INTRODUCTION
TO THE
HISTORY OF SCIENCE

VOLUME III

SCIENCE AND LEARNING IN THE FOURTEENTH CENTURY

BY
GEORGE SARTON
Associate in the History of Science
Carnegie Institution of Washington

IN TWO PARTS

PUBLISHED FOR THE
CARNEGIE INSTITUTION OF WASHINGTON
BY
THE WILLIAMS & WILKINS COMPANY
BALTIMORE
1948

CARNEGIE INSTITUTION OF WASHINGTON
PUBLICATION 376

Reprinted 1953

CONTENTS

PART II

The Time of Geoffrey Chaucer, Ibn Khaldūn, and Ḥasdai Crescas
(Second half of the fourteenth century)

CHAPTER XV — PAGES

SURVEY OF SCIENCE AND INTELLECTUAL PROGRESS IN THE SECOND HALF OF THE FOURTEENTH CENTURY 1019–1333

I. General Background, 1019

II. Religious Background, 1031: A. Western Christendom, 1031: 1. The government of the church, 1031; 2, The Crusades, 1035; 3, Religious orders, 1036; 4, Biblical studies and translations, 1039; 5, Homiletics and paraenesis, 1040; 6, Art and religion, 1041; 7, Saints, 1041; 8, Relics, 1044; 9, Apologetics, 1045; 10, Internal criticism of the church, 1046; 11, Superstition, 1048. A1, Italy, 1052; A2, Catalonia, 1052; A3, Judeo-Spanish converts, 1053; A4, France, 1053; A5, England, 1054; A6, Germany, 1055; A7, Bohemia, 1055; A8, Sweden, 1056; A9, Netherlands, 1056. B. Eastern Christendom, 1057: B1, Byzantium, 1057; B2, Russia, 1058. C. Israel, 1059: C1, Spain, 1060; C2, Catalonia, 1061; C3, Provence, 1063; C4, Germany, 1063; C5, East, 1064. D. Islām, 1064: D1, Western Islām, 1064; D2. Eastern Islām, 1065. E. India, 1069. F. Tibet, 1069. G. China, 1070

III. The Translators, 1071: 1. Arabic, 1071: 1a, From Arabic into Hebrew, 1071; 1b, From Arabic into Latin, 1072; 1c, From Arabic into Catalan, 1072; 1d, From Arabic into Persian and Turkish, 1072. 2. Greek, 1072: 2a, From Greek into Latin, 1072; 2b, From Greek into Hebrew, 1073. 3. Latin, 1073: 3a. From Latin into Hebrew, 1073; 3b, From Latin into Greek, 1074; 3c, From Latin into French, 1075; 3d, From Latin into Spanish, 1075; 3e, From Latin into English, 1076; 3f, From Latin into Czech, 1076. 4. Hebrew, 1076: 4a, From Hebrew into Greek and Latin, 1076; 4b, From Hebrew into Spanish, 1077. 5. French, 1077: From French into English, 1077. 6. Persian, 1077: From Persian into Turkish, 1077. 7. Sanskrit, 1077: From Sanskrit into Bengali, 1077. Conclusion, 1078

IV. Education, 1078: A. Christendom, 1078: 1, Universities, 1078; 2, 3, English colleges and schools, 1079; 4, Education in France, 1079; 5, Italy, 1080; 6, Netherlands, 1081. B. Islām, 1082. C. China, 1083. D. Japan, 1084

V. Philosophic and Cultural Background, 1085: A. Western Christendom, 1085: A1, Italy, 1086; A2, Catalonia, 1086; A3, France, 1087; A4, England, 1089; A5, Germany, 1091; A6, Netherlands, 1092; A7, Bohemia, 1093. B. Eastern Christendom, 1094: B1, Byzantium, 1094; B2, Armenia, 1095. C. Israel, 1096: C1, Spain, 1096; C2, Catalonia and Aragon, 1096; C3, Provence, 1097; C4, East, 1097. D. Islām, 1098: D1, Granada, 1098; D2, Ifrīqīya, 1098; D3, Mamlūkīya, 1099; D4, Īrān, 1100; D5, Anatolia, 1100; D6, The Destroyer, Tīmūr Lang, 1101. E. India, 1102. F. China, 1102. G. Korea, 1103. Notes on various superstitions which deeply colored the cultural background everywhere, 1103

VI. Mathematics and Astronomy, 1105: A. Western Christendom, 1105: A1, Italy, 1105; A2, Catalonia (and the rest of the Hispanic peninsula), 1107; A3, France, 1108; A4, England, 1110; A5, The Netherlands, 1111; A6, Germany, 1112; A7, Poland, 1114; A8, Bohemia, 1114; A9, Scandinavia, 1114. B. Eastern Christendom, 1115: Byzantium, 1115. C. Israel, 1115: C1, Spain, 1115; C2, Catalonia, 1115; C3, Provence, 1116; C4, Greece, 1117; C5, Yaman, 1117. D. Islām, 1117: D1, Maghrib, 1118; D2, Ifrīqīya, 1118;

CHAPTER XV—*Continued* PAGES

D3, Mamlūkīya, 1118; D4, Anatolia, 1119; D5, Farther East, 1119; D6, Islām (undetermined), 1121. E. India, 1121. F. China, 1121. G. Korea, 1122

VII. Physics, Technology, and Music, 1122: 1. Optics and optical meteorology, 1123. 2. Weights and measures, 1124. 3. Magnetism, 1124. 4. Mechanical clocks, 1124. 5. Arms and armor; dinanderie, 1125. 6. Printing, 1125. 7. Hydrostatics, 1126. 8. Canals, 1126. 8 bis. Metallurgy and mining, 1126. 9. Mechanical theories, 1126. 10. Discussions concerning the vacuum, 1127. 11. Technical improvements and their social impact, 1127. 12. Musical theories, 1128: Music in the Latin West, 1128; Music in Islām, 1129

VIII. Chemistry, 1129: A. Christendom, 1130: A1, Catalonia, 1130; A2, Italy, 1131; Note on early maiòlica, 1133; A3, France, 1135; A4, England, 1136; A5, Germany, 1137; A6, Russia, 1138; A7, Addition, 1138. B. Islām, 1138. C. India, 1139. D. China, 1139

IX. Geography, 1140: Catalonia, 1140. A. Christendom, 1142: A1, Spain, 1142; A2, Italy, 1143; A3, France, 1147; A4, England, 1148; A5, The Netherlands, 1150; A6, Germany, 1152; A7, Scandinavia, 1154; A8, Russia and Byzantium, 1155. B. Israel, 1156. C. Islām, 1156: C1. Maghrib, 1157; C2, Mashriq, 1160. D. Java, 1161. E. China, 1161

X. Natural History, 1162: *Geographical survey*, 1162: A. Christendom, 1162: A1, Hispanic peninsula, 1162; A2, Italy, 1163; A3, France, 1164; A4, Pays de Liége, 1165; A5, England, 1165; A6, Germany, 1166; A7, Bohemia, 1166; A8, Byzantium, 1167. B. Israel, 1167. C. Islām, 1167: C1, Maghrib, 1167; C2, Arabia, 1168; C3, 'Irāq and Mamlūkīya, 1168; C4, Turkey, 1169; C5, Transoxiana (Mā warā'-l-nahr), 1169. D. China, 1169

Special subjects, 1170: 1. General surveys. Theory of evolution, 1170. First Kingdom: Minerals, 1170: 2. Geological theories, 1170. 3. Lapidaries, 1171. 4. Earthquakes and volcanoes, 1172. 5. Mining and metallurgy, 1173. Second Kingdom: Plants, 1176: 6. Herbals, 1176. 7. Botanic gardens, 1177. 8. Plant (and animal) iconography, 1177. 9. Husbandry, 1180. 10. Spices, 1182. Third Kingdom: Animals, 1183: 11. Hunting and falconry, 1183. 12. Fishing, 1185. 13. Special animals, 1186: insects, 1187; menageries, 1189; voles and lemmings, 1190. 14. Translations, 1191

XI. Medicine, 1191: The Black Death, 1191. *Geographical survey*, 1192: A. Christendom, 1192: A1, Italy, 1192; A2, Hispanic peninsula, 1199; A3, France, 1200; A4, England, 1202; A5, Germany, 1205; A6, Bohemia, 1207; A7, Iceland, 1208; A8, Christian East, 1208. B. Israel, 1211. B1, Spain, 1211; B2, Catalonia, 1211; B3, Provence and Languedoc, 1211; B4, Germany, 1212; B5, Serbia, 1213; B6, China, 1213. C. Samaritan medicine, 1213. D. Islām, 1213: D1, Andalusia, 1213; D2, Ifrīqiya, 1214; D3, Mamlūkīya, 1214; D4, Yaman, 1215; D5, Anatolia, 1215; D6, Īrān, 1217. E. India, 1217. F. China, 1218. G. Japan, 1218

Topical survey, 1219: 1. Medical astrology and alchemy, 1219. 2. Translations and commentaries, 1220. 3. Literary and scholastic background, 1222. 4. Anatomy, 1223; Note on dwarfs and giants, 1227. 5. Physiology, 1228. 6. Embryology and obstetrics, 1229. 7. Anatomical (and medical) iconography, 1230; The dance of death, 1231. 8. Physiognomy, 1232. 9. Surgery, 1232. 10. Eye diseases, 1234. 11. Various other diseases, 1236. 12. Leprosy and cagots, 1237. 13. Famines, 1237. 14. Veterinary medicine, 1238. 15. Regimina et consilia, 1238. 16. Balneology, 1240. 17. Pharmacy, 1241. 18. Medical teaching and profession, 1242. 19. Faith healing, 1246. 20. Medical deontology, 1247. 21. Hospitals, 1247; List of fourteenth-century Muslim hospitals (derived from Sayili 1941), 1249. 22. Erotics, 1249

XII. Historiography, 1249: A. Christendom, 1249: A1, Hispanic peninsula, 1250; A2, Italy, 1251; A3, France, 1253; A4, Ireland, 1254; A5, Scotland,

Chapter XV—*Continued*

PAGES

1254; A6, England, 1254; A7, Belgium, 1257; A8, Germany, 1258; A9, Bohemia, 1258; A10, Poland, 1259; A11, Byzantium, 1259; A12, Armenia, 1260; A13, Egypt, 1260. B. Israel, 1261. C. Samaritan, 1261. D. Islām, 1261: D1, Granada, 1261; D2, Morocco, 1262; D3, Algiers, 1262; D4, Tunis, 1262; D5, Yaman, 1263; D6, Mamlūkīya, 1264; D7, Turkey, 1266; D8, Īrān, 1267. E. Ceylon, 1267. F. Java, 1268. G. China and Korea, 1268. H. Japan, 1270

XIII. Law and Sociology, 1271: A. Islām, 1271: A1, Maghrib, 1271; A2, Mashriq, 1271. B. Christendom, 1272: B1, Italy, 1273; B2, France, 1275; B3, Germany, 1277; B4, England, 1278; B5, The Netherlands, 1280; B6, Byzantium, 1280. C. India, 1281. D. China, 1281. Appendix: Monetary difficulties and theory of money, 1282

XIV. Philology, 1284: 1. The linguistic situation, 1284. 2. Latin, 1287: i, Humanism in Italy, 1288; ii, Humanism in France, 1293; iii, Humanism in England, 1295; iv, Humanism in Germany, 1296; v, Humanism in the Netherlands, 1297; vi, Books and libraries, 1297; vii, Latin vs. the vernaculars, 1298. 3. Italian, 1299. 4. Castilian (Spanish), 1301. 5. Provençal, 1302; Felibrejado, 1303. 6. Catalan, 1304. 7. Portuguese, 1306. 8. French, 1307; French in England, 1310. 9. English, 1313. 10. Dutch, 1316. 11. German, 1318. 12. Scandinavian, 1319. 13. Greek, 1320; Greek in the West, 1320. 14. Slavonic languages, 1322. 15. Armenian, 1323. 16. Georgian, 1323. 17. Syriac, 1323. 18. Coptic, 1323. 19. Aethiopic, 1323. 19 bis. Zyrian, 1323. 20. Hebrew, 1324; Hebrew studies in the West, 1324; Yiddish, 1325. 21. Arabic, 1326. 22. Persian, 1328. 23. Turkish, 1328. 24. Mongolian, 1329. 25. Manchu, 1329. 26. Sanskrit, Pāli, Siṅhalese, 1330. 26 bis. Other Aryan languages of India, 1330. 27. Dravidian languages (Canarese), 1330. 27 bis. Javanese, 1331. 28. Tibetan, 1331. 29. Chinese, 1331. 30. Korean, 1331. 31. Japanese, 1331

Chapter XVI

Religious Background (Second Half of the Fourteenth Century).....1334–1372

A. Western Christendom, 1334: A1. Italy, 1334: St. Catherine of Siena, 1334. A2. Catalonia, 1338: Eymeric, 1338; St. Vincent Ferrer, 1339; Turmeda, 1341. A3. Judeo-Spanish converts, 1343: Solomon ben Isaac ha-Levi, 1343. A4. France, 1344: Mézières, 1344. A5. England, 1346: Wycliffe, 1346. A6. Germany, 1350: Gelnhausen, 1350. A7. Bohemia, 1351: Milič, 1351; Matthew of Janov, 1352; Štitný, 1353. A8. Sweden, 1354: St. Birgitta of Sweden, 1354. A9. Netherlands, 1356: Groote, 1356; Zerbolt, 1362

B. Eastern Christendom, 1363: B1. Byzantium, 1363: Manuel Calecas, 1363

C. Israel, 1364: C1. Spain, 1364: Joseph ben Eliezer Bonfils, 1364. C2. Catalonia, 1364: Nissim ben Reuben Gerondi, 1364. C5. East, 1365: Abraham Qirimi, 1365; Eleazar ben Nathan ha-Babli, 1365

D. Islām, 1365: D1. Western Islām, 1365: 'Abd al-Ḥaqq al-Islāmī, 1365

E. India, 1366: Mādhava, 1366; Sāyaṇa, 1368; Dhammakitti IV, 1370; Dhammakitti V, 1370

F. Tibet, 1371: Tsong Kapa, 1371

Chapter XVII

The Translators (Second Half of the Fourteenth Century)..........1373–1396

1a. Translations from Arabic into Hebrew, 1373: Joseph ben Joshua I ha-Lorqi, 1373; Joseph ben Joshua II ha-Lorqi, 1373; David ibn Ya'īsh, 1373; Judah ben Solomon Nathan, 1374; Jacob Carsono, 1375; Samuel ibn Moṭoṭ, 1375; Solomon ben Labi, 1376; Judah ben Solomon ibn Labi, 1377

2a. Translations from Greek into Latin, 1377: Leonzio Pilato, 1377

CHAPTER XVII—*Continued* PAGES

2b. Translations from Greek into Hebrew, 1378: Solomon ben Elijah, 1378

3a. Translations from Latin into Hebrew, 1378: Moses of Roquemaure, 1378; Leon Joseph of Carcassonne, 1379; Jekuthiel ben Solomon, 1380; Abraham Abigdor, 1380; Solomon Abigdor, 1382; Solomon ben Nathan Crescas, 1382; Solomon ben David Davin, 1382; Benjamin ben Isaac of Carcassonne, 1383; Jacob ben Judah Cabret, 1383; Meir Alguadez, 1384; Shemṭob Shapruṭ, 1385

3b. Translations from Latin into Greek, 1386: Prochoros Cydones, 1386; Demetrios Cydones, 1387

3c. Translations from Latin into French, 1389: Jean de Sy, 1389; Martin de Saint-Gilles, 1389; Jean Corbechon, 1390; Foulechat, 1390; Presles, 1390; Jean Dandin, 1390; Hesdin, 1391; Eudes, 1391; Jacques Bauchant, 1391; Golein, 1392; Evrard de Conty, 1393

3c. Translations from Latin into English, 1393: Trevisa, 1393

4. Translations from Hebrew into Greek and Latin, 1394: Atumanos, 1394

7. Translations from Sanskrit into Bengāli, 1395: Kṛittivāsa, 1395

CHAPTER XVIII

EDUCATION (Second Half of the Fourteenth Century) 1397–1408

A. Christendom, 1397: 1. Creation of new universities, 1397: Huesca (1354), 1397; Pavia (1361), 1397; Cracow (1364, 1397), 1398; Orange (1365), 1398; Vienna (1365), 1398; Pécs or Fünfkirchen (1367), 1399; Erfurt (1379, 1392), 1399; Heidelberg (1385), 1400; Cologne (1388), 1400; Buda (1389, 1395), 1400; Ferrara (1391), 1400. 2. English colleges, 1401: Oxford, 1401: Canterbury (1361), 1401, New College (1379), 1401; Cambridge, 1402: Corpus Christi (1352), 1402. 3. English schools, 1402: Winchester (1378), 1402. 4. Education in France, 1404: The University of Paris, 1404; Parisian colleges, 1405; Education in the provinces, 1405; La Tour-Landry, 1406. 5. Italy, 1407: Giovanni da Ravenna (I), 1407. 6. Netherlands, 1408: Cele, 1408

D. Japan, 1408: The Ashikaga-gakkō, 1408

CHAPTER XIX

PHILOSOPHICAL AND CULTURAL BACKGROUND (Second Half of the Fourteenth Century) 1409–1479

A. Western Christendom, 1409: A1. Italy, 1409: Domenico di Bandino, 1409. A2. Catalonia, 1410: Francesc Eiximènis, 1410. A3. France, 1410: Deschamps, 1410. A4. England, 1412: Strode, 1412; "Langland," 1413; Hilton, 1415; The cloud of unknowing, 1416; Chaucer, 1417; Gower, 1427. A5. Germany, 1428: Albert of Saxony, 1428; Henry of Oyta, 1432; Dinkelsbühl, 1432; Dambach, 1433. A6. Netherlands, 1434: Marsilius van Inghen, 1434; Jan de Weert, 1437

B. Eastern Christendom, 1438: B1. Byzantium, 1438: John of Cypros, 1438; Cabasilas, 1438; Peter of Crete, 1440. B2. Armenia, 1441: John of Orodn, 1441; Gregory of Tathev, 1441

C. Israel, 1442: C1. Spain, 1442: Meir ben Aldabi, 1442; Ibn Malkah, 1444; Menahem ben Zeraḥ, 1444; Ibn al-Naqawa, 1445. C2. Catalonia and Aragon, 1446: Ḥasdai Crescas, 1446. C3. Provence, 1449: Jacob ben Solomon Ẓarfati, 1449; Bonsenior ben Yaḥya, 1449. C4. East, 1450: Isaiah ben Joseph of Tabrīz, 1450; Judah ben Moses Mosconi, 1450; Joseph ben Moses ha-Kilti, 1452

D. Islām, 1452: D1, Granada, 1452: Ibn 'Abbād, 1452; Ibn 'Āṣim, 1453. D3. Mamlūkīya, 1453: 'Abd al-Raḥīm ibn al-Ḥasan al-Isnawī, 1453; 'Umar ibn Isḥāq al-Hindī, 1454; Sīdī Khalīl, 1455; Muḥammad ibn Muḥammad al-Jazarī, 1455. D4. Īrān, 1456: Ḥāfiẓ, 1456; 'Alī ibn Shihāb al-dīn, 1458; 'Abd al-Karīm al-Jīlī, 1459; Ni'mat Allāh Walī, 1459; Faḍlallāh al-Ḥurūfī, 1459; al-Jurjānī, 1461. D5. Anatolia, 1462: al-Taftāzānī, 1462;

CHAPTER XIX—*Continued* PAGES

Ṣalāḥ al-dīn, 1464; Aḥmedī, 1464; al-Fanārī, 1465. D6. The Destroyer: Tīmūr Lang, 1467
E. India, 1474: Taruṇaprabha, 1474; Lal Ded, 1475; Banda Nawāz, 1476
F. China, 1477: Hsieh Ying-fang, 1477
G. Korea, 1478: Chêng Mêng Chou, 1478

CHAPTER XX

MATHEMATICS AND ASTRONOMY (Second Half of the Fourteenth Century) 1480–1538

A. Western Christendom, 1480: A1. Italy, 1480: Thomas de Pisan, 1480; Montulmo, 1481; Gentile degli Mainardi, 1482; Andrea da Sommeria, 1482; Guarimbertus, 1483; Early arithmetic, 1483; Italian computus of 1393, 1484; Alçune cose di abaco, 1484. A2. Spain, 1485: Dalmau Ces-Planes and Pere Engelbert, 1485. A3. France, 1486: Oresme, 1486; Jean Fusoris, 1497; Pèlerin de Prusse, 1498; Bertran Boysset, 1498. A4. England, 1499: Rede, 1499; Brit, 1500; Nicholas of Lynn, 1501; Somer, 1501. A5. Netherlands, 1502: Jan de Heusden, 1502. A6. Germany, 1502: Langenstein, 1502; Evno, 1510; John of Livania, 1510. A7. Poland, 1510: Hermann de Przeworsko, 1510
B. Eastern Christendom, 1511: Byzantium, 1511: Isaac Argyros, 1511; Theodoros Meliteniotes, 1512
C. Israel, 1514: C1. Spain, 1514: Joseph ben Isaac ibn Waqar, 1514; Note on Ibn al-Kammād (XII-2?), 1514; Isaac Alḥadib, 1515. C2. Catalonia, 1516: Jacob Bonet, 1516. C3. Provence, 1517: Immanuel Bonfils, 1517; Samuel ben Simeon Kansi, 1520; Profiaṭ Duran, 1520
D. Islām, 1523: D1. Maghrib, 1523: 'Alī ibn abī 'Alī al-Qusṭanṭīnī, 1523; al-Jādarī, 1524. D3. Mamlūkīya, 1524: al-Bahāniqī, 1524; Ibn al-Shāṭir, 1524; Ibn Zuraiq, 1526; al-Khalīlī, 1526; Taqī al-dīn al-Ḥanbalī, 1527; Ibn al-Hā'im, 1527; Ibn al-Majdī, 1528; Ibrāhīm al-Ḥāsib, 1529. D5. Father East, 1529: 'Aṭā' ibn Aḥmad, 1529; 'Abd al-Wāḥid ibn Muḥammad, 1530; 'Abdallāh ibn Khalīl al-Māridīnī, 1530. D6. Islam (undetermined), 1533: 'Abd al-Qādir ibn 'Alī, 1533; Other Oriental texts on finger reckoning, 1534
E. India, 1534: Nārāyaṇa, 1534
F. China, 1536: Ting Chü, 1536; Yen Kung, 1536; Liu Chi, 1536
G. Korea, 1537: Korean astronomy at the end of the fourteenth century, 1537

CHAPTER XXI

PHYSICS, TECHNOLOGY, AND MUSIC (Second Half of the Fourteenth Century) 1539–1571

1. Optics and Optical Meteorology, 1539: Themon son of the Jew, 1539
4. Mechanical Clocks, 1540
5. Arms, Armor, Dinanderie, 1547: Arms, 1547; Treatises on military technology, 1550; Armor, 1555; Dinanderie, 1561
6. Printing, East and West, 1561: Far East, 1561; West, 1563
9. Mechanical Theories, 1564: Pelacani, 1564
12. Musical Theories, 1567: Landino, 1567; Tunsted, 1568; Theinred, 1569; Acoustic vases, 1569; 'Abd al-Qādir ibn Ghaibī, 1570

CHAPTER XXII

CHEMISTRY (Second Half of the Fourteenth Century) 1572–1590

A. Christendom, 1572: A1. Catalonia, 1572: Rupescissa, 1572; Tárrega, 1574; Sedacer, 1574. A3. France, 1575: "Ortolanus," 1575; Flamel, 1576. A4. England, 1578: Dombelay, 1578. A5. Germany, 1579: Wimandus, 1579; Stromer, 1579; Note on the Visierruthe and the Visierkunst, 1580; "Berthold

CHAPTER XXII—*Continued* PAGES

der Schwarze," 1581; Leonard of Maurperg, 1582. A6. Russia, 1583: Introduction of the Byzantine technique of painting into Russia, 1583

C. India, 1584: Merutuṅga, 1584

D. China, 1585: T'ao Tsung-i, 1585; Note on Chinese Muslims, 1586; Shên Chi-sun, 1590

CHAPTER XXIII

GEOGRAPHY (Second Half of the Fourteenth Century)................1591–1627

Catalonia, 1591: Catalan mappemonde 1375, 1591; Soleri, 1592; Abraham Cresques, 1592; Jahuda Cresques, 1593

A. Christendom, 1593: A2. Italy, 1593: "The brothers Zeni," 1593; Gucci, 1595; Frescobaldi, 1595; Sigoli, 1596; Niccolò di Martoni, 1596; The Medicean atlas, 1351, 1597; Pizigano, 1598; Two anonymous Italian portolani dating probably from the last quarter of the fourteenth century, 1599; Fazio degli Uberti, 1600. A3. France, 1601: Anglure, 1601. A4. England, 1602: Mandeville, 1602; Thomas Swinburne, 1606. A5. Netherlands, 1606: Hese, 1606. A7. Scandinavia, 1607: Ivar Bárðarson, 1607; Björn Jórsalafarer, 1608; Scandinavian exploration of North America, 1608. A8. Russia and Byzantium, 1613: Ignatius of Smolensk, 1613; Alexander the Pilgrim, 1614; Grethenios, 1614

C. Islām, 1614: C1. Maghrib, 1614: Ibn Baṭṭūṭa, 1614. C2. Mashriq, 1623: Aḥmad ibn Muḥammad al-Maqdisī, 1623; al-Bākuwī, 1623

D. Java, 1624: Nāgarakṛitāgama, 1624

E. China, 1627: Chinese knowledge of geography and zoology at the end of the fourteenth century or the beginning of the fifteenth, 1627

CHAPTER XXIV

NATURAL HISTORY (Second Half of the Fourteenth Century)..........1628–1649

A. Christendom, 1628: A2. Italy, 1628: Rotario d'Asti, 1628. A3. France, 1629: Gaston Phoebus, 1629; Jehan de Brie, 1631; Taillevent, 1632; "Cybo of Hyères," 1633

B. Israel, 1634: Gatigno, 1634

C. Islām, 1635: C1. Maghrib, 1635: Ibn Hudhail, 1635; Ibn Juzayy, 1636. C2. Arabia, 1637: al-'Abbās ibn 'Alī al-Rasūlī, 1637. C3. 'Irāq and Mamlūkīya, 1638: Ibn al-Duraihim, 1638; Iconography of animals (and plants), 1638; al-Damīrī, 1639; Muḥammad ibn Mangalī, 1641; Muḥammad ibn Lājīn, 1642; Ṭaibughā, 1643. C4. Turkey, 1643: Maḥmūd ibn Muḥammad al-Bārjīnī, 1643

D. China, 1644: Chu Hsiao, 1644

CHAPTER XXV

MEDICINE (Second Half of the Fourteenth Century)..................1650–1733

Plagues, 1650: The Black Death, 1650: Development of public sanitation, 1658; Plague treatises, 1659; List of plague treatises, 1661. Other epidemics, 1664: Cholera, 1664; The dancing mania, 1665

A. Christendom, 1668: A1. Italy, 1668: Dionisio II Colle, 1668; Franciscus de Gianellis, 1669; Dino Dini, 1669; Giacomo de' Dondi, 1669; Marra, 1671; Guido da Bagnolo, 1672; Tommaso del Garbo, 1672; Cardo of Milan, 1674; Niccolò di Burgo, 1674; Francischino de Collignano, 1675; Iacopo da Arquà, 1676; Giovanni de' Dondi, 1676; Giovanni da Santa Sofia, 1677; Nicholas of Udine, 1678; Christophorus de Honestis, 1679; Syllanus de Nigris, 1680; Bartolommeo da Pisa, 1680; Marsiglio da Santa Sofia, 1681; Pietro da Tossignano, 1681; Francesco Casini, 1684; Ugolino da Montecatini, 1686; Jacopo da Prato,

CHAPTER XXV—*Continued* PAGES

1686. A2. Hispanic peninsula, 1687: Joannes Jacobi, 1687. A3. France, 1689: Fromont, 1689; Bernard Alberti, 1690; Guy de Chauliac, 1690; Pierre de Nadilz, 1694; Pataran, 1694; Raymond Chalmel de Viviers, 1694; Jean Le Fèvre, 1695; Harcigny, 1696; Jean de Tournemire, 1696; Molinier, 1698; Boucher, 1698; Auxon, 1699; Jean Le Lièvre, 1699. A4. England, 1700: John Arderne, 1700; John of Mirfeld, 1704. A5. Germany, 1706: Thopping, 1706; Tilmann, 1706; John of Glogau, 1707; Thomas of Sarepta, 1708; Bernard of Frankfurt, 1709; Heinrich Ribbenicz, 1710; Low German medical writings, 1710. A6. Bohemia, 1712: Gallus de Strahov, 1712; Jean de Grandville, 1713; Sigismund Albic, 1713. A8. Christian East, 1715: Jacob the Armenian, 1715

B. Israel, 1716: B1–2. Spain, 1716: Joshua ben Joseph II ha-Lorqi, 1716; Samuel Esperial, 1717. B3. Provence and Languedoc, 1717: Violas of Rodez, 1717; Isaac ben Jacob Lattes, 1718; Isaac ben Ṭodros, 1718; Ṭodros de Cavaillon, 1719; Bendig 'Ain, 1719. B4. Germany, 1720: A medical treatise of 1396 in Yiddish, 1720; Note on early Yiddish literature, 1720

C. Samaritan Medicine, 1721: Abū Sa'īd al-'Afīf, 1721

D. Islām, 1721: D1. Andalusia, 1721: Muḥammad ibn Muḥammad of Almeria, 1721; Muḥammad ibn 'Alī al-Shaqūrī, 1721. D2. Ifrīqīya, 1722: Ibn abī Ḥajala, 1722. D3. Mamlūkīya, 1723: al-Shādhilī, 1723; al-Manbijī, 1724. D4. Yaman, 1725: Muḥammad al-Mahdī, 1725. D5. Anatolia, 1725: al-Āqsarā'ī, 1725; Isḥāq ibn Murād of Gerede, 1726; Muḥammad ibn Maḥmūd, 1726; Ḥājjī Pāshā, 1727. D6. Īrān, 1728: al-Rāmī, 1728; Zain al-'Aṭṭār, 1728; Manṣūr ibn Muḥammad, 1729

E. India, 1730: Maṅgarāja, 1730; Madanapāla, 1730; Yoga-Ratnākara; 1731

F. China, 1721: Wang Li, 1731; Chia Ming, 1731; Tsi Ssŭ-kung, 1732; Yüan Kung, 1732

G. Japan, 1733: Yūrin, 1733; Majima Seigan, 1733

CHAPTER XXVI

HISTORIOGRAPHY (Second Half of the Fourteenth Century)...........1734–1791

A. Christendom, 1734: A1. Hispanic peninsula, 1734: Pere III el Cerimoniós, 1734; López de Ayala, 1735. A2. Italy, 1737: Filippo Villani, 1737; Michele da Piazza, 1737. A3. France, 1738: Venette, 1738; Dardel, 1739. A4. Ireland, 1740: "Pembridge," 1740. A5. Scotland, 1740: Barbour, 1740; Fordun, 1741. A6. England, 1742: Geoffrey le Baker, 1742; Robert of Avesbury, 1742; Knighton, 1742; Thorne, 1743; Cirencester, 1743; Malverne, 1744; Walsingham, 1744; Burton, 1746; Gray, 1746. A7. Belgium, 1746: Le Muisit, 1746; Jean le Bel, 1748; Jean d'Outremeuse, 1748; Hemricourt, 1750; Froissart, 1751; John of Ypres, 1753. A8. Germany, 1754: Northof, 1754; Tilemann, 1755; Closener, 1756; Jacob Twinger, 1756. A9. Bohemia, 1757: Beneš of Weitmil, 1757; Přibik Pulkava, 1758. A10. Poland, 1759: Jan Czarnkowski, 1759. A11: Byzantium, 1759: John VI Cantacuzenos, 1759. A12. Armenia, 1761: Gregory of Khlath, 1761

C. Samaritan, 1761: Abu-l-Fatḥ ibn abī-l-Ḥasan, 1761

D. Islām, 1762: D1. Granada, 1762: Ibn al-Khaṭīb, 1762. D3. Algiers, 1764: Ibn al-Qunfūdh, 1764. D4. Tunis, 1766: Yaḥyā ibn Khaldūn, 1766; Ibn Khaldūn, 1767. D5. Yaman, 1779: Ibn Wahhās, 1779. D6. Mamlūkīya, 1780: Mufaḍḍal ibn abī-l-Faḍā'il, 1780; Ibn Shākir, 1781; 'Abd al-Wahhāb al-Subkī, 1781; Ibn Kathīr, 1782; Muḥammad ibn Qāsim al-Nuwairī, 1782; Ibn Ḥabīb, 1783; Ibn al-Furāt, 1783; Ibn Duqmāq, 1784; Ibn al-Shiḥna, 1785; al-Qalqashandī, 1785

G. China, 1788: T'o-T'o, 1788; Sung Lien, 1789; Li Shan-ch'ang, 1790; Wu Hai, 1790; Hsia Wên-yen, 1791

Chapter XXVII

PAGES

Law and Sociology (Second Half of the Fourteenth Century) 1792–1801

A. Islām, 1792: A1. Maghrib, 1792: Mūsā (II) ibn Ziyān, 1792
B. Christendom, 1792: B1. Italy, 1792: Albornoz, 1792; Bartolus, 1793; Baldo, 1795; Giovanni da Legnano, 1796. B5. Netherlands, 1798: Philip of Leiden, 1798
C. India, 1799: Viśveśvara, 1799
D. China, 1800: Hung Wu, 1800; Liu Wei-ch'ien, 1801

Chapter XXVIII

Philology (Second Half of the Fourteenth Century) 1802–1829

Latin and Italian, 1802: Giovanni Boccaccio, 1802; Benvenuto de' Rambaldi, 1812; Marsiglio of Florence, 1815; Salutati, 1815; Giovanni da Ravenna (II), 1817; Vergerio, 1818; Dietrich von Niem, 1819
Catalan, 1820: Bernat Metge, 1820
Greek, 1821: Diassorinos, 1821; Chrysoloras, 1822; Manuel II Palaeologos, 1823
Czech, 1824: Flaška z Pardubic, 1824
Zyrian, 1825: St. Stephen of Perm, 1825
Hebrew, 1825: Pereẓ Trabot, 1825; Menahem ben Abraham Bonafos, 1826
Arabic, 1826: al-Fīrūzābādī, 1826
Canarese, 1828: Abhinava Maṅgarāja, 1828
Chinese, 1828: Chao Hui-ch'ien, 1828; Ting Hao-nien, 1829

Addenda 1830–1871

General Bibliography 1872–1911

Indexes 1913–2155

General Index, 1913
Greek Index, 2092
Chinese Index and Glossary to Volumes 1, 2, and 3, 2100
Japanese Index and Glossary to Volumes 1, 2, and 3, 2141

LIST OF ILLUSTRATIONS

For further explanations and acknowledgments of courtesies received, see the legends under the illustrations.

PART II

FIGURE PAGE
23. Post-mortem examination, 1363....1225
24. Instructions for the Chinese census of 1370....1269
25. Early portrait of Geoffrey Chaucer in the Harvard Library....1419
26. Title page of astronomical treatise written for a Mongol prince in 1362...1531
27. Ancient works of the Wells Cathedral clock, c. 1392....1543
28. Interior dial of Wells Cathedral clock....1544
29. Brass plate to the memory of Willem Wenemaer and his wife (Ghent, after 1325)....1557
30. Drawing of Wenemaer's armor....1558
31, 32. The Stone Man of Ghent, 1338....1559
33. Muslim Chinese publication....1588
34. Various forms of runic numerals....1611
35. Possible itinerary of Scandinavians from the coast of Labrador to Minnesota....1612
36. Page of the Ming encyclopaedia of 1609, reproducing the I-yü t'u-chih...1626
37. Another page of the same text....1627
38. Page from the Famine herbal, c. 1406....1647
39. Map of Central Europe showing location of anti-Jewish outbreaks....1657
40. Instruments used by John Arderne in the cure of fistula....1701

PART II

The Time of Geoffrey Chaucer, Ibn Khaldūn, and Ḥasdai Crescas

(Second half of the fourteenth century)

It is claimed that the following words were written upon Plato's door: "Nobody should enter our house who is not a mathematician."* And our own elders, may God have mercy upon them, used to say, "The study of mathematics† is for the mind like soap for the clothes, which washes away from them the dirt and cleans the spots and stains." This is due to the arrangement and order of that science . . . .

—*Ibn Khaldūn*

(Muqaddama. Arabic ed., vol. 3, p. 102, Paris 1858;
French ed., vol. 3, p. 142, Paris 1868.)

*Or geometer, muhandis. The words written upon the door of the Academy were Μηδεὶς ἀγεωμέτρητος εἰσίτω μου τὴν στέγην. This tradition has been preserved for us by a very late Byzantine author, Joannes Tzetzes (XII-1), in his Βίβλος ἱστοριῶν (VIII, 972), Historiarum variarum chiliades, which I failed to mention in the note devoted to him (Introd. 2, 192). See the Greek edition by Theophil Kiessling (p. 322, Leipzig 1826).

†Or geometry, 'ilm al-handasa.

CHAPTER XV

SURVEY OF SCIENCE AND INTELLECTUAL PROGRESS IN THE SECOND HALF OF THE FOURTEENTH CENTURY

I. GENERAL BACKGROUND

The division of the past into half-century periods is artificial, but, as we explained before (Introd. 1, 37–39), no division would apply equally well to every branch of science or to every nation. Hence, it is more convenient to divide the past into periods of equal length and sufficiently brief. Half a century is a period which almost every man can measure and encompass in his own life; for every such period, say the present one, 1351–1401, there are always enough men who have lived through it from the beginning to the end to insure a modicum of homogeneity.

The second half of the fourteenth century, however, had the remarkable peculiarity of being limited at its two ends by two series of events of international importance and of such magnitude that millions of men were deeply affected by them. The first is the Black Death, which began in 1348–49, and the second is the conquests of Tīmūr Lang, which ended in 1405. These two calamities did not cover exactly the same territory, but the territory of each was so enormous that they overlapped considerably, and millions of people had the sad privilege of witnessing both. Some escaped the Black Death only to be destroyed by Tīmūr.

Nor were those two calamities the only ones; think of the Babylonian captivity followed by the Great Schism, the Hundred Years' War, etc. Look around the civilized world and you will hardly find a place, certainly not a country, which was ever free for a whole year from war, plague, or starvation. No place was ever delivered from fear for a single day, for to the natural fears caused by physical calamities, wars, revolts, and general lawlessness were added the artificial fears bred by superstitions and unreason. One could possibly escape natural miseries, but no one could escape the nightmares of his own mind; one could get away from tyrants or bezonians, but how could one elude the devils, the witches, the evil-eyed? There might be for once no real danger in the offing, but if an astrologer insisted on interpreting a comet or an occultation as a portent of evil, what could a man do except shrive and tremble?

We assume that the reader has some knowledge of general history, and that all he needs now is simply to refresh his memory. The notes of this section are meant to answer that humble purpose.

It is well to speak of Europe as Christendom, for the church dominated every person, every thing. Emperors and kings might dispute the pope's authority, the people as a rule did not. Every action or idea had its theological aspect; every form of nonconformism, every velleity of protest might be (and often was) construed as heresy. Thus, anything concerning the church would affect everything else. From 1309 to 1376 the popes, having been frightened out of Rome by continual turbulences, were established in Avignon. During their so-called Babylonian captivity, the French popes reorganized the administration of the church, increased its power but did not put an end to many abuses, and managed to outrage almost everybody except the profiteers. When peace had been re-established in Italy by cardinal Albornoz, and the popes returned to Rome, another papacy and another curia continued in Avignon. For half a century the Great Schism divided Western Christendom into two hostile parties which excommunicated each other.

The Golden Bull issued in 1356 by the emperor Charles IV of Luxemburg (ruled 1347–78) transformed the Holy Roman Empire into a federation of seven sovereign electors.[1] The emperors ceased to be the only representatives of worldly power versus the spiritual power wielded by the popes. Their power decreased while the power of foreign kings increased; on the other hand, the spiritual power of the popes was weighted by a growing ballast of material interests.

Feudal institutions were broken down everywhere by the jealousy of the kingly overlords and by the growing independence and insubordination of the townspeople. The lords were ground between the royal upperstone and the popular netherstone. The feudal world was on the decline.

In short, the outstanding paraphernalia of the world were steadily changing, vanishing. The two pillars, the pope and the emperor, were crumbling. The lords were obliged to negotiate and compromise. The outside world of 1400 was utterly different from that of 1300.

The main series of wars was the Hundred Years' War (1337–1453) between England and France. Those wars were fought on French territory and, being aggravated by civil wars among the French people, caused them to be the victims of infinite miseries. It has been guessed that one-third of the French population was destroyed; the destruction of wealth was at least as great. The average reader who is not a historian of this period is generally hypnotized by the great and mysterious figure of Joan of Arc, but St. Joan's miracles began only in 1428 or 1425; she was captured by the Burgundians in 1430, and condemned to death by an ecclesiastical court in Rouen 1431. By this time the war had lasted almost a century, and the destruction of France was at least as great as it is today. The battle of Poitiers (1356) had been as great a catastrophe as Waterloo or the two Sedans. John the Good, his son, his two brothers, and a great many French lords had been made prisoners by the Black Prince. John's ramson ruined France. Limoges was put to fire and sword in 1370. In spite of having better generals, like the Breton Bertrand du Guesclin (c. 1320–80), France was bled to death.

The growth of the communes was interrupted by many vicissitudes. Thus, Flemish democracy received a terrible setback when their militia, especially that of Ghent, led by Philip van Artevelde (less able than his father Jacob), was defeated on November 27, 1382 at Roosebeke (East Flanders) by Philip II the Bold, duke of Burgundy. The duke of Burgundy had married Marguerite, daughter of Louis II de Male, count of Flanders, and when Louis died, in 1384, the county of Flanders escheated to Burgundy.

In order to understand the situation around the Baltic one has to take into account the vicissitudes of the Scandinavian kingdom, of the Teutonic Order, and of the Hanseatic League. Valdimarr V Atterdag (king of Denmark 1340–75) attacked Gotland and ruined Visby in 1361. Visby had been the cradle of the Hansa (Introd. 2, 1063). Thus began a war between him and the Hansa; Copenhagen was sacked, but the Hansa fleets were defeated in 1362 at Helsingborg (on the Swedish side of the Sound). A few years later the Hansa, supported by Sweden, Norway, Holstein, and Mecklenburg, defeated Valdimarr and obliged him in 1370 to accept the peace of Stralsund (in Pomerania). The Hansa was strengthened in

[1] The archbishops of Mayence, Treves, and Cologne, the count palatine of the Rhine, the duke of Saxony, the margrave of Brandenburg, the king of Bohemia.

the Baltic, but political instability in Scandinavia favored piracy.[2] Scandinavian unity was achieved for a time under Margareta of Denmark (1387–1412), the "Semiramis of the North," who ruled the three kingdoms. She caused the establishment of the Union of Kalmar[3] in 1397. The Hanseatic League declined rapidly in the following century.

The emperor Charles IV of Luxemburg (1347–78) was king of Bohemia under the name of Charles I, and his rule was the golden age of his country. Many proofs of the efflorescence of Bohemian culture will be given in this volume.

The administration of Poland was reformed by Kasimierz III Wielki (Casimir the Great), who ruled from 1333 to 1370 and promoted Polish business and culture. He was succeeded by a prince of Anjou, Louis, whose daughter, Jadwiga (Hedwig), married in 1386 Jagiello, grand duke of Lithuania. This Jagiello was the first ruler, under the name of Wladyslaw V (1386–1434), of the Jagellonian dynasty. The union of Poland and Lithuania provided a strong barrier against the Teutonic Order.

The Swiss federation in spite of its smallness and youth was already strong enough in 1386 to defeat at Sempach (not far from Lucerne) the Austrian invaders led by the Hapsburg Leopold II of Swabia. The Swiss peasants were inspired by the legendary hero Arnold Winkelried. The battle of Sempach and that of Näfels soon afterward (1388) are important landmarks, even as the battle of the Golden Spurs, 1302, in the history of democracy and freedom.[4]

In the Hispanic peninsula the age-long fight against the Muslims was almost completed. Somebody has calculated that 3,700 battles were fought between Christians and Muslims from 710 to 1492. How he reached that figure, and how big a fight must be to be called a battle, I do not know, but it is certain that by this time almost all those battles were already fought, and Spaniards had more energy left to fight among themselves or to attack other Christians. Peter the Cruel ruled Castile from 1350 to 1369, spending a good part of his time fighting his half-brother, the bastard Henry Trastamara. That civil war became an international war, because the Black Prince defended Peter, while the French supported Peter's wife, Blanche de Bourbon, and sent Bertrand du Guesclin to help Henry. In 1369, the latter killed his adversary and succeeded him (Henry II, 1369–79).

Peter the Cruel was a brute, but he deserves our gratitude for his construction of the Alcázar of Seville. It speaks volumes for Muslim influence in Christian Spain that that admirable palace was built in Mudejar (i.e., Moorish) style, though the Moors had been driven out of Seville more than a century before (in 1248).[5]

In 1385, the king of Portugal, João I de Boa Memória, defeated the king of Castile, Juan I, in the battle of Aljubarrota (in Leiria). Thus was the independence of Portugal established and its future glory prepared. In the following year, João I married Philippa of Lancaster, daughter of John of Gaunt, and the treaty of

[2] David K. Bjork: Piracy in the Baltic, 1375–98 (Speculum 18, 39–68, 1943).

[3] In Småland, on the southeast coast of Sweden, opposite the island of Öland.

[4] Theodor von Liebenau: Die Schlacht bei Sempach. Gedenkbuch zur fünften Säcularfeier (468 p., 10 pl., Luzern 1886).

[5] The best parts of the Alhambra of Granada were built at about the same time but by Moorish princes of the Naṣrī dynasty, Yūsuf I, 1333–54; Muḥammad V, 1354–59, 1362–91; Muḥammad VII, 1392–1407. It is purely Moorish and superior to the Alcázar. The Alcázar, however, built by a Christian prince, is one of the best specimens of Moorish castle.

Windsor (1386) sealed the amity of Portugal and England. The famous organizer of maritime discoveries, Henrique o Navegador (1394–1460),[6] was a son of the victor of Aljubarrota and of the English princess.

Reference has already been made to Italian conditions, which were so chaotic that the popes had been obliged to flee Rome and find a refuge in Avignon. The revolt of Cola di Rienzo in 1347 had raised ardent hopes in the hearts of the poor and the scholars, but it was a flash in the pan, and the feudal chaos was allowed to continue until cardinal Albornoz repressed it with an iron hand. Outside the papal domains the main conflict was between Venice and Genoa. In 1354, the Venetian fleet was destroyed by the Genoese at Sapienza.[7] John V Palaeologos having in 1377 given the island of Tenedos, key to the Dardanelles, to the Venetians, the Genoese felt the need of revenge, and their admiral, Luciano Doria, defeated the Venetians near Pola (southern end of the Istrian peninsula, upper Adriatic), landed in Chioggia (south of Venice lagoon), and blockaded Venice. The Venetians, however, were able to cut the Genoese fleet off from its supplies and to cause its surrender (1381). Venice was now mistress of the Adriatic and the Mediterranean and of the Western trade with the East. In order to protect its privileges, Venice concluded a treaty in 1388 with the Turks, who were then the most dangerous enemies of Christendom. The Venetians said, "We cannot allow Christianity to interfere with our business," or if they did not say so, that was their thought. We should not cast stones at them, for many of our own politicians of a few years ago proved to be on the same level.

One of the main causes of chaos and misery was the existence of mercenary troops (grandes compagnies, compagnie di ventura), recruited by captains (condottieri) from among the most lawless and restless elements of many nations. These companies were hired by princes or towns when the latter needed military assistance and discharged when the need was over. In wartime such companies were not necessarily more dangerous than other regiments; sometimes they were definitely less dangerous, for when companies facing each other were equally matched, their captains preferred sometimes to replace too hazardous a battle by a bargain. In time of peace between two campaigns, however, these companies, drawing no pay, lived by rapine and brigandage, robbed and tortured the peasants, sacked the cities or blackmailed them. Kings, lords, or governors employing mercenaries paid them well according to contract as long as the mercenaries were victorious, but as soon as the latter began to suffer reverses, their employers were likely to cut their pay off, and then the mercenaries exacted compensation in their own criminal manner. Mercenaries had been used long before this time, but that evil did not attain its climax until after the middle of the fourteenth century. As far as France is concerned, it was carried to a height during the chaos caused by the Hundred Years' War; as far as Italy and Spain are concerned, it was favored by endless internecine jealousies between princes or cities. Considerable pillage was done by free companies at the beginning of the rule of Charles V (ruled 1364–80), but Bertrand du Guesclin managed to enlist many of them and take them across the Pyrénées to support Henry of Trastamara against Peter the Cruel; another French leader, Bernard d'Armagnac, took disbanded mercenaries to Italy. This saved one country momentarily at the expense of another.

The outstanding condottiere of this age was the Englishman Sir John de Hawk-

[6] See his portrait by Nuno Gonçalves in Isis (22, 442, 1935). See also Isis 24, 7–14, 1935.

[7] Little island off Modon, southwestern point of Greece.

wood[8] (d. 1394), a man of Essex, who was apparently a captain of genius, as courageous as a lion and as resourceful as a fox, but brutal, unscrupulous, ready to fight or blackmail anybody if it was profitable to do so. One of his earliest achievements was to menace Avignon in 1360 and extort sixty thousand francs blackmail from the pope, Innocent VI. Most of his life was spent in Italy; the briefest list of his adventures would be very long and monotonous.[9] He died in Florence in March 1394 and was given a magnificent funeral in the Duomo. In one of his novelle (no. 181), the Florentine storyteller Franco Sacchetti, who was one of Acuto's contemporaries, tells us that the latter, being greeted by friars with the customary salutation "Pace," answered, "Dio vi tolga la vostra limosina." As these unkind words astonished them, he added, "Non sapete voi che io vivo di guerra e la pace mi disfarebbe?"

Indeed, Hawkwood and the other condottieri were professional warriors; they did not deal in munitions for use in distant emergencies, but in men anxious to fight immediately. Happily for them, emergencies were never lacking, here or there, and if they did not exist, it was easy enough to create them.

Before judging them too harshly we should pause and consider that the crowning indignities in that direction were reserved for a much later age, "the age of enlightenment," when one of the German princelings, Friedrich II, Landgraf von Hessen-Cassel, sold his own subjects (the "Hessians") for military use against our people during the American Revolution.

E. de Fréville: Des grandes compagnies au quatorzième siècle (Bibliothèque de l'Ecole des chartes 3, 258–81, 1842; 5, 232–53, 1844). Ercole Ricotti: Storia delle compagnie di ventura in Italia (4 vols., Torino 1845). Alfred Semerau: Die Condottieri (410 p., Jena 1909). Philipp Losch: Soldatenhandel. Mit einem Verzeichnis der Hessen-Kasselischen Subsidienverträge und einer Bibliographie (112 p., Kassel 1933). Including a list of 37 contracts for the sale of "Hessians" to other nations from 1677 to 1815.

When conditions became intolerable the long-suffering peasants revolted, but such spasmodic and ill organized revolts as theirs could only produce more evils and more pains; they did not help much to hasten the days of retribution and equitable repartition, of justice and mercy. The only thing which these revolts achieved was to cause the more thoughtful people to realize the evils of their times and the need of reform. One of the first examples had been given by the West Frisians, who revolted in 1254–88 against the count of Holland. Half a century later, 1323–28, the people of West Flanders, led by Claes[10] Zannekin, tried to establish a rural democracy and to replace manorial tenure of the land by farmers' ownership. The most terrible agrarian troubles occurred after the middle of the century, first in France, then in England.

The French troubles were aggravated and precipitated by the disaster of Poitiers (1356) and by the brigandage of the grandes compagnies. Not only were the French peasants oppressed by their lords, as was the case in every other country, but those lords failed to protect them against the bandits and sometimes even betrayed them and shared profits with the condottieri. By 1358 the French peasant

[8] Froissart often speaks of him, calling him Jean Haccoude. See Kervyn de Lettenhove's edition (21, 533–35, Bruxelles 1875). In Italy he was called Giovanni Acuto.

[9] John Temple-Leader and Giuseppe Marcotti: Giovanni Acuto (306 p., ill., Firenze 1889), Englished by Leader Scott (370 p., ill., London 1889). Including text of 72 documents. J. M. Rigg (DNB 25, 236–42, 1891), good summary.

[10] Claes = Nicholas.

"Jacques Bonhomme" could not stand it any longer, and realized that death itself was sweeter than the continuation of his slavery and sufferings. His revolt, called Jacquerie, burst out in May–June 1358 in the Beauvaisis (Oise), the first leader being Guillaume Carle or Karle. It spread quickly in the neighboring "pays," but the cities refused to help the peasantry, except that Etienne Marcel, provost of the merchants of Paris, sent troops to their rescue. Marcel was murdered in Paris; many other efforts miscarried, the revolt failed.[10a] The Jacquerie had been brutal, its repression was merciless.[11]

The English revolt began twenty-three years later, in 1381, being led by Wat Tyler and John Ball. Its chief cause was serfdom, but many other grievances had clustered around that central one. As in the case of the Pastoureaux, the social unrest was leavened with religious aspirations. Their religious leader was the Wycliffian John Ball, who preached from the text,

When Adam dalf and Eve span
Wo was thanne a gentilman?

The religious malcontents were called Lollards, and for a short time their popular success was such that it was said every fourth man in England was a Lollard. They marched on London, made wise demands but committed stupid excesses, were hoodwinked and defeated. The repression was terrible. Wycliffism and Lollardy, which had been welcome in Oxford, were driven out by William of Courtenay, archbishop of Canterbury (1381–96), in 1382. This opened a very sad period of enslavement for the University of Oxford (Rashdall 3, 125 f., 1936).

For more details see Norman Scott Brien Gras: History of agriculture (p. 103–27, New York 1925). John Ball's preaching was very effectively reported by Froissart. Translation in the Cambridge medieval history (7, 739, 1932).

The most hopeful events in Christendom were those concerning the growth of parliamentary institutions in England. The development of those institutions was greatly helped by the government's need of money for war purposes, money which could be obtained in sufficient quantity only from the burgesses. The king's initiative and power were steadily encroached upon by Parliament. In 1341, all the king's ministers were subjected to parliamentary approval; in 1344 it was voted that a grant should be spent exactly as directed. By the end of the century both the House of Commons and the House of Lords were beginning to shape themselves. The "Good Parliament" of 1376, led by the Black Prince, refused credits until an audit of accounts had been approved, and it impeached William, fourth baron Latimer (1329?–81), as a bad adviser and war profiteer, this being the earliest record of the impeachment of a minister of the crown by the

[10a] Arthur Layton Funk: Robert le Coq and Etienne Marcel (Speculum 19, 470–87, 1944). Robert le Coq, bishop of Laon, was closely associated with Marcel. After the latter's death (1358) Robert was translated by Innocent VI to the see of Calahorra, where he remained until his death, in 1372. Funk's paper shows that the basis of the Jacquerie was much broader than is generally realized.

[11] The Jacquerie of 1358 had been preceded by various other revolts of peasants or "pastoureaux" (= small shepherds). The first had occurred in 1214 in the Berry and the surrounding region; the second, beginning in Picardy 1251, was instigated by a mysterious character, the "master of Hungary," whom Our Lady had sent to preach a social crusade; the third revolt, in 1320, was also led by religious enthusiasts. All these revolts had failed and been cruelly repressed.

Commons. In 1382, archbishop Courtenay held a synod to condemn Wycliffe's opinions; he obtained the king's license to persecute the Lollards, but Parliament refused to allow those persecutions. These parliamentary victories were sometimes followed by defeats, but in spite of many vicissitudes the general movement was in the direction of modern democracy.

In Eastern Europe, the Byzantine empire was steadily diminishing in proportion as Turkish power was increasing. The two stories are complementary; it will suffice to tell one of them. The decadence of Byzantium was due mainly to internal causes, and no help could be obtained from the West because of the unconquerable aversion separating the Latins from the Greeks and the deadly jealousies obtaining between Western powers. The perennial hatred of the Venetians for the Genoese has already been referred to. Here is another illustration of it which may help us to understand more completely the hopelessness of a Christian stand against the Turks in the Near East. The Lusignan rulers of Cyprus used to be crowned in Nicosia as kings of Cyprus and in Famagusta[12] as kings of Jerusalem. In the Famagusta ceremony the consuls of Genoa and Venice were wont to lead the king's horse in the procession, one on either side. When Peter II was crowned, in 1369, the two consuls quarreled on a matter of precedence; the king sided with the Venetian, a battle followed, and the Genoese sent an avenging fleet in 1372, captured and sacked the island; the Genoese kept Famagusta from 1372 to 1464.[13] The failure of the crusade of Nicopolis in 1396 may be ascribed partly to the fact that the sulṭān Bāyazīd had been forewarned by Gian Galeazzo Visconti, duke of Milano.[14]

The increase of Turkish power and of the Turkish menace to Byzantium and Christendom may be summarized with the following facts. Under the second 'Uthmānlī sulṭān, Urkhān (1326–60), the Turks secured their first foothold on European ground, namely at Tzympe, Gallipoli, 1354, and they spread rapidly through Thrace. This invasion was caused by an appeal for help made by Joannes VI Cantacuzenos! Under Murād I (1360–89), the Turks took Adrianople, 1365, and made it their capital; they began the conquest of Bulgaria (1369–72), whose ruler, Iovan Shishman III, became their vassal; they defeated the Serbs (1371), conquered Macedonia, made raids into Greece and Albania, took Sofia (1385), Nish (1386), defeated a Balkanic coalition led by Lazar of Serbia in 1389. By this time both Genoa and Venice had already made treaties with the Turks. The process of attrition continued under Bāyazīd Yildirim (1389–1402); Constantinople was besieged (1391–98), a Christian host led by Sigismund of Hungary was defeated at Nicopolis on the Danube 1396, Greece was invaded as far as the gulf of Corinth.[15] Byzantium was in its agony when it was saved by a miracle, the arrival from Central Asia of Tīmūr Lang, who defeated Bāyazīd in Ankara (1402). A strange fate had granted the empire half a century of respite, but it was doomed nevertheless.

In the meanwhile, Tatars of the Golden Horde had been settling in Russia, Lithuania, and Poland. During the fourteenth century Tatars helped Lithuanians

[12] After the loss of 'Akkā (St. Jean d'Acre), 1291.

[13] Sir Ronald Storrs and Bryan Justin O'Brien: Handbook of Cyprus (9th ed., p. 21, London 1930).

[14] Atiya (p. 9, 435–62, 1938).

[15] Not Athens! Since 1204 the glorious city had suffered many vicissitudes. It had been ruled in turn by Frenchmen, Catalans, Sicilians, Aragonians. In 1385, the Florentine Nero Acciaiuoli assumed the title of duke of Athens. The Acciaiuoli dynasty continued to rule until the Turkish conquest by Muḥammad al-Fātiḥ in 1456–58 (Stokvis 2, 465–69, 1889).

to resist encroachments of the Teutonic Knights. Tīmūr having defeated the khān of the Golden Horde, Tūqtāmish Ghiāth al-dīn, in 1391, more Tatars moved westward. The Tatar or Muslim culture of Kazan (near the confluence of the Volga and Kama rivers), a culture called in Arabic Qāzānī or Bulghārī, began only in the following century; from the religious point of view, it drew its substance from the mosques and schools of Bukhārā.

W. Barthold: Qazān or Qāzān (EI 2, 837-38, 1925); Tatar (EI 4, 700-2, 1929). L. Bohdanowicz: The Muslims in Poland (Journal of the Royal Asiatic Society, 1942, p. 163-80).

The expeditions and conquests of Tīmūr from 1369 to his death in 1405 influenced the whole of Asia and of Eastern Europe, either directly or indirectly through the nomadic populations which were hustled out of their usual territories, or through the sedentary populations which were uprooted and violently displaced. The main result on the credit side was the creation of a new (Tīmūrī) culture in central Asia, "beyond the river,"[16] especially in Samarqand. That culture did not last very long as Tīmūr had planned it, but his descendants extended it in various forms, the most remarkable being the so-called "Mogul" culture of India. Bābar Ẓahīr al-dīn, the first Mogul emperor (1526-30), was a descendant of Tīmūr in the fifth generation; the great Akbar (1556-1605) was a descendant in the seventh generation.

On the debit side, we must note in the first place the unsettlement and sterilization for centuries of the Arabic cultures of the Near East, already weakened by the Black Death (1348, 1381) and by Turkish hegemony.

The Timurian invasions caused a fantastic reshuffling of Asiatic cultures, because whatever knocks Tīmūr delivered here or there were transmitted from one end of Asia to another with incredible speed. In order to understand the history of Asia, north of India, one must always bear in mind the extreme mobility of the nomadic tribes.[17] Tīmūr was not the inventor of "Blitzkrieg"; he simply improved in some technical details an immemorial tradition of the peoples of the plains.

Reference has often been made in this volume to the nefarious influences of astrology and magic in all kinds of private and political affairs. Those influences were strong in the West, yet to some extent mitigated by the church. In the Muslim East they might be mitigated by wise theologians, but the interference of the latter was rarer and more casual. In Central and Eastern Asia, they were apparently unmitigated. Every event could be explained by astrologers or prophesied; in many cases a prediction became a cause. In the fourteenth century, it would not have been necessary to teach preparedness against hypothetical enemies; it would have sufficed to foretell a definite war with sufficient technicality and solemnity. There were always court astrologers and soothsayers to do that.

The power of the great Muslim sulṭān of northern India, Muḥammad ibn Taghlaq, began to wane before the end of his rule. His immense empire preserved its integrity for only a few years. Indeed, his mad tyranny had excited implacable hostilities and caused a series of rebellions from 1343 to 1351. One of these revolts insured the liberation of the northern part of the Deccan, above the Kistna river. That revolt was led by an Afghān or Turkī official, Ḥasan Gāngū, who had risen to high office and had received the title Ẓafar khān. He defeated the royal armies,

[16] Beyond the river Oxus = Transoxiana = Mā warā-l-nahr (Jayḥūn, Āmū Daryā).

[17] See application of this idea to linguistics by Jean Deny in Meillet and Cohen (p.187,1924).

occupied Dawlatābād in 1347, proclaimed himself king under the style 'Alā' al-dīn Ḥasan Bahmanī,[18] and established his capital in Kulbargā (in the Niẓām's dominion), which he called in Muslim style Aḥsanābād. He ruled twelve years, 1347–58, and the Bahmanī dynasty which he founded lasted almost two centuries (1347–1526). Between the death of Muḥammad ibn Taghlaq in 1351 and his own in 1358, 'Alā' al-dīn conquered a large part of the Deccan. His kingdom finally extended from Berār in the north to Vijayanagar to the south, and from sea to sea east and west.

His successor, Muḥammad Shāh I (1358–75), conducted a ferocious war against his southern neighbors. This was largely a racial and religious war against the Hindu culture of Vijayanagar; the Hindu infidels had to be destroyed or Islamized. That fanatical task was continued by the other Bahmanī salāṭīn, the most splendid of whom was Tāj al-dīn Fīrūz Shāh (1397–1421). It is remarkable that in spite of Bahmanī efforts to exterminate the Hindu people of the Deccan, the population of that selfsame territory today is overwhelmingly (say, 90 per cent) Hindu.

This Fīrūz Shāh should not be confused with another sulṭān of the same name who succeeded Muḥammad ibn Taghlaq and ruled northern India from 1351 to 1388. Fīrūz Shāh Taghlaq left the Bahmanī kingdom in peace and tried to reorganize what remained of his own; he built a new Delhi called Fīrūzābād, also other cities, and he abolished torture; he was charitable and well meaning, but self-righteous and intolerant. After his death, in 1388, there was much confusion, changed into chaos by the invasion of Tīmūr ten years later. Tīmūr killed people by the hundred thousand, sacked cities, and when further destruction became unprofitable and tiresome withdrew from India, "leaving anarchy, famine and pestilence behind him."

The contemporary history of Vijayanagar has already been told, for the main events of this period were its struggle against the fanatical and predatory Muslims of the Bahmanī kingdom, its close neighbors to the north. More information on Hindu history may easily be obtained in Vincent A. Smith's excellent textbook (1923).

As to China, the Pax mongolica, thanks to which so many Western travelers had been able to cross Asia in relative safety, had almost ceased to obtain by the middle of the fourteenth century. The last capable rulers of the Yüan dynasty had been Ch'êng Tsung (1294–1307), grandson of Kublai Khān (XIII-2), and Jên Tsung (1311–20), the latter already far less capable than the former.[19] After Jên Tsung matters had gone rapidly from bad to worse. Rebels and bandits desolated the provinces. The Mongols were losing their grip. The fifteenth and last emperor of the Yüan dynasty, Hui Tsung,[20] whose unauspicious rule began in 1333, was soon obliged to devote all his energy to the suppression of plots and rebellions. The crisis became so grave that in 1340 he suspended the public examinations (keystone of the civil service), using the funds thus released for the imperial bodyguard. As the Chinese became more refractory, new methods of restraining them were introduced, and thus new tensions and new causes of mutiny produced.

[18] He assumed the title Bahman or Bahmanī, because he claimed descent from the Achaemenian king of that name, better known as Artaxerxes I Longimanus (465–424 B.C.) = Ardashīr Darāzdast = Ahasuerus in the book of Esther.

[19] Ch'êng Tsung is the dynastic title of Tīmūr, alias Olcheitu (Giles no. 1929); Jên Tsung, that of Ayuli Palpata (Giles no. 13).

[20] Dynastic title of Tughān Tīmūr; Ming historians give him the title Shun Ti. He was born in 1320 and died at Qaraqorum in 1370 (Giles no. 1953).

It was proposed to slay all the men called Li, Liu, Chao, Chang, and Wang! this might have saved the Mongols but depopulated China. The Yang tzŭ chiang joined the rebels, flooding the country. Famine ensued. The government, being desperately short of funds, issued fiat money, which paralyzed trade. In short, everything was ready for the end of the Yüan dynasty, everything including the necessary leader of the revolution, a poor man called Chu Yüan-chang.[21] After having been a novice in a Buddhist monastery, he became a revolutionary leader by the force of circumstances. By 1367, he was holding the Yang tzŭ valley; in the following year he took Peking, and ascended the imperial throne, assuming the title Hung Wu. His military genius enabled him to conquer and pacify the empire; his administrative genius, to reorganize it completely. He was just and merciful. He unified China, driving Mongol remnants out of Qaraqorum (1372, 1388) and Yünnan (1381). He did his best to re-establish the purest Chinese traditions (those of the T'ang dynasty), improved the system of examinations, patronized education, arts, and letters, codified the law, regulated the coinage and taxation, revived Confucianism, recognized Buddhism and Taoism as state religions.

All that was admirable, but the dark side of the picture was that the institutions of the new Ming dynasty tended to be considered excellent and to be crystallized with no possibility of reform. The empire itself, Chung Kuo,[22] was perfect and self-sufficient. From 1350 on, and more completely from 1368 on, China was cut off from the West. At the very time when Europe was beginning to progress and was gradually discovering the secret of perpetual youth (the experimental method), the Ming were so convinced of their superiority over all the foreign barbarians that they became unable to learn anything. Foreign contacts, they thought, could only spoil their own excellence. Every effort was made to avoid the possibility of such contacts; the leaven which the Jesuits succeeded in smuggling in could hardly operate. Ming autarchy and self-righteousness were continued and aggravated by the Manchus until our own days—but that is another story, which does not concern us now.

To return to the fourteenth century, the anti-Mongol rebellions had naturally spread to Korea. A Korean revolt occurred in 1356. The Korean kings, however, remained loyal to the Yüan rulers. The result was a series of civil wars between the kings and some of their vassals, and popular disorders. The situation was aggravated by increasing depredations of Japanese pirates and by economic difficulties. The establishment of the new Li dynasty in 1392 put an end to these civil troubles; that dynasty lasted more than five centuries (until 1910), and but for Japanese greed it would still exist today. The dynastic change in Korea was partly a consequence of the dynastic change which had occurred in China twenty-five years before. Korean loyalty to China was not affected, but a new China caused the emergence of a new Korea.[23] To the prosperity of the early Ming corresponded in Korea the prosperity of the early Li.

Up to 1392 the Chinese had called their little neighbor Kao-li-kuo; from 1392 on they called it Chao-hsien-kuo.[24]

[21] Born in Anhui 1328, died on the dragon throne in 1399. Canonized as T'ai Tsu (Giles no. 483).

[22] The Middle Kingdom (surrounded by the four seas, beyond which are barbarians living on islands). The term is very old, pre-Han.

[23] L. Carrington Goodrich: Sino-Korean relations at the end of the fourteenth century (Transactions, Korea branch, Royal Asiatic Society, 30, 33–46, Seoul 1940).

[24] The Japanese pronunciation of the first two characters of these names is, respectively, Kōrai and Chōsen. Our name Korea is derived from the earlier Chinese name.

In Japan, the Ashikaga period had begun unauspiciously with civil wars and even with a dynastic schism. Indeed, from 1331 to 1393 there were two imperial dynasties, the Southern one and the Northern (schismatic) one. Go-Daigo-tennō[25] had been obliged to flee from his capital, Kyōto, and the first emperor of the Northern dynasty, Kōgon-tennō, had been put in his place in 1331. The sixth emperor of the Northern dynasty, Go-Komatsu-tennō, ruled from 1383 on, but in 1392 the legitimate emperor Go-Kameyama-tennō abdicated in favor of his rival. Go-Komatsu then became legitimate emperor, the one hundredth (1393–1412) according to Japanese mythologists. At the time of Go-Kameyama's abdication it had been solemnly covenanted that Go-Komatsu's successors should be chosen alternately from the two branches of the imperial family. That covenant was not kept. Go-Kameyama lived long enough to see it violated twice; his descendants were excluded forever from the imperial throne.

Of course, the actual ruler was not the lord of heaven Go-Komatsu, but the Ashikaga shōgun Yoshimitsu (1367–95), succeeded by his son Yoshimochi (1395–1423). This was a great age of art. To mention a single example, the memory of Yoshimitsu is immortalized by the exquisite Kinkaku-ji (golden pavilion) which he built near Kyōto in 1397 (that is, after his retirement; he died in 1408).

In spite of the civil war and the imperial schism, the work which Kitabatake Chikafusa had completed c. 1342 was already bearing its fruits. The Japanese emperors and feudal princes (daimyō) had already swallowed the mythological politics explained in the Jingō shōtō-ki. Though they were hardly emancipated from Chinese culture, and would not be for centuries to come, they were already believing in their own divine superiority. Thus is the future prepared by individual fantasies and collective hallucinations.

Japanese intercourse with China and Korea was made difficult by dynastic troubles; it was jeopardized and brought into disrepute by the increasing activities of Japanese pirates[26] operating along the coasts of their western neighbors. Buddhist needs, however, caused the importation of art objects, books, and missionaries from the mother country, China. For example, some celadon porcelain is known to this day in Japan as Tenryū-ji-seiji, because it was imported mostly by the Tenryū-ji founded by Soseki in 1342; the vessels used in that trade (limited to two per year) were called Tenryū-ji-bune.

The history of Siam as an independent country (Muang Thai, land of the free) may be said to begin in 1350. To be sure, the valley of the great river Menam Chao Phya (or Menam River) had been inhabited from time immemorial by Mon-Khmer peoples, but we know very little about their history. Another nation of Sino-Tibetan origin, the Lao Thai, came down from the mountains in the north and invaded the rich valley gradually. These migrations on the familiar pattern, from the inhospitable mountains into the fertile valley, were accelerated when the Mongols under Kublai Khān (XIII-2) invaded southern Ssŭch'uan and Yünnan. The Thai people inhabiting these southern provinces of China moved southward, pushing before them others, and so on. The gradual conquest of the many kingdoms scattered in the Menam valley is too long a story to be told here. The climax occurred when Phra Chao U'thong (Phra Chao Rama Tibodi I, 1350–69) consoli-

[25] The word tennō, Japanese reading of the Chinese characters t'ien huang (lord of heaven), is generally added to the emperor's name, but it is a title, not a name. There are many other imperial titles, but this is the standard one, so much so that it means "emperor."

[26] An account of these Japanese pirates (wo k'ou), who infested the Chinese coast during the Ming dynasty, was written by Chiang Ch'ên-ying, d. 1699 (Hummel p. 135, 1943).

dated these gains and became the first king of Siam, establishing his capital in Ayuthia (east of the Menam, 43 miles north of Bangkok). King Rama Tibodi's power extended not only over the lower Menam valley, but also over a good part of Burma (Moulmein, Mergui, Tenasserim), the Bengal Gulf, and parts of the Malay Peninsula. One must not think of such dominion in terms of contiguous territory with definite boundaries, but rather in terms of separate outposts. For example, the Thai might dominate Moulmein and Mergui without being able to control the mountainous districts lying east of those points. Siam proper is a natural region neatly limited to the west by the Burmese chains, to the north by the last counterforts of the Tibetan mountains, and to the north and east by the mountains dividing the Menam basin from the Mekong basin. During the second half of the fourteenth century the Thai rulers made frequent incursions into the Mekong territory (that is, Cambodia, their eastern neighbor). Thus the Khmer power was gradually undermined, and this meant the destruction of the magnificent monuments of Angkor-Vat.[27]

The Thai rulers of Ayuthia had frequent conflicts with another Thai kingdom, capital Chiengmai, in the western upper reaches of the Menam valley. Burma was involved, and this caused a series of triangular wars between Burma, Ayuthia, and Chiengmai. The Thai rulers of Ayuthia sent a "tributary" mission to Nanking in 1371 to congratulate the first Ming emperor. By the end of the century, however, and down to 1450 or 1500 they were the dominant power in Southeastern Asia.

The first king of Ayuthia, Phra Rama Tibodi, was not simply a conqueror, but a great administrator, who codified the customs of his people and organized Siamese culture. Ayuthia remained the capital for four centuries, that is, until 1767, when it was destroyed by the Burmese. The Thai capital was then moved nearer to the mouth of the Menam, to Bangkok, where it has continued to be to this day.

There is a whole family, fairly homogeneous, of Thai languages, the most important of which is the Siamese. The Siamese script was created in 1284, and the oldest known Siamese inscription dates from 1293. See Jean Przyluski in Meillet and Cohen (p. 379-84, 1924). The Thai tribes were often called by themselves Tshām or Shām (Burmese pronunciation, Shān), hence the word "Siam" and also the Chinese name of their country.[28]

The Thai culture was Buddhist but on a Brahmanic foundation, which was carefully preserved because of its use in royal ceremonies and other temporal matters, for which Buddhism did not provide a proper ritual. In the absence of documents, the history of Thai sculpture affords one of the best approaches to the understanding of the early Thai culture.

Alfred Salmony: Sculpture in Siam (folio, London 1925). William Alfred Rae Wood: History of Siam (Bangkok 1926; reprinted 1933). Ananda K. Coomaraswamy: History of Indian and Indonesian art (quarto, p. 175-80, London

[27] These monuments, dating from the twelfth and thirteenth centuries, were seen by Chou Ta-kuan (XIII-2) in 1296. When the Thai conquered the Khmer, these immense monuments were neglected and soon conquered by the jungle. For the history of their ruins see Introd. 2, 1067. Angkor-Vaṭ is outside Siam proper, in Cambodia, west of the Mekong but in the Mekong basin.

[28] That Chinese name is Hsien lo kuo. The first character is probably a Chinese imitation of the sound Shān, just as "Siam" is a European imitation of it. The second character, lo, is the same as that used in "lo lo" to designate some hill tribes of Ssŭch'uan and Yünnan, called Lolos in English. May we remark in passing that the name "Thailand" upon which the Siamese government insisted until recently is far more outlandish than the name "Siam."

1927). Reginald Le May: Concise history of Buddhist art in Siam (quarto, 188 p., 206 ill., Cambridge 1938).

These notes, which could be lengthened indefinitely, are sufficient to give the reader a general view of the political background of the world in the second half of the fourteenth century. Enough of them have been devoted to Eastern matters to make him realize the necessity of considering always the Eastern side of the world as well as its Western one if he would see it as a whole. More historical notes have occasionally been given in separate articles of this volume whenever it was thought necessary to refresh the reader's memory, and whenever this could be done within a brief compass. The intellectual history which is our main concern is of course dominated by military, political, and economic events, but small events may have a disproportionately large influence. For example, a school or an academy might be destroyed in a little affray between rival lords or bandits just as thoroughly as in an international war. It is difficult to say just how much political history the historian of science should know. He should be able to understand the general situation, without going into too many details, yet the little affray just mentioned would arrest his curiosity, and thus he might be led to consider historical events too small to interest the political historian. Or else events would suddenly assume a new importance in his eyes because of casual results. To illustrate, the almost accidental murder of Archimedes by a Roman s ldier in 212 B.C. obliges him to investigate the sack of Syracuse more carefully. Archimedes is of far greater importance in the history of mankind than Claudius Marcellus, yet the latter unwittingly caused the death of the former, and we must take him into account. Many similar examples will be found in this volume. Not only is it not possible to disregard the historical background, but we cannot tell beforehand how much history must be studied.

II. RELIGIOUS BACKGROUND

A. *Western Christendom*

Before we try to determine the religious efforts made in different parts of the West and to ascertain as it were the religious color of the various countries submitted to papal obedience, it is useful to set forth a few generalities.

1. *The government of the church*

The first French popes[1] have been introduced above (chapter I, section II); to wit, Bertrand de Got (Clement V), Jacques Duèse (John XXII), Jacques Fournier (Benedict XII), and Pierre Roger (Clement VI). The last named, who ruled until 1352, had done much to increase and adorn the pontifical palace in Avignon; he had fought with success the gangsters who terrorized Rome, and had extended his protection to persecuted Jews. Clement VI was followed by Innocent VI (1352–62), whose original name was Etienne Auber (or d'Albert), a Limousin, professor of canon law in Toulouse, bishop, cardinal. He had called Petrarca a sorcerer for reading Virgil, but later favored him, and was not an enemy of letters. He founded the "Chartreuse" (Carthusian monastery) at Villeneuve,[2] across the Rhône from

[1] The first French popes ruling, as it were, in French territory. There had been other French popes ruling in Rome, the first being Gerbert of Aurillac or Sylvester II (X-2), two more in XI-2, one in XII-1, and three in XIII-2, to wit Urban IV, Clement IV, and Martin IV.

[2] During the Avignonese papacy many cardinals built palaces in Villeneuve, where they were close to the curia yet in French territory.

Avignon, and fought the grandes compagnies (bands of freebooters) which were devastating the French country; his legate, cardinal Albornoz (appointed by Clement VI in 1350), assured (?) the pacification of his Italian subjects and gave them a new code in 1357. After him came Guillaume de Grimoard, blessed Urban V (1362–70), a Benedictine from the Gévaudan, who had taught law in various universities; he completed the building of the immense palace of Avignon,[3] a task which had kept four popes busy for more than thirty years. He was the first pope to return to Rome, this being made possible by cardinal Albornoz' "pacification." In spite of the remonstrances made by Oresme and other Frenchmen, he left in 1367, but was so pestered by the Romans and other Italians that he was already back in Avignon in 1370! The next pope, the last French one, was Pierre Roger de Beaufort, Gregory XI (1370–78), a nephew of Clement VI and thus cardinal at the age of 18. He was still in deacon's orders at 39 when elected pope, was made a priest one day and elevated to the pontificate on the next one. He worked for spiritual peace according to his lights, condemning Lullists and Beghards. Under the influence of St. Catherine of Siena he reconciled Florence with the church, left Avignon in 1376, and after a very painful journey arrived in Rome in 1377. The eternal city was then ruined by protracted anarchy, misery, epidemics; its population reduced to some 17,000 people.[4] Thus ended the Babylonish captivity, and to some it might seem that the church was finally liberated from dire perils, yet her real troubles were only beginning.

Gregory XI died in 1378, soon after his return to Rome. Under pressure of the Roman people, who feared the election of a French pope, the sacred college (sixteen cardinals, only four of them being Italians) gave the tiara to a Neapolitan, Bartolommeo Prignano. This pope, Urban VI (1378–89), turned out to be so despotic that fifteen of the cardinals, having escaped to Anagni (40 km. from Rome), declared the election voided because of external pressure and elected a new pope, Robert of Geneva, ruthless soldier and cardinal, under the name Clement VII (1378–94). There were now two competing popes, a dismal situation which lasted half a century.

The Roman pope, Urban VI, was followed by three other Italians: Piero Tomacelli of Naples, Boniface IX (1389–1404); Cosmo Megliorati of Sulmona (Abruzzi), Innocent VII (1404–6); and Angelo Corrario (or Correr) of Venice, at one time titular patriarch of Constantinople, Gregory XII (1406–15). In the meanwhile, the antipope Clement VII was followed by the Aragonese Pedro de Luna, Benedict XIII (1394–1417, 1424).

The schism had taken on a political aspect, for the "Urbanists," as they were called at first, or the popes of Rome, received the obedience of northern and central Italy, Corsica, the Empire (with a few exceptions), Hungary, Poland, Scandinavia, England, Ireland, while the Avignonese popes were supported by France, Spain, the kingdom of Naples and Sicily, Sardinia (enfeoffed to Aragon), Scotland, Rhodes, and Cyprus. The situation became so unbearable that at the initiative of the University of Paris, drastic means were taken to cure it. A council assembled in

[3] Léon Honoré Labande: Le palais des papes et les monuments d'Avignon au XIVe siècle (quarto, 2 vols., ill., Marseille 1925). Most readers will be satisfied with the shorter study by Brun (1928).

[4] The population of Rome had reached c. 1377 its absolute minimum in Christian times; in 1198 it was still c. 35,000, in 1513, c. 40,000. That minimum was partly caused by the Black Death of 1348 and the earthquake of 1349. Pietro Castiglioni: Della populazione di Roma dalle origini ai nostri tempi (Roma 1878). For the sake of comparison, there were in Athens in 1394 according to Niccolò di Martoni (q.v.) about 1,000 hearths.

Pisa 1409 deposed Gregory XII and Benedict XIII and elected in their stead one Pietro Philargo,[5] Alexander V (1409–10), a Cretan waif, who had assumed the Franciscan habit, received a splendid education, and been finally elevated to the cardinalate. The council's preference for a man without family and without country was natural enough, too many popes having exploited their position for the benefit of their kinsmen or countrymen.

Alexander V sat in St. Peter's chair for hardly more than ten months, being replaced in Bologna 1410 by Baldassare Cossa of Naples, John XXIII (1410–15), while Benedict XIII continued to hold sway in Avignon. Under the combined pressure of the University of Paris and the emperor Sigismund, John XXIII in 1414 summoned a new council in Constance. He even attended it, but was soon obliged to make himself scarce because of the terrible accusations preferred against him. Gregory XII, who was still living, submitted to the council's authority, John XXIII was deposed, Benedict XIII excommunicated, and a new pope elected. This was Oddone[6] Colonna (of the illustrious Colonna family), crowned in Constance 1417 under the name Martin V.[7] The rule of Martin V (1417–31) may be said to have ended the schism.[8]

I trust this digression into the fifteenth century will be forgiven me. I wrote it mainly for scientific readers unfamiliar with ecclesiastical history. In order to understand the meaning of the Great Schism, which began in 1378 and continued until Martin's election in 1417 (or Clement's abdication in 1429), one must have some idea of its length and vicissitudes. It was not a short interlude of misunderstanding and papal duplication such as had happened before and would happen again, but an endless period of struggle which divided Catholicism and Europe into two inimical factions at the very time when the unity of Christendom was more needed than ever to resist Turkish encroachments.

The following table summarizes the complicated story which has been told:

Regular popes[9]		*Antipopes*	
202. Urban VI	1378–89	Clement VII	1378–94
203. Boniface IX	1389–1404	Benedict XIII	1394–1417, 1424
204. Innocent VII	1404–6		
205. Gregory XII	1406–9, 1415		
206. Alexander V	1409–10		
207. John XXIII	1410–15		
208. Martin V	1417–31	Clement VIII	1424–29

All the regular popes in this list were Italians, except the Cretan Alexander V. The antipopes were French or Aragonese. The old Aragonese Pedro de Luna (Benedict XIII) was the bastion of resistance to Rome. As Jean Gerson put it, "there would be no peace in the church as long as that moon was not eclipsed."

5 See the note devoted to Peter of Crete.

6 Oddone = Otto, Eudes.

7 He was a subdeacon at the time of his election and within a week's time was consecrated priest, bishop, pope. This is the third example of such rapid elevation in those troubled days, the other two being Gregory XI and John XXIII.

8 In 1424, the last antipope, Gil Muñoz, canon of Barcelona, was elected by Benedict's cardinals pope Clement VIII. He resigned in 1429 when his king, Alfonso V of Aragon, was reconciled with Martin V; he died bishop of Majorca, 1446.

9 As given in CE (12, 274, 1911). The numbering of the early popes is difficult; the ordinal numbers here given are tentative.

Excommunicated by two councils, he fought and wore out five popes; after being besieged in Avignon, he ran away and spent his remaining years in Peñiscola (Valencia), dying there at 90, unshakable until the end.

The Babylonish captivity had done considerable harm to the church. It was agreeable to France, but the rest of the world, most of all the Italians, could not bear to pay Peter's pence and other taxes for the special benefit of French pontiffs and French prelates.[10] Out of 134 cardinals created by the Avignonese popes, 113 were French (Brun p. 264, 1928). That seems terrible, but after all it was not much worse than what has been done by Italian popes ever since. The majority of the sacred college has always been overwhelmingly Italian, though nobody would claim that Italy has more merit than all the rest of Catholic Christendom put together. Such policy can be justified only by the specious arguments used to defend nepotism pure and simple.[10a]

In many countries, such as England, French exactions, being a novelty, were resented more than the Italian ones, which were already in the nature of vested interests. During the rule of Edward III various defensive measures were taken against Avignonese greed of money and power. In 1351, the Statute of Provisors was issued to prevent the pope from exercising the right of provision and reservation of benefices in England; the fact that that statute had to be confirmed in 1362 and 1390 suggests that it was often disregarded. In 1353, the Statute of Praemunire (= praemonere facias) forbade appeals to foreign courts. In 1366, the Parliament rejected the papal request for renewal of the tribute which John Lackland had promised to pay in 1213 and which Edward III had stopped in 1333; it declared that no king had power to enfeoff England to the pope; in 1371, it declared bishops unfit for state offices. The general trend of these royal and parliamentary decisions is clear enough; it prefigures the creation of the church of England, which was finally established (1563) under the combined pressure of English nationalism and endless papal encroachments.

Bad as the Babylonish captivity was, it was nothing as compared with the Great Schism which followed. Passions ran high and innumerable misdeeds were committed on both sides. To cite a single instance, six cardinals of Clement VII's party were dragged in chains to Genoa by order of Urban VI, and the doge Antoniotto Adorno caused them to be tortured and murdered (Atiya p. 400, 1938). There were not only antipopes, but anticardinals, antigenerals of the orders. Catholic Christendom was divided into two halves excommunicating each other.[11]

[10] The hatred against the Avignonese popes can be deduced from such documents as the letter of congratulations addressed c. 1351 "ad malos principes ecclesiasticos" (i.e., Clement VI and his curia) supposedly by Lucifer! (HL 24, 34, 1862).

[10a] Those iniquitous conditions have been finally remedied by the present pontiff, the Roman Eugenio Pacelli, who assumed the name Pius XII at the time of his consecration in 1939. At the consistory of February 18, 1946, he created thirty-two new cardinals, bringing the Sacred College to its full complement of seventy. Never have as many cardinals been created in a single consistory. Pius XII did it to increase the internationality of the college; for the first time in many centuries the Italian cardinals do not constitute its majority.

[11] In some extreme cases the sacraments (such as baptisms and marriages) administered by priests of the one obedience were called invalid by priests of the other! (Connolly p. 73, 1928). Connolly's book contains much information on the schism apropos of Jean Gerson, who labored indefatigably to heal it, as chancellor of the University of Paris and royal legate to the council of Constance. Gerson tried hard to end the schism by the voluntary abdication of the popes and by compromise, and accepted the conciliar method only c. 1409, when other avenues of peace proved to be closed.

If one were to listen to the publicists of either party, the other party was living in a state of mortal sin. Even the saints were divided; the two Catherines were on the side of Urban and anathematized Clement, while St. Vincent Ferrer and St. Colette[12] were on the other side. What were the plain people to believe when the very saints disagreed? It is true they were not asked anything. They were told partisan untruths by their leaders; the lines of cleavage were largely national. Yet every thinking man was aware of the schism; the whole literature of the time, whether religious or profane, is permeated with the feeling of that growing horror. If God chose his vicar, how could he countenance two or three at a time? The accumulated lies and crimes of both sides stank to heaven. People who had been faithful began to wonder and to doubt, and those who had been firm trembled. It was as if the spiritual basis of the world had been shaken and shattered. The world recovered, but the church never did; the latter had been weakened so much that it was unable to resist the greater and lasting schism which was to occur a century later. The Great Schism was indirectly one of the main causes of the Reformation.

2. *The Crusades*

After the fall of 'Akkā (Acre) in 1291, the Frankish trade had concentrated on the Cilician coast (kingdom of Little Armenia), especially in the harbor of Ayās (Italian, Lajazzo). Ayās was destroyed by the Mamlūk sulṭān al-Nāṣir Muḥammad in 1322, rebuilt, and destroyed again in 1347 by the Mamlūk al-Nāṣir Ḥasan. That was the end of it and almost the end of Armenia;[13] some scholars[14] would call the fall of Ayās the final blow to the Crusades. And yet the Crusades continued, and some important ones were still to come, those of Peter I of Lusignan, of Amedeo VI of Savoy, of Louis II of Bourbon, and finally the most dismal one of Nicopolis (1396).[15] Religious enthusiasm for the conquest of the Holy Land and the submission of the Turks might have been awakened at the end of the century by the appeals of illustrious refugees, such as Peter I of Lusignan, king of Cyprus, who traveled in Western Europe in 1362–65; Leo V, king of Armenia, who visited in vain the courts of Urban VI and Clement VII; or Manuel II Palaeologos, who wandered as a pilgrim in Italy, France, and England, 1399–1401. All these efforts failed because the selfishness and greed of the Western nations were far greater than their faith. Their faith was intermittent and weak; their greed, enduring and insatiable. The Venetians said, "Siamo Veneziani poi Cristiani." The Genoese did not say such things, but did worse. They took advantage of the tumult to attack Chios and indulge in piracy; they betrayed the Crusaders and carried on a flourishing trade in Christian slaves, whom they collected in Caffa,[16] in order to reinforce the Mamlūk army! It was not possible to carry the ignominy any farther.

The church helped to destroy the crusading ideal in other ways, for its hatred of Islām and the Turks, intense as it was, was never sufficient to make it forget its

[12] Colette Boilet, born in Picardy 1380, died in Ghent 1446. She reformed the order of Poor Clares.

[13] The last king of Armenia, Leo V, was conquered in 1375 by the Mamlūk governor of Aleppo, Sayf al-dīn 'Ishq Tīmūr (Morgan p. 233, 1919). Leo V was prisoner in Cairo from 1375 to 1382, then released; he died in Paris 1393.

[14] E.g., Henri Lammens.

[15] Aziz Suryal Atiya: The crusade of Nicopolis (246 p., London 1934). Atiya (1938).

[16] Or Cafa, Κάφα, a Crimean harbor controlled by the Genoese from the second half of the thirteenth century until the middle of the fifteenth century. W. Barthold (EI 2, 617–18, 1924).

hatred of the Greeks and of Orthodoxy, and it tried repeatedly to take advantage of the misery of Oriental Christians, in order to reduce them to obedience. How could any idealism thrive in an atmosphere poisoned with such perfidies, jealousies, base motives, and double-crossings?

After the calamity of Nicopolis (1396) the crusading spirit was apparently quenched, and it became impossible to find rulers and knights naïve enough to plan common action in the defense of the East for the ultimate benefit of Venetian merchants and Genoese pirates. The propaganda literature of which we could still quote so many examples in the first half of the fourteenth century ceased almost completely; the only publicist whose activity was not stopped by the Nicopolis disaster was Philippe de Mézières, who lived until 1405. Other disasters followed thick and fast. Cyprus was conquered in 1424–26, Rhodes in 1440–45, Constantinople in 1453. In 1461, Thomas Palaeologos[17] took refuge in Rome, bringing the head of St. Andrew the Apostle. He revived the crusading flame in the heart of Pius II (Enea Silvio de' Piccolomini, pope 1458–64). That was really the last flame. After that the crusading ideal may still have flickered from time to time, but only in the minds of visionaries such as Christopher Columbus.[18]

To complete this dark picture, the missionary efforts in China were brutally stopped in 1368 when the Mongol dynasty, which was cosmopolitan and tolerant, was replaced by the Ming dynasty, which was militantly Chinese and exclusive. Thus ended for centuries the hope, not only of Christianizing China, but also of obtaining allies in Eastern and Central Asia with whom to crush the Muslim hosts of the Near East. After a century of intercourse with the West, China became again a remote, inaccessible country.

3. *Religious orders*

The main possibilities in the organization of religious orders had already been explored before the fourteenth century began, and no startling novelty occurred until the creation of the Society of Jesus by San Ignacio de Loyola in 1534.

The creation of the following orders, however, should be mentioned:

(1) The *Brigittines* or Order of St. Saviour is a contemplative order created in Vadstena 1346 by St. Birgitta of Sweden. The constitution of the order was confirmed by Urban V in 1370. St. Birgitta's daughter, St. Catherine of Sweden, was the first sovereign of the order, in 1375. See my note on St. Birgitta.

(2) *Jesuati.* Blessed Giovanni Colombini (born Siena c. 1300, died July 31, 1367) founded the order of Jesuati, the purpose of which was to take care of the sick, particularly the plague-stricken, to attend the burial of the dead, and to mortify the self (daily scourging). This Giovanni belonged to a patrician family of Siena and was for a time gonfalionere; he abandoned all his belongings to live in poverty and charity. The rule of the order was derived from the rules of St. Benedict and St. Augustine. Its constitution was approved by Urban V in 1367, a week before Giovanni's death. The order spread rapidly in Italy, but degenerated so much that in the seventeenth century its members were derisively called Aquavitae fathers. It was suppressed in 1668 by Clement IX.

[17] Thomas Palaeologos (b. 1409; d. Rome 1465), porphyrogennetos, sixth son of Manuel II Despotes of Peloponnesos 1429–60, then driven out by Muḥammad II al-Fātiḥ. His children were educated in Rome under cardinal Bessarion's supervision, suffered strange vicissitudes.

[18] The ambition to recover the Holy Sepulcher was one of Columbus' "idées fixes," which he continued to entertain until the very end of his life. Samuel Eliot Morison: Admiral of the Ocean Sea (2 vols., Boston 1942; Isis 34, 169–72), see index s.v. Jerusalem.

A similar order for women, the Jesuatesses or Sisters of the Visitation of Mary, was founded in 1367 by Giovanni's cousin, Blessed Catherine Colombini of Siena (d. 1387). It was devoted to prayer, silence, fasting, scourging. It survived in Italy until 1872 (CI 8, 458–89, 1910).

By a curious coincidence, the feasts of Beato Giovanni, founder of the Jesuati, and of San Ignacio de Loyola, founder of the Jesuitae, are celebrated on the same day; they both died on July 31, the first in 1367, the second in 1556.

(3) *Hieronymites.* Various hermit groups have been named in honor of St. Jerome (IV-2). Their organization was often informal and loose, but more definite groups were established in Spain and Italy in the second half of the fourteenth century.

(a) Hieronymites of Lupiana: One of the first formal organizations occurred in Spain in the monastery of San Bartolomé de Lupiana (Guadalajara, dioc. Toledo), the first prior being Fernando Pecha, formerly chamberlain to Peter the Cruel (king of Castile 1350–69). Fernando obtained in 1373 a bull of confirmation from Gregory XI. In spite of the Hieronymites' name, their rule is Augustinian rather than Hieronymian. In 1389, they received the monastery of Nuestra Señora de Guadalupe in Estremadura, which has remained one of the most famous centers of pilgrimage.[19] The Spanish and Portuguese houses of the order were united under a single constitution in 1595.

The Hieronymites, many of whom belonged to the aristocracy, received many favors from the kings of both countries. The monastery of Belem (near Lisbon), which was founded by king Manuel in 1497 and where the kings of Portugal are buried, belongs to their order. So do the monastery of Yuste (in Estremadura), founded in 1402, where Charles Quint spent the end of his life and died in 1558, and the immense monastery of Escorial, founded by Philip II in 1557 and completed in 1584. The Escorial contains the remains of the kings of Spain, but is especially dear to scholars because of its library (Isis vol. 34, p. 34).

The monks were celebrated for the abundance of their alms, they took an inglorious part in the evangelization of the New World. Their purpose was contemplative, but they engaged in study and preaching. They concerned themselves with sacred music and helped to preserve and purify musical traditions in the churches of Spain; they patronized the fine arts.

An order of Hieronymite nuns was founded in Toledo in the fourteenth century by Maria Garcias (d. 1426).

(b) Hieronymites of the Congregation of Blessed Peter of Pisa (Frati mendicanti di San Gerolamo): This order was created in 1377 by Pietro Gambacorta (1355–1435), later called Beato Pietro da Pisa. It is a mendicant order submitted to considerable fasting and penitence. Their rule was not approved until 1567, by Pius V. Their mother house is in Montebello (Umbria), but they have many other monasteries in Italy, the most famous being the Roman one of Sant' Onofrio sul Gianicolo, where Torquato Tasso died in 1595 and was buried.

(c) Hieronymites of Fiesole: This branch was founded in 1360 by Blessed Carlo de Montegraneli in Fiesole near Florence. It was approved by Eugene IV in 1441 and suppressed by Clement IX in 1668.

(d) Hieronymites of the Observance, or of Lombardy: Branch of the Spanish

[19] It is after that Guadalupe that the many other Guadalupes in Colombia, Mexico, Peru, Uruguay, and Texas have been named, as well as the French Guadéloupe island in the West Indies.

order of Lupiana, established in Italy by Lupo d'Olmedo. It was recognized as an independent order by Martin V in 1424, and later had various affiliated houses in Andalusia.

(4) *Brothers and Sisters of the Common Life* (Fratres et sorores communis vitae). A congregation organized by Geert Groote after 1374 in Deventer. It was a fraternity of laymen and clerks united for devotional, practical, and educational purposes.

(5) *Windesheim Canons.* This order of "Augustinian canons of the new observance" was organized after Groote's death (1384) to foster the same endeavors as the Brothers of the Common Life, but along purely monastic lines. An order of canonesses was established near Deventer in 1400.

For these two foundations (4, 5) and their far-reaching influence see my note on Geert Groote.

Though born in the fourteenth century, the orders mentioned in this chapter did not have much importance except later. The main religious orders of the fourteenth century were the Franciscans and Dominicans, many members of which will be spoken of in this volume. These two orders were very much alive and were so large and widespread that they combined within their habit a great diversity of types. The fermentation was particularly intense among the Franciscans, and quarrels between the more conservative brethren and the more liberal (Spirituals) were flaring up repeatedly; we shall come across many examples of that. The Dominicans were less turbulent, or else they spent their energy fighting heretics, yet they experienced many vicissitudes which cannot be told here. See histories of their order such as that by Angelus Maria Walz: Compendium historiae ordinis Praedicatorum (Rome 1930). To quote a single instance, there was formed within the order at the beginning of the century a society of missionaries, Societas fratrum peregrinantium propter Christum, which established many houses in Eastern Europe and in Asia, but was almost exterminated by the Black Death. It was restored in 1373. From 1603 to its final suppression, in 1857, it was called the Congregation of the Orient and of Constantinople.[20]

Considering the growing success of the friars and their intellectual leadership, we may expect the struggle between seculars and regulars to continue. There is no point in discussing it again. As an example of its persistence let me cite the sermon Defensio curatorum which Richard Fitzralph, archbishop of Armagh (Ireland), preached before Innocent VI in 1357 and which was put into English by John of Trevisa.

The great military orders were now a thing of the past, the Templars had even been suppressed, but orders of chivalry were still created. They were generally established with a religious intention, as well as with a military or political one, but the religious aspect tended to remain superficial and insignificant. As examples, consider the Order of Christ, created by Dom Dinis o Lavrador, sixth king of Portugal, and approved by John XXII in 1319. That order had been created largely to replace under a new name the suppressed order of Templars. It was really a militant order which helped Portugal in its fight against the Moors, and the religious motive was strong.

The Order of the Garter was created in 1348 by Edward III, and placed under St. George's patronage. It included twenty-five knights not counting members

[20] Raymond Loenertz (O.P.): La Société des Frères pérégrinants (222 p., Romae ad S. Sabinae 1937; Speculum 13, 247).

of royal families. It is centered in the St. George Chapel of Windsor. It was reformed by Henry VIII in 1522.

The Order of the Bath was created in 1399 by Henry IV, and was many times reformed.

The Order of St. George of Alfama (near Tortosa, Catalonia), created by Peter II of Aragon in 1201, was approved in 1363 by Urban V and merged in 1399 with the Order of Our Lady of Montesa (Valencia), which had been established in 1316 by James II of Aragon to replace the Templars.

This list might be lengthened, and similar orders were created in increasing numbers during the following centuries, each royal family, each country establishing its own. The religious motives have become weaker and weaker, and membership is now simply an official reward and a matter of social distinction.

4. *Biblical studies and translations*

It is hardly necessary to enumerate Biblical commentaries, for these were a commonplace avocation in the life of every Christian scholar. It is more important to lay stress on the growing number of translations into many vernaculars. These translations are also too numerous to be recorded here. References to them will be found in the body of this work and in the linguistic sections of chapters I and XV.

Three examples will suffice. Jean de Sy began a new translation of the Bible into French which king John the Good had ordered to be made at the expense of the Jews. Wycliffe and his associates produced two English versions. Gerard Zerbolt defended the translations into Dutch made by the Brothers of the Common Life. All these translations were made from the Vulgate. A demand for vernacular Bibles occurred almost everywhere, and it was heard by the most orthodox as well as by other men having conscious or unconscious leanings toward spiritual independence and heresy. The clerical hostility to that demand and to its satisfaction did not crystallize equally fast in different countries. In England, it hardly began before 1391, but then under the fear of Lollardy it soon assumed a violent form. By 1406 the penalty for reading the Bible in the vernacular was excommunication, by 1414 forfeiture of life and property! Yet the Bible was translated and the translations copied in increasing quantities, witness the relatively large number of MSS which have survived.

In this case as in many others the church seems to have behaved with incredible stupidity. The desire to read the Bible was at first a symptom of religious fervor. Was it not natural enough for a pious man or woman to want to read or hear the words of God in his own language? The desire was innocent, but the church caused it to become guilty. Ecclesiastical repression created or excited heretical tendencies which might have been avoided or canalized in the right direction. Persecution completed the transformation of good people into implacable rebels. It is certain that the prohibition of vernacular Bibles was one of the latent causes of the Reformation.

It is interesting to note the existence of apocryphal writings among the Biblical versions. For example, John of Trevisa translated into English the Gospel of Nicodemos or the Acts of Pilate. A comparative study of all the vernacular Biblical texts might reveal curious preferences for certain apocrypha or pseudepigrapha. This would be a considerable task which we cannot undertake, though we should like to know its conclusions.

5. *Homiletics and paraenesis*

One of the best means of evaluating popular religion in various countries is to study the sermons which were preached, especially those delivered in the vernacular. The substance, style, and method are revealing, as well as the circumstances determining their delivery. A good number of studies have been devoted to sermons, and though their authors were often more interested in literature than in religion, the conclusions of their researches are of interest to us.

The interest of seculars and regulars in homiletics was natural enough, as sermonizing was one of their main duties and their best means of teaching and guiding their flocks. Thus it is not surprising to find many mediaeval treatises on homiletics. It is true, many books entitled "ars praedicandi" (e.g., the three written by Ramon Lull) are not such treatises, but rather discussions of vices and virtues or collections of sermons. Nevertheless there are enough genuine treatises on the art of preaching to prove the popularity of that subject in mediaeval times. These treatises have been studied by Thomas M. Charland (O.P.): Artes praedicandi. Contribution à l'histoire de la rhétorique au Moyen âge (Publications de l'Institut d'études médiévales d'Ottawa vol. 7, 421 p., 1936). Father Charland's elaborate memoir contains critical editions of two outstanding texts of that kind, both of the fourteenth century: the first is the Forma praedicandi, written not by Jean de la Rochelle (XIII-1), as was formerly believed, but in 1322 by an unknown Englishman, Robert de Basevorn; the second is the De modo componendi sermones, by the English Dominican Thomas Waleys (still living in 1349).[21] Neither treatise had been published before; in Charland's edition they cover respectively p. 231–323 and p. 325–403.

A list of mediaeval tracts on the art of preaching, already published or not, has been compiled by Harry Caplan: Mediaeval artes praedicandi (Cornell studies in classical philology vols. 24–25, 52+36 p., Ithaca, N. Y. 1934–36).

As to the preaching itself, in addition to treatises on ecclesiastical history one may consult:

For England, the excellent books of Gerald Robert Owst: Preaching in medieval England, 1350–1450 (400 p., Cambridge University 1926); Literature and pulpit in medieval England (640 p., Cambridge University 1933). Homer Garrison Pfander: The popular sermon of the medieval friars (70 p., New York University 1937). Mary Aquinas Devlin: Bishop Thomas Brunton and his sermons (Speculum 14, 324–44, 1939); this Thomas Brunton or de Brynton, one-time Benedictine of Norwich, was bishop of Rochester 1373–89.

For Germany, Felix Richard Albert: Die Geschichte der Predigt in Deutschland bis Luther (3 vols., Gütersloh 1892–96); vol. 3 is devoted to the "golden age" of German homiletics, 1100–1400. Landmann Florenz: Das Predigtwesen in Westfalen in der letzten Zeit des Mittelalters (Münster i.W. 1900).

For France, Albert Lecoy de La Marche: La chaire française au Moyen âge specialement au XIIIe siècle (520 p., Paris 1868; revised ed., 566 p., Paris 1886). Louis Bourgain: La chaire française au XIIe siècle (410 p., Paris 1879). Marie Magdeleine Davy: Les sermons universitaires parisiens de 1230–31 (428 p., Paris 1931). Though these French studies do not deal with the fourteenth century, I have cited them faute de mieux.

For Italy, Francesco Zanotto: Storia della predicazione nei secoli della letteratura italiana (572 p., Modena 1899).

[21] Not to be confused with other men called Thomas Waleys or Wallensis; there were of course many Thomases in Wales. See note on Thomas Jorz (XIV-1).

It is hardly necessary to point out that many of these sermons contain valuable information on mediaeval society, manners, and customs, as observed from an ecclesiastical point of view.

6. *Art and religion*

The best means of religious education was not the pulpit, but the art of the architect, the painter, and sculptor, illustrating for the unlettered people the stories of the Bible and church and the legends of the saints—or rather it was the pulpit combined with the plastic arts. Sermons did not last very long, but the faithful could examine the paintings and statues as long and as often as they pleased. Christian art of the thirteenth and fourteenth centuries was truly encyclopaedic in its purpose. The cathedral was like a picture book always available to visitors. It is thus very important for historians of mediaeval thought to be as well acquainted as possible with Christian art (see Introd. 2, 162, 334, 824). Every history of art will help them, but above all the exemplary studies of the French scholar Emile Mâle: L'art religieux du XIIe siècle en France (464 p., 253 ill., Paris 1922; Isis 6, 52–56); L'art religieux du XIIIe siècle en France (548 p., ill., Paris 1898); L'art religieux à la fin du Moyen âge en France (570 p., 250 ill., Paris 1908); L'art religieux après le Concile de Trente en Italie, France, Espagne et Flandres (540 p., 294 ill., Paris 1932). These works have been frequently reprinted, especially the second, which was the first to appear and has been translated into English and German. Though they are restricted to France except the last one, they apply as well to other countries of Western Europe; the illustrations are French, but the subject is international. See also Louis Bréhier: L'art chrétien (456 p., 233 ill., Paris 1918; Isis 4, 540–44); Hippolyte Delehaye: Cinq leçons sur la méthode hagiographique (p. 117–46, Bruxelles 1934).

The subject of iconography is closely related to that of art. What were the graphical symbols of the Christian faith? How were the saints represented? It is clear that the paintings and sculptures could teach only if there was sufficient agreement on their conventions, on their language. Mâle's books are more concerned really with iconography than with art. See also my note on reliquaries below, and Karl Künstle: Ikonographie der Heiligen (620 p., ill., Freiburg i.B. 1926); Ikonographie der christlichen Kunst (Freiburg i.B. 1928); and the admirable book of Yrjö Hirn (1912).

7. *Saints*

The outstanding fact of mediaeval Christendom is the devotion to the saints. This is proved by the whole of Christian art, by Christian literature, and above all by the manners and customs of Christian people. The saint—man or woman—is the real hero of mediaeval life. The whole of Christian education tended to give at least as much reality to the "other" world and the new life beginning in hell, purgatory, or heaven as to the nether world, this side of death. The saint was the supreme hero, because he alone was the hero of both worlds. On that account he was the natural intercessor between men and God, or at least between men and Christ or his Mother. This was and is orthodox doctrine, confirmed by the council of Trent (1545–63). It opened the door to many exaggerations and superstitions, which are abundantly illustrated in the Legenda aurea put together by James of Voragine (XIII-2) and in innumerable other writings the authors of which outbade one another in their miraculous tales.

The cult of saints originated with the cult of martyrs and developed slowly at first. The competition between rival centers of pilgrimage, the recurring need of supernatural consolation in times of disaster, which were many (wars, plagues, famines, etc.), the insatiable love of marvels, etc. caused that cult to increase more and more rapidly and finally to grow out of bounds. Some of the churchmen realized the dangers implied, but the church did little to avoid them, except that it gradually tried to limit the number of saints, and to recognize as such only those who had been regularly canonized. Even so, much latitude was left to particular dioceses or localities. In the course of time the processes of beatification and canonization have become more and more severe, but they have often been preceded and prepared by long periods of popular cult. The four main saints of our period died and were canonized in the years given below:

St. Birgitta	died 1373,	canonized 1391
St. Catherine of Siena	1380	1461
St. Catherine of Sweden	1381	1484
St. Vincent Ferrer	1419	1455

The devotion to saints became the main prop of the church at the very time when its financial and political methods tended to alienate many people, and thus instead of regulating that devotion, the church, or at least particular churches, was often tempted to exploit it.

From early days on, accounts of the lives and deaths of martyrs and saints were written, but since they were composed by men who were as uncritical as they were pious, all kinds of legends and commonplaces were mixed with the facts. Two collections of such lives enjoyed an extraordinary popularity in spite of or rather because of their complete lack of criticism; the first was written toward the beginning of the Middle Ages by Gregory the Great (VI-2), Dialogus de vita et miraculis patrum italicorum et de eternitate animarum, the second toward their end by James of Voragine (XIII-2), Legenda aurea. Both collections are represented by many MSS, incunabula, and later editions.

Facts and fancies are so thoroughly confused in a large part of hagiographical literature that their separation is hopeless. In other cases it is possible, if difficult, to remove apocryphal stories, to edit purer texts, to reconstruct the original data and come closer to the truth. That enormous task has been undertaken by a group of devoted scholars, the Bollandists, recruited within the Belgian province of the Jesuit order and now established in the Collège St. Michel, Brussels. Their name is derived from that of one of their founders, John Bolland (born in Bolland near Liége 1596, died 1665). Their main purpose was (and is) to edit the lives of saints in a scientific manner. The saints are arranged in order of death days (i.e., their days of birth to eternal life, their feast days).[22] The Acta Sanctorum for January appeared in Antwerp 1643. They had reached the month of November when their labor was twice interrupted by German invasions of Belgium. In addition, the Bollandists have done considerable work in teaching and diffusing sound hagiographic methods. This has been done admirably by the late Hippolyte Delehaye (1859–1941), who, in addition to his articles for the Acta Sanctorum and the Analecta Bollandiana (1882 ff.), had published (all in Brussels) Les légendes

[22] That order may puzzle lay readers. It is a natural one if one considers the needs of the liturgy. Moreover, the fundamental facts in the life of a saint, its "coordinates" (as father Delehaye has put it), are the date (day, month, year) and place of death. The cult of a saint often began in the locality where he died on the first anniversary of his death.

hagiographiques (1905, reprinted 1906, 3d ed., 242 p., 1927; English translation 1907); Origines du culte des martyrs (1912; 2d ed., 450 p., 1933); Les passions des martyrs et les genres littéraires (1921); Sanctus, essai sur le culte des saints dans l'antiquité (274 p., 1927); Cinq leçons sur la méthode hagiographique (148 p., 1934), etc. He has also written a history of the Bollandist undertaking, A travers trois siècles. L'oeuvre des Bollandistes 1615–1915 (280 p., 1920; Englished 1922). These books represent the most enlightened opinion on saints as well as on hagiography; unfortunately, there is an enormous distance between that opinion and popular superstitions, which are more often encouraged than discouraged by the church, and more often exploited than repressed.

The best survey of the question from the point of view of comparative religion will be found in ERE (11, 49–82, 1921); from a Christian but non-Catholic standpoint, John M. Mecklin: The passing of the saint. A study of a cultural type (206 p., University of Chicago 1941); from a rationalistic standpoint, P. Saintyves (1930).

Clerical abuses have caused the publication of many anticlerical studies, most of which are marred not only by lack of impartiality, but also by lack of criticism and lack of taste.

The great increase in the number of saints caused a similar increase in the number of holidays. There were far too many holidays in mediaeval times, and holidays were not always observed in the best manner, being more often a source of dissipation than of edification. Thus holidays, especially excessive ones, introduced social, economic, and moral difficulties. Edith Cooperrider Rodgers: Discussion of holidays in the later Middle Ages (147 p., Columbia University, New York 1940).

One of the results of the cult of saints was the establishment of pilgrimages to the holy places where those saints had lived or died (Introd. 2, 33–34, and this volume by index). It would seem necessary here to refer to another pilgrimage which became eventually the greatest one of Western Europe, until it was somewhat eclipsed by the pilgrimage to Lourdes (1858). According to a legend, the Santa Casa wherein the Annunciation and the Incarnation had taken place in Nazareth, or the Santa Casa restored by St. Helena[23] on the same spot to celebrate those events, was translated by angels to Dalmatia in 1291 in order to save it from profanation by the Muslims; later it was translated to the opposite coast of the Adriatic, to two different places; a fourth translation took it finally to Loreto (on the coast, south of Ancona), where it can be seen to this day. It is a small building, a single room measuring 10.60 × 4.36 × 6.20 m., without roof and without foundations, lying under the cupola of the basilica of Loreto. That basilica was built by Donato Bramante from 1464 to 1513, and the portal by Sixtus V in 1587. A festival took place in Loreto at least as early as 1313 in honor of the Virgin, but that festival was celebrated on the date of her Nativity (September 8), not of the Annunciation (March 25). The legend of the translation of the Santa Casa was born only in 1472, but it was already fully developed by 1531, when a sumptuous marble covering was built around the monument in the middle of the church. The festival of the translation, on December 10, was not celebrated until 1590. The late development of that legend (almost two centuries after the alleged event) and its prodigious success once it was started have been admirably investigated by canon Ulysse

[23] St. Helena (c. 248–c. 327), mother of Constantine the Great. She is said to have discovered the True Cross in Jerusalem on May 3, 326. Therefore, the Invention of the Cross is celebrated every year on May 3.

Chevalier: Notre-Dame de Lorette. Etude historique sur l'authenticité de la Santa Casa (Bibliothèque liturgique vol. 11, 520 p., Paris 1906). The book is a credit to the integrity of the best kind of Catholic scholarship (comparable to the Bollandist scholarship referred to above); it must be added, however, that the church has never ceased to encourage the cult and the pilgrimage, and the legend is generally believed in by the faithful.

The cult of saints in Islām answers the same emotional purposes but is very different from the Christian cult in that it is essentially popular, heretical, and equivocal rather than orthodox; its organization, so far as it is at all organized, is generally due to dervish initiative. For comparison between Jewish, Christian, and Muslim saints and for syncretic cults see Frederick William Hasluck (1878–1920): Letters on religion and folklore (268 p., London 1926); Christianity and Islam under the sultans (2 vols., 952 p., Clarendon Press, Oxford 1929); both works very carefully edited by his widow, Margaret M. Hasluck.

8. *Relics*

The most significant feature in the cult of saints was the veneration of their relics (reliquiae, λείψανα). This aspect of the cult originated,[24] like the cult itself, in the early Christian centuries with reference to the holy martyrs. The theory that divine grace could be obtained through the relics of martyrs and saints was soon developed and has remained an article of Catholic doctrine (confirmed by the council of Trent, sess. XXV). In order to distribute that divine grace and make it available to more people, the bodies of saints were divided into small fragments.[25] Moreover, similar virtues were gradually ascribed to hallowed objects[26] (objects used by saints) and even to objects (such as pieces of cloth, medals, scapularies, rosaries) placed momentarily in contact with relics.

Relics were needed for the consecration of altars[27] and for the oaths of both parties and their compurgators in every lawsuit;[28] moreover, belief in their miraculous power awoke insatiable greed with regard to them in the souls of many people, good and bad. Though the sale of relics was forbidden, all kinds of transactions from the most innocent down to the most sinful were implied in their transmission from one owner to another. Impostors prepared and sold false relics; other men, not necessarily bad men, were so carried away by their desire to obtain relics that they did not hesitate to steal them or to commit other crimes for the sake of obtaining them. There arose a tremendous rivalry among churches and monasteries for the possession of relics far in excess of their ritual needs. Monastic orders whose branches were spread all over Europe had special facilities for the collection of relics from everywhere, and some of their abbots were seized with a kind of collector's mania, they wanted "to complete this or that series," or to have relics for every day of the year. Some princes were seized with the same mania; a collection

[24] As far as Christendom is concerned, but the veneration of relics was (and is) practiced by many non-Christian peoples.

[25] For a time the translation and dismemberment of the remains of martyrs were forbidden, e.g., by the Theodosian Code (V-1) and by Gregory the Great (VI-2).

[26] The most important of hallowed objects is the Holy Cross invented by St. Helena. Pieces of it and other objects connected with the life and passion of Christ are scattered all over the world.

[27] As early as the second council of Nicaea (787) it was ordered that each altar should contain some relic; the order was not a novelty, but consecrated old usage.

[28] Read the chapter Wager of law in Henry Charles Lea: Superstition and force (Philadelphia 1866; 4th ed., revised, 1892).

of relics they thought would take them straight to heaven, and strangely enough those sacred collectors were often utterly unscrupulous. Some sanctuaries or royal chapels owned hundreds and even thousands of separate relics, and the ancient inventories which have been preserved afford the best proof of the superstitious spirit (i.e., utter lack of criticism) in which those collections were made.

The veneration of relics had great influence on the arts. Indeed, special containers had to be prepared for them, and there was every desire to make those reliquaries as beautiful as possible. The reliquaries were generally made of the most precious materials, and they were often very beautiful objects. Our great museums boast many of them. Some churches had so many relics that they established special rooms to contain the reliquaries, and those rooms were themselves like giant reliquaries. Such leipsanothecas might be seen, e.g., in the Sainte Chapelle of Paris, the church of St. Ursula, Cologne, the Casa Santa de Loyola in Azpeitia, Guipúzcoa (Osiris 5, 87).

The abuses which crept inevitably into the veneration of relics because of human weaknesses were criticized by some courageous men, such as the Benedictine Guibert of Nogent (XII-1), but on the whole the church showed more readiness to countenance them and even to take advantage of them than to hold them in check.

Collin de Plancy: Dictionnaire critique des reliques et des images miraculeuses (3 vols., Paris 1821–22), antireligious. Hermann Siebert: Beiträge zur vorreformatorischen Heiligen- und Reliquienverehrung (75 p., Freiburg i.B. 1907). Ernst Alfred Stückelberg: Geschichte der Reliquien in der Schweiz (2 vols., Zürich 1902, Basel 1908). Herbert Thurston (CE 12, 734–39, 1911). Friedrich Pfister: Der Reliquienkult im Altertum (2 vols., Giessen 1909–12). P. Saintyves (= Emile Nourry): Les reliques et les images légendaires (334 p., Paris 1912). J. A. MacCulloch: Primitive and Western relics (ERE 10, 650–58, 1919). Vincent A. Smith: Eastern relics (ERE 10, 658–62, 1919). Hippolyte Delehaye: Les reliques des saints (Cinq leçons sur la méthode hagiographique, Bruxelles 1934; p. 75–116). Joseph Braun: Die Reliquiare des Christlichen Kultes und ihre Entwicklung (768 p., 602 fig., Freiburg i.B. 1940), very elaborate artistic and archaeological study of more than 4,000 reliquaries, representing an infinite variety of forms and techniques.

9. *Apologetics*

Section II, subsection 7 of chapter I, giving an account of apologetic literature in the first half of the century, would apply equally well mutatis mutandis to the second half. Anti-Islamic writings continued to be circulated because they were needed to keep alive the crusading spirit and because the growing fear of the Turks increased the hatred of Islām. There were no novelties in that literature, however, the outstanding book remaining that of Ricoldo di Monte Croce (XIII-2). Unfortunately, the average Christian, even the well educated one, did not derive his knowledge of Islām or of its Prophet from books, but rather from the tales brought back by Crusaders and adventurers, and his views on those subjects were fantastic. He was ready to identify the Prophet with an idol, a heretic, an impostor, Antichrist, etc., and all kinds of fables not only malicious but stupid were circulated about him. For example, the story about the Prophet's coffin suspended in the air goes back to the eleventh century.

John S. P. Tatlock: Mohammed and his followers in Dante (Modern language review, 4 p., 1933). C. Meredith Jones: The conventional Saracen of the songs of geste (Speculum 17, 200–25, 1942). Samuel Claggett Chew: The Crescent and the Rose, Islam and England during the Renaissance (600 p., ill., New York 1937); though this book deals with a later period, many of the stories it relates are much older, e.g., the one about the Prophet's coffin (p. 414–22).

Closer to our period is John Lydgate (1370?–1451?), and the more so that his Fall of princes is an adaptation of Boccaccio's De casibus virorum illustrium. See his book IX, lines 50–161, "Off Machomet the fals prophete and how he beyng dronke was deuoured among swyn," which is packed full with absurdities and evil nonsense.

As to the anti-Jewish literature, it was "enriched" with the books produced by two renegades, Jerome of the Holy Faith and Paul of Burgos.

The existence of Jewish renegades is not surprising, for not only were the Jews persecuted beyond endurance, but many were forcibly baptized. It would have been more surprising to find Christians having become Jews, and I found none in this period, but I came across another case hardly less singular. The Franciscan Anselmo Turmeda settled in Tunis, embraced Islām, and toward the end of his life wrote in Arabic a book against Christendom which enjoyed some popularity among Muslims. Like other renegades, he had the advantage of knowing inside out the religion he was attacking. He was aware of its weaknesses, because, as we shall see in the following section, these weaknesses had by this time become obvious to all except those who were obstinately blind to them.

It was part of the popes' duty to promote missionary enterprises and, as much as possible, crusades, to organize the teaching of sound theology, the supervision of the faith, and the repression of heresy. That was also the duty of Christian sovereigns, and most of them took it very seriously. In England the fight against Lollards and other heretics became more violent, and the statute De haeretico comburendo was passed in the second year of Henry IV (1401; it was abolished only in 1676!). The first victim of that statute, the first martyr, was William Sawtrey, priest at St. Margaret's, Lynn, Norfolk, who was burnt at Smithfield in 1401 (DNB 50, 380, 1897). May God forgive those who persecuted him!

There was also anti-Christian literature written by Muslims. For example, in the Mamlūk state, some of the Coptic subjects had gradually obtained considerable wealth and influence because of their superior abilities. This excited the jealousy of good Muslims, who raised a hue and cry, saying that the Copts were claiming the land of Egypt as their own and misappropriating Muslim lands and awqāf for the benefit of Christian subjects or Christian churches. A good example of such anti-Coptic propaganda was given by 'Abd al-Raḥīm al-Isnawī. It is interesting to compare his Kalimāt muhimma with much anti-Semitic propaganda, concerned not at all with apologetics, but only with the defense of vested power and property.

10. *Internal criticism of the church*

Unrest among the faithful increased considerably during the second half of the century because their situation was aggravated by natural calamities such as the Black Death and by human ones such as the Great Schism. Repression and persecution did not ease matters, but on the contrary turned good people into rebels. There is no difficulty in proving these statements, the only difficulty is to choose a few significant facts among thousands and thousands.[29]

Let us first consider France, which had been the leading Christian nation in the

[29] For the shortcomings of the religious orders, see G. G. Coulton: The last generations of mediaeval monachism (Speculum 18, 437–57, 1943; Isis 35, 252).

Crusades and had now become the hostess or guardian of the popes and their court. A proverb illustrates the fact that instead of being loved and blessed by the common people, the clergy whether secular or regular was often feared: "Un grand seigneur, un grand clocher, une grande rivière sont trois mauvais voisins." That impression is fortified by contemporary literature, whether the popular literature wherein the villain is as often as not a clerk or a monk, or the learned writings of a poet like Eustache Deschamps. The whole literature is tainted with anticlericalism. Whose fault is that? The masses were religious enough, to the point of superstition; they were always ready to look up to the clerks. Where did they learn to look down on them? Who perverted them? The clerks abused their privileges and took unfair advantage of the almost unlimited confidence which had been placed in them. The reaction was brutal, but what else would you expect? The violent criticisms made by Reformers in the sixteenth century were all anticipated by faithful members of the church, some of them in orders. One could easily compile an anthology of Catholic animadversions upon the church written in the fourteenth century, by good men, even by saints like St. Catherine of Siena, the strength and bitterness of which could not be exceeded.

Instead of trying to win the hearts of the people in a fatherly way, the church was often tempted to subjugate them by means of punishments, above all excommunications, and the latter were then not infrequently commuted for financial contributions.[30] Ecclesiastical tribunals continued the barbaric custom of trial by combat and added inquisitorial methods and the criminal use of torture. The clerks themselves were protected from lay justice.[31] Many punishments could be avoided with a payment of money; even religious punishments such as expiatory pilgrimages could be compensated in that way (Introd. 2, 34). It is clear enough that such a system of evils could not be prolonged without danger. Corruption is like a disease. The church was wasted with an incurable cancer, or rather with a cancer which would have caused its death if it had not been extirpated by the Reformers, then again by the Counter-Reformers.

The situation was not better in England. The popular aspect of it has been amusingly set forth by Jusserand (1884) on the basis of contemporary writings, primarily those of Chaucer. Remember Chaucer's account of the "pardoners," account in no way exaggerated, for it can be entirely justified on documentary evidence; then his "palmers" or professional pilgrims, his false pilgrims and all kinds of religious vagrants. Jusserand's book explains the curious and complicated organization of pilgrimages, which is equally interesting from the religious and the social point of view (e.g., the guilds facilitated them in many ways). Much of that was innocent enough, but the same abuses, the identical simony, which we observed in France flourished in England, with this formidable aggravation, that the simo-

[30] On the abuses of excommunication, see Henry Charles Lea: Studies in church history (p. 223–487, Philadelphia 1869). For the wager of battle and ordeal referred to below, see the same author's Superstition and force (Philadelphia 1866; 4th ed., revised, 1892). ERE (9, 507–33, 1917).

[31] For an account of growing anticlericalism in Flanders see Vanderkindere (ch. 9, also p. 262, 1879). To realize how much clerical immunity must have irritated the people, even the most faithful, you have only to imagine what your feelings would be if members of one of our administrations, say, the Treasury, were put out of reach of the common courts and then proceeded to exact all kinds of fancy taxes. They would not enjoy much popularity. Clerical immunity or benefit of clergy is discussed by H. C. Lea in his Studies in church history (p. 169–221, 1869).

niacal prelates were often foreigners treating England like a conquered land. The religious and social reactions which occurred are thus natural enough. The Vox clamantis of John Gower, the grumbles of Piers Plowman, the good-natured satire of Geoffrey Chaucer, the gentle warnings of William Thorne should have been listened to and heeded. Nobody did, the abuses continued, and not only that, but instead of the abusers' and simoniacs' being restrained, it was the critics and malcontents who were punished. No wonder, then, that the writings of Wycliffe found more readers, assenters, and zealots, and that the plain people—those who could not read but were made to suffer in their bodies as well as in their souls—fell deeper and deeper into Lollardy and revolt. I am asking once more, Who created the Lollards? The flocks revolted against their shepherds, because the shepherds were bad.

Under the influence of similar abuses and of Wycliffe, the Czech people revolted in the same way as the English. Their revolt was national as well as religious; it led to Jan Hus and the Hussite wars. It is less instructive than the English revolt, because it is more difficult to disentangle the purely religious issue from the national one. It is clear, however, that the church was festering in Bohemia, even as it did in France and England.

The situation was bad enough during the Babylonish captivity, the Great Schism made it worse. To the best minds and the most generous hearts it seemed at times hopeless.

11. *Superstition*

Did the superstitious practices encouraged or at least countenanced by the church increase superstition? It is very difficult, if not impossible, to answer that question. To begin with, it would be helpful to ask ourselves how the matter stands today, in this so-called "age of science." Are our people free of superstitions? How is it that so many charlatans, palm readers, astrologers manage to subsist in our cities? A distinguished scientist[32] has published distressing revelations on the subject: "Recently in New York's Pennsylvania Station I purchased seven different magazines on astrology. One of them, and this not the best seller according to my newsdealer, I found had a monthly paid circulation of over 132,000 copies (The circulation of our journal Science is about 15,000)." Do you want other examples of irrationality in our midst, you will find a large choice of them in Gilbert Seldes: The stammering century (New York 1928) and Charles W. Ferguson: The confusion of tongues (New York 1929). By the way, all this suggests that literacy is not by any means the panacea which some people have believed it to be. Illiterate people may be better off than the so-called literate ones who find their daily pabulum in irrational and senseless publications. Mediaeval men have been blamed or pitied for reading too little; a good many of our contemporaries are hopelessly confused because they read too much without rhyme or reason. Thus we should be very humble in our judgments of our predecessors, we could not be too humble.

The second point to bear in mind is that the church did fight superstitions to some extent. I have already discussed the matter apropos of the popes of the first half of the fourteenth century; the popes of the second half were less outspoken than John XXII and Clement VI, but they pursued on the whole the same policies. Superstitions useful to the church were hardly tampered with, and on the other

[32] Albert Francis Blakeslee: Individuality and science (Science 95, 1–10, 1942; see p. 8).

hand no objection was made to the purer kind of astrology, such as is represented by the Tetrabiblos[33] of Ptolemy (II-1) and its more "scientific" commentaries. Both policies were expedient and the second was wise, for the scientific core of astrology had some plausibility and it was accepted by all the leading philosophers and scientists. The popes' toleration of astrology was comparable to their present toleration and encouragement of science. They were aware, however, that dangerous thoughts were lurking around astrology, and they condemned magic repeatedly. We find various superstitions denounced in the Directorium inquisitorum of Nicholas Eymeric, in the writings of Eustache Deschamps, of Geert Groote, etc.

In spite of these denunciations, superstitions were rife, and I am under the impression that they were actually increasing. Such a calamity as the Black Death may have had a large share in the increase, for it created widespread terrors, and terrified people are in the best psychological condition to accept any kind of superstitious ideas. Alas! the Black Death was not alone in spreading fears, insecurity, distress. There were repeated floods and famines, uprisings and wars; civil and clerical lords vied with one another in the exploitation of their subjects and the maladministration of justice. The poor people did not know to whom to turn for protection—it is true they could appeal to the saints and pray, but sometimes they placed their confidence in soothsayers. Successful predictions might (and did) give the latter some prestige. If an intelligent man, a good psychologist, foretells many events he is bound to succeed sometime; it is part of his skill to play up his good predictions and to cause the bad ones to be forgotten. Moreover, predictions concerning the conduct of individuals often came true for the very reason that they were made. The love of marvels, of adventures, and all manner of unclear and confusing ideas, the frequent excommunications (extended to the popes themselves by their rivals), the immorality of many clerks and monks, their greed and simony, all that helped to increase the spiritual chaos and hence to favor the growth of superstitions and magical practices.

The main single factor, however, in the increase of irrationality and superstition was the spread of the witchcraft mania. The beginnings of it have been described in chapter II, and the more violent phase did not set in before the end of the fifteenth century,[34] but the disease grew steadily during the fourteenth and fifteenth centuries, infecting gradually more and more minds and transforming individual aberrations into social ones. In this case the contemplation of the calamities occurring within our own times ought to incline us to humility and indulgence. Indeed, the spirit and methods of anti-Semitism in Germany remind us of the early witch mania and of inquisitorial procedure.

After the Black Death there were many more witches and witch-hunters than

[33] That treatise was very popular in mediaeval times, witness a great many MSS in Arabic, Latin, Greek, etc. Though the Almagest was not printed completely until 1515 (in Latin from the Arabic, see Introd. 1, 274), the Quadripartitum (and Centiloquium) is represented by two incunabula, 1484, 1493 (Klebs no. 814). Two critical editions of it have appeared recently, by Franz Boll and Aemilia Boer (Leipzig 1940) and by Frank Egleston Robbins (Cambridge, Mass. 1940; Isis 33, 718–19). An English translation was published for modern astrologers in Chicago as recently as 1936 (Isis 35, 181).

[34] More exactly, it began with the bull Summis desiderantes affectibus issued by Innocent VIII on December 5, 1484, and with the publication of the Malleus maleficarum (The witch hammer) by the Dominicans Jacob Sprenger and Heinrich Kraemer (Institoris) in Speier c. 1485 (at least 7 incunabula editions). English translation by Montague Summers (324 p., London 1928), excellent review by George L. Burr (American historical review 34, 321–25, 1928–29). See also Isis (25, 147–52).

before. For well balanced and well fed people the fear of the Devil was simply another, a cruder form of the fear of sin; for people who were nervously unbalanced, and possibly weakened by illness and hunger, that fear could easily become morbid and bring about mental aberrations of various kinds, some of which were highly contagious. The soil was made ready in the period 1348–1484 for a whole gamut of pathological delusions, individual and collective. One of the main items in that sinister preparation was the declaration made in 1398 by the University of Paris. That university was a sort of high court of theology, whose international importance was greater than ever during the Schism. It adopted a series of twenty-eight articles against demonology and declared it was a theological error to doubt the reality of sorcery and its effects.[35] Thus it is not surprising that an increasing number of people were willing to believe that others, or even themselves, had become the accomplices and the tools of some infernal power.

It was a terrible tragedy counting numberless victims, not only, mind you, those who died or were tortured, but also, and hardly less so, those who did the killing or the torturing or who organized it. The total number of victims, high as it was, was very small as compared with the number of victims of the recurring famines, plagues, or wars, but we must bear in mind that human deaths caused by the injustice of other men, or worse still by the miscarriage and the essential perversion of justice, are infinitely more tragic than those due to the blind action of microbes, the soulless forces of nature, or the vicissitudes of war.

The most painful aspect of the witchcraft delusion has not yet been shown. We discover it when we realize that with the exception of a few monsters, the inquisitors and other persecutors were on the whole well meaning men. They were full of superstitions and lacked rational knowledge, and they had been swept off their feet by a kind of panic. Their purpose was often lofty and good, at least in their own eyes. They perpetrated atrocities and abominations for the sake not of hatred, but of love. Indeed, they professed to love God and their neighbors above themselves.

Mention of the Inquisition should not confuse the reader. As far as Spain is concerned, Lea has shown that the witchcraft mania was repressed there and rendered comparatively harmless "because of the wisdom and firmness of the Inquisition." The Spanish inquisitors' main purpose was to fight heresy, especially the relapsing of converted Jews and Moors, and magic; they were not obsessed by witchcraft delusions. The same might be said about Italy. The witchcraft mania was a northern disease. It is true the witch could be classified with the heretics or the magicians, but only if the reality of his crime were accepted; the delusion consisted in admitting the possibility of such a crime, whether for oneself or for others; as soon as the persecution of witches was started it tended to create its own victims.

Bibliography. The literature on witchcraft is abundant, and it cannot be separated from that on the Inquisition, though the two subjects are different. Only a few titles can be given here. Those quoted apropos of the Inquisition (Introd. 2,

[35] G. G. Coulton: Medieval panorama (p. 117, 1938). Organized witchcraft persecutions began after the bull of 1484 with the help of the Malleus. They did not reach their climax until the second half of the sixteenth century, or even the beginning of the seventeenth. The witchcraft trials of Salem (Massachusetts) took place in 1692, the last English trial in 1712, the last Scotch execution of a witch in 1722. Executions occurred as late as 1782 in Spain, 1793 in Germany (Posen), 1888 in Peru! . . .

553) are not repeated, though the works of Henry Charles Lea (1825–1909) and Joseph Hansen (1862–) are fundamental. But I should have added that Lea's three-volume History of the Inquisition of the Middle Ages (New York 1887–88) was reprinted in 1895, revised 1906, 1922. French translation by Salomon Reinach on text corrected by Lea, introduction by Paul Fredericq[36] (2 vols., Paris 1900–2, reprinted 1910). German translation directed by Joseph Hansen (3 vols., Bonn 1905, 1909, 1913). Abridged Italian translations by Pia Cremonini (Torino 1910) and by Don Libero (Mendrisio, Ticino 1914).

Lea also wrote a History of the Inquisition of Spain (4 vols., New York 1906–7), abbreviated translation into French by Salomon Reinach (Brussels 1908), translation into German by Prosper Müllendorff (3 vols., Leipzig 1911–12), and The Inquisition in the Spanish dependencies: Sicily, Naples, Sardinia, Milan, the Canaries, Mexico, Peru, New Granada (New York 1908). The Spanish Inquisition began only in 1480 and thus does not concern us at present, but it is well to know of the existence of these thorough studies. The three works were reprinted in a complete and uniform edition, History of the Inquisition (8 vols., New York 1922). Unfortunately, these works have never been translated into Spanish; that is, Spanish readers unfamiliar with foreign languages have not been permitted to know the truth about the Inquisition, but only the lies and exaggerations of the clerical or anticlerical parties. Lea, it should be noted, was impartial and honest; he could not satisfy the fanatical clericals, but he was praised by the leading Catholic historians, such as Lord Acton (first baron Acton of Aldenham, 1834–1902).

At the time of his death, in 1909, Lea had been preparing for years a history of witchcraft. His "Materials for a history of witchcraft" were edited by Arthur C. Howland, introduction by George Lincoln Burr (3 vols., 1592 p., University of Pennsylvania, Philadelphia 1939; Isis 34, 235). This edition was facilitated by the fact that Lea owned practically all the books which he used, and his library is preserved in its integrity in a separate room of the Library of the University of Pennsylvania; unfortunately the edition is not indexed.

Wilhelm Gottlieb Soldan: Geschichte der Hexenprozesse (Stuttgart 1843), re-edited by Heinrich Heppe (2 vols., Stuttgart 1880) and abridged with illustrations by Max Bauer (2 vols., Munich 1912). Gustav Roskoff: Geschichte des Teufels (2 vols., Leipzig 1869). George Lincoln Burr: The literature of witchcraft in Europe (Papers of the American Historical Association, 32 p., New York 1890), bibliography; The witch persecutions (Translations and reprints vol. 3, part 4, 36 p., Philadelphia 1897), excellent introduction for class use. Jules Regnault: La sorcellerie (medical thesis, 352 p., Paris 1897, 2d ed., 375 p., Paris 1936). George Fraser Black: List of works relating to witchcraft in Europe (Bulletin of the New York Public Library, 1911, 727–55, Isis 31, 486–87). Oswald Weigel: Geschichte der Hexenprozesse (39 p., Leipzig 1912), bibliography. Sister Antoinette Marie Pratt: The attitude of the Catholic church towards witchcraft and allied practises of sorcery and magic (thesis, 138 p., Washington 1915). Margaret Alice Murray: The witch-cult in Western Europe (304 p., Clarendon Press, Oxford 1921; Isis 4, 644). Ian Ferguson: The philosophy of witchcraft (219 p., London 1924) Montague Summers: The history of witchcraft and demonology (370 p., London 1926); The geography of witchcraft (630 p., London 1927); these two volumes complete each other, and the author, a Catholic who believes in the reality of witchcraft

[36] Paul Fredericq (1850–1920) of Ghent completed Lea's work with reference to the Netherlands, his main works ad hoc being: Inquisitio haereticae pravitatis neerlandica (2 vols., in Dutch, Ghent 1892–97). Corpus documentorum inquisitionis haereticae pravitatis neerlandicae (5 vols., Ghent 1889–1906); this is his main work, unfortunately not finished; parts I–III (1889–1906) deal with the period 1025–1520, parts IV–V (1900–2) with the period 1514–28. Codex documentorum sacratissimarum indulgentiarum neerlandicarum (708 p., 's Gravenhage 1922). In both works editorial commentaries are in Dutch.

(Isis 25, 149), has devoted other books to the same subject; they have been judged with deserved severity by G. L. Burr (American historical review 34, 321–25, 1929); reprinted in George Lincoln Burr: Life and selections from his writings (p. 491–95, Cornell Univ., Ithaca 1943; Isis 35, 147–52). Margaret Alice Murray: The God of the witches (224 p., London 1933). Charles Edward Hopkin: The share of Thomas Aquinas in the growth of the witchcraft delusion (historical thesis, University of Pennsylvania, 196 p., Philadelphia 1940). Charles Williams: Witchcraft (316 p., London 1941), derived from Lea and Summers.

A1. *Italy*

The outstanding religious worker in Italy and one of the greatest in mediaeval Europe was a young woman, Santa Caterina of Siena, who died in 1380 at the age of 33, after ten years of activity for the return of the popes to Rome, and above all for the peace and unity of the church.

If Caterina failed in her main purpose it is not surprising that others did, but the unrest was steadily growing among the faithful. In fact, it was growing everywhere, but in Italy the disappointment was keener than anywhere else when the return of the popes to Rome, instead of improving the situation, caused it to become considerably worse. The church was gravely ill. That could be read in the Decamerone of Boccaccio, but more definitely, and far more impressively, in the Trattato delle lagrime of Santa Caterina. A jurist like Giovanni da Legnano wrote treatises in defense of papal authority and especially for Urban VI against Clement VII. Benvenuto di Rambaldi was especially shocked by the sins of Avignon, which he compared to Babylon. A little later Pietro Paulo Vergerio the Elder would insist that the reform of the church from head to foot was the primary need. If the church were healthy, there would be no schism.

A2. *Catalonia*

In the meanwhile, the Dominicans of Catalonia continued their fight against heresy. They were trained to scent heretical thoughts ahead of other Dominicans, not to speak of other people. The views of their own countryman Ramon Lull seemed particularly dangerous to them just now, and Nicholas Eymeric led the investigations necessary to condemn Lull, yet he failed. He compiled a new guide for inquisitors which was more elaborate than that of Bernard Gui and remained the standard work for centuries. Eymeric's Directorium was the second breviary of inquisitors and the book which every prudent theologian would always keep in mind, if he cared for his health. San Vicente Ferrer, when not engaged in political work for the "antipopes," was converting Jews and Muslims by the thousand. He was one of the most successful hell-fire preachers of his time, but we cannot help suspecting that many of his conversions were due less to his eloquence than to more insidious arguments.

The Franciscans were never comparable to the Dominicans as champions of orthodoxy; their religious ardor was of a different kind, and they often exposed themselves to spiritual temptations. Ramon Lull was a Franciscan tertiary, he had been playing all his life with new ideas. He was a spiritual adventurer, the kind of man whom Dominicans must watch with special caution, but to whom mankind owes most of its blessings. Roger Bacon was another Franciscan and an Englishman to boot, but let us return to Catalonia and the fourteenth century. Toward the end of this century there was living a Franciscan of Majorca, Anselmo Turmeda, who was of a particularly unbalanced type, for his religious meditations led him not only to heresy but to complete apostasy. He proceeded of his own will to Tunis, became a Muslim, and wrote apologetic treatises defending Islām against Christendom.

A3. *Judeo-Spanish converts*

Inasmuch as we have spoken of the apostate Turmeda, we should say a few words also of two other apostates[37] (representing a much larger group, anonymous and silent), Jews who became Christians, militant Christians. The first is one "Jerome of the Holy Faith," physician to the antipope Benedict XIII; he has been tentatively identified with Joshua ben Joseph ha-Lorqi and he wrote two anti-Jewish treatises. The second, known to the Christian world as Paul of Burgos, was originally named Solomon ben Isaac ha-Levi. He was even more rabidly anti-Jewish than the first. It should be added, in extenuation of their violent attacks on their former brethren, that converts are irresistibly led to exaggerated and ungenerous expressions of their new faith in order to justify their own conduct to themselves and prove their loyalty to other people. They are all the time on their mettle, obliged to answer the suspicions of their neighbors and the doubts of their own conscience.

A4. *France*

The French writers on religion constitute a remarkably quiet little group. I found no exalted souls among them comparable to Catherine of Siena or St. Vincent Ferrer, nor tormented ones like Anselmo Turmeda or Paul of Burgos. Consider Jean de Sy, Philippe de Mézières, and Eustache Deschamps.

Jean translated the Bible from Latin into French for Jean le Bon, or rather he began that translation about the middle of the century; it was not completed, by others, until 1410.

Philippe was a moralist and publicist, who took part in the ill-fated crusade of Humbert II of Viennois, and devoted the end of his life to crusading propaganda. Most of his writings, even his biography of Peter of Thomas, were permeated with the ideals which had made possible and relatively successful the earlier crusades; these ideals, however, were now obsolescent. He spoke of European unity against Islām at a time when political unity was becoming more and more chimerical and when Roman Christendom itself was cleft asunder.

The poet Eustache Deschamps wrote a "complaint of the church," a type of composition popular in those days, the lamentations of the ailing church. He wrote it in Latin and also in French, at the request of the antipope Benedict XIII. During the Great Schism, there was not much to choose between the two popes, who were equally anxious and miserable, but the church itself suffered most.

Toward the end of the century there were among the leaders of the French church two men of extraordinary ability and wisdom, Pierre d'Ailly and Jean Gerson. Though the kingdom of France continued to own obedience to the popes of Avignon, whose claims were supported by the University of Paris, Ailly and Gerson were among the first to see the need of a different solution. In 1381 Ailly tried to persuade the French court that the schism could and should be ended by the

[37] The word "apostate" is of course colored, just as "convert" is. A baptized Jew is an apostate from the Jewish angle and a convert from the Christian one. I use both words without animus. When a man changes his religion, we should assume that he is honest as long as he is not proved to be dishonest.

mediation of a council. Though he was in the service of Clement VII and Benedict XIII, both of whom showered benefices on him, he remained comparatively free because he valued the peace and unity of the church above everything else. From 1384 on he was director of the College of Navarre, and in that capacity was able to recruit and train his best assistants, Jean Gerson and Nicolas Clémanges, who continued with increasing vigor and ability his campaign for a peaceful healing of the disastrous schism. Though Gerson was an appointee of the Avignonese curia, he was bold enough in 1391 to suggest that both popes should resign. These three men, and especially Ailly and Gerson, redeemed the church of France in those critical days; they were among the main artisans of the councils of Pisa (1409) and of Constance (1414–18), and of the peace which followed.[38]

A5. *England*

England having become increasingly restive under the Avignonese regime, it is not surprising that at the time of the schism it transferred its allegiance to the Roman popes. It had good reasons to expect more justice and to dread fewer exactions from Rome than from Avignon. Unfortunately, the trouble made by greedy prelates and wretched underlings could not be easily unmade. Evil traditions had been established which could not be stopped. Clerical errors were producing their natural harvest in the form of anticlerical prejudices. Thus it came to pass that England was the cradle of the earliest form of reformation within the Roman church, Wycliffism. The originator of that movement, John Wycliffe, came from Yorkshire. He translated the Bible into the vernacular, and challenged papal authority. All authority, he claimed, rests in God and is forfeited by God's representatives as soon as they fall into sin. Monkish lapses from virtue, which were undoubtedly numerous, caused him to denounce monasticism, root and branch. His revolt was economic as well as religious, and the social aspects of it were stressed more and more by his followers, especially the humbler folk, the Lollards.[39] Wycliffe lived long enough to spread abundant seeds, yet he died early enough (in 1384) to escape violent persecution. A lay follower of his, Walter Brute, who had calmly suggested expropriating the clergy, was tried in 1391; happily he had had the good taste to publish his revolutionary ideas in Latin, and as he recanted he escaped punishment. The anger against the Lollards grew with the new century, and in 1428 Wycliffe's remains were ignominiously cast out. The religious views of Wycliffism and even more its social views were admirably expressed in the Vision of Piers Plowman, one of the masterpieces of Middle English literature. The author of it, William Langland or whoever he was, was a man of the people but not a Lollard, not an extreme radical. His condemnation of eccle-

[38] Pierre d'Ailly (born Compiègne 1350, died Avignon 1420), bishop from 1395, made a cardinal by John XXIII in 1411. Jean Gerson (born in Champagne 1363, died Lyon 1429), chancellor of the University of Paris 1395, from 1410 on recognized as the leader of the liberal party in the church. Nicolas of Clémanges or Clamenges (born in Champagne c. 1360, died c. 1440), rector of the University of Paris 1393, secretary to Benedict XIII. Good account of their efforts to heal the schism in Flick (1930).

[39] Meaning originally the "mutterers" or "mumblers." According to OED the name was first applied c. 1300 to the humblest brethren (lollebroeders), who mumbled prayers over the sick and the dead. In the fourteenth century it was applied to other monks, to Beghards, and finally to men who professed to be more genuinely humble and pious than the monks, and were drifting out of the church into heresy. By the end of the century, Lollard had become in the upper classes a term of opprobrium; it was used by them as vaguely yet as decisively as the term bolshevik is used today.

siastical abuses and social crimes is the more impressive because of his relative moderation and charity.

In England, as elsewhere, criticism of the church was voiced not only by the poor and the rebellious. William Thorne, a monk of St. Augustine's Abbey, Canterbury, who had traveled to the curia in 1387 on monastic business, did not hesitate to describe its corruption. Mind you, this was not the wicked Avignonese curia, but the good Roman one! In his Vox clamantis (written between 1381 and 1400), the poet John Gower explained the vices of the clergy and the urgent need of reform. This was a Latin poem written for the learned people, yet it is sometimes as outspoken as Piers Plowman. Another note was struck by Richard Fitzralph in his Defensio curatorum (in defense of the seculars and against the silly notion of evangelical poverty!), but this was a sermon preached in 1357 before the pope of Avignon. It was translated by John of Trevisa. Among John's many other translations from Latin into English was one of the apocryphal Gospel of Nicodemos.

A6. *Germany*

The German views on church matters which have remained in my sieve are all expressed by seculars. To be sure, if one wanted it one could very probably find many expressions of monastic opinion, but it so happened that none arrested my attention.[40]

German clerics were specially responsible for the development of the conciliar theory. The first to advocate that theory was Conrad von Gelnhausen; that is, as early as 1379 (thus two years before Ailly) he advocated the healing of the schism by appeal to a carefully selected council which would have the authority to mediate between the rival popes. Heinrich von Langenstein carried the theory much farther (1381), for he saw in the council a means not only of ending the schism but of cleansing the church. The careers of these two men were curiously symmetrical; both had been driven out of the University of Paris because of their loyalty to the Roman pope. Heinrich proceeded to the University of Vienna, Conrad to the University of Heidelberg; both universities had been chartered by Urban VI, in 1384 and 1385 respectively, and had become citadels of Urbanism. A third German cleric, Dietrich von Niem, wrote various pamphlets on the schism and the need of papal reform; he was one of the main artisans of the council of Constance.

It was because the activities of these men working on the Roman side were supported by outstanding Frenchmen such as Ailly, Gerson, and Clémanges working on the Avignonese side that the conciliar theory became a reality, and that the schism was finally healed, but not, alas! before irreparable damage had been done.

A7. *Bohemia*

The same wind of freedom which blew over England also blew over Bohemia. It is true, some Bohemians were influenced by Wycliffian books, but they could be influenced only because they were in a similar state of mind, ready to vibrate and react even as some of their English brethren did. Thus did it come to pass that ideals that had germinated in England were incubated in Bohemia and reached their maturity in Germany.

[40] The reader should always bear in mind that the author was not hunting for religious opinions as such; he is giving the religious opinions of men who interested him primarily for other reasons.

The new ideas were preached timidly in the Teyn church, Prague, by Conrad Waldhauser, then far more boldly by Milič of Kremsier, Matthew of Janov, and Thomas of Štitný. Matthew used the Czech language occasionally and Thomas always; thus they were able to move Bohemian hearts far more deeply than would have been possible otherwise, and their efforts were correspondingly obnoxious to prelates who preferred their flocks to be as blind and dumb as possible. Thomas, it should be observed, was not at all a revolutionary, but a quiet mystic, who transmitted to his people the thoughts of St. Augustine, St. Bonaventura, and his own contemporary St. Birgitta.

All these men were gentle enough, and their influence would have been wholly on the side of sweetness had not persecution embittered it. They, as well as Wycliffe, were the forerunners of Jan Hus, who died a martyr of his faith in Constance 1415. Thus were sown the dragon's teeth of the Hussite wars and of endless miseries; the Reformation was brought one step nearer and made unavoidable.

A8. *Sweden*

The difference in religious climate between Bohemia and Sweden is great. In the first country, stupidity and lack of sensitiveness on both sides had driven generous souls into rebellion; in the second, peace remained undisturbed. The best way to illustrate this would be to carry the reader from Prague to Vadstena, on the shore of Lake Vettern in Sweden. It was the author's privilege to spend there hours far too brief yet blessed (Isis 23, 450–52). The religious leader of Sweden was a woman, St. Birgitta, and the new order which she founded, the Brigittines, originated in Vadstena (1346). Like her contemporary St. Catherine of Siena, St. Birgitta took part in the ecclesiastical polemics of her days; from 1349 on she lived mostly in Rome, and she died there in 1373. She urged Urban V to return to Rome and he listened to her, but his return was a failure. She was spared the torture of witnessing the tearing asunder of the church. St. Catherine of Sweden continued her mother's task and completed it beautifully.

For the understanding of the Swedish fervor of those days we should go to Vadstena, then to Rome. During the third quarter of the century we might have met in the Eternal City St. Birgitta, and if we had chanced to be there in 1375 we might have seen sitting together in a cell and praying together St. Catherine of Siena and St. Catherine of Sweden.

A9. *Netherlands*

Dutchmen, that is, roughly speaking, the northern Netherlanders, have always had the reputation of being hard-headed business people, rich in common sense, practical, steady. That reputation is borne out magnificently by their painters, excepting, of course, Rembrandt, who introduced outlandish elements derived from the secret recesses of his genius and possibly from the stories of his Jewish friends. Those qualities (I mean the Dutch ones, not those peculiar to Rembrandt) enabled them to create the most promising religious movement of the fourteenth century, what has been aptly called the Christian renaissance. The founder was Geert Groote, who had been influenced by the mystics, especially the Fleming Ruysbroeck (XIV-1), but not excessively, being protected from any such excess by his Dutch carapace impervious to nonsense of any kind. Thus he read Ruysbroeck, maybe conversed with him (for Ruysbroeck lived to be a very old man and died only in 1381); he probably read Eckhart, Tauler, and Suso and retained from their teachings all that might help him to travel the middle road to the good life. The most remarkable fruit of that spiritual movement was the Imitatio Christi, one of the golden books of mankind. The Imitation was not really completed, in the form familiar to us, until the first quarter of the fifteenth century, that is, until many years after Groote's death (he died in 1384). The editor was in all probability the Dutch canon Thomas a Kempis (1380–1471). Thomas was not trying to be original, but rather to put together as well as possible favorite evangelical quotations and sayings of his revered teachers Groote, Radewijns, Zerbolt, and others. His success was immense. Thanks to the Imitation and the educational activities of his brethren, the influence of the "moderna devotio" founded by Groote was incalculable. It had this remarkable particularity, that it was felt by the Reformers (some of them at least, such as Luther) as well as by the Counter-Reformers, beginning with St. Ignatius. It is felt deeply to this day by any thoughtful Christian, whether rational or mystical.

B. *Eastern Christendom*

B1. *Byzantium*

There is no need of discussing the main problems of the Orthodox church as lengthily (considering the main purpose of our work) as we discussed those of the Catholic church. The latter touch the evolution of science in many ways. For example, the reckless and arbitrary persecution of heresy and witchcraft imperiled the freedom of thought without which science cannot thrive. Moreover, the main difficulty of the Orthodox church has already been discussed in chapter I.

The quarrel continued between a small band of highly educated Latinizers and the bulk of the Orthodox church, which Rome had hurt so deeply and so often that a reconciliation seemed impossible, unthinkable. The two parties, Catholic and Orthodox, hated each other so vigorously that to either party Muslims and Turks seemed lesser enemies than the other. And yet how much they needed each other! The Catholics had not renounced their crusading dreams, and how could they hope to win without the help, or at least the benevolent neutrality, of the Greeks? The situation of the latter was much worse, for the Byzantine Empire was threatening collapse, and how could it resist the Turks without Catholic assistance? The Crusades were a ruinous luxury (many Catholics admitted that much), but the defense of the empire was a necessity. And yet the union so deeply needed on both sides could not be accomplished.

The projects of union must have been thwarted or at least pigeonholed during the interminable schism, for if the Orthodox church had reconciled itself with one half of the Catholic one, the schism between itself and the other half would have increased. What was the use of diminishing one schism to increase another? As the Turkish peril became more ominous, some Orthodox politicians were in the best mood to compromise with Rome, but Rome would make no concessions whatsoever. Is it surprising that some Greeks reached the conclusion that, servitude for servitude, one might expect more toleration from the Muslims than from the Latins?

No startling novelty changed the situation in the second half of the fourteenth century, but if we may briefly anticipate later events, the Latin schism was healed by the council of Constance (1414–18) and the election of Martin V (1417), but the same council condemned Wycliffe and Hus and hence the Bohemian schism continued. During the council of Ferrara-Florence (1438–45), the schism between

Rome and Constantinople was healed, but only by the complete submission of the Greek representatives (1439), and this the Greek people could not accept. In any case, the union came too late, and Constantinople was conquered by the Turks in 1453.

To return to our own period, the Latinizers constituted a small but very learned and very aggressive minority. They had obtained considerable theological knowledge from the works of St. Thomas Aquinas, which were incomparably more elaborate than their Greek equivalents. The leaders were Demetrios Cydones of Salonica, educated in Milano, who translated treatises of St. Thomas and others into Greek, and his younger brother Prochoros Cydones, who had the courage to defend Latin theology in the great lavra of Mt. Athos, that is, in the very citadel of Hesychasm. Needless to say, he was cruelly punished. The third was Manuel Calecas, who assumed the Dominican habit in the monastery which had been established in Pera, a suburb of Constantinople. His activity in defense of Catholic theology was considerable. It should be observed that the Catholics had been very successful in obtaining the enthusiastic cooperation of men who could preach the Latin religion in the best Greek style and with an inside knowledge of the Orthodox weaknesses. Their influence, however, would hardly be felt beyond the walls of the Pera monastery, or of their own little circles; the Greeks would not even listen to them or read their books, for their eyes and ears were shut by irremovable prejudices.

Thus, if one had to describe the theological and ecclesiastical literature of that day, which is of course beyond our scope, one would find that the Latinizing treatises were lost in a sea of Orthodox ones. It will suffice to name briefly the outstanding advocates of the Orthodox faith. We may begin with the emperor John VI Cantacuzenos, who outlived his abdication almost thirty years in the monastery τῶν Μαγγάνων and in Vatopedi, writing historical and theological treatises. His son Matthew, who had also withdrawn from the world on the Holy Mountain, wrote gentle books of edification and Biblical commentaries. The astronomer Theodoros Meliteniotes composed a kind of diatessaron, an enormous commentary on the four Gospels, of which only a small part has come down to us. One of the leading ecclesiastics was Joseph Bryennios, patriarchal vicary in Crete, then in Cyprus (countries under Catholic governments), whose library was bequeathed to Hagia Sophia.

Such was the peril and misery of the empire and its church, however, that the emperors themselves were obliged to forget their pride and travel westward in order to beseech the assistance of their old enemies, the Latin prelates and the Latin princes. Thus John V Palaeologos went to Italy in 1369, and Manuel II Palaeologos spent three years in the West, 1399–1402. These visits were made in vain as far as their main purpose was concerned, but they hastened materially the diffusion of Greek humanism and the dawning of the Renaissance. The Latins had no use whatsoever for Greek theology, but the very mention of the ancient Greek letters—never completely forgotten—was as it were awakening them out of a long lethargy.

B2. *Russia*

Russia was more remote from the popes, and instead of quarreling with them devoted a part of its own religious zeal to missionary undertakings. The most remarkable example is St. Stephen of Perm, who was one of the first evangelists of the northern and northeastern regions of Russia. As is always the case with missionaries, his activity is almost as interesting from the purely linguistic or cultural point of view as from the religious one. We shall come back to St. Stephen in our last chapter and in the last section of this one. He died in Moscow in 1396.

C. *Israel*

In spite of increasing persecutions, Jewish contributions to learning continued to be remarkable for their quality as well as for their number. This will appear not so much in this section as in the following ones. The Jewish difficulties were made worse by Christian proselytism and by many instances of compulsory baptism. The Catholic theory of baptism was very strange. Though the best men recognized the danger of forcible and promiscuous baptism, the sacrament of baptism, once conferred, and no matter how (provided the liturgical forms were observed), was held to change the nature of the individual.[41] A converted Jew became a favorite object of inquisitorial solicitude. The men, women, and children who had accepted baptism under compulsion were distrusted, not only by their former brethren, but even more by their new ones. The wisest kept their secrets in their own hearts; others could not bear the situation, fled or recanted; others still were so anxious to prove the reality of their conversion that they flaunted anti-Semitic opinions, which, whether genuine or not, were in their case equally odious. The Christians were as demoralized as their victims. Mass conversions of infidels at first elated them, but in spite of their faith in the miraculous efficacy of baptism, they soon doubted the value of their victory. Judging from what their own feelings would be if the situation were reversed, they could not but think that the converted Jews were simply biding their time, preparing revenge and perhaps practicing it already in secret. This explains the monstrous crimes which were ascribed to converts and which had no existence except in the imagination of the tormentors.

A good example is the so-called host tragedy which occurred in Brussels 1369. The Jewish banker Jonathan of Enghien and the convert John of Louvain were accused, the first of having planned, the second of having realized the stealing of consecrated wafers. The latter were stolen from the tabernacle in St. Catherine Church, Brussels, in October 1369, and taken to the synagogue, where they were reviled and transfixed, when they began to bleed profusely. That is "the miracle of St. Gudule" commemorated ever since by periodical festivals and by a special chapel in the cathedral St. Gudule of Brussels, the "chapelle du St. Sacrement de miracle" (sic), built in 1534-39 and decorated with a splendid series of stained-glass windows, describing the events, presented in 1540-47 by the kings of Portugal, Hungary, France, and Austria. Those incredible events caused a terrible pogrom in Brussels 1370.

[Henri Griffet]: Histoire des hosties miraculeuses qu'on nomme le Très saint sacrement de miracle, qui se conserve à Bruxelles depuis l'an 1370 et dont on y célèbre tous les cinquante ans l'année jubilaire (124 p., ill., Bruxelles 1770). Hirn (p. 132, 1912).

[41] According to Catholic (and Orthodox) doctrine, the sacraments are efficacious by the very fact that the rites have been properly followed (ex opere operato); according to Protestants, their efficacy depends on the disposition of the people receiving them (ex opere operantis). In particular, baptism, according to the Catholic faith, is entirely independent of the receiver's intention; it transforms his nature miraculously (see Isis 30, 309), gives him grace, and is indelible. This was clearly explained by St. Augustine at the time of his controversy with the Donatists (De baptismo III, 14).

The endless tragedies caused by compulsory baptism have been very well set forth by Henry Charles Lea: The Moriscos of Spain, their conversion and expulsion (Philadelphia 1901). Though this book deals mainly with the forcible conversion of Moors, it refers also to the conversion of Jews, which occurred at the same time (fifteenth and sixteenth centuries). See also Lea's Chapters from the religious history of Spain (p. 437–68, 445, Philadelphia 1890). Baruch Braunstein: The Chuetas of Majorca. Conversos and the Inquisition of Majorca (242 p., Columbia University Oriental series, Scottdale, Pa. 1936; Isis 36, 60).

One would think that the Jews, obliged to move in an atmosphere of hatred, contumely, and suspicion, trembling for their lives and belongings almost without surcease, would be unable to do any intellectual work, but that is not so. In fact, there are so many Jewish contributions that it is expedient to subdivide our account into five sections: (1) Spain, (2) Catalonia, (3) Provence, (4) Germany, (5) East.

C1. *Spain*

The tensions between Jews, Christians, and conversos were especially high in Spain, which has always proved herself to be, even in our own days, a hotbed of fanaticism and intolerance. These tensions were due to appear more conspicuously after the Catholic rulers, Ferdinand and Isabella, had established the Inquisition (1478),[42] but their potential was already dangerously high in the fourteenth century and many irreparable crimes were then perpetrated, which became the source of more crimes, and so on, ad majorem Satanae gloriam. As in other countries, anti-Semitism was considerably aggravated by the Black Death, which was often ascribed to Jewish malefices. Certain Jews were very wealthy, and their expropriation was so desirable that acute theologians had no difficulty in justifying it. In 1391, a series of pogroms occurred in Seville, Toledo, Valencia, and even in Barcelona. The mass conversions of Jews by St. Vincent Ferrer belong to the next century (1411), but St. Vincent himself had assumed the Dominican habit in 1367 and been very active ever since. They illustrate the remarks made about baptism above; St. Vincent baptized the Jews by the thousand (25,000 or 35,000?!); how could such wholesale conversions be genuine and worth while? how could the baptisms themselves be ritually valid?

The Jews were sustained by their religious faith and by their unshakable belief in their own superiority. Thus, Meir ben Aldabi, who was possibly himself a victim, for he fades out completely after 1360, ascribed to the genius of his ancestors not only the Hebrew writings but even the Greek ones! The latter, he could not help but surmise, were probably derived from Hebrew originals. Such conceptions are remarkable enough in Jewish minds; what is more remarkable is that Christian doctors were sharing them. Joseph ben Eliezer Bonfils (note the Provençal name, yet Joseph flourished in Saragossa) wrote commentaries on the Torah; most of his work seems to have been done in the East, where he was from 1370 on. Shemṭob Shapruṭ of Tudela wrote one of the most elaborate mediaeval apologies for Judaism; he translated the whole of Matthew and parts of the other Gospels from Latin into Hebrew; he composed many commentaries on the Bible and the Talmud; he took part in the public disputation on original sin and redemption in Pamplona 1375.

[42] Henry Charles Lea: History of the Inquisition of Spain (4 vols., New York 1906–7). Salvador de Madariaga: Christopher Columbus (p. 119–35, New York 1940; Isis 33, 95). In that provocative book Madariaga remarks (p. 329) that anti-Semitism was always a democratic, and pro-Semitism an aristocratic attitude in Spain.

Public disputations were one of the favorite means of that period for solving the Jewish-Christian difficulties. They illustrate the Christian naïveté and complacency of that age. Everybody realizes today that dogmatic beliefs cannot be refuted and reversed by formal discussions, least of all public ones. At best, that is, if there were no suggestion of pressure or unfairness, the disputation might cause doubts and thus prepare a conversion. The conditions under which those disputations were held, however, were very remote from fairness, every effort being made to impress the Jews with their guilt and unworthiness. This was perhaps due to ignorance and pharisaism as much as to malice. The outstanding tournament of that kind took place in Tortosa (Catalonia) in 1413–14; it occupied no less than 69 sessions and lasted 21 months! Some of the sessions were presided over by the antipope Benedict XIII,[43] attended by an impressive galaxy of prelates and nobles; the Jews were more like criminals brought before a court of justice than equal partners in an unprejudiced debate. The main accuser was the convert Jerome of the Holy Faith (Geronimo de Santa Fé); the defendants included Vidal Benveniste, Astruc ha-Levi,[44] etc. In conclusion, Benedict XIII issued a bull forbidding the Jews to study the Talmud, to have intercourse with Christians, to disinherit their baptized children, etc. The implementation of the bull was entrusted to Gonzalo de Santa Maria, son of the convert Paul of Burgos. (Margolis and Marx p. 454–56, 1927.)

C2. *Catalonia*

The two disputations referred to in the preceding section occurred in Pamplona and Tortosa, that is, respectively in the Basque and Catalan territories, not in the Spanish ones, yet it was not improper to call them Spanish events. Let us now consider the Jews of Catalonia.

Solomon Astruc Gatigno and Ezra ben Solomon Gatigno, probably father and son, devoted themselves to Biblical studies. The first flourished in Barcelona, the second in Saragossa and Lerida. Responsa and commentaries on the Talmud were published by Nissim ben Reuben Gerondi. As a Talmudist he was a worthy follower of Moses ben Naḥman Gerondi (XIII-2) and Solomon ben Adret (XIII-2). These three great men were for over a century the outstanding Talmudists of Catalonia; Moses died c. 1270, Solomon in 1310, and Nissim ben Reuben c. 1376. Nissim's main title to fame, however, is perhaps the fact that he was the teacher of Ḥasdai Crescas. We may call the latter Crescas, for though the name is not uncommon on both sides of the Pyrénées, when we say Crescas alone, we mean Ḥasdai Crescas, one of the leading philosophers of his time. He was more important from the philosophical than from the religious point of view, yet he was the leader of the Barcelona community at a most critical time. He was a witness of the tumult of 1391, during which his own son was killed, and he described it in a letter addressed to the Avignon community. In spite of the terror which was thus created, he did not hesitate a few years later to write in Spanish an apology for Judaism.

Gerondi's Responsa are among the most significant of their time and place,

[43] We call him antipope according to Roman usage, but to the audiences of Tortosa he was the true and only pope.

[44] Vidal Benveniste of Saragossa (EJ 3, 41, 1902). Astruc ha-Levi of Daroca in the province of Saragossa (EJ 2, 254, 1902). They had been selected not only for their theological learning, but also for their ability to debate in Latin.

but of course every rabbi was asked questions by members of his community (and if he was sufficiently famous, by members of distant communities) and it was an essential part of his rabbinical duty to give considered and learned answers. These questions and answers (she'elot u-teshubot) were often collected, and a good many of them have been published, printed, reprinted, etc. These collections constitute by far the most valuable documents for the study of Jewish life and thought from almost every angle, for the queries cover practically the whole field of theology, religion, rites, science, manners, etc. Most of them are practical, or of a mixed kind, e.g., the numerous ones related to calendaric difficulties. The habit began after the completion of the Mishnah[45] and has continued to our own days, East and West. These "responsa prudentium" give us, or will give us when they are properly analyzed, digested, and indexed, a large amount of information relative to eighteen centuries of Jewish life in many countries. No nation has produced or preserved a casuistic literature of such magnitude, illustrating at once the virtues and weaknesses of its authors. Many references to responsa have been made in my work, to those of Saadia ben Joseph (X-1), Alfasi (XI-2), Abraham ben Nathan (XIII-1), Solomon ben Adret (XIII-2), Asher ben Jehiel (XIII-2), etc., but hundreds more could be cited.

Many collections of responsa written by individual rabbis have been published and some of them are quoted in this volume; there are also collections including responsa by more than one author. Cowley (p. 592, 1929). Jacob Zallel Lauterbach (JE 11, 240–50, 1905). Much use of responsa has been made by Israel Abrahams (1896), see long list of his responsa sources, p. 434–36.

In addition to the authors of responsa quoted passim in this volume, let us introduce two who were perhaps the most important of the second half of the fourteenth century, whose curricula were similar, and who became bitter rivals.

The older one was Isaac ben Sheshet Perfet (or Barfat), born in Barcelona, 1326, rabbi in Saragossa and Valencia; the persecution of 1391 drove him to Africa and he established himself in Algiers, where he soon enjoyed considerable honor and influence; he died in Algiers in 1408; his tomb has remained a center of pilgrimage to this day (EJ 8, 551–56, 1931). His 518 responsa were printed in Constantinople 1547, then again in Riva di Trento 1559, and Lemberg 1805; additional ones were edited by D. Frenkl (Munkács, Hungary 1901). General study by Abraham M. Hershman: Rabbi Isaac ben Sheshet Perfet and his times (276 p., New York 1943; Isis 36, 28).

The younger man, Simeon ben Ẓemaḥ Duran, was born thirty-five years later in Majorca, 1361. He belonged to the important family of Duran (Durand, Durante, Douran), which originated in Provence but scattered to Majorca and North Africa. The persecution of 1391 drove him to Algiers, where his father, Ẓemaḥ, died in 1404 and himself in 1444. He had received a far better training in science and philosophy than Isaac ben Sheshet, and was not simply a Talmudist and casuist like the latter, but a theologian. His main work is the Magen abot (Shield of fathers), dealing with the philosophy of religion; in another entitled Or ha-ḥayyim (1436) he defended Maimonides against the Or Adonai of Ḥasdai Crescas. His is an important personality, far more so than that of his old rival, but he belongs to the fifteenth century, as most of his nineteen works were written late in life. His 802 responsa were published under the title Ha-tashbaẓ (folio, 3 vols., Amsterdam 1738–39; same edition with new title page, Amsterdam 1741). For more information on

[45] Mainly by Judah ha-Nasi (II-2). See also Introd. 1, 401.

him see JE (5, 17, 1903), EJ (6, 130–35, 1930), Isidore Epstein: The responsa of Rabbi Simon ben Ẓemaḥ Duran (118 p., Jews' College publications no. 13, London 1930); and on both men and their environment, Abraham Aaron Neuman: The Jews in Spain. Their social, political and cultural life during the Middle Ages (2 vols., Philadelphia 1942; Isis 35, 40). See also articles on Algeria and Algiers (JE 2, 381–87, 1901; EJ 2, 296–308, 1928).

C3. *Provence*

An intense Jewish life was continued in Provence until the end of the century, and that life was very largely expressed in the Hebrew language. In mediaeval days (and until much later) Jews, who had taken so easily to Arabic, did not consider that any other language, such as Latin, French, or Provençal, could be substituted for Hebrew for their own literary purposes. The word "literary" is perhaps misused in this case, for there is hardly any evidence of bonae literae in Jewish Provence, all their abundant literature being devoted to theology, religion, ritualism, responsa, grammar, and science. Their fidelity to the Hebrew script was equal to their love of the language itself, and they used it to transcribe French and Provençal texts. When the inquisitors began to burn indiscriminately every book or paper bearing the easily recognizable Hebrew script, they did not know that they were destroying a part of French and Provençal as well as of Hebrew literature.

Almost every Judeo-Provençal writer of this time composed Biblical[46] or Talmudic commentaries or religious books of one kind or another, but it will suffice to consider one, Profiaṭ Duran, one of the outstanding defenders of his persecuted faith in the Middle Ages. This is the more remarkable in that he was forcibly converted to Christianity in 1391,[47] but he planned (and perhaps accomplished) a pilgrimage to the Holy Land in order to atone for his apostasy, and renewed his covenant with the God of his fathers. He wrote c. 1396 a satire on Christianity which was so subtle that some Christian doctors mistook it for a eulogy and helped to distribute it. A year later he addressed to Crescas a treatise against Christianity. Finally, he wrote a history of the persecutions which his brethren had had to suffer throughout the ages.

Before leaving Provence it is well to recall that the most peaceful haven for Jews was the papal city of Avignon. The French popes were not only tolerant of Jews, but capable of kindness to them.

C4. *Germany*

The only representative of Judeo-German religion whom I came across is so strange that I am afraid he is not very typical. This is Yom-ṭob ben Solomon

[46] In spite of the abundance of Biblical commentaries written in Hebrew, the earliest Hebrew concordance to the Old Testament was not available until the middle of the fifteenth century. That concordance, entitled Meir netib or Or netib (Light of the path), was compiled in 1437–47 in Arles and perhaps also in Avignon by the Provençal Isaac Nathan ben Qalonymos ben Judah Nathan. Neubauer-Renan (p. 582–85, 1893); Isaac Broydé (JE 6, 628, 1904). In the printed editions (Venice 1524, etc.) it was wrongly ascribed to Mordecai Nathan. In spite of its incompleteness, it was the basis of the later concordances, including that of Johannes Buxtorf I (1564–1629), published posthumously, Concordantiae Bibliorum hebraicae (Basel 1632), by his son Joh. Buxtorf II (1599–1664). A concordance to the Vulgate had been begun two centuries earlier by the Dominicans under the direction of Hugh of Saint Cher (XIII-1) and was printed forty years before the Hebrew one, Concordantiae sacrorum bibliorum (Nuremberg 1485).

[47] See my remarks on the dangers of forced baptism, above.

Lipmann. To begin with, is he to be counted a German? He came from Mülhausen in Alsace and flourished in Prague. He wrote the Sefer ha-niẓẓaḥon (Book of victory), refuting Christianity and Qaraism and defending rabbinical Judaism and to some extent the qabbala. His work must be ascribed some importance, for it provoked considerable discussion. Like many of his learned contemporaries in other countries, Lipmann knew Latin and was well acquainted with the New Testament in that language. The need of defending themselves against Catholic persecutors had obliged some Jewish doctors to learn Latin; it was not sufficient for their purpose to have a smattering of it, they had to know it very well in order to understand scholastic quibbles and to ward off hairsplitting arguments; they had to know it even better if they wanted to take a useful part in disputations, which were conducted exclusively in that language.

Yom-ṭob ben Solomon Lipmann is not dealt with in this volume, for his activities as we know them belong rather to the following century. We first hear of him in 1399, when he was thrown into prison upon the denunciation of an apostate Peter (Pesaḥ). His Sefer ha-niẓẓaḥon was completed before 1410 (probably c. 1401–5); it is divided into seven parts and 354 sections, to symbolize the days of the week and of the lunar year. The seven parts are: (1) refutation of Christian charges; (2) justification of the pious Jewish life; (3) explanation of difficult passages in the Bible; (4) foundation of the commandments; (5) condemnation of heretics and Qaraites; (6) condemnation of skeptics and scoffers; (7) the sixteen bases of faith. The book was first printed in Nuremberg 1644 and many times afterward; a Latin translation appeared in Altdorf 1643 (JE 8, 97–98, 1904; EJ 10, 988–91, 1934).

Lipmann was typical in at least one thing, his name, which has become one of the best-known Jewish names all over the world.[48] (Of course, there are variants in the spelling, one or two p's or n's.)

C5. *East*

We have already remarked that Joseph ben Eliezer Bonfils, though we counted him among the Spaniards, flourished in the East. His main work, Ẓafenat pa'neaḥ, was written in Damascus 1370. Thus he might be counted a Syrian Jew. Three other men represent, respectively, the Crimea, Egypt, and Greece.

These three men wrote commentaries on the Torah which have this in common, that they represent rabbinical Talmudism against Qaraism. This is remarkable, for Qaraism was still an important school of Jewish thought in the East and nowhere else. The first was Abraham Qirimi (= the Crimean); the second, Eleazar ben Nathan ha-Babli, was acquainted with Arabic and Coptic, hence he must have flourished in Egypt; the third, Solomon ben Elijah, flourished in Salonica and Ephesos. The three had in common also some rationalistic velleities, probably due in part to their anti-Qaraite fixation.

For Chinese Jews, see section G, on China, below.

D. *Islām*

We shall consider successively the Maghrib and the Mashriq.

D1. *Western Islām*

Few people are able to appreciate their religion without contrasting it with the poorer kind of religion of other people. Hence apologetics has a sad way of degen-

[48] To men of science it has been endeared by the French physicist Gabriel Lippmann (1845–1921) and the German historian of chemistry Edmund O. von Lippmann (1857–1941?), about whom see Osiris vol. 3, 1937.

erating into controversy, irenics into polemics. Two Moors of this period wrote treatises against the Jews; it is possible that the expulsion of the Moors from almost the whole of Spain by the Christians caused them to vent their anger on other men who were treated even worse than themselves. It must be added, however, that there was no persecution of Jews in the Dār al-Islām comparable to that obtaining in Christian countries; the Jews were segregated (as were often other non-Muslims), they were generally not ill treated.[49]

These two Moors are Muḥammad ibn 'Alī al-Shaqūrī and 'Abd al-Ḥaqq al-Islāmī. The first wrote a book on jihād and another the title of which is transparent, "Knocking the Jew down to prevent him from exceeding the limits . . . ." 'Abd al-Ḥāqq, whose very name al-Islāmī suggests a recent conversion, being anxious to prove his zeal for the destruction of his own people, wrote a treatise entitled "The sharpened sword to answer the Jews."[50]

In contrast with this Jewish renegade we may recall the Christian one, Anselmo Turmeda, a Franciscan of Majorca, who embraced Islām and wrote an Islamic apology against Christendom. It is difficult to choose among renegades or converts (as you may please to call them), but it must be admitted Turmeda's conversion is more likely to have been genuine than that of that "servant of the truth" 'Abd al-Ḥaqq. The latter had very much to gain, and the former little, by turning his coat. We cannot read in their hearts, however, and we should not judge.

D2. *Eastern Islām*

Religious life in the Mashriq was more complex because of the rivalry not only between Sunnī sects, but also between Sunnī and Shī'a. These matters have already been explained sufficiently for our readers, though far too briefly for students of Islamic thought. I can but refer the latter to other works often mentioned by me.

In addition to the Qur'ān and its commentaries (tafsīr), the main source of theological knowledge in Islām is the tradition (ḥadīth, pl. aḥādīth), that is, the unread revelation (waḥy ghair matlū) through the Prophet's sayings (ḥadīth) or customs (sunna, pl. sunan). Muslims gave from the very beginning an enormous importance to ḥadīth and took considerable pains to insure its accuracy. This involved the development in early Islām of methods comparable to our modern methods of historical criticism, long before Western people had any idea of them. Each ḥadīth was scrutinized in itself and in every link of its transmission. Moreover, collections of aḥādīth were soon established; in fact, innumerable collections were published, out of which six have emerged which enjoy a kind of canonic authority; they are called the six books (al-kutub al-sitta) or the six correct books (al-ṣiḥāḥ al-sitta):

1. The Ṣaḥīḥ of Muḥammad ibn Ismā'īl al-Bukhārī (IX-1), who died in 870.
2. The Ṣaḥīḥ of Muslim (IX-2) ibn al-Ḥajjāj al-Nīsābūrī, d. 875.
3. The Sunan of Abū Dā'ūd Sulaimān ibn al-Ash'ath al-Sijistānī, d. 888.
4. The Jāmi' of Muḥammad ibn 'Īsā al-Tirmidhī (of Tirmidh on the Oxus), d. 892.
5. The Sunan of Abū 'Abd al-Raḥmān al-Nasā'ī (of Nasā in Khurāsān), d. 914.
6. The Sunan of Muḥammad ibn Yazīd ibn Māja al-Qazwīnī, d. 886.

[49] Jews were often very well treated in Muslim Spain, and therefore when they were expelled from Christian Spain many of them took refuge in Turkey. Many Hispanic Jews embraced Islām (Arnold p. 113, 134, 1896).

[50] On controversial literature between Muslims and the followers of other faiths see Arnold (p. 359–60, 1896).

Please note that these six writers were Orientals, we might call them Persians, and that they all died in the second half of the ninth century except al-Nasā'ī, who lived until 914. Traditional ḥadīth was thus established within half a century or little more. The first two collections, called al-Ṣaḥīḥān, are considered the most precious; the other four, dealing more with usage (sunna) than with sound sayings, are called Sunan (al-sunan al-arba'a). To these "six books" may be added at least three others which are given, at least by certain groups, almost equal authority:

7. Kitāb al-muwaṭṭa' of Mālik ibn Anas (VIII-2), of al-Madīna, the imām of the Mālikī school, d. 795.

8. Musnad of Aḥmad ibn Muḥammad Ibn Ḥanbal (IX-1) of Baghdād, imām of the Ḥanbalī school, d. 855.

9. Al-musnad al-jāmi' of 'Abdallāh ibn 'Abd al-Raḥmān al-Dārimī al-Samarqandī, who was a teacher of the authors of nos. 2, 3, 4, and died in 869.

All these books are authoritative for the Sunnī community, except that each of the orthodox schools attaches more importance to this or that one.

For more information on the enormous field of ḥadīth, see the notes of my Introduction implicitly referred to apropos of nos. 1, 2, 7, and 8, and Hughes (p. 639–46, 1885), Brockelmann (1, 156–68, 1898, and suppt.), Th. W. Juynboll (EI 2, 189–94, 1914–15). Alfred Guillaume: The traditions of Islām, an introduction to the study of ḥadīth literature (184 p., Clarendon Press, Oxford 1924).

Two vast concordances are in course of publication:

(a) Taisīr al-manfa'a bi-kitābai Miftāḥ kunūz al-sunna wal-Mu'jam al-mufahras li-alfāẓ al-ḥadīth al-nabawī (8 parts seen, Cairo 1935–40); each part is an index to one of the collections enumerated above, in the following order, 1 to 6, 9, 7; I assume that a ninth part, not seen by me, will contain an index to no. 8.

(b) A. J. Wensinck: Concordance et indices de la tradition musulmane. Les Six livres, le Musnad d'al-Dārimī, le Muwaṭṭa' de Mālik, le Musnad de Aḥmad ibn Ḥanbal (al-mu'jam al-mufahras li-alfāẓ al-ḥadīth al-nabawī), published by many scholars under the auspices of the International Academic Union. I have seen 11 parts in folio, 2 col., dated Leiden, Brill, 1933–38, forming 1 vol. of 552 p., and 320 p of vol. 2. This reaches the catchword rawā or rawiya, hence less than one-half o that fundamental work is available. Book (a) facilitates the use of (b).

As the completion of the great work begun by Arent Jan Wensinck (1882–1939) may be considerably delayed because of his death and of the war, we should mention his preparatory volume, A handbook of early Muhammadan tradition alphabetically arranged (488 p., Leiden 1927; Isis 11, 231). This is an English index enabling one to find definite traditions in the Arabic collections.

The most popular treatise on ḥadīth in the Orient, especially in India, is the Mishkāt al-maṣābīḥ (Niche of lamps) compiled by Walī al-dīn Muḥammad ibn 'Abdallāh al-Khaṭīb al-Tibrīzī c. 1336–39. Many lithographed editions of it have appeared in India, e.g., Bombay (1854, 1865, 1878–80), Delhi (1883–85, 1890); other lithographed editions include a Hindustānī translation (Amritsar 1895–96; Lahore 1902, 1906). The Arabic text was also published in St. Petersburg 1898, and in Kazan 1909. English translation by A. N. Matthews: Collection of the most authentic traditions regarding the actions and sayings of Muhammed; exhibiting the origin of the manners and customs, the civil, religious and military policy of the Muslemans (folio, 2 vols., Calcutta 1809–10). There are many commentaries in Arabic, Persian, Hindustānī.

The Mishkāt al-maṣābīḥ was founded upon an older work, the Maṣābīḥ al-sunna by al-Ḥusain ibn Mas'ūd al-Farrā' al-Baghawī of Baghshūr, Khurāsān, who died c. 1116–22 in Marv al-Rūd, or Little Marv, not very far from his native city. Brockelmann (1, 364; 2, 195; suppt. 1, 621; 2, 262). Alfred Guillaume remarked in his Traditions of Islam (p. 5, Oxford 1924), "It would be difficult to overestimate the value of the Mishkāt as a synopsis of the ḥadīth literature."

All the collections and concordances thus far mentioned concern the Sunnī community, which is by far the largest. The Shī'a attach just as much importance to ḥadīth as the Sunnī, but of course their canonic collections are different. They recognize four such collections, all of which were established much later than the Sunnī ones:

1. Al-Kāfī fī 'ilm al-dīn, by Muḥammad ibn Ya'qūb al-Kulīnī, d. 940.
2. Kitāb man lā yaḥḍuruhu-l-faqīh, by "shaikh 'Alī" = Abū Ja'far Muḥammad ibn 'Alī ibn Bābūya al-Qummī, d. 991.
3. Tahdhīb al-aḥkām, by Abū Ja'far Muḥammad ibn al-Ḥasan al-Ṭūsī, d. Najaf 1066/67.
4. Al-istibṣār fīmā 'khtulifa min al-akhbār, by the same. Brockelmann (1, 187, 405, 1898). R. Strothmann: Shī'a (EI 4, 354, 1926).

This digression on ḥadīth was introduced to help the reader to realize the enormous importance of that subject in Islamic thought; it was introduced here because the purification and canonization of ḥadīth was exclusively an Oriental contribution, though commentaries on ḥadīth could be made and were actually made by Western Muslims as well as by Eastern ones.

To return to the Eastern doctors, their religious publications dealt not only with ḥadīth, but with many other subjects. To begin with, we may recall al-Yāfi'ī (XIV-1), who lived until 1367 and was one of the greatest ṣūfī exponents in the Shāfi'ī school; he exerted a strong influence in Arabia as the main transmitter there of the ideas of Ibn 'Arabī (XIII-1) and others. Of course, the views set forth by a famous teacher in the mosques of Mecca and Madīna were bound to circulate throughout the Dār al-Islām. Muḥammad ibn Muḥammad al-Jazarī wrote a great many books on ḥadīth and tafsīr; he flourished in Syria and Persia. Meanwhile, there was considerable religious and theological discussion in Anatolia. That vast country had been behind Syria, Egypt, and 'Irāq, but was now catching up with astonishing energy. To illustrate, consider three outstanding Turks, al-Āqsarā'ī, Ḥājjī pāshā, and al-'Ainī. I may call them Turks without hesitation; the name of the first is Turkish and the two others knew Turkish as well as Arabic.

Al-Āqsarā'ī wrote a commentary on the Qur'ān, or, more exactly, annotated the famous commentary al-Kashshāf of al-Zamakhsharī (XII-1). In the same way Ḥājjī pāshā took as his text the Anwār al-tanzīl of al-Baiḍāwī (XIII-2), itself derived from the same al-Kashshāf. Al-'Ainī was primarily a historian and a traditionist.[51] He discussed the Ṣaḥīḥ of al-Bukhārī (IX-1). Note that Ḥājjī

[51] No special note is devoted to al-'Ainī because most of his activities belong presumably to the fifteenth century. Maḥmūd ibn Aḥmad al-'Ainī al-Ḥanafī was born at 'Aintāb, between Aleppo and Antioch, in 1360, but spent most of his life in Cairo, at first as a ṣūfī, later as a civil servant to the Mamlūk rulers. In 1399 he was muḥtasib, later nāẓir al-aḥbās, and from 1425 to 1442 qāḍī al-quḍā of the Ḥanafī rite. He wrote a general history, which he translated at sight from Arabic into Turkish for the sulṭān al-Ashraf Bars-bey (ruled 1422–38). He wrote many books, some in Turkish, most in Arabic, and died in 1451. He had founded a school called after him madrasa 'ainīya. Wüstenfeld (p. 50–52, 1882). Brockelmann (2, 52–53, 1902; suppt. 2, 50, 1938). Marçais (EI 1, 212–14, 1909).

pāshā and al-'Ainī were educated in Cairo; al-'Ainī was born in northern Syria and spent most of his life in Egypt, but he was a Turk and translated popular Ḥanafī books into Turkish. We have already remarked that the Turkish language was used at the Mamlūk court even as it was to be used centuries later at the Khedivial one.

The Persian Shī'a Faḍlallāh al-Ḥurūfī created a new kind of mystical doctrine wherein much stress was laid on the numerical value of letters, even as in the Jewish qabbala. It is not necessary, of course, to assume that he was submitted to Jewish influences. The logical and illogical reactions of men being very much the same everywhere, the same spiritual conditions are bound to produce the same fruits. These conditions were mystical tendencies, and the fact that letters believed to be as sacred as the language chanced to have numerical values which everybody recognized at once. For example, the symbols yod daleth (yā dāl) suggested immediately to the Jewish (or Arabic) mind two ideas, hand and 14; what could be more natural than to equate them? This harmonized with the universal habit of counting things and attaching as much importance to the numbers as to the things themselves.[52] Muslim, especially Ḥurūfī, mystics developed their special kind of gematria in the most extravagant manner. Anybody accepting their fantastic premises, and endowed with enough numerical imagination, was almost bound to carry them to the point of absurdity. This Faḍlallāh has not taken us away from Turkey, for his doctrines obtained special popularity in that country thanks to their rapid assimilation by the Baktāshī dervishes.

Ṭuruq. The Muslim brotherhoods were discussed in chapter II (p. 420–21), and some information was given about the earlier ones, (1) Qādirīya, (2) Qalandarīya, (3) Suhrawardīya, (4) Aḥmadīya, (5) Mawlawīya, and those created in the first half of the fourteenth century, (6) Ṣafawīya, (7) Baktāshīya. The Baktāshīya was especially welcome in Turkey, and, as we have just seen, it was the vehicle in that country of Shī'a doctrines and fantastic ideas.

In the second half of the century there were created at least two more ṭuruq which deserve to be briefly examined, for their influence on Muslim people was as great as that of monkish orders on Western ones.

(8) Naqshbandīya: This ṭarīqa is called after its founder Naqshband, Muḥammad ibn Muḥammad Bahā' al-dīn al-Bukhārī (1317–89). The nickname Naqshband, signifying (in Persian) painter, embroiderer, was taken to mean here the painter of God, of the divine truth.[53] Much information about his life and doctrines is collected in a Turkish book called Rashaḥāt 'ain al-ḥayāt (Drops from the fountain of life). He was born near Bukhārā and at 18 went to Sammās, a neighboring village, to become the disciple of the ṣūfī leader Muḥammad Bābā al-Sammāsī, who on his deathbed appointed him his khalīfa. Most of his life was spent in and about Bukhārā and Samarqand. His followers were protected by Tīmūr Lang. The order spread considerably in Turkey and all over the Ottoman empire.

Brown-Rose (p. 139 et passim, 1927). D. S. Margoliouth (EI 3, 841, 1934). Russian memoir by V. Gordlevskii in the collection of essays presented to Sergei Fedorovich Oldenburg (p. 147–64, Leningrad 1934).

[52] See index to Introd. vol. 1 under *number* 1, 2, 3, 4, 5, 7, 9, 10, 11, 12, and to vol. 2 under *number* 6.

[53] In Persian, naqshbandī ḥawādith (he who adorns the calamities) is an epithet of God; naqshbandīya refers to ṣūfī rites, not necessarily of this sect.

(9) Khalwatīya: This is an offshoot of the Suhrawardīya (Introd. 2, 363); it was created in Khurāsān by Ẓāhir al-dīn 'Umar al-Khalwatī (d. 1397). Its name is derived from a much used mystical term, khalwa (retirement from the world for deep devotion; from the root khalā, to be empty, vacant). The Khalwatīya obtained much popularity, but, its founder having left it without organization, after his death it soon split up into some fifteen suborders, eight in Anatolia, five in Egypt, one in Nubia, Hijāz, Somaliland, one in Kabylia. Each of these branches has a name of its own, and it is a moot point whether to consider them separate orders, or parts of the Khalwatīya, or parts of the Suhrawardīya. At any rate, that darwīsh exuberance corresponds to the monkish exuberance obtaining in Christendom and shows that the same fundamental desires were inspiring men in both cases. As the world was bad, it was better to withdraw from it and live with one's brethren and with God.

Brown-Rose (1927). Louis Massignon (EI 4, 670, 1929).

For Chinese Muslims (hui-hui) see the note on Chinese religions below, and the article on T'ao Tsung-i.

E. *India*

In the peninsula of Hindustān, irrespective of the Muslim conquerors, the religious development was Jaina or Hindu; in Ceylon, Buddhism continued to flourish.[54]

The beginnings of Jainism, which can be traced back to the sixth century B.C., were explained in volume 1 (p. 69). Jainism has continued to grow ever since, though exclusively in India. Jains scattered over the peninsula in small groups, remaining more numerous along the Malabar coast or not very far from it, below Bombay and also above it. Even in the countries where they were most numerous they remained a small minority among Hindus.[55] They made proselytes in the Gujarāta territory and therefore Taruṇaprabha (fl. c. 1355) wrote a treatise in Gujarātī explaining Jaina ethics.

Muslim rulers had destroyed, if not Hinduism—that was as impossible as destroying the jungle—at least the literary and philosophical efforts which were the purest expression of that culture. Happily, Hindu and Vedantic studies could continue to flourish in southern India under the patronage of the Vijayanagar dynasty. Thus we have at this time two of the greatest Vedantic scholars, Mādhava and Sāyaṇa, said by some to be brothers and by others to be identical. Many Sanskrit writings are ascribed to them.

For Buddhism we must pass from the continent to Ceylon. Two abbots of the vihāra of Gaḍalādeṇi, Dhammakitti IV and Dhammakitti V, distinguished themselves with a number of edifying books in Pāli.

F. *Tibet*

A reform of Tibetan Buddhism was successfully completed by Tsong Kapa c. 1392. The sect which he created was less ascetic and more ritualistic than the older one; it attained considerable popularity. Its members, called Yellow Hats

[54] Buddhism was not completely extinguished in India proper, witness such a document as was published by Arthur Waley: New light on Buddhism in medieval India (Mélanges chinois et bouddhiques 1, 355–76, 1932; Isis 35, 227).

[55] Imperial gazetteer of India (vol. 26, Atlas, Oxford 1931; pl. 16).

(vs. the Red Hats of the old observance), were so successful that they gradually superseded their predecessors and became the temporal as well as the spiritual masters of the country.

Tsong Kapa's reform was purely formal, it did not touch the doctrines, which he left as Atīsha had reformulated them about the middle of the eleventh century; one might perhaps compare it to the Cistercian reform in the Benedictine order. It was certainly not a reform in the liberal sense, and to call Tsong Kapa a Luther of Lamaism is foolish. He did not repudiate tantrism,[56] but proclaimed the need of using the teachings explained in tantra form as well as those explained in sūtra form.

Lawrence Austine Waddell: The Buddhism of Tibet or Lamaism (London 1895). In his admirable book, Peaks and lamas, Marco Pallis makes some interesting remarks on Tsong Kapa's reform (p. 256, London 1939).

G. *China*

In China the agelong struggle between Confucianism, Taoism, and Buddhism continued with moments of dual or even triangular harmony. The vicissitudes of each religion make me think of a gigantic dragon moving its coils up and down and sliding forward, backward, or sideways as conditions require. Now imagine three such dragons mixing or unmixing their coils, and trying to move either in one direction, or else in two or three different ones. The Confucian dragon was the steadiest of the three and the most Chinese, the two others were always a bit outlandish. The government and the administration of China were overwhelmingly Confucian, the classics which every ambitious boy had to memorize were Confucian classics. Thus it is not surprising that Confucianism had always the upper hand, though it generally preferred to subordinate Buddhism and Taoism to its purposes rather than persecute and destroy them. Indeed, even when they were decidedly out of favor Buddhism and Taoism never disappeared far below the surface of life, for women maintained the former, and adventurous spirits the latter.

The historian Wu Hai (d. 1391) is a good example of Confucian orthodoxy, but his lack of toleration is not representative. If he could have had his way, the printing and circulation of "heterodox" (i.e., Buddhist and Taoist) books would have been forbidden. He was not listened to, but even if he had been, heterodox books would have continued to circulate. It was not as easy to suppress books in the China of the fourteenth century as in the Germany of the twentieth!

A similar situation obtained in Korea, where Confucianism had made enormous progress after 1313, though it did not receive official consecration until 1392, when the new Li dynasty was established. Taoism had far less vitality in Korea than in China, but Buddhism had quite as much if not more, and persecutions fortified it.

In both countries the three religions mixed but did not combine.[57] The mixture was even more complex, for there were still other religions, chiefly Islām, Judaism,

[56] The Sanskrit word tantra has many meanings (Monier-Williams' Sanskrit dictionary p. 436, 1899): warp, framework, doctrine, treatise; in English usage tantra and tantrism often designate doctrines or treatises dealing with Śiva and Śakti mysticism and magic (Śakti being the primordial female energy corresponding to the primordial male energy Śiva). There is no canon of tantra literature, and it was only in this century that it began to be investigated by European scholars. One of the leaders was Arthur Avalon (= Sir John Woodroffe), whose series of tantric texts began to appear in 1913 (Isis 3, 77-81). L. de la Vallée Poussin (ERE 12, 193-97, 1922). Emeneau (p. 313 and by index, 1935). Ernest A. Payne: The Śāktas, an introductory and comparative study (Religious life of India, 153 p., Calcutta 1933; p. 49-60).

[57] This chemical metaphor is selected as the best means of expressing our thought. If the religions had combined, they would have created a new religion, which was not the case. They mixed but remained independent, like the three dragons.

Nestorian and Catholic Christianity. All these religions recognized Confucianism, for they could not have been tolerated otherwise. They were not expected to bow to Taoism or to Buddhism, but the latter had such a strong hold on the hearts of the people that it was decidedly better to be friends with it. An interesting example of Muslim-Buddhist symbiosis is afforded by the Monastery of the Five Flowers (Wu hua ssŭ) built in Yünnan-fu in 1277 by the prince of Yünnan and the minister-governor, the Muslim Sayyid al-Ajall (see my note on Chinese Muslims in chapter XXII). A Buddhist temple built by a Muslim! The story is told in a long Chinese inscription of 1368, still in situ (Ollone p. 132–39, 1911).

We need not speak of Chinese Christians, for there are many references to them throughout this book, but the story of the Chinese Jews is less well known. The ultimate source of information concerning them is a group of Chinese Jewish inscriptions in K'ai fêng fu (dated 1164, 1489, 1512, 1663). Jews came to China during the Han dynasty and again during the Sung. There has been a synagogue in K'ai fêng fu, Honan, at least since 1163. In 1421 the Jewish physician Yen Ch'êng obtained the emperor's permission to restore it. Later he was appointed a magistrate in Chehkiang.

Jérôme Tobard (S.J.): Inscriptions juives de K'ai-fong-fou (Variétés sinologiques no. 17, 120 p., Shanghai 1900), elaborate study including Chinese texts, rubbings, and other illustrations. Kaufmann Kohler and Henri Cordier (JE 4, 33–36, 1903). S. M. Perlmann: History of the Jews in China (95 p., London 1913). Albert M. Hyamson (ERE 3, 556–60, 1911; EJ 5, 475–82, 1930). William Charles White: Chinese Jews (3 vols., Toronto 1942; Isis 35, 257).

The three religions which we call Nestorianism, Zoroastrianism, and Manichaeism were called by the Chinese ching chiao (ta-ch'in), huo chiao (hsien, mu-hu), and mo-ni, but they were gradually confused under the global name, the three *foreign* religions.[58] For example, in the edict of secularization of the Taoist emperor Wu Tsung, dated 845, these three religions are already lumped together as wai-kuo, that is, foreign (Introd. 1, 552).[59]

A. C. Moule (1930). F. S. Drake: Foreign religions of the T'ang dynasty. I. Zoroastrianism, II. Manichaeism (Chinese recorder 71, 343–54, 643–49, 675–88, Shanghai 1940). Thanks to L. Carrington Goodrich and James R. Ware.

III. THE TRANSLATORS

During the first half of the century a number of books were translated from some nine languages into other languages; during the second half of the century the languages from which the translations were made were the same with the exception of Spanish (or Catalan) and Tibetan. Let us consider the various groups one by one.

1. *Arabic*

1a. *From Arabic into Hebrew*

This is again the largest subgroup in the Arabic group. With the exception of a single Easterner, all the workers were in Spain or southern France. The transla-

[58] When the Chinese speak of the three religions or three doctrines (san chiao), they mean of course Confucianism, Taoism, and Buddhism.

[59] English translation of the edict by Ignatius Ying-ki: The secularization decree of Wu-tsung (Catholic University, Peking, bulletin no. 6, p. 119–24, July 1929). Ying-ki translated mu-hu by Mohammedans, which is, I believe, incorrect. Giles' dictionary (p. 1001, 1912); mu-min means Mohammedans, mu-hu, Zoroastrians.

tions are of many kinds—medical, astronomical, philosophical. Joseph ben Joshua ha-Lorqi translated the logic of Maimonides; another scholar bearing the same name (grandson of the former?) translated part of the Qānūn of Ibn Sīnā; David ben Solomon ibn Ya'īsh of Seville translated the domestic economy ascribed to "Bryson"; Judah ben Solomon Nathan, various medical books and the Maqāṣid al-falāsifa of al-Ghazzālī; Jacob ben Isaac Carsono, his own treatise on the astrolabe; Samuel ibn Moṭoṭ, Solomon ben Labi, and Zerahiah ben Isaac ha-Levi, theological and philosophical treatises. All told, a fine collection of earnest Arabic books were made available to Hebrew readers. The Jewish communities realized the value of such work, and a financier like Judah ben Solomon ibn Labi of Saragossa was willing to subsidize the scholars engaged in it.

The single Easterner, Solomon ben Elijah, translated a Ptolemaic treatise on the astrolabe from the Greek but with the help of an Arabic version, or else he translated it from the Arabic with reference to the Greek original.

1b. *From Arabic into Latin*

That mighty stream of earlier centuries had become a rivulet at the beginning of this one, and by the middle of it, it was beginning to dry up. We can quote only one possible translator, Joannes Jacobi, who knew Arabic and wrote many treatises in Latin derived from Arabic sources. The translations which can be definitely ascribed to him, however, are written in Catalan.

1c. *From Arabic into Catalan*

This subgroup is relatively large; it helps to prove the vitality of the Catalan language. We have, to begin with, the translation of two ophthalmological texts by Joannes Jacobi, referred to in the previous section. The king of Aragon and Catalonia, Pere el Cerimoniós, caused various treatises, notably an agricultural one, to be translated. The Franciscan Anselmo Turmeda translated a part of the Rasā'il ikhwān al-ṣafā'; it is true his Disputa del ase was supposed to be an original text, but it was really a translation and must be judged as such.

1d. *From Arabic into Persian and Turkish*

The Turkish book on falconry, Bāz-nāma, by Maḥmūd ibn Muḥammad al-Bārjīnī was probably first written in Arabic, then turned into Persian, finally into Turkish. Many Turkish writings have an Arabic and (or) Persian origin, which simply means that Turkish culture is largely derivative from the Arabic (or Islamic) and from the Persian.

2. *Greek*

2a. *From Greek into Latin*

With the more general recognition of the Greek origin of many of the philosophical and scientific classics, which the majority of Western scholars had known only in the form of translations from the Arabic, one would expect the Greco-Latin stream to increase considerably. It did increase, but very little and slowly, the obvious reason for that slowness being the deep schism separating the Latin from the Greek world. The number of scholars knowing the Greek and Latin languages sufficiently well to translate from the one into the other was exceedingly small, and not all of them were willing and ready to do such work.

These translators may be divided into two groups, the Western or Italian, and the Eastern or Greek.

The outstanding man of the first group was the Calabrian Leonzio Pilato. The Calabrians had never lost touch completely with Greek culture, and moreover Leonzio had followed his teacher Barlaam to Constantinople. His achievement as a translator, however, was cut short by his accidental death in 1366. The only translations of his that have come down to us are those of the first canti of the Iliad and of the Odyssey. The other Italians, Giacomo d'Angelo, Poggio Bracciolini, and Guarino Veronese, belong rather to the fifteenth century than to the fourteenth, for their main work was not completed until after 1400. The first of these is also called Giacomo da Scarperia, because he was born at Scarperia in the Mugello district;[1] he was a pupil of Manuel Chrysoloras in Venice and accompanied him to Constantinople in search of MSS. He translated Ptolemy's Quadripartitum and five of Plutarch's lives, but his main title to fame was his translation of Ptolemy's Geography, completed in 1409. The famous humanist Poggio (born near Florence 1380, died in that city 1459) wrote translations of Xenophon's Cyropaedia and of the histories of Diodoros of Sicily (I-2 B.C.). Guarino (born in Verona c. 1370, died at Ferrara 1460), another pupil of Chrysoloras, traveled to the East to collect MSS and translated the whole of Strabo, a few of Plutarch's lives, and the latter's treatise περὶ παίδων ἀγωγῆς (1411).

Passing to the Orientals, the first to attract our attention is Symeon Atumanos, who translated the New Testament and Plutarch's treatise on the control of anger, περὶ ἀοργησίας. Petros Philarges, who in 1409 became pope Alexander V (to whom Giacomo d'Angelo dedicated his Ptolemy), is said to have translated a few books. Manuel Chrysoloras began a translation of Plato's Republic. Atumanos and Chrysoloras were born in Constantinople, Petros Philarges in Crete. The three had a native knowledge of Greek, but they had to acquire their Latin, and in the case of Atumanos that acquisition remained very imperfect.

For the reverse translations from Latin into Greek, see section 3b.

2b. *From Greek into Hebrew*

Solomon ben Elijah translated the Ptolemaic treatise on the astrolabe, and Atumanos, the New Testament. Both translations are subject to doubt, the first because it was made partly, largely, or completely from the Arabic, the second because the text is lost. Atumanos intended to translate the New Testament into Hebrew, but was his intention realized? Both men had a good knowledge of Greek; Solomon had a deep knowledge of Hebrew, but can we say the same of Atumanos?

For the reverse translation from Hebrew into Greek, see section 4a.

3. *Latin*

3a. *From Latin into Hebrew*

This is by far the largest subgroup of translations of this period, a fact which confirms the impression we explained in chapter I. Latin has now become a source of knowledge for the Jews as well as for the Christians. The Latin-Hebrew stream is so large that it will be convenient to consider separately the Provençal and the Spanish contributors. It is noteworthy that the majority of them on both sides of the Pyrénées were primarily, if not exclusively, translators.

[1] In the Appennino. Mugello is the upper valley of the Sieve, affluent of the Arno.

Provence. The Provençal scholars, realizing the growing importance of Latin medicine, devoted themselves chiefly to the version of medical treatises. Thus, Moses of Roquemaure and later Jekuthiel ben Solomon of Narbonne translated the Lilium medicinae of Bernard of Gordon; Leon Joseph of Carcassonne and Abraham Abigdor, Gerald de Solo's commentary in nonum Almansoris; Leon Joseph also translated other treatises by Gerald de Solo and Jean de Tournemire; Abraham Abigdor, treatises by Bernard Alberti, Arnold of Villanova, and Gerald de Solo; Ṭodros ben Moses Yomṭob, treatises by Mesuë major and Arnold of Villanova; Benjamin ben Isaac of Carcassonne, a plague tract by John of Burgundy; Judah ben Solomon Nathan, Latin notes to a treatise of Ibn Wāfid, a treatise on wine by Arnold of Villanova, remarks by Gilbert the Englishman and Bernard of Gordon. This last item suggests that the list might be lengthened if Hebrew elaborations of Latin treatises were added to the translations pure and simple. It is clear that some Jewish doctors were taking pains to make the latest Latin compilations and commentaries available in Hebrew and enable their brethren to compete on equal terms with their Christian colleagues. I mean equal scientific terms; the social terms, alas! were far from equal. It is no accident, however, that these translations were composed in Provence, where Jewish physicians were more or less tolerated; in the comtat Venaissin they even enjoyed some amount of protection from the French popes.

There were also a number of nonmedical translations. Abraham Abigdor translated the Summulae logicales of Peter of Spain and some of the logical commentaries of Ibn Rushd; Solomon Abigdor, the Capitula astrologiae of Arnold of Villanova and the Sphaera mundi of Sacrobosco; Solomon ben Nathan Crescas, a magical book by Apollonios of Tyana; Solomon ben David Davin, astronomical tables for Paris and an astrological treatise by Ibn abī-l-Rijāl. The astrological treatises might have been added to the medical ones, because they were considered necessary for medical practice.

Spain. Spain should be understood largo sensu, for at least one of the translators, Jacob ben Judah Cabret, should be called a Catalan. He translated the Capitula astrologiae of Arnold of Villanova. A little later (1403) another member of that family, Isaac ben Abraham Cabret, translated the commentary of John of Saint Amand on the Antidotarium Nicolai.

Thanks to conditions similar to those obtaining in Provence and to the patronage of Judah ben Solomon ibn Labi, many other translations were made in Spanish lands. Meir ben Solomon Alguadez translated the Nicomachean ethics; Shemṭob ben Isaac Shapruṭ, the Gospel of Matthew and parts of the other Gospels; Jacob ben Isaac Carsono, the astronomical tables of Engelbert and Dalmau.[2]

For the reverse translations from Hebrew into Latin, see section 4a.

3b. *From Latin into Greek*

The Latin-Hebrew stream was a natural one; Jewish scholars translated Latin books into their own language because they needed them. On the contrary, the Latin-Greek stream was a forced one which could not have existed but for the outside pressure which kept it going. That pressure was the Catholic propaganda, which was anxious to place as many Catholic writings as possible before the eyes of the Orthodox flock. Two brothers Cydones, who came from Salonica, were converted to Catholicism or at any rate to the Catholic views of church unity, and

[2] The text of these tables may have been in Catalan, instead of Latin.

learned to appreciate the theological writings of the Catholic doctors. Prochoros Cydones translated writings of St. Jerome, St. Augustine, Boetius, and St. Thomas. His brother Demetrios translated a mass of the Ambrosian liturgy, writings of St. Augustine, Fulgentius, St. Anselm, Ricoldo di Monte Croce, and the Summa contra gentiles of St. Thomas. Demetrios spent part of his life in Milano and died in Venice (?); Prochoros, having imprudently remained in the Orthodox world, was anathematized by his former brethren, died unhouseled, and was buried like a dog.

For the reverse translations from Greek into Latin, see section 2a.

3c. *From Latin into French*

In contrast with the artificial Latin-Greek stream, the Latin-French was a very natural one, full of youthful vigor, announcing the increasing importance of the French language. Indeed, French was destined to become the main heir of Latin.

The list of scholars engaged in the task of pouring Latin culture out into French vessels is long and distinguished.

Jean de Sy translated part of the Old Testament; Martin de Saint-Gilles, the Aphorisms of Hippocrates; Jean Corbechon, the encyclopaedia of Bartholomew the Englishman; Denis Foulechat, the Polycratus of John of Salisbury; Raoul de Presles, the Civitas Dei of St. Augustine and a political treatise by Giles of Rome; Nicole Oresme, the Ethics, Politics, and Astronomy of Aristotle; Jean Dandin, moral treatises by Vincent of Beauvais and Petrarca; Simon de Hesdin and Nicolas de Gonesse, the Memorabilia of Valerius Maximus; John of Ypres, various travel books; Richard Eudes, the balneological poem of Peter of Eboli; Jacques Bauchant, one of Seneca's books; Jean Golein, the Collationes of Joannes Eremita, the Rationale divinorum officiorum of William Durand, the Chronicle of Burgos, treatises by Bernard Gui, etc.; Evrard de Conty, the Aristotelian Problems; Eustache Deschamps, his own complaint apropos of the Great Schism. A good part of that considerable activity was patronized by king Charles the Wise (ruled 1364–80), whose munificence was emulated by other princes, such as Jean de Berry (1340–1416).[3] It is probably because of that royal and lay patronage that the list of translations is so varied and eclectic. I did not try to mention all the translations, but left out deliberately a number which would hardly concern my readers; nevertheless, the presence of so many pagan and scientific books is remarkable. In the courts of Charles the Wise and Jean de Berry we are already breathing the air of the Renaissance, only a few puffs to be sure, but the new atmosphere is unmistakable.

3d. *From Latin into Spanish*

A great many books were translated into Spanish, but in this case we cannot speak of a general movement as in France, for most of the translations are credited to a single man, Don Pedro López de Ayala el Canciller. He is said to have translated three decades of Livy, Valerius Maximus, the Consolatio of Boetius, the

[3] John II the Good, king of France 1350–64, had three sons, Charles V the Wise who succeeded him, John duke of Berry, and Philip II the Bold, duke of Burgundy (1363–1404). The three brothers were patrons of letters and arts. They did not subsidize translators only, but even more copyists, limners, and artists of many kinds. Some of the most precious MSS of the fourteenth century in the Bibliothèque nationale of Paris and elsewhere are due to the munificence of the first two. A large part of the Burgundian library is still available in the Royal Library of Brussels. Until the end of the eighteenth century that library was actually called Bibliothèque des ducs de Bourgogne. See Catalogue des MSS (folio, 3 vols., Bruxelles 1842). Otto Cartellieri: The court of Burgundy (p. 164–80, London 1929).

Moralia of St. Gregory, the Historia trojana of Guy of Colonna, and treatises by St. Isidore of Seville and Boccaccio. Whether he did that work himself or had it done under his direction, the fact remains that all these texts, most of them pagan, became available to the men and women of Castile. The Spanish Renaissance was on the way, even as the French one.

3e. *From Latin into English*

The English were drinking from two main sources, Latin and French. The most important text derived from the first of these sources was the translation of the Vulgate by John Wycliffe and his associates. To Chaucer we owe a translation of the Consolatio of Boetius, but it was probably made from the French as much as from the original; his treatise on the astrolabe is so close to the Latin version of Māshāllāh's book that it might be called a translation. In fact, it is closer to Māshāllāh than Chaucer's Consolation is to Boetius. The main translator of the age was John of Trevisa, who produced English versions of the Gospel of Nicodemos and of writings by Bartholomew the Englishman, Giles of Rome, Ranulf Higden, Pierre Dubois, and Richard Fitzralph. Many of these writings were of recent origin; their translation proves not only that the English people (that is, the English clerks) wanted to read them, but also that Latin was ceasing to be a vehicle of thought. Instead of being a vehicle, Latin was becoming an impediment.

3f. *From Latin into Czech*

Even as Charles the Wise promoted French translations, the emperor Charles IV of Luxemburg, king of Bohemia (1347–78), otec vlastí, encouraged Czech ones. For example, he caused the Legenda aurea to be adapted to Bohemian use and published in the Czech language. His autobiography was translated by Pulkava, and Pulkava's own chronicle could soon be read in Czech as well as in Latin. Mandeville's travels were translated by Vavřinec of Březova.[4]

The Gospels had been translated into Czech and were actually read in that language. For example, Anne of Bohemia, queen (1382–94) of Richard II, read the Gospels in Czech as well as in Latin and German. Her Bohemian friends as well as the Bohemian students who came to Paris and Oxford (where scholarships were available to them from 1388 on) contributed to the spreading of Wycliffism in Bohemia, and eventually caused the translation of Wycliffian literature into Czech.

4. *Hebrew*

4a. *From Hebrew into Greek and Latin*

Very few people cared to translate anything, except the Old Testament, from Hebrew into other languages. The Old Testament itself was generally neglected by the Christians, except in its Vulgate form if these were Latins or in the Septuagint if they were Greeks. Symeon Atumanos of Constantinople undertook to translate it into Greek and into Latin for Urban VI; he was thus preparing the edition of a triglot Bible. His Greek version of the Old Testament is extant in the famous MS Marcianus Graecus VII.

For the reverse translations from Greek into Hebrew and from Latin into Hebrew, see sections 2b and 3a.

[4] Březova is 54 miles southeast of Brno (Brünn). Vavřinec's Latin name is Laurentius Byzinius (or Byzynius). He flourished from 1365 to 1437, wrote a chronicle of Bohemia from 1414 to 1422 (preparation and beginning of the Hussite wars), and various books in Czech (Potthast p. 712, 1895).

4b. *From Hebrew into Spanish*

The Psalter had been translated into Castilian from the Vulgate, with due reference to the Hebrew text, by Hermann the German (XIII-2). It is probable that other attempts were made to translate the Old Testament from Hebrew into Castilian during the fourteenth century, witness the texts of the Escorial MS and of the Evora MS (the latter written in 1429), and the so-called Ferrara Bible (printed Ferrara 1553), which is essentially the Evora Castilian text written in Hebrew characters for the use of the descendants of the Jews expelled from Spain (this Ferrara Bible is used to this day by the Sephardim of the Near East). In 1422, rabbi Mose Arragel was ordered by the grand master of the Order of Calatrava to prepare a new Castilian translation; that translation was made with constant reference to the Castilian versions of the thirteenth and fourteenth centuries. It is preserved in the magnificent Bible of Olivares.[5] The Castilian versions were the earliest translation in any European vernacular made directly from the Hebrew text. The contemporary (or earlier) versions in English, German, Italian, etc. were all made from the Vulgate.

Though Arragel's work belongs to the fifteenth century, it implies much work done in the second half of the fourteenth.[6]

5. *French*

From French into English

We have but one scholar to quote in this section, but he is a great one, Chaucer. He has already been mentioned as a translator from Latin, but his translations from the French are far more important, that is, if we assume, as we must, that his Boetius was largely derived from the French versions, and, as we may, that he had a share in the translation of the Roman de la rose.

6. *Persian*

From Persian into Turkish

A book on sexual hygiene by Nāṣir al-dīn al-Ṭūsī was translated by one Ṣalāḥ al-dīn. Another possible translation from Persian into Turkish has been referred to above in section 1d.

7. *Sanskrit*

From Sanskrit into Bengali

By the end of the century the two great epics of Sanskrit literature, the Mahābhārata and the Rāmāyaṇa, were partly available in Bengali form, and thus the Bengali language was established on a solid basis. The early translation of the Rāmāyaṇa is ascribed to Kṛittivāsa (b. 1346); its text has been so much corrected and modified by later translators that it cannot be reconstructed. The Mahābhārata was summarized in Bengali at about the same time by Sañjaya.

[5] Biblia (antiguo testamento) traducida de hebreo al castellano por Rabi Mose Arragel de Guadalfajara y publicada por el Duque de Berwick y de Alba (folio, 2 vols., Madrid 1920–22). Also privately printed for presentation to the members of the Roxburghe Club, 1918–21.

[6] For the history of the Spanish Bible, see Henry Charles Lea: Chapters from the religious history of Spain (p. 44–56, Philadelphia 1890). In Spain, the interdiction of the vernacular Bible did not become harsh until after the Reformation.

Conclusion

Though the list of translations is less complex than that relative to the first half of the century, a synopsis like the one given on page 70 will be useful for a better understanding of the cultural exchanges involved, and a comparison of this period with others.

Table 3

Linguistic classification of translations (XIV-2)

1. A→H	3. L→H*	4. H→G*, L*
→L	→G*	→Sp
→Cat	→F	5. F→E
→P→T	→Sp	6. P→T
2. G→L*	→E	7. S→Ben
→H*	→Cz	

There are only 18 combinations as against 34[7] in table 1 (p. 70). These combinations are not equally important. The most important by far are A→H, G→L, L→H, L→F. The asterisks refer to the translations which were reversed; only three pairs. Most translations were not reversed. For example, books were translated from Arabic into Hebrew, but not from Hebrew into Arabic.

Table 4

(Reverse of table 3)

L	was	translated	from	A, G, H
H	"	"	"	A, G, L
G	"	"	"	L, H
Cat	"	"	"	A
Sp	"	"	"	L, H
F	"	"	"	L
E	"	"	"	L, F
Cz	"	"	"	L
P	"	"	"	A
T	"	"	"	P, A
Ben	"	"	"	S

The superiority of Latin appears in its double connection as a reservoir filled from three sources and emptying itself in the largest number (six) of directions. The continued superiority of Latin and its derivatives symbolizes the growing supremacy of Western culture.

IV. EDUCATION

A. *Christendom*

1. *Universities*

Of the eleven universities founded in the second half of the fourteenth century, five were of lasting importance, to wit Pavia (1361), which became the center of learning of Lombardy; Cracow (1364), the first Polish university; Vienna (1365),

[7] Or 37 if the data of the appendix to that list are counted.

the first Austrian one; Erfurt (1379) and Heidelberg (1385), the first two German universities. Each of these institutions suffered its own vicissitudes and was gradually colored by its own environment, but they were not essentially different from one another.

The University of Paris continued to be in many respects the most important university of Europe, and it played an important part in reaching decisions concerning theological and philosophical orthodoxy. This helped to preserve unity of thought, especially during those critical years when the unity of the church was jeopardized by the Great Schism (1378–1429).[1] On the other hand, orthodox decisions, however supreme they may be, have the unavoidable consequence of inviting heresy, and causing it, as it were, to exist where it did not exist before. To illustrate the evil side of the spiritual leadership which the University of Paris had assumed, it will suffice to recall that the condemnation, the judicial murder, of Joan of Arc was accomplished in Rouen in 1431 upon its most emphatic advice.[2] This was the outstanding murder to weigh upon the university's conscience (if a university may be said to have a conscience), but it committed a good many others.

The decisions of the University of Paris originated various emigrations of refugee scholars and to that extent favored the diffusion of science (many examples will be found in this volume).

2, 3. *English colleges and schools*

Two new colleges were established in Oxford, Canterbury (1361) and New College (1379), and only one in Cambridge, Corpus Christi (1352). Among the founders of these institutions the most original was undoubtedly William of Wykeham, who created not only New College, but also a preparatory school for it, Winchester (1378), which was the earliest "public school" of England.

There were a number of grammar and chantry schools all over the country, but their level was relatively low and the ignorance of many clerks was shocking. Some of them were not even able to understand exactly their breviary or the Gospels.

4. *Education in France*

Reference has already been made to the University of Paris, which was truly an international institution. In a minor degree every university was, for the papal bull conferred on their graduates the privilege of teaching everywhere.

Eleven more colleges were created in Paris, but none of importance. The provincial universities continued to do their share of the educative work, and they were helped by the universities of Montpellier,[3] Avignon, and Orange, which were outside French territories but close enough to function for them almost as well as if they had been French institutions. The library of Avignon became under Urban V the largest library of France.

[1] For the part played by the University of Paris in healing the schism and also in mediating between regulars and seculars, see Connolly (p. 90–203, 1928).

[2] The condemnation of 1431 was declared iniquitous and Joan rehabilitated by another tribunal in 1456. She was beatified by Pius X in 1909 and canonized by Benedict XV in 1920. St. Joan's day is May 30, day of her martyrdom in Rouen. The judgments of 1456, 1909, 1920 were implicitly condemnations of the University of Paris.

[3] Montpellier, it is true, was under French rule from 1349 to c. 1364, then again after 1382. See Stokvis (2, 131, 1889).

There were many cathedral and monastic schools in every part of the country, and for the illiterate, who formed the large majority of the nation, was provided the silent teaching of the paintings and the works carved in stone or wood which decorated the churches. Each church was like a book illustrating the main doctrines in the most reverential manner. Occasional sermons helped the ignorant to direct their attention to this or that, and those who were sufficiently intelligent and susceptible to such influences would learn much without the need of letters; they would learn enough, claimed the priests, to insure their salvation, and what more did they need? The feeling is neatly expressed in the prayer which François Villon wrote for his mother:[4]

Femme je suis povrette et ancienne,
Qui riens ne sçay; oncques lettre ne leus.
Au moustier voy dont suis paroissienne
Paradis paint, ou sont harpes et lus,
Et ung enfer ou dampnez sont boullus:
L'ung me fait paour, l'autre joye et liesse.
La joye avoir me fay, haulte Deesse,
A qui pecheurs doivent tous recourir,
Comblez de foy, sans fainte ne paresse.
En ceste foy je vueil vivre et mourir.

One of the most popular educational books of mediaeval times was written in 1371 by La Tour-Landry for his daughters, "Le livre du chevalier de la Tour." It explains the course of conduct which gentlewomen ought to follow in order to do their duty and avoid pitfalls. The book was soon translated into English and into German, but not into Latin. According to his own statement, La Tour-Landry had written a similar book for his sons, but that book is unfortunately lost.

5. *Italy*

The only new universities were those of Pavia (1361) and Ferrara (1391), the second of which did not last very long, whereas the former has continued to this day to accumulate fame and merit in spite of the fact that it has remained relatively small. In this period, however, the main centers of learning were much less these new foundations than the older ones, above all the venerable Bologna. Bologna was not only the main studium of Italy, it competed in the international field with Paris.

Some of the most famous Italian teachers of those days were connected not with the old or new universities, but with humbler institutions. We may say that the Italians were the first to give glamour and fame to grammar schools. The two greatest teachers of Europe were Giovanni da Ravenna and Vittorino da Feltre.

Giovanni da Ravenna or Giovanni di Conversino taught in many schools of northern Italy, being an early exemplar of the itinerant and restless humanist. His publications are not important, but he was a persuasive teacher who instinctively used friendly and intuitive methods instead of trying to cram his pupils like poultry, doing violence to them, causing their resentment, and then revenging

[4] Villon lived a century later (1431–89), but that does not matter. The quotation is taken from the "Ballade que feit Villon a la requeste de sa mere pour prier Notre-Dame." It is included in the Grand testament (Paris 1489). Paul Lacroix's edition of the Oeuvres (p. 64, Paris 1877).

himself upon them. His main reward was less his own fame than that of some of his pupils, like Pietro Paolo Vergerio, Guarino da Verona, and above all Vittorino da Feltre. Let us say a few words about each of them. Vergerio the Elder was a teacher of many things in many places, but above all a humanist. He distinguished himself so much at the council of Constance—where distinguished people had gathered from every Catholic country—that the emperor Sigismond became anxious to gain his collaboration. He spent the rest of his life in the imperial service, being one of the earliest models of a secretary who does not simply write letters according to the proper formulas but fully deserves to be called a man of letters. Guarino Veronese was a successful hunter of MSS, and he translated many books from Greek into Latin. The greatest of all these men was Vittorino da Feltre, who founded the Casa giocosa (the Joyous house) in Mantua, a new school where he tried to develop simultaneously the minds, the bodies, and the hearts of his pupils, to combine the highest ideals of ancient times with those of Christianity, to harmonize individualism with moral discipline, temperance and piety with joy. We have trespassed into the fifteenth century; Vergerio it is true was born as early as 1349, but he lived until 1420, Guarino until 1460, Vittorino until 1446; the Casa giocosa was opened only in 1423. Yet the seeds were put in the hearts of these men by the elder Giovanni da Ravenna in the fourteenth century. New methods of education were then being tried in Italy, the like of which was not known in many civilized countries until our own times. The great majority of the present "grammarians" or classical scholars are not fit to clean Vittorino's shoes, and Vittorino's own education was certainly completed in our period, for he was 22 years old when the new century began.

6. *Netherlands*

While this admirable renaissance of education was beginning to blossom in northern Italy, another renaissance, equally admirable but of a very different temper, was unfolding itself in the Netherlands. This is what is called the Christian renaissance or the moderna devotio. The father of it was Geert Groote of Deventer (1340–84). Though the first house of the Brothers of the Common Life was not opened until 1391, we may truly say that he was the originator of the new society. It was he also who suggested the organization of a new order, the Windesheim canons, whose ideals were the same as those of the Brothers but who submitted themselves, in addition, to monastic discipline. Both organizations, the monastic one and the semimonastic one, were well under way before the end of the century.

The Brothers of the Common Life were tremendously interested in education, and their idea of teaching was strongly opposed to scholasticism. Though mainly concerned with grammar (vs. science), their teaching was fresh and alive,[5] because it was permeated by a new spirit. That spirit was not humanistic like Vittorino's, but mystical. Groote had been profoundly influenced by Henry of Calcar, by the "Gottesfreunde," and by Ruysbroeck. Such mysticism as theirs is truly a fountain of youth, and educators who had drunk from that fountain were likely to be more imaginative, more persuasive, more amiable than were the schoolmen. Yet their schools were not "gay" like Vittorino's. For one thing, the climate of Holland is not so gay as that of Lombardy; then, their Christian fervor was more

[5] Or at least had possibilities of freshness and aliveness, but then as now, all teachers were not equally alive; some of them, we may be sure, were pretty dull.

intense, and such fervor is often tinged with sadness. It would be equally misleading, however, to think that Vittorino's education was not Christian, or that the Brothers completely disregarded pagan letters. Between the Brothers' schools and Vittorino the difference was not of essence, but of emphasis. One of Vittorino's superiorities was his interest in physical education. On the other hand, his own school was an exception even in Italy, and its success was due very largely to his own genial personality. The Brothers of the Common Life established not one school, but a good many; before the middle of the fifteenth century there were already some hundred and fifty of them in the Netherlands, France, and Germany. The schools were the best available until the middle of the sixteenth century.

The greatest teacher among the Brothers in their early days was Joannes Cele, who conducted the school of Zwolle during forty-two years (1375–1417) and thus created a model and a standard. The pedagogical success of the Brothers was very largely due to Cele's genius and to the Zwolle community. During the fifteenth century their influence was considerable. Nicholas of Cusa (1401–64) was one of their pupils and main defenders. Unfortunately, even the best examples lose their glamour and ideals, their life-giving power, unless they be refreshed from time to time. Erasmus, who was also one of the Brothers' pupils, was no longer as ready to defend them as cardinal Nicholas was. By the middle of the sixteenth century the schools of the Brothers of the Common Life had become commonplace and dull; they were then replaced by the Jesuit schools, partly modeled upon them but rejuvenated by a new ideal.

B. *Islām*

For Jewish education it will suffice to refer to the remarks made in chapter I, section IV B, because I am not aware of any novelty introduced by Jews during the second half of the century. On the contrary, Islamic views on education were refreshed by two men of singular genius, the traveler Ibn Baṭṭūṭa and the historian Ibn Khaldūn. Of course, they will be dealt with more fully later on, for they were not educators like Muḥammad ibn Aḥmad al-Riqūṭī (XIII-2), but interested observers.

Ibn Baṭṭūṭa is scarcely more (as far as education is concerned), but he is a very intelligent and faithful one. We owe him some of the best information available on the mediaeval schools of Islām and on the tradition of knowledge from the older teachers to the younger ones. Ibn Khaldūn is not simply an observer, but a critic, one who, considering his milieu and the increasing obscurantism which was restraining Islamic life, was remarkably bold and foreseeing. Ahead of other Muslims for centuries he saw the need of reforming educational methods from top to bottom; he saw that clearly and was not afraid of saying so. It is interesting to note that both Ibn Baṭṭūṭa and Ibn Khaldūn were Westerners; interesting and a bit puzzling, for we should not expect the Maghrib of that time to be more progressive or less trammeled by obsolete conventions than the Mashriq.

The conventional methods of teaching may be represented by the Syrian Ibn al-Shiḥna, who was a famous textbook writer. That "business" indeed is not new, though it was less profitable then than it is now. Ibn al-Shiḥna wrote a whole series of short textbooks on many subjects *in verse*. As the outstanding, if not exclusive, educational method was memorizing, textbooks written in verse were naturally more popular than others. Ibn al-Shiḥna was earning his living as a judge, and we must assume that he composed his manẓūmāt for the fun of it, or, if you please, for the sake of glory, not of money. There was no money in that business then, but a good collection of rhymed lines giving all the essentials about grammar, logic, or medicine would be eagerly copied and handed out from one student to another, and soon the rhymester would be spoken of as a master, if not as the creator, of the subject!

C. *China*

The system of examinations for civil service which dominated Chinese administration has often been referred to. It developed very early and continued to exist until 1905–6, modifications being made from time to time but no essential change. In order to obtain any post in the civil service, Chinese scholars had to prove their ability by passing a series of examinations. The first, taken in district examination halls, led to the degree hsiu ts'ai (budding ability). A second series of competitive examinations, held every three years in the provincial capitals, entitled the winners to the title chü jên. The final examination, taken in Peking, led to the degree chin shih, which is very often mentioned in our notes on Chinese scholars. That degree opened the candidate's administrative career, lots being often drawn between them for the vacant posts. The most ambitious of these men tried to pass a final examination, tien shih (palace examination), which admitted them into the imperial academy of literature, Han-lin yüan.

The advantages of this system were many. It kept alive among a selected minority a deep knowledge of letters and of the Confucian classics. It made possible the recruitment of a class of literate civil servants from among all the most intelligent people of the country, without respect for place, family, or wealth. It was essentially fair and provided for the needs of the state and for the constitution of a changing nonhereditary aristocracy.

The disadvantages were even greater. In the first place, these examinations were almost exclusively literary. The aim was always the writing of standard essays (wên chang) in classical and stereotyped language, the goodness of which was measured chiefly by the number of quotations or semiquotations[6] from the classics or cryptic allusions to them. Far from adapting minds to changing conditions, the examinations tended to anchor them to a past which, being out of touch with reality, was less and less understood, or more and more misunderstood. It put an absurd premium on memory, the other intellectual qualities being neglected and sterilized. Some feeble attempts were made to change the nature of the examinations, some of them in extremis at the very end of last century, but the system was too deeply rooted and fossilized to be correctible.

Throughout the Middle Ages and later the Chinese people attached an enormous importance to these examinations, the successful candidates being the heroes of their communities, and all kinds of festivities being organized in their honor. This may seem funny, but it was a popular recognition of learning as an avenue to goodness. The popular reverence for learned men is less objectionable than the idolization of movie stars, baseball players, toreadors, or jockeys. Another feature of the Chinese system was the relative contempt for military and naval vs. civil training, a contempt which was pretty dangerous in a hard competitive world, but

[6] Semiquotations or silent, implicit quotations. Western readers can understand this by comparison with their own mediaeval writings. E.g., there is hardly a page in the Confessions of St. Augustine or in the Imitation of Christ which does not contain a few words or a whole sentence taken from the Holy Scriptures.

was not at bottom dishonorable. A Chinese statesman of our own times remarked in favor of the examination system, "It has repressed rebellion by keeping the minds of ambitious men cramped by the pursuit of useless knowledge" (Ball, p. 231, 1926). A specious argument! On the other hand, candidates who had spent the best part of their life in obtaining the chin shih were likely to think that they had a claim on society and become disgruntled when out of employment, the more so that their education had unfitted them for any useful activity outside the yamens. These disgruntled mandarins might become rebels and often did. Of course, this is a weakness of every examination system, otherwise good or bad, which does not adjust carefully the number of graduates to the actual needs. If it sends out too many graduates, it creates déclassés and potential troublemakers.

The system of examinations and the social mandarinism[7] deriving from it are not exclusive to China; there was enough mandarinism in French and English culture to enable us to understand better its good and evil points. Thanks to the extreme difficulty of Chinese classical studies (even for the Chinese), the system became particularly obnoxious in China. On the other hand, one cannot admire too much the democratic spirit which informed it from first to last.

Robert des Rotours: Le traité des examens. Traduit de la Nouvelle histoire des T'ang, ch. 44, 45 (Bibliothèque de l'Institut des hautes études chinoises vol. 2, 422 p., Paris 1932), including Chinese texts. Victor Purcell: Problems of Chinese education (270 p., London 1936; Isis 36, 47), especially first 2 chapters. Ssu-yü Têng: Chinese influence on the Western examination system (Harvard journal of Asiatic studies 7, 267–312, 1943; Isis 35, 75), concluding that the Chinese system of examinations did influence the Western systems in a general way.

A curious addition to the Chinese educational system was made by the early Ming emperors. Already the first of these, Hung Wu (ruled 1366–99), had realized the need for a school for the study of the Mongolian language, and for a Chinese-Mongolian dictionary. The idea was developed by the third Ming emperor, Yung Lo (ruled 1403–24), he who immortalized himself with the great encyclopaedia Yung Lo ta tien. In 1407, he established the Ssŭ-i-kuan or college of four (meaning, all) foreign people, a kind of "Oriental school" or "Ecole des langues orientales vivantes," organized for official purposes, e.g., to train interpreters for the diplomatic service. At first eight languages were taught, to wit, Tatar or Mongolian, Yü-chêng (Nü-chên) or Oriental Tatar, Tibetan, Sanskrit, Persian, Uighūr, Mien tien = Burmese, Siamese. Later, when the Ch'ing dynasty reorganized the school in 1644, two more languages were added, two of the Shan or Tai (T'ai, Thaī) languages spoken on the borders of Yünnan.

E. Denison Ross: New light on the history of the Chinese Oriental college and a 16th century vocabulary of the Luchuan language (T'oung pao 9, 689–95, 1908).

D. *Japan*

Japanese education was dominated by Zen Buddhism, which enjoyed the favor of the imperial court, of the shōgun, and of the upper classes. The main teachers who transmitted the influence of their own master Soseki (XIV-1), Myoō and Chūshin in the Rokuon-ji, and Ryōken in the Nanzen-ji (both temples near Kyōto), were the spiritual leaders of the nation.

[7] For the explanation of the curious Portuguese term mandarin, see Yule and Burnell: Hobson-Jobson (p. 550–52, 1903).

By the middle of the century the Ashikaga-gakkō, a school which was then already old but had remained unimportant, became the main center of Chinese learning. Near the end of the century the school was established in Ashikaga, province of Shimotsuke (Tōsandō). We may call it a creation of the second half of the fourteenth century, though its prestige did not reach its climax until the fifteenth and sixteenth centuries.

Thanks to that school and to the Zen schools, the doctrines of Buddhism and of Neo-Confucianism were now very deeply rooted in Japan, and every social factor was helping their development. Their double action upon Japanese minds was comparable to the double action of Christianity and Hellenism upon ours.

For education in the Far East and elsewhere, see ERE (5, 166–216, 1912).
For Korea, see H. B. Hulbert: National examinations in Korea (Transactions, Korea branch, Royal Asiatic Society, 14, 9–32, 1923).

V. PHILOSOPHIC AND CULTURAL BACKGROUND

A. *Western Christendom*

The philosophic background in the West was very much the same in the second half of the century as it had been in the first half, hence the general remarks made in chapter I, section V, might be repeated here. The Book of sentences continued to be the most popular vehicle of theology, and to the average clerk its importance was almost equal to that of the Bible itself. On the other hand, some of the leading thinkers were tormented with the same need of unity as their immediate predecessors, and that burning desire informed their logical and encyclopaedic efforts. The Truth must be one, hence the outstanding intellectual problem was to reconcile Aristotle with the Holy Scriptures. This had been done, as much as it could be done, by St. Thomas. It could not be done completely, and hence there was room for discussion; as some of the difficulties were irreducible, the discussions were bound to be endless. (Of course, Jewish and Muslim rationalists were struggling with the same inherent contradictions.) The fight between nominalism and realism was still the main philosophical issue, but the situation was very different from what it had been a century before. Toward the end of the thirteenth century, thanks to St. Thomas' genius, moderate realism was the favorite point of view; but as the fourteenth century grew older, Occamism, that is, moderate nominalism, was in the ascendant. The growing popularity of nominalism and rationalism favored the development of science, but it unavoidably created reactions against itself. The reaction might be literary, humanistic, as with Petrarca; more often it came straight from the heart, it was mystical, and the mystics of this time were so remarkable that we must give much space to them. In most cases the mystical reaction was so intensely individual that its message could not be transmitted except to a very few people, and remained inefficient; in the Netherlands, however, it was combined with so much common sense and practical charity that it became itself a means of spiritual progress. The "moderna devotio" helped to create better Christians; because of its moderation and charity, it helped rather than hindered the progress of science.[1] Science, we should remember, implies devotion and

[1] For the spread of nominalism in the universities, see Franz Ehrle: Der Sentenzenkommentar Peters von Candia (Münster 1925; Isis 29, 488). A movement somewhat comparable to the moderna devotio was initiated in Paris by Jean Gerson. Gerson had been trained as a

humility at least as much as religion does. Now let us review briefly the contributions and characteristics of each country.

A1. *Italy*

There was no outstanding philosopher, but many among the educated people were interested in philosophical questions and in general knowledge. To begin with, there are a few commentators, that is, learned men who read Aristotle pen in hand, and discuss his statements. Thus the physicians Pietro da Tossignano and Tommaso del Garbo and the physicist Biagio Pelacani. The first of these was especially interested in the Problems and arranged them in tabular form; Tommaso studied the De anima. Biagio Pelacani of Parma was more of a philosopher; his commentaries ranged over a large part of the Aristotelian corpus and in addition he pondered on the logic of Peter of Spain, Buridan's questions, and the mathematico-philosophical treatises of Bradwardine, Swineshead, and Oresme. In this connection, we might mention also the Aristotelian commentaries and the Aristotelian encyclopaedia (Summa totius philosophiae) of Paul of Venice, an Austin friar, who was a younger contemporary of the men just mentioned. Born at Udine, c. 1370, he flourished mainly in Padua and lived until 1429; his dated writings belong to the fifteenth century. He was influenced by Albert of Saxony and the Parisian nominalists and popularized their thoughts in the schools of northern Italy.

The diffusion of scientific knowledge was assured by two treatises, the De mundi fabrica, written in Latin prose by Domenico di Bandino, and the Dittamondo composed in Italian verse by Fazio degli Uberti. Philosophic humanism was represented by Boccaccio and by two interpreters of Dante, Benvenuto Rambaldi and Filippo Villani. The latter, Filippo "il Solitario" as he was called, was primarily a historian continuing on a lower plane the chronicles of his father and uncle; the lectures on the Divina commedia which he was invited to deliver toward the end of his life were secondary activities. On the contrary, Rambaldi (d. 1390) was the greatest among the early commentators, the gonfaloniere of the Dante tradition. This reminds us of a significant fact; a new spring of thought had been created in Italy at the beginning of this century, and it was now already fertilizing Italian minds. Dante belongs definitely to the Italian background; within the following century and the sixteenth he will take his place in the background of every Catholic country.

The Dialogo composed in 1378 by St. Catherine of Siena was one of the outstanding mystical treatises of the age.

In one way this age differed profoundly from the preceding one. In the first half of the fourteenth century, the majority of the Italian thinkers were monks—Dominicans, Franciscans, Carmelites, Augustinians. In the second half of the century, most of them are laymen, the only exceptions being St. Catherine, who was a Dominican tertiary, and Paul of Venice, who had assumed the Augustinian habit.

A2. *Catalonia*

When we pass from the Italian to the Hispanic peninsula, the first fact to draw our attention is the continued superiority of the Catalans over their Castilian neighbors. So much so that we must entitle this section not Spain, but Catalonia!

---

nominalist, but was temperamentally more of a realist; it was because of his influence that the realists controlled the teaching of philosophy in Paris from c. 1405 to 1437. As late as 1418, however, he tried to reconcile Occamism and realism (Connolly, p. 85, 190, 1928).

Two only of these Catalans could be called philosophers, and they were indeed very distinguished theologians. The first, Francesc Eiximènis, was a Franciscan, author of a religious encyclopaedia called Lo Crestià (The Christian) and of various other books which enjoyed some popularity, witnessed by incunabula editions not only in Catalan, but also in Castilian and French. The other, Ramon Sebonde, continued the Lullian tradition, prudently mixing the wisdom of his master with that of St. Thomas. He was born in Barcelona, but flourished mainly in Toulouse, where he died in 1432. He wrote in Latin (c. 1425) a "natural theology," a combination of rationalism and mysticism which was very much esteemed in Western Europe down to the middle of the seventeenth century. Sebonde's residence in Toulouse accounts for his popularity in France. It was natural that Pierre Eyquem, lord of Montaigne, would hear Sebonde quoted as an admirable defender of Christian dogmatism, and, noticing with pain the skeptical tendencies of his son Michel, beg the latter to translate the Theologia naturalis into French. Montaigne (1533–92) did not simply translate the book (Paris 1569), but included an apology for the author in his famous Essays (Bordeaux 1580).[2] Thus did Sebonde participate in Montaigne's fame, and influence, among others, Pascal.

The two other Catalans are of little importance as philosophers, yet striking personalities. Bernat Metge was the greatest Catalan writer of his time; he helped to transmit to his own people the vivifying waters of Italian humanism and lifted his native language almost to the same level as Italian and French. We cannot explain the cultural background of Catalonia without speaking of him, indeed without leaving him, where he belongs, in the center of the stage. The Majorcan Anselmo Turmeda passed off as his own creation a Catalan translation of one of the Arabic treatises of the Brethren of Purity.

Of these four Catalans, two, Metge and Sebonde, were laymen, the two others, Eiximènis and Turmeda, were Franciscans. Unfortunately, the second of these, brother Anselmo, apostasized not only from his order, but also from his faith, and became a Muslim! The story of his recantation and of his Christian martyrdom is a legend, hence we should count him out of this Christian section. He left his mark, however, on Catalonian and French thought.

A3. *France*

The leading philosophers and theologians of France are very different in many respects from their predecessors, except one, Peter of Thomas, who wrote books of Scotist theology, but he probably wrote them in the first half of the century, for from 1354 to his death in 1366 various ecclesiastical and diplomatic missions took most of his time.

The outstanding thinker was Nicole Oresme (d. 1382), who was primarily a mathematician and physicist, and developed a scientific philosophy which was admirable in its restraint, humbleness, and rationalism. His translations of the Ethics, Politics, and Economics of Aristotle, and his commentaries on these works, opened to the French reading people a treasure of wisdom hitherto available only in Latin. This is a sign of the times. Philosophy is democratized as everything else, democratized and laicized. It is becoming possible for men to study the problems of divinity and humanity, of nature and nurture, without undergoing a Latin preparation divorcing them from everyday life. They can now increase their

[2] Essais (livre II, ch. 2), Apologie de Raimond Sebond. This covers 183 pages in Fortunat Strowski's edition (3, 155–337, Paris 1828).

knowledge and develop whatever innate wisdom is theirs without isolating themselves from their fellow men as priests, clerks, or monks.

Oresme was for a time the grand master of the Collège de Navarre, which was then the best college of France; he spent the end of his life as bishop in his native province, Normandy. Two other prelates distinguished themselves as educators of the French people, Pierre d'Ailly (1350–1420) and Jean Gerson (1363–1429). The word "educator" is used with reference to them in its broadest acceptation; they educated their people in the way philosophers do, whether they actually teach or not. Their main work was done in the fifteenth century, but Pierre d'Ailly was already 51 at the beginning of it, and Jean Gerson 38. Pierre d'Ailly was a follower of Oresme as a natural philosopher, whereas Jean Gerson restricted himself to ethical, theological, and ecclesiastical questions. Each took a prominent part in the deliberations of the council of Constance. Pierre d'Ailly was a bishop and became eventually a cardinal (1411); in his youth he had written logical treatises and commentaries on the Books of sentences and Boetius' Consolation. Gerson was so famous as a writer of devotional books that the Imitation of Christ was long ascribed to him. He did not write the Imitation, but when the exhausting business of the council was finally over, he retired to Rattenberg in Tirol and composed the De consolatione theologiae. His philosophical point of view was Occamism tempered with mysticism.

To return to the French translations, Oresme was by no means alone in making them, though his were by far the most important. Other philosophical books were put into French at about the same time: Boetius by Jean de Sy; the De remediis utriusque fortunae of Petrarca and the De eruditione filiorum of Vincent de Beauvais by Jean Dandin; the Civitas Dei of St. Augustine and the De utraque potestate of Giles of Rome by Raoul de Presles; the De proprietatibus rerum of Bartholomew the Englishman by Jean Corbechon; the Polycratus of John of Salisbury by Denis Foulechat. It is very significant that, with the exception of Oresme translating Aristotle, all these men were translating mediaeval texts, some of them written by recent authors like Giles of Rome (d. 1316) or even by a contemporary like Petrarca (d. 1374).

To complete our picture of French thought, we may still introduce two men of letters. The first was the poet Eustache Deschamps. The other "man" of letters was a woman, the first professional woman of letters in France (and perhaps in the world), Christine de Pisan.[3] Her father was Italian and she herself was born in Venice, but she was moved to Paris as a child in 1368 and spent practically the whole of her life in France. She became one of the leading writers of her time. Her writings and those of her older contemporary Eustache Deschamps constitute an excellent mirror of their age and "milieu."

We may now repeat the remark made above about the Italian writers. In the first half of the fourteenth century most of the writers were regulars—Dominicans, Franciscans, Cistercians; in the second half of the fourteenth century, most of them are seculars or laymen. The only ones who were certainly regulars were Peter of Thomas, Carmelite, and Foulechat, Franciscan; Jean de Sy was perhaps a friar. Oresme, Ailly, and Gerson were seculars. Oresme ended his life as a bishop,

[3] Married at 15, a widow at 25, she wrote to support herself and bring up her children. Her literary activity was prodigious and exceedingly varied. It is not easy for a woman to earn a living as a professional writer in the twentieth century; it was almost impossible in the fourteenth; yet Christine did it.

Ailly as a cardinal, and Peter of Thomas as Latin patriarch of Constantinople. All the others were laymen.

A4. *England*

The professional philosophers of the English group were two Mertonians, Ralph Strode and John Chilmark. Both were logicians. Ralph Strode, "the philosophical Strode," wrote two treatises on logic and tried to follow a middle road between nominalism and realism. Chilmark summarized a part of Dumbleton's Summa logicae and composed a few treatises on physical questions, which have not yet been investigated.

The most original members of the group are the religious and social reformers, John Wycliffe and William Langland. Wycliffe was one of the most learned theologians of his age, the precursor of Hus and to some extent of Luther. His political radicalism was combined with conservatism (Scotism) in philosophy. The combination is strange but by no means exceptional. William Langland wrote the greatest poem in Middle English next to the Canterbury Tales. Indeed, we may say that Piers the Plowman is one of the most remarkable literary achievements of the Middle Ages. Its creation is an excellent symptom of the revolutionary changes which were then taking place, though so deep under the surface that few people realized their existence, and had sufficient vision and courage to advertise them. Of course, the miseries which the plain people had to endure were tangible enough and widespread, but the clerks and the people who could write were for the most part blind to them or indifferent. These sufferings seemed to them an inherent part of nature, and would not the sufferers receive in heaven all the compensations which they deserved?[4] Piers the Plowman, however, saw things in a different light and was not afraid of saying so. John Wycliffe, speaking with greater authority, joined his voice to that of humble Piers, and together they were heard by an increasing number of people, not the sufferers only, but the men and women who are generous enough to feel the sufferings of others as if they were their own. The messages of Wycliffe and Langland were repeated first by Lollards and Beghards, then were gradually and slowly taken on by others; they are not yet understood by everybody today; it is still necessary to repeat them from time to time.

Another form of reaction to the material and spiritual evils was the mystical one. The task so well begun by Richard Rolle was continued by Walter Hilton in his Scale of perfection, and by the author of the Cloud of unknowing. These and other writings are by far the best specimens of English prose, and they prove the depth and originality of the English culture of that time, a culture hidden to most eyes under the surface, which was crude and barbaric. Most Englishmen were brutish, without taste or mercy, but they were redeemed by men like Rolle, Hilton, and others whose name is unknown but whose writings are immortal. To these men might be added at least one woman, mother Julian of Norwich. I have not spoken of her in my main text, but it is not too late to say a few words about her now.

[4] To illustrate the past by means of the present, here is a remark made by Francis Herron in a memorandum dated August 11, 1942, sent from the Argentine as private information to the Institute of Current World Affairs, New York: "Those who favor tradition in the Church (what is called here the diplomatic church) say that there is democracy—but on the other side of the tomb. They see in poverty and disease a condition which the people must face in a resigned and passive manner for it is naught but the will of God. . . ."

Julian (or Juliana) was an "ankress" or anchoret living in a cell attached to St. Julian's at Norwich.[5] The foundations of that cell may still be seen, with the "squint" (or low side window) through which she heard Mass. In the year 1373, May 8, being then 30½ years old, she received sixteen revelations, which she wrote down and which have come down to us in four MSS. The oldest of these MSS (British Museum) was written in 1413, when she was still alive, being then 71. She continued to ponder on those divine revelations, the meaning of which was explained to her fifteen years later. We may pause a moment to listen to her own quaint words:

"And from that time that it was shewed I desired oftentimes to witten what was our Lord's meaning. And fifteen years after, and more, I was answered in ghostly understanding, saying thus: 'Wouldst thou witten thy Lord's meaning in this thing? Wit it well: Love was his meaning. Who shewed it thee? Love. What shewed he thee? Love. Wherefore shewed it he? For Love. Hold thee therein and thou shalt witten and know more in the same. But thou shalt never know nor witten therein other thing without end.' Thus was I learned that Love was our Lord's meaning."[6]

The "XVI Revelations of divine love" were first edited by R. F. S. Cressy (s.l. 1670);[7] reprinted Leicester 1843, Boston 1864, London 1902, 1920. Revelations of divine love, with a preface by Henry Collins (London 1877); new edition by Grace Warrack, with glossary (London 1901), reprinted 8 times between 1901 and 1923. Comfortable words for Christ's lovers, edited by Dundas Harford (London 1911); reprinted in 1912, then again in 1925 under new title, The shewings of the lady Julian; new edition by Dom Roger Hudleston, with glossary (304 p., London 1927). French translation by Dom G. Meunier: Mystiques anglais. Révélations de l'amour divin à Julienne de Norwich (Paris 1910; reprinted 1925).

Wells (p. 464, etc., 1926). William Ralph Inge: Studies in English mysticism (St. Margaret's lectures, London 1906). R. H. J. Steuart (S.J.): Diversity in holiness (p. 3–17, New York 1937).

Having thus proved the richness of English mystical literature, let us now consider three profane authors of the same time, whose influence was considerable, Geoffrey Chaucer, John of Trevisa, John Gower. It is almost superfluous to speak of the first one to English readers. He did for England what Dante, Petrarca, and Boccaccio did for Italy. To most people he is the author of the Canterbury Tales, but his services were not restricted to that. He translated the Consolation of Boetius and probably the Roman de la rose (the Middle English text Romaunt of the rose exists, but the ascription to him is uncertain). More translations were made by his Cornish contemporary John of Trevisa, e.g., the De proprietatibus rerum of Bartholomew the Englishman and the De regimine principum of Giles of Rome, to cite only, out of eight, the two which would interest philosophical readers most. Chaucer and Trevisa rendered to England the same kind of service which their contemporaries Oresme, Jean de Sy, Jean Dandin, Jean Corbechon, etc. were rendering to France.

[5] That church belonged to the Benedictine nunnery of Carrow; it does not follow that mother Julian was a Benedictine.

[6] Text as given by Hudleston (p. 244, 1927).

[7] The name is thus printed on the title page. The author was Hugh Paulinus Cressy (1605–74), who explained his passage from the Church of England to the Church of Rome in a curious book, Exomologesis (655 p., Paris 1647; 2d ed., 580 p., Paris 1653). He assumed the Benedictine habit and then was named Dom Serenus Cressy (DNB 13, 74).

"Moral Gower" did something more ambitious, he wrote long didactic poems dealing chiefly with ethics, but including a variety of other matters. The most remarkable thing about him is that he wrote in three languages, for England had the misfortune to be then a trilingual country (see our note in chapter I, p. 347 f.). He wrote the Speculum hominis in French, the Vox clamantis in Latin, and the Confessio amantis in English (note that the three titles are in Latin). Book VII of the Confessio is an account of popular science. In general, we may say that the poems of Chaucer and Gower contain a vast amount of information on the folklore and the folk manners of their day; they are a mirror of their time and "milieu" in the same manner that the writings of Eustache Deschamps and Christine de Pisan are of contemporary France.

Most of the men I have spoken of were seculars or laymen. The only regular was Walter Hilton, an Austin canon. No mention has been made of any Dominican or Franciscan, whereas in the first half of the century most of the work was done by friars.

A5. *Germany*

The German group is a very distinguished one and of special interest to the historian of science, as many of its members were engaged in scientific work and in the discussion of scientific principles and methods. These scientific philosophers, though German, were really offshoots of the University of Paris; much of their work was actually done in Paris or under Parisian influence, and hence their activities should be credited to France as well as to Germany. The greatest of these Parisian-German masters was Albert of Saxony, who was the founder of the University of Vienna and its first rector, in 1366. He wrote a treatise on the new logic and a dozen Aristotelian commentaries. Another outstanding Occamist would have been disowned by the German leaders of yesterday, for he was the son of a Jew. Themo Judaei was born in Westphalia, but educated in Paris, where he became a famous teacher and was the recipient of many honors. He wrote a commentary on the Meteorologica similar in form and contents to Albert's commentaries. Henry of Oyta and Henry Langenstein were obliged to leave Paris because of ecclesiastical difficulties springing out of the Great Schism. Both were among the first teachers of the University of Vienna, and they explained their philosophical views very largely in the form of commentaries on the Books of sentences. Nicholas of Dinkelsbühl did not study in Paris, but in Vienna, for he belongs to a younger generation. The Parisian influences came to him indirectly through his teachers, Langenstein and Oyta. He wrote a commentary on Aristotelian physics. All these men were moderate Occamists, and they created in Prague and Vienna the philosophical preparation for the purely scientific work to be accomplished later. They may be counted among the forerunners of the German scientists of modern times.

The contrast between the work done in the second half of the century and that done in the first half is even more startling in Germany than it was in other countries. The main achievement of the second half was the transmission of Parisian Occamism to Germany; the main achievement of the first half had been the magnificent efflorescence of Christian mysticism due to Meister Eckhart and the Friends of God. Of course, we should bear in mind that our classification is, like every classification, somewhat artificial. We put all these mystics in the first half of the fourteenth century, and indeed the greatest of them, Eckhart, died in 1327, but Tauler lived until 1361 and Suso until 1366; moreover, the Theologia Deutsch, the date of which can only be guessed, may have been composed after 1350 as well as before. Other mystical and ascetic writers were at work in the monasteries. Let me speak of one more who achieved considerable fame, Ludolf of Saxony,[8] who died in old age on April 13, 1378. After having been a Dominican for thirty years, he entered the Charterhouse of Strassburg c. 1340. He wrote various works, In psalmos Davidicos or Expositio in Psalterium (princeps Speier 1491), De remediis contra tentationes spirituales novissimi temporis, but his masterpiece was the Vita D. Jesu Christi ex quattuor evangeliis aliisque scriptoribus orthodoxis concinnata. This is not simply a life of Jesus Christ, but a vast compilation of facts, commentaries, exhortations, etc. concerning the beginnings of Christianity, a Summa evangelica. The book was exceedingly popular in many countries, witness the large number of MSS and of editions in many languages. The two earliest editions appeared in 1474 (Strassburg and Cologne) and there are at least 11 more incunabula in Latin. Many incunabula appeared in other languages, Dutch (Antwerp 1485, 1487, 1488, Delft 1488, Zwolle 1495), French (Lyon 1487?, 1493, Paris 1500–3), Catalan (Valencia 1495, 1500), Portuguese (Lisbon 1495). German, Spanish, and Italian translations were printed later. The latest Latin editions appeared in Paris 1865, 1878. Ludolf is one of the many writers to whom the Imitation of Christ was ascribed; the author of the Imitation was certainly acquainted with Ludolf's Vita Christi, which was read aloud in the monasteries. It is said that Ludolf introduced the word Jesuita, namely in his remark that baptism makes of us Christiani, but the life of glory in heaven, Jesuitae.

It is natural that books like the Vita Christi found more readers than the writings of the Occamists. The Occamists were only a very small group after all (like the genuine relativists today); they constitute a vanguard, and the vanguard is necessarily small. Most of the writers continued the old traditions. Thus the mysterious John of Livania, who flourished in Treves c. 1374, wrote *against* Occam. John of Dambach completed in 1366 a Consolatio theologiae which included curious psychological speculations (perhaps we might call him a psychoanalyst avant la lettre?). Toward the end of the century Henry of Hessen junior (not to be confused with Henry of Hessen senior, who is none other than Henry Langenstein) was teaching in Heidelberg and writing commentaries on the Bible and the Sentences, a treatise on politics, etc.

All the men referred to in this section were laymen or seculars, except Dambach, who was a Dominican; the younger Henry of Hessen, who was a Carthusian; and Ludolf of Saxony, who was both.

A6. *Netherlands*

It is curious that the Netherlanders who distinguished themselves in the first half of the fourteenth century were southerners, Flemings, whereas those of the following period were mostly northerners, Hollanders. Let us deal first with the solitary Fleming, Jan de Weert, a late follower of Jacob van Maerlant. The latter had died in 1299, but his influence had been kept alive by his disciples. Though Jan De Weert was a master surgeon, his writings (in Flemish verse) were devoted exclusively to divinity and morality.

[8] Leutolf von Sachsen, Ludolphus de Saxonia (NBG 32, 202, 1860; ADB 19, 388, 1884; CE 9, 416, 1910). In case of contradictions, I have preferably followed CE.

Marsilius van Inghen, who was born in the diocese of Utrecht, was the Dutch equivalent of Albert of Saxony. That is, like Albert he was an alumnus and notable member of the University of Paris; Albert founded the University of Vienna, and Marsilius may be said to have founded that of Heidelberg. The cosmopolitanism of mediaeval life is remarkably well illustrated in this case of a Dutchman, educated in Paris, establishing on the Parisian basis a new German university! Marsilius was a moderate Occamist, who brought to Heidelberg not only the new logic but the knowledge and methods he had obtained from Buridan and Oresme. He wrote commentaries on various parts of the Aristotelian corpus and on the Books of sentences.

The two other Dutchmen represent the main contribution of their country to mediaeval culture, the Christian renaissance or moderna devotio. We have already spoken of them in the sections on religion and education, but they must be mentioned once more here. Geert Groote and Gerard Zerbolt were not only great educators and religious leaders, they were theologians, moralists, philosophers in the old sense. Their main concern was the good life, informed with Christian and ancient wisdom. They followed a middle path between scholasticism on the one hand and exaggerated mysticism on the other. Zerbolt was more of a theologian than Geert Groote; he devoted part of his time to comment on the Books of sentences, but never lost sight of his main duties to the Brothers of the Common Life, whom he helped to defend against the snares of the world and the criticisms of the regulars.

A7. *Bohemia*

The circumstances and affinities which united Bohemia and England have been pointed out at the end of my note on Wycliffe. The main exponent of Bohemian thought was Thomas of Štitný, who had been deeply influenced by St. Augustine and St. Bonaventure and was explaining theology and morality according to realist (antinominalist) traditions. In his insistence on conduct, on the "good life" rather than on hairsplitting technicalities, he was very close to the Dutch Brothers of the Common Life; on the other hand, his denunciations of ecclesiastic and monastic sins suggest comparison with Wycliffe. His defense of the use of the vernacular (Czech) instead of Latin for religious purposes was similar to the defense of English by Wycliffe and of Dutch by Zerbolt. It is impressive to witness convergent activities for reform in three countries; later on these activities would diverge because national conditions were so different. Wycliffe would prepare the Reformation abroad but the Church of England at home; the Brothers of the Common Life would remain orthodox, though they would occasionally hatch singular birds like Erasmus; Štitný prefigured Jan Hus, the martyr, and many miseries which followed. By the way, Hus was a true child of the fourteenth century, for he was already 27 years old at the beginning of the fifteenth. It was only later, c. 1410, that he fell more completely and directly under Wycliffian influences. Hus was condemned to be burned at the stake in Constance in 1415. In the meanwhile, another child of the fourteenth century, Vavřinec of Březova, had grown up. Vavřinec (i.e., Laurence, Laurentius) was born in 1365, and lived long enough to write a chronicle of the Hussite wars (1414–22). He may have composed his dream book (in Czech) before the end of the century, for it is dedicated to Wenceslas IV (king of Bohemia 1378–1419).

B. *Eastern Christendom*

This account will be restricted to two nations, the Byzantine and the Armenian, and for each of them we shall be obliged to consider separately two groups, the national or Orthodox group on the one hand, and the Catholic or Latinizing one on the other.

B1. *Byzantium*

The main theologians on the Orthodox side were John of Cypros, author of an elaborate treatise on dogmatics, and Nicolaos Cabasilas, who wrote mystical interpretations of Christian life and of the liturgy. Wherever mystical tendencies are strong, and they certainly were among the Hesychasts, theologians have to be extremely vigilant, lest enthusiastic[9] people become unwieldy, neglectful of rites, and even antinomian. Cabasilas' function was to reconcile mystical intuitions with orthodoxy. On the other hand, Isaac Argyros wrote treatises *against* the Palamites (Hesychasts). There is no reason for suspecting his orthodoxy, but he was a disciple of Nicephoros Gregoras and like him an astronomer; he resented mystical extravagances and the insatiable mystical pride hidden under the cloak of humility; he represents to us the more rationalistic aspect of the Orthodox church. To Neilos Diassorinos, who came from Chios and was metropolitan of Rhodes until the Knights of St. John drove him out, we owe a number of religious books as well as a history of the councils. Demetrios Chrysoloras composed theological treatises. The ethical side of Christian life was stressed by the monk Joseph Christodulos (formerly John VI Cantacuzenos), his son Matthew, and Manuel II Palaeologos. Joseph wrote a paraphrase of the Nicomachean Ethics; Matthew, commentaries on the Song of songs and the Book of wisdom and various essays. Many books were produced by Manuel II Palaeologos, though he was able to remain on the throne almost to the end of his life. Another activity of these men was polemics against non-Christians: Joseph Christodulos wrote a treatise against Jews and Muslims, and Manuel II Palaeologos, who had been before his accession a hostage at the Turkish court, explained the errors of Islām. Among Manuel's treatises are one in which he sets forth the rules of conduct of a Christian prince, another on the procession of the Holy Ghost (Paris 1400), and one on dreams. The writings and correspondence of Manuel would suffice to give us a pretty good idea of the Byzantine via media of his age; he avoided mystical and rationalistic extremes, and his intimate knowledge of Catholic and Muslim ways of thinking and of their manners of living saved him from provincialism. He may serve to illustrate the more enlightened common sense which, rare as it was, is nevertheless representative of his age and milieu.

Meanwhile, the Latinizing party was very active, but the number of distinguished men in its ranks should not deceive us with regard to its popularity. Whereas the Orthodox had the whole people solidly behind them, the Latinizers were like a general staff without an army. Their activity was comparable to that of fifth columnists in an unreceptive country; they tried to seduce individual men, especially

[9] This word is used here in its original meaning. The ἐνθουσιασταί were the God-intoxicated, God-possessed (ἔνθεοι) people. For a discussion of this see Karl Holl: Enthusiasmus und Bussgewalt beim griechischen Mönchtum (Leipzig 1898); L. Radermacher (ERE 5, 316–17, 1912); Jeanne Croissant: Aristote et les mystères (Liége 1932; Isis 34, 239).

prominent ones, from their natural allegiance, but their gains were small and precarious; they made no headway. Though disastrous military and economic events gave them a good purchase on the people, they failed to convert it; the temperamental differences between Greeks and Latins were too great, and the memory of evil deeds was too painful to be overcome by means of political arguments or theological subtleties.

The most important Latinizers were Prochoros Cydones (a younger brother of Demetrios), who paraphrased St. Thomas in Greek and turned the latter's arguments against the Hesychasts; and Manuel Calecas, who assumed the Dominican habit in the Pera monastery and wrote many treatises explaining Catholic dogmatics. Among the Latinizers we might count also some of the men who moved westward and did so much for the spread of humanism in Western Europe; from the point of view of Byzantium they were Latinizers, but from the Italian point of view they were the annunciators of Hellenism. Such were Manuel Chrysoloras, who translated Plato's Republic into Latin, and Gemistos Pletho, who explained to the Florentines the difference between Plato and Aristotle.

Petros Philarges assumed the Franciscan habit in his native island, Crete.[10] Of all the Greeks, he was the one who carried the Latinizing tendency to its limit and climax; no one could go farther along that road than he did, for he became pope under the name Alexander V (1409–10). Like every other Catholic theologian, he had composed a commentary on the Books of sentences (1380); the fact that he was a foreigner made it probably easier for him to preserve a certain neutrality with regard to the main dispute of the age (nominalism vs. realism), and thus his commentary is remarkably eclectic in that respect.

B2. *Armenia*

Philosophical and theological studies were carried on by Armenian doctors writing for their own flocks in their own language. Thus, the archimandrite John of Orodn wrote commentaries on Aristotelian logic and the New Testament; his main pupil, Gregory of Tathev, composed the Book of questions, a theological catechism wherein the orthodox Armenian doctrines were contrasted with the errors of other Christians, Jews, Muslims, etc. Other theological treatises and commentaries were written by him and by his friend George of Erseng. One of Gregory's nephews, Arakel of Sunik, was the author of an Adamic and other mystical poems.

The work of Catholic propagandists was continued, notably by one John Golodik, who wrote commentaries on the Bible, on Dionysios the Areopagite, and on the treatises of the unknown Dominican Peter of Aragon, recently translated into Armenian by Jacob the Dragoman.

[10] At the partition of the Greek empire which followed the fall of Constantinople (1204), Crete was granted to Boniface, marquis of Montferrat, who promptly sold it to the Venetians; it remained under Venetian power until the Turkish conquest (1645–69). The Venetians established the seat of government in the Muslim capital, Khandaq (Persian-Arabic word meaning ditch, moat, see EI 2, 899; 1, 879), and Khandaq was adulterated into Candia, name gradually given by Westerners to the island itself. In the fourteenth century the rulers of Crete or Candia were thus Venetian and Catholic, but the majority of the native Christian population remained Orthodox. For the uninterrupted existence of both cults see Flaminio Cornelio (or Cornario): Creta sacra, sive de episcopis utriusque ritus graeci et latini (2 vols., Venice 1755).

C. *Israel*

We may now pass to the consideration of Jewish efforts, which were remarkable in quantity as well as in quality, especially if one bears in mind the fact that, with the exception of a few isolated individuals in the Near East, they were restricted to the Hispanic peninsula and southern France. The account will be divided into four parts: (1) Spain, (2) Catalonia and Aragon, (3) Provence, (4) Near East.

C1. *Spain*

Jewish Spain boasted a number of original or ambitious thinkers, such as Meir ben Aldabi, who in 1360 completed the Shebile emunah, an elaborate theological, philosophical, and scientific compilation; Ibn Malkah, who wrote a Neoplatonic commentary on the Sefer yeẓirah and on Pirqe rabbi Eli'ezer; Menahem ben Zeraḥ, who wrote the Ẓedah la-derek (c. 1374), a summary of the Jewish commandments; Israel Ibn al-Naqawa, who collected the ethical and ritual traditions of his people in the Menorat ha-maor, a book which was indirectly a powerful tool for the preservation of those traditions. We might still mention two younger contemporaries who were born in the last quarter of the fourteenth century, but whose main activities occurred in the following: Shemṭob ibn Shemṭob (fl. 1390–1440) and Ephraim ben Israel Ibn al-Naqawa (d. 1442). Shemṭob ibn Shemṭob was the author of the Sefer ha-emunot,[11] a treatise on the articles of faith written from the qabbalistic angle against the rationalistic and Aristotelian point of view; he criticized with special vigor Ibn Ezra, Maimonides, and Levi ben Gerson. As his book was much used by later qabbalists, it is of importance in the history of the qabbala. Rabbi Ephraim, son of the Israel Ibn al-Naqawa mentioned above, fled to Africa in 1391 and flourished in Tlemcen until 1442, but remains there to this day a legendary thaumaturge and protector of the community, affectionately called "the Rab."

To these wise collectors of the wisdom and traditions of their people should be added a number of men who were primarily translators. Joseph ben Joshua ha-Lorqi revised the Hebrew translation of Maimonides' logic and wrote a treatise of his own on the elements; David Ibn Ya'īsh translated the Arabic version of the economics ascribed to "Bryson"; Samuel ibn Moṭoṭ, the Orchard of al-Baṭalyūsī, the Sublime faith of Abraham ben David ha-Levi, the Book of substances wrongly ascribed to Abraham ben Ezra; Meir Alguadez, the Nicomachean Ethics. Biblical and Talmudic commentaries were written by Samuel ibn Moṭoṭ (already mentioned) and by Shemṭob Shapruṭ. To the former of these last named we owe also a commentary on the Sefer yeẓirah, and to the latter, the Eben boḥan, one of the best mediaeval defenses of Jewish theology.

C2. *Catalonia and Aragon*

The most important Jewish philosopher of this time and perhaps the only one who may be considered an original and creative thinker was Ḥasdai Crescas, a son of Barcelona. He was born c. 1340 and thus is truly a man of the fourteenth century; yet his main work, Or Adonai, was completed only in 1410, when he was about 70 years old. It was a criticism of Aristotelianism and of Maimonidism in the light of Talmudism as interpreted by a vigorous personality. To measure Crescas' importance, it will suffice to remember that his cosmological views have been considered a partial anticipation of those of Giordano Bruno, and that Spinoza

[11] First published in Ferrara 1556. Max Schloessinger (JE 6, 541, 1904).

was deeply influenced by him. The defense of Maimonides was soon taken up by another Catalan, Simeon ben Ẓemaḥ Duran (born in Majorca 1361; in 1391 persecution drove his family to Algiers, where his father, Ẓemaḥ, died in 1404 and himself in 1444). The Or ha-ḥayyim of Simeon Duran was composed as a kind of Maimonidean answer to the Or Adonai. Simeon's main work was the Magen abot, a commentary on Pirqe abot.[12]

Two translators must still be mentioned, Zerahiah ben Isaac ha-Levi (called Saladin) and Solomon ben Labi. Zerahiah translated the Kitāb al-tahāfut of al-Ghazzālī, and Solomon, the Kitāb al-'aqīdah al-rafī'ah of Abraham ben David ha-Levi. That is, Zerahiah and Solomon devoted their zeal to books which were truly worth while. This redeems their memory. Translation is by no means an inferior activity, and translators may do more meritorious work than self-styled "original" writers; translators are often fools, however, and prove it by their stupid selection of the books on which they spend their efforts. This reproach cannot be made against Zerahiah and Solomon.

The Catalan Jewish group is small but worthy of the splendid culture which the Catalan Christians were then developing in Barcelona, on the eastern coast of Spain, and in the Balearic islands.

C3. *Provence*

Some translators were at work also across the Pyrénées, in Provence, the most remarkable being Maestro Bongodas (Judah ben Solomon Nathan) and Abraham ben Meshullam Abigdor. The first translated a very important book, the Maqāṣid al-falāsifa of al-Ghazzālī, and he wrote a defense of philosophy against the Talmudists. Abraham Abigdor wrote a Hebrew adaptation in rhymed prose of the same work (Maqāṣid). He was interested especially in logic, translated the Summulae logicales of Peter of Spain, and commented on Ibn Rushd's middle commentary on the first three parts of the Organon. As Abraham had no knowledge of Arabic, his study of the Organon was probably made on the basis of a Latin version. This strange twist in cultural exchanges, Arabic knowledge reaching Jewish scholars via Latin channels, illustrates more vividly than anything else the deep transformation which had taken place, most of it below the surface, during the past two centuries.

The historical work Qiryat sefer written in 1372 by Isaac ben Jacob Lattes is not simply a chronicle, it contains much information on theology, ethics, Biblical commentaries, etc. It was a sort of historical, ethical, and philosophical vade mecum and viaticum for the Jewish reader, especially valuable in the days of persecution. Profiaṭ Duran completed his Talmudic studies with various scientific investigations which gave him a more rationalistic outlook; he was a generous defender of Maimonides. On the other hand, the mystical aspect of theology was represented by Jacob ben Solomon Ẓarfati.

The great philosopher Abraham ben Ezra (XII-1) had not thought it unworthy of himself to write a book on chess; a new one was composed in rhymed Hebrew prose by Bonsenior ben Yaḥya at about this time or a little later.

C4. *East*

Though many Jews lived in Eastern countries, the intellectual center of Israel had long passed to the West, and the life of Eastern Jewry seemed pretty stagnant

[12] JE (5, 17, 1903). Cowley (p. 637, 1929). EJ (6, 130–34, 1930).

(except perhaps in medicine). Persecutions were driving Jewish scholars out of Provence and Spain, but their habitual refuge at this time was Morocco, Algiers, or Tunis. A few Jews like Profiaṭ Duran made (or contemplated) pilgrimages to the Holy Places, others traveled east to find peace in Palestine and spend there the end of their life, with the hope of being finally buried in Jerusalem. It is possible that Meir ben Aldabi did so, but we cannot be sure, for the story of his life after his departure from Spain is unknown. Strangely enough, I cannot name a single Jew who distinguished himself as a philosopher or theologian in the Holy Land in this period, but I shall name three who were connected respectively with Persia, Serbia, and Greece.

The Persian Isaiah ben Joseph finished in Tabrīz 1351 a qabbalistic treatise, 'Eẓ ḥayyim. The Serb Judah ben Moses Mosconi was a very learned Talmudist who in his Eben ha-'ezer discussed the Biblical commentary of Abraham ben Ezra. The Greek Joseph ben Moses ha-Kilti summarized the Aristotelian Organon in aphoristic form.

D. *Islām*

The account of Islamic thought is divided into six sections, devoted respectively to (1) Granada, (2) Ifrīqīya, (3) Mamlūkīya, (4) Īrān, (5) Anatolia, and (6) the destroyer Tīmūr Lang.

D1. *Granada*

In the little kingdom of Granada, which was the last Muslim stronghold in Western Europe, there flourished Ibn 'Abbād and Ibn 'Āṣim. The first was born and educated in Ronda, but he spent a great part of his life in Morocco and died in Fez, 1390. He wrote ṣūfī commentaries which are studied to this day and influenced not only Muslim thought, but Christian thought as well. For example, traces of his influence have been detected in the writings of the great Spanish saint San Juan de la Cruz. Ibn 'Āṣim, who flourished in Granada until his death (1427), is far less distinguished, yet his poem on the principles of Mālikī law enjoyed much popularity.

D2. *Ifrīqīya*

The word Ifrīqīya is the Arabic designation (derived from the Latin "Africa") for the middle part of North Africa or the eastern part of Barbary, leaving out the Maghrib (or Morocco) in the west and Egypt in the east.[13] We have no Moroccan to deal with, unless we count as such Ibn 'Abbād, who emigrated there from Granada in middle life; as to the Egyptians, they will be dealt with in the Mamlūk group with the Syrians.

Ifrīqīya gave the world one of its outstanding personalities, Ibn Khaldūn, whom we may call the founder of the philosophy of history, one of the most learned and wisest men of his time anywhere. We shall come back to him so often that it is hardly necessary to devote much space to him now. As compared with him, Ibn abī Ḥajala is insignificant; he has no claim on our attention as a philosopher, but only as a man of letters dealing eventually with theological matters, as was un-

[13] G. Yver (EI 2, 453–55, 1919). Arabic geographers and historians differ as to its inclusiveness and limits, but we need not bother about that. The rough definition is sufficient for our purpose.

avoidable in Muslim communities. For example, among his many writings is a treatise on chess, wherein the theological aspects of the game are discussed. Is the game permitted to a good believer, and if so under what conditions and with what restrictions? Ibn abī Ḥajala was primarily a man of letters, but he helped as such to constitute the intellectual atmosphere of his time. He came from Tlemcen; Ibn Khaldūn hailed from Tunis.

D3. *Mamlūkīya*

The scholars and thinkers who flourished under Mamlūk patronage constitute as usual a very fine group, though its supremacy is not obvious as it was in the first half of the century, but on the contrary debatable, for the group could boast no man comparable to either Ibn Khaldūn or Ḥāfiẓ.

In order to emphasize the importance of the different schools of jurisprudence, I shall divide the Mamlūk scholars according to the schools to which they belonged. Let it be remembered that the members of the four schools were equally "orthodox" Sunnites (that is why it is misleading to call those schools sects); their differences were restricted to interpretation, ritualistic details, legal matters. Though small, these differences were sufficient to divide the community and to unify more intimately the men belonging to the same group (as, e.g., the people belonging to the same political party with us).

The main subgroup was that of the Shāfi'ī school, represented by four 'ulamā', 'Abd al-Raḥīm ibn al-Ḥasan, 'Abd al-Wahhāb ibn 'Alī al-Subkī, Muḥammad ibn Mūsā al-Damīrī, and Aḥmad ibn 'Alī Ibn Ḥajar al-'Asqalānī. 'Abd al-Raḥīm was a theologian of the legalistic type; he explained Shāfi'ī law in many publications. Al-Subkī was also interested in jurisprudence (every Muslim theologian was), but less exclusively. He wrote a book on the methods of reobtaining divine grace when one had lost it. Al-Damīrī was an encyclopaedist, but he found time to compose treatises on tawḥīd (the unity of God) and other theological subjects and even to write an elaborate commentary on al-Nawawī's manual of Shāfi'ī, law. The last named, Ibn Ḥajar al-'Asqalānī, is a "fin de siècle" individual, for he was not born till 1372; in the course of time he became the official leader, the chief Shāfi'ī judge (qāḍī al-quḍat, muftī), of Egypt, and as such was invited to give legal and theological decisions (fatwā; pl. fatāwā) binding the community. Whether he might be called a shaikh al-Islām or not is a moot question (J. H. Kramers, EI 4, 275–79, 1926). At any rate, he had plenty of judicial and administrative duties, but in spite of them managed to write a large number of books on theological and other subjects. He lived in Cairo until 1449.[14]

There were two distinguished theologians of the Ḥanafī rite, but both of foreign origin. 'Umar ibn Isḥāq al-Hindī was, as his nisba indicates, a Hindu; Ibrāhīm ibn Muḥammad ibn Duqmāq was probably of Turkish ancestry. The first wrote a treatise wherein he analyzed the differences obtaining between the four schools of law; he also wrote many books wherein he explained Ḥanafī or mystical views. He became the grand muftī of his school, and many of his fatāwā have been preserved. Ibn Duqmāq was mainly a historian, but he devoted much attention to the Ḥanafī doctrines and realities and to taṣawwuf. He wrote a book on the interpretation of dreams.

We came across a single Mālikī doctor and a single Ḥanbalī one. Sīdī Khalīl wrote a textbook of Mālikī law which was very popular, especially in Algeria,

[14] C. Van Arendonck (EI 2, 379, 1916). Brockelmann (2, 67–70, 1902; suppt. 2, 72–76, 1938).

though he himself was an Egyptian who hardly left Cairo except for the Pilgrimage. The single Ḥanbalī 'ālim was the Algerian Ibn abī Ḥajala, who after his return from the Pilgrimage stopped in Cairo and stayed there. Finally, we should mention Muḥammad ibn Muḥammad al-Jazarī, whose school is not known and does not appear from his writings, for he was primarily a traditionist and a student of the Qur'ān. He spent the first part of his life in Damascus and Cairo, but after 1395 various vicissitudes took him to Brussa, Samarqand, and Shīrāz, where he died (1429).

D4. *Īrān*

The Persian group is particularly brilliant. It is headed by no less a person than Ḥāfiẓ, who is not only the greatest poet of his people, but one of the greatest in world literature. Every great poet helps powerfully to create the spiritual atmosphere of his time, and hence deserves to be included in a survey like this one. This is especially true for one like Ḥāfiẓ, who was a ṣūfī; many of his poems are mystical effusions. He has done more to popularize the mystical philosophy of Islām than any textbook writer, for his verse was read, recited, and remembered by countless men and women. His poems were the vehicles of serene ideas which they carried to every court and to every home.

Taṣawwuf was the most popular philosophy of Persia. It was developed intuitively by Ḥāfiẓ and explained more systematically by many doctors, such as 'Alī ibn Shihāb al-dīn, 'Abd al-Karīm al-Jīlī, Ni'mat Allāh Walī. They wrote many treatises on mystic doctrines, which found their best public in the communities of dervishes, even as the mystical books of Christendom were received with special favor in the monasteries and nunneries. The bond between monasticism and mysticism was even stronger in Islām than in the Christian world. 'Abd al-Karīm was a descendant of the founder of the Qādirīya; Ni'mat Allāh was the founder of a new order called after him Ni'mat Allāhī. Both 'Abd al-Karīm and Ni'ma contributed much to the diffusion of the Western mysticism of Ibn 'Arabī into the Eastern countries. Ni'ma was a Shī'a and so was Faḍlallāh al-Ḥurūfī, creator of a kind of Muslim gematria, which attained considerable success in Turkish lands.

In so far as all these men were mystics and poets, their philosophy was very eclectic, subjective, and vague. Treatises of a more objective and rational kind were written by al-Jurjānī. We owe to him treatises on law, philosophy, logic, on the definition of technical (philosophical) terms, and on the classification of sciences. Al-Jurjānī was a rival of his Turkish contemporary Taftāzānī, with whom we shall deal presently. Let me repeat once more that the differentiation between Turks and Persians in this period is often arbitrary; we are on safer ground only when the former wrote in Turkish and the latter in Persian, but most of them wrote in Arabic, which was as international as Latin.

D5. *Anatolia*

Mas'ūd ibn 'Umar al-Taftāzānī was one of the best Eastern scholars of his time. He flourished mainly in the eastern part of the Dār al-Islām, and died in Samarqand (1390). We feel justified, however, in placing him here at the head of the Turkish group, for he wrote occasionally in Turkish as well as in Arabic, and his books on Ḥanafī law, logic, metaphysics, theology, etc. exerted a deep influence on the Turkish renaissance. His fame was international, at least in the Eastern world. Philosophic ideas were popularized in Turkish verse by Ṣalāḥ al-dīn and his sons and by Aḥmedī. They were explained in prose by Ḥājjī pāshā and al-Fanārī. The latter may be called the first great teacher of Turkey, and his tradition was continued by his son, Muḥammad shāh Čelebī, in the following century.

Turkish scholars had been much impressed apparently by the encyclopaedic works available in Arabic and Persian,[15] e.g., the Ḥadā'iq al-anwār of Fakhr al-dīn al-Rāzī, and we witness the blossoming of these encyclopaedic tendencies in the works of Muḥammad shāh Čelebī (d. 1435) and al-Bisṭāmī (d. Brussa 1454). The latter, 'Abd al-Raḥmān ibn Muḥammad al-Bisṭāmī al-Ḥanafī al-Ḥurūfī, was a Syrian, but after a period of study in Cairo, he had established himself in Brussa. He devoted a good part (1392–1441) of his life to the compilation of an encyclopaedia of the "hundred sciences."[16] This was continued on a larger scale later by Aḥmad ibn Muṣṭafā Ṭashköprüzāde in his great encyclopaedia Miftāḥ al-sa'āda wa miṣbāḥ al-siyāda, dealing with a hundred and fifty sciences, and on a larger scale still by Muṣṭafā ibn 'Abdallāh Kātib Čelebī Ḥājjī Khalīfa, whose classification at the head of his Kashf al-ẓunūn enumerated 307 branches of knowledge.[17] These encyclopaedic-bibliographic-classificatory tendencies are decidedly a Turkish trait, which we have seen originate (in its Turkish form) at the end of the fourteenth century.

D6. *The destroyer*

There occur from time to time in the course of history, happily not too often, men who have a special genius for conquest and destruction. Think of Alexander the Great; Attila (d. 453), properly named flagellum Dei, "the scourge of God"; Chingiz Khān (XIII-1); Hūlāgū, who sacked Baghdād in 1258. The methods of these men were very much the same, "Blitzkrieg" accompanied by ruthlessness. Of course, these monsters did not think of themselves as "destroyers," but as builders of a "new order." They did establish a kind of order, for when their work was done, there ruled in their dominions the order of exhaustion and death. We may apply to them the incisive words which the British chieftain Calgacus applied to the Romans: "To plunder, butcher, steal, these things they misname empire; they make a desolation, and they call it peace."[18]

At the end of the fourteenth century the "scourge of God" was a Turk or Mongol called Tīmūr Lang, who conquered a large part of the world and destroyed the leading cities of Asia, building pyramids of skulls to remind the people of his merciless "Schrecklichkeit." When the destruction was sufficiently complete to assure the foundation of a new order, Tīmūr built himself an imperial city, Samarqand, and posed as a patron of science and arts. The scientific or artistic creations which may be credited to his patronage are not few, yet negligible as compared with the lives and goods which he had caused to be destroyed.

[15] We may assume that well trained Turkish scholars were often as familiar with Persian as with Arabic, for they were very much exposed to Persian influences.

[16] Brockelmann (2, 231, 1902; suppt. 2, 323, 1938).

[17] For Ṭashköprüzāde (born Brussa 1495, died Istanbul 1561) see Brockelmann (2, 425–26, 1902; suppt. 2, 633, 1938); Franz Babinger (EI 4, 689, 1929). For Ḥājjī Khalīfa (born Istanbul 1608/9, died there 1657) see Brockelmann (2, 427–29, 1902; suppt. 2, 635–37, 1938) and our general bibliography. Readers having no access to Gustav Flügel's monumental edition of the Kashf al-ẓunūn may find the classification in Julius Theodor Zenker: Bibliotheca orientalis (p. xviii–xliii, Leipzig 1846).

[18] "Auferre trucidare rapere falsis nominibus imperium, atque ubi solitudinem faciunt, pacem appellant." Tacitus (I-2): Agricola (ch. 30; Loeb library ed., p. 220).

In order to give a correct idea of the cultural background of the fourteenth century one must speak of this monster, even as one has to speak of the Black Death and of the earthquakes, famines, and other calamities. They were the agents of destruction, but life never stops. They caused the scenery to be shifted more rapidly, and the play continued. We must evoke the memory of such monsters as Tīmūr, who interrupt brutally the peaceful activities of millions of men, women, and children; we must evoke it if only to curse them and to pity their innumerable victims.

Tīmūr was received into the mercy of God in 1405. The proud city which he had raised as a witness of his glory and splendor continued to be a center of culture for less than a century and then sank into oblivion. His memory is celebrated to this day by his mausoleum and jade tomb and by the universal execration of gentle people.

E. *India*

The dominant figure in the Indian panorama is that of Mādhava Vidyāraṇya, who revived Vedantic philosophy under the patronage of the Vijayanagara rulers. His main work, the Sarvadarśanasaṃgraha, is an account of the philosophical systems of India culminating in that of Śaṅkara.

In the same period Dhammakitti V, flourishing in Ceylon, wrote one or two books devoted to the history of Buddhism; Taruṇaprabha explained Jaina ethics; the poetess Lal Ded composed mystic verse reconciling Hindu and Muslim aspirations; another mystic, Banda Nawāz, wrote treatises on taṣawwuf.

Note the great diversity of those efforts, which illustrate the infinite complexity of Indian life. The first of these five was a Vedantist, the second a Buddhist, the third a Jain, the fourth a Śaiva yōginī, the fifth a ṣūfī. The first wrote in Sanskrit, the second in Pāli and Siṅhalese, the third in Gujarātī, the fourth in Kashmīrī, the fifth in Urdū. This is the more remarkable if one bears in mind that I did not select these persons for the sake of representing five religions, five philosophies, and five languages. They selected themselves, they stood out among their contemporaries in the Indian world, and it was only after having considered them one by one that I realized their differences.

F. *China*

An account of Chinese superstitions was written by Hsieh Ying-fang, who was director of education in Kiangsu. It would be worth while to investigate, analyze, and perhaps translate that work (or parts of it). In the meanwhile, we are unable to appraise its rationalism and its value.

The end of the Yüan dynasty and the beginning of the Ming was a period of trouble and chaos. The new Chinese order was profoundly different, for good or evil, from the old Mongolian one. It was only at the beginning of the following century, under the rule of the third Ming emperor, Yung Lo (ruled 1403-24), that there was enough peace for philosophy or scholarship. Yung Lo was a famous patron of learning, witness the encyclopaedia, Yung Lo ta tien, which he patronized. That encyclopaedia was by far the largest ever compiled anywhere; it was completed in 1409 and remained unprinted, this lack of publicity being probably the result of its unwieldy size.[19]

[19] See my note on it in the article on Wang Chên (XIV-1), p. 830.

G. *Korea*

The Korean statesman Chêng Mêng Chou was one of the greatest educators of his people, and he completed the establishment of Confucianism, or rather Neo-Confucianism (hsing li), in his country. He witnessed the fall of the Yüan dynasty in China, and in Korea that of the Koryu one, to which he remained faithful unto death. His abundant writings are literary rather than philosophical, and yet he has been called the grandfather of metaphysics. His personality symbolizes the Korean renaissance. For the progress of Confucianism (vs. Buddhism) under the new Korean dynasty see Youn (p. 139 f., 1939).

Notes on Various Superstitions Which Deeply Colored the Cultural Background Everywhere

The references above to books on the interpretation of dreams written in Czech by Vavřinec of Březova, in Greek by Manuel II Palaeologos, in Arabic by Ibn Duqmāq[20] may seem out of place in a chapter devoted to philosophy, but oneirocriticism or oneirology was then considered a legitimate branch of science, and belief in its value was an integral part of everyman's philosophy. A. C. Klebs did very well to include such books among his Incunabula scientifica et medica (1938).

Divination, that is, the art of foretelling events or discovering hidden knowledge from present tangible facts of any kind, is probably as old as human thought. Note that the definition of it which we have given would include legitimate science, but the latter was gradually separated from it. Science implies the exclusive use of experimental and rational methods, whereas divination is irrational, occult, and depends primarily on ritual and magic formulas. The distinction is very clear today to men of science, but it is far from clear to other men, and in antiquity, the Middle Ages, and for centuries later it was unclear even to the wisest people. Remember Cicero's defense of divination in his De natura deorum.

The best general account for ancient times is still that of L. A. T. Bouché-Leclerc: Histoire de la divination dans l'antiquité (4 vols., Paris 1879–82). Theodor Hopfner: Μαντική (PW 27, 1258–88, 1928). Alfred Boissier: Choix de textes relatifs à la divination assyro-babylonienne (2 vols., Genève 1905–6); Mantique babylonienne et mantique hittite (80 p., 5 pl., Paris 1935), including brief notes on divination among the Arabs, in Africa, Insulinde, Mongolia, and China. François Lexa: La magie dans l'Egypte antique de l'Ancien empire jusqu'à l'époque copte (3 vols., Paris 1925; Isis 9, 450–52).

Among the hundred or more classical forms of divination, oneiromancy was one of the most natural and the most popular. We may assume that the interpretation of dreams was practiced always and everywhere. References to it are found in every ancient literature and in many folk tales. Immemorial traditions of Western people ascribe its invention to the people of Mesopotamia and of Egypt. An Egyptian dream book of the XIIth dynasty (c. 2000–1790 B.C.) was edited by Alan H. Gardiner (London 1935; Isis 25, 476–78). Many dream books, Greek, Arabic, Latin, etc., are mentioned in my Introduction (see index s.v. dreams). In accordance with the Oriental origin ascribed to oneirology, the earliest dream

[20] It is probable that many more such books could have been quoted if I had hunted for them, but I mentioned only those which I came across involuntarily. As it is, they suffice to illustrate a curious aspect of contemporary thought and its universality.

book was supposed to have been written by the prophet Daniel for king Nebuchadrezzar, and the earliest printed dream book appeared under the title Somnia Danielis (princeps, Rome 1475). There are no less than 39 incunabula editions of that book (Klebs no. 319). Maurice Hélin: La clef des songes. Facsimilés, notes et liste des éditions incunables (99 p., Paris 1925). P. Saintyves (p. 3–163, 1930), on the importance of dreams in hagiographic traditions. Joseph de Somogyi: The interpretation of dreams in Ad-Damīrī's Ḥayāt al-ḥayawān (Journal of the Royal Asiatic Society, 1940, 1–20).

Another form of divination which enjoyed considerable popularity in the past and enjoys it still on all the uneducated and irrational fringes of mankind is physiognomy. There is a considerable literature about it in Greek, Latin, Arabic, etc. See, e.g., my notes on the pseudo Aristotle (Introd. 1, 135–36), Polemon of Laodicea (II-1), Apuleius (II-2), Adamantios Sophista (IV-1), Sirr al-asrār (IX-1), al-Rāzī (IX-2), Giles of Corbeil (XII-2), Michael Scot (XIII-1), Bartholomew of Messina (XIII-2), pseudo Albert (Introd. 2, 941), Aldobrandin of Siena (XIII-2), and more in this volume by index. The Arabic tradition has been investigated recently by Youssef Mourad: La physiognomonie arabe et le Kitāb al-firāsa de Fakhr al-dīn al-Rāzī (XII-2) (252 p., Paris 1939; Isis 33, 248–49).

It is remarkable that physiognomy has been gradually and almost completely restricted to the consideration of hands (chiromancy or palmistry). The literature of palmistry is enormous. To speak of the incunabula only, the earliest was perhaps the block book bearing the name of Johann Hartlieb: Die Kunst Chiromantia,[21] printed in Augsburg in or after 1478. A facsimile copy of it (46 pl.) was published in Munich 1926. Another Chiromantia was first printed in Venice 1481; there are 10 Latin and 2 Italian incunabula editions of it, and to these may be added the Chiromantia of Aristotle (Ulm 1490). See Klebs (nos. 86, 272, 499), a total of 14 incunabula dealing with palmistry, to which should be added a great many more referring to it.

More information on these subjects and related ones may be found in Thorndike's monumental work. I simply wanted to indicate their importance if one wishes to evaluate the scientific and philosophic thought of the fourteenth century. There is little to be gained by investigating the history of such superstitions, for they were inherently unprogressive. A dream book printed today is not essentially different, better or worse, from the one written on an Egyptian papyrus four thousand years ago; the palmistry of today is not essentially different from that of the Middle Ages, but of course there are considerable differences between the rascals practicing those arts. Some are so clever and such good psychologists and thought readers that they can give their customers welcome, intriguing, and even valuable advice.

Albert L. Caillet: Manuel bibliographique des sciences psychiques ou occultes (3 vols., Paris 1912; Isis 1, 285–87).

The best account of superstition in the Muslim world will be found in the Muqaddama of Ibn Khaldūn. For Chinese superstitions see the Pien-huo p'ien of Hsieh Ying-fang.

Very elaborate surveys of divination in many ages and places by 18 specialists (ERE 4, 775–830, 1912); see also the surveys concerning charms and amulets (ERE 3, 392–472, 1911), dreams and sleep (ERE 5, 28–40, 1912), magic (ERE 8,

[21] Johann Hartlieb was physician to Albert III, duke of Bavaria-Munich; he wrote the Chiromantia for the latter's wife, Anna of Braunschweig, in 1448. He died in 1471–74 (ADB 10, 670–72, 1879). Sudhoff (p 97–99, 1908).

245–324, 1916), occultism (ERE 9, 444–48, 1917), palmistry (ERE 9, 591, 1917), possession (ERE 10, 122–39, 1919), prodigies and portents (ERE 10, 362–76, 1919), superstition (ERE 12, 120–22, 1922). Sir E. A. Wallis Budge: Amulets and superstitions (583 p., 22 pl., 300 ill., Oxford 1930).

VI. MATHEMATICS AND ASTRONOMY

A. *Western Christendom*

Our account of mathematical knowledge in Western Christendom is divided into nine sections, relative to (1) Italy, (2) Spain, (3) France, (4) England, (5) Netherlands, (6) Germany, (7) Poland, (8) Bohemia, (9) Scandinavia.

A1. *Italy*

We might begin with the most characteristic fruit of Italian mathematics, the study of perspective and its application to painting, though that fruit did not ripen until the fifteenth century. Leaving out of account Greek speculations on the painting of stage scenery (scenography), for which see my notes on Anaxagoras and Agatharchos (V B.C.), or the Arabico-Latin ones on "perspectiva" as part of meteorology, which were never properly focused on the problems of linear perspective, we may say that these problems were first investigated in Tuscany. This is not surprising, for that country was experiencing a great revival in painting and architecture. The artist preparing architectural sketches or wishing to introduce buildings in his paintings realized the need of rules to create and sustain the necessary illusions. It is said that the Florentine artist Lorenzo Ghiberti (1378–1455) was the first to investigate such questions; discussions of them are included in his Commentarii, written only toward the end of his life but embodying the whole of his experience. This Ghiberti is immortalized by two of the bronze doors of the Battistero of Florence.[1] He was the teacher of the painter Paolo Uccello (1397–1475), who is sometimes called the founder of perspective. The same title has been given to still another Florentine, the architect Filippo Brunelleschi (1377–1446), who built (1419–34) the magnificent dome of Santa Maria del Fiore. The study of perspective was continued by Leon Battista Alberti (1404–72), Piero della Francesca (c. 1416–92), and Leonardo da Vinci (1452–1519), all of them Florentines, except Piero, who was an Umbrian, but who had spent at least ten years of his life in Florence, c. 1439–50. We may say that linear perspective was born in Florence about the end of the fourteenth century.[2]

Another mathematical seed was sown at that time in Italy—the seed of the calculus of probabilities, which is found in the Dantesque commentary of Benvenuto di Rambaldi. That seed did not really germinate until the second half of the seventeenth century.

The majority of the Italian mathematicians were primarily interested in astronomy. Thus, Giacomo de' Dondi published under the title Planetarium a set of astronomical tables based on the Alphonsine ones but adjusted to the meridian of

[1] There are three bronze doors to that Baptistery (San Giovanni Battista). The first was modeled by Andrea Pisano in 1330–36, the second by Ghiberti in 1403–24, and the third, facing the Duomo, also by him, 1425–52. It was of this third one that Michelangelo said it was worthy to be the gate of Paradise.

[2] For different views on this subject see Miriam Schild Bunim: Space in medieval painting and the forerunners of perspective (280 p., 79 ill., Columbia University, New York 1940; Speculum 20, 484–86). Erwin Panofsky: Albrecht Dürer (quarto, 2 vols., revised ed., 1, 247, Princeton 1945; Isis 36, 183); the first edition appeared in 1943.

Padua; he wrote a treatise on tides wherein he ascribed the fluctuations of the latter not only to the sun and moon (as did the Greeks), but also, in some cases at least, to Venus and Jupiter. Biagio Pelacani wrote a Theoretica planetarum and a commentary on the Sphere of Sacrobosco. The author of the encyclopaedia Fons memorabilium universi, Domenico di Bandino, knew enough of astronomy to foretell eclipses, but he did not do it well. Two younger men should still be mentioned, both born about 1370. The first, Paul of Venice,[3] might be neglected, for his astronomical contribution was simply a Latin translation of the Della composizione del mondo of Ristoro d'Arezzo (XIII-2), and his mathematical one a treatise on quadrature, but his contemporaries had an exalted opinion of him. The second, on the contrary, Prosdocimo de' Beldomandi,[4] was one of the outstanding mathematicians and astronomers of his time, but his many treatises belong definitely to the first half of the fifteenth century.

The five men enumerated in the preceding paragraph might be called astronomers; at any rate they were interested in astronomy, and also to some extent in astrology. For example, Biagio Pelacani made astrological predictions, and we might call him a moderate and rational believer in astrology (rational, we should remember, is a relative term; nobody is absolutely rational or absolutely irrational). The six men to be mentioned now were more deeply interested in astrology than in astronomy. Indeed, we might call them astrologers. The first of these, Thomas de Pisan, was astrologer to the kings of France, Charles V and Charles VI. The practical importance of astrology for the wise conduct of affairs being then conceded by everybody, a pope, emperor, king, prince, bishop, in short any man of power and leader of men, would have his private astrologer to guide him. In addition to the astrologers who had found a royal or episcopal berth or a chair in one of the universities, there were many others less lucky, who had no stable position but sold their astrological knowledge as well as they could and wrote treatises ad hoc in order to justify themselves or increase their qualifications. Thus, Antonio da Montulmo taught for a while in Bologna and wrote astrological treatises. Gentile degli Mainardi introduced astrological arguments and comparisons in his treatise on chivalry. Giovanni da Legnano was primarily a jurist, but he applied astrology to politics. He wrote two astrological treatises relative, respectively, to a conjunction of Saturn and Jupiter in Scorpio (1365) and to the comet of 1368. He saw connections between these events and the miseries of his time. He thought it necessary to add an astrological introduction to his masterpiece, the De bello, one of the earliest treatises on international law. More astrological treatises were composed by Andrea da Sommeria and Matthaeus Guarimbertus. It is hardly worth while to try to determine the relative value of these writings; their intrinsic value was negligible, but their extrinsic importance varied according to circumstances. For example, treatises of Antonio da Montulmo and of Guarimbertus fell under the eyes of the great German astronomer Regiomontanus (1436–76), who

[3] Paul of Venice was born at Udine (Friuli, north of the Adriatic) c. 1370; he became an Augustinian Hermit and flourished chiefly in Padua, where he died in 1429. He was mainly an Aristotelian commentator. His Summa totius philosophiae (Expositio librorum naturalium Aristotelis), popularizing the views of Albert of Saxony and the Parisian Nominalists, attained an immense success. First edition 1476 (Klebs no. 732). Duhem: Etudes (2, 90–94, 323–27, 1909); Système (4, 280–89, 1916).

[4] Prosdocimo de' Beldomandi, born at Padua c. 1370–80, flourished there, and died in 1428. Antonio Favaro: Vita ed opere di Prosdocimo de' Beldomandi (Boncompagni's Bullettino 12, 1–74, 115–251, 1879; 18, 405–23, 1886; BM 1890, 81–90). See also BM (1890, 113–14; 1891, 32). Cantor (2, 204–9, 1899). D. E. Smith (p. 13–15, 1908). Duhem: Système (4, 289–301, 1916). Gino Loria (Isis 12, 322, 1929). Klebs (no. 167).

did them the honor of discussing them and thus keeping them a little longer in the limelight.

It is very much to the credit of the humanists that their leaders, such as Petrarca and later Coluccio Salutati, resisted and discouraged superstitious tendencies. Salutati was not bold enough to make a frontal attack on astrology (nobody was in those days), but he did not hide his skepticism.

A survey of Italian mathematics would not be complete without the consideration of a few anonymous treatises. Three among others have arrested my attention. The first (the Italian origin of which is uncertain) is a treatise on plain arithmetic, combining the new numerals with Roman fractions, that is, representing a kind of compromise. In our judgment of it we should not forget that decimal fractions were not clearly and definitely introduced until 1585 and that even as late as that they would have been unable to establish themselves but for the introduction of logarithms within the following generation.[5] The second is an elaborate compotus written in Tuscany c. 1393. The third is a curious algebra wherein a number of problems are exactly solved according to rules which are not explained and some of which are prematurely generalized. The date of this third treatise, "Alcune cose di abaco," cannot be determined, but even if we put it as late as possible (end of fourteenth century), it is an interesting document concerning the algebraic fermentation which was then going on, and the maturation of which would take at least two more centuries. It is a remarkable fact that mathematical (or other scientific) ideas do not mature in order of growing difficulty, or in logical order. On the contrary, many concepts grow together irrespective of difficulty, according to the needs of the time and sometimes even without the stimulation which material needs supply.

A2. *Catalonia (and the rest of the Hispanic peninsula)*

The leading astronomers were Dalmau Ces-Planes and Pere Engelbert, who were employed in Barcelona by the king of Aragon and Catalonia to compile ephemerides, build instruments, etc. They realized the imperfections of the Alphonsine tables and tried to remove them.

It is interesting to note that in his great treatise on inquisitorial principles and procedure, Directorium inquisitorum, Nicholas Eymeric did not hesitate to condemn astrological practice. That was indeed the traditional attitude of the church. The postulates of astrology were tentatively accepted, but the astrological convictions, being incompatible with the freedom of the will, were rejected;[6] astrological mummeries were formally anathematized.

I am not acquainted with any astronomical or mathematical work done outside Catalonia in the peninsula, but there was increasing dissatisfaction with the calendar. In addition to the difficulties with the Julian calendar which the Spaniards shared with the rest of Europe,[7] they had a special nuisance in their era, the Spanish

[5] Sarton (1934–35).

[6] For example, remember the condemnation of astrology included in the Confessions of St. Augustine (V-1), in VII, vi, where he describes the different fates of people born at exactly the same time, or of twins. It is true St. Augustine ascribed astrological ideas and practice to the Manichaeans, and his hatred of astrology was part of his conversion from Manichaeism to Catholicism.

[7] The length of the Julian year was 365¼ days, that is, 11^m4^s longer than the tropical year. Small as that difference was, it amounted to more than 3 days in 4 centuries. By 1582 the vernal equinox fell on March 11; therefore, a new calendar (our Gregorian calendar) was finally established by pope Gregory XIII, who decided also that the morrow of October 4, 1582 would be called October 15.

era, the use of which dated back to the fifth century. Its epoch was January 1, 38 B.C. Thus every one of their dates was out of step with the European dates:

Spanish year 1370 = Julian year 1332
Julian year 1370 = Spanish year 1408

This must have been an annoying source of confusion. After having been accepted not only in the peninsula but also in southern France and Vandal Africa, the Spanish era had been gradually restricted to the peninsula. It was forbidden in Aragon 1349, in Valencia 1358, in Castile and León 1383; in Navarre even later. It should be noted that Alfonso X el Sabio (XIII-2) in his dealings with foreign chanceries had sometimes used the Spanish era, sometimes not. It is probable that the discontinuance of the Spanish era was not immediate in any kingdom, but gradual. According to Ginzel (3, 175, 1914), the Spanish era was customary until the end of the fourteenth century, and in Portugal until as late as 1422, where it was abolished by João I de Boa Memória (king 1385–1433).

A3. *France*

The best mathematicians and astronomers of the age were two Frenchmen, Nicole Oresme and Pierre d'Ailly. Oresme had been pondering on the use of coordinates and the use of graphs to represent the growth of a function; his ideas were still vague, but he seems to have had some intuition of the nature of maxima. He had been thinking of a fourth dimension, but rejected it. He busied himself with combinatorial analysis and the meaning of fractional exponents. In short, he had a mathematical mind but lacked intensity and persistence, or was too readily distracted from mathematical topics by the necessity of investigating many others. It is difficult to say where the fault lay and whether we should blame his own weakness or the strength of overwhelming circumstances. His work in astronomy has the same characteristics as his mathematical work. It includes brilliant ideas which did not receive sufficient development. He was the first to suggest that the incommensurability of planetary periods would cause special difficulties in the determination of planetary motions. He criticized Ptolemaic astronomy and argued in favor of the diurnal motion of the earth.[8] He wrote an astronomical treatise in French, Traicté de l'espère, and translated into the same language the De coelo et mundo, adding a commentary of his own to bring the subject up to date. This was not so much a contribution to astronomical knowledge as a means of bringing that knowledge within the reach of the growing audience which was not able or not inclined to read Latin. Perhaps his main service to astronomy and to science in general consisted in his persistent antagonism to astrological predictions. That antagonism was partly theological, but he had over other theologians the advantage of speaking as a master of the subject; he enjoyed the authority of an expert, which the others lacked. His aversion to astrology was probably intensified by the alarming popularity of that aberration among "educated" people, especially

[8] This was by no means a novelty. The idea cropped up again and again, not only in the Middle Ages but also in antiquity. It is discussed (but refuted) in the Almagest (I, VI). For other early examples, see Grant McColley: The theory of the diurnal rotation of the earth (Isis 26, 392–402, 1937). The idea was clearly expressed by Ibn Rusta (X-1), see text in Blachère (p. 35, 1932). As long, however, as an idea crops up and disappears again and again, it simply means that it has failed to be established. This one was not really established until 1543, by Nicolaus Copernicus.

in court circles, and above all by the fascination it exerted on king Charles V, who had been tutored by him and for whom he could not help feeling responsible.

The other astronomer, Pierre d'Ailly, belongs to the following century if we consider the date of completion of his main work, the Imago mundi (c. 1410), but Pierre is to a large extent a man of the fourteenth century. He was born at Compiègne in 1350, studied at the College of Navarre, of which he became the head in 1384; he flourished mainly in Paris, became a bishop in 1395, a cardinal in 1411, and died in Avignon in 1420. He took a prominent part in the council of Constance (1414–18), which re-established the unity of the Roman church. He was a good popularizer of Ptolemaic astronomy, chiefly in the form of a commentary on the Sphaera mundi of John of Sacrobosco (XIII-1); he prepared for the council a memoir on the reform of the calendar, the necessity of which became more and more obvious as the divergence between the Julian year and the seasonal one increased. His cosmographical views influenced Christopher Columbus. His opposition to astrology was less outspoken than that of his older contemporary Oresme, and that is hardly surprising, for he lacked the mathematical training, the rationalism, and the originality of the latter. In 1410 he wrote a Tractatus de legibus et sectis contra supersticiosos astronomos, but in 1414 he composed a whole series of treatises (nos. 11–16 in the Ymago mundi)[9] wherein he explained the concordance of theological and historical events with astronomical ones. Judging from the apostils written by Christopher Columbus in the margin of his copy (edition of Louvain c. 1483; Klebs no. 766), treasured in the Biblioteca Colombina in Seville, Christopher was much impressed by the astrological coincidences pointed out by Pierre d'Ailly.[10] For example, he emphasized (folio dd5 verso) Pierre's statement that 1489 would be like 1414, a year during which calamities or prodigies might be expected, writing in the margin "Anno christi 1489 erit complementum aliorum 10 revolucionum." It is clear that for Pierre or Christopher, as well as for their predecessors, the occurrence of conjunctions (especially the conjunction of the three superior planets, Mars, Jupiter, and Saturn) would cause or at any rate signalize extraordinary historical events.

On the other hand, the anti-astrological campaign was continued vigorously by one of Ailly's pupils, Jean Gerson, who wrote a special tract Trilogium astrologiae to warn the Dauphin against the dangers of astrology. He ascribed astrological errors to the Averroists, because it was now the fashion to blame the latter for everything which deviated from orthodoxy, especially for every error parading as science (Introd. 2, 358). This was entirely unwarranted. It is true that Babylonian, Egyptian, and Greek astrology had reached the West largely through Arabic channels, but the Arabic astrological treatises from which Western astrology was derived were all anterior to Ibn Rushd.

The attacks of Oresme, Ailly, and Gerson suggest that astrology was flourishing in their time. Indeed, it would not be difficult to name many astrologers whose ill-gotten prestige must have excited their anger. The most famous of all, Thomas de Pisan, has already been dealt with in the Italian section above, but we should remember that he was in the service of Charles V and Charles VI. Another

[9] (11) Vigintiloquium de concordia astronomicae veritatis cum theologia, (12) De concordia astronomicae veritatis et narrationis historicae, (13) Elucidarium astronomicae concordiae cum theologia et cum historica veritate, (14) Apologetica defensio astronomicae veritatis, (15) Secunda defensio eiusdem, (16) De concordia discordantium astronomorum.

[10] I examined the photostat reproduction of that very copy published by the Massachusetts Historical Society (Boston 1927). Edition of 22 copies.

astrologer, Pèlerin de Prusse, wrote a treatise on astrology in French for Charles V, in 1361 (that is, before Charles's accession to the throne). On the other hand, Jean Fusoris, who made astrolabes and constructed an astronomical clock for the cathedral of Bourges, was not strictly speaking an astrologer. He was employed by the king of Aragon and by the pope for the purpose of preparing astronomical instruments rather than for the making of predictions. He compiled trigonometrical tables and wrote treatises on the use of the astrolabe and on cosmography. The great surgeon Guy de Chauliac dedicated to Clement VI (pope 1342–52) a treatise wherein he discussed the applications of astrology to medicine. The poet Eustache Deschamps had indulged in astrology, which he curiously called the "art of Toledo,"[11] in his youth, but as he grew older and more concerned with the hereafter he avoided predictions. The list of fourteenth-century astrologers flourishing in France could easily be lengthened by the study of a document written by Symon de Phares toward the end of the following century. The "Recueil des plus célèbres astrologues et quelques hommes doctes" which Symon compiled for Charles VIII in the last year of the latter's reign (1498) was meant to be a history of astrology from Adam down to his own days. He lists a very large number of "astrologers," but we should bear in mind that his use of that term was more inclusive than our own. The center of interest, however, is astrology proper, judicial astrology, and a good many of his notices, in fact the most reliable of them, refer to the fourteenth and fifteenth centuries. That Recueil was edited on the basis of the unique MS in the Bibliothèque nationale by Emile Wickersheimer (320 p., Paris 1929; Isis 13, 167).

A book on surveying written in Provençal, probably by Bertran Boysset, is more interesting to philologists and folklorists than to historians of mathematics. It illustrates the survival, for the needs of everyday life, of traditional methods uninfluenced by mathematical progress. As far as mathematics is concerned, that book might have been written before the days of the Roman agrimensores (i.e., before the Christian era).

A4. *England*

We may well begin our survey of English mathematics with a document as interesting from the linguistic as from the scientific point of view, the Anglo-Norman algorism edited by Louis C. Karpinski and Charles N. Staubach (Isis 23, 121–52, 1935; 25, 202). It is a poem of 328 lines in Anglo-Norman explaining the elements of the new arithmetic, that is, how to write numbers and to perform the six operations. The Hindu numerals from 1 to 10 are written in the very first line, constituting a kind of symbolic beginning.

So much for primary education; we may now pass to more difficult matters. Mathematical progress was assured by the continuance of the Merton tradition. The musician Simon Tunsted of Norwich improved Wallingford's Albion. William Rede, founder of the Merton library, compiled many ephemerides. Walter Brit was another Merton astronomer, but his importance has been much deflated by the discovery that various writings formerly credited to him are apocryphal. Thus the Merton tradition continued, but on a lower level and more feebly than during the first half of the century.

In 1391 Geoffrey Chaucer wrote a treatise on the astrolabe which was the first of its kind in the English language, and one of the earliest monuments of English

[11] See the remarks on Toledan letters below in the German section.

astronomy. It contained no novelty, but was a clear exposition of the astronomical knowledge generally available in his days.

Two monks, the Carmelite Nicholas of Lynn and the Franciscan John Somer, computed calendars including astronomical tables. Neither spoke of the reform of the calendar, the necessity for which was realized by many people on the continent, not only mathematicians but also churchmen. Their unconcern is the more remarkable when one remembers that Englishmen, Robert Grosseteste and Roger Bacon, had been the first to recognize and proclaim that need.

A5. *The Netherlands*

In this period, Bruges was the most prosperous city of Flanders. It was a center of international commerce, and hence we should not be surprised if we found there indications that the art of accounting was being developed. There have come to us the account books of two money-changers, Collard de Marke and Guillaume Ruyelle, who flourished in Bruges c. 1366–69. These precious accounts have been investigated by Raymond De Roover,[12] who declared them to be very well kept though without the use of the double-entry method. That method was used by the stewards of Genoa in 1340 and in the Medici accounts, Florence 1395, but apparently it had not yet found its way to Bruges. It is thus probable that the method was invented in Italy; the earliest printed treatise on the subject was included in the Summa de arithmetica of Luca Pacioli (Venice 1494). Other initiatives related to that one may be ascribed to Italy. The earliest textbook on commercial practice that has come down to us was composed by the Florentine Francesco Balducci Pegolotti (XIV-1) c. 1340; that book included among other things the earliest tables of interest. Yet it is fair to remember that the earliest tables of interest to appear in print were edited by the illustrious Fleming Simon Stevin (Antwerp 1582).[13] In short, the traditions of accounting and commercial science developed, as we should expect, in the great commercial cities of Italy and Flanders, the Italians being the initiators, the Flemings adept pupils. The complete investigation of these questions is of course impossible, for only a few of the fourteenth-century account books have survived and the archaeological mementos of early commerce have almost completely vanished. A good but rare example of such mementos is the customs tariff of Antwerp dating from the end of the fourteenth century or the beginning of the fifteenth. It is written on slips of paper glued to wooden leaves forming a book, and is preserved in the National Archives, in Brussels.[14] The remarks which have just been made do not by any means exhaust the subject. They are sufficient to remind the reader of the necessity of investigating economic history if he wishes to watch the growth of commercial arithmetic.

[12] Quelques considérations sur les livres de compte de Collard de Marke précédées d'un aperçu sur les archives commerciales de Belgique (Bulletin d'études et d'informations de l'Institut de commerce St. Ignace, avril 1930, p. 445–75); Le livre de comptes de Guillaume Ruyelle (Annales de la Société d'émulation de Bruges 77, 15–95, 1934; Isis 24, 481).

[13] Sarton (p. 247, 264, 1934). For the study of later developments, see Richard Brown: History of accounting and accountants (476 p., Edinburgh 1905). Cornelis Marius Waller-Zeper: De oudste intresttafels in Italië, Frankrijk en Nederland (192 p., Amsterdam 1937; Isis 36, 185), including reprint of Stevin's tables of 1582.

[14] Photograph in Rob. Van Roosbroeck: Geschiedenis van Vlaanderen (vol. 2, opp. p. 216, Amsterdam 1937). Read in that volume the account of economic conditions in Flanders in the fourteenth and fifteenth centuries (p. 191–267) by Frans Lodewijk Ganshof.

The only Flemish astronomer of that time was Jan de Heusden, who was physician in turn to the count of Flanders and the duke of Burgundy. He built a kind of celestial sphere or orrery.

In the northern provinces, the Brothers of the Common Life, led by Geert Groote, discouraged astrological tendencies as much as they could. The leading Dutch philosopher, Marsilius van Inghen, was also the leading mathematician. He was a follower, in mathematics, of Oresme, and in astronomy, of Bernard of Verdun and Giles of Rome.

A6. *Germany*

We have two very interesting documents for the history of geometry. The first, included in the family chronicle of a Nuremberg patrician, Ulman Stromer, is the earliest example of the "Visierkunst," a method for the determination of the contents of barrels or casks, which obtained much popularity in German lands, and became a sort of German specialty. Stromer's text was the first of a long series published in Germany, many in German, others in Latin, leading as a sort of climax to the Nova stereometria doliorum vinariorum of Johann Kepler (Linz 1615).[15]

The second is the so-called Geometria culmensis, a geometrical treatise compiled by an unknown author for Conrad von Jungingen, grand master of the Teutonic Knights from 1393 to 1407, and published in two editions, Latin and German. The Geometria culmensis gives us a good idea of the geometrical knowledge available in Germany at the end of the century.

The leading mathematicians were interested chiefly in astronomy, either for its own sake, or for astrological purposes. Astrology, we should remember, provided a livelihood; if this was still true in Kepler's time, it was far more so in this time, a century and a half earlier. A mathematician satisfied to remain on the computer's level might find a job as accountant or clerk in one of the commercial centers. If he was more ambitious, there was for him no opportunity but teaching or astrologizing, both implying astronomical work. If he was a philosopher or theologian trying to explain the universe, a good deal of his time would still be devoted to astronomical research. Thus a list of the leading German astronomers would include Albert of Saxony, Heinrich Langenstein, Nicholas of Dinkelsbühl, Johann von Gemunden.

Albert wrote treatises on the "latitudes of forms," on proportions, on the quadrature of the circle, treatises which did not help to clarify those subjects but left them as confused as they were; his astronomical interest took the form of a commentary on the Sphere of Sacrobosco. Though his views were essentially Ptolemaic, he believed in the existence of the trepidation of the equinoxes and tried to account for it. Heinrich devoted much of his energy to the refutation of astrological fallacies, being in that respect Oresme's emulator. Nicholas and Johann were primarily teachers. Nicholas lectured on the latitudes of forms, on Euclid, and on astronomy, using the textbooks of John of Sacrobosco and Gerard of Sabbioneta. In addition to his teaching, Johann compiled ephemerides and published many astronomical treatises. He may be considered one of the introducers of decimal fractions, though he was still combining them with sexagesimal ones. His table of sines was computed with reference to a radius of length 600.000; this, of course, to

[15] Christian Frisch: Kepleri opera omnia (4, 551–646, 1863). Max Caspar: Bibliographia Kepleriana (no. 48, München 1936; Isis 26, 513).

avoid fractions, but the unit was a strange (Babylonian) combination, 60.10^4. For the extraction of square roots he recommended the method which can be represented by the following equation,

$$\sqrt{a} = \frac{1}{60^n \cdot 10^m} \sqrt{a\ 60^{2n}\ 10^{2m}}\ ,$$

but the final result was written in sexagesimals. Thus persisted the confusion which was not cleared up until 1585, by Simon Stevin (Sarton p. 169–71, 1935). Johann was born c. 1380 and most of his work belongs to the fifteenth century.[16]

These four men, the leading mathematicians of German lands, were all connected with the University of Vienna. Albert was really the founder of that university and its first rector, 1366. Heinrich came later and may be called the inceptor of the mathematical tradition which gave so much fame to that university in the following century. Nicholas conducted a number of mathematical and astronomical courses in 1391–95. It is necessary to insist on that because Johann, whose teaching in Vienna did not begin until 1408, is often called the first mathematical teacher in a German university. This may be true if one means a teacher of mathematics only. Johann taught theology and philosophy until 1420, and then restricted himself to mathematics and astronomy. The difference may be interesting from the administrative point of view; it has little importance otherwise.

Astrologers were established in other cities, writing books, making general predictions, and casting private horoscopes. Thus Evno in Würzburg, John of Livania in Treves, John of Stendal in Erfurt, John of Glogau in Silesia, and Bernard of Frankfurt in that city. It is hardly worth while to differentiate between them, their doings being much of a muchness. The German collections of archives are full of unpublished astrological papers or treatises, a good many of which have not yet been investigated. See Zinner's Verzeichnis (1925), e.g. under the heading Zusammenkünfte (conjunctions), listing 191 MSS plus hundreds appearing under the names of known authors. Much astrological literature was connected with John of Toledo, a name which may refer to John of Seville (XII-1), but more frequently refers to a mythical personality. For a couple of centuries every portent, such as a comet, an earthquake, or an extraordinary conjunction of planets, every calamity might and often did cause the publication or diffusion of a "Toledan letter," containing dire prophecies and aggravating the disquiet of afflicted people. We owe an elaborate study of that kind of apocalyptic literature to Hermann Grauert: Meister Johann von Toledo (Sitzungsberichte der Bayerischen Akad., philol. Kl., p. 111–325, Munich 1901). Much of it concerns the fourteenth century, not only in Germany, but in Bohemia, the Netherlands, and Italy. That literature is extremely repetitious and of no interest to the historian of science, except in bulk. Many examples of it are quoted in this volume, passim, under the names of known astrologers.

The following item is interesting for the study of German arithmetic. Maximilian Curtze: Arithmetische Scherzaufgaben aus dem 14. Jahrhundert (BM 1895, 77–88). Latin text from Cod. lat. Monac. 14684, f. 30–33. Incipiunt subtilitates enigmatum. There is a similar text in Cod. Amplonianus Qu. 345, f. 16, entitled Cautele algorismorum.

[16] John Mundy: John of Gmunden (Isis 34, 196–205, 1943).

The earliest examples of Hindu numerals in monumental inscriptions (excluding doubtful cases) are found at Pforzheim 1371 and Ulm 1388 (Smith and Karpinski p. 142, 1911).

A7. *Poland*

Polish mathematicians writing in Latin are difficult, if not impossible, to separate from German ones using the same language. The intense nationalism of our times was unknown in the Middle Ages; there was more provincialism and parochialism on the one hand, and more internationalism on the other.

John of Glogau, named in the previous section, might perhaps be counted as a Pole. Glogau on the Oder had been a Polish city; from the beginning of the fourteenth century the duchy of Silesia, of which it was a part, was under Bohemian suzerainty. Should we call him a Pole, a Bohemian, a German? The case of Hermann de Przeworsko seems clearer. He devoted a short astrological treatise to the comet of 1368, writing it in Latin. We may call him a Polish astrologer.

A8. *Bohemia*

In addition to canon John of Glogau, whose treatise on the plague (1371–73) contains much astrology, one must cite another physician, Christian of Prachatice (not far from Budějovice = Budweis on the Moldau), who was born in 1368 and flourished mostly in Prague. He was astronomer to the emperor and the king of Bohemia; dean and rector of the philosophical faculty of Prague in 1403; vicar of St. Michael in that city from 1405; visited John Hus in Constance 1415; exiled from Prague from 1427 to 1429; rector of the university in 1434; died in 1439. He wrote various books in Czech and in Latin. The most popular perhaps was his Astrolabium Ptolemaei, a treatise on the astrolabe in 53 chapters, represented by more than 40 MSS. He also wrote an Algorismus prosaycus (c. 3,500 words) derived from Sacrobosco. One of his Czech writings deals with iatromathematics.[17]

A9. *Scandinavia*

We have already spoken in volume 2 (p. 212, 404) of the Icelandic compotus or rím, as it was established in the twelfth century by Stjörnu Oddi (XII-1) and Bjarni Bergthórsson (XII-2). Icelandic chronology was derived from foreign treatises, mainly the De temporum ratione of Venerable Bede (VIII-1). These early Icelandic calendars were included in the Alfraethi íslenzk, an encyclopaedic treatise the MS of which was written in 1387. The Alfraethi íslenzk contains also two later rím derived from Sacrobosco (XIII-1).

Text. Stephanus Biörnonis (Björnsen): Rymbegla, sive Rudimentum computi ecclesiastici et annalis veterum Islandorum (Copenhagen 1780), Icelandic and Latin. New edition (Copenhagen 1801).

Natanael Beckman and Kristian Kålund: Alfraethi Islenzk. Islandsk encyklopaedisk Litteratur. II. Rímtol (538 p., Copenhagen 1914–16), Icelandic text, with notes, of three rím. The second and third rím (p. 81–222), derived from Sacrobosco, are probably fourteenth-century texts, not much earlier than the MS.

[17] František Josef Studnička (1836–1903): Algorismus prosaycus magistri Christiani anno fere 1400 scriptus (Sitzungsberichte der K. böhmischen Gesellschaft der Wissenschaften, 6, Prag 1893). Benedict (1914). Zinner (p. 266, 483, 1925).

B. *Eastern Christendom*

Byzantium

Mathematical, and especially astronomical, thought was represented by three very distinguished men, Nicolaos Cabasilas, Isaac Argyros, and Theodoros Meliteniotes.

Nicolaos was primarily a theologian, but his interest in astronomy is proved by his attempt to reconstruct the commentary on book III of the Almagest (dealing with the length of the year and the average solar motion) by Theon of Alexandria. The two other men, Isaac and Theodoros, were primarily mathematicians. They continued the astronomical renaissance which had been caused by the discovery and study of Persian treatises. Theodoros composed his Tribiblos c. 1361, and Isaac (or somebody else) the Paradosis in 1371. These dates should not be given too much importance; it would be unwise to conclude that the Paradosis, being somewhat posterior, was derived from the Tribiblos. In the present state of our knowledge (there is no critical edition of either treatise) it is better to consider both as coeval monuments of the same stage in Byzantine astronomy. It is sad to think that Byzantine scientific thought had been so debased that Greek-speaking scholars needed Arabic or Persian stimulation in order to rediscover the ideas of their own ancestors.

Many scholia which have come to us under Isaac's name show that the latter had studied Euclid, Heron of Alexandria, Nicomachos, Ptolemy, Proclos, Philoponos, Planudes' arithmetic, etc. He had also given some attention to the compotus, but his work in that field was ecclesiastical rather than scientific and thus is not comparable to that of his older contemporary Nicephoros Gregoras (XIV-1).

C. *Israel*

Jewish efforts will be considered under five headings, three of which refer to the West and two to the East: (1) Spain, (2) Catalonia, (3) Provence; (4) Greece, (5) Yaman.

C1. *Spain*

Meir ben Aldabi completed his encylopaedia, Shebile emunah, in 1360. The second "path," dealing with the creation of the world, contains a summary of cosmology, astronomy, and mathematical geography. The astronomical knowledge was derived from al-Farghānī. The Ẓedah la-derek̲ of Menahem ben Zeraḥ discusses the calendar and explains two astronomical tables. The revision of the Alphonsine tables completed by Pere Engelbert and Dalmau Ces-Planes was put into Hebrew form by Jacob Carsono. While Latin (or Catalan) tables were thus made available to the Jewish community, Arabic tables were translated into Hebrew by Joseph ben Isaac ibn Waqar and by Isaac Alḥadib. In addition to the canons which accompanied each table, Alḥadib wrote treatises explaining the use of astrolabes and other instruments. We may conclude that, though the Jews of Spain added nothing to astronomical knowledge, they were well acquainted with the Latin and Arabic writings circulating in their days.

C2. *Catalonia*

Less work was apparently done in the Catalan than in the Spanish provinces. Nevertheless, Jacob Bonet in 1361 compiled astronomical tables for the latitude of

Perpignan and Jacob ben Judah Cabret translated the De judiciis astronomiae (medical astrology) of Arnold of Villanova into Hebrew (Barcelona 1381). Bonet's tables were very popular, being represented by many Hebrew MSS; they were even translated into Latin and later retranslated from Latin into Hebrew! The same Bonet wrote geometrical notes to the tables of Jacob ben Maḥir.

Other geometrical notes are found in the correspondence of Simeon ben Ẓemaḥ Duran (born in Majorca 1361; moved in 1391 to Algiers, where he died in 1444). Simeon's mathematical adviser was one En Bellshom Ephraim Gerondi.[18] He wrote to him to obtain information on mathematical passages of the Talmud and for the determination of areas and volumes. For example, Ephraim gave him a formula equivalent to $S = 2\pi rh$, where S is the surface of a spherical segment, h its altitude, and r the radius of the sphere. This was written by Ephraim in Majorca after 1391, for he asked rabbi Simeon to assist him in escaping from the island, where anti-Semitic persecutions were increasing.[19]

C3. *Provence*

Some of the best mathematical work was done by the Jewish scholars of Provence. The greatest of them was Immanuel ben Jacob Bonfils of Tarascon. That sleepy little town of the lower Rhône (near Arles) is best known to most people because of a legendary character, "Tartarin de Tarascon," the type of the cheerful and candid braggart, created in 1872 by Alphonse Daudet (1840–97). It is probable that very few people, even in Tarascon itself, are aware of the fact that that town gave birth to one of the greatest mathematicians of the Middle Ages. Immanuel Bonfils compiled various astronomical tables and ephemerides, one of which, called the Wings of eagles, enjoyed considerable popularity not only in its original Hebrew form, but also in Latin, and even in Greek. His astronomy was derived mainly from al-Battānī and Levi ben Gerson; that is, it was Greek-Arabic astronomy, as it had been gradually corrected in the Christian and Jewish circles of Western Europe. It is truly remarkable that that Western knowledge was transmitted to the Byzantine world via a Hebrew channel, and that that transmission was completed before the middle of the next century. This illustrates the complexity of intellectual exchanges in that period. Immanuel's main contribution, however, was not astronomical but algebraical. One of his little treatises, Derek ḥilluq (Way of division), contains anticipations of the exponential calculus as well as of decimal fractions. On the strength of this we may call him a forerunner of Simon Stevin (1585) as well as of Nicholas Chuquet (1484), and if we had to name the three outstanding mathematicians who flourished at century intervals during these centuries, we should say, Bonfils, Chuquet, and Stevin. It is a pity we have no better knowledge of his life, but the new fame given to him in this volume may stimulate further investigations and alleviate our ignorance.

The other Provençal Jewish mathematicians are not comparable to Immanuel Bonfils, and what we have to say of them will seem an anticlimax. That is unavoidable; men of genius dwarf their neighbors.

Jacob Bonet (or Jacob Po'el) in 1361 compiled astronomical tables for the latitude of Perpignan.

Samuel ben Simeon Kansi wrote an abridgment of the Eagle wings, and he also explained the tables of Jacob Bonet. Solomon ben Abraham Abigdor translated

[18] En is a Catalan title, the equivalent of Dom or Sir. Bellshom or Bellsom is probably a corruption of belhomme (Neubauer-Renan p. 666, 1893).

[19] Jekuthial Ginsburg: An unknown mathematician of the fourteenth century (Scripta mathematica 1, 60–62, 1932).

the medical astrology of Arnold of Villanova and the Sphaera mundi of Sacrobosco; Solomon ben David Davin, the astronomical tables of Paris and the astrology of Ibn abī-l-Rijāl; all these translations were made from Latin into Hebrew. Isaac ben Moses ha-Levi (Profiaṭ Duran) wrote a treatise on the calendar, and a discussion of the length of the days according to seasons and latitudes. There have come to us also under his name astrological notes and remarks on the numbers seven and ten. The sacredness of those numbers was a favorite subject of commentary, and not only among qabbalists and students of gematria, but in almost every scholarly circle.[20]

C4. *Greece*

The title of this section refers not only to Greece proper, but to all the Eastern countries where Greek was spoken. The Jews of those countries we may be sure knew Greek as well as Hebrew. One of them, Solomon ben Elijah, who flourished in Salonica and Ephesus, translated into Hebrew the Ptolemaic treatise on the astrolabe and compiled astronomical tables, which were probably derived from those of Georgios Chrysococces. Joseph ben Moses ha-Kilti wrote a Hebrew commentary on the mathematical books of Abraham ben Ezra. We may recall here that the "Eagle wings" of Immanuel Bonfils circulated among Qaraites, who commented upon them and adapted them to the coördinates of the Crimea and Constantinople. Sometime later these tables were even translated from Hebrew into Greek, either for other Jews who were more familiar with Greek than with Hebrew at least for profane and scientific purposes, or for their Christian neighbors. This Greco-Hebrew tradition was continued in the following century by the Turkish Quaraite Mordecai ben Eliezer Comtino (ha-Qusṭadini ha-Yawani), who flourished at Adrianople and Constantinople and died in the latter place c. 1480–87 in very old age.[21]

C5. *Yaman*

We have already had various opportunities for referring to the learned Rasūlī dynasty (1229–1454), which was then ruling Arabia Felix. For a brief account of it see Lane-Poole (p. 99–100, 1893) and A. S. Tritton (EI 3, 1128–29, 1936). Thus it is not surprising that they encouraged astronomical work. In 1389 a Yamanī astronomer adapted Jerusalem tables to the latitude of Ṣana'ā, which was then the capital. About 1420 another astronomer called Joseph ben Japhet ha-Levi compiled new tables for Ṣana'ā, preceding them with an introduction written in Arabic and partly translated into Hebrew.[22] He called himself the disciple of an unknown Solomon ben Benaya. Was that perhaps the author of the tables of 1389?

D. *Islām*

The account of Muslim mathematics will be divided into five sections—two Western ones, one middle one, and two Eastern ones: (1) Maghrib, (2) Ifrīqīya, (3) Mamlūkīya, (4) Anatolia, (5) Farther east.

[20] For a general discussion of sacred numbers in Semitic tradition, see William Cruickshank (ERE 9, 413–17, 1917). See articles by Thomas Davidson and Arthur Berriedale Keith (ibid. p. 406–13) for similar ideas in other traditions. Vincent Foster Hopper: Medieval number symbolism (254 p., Columbia University, New York 1938; Isis 31, 101–3).

[21] B. Suler (EJ 5, 637–40, 1930). Pincus Schub: A mathematical text by Mordecai Comtino (Isis 17, 54–70, 1932).

[22] The tables were called in Hebrew Nir yisrael. They were compiled c. 1420 but contain an interpolation dated 1448. Steinschneider (p. 248, 1902). EJ (9, 347, 1932).

D1. *Maghrib*

Astronomical thought was kept alive in the Maghrib by 'Alī al-Qusṭanṭīnī, who wrote c. 1360 for a Marīnī sulṭān an astronomical poem accompanied by tables; and by 'Abd al-Raḥmān al-Jādarī, who thirty years later, in Fās, wrote a treatise on the determination of praying times. Al-Jādarī was muwaqqit[23] in the masjid al-Qarawīyīn and was primarily interested in the calendar and chronology.

D2. *Ifrīqīya*

To the Algerian man of letters Ibn abī Ḥajala we owe a treatise on chess and an anthology illustrating the importance of the number seven. We need not repeat the remarks made about this on previous occasions; numerology was a favorite subject of learned discussion everywhere; it will never be completely extirpated. Ibn al-Qunfūdh, qāḍī of Constantine, wrote commentaries on astronomical and arithmetical treatises of Ibn al-Bannā' and on the astrology of Ibn abī-l-Rijāl.

The great Tunisian historian Ibn Khaldūn was not a mathematician, but he had obtained from his own teacher Muḥammad ibn Ibrāhīm al-Abulī (XIV-1) the knowledge systematized by Ibn al-Bannā' (XIII-2). He had also studied the zā'irja-l-'ālam of Abū-l-'Abbās al-Sibtī (XII-2). There is much mathematical lore in his Muqaddama; for example, curious applications of the Arabic (literal) number system (Prolégomènes I, 242–45), and, what is more remarkable, a discussion of the amicable numbers 220 and 284 and their astrological use (ibid. III, 178–81; Dickson 1, 39, 1919). He was a moderate believer in astrology; in spite of a strong curiosity about occult matters, his robust common sense safeguarded him from the worst abuses of magic and divination.

The Tunisian astronomers shared the interest of their Muslim contemporaries (and followers) in all the calculations concerning their rites, notably the determination of the qibla and of the times of prayers. They built and used gnomons and astrolabes. Their determination of the qibla was often shockingly incorrect.[24]

D3. *Mamlukīya*

The Mamlūk empire was then the most civilized part of the Dār al-Islām, and this estimate is verified in this field as in many others. We can enumerate at least eight astronomers and arithmeticians.

Al-Bahāniqī wrote a treatise on the quadrant. Ibn al-Shāṭir, timekeeper in the mosque of the Omayyads in Damascus, made astronomical observations and wrote various treatises on the construction and use of instruments; his determination of the obliquity of the ecliptic was remarkably correct; he compiled new tables and explained their significance; he did not hesitate to criticize Ptolemaic astronomy; in short, he was one of the outstanding astronomers of his age. Ibn Zuraiq was employed in the same mosque and his activities were of the same kind. Similar statements apply to Muḥammad al-Khalīlī, and to the latter's son (?), Mūsā ibn

[23] The muwaqqit's function was to determine the times of prayers and other ritual times. He was an indispensable officer of the mosque, and a special room was generally devoted to his needs. Good example in the jama' Andalus in Fez. Henri Terrasse: La mosquée des Andalous à Fès (2 vols., Paris c. 1940; Isis 35, 76).

[24] Sarton: Orientation of the miḥrāb (Isis 20, 262–64, 1933). Henri Terrasse (Isis 24, 109–10, 1935). H. P. J. Renaud (Isis 34, 24, 1942). Sarton (Isis 35, 176, 1944).

Gonzague Ryckmans and Fernand Moreau: Un gnomon arabe du XIVe siècle (Muséon 39, 33–40, 1 pl., Louvain 1926), a gnomon made by Abū-l-Qāsim ibn Ḥasan al-Shaddād in Tunis 1355.

Muḥammad al-Khalīlī. Taqī al-dīn al-Ḥanbalī was an arithmetician, who discussed the proofs by casting out of sevens, eights, nines, and elevens. A good many textbooks bearing the name of Ibn al-Hā'im have come down to us, dealing with arithmetic, inheritance problems, and algebra. Ibn al-Majdī was even more prolific as a writer; he dealt with a great variety of subjects—the use of quadrants, the determination of the qibla, arithmetic, inheritance problems—and compiled many almanacs and ephemerides.

To these men, who explained the knowledge available in their days and were honest if not original teachers, might be added astrologers like Ibrāhīm al-Ḥāsib. A complete account of contemporary astrology would oblige us to drag in once more a good many authors mentioned in other sections. It will suffice to refer, e.g., to al-Damīrī's encyclopaedia, which includes a discussion of the licitness of astrology. He distinguishes many degrees of licitness, ranging all the way from good to bad according to the astrologer's purpose. Christian theologians would have generally agreed with his conclusions. Astrology is not good or bad per se, it all depends on the interpretation and use which are made of it.

We cannot leave Egypt without recalling the memory of one of her greatest astronomers, Ibn al-Haitham (XI-1). This is the more necessary because his services to optics are far better known than his astronomical investigations; the account of the latter in my volume 1 (p. 721) and in Brockelmann's volume 1 are equally insufficient.[25] One of his astronomical treatises, on the shape of the universe (fī hai'at al-'ālam), attracted more attention in Christian and Jewish than in Muslim circles. It had been translated from Arabic into Spanish by Abraham of Toledo (XIII-2), and into Hebrew by Jacob ben Maḥir ibn Tibbon (XIII-2) and by Solomon ben Paṭer (XIV-1). Later Jacob's Hebrew version was translated into Latin by Abraham de Balmes (born at Lecce in the heel of Italy, died at Venice 1523 in extreme old age). As against these multiple translations, there is no evidence (e.g., in the form of commentaries) that this treatise interested the Arabic astronomers.

D4. *Anatolia*

Turkish astronomy is represented by two men who belong to this age yet did their main work at the beginning of the next century, and the second of them far away from his native land. Ṣalāḥ al-dīn was a famous poet who wrote in Turkish under the rule of Bāyazīd and later. We speak of him here because one of his Turkish poems, the so-called solar poem, was an astrological calendar; it was completed only in 1408. Qāḍī Zāde al-Rūmī was more of an astronomer; indeed, he was the second director of the observatory founded by Ulūgh Beg in Samarqand. His name tells his story, for one could not call a man Rūmī in his native Rūm (he was born in Brussa), but only in exile. He was one of the leading mathematicians and astronomers of his time and died c. 1436–46.

D5. *Farther East*

It is better to classify the remaining Muslim mathematicians under the vague designation Easterners than to call them Persians, for they might be Persians or not.

We may begin with a remarkable illustration of the relations existing at this time in Samarqand (and Central Asia) between Muslim and Chinese people. It is an astronomical treatise by one 'Aṭā' ibn Aḥmad written in Arabic c. 1362 for a

[25] See Brockelmann (1, 469–70; suppt. 1, 851–54).

Mongol prince of the Yüan dynasty and bearing Chinese characters which I was not able to identify (see facsimile in text, fig. 26).

'Abd al-Wāḥid ibn Muḥammad wrote commentaries on astronomical treatises by Nāṣir al-dīn al-Ṭūsī and al-Jaghmīnī, and a poem on the use of the astrolabe. 'Abdallāh ibn Khalīl of Mārdīn flourished in Damascus, where he was timekeeper in the Omayyad mosque; we might have mentioned him above when we named other men holding the same office in the same mosque. He wrote various astronomical treatises, similar to those composed by his colleagues. The philosopher al-Jurjānī wrote commentaries on the astronomy of Nāṣir al-dīn al-Ṭūsī and al-Jaghmīnī.

Ulūgh Beg, a grandson of Tīmūr Lang, himself governor of Turkistān, emperor in 1447, murdered by his own son in 1449, is dear to us because of his foundation of an observatory northeast of Samarqand in 1420.[26] This was the main center of astronomical research in the world, after the destruction of the Marāgha observatory. The latter had been created by Nāṣir al-dīn al-Ṭūsī c. 1259, and did not last more than two generations. It had ceased to function probably before the end of the thirteenth century, certainly before the middle of the following century. Thus a whole century elapsed before Ulūgh Beg attempted an astronomical renaissance in Samarqand. Observations were made there by Jamshīd ibn Mas'ūd, the first director, Qāḍī Zāde al-Rūmī, the second director, and 'Alī ibn Muḥammad al-Qūshchī.[27] The results of their observations were the so-called tables of Ulūgh Beg, written originally in Persian but soon translated into Arabic.[28] All these men probably knew both languages equally well; some knew Turkish also. At any rate, Ulūgh Beg and Qāḍī Zāde were Turks, and 'Ali ibn Muḥammad al-Qūshchī spent the end of his life in Constantinople. The observatory of Samarqand was as short-lived as that of Marāgha, and the Zīj Ulūgh Beg was the last great monument of Muslim astronomy. A critical edition of the catalogue of stars included in those tables was prepared by Edward Ball Knobel and published by the Carnegie Institution (Washington 1917; Isis 2, 413–15). The first director of the Samarqand Observatory, Jamshīd ibn Mas'ūd, was one of the first mathematicians deliberately to use decimal fractions (Sarton p. 170, 1935).

I trust the reader will forgive this excursion outside the frame of the fourteenth century, because it will help him to measure the work done in that century. Moreover, all these men were children of the fourteenth century, except 'Alī ibn Muḥammad al-Qūshchī; all died before the middle of the fifteenth century, except 'Alī, who lived until 1474.

[26] L. Bouvat (EI 4, 994–96, 1932). Wilhelm Barthold: Uluġ Beg und seine Zeit. Deutsche Bearbeitung von Walther Hinz (Abhandlungen für die Kunde des Morgenlandes 21, part 1, 262 p., Leipzig 1935). The original Russian text was published by the Academy of Sciences, Petrograd 1918; a Turkish translation appeared in Istanbul 1930. Chapter VI (p. 161–78) deals with Ulūgh's scientific work and private life.

[27] Qūshchī is a Persian word, and the last consonantal group of our transcription is the jīm 'ajamī, pronounced like ch in church. The word means falconer. Indeed, 'Alī's father, Muḥammad, had been Ulūgh's falconer.

[28] That is my conclusion, but it may be argued that the tables and their elaborate introduction were written originally in Arabic or in Turkish. The popularity of these tables in the East is proved further by the existence of a Georgian translation made by Wakhtang VI (alias Ḥusain Qulī Khān), king of Georgia 1703–9, 1711–14, 1719–24 (Stokvis 1, 78). This has been studied by Yurii Nikolayevich Marr (1893–1935) in the Perso-Georgian studies (part 1, 1–53, 1926) edited by him and Karpez Darespanovich Dondua, under the title (in Russian) The Zīj of Ulūgh Beg, translation by Wakhtang with Perso-Georgian glossary.

D6. *Islām (undetermined)*

Our account of Muslim mathematics may be concluded with a mention of one 'Abd al-Qādir ibn 'Alī, of unknown racial or geographical origin. He was a ṣūfī, but that does not help us. He wrote a treatise on finger reckoning which is as puzzling as his own personality, for it is, together with the poem it professes to explain, the earliest text of its kind in Arabic, though Arabic people must have used finger reckoning long before that time. The earliest Latin text ad hoc was written by Bede (VIII-1). Popular lore, however, has a curious way of escaping publication, and such escape would be particularly natural for a manual (vs. verbal) symbolism and technique.

E. *India*

The Hindu tradition of arithmetic and algebra was continued by Nārāyaṇa, who flourished c. 1356. He derived his knowledge mainly from Bhāskara, and transmitted it, without substantial additions of his own, to the Hindu mathematicians of the sixteenth century.

F. *China*

By the middle of this century the golden age of Chinese mathematics was already over, and the work done in the second half of the century was comparatively unimportant.

Ting Chü published a collection of arithmetical problems, without rules and without order. The solution of some congruence equations is ascribed to Yen Kung; this was not a novelty in China, for such equations were considered by Chinese mathematicians in relatively early days (say, third century).

The end of the Yüan dynasty was a period of great confusion, not only political but also cultural. This appears in the mathematical field and will appear more and more clearly as we obtain a better knowledge of the conflict between Mongol (partly Muslim) methods and original Chinese ones. That conflict was naturally accentuated by the fight between the Yüan and the Ming, but it is much older.

About the year 1370 two calendars were prepared, a purely Chinese one by the astronomer Liu Chi, and a Muslim[29] one by the Uighūr mathematician Chêng A-li.

For the history of the suan p'an or Chinese abacus, see the note on T'ao Tsung-i. It is curious that the Chinese, who are more likely to antedate their discoveries than to postdate them, assign a relatively late origin to their abacus. That theory is so unplausible that it must be caused by some misunderstanding; it is possible also that the abacus, being considered a part of folklore, had been unconsciously or deliberately neglected by the Chinese mathematicians. Manual techniques often remain unrecorded for centuries.

The Chinese astronomers were good and patient observers, and, not to speak of the star catalogues, we owe to them continuous series, of considerable length, of observations relative to eclipses, comets, sunspots, meteors, and meteorites.

For the eclipses, see the list given by Alexander Wylie: Eclipses recorded in Chinese works (Journal of the North China branch, Royal Asiatic Society, Dec. 1867, p. 87-158).

For comets, Edouard Biot: Catalogue des comètes observées en Chine de 1230 à

[29] The word Muslim here has no religious implication. The reference is to culture and especially mathematics, not to religion or language. It is unlikely that a man like Chêng A-li knew Arabic; his languages were Chinese, Mongolian, and perhaps Turkish.

1640 (Additions à la Connaissance des temps pour 1846, 43 p.). This is a continuation of the list of comets down to 1222 given by Ma Tuan-lin (XIII-2) in his Wên hsien t'ung k'ao; the Ma Tuan-lin comets are listed also in Alexandre Guy Pingré: Cométographie (2 vols., Paris 1783-84). E. Biot: Recherches faites dans la grande collection des historiens de la Chine sur les anciennes apparitions de la comète de Halley (Connaissance des temps 1846, p. 69-84). John Williams: Observations of comets from B.C. 611 to A.D. 1640 extracted from the Chinese annals (156 p. plus lithographed atlas, London 1871).

Incidentally, the Chinese were the first to observe that the comets point their tails away from the sun. There is in the T'ang annals a statement relative to a comet observed in 837, March 22 and following days: "In general, when the comet appears in the morning it is directed toward the West, when it appears in the evening it is directed toward the East. That is a constant rule." Edouard Biot: Sur la direction de la queue des comètes (C. R., Acad. des sciences 16, 751, 1843). The first to state with words and illustrations, not only that the tail of the comet points away from the sun, but that its direction coincides with the radius vector, was Peter Apian in 1532. A. Pogo (Isis 20, 443-46, 1934). The Chinese name for a comet is broom star, "sui hsing" or "sao chou hsing."

For sunspots, John Williams: Chinese observations of solar spots (Monthly notices of the Royal Astronomical Society 33, 370-75, 1873), 45 observations ranging from 301 to 1215, taken from Ma Tuan-lin (XIII-2); many dates are badly reduced to our calendar. Alexander Hosie: Sunspots and sun shadows observed in China B.C. 28—A.D. 1617 (Journal of the North China branch, Royal Asiatic Society, 12, 91-95, 1878). Joseph de Moidrey: Observations anciennes de taches solaires en Chine (Bulletin astronomique vol. 21, 11 p., 1904), 84 observations ranging from B.C. 28 to A.D. 1638.

For meteors and meteorites, Abel Rémusat: Observations chinoises et japonaises sur la chute des corps météoriques, 1819 (in his Mélanges asiatiques 1, 184-208, 1825). Edouard Biot: Catalogue général des étoiles filantes et des autres météores observés en Chine pendant vingt quatre siècles, depuis le VIIe avant J. C. jusqu'au milieu du XVIIe (Mémoires présentés . . . à l'Académie des sciences 10, 129-352, 1848); Note supplémentaire (ibid. p. 415-22).

G. *Korea*

Much astronomical work was undertaken by the Li dynasty soon after its beginning in 1392. New calendars and tables were compiled in 1394, and a celestial planisphere was completed in 1395 and engraved on stone. Copies of that monument have come down to us, and we are thus in a good position to evaluate Korean knowledge of the stars at the end of the fourteenth century. The map of 1395 was not based upon new observations, but slavishly derived from early Chinese models.

VII. PHYSICS, TECHNOLOGY, AND MUSIC

The same order is followed as in section VII of chapter I. That is, the items gathered under this general heading are not classified along geographical or political lines, but according to subjects.

Mining and metallurgy will be dealt with in the geological paragraphs in section X below.

The twelve parts of this section are as follows: (1) Optics and optical meteorology. (2) Weights and measures. (3) Magnetism. (4) Mechanical clocks. (5) Arms and armor; dinanderie. (6) Printing. (7) Hydrostatics. (8) Canals. (9) Mechanical theories. (10) Discussions concerning the vacuum. (11) Technical improvements and their social impact. (12) Musical theories.

1. *Optics and Optical Meteorology*

Optical and meteorological questions continued to be discussed by every commentator. They crop out everywhere, and a complete list of the scholars discussing them incidentally would be long and of little use. Every scientific book included such questions. Take, for example, the Problemata ascribed to Aristotle;[1] the majority of the problems are physiological or medical, yet some deal with meteorologic topics (such as winds, thunder) or optical ones (rainbows and halos) These Aristotelian problems opened a tradition of "queries and answers" which can be traced throughout the centuries in every language of the West—Greek, Arabic, Hebrew, Latin, etc. Futile as many of the queries may seem to us, they were nevertheless one of the main springs of physical thinking. The futility of a question, by the way, can only be determined after long investigations; or, to put it otherwise, wise, pertinent questions can only be asked by men of great experience; when one is finally able to ask the right question, it is already half answered.

To return to meteorology and optics, the main student of it in Italy was Biagio Pelacani of Parma, who wrote a commentary on the Perspectiva communis of John Peckham, so elaborate that it exceeded the original work in length. He tried to explain some optical phaenomena by the reflection of light from the clouds.

Similar habits of speculation were cultivated in Germany by Themon son of the Jew, and Nicholas of Dinkelsbühl, and in England by Henry Knighton and Simon Tunsted.

Themon wrote a commentary on the Meteorologica, speculating on the nature of vision and discussing the rainbow as thoroughly as was possible in his time. The scholastic method of referring to conflicting opinions and putting them all as it were on the same level without choice makes it sometimes difficult, if not impossible, to determine his own conclusions. Nicholas published a commentary on Aristotle's Physics and gave a course in Vienna on the "perspectiva communis." Henry Knighton was not a physicist, but his chronicle contains valuable meteorological observations, and the same tendencies appear in the work of his anonymous continuer (to 1395). Of course, almost every chronicle would contain some meteorological remarks, but these would generally be restricted to phaenomena of practical importance (e.g., severe winters, droughts), whereas Henry and his continuer refer to such things as northern lights (?) and a "rain of blood." A commentary on the Meteorologica has been ascribed to the musician Simon Tunsted; it is comparable to the commentaries of Themon and Oresme.

Many studies have been devoted to the early printed almanacs containing the kind of meteorological information which may still be found in the "farmer's almanacs" of today. It is true these studies are largely restricted to external bibliography, no attempt being made to appraise the contents. The incunabula calendars are partly derived from the astrological literature of the thirteenth and fourteenth centuries.

[1] The Problemata are of Peripatetic origin but with many later accretions; it may be that the text as we have it was not completed until the fifth century or even the sixth. In the fourteenth century, it was available to Western scholars, Moses ibn Tibbon (XIII-2) having translated it from Arabic into Hebrew, Bartholomew of Messina (XIII-2) from Greek into Latin, and Evrard de Conty from Latin into French.

Gustav Hellmann: Wetterprognosen und Wetterberichte des XV. und XVI. Jahrhunderts. Facsimiledrucke mit einer Einleitung (Berlin 1899); Die Wettervorhersage im ausgehenden Mittelalter, XII bis XV. Jahrh. (Beiträge zur Geschichte der Meteorologie no. 8, 169–229, Berlin 1917; Isis 4, 185); Über den Ursprung der volkstümlichen Wetterregeln, "Bauernregeln" (Sitzungsberichte der K. preussischen Akad. der Wissenschaften, phys. Kl., p. 148–70, 1923; Isis 9, 586); Zur Geschichte der Wettervorhersage in Kalendern (Archiv für Geschichte der Mathematik 10, 291–93, 1927; Isis 11, 193). Gustav Hellmann (1854–1939), who was the outstanding student of the history of meteorology, wrote a good many other studies on the subject, the list of which from 1883 to 1922 was published at the end of his Beiträge (3, 99–102, Berlin 1922); additional bibliographies to 1935 were kindly compiled for me by the Reichsamt für Wetterdienst in Berlin (1937) and by the Weather Bureau in Washington (1937), but it has not yet been possible to publish them.

In addition to Hellmann's studies, see Paul Heitz and Konrad Haebler: Hundert Kalender-Inkunabeln (40 p., 103 pl., Strassburg 1905). Wilhelm Hess: Himmels- und Naturerscheinungen in Einblattdrucken des XV. bis XVIII. Jahrhunderts (114 p., 30 fig., Leipzig 1911). Eustace F. Bosanquet: Early printed almanacks and prognostications (Bibliographical Society, London 1917); the earliest English almanac was printed in 1492. Le grant Kalendrier et compost des Bergiers (Paris 1925; Isis 8, 354–55). P. Saintyves: L'astrologie populaire étudiée spécialement dans les doctrines et les traditions relatives à l'influence de la lune (464 p., Paris 1937; Isis 30, 387).

For further comparison with later American conditions, George Lyman Kittredge: The Old Farmer and his Almanack (418 p., Boston 1904; reprinted Harvard University 1920).

2. *Weights and Measures*

Metrological information may be derived from the chronicle written by the Nuremberg patrician Ulman Stromer.

Isaac Alḥadib is said to have written a treatise on Biblical weights and measures. Unfortunately, that treatise is lost.

3. *Magnetism*

It is possible that some knowledge of magnetic declination was more common by the end of the century than was formerly assumed. Intelligent sailors must have noticed that their compass did not point to the true north, which they could determine at night, but even if they noticed that discrepancy they were not prepared to publish it, because they were too ignorant or too inarticulate, or they preferred to keep the knowledge for themselves. It has been suggested that the Vikings had such knowledge; this is plausible but not proved.[2]

It has even been suggested, on the basis of a line in the Parlement of foules, that Chaucer was aware of the declination. This seems less plausible. It would be strange indeed if Chaucer were the only contemporary writer to refer to it.

4. *Mechanical Clocks*

Town clocks and other monumental clocks became more frequent in this period. We have good descriptions of many, and, what is even more convincing, at least three clock mechanisms have come down to us.

[2] Heinrich Winter: Die Nautik der Wikinger und ihre Bedeutung für die Entwicklung der europäischen Seefahrt (Hansische Geschichtsblätter 62, 173–84, 1937; Isis 30, 165).

This invention, important as it was from the mechanical point of view, was even more so from the social one, for the mechanical clocks introduced equal hours instead of the unequal ones, and helped to replace the religious government of the day by a lay one.

The dials of those early clocks were generally divided into 24 parts. Smaller clocks for use in a chamber were not made before the following century, and pocket watches not before the sixteenth century.

Many of the early clockmakers are known to us, the most illustrious being Giacomo de' Dondi (nicknamed Giacomo dall' Orologio) and his son Giovanni. Giacomo had built a clock for the Carrara palace at Padua in 1344; Giovanni devised a more elaborate clock and completed it twenty years later for the Visconti castle in Pavia. Moreover, he wrote a full account of it, explaining how to build similar clocks (and orreries). Another description of a contemporary clock may be found in the Traité de cosmographie of Jean Fusoris.

5. *Arms and Armor; Dinanderie*

A great many cannon, some of which were of considerable size, were made in the second half of the fourteenth century, not only on the Continent but also in England. These early firearms were not very efficient, but their founding occupied a large number of artisans in many countries. The activities of these craftsmen were extended to the making of other weapons and also of instruments used for offensive or defensive purposes. A military technology, essentially different from the ancient one, was now steadily developing. The best witness of this is the existence of a number of special treatises, the earliest of which was begun in 1395 by Konrad Kyeser of Franconia and was followed in the fifteenth and sixteenth centuries by many others. Bearing in mind the fact that the majority of military engineers and craftsmen were inarticulate or secretive, each author of such a treatise represents hundreds of companions who could not or did not write.

The early firearms were not yet sufficient to destroy the usefulness of body armor; on the contrary, the golden age of Western armor was being ushered in in this very period when so many and such big guns were produced everywhere. The study of armor is facilitated not only by many monuments illustrating it, but also by a not inconsiderable number of contemporary specimens of very fine workmanship. The richest trove of armor was found recently in Gothland, when some twelve hundred bodies of soldiers, killed in the battle of Visby, 1361, were excavated.

Gunsmiths, harquebushers, and makers of armor increased materially the knowledge of metalwork and encouraged the development of other crafts involving the use of metals. Magnificent specimens of brass and copper work ("dinanderie") dating from this time are extant to this day, and speak loudly for the technical lore as well as for the artistic taste of their creators.

6. *Printing*

Printing was continued on a large scale in China, Korea, and Japan. Though typography had been invented, it was hardly used before the fifteenth century, as the enormous fonts needed to print analphabetic scripts destroyed the economic value of the invention. Typography must have been to scholars of the Far East a kind of curiosity, but the engraving of texts on wooden plates was far more convenient, especially for the texts in which they were interested, not ephemeral ones, but standard religious and philosophic texts which it should be as easy as possible to reprint at any time ne varietur. Putting this in a paradoxical form, it is as if the Chinese had jumped immediately to the stereotypic stage without stopping long at the typographic one.

Xylography was discovered independently in the West in the last quarter of the fourteenth century, but it did not develop very much as far as the printing of texts (vs. images) was concerned. While the Chinese were printing whole libraries from blocks, the Christians used blocks only for illustrations and relatively short texts. There is no xylographic literature to speak of; Western printing may be said to have really begun with the Western rediscovery of typography in the second quarter of the fifteenth century. Once discovered, printing developed with a constantly accelerated speed in the second half of that century, but even so, fewer words or pages had probably been printed in Europe before 1500 than had been printed in the Far East many centuries earlier.

7. *Hydrostatics*

The Archimedean tradition was continued feebly by Biagio Pelacani of Parma, who resurrected the idea of the areometer of constant weight. For a material addition to Archimedean hydrostatics one has to wait for Giambattista Benedetti, 1585, and especially for Simon Stevin, 1586 (Sarton p. 276–78, 1934).

8. *Canals*

Nothing to add to chapter I, section VII, p. 145, and chapter VII, section 8, p. 735.

8 bis. *Metallurgy and Mining*

Mining is so closely connected with geology, and metallurgy with mining, that these two topics will find a more appropriate place in chapter XXIV (or section X of chapter XV), dealing with natural history.

9. *Mechanical Theories*

The main centers of mechanical speculation in the first half of the fourteenth century were Merton College in Oxford and the University of Paris. In the second half of the century, Merton mechanics was discussed by William Heytesbury, but by him alone. The Parisian school of mechanicians continued to flourish for a time, but the controversies and enmities caused by the Great Schism drove some of the best scholars away to Germany. Thus was Parisian mechanics transplanted into other universities, chiefly Vienna and Heidelberg. Many examples can be found in the annals of science which prove that the development of ideas is favored by their transplantation. In this case, however, the problems to be solved were too difficult in spite of their apparent simplicity, and the transplantation did not suddenly bring favorable mutations into being. Instead of that, mechanical problems would still have to germinate for more than two and a half centuries before it would become possible to formulate them with sufficient clearness.

The main protagonists were now Nicole Oresme, Albert of Saxony, and Marsilius van Inghen, all members for a time of the University of Paris. This illustrates well the cosmopolitanism of that university, for Nicole was a Frenchman, Albert a German, and Marsilius a Dutchman.

Oresme had made a deep study of Aristotelian mechanics and had digested the new views on impetus explained by Peter Olivi. His presentation of these views and of the fluxus formae, though it was still too obscure to be convincing, brought one a little nearer to the Galilean revolution. One of his most pregnant remarks was to the effect that gravitation can be conceived without postulating the existence of a fixed center of attraction coincident with the center of the universe. Oresme and Albert of Saxony continued Buridan's meditations on the accelerated speed of falling bodies. Albert could not decide whether the speed was proportional to the time or to the space; it is significant that he considered both possibilities, though he ended by rejecting them. In this case, again we witness as it were the embryological development of Galileo's discovery of the law of falling bodies (published by him only in 1638). Jean Buridan and Albert of Saxony tended to assimilate celestial to sublunar mechanics, and thus were dealing a new blow to Aristotelian prejudices. Albert explained the new points of view in Vienna, and Marsilius discussed them in Heidelberg. These acute minds suffered from the same weakness: they had no idea of submitting their theories to experiment. A few experiments had already been devised before their time, e.g. by Peter the Stranger (XIII-2), but these were accidental; the experimental method was not understood (Introd. **2**, 94). The inhibition was a purely mental one; the experiments finally conceived by Stevin and Galileo were so simple that they could have been instituted in Oresme's time as well as in their own.

It is remarkable that at this stage the gestation of the new mechanics took place chiefly in northern places—Oxford, Paris, Vienna, Heidelberg. The only southern scholars who were sharing in the work at this time were Giovanni da Casale and Biagio Pelacani; no definite contributions can be ascribed to them, but they helped to transmit the new ideas to the Italian mechanicians of the fifteenth and sixteenth centuries, Giovanni Battista Capuano of Manfredonia (fl. 1475), Alessandro Achillini of Bologna (1463–1512), Leonardo da Vinci (1452–1519), Agostino Nifo (1473–1538), Niccolò Tartaglia of Brescia (1506–59), Girolamo Cardano of Pavia (1501–76), Alessandro Piccolomini of Siena (1508–78), Giovanni Battista Benedetti of Venice (1530–90), Guido Ubaldo del Monte of Pesaro (1545–1607), Bernardino Baldi of Urbino (1553–1617). This long enumeration has been given to show that the new mechanics, if it was born in the north, owed much eventually to Italian genius. This helps to explain Galileo, but it does not explain Stevin. "The wind bloweth where it listeth."

10. *Discussions Concerning the Vacuum*

The horror vacui dominated the second half of the century even more completely than the first, for the most independent spirit in that respect, Walter Burley, did not live long after 1337. Even for a man as original as Marsilius van Inghen the Aristotelian impossibility of a vacuum was still an uncontrovertible dogma. We may assume that almost every one of his contemporaries shared that prejudice; I can name only one who did not, Albert of Saxony, and perhaps a second, Heinrich von Langenstein. As long, however, as a vacuum could not be created experimentally, it was permissible to deny its possibility; the experimental creation was not effected until 1641 and 1654 (by Otto von Guericke).

11. *Technical Improvements and Their Social Impact*

No technical improvements of importance can be definitely assigned to this period, that is, none occurs to us, but information concerning labor conditions could be derived from the books on guilds cited in section VII of chapter I.

A curious document illustrating labor conditions is preserved in the town library of Nuremberg. It is the Hausbuch der Mendelschen Zwölfbrüderstiftung. A citizen of Nuremberg, Konrad Mendel, created in 1388 an asylum for twelve old workmen. It was not a hospital; the men accepted were in tolerably good health and able to continue their work as much as their age permitted. Volume 1 of the Hausbuch contains the portrait of every brother at his work, 333 illustrations, and reaches the year 1549. Unfortunately, the beginning of the MS, which included portraits of four brethren, and very probably those of the founder and his wife, is lost. It was only with the ninety-eighth brother that the habit of adding his death date was introduced; that brother died in 1426. The preceding portraits relate to workmen who died earlier. We have thus a good collection of portraits of artisans of the end of the fourteenth century, represented each one in his peculiar costume and with the tools of his craft, some of which he is actually using.

Friedrich Bock: Deutsches Handwerk im Mittelalter (36 ill., text p. 38-48, Leipzig 1936). Ernst Mummenhoff: Der Handwerker in der deutschen Vergangenheit (Monographien zur deutschen Kulturgeschichte no. 8, 142 p., 151 fig., Leipzig 1901). Feldhaus (p. 702, 1914); many portraits are used in his book to illustrate the articles entitled Bohrapparate, Draht, Drehstuhl, Feile, Fingerhut, Pumpe 11, Seiler. Other illustrations have been used by the same author in Geschichtsblätter für Technik (vol. 5, pl. 6, 1918; vol. 6, 160, 1919). See also his study Alte Nürnberger Apotheker- und Wundarzt-Porträts (AGM 12, 78-81, 1920).

12. *Musical Theories*

Music in the Latin West

The musical movement which was already in full swing before the middle of the century continued with increasing vigor. Whether the French were the true initiators or not, their contributions were particularly important. Guillaume de Machaut lived until 1377. His masterpiece, a mass in four voices, was written for the coronation of Charles V at Reims in 1364. Assuming that the ascription and date are correct (there are difficulties involved which have not yet been completely solved), that mass is a definite landmark in the history of music.

The main defender of the new art in Italy was the Florentine Francesco Landino, organist in San Lorenzo. Landino was simply a practical musician, a composer and player, a representative of the musica instrumentis constituta (the third kind of music according to Boetius, but the best kind to us). For Italian treatises on the theory of music we have to wait until the beginning of the new century, when the mathematician Prosdocimo de' Beldomandi wrote a whole series of them (1403-13). Prosdocimo discussed mensural music, monochord divisions, etc. One of his treatises, dated 1404, was a commentary on Jean de Meurs; another, dated 1420, a violent attack against his fellow townsman Marchetto (they were both Paduans).

The main musicologists of this period were Englishmen: Simon Tunsted, Theinred, and Thomas Walsingham. The first was a Franciscan, the two others Benedictines; Simon and Thomas were Norfolkers, Theinred came from Kent, at any rate he flourished in Dover. One of the best contemporary treatises, the De quattuor principalibus musices, is ascribed to Simon Tunsted (and our listing him here is justified only if that assumption is correct). The author of the Quattuor principalia (1351), whoever he was, expressed his deep admiration for Philip of Vitry. Theinred composed in 1371 the De legitimis ordinibus pentachordorum et tetrachordorum, and Thomas Walsingham wrote the Regulae de figuris compositis, wherein he stated that notes should not be divided beyond the minim.

The increasing popularity of music is proved by abundant literary references, e.g. in the Decamerone and the Canterbury tales, and by incidental remarks of annalists and historians such as Froissart. The coronation of Charles VI (1380) was a musical event, even as that of his predecessor, Charles V (1364). Other monarchs such as Edward III of England (ruled 1327–77) and Joan I of Aragon (ruled 1387–95) appreciated the beauty and the political value of music. By the end of the century music was becoming an essential part of every ceremonial, public or private. In addition to the musical doctors and to the musicians attached to the courts, there were many minstrels in the cities, and many more were roaming through the country, from manor to manor, or from kermis to village fair. So numerous were they that they had realized the necessity of organizing themselves. The earliest guild of musicians was the Nicolaibruderschaft of Vienna, established as early as 1288 (that is, 654 years before the unionization of the Symphony Orchestra of Boston); then followed the company of trumpeters of Lucca and the Confrérie de St. Julien des ménétriers in Paris (1331),[3] which was important enough to have its own hospital.

More information of this kind may be found in the histories of music, e.g. in Gérold (1936), Reese (1940), or Láng (1941). Of course, our readers are concerned chiefly with the theory of music, but theory and practice cannot be separated very long, and their evolutions are necessarily mingled.

Before passing to the East, reference may be made to the "acoustic vases," fourteenth-century examples of which are found in various countries of Western Europe and also in Cyprus. The idea was Greek or Roman, but mediaeval architects gave it a new try.

Music in Islām

The elaboration of musical theory had reached its climax in the work of Ṣafī al-dīn 'Abd al-Mu'min (XIII-2). A century later the outstanding musician was the Persian 'Abd al-Qādir ibn Ghaibī, who lived until 1435. 'Abd al-Qādir was not only a famous theorist, but also a distinguished composer and player who flourished at the Jalāir (Mongol) court of Persia, then at the courts of Bāyazīd and Tīmūr. His theoretical writings belong to the end of his life, that is, to the fifteenth century, but they may be considered as representing fourteenth-century thought.

Other musical treatises were written by the mathematician 'Abdallāh ibn Khalīl al-Māridīnī and by the philosopher al-Jurjānī. All these treatises were written in Arabic.

The musical theorists of this century were apparently all Easterners. Of course, this does not mean that music was not studied in Andalusia and North Africa; in all probability it was, but the books which have come down to us were composed exclusively in the eastern part of the Dār al-Islām.

VIII. CHEMISTRY

It is not necessary to continue the discussion, outlined in section VIII of chapter I, of a number of topics, such as alchemical traditions, colors, glass, paper, chemical substances, because that discussion was sufficient for general orientation. The reader will easily add to it the few relevant items relative to the second half of the fourteenth century. We may thus begin immediately with the consideration of the

[3] Láng (p. 166, 1941).

work done in various parts of the world: (A) Christendom, (B) Islām, (C) India, and (D) China.

A. *Christendom*

The information gathered in this volume may be subdivided under six headings: (1) Catalonia, (2) Italy, (3) France, (4) England, (5) Germany, (6) Russia.

A1. *Catalonia*

The Catalan group (assuming that every member of it is truly a Catalan) consists of three monks belonging respectively to the Franciscan, Dominican, and Carmelite orders. The first, John of Rupescissa, was a gray friar. He was also known as Jean de Roquetaillade and may have been of French origin; he certainly spent the best part of his life in the monasteries and the monastic prisons of southern France. He wrote at least two books dealing with alchemy and alchemical medicine, in the occult Lullian manner. Ramon de Tárrega was a black friar, and many of the Lullian alchemical writings were ascribed to him; like John he was persecuted and imprisoned. We do not know whether John died in prison in 1356, or later out of it, but Ramon actually died in the cell in which he had been detained pending judgment of his heresies, in Barcelona 1371. The third, Guillem Sedacer, was a white friar. He was the author of at least one alchemical treatise, named after him the Summa sedacina, and possibly of a second. That treatise is also of the occult type and very learned. Guillem was apparently well acquainted with the alchemical traditions, as far as these were available in Latin (and by that time not only had the bulk of the alchemical writings, whether Greek or Arabic, been translated into Latin, but many new treatises had already been composed in that language). A good deal of alchemical syncretism had been achieved. It has been pointed out before that contemporary Byzantine alchemy was substantially of the same kind as the Latin, and the Sedacina is very close to an anonymous Greek text, περὶ μεταλλικῆς τέχνης, probably a little anterior. This is easily accounted for by borrowings from the same (Arabic) sources. The alchemical purposes of the Lullian school, to which these three men belonged, were not only the transmutation of base metals into noble ones, but also the conservation of health and youth. These alchemists were not concerned so much with finding the truth as with gratifying the elemental desires of mankind, the obtaining of money, health, and longevity, or with alleviating their constant and irrepressible fears of poverty, sickness, and death. This does not mean that they were deceitful or insincere, but their minds lacked clearness and vigor, and they indulged, as so many other men had done before or would do later, in wishful thinking.

The alchemical treatises of these three friars were all written in Latin. We should still mention an anonymous one entitled Phoenix,[1] which was probably written after their death yet before the end of the century, for it was dedicated in 1399 to Martin I the Humane, king of Aragon (1395–1410) and count of Catalonia. It is divided into 11 chapters and belongs to the same occult and meaningless group as the treatises of the three friars. It has been ascribed without proof to Blasius of Barcelona, physician to the same king, to whom he dedicated a plague

[1] Tractatus compositus super lapidem philosophorum . . . ; Liber fenicis; Phenix vocor ego moriens. . . . Unpublished. See Thorndike (3, 637, 1934).

treatise in 1406. This Blasius may have been a Catalan, but we do not know; he flourished in Toulouse, Montpellier, and Sicily, as well as in Barcelona.[2]

Another Catalan friar, a black one like Ramon, realized the religious dangers of such thinking and prosecuted the alchemists of his day with the same energy which he used in prosecuting other heretics. This was the famous inquisitor Nicholas Eymeric. Disregarding for the nonce the inquisitorial methods, he was certainly right in his estimate of alchemical purposes, which did not tally with Christian dogmas or Christian morality. Many Christians of that time (and later), however, did not see those discrepancies, being willfully or unwillfully blind to them. It is significant that the leaders of alchemical thought in Catalonia were monks.

A2. *Italy*

Thomas de Pisan exchanged alchemical letters with one Bernard of Treves. Since he was primarily an astrologer, it is not surprising to find him dabbling in alchemy, nor could we expect his alchemical thinking to be on a higher level than his astrological thinking. In spite of his initial success in Bologna, his fame was gained abroad in the service of the French kings. We may thus leave him out of the Italian picture, and if we do so, we find the Italian group very different from the Catalan. The latter was chiefly Lullian, that is, fantastic; the former was technical, practical, and thus rational. The man who tries to solve simple practical problems (such as, how to give a definite color to an object) is obliged to use rational methods; he cannot explain the need away with fantastic suggestions. Either he succeeds or he does not, and his success cannot be repeated without acceptance of some kind of scientific discipline. His recipes must work, or else they are soon disregarded and rejected.

The two Italians to be considered did not accomplish their task until the fifteenth century, but they flourished and let it mature in the fourteenth. Cennino Cennini[3] was a painter to whom his master Agnolo Gaddi, son and pupil of Taddeo Gaddi of Florence, had handed down the glorious tradition of Giotto. According to Cennino himself, Giotto it was "who had changed the art of painting from Greek into Latin and modernized it."[4] He completed in or before 1437 his Libro dell' arte, which is a rich collection of recipes, not only for ordinary drawing and painting, but for painting on diverse surfaces (mosaic, glass, etc.) and for various other techniques. Another collection of recipes relative to painting and other crafts was completed in Paris 1411 by John Alcherius.[5] In a way it continued the tradition of earlier collections, such as the Compositiones ad tingenda (VIII-2), the Mappae clavicula (VIII-2), Heraclius (X-2), Theophilus (XII-1), Peter of Saint Omer (XIII-2). That could not be otherwise, most recipes being handed down continuously by each craftsman to his apprentices. Many of Alcherius' recipes, however, were not

[2] This Blasius is not mentioned by Rubió i Lluch (1908–21). Dorothea Waley Singer: Some plague tractates (p. 31, London 1916). K. Sudhoff: Die Pestschrift des Blasius Brascinonensis 1406 (Pestschriften no. 273; AGM 17, 103–19, 1925).

[3] Cennino di Drea (= son of Andrea) was born in Colle di Val d'Elsa (Siena) c. 1360; died at Padua 1440.

[4] "Il quale Giotto rimutò l'arte del dipignere di greco in latino, e ridusse al moderno" (ch. 1 of Cennino's Libro dell'arte).

[5] Alcherius or Alcerius, Archerius, Algerius. Flourished c. 1382–1411 in Milano, Paris, Bologna, Venice. I call him Italian; he may have been French. Most of his recipes were written in Latin, some in French or Italian. Cennino wrote only in Italian.

taken down from earlier books, but dictated to him by artists. Thus, in Milan 1382, Alberto Porzello gave him a recipe for making ink; in Paris 1398, Jacob Cona, a Flemish (?) painter, dictated to him the treatise De coloribus diversis modis, on limning and gilding; a few weeks later another similar treatise was dictated to him by Antonio de Compendio, limner; some 88 recipes dealing with painting, limning, working in metals, hardening iron, etc. were obtained from Fra Dionisio, a Servite in Milan 1409; in 1410, Master Johannes, a Norman, showed him how to prepare ultramarine; in Bologna 1410, Theodore, a Flemish embroiderer, taught him how to prepare and use dyes; in the same year Giovanni da Modena, then living in Bologna, lent him a book containing recipes of colors and mordants for laying on gold; in Venice 1410, Michelino di Vesuccio gave him another ultramarine recipe. This enumeration of Alcherius' new sources has been given because it is not too long, yet typical.

Text. The Trattato della pittura of Cennino was first edited by Giuseppe Tambroni (224 p., Roma 1821). That first edition, dedicated to a Danish royal prince, was incomplete and inaccurate. A better edition under the title Il libro dell'arte was prepared by Gaetano and Carlo Milanesi (240 p., Firenze 1859).

The first English translation, by Mary Philadelphia Merrifield: A treatise on painting written by Cennino Cennini in 1437 . . . (250 p., 9 pl., London 1844), and the French translation, by Victor Mottez: Le livre de l'art (230 p., Paris 1858), were derived from Tambroni's imperfect edition.

The Milanesi text was translated into German by Albert Ilg: Das Buch von der Kunst (Quellenschriften für Kunstgeschichte 1, 212 p., Wien 1871); into English, by Lady Christiana J. Herringham: The book of the art (London 1899; reprinted 1922); into German, by Willibrord Verkade: Handbüchlein der Kunst (Strassburg 1916).

Two critical editions of the Italian text, based on the MSS, have been prepared by Renzo Simi: Il Libro dell'arte. Edizione riveduta e corretta sui codici (144 p., Lanciano 1913) and recently by Daniel V. Thompson, Jr.: Il Libro dell'arte (148 p., 3 pl., Yale University, New Haven 1932). The latter has prepared also a new English translation (172 p., Yale University 1933; reprinted 1936).

Alcherius' collection was edited by Mrs. Merrifield: Original treatises of the arts of painting (1, 1–321, London 1849).

Criticism. Arthur Pillans Laurie: The materials of the painter's craft (London 1910). D. V. Thompson (1936).

To return to the texts, there is a great literary difference between them, for Alcherius was simply a compiler who tried to build up a large collection of recipes, copied them as he found them, in prose or verse, and did not even bother to reduce them to a single language, that is, to translate into Latin the non-Latin recipes. On the contrary, Il libro dell'arte was written completely in Italian, and Cennino did not simply compile it; he composed it, and though his literary efforts were sometimes clumsy, they are very touching. Just consider how he broaches the subject: "Here begins the Book of the Art. Made and composed by Cennino da Colle, in the reverence of God, and of the Virgin Mary, and of St. Eustachius, and of St. Francis, and of St. John the Baptist, and of St. Anthony of Padua, and generally of all the saints of God, and in the reverence of Giotto, of Taddeo, and of Agnolo the master of Cennino, and for the utility and good and advantage of those who would attain perfection in the art"; and before proceeding to the recipes he explains the moral basis of the art and the importance of pursuing it in a noble spirit. Let me quote a few more lines: "There are some who follow the arts from poverty and necessity, also for gain, and for love of the art; but those who pursue them from love of the art and true nobleness of mind are to be commended above all others. Now then, you of noble mind, who are lovers of this good, come at once to art and adorn yourselves with this vesture,—namely, love, reverence, obedience, and perseverance. And as soon as thou canst, begin to put thyself under the guidance of the master to learn, and delay as long as thou mayest thy parting from the master."[6]

Note on early maiòlica. The making of maiòlica or faïence attained considerable popularity in Italy in the fourteenth and fifteenth centuries and even more so in the sixteenth. The very names given to glazed earthenware betray the Italian origin, for faïence is a French word derived from the Italian town Faenza (Ravenna district); maiòlica (Eng. majolica) is Italian, derived from the Italian name (Majorica) of the Balearic island Majorca. This implies a Spanish origin behind the Italian one.

Let us recapitulate the story. The application of glaze to pottery is very ancient; it goes back to Egypt and the ancient Near East, though strangely enough it was seldom practiced by the Greek artists in terra cotta. The use of glazes implies a good amount of chemical knowledge: "All faïence glaze consists essentially of silicic acid in the form of quartz sand, which is combined with a flux as an aid to fusion; on the nature of this flux depend the different kinds of glaze which determine different kinds of faïence" (Hannover 1, 49, 1925). Early Egyptians used an alkaline flux for thousands of years, knew how to color it with metallic oxides and also how to control the appearance by various methods of firing. Alkaline glazes were hardly used outside of Egypt or the Near East. Lead glazes were also invented in the East and spread considerably East and West, but were not fully developed until Islamic times. Tin glazes, of great importance in faïence technique, are also very ancient. There seems, however, to be a gap between ancient faïence and the mediaeval Islamic kind, as if the art had been lost and then after a long time rediscovered.

As to Islamic wares, we have a very valuable written document, the Persian treatise composed in Tabrīz 1300 by 'Abdallāh ibn 'Alī al-Kāshānī (XIV-1). Eastern Muslims seem to have invented the "luster" technique, i.e., the employment of iridescent metallic pigments; the disapproval of the use of precious metals by Muslim puritans may have stimulated the invention, it certainly helped its early and wide distribution. In the twelfth century lusterwares were already spread throughout the Dār al-Islām, and some examples found their way to Christian Europe. The art was admirably developed by the Moors of Spain (Hispano-Moresque faïence), and from Muslim Spain specimens of it could easily be carried to Christian Spain and other parts of Christendom. According to al-Idrīsī (XII-2), lusterware was made in Calatayud (prov. Zaragoza), which was then a Christian city, having been reconquered in 1120 by Alfonso I of Aragón. The main center of production in the fourteenth century, however, was still in Muslim Spain, chiefly in Malaga (Mālaqa; conquered only in 1487, by Ferdinand and Isabella). Admirable examples of Malaga fourteenth-century ware exist in the Alhambra of Granada, the Hermitage of Leningrad, in Palermo, Stockholm, etc. From Malaga the art spread to Italy, probably via the Baleares, hence the name maiòlica.

[6] The two quotations are borrowed from Lady Herringham's translation (p. 3, 6, 1899).

The Moors developed considerably not only the Eastern use of faïence vessels, but also the Eastern use of faïence tiles. Tiles were an essential part of Muslim architecture (outside and inside), later of Moorish architecture, finally of Christian Spanish and Portuguese architecture. The Spaniards learned to say of a poor man, "no hará casa con azulejos" (he will never get a house with tiles, meaning he will never get rich).[7]

It was long believed that Italian maiòlica began with maestro Giorgio Andreoli of Pavia (established in 1485 in Gubbio), his brothers Giovanni and Salimbene, and his son Vincenzo (maestro Cencio), or that it began with Luca della Ròbbia of Florence (1399–1482), his nephew Andrea (1435–1528), and the latter's sons, Giovanni, Gerolamo, and Luca. That belief rested on misunderstandings. The Andreoli were painters of maiòlica, and the Della Ròbbia were sculptors. The latter invented the art of creating "figure vetriate," majolica sculpture; the former developed majolica painting.

The technical knowledge ad hoc existed in Italy, witness the Pretiosa margarita novella of Pietro Buono (XIV-1) of Ferrara, wherein tin enamels are mentioned, and the early treatises edited by Gaetano Milanesi: Dell'arte del vetro per musaico. Tre trattatelli (Scelta di curiosità letterarie vol. 51, 200 p., Bologna 1864). Two of these treatises date from the end of the fourteenth century or beginning of the fifteenth, the third from 1443. They contain much experimental knowledge concerning colored glasses and glazes, e.g. with reference to gold luster effects.[8] The reality of that knowledge has since been confirmed by the discovery of specimens of Italian maiòlica anterior to the fifteenth century. For example, in the Victoria and Albert Museum there are such specimens dug up at Orvieto, Faenza, Florence, Ravenna (Rackham 1940).

The albarello[9] vases so popular in Italy from the early days of maiòlica trade are probably of Oriental (Persian) origin via Spain.

Select references. Emile Molinier: La céramique italienne au XVe siècle (98 p., Paris 1888). Henry Wallis: The Oriental influence on the ceramic art of the Italian Renaissance (80 p., London 1900); The art of the precursors (99 p., London 1901). Marc Louis Solon: History and description of Italian majolica (224 p., 49 fig., 23 pl., London 1907). Wilhelm Bode: Die Anfänge der Majolikakunst in Toskana (38 p., 37 pl., Berlin 1911). Emil Hannover (1864–1923): Keramisk haandbog (3 vols., ill., Copenhagen 1919–24); translated into English under the title Pottery and porcelain, with notes by Bernard Rackham (3 vols., London 1925; 1, 13–109).[10] Seymour de Ricci: Catalogue of early Italian majolica in the collection of Mortimer L. Schiff (New York 1927). Gaetano Ballardini: Corpus della maiolica italiana. I. Le maioliche datate fino al 1530 (Roma 1933). Bernard Rackham: Catalogue of Italian maiolica (2 vols., Victoria and Albert Museum, London 1940).

This artistic digression may seem to have taken the reader a long way off from chemistry, but it has not. One cannot insist too much on the fact that the arts

[7] For a curious use of tiles in Portugal, see Sarton: Les azulejos géométriques de Coimbra (Isis 24, 106–7, 1 fig., 1935).

[8] Wilhelm Ganzenmüller: Ein italienisches Goldlüsterrezept vom Ende des 14. Jahrhunderts (Zeitschrift für angewandte Chemie 51, 254–56, 1938).

[9] Italian word albarèllo or alberèllo (Crusca), designating cylindrical vases with concave sides often used as drug jars; later, drug jars of different shapes. The word may be derived from the Persian barnī or baranī, earthen or glass vessel for medicines or confections.

[10] Hannover's book is, I believe, the best book of its size on ceramics. It is a masterpiece of condensation and relative accuracy.

were for many centuries the best source of chemical knowledge, the best and almost the only nursery of the experimental method. In the second place, the chemist might do well to conduct his research in the humble and reverent spirit of Cennino Cennini, and should never think that the recipes, however good, are the whole of science. The recipes and even the theories are insufficient without love.

Of course, the Italian astrologers, jurists, theologians, philosophers, and even the men of letters could not help discussing alchemical questions, for such were questions of the day. For example, the greatest mediaeval commentator on the Divina commedia, Benvenuto di Rambaldi, discussed the alchemical hypothesis apropos of Inferno XXIX. His conclusions represented the moderate point of view; the transmutation of metals may be theoretically possible, but is difficult if not impossible to accomplish here below. Such discussions might be interesting, yet they were essentially futile. No chemical progress could be expected, except from the genuine experiments of honest craftsmen.

A3. *France*

The mysterious Ortolanus wrote various alchemical treatises; his Practica—to be completed a few years later by the Englishman John Dombelay—may have been composed in Paris 1358, and Ortolanus (or Ortolan, Lortholain) may have been a Frenchman, but we do not know. We have to place him somewhere, and we place him here but without conviction. He had apparently made some experiments, but the writings ascribed to him are as diffuse, obscure, and futile as the Lullian ones.

With Nicolas Flamel, we fall back upon solid ground. Though he became a legendary personality, his achievements are tangible enough. He did not find the method of transmutation, but practiced with considerable success the art of transferring gold from the savings boxes of other people to his own. That had nothing to do with alchemy, but people whose imagination was saturated with alchemical nonsense could not think of a better explanation of Flamel's wealth than an alchemical one, and in the course of time a number of alchemical writings were ascribed to him. This was even more fatuous. Alchemical treatises were generally composed by poor devils who, if they could not find a protector, were never sure of the next meal, let alone the transmutation of metals; on the other hand, rich men, then as now, had no time or wish to write books "on how to get rich." Such books are only written by the very people who do not know how.

The poet Jean de La Fontaine,[11] born c. 1381 at Valenciennes in Flanders (that is, he was a fellow townsman of Froissart and Watteau!), wrote in Montpellier 1413 an alchemical poem which he wittily entitled "La fontaine des amoureux de science" (a title which Arabic writers would have appreciated and envied). That poem of about a thousand lines witnesses the popularity of alchemical fancies; its scientific value is negligible. Jean de La Fontaine was mayor of Valenciennes in 1431; nothing else is known about him.[12]

[11] Not to be confused or compared with his namesake, the author of Fables and Contes (1621-95). The early one was a second-rate poet; the later one must be considered one of the very greatest in world literature.

[12] His poem was first published in Paris, Gothic type, undated (early sixteenth cent.). Later editions: Lyon 1547, Paris 1561, Lyon 1571, 1618; Paris 1735 with Roman de la rose; by Achille Genty (95 p., Paris 1861). The editions of 1561 and 1618, entitled La transformation métallique, contain also Les remonstrances de la nature à l'alchymiste errant avec la réponse dudict alchymiste, by Jean de Meung (XIII-2), and Le sommaire philosophique de N. Flamel. These three French poems are followed in the edition of 1561 by a defense of alchemy against

Ortolan, Flamel, and La Fontaine, the three together do not give us a very high idea of French alchemy. It is true one might add to them John of Rupescissa (Jean de la Roquetaillade), whom we counted somewhat arbitrarily as a Catalan, Thomas Pisan, and Alcherius. Pisan became a Frenchman and Alcherius may have been born one. Alcherius' collection was copied in 1431 by a real Frenchman, Jean le Bègue, who contributed fifty more recipes, chemical and medical, all written in French, and a technical glossary, for which he made use of the Catholicon of Giovanni Balbi (XIII-2). This Jean le Bègue was born in 1368, and became a licentiate in the law and notary of the masters of the mint in Paris.[13]

According to White,[14] "Charles V [the Wise, king of France 1364–80] forbade in 1380 the possession of furnaces and apparatus necessary for chemical processes; under this law the chemist, John Barrillon, was thrown into prison, and it was only by the greatest effort that his life was saved. In England, Henry IV, in 1404, issued a similar decree. In Italy, the Republic of Venice, in 1418, followed these examples."

A4. *England*

John Dombelay composed the Stella alchimie in 1384 and two years later wrote a commentary on Ortolanus' Practica, whose mystical tendencies he accentuated in spite of occasional references to experimental efforts.

In one of the Canterbury tales (the Canon's Yeoman's tale) Chaucer wrote an amusing and cutting satire against alchemists. The villain of his story, the "alkamystre" (l. 1204), was a canon regular of St. Augustine; some scholars would identify him with William Shuchirch, a canon of the King's chapel at Windsor (Speculum 16, 103). In any case, Chaucer did not want to hurt the feelings of canons in general, and remarked that there might be a rogue in every monastery, God forbid that all should pay for what one rascal did (l. 992–97). In spite of the church's unmistakable opposition to alchemy, it is not surprising that clerics indulged in it, for their singular ability to read Latin exposed them to temptations from which illiterate people were spared. What interests me most in the story is Chaucer's conviction that alchemists were evil men. No doubt he was not alone in feeling that. By the end of the fourteenth century alchemy was already discredited among knowing people, but such was the intensity of the desire for the goods which alchemists promised—wealth, health, and longevity—that they could always obtain a foothold in some of the best and highest places. The hidden competition between quacks and rascals on the one hand, and honest craftsmen on the other, was destined to continue for three or four centuries before a sufficient amount of chemical light would put an end to it.

I. Girard. I have seen only the editions of 1561 and 1861. German translation, Die Fontina der Liebhaber der hohen Wissenschaft, in Vier nützliche Chymische Tractat vom Stein der Weisen (Halle i.S. 1612).

NBG (28, 767, 1859). Ferguson (1, 433, 1906).

[13] His recipes etc. were edited by Mrs. Merrifield: Original treatises of the art of painting (1, 1–321, London 1849). Vol. 2 of the same work, published in the same year, contains Italian texts of the fifteenth and sixteenth centuries continuing the same tradition, a note on the weights and measures used in these texts (p. 896–98), and an elaborate index.

[14] Andrew Dickson White (1, 391, 1896). I was not able to check White's statements, but they are plausible. Barrillon is completely unknown to me; he is not even mentioned by Chevalier (1907).

An alchemical treatise, De serpente alchemico breviloquium, was composed by Thomas Holcote, said to be a disciple of Chaucer's.

A5. *Germany*

The German group is the largest of all in the West, but that does not mean much, for when two unknown or fabulous men have been weeded out there remain only four deserving full consideration.

John of Livania wrote a treatise against Rupescissa. He was a canon in Treves, and that reminds us that Thomas de Pisan exchanged alchemical letters with an unknown Bernard of Treves (it is true this Bernard might be connected with Treviso as well as with Treves = Trier). The great man of science and philosopher Heinrich von Langenstein, one of the creators of the University of Vienna, expressed moderate opinions concerning alchemical claims and possibilities; there was, he thought, a kernel of truth in alchemy which should be carefully dissociated from magic and quackery, and encouraged. Heinrich was right!

The main alchemical writer in Germany was one Wimandus de Ruffo Clipeo (Rothschild!). The most popular of his works, entitled Gloria mundi, represents alchemy at its worst, that is, the most occult and fatuous kind.

The Nuremberg patrician Ulman Stromer was the first German to produce paper on a relatively large scale. With the assistance of two Italians, he established a paper mill near Nuremberg in 1390. That year may be called the birth year of paper manufacture in Germany.

The invention of gunpowder and firearms has been gratuitously ascribed to one "Berthold der Schwarze," about whom we know nothing for certain.

As was remarked above (ch. I, p. 177), a good deal of information on the knowledge of chemical substances will be available when facts concerning each have been carefully extracted from dated or datable writings or monuments. To illustrate the use of the latter, it has been shown that some mediaeval paintings in the Germanic Museum, Nuremberg, have been made upon a preliminary layer of bismuth. According to Lippmann, that practice can be traced back to the fourteenth century. Of course, it does not follow that the identity of bismuth was clearly realized. Ancient people could not distinguish bismuth from lead and tin, and the idea that bismuth was a kind of lead persisted until the eighteenth century. Miners spoke of three kinds of lead (lead, tin, bismuth) and considered the third kind the most advanced on the way to silver (tectum argenti). When they struck a vein of bismuth they said, "Alas, we have come too soon." Georgius Agricola spoke of bismuth (bisemutum) in his mining catechism Bermannus (Basel 1530). The paintings of the Germanic Museum prove that bismuth was actually used as early as the fourteenth century for a definite purpose.[15]

A collection of recipes gathered in 1394 by one Leonard of Maurperg affords us curious glimpses into the alchemical fraternity, or more exactly into the loose tribe of cognoscenti of various intelligence and integrity who were then already dispersed across Europe and the Near East. Indeed, he tells us, about each recipe, from whom and where he got it. We follow him in Montpellier, Rome, Sicily, Cologne, Posen, Cracow, etc. and if we may believe him he even traveled as far as Jerusalem and Tabrīz in search of the alchemical secret.

[15] Edmund O. von Lippmann: Zur Geschichte des Wismuts (Chemiker Zeitung, 1905, p. 719; Abhandlungen und Vorträge 1, 247–48, 1906). Georgius Agricola: De re metallica, translated by Mr. and Mrs. Herbert Clark Hoover (p. 433, London 1912; Isis 13, 113–16). Weeks (p. 13, 1933). No mention of bismuth in D. V. Thompson (1936).

A6. *Russia*

For the study of Byzantine chemistry no other written sources are known to us for this period than manuals of Christian iconography, which may contain information similar to that given by Cennino Cennini and Alcherius. The methods of Byzantine painting and of the Byzantine arts and crafts were practiced during the fourteenth century with increasing frequency not only in the Byzantine empire, but throughout the Slavonic world. The fruits of these methods can be investigated in churches of Mistra, Verria, Nagoritchino, the Holy Mountain, Novgorod, Moscow, etc.

A7. *Addition*

A study by Wilhelm Ganzenmüller: Liber florum Geberti. Alchemistische Oefen und Geräte in einer Handschrift des XV. Jahrh. (Quellen und Studien zur Geschichte der Naturwissenschaftens vol. 8, parts 1-2, Berlin 1941) was not available to me on account of the war. Though devoted to a fifteenth-century MS, it may, and probably does, contain materials of value for the study of fourteenth-century alchemy. Similar remarks apply to the various catalogues of alchemical MSS; I have mentioned them apropos of definite facts, but the student of mediaeval alchemy should be prepared to use them repeatedly and extensively. Let me cite them once more for good measure: (1) Catalogue des MSS alchimiques grecs (8 vols., Bruxelles 1924-32; Isis 7, 507-11, etc.). (2) Dorothea Waley Singer: Catalogue of Latin and vernacular alchemical MSS in Great Britain and Ireland (3 vols., Brussels 1928-31; Isis 18, 398). (3) Catalogue des MSS alchimiques latins (vol. 1, Bruxelles 1939; Isis 32, 211), only one volume published, relative to the Paris libraries, by James Corbett. (4) William Jerome Wilson: An alchemical MS by Arnaldus de Bruxella (Osiris 2, 220-405, 2 pl., 2 fig., Bruges 1936); Catalogue of Latin and vernacular alchemical MSS in the United States and Canada (Osiris 6, 854 p., Bruges 1939).

B. *Islām*

The best account of Islamic enlightened thought on alchemy will be found in the Muqaddama of Ibn Khaldūn (3, 207-27, 249-64). His main sources were Khālid ibn Yazīd ibn Mu'āwiya (VII-2); Jābir ibn Ḥaiyān (VIII-2), whose seventy enigmatic epistles on the subject are given so much importance that many people call alchemy 'ilm jābir; al-Fārābī (X-1); Maslama ibn Aḥmad al-Majrīṭī (X-2); Ibn Sīnā (XI-1); al-Ghazzālī (XI-2); Abū Bakr ibn Bashrūn, a disciple of Maslama; al-Ḥusain ibn 'Alī al-Ṭughrā'ī (XII-1); and one unknown poet, Ibn al-Mughairibī. He rejected the authenticity of the alchemical writings ascribed to Khālid ibn Yazīd, who was a Bedouin and hence ignorant of arts and sciences, and of those bearing al-Ghazzālī's name, for the latter was a man of too high intelligence to share the views of the alchemists, let alone teach them. Al-Fārābī and Ibn Sīnā had expressed views on alchemy but were not alchemists. Ibn Khaldūn quotes verbatim a very long letter (p. 210-25) written by Abū Bakr ibn Bashrūn to his condisciple Ibn al-Samḥ (XI-1), probably identical with the well known Spanish mathematician. He had the wit to ask himself, Why are the alchemical writings so obscure and why is their terminology secret?[16] He concluded that if the al-

[16] Alchemists never called things, say metals, by their true names, but used other names or symbols known only to initiates. For the secret names, see Julius Ruska and Eilhard Wiede-

chemists could do at all what they claimed to do, they must use magical means condemned by diverse religions. Orthodox Islām was as intolerant of magic (and, we may add, as impotent to restrain its use) as orthodox Christendom. It is typical of Ibn Khaldūn, orthodox as he was, that he refers to the reprobation not of one kind of religious law (shar'iyya), but of many kinds. He finally concluded that the transmutation of metals was impossible, that the philosopher's stone or egg did not exist, and that the practice of alchemy was baleful.

C. *India*

Chemical experiments and alchemical speculations were made by the Jaina physician Merutuṅga (fl. 1386), who continued the Hindu tradition of rasa studies. That is an iatrochemical tradition, involving pharmaceutical experiments with metallic salts, especially mercurial ones. It is not yet possible to appraise its scientific value or to compare it with contemporary alchemical traditions in other countries.

Additional information may be obtained from the dictionary of materia medica compiled by the Hindu prince Madanapāla (fl. 1375). For example, that dictionary seems to consider as a special entity the zinc (jasada) extracted from calamine; this is remarkable because there was no mention of zinc in Western writings before Agricola and Paracelsus. It may be that the smelting of zinc began in India.[17]

D. *China*

The value which Chinese scholars attached to ink has already been referred to (ch. I, p. 181). More information concerning ink manufacturers was published at this time by the famous essayist T'ao Tsung-i, and, what is more important, by one of the manufacturers, Shên Chi-sun. Shên's treatise Mo-fa chi-yao (1398) is exceptional in that it actually explains how to make ink. To be sure, the Western collections of recipes, such as Cennino's, contained ink recipes,[18] but essays or books exclusively devoted to ink are a Chinese specialty, symbolic of Chinese humanism.

There is nothing to add at present to the general remarks on Chinese alchemy offered in chapter I (p. 180). Our knowledge of the texts is still very imperfect. A good many are available in the Taoist and Buddhist patrologies, but we have no critical edition prepared by historians sufficiently familiar with chemical facts and theories; only very few texts are available in translation. For further research see Alfred Forke: The world-conception of the Chinese (314 p., London 1925; Isis 8, 373–75), chiefly book 4, p. 227–300. Obed Simon Johnson: A study of Chinese alchemy (170 p., Shanghai 1928; Isis 12, 330–32). Evan Morgan: Tao the great luminant. Essays from Huai Nan tzŭ[19] (336 p., 3 pl., London 1936; Isis 27, 504–7). Masumi Chikashige: Oriental alchemy (112 p., 17 pl., Tokyo 1936; Isis 27, 79–81).

---

mann: Alchemistische Decknamen (Beitr. 67, Sitzungsberichte der Physikalisch-medizinischen Sozietät in Erlangen 56, 17–36, 1924; Isis 8, 794). For symbols, see Fritz Lüdy, Jr.: Alchemistische und chemische Zeichen (Gesellschaft für Geschichte der Pharmazie 1928; Isis 13, 232); C. O. Zuretti: Alchemistica signa (Catalogue vol. 8, 1932; Isis 19, 440); Wilson (1939).

[17] Monier-Williams (p. 416, 1899). Ray (p. 157, 1903; p. 17, 19, 22, 1909). Hoover's translation of Agricola (p. 408–10, London 1912). Weeks (p. 20, 1933).

[18] D. V. Thompson (p. 19, 80–84, 120–21, 206, 1936).

[19] Huai Nan tzŭ (II-2 B.C.), d. 122 B.C., grandson of the first Han emperor. His work is a part of the Taoist patrology.

See also Tenney L. Davis' papers written with the cooperation of Chinese students from 1930 on (Isis 15, 456; etc.). The field of Chinese alchemy is immense, and our knowledge of it more tantalizing than sufficient.

The following two memoirs on Chinese alchemy will appear presently in Isis: Roy C. Spooner and C. H. Wang: The divine nine turn tan sha method, a Chinese alchemical recipe (accepted for publication Feb. 23, 1945); tan sha means cinnabar. Homer H. Dubs: The beginnings of alchemy (accepted July 13, 1945). According to Dubs the earliest mention of alchemy is found in a Chinese imperial edict dated 144 B.C. and its origin probably goes back to the fourth century B.C. in the school of Tsou Yen (Giles no. 2030, 1898).

IX. GEOGRAPHY

We shall begin with a section devoted to Catalonia, then deal successively with (A) Christendom, (B) Israel, (C) Islām, (D) Java, (E) China.

Catalonia

It is necessary to deal separately with Catalonia, because the very important geographical activities which occurred in that country cannot be credited to Christians alone or to Jews alone, but only to their combined efforts. The periods of prosperity and progress in the Iberic peninsula coincided with periods of international cooperation—with Carthaginians, Romans, Muslims, or Jews; the periods of fanaticism and "limpiéza"[1] were periods of decadence and increasing poverty. Not only was the "limpiéza de sángre" soon followed by a "limpiéza de bólsa" (and do not say that this did not matter so much; it mattered very much indeed, for it meant starvation or semistarvation for the multitude), but the "purity of blood" was always accompanied by increasing narrow-mindedness, bigotry, inhumanity. The practice of intolerance, and especially of its most heinous form, limpiéza, enervated and ruined Spain even as it is destroying Germany under our own eyes.

The fourteenth and fifteenth centuries, and especially their middle period (c. 1350–c. 1450), constitute the golden age of Catalonia; in spite of sporadic persecutions, it was a period of cooperation between Jews and Christians. Nowhere was that cooperation more fertile than in the field of geography, and especially cartography. The attention paid by the Catalan people to cartography was natural enough, for they were at that time the outstanding Mediterranean navigators. The Llibre del consolat de mar (see ch. I, p. 325) compiled about the middle of the century remains to this day a monumental witness to their wise leadership. Seafaring people needed charts, instruments, and every kind of up-to-date information for navigation and business. A center where such information could be collected was gradually formed in Majorca. There is no reason to believe that it ever reached a stage of organization comparable to that of the colonial and naval institute which Dom Henrique o Navegador founded in Sagres (Faro) in 1437 or a little before. It could not reach that stage, because it was due to the initiative, not of kings or princes, but of learned men. We must assume that it simply grew around these men.

The most remarkable achievement of the "school of Majorca," as that spontaneous group of cartographers is often called, is the Catalan mappemonde of 1375.

[1] For a definition of this and an abundance of illustrations see Henry Charles Lea: History of the Inquisition of Spain (4 vols., New York 1906–7).

It is an atlas of six large maps prepared for Charles V of France, materially superior to earlier portolani. Indeed, Beazley went so far as to say (3, 525, 1906), "This splendid *quarte de mer en tableaux* ... is unquestionably the most magnificent and comprehensive map design and in relation to Asia by far the most scientific yet produced in Christendom." Whereas portolani compiled for the use of sailors focused their attention almost exclusively on the coast lines, the Catalan atlas incorporated a considerable amount of information relative to the lands of Asia and North Africa. Other maps, less remarkable yet significant, were compiled by William Soleri (1385), and others still by Abraham Cresques and the latter's son, Jahuda Cresques. The Catalan atlas of 1375 has sometimes been ascribed to Abraham Cresques, but without sufficient proof, simply because Abraham appears to have been the leading cartographer flourishing about that time. Abraham died in 1387; Jahuda lived at least until the end of the century. All were Majorcans. Soleri was probably a Christian, the Cresques were Jews, but Jahuda was forcibly converted during the persecution of 1391 and then called Jayme Ribes. Thus by the end of the century the general situation had already deteriorated because of intolerance, and further progress, if not altogether stopped, was at least slowed down. Moreover, instead of two rival groups, Jewish and Christian, living in a state of amity or mutual forbearance, there was now a triangular conflict between Jews, Christians, and converts, each of the three groups suspecting the other two, and the bitterness growing all around with compound interest.

Let us cast a glance over the beginning of the fifteenth century to see how matters turned out. There were still two distinguished cartographers of the Majorcan school, Mecia (= Matthew) de Viladestes, who completed in 1413 a remarkable map preserved in the Bibliothèque nationale, Paris, and Gabriel de Vallsecha, who completed in 1434 or 1439 the famous mappemonde of the Institut d'Estudis catalans in Barcelona, and made another one in 1447. Their efforts were the swan song of Majorcan cartography in Majorca.[2]

The result of intolerance was to drive the Catalan genius outside for the enrichment, spiritual as well as material, of rival nations, chiefly Genoa and Portugal. It has been claimed that Jahuda Cresques himself went to Portugal, and he has been tentatively identified with one Jacme de Majorca, who entered the service of Dom Henrique. The main point is that Majorcan scientists did participate in the foundation of the Sagres institute and thus helped to build up Portuguese wealth and fame. On the other hand, one Battista Beccario, who was active in Genoa and published maps there in 1426 and 1435, showed unmistakable traces of Catalan influence. The same can be said of the "table of Velletri," a copper mappemonde formerly in the Borgia Museum in Velletri (near Rome), now in the Archives of the Propaganda in Rome, dating probably from the beginning of the fifteenth century.[3]

During the fifteenth century Majorcan genius and initiative were transplanted to

[2] The map of Mecia de Viladestes (1413) is especially valuable with reference to Majorca and West Africa; e.g., it shows the roads converging on Timbuktu from Egypt, Tunis, Morocco, and the Sūdān. The map which Gabriel de Vallsecha (a member of the Cresques family, still living in 1447) completed in 1439 once belonged to Amerigo Vespucci; George Sand made a blot of ink upon it! Excellent partial facsimiles of both maps in La Roncière (vol. 1, 1925).

[3] The atlas of Battista Beccario (Becharius), 1426, formerly in the library of Ratisbon, is now in the National Museum, Munich. Both the "table of Velletri" and the Beccario atlas betray their Catalan affinities in their representations of Western Africa. La Roncière (1, 139–41; 2, pl. xxii, 1925), including full bibliography relative to the Velletri table.

Genoa, Marseille, Messina, Venice, Florence, Malta, Fez, etc.; but nowhere did they succeed so well or bring forth so many fruits as in Portugal. One curious consequence of this may still be cited. As Dom Henrique was primarily interested in sea routes as opposed to the land routes, the Sūdān, about which much knowledge had been obtained, was gradually abandoned for the western Atlantic coast and the Atlantic islands. In the sixteenth century Timbuktu became a city of mystery, and it remained almost inaccessible to Europeans until the middle of the nineteenth century.[4]

A. *Christendom*

A1. *Spain*

About the middle of the century a geographical treatise was derived from the portolani or from their contemporary sources by an unknown Franciscan. In its turn, this Libro del conosçimiento exerted some influence on later maps, such as the Catalan map (middle fifteenth century) preserved in the Este library of Modena.

Another Castilian, but a layman, was destined to attain a kind of literary immortality. This was Ruy González de Clavijo, member of an embassy sent by Enrique III (king of Castile 1390–1406) to Tīmūr Lang. The embassy sailed in May 1403 from Cadiz to Trebizond, via Gaeta, Rhodes, Constantinople (where they spent five months); from Trebizond they traveled inland via Erzerum, Tabrīz, Nīshāpūr, Marv, Balkh, reaching Samarqand in July 1404. The journey home was made in the same way (with minor differences) and consumed about the same time, as they spent six months in Tabrīz. They arrived in Genoa on January 3, 1406, visited the antipope Benedict XIII (Pedro de Luna) at Savona near by; sailed from Genoa, and finally landed in San Lúcar de Barrameda in March 1406. González de Clavijo wrote in Spanish an account of their immense journey, which is considered by good judges (such as George Borrow and Sven Hedin) one of the most entertaining books of travel ever written. It includes a valuable description of Constantinople (being one of the last before the Turkish conquest), a striking portrait of Tīmūr, and descriptions of his court and peoples, Tatar trade and arts, and various curiosities, such as a giraffe sent to Tīmūr from Egypt and fourteen elephants he had brought from India. Of course, this is a fifteenth-century book, but González de Clavijo as well as Tīmūr is a child of the fourteenth century; in 1400 the former was still young (we do not know the date of his birth, but it is stated that he served from youth as chamberlain to Enrique III), but Tīmūr was an old man, almost blind, nearing the end of his tumultuous life.[5] González de Clavijo must have written his account between 1406 and 1412, when he died.

Text. First edition, Historia del gran Tamorlan, edited by Gonçalo Argote de Molina (Seville 1582). Reprinted Madrid 1782. First English translation by Sir Clements Markham (Hakluyt Society, 260 p., map, 1859). Russian translation, with Spanish text, and notes by I. Sreznevski (Imperial Academy, St. Petersburg 1881). Filip Jacob Bruun: Constantinople, ses sanctuaires et ses reliques au commencement du XVe siècle. Fragment traduit et annoté (48 p., Odessa 1883). New English translation by Guy Le Strange (Broadway Travellers, 390 p., London 1928).

Criticism. Beazley (3, 332–56, 1906). Browne (3, 199–202, 1920).

[4] La Roncière (1, 167–72, 1925). The same book contains much information, admirably illustrated, concerning Jewish cartography of northwestern Africa (Sahara, Senegal, Niger). Carra de Vaux (EI 4, 776–77, 1930).

[5] The Spaniards were kindly received by Tīmūr on November 1, 1404 and saw him frequently afterward; he died on February 18, 1405, at the (Muslim) age of 71.

A2. *Italy*

There were a good number of Italian sailors, Genoese, Venetians, Amalfians, etc., and the knowledge incorporated in the portolani was partly due to them. Niccolò Zeno was a Venetian sailor, of great experience in the Mediterranean; after a lapse of almost two centuries some daring navigation among the islands of the western Atlantic (Faroe Islands?) was ascribed to him or to a contemporary namesake. That is not impossible but unproven.

The Italians were more familiar with the Mediterranean, which they were crossing in every direction for war and business, and some of them at least for the sake of pilgriming to the holy cities of the Near East. Quite a few can be named for this period, but none of outstanding merit, none ready or privileged to repeat the exploits of Giovanni de' Marignolli (XIV-1). Giovanni came back from the East after an absence of thirteen years in 1352, received a bishopric, became secretary and historiographer to the emperor Charles IV, and died in 1358/59.

The main Italian pilgrims to the Holy Land were Leonardo Frescobaldi, Giorgio Gucci, Simone Sigoli, and Niccolò di Martoni. The first three traveled in 1384, and each of them has left us an account of the journey, the best being Frescobaldi's, especially with regard to Egypt. Ten years later Niccolò di Martoni went to Jerusalem, visiting Egypt and the Sinai on his way and returning via Cyprus, Rhodes, and Greece. His account is particularly valuable with regard to Greece. Niccolò wrote in Latin, but the three others in Italian.

The Italians (as well as the Catalans) were much concerned about Abyssinia. This appears in Sigoli's account, which includes a reference to Prester John, the powerful ruler of India, to whom the sulṭān of Egypt was obliged to bow, otherwise the life-giving waters of the Nile might be diverted from him. This confusion between India and Abyssinia is a good symbol of the geographical knowledge (or ignorance) of those days. And yet during the rule of Kerenbes, the last Christian king of Dongola[6] (c. 1311), some contact had been established with Rome, and in 1316 John XXII had sent a mission of eight Dominicans to Nubia and Abyssinia. When they reached the latter country they received the names Grima, Argaï, Luanos, Pantaleon, Sama, Aleph, Assen, and Aguloa; a tertiary sister called Imea had come with them to establish a nunnery. In 1329 pontifical letters were addressed to the emperor, and this aroused the jealousy of the sulṭān of Egypt. In 1330 the Dominican Bartolommeo da Tivoli was consecrated bishop of Dongola. The knowledge which he and his associates obtained about that country may be seen in the Pizigano map of 1367. On the other hand, a Franciscan who had lived for many years in Prester John's country was summoned in 1391 by Juan I of Aragon. During the rule of Dāwit I (= David; emperor 1382–1411), there was prepared an itinerary from Venice to Axum (Iter eunti de Venetiis ad Indiam ubi jacet corpus beati Thome apostoli) together with conversational manuals in Arabic and Amharic.[7] In 1402, the Florentine Antonio Bartoli accompanied to Venice Abyssinian ambassadors bringing with them as presents leopards and aromatics. Yet the fundamental confusion could not be eradicated. Indeed, as long as itineraries and verbal accounts are not anchored on definite coordinates, geographical

[6] Harold Alfred Macmichael: History of the Arabs in the Sudan (1, 186, Cambridge 1922). Dongola (Ar. Dunqula) is a district of Nubia on both banks of the Nile between 19°42′ and 18°N., at present a mudīrīya (capital, Merowe) of the Anglo-Egyptian Sūdān (E. Graefe, EI 1, 1072–73, 1913).

[7] The text of the itinerary is given by La Roncière (2, 113–14, 1925) together with abundant information (1, 61–70; 2, 112–22).

knowledge remains vague and drifting, and every kind of confusion may occur and reoccur.[8]

To be sure, a number of portolani were compiled, but the information which they provided was not sufficient, or they were not considered with sufficient earnestness, except by sailors. We have spoken in a preceding section of the maps provided by the school of Majorca; these maps were not used by Catalans alone; indeed, the most remarkable of them was the magnificent atlas completed in 1375 for Charles V of France. And not only did the maps emigrate, but the map makers themselves, as religious intolerance drove them out. Next to Majorca, the best maps were produced in Italy, and enough of these early Italian portolani are extant to give us a fair idea of their general value.

The Medicean (or Laurentian) atlas of 1351 is perhaps the most important monument of the Italian cartography of that period, even if we eliminate from it some of its prophetic features. Indeed, either the date of the whole map must be postponed by at least a century, or we must admit that it was actually compiled in or about 1351 together with the lunar calendar prefacing it, but that interpolations were introduced when Portuguese discoveries revealed the West African coasts. The second alternative seems preferable.

In addition to the Medicean atlas we have maps compiled by the Venetian Francesco Pizigano in 1367 and 1373, the Combitis atlas, the Pinelli atlas of c. 1384, the Velletri table, and the atlas completed by the Genoese Battista Beccario in 1426.

Giacomo de' Dondi of Padua, better known under the nickname Giacomo dall' Orologio, wrote a treatise on tides wherein he postulated planetary influences in addition to the solar and lunar ones. The tides were smaller and less regular in the Mediterranean, he said, because of the isolation of that sea from the ocean. The Dittamondo is a long didactic poem in terzine completed by Fazio degli Uberti c. 1360. Its form illustrates the strength of the Dante tradition. It is so largely devoted to geographical matters that one might call it a geographical poem (probably the longest ever written), but we should bear in mind that it deals with geography in a historical rather than in a scientific mood; it is geography in terms of human history rather than in terms of natural history, but that is very much what we should expect.

The same interest in historical geography was very strong in Boccaccio, to whom we owe the first description of the Canaries, apropos of the rediscovery of those islands by Nicoloso da Recco (XIV-1), a Genoese in Portuguese service. Moreover, Boccaccio compiled a geographical dictionary, the first of its kind in Latin, though preceded by many Arabic dictionaries of far greater importance, such as the Mu'jam al-buldān of Yāqūt (XIII-1) and the 'Ajā'ib al-buldān of al-Qazwīnī (XIII-2). Boccaccio's dictionary was primarily historical or humanistic, yet he made occasional references to natural phaenomena, this being readily explained by the fact that some of his authorities, such as Aristotle, Pliny the Elder, and Seneca, were the leading men of science of their days. It was only the humanists restricting their own pabulum to Livy, Horace, and Virgil, or more generally to the bonae

[8] See discussion concerning the Niger and Nile rivers below, and, with regard to a smaller matter, my note A sidelight upon geographical knowledge in the first half of the fifteenth century (Isis 9, 118, 1927), wherein it is shown that as late as 1440 the people of Ghent did not know and could not find the distances from their town to Amiens and Liége!

litterae pure and simple, who could completely ignore the scientific aspects of nature. Boccaccio's geographical curiosity appears occasionally even in such a book as the De casibus virorum illustrium, wherein he refers to inhabitants of the polar regions.[9] A certain amount of geographical knowledge may be found also in the Mundi fabrica of Domenico di Bandino, and, strangely enough, Domenico mentions the same expedition to the Canaries that Boccaccio does. I suppose that it should be possible to compile a survey of geographical knowledge in the trecento on the basis of the works of Riccobaldo da Ferrara, Dante, Petrarca, Boccaccio, Fazio degli Uberti, Domenico di Bandino. Such a survey should be published in the form of a dictionary, completed with a systematic classification of the catchwords, synoptic tables, and maps. This would be for us too long an intermezzo. The point to remember is that an educated man of the year, say, 1375 had, or could have if he took the trouble, a mass of geographical knowledge which was considerable enough, though seldom accurate and sometimes grossly inaccurate.

The humanistic tradition already so strong in Italy led naturally enough to the revival of Ptolemaic geography. What is more remarkable, and symptomatic of a new spirit, scholars—even such as Petrarca—not only were interested in the ancient geographical texts, but wanted to obtain and discuss ancient maps. The primices of that movement did not really appear until the first decade of the next century, but they were prepared in the fourteenth century. Upon the insistence of Coluccio Salutati (1331–1406) and other humanists, great efforts were made to obtain Greek MSS. The most fruitful of these efforts was made with the help of Manuel Chrysoloras. When the latter returned to Constantinople after his first mission to Venice (1394/95), he took with him two of his disciples, Guarino da Verona and Giacomo d'Angelo, whose main purpose was to search for manuscripts. Giacomo found a copy of Ptolemy's Cosmographia with maps, and by 1406 he had already translated it into Latin. He dedicated his translation then to Gregory XII; in 1409 he dedicated it again to Alexander V.[10] The maps appended to Giacomo's translation had been prepared by a Florentine artist, Francesco di Lapacino, who had simply copied the original outlines, replacing Greek names by Latin ones.

Giacomo's own Latin name was Jacobus Angelus; he should not be confused with a contemporary namesake (in Latin) who wrote a treatise on the comet of 1402. Our Jacobus came from the Mugello valley and his original name was Giacomo da Scarperia, the other one was a German, Jacob Engelhart of Ulm.[11]

To return to the Latin translation of the Cosmographia, allow me to pursue its history a little farther. To begin with, Giacomo's translation and maps are easily available. The Latin MS 4802 (Bibliothèque nationale, Paris) was reproduced in facsimile, text and maps, by the care of Henry Omont (Paris 1925). The first printed edition of the Cosmographia (H. Liechtenstein, Vicenza 1475) reproduced that very text, but without the maps! The idea of adding maps occurred about

[9] See ch. I, p. 197.

[10] The reader will recall that Gregory XII, elected during the schism, had been declared heretic and asked to abdicate by the council of Pisa in 1409, and had refused and fled to Gaeta; he resigned only in 1415. Alexander V (= Peter of Crete) was the union pope elected by the council in 1409; he soon disappointed the hopes of the peacemakers, and died ten months after his election.

[11] Engelhart's De cometa was first printed in Memmingen 1490 (Klebs no. 69). See Thorndike (4, 80–87, 662–65, 1934).

the same time to four printers, as is witnessed by the four successive editions (2d to 5th), following one another within five years; all of them including maps—different maps.

2d ed., Lapis, Bologna 1477. (The date actually printed is 1462,[12] which is certainly an error; the symbol XV or XX has been omitted in the Roman date; the real date would then be 1477 or 1482; if the second [less probable] alternative were correct, this would be not the second edition, but the fourth.) This edition, including 26 maps, was prepared by Taddeo de' Crivelli and completed by him in 1477.

3d ed., Conrad Sweynheim and Arnold Buckinck, Rome 1478. 27 maps.

4th ed., Nicolaus Laurentii Alemannus, Florence 1480. The text is an Italian metrical version by Francesco Berlinghieri. 31 maps. (More books, 1943, p. 114-19).

5th ed., Holle, Ulm 1482. 32 maps.

(All the incunabula editions are in Latin, except the edition of Florence 1480, in Italian.)

The maps of the editions of 1478 to 1490 were prepared by Nicholas the German (Donnus Nicolaus Germanus), who dedicated his first atlas in 1466 to the duke Borso of Este. This atlas contained 27 maps; Nicholas presented a larger atlas to Paul II (pope 1464-71), including 3 new maps—Spain, Italy, Scandinavia; in 1482 he added 2 more maps (thus 32 in all), France and the Holy Land.

Nicholas had introduced a new kind of projection, the trapezoidal,[13] also called after his own misquoted name "Donis" projection. He improved the outlines of the old maps and, as we have seen, introduced five new ones. It is noteworthy that with special regard to Greenland, Nicholas' second atlas showed its true position to the west of Scandinavia and Iceland after Claudius Clavus, but in his third atlas, being misled by learned traditions, he placed it wrongly to the north of Scandinavia and the east of Iceland. Henricus Martellus, Nicholas' successor, reintroduced the correct disposition of Greenland (c. 1490 sq.), but in spite of that the wrong delineation continued to appear on many maps. After the rediscovery of Greenland early in the sixteenth century, the two positions were sometimes combined upon the same maps! This example may serve to illustrate the vagaries of cartographic traditions.

Nicholas' atlas of 1466 (27 maps) was the basis of the Roman editions, 3d 1478 and 7th 1490. His intermediary atlas (30 maps) was the prototype of the maps of the Canerio or Cantino type, as far as concerns Northern Europe and Greenland. The atlas of 1482 (32 maps) was the basis of the Ulm editions, 5th 1482 and 6th 1486.

It is not true that Nicholas wrote the two tracts appended to the Ulm edition of 1486, namely, the index, Registrum alphabeticum super octo libros Ptolemaei, and the De locis ac mirabilibus mundi. This was done by the printer of that edition, Johann Reger of Kemnath (near Bayreuth, Bavaria). Nicholas was probably dead then, for one hears nothing of him after 1482.

The Ulm maps were engraved on wood, all others on copper. The maps of Bologna 1477 (or if that date should be read 1482, of Rome 1478) are the first examples of copper engraving for books.[14]

[12] Facsimile of colophon in Sarton: Study of the history of science (p. 13, Harvard University 1936).

[13] Straight parallels and converging straight meridians divide the map into trapezoids.

[14] The earliest printed map is the diagram of the world in the Etymologiae of Isidore of Seville (VII-1), 1st or 2d ed., Zainer, Augsburg 1472 (Klebs 536.2; Isis 34, p. 32 n. 2). Note kindly communicated by William A. Jackson (Feb. 3, 1943).

After the publication of the printed maps, MS maps fell gradually into disuse. The history of the early printed editions is symptomatic of later development; that is, in each atlas maps were gradually replaced by better ones, new maps added. It is a process of gradual and continuous change, the detailed explanation of which would be very long. Seven editions (including the first, mapless) appeared in the fifteenth century; some 33 before 1570, and more than 50 before 1730. A comparative study of these editions forms an essential part of the history of cartography down to the end of the seventeenth century. The gradual improvements concerned not only the contents of the maps, but the systems of projection and other cartographic methods.

For further information see father Joseph Fischer: Claudii Ptolemaei Geographiae codex Urbinas graecus 82 (folio and quarto, 4 vols., Leiden 1932; Isis 20, 267–70); Edward Luther Stevenson: Geography of Ptolemy in English (New York Public Library 1932; Isis 20, 270–74; 22, 533–39). Klebs (no. 812.1–7). Sarton (p. 103, fig. 10–11, 1938).

We may say that that tremendous cartographical development, implying the recovery of the Ptolemaic maps and their gradual improvement and enrichment from a great variety of other sources, began in the fourteenth century thanks to the initiative of Salutati, Chrysoloras, and Giacomo d'Angelo. It continued with increasing strength throughout the fifteenth and sixteenth centuries. The production of standard atlases was naturally benefited by the invention of engraving; it is very strange that the West was so far behind in that respect and that no engraved map existed in the West before 1477 or 1478, though Chinese maps were engraved on stone as early as 1137 (Introd. 2, 225) if not earlier.

A3. *France*

It has been claimed, for the first time in 1669 by Villault de Bellefond,[15] that sailors of Dieppe and Rouen in 1364 and following years sailed along the West African coast far beyond Cape Bojador (26°6'N.; in Rio de Oro) and traded at various points between Cape Verde and the Bight of Benin (i.e., all along the horizontal sector of the West African coast). That trade flourished until c. 1410. Unfortunately, no archival documents are extant wherewith to substantiate these claims. The story is not implausible, but it is unproven. Even La Roncière (2, 10–17, 1925) entitled his chapter ad hoc "Hypothétiques Petit-Dieppe et Petit-Paris en Guinée 1364." After a careful analysis of the question (with apparently exhaustive bibliography), he concluded, "Autant les voyages des Normands aux côtes de Guinée en 1364 sont du domaine de la légende, autant la conquête des Canaries par l'un d'entre eux tient de l'épopée." Indeed, the Canaries were conquered by Norman sailors led by Gadifer de La Salle, but that happened only after the fourteenth century, though very soon after, in 1402–5.

The outstanding French pilgrims to the Holy Land were Ogier VIII, lord of Anglure in Champagne, and four knights of Metz. Ogier's account was in French, and so was that of the four knights, yclept Jehan de Raigecourt, Rémion de Mitry, Poince Le Gournaix, and Nicolle Louve. The last named wrote the account of their journey, Relation d'un voyage de Metz à Jérusalem entrepris en 1395 par quatre chevaliers messins. It was published in L'Austrasie, Revue du Nord-Est de la France (3, 149–68, 221–36, Metz 1836), not available to me, cited by Röhricht

[15] Relation des costes d'Afrique appellées Guinée . . . dans le voyage qu'il y a fait en 1666 et 1667 (p. 410–25, Paris 1669). Beazley (3, 430–39, 1906). Hennig (3, 300–14, 1938).

(p. 95, 1890). Some years later (1428) a ballad bearing Nicolle Louve's name described the dangers and sufferings of their voyage.

The Songe du vieil pelerin composed by Philippe de Mézières in 1388–89 is an allegorical journey across the whole of Europe and the known parts of Africa and Asia under the guidance of queen Truth.[16]

The leading French writer on geography and cosmography was Pierre d'Ailly (b. 1350), but his main work, the Imago mundi, was not completed until 1410. It is mainly a summary of patristic and scholastic ideas; all in all, it is the best account of the cosmographical and geographical knowledge available at the beginning of the fifteenth century, and it derives additional importance from the fact of its having been studied very thoroughly by Christopher Columbus. The latter's copy of the original edition (Louvain 1483; Klebs no. 766) contains 2,125 postils, varying in length from one word to over a thousand, written in his own hand. The Imago mundi is innocent of the Ptolemaic knowledge which was then being rediscovered, but Ailly became acquainted with it somewhat later and discussed it in other tracts included in the edition of 1483. Columbus derived from that edition an exaggerated notion of the length of Eurasia, and this increased his hope of the possibility of reaching the eastern shores of Asia by westward navigation. The Imago mundi and other tracts can now easily be consulted, together with Columbus' notes, in the Latin-French edition by Edmond Buron (3 vols., 828 p., 36 pl., Paris 1930; Isis 18, 345). See also Samuel Eliot Morison: Admiral of the Ocean Sea (2 vols., Boston 1942; 1, 53–55, 120–25; Isis 34, 169–72).

A4. *England*

Among the commonplaces discussed by learned men, in England as well as elsewhere, were a number of questions which we should call today geodetic. They concern the size, shape, and equilibrium of the earth, the relations between the land and water areas or between the land and the water spheres. Such questions suggested themselves through the study of the Aristotelian Meteorologica and De mundo. In the commentary on the Meteorologica ascribed to Simon Tunsted we find curious variations on these themes; Simon (or whoever the author was) discusses the eccentricity of the earth and water spheres, explains that the volume of water must be smaller than the volume of earth, and wonders whether the volumes of the four elements form a geometrical progression.

The Benedictine chronicler Richard of Cirencester must be mentioned here, in order to be properly dismissed. The De situ Britanniae formerly ascribed to him and assumed to be an important source for English toponymy has been proved to be an eighteenth-century forgery. Unfortunately, much harm had already been done before that discovery was made. A number of incorrect place names have attained some kind of consecration and popularity because of the reliance placed on that text.

The Oxford Franciscan Nicholas of Lynn (not to be confused with his Carmelite namesake and contemporary) is said to have traveled to the Arctic in 1360. The treatise ascribed to him, Inventio fortunata, is lost, but the story itself is credible because we know that many people had actually traveled to the frozen lands for various reasons (see ch. I, p. 193–97). In particular, we might expect Englishmen to do so because of some of their traditions going back to Alfred the Great (IX-2), and of the reputation as travelers and adventurers which they had already acquired.

[16] Nicolas Jorga: Philippe de Mézières et la croisade au XIVe siècle (p. 468, Paris 1896).

Foreigners agreed that Englishmen were restless people, always on the move from one country to another, and this was queerly explained on the assumption that Englishmen were dominated by the moon! Some of them admitted that much themselves, even such eminent ones as Ranulf Higden, John Gower, and John Wycliffe,[17] and that curious fancy was still entertained a century later by the illustrious prototypographos William Caxton (1422?–91). In the prologue to his Boke of Eneydos compyled by Vyrgyle (1490), he remarked, "For we englysshe men ben borne under the domynacyon of the mone, whiche is neuer stedfaste but euer wauerynge." Incidentally, this illustrates the utter vagueness of astrological conceits, for how could all Englishmen or more Englishmen than other people be born under the moon? Astrological explanations were mostly nonsense or plays on words, feeble and idiotic puns.

The geographical best seller of the Middle Ages was composed c. 1365 by a mysterious Englishman, Sir John Mandeville. No one can produce a best seller unless he has an instinctive knowledge of what the public wants; Sir John had that quality to a supreme degree. He knew full well that most people did not care about accurate information, but preferred fantastic tales; the more fantastic the better. He had it in him to tell them just the kind of stories which they would like to hear, and let himself go. It is now generally admitted that the original text of his Travels was written in French, and some critics have gone so far as to suggest that the real author was not an Englishman, Sir John of St. Albans, but a Liégeois, Jean d'Outremeuse. That second hypothesis is unproven. There is no reason to suppose that a noble Englishman of that time could not or would not write in French and do it well; it is true the accomplishment was becoming rarer than it had been a century or two earlier, but it was perfectly possible. Whoever wrote the Travels knew what the people wanted, not only in England but all over Christendom, and gave it to them thick. "Some 300 MSS of the work [Middle English version] survive and there are said to be more copies of it dating from the fourteenth [?] and fifteenth centuries than there are of any other book except the Scriptures" (Wells p. 433). There are also innumerable MSS in French, Latin, German, Dutch, Italian, etc. It should be noted that the Latin MSS and all the English MSS but one (Cotton) give one the impression that their language is the original one. In the Cotton MS it is stated that Sir John himself translated his book from Latin into French, thence into English in order "that every man of my nation might understand it." The oldest MS is French, 1371; the Latin and English MSS date from the following century. The Cotton is one of the earliest English MSS, c. 1410–20. As usual, the popularity of the incunabula confirmed that of the MSS. Klebs (nos. 648–52) listed 35 editions in five languages, whereas he could find only 4 editions of Marco Polo. Marco was too honest! (Sarton p. 67, 82, 111, 183, 186, 189, 191, 1938.)

Sir John was utterly unreliable, but it does not follow that everything he wrote was wrong. His success was due to a proper blending of agreeable fancies with enough verisimilitude and with easily controllable statements, plausible statements, and statements which ought to be true. One of his predictions seemed more fanciful than all the others: he spoke of a man who traveled continually eastward and came back to his own country. . . .

His account began as if he were writing a guide to Jerusalem, and though he soon forgot that purpose, it was the right touch to win the reader's benevolence

[17] Jusserand (p. 236, 1884).

at the start. Indeed, a pilgrimage to Jerusalem was as it were the ideal journey, for sinners as well as for saints and for everybody. The name Jerusalem was like a magic name, yet the journey required so much time that few Englishmen could accomplish it. We cannot name many. There is a Walter Wiburn c. 1367, then Henry of Lancaster "earl of Derby" (the future Henry IV) in 1392-93, and in the same year Thomas Swinburne and Thomas Brygg. The accounts of those journeys were all written in Latin. For Swinburne, see the note in chapter XXIII; for the others, Röhricht (1890) sub annis. A few words may be added here concerning the pilgrimage of Henry of Bolingbroke (or of Lancaster), the future king. Henry was very pious and had thought of joining the crusade of Louis II de Bourbon, but at the last moment allowed his brother John Beaufort to replace him. Then he volunteered to fight with the Teutonic Knights against the heathen Lithuanians, and he set sail for that purpose from Boston in 1390. That story does not concern us. In July 1392 Henry left England again, sailing from Lynn to Danzig. After a while, having probably realized that there were better things for an English prince to do than to fight for the aggrandizement of Prussia, he decided to pilgrim to Jerusalem. He traveled via Prague, Vienna, Venice, Zara, Rhodes, Jaffa; the return journey was via Cyprus, Venice, Milano, Paris. He was back in London on July 5, 1393. The account or rather the accounts of his travels were kept by his treasurer, Richard Kyngeston (d. 1418), archdeacon of Hereford, and have come down to us.[18]

In addition to the narratives of pilgrimages, there were also a number of itineraries, represented in Middle English by such texts as the Stations of Rome and the Stations of Jerusalem, the dating of which is difficult. The Stations of Rome was probably first put together about the end of the thirteenth century, the purpose being not only to describe the shrines of Rome, but to win pilgrims away from Santiago and Jerusalem. Were there not more indulgences to be won in the Eternal City than anywhere else? It was first written in verse, the number of lines varying considerably from one MS to another; there are also prose versions. The Stations of Jerusalem is a later composition (fifteenth century?), also in verse (848 lines). The journey from Venice to Jerusalem is described, then the Holy Places and the New Testament events connected with them.[19]

A5. *The Netherlands*

The Netherlandish group of travelers and geographers is very diversified and distinguished. We may begin with the least important and the most popular member of it, Johannes de Hese, whose Itinerarius ad Jerusalem per diversas mundi partes is one of the best collections of geographical lore. It is a mixture of a little truth with a wealth of fancy, and enjoyed a popularity comparable to that of John Mandeville's Travels and explainable on the same grounds, yet much smaller. Its circulation was restricted to the Latin and Dutch groups, whereas Mandeville's inventions were available in as many as six languages, and the number of its incunabula editions was only 8 as against 35 for Mandeville. Such books as were written by these two Johns, Hese and Mandeville, are very precious sources for the

[18] Hans Prutz: Rechnungen über Heinrich von Derby's Preussenfahrten 1390-92 (336 p., Leipzig 1893). Lucy Toulmin Smith: Expeditions to Prussia and the Holy Land made by Henry earl of Derby in 1390-93, being the accounts kept by his treasurer (Camden Society, 474 p., 1894).

[19] Jusserand (p. 296-99, 1884). Wells (p. 432). For the meaning of stations, see A. J. Maclean (ERE 11, 854-57, 1921).

understanding of mediaeval thought. The historian of science may exclaim with some impatience, "I am not concerned with dreams and fancies, I can take stock only of real knowledge, factual knowledge, I want to register only what the best people knew for certain." That is all very well, but it cannot be done. Knowledge was not analyzed, and differentiated as to its sources, as with us. There was no touchstone for scientific truth. The fables told in those books were as certain to their readers as the controllable facts. And where could the facts be controlled? Perhaps the only place where the analysis of geographical facts was then seriously attempted was in Majorca, and the only men who contemplated it, the Jewish map makers of that island.

To return to the Netherlands, a far greater personage than John of Hese (or John of Utrecht) was John of Ypres or "Long John" (Jan De Langhe), who was abbot of the Benedictine house of St. Omer until his death in 1383. Long John was one of the first to appreciate the pregnancy of geographical discoveries and to collect travelers' accounts; this is very remarkable because the golden age of scientific discoveries had not yet begun (the usher of it was the Portuguese infante Henrique o Navegador, who was born only eleven years after Long John's death). We must consider him the forerunner of the Italian Ramusio and the Englishman Hakluyt; unfortunately, whereas the Raccolta of Giambattista Ramusio appeared in 1550–59 and the Principall navigations of Richard Hakluyt in 1589, 1598–1600, the texts put together by Long John remained unpublished in their entirety until modern times. By the way, Long John's collection was meant to appear in French, whereas Ramusio's and Hakluyt's were respectively in Italian and English.

Problems of geodesy and the nature of gravitation were discussed by Marsilius van Inghen.

The Low Countries must have produced their share of pilgrims, yet I can only mention one relevant text. That is one of c. 1380, Via prima quae est diversorum locorum mundi distantia demonstrativa, explaining pilgrim ways leading from Bruges to every country of Europe, except Great Britain and Portugal. It has been edited by Joachim Lelewel: Géographie du Moyen âge (Epilogue p. 281–308, Bruxelles 1857). Of course, one might add to that the Itinerarius ad Jerusalem of John of Utrecht or its Dutch translation,[20] but that is hardly more legitimate than to count John Mandeville among the English pilgrims. For the next Netherlandish pilgrim one has to wait until 1403, when the illustrious[21] Belgian knight Ghillebert de Lannoy (1386–1462) made his first voyage to the Near East. This Ghillebert (variant of Gilbert) was an outstanding type of knight errant, who began his military career as early as 1399, at the ripe age of 13. He spent his life as a soldier, diplomat, statesman in the service of the dukes of Burgundy. He traveled and fought all over Europe including Russia, in the Near East, and in North Africa. He visited the Near East thrice, in 1403–4, 1421–23, 1446–47. He wrote in French accounts of his journeys and embassies and two books of moral precepts. All this, however, concerns the fifteenth century, even if Ghillebert himself was a fin-de-siècle product of the fourteenth.[22]

[20] Bearing by mistake the name of John Voet of Utrecht (Röhricht 1890, year 1398).

[21] When the order of the Golden Fleece was established in Bruges 1430 by Philip the Good, duke of Burgundy, out of the thirty original knights three belonged to Lannoy's family, including himself.

[22] Constant Philippe Serrure: Voyages et ambassades de messire Guillebert de Lannoy, 1399–1450 (140 p., Mons 1840), based on Lannoy's MSS, with geographical notes, glossary, and map by Joachim Lelewel. Charles Potvin: Oeuvres de Ghillebert de Lannoy (Louvain 1878),

Of the Netherlanders mentioned in this section, two were southerners (Belgians), John of Ypres and Ghillebert de Lannoy, and two northerners (Dutch), John of Utrecht and Marsilius van Inghen. All except Ghillebert wrote in Latin; the two Belgians wrote also in French, but not in Dutch. This requires some explanation. Lannoy's case is simple; he was a familiar of the Burgundian court and a diplomat; French was then already the main diplomatic language, especially in the Near East. As to Long John, though he was born at Ypres, in the heart of Flanders, he had been educated in Paris and then had withdrawn to the abbey of St. Bertin in St. Omer, of which monastery he was the abbot for eighteen years (1365-83). Now the county of Artois (almost coextensive with the department Pas-de-Calais) had many connections, too difficult to explain, with the duchy of Burgundy. The Artésiens and more particularly the Audomarois (= inhabitants of St. Omer) were partly Flemish and partly French; it is probable that the upper classes spoke French. A good witness thereof is the courtly romance Le livre du très chevalereux comte d'Artois et de sa femme, written not long afterward, one of the most gracious monuments of the old French prose.[23] The story is centered upon the romantic personality of Philippe de Bourgogne, born in 1323, the son of Eudes IV de Bourgogne (count of Artois 1330-47) and Jeanne de France; in 1338, he married Jeanne de Boulogne; he died at the siege of Aiguillon (Lot-et-Garonne) in 1346. The title of count of Artois given to him in the romance is an anticipated courtesy title, for he died before his father. Though the hero belongs to the first half of the fourteenth century, the romance dedicated to him was not written before the fifteenth; there are no MSS anterior to the fifteenth century.[24]

A6. *Germany*

My notes relative to Germany are surprisingly few. Indeed, they relate only to two men, each of whom might have been rejected, the first because he was a Jew or a Frenchman, the second because his achievement was posterior to 1400.

Themon son of the Jew was a Westphalian and a convert. He studied in Paris and became one of the luminaries of that university. His study of the Meteorologica implied as usual the discussion of geodesic and geological problems. Do the centers of gravity of the earth and the universe coincide? and how are we to understand the first? What are the densities of each of the four elements? On these and similar questions he held (or seemed to hold) opinions which were original but in the absence of factual knowledge highly arbitrary. Like many other schoolmen, he seemed to be satisfied with queries and many answers to each, illustrating his curiosity and his learning, but leading nowhere.

The Bavarian Hans Schiltberger was one of the victims of the baleful crusade of

---

with geographical notes and maps by Jean Charles Houzeau. Ferdinand Loise (Biographie nationale de Belgique 11, 308-22, 1891). Oscar Halecki: Gilbert de Lannoy and his discovery of East Central Europe (Bull. Polish Institute 2, 314-31, New York 1941). Petras Klimas: Ghillebert de Lannoy in medieval Lithuania (New York 1945; Speculum 20, 486-91).

23 Abbé Mercier: Extrait d'un MS intitulé Le livre du très chevalereux comte d'Artois (48 p., ex Bibliothèque des romans, vol. 1, janvier 1783), reprinted in 25 copies. J. Barrois: Le livre du très chevalereux comte d'Artois (quarto, 236 p., ill., Paris 1837), first edition of whole text.

24 According to Gaston Paris: Littérature française au Moyen âge (4th ed., Paris 1909; p. 113), the prose story was preceded by a poem, which is related to Oriental tales and to a tale of Boccaccio, imitated by Shakespeare in All's well that ends well. If so, the adaptation to Philippe de Bourgogne is a later invention.

Nicopolis. Being then a boy of 15, he was made prisoner by the Turks and remained thirty years (1396–1426) in their servitude or dependence, being moved about by his masters and his own reckless spirit in Turkey, Armenia, Georgia, Turkestan, Siberia, and Russia. After his return he wrote a Reisebuch, containing an account of his own adventures and of many countries he had visited or heard of. Schiltberger was the first of the great German travelers, the first non-Russian European to explore a part of Siberia, i.e., parts of the Ob and Irtysh valleys; he may have visited the holy places of Islām, and if so he was the first German to do so.

His relation, poor as it was and full of imperfections, contained so much that was true and novel, and so much that was striking and pathetic, that it was very well received. Klebs lists only 1 incunabula edition (no. 894), Reisen in den Landen der Heidenschaft (Augsburg 1478), because that is the only independent one, but at least 3 more editions appeared before 1500, and at least 6 more in the sixteenth century. There are also many modern editions, by Karl Friedrich Neumann (182 p., Munich 1859); by Filip Jacob Bruun in the Records of the Imperial Novorossiisk University (vol. 1, Odessa 1866) with Russian commentary; by Valentin Langmantel (205 p., Tübingen 1885).

Englished by Buchan Telfer with Bruun's notes (Hakluyt Society, 295 p., map, London 1879).

V. Langmantel (ADB 31, 262–64, 1890). Beazley (3, 356–78, 1906). Hennig (3, 325–32, 1938).

In the section devoted to Italian geography reference was made to the revival due to the rediscovery of Ptolemy's Cosmographia, text and maps. That revival was initiated by Italians, and continued vigorously by other Italians and Germans. A study of the early cartography of Germany and Central Europe made by Dana B. Durand confirmed this (Isis 19, 486–502, 3 pl., 1933; Isis 21, 367). To be sure, most of this concerns the fifteenth century, but it is worth while to announce here the German fruits which were soon to be obtained from the Italian initiative of the fourteenth century. According to Durand, the earliest maps of North European nations can now be placed with certainty in the first half of the fifteenth century, perhaps as early as the third decade. Durand developed his views in a book the printing of which was completed in Leiden at the time of the German invasion;[25] no copy has yet reached me (January 1947).

Finally, we have a few accounts written by German pilgrims to the Holy Land or concerning them. According to Röhricht (1890) we have c. 1356–57, Johannes de Oosterroyck: Tractatus de Terra Sancta; 1376, Johannes von Bodman and Diethalm Schilter: Die Fahrt zu dem heiligen würdigen Grab zu Jerusalem; 1377, Hertel [Johann] von Lichtenstein: Pilgerbüchlein; 1385, Lorenz Egen: Wie Lorenz Egen von Augsburg . . . zoch gen Sant Kathareinen; 1385, Peter von Sparnau and Ulrich von Tennstädt: Reise nach Jerusalem.

For Johann von Lichtenstein, see Iosef Haupt: Philippi Liber de Terra Sancta in der deutschen Übersetzung des Augustiner-Lesemeisters Leupold vom Jahre 1377 (Oesterreichische Zeitschrift für katholische Theologie 10, 511–40, Wien 1871; reprinted separately, Wien 1872). It has been shown by father Wilhelm Anton Neumann: Philippi Descriptio Terrae Sanctae (ibid. 11, 1–79, 165–74, 1872; reprint 88 p., Wien 1872) that the text translated in 1377 on the occasion of Johann

[25] The Vienna-Klosterneuburg map corpus of the fifteenth century (2 vols., Brill, Leiden 1940).

von Lichtenstein's return from the Holy Land was simply an abbreviation of the Descriptio Terrae Sanctae written in 1285-91 by Philippus Brusserius Savonensis; Neumann's paper contains a critical edition of the thirteenth-century text.

Note that the five accounts mentioned above are all in German, except possibly the first (a German text might have a Latin title). This is what we should expect. Such accounts were not written for learned men, but for the edification of pious people and the use of would-be pilgrims.

A7. *Scandinavia*

An Icelandic description of the Holy Land dating from about the middle of the fourteenth century, if not earlier, is included in the same Codex arnamagn. 194,736 (Copenhagen) which contains the account written by Nikulás Saemundarson (XII-2). This anonymous description was edited in Icelandic and translated into Latin by Carl Christian Rafn: Antiquités russes d'après les monuments historiques des Islandais (2, 415-20, Copenhague 1852). The text begins "I Miklagarði er kirkja, er heitir Aegisif . . . " (In Constantinople is a church called Hagia Sophia . . .). There are other geographical documents in Icelandic in that sumptuous publication (p. 388-452) which I have not been able to analyze; it is unfortunately not indexed.

Greenland had been discovered by Icelanders before the end of the ninth century and colonized by them a century later. It remained an Icelandic colony until the end of the Icelandic republic. In 1262 the Icelanders lost their independence and became subjects of Norway; in 1380 the Norwegians themselves became Danish subjects. Thus from 1262 to 1380 Greenland was a Norwegian colony.

It is not surprising, then, to find Norwegian sailors, priests, administrators, or adventurers proceeding all the way to Greenland. The priest Ivar Bárðarson was sent to Greenland in 1341 (or 1349?) by the bishop of Bergen. He remained there until 1379. He wrote an account of Greenland which is lost in its original (Norwegian) form, but survives partly in a Danish translation. Another account was written by Björn Einarsson Jórsalafarer, who visited Greenland in 1385-87, and lived there with two Eskimos whom he had rescued.

It is highly probable that Norwegian or Icelandic sailors proceeded from Greenland to those coasts of North America which had been discovered by their ancestors in the year 1000. Indeed, the Greenland colonists needed a certain amount of timber in order to build houses, churches, bridges, ships, etc.; no timber was available in Greenland (nor for that matter in Iceland), and it took considerably less time and pains to import what was needed from Labrador and even from other American shores farther south than from Norway.

We know of a mission sent by king Magnus Smek in 1355 in order to investigate the weakening Christianity of Greenland. That mission, headed by Poul Knutsson, was absent ten years; it probably extended its inspection to Vinland, which was a part of the diocese of Gardar (Greenland).

It is possible that some of the Norse colonizers of America or some of the Norse visitors tried to obtain a better idea of the American "island" by its circumnavigation, even as their ancestors Naddodd the Viking and Gardar Svavarsson had circumnavigated Iceland c. 860-70 (Introd. 1, 605). This may have led them via the Hudson Strait, the Hudson Bay, the Nelson River, and Lake Winnipeg to the region of Manitoba, Dakota, Minnesota. That hypothesis has been somewhat confirmed by recent discoveries of various implements similar to the Viking implements, and of the much discussed runic inscription of Kensington, dated 1362. If that inscription be genuine and the date 1362 certain, we must admit that Norsemen visited that region in 1362, but they may have reached it along other roads.

The discoveries made by Norse sailors were eventually mapped by the great Danish cartographer Claudius Claussøn Swart, better known under the name Claudius Clavus.[26] He was the earliest cartographer of the northern countries, having prepared before 1427 a map of them for cardinal Guillaume Filastre.[27] This map is often called the Nancy map, because it is included in the MS of the translation of Ptolemy by Giacomo d'Angelo kept in the library of that city (Cod. lat. 441, completed 1427). After his return to the north Clavus collected material for a better map, his "second" map, which influenced the cartographic incunabula (e.g., the Ulm editions of Ptolemy 1482, 1486). Clavus' maps, furnished with lines of latitude and longitude, are of great importance because they were the first scientific extension of Ptolemy's geography. They contain the earliest representation of Greenland and a fairly good drawing of the Danish isles (e.g., Fünen, Seeland), far superior to that found in much later maps (end of seventeenth century).

We have again outrun our boundary, but it was justified because Clavus' work (e.g., that concerning Greenland) was largely the fruit of discoveries made in the fourteenth century and before.

A8. *Russia and Byzantium*

The geographical literature of this time is almost exclusively restricted to accounts of pilgrimages.

The University of Ghent owns a Slavonic MS which was written by an unknown person at Vidin (on the Danube) in 1360 for Anna, wife of Iovan Sracimir, one of the two last Bulgarian tsars. It is a very long text (c. 4,266 lines), a synaxary of saintly women, ending with a short description of the Holy Places. That description is very similar to those given by Daniel of Kiev (XII-1) and Stephen of Novgorod (XIV-1).

[26] His family name was Swart, also written Suartho or Niger. Claussøn = filius Nicolai. Hence he is also named Nicolaus Niger, or more correctly Claudius Niger; Poggio called him Nicolaus Gothus. Clavus was born on September 14, 1388 in Sallinge, Fünen, Denmark; educated at the Cistercian monastery of Sorø, near Roskilde; "peragravit magnam partem orbis," said Poggio; was in Rome 1423/24; returned not long after to the northern countries; date and place of death unknown.

Axel Anthon Björnbo (1874–1911) and Carl S. Petersen: Fyenboen Claudius Claussøn Swart (260 p., maps, Copenhagen 1904), in Danish with French summary; Der Däne C. C. Swart, der älteste Kartograph des Nordens, der erste Ptolemäus-Epigon der Renaissance (266 p., 3 maps, facs., Innsbruck 1909), really a new edition of the Danish memoir of 1904, superseding it. A. A. Björnbo: Cartographia Groenlandica (345 p., Copenhagen 1912), in Danish. Nansen (2, 248–76, 1921), detracting much from Clavus' reputation. Vilhjalmur Stefansson: Greenland (p. 198, New York 1942; Isis 34, 379–80).

[27] Guillaume Filastre (or Fillastre), born in 1347/48, died in Rome 1428. Educated in Angers, taught in Reims. Archbishop of Aix-en-Provence, cardinal 1411. Took a distinguished part in the councils of Pisa and Constance, laboring for the healing of the schism and the election in 1417 of Martin V, who appointed him his legate in France. Filastre was a friend of Pierre d'Ailly and deeply interested in cosmography. He wrote a commentary on Ptolemy included in the Nancy MS (NBG 17, 687–88, 1856). He received undeserved credit for the innovations introduced by Clavus, e.g. concerning Greenland. In fact, in his commentary he stated, in opposition to Clavus, that Greenland lay north of Norway, an error which was often repeated and was difficult to eradicate.

The Slavonic (Serbian) text was partly edited by Jean Martinov in the (Russian) Monuments of ancient literature and art, no. 14 (quarto, 28 p., 5 facs., Synodal press, St. Petersburg 1882); the same father Martinov translated the description into French (Archives de l'Orient latin 2 B, 389–93, 1884).

Three other accounts, all dealt with in chapter XXIII, were written in Russian by Ignatius of Smolensk, Alexander the Pilgrim, and Grethenios. All these pilgrims wrote in their Russian vernacular, which confirms the remark made above about the German pilgrims. Ignatius and Grethenios described the itinerary from Moscow to Jerusalem and the Holy Places; Alexander did not go beyond Constantinople.

The case of Grethenios is especially interesting. His name being Greek, he was probably a Byzantine priest. Many such priests came to Russia to impart religious education and insure ritual continuity, even as Italian priests had come to England in earlier times. Strangely enough, we have no pilgrim accounts of this time in Greek, except perhaps an anonymous short text, Ἀπόδειξις περὶ τῶν Ἱεροσολύμων, of uncertain date which may have been composed before 1400. Edited in Greek and Latin by Leone Allacci: Συμμικτα (p. 80–102, Cologne 1623); by Stephan Bergler in Josephi Genesii[28] De rebus Constantinopolitanis (folio, suppt. p. 33–40, Venice 1733), forming vol. 22 of the Venetian Byzantine corpus; in PG (133, 973–90, 1864).

To conclude our survey of Byzantine geography, reference may be made pro memoria to the discovery of the São Miguel island in the Azores archipelago by an unnamed "Greek," said to have been thrown upon that island by a storm. The story is not impossible but it is not very plausible, as we have never heard of any mediaeval Greek or Byzantine navigator's venturing into the Atlantic. Moreover, it was told for the first time very late, by Antonio Cordeyro (S.J., 1641–1722) in his Historia insulana das ilhas a Portugal sugeytas no Oceano Occidental (quarto, p. 117, Lisboa 1717), with the marginal caption "Fabulosos descubrimentos da Ilha de S. Miguel."[29] As was explained in chapter I, the Azores were probably discovered before the middle of the fourteenth century, but the effective discovery was not made until 1431–44.

B. *Israel*

The most important work done by Jewish geographers has already been discussed in the Catalonian section above, because we found it impossible to deal with the cartographic school of Majorca except if Jewish and Christian efforts were considered together.

Geographical information may be found in compilations like the Shebile emunah of Meir ben Isaac ibn al-Dabi, and in some theological commentaries such as the Ẓafenat pa'neaḥ of Joseph ben Eliezer Bonfils, who flourished in Spain but spent the latter part of his life in Damascus, Egypt, and Jerusalem. Jacob ben Nathaniel ha-Kohen (XII-2), who visited the tombs of the saints in the Holy Land and wrote an account of them, may be of a later date than we thought; according to Steinschneider the account might be as late as the fourteenth century.

C. *Islām*

The geographical writings of Muslim travelers and learned men are not very numerous, but of outstanding value. They include the most important ones of this

[28] Γενέσιος, author of four books of imperial annals of the ninth century (813–86). He flourished about the middle of the tenth century (Krumbacher p. 264).

[29] German translation in Hennig (3, 315–16, 1938).

time. It will suffice to divide them into two groups, relating to the West and the East.

C1. *Maghrib*

The greatest traveler of the Middle Ages, not excepting Marco Polo, was a Maghribī of Berber ancestry, Muḥammad ibn 'Abdallāh Ibn Baṭṭūṭa of Tangiers. He is so well known even to non-Orientalists, to whom the whole text of his travels is available in French and well selected extracts in English, that it is not necessary to do more than to recall the main facts. For thirty years he traveled over a great part of the world in the three continents. The initial stimulation was given him by the religious duty of the pilgrimage to Mecca. Learned men took their time accomplishing that duty, and might be absent for two or three years; Ibn Baṭṭūṭa, however, beat them all. His first absence from home lasted twenty-five years, during which it is true he accomplished the Pilgrimage at least five times. All in all he must have traveled some seventy-five thousand miles by land and sea. He not only visited every part of the Dār al-Islām and many Muslim colonies abroad, but also penetrated the lands of Christians, Hindus, and Chinese. We owe him an abundance of information concerning North Africa, Egypt, Anatolia, Persia, India, China, and, in the west, Spain, his native Morocco, and, most interesting of all, West Africa, the mysterious country watered by the Niger, the ancient culture centered in Timbuktu.

For the fascinating account of those journeys we are indebted not only to Ibn Baṭṭūṭa, but also to his secretary, Ibn Juzayy, to whom he dictated it. Ibn Juzayy did not simply take the dictation, but edited his notes, added various literary embellishments and complementary information taken from earlier narratives. Though many interpolations by the editor are formally given as such, being introduced by the words "Qāla [= dixit] Ibn Juzayy,"[30] other interpolations or modifications are probably hidden. Such questions being of their nature insolvable, it is better to consider the Riḥlat ibn Baṭṭūṭa, completed 1355, as the joint work of the two men, Ibn Baṭṭūṭa remaining the main creator and the hero.

The Riḥla does not pay much attention to physical geography; Muslim doctors were far more interested in men than in climates, plants, and animals; Ibn Baṭṭūṭa was no exception to that rule, and his account is a monument of anthropogeography ("géographie humaine"). It is clear that Ibn Baṭṭūṭa was not map-minded, for I do not remember his referring a single time to a map, which he would have needed, according to our own ideas, in order to "map out" his travels, if not to direct his steps from place to place. A curious exception concerns his mention of a map of Gibraltar (Defrémery 4, 359), which, if we do not misunderstand his description of it, was a relief or raised map, the first mentioned anywhere.

The great Spanish historian Ibn al-Khaṭīb, who lived until 1374, wrote an account of a journey in eastern Granada and a description of Spanish cities and their libraries. Ibn Khaldūn realized how deeply the behavior of men is conditioned by geographical factors, and therefore described these factors at length in his immortal Muqaddama. He was well versed in Ptolemaic and Idrisian geography and continued the ancient speculations on the proportion of land areas to sea areas, the seven climates, etc. He discussed the relative importance of race and environment, nature and nurture. The significance and importance of Ibn Khaldūn as a pioneer in geographical as well as in historical thinking cannot be overestimated.

[30] In addition to his preamble and conclusion, there are at least 47 interpolations which can be definitely ascribed to him. See Defrémery's index (p. 47, 1859).

One question of western Sudanese geography deserves special consideration, because it illustrates the fundamental ignorance which existed in those days and was bound to continue for centuries, as long as the sites discovered by travelers were not mathematically determined and their relations with other sites could not be seen on reliable maps. We refer to the ambiguities and mysteries concerning the river Niger, one of the greatest rivers of Africa, next to the Nile and Congo.

Ibn Khaldūn (Muqaddama, French text 1, 116, Arabic text 1, 96) and Ibn Baṭṭūṭa (Defrémery 4, 395) both speak of the Niger as if it were a branch of the Nile; in fact, they call it Nile. In order to understand that error it is necessary to look backward and forward.

Herodotos (ii, 32–33) reported the existence of a great river crossing North Africa, a western branch of the Nile, flowing from west to east, symmetrically with the Danube in Europe. Juba II, king of Mauretania (I-2 B.C.), and Pliny (I-2) told similar stories. On the other hand, Ptolemy (II-1) placed the sources of the Nile in the Lunae mons (τὸ τῆς Σελήνης ὄρος) somewhere in equatorial East Africa (Geogr. IV, 8). That tradition was elaborated by the Arabs. For example, al-Khwārizmī (IX-1) represented on his map[31] the following schema. Ten rivers issue from the Jabal al-qamar (= Lunae mons), each group of five reaches a lake, from each lake rivers flow northward to a third lake, whence the Nile originates. That Ptolemaic-Khwarizmian theory was soon contaminated by others, to wit the one alluded to before ascribing a western source to the Nile, and the Jewish-Christian legend ascribing it a source in Paradise.

The western theory was confirmed by al-Bakrī (XI-2), who was the first Muslim to identify Nile with Niger; this error was continued in various ways by other Arabic geographers such as al-Idrīsī (XII-2), Ibn Sa'īd al-Maghribī (XIII-2), Abū-l-Fidā' (XIV-1), al-Dimashqī (XIV-1), etc. The error was given a strange twist by al-Idrīsī, who imagined that the Niger flowed from east to west, identifying it with such a river as the Senegal. This was not incompatible with the idea that Niger and Nile originated in the same localities. On the other hand, one of the commonplaces of Arabic geography was a remark to the effect that the Nile flows from south to north and is the only river in the world for which this is the case. How could this be reconciled with the knowledge of the middle Niger flowing from west to east, and the lower Niger flowing from north to south? It is very puzzling.

Ibn Baṭṭūṭa described the Niger (which he called Nile) as flowing from west to east, but al-Idrīsī's conception of a flow in the opposite direction prevailed, and was adopted by Leo Africanus (1526)[32] and by the subsequent cartographers down to as late as 1792 (as shown in the map by Guillaume de l'Isle or Delisle in the atlas of J. B. Elwe, Amsterdam 1792).[33]

[31] Hans von Mžik: Afrika nach der arabischen Bearbeitung der γεωγραφικὴ ὑφήγησις von al-Khwārizmī (Denkschriften der Akad. der Wissenschaften vol. 59, 105 p., Vienna 1916; Isis 5, 208), with Arabic map of the Nile, explained p. 42–45.

[32] Joannes Leo Africanus was a Christian convert from Islām, formerly named al-Ḥasan ibn Muḥammad al-Wazzān al-Zaiyātī. Born in Granada 1495, educated in Fās, taken by corsairs in 1520 and converted; died in Tunis c. 1550, a good Muslim. The most popular of his works was a description of Africa which he wrote in Arabic and translated into Italian 1526, and which was first published in Ramusio's Navigationi (Venice 1550). It was translated into Latin, French, English, Dutch. L. Massignon (EI 3, 22, 1928).

[33] The map is reproduced in Bovill (1933), as well as the Africae tabula nova of Abraham Ortelius (Antwerp 1570) and the Africae nova descriptio of Jan Blaeu (Amsterdam 1664–65), the three maps showing the Niger flowing into the Atlantic together with the Senegal. In the Delisle map, there is added a legend "Quelques uns croyent que le Niger est un bras du Nil et l'apellent à cause decela le Nil des Nègres." In 1792!

Considering the chaotic knowledge of the Niger, the Senegal, and the Nile which obtained as late as 1792, we should not judge Ibn Baṭṭūṭa or Ibn Khaldūn too severely for the confusion of their own thoughts. It may be added that when David Livingstone (1813–73) reached the Lualaba river in 1866, he wondered whether it was the Nile, the Niger, or the Congo! Having said so much, we may be permitted to indicate briefly how the veil was gradually lifted. Mungo Park reached the upper Niger near Segu on July 20, 1796 (published with James Rennell 1799); on a second expedition Mungo Park reached the upper Niger again in August 1805 at Bamako, traveled downstream, and lost his life at the rapids of Busa (lower Niger) in 1806. As a final vindication of the fourteenth-century geographers, if such were needed, as late as 1829 general Sir Rufane Shaw Donkin (1773–1841) published a Dissertation on the course and probable termination of the Niger (205 p., 2 maps, London 1829) wherein he claimed that the Niger enters the Mediterranean at the Gulf of Syrtis! The mystery of the Niger was finally solved by two brothers, Richard Lemon Lander (1804–34) and John Lander (1807–30), who reached Busa in the middle of 1830 and sailed down the river to the sea. The course of the Niger was now for the first time completely understood from its upper reaches down to the delta.[34]

The disentanglement of the Nile from the Niger might have been reached as well by a fuller knowledge of the Nile. Though Muslim territory ended at the first cataract, near Uswān (Assuan), some of the conquerors went up the river at least as far as Dongola, and they received information concerning the upper reaches of the Nile from caravans. At any rate al-Khwārizmī's schema, fantastic as it seems, contains a remarkable amount of truth. The Jabal al-qamar has been identified with the Ruwenzori range, rising between lakes Albert and Edward, not far above the equator. The Ruwenzori range was discovered by Henry Morton Stanley (1841–1904) in 1888. The exploration of the upper Nile and the exact determination of its sources was completed only in the second half of the nineteenth century by European and Egyptian explorers; the history is too complicated to be told here.

The confusion of Niger with Senegal implies some knowledge of the latter. Indeed, the Senegal River was known to the ancients, even perhaps to Hanno (V B.C.), yet it was not recorded in Ptolemy's geography. The Senegal country was conquered by Arabs in the first half of the eleventh century, being perhaps the first Negro country of Africa to be Islamized (EI 4, 223, 1926). It has been claimed but not proved that Dieppe seamen rediscovered the mouth of the Senegal c. 1364. That discovery was made in 1445 by the Portuguese Dinis Dias. In 1455, Alvise Cadamosto (1432–77), Venetian sailor in the service of Henrique o Navegador, ascended the Senegal River (as well as the Gambia) for some distance. The upper reaches of the river were explored in 1638 by Claude Jannequin sieur de Rochefort, and c. 1698 by André Brue, who went beyond the Felu falls. The source of the Senegal (more exactly of the Bafing) was discovered in 1818 by Gaspard Mollien in the Futā Jallon. This is the most important range in West Africa and the most important hydrographic center in the whole continent; it contains the sources not only of the Bafing, but also of the Niger and the Gambia (EI 2, 120–23, 1914).

As to the Congo, it was unknown to the Greek and Arabic geographers. Its mouth was discovered by the Portuguese Diago Cão in 1482. The Zaire (as the

[34] Parts of the delta had been observed before, but without realization that these waters were identical with those flowing near Timbuktu.

Congo was then called) was mentioned in the Lusiadas of Camões (1572). Apparently the river remained completely unexplored until the nineteenth century.[34a] As it is an immense river basin, second only to that of the Amazon, the story of its gradual exploration is too long to be summarized here. It is the story of the unveiling of central Africa, a chapter of geographical discovery, and even more so of colonial history, in the nineteenth century.

August Knötel: Der Niger der Alten (48 p., Glogau 1866), with a map of northwestern Africa after Ptolemy. La Roncière (2, 107–11, 1925). Bovill (1933). Johannes Hendrik Kramers: Al-Nīl (EI 3, 918–21, 1935). There is a very large literature on the great rivers Nile, Niger, Senegal, Congo, but this is not the place to refer to it, even in selection. An exception might be made for the book of Emil Ludwig: Der Nil, Lebenslauf eines Stromes (Amsterdam 1935; English translation London 1936), a popular but well documented "biography" of the Nile outside Egypt.

C2. *Mashriq*

The Eastern geographers were far less important not only than their Western contemporaries, but than their own predecessors, for there was not a single one among them comparable to Abū-l-Fidā', who had died in 1331, or even to al-Dimashqī, who lived only until 1326.

The Muslims' repeated victories over the Crusaders had intensified their pride in their holy places, especially those of Egypt and Palestine which had been menaced. Hence there arose in this century a pilgrim literature, concerned not only with the sacred places of Arabia, but also with those of the Near East. That pilgrim literature is sometimes polemical, or, to use Atiya's apt expression, it takes the nature of a counter-crusade propaganda. Muslims were urged to go to Jerusalem to insure their salvation. Thus, in an anonymous book of the middle of the fourteenth century dealing with the virtues of Syria (faḍā'il al-shām) and the virtues of Jerusalem (faḍā'il bait al-maqdis, or al-muqaddis) it was stated that a prayer said in the mosque of 'Umar was equal to 40,000 prayers elsewhere, and that one said in the mosque of Damascus was worth 30,000 prayers elsewhere. One recognizes the same kind of quantitative superstitions as those which abounded in the sanctuaries of Christendom, accidental coincidences which illustrate the identity of human minds in various climes. The comparison can be carried farther, for in this case also piety was combined with worldly concerns. The pilgrims were reminded that Syria possessed nine-tenths of the wealth of the world, and hence was truly worth keeping and defending. Another book enumerating the blessings to be obtained in Jerusalem was written in 1351 by Aḥmad ibn Muḥammad al-Maqdisī. Two other books of the same kind may still be cited: the Muthīr al-gharām fī ziyārat al-Khalīl 'am, by Isḥāq ibn Ibrāhīm al-Tadmurī al-Shāfi'ī (d. 1429), dealing with the pilgrimage to Hebron;[35] and Al-kawākib al-saiyāra fī tartīb al-ziyāra fī-l-Qarāfatain

[34a] It was explored by the Portuguese Duarte Lopes in 1578. He came back to Europe eleven years later and met in Rome Filippo Pigafetta (1533–1603). The story which he told Pigafetta in Portuguese was published by the latter in Italian, Relatione del reame di Congo (Roma 1591), with two maps of Africa and Central Africa. Though the book was translated into Dutch, English, German, and Latin, its contents were strangely forgotten or discounted, and Lopes' discoveries had to be made anew in the second half of the nineteenth century. Further information will be found in my article on Camillo Agrippa, Domenico Fontana, and Filippo Pigafetta, as yet unpublished.

[35] The Arabic name of Hebron is al-Khalīl = the friend (of God), with reference to the prophet Abraham, who was buried there (EI 2, 431–32, 1918; 886–87, 1925).

al-kubra wal-ṣughrā,[36] written in 1401 by Muḥammad ibn ʿAbdallāh al-Suʿūdī ibn al-Zayāt, describing the tombs venerated in Cairo.

See Brockelmann (2, 131; suppt. 2, 162). Atiya (p. 468–69, 545, 1938).

Such books belong to the literature of topography. Humble as they are, they may help one sometime to correct or precise historical facts. They had to be mentioned here, if only because similar books relative to Christian and Jewish pilgrimages had been mentioned before. Religious needs, and particularly the urge to visit holy places and the faith that such good deeds will favor one's salvation, are truly universal.

Al-Bākuwī's summary of the geography of al-Qazwīnī was written at the end of the fourteenth century or the beginning of the fifteenth. It has over the original text the superiority of giving the mathematical coordinates of the places mentioned, but it continues the inconvenient subdivision of the materials into seven alphabets, a separate classification being used for each climate.

Al-Qalqashandī began in 1387 and completed twenty-five years later an immense encyclopaedia, which includes a considerable amount of geographical information. The Ṣubḥ al-aʿshā, as it is called, was modeled upon the Masālik al-abṣār which Ibn Faḍlallāh al-ʿUmarī had compiled half a century before. Both works were composed for the same clientele, the administrators of the Mamlūk empire and their chancellors and secretaries, who could not accomplish their task well enough without all the historical, geographical, administrative, and literary information which each case required. Come to think of it, it is highly probable that a good many mediaeval encyclopaedias—Latin, Arabic, Persian, Chinese—were patronized by kings and ministers for similar reasons. The administrative needs of rulers and governors were more urgent than the needs of scholars, and the rulers had means which scholars had not of promoting those vast undertakings.

D. *Java*

The Nāgarakṛitāgama, a poem written in old Javanese in 1365 by Prapañca, contains information concerning the historical geography of the Malay Peninsula and Archipelago, which is especially valuable as such information is otherwise almost unobtainable in contemporary documents.

E. *China*

The Pax Mongolica, making possible exchanges of wares and ideas between China and the West, became more and more precarious as the fourteenth century advanced, and ceased to exist after 1360. The last news to reach the West from China before the fall of the Ming curtain was brought by the great Moroccan traveler Ibn Baṭṭūṭa.

By the middle of the century chaos obtained in China instead of peace and order, yet such was the strength of Chinese traditions that the Mongolian historian T'o-t'o continued during these troubled times to edit official histories of earlier dynasties. These histories contained, as usual, a fair amount of geographical

[36] The two Qarāfa cemeteries in Cairo, where many saintly and learned people are buried, the most venerated being the imām al-Shāfiʿī (IX-1).

knowledge. For example, the Sung chih explains the geography not only of China itself (under the Sung), but also that of a number of barbarian countries.

The tradition of topographical studies so dear to the Chinese heart was also continued. During the distressful period of transition from the Yüan to the Ming regime we may imagine that many civil servants were rusticated and withdrew willy-nilly from their yamens to their country retreats. Those of a studious turn of mind took advantage of their enforced leisure to undertake some kind of literary work. Thus Hsieh Ying-fang, having taken refuge in a mountain hermitage, edited the topography of his native province, Kiangsu.

A remarkable document of the early Ming period is the album I-yü t'u-chih, containing illustrations of 168 countries or places, with brief legends.

The tremendous effort begun by the first Ming emperor, Hung Wu, to renovate Chinese institutions and Chinese learning could not bear many fruits until the following century. It will suffice to recall the gigantic encyclopaedia Yung Lo ta tien, completed in 1409, which was a treasury (in great part lost) of geographical as well as other knowledge; then also the Ta Ming I-t'ung-chih, the Ming geography completed c. 1450 under the direction of Li Hsien. This Li Hsien was born in Hupeh province in 1408, rose very high in the imperial service, and died in 1466 (Giles no. 1137). Both works, it should be borne in mind, were undertaken and carried through by imperial order. They are among the proudest monuments of the early Ming dynasty.

Two Ming editions of the Ta Ming I-t'ung-chih are available in the Library of Congress, the one in 40 vols., the other in 80 vols.

X. NATURAL HISTORY

The same arrangement will be followed in this section as in section X of chapter I, that is, a review of the work done in various countries in cultural and geographical order, followed by a review of main subjects in topical order.

Geographical survey

The first survey is divided into four main parts: (A) Christendom, (B) Israel, (C) Islām, (D) China.

A. *Christendom*

The Christian part has eight subdivisions: (1) Hispanic peninsula, (2) Italy, (3) France, (4) Pays de Liége, (5) England, (6) Germany, (7) Bohemia, (8) Byzantium.

A1. *Hispanic peninsula*

It is necessary to entitle this section "Hispanic peninsula," for neither of the two men to be quoted was a Spaniard in the strict sense; the one was Catalan and the other Basque. Much of Spanish glory is of either Catalan or Basque origin, and yet Spain has consistently ill-treated these "foreigners" on its own territory. Too often, alas! Spain makes us think of a stepmother living at the expense of two despised stepchildren.

The Aragonese or Catalan is none other than the king Pere III el Cerimoniós, who continued the fine tradition of Jaume I el Conqueridor (XIII-2). Pere was not simply a historiographer like his ancestor Jaume, but a patron of learning. He caused books to be translated from Arabic into Catalan, notably a book of agriculture. This is an interesting illustration of the continuity of Arabic influence in husbandry in spite of the fact that by this time the Moors had been driven out of the whole peninsula except Granada and that their last Aragonese and Majorcan strongholds had been abandoned for more than a century. Indeed, Moorish gardens and relics of Moorish husbandry can be seen in the peninsula to this day.

To the Basque soldier and man of letters López de Ayala we owe an elaborate treatise on falconry.

A2. *Italy*

We may begin our account with the legendary personality of Rotario d'Asti, who is believed to have ascended the Rocciamelone, a relatively high mountain, in 1358. He is one of the early heroes of alpinism.

The two Dondi, Giacomo de' Dondi and his son Giovanni, were interested in what might be called geological problems. The first wrote a treatise on that perennial riddle, the saltness of the sea and of certain springs; he discussed methods of extracting salt from the sea and was first to recommend the extraction of salts from mineral waters. Giovanni continued his father's speculations and investigated more thoroughly the springs of Abano, near Padua. Neither was able to solve the many problems involved, but that was hardly possible considering the imperfection, or rather the utter insufficiency, of their frame of reference. Though Boccaccio's geographical dictionary was essentially of the humanistic type, it includes occasional references to natural objects. Boccaccio asked himself a few geological questions (e.g., concerning sulphurous exhalations or calcareous deposits). Of course, he had no means of solving them, but he deserves some credit for having put them on record. It would take four more centuries for geology to become a branch of science.

The third part of Domenico di Bandino's encyclopaedic treatise, Fons memorabilium universi, is a summary of natural history.

A splendid herbal, Liber de simplicibus, was completed in Venice shortly after the end of the fourteenth century, in 1410. The author, Benedetto Rinio (or Rin) of Venice, was helped by his father Lodovico and by his teacher Nicola Roccabonella of Conegliano (Treviso).[1] That herbal is essentially a collection of plates, drawn and colored by the Venetian artist Andrea Amodio (or Amoglio). To the pictures, however, are added brief botanical notes indicating collecting seasons, the part of each plant containing the drug, authors who have dealt with it, and the names of each plant in many languages, not only Latin, Greek, Arabic, German, and various Italian dialects, but even Slavonic. It is true some of the names, chiefly the Arabic, Germanic, and Slavonic, are later interpolations. The main feature is the iconography, 450 plants (some of them exotic) being admirably reproduced upon 440 plates. These illustrations were so much admired by Ruskin that he had some of them copied by the painter Caldara.

Venice was then carrying on an extensive trade in herbs and drugs with Eastern and Western customers, and special pains were taken to detect adulterations and prevent errors in identification. Rinio's herbal was certainly composed and used for such purposes. Indeed, it was deposited for a long time in one of the main apothecary shops of Venice, the Testa d'oro, where the pharmacist and the physi-

[1] Ulisse Aldrovandi believed erroneously that Roccabonella (M.D. 1410) was the author.

cians gathering in his shop[2] would consult it for the identification of simples. From 1604 to 1789 this herbal was kept in the library of the Dominican fathers of SS. Giovanni e Paolo, and was then transferred to the Biblioteca Marciana, where it has remained until now.

The introduction to Rinio's herbal was published in 1782 by one of its Dominican custodians, father Domenico Maria Berardelli, in the Nuova raccolta d'opuscoli scientifici e filologici founded by the Camaldolite abbot Angiolo Calogerà.[3] The herbal itself has been edited by Ettore De Toni: Il libro dei semplici di Benedetto Rinio (Memorie dei Nuovi Lincei 5, 171–279, 1919; 7, 275–398, 1924; 8, 123–264, 1925) with abundant notes and indexes, list of authors mentioned, but, alas! without illustrations. There is a long review of this edition by Achille Forti in the Rivista di storia delle scienze mediche (1926, p. 294–300). Emilio Teza: Il De simplicibus di B. Rinio nel codice Marciano (Atti R. Istituto veneto 56, 18–29, 1898).

A3. *France*

One of the outstanding mediaeval treatises on hunting, Le miroir de Phoebus, is ascribed to Gaston count of Foix, better known under the nickname Gaston Phoebus. Though written mainly for practical purposes, it contains so much information on the animals which were hunted as well as those which took part in the hunt that it is truly a mirror of the natural history of those days. Thanks to its lively style as well as to its intrinsic value, the book was very popular in the aristocratic circles for which it was meant. Gaston's book was begun in 1387. Some thirty years earlier a French poem, Le roman des oiseaux, had been composed by Gace de la Bigne for king Jean le Bon, then prisoner in England.

A delightful treatise on shepherdy was written by Jean de Brie in 1379 and dedicated to Charles le Sage. It deals in savorous language with the lore of shepherds, and explains their duties and dignity. The book honors its author and the shepherds of France, a gentle class of people, humble yet conscious of their value, meditative and slow, submissive and obedient, except when they were raised to anger as happened in the tumults of the Pastoureaux and the Jacques.

This is perhaps the best place to mention two remarkable books of domestic economy. Le viandier, composed before 1380 by the royal "chef" Guillaume Taillevent, is a cookbook, the first elaborate one in the French language. A more ambitious book was published anonymously c. 1393 under the title Le ménagier de Paris. It deals with family ethics, the government of the home, cooking recipes, hunting and hawking.

Finally, mention should be made of a contemporary MS admirably illustrated by Cybo of Hyères. The miniatures include astonishing representations of insects and caterpillars. These illustrations bear no relation to the text which they surround. That text is in Latin, but all the other texts referred to in this section were written, as we should expect, in French.

[2] Italian physicians often expected and met patients in apothecary shops, where they spent definite hours each day. For the relations between Italian physicians and apothecaries see Kremers and Urdang (p. 49, 1940).

[3] D. M. Berardelli: Codicum omnium latinorum et italicorum qui manuscripti in Bibliotheca SS. Joannis et Pauli Venetiarum apud P. P. Praedicatores asservantur catalogus (pars I, 96 p., Nuova raccolta 37, 51–58, Venezia 1782). 42 vols. of that Raccolta appeared in Venice from 1755 to 1787. Angiolo Calogerà, born in 1699, died in 1768; vol. 37 was edited by another Camaldolite, father Fortunato Mandelli.

A4. *Pays de Liège*

The chronicler Jean d'Outremeuse compiled a curious scientific treatise which, as its title, Trésorier de philosophie naturelle des pierres précieuses, indicates, is centered on a lapidary. Incidentally, this is the earliest use of the phrase "philosophie naturelle" known to me.[4] The phrase (or its Latin or English equivalent) is not mentioned in Ducange; Littré's earliest reference is to Pascal; the earliest one in OED is to Compound of alchymy (1471) of George Ripley. Jean was not satisfied with descriptions of stones, he wanted to explain them, and therefore he fancied his work as a "natural philosophy" rather than a "natural history." His achievement fell considerably short of his intention.

A5. *England*

We might expect to find in England treatises on the chase and hunting, and we do find them, but the early ones are entirely of French derivation. This is not surprising, for the English squirearchy was still largely subservient to French patterns, and its snobbishness more often than not assumed French colors. A treatise on hunting had been written in Anglo-Norman by William Twici and John Gyfford for Edward II. An English version of it appeared in the second half of the fourteenth century. Gaston Phoebus' Miroir was translated into English under the title The master of game, at the beginning of the following century, by Edward Plantagenet, second duke of York. The first English book, English in substance as well as in language, appeared just a little later (that is, in the first half of the fifteenth century), being the famous Boke of St. Albans ascribed to dame Juliana Berners (variants: Bernes, Barnes), of whom practically nothing is known but who is supposed to have been born c. 1388. She was probably the prioress of Sopwell Nunnery, near the Abbey of St. Albans, in Hertfordshire. The Boke of St. Albans was first issued by an unknown printer, sometime schoolmaster of St. Albans, in that place 1486. It includes four separate treatises, on hawking, hunting, the "lynage of coote armiris," and the "blasyng of armys." The second edition, issued by Wynkyn de Worde (Westminster 1496), contains a fifth treatise, fuller and clearer than the first four, dealing with fishing (Treatyse on fysshinge with an angle), the earliest treatise of its kind in English.[5] These treatises enjoyed great popularity in the sixteenth century, witness a number of additional editions under various titles. According to a modern editor, Joseph Haslewood (1810–11), the parts ascribable to dame Juliana are to be restricted to (1) a part of hawking, (2) the whole of hunting, (3) a short list of the beasts of the chase, (4) a short list of beasts and fowls. The books on heraldry are not hers, but they do not concern us anyhow.

Text. First edition St. Albans 1486, 2d Westminster 1496, with 3 quaint woodcuts. For later editions, see Thomas Westwood and Thomas Satchell: Bibliotheca piscatoria (p. 24–29, London 1883).

Modern reprint of the five treatises with notes by Joseph Haslewood (London

[4] With the possible exception of the Philosophia sive physica pauperum ascribed to Albert the Great (XIII-2), first printed in 1482; the 4th to 6th editions, 1490, 1493, 1496, bore the alternate title Philosophia naturalis (Klebs no. 23; Introd. 2, 941–42). It is probable that this new title was an invention of the editor of 1490.

[5] There is, however, an earlier description of fishing in the Latin-English Colloquium of Aelfric (X-2).

1810–11). Often reprinted in Europe and America, but many of the reprints are restricted to the fifth treatise. Facsimile editions of the original editions, Boke of St. Albans, introduced by William Blades (London 1881), Treatyse on fysshynge, introduced by M. G. Watkins (London 1880). A jewel for gentrie (London 1614) is a plagiarized edition of the five treatises.

Alfred Denison has edited a MS in his possession of the Treatyse of fysshinge, the text of which is different from that printed in 1496 and apparently older (46 p., London 1883), with preface and glossary by Thomas Satchell.

Criticism. M. G. Watkins (DNB 4, 390–92, 1885). Robert Bright Marston: Izaac Walton and some earlier writers on fish and fishing (London 1894). Walter John Turrell: Ancient angling authors (London 1910). William Radcliffe: Fishing from the earliest times (New York 1921; Isis 4, 568–71).

To return to the fourteenth century, a lapidary is ascribed to John Mandeville and a treatise on herbs to Joannes ad Barbam. The lapidary is copied from Marbode (XI-2). The herb book may have been written by the author of the Travels; it is dated 1357. Another herb book was composed by John Arderne.

There are references to earthquakes (1382) in the chronicle of John Malverne.

The student of natural history may find some grist for his mill in the many books bearing Chaucer's name. The following item may suffice: Chaucer it was who introduced the cat into English literature!

A6. *Germany*

Thomas of Sarepta or of Breslau, who in our ignorance might be called a Pole as well as a German, had a better knowledge of botany than most physicians. In his youth he had collected plants and prepared a herbarium.

Albert of Saxony continued the geological tradition of the Arabs, chiefly Ibn Sīnā (XI-1). He gave a good account of the geological action of water. Considering the enormous erosive power of water, Albert had the shrewdness to suggest that in the course of time the land areas would be finally washed out into the sea, except that continents were periodically uplifted in order to re-establish the static equilibrium disturbed by erosion. In other words, if we take a sufficiently generous view of his groping thoughts, we may consider him an adumbrator of isostasy![6]

Henry of Langenstein, who was like Albert one of the founders and animators of the University of Vienna, speculated on the origin of life. He tried to account for the spontaneous generation of various pests (such as mice and vermin) and even of diseases by astrological arguments. Special celestial conjunctions might even bring about the creation of new kinds of men! The very boldness of such views gives us a new insight into the strength of astrological prepossessions.

A7. *Bohemia*

The nationality of Latin-writing men may be difficult, if not impossible in special cases, to determine. For example, we cannot decide whether Thomas of Sarepta should be counted as a German or as a Pole, for he wrote in Latin. But when a Bohemian writes in his own Bohemian (Czech) language, we must call him a Bohemian.

Two Czech writings of this time deserve to attract the attention of the historian

[6] William Bowie: Isostasy (New York 1927; Isis 11, 252); starting the history of isostasy in 1855 with George Biddell Airy and John Henry Pratt, or at the beginning of the nineteenth century with Babbage and Herschel.

of the natural sciences. In 1394, Jan Flaška composed a beast epic entitled the New council. A few years later the physician and mathematician Christian of Prachatice[7] wrote a herbal, Lekarszké knizky, wherein some 156 plants were listed.[8] These two writings are probably more valuable from the linguistic than from the scientific point of view.

A8. *Byzantium*

A long Greek poem (more than 3,000 verses) bearing the illustrious name of Meliteniotes deals with all kinds of natural and mythical subjects, chiefly precious stones and minerals. The philologist would call it a glossary of mineralogy; it is a hotchpotch of Byzantine mineral lore.

Neilos Diassorinos of Chios wrote treatises on stones and on artificial generation (?) which have not yet been published, nor even explored.

B. *Israel*

A Catalan Jew named En Solomon Astruc Gatigno wrote a commentary on the Torah, including among other things an account of a locust plague which occurred in 1359.

C. *Islām*

The survey of Muslim natural history is divided into five sections: (1) Maghrib, (2) Arabia, (3) 'Irāq and Mamlūkīya, (4) Turkey, (5) Transoxiana (Mā warā'-l-nahr).

C1. *Maghrib*

Two Andalusians wrote books on horses. The most important as well as the best known is Ibn Hudhail, to whom we owe no less than three such books. The other, 'Abdallāh ibn Muḥammad Ibn Juzayy, has the distinction of being the brother of Muḥammad ibn Muḥammad Ibn Juzayy, who edited Ibn Baṭṭūṭa's travels. Horses and horse lore were one of the favorite topics of Arabic (or Muslim) letters. According to the author's personality and his training, his "horse book" might vary all the way from pure science to pure literature. If it was scientific, its interest might be centered on natural history, or venery, or husbandry and breeding, or veterinary medicine, or it might be sufficiently eclectic to deal with every aspect of hippology. Ibn Hudhail's main work was the Tuḥfat al-anfās, divided into two parts treating, the first, the art of cavalry (in the military sense); the second, what we might call equitation, the care of horses, and all the things which a gentleman rider might wish to know about his mounts. Ibn Juzayy's book was more exclusively philological and anecdotic.

When we turn from Andalusia to North Africa, we must naturally meet the two learned men who dominated this age, Ibn Baṭṭūṭa and Ibn Khaldūn—we come across them and nobody else. Though Ibn Baṭṭūṭa was not a naturalist, and like most Muslim travelers was far more interested in men than in natural objects, yet

[7] Prachatice is the Czech spelling, Prachatitz the German.

[8] Gerald Druce: Some early Czech contributions to botany (Nature 151, 98–100, 1943). Christian of Prachatice heads the list, the next one being Jan Černý (1480–1530), whose illustrated herbal, Kniha lekarzská kteraz slowe Herbarz, aneb Zelinarz, was printed in Nuremberg 1517, then Prague 1544, 1554, Olomouc 1554. Then Thaddeus Hájek (1525–1600), Herbarz ginak bilinarz (Prague 1562).

his long Riḥla is so full of information on plants and animals that the student of natural history will find it worth his while to excerpt it. Since he was chiefly concerned with God and man, the rest of nature—mere minerals, plants, or animals—attracted his attention only in proportion to their usefulness to man. He had no scientific curiosity, but a good deal of human curiosity, which is reflected throughout the account of his journeys and gives to that account so much vitality.

Ibn Khaldūn has little to tell us about particular plants or animals, but he continued the old Muslim speculations on the scala naturae, evolution, and harmony of the world.

C2. *Arabia*

The most elaborate treatise on agriculture of this age was composed in Arabia. This may astonish some readers, but it is not very difficult to explain. It was written by a member of the Rasūlī dynasty of Yaman, al-'Abbās al-Rasūlī, and that dynasty had fostered learned traditions for at least a century and a half. Al-'Abbās was well acquainted with the geoponica as well as with Nabataean and Muslim husbandry. There was no reason why such MSS could not be collected just as well in Ṣana'ā' as in other Muslim capitals; all that was needed was sufficient interest, and this was provided by the rulers.[8a] Moreover, the proximity and relative accessibility of Mecca opened up all the resources of the Muslim world. For a Yamanī scholar a visit to Mecca, which he could repeat frequently, was almost as good as a journey around the Islamic world, for that whole world would presently walk before his eyes, and it was up to him to make the most of it.

C3. *'Irāq and Mamlūkīya*

The most cultured part of Islām was still the Mamlūk empire, where many prosperous cities were large enough to supply the necessary concentration of human efforts, mutual stimulation, and emulation, yet not so large as to lose touch with the fallāḥīn of the rīf and the badāwī of the saḥrā'. Moreover, the Mamlūk cities were closely associated with those of 'Irāq, such as Baghdād, Mūṣul, or al-Baṣra. It is thus proper to speak of the Iraqians together with the Syrians and the Egyptians.

The single 'Irāqī to be considered, Ibn al-Duraihim, spent most of his life in Egypt and Syria and died at Qūṣ, in Upper Egypt, on his way to Abyssinia. He composed a treatise on the properties of animals, or revised an earlier text on the same popular subject. His text is represented by an admirable Escorial MS dated 1354, including some 250 zoological miniatures. Ibn al-Duraihim's book or album, Kitāb manāfi' al-ḥayawān, and earlier books bearing the same title constitute the best approximation to an elementary zoological treatise in mediaeval Islām.

A far more ambitious zoological task was undertaken by al-Damīrī. His Kitāb ḥayāt al-ḥayawān (Lives of animals) is a zoological dictionary, dealing with more than a thousand animals, in alphabetical order (except that the lion, being the king of beasts, is given precedence over all others!). There is very little zoology, as we understand it today, in that compilation; the description of each animal is rudimentary, and much of the information is not zoological, but traditional (in the Muslim sense), legal, proverbial, medical, literary, oneirocritic, etc. We might call

[8a] The richness of the Ṣana'ā' libraries was proved by the fact that the Lombard merchant Giuseppe Caprotti was able to collect there an enormous quantity of MSS; most of them are now in the Ambrosiana of Milano, the remnant was given to the Vatican in 1922. Giorgio Levi Della Vida: Elenco dei manoscritti arabi islamici della Biblioteca Vaticana (Roma 1935; Isis 36, 273–75).

al-Damīrī's voluminous work a dictionary of parazoology; it is a mine of zoological folklore, the popularity of which was considerable, witness the number of MSS complete or partial, commentaries, adaptations, imitations, elaborations, summaries, anthologies—not only in Arabic, but also in Persian and Turkish.

Books on equitation, hippiatry, cavalry tactics were at least as popular in the Mamlūk world as in other parts of the Dār al-Islām. Such books were composed by Muḥammad ibn Mangalī, by Muḥammad ibn Lājīn (who followed the example of his father Lājīn), and by Ṭaibughā ibn 'Abdallāh al-Baklamishī. The last named was of Turkish-Greek origin; that is not very strange, for there were many Turks and Greeks in Egypt then even as now.

The first named, Muḥammad ibn Mangalī, also wrote one of the most elaborate and original hunting books in the Arabic language. That book gives much information about hunting with various cats as well as with falcons, or with a leopard trained for teamwork with a falcon.

The Shāfi'ī doctor 'Abd al-Raḥīm ibn al-Ḥasan al-Isnawī wrote a dissertation on hermaphrodites (khunthā), a subject which exercised the legalistic mind of theologians. As men and women have different responsibilities and duties, theologians and jurists asked themselves what might be the duties and rights of these intermediate types; how should they pray? inherit? etc. They did not question the reality of such types. It is probable that they were acquainted mainly with people whose sexuality could not be clearly established (al-khunthā-l-mushkil), and who for psychic as well as physical reasons could and did pass themselves off either as men or as women. Similar cases are discussed from time to time in our own law courts and in the newspapers.

C4. *Turkey*

Two popular types of natural history are found in Turkish writings.

Isḥāq ibn Murād of Gerede composed a herbal, dealing with the medical properties not only of herbs, but also of other plants, animals, and minerals. This Isḥāq had done some herborizations himself in the mountains of northern Anatolia.

Maḥmūd ibn Muḥammad al-Bārjīnī wrote a treatise on falconry which seems to be largely derived from the twelfth-century Greek and Arabic books.

C5. *Transoxiana* (*Mā warā'-l-nahr*)

The great conqueror Tīmūr Lang, who made Samarqand the capital of his empire, caused an artistic revival but does not seem to have stimulated scientific efforts of any kind. His tombstone in the Gūr-i-Mīr is one of the largest jade objects in the world. It was probably carved out of a block quarried in eastern Turkestan, which has always been one of the main sources of the best Chinese jade (pi yü).

D. *China*

T'ao Tsung-i wrote an essay on the precious stones of the Muslims. The title refers to the fact that many of the gems sold, say, in Peking were brought from Central Asia, Īrān, etc., by Muslim traders.

We have an album of the beginning of the Ming dynasty, entitled I-yü t'u-chih, containing many illustrations of plants and animals considered characteristic of some 168 countries or places.

The Yung Lo ta tien (1409) contains an abundance of information on minerals, plants, and animals, mostly of the literary and anecdotic rather than the purely scientific type.

The first Ming emperor, Hung Wu, had many sons, one of whom, called Chu Hsiao or more often Chou Wang Hsiao, was banished from the court for political reasons and obliged to spend a good part of his life (1382–1400) in exile near Kai-fêng-fu, Honan. He improved the opportunity which this enforced rustication gave him to create in his estates a botanical garden and even an experimental garden for the acclimatization of wild plants which might be used in times of famine. It has been shown above that China was frequently visited with famines, which decimated the people and brought terror everywhere. Chu Hsiao investigated means of increasing the food resources in the recurrent periods of scarcity. In 1406 he completed an account of his investigations in the "famine herbal" (Chiu-huang pên-ts'ao), which may perhaps be considered the most remarkable herbal of mediaeval times. It describes 414 plants, a good many new, and is admirably illustrated.

Special subjects

In order to facilitate cross references, the sections are numbered in the same way as they were in chapter I, section X. Thus one may read the article on herbals (no. 6) in chapter I, section X, then pass immediately to the article on herbals (no. 6) in chapter XV, section X. The classification is tentative rather than exclusive and final. Experienced readers always consult other sections than the one which concerns them immediately, and may thus find valuable hints.

1. *General surveys. Theory of evolution*

The best example of encyclopaedic survey is given us of course by the great Chinese encyclopaedia, Yung Lo ta tien, which was completed only in 1409, but may be said to represent the knowledge accumulated by the end of the fourteenth century. There was no work at all comparable in Western or Arabic literatures. To find the nearest equivalent in Latin one would have to go back to the Specula of Vincent of Beauvais (XIII-2). In the present period the encyclopaedic point of view is found only in small and unimportant publications such as the De mundi fabrica of Domenico Bandino, or the Trésorier de philosophie naturelle of Jean d'Outremeuse. One might add the Riḥla of Ibn Baṭṭūṭa, because of the latter's curiosity extending to the three kingdoms of nature.

For biological speculations one should turn to some writings of Henry of Langenstein wherein he discusses astrological causes of generation, and perhaps to the περὶ γεννήσεως τεχνικῆς of Neilos Diassorinos. The Arabic treatise on hermaphrodites by 'Abd al-Raḥīm ibn al-Ḥasan al-Isnawī might also be consulted. One might expect to find biological speculations in the Muqaddama of Ibn Khaldūn because of the latter's inquiring and philosophical mind, but his work is in this respect disappointing. Ibn Khaldūn was not a naturalist like al-Mas'ūdī, but rather a humanist, or we might venture to say a supernaturalist, more anxious to find the relation upward between man and the angels than that connecting man downward, with the monkeys and the date palms.

First Kingdom: Minerals

2. *Geological theories*

We owe to Albert of Saxony the only worth-while addition to geological theory. Following the lead taken by Arabic authors, he emphasized the geological activity of water and added views suggesting an adumbration of isostasy.

The two Dondi, Giacomo and Giovanni, father and son, investigating hot and mineral springs, were led to ask themselves a number of geological questions. How are such springs heated? and how are they salted? why is the sea salted? Perennial queries which would remain unsolved for a long time to come.

Being stimulated by such writers as Aristotle, Vitruvius, Pliny, Seneca, Albert the Great, and Vincent of Beauvais, Boccaccio was also able to ask natural questions (chiefly in his De montibus), but his main interest was humanistic.

Scholars living in the neighborhood of mountainous districts might have learned something from the observation of mountains, canyons, glaciers, and other alpine wonders, but unfortunately their curiosities were inhibited by superstitious fears. As contrasted with the Buddhists, for whom the mountains (or some mountains at least) were sacred[9] and very early became centers of pilgrimage, the Christians regarded them as accursed and diabolical. Hence mountain ascents, which were a commonplace of religious life in China (and Japan), were so exceptional in Christendom that the very few which occurred, or are remembered, are cited as extraordinary events, e.g. Petrarca's ascent of 1336, and the probably apocryphal one made by Rotario d'Asti in 1358.

3. *Lapidaries*

Mineralogical knowledge or rather lore, what little there was of it, must be looked for in the lapidaries, which continued such hoary and venerable traditions that one can hardly expect to find any novelty in them. A few more lapidaries were composed: in French, by John Mandeville (?) and Jean d'Outremeuse; in Greek, by one Meliteniotes and by Neilos Diassorinos; in Chinese, by T'ao Tsung-i, etc. Of course, every encyclopaedia of natural history would contain some mineral lore, every Biblical commentary would include a discussion of the twelve stones adorning the high priest's breastplate (Exodus 28:15–21; 39:10–13); etc.

The English lapidaries are either anterior to this period or posterior. Elaborate studies of the earlier (Anglo-Norman) ones have been made by Paul Studer and Joan Evans: Anglo-Norman lapidaries (424 p., Paris 1924; Isis 9, 123–24), and of all of them by Joan Evans: Magical jewels of the Middle Ages and the Renaissance particularly in England (264 p., 4 pl., Clarendon Press, Oxford 1922; Isis 6, 222); English mediaeval lapidaries, with Mary S. Serjeantson (Early English Text Society no. 190, 218 p., London 1933), edition of seven English texts, one of them of the eleventh century, all others of the fifteenth, with indexes, synoptic table, and glossaries.

For jade one would have to turn to Chinese sources. An elaborate catalogue of 700 pieces of ancient jade, the Ku yü t'u p'u, had been completed by Lung Ta-yüan as early as 1176 (Introd. 2, 263). The Chinese passion and reverence for jade,[10] the gem par excellence, was shared by the Mongol rulers and indeed by all the people who fell into the orbit of Chinese culture.

The most famous piece of jade in the world, as well as one of the largest, is the one forming the tombstone of Tamerlane in Samarqand. The great conqueror died in 1405, but it is probable that he had ordered the preparation of that unique

[9] E.g., the "five mountains," wu shan, also wu yo (or yüeh), see Soothill and Hodous (p. 117, 1937). William Frederick Mayers: Chinese reader's manual (p. 320, no. 176, Shanghai 1874). H. A. Giles (no. 13,367, 1912), naming the five mountains.

[10] Hence the word for jade, yü, is a Chinese glamorous word, just as 'arūs in Arabic, queen in English, etc. Examples of the glamorous use of yü are given by Ball (p. 306, 1926), and in every Chinese dictionary sub voce. For Buddhist use see Soothill and Hodous (p. 195, 1937).

monument long before his death. In its extravagant grandeur and simplicity, it was a perplexing memorial of his awful deeds.

For comparison see various articles on stones and precious stones in ERE (10, 224, 1919; 11, 864–77, 1921).

4. *Earthquakes and volcanoes*

No new attempts were made to explain volcanic and seismic phaenomena, but chroniclers recording the fairly frequent catastrophes of this period could not always help adding their own interpretations. Sometimes the interpretation was implicit: the chronicler simply mentioned the close succession of events, causal relations being suggested. Thus earthquakes were connected not only with volcanic explosions (as in Iceland), but with comets, conjunctions, floods, famines, and pestilences.

There were certainly enough earthquakes and concomitant tragedies to excite the fears of people and strengthen their superstitions. Let me quote the most important from Mallet's list (p. 40–45, 1852).

A heavy earthquake began on Christmas 1352 at Borgo San Sepolcro and continued for the whole week; violent shocks were followed at intervals by lighter ones for more than a month; 2,000 people lost their lives. In 1356, there was a violent earthquake in the upper Rhine valley, especially at Strassburg and Basel, and throughout a good part of Switzerland. At Basel, many buildings were destroyed by the shocks and by concomitant fires. Thirty-eight castles were ruined in the diocese of Constance. Shocks continued to be felt at Basel for a year. Other quakes desolated the same region in 1357. In 1361, the southern Adriatic coast of Italy was violently shaken; at Ascoli 4,000 persons died; at the end of the same year quakes shocked Siena during four days, destroying many buildings. In 1382 occurred one of the most violent earthquakes ever recorded in England; the center was in Canterbury, but shocks were felt in other parts of England and on the Continent. John Malverne spoke of that quake.[11] In 1383, there was such a violent earthquake in Mytilene that "buildings were rocked from side to side like trees in a tempest"; the city was ruined, 500 persons died. In 1391, Swiss quakes were accompanied by the apparition of a comet and followed by heavy rains, floods, famine, and pestilence. The quake of 1393 in Bologna was followed by smallpox and by a terrible tempest. On the other hand, another quake felt in 1394 in Switzerland, France, and Germany was followed by excessive heat and abundant harvest. At the end of 1395 quakes were felt along the eastern coast of Spain, and at Alcira (Valencia) two fountains gave forth water of an abominable smell and the color of ashes. The quake of Montpellier 1397 was accompanied by a plague.

Earthquakes and volcanic explosions were recorded in Iceland under the following dates: 1360, 1370, 1389–90, 1391. George Hans Boehmer: Volcanic eruptions and earthquakes in Iceland (Smithsonian report for 1884–85, p. 495–541), derived from Thorvaldur Thoroddsen.

Father Hoang (p. 146–53, 1931) lists 71 Chinese quakes for the second half of the century, against 139 for the first half. Apparently many of these quakes were weak, too weak to cause the loss of life or property, and would probably have remained unrecorded in Europe. On the whole, this was a period of relative seismic calm in China, whereas seismic agitation increased in Japan, especially from 1361 to c. 1380.

[11] **Charles Davison: History of British earthquakes (p. 330, 384, Cambridge 1924; Isis 8, 628).**

5. *Mining and metallurgy*

The trends which were noticeable about the middle of the century became clearer and clearer as the century proceeded toward its end. Coal mining and the metallurgical industries deriving from it their main sustenance continued to expand in Western Europe, chiefly in England. The expansion, however, was more economic and industrial than technical. It did not imply new technical discoveries of a revolutionary kind.

The proverbial importance of Newcastle-on-Tyne as a center of coal distribution was emerging. From the beginning of the fourteenth century the coal trade was already thriving, not only on the Tyne, but also on the Firth of Forth, and to a smaller extent on the estuaries of the Dee and the Severn. Under Edward II coal was already being exported to France. Indeed, we hear in 1325 of a ship bringing corn from Pontoise to Newcastle and returning freighted with coal. Coal was already used for domestic as well as for industrial purposes. Thus in 1313 the monks of Jarrow were using coal. The monks of Tynemouth leased out various collieries from 1330 on, and so did the bishop of Durham in 1356. Edward III was the first king to interest himself in the Tyne coal trade; he permitted the delivery and measuring of coal by the keel, that is, in relatively large quantities (a keel was a kind of ship special to the Tyne, a broad, flat-bottomed boat designed to carry the heaviest load with the least draught of water). There were already regular mine works consisting of pit and adit, or vertical shaft and horizontal gallery above the level of free drainage.[12]

This development, however, must not be exaggerated. The sea-coal[13] trade, large as it was from the mediaeval point of view, was very small as compared with later developments (end of seventeenth century and later). Exports from Newcastle fluctuated from 2,000 to 7,000 tons per annum during the period 1375 to 1515, and were not much larger at the end than at the beginning of that period. Neither did the imports of Newcastle coal at London increase much between the accession of Edward II (1307) and the end of the sixteenth century, for the number of coal meters, used to measure the coal unloaded on the Thames, remained the same. The export trade in coal was taken care of very largely by foreign ships owned and manned by Normans, Bretons, Gascons, Flemings, who brought other wares to England and took sea coal as ballast for the return trip. John Ulric Nef: The rise of the British coal industry (2 vols., London 1932; part I).

A similar importance was gradually taken on by the land of Liége, so much so that the old city was losing its clerical character and becoming an industrial center. It was surrounded by mines and smithies. Whereas Flanders, abounding in wool, was a land of drapers, Liége was being transformed into a city of smiths, and more and more of those smiths were gunsmiths. The corporation of the smiths surpassed by far all the others. The rapidly growing manufacture of firearms accentuated the transformation of Liége, which was so deep, and relatively speaking so rapid, that a kind of industrial revolution occurred in the fifteenth century. The industry expanded so much that additional workingmen had to be continually imported, and at the beginning of that century, foreigners were already more numerous than

[12] Details quoted from Robert L. Galloway: History of coal mining in Great Britain (p. 11–18, London 1882).

[13] The term sea coal originated in the thirteenth century. It was coined to differentiate mineral coal from charcoal; the mineral coal was often found near the sea or the estuaries, and it was largely carried along sea lanes (OED, sea-coal).

citizens. These matters are well explained by Henri Pirenne in his Histoire de Belgique (3d ed., 2, 289 f., 1922).

Pirenne claims (p. 288) that German coal miners were trained in Liége; that is possible, but there were also ancient centers in Germany, and many Germans may have been attracted to Liége to work as masters as well as apprentices. Moreover, Germans emigrated to England. Hermann de Allemania (1314) and Thomas de Almaigne (1324) have already been mentioned; in 1359, Tilman de Cologne was working the lead mines of Alston moor, in Yorkshire (Rickard 2, 535, 1932).

The fundamental metallurgical process was the smelting of iron out of the ores. We have already explained that blast furnaces were first used near Namur (1340) and Liége (before 1400), and that the invention was taken from Liége to England. Blast furnaces (haut-fourneaux) and even pit furnaces, however, remained very exceptional in the fourteenth century. Most of the iron was probably smelted by means of the so-called sponge iron process. That is, the ore was mixed with charcoal and heated in a small furnace or even on a forge; air was blown in by means of bellows. The temperature thus reached (say 1,400° F.) was not sufficient to melt the iron, which was found in a porous "spongy" form at the bottom of the furnace. The remaining slag could be hammered out, and one finally obtained wrought iron. The process was eased by the addition of a limestone flux.[14] A good smith could improve a bloom[15] gradually by repeated heating and hammering. The smith's work was facilitated by olivers, i.e., treadle hammers. Olivers are mentioned in English documents of 1352 and 1375.

Rods of metal could be obtained by shearing or slitting sheet metal; the rods were then drawn through successively smaller holes in a tempered steel plate (the draw plate, whirtle or wortle), and thus were metal wires made. This was done in Nuremberg at least as early as 1389 (picture of the Mendel foundation); it was probably done in England in the fourteenth century, if not before.

Feldhaus (p. 199–204, 1914). Rhys Jenkins: The oliver. Iron making in the fourteenth century (Transactions, Newcomen Society 12, 9–14, 1933). John James Hall: Iron work fastenings of the fourteenth century (ibid. 16, 129–39, 4 fig., 1937).

A great variety of other metallurgical processes were practiced by the gunsmiths and other craftsmen, but they remained traditional and, if not familial and secret, at least unpublished almost until the sixteenth century. It is certain that much technical progress was made between 1300 and 1400; that progress was controlled by the growth of urbanization and by military rather than peaceful needs. Therefore, accounts of it are found, if at all, in the books on military technology, a long series of which is enumerated in chapter XXI. For mining and metallurgical treatises, we have to wait until the sixteenth century, i.e., until the Bergbüchlein of Rülein von Kalbe (physician and burgomaster of Freiberg) printed c. 1505, the Probirbüchlein of c. 1518 (first treatise on assaying), the Bergwerk und Probirbüchlin (Francfort 1533),[16] and finally the great books of Vannoccio Biringuccio (Venice 1540) and Georgius Agricola (Basel 1556).[16a]

[14] In a blast furnace the temperature is twice as high, and the final product is cast iron.

[15] A bloom is a mass of relatively pure wrought iron, a pig of iron.

[16] Ernst Darmstaedter: Berg-, Probir- und Kunstbüchlein (Münchener Beiträge no. 2/3, 112 p., München 1926; Isis 10, 143).

[16a] These two great books are available in convenient English translations: Biringuccio by Cyril Stanley Smith and Martha Teach Gnudi (New York 1942; Isis 34, 514–16); Agricola by Herbert Clark Hoover and Lou Henry Hoover (London 1912; Isis 13, 113–16).

So much for the West; with regard to Eastern methods our information is even poorer. We know that the Muslims had developed Hindu methods, or reinvented them, for the making of exceptionally good steel, and the blades of Damascus (and Toledo) were famous. No Arabic or Persian descriptions of these methods are known to us, but there are in our museums many specimens of the art (though perhaps none as ancient as the fourteenth century). Eastern people had perfected at an early date the making of watered (or damascened) steel, famous for its hardness, elasticity, and decoration with wavy lines. According to Grancsay,[17] "This pattern, as well as the qualities of strength and toughness shown in the metal, is the result of the irregular crystallization which takes place with the slow cooling of a crucible steel of high carbon content, and the subsequent reheating and forging required to fashion the blade. Since the ore is converted into steel cakes of small size, the blade is of necessity composed of many bars welded together in layers. By doubling the complex bar on itself, thus increasing the number of laminae, the beauty and the quality of the blade are improved. The forging is done at low temperature so as not to lose the cementite (a hard, brittle carbide of iron) which crystallizes in the dots and long lines, or needles, that are the foundation of the pattern. During the process of forging, the crystals spread and elongate into delicate, tortuous lines. Repeated hammering of the bar—especially if twisted, rippled, or bent irregularly in the doubling process—converts the lines into patterns, one of the most familiar being the ladder pattern, the ladder on which the faithful ascend to heaven."

The Muslims' attitude toward iron was colored by the sūrat al-ḥadīd (no. 57), in which God announces that he has sent down iron, wherein there are both keen violence and advantages to man.[18] Iron is both evil and good! Cosmographers like al-Qazwīnī (XIII-2) distinguished between natural iron, sābūrqān[19] (iron ores?), and artificial iron, which might be weak and female (Pers. narm-āhan), that is, soft iron, or hard and male, that is, steel (fūlādh). According to the Muslims themselves, the best iron came from India and China.

It is possible that the best methods were invented and developed first in India. Witness the Kutub pillar in Delhi, which is the most impressive iron monument in the whole world. It is an iron pillar 24 feet high and 6½ tons in weight, dating back to early days (c. A.D. 400) and (in spite of the hot and damp climate) showing no trace of rust—the inscription upon it (unfortunately undated) is as clear as when it was engraved, fifteen centuries ago.[20]

From India the arts of iron and steel making might have been transmitted to the West via the Muslims, and to China (and Japan) via Central Asia. At any rate, the Japanese were soon able to produce steel blades of astounding excellence. To be sure, the Japanese might have invented that art independently. Ingenious swordsmiths anxious to improve the quality of their blades, and trying every kind of heating, cooling, and tempering, as well as every kind of ore, might eventually discover or rediscover similar secrets.

It is probable that information concerning Chinese mines and metallurgy might

[17] Stephen V. Grancsay: An Indian scimitar (Bull. of the Metropolitan Museum 30, 141–42, 1935).

[18] Wa anzalnā-l-ḥadīd fīhi bā's shadīd wa manāfi'u li-n-nās (57, 25).

[19] As quoted by J. Ruska (EI 2, 189, 1914). I do not understand that word.

[20] Nil Ratan Dhar in Cultural heritage of India (3, 451, 1936). Verrier Elwin: The Agaria (328 p., ill., Calcutta 1942; Isis 35, 253), account of primitive iron metallurgy in central India, and the marriage of craft with magic.

be found in the remaining volumes of the Yung Lo ta tien or in the Ch'in ting ku chin t'u shu chi ch'êng (e.g., in article t'ieh, XXVII, 343, 344).

With regard to Japan our documents are relatively late. An early treatise was translated by Samuel Wells Williams: "Ko doü dzu roku, or a memoir on smelting copper illustrated with plates, small folio 20 p." (Chinese repository 9, 86–101, Canton 1840). William Gowland: The early metallurgy of copper, tin and iron in Europe, as illustrated by ancient remains and the primitive processes surviving in Japan (Archaeologia 56, 267–322, 27 fig., 1899); The early metallurgy of silver and lead (ibid. 57, 359–422, 21 fig., map, 1901); Metals and metal working in old Japan (Transactions of Japan Society 13, 20–99, 1915). C. N. Bromehead: Ancient mining processes as illustrated by a Japanese scroll (Antiquity 16, 193–207, 2 pl., Gloucester 1942), apropos of a scroll 22 feet long and 1 foot wide illustrating gold mining in Sado island (west coast of Japan), and all the subsequent processes to the minting of refined gold. Gold mining on Sado was begun only in 1601.

The earliest reference to gold mining in Korea is of the year 1079. In 1340 the king sent gold and silver to China "to purchase many things of foreign manufacture." About 1380 general Li T'ai tsu was given fifty ounces of gold for having defeated Japanese pirates. About the same time the king of Korea paid each year to the Ming emperor a tribute including a hundred pounds of gold. Edwin W. Mills: Gold mining in Korea (Transactions, Korea branch, Royal Asiatic Society, 7, 5–39, Seoul 1916).

This section on mining and metallurgy is more tantalizing than satisfying; very few references are made to contemporary or almost contemporary writings; references to monuments are chronologically vague. Such as it is, however, it may help scholars to begin a deeper study of these difficult questions.

Second Kingdom: Plants

6. *Herbals*

More herbals were published in Latin by Joannes ad Barbam (John Mandeville?), John Arderne, Thomas of Sarepta, and Benedetto Rinio; in Czech by Christian of Prachatice; in Turkish by Isḥāq ibn Murād of Gerede; in Chinese by Chu Hsiao. To these herbals might still be added an anonymous French one, compiled c. 1380 in the pays de Vaud, Switzerland. Like every other herbal, it is largely derived from earlier ones, beginning with the Macer floridus, but includes new data. It was edited by Paul Aebischer and Eugène Olivier: L'herbier de Moudon (Publications de la Société suisse d'histoire de la médecine, 102 p., pl., Aarau 1938; Isis 29, 487).

The history of the pên ts'ao has been discussed sufficiently in chapter I (p. 222–24); but it is worth while to stress once more the exceptional importance of the Chiu-huang pên-ts'ao, which was probably the most original compilation of its kind, not only in China, but anywhere. As to the European herbals, a detailed comparative analysis, which nobody has yet attempted, would be necessary to determine their respective merits or demerits. We may naturally expect each one to include local novelties in addition to the traditional commonplaces. This is especially true of the herbals written in colloquial languages, non-Latin in Christian Europe, non-Arabic in the Dār al-Islām, non-Chinese in the Far East. We do not, however, know Korean, Japanese, Annamese, Balinese, or Malay herbals which can be definitely assigned to this period.

The reader wishing to investigate Far Eastern non-Chinese herbals might begin with the following books: Albert Sallet: L'officine sino-annamite. Le médecin annamite et la préparation des remèdes (160 p., 16 pl., Paris 1931; Isis 22, 267–72). Wolfgang Weck: Heilkunde und Volkstum auf Bali (260 p., 27 fig., Stuttgart 1937; Isis 28, 235). John Desmond Gimlette: Malay poisons and charm cures (135 p., 1915; 2d ed., 272 p., London 1923; Isis 8, 810); The medical book of Malayan medicine (152 p., Singapore 1930; J. R. A. S., 1931, 475–77); Dictionary of Malayan medicine (272 p., London 1939; Isis 33, 130). Isaac Henry Burkill: Malay village medicine (Gardens' bulletin 6, 165–321, Straits Settlements 1930; Isis 17, 551); Dictionary of the economic products of the Malay peninsula (2 vols., 2414 p., London 1935).

It would seem that the Silesian doctor Thomas of Sarepta did not simply compile a herbal, but collected plants and made himself a herbarium in the modern sense, i.e., a collection of dried plants.[21] This is the earliest mention of such a collection known to me, though it is clear that every herborizer must have preserved or tried to preserve at least some specimens for future reference. When is such a collection large enough and systematic enough to deserve the name herbarium? That is a moot question. At any rate, I never heard of any such collection anterior to that of Thomas of Sarepta, except that Villard de Honnecourt (XIII-2) gave a recipe for the preservation of colors in dried flowers.

7. *Botanic gardens*

It is probable that the herb gardens or botanic gardens created in the first half of the fourteenth century continued in the second half of the century, and that new ones were established, though none is definitely mentioned. A monastery garden might resemble a botanic garden more or less according to the tendencies of its guardian, the hortulanus, and of the physician, herbalist, or hospital attendants. No herb garden of the second half of the fourteenth century was sufficiently remarkable to attract the attention of chroniclers.

Dietrich Laurenstein: Der deutsche Garten des Mittelalters bis 1400 (Diss., 52 p., Göttingen 1900). H. Fischer (1929).

The outstanding achievement occurred in China. The Ming imperial prince Chu Hsiao, being exiled from the dragon's court, improved the opportunities which his banishment gave him to establish in his estates near Kai-fêng-fu, Honan, not only a botanical garden, but also an experimental one for the introduction of useful plants. This is so important that one wishes Chinese scholars would investigate the matter and give us more information about it.

8. *Plant (and animal) iconography*

The most remarkable iconographic monuments of this period are the herbal of Benedetto Rinio and the miniatures of Cybo of Hyères.

The colored plates which Rinio added to his herbal in order to illustrate some 450 plants are pleasant and even beautiful, but their purpose was utilitarian. On the contrary, Cybo's purpose was purely artistic and full of fancy. His idea was to embellish a manuscript with the beauties of nature, without so much as bothering about the text. His drawings of all kinds of leaves, flowers, insects, birds, even mollusks, are remarkably naturalistic, but he gave free play to his imagination in their selection and grouping. His work is of deep interest to the humanized

[21] According to Ducange (s.v.), the mediaeval term herbarium never had the modern meaning. Latin herbals were often called herbarium or herbarius (Klebs nos. 505–7).

naturalist in that it is symbolic of the triumph of free and naturalistic interpretations over the somewhat stilted and conventional ones. Should we speak of renaissance apropos of this? Renaissance against mediaevalism? I think not; the two tendencies may be shown to have coexisted in various degrees throughout the Middle Ages. A study of all the illuminated MSS from this special angle would be very worth while. It could be carried out under ideal conditions in the Pierpont Morgan Library of New York, where many valuable MSS are assembled, together with photographs of many more and the relevant literature almost in its entirety.[22] Much additional information might be culled from the histories of art or from such books as Joan Evans: Pattern. A study of ornament in Western Europe from 1180 to 1900 (folio, 2 vols., Clarendon Press, Oxford 1931); Nature in design. A study of naturalism in decorative art from the bronze age to the Renaissance (134 p., ill., London 1933). Denise Jalabert: De l'art oriental antique à l'art roman. Recherches sur la faune et la flore romanes. I, Le sphinx (Bulletin monumental vol. 94, 71–104, 28 fig., 1935); II, Les sirènes (ibid. vol. 95, 433–71, 42 fig., 1936); III, L'aigle (ibid. vol. 97, 173–94, 26 fig., 1938).

Zoological iconography cannot be separated from the botanical; the very herbals contain occasionally a few animal pictures. Artists like Villard de Honnecourt (XIII-2) and Cybo of Hyères did not draw any lines between the two kingdoms, or for that matter between the three. They let them mix in their drawings even as they do in nature. The same remark applies to many of the Arabic miniaturists.

Some books, however, called bestiaries or volucraries were more restricted in their scope. There are definite bestiary iconographical traditions comparable to the herbal ones, but less clear, not established by incunabula, and more difficult to investigate. Bestiaries were popular; it would seem that some of them were produced in quantities, a "pouncing" process being used to reproduce the images as rapidly and accurately as possible.[23]

The vicissitudes of plant and animal illustrations may be followed not only in Western MSS, but also in Oriental ones, Christian and Islamic. For example, there is in the Pierpont Morgan Library an Armenian prayerbook (MS 803) written in 1335 by Vardan of Lori (Georgia) and his sons and decorated by Megherditeh. The decoration includes foliage, birds, and monsters. Other Armenian MSS with similar decoration may be found in the catalogue raisonné compiled by Sirarpie der Nersessian: MSS arméniens illustrés des XIIe, XIIIe et XIVe siècles de la bibliothèque des pères Mékhitharistes de Venise (Paris 1936–37).

A large collection of Islamic animal designs was published by Mrs. Cleves Stead: Fantastic fauna, with foreword by Gaston Wiet (38 p., 177 pl., Cairo 1935). It contains some 630 designs taken from mediaeval Egyptian ceramics, preserved in the Arabic Museum, Cairo; very full index. The book is known to me only through L. A. Mayer's very favorable review of it in Journal of the Palestine Oriental Society (19, 122, Jerusalem 1939).

The amount of work remaining to be done in the Oriental field may be judged from the lists published by Kurt Holter: Die islamischen Miniaturhandschriften vor 1350 (Zentralblatt für Bibliothekswesen 54, 1–34, 1937); Hugo Buchthal, Otto Kurz, and Richard Ettinghausen: Supplementary notes (Ars islamica 7, 147–64,

[22] The Pierpont Morgan Library, 1924–29 (148 p., 14 pl., New York 1930; Isis 16, 574); 1930–35 (164 p., 14 pl., New York 1937); 1936–40 (140 p., 19 pl., New York 1941; Isis 34, 280).

[23] Samuel A. Ives and Hellmut Lehmann-Haupt: An English 13th century bestiary. A new discovery in the technique of medieval illustration (45 p., 8 pl., New York 1942; Isis 34, 366–67).

1940); Hugo Buchthal and Otto Kurz: A handlist of illuminated Oriental Christian MSS (120 p., 1 pl., Warburg Institute, London 1942). The last-mentioned authors have listed no less than 555 MSS in Syriac, Arabic, Coptic, Nubian, Aethiopic, Armenian, and Georgian, ranging from the sixth to the fifteenth century; 44 are ascribed to the fourteenth century.

There are also a good number of illuminated Muslim MSS, mostly in Arabic, but also in Persian and Turkish. In addition to the hints given in Introd. 2, 1073, it will suffice to refer to the magnificent MS of the Manāfi' al-ḥayawān of Ibn al-Duraihim, written, probably under the author's inspection, in 1354 and illustrated with some 250 miniatures. That MS is the pride of the Escorial library (Renaud 1941, no. 898).

More information may be found in Sir Thomas Walker Arnold: Painting in Islam (178 p., 64 pl., Oxford 1928). Edgar Blochet: Musulman painting (London 1929). Hugo Buchthal: Indian fables in Islamic art (Journal of the Royal Asiatic Society, 1941, 317–24, 4 pl.).

It is clear that generalizations should be avoided until all these documents, Christian and Muslim, have been properly analyzed and classified from our point of view. What is certain is that naturalistic trends can be detected in most of the fourteenth-century ones, together with the occasional persistence of conventional and stereotyped motives.

Passing to China, the admirable iconographic traditions preserved and developed for centuries in the pên ts'ao have been discussed previously. It will suffice to remark that the illustrations included in the early printed pên ts'ao represent an iconographic corpus much larger than that included not only in the MS herbals of the West, but also in the Western incunabula. In this respect China was far ahead of Europe.

To the pên ts'ao may be added a curious album of natural history, the I-yü t'u-chih, containing the images of many animals. The Chinese had a great fondness for picture albums. Many such albums have been mentioned before; it will suffice to recall the Kêng chih t'u shih of Lou Shou (XII-2), 45 woodcuts illustrating husbandry and weaving, and the twelve books of images completing the treatise on agriculture, Nung shu, of Wang Chên (XIV-1). The Chinese encyclopaedias contain abundant figures. This fondness for illustrations may be explained partly by the fact that the written language was very difficult (images would encourage the reader, sometimes they might replace the text), and partly by the fact that it was hardly more difficult to engrave the pictures than the text, and hence it was more tempting to have pictures than not, or to have many than few. However that may be, there is a wealth of iconographic documents to illustrate almost every aspect of Chinese life.

Interesting information may be found also in the richly illustrated book of Arthur de Carle Sowerby: Nature in Chinese art (204 p., New York 1940; Isis 34, 68), but the monuments to which the author refers and which he often reproduces are seldom dated or datable.

It is remarkable that in earlier times the animal motif was much more popular than the floral one. The full efflorescence of floral motives did not occur till the Sung dynasty (Sowerby p. 129–31).

The perennial conflict between realism on the one hand and idealization or stylization on the other, and the rhythmical oscillation from naturalism to idealism and vice versa, are as conspicuous in Chinese as in Western art. Many of the Chinese drawings of plants, and even more so of animals, are highly conventional, others are so realistic that the natural objects which they represent can be determined (at least the genus). It is clear that that rhythm is an essential characteristic of human nature; its wave length and amplitude vary from place to place and from time to time, but it can be detected somehow everywhere.

9. *Husbandry*

The main agricultural treatise of this period was written in Arabic, and not only that, but it was written by an Arabian prince in Arabia! This was the Bughyat al-fallāḥīn composed by al-Malik al-Afḍal al-'Abbās ibn 'Alī, the sixth Rasūlī sulṭān of Yaman. This treatise is unusually comprehensive.

The Arabic superiority in husbandry was recognized in Aragon and Catalonia, witness the fact that Pere III el Cerimoniós ordered the translation from Arabic into Catalan of a treatise on agriculture formerly put together for the Moorish kings of Seville.

Agricultural improvements gradually introduced during the Middle Ages are very difficult to date, even approximately. Allusion has already been made (ch. I, p. 227) to the rotation of crops as being common in Flanders at the beginning of this century. It is difficult to be more precise, or to determine more exactly which crops were rotated in different countries. How was the land enriched? The value of manure had been recognized from ancient times; stercus quod plurimum prodest, said Varro (I-2 B.C.). Not only was stable manure widely used wherever it was available, but also the dung of birds, especially pigeons. More manure was obtained by scattering straw and stubble in the farmyards and allowing cattle to trample and foul it. Wood ashes were also used, as well as green manure, i.e., the burying of lupines, beanstalks, and vetches. All this was already done in Roman times. It is interesting, by the way, that the special value of leguminous plants was thus empirically recognized, though their function (the capture and fixation of atmospheric nitrogen) could be understood only in the nineteenth century. It is possible that economists will eventually be able to tell us when various improvements were observed in various places, but there is little hope of establishing the emergence in definite years (or even definite centuries) of real agricultural inventions.

The recent publication of volume 1 of the Cambridge economic history of Europe, edited by John Harold Clapham and the late Eileen Power, was eagerly awaited, for it was hoped it would bring light on these questions. It is a rich mine of information for the economist. Among other things, François Louis Ganshof, one of the fifteen contributors, has investigated the transformation of Western European domains between the eleventh and the fourteenth centuries with regard to the extent of land under cultivation, the management of the soil, and the character and distribution of landed property. He has shown how the classical domain was broken up, and how church property was repeatedly caused to shrink, instead of expanding as the conception of mortmain would have suggested. The explanation is that the church, in spite of its immortality and other advantages, did not escape social vicissitudes of many kinds; it was occasionally obliged to sell some of its holdings, it might be robbed by neighboring lords, by its own avoués, by sharecroppers or squatters; its property might be squandered by incompetent and reckless abbots, or by dishonest stewards and bailiffs. Ganshof adduces many documented instances of each of these possibilities, and concludes (p. 287): "We shall not venture to express a categorical opinion on the question whether as a whole the rural property of the Church increased or diminished between the eleventh and the fourteenth centuries. If the terminus a quo be placed towards the end of the third quarter of the ninth century, there can be no doubt that there was a decrease, and indeed a very marked decrease." These lines have been quoted as a correction to the remarks made about mortmain in a previous chapter (ch. I, p. 327). The evil of mortmain did exist, but it was somewhat mitigated by antagonistic forces. Nobody in those days objected to mortmain or even was very conscious of it, but property, whether lay or ecclesiastical, will never be secure as long as landowners, not to speak of landless people, are hungry for more land than they have.

As to the kind of technicalities which the historian of science is hunting for, the Cambridge economic history is disappointing. Whatever technicalities are discussed are undated, and probably undatable. We shall never know except in a very rough way when the mediaeval agricultural inventions were made, and how they spread from country to country. Outside of the information given in dated agricultural treatises[24] or incidentally in other books, providing us with termini ante quem, we have to be satisfied with the few crumbs which may fall from time to time from the economist's (or the historian's) table.

A good example of such a crumb is the list of seeds bought in 1360 for the household of king Jean le Bon, who was then prisoner in England. This list gives us a good idea of a kitchen garden of that time. It includes "cabbage, onion, 'porète' (in all probability leeks), lettuce, mountain spinach, beet, parsley, hyssop, borage, purslain, garden cress, etc."[25] This is quoted from the article by Charles Parain: The evolution of agricultural technique, in the same volume (p. 118–68, especially 155; 573–75), who adds, "Borage is a newcomer to such a list; it probably dates from the thirteenth century."

The most delightful book in the agricultural literature of this period is the book on shepherdy written in French in 1379 by Jehan de Brie "Le bon berger." It explains in simple but delectable language all that a good shepherd should know, not only about the sheep, but about the weather, the dogs, the herd's calendar, his duties and privileges. The good shepherd must be able to tend the animals in his charge when they are ailing. In short, his duties are many and complex, and his dignity should be measured by them and by the services he renders to the community, not simply by the humbleness of his position in the social order.

The economic value of sheep was high, not only because of their wool, but also because of the manure which they produced. That was well understood in England, though by this time the golden age of demesne farming was already over. Said the late Eileen Power in her excellent little book on the English wool trade (p. 35, 1941): "The later fourteenth century, from about 1340, was the critical age, and the fifteenth century the age of stagnation. Against the background of pestilence and war, prices fell, agrarian profits dwindled, the population decreased and colonisation came to a stop. The slump was most strongly marked in arable farming, but the

[24] In the West, Walter of Henley (XIII-1), near 1250; Pietro dei Crescenzi (XIV-1), c. 1306; Jehan de Brie, 1379; Mayster Ion Gardener: The feate of gardeninge, poem of 196 English lines, written c. 1440–50, edited by Alicia M. Tyssen-Amherst (Archaeologia 54, 157–72, 1894); John Fitzherbert: Husbandrie (1523), etc.

[25] This list of 1360 might be compared with that of a little before 1328 in the accounts of Thierry d'Hireçon, mentioned in chapter I, p. 227.

same thing, though possibly to a less extent, occurred in sheep farming. It is difficult to find signs of that wholesale substitution of pasture for arable farming which, according to textbooks, happened after the Black Death. It is quite true that there was a decline in arable cultivation, and rolls sometimes show lands being turned back from arable to pasture. But these were 'marginal' lands, put under plough during a boom period and lapsing again during the slump. And this did not necessarily mean more sheep. What happened probably was that the rougher grazing was in turn abandoned for the lands newly laid to pasture. One is indeed forced to the irresistible conclusion that there was a serious drop in sheep farming during this period."[26]

Some glimpses into the actual conditions of English agriculture may be obtained in the poem Piers Plowman, about which see the note on William Langland. These glimpses have been put together in part 1 of Jack Cecil Drummond and Anne Wilbraham: The Englishman's food (London 1939; Isis 33, 300), and explained in their relation to the all-important subjects of food and diet.

Our account of husbandry may properly end with the mention of two French books of domestic economy: Le viandier, composed by the royal chef Guillaume Taillevent, and the anonymous Ménagier de Paris. The first of these is hardly more than a cookbook, but it has the distinction of being the first elaborate one in the French language. The second is more ambitious, for it is not by any means restricted to cookery (essential as the latter may be in every home), but discusses other aspects of domestic life, such as gardening and hunting, and the respective duties of husband and wife, master and servant.

10. *Spices*

There is little to add to the account of spices given in chapter I (p. 229-31). Much information may be culled from the geographical and medical books of the second half of the fourteenth century, but none obliging us to reconsider our views. Perhaps the best description of pepper as cultivated on the Malabar coast is that given in the Riḥla of Ibn Baṭṭūṭa (Defrémery 4, 76-78, 80). Other spices attracted Ibn Baṭṭūṭa's curiosity, for he was interested in good cooking and all that pertains to it, and referred many times to such condiments as ginger, nutmeg, cloves (in Java and Sumatra), cinnamon (in Malabar and Ceylon), etc.

Spices were among the most important articles of trade between the East and the West. Their importance appears especially in such international emporia as Alexandria and Venice, which were respectively the main outlet of the East and the main inlet of the West. The beautifully illustrated herbal completed by Benedetto Rinio in 1410 was produced because of the requirements of the Venetian dealers in spices, condiments, and herbs.

There was an eager market for spices because they were not simple luxuries, but answered physiological cravings. For many people pepper had become a necessary ingredient for the preparation of meat and fish, especially when these viands were not quite as palatable as one might have wished or had lost their freshness. This must have happened often enough in an age of slow communications. Monasteries tried to put up large provisions of preserves of various kinds, pickled and smoked

[26] For further ideas on mediaeval shepherdy, see Clapham and Power (vol. 1, by index s.v. "farming, sheep"), though their survey concerns almost exclusively times anterior to the fourteenth century. On the wool trade see J. W. Shilson: Weighing wool in the Middle Ages (Antiquity 18, 72-77, 1944).

viands, as well as spices. We hear an echo of this in the chronicle of the religious troubles in Flanders in 1566–68, written by Marc Van Vaernewyck.[27] When the Protestant iconoclasts sacked the Dominican monastery in Ghent, they found there large quantities of pepper, cane sugar, saffron,[28] and other spices. And Marc Van Vaernewyck adds by way of explanation: "The monks who do not take any physical exercise had always a large provision of pepper on hand in order to facilitate the digestion of fish of which they eat considerable amounts. Those among them who were ailing or did not feel comfortable made also use of it [pepper]." Though this remark refers to the sixteenth century, it would apply equally well to the fourteenth century, except that the spices then were much rarer and more valuable.

Third Kingdom: Animals

11. *Hunting and falconry*

Of all the books touching upon natural history, none were more numerous or more popular than those dealing with hunting in its various forms, and especially with the royal sport of falconry.

The best examples of cynegetic literature came from France, which was in many respects the home of Western knighthood and was giving Europe the most elaborate conceits of chivalresque romance as well as the latest patterns and fashions of chivalresque usage.

The first of these examples is the poem, entitled Roman de detuits (des deduis), which Gace de la Bigne began at Hertford in 1359 for his king, Jean le Bon, then prisoner of the English; it was completed in France in or after 1370.

The second is a very elaborate treatise in prose and verse entitled "Les livres du roy Modus et de la royne Ratio," made up of two very different parts, the first, "Le livre des déduis," discussing many forms of hunting, the second, "Le songe de pestilence," being devoted to moralities. The first part was written in or after 1354; the second was begun twenty years later; both were completed in 1376–77. These two parts are so different that one might be tempted to ascribe them to two authors, but it does not seem necessary to do that. All considered, it is more likely that both works were written by the same man, and that the second was copied by another man, the names of both being concealed in a circular anagram placed at the end. The author was certainly a Norman, and probably Henri de Ferrières; the Songe de pestilence was copied by Denis d'Hormes (the two noble Norman families de Ferrières and d'Hormes or d'Ormes, d'Ourmes, were related).

The popularity of that text is proved by the existence of 32 MSS (the earliest dated 1379) and by many printed editions: (1) Chambéry 1486, with woodcuts, (2) Paris, s.a., between 1518 and 1526, (3, 4) Paris, s.a., (5) Paris 1526, (6) Paris 1560, (7) Paris 1839, (8) transcription in modern French by Gunnar Tilander (232 p., 51 fig., Paris 1931).

The same has prepared a critical edition for the Société des anciens textes français. Gunnar Tilander: Les livres du roy Modus et de la royne Ratio (2 vols., 28 pl., Paris 1931–32), with elaborate introduction, notes, glossary, and indexes; the glossary is particularly rich in cynegetic terms. In this edition the Livre des

[27] Ferdinand van der Haeghen: Van die beroerlicke tijden in die Nederlanden en voornamelijk in Ghendt (5 vols., Ghent 1872–81). French translation by Hermann Van Duyse (2 vols., Ghent 1905; Isis 33, 61–63). My reference is to the French translation (1, 108).

[28] Crocus sativus. The name comes from the Arabic za'farān (Meyerhof no. 135, 1940). Much used as a spice and drug by Muslims, and all over Europe.

déduis is divided into 139 sections and covers 309 p.; the Songe de pestilence, sections 140 to 259, covers 225 p.

We need not speak long of the third French treatise, Le miroir de Phoebus, though it is the best of all, because the reader will find all the needed information in the article devoted to its author, Gaston III count of Foix, nicknamed Gaston Phoebus. That treatise was begun in 1387, and it is perhaps the best of its kind, not only in France, but also in Christian Europe. The personality of its author, one of the most powerful lords of southern France, emphasizes the fact that hunting, and especially the chase, was a sport reserved for the lords of the land and their attendant gentlemen. Some kings and lords who distinguished themselves in the exercise of that prerogative were greatly admired and quoted as paragons of knightly behavior. The keeping of hounds and falcons required considerable care; falcons were very delicate, especially during molting, and liable to suffer various ailments; they were hard to replace (falcons do not breed in captivity) and were treated far more tenderly than poor human beings. The maintenance of stables, kennels, and mews on a princely scale was very expensive; many kinds of servants and officers were required not only for the service of such an establishment, but even more for the ceremonial of the chase. Some idea of these expenditures may be obtained from the royal accounts, or from the account of such a prince as Louis d'Orléans,[29] who displayed extraordinary magnificence in his cynegetical exploits.[30] All this, however, concerns the social historian rather than the naturalist.

Information on hunting of a humbler kind is provided in the Ménagier de Paris (c. 1393).

French fashions were eagerly imitated by the English lords. The latter were familiar enough with French usage. Gace de la Bigne had begun his Roman des deduis in England, and we may imagine that English gentlemen in attendance on the royal prisoner were acquainted with that poem. The earliest English treatise on hunting is the translation of an Anglo-Norman one written in the first quarter of the century by William Twici and John Gyfford; that translation was probably made in the second half of the century. Soon afterward (c. 1410), Le miroir de Phoebus was Englished by Edward Plantagenet, duke of York, under the title The master of the game. Treatises on hawking and hunting are included in the Boke of St. Albans ascribed to dame Juliana Berners and supposed to have been written in the first half of the fifteenth century.

A Spanish treatise on falconry, Libro de las aves de caça, was written in 1386 by López de Ayala, during his captivity in Portugal. It should be noted that López quoted the book of king Modus as an authority. Hence in the Spanish as well as in the English case, the French influence is clear. It is possible that treatises on hunting and hawking were written also in other European languages, but the examples taken from the three foremost literatures, next to Italian, may suffice to indicate the trends of Catholic Europe.

The earliest German text on falconry, the Aucupatorium herodiorum, was written somewhat later, c. 1430–50, by Eberhard Hicfelt. It is derived from Latin writings

[29] Louis I, son of king Charles V and queen Jeanne de Bourbon; born in Paris 1372, duke of Orléans 1391; murdered in Paris 1407 by the men of Jean sans Peur, duke of Burgundy. He was not only a magnificent huntsman, but a great patron of arts and letters.

[30] Etienne Charavay: Etude sur la chasse à l'oiseau au Moyen âge. Une fauconnerie princière et l'éducation des faucons d'après des documents inédits du XIVe siècle et du XVe (Paris 1873), only 100 copies printed, one of which is in Harvard.

rather than the French ones, and is very elaborate, being divided into three main parts dealing respectively with the nature and habits of falcons, the training of falcons and their ordinary care, their ailments and how to cure them.[31]

It is always well to complete one's study of the fourteenth-century texts with an examination of the incunabula, which may, and more often than not do, represent older traditions. The author has no time to analyze these incunabula, but simply mentions them.

The oldest printed text is, curiously enough, in German, the Habichtbuch (Augsburg 1480, 1497); then we have the English text, the Boke of St. Albans already referred to (St. Albans 1486, Westminster 1496); then only the French texts, Guillaume Tardif: Art de faulconnerie et des chiens de chasse (Paris 1492). Le livre du faulcon (4 incunabula editions, Paris c. 1495–1500); Le livre de la chasse du grand seneschal de Normandie (Paris c. 1500). The French printed texts appeared later than the German and English ones perhaps because of the availability of French MSS in every aristocratic house. See Klebs (nos. 500, 501, 502, 609, 950). Note that all these French texts are anonymous, except that bearing Tardif's name. Guillaume Tardif of Puy-en-Velay was a professor at the College of Navarre and reader to Charles VIII (king 1483–98); his treatise was largely derived from the book of "king Dancus" (XIII-2), which has come down to us in a French version of 1284. His Art de faulconnerie was reprinted with notes by Ernest Jullien (2 vols., Paris 1882). Harting (no. 142, 1891).

Strangely enough, the only Eastern treatise on falconry of this period is that of Maḥmūd ibn Muḥammad al-Bārjīnī, written in Turkish, but obviously derived from Arabic and Persian patterns.

Though falconry was originally an Eastern sport which did not attain much glamour in the West until after the Crusades, it is remarkable that Arabic treatises on the subject are relatively few. On the other hand, we have a long series of books devoted to horses, their use for hunting or raiding, their care in health and sickness, and their breeding. To the books mentioned in chapter I may be added those of two Andalusians, 'Abdallāh ibn Muḥammad Ibn Juzayy and Ibn Hudhail, and of three Orientals, Muḥammad ibn Mangalī, Muḥammad ibn Lājīn, and Ṭaibughā ibn 'Abdallāh. The last named was of Turkish-Greek origin, a representative of a not inconsiderable group of men, whom one can observe in the Near East in our century as well as in the fourteenth.

The characteristics of Arabic hippology have already been discussed. It will suffice to repeat that these books are very different from the Western cynegetical treatises, though in so far as they occasionally discuss the same problems they must be similar. Their differences lie in the general point of view and the arrangement.

12. *Fishing*

The only treatise on fishing is perhaps the one contained in the second edition of the Boke of St. Albans (Westminster 1496). There is of course no doubt as to the existence of that treatise, the earliest fishing treatise in English, but the ascriptions to dame Juliana Berners and the first half of the fifteenth century are doubtful.

The text of other fishing incunabula in German and Flemish may be equally old if not older. The German text entitled Fisch- und Vogelfang was printed thrice in

31 Ernst von Dombrowski: Altdeutsches Weiderwerk, 1. Band. Aucupatorium herodiorum. Eine deutsche Abhandlung über die Beizjagd aus der ersten Hälfte des 15. Jahrh. (78 p., Wien 1886). Harting (no. 46, 1891).

Strassburg and Erfurt 1498; and the Flemish one, Visschers ende vogheleers, was issued twice in Antwerp 1500 (Klebs nos. 407-8). These German and Flemish texts deal with birding as well as fishing, poor men's sports.

13. *Special animals*

Before speaking of books or facts relative to single animals or groups of animals, let us consider two Arabic works devoted to zoology in general. The first is the treatise on the properties of animals, Manāfi' al-ḥayawān, of which an admirable illustrated MS exists in the Escorial. It contains short descriptions of many animals and their properties or virtues. The other is the treatise on the lives of animals, Ḥayāt al-ḥayawān, a collection of notices on more than a thousand animals put together by al-Damīrī. This gives us precious little information of zoological interest in the strict sense, but the general intention and arrangement were zoological. Al-Damīrī wanted to collect all the lore available concerning animals, that is, all that his readers would want to know about each and every animal of which they had heard, including some mythical ones.

By far the most numerous books devoted to special animals were those dealing with hunting, and discussing the animals which were chased—the hare, hart, buck, roe, wild boar, wolf, fox, badger, wildcat, otter, etc.—and those that were used as auxiliaries—the horses, hounds, various kinds of felinae and cheetahs, hawks and falcons, cormorants. These hunting books, Western and Oriental, have already been considered.

Though cats had been known from time immemorial and had shared the life of the ancient Egyptians,[32] their first appearance in English literature is due to Chaucer!

Ivory has been used for artistic purposes from very early, even prehistoric, times. In antiquity and throughout the Middle Ages most of the ivory carved in the Western world was probably elephantine. The elephant tusks were obtained in India and Africa; the distinction can be safely made, for Asiatic ivory is of a purer white, not so hard and less close in texture. It is probable that the great bulk of European ivory came from Central Africa; Marco Polo (XIII-2) saw great stores of it at Zanzibar. From the eleventh century on, if not before, much use was made of morse ivory, that is, walrus ivory (morsa means walrus in Lapp). That ivory, obtained in arctic regions, was one of the main articles of Scandinavian (Icelandic) trade. Most of the draughtsmen and chessmen of the twelfth century are made of morse ivory. The arctic regions provided also narwhal ivory. The single tusk of the narwhal, however, was often kept entire as a curiosity; this may have helped to accredit the legends concerning the unicorn or monoceros.

Arctic ivory was also exported across Siberia and northeastern Asia and was early known to Chinese, Japanese, Hindus. The same can be said of fossil ivories found in the Siberian tundras.[33] The precious substance found its way to Chinese markets and was widely distributed under the Yüan dynasty.

Finally, the teeth of the hippopotamus were also used, but only for smaller objects, since hippo tusks, being hollow, produce but little ivory. My attention was drawn to hippo ivory by the extraordinary series of forty ivory panels made by

[32] Neville Langton: The cat in ancient Egypt (104 p., 259 fig., Cambridge 1940). Cats appear on monuments of the first dynasty.

[33] There are references to fossil ivory in Theophrastos (IV-2 B.C.), Pliny (I-2), and al-Māzinī (XII-2). See Introd. 2, 412.

the Florentine sculptor Baldassare degli Embriachi, now in the Metropolitan Museum, New York. This Baldassare had a flourishing workshop in Venice at the end of the fourteenth century, and these particular panels were already in the Certosa of Pavia in or before 1400. Mary Alice Wyman: The Helyas legend as represented on the Embriachi ivories at the Metropolitan (Art bulletin 18, 5–24, 1936).

These remarks on the widely spread use of ivory in mediaeval times suggest a kind of hunting, not spoken of in the hunting books, which must have increased some people's knowledge of natural history—hunting for elephants, walruses, narwhals, hippos, not to speak of the search for and trade in fossils, always exceedingly popular in China.[34]

Readers wishing to pursue these inquiries may be embarrassed by the abundance of the ivory literature. Here are a few first-aid references:

Alfred Maskell: Ivories (Connoisseur's library, 458 p., 88 pl., London 1905). Ormonde Maddock Dalton: Catalogue of the ivories in the British Museum (246 p., 125 pl., London 1909). Berthold Laufer and Paul Pelliot: Arabic and Chinese trade in walrus and narwhal ivory (T'oung pao vol. 14, 58 p., 1913). Otto Pelka: Elfenbein (420 p., 316 fig., Berlin 1923). Adolph Goldschmidt: Die Elfenbeinskulpturen (4 vols., Berlin 1914–26); (with Kurt Weitzmann) Die byzantinischen Elfenbeinskulpturen des X.–XIII. Jahrh. (2 vols., Berlin 1930–34). Etsujiro Sunamoto: Zô. Elephants (2416 p., 431 pl. and fig., Osaka 1931–32; Isis 26, 191), in Japanese. Perry Blythe Cott: Siculo-Arabic ivories (Princeton monographs, folio ser. 3, 68 p., 80 pl., Princeton 1939), with a catalogue raisonné of 180 items ranging from the twelfth to the fourteenth century.

Insects. Various invasions of locusts were duly recorded by the chroniclers. According to Bodenheimer (2, 47, 1929), the following occurred in Europe: invasion of Italy in 1363–65, 1389; of Germany in 1353/54, 1363/64, 1373, 1376, 1388; of France in 1353, 1364, 1374. To that list I can add at least one more, that of 1359 in Catalonia, which escaped Bodenheimer's attention, perhaps because it is recorded only in a Hebrew text, the Midrashe ha-Torah of Gatigno.

It is a curious fact that Western writers paid relatively little attention to insects (except as pests), and yet they had or might have inherited Egyptian and Greek traditions of devotion to insects and even of worship. It is probable that these traditions were destroyed by the Jewish, Christian, and Muslim religions. The Egyptians had a great respect for scarabs (Scarabaeus sacer, dung beetle), dedicated to the sun god; the scarab became for them a symbol of resurrection, and their artists produced innumerable scarabs of all sizes and kinds, in many materials. Visitors to Egypt remember the gigantic scarab in granite of Amenophis III (1411–1375 B.C.) near the sacred lake (Birkat al-mallāḥa) of Karnak.[35] Another enormous scarab, in green granite, may be seen in the British Museum; but this one is of considerably later date (Ptolemaic).

The Greeks were interested mainly in the singing cicada (ὁ τέττιξ), and there are various graceful poems in the Greek Anthology celebrating these insects, e.g., by

[34] For walruses and narwhals some information is given in Scandinavian chronicles and other books such as the Konungs skuggsjá (XIII-1). As to the Chinese trade in fossils, see Max Schlosser: Die fossilen Säugethiere Chinas (Abhandlungen der K. bayerischen Akad. der Wissenschaften vol. 22, 1903; Isis 23, 271; 33, 277).

[35] It was my great privilege to see it there in November 1931. G. Sarton: Monumental representations of insects apropos of a pre-Columbian Aztec grasshopper (Isis 32, 1 pl.).

Evenus (Εὔηνος) of Paros, contemporary of Plato, and by Meleager (Μελέαγρος) (fl. c. 60 B.C.). A reference of the latter to the feeding of cicadas with chopped leeks would suggest that the Greeks had insect pets. According to Greek mythology, the cicada was beloved of the Muses and dedicated to Apollo.[36] It is possible that the dedication to Apollo, god of light and sun, was of Egyptian or Oriental origin. No trace of the Greek fondness for cicadas can be found in Latin literature, whether ancient or mediaeval. The love of insects disappears completely until recent days,[37] the days of Keats, Tennyson, and especially Lafcadio Hearn, who was influenced by the Japanese.[38]

Indeed, the Chinese and the Japanese had developed very early an appreciation and love of insects, of which there is no comparable example in the world, not even in Greece. See the note on Chia Ssŭ-tao (XIII-1). I do not know writings of the fourteenth century similar to Chia's, in Chinese or Japanese, but the love of insects continued during that period and must be taken into account in any assessment of their knowledge of nature. In Japan the popular interest in insects is illustrated by a better knowledge of them than can be found among similar classes in other countries. This is evidenced in the children's drawings; every Japanese child will draw insects with three pairs of legs, spiders with four, higher crustaceans with five; he is likely to be acquainted with rare particularities of some insects, e.g., the ability of an elater beetle to jump into the air when placed on its back. Moreover, the Japanese popular vocabulary concerning insects is considerably richer than that of other nations.

The love of insects is abundantly reflected in Japanese poetry and in Japanese art, e.g., in the making of netsuke, ceramics, and other objects, many of which include remarkably accurate representations. I cannot give fourteenth-century examples, but I am sure there are plenty. These tendencies permeate the whole of Japanese culture. For a later example let me recall the delightful picture book of insects (Ehon mushi erami) published in 1788 by the great artist Utamaro (= Kitagawa, 1754–1806). Laufer collected for the Field Museum of Chicago in 1923 a very fine series of objects illustrating Japanese care of crickets and grasshoppers (gourds, boxes, clay beds for the crickets, feeding dishes, nets, brushes, traps, etc.).

Edward S. Morse: Japan day by day (1, 273; 2, 205, Boston 1917). Berthold Laufer: Insect musicians and cricket champions of China (27 p., 12 pl., Field Museum, Chicago 1927; Isis 10, 510–11). John Golding Myers: Insect singers. A natural history of the cicadas (324 p., 7 pl., 116 fig., London 1929; Isis 31, 251).

[36] There are references to grasshoppers and cicadas (ἡ ἀκρίς, ὁ τέττιξ)) in the gracious story Daphnis and Chloë, composed by Longus (Λόγγος) toward the end of the second century or later (book I, 10; I, 25–26; III, 24). Chloë even makes a cage for a grasshopper (ἀκριδοθήκη)', just like a Chinese or a Japanese woman! The epithet τεττιγοφόρος applied to an Athenian is explained by the fact that in early times Athenians wore a golden cicada in their hair to proclaim that they were αὐτόχθονες, not foreign settlers.

[37] A partial exception is the mediaeval interest in bees, but the exploitation of insects is different from the love of them. Bees were often used as virtuous illustrations by the moralists, e.g. in the Bonum de apibus of Thomas of Cantimpré (XIII-1) and in a Syriac treatise of Solomon of Baṣra (XIII-1). Another partial exception is the occasional praise of butterflies.

[38] The golden cicada (cigalo d'or) which the Felibres have chosen as the insignia of majourau (mayor, chief) is derived from the Greek example quoted in footnote 36 and perhaps from Troubadour tradition. Frédéric Mistral: Lou tresor dóu felibrige (1, 556, Aix-en-Provence 1879–86). A century ago the people of Madrid were keeping pet crickets in cages. Théophile Gautier: Tras los montes (ch. 8, Paris 1843); that book was often reprinted, in 1845 and later, under the title Voyage en Espagne.

Lafcadio Hearn: Insects and Greek poetry (William Edwin Rudge, New York 1926); Insect literature translated and annotated (515 p., 8 pl., Tokyo 1921). The latter book is a collection of Hearn's articles on insects taken from many books, with the text of the Japanese quotations given by Hearn in English, and Japanese translation of Hearn's own text; the Japanese and English being printed on opposite pages. This book was prepared by Masanobu Ōtani, who had gathered the Japanese insect lore used by Hearn.

Menageries. One of the best ways of knowing animals is to live with them, or at least near them. The wish for pet animals is as old as civilization. Some animals, like cats, were attracted by man and to him, and have lived with him for uncountable millennia without allowing him to exploit them. Others could not be tamed at all, yet men wanted to have them near; thus were "menageries" created. We owe to Loisel a history of menageries[39] which begins in Egypt. He speaks of menageries in China, India, Babylonia, etc. Many existed in the Hellenistic world (e.g., in Alexandria) and in the Roman one. Throughout the Middle Ages we may assume that some princes, here and there, kept wild animals in cages. This was tempting and plausible enough. Such animals might be given them from time to time by other princes or by their own vassals or retainers. The personnel of their stables and mews could easily take care of a few more beasts, such as bears, wolves, foxes, wildcats, or even of rarer ones such as ostriches or giraffes. One of the best mediaeval examples of royal interest in animals was given by Frederick II of Hohenstaufen (XIII-1). Frederick maintained menageries in Palermo and in Luceri dei Pagani, and he had a movable one which accompanied him on his travels. The first giraffe to be seen in Europe was thus exhibited by him.

One of the most important menageries was that of the kings of France, which can be traced to the time of St. Louis (king 1226-70) and which became gradually more ambitious. There was a menagerie in the Louvre from 1333 to c. 1375, but the main one was in another part of Paris, the Hôtel Saint-Pol, under Charles V and Charles VI (1364-1422).

The popes of Avignon tried to emulate the kings. John XXII (pope 1316-34) had stocked his gardens with white peacocks and had organized a real menagerie. In 1324 his foreman was ordered to prepare a large cage for bears and others for the lion and the ostriches. A few years later a camel and deer were added. These animals inspired the artists who decorated the palace and churches of Avignon. In 1335, Benedict XII ordered a new lion from Sicily. Clement VI (1342-52) had parrots and other exotic birds. In 1384, Clement VII, who did not care for birds, gave them to the duke of Burgundy, and caused the whole menagerie to be moved to his castle of Sorgues,[40] keeping in town only a single lion. In addition to the menageries kept by feudal princes, there were also municipal ones. For example, Bertrand Boisset tells us that the city of Arles had a lion of its own. One day they managed a fight between the lion and a ram, and the ram won! This does not gives us a very high idea of the Arlesian lion. . . . Brun (p. 227, 1928), from whom I gather these anecdotes, adds that the duke of Berry had a predilection for bears and swans, and took a bear with him wherever he went. The duke of Burgundy had so

[39] Gustave Loisel: Histoire des ménageries de l'antiquité à nos jours (3 vols., Paris 1912). Vol. 1 tells the story to the sixteenth century inclusive; vol. 2, seventeenth to eighteenth century; vol. 3, nineteenth to twentieth century.

[40] Sorgues-sur-l'Ouvèze, in Vaucluse, 10 km. from Avignon.

many monkeys that he made presents of them to his friends, and a tamed leopard was his traveling companion.

The same habits obtained in Germany. A kind of zoological garden existed in 1365 in Schönberg near the Moritzberg. Joseph Reindl: Ehemalige zoologische und botanische Gärten in Bayern (Archiv für Geschichte der Naturwissenschaft 4, 79–86, 1913; p. 80). At the end of the century there was another "Tiergarten" in Stuhm, near Marienburg, West Prussia. Definite information ad hoc is to be found in the accounts of the Teutonic Order (XII-2), as published by Erich Joachim: Das Marienburger Tresslerbuch der Jahre 1399–1409 (698 p., Königsberg i.Pr. 1896). Among the boarders of that Tiergarten or Wildpark, so different from those of Western Europe, were specimens of Wisent, Urochs, and Meerochs. The first two names refer to the European bison (Bison bonasus) and the ure-ox, urus, or aurochs (Bos primigenius), but what is the Meerochs? This has caused considerable discussion. The word Meer has been affixed to many names of animals and plants in Middle German to denote an outremer or exotic origin.[41] The Meerochs was thus probably an exotic animal. Szalay concludes that it was the zebu (Bos indicus).[42] If so, there were in 1407 eight specimens of zebu in the Stuhmer "zoo."

It is legitimate to include in the zoological literature of this period the animal tales, such as the Czech ones of Flaška z Pardubic and the Byzantine ones enumerated in chapter X, pages 823–25. One of these, the *Διήγησις παιδιόφραστος τῶν τετραπόδων ζῴων*, is a poem describing an assembly of animals; the assembly is said to have taken place in 1365, and this may be the true date of the poem itself; the date is plausible. These stories, Czech, Greek, etc., may be connected with the cycle of Reynard the Fox (XII-2),[43] but may just as well be independent of it, or both cycles may derive from earlier sources. The personification of animals and their use for didactic, satirical, humorous, or fabular purposes is spread all over the world. It is a universal characteristic of the human mind; it reveals an instinctive feeling of kinship with animal life in all its forms.

The Dialogus creaturarum ascribed to Maino de Maineri (XIV-1; d. c. 1364), a collection of animal moralities, may also be cited in this connection. That book, whoever was its author—the mysterious Nicholas of Pergamon, or Maino de Maineri, or a tertius quis—attained considerable success, witness the number of incunabula editions in Latin, Dutch, and French, and early ones in English.

Voles and lemmings. Outbreaks of voles or field mice (Microtus arvalis and related species, campagnol) occurred in 1271, 1278–79, 1366, 1378, 1468, etc. Charles Elton: Voles, mice and lemmings. Problems in population dynamics (500 p., ill., Clarendon Press, Oxford 1942; Isis 35, 82); no information is given on the fourteenth-century outbreaks.

[41] Meerkatze, Meerschwein, Meergans; Meerbirnbaum, Meercucumer, Meerkirsche, Meerklee, etc. A similar formation exists in Magyar, with tengeri = Meer.

[42] B. Szalay: Der Meerochs. Ein Beitrag zur Geschichte des Zebu, des "Büffels," des Elches, usw. (Zoologische Annalen 6, 75–111, Würzburg 1914).

[43] The cycle obtained so much popularity in France that the early French name of the fox, goupil, derived from vulpecula, little vulpes, was replaced by the name renard (from Reynard). Even so the word espiègle is derived from another Germanic cycle of stories, Eulenspiegel or Uilenspiegel. Reynard was as familiar to mediaeval men as Micky Mouse or Donald Duck is to us; in both cases the association of ideas was solidly established in childhood. The word goupil survives in goupillon, meaning aspergillum or sprinkler (for holy water), which was made of a fox's tail.

As to the lemmings (Myodes lemmus, and related species), though their name occurs in an Old Norse text of the second half of the thirteenth century, the first author to deal with them was the Bavarian Jacob Ziegler: Quae intus continentur (Strassburg 1532). Thus the history of lemmings begins only in 1532.

Konráð Gíslason: 44 prøver af oldnordisk Sprog og Literatur (404 p., Copenhagen 1860). Robert Collett: Myodes lemmus, its habits and migrations in Norway (Videnskabs-Selskabs Forhandlinger no. 3, 62 p., Christiania 1895). Charles Elton (1942).

14. *Translations*

The only translations of this period bearing on natural history are those made from Arabic into Catalan by order of Pere III el Cerimoniós.

XI. MEDICINE

The Black Death

Instead of beginning as usual with an account of the medical work done in each country, we must speak first of all of the great calamity which shook Europe, nay, the whole world, about the year 1348. That calamity was so intense and caused so many victims (say, a quarter of the population) that it created a solution of continuity in history and dominated everything. Some people have gone so far as to suggest that the Black Death of 1348 might be selected as one of the major divisions of the human past, and that it was a more brutal, complete, and international separation than, say, the fall of Constantinople a century later.

There are many objections to this. In the first place, my book will show that in spite of the calamity (which we do not in any way depreciate), the second half of the fourteenth century was not essentially different from the first. As far as the history of science and learning is concerned, it is certain that the plague caused the untimely death of many scholars or future scholars, but apparently other scholars took their place and continued their work. It is vain to speculate on what might have happened if men whose genius was cut short by the atra mors[1] had been able to live or to live longer, for after all the same hazards obtain always and everywhere. If one bears in mind that a single man of genius may change profoundly the course of history, and that that very man may be killed at almost any time by the most futile and unpredictable accident, one realizes that chance plays a tremendous part in human affairs. Such a reflection makes us feel very humble; so far, so good; but it is otherwise not very helpful. We have to take history as it is, not as it might have been if some men had lived longer or not lived at all. No matter how many good men died in 1348, the philosophers, the men of science and learning, were substantially the same kind of people after that fateful date as before.

Moreover, though the mortality was highest about the middle of the century, the plague remained pandemic in the Old World in the second half of the century.

The medical art was helpless, except in so far as it advised cleanliness and segregation. The possibility of contagion was fully recognized, but its mechanism was not understood until centuries later, hence the methods of prophylaxy were neces-

[1] On the use of that phrase see Stephen d'Irsay (Isis 8, 328–32, 1926).

sarily haphazard. One might, for example, forbid markets or kermesses but permit religious processions; one might discourage the kissing of women but encourage the kissing of patens or reliquaries; or one might close the gates of a city to people and be unaware of the rats coming in through the same gates or otherwise. Isolation, it was felt, was the best guaranty of health; only very few people could afford it, and even those might fall victims to the disease, for their isolation was never as complete as they imagined it to be.

Other epidemics than the Black Death were all the time jeopardizing the well-being of the people and disturbing their peace. The most singular of them was the dancing mania which began in the Rhine region about 1374 and spread itself across a good part of Europe during a couple of centuries.

Geographical survey

A. *Christendom*

Our account of medicine in Christendom will be divided into eight sections: (1) Italy, by far the longest, (2) Hispanic peninsula, (3) France, (4) England, (5) Germany, (6) Bohemia, (7) Iceland, (8) Christian East.

A1. *Italy*

The Italian group is so large (some thirty men) that one would be tempted to subdivide it into smaller groups, but that would be a little tiresome, because many of the physicians would reappear in diverse groups. It may be more interesting to take them as they come in a rough chronological order.

The first was Dionisio II Colle, who about the middle of the century represented in Belluno a famous medical family then already old. He wrote a treatise on the plague, which had almost claimed his own life. Another plague treatise was composed by Franciscus de Gianellis, who in 1351, being then professor at the University of Perugia, had been asked for advice by that city when the dreadful disease was menacing its inhabitants. Dino Dini of Florence continued the tradition of veterinary art. Giacomo de' Dondi compiled a large collection of recipes, the Aggregatio medicamentorum (or Promptuarium medicinae), which enjoyed some popularity and continued to be used for almost two centuries. William de Marra of Padua wrote a treatise on poisons, a very timely subject in a country distracted by passionate hatreds and demoniac jealousies. In our gallery Guido da Bagnolo represents the type of the royal physician and humanist; he spent a part of his life in Cyprus and had gathered a rich library. We have no writings of Guido; on the other hand, another medical humanist, Tommaso del Garbo, bequeathed a large mass of writings which were studied until the sixteenth century. The main one was his Summa medicinalis, a kind of medical encyclopaedia. Tommaso vied with Taddeo Alderotti and with his own father, Dino del Garbo. A good part of his activity was devoted, like theirs, to the interpretation of the ancient classics; in his case, books of Galen and Ibn Sīnā and even the De anima of Aristotle. Plague treatises were written by him (after 1348), and also by Giovanni de' Dondi before 1371, Cardo da Milano 1378, Niccolò di Burgo 1382, Francischino Collignano 1382, Giovanni da Santa Sofia, Niccolò da Udine 1390, Pietro da Tossignano 1398, etc. Iacopo da Arquà, who was honored with the title of physician to the king of Hungary, has left consilia and Galenic commentaries. Giovanni de' Dondi was physician to the emperor Charles IV, and like his father, Giacomo, cited above, was interested in the medical virtues of the hot springs of

Abano (near Padua). He was scientifically minded and approached medical problems from a physical angle. Giovanni da Santa Sofia wrote a Practica, and commentaries on Hippocrates, Galen, and Ibn Sīnā. Many works are ascribed to Christophorus de Honestis, the best-known being a materia medica in the form of a commentary on the Antidotarium of Mesuë the Younger. Syllanus de Nigris composed a commentary on the ninth book of al-Rāzī's Kitāb al-manṣūrī; that was his way of putting together his views on practical medicine. An epitome of medicine is ascribed to Bartolommeo da Pisa; this is remarkable, for Bartolommeo was a Franciscan friar, and friars did not generally devote their attention to medical subjects. Marsiglio da Santa Sofia was mainly a commentator, a very prolific one, studying in turn Hippocrates, Galen, al-Rāzī, Ibn Sīnā; he was the best-known member of an illustrious medical family. We have already spoken of two of them, Niccolò da Santa Sofia (XIV-1) and his son Giovanni. Marsiglio was a younger brother of the latter. His commentary on the ninth book of Almansor was written with the cooperation of his two nephews (Giovanni's sons), Galeazzo and Bartolommeo da Santa Sofia. Both his nephews taught in Padua, but Galeazzo was for a time professor in Vienna, where he is said to have performed the first anatomical dissection (before 1405); he was physician to Albert IV, duke of Austria (ruled 1395-1404). Galeazzo returned to Padua in 1405 and died there in 1427; his younger brother Bartolommeo seems to have remained all his life in Padua; he taught there from 1388 to 1437 and died in 1448.[2] With the exception of short interludes (Giovanni in Bologna, Marsiglio in Pavia, Galeazzo in Vienna), the Santa Sofia doctors flourished in Padua, and their fame is part and parcel of the fame of the University of Padua. On the other hand, Bologna could boast Pietro da Tossignano, who wrote so much that his works were first ascribed to different members of the Tossignano family; it is now accepted that the three or two Tossignani are only one, namely Pietro, who died about 1407. He wrote regimina, and commentaries on the Problems of Aristotle, the ninth book of Almansor, and the Thesaurus pauperum of Peter of Spain. A treatise on surgery is also ascribed to him, but may be apocryphal. His books remained in circulation at least until the end of the sixteenth century, and the name Tossignano is one of the best-known medical names of his age. Francesco Casini wrote treatises on balneology and toxicology, but is best remembered as a pontifical archiater and a Sienese agent at the curia. It was lucky for Siena to be represented at the curia by one of her own sons, who had captured the popes' confidence so completely that he was personal physician to six of them. The name of Ugolino da Montecatini is familiar to us only because of a book of his on the springs of his native region (between Lucca and Florence) and their medical virtues.

Jacopo da Prato composed a treatise for the use of surgeons, containing not only a summary of surgical experience (as surgery was understood in those days), but also a general medical introduction.

Long as it is, this list could have been lengthened considerably if we had not restricted our choice to doctors whose writings have come down to us and hence whose medical thought can be investigated. Not only have all these men left tangible witnesses of their knowledge in the form of medical texts, but most of these texts have been published[3]—some of them repeatedly.

[2] BL (5, 17, 1934). K. Sudhoff has published plague treatises written by Galeazzo da Santa Sofia for Albert IV (AGM 6, 357-61, 1913) and by Bartolommeo (AGM 6, 349-53, 1913).

[3] The exceptions are Franciscus de Gianellis, Dino Dini, Guglielmo da Marra, Guido da Bagnolo, whose works exist only in MS form.

If one wished to investigate not only medical thought, but also the medical profession and the medical manners and customs which obtained in Italy, it would be necessary to take into account many more physicians, who wrote nothing or whose writings are lost, yet who practiced medicine. Even in our own days the best practitioners are not necessarily the writing ones, or those who write most, or whose writings are the most popular. In this field more perhaps than in any other, there are considerable differences between knowing and saying, between doing and writing. The Italian archives contain many valuable documents illustrating medical life and practice in the trecento. Let me cite a single instance. The state archives of Lucca have in their custody the chartulary and other documents of the ancient hospital (Ospedale di S. Luca) of that city. This includes the notes and journal of a physician Jacopo di Coluccino, who practiced in Lucca from 1364 to 1402. We are thus given information concerning his studies and diplomas, his professional contract with a pharmacist (speziale), Giovanni di Ser Cambio, for four years (1376–79),[4] some of his cures, his relations with colleagues, his honoraria, the philosophical advice he obtained from a friar Gregorio da Pistoia in 1379,[5] his library, family matters, the domestic slaves (schiave) in his service, wet nurses, etc. Apparently, maestro Jacopo was an important physician, and a distinguished citizen of Lucca. From 1372 to 1395 he was frequently elected a member (anziano) of the town government, and in 1390–91 he was even a member of the general council of Lucca. His journal ends in 1402, but he lived until 1418.[6] Brief as it is, my summary of these documents is sufficient to indicate their very high interest for the student of medical life and the sociologist. In order to reach valid conclusions, however, it would be necessary to investigate a good many documents of a similar kind. I am sure that they exist, but there might be some difficulty in collecting a sufficient number of them.

The list of physicians must be completed also with brief accounts of a few who did their best work in the following century yet were children, and more than children, of the trecento. Here are eight of them: Falcucci, Jacopo della Torre, Argelata, Benzi, Cermisone, Aurispa (or Giovanni da Noto), Savonarola, and Polcastro.

Niccolò Falcucci (Nicolaus Falcutius, de Falconiis, Florentinus) was a Florentine who died in 1411/12. He composed an immense encyclopaedia of medicine, Sermones medicinales, arranged in the scholastic manner, and largely derived from the Arabic compilations available in Latin. (He knew neither Greek nor Arabic.) It is divided into eight parts or sermones, of which only seven were written or at any rate printed: (I) De conservatione sanitatis; (II) De febribus; (III) De membris capitis; (IV) De membris spiritualibus; (V) De membris naturalibus; (VI) De membris generationis; (VII) De cyrurgia et de decoratione; (VIII) De medicinis simplicibus et compositis. It is typical that the more modern authors (Lanfranchi, Mondeville, Chauliac) are ignored, whereas a great many others (ancient, Arabic, early mediaeval) are quoted repeatedly. Falcucci wrote a commentary on Hippocrates' aphorisms; he may have been the first compiler to proclaim the infallibility of Galen.

[4] The association of Italian physicians with pharmacists has already been mentioned.

[5] Among the texts which fra Gregorio lent him were the Sentences of Peter the Lombard, and such authors as Albert of Saxony, Peter of Spain, Buridan.

[6] Alberto Chiappelli: Maestro Jacopo di Coluccino da Lucca medico ed i giornale delle sue ricordanze (Rivista di storia delle scienze p. 121–33, Siena 1921).

Text. The contents of the following editions vary; they seldom contain seven sermones, but only a smaller number. For the incunabula, see Klebs no. 389: Pavia 1484 (sermones I, II, VII), Venice 1490–91 (I–VII), Venice or Pavia 1491–93 (IV, V), Venice 1491 (II, VI), Venice 1495? (V, VI). Later editions Venice 1507, 1515, 1533.

Criticism. Gurlt (1, 803–29, 1898). Ignaz Schwarz: Eine unbekannte Ausgabe der Pars II der Sermones, 1491 (AGM 4, 79–80, 1910). Neuburger (2, 422, 457, 488, 1911). K. Sudhoff: Prophylaxe und Kur pestilentialischer Fieber nach Falcucci in Form eines Pestregimen zusammengezogen von einem Ungenannten (AGM 6, 338–41, 1913). Dorothea Waley Singer: Some plague tractates (p. 36–38, London 1916). J. G. A. Heerklotz: Falcucci in seinen die Zahnheilkunde berührenden Kapiteln (Diss. Leipzig, 33 p., Dresden 1921).

Jacopo (or Giacomo) della Torre, or Jacopo da Forlì (Jacobus Foroliviensis) after his native country or city Forlì in Emilia, was born about the middle of the fourteenth century. He taught logic and later medicine in Bologna; in 1399–1402 he taught in Padua, then returned to Bologna; in 1407 he was again professor in Padua, where he died in 1413/14. He published commentaries on Hippocrates, Galen, and Ibn Sīnā, which enjoyed a great and long popularity.

Text. Klebs nos. 546–50. In aphorismos Hippocratis expositio (Venice 1473, Padua 1477, bef. 1480, Pavia 1484, Venice 1490, 1495).

Super I, II, III tegni Galeni (Padua 1475, Venice 1484, Pavia 1484, 1487, Venice 1491, 1495/96).

Expositio in primum Avicennae canonem (Padua? 1475?, Venice 1479, Pavia 1488, Venice 1495, Pavia 1500).

Expositio in Avicennae aureum capitulum (canon III, 21, 2) de generatione embryonis (Pavia 1479, Siena 1485/86, Venice 1489, 1501, 1502, 1518).

Quaestiones extravagantes (Pavia 1484, 1487, Venice 1495/96, Pavia 1500).

De intensione et remissione formarum (Padua 1477).

Opera omnia (Venice 1547).

Criticism. NBG (45, 503, 1866). Gurlt (1, 802–3, 1898). Neuburger (2, 487, 1911). BL (5, 511, 1934).

Pietro d'Argelata[7] was a Bolognese; he taught medicine in Bologna and died in 1423. He was primarily a surgeon, and composed an elaborate treatise on surgery, De chirurgia libri VI, largely derived from earlier works (Ibn Sīnā, Chauliac, etc.), but also from his personal experience. It contains a good deal of therapeutics and, as usual, a part is devoted to gynaecology and obstetrics. When pope Alexander V (Peter of Crete) died at Bologna in 1410, Argelata made a post-mortem examination which is described in his work.

Text. Klebs no. 777. Chirurgia (Venice 1480, 1492, 1497/98, 1499). Later editions 1513, 1520, 1531.

Criticism. Gurlt (1, 831–56, 1898), analysis of the Chirurgia. BL (1, 191, 1929).

Ugo Benzi[8] was born in Siena c. 1370; he taught medicine in Pavia 1399, Bologna 1412, Padua 1420, Florence, then again Padua 1430. He took part in the council of Ferrara and died at Ferrara in 1439. He is the type of the learned physician

[7] Argilata, Arzelata (also variants of each form with two l's), Largelata, La Cerlata. Pierre de l'Argenterie, de Largenterie.

[8] Ugo or Ugone da Siena. Hugo Senensis, Bencius, de Benciis (or with t instead of c).

whose knowledge appeared chiefly in the form of commentaries on the old masters, Hippocrates, Galen, and Ibn Sīnā. We have also from him, however, a number of consilia including original observations, and a treatise on personal hygiene, one of the earliest if not the earliest to be printed in Italian (1481). It is probable that he wrote it in Latin and that someone else (or himself) translated it into Tuscan. He was not the earliest Italian to write such a treatise, but his Salernitan predecessors wrote in Latin, and his fellow citizen Aldobrandino (XIII-2) wrote in French. His treatise is far more original than Aldobrandino's. He had two sons, Francesco Benzi, professor in Ferrara c. 1450, and Socino Benzi, archiater to Pius II (pope 1458–64).

Text. Klebs nos. 997–1003, 548. Trattato utilissimo circa la conservazione della sanità (Milano 1481, reprinted 1507). Later editions under the title Le regole della sanità e natura dei cibi con le annotazioni di Giovanni Lodovico Bertaldi (Torino 1618, 1620).

Subtilis quaestio de malitia complexionis diversae (Pavia 1488, 1500, Venice 1495).

In aphorismos Hippocratis et commentaria Galeni resolutissima expositio (Ferrara 1493, Venice 1498).

Super quartam fen primi canonis Avicennae praeclara expositio (Pavia 1478, 1496, Siena 1485/86, Venice 1485, 1517, 1523).

In primum canonis Avicennae expositio. Fen I (Ferrara 1491), fen I, II (Venice 1498).

In primam fen quarti canonis (Pavia 1498), together with Ugo's Quaestio de modo augmentationis.

In tres libros Microtegni Galeni luculentissima expositio (Pavia 1496, Venice 1498, 1523).

Consilia saluberrima ad omnes aegritudines a capite ad calcem perutilia (Bologna 1482, Pavia 1498, Venice 1518).

Opera omnia (Venice 1518).

Criticism. Gurlt (1, 806–68, 1898). Arturo Castiglioni: Ugo Benzi (Rivista di storia delle scienze, 30 p., 1921; Isis 5, 504). Reinhard Nossol: Mund- und Zahnleiden in Consilien des Ugo Benzi, Bartolommeo Montagnana und Giambattista da Monte[9] (Diss. Leipzig, 39 p., 1922; Isis 5, 221). BL.(1, 465, 1931).

Dean P. Lockwood has completed a very elaborate study on Benzi (Isis 34, 215).

Antonio Cermisone, born at Padua, taught there from 1413 to his death in 1441. He compiled a collection of consilia, including personal observations. This was the second such collection to be printed, being preceded only by the Consilia of Bartolommeo Montagnana, printed four months earlier (Padua, May 1476).

Text. Klebs nos. 263–66, 548.1–2, 689.4. Consilia medica (Brescia, Sept. 1476, Venice 1497). The Venetian edition included Montagnana's Consilia, being the second edition of Cermisone and the fourth of Montagnana. Later editions, Venice 1503, 1514, 1521, including also other consilia.

Consiglio per preservazione della peste (Naples 1475). Ricette contra pestilenza (Milano 1480, 1483). Recollectae de urinis (Italy 1475), also printed with Jacopo della Torre: Super primum Canonis Avicennae expositio (Padua? 1475?, Venice 1479).

Criticism. Gurlt (1, 868, 1898). Ernest Wickersheimer: Un portrait de Cermisone (Bull. de la Société française d'histoire de la médecine 9, 278–83, 1 pl., 1910), miniature in Munich MS Latin 207, which seems to be a genuine portrait; the text

[9] Bartolommeo Montagnana died c. 1460; Giambattista da Monte, 1551.

of the MS was written by Hermann Schedel of Nuremberg (1410-85), physician and humanist, not to be confused with his nephew Hartmann Schedel of Nuremberg (1440-1514), historian, archaeologist, author of the Liber chronicarum, the famous Nuremberg chronicle. Hermann Schedel was a student of Cermisone in Padua 1439. He may himself have limned his teacher's portrait; the beginning of his notes on Cermisone's consilia contains most interesting remarks on the latter's personality, and a note by Hartmann on the MS. Karl Sudhoff: Receptae contra la pestilentia (Pestschriften no. 208; AGM 16, 119, 1925).

Giovanni da Noto, Sicilian, wrote a plague regimen in Latin, Bologna, September 1398. He is probably identical with the humanist Giovanni Aurispa, to be dealt with later. He had written another paper, Consilium contra arteticam,[10] which is lost.

Text. Karl Sudhoff: Pestkonsilium Johannis de Noctho aus Sizilien (Pestschriften no. 40; AGM 5, 384-90, 1911).

The six physicians just dealt with, Niccolò Falcucci, Jacopo della Torre, Pietro d'Argelata, Ugo Benzi, Antonio Cermisone, and Giovanni da Noto, completed their education and did part of their work in the fourteenth century, even if their main work was done after 1400.[11] The two following are really fin de siècle, and their inclusion is disputable. No great harm is done, however, in saying a few words about them.

Sigismondo Polcastro[12] was born at Vicenza c. 1379, and taught philosophy or medicine at the University of Padua for half a century; he died in 1473 at the age of 94. He composed a treatise on various questions, some of them medical, in the scholastic manner.

Text. Klebs no. 791. Quaestio de restauratione humidi (folio, 10 leaves, 2 col., Padua 1473, Venice 1490).

Quaestiones quarum prima de actuatione medicinarum, secunda de appropinquatione ad aequalitatem ponderalem, tertia de restauratione humidi substantifici, quarta de reductione corporum, quinta de extremis temperantie, etc. (Venice 1506).

It is possible that the second edition, Venice 1490, contained more than one question, perhaps as many as the third edition.

Criticism. Gerolamo Tiraboschi: Storia della letteratura italiana (2d Modena ed., 6, 457, 1790). Osler (p. 59, 1923). BL (5, 645, 1932).

Giovanni Michele Savonarola, born c. 1384 of an old Paduan family, studied medicine, one of his teachers being Jacopo da Forlì; then he taught it in Padua and later in Ferrara; he died c. 1467 (rather than c. 1461). He was one of the greatest physicians of the first half of the fifteenth century, and his works may be said to mark the beginning of a wholesome reaction against medical scholasticism. For example, in the most important of them, a general medical treatise, Practica de aegritudinibus, the description of cases is placed in the foreground. This indicates a revival of the clinical spirit, and of experimental vs. ratiocinative medicine. He was the first to recommend a palliative treatment of varices by means of strong bandages, etc.

[10] Artetica gutta, badly derived from ἀρθριτική νόσος, arthritis; (Ducange s.v.) podagra, gout.

[11] Giovanni da Noto would belong completely to the fourteenth century if he were not identical with Aurispa. Our placing him here is based on the assumption of that identity.

[12] Sigismundus de Polcastris, Porcastris, Porchrastis, etc.

Text. Klebs nos. 882–86. Practica de aegritudinibus a capite ad pedes (Colle 1479, Venice 1486, 1497, 1502, 1518, 1547, 1559, 1560, 1561).

De aqua ardenti (Pisa 1484). De arte conficiendi aquam vitae simplicem et compositam (Hagenau 1532, Basel 1597).

De balneis et thermis naturalibus omnibus Italie (Ferrara 1485, Bologna 1493, Venice 1496, 1498, 1592).

Practica canonica de febribus (Bologna 1487, Venice 1496, 1498, 1503, 1543, 1552, 1562, Lyon 1560).

In medicinam practicam introductio, sive de compositione medicamentorum liber (Strassburg 1533).

De pulsibus, urinis et egestionibus (Bologna 1487, Venice 1497, 1498, 1552).

De gotta, la preservatione e cura (Pavia 1505).

Libreto de tutte le cose che se manzano communamente . . . e le regule per conservare la sanità (Venice 1508, 1515, 1575).

Criticism. Gurlt (1, 871–79, 1898). Emanuel Roth: Savonarola und die Balneologie (Zeitschrift für Balneologie, 1910). Neuburger (2, 442, 506, 513, 1911). Romolo Meli: Trattati di medicina del XIII secolo e codice del 1462 dell' opera de balneis nella biblioteca S. Scolastica in Subiaco (Rivista di storia delle scienze, anno 8, 339–44, 1917). BL (5, 36, 1934).

We could not resist the temptation to give an account, however brief, of this Savonarola, because he was the grandfather and the devoted tutor of Girolamo Savonarola, the Dominican reformer and martyr (born Ferrara September 21, 1452, died at the stake in Florence on May 23, 1498), one of the outstanding personalities of the quattrocento. Thus Doctor Savonarola is important not only in himself, but as a living link between the fourteenth century and the late triumphant Renaissance. A very good account of fra Girolamo has been given by Pasquale Villari: La storia di fra Girolamo e de' suoi tempi (Florence 1857), Englished by his wife, Linda Mary Villari (2 vols., London 1888, again 1899). Unfortunately, Villari has very little to say about Girolamo's grandfather.

The latter dedicated his Practica canonica de febribus to Polcastro. Hence Polcastro and Savonarola are linked, and through the latter our imagination is able to project itself from the end of the fourteenth century to the end of the fifteenth.

My account of Italian medicine in the second half of the fourteenth century may seem endless, and yet it is necessary to add a few words concerning men of letters whom the historian of medicine could not possibly neglect—Matteo Villani, Boccaccio, and Giovanni da Ravenna I.

Matteo was the brother of the great Florentine chronicler Giovanni Villani (XIV-1), who was a victim of the plague in 1348. Giovanni's chronicle stopped at 1346, Matteo continued it from 1346 to 1363, and gave us one of the best accounts of the plague and of its social consequences. To Boccaccio we owe another description of the same plague (Florence 1348), less detailed but equally impressive and far better known. The humanist Giovanni da Ravenna I (or Giovanni di Conversino) wrote a booklet on the gout. To be sure, that Conventio inter podagram et araneam is simply a literary exercise, but it reminds us that not only this Giovanni, but many well-to-do people of his time suffered from various forms of arthritism. This is a part of the medical background of the Renaissance.

It is remarkable that all the Italians mentioned in this section were northerners except the Sicilian Giovanni da Noto. The main medical centers were Padua, Bologna, and Florence, then Pavia and Perugia.

A2. *Hispanic peninsula*

Passing from Italy, chiefly northern Italy, to Spain is like passing from the brilliant sun into the darkness. As against the number and diversity of Italian doctors, we came across only two in the Hispanic peninsula, and of these two the first is certainly a Catalan, the second possibly a Portuguese! Would this be due to a relative neglect of Spanish sources? Not likely. Any Latin-writing physician of the peninsula would have had almost as good a chance of being known abroad as his Italian colleagues. The courts of Aragon and Castile were not isolated from the other European courts; the Spanish universities were (and have always remained) far more provincial than the Italian ones, but Montpellier was for more than half of the century an Aragonese university, and Spaniards continued to resort to it after it had become French. Montpellier was the main academic link of the peninsula with the rest of Europe; it was an excellent link.

There were of course a good many practitioners, some of them famous or favored by the patronage of kings and prelates, but we can deal with them only if they wrote books, added to our knowledge or tried to do so. We need not repeat the remarks ad hoc made in the preceding section. On the other hand, Spanish doctors who had left behind them medical treatises of some importance could hardly have failed to arrest the author's attention. One of the main functions of his survey, however, is to act as a challenge. If you know of other physicians than the two to be named presently, dear reader, please let him know.

The first (and the only one belonging completely to the fourteenth century) is Joannes Jacobi, a Catalan, who wrote a number of medical treatises, among them a plague tract (c. 1373) which was the most popular book of its kind. Five years later he compiled a general treatise of practical medicine, the Secretarium or Thesaurarium. We also owe to him ophthalmological texts translated from Arabic into Catalan.

The second, Valescus de Taranta,[13] is said to have been of Portuguese origin, but nothing is known of his early years before 1382, when he appeared in Montpellier. He belongs rather to the following century, for the two works bearing his name were both completed after 1400. The first is a plague tract, Tractatus de epidemia et peste (1401); the second is a general treatise of medicine and surgery, the Practica, better known under the name Philonium (1418). It is very clear and arranged in a very orderly manner,[14] and remained popular until the end of the seventeenth century. It includes brief anatomical descriptions. Valescus recognized three degrees of burning or scalding (adustio ignis vel aquae; dolor, vesica, ulcera).

Text. Klebs nos. 78, 98, 575, 774, 1007–10. De epidemia et peste (Turin or Piedmont 1473, Basel 1474, Hagenau 1497). Also printed with Arnaldo de Villanova: De arte cognoscendi venena (in all the latter's incunabula editions, Mantua 1473, Padua 1473, Turin or Piedmont 1474, Milan 1475, Rome 1475); with 4 incunabula of Pietro d'Abano: De venenis (Mantua 1473, Padua 1473, Milan 1475, Padua 1487), and in the unique incunabulum Arcana medicinae (Geneva 1500).

To these 13 Latin incunabula must be added 5 vernacular ones: Low German (Lübeck 1484), Catalan (Barcelona 1475), Spanish in the Spanish Fasciculus

[13] Many variants, Valascus, Balescus, Balescon; Tarenta, de Tharare.

[14] A capite ad calcem, then for each disease: declaratio (nomina, differentia), causae, signa, prognosticatio sive judicia, curatio.

medicinae (Saragossa 1494, Burgos 1495, Pamplona 1495), in all 18 incunabula editions. Anonymous Hebrew translation (Constantinople, s.a., c. 1510) followed by a Hebrew-Arabic glossary. Steinschneider (p. 818–20, 1893).

The Practica sive Philonium pharmaceuticum et chirurgicum de medendis omnibus cum internis tum externis humani corporis affectibus. Four incunabula, Barcelona 1484, Lyon 1490 (twice), 1500. Later editions, Lyon 1521, 1526, 1531, 1560, Frankfurt 1599, Leipzig 1680, 1714.

Criticism. Gurlt (2, 108–20, 1898). Frederick Porteous Henry: Life and writings of Valescus de Tarenta (Maryland medical journal, 16 p., June 1901). Neuburger (2, 411, 510, 1911). Meinolf Ebbers: Zahnheilkundiges bei Valescus (Diss., 8 p., Leipzig 1922; Isis 5, 502). Klebs and Sudhoff (p. 159–67, 1926). BL (1, 302, 1929).

It is remarkable that these two men (the second of whom does not really belong to our period) were both connected with Montpellier, Joannes Jacobi from c. 1360, Valescus from 1382. Moreover, Joannes dedicated his Secretarium to Charles V c. 1378. From 1382 on Montpellier was under French influence. Hence these two "Spaniards," the first Catalan, the second Portuguese, flourished under French patronage. And that is all the Hispanic peninsula has to offer us in this period!

A3. *France*

Leaving out the mysterious Jean de Bourgogne, who may be identical or not with Jean de Bordeaux and with John Mandeville, it will be convenient to divide the French physicians into two groups, southern and northern. The division is a natural one, but it should not be considered mutually exclusive, for Paris was already a powerful magnet attracting men of the south, while Montpellier and Avignon, not to speak of Italy, caused many northerners to move southward. Some of them never returned to their homeland.

Southern physicians. Bernard Alberti compiled a collection of prescriptions largely derived from Ibn Sīnā. Guy de Chauliac was the greatest surgeon of his age, and he influenced the development of his science deeply for almost two centuries. Pierre de Nadilz and Jean Pataran discussed the impregnation (or conception) of women. Raymond Chalmel de Viviers and Jean Tournemire wrote plague treatises, and to the latter we owe also a general treatise of medicine, the Clarificatorium, in the form of a commentary on the ninth book of Almansor.

This group is not very remarkable except for the gigantic personality of Guy de Chauliac. It could be easily increased, however, if famous practitioners were added to the medical writers. Of course, this would hardly improve our knowledge of contemporary medicine, but it would help us to understand medical manners and customs. Two examples will suffice. Not only did the popes appoint private physicians who became outstanding ipso facto, but the cardinals of Avignon did the same, each cardinal having his own princely court. It was a great honor for any physicus to be attached to a reverendissime cardinal; it was also or might be very profitable. One Guillaume de Lafont (Guillelmus de Fonte) was in the service of the "white cardinal," the Cistercian Guillaume Curti (d. 1361). This Lafont was born in Castres (Tarn, Languedoc) and had received his medical education in Montpellier; he had become wealthy and lived in great style; he had collected a number of books, and in his will (dated Avignon, May 19, 1361) he disposed of them in various ways. His Bible in five volumes was bequeathed to the monks of Marvéjols, his missal to the church of Caussade, his theological books to Blacas de

Laprade. His medical books, he directed, should be sent to Montpellier. Two books of Avicenna and one of Galen should be sold and the proceeds (considerable) given to the Montpellier hospitals; the other medical books were to be distributed by the chancellor of the medical school to poor students. Pierre Pansier: Guillelmus de Fonte, maître en médecine, bienfaiteur des étudiants pauvres de Montpellier en 1361 (Bull. de la Société française d'histoire de la médecine 11, 25–32, 1912), including full text of the will.

The court of Avignon attracted Italian physicians as well as French ones. Master Naddino di Aldobrandino Bovattieri came from Prato (near Florence) and entered the service of Clement VII (antipope 1378–94). A few letters which he wrote throw curious light on life in Avignon; it was very expensive, and physicians dealing with members of the curia must be prepared to answer difficult questions of medicine and philosophy. In spite of the studies which he continued day and night, Naddino found it difficult to hold his own with them. It is clear that the Avignonese community was very sophisticated; it was a promising field for a physician, but whatever rewards he obtained had to be earned. This Naddino lived until 1410 or later. Robert Brun: Naddino de Prato médecin de la cour pontificale (Mélanges d'archéologie et d'histoire, Ecole française de Rome, 40, 219–36, 1923).

Northern physicians. Many of the northern physicians were in the royal service. Pierre Fromont was a surgeon, Le Fèvre wrote a treatise on gout, Guillaume de Harcigny was one of the doctors who were consulted concerning the insanity of Charles VI, Jean Molinier investigated weakness of sight, consilia are ascribed to Guillaume Boucher and also to Pierre d'Auxon, Le Lièvre was an anatomist and compiled a treatise on bloodletting. None of these activities were new or important, but taken together they give us a general view of medical practice in northern France between the Black Death and the end of the century.

A few other doctors were engaged in the translation of medical books from Latin into French. Martin de Saint-Gilles translated Hippocrates' aphorisms with Galen's commentary; Richard Eudes, the poem of Peter of Eboli on the mineral waters of Pozzuoli; Evrard Conty, Aristotle's Problems. The second of these translations might have been made for laymen, the two others could interest only physicians. It is significant that the latter were already losing their hold on Latin and needing French versions; yet professional snobbishness would oblige them to speak some kind of Latin for another three centuries. (Remember Molière's amusing parodies.)

The poems of Eustache Deschamps contain much information on the medical manners and even on the medical ideas of his time. Like many of his contemporaries, he was a sufferer from the mal Saint Maur, i.e., gout, and like Jean Le Fèvre he made a distinction between hot and cold gout. Our own knowledge of arthritism and our means of curing it are still so imperfect that we should not judge those old conceits too severely.

The most talked-of pathological event of this period in France was the madness of Charles VI le Bien-aimé (or le Fou), which broke out suddenly in August 1392. Among the half-dozen physicians called to the rescue were Guillaume de Harcigny, already named, Guillaume Le Touzé, etc. Of course, they were not able to do anything, and the madness continued its natural course. Charles VI (born in 1368, son of Charles V) was king from 1380 to his death in 1422, but he never ruled; the power was actually in the hands of his councillors, nicknamed Marmousets

(Hommes de peu); at the time of his insanity the Marmousets were exiled by his uncles, the dukes of Berry and of Burgundy,[15] and effective power remained from then on in the dukes' hands. Toward the end of his life Charles VI found some comfort in music; judging from his library he (or his librarian!) had also various intellectual interests.

For music see André Pirro: La musique à Paris sous le règne de Charles VI (36 p., Strassburg 1930). Louis Claude Douët-d'Arcq: Inventaire de la bibliothèque du roi Charles VI fait au Louvre en 1423 par ordre du régent duc de Bedford (362 p., Paris 1867). Charles VI's library was a development of the library of Charles V, the inventory of which had been made in 1373, by Gilles Malet. The inventory made in 1423 by order of the duke of Bedford is especially interesting because the estimated value of each of its 832 items is given. Charles VI's library included a good number of scientific books, dealing with arithmetic, geometry, astronomy, astrology, geomancy, chiromancy, alchemy, meteorology, agriculture, natural history, medicine, surgery. For comparison see the inventory of the library of Jean de Dormans, cardinal bishop of Beauvais 1373, published in the same book (p. 220-30), and Hiver de Beauvoir: La librairie de Jean duc de Berry au château de Mehun-sur-Yèvre, 1416 (108 p., Paris 1860). Jean de Berry was a younger brother of Charles V; he was born in Vincennes 1340 and died in Paris 1416; he was one of the most magnificent princes of his time.

The following item, petty as it is and belonging to what the French call "la petite histoire," may interest historians of the medical profession. In May 1381 a surgeon called Jehan Merlin, "cirrurgien de rompture et de taille," was traveling with a "triachier" (= seller of theriaca, a druggist) called Adam Le Lièvre "pour aler par païs pour leur pain gaigner de leurs sciences ou mestiers." They fell out and the surgeon killed his partner. The original document is edited by Louis Claude Douët d'Arcq: Choix de pièces inédites relatives au règne de Charles VI (2, 153-55, Paris 1864).

A4. *England*

The most distinguished member of the English group was a surgeon, John Arderne. His fame did not begin to compare with that of his French contemporary Guy de Chauliac, yet he was a physician of experience, a surgeon of genius, and his mind was open to novelties. The case of John of Mirfeld is different. He was very learned, but it would be difficult to find anything new and important in either his Breviarium or his Floriarium. Both works are simply compilations of all the medical flotsam of Greek, Arabic, or mediaeval origin which had reached England by that time, together with a fair amount of native folklore and traditional nonsense. They give us a very definite idea of the medical learning then available in the Hospital of St. Bartholomew (the dear old "Bart's" of today), though we must assume that good practitioners, whose names have been forgotten, may have transcended that learning and corrected it with their own unpublished experience, and their own common sense.

Treatises on the plague were composed in 1365 by Joannes ad Barbam, probably identical with John Mandeville (see below), and somewhat later, about the turn of the century, by a priest called John Malverne (not to be confused with a contemporary chronicler bearing the same name).

[15] Jean II le Bon (king of France 1350-64) had three sons, Charles V le Sage (b. 1337, king 1364-80), Jean duc de Berry (1340-1416), Philippe II le Hardi duc de Bourgogne (b. 1342, duke 1363-1404). These three sons were great bibliophiles and patrons of letters. Otto Cartellieri: Am Hofe der Herzöge von Burgund (Basel 1926); The court of Burgundy (London 1929).

Valuable information on the Black Death in England is to be found in the chronicle of Henry Knighton. A collection of medical recipes, entitled Cirurgia, is ascribed to Walter Brit, identified on insufficient grounds with a fellow of Merton College who flourished c. 1390.

Medical texts in Middle English. Many texts in Middle English or fragments of such texts are preserved in the archives and libraries of Europe and America. These texts are perhaps of greater interest to the English philologist than to the historian of science; in any case the philologist must prepare the way. Whenever all such texts have been registered and classified, a comparative edition of them, in as strict a chronological order as possible, will be very valuable. The historian of medicine (and of botany) may then be able to draw conclusions. In the meanwhile, here is a list of the most important of these texts. A few more could probably be added by a more systematic exploitation of Wells' Manual and its eight supplements (New Haven 1916–41). It should be noted that our list includes only late Middle English texts, i.e., dating from about 1350–1450, or 1300–1400, whereas Wells' limits are 1050–1400.

George Stephens: Extracts in prose and verse from an old English medical MS preserved in the Royal Library at Stockholm (Archaeologia 30, 349–418, London 1844), with glossary. Many herbs are named in Latin as well as in English. There seems to be a reference to Philippa of Hainault, who was the queen of Edward III from 1328 to her death in 1369. The MS was probably written in the second half of the fourteenth century.

Thomas Wright and James Orchard Halliwell[-Phillipps]: Reliquae antiquae (2 vols., London 1845). Medical recipes (1, 51–55) in rather a Northern dialect. These recipes often remind us of the old Anglo-Saxon ones (see Introd. 1, 633).

Fritz Heinrich: Ein mittelenglisches Medizinbuch (235 p., Halle a.S. 1896). Derived from many British Museum MSS, chiefly Add. MS 33,996, probably written c. 1430–50.

George Henslow: Medical works of the fourteenth century together with a list of plants recorded in contemporary writings with their identifications (293 p., 1 facs., London 1899). On the basis of a MS in Henslow's possession; it is a commonplace book written mainly in Latin, beginning thus: Incipit liber de aquis et primo de aqua preciosa herbarum; dealing with many scientific and technical subjects; it contains many English recipes. The MS was written before 1400 but contains later interpolations, the latest 1464. Midland dialect with lapses into Southern dialect. The "plants recorded in the fourteenth century" are listed p. 147–269.

For John of Burdeux (or John of Bordeaux, John of Burgundy) see note on John Mandeville. The early English text of his plague treatise was edited by Alexander Gardner: John de Burdeux or John de Burgundia otherwise John de Mandeville and the pestilence (40 p., privately printed, David Murray, Paisley 1891), and by Karl Sudhoff (AGM 5, 72–75, 1911). Herbert Schöffler: Beiträge zur mittelenglischen Medizinlitteratur (326 p., Halle a.S. 1919), divided into two parts: (I) Lexikographische Studien, (II) Practica phisicalia magistri Johannis de Burgundia, with elaborate index and long list of similar writings (21 items). The Practica phisicalia is a collection of recipes; the MS (Bodleian Rawl. D 251) can be dated only on palaeographical grounds, c. 1425–50. Wells (p. 1070, 1127, 1461, 1511).

Lanfrank's Science of cirurgie. English version of the Chirurgia magna of Lanfranchi of Milano (XIII-2), made c. 1387–1400. Edited by Robert von Fleischhacker (Early English Text Society no. 102, part 1, text 355 p., London 1894).

Glossary of drugs in the Library of the Medical Society of London (MS 131). Including a leaf from a glossary of medical terms, an alphabetical Latin list of drugs with English equivalents, an alphabetic English list of herbs indicating the virtues of each, a table of weights and measures. Wells (p. 1461, 1511).

Leechbook in the Army Medical Library, Washington, D. C. A book of 117 leaves in various hands, containing recipes, of the period 1320–1420. Claudius F. Mayer: A medieval English leechbook and its fourteenth century poem on blood-letting (Bull. of the history of medicine 7, 381–91, 1 pl., 1939).

Medical practice. The outstanding practitioners were those connected with the English court. As usual, these worthy physicians were satisfied with their present fame and comfort and had no ambitions for the future. We know the names of four medical men in the service of Edward III, to wit, two physicians, Pancius de Controne (fl. 1317–38) and Jordan of Canterbury (fl. 1326–60), and two surgeons, Roger de Heyton (d. 1349) and Adam Rous (d. 1379). None of these men left any writings, none is remembered in DNB. George E. Gask: The medical staff of king Edward the Third (Proceedings of the R. Society of Medicine 19, hist. sec., 1–16, 1926; Isis 10, 130).

To pass to the other extreme, there were in England as elsewhere a number of men who practiced medicine or surgery, or sold drugs, without license or diploma. Some of these men were quacks, though they were not necessarily more quackish than their licensed contemporaries. The main difference between a charlatan and a scientific doctor does not lie so much in a diploma as in the mind and conscience. At any rate, unlicensed quacks became so numerous that it was found necessary to prosecute them. See "Punishment of the pillory for pretending to be a physician" in London 1382, the victim being one Roger Clerk of Wandsworth. English translation of the Latin judgment in Henry Thomas Riley: Memorials of London and London life (p. 464–66, London 1868). In 1421, Henry V decreed an "Ordinance encontre les entremettours de fisik et de surgerie" (Jusserand p. 110, 1884). All of which shows that the medical profession was already well organized and ready to defend its monopoly and privileges.

The best portrait of the contemporary physician is given us in the general prologue to the Canterbury tales (lines 411–44). It is so short and pregnant that we may be permitted to print it here (after F. N. Robinson's edition):

> With us ther was a Doctour of Phisik;
> In al this world ne was ther noon hym lik,
> To speke of phisik and of surgerye,
> For he was grounded in astronomye.
> He kepte his pacient a ful greet deel
> In houres by his magyk natureel.
> Wel koude he fortunen the ascendent
> Of his ymages for his pacient.
> He knew the cause of everich maladye,
> Were it of hoot, or coold, or moyste, or drye,
> And where they engendred, and of what humour.
> He was a verray, parfit praktisour:
> The cause yknowe, and of his harm the roote,
> Anon he yaf the sike man his boote.
> Ful redy hadde he his apothecaries
> To sende hym drogges and his letuaries,
> For ech of hem made oother for to wynne—
> Hir frendshipe nas nat newe to bigynne.
> Wel knew he the olde Esculapius,

And Deyscorides, and eek Rufus,
Olde Ypocras, Haly, and Galyen,
Serapion, Razis, and Avycen,
Averrois, Damascien, and Constantyn,
Bernard, and Gatesden, and Gilbertyn.
Of his diete mesurable was he,
For it was of no superfluitee,
But of greet norissyng and digestible.
His studie was but litel on the Bible.
In sangwyn and in pers he clad was al,
Lyned with taffata and with sendal;
And yet he was but esy of dispence;
He kepte that he wan in pestilence.
For gold in phisik is a cordial,
Therefore he lovede gold in special.

A long commentary might be written on this, with abundant references to mediaeval science, but the reader can do that for himself.[15a]

A5. *Germany*

The writings have come down to us of a number of German physicians, none of whom was of exceptional distinction. Heinrich Thopping was asked to prescribe regimina for a count palatine and one of the popes. The name of Tilmann is attached to a series of clinical observations and to a collection of recipes for men and beasts. The Silesian doctor Thomas of Sarepta (should we call him a German or a Pole?) is more important. We owe to him two large medical compilations, the Michi competit (1360) and the Collectorium secundum alphabetum, which, as its title indicates, is a kind of medical dictionary. Thomas' distinction is greater as a botanist than as a physician. The indispensable plague treatises (such as were published at that time in every plague-stricken country) were composed by John of Glogau (c. 1372), by Bernard of Frankfurt (1381), and by Heinrich Ribbenicz (1370). The last named was rector of the University of Prague, and his patronymic is of Czech (Slavonic) formation. Perhaps we should call him a Czech? The German Nazis, however, would have a good argument for claiming him as one of their own brethren. Indeed, this Ribbenicz was the first (or one of the first) to blame the plague on the Jews!

We have four medical treatises written in the vernacular, that is, presumably for lay readers as well as for doctors, and for women as well as for men. It is remarkable that they are all written in Low German; they are called (after the main MSS) the Utrecht, Wolfenbüttel, Gotha, and Bremen Arzneibücher. They are anonymous except the last, which bears the name of Arnoldus Doneldey. This Arnold, however, was not necessarily the author; he was a Bremen patrician for whom that particular collection had been copied. These works are perhaps of greater value to

[15a] It will suffice to indicate the physicians quoted, some of whom are difficult to identify. They are, in Chaucer's order, Dioscorides (I-2), Rufus (II-1), Hippocrates (V B.C.), 'Alī ibn 'Abbās (X-2), Galen (II-2), Serapion the Elder (IX-2) or Serapion the Younger (XII-1), al-Rāzī (IX-2), Ibn Sīnā (XI-1), Ibn Rushd (XII-2), Damascien is probably Mesuë the Elder (IX-1) or Serapion the Elder (IX-2), Constantine the African (XI-2), Bernard of Gordon (XIV-1), John Gaddesden (XIV-1), Gilbert the Englishman (XIII-1). Physicians of many ages and nations are all mixed up. Chaucer and his contemporaries saw them all, as it were, in the same plane, at the same distance.

philologists than to historians of medicine, who do not expect to find much novelty in them. They illustrate the diffusion of medical knowledge into the northern German lands, the pouring of that knowledge out of Latin vessels into Low German ones. How is it that we do not have High German collections of the same kind and age?

Another remarkable fact is the number of German clerks engaged in medicine. In the other countries physicians were generally if not exclusively laymen. In Germany the situation was different, for Tilmann, John of Glogau, and Thomas of Sarepta were priests; the last one was so called after his bishopric Sarepta (in Palestine); of course, that bishopric was an honorary one, Palestine being then in Muslim hands. Still another priest should be mentioned, the famous Heinrich von Langenstein, one of the founders of the University of Vienna. His curious biological and anthropological ideas have already been discussed; the same conceptions were applied by him to medicine; new diseases might be created by new shufflings of pathological causes, and corresponding remedies by appropriate shufflings of known remedies. He was also one of the first to suggest pathological interpretations of dreams and hallucinations. All of which reveals in him a good scientific imagination, unfortunately lacking experimental restraint.

To complete this picture of German medicine we may refer to two "fin de siècle" physicians whose accomplishments were delayed until the beginning of the following century.

John of Saxony studied in Montpellier and practiced in Strassburg; he may be identical with a priest who flourished in that city c. 1392. However that may be, he had obtained some local fame c. 1409, witness the following story. A Strassburger, Ulin Apt, being ill, wanted to send a specimen of his urine to him; but Ulin's wife thought it was better to take the urine to a quack. The latter, being deceived by some circumstance, assumed that the urine came from a pregnant woman and made some fantastic prognosis. The poor wife went then to John of Saxony, who said at once, "This is the urine of a man of about forty, his liver is sick and blood is gathering around his heart," and that was true! John of Saxony wrote a plague treatise, Compendium de epidemia, which was soon translated into German.[16]

The other case is that of Ortolff the Bavarian. He flourished at Würzburg, Bavaria, at the beginning of the fifteenth century or before. He wrote a popular book on medicine in German (Arzneibuch) derived from the Pantegni,[17] Platearius (XI-2), and other Salernitan writings. The botanical part is taken from Conrad von Megenberg (XIV-1), so much so that the two authors have often been confused. A German book on midwifery (Büchlein der schwangeren Frauen) is also ascribed to Ortolff.

Text. Klebs nos. 715–16. Arzneibuch (Augsburg 1477, Nürnberg 1477, Augsburg 1479, 1482, 1488, 1490). Same in Low German (Lübeck 1484).

Biechlin wie sich die schwangern frawen halten süllen vor der gepurt in der gepurt und nach der gepurd (Ulm c. 1495). Two later editions 1525, simply

[16] Karl Sudhoff: Pestschriften (AGM 16, 20–29, 1924; 16, 187–88, 1925), including Latin text. Ernest Wickersheimer: Le régime de Jean de Saxe suivi d'une étude sur le régime des cinq médecins strasbourgeois (Janus 28, 369–79, 1924; Isis 8, 751), with German text; Recettes contre la peste extraites d'un MS du XVe siècle ayant appartenu à l'abbaye de Maulbronn (Janus 30, 1–7, 1926; Isis 9, 156); Dictionnaire (p. 475, 1936).

[17] That is, the Latin version by Constantine the African (XI-2) of the Kitāb al-malikī of ʿAlī ibn ʿAbbās (X-2).

entitled Frauenbüchlein. Facsimile edition with notes by Gustav Klein: Das Frauenbüchlein des Ortolff von Bayerland (Alte Meister der Medizin 1, München 1911), containing also a few extracts from the Arzneibuch.

Criticism. Neuburger (2, 515, 1911). Sudhoff: Deutsche Inkunabeln (p. 20–34, 1908); Pestvorschriften im Arzneibuch (AGM 14, 81–84, 1923). Henry E. Sigerist: Meister Blumentrosts Arzneibuch (AGM 12, 70–73, 1920; Isis 8, 750), apropos of a Zürich MS once owned by Conrad Gesner, the text of which is very close to Ortolff's Arzneibuch.

Medical practice. Medical practice was not essentially different in Germany from that obtaining in other Christian countries of Western Europe. For one thing, German physicians had often obtained their medical education abroad, e.g., Tilmann in Montpellier, Langenstein in Paris, and Ribbenicz in Prague, or at least they had traveled abroad, like Thomas of Sarepta. On the other hand, foreign doctors sometimes taught in German universities, the best example being Galeazzo da Santa Sofia, who was professor in Vienna c. 1398–1405.

In the course of his extensive analysis of medical archives Karl Sudhoff has dug out and published in AGM many items throwing light on the manners and psychology of German doctors. For example, Schlimme Prognose und ärztliche Politik. Aufzeichnungen eines deutschen Praktikers im Meissnischen aus dem 14. Jahrh. (AGM 8, 350–51, 1915); Analekten aus einer Breslauer Handschrift vom Ende des 14. Jahrh. (AGM 10, 207–8, 1917).

A6. *Bohemia*

Bohemian medicine is represented by three royal physicians, Gallus de Strahov, Jean de Grandville, and Sigismund Albic. The first wrote a regimen for the emperor Charles IV, a book on medicinal waters, and treatises on the plague, bloodletting, and urinomancy. Jean de Grandville (we give him a French name, for he spent most of his life in France, but he originated in the diocese of Prague) is better known as a poisoner than as a healer, but it is important to speak of him, for he was not by any means the only exemplar of that sinister profession. He worked for Louis II de Bourbon and the latter's sister, Bonne de Bourbon, and helped them to get rid of their enemies as well as of their diseases. Princes of those days found it as natural to use a poisoner as to use an astrologer or an alchemist, and there were virtuosi able to satisfy them on all those grounds. Sigismund Albic was a far greater man than the two preceding ones, in fact the most important Bohemian physician of the Middle Ages. A good many Latin writings are ascribed to him, dealing in a learned way with all the medical topics of the day, the foremost being the plague and prophylactic regimina. Some of these works are probably posterior to 1400, for he lived until 1427.

The two following belong more definitely to the fifteenth century.

Sulko (or Sulken) of Hosstka, doctor of medicine, flourished in Prague 1395–1413, and was rector of the university in 1413. He wrote a Regimen in febribus in Latin and a Regimen et cura colicae in German,[18] both very short. Karl Sudhoff: Meister Sulko (AGM 2, 47–54, 1908; Mitt. 9, 68, 1910).

Christian of Prachatice, who became rector of the same university twenty years later, has been dealt with in the mathematical section above. Born at Prachatice in 1368, he lived until 1439; he wrote in Czech as well as in Latin. His medical

[18] At any rate it has come to us in German.

writings include a herbal and treatises on iatromathematics and bloodletting (these three in Czech), and a herbal and plague tract (both in Latin). The plague tract dates from 1409. K. Sudhoff: Pestschriften nos. 65–67. Ein lateinisches Remedium reportatum für die Pest des Meister Christannus von Prachatice und ein Exkurs über die Kur der Apostemata. Ein Traktat über Apostembehandlung aus Prag. Ein deutsches Pestregimen unter dem Namen des Magister Christianus Pragensis (AGM 7, 99–106, 1913).

A7. *Iceland*

The Icelandic knowledge of this time can be inferred approximatively from an old Icelandic miscellany, the MSS of which are preserved in Dublin (Royal Irish Academy, 23 D 43; Trinity College, L 2,27). The MS of the Royal Irish Academy is the most important Icelandic medical document of mediaeval origin; the compiler made an effort to gather in one volume everything that was known in his day. Though it is comparatively late (end of the fifteenth century), the bulk of the material is more likely to be anterior than posterior to the fourteenth century. It contains: (1) charms and conjurations to cure fevers or stop haemorrhages; (2) brief section on the depth of the sea; (3) book of simples; (4) antidotarium; (5) lapidary (small fragment); (6) leechbook (or parts of several); (7) cookbook. Linguistic evidence shows that the compiler used Danish and Norwegian sources as well as Icelandic ones, but that is not surprising. The main source of the book of simples is Henrik Harpestraeng (XIII-1); that of the antidotarium is the Salernitan Antidotarium Nicolai (XII-1; Introd. 2, 239); that of the lapidary, Harpestraeng again. The leechbook is apparently independent; that is, no direct source of the whole has been found, but it derives through other Scandinavian texts from the ancient and mediaeval lore preserved in Latin.

Henning Larsen: An old Icelandic medical miscellany (336 p., Norwegian Academy, Oslo 1931; Isis 17, 436–38). Includes Icelandic text, English translation; elaborate notes and indexes.

A8. *Christian East*

The poverty of late medical Byzantine literature cannot be denied even by the most fervent admirers of Byzantine culture. The few great names of Byzantine medicine are early ones, Oribasios of Pergamon (IV-2), Aëtios of Amida (VI-1), Alexander of Tralles (VI-2), Paulos Aegineta (VII-1)—all of them, except Paulos, Asiatics. The later doctors are decidedly on a lower level, Theophanes Nonnos (X-1), Michael Psellos the younger (XI-2), Symeon Seth (XI-2), Nicolaos Myrepsos (XIII-2), Joannes Actuarios (XIV-1). After the middle of the fourteenth century medical writing seems to stop completely, that is, creative writing as distinguished from mere copying.

For example, a Paris MS (suppt. grec 764) written at the end of the fourteenth century or the beginning of the fifteenth contains a vast medical encyclopaedia, Τὰ εὐπόριστα (usual remedies), divided into 725 articles. Its contents may be analyzed as follows: (1) pathological summary; (2) collection of recipes: purgatives, antidotes, oils, dry powders, potions, preparations with honey, plasters; (3) therapeutical summary; (4) dietetics; (5) various kinds of food; (6) hygienic guide for each season; (7) varia. The first item is simply Τὰ εὐπόριστα of Theophanes

Nonnos (X-1). Items 2 and 4 are derived from the same collection. Item 5 follows closely the περὶ τροφῶν δυνάμεως of Galen; item 6 is Hippocratic; item 7, eclectic. The most curious part is item 3, entitled Θεραπευτικαὶ ἰατρεῖαι συντεθεῖσαι παρὰ διαφόρων ἰατρῶν κατὰ τὴν ἐκτεθεῖσαν ἀκολουθίαν τοῦ ξενῶνος. It is a collection of therapeutic rules put together by the physicians of a particular hospital (ξενῶν). Such collections were probably prepared then as now for the guidance of doctors who were expected to work together in agreement. This was the more natural in that the main Byzantine hospitals were also to some extent medical schools. According to the τυπικόν[19] of the Pantocrator (Παντοκράτωρ) founded by Joannes II Comnenos (ruled 1118–43), there was appointed a full-time διδάσκαλος whose duty it was to teach the sons of the doctors attached to that famous νοσοκομεῖον. (Incidentally, the hereditary transmission of the medical profession was thus established at the same time.) It is highly probable that similar arrangements existed in the other hospitals.

Another medical document which we quote faute de mieux is a curious prognostic from the blood edited by Singer in 1917. It is a single page written in the late fourteenth century or early fifteenth in the monastery of the Holy Trinity in Chalcis (now in Bodleian), περὶ αἱμάτων σωτηρίων καὶ ὀλεθρίων (concerning safe and dangerous bloods), a series of brief rules indicating conclusions to be drawn from the aspect of the blood obtained in bloodletting.

Some of the witnesses of the last century of Byzantium were aware of the decadence, which was not simply medical, alas! but involved many moral and intellectual factors. One of those witnesses, Joseph Bryennios (fl. 1381–1405), has left a vivid and forceful description of that moral and intellectual abasement. In a treatise of his divided into 49 chapters (κεφάλαια ἑπτάκις ἑπτά), he devotes the whole of chapter 47 to an examination of the causes of their miseries (τίνες αἰτίαι τῶν καθ' ἡμᾶς λυπηρῶν). Medicine, he remarked, was abandoned to Jewish physicians, and his own countrymen were dominated by all kinds of superstitions. "Our face has become like that of a prostitute and convinced sinner" (ὅτι ὄψις ἡμῖν πόρνης ἐγένετο καὶ πρόληψις ἁμαρτίας). One could not express the terrible truth of Byzantine decadence more strongly. No wonder Byzantium fell, in spite of miraculous events like the untimely death of the Serbian tsar Stephen Dushan (Stephen Urosh IV) in 1355, or the defeat of Bāyazīd by Tīmūr Lang in 1402. Byzantium fell in 1453, because there was not enough strength and virtue within to hold her up. The rotten tree is destroyed by the storm. Rottenness is the real cause of its fall, the storm being simply the occasion or the instrument.

Charles Singer: Byzantine medical fragments (Annals of medical history 1, 333–41, 1 facs., New York 1917). Edouard Jeanselme: Sur un aide-mémoire de thérapeutique byzantin. Traduction, notes et commentaire (Mélanges Charles Diehl 1, 147–70, Paris 1930). Lysimachos Oeconomos: L'état intellectuel et moral des Byzantins vers le milieu du XIVe siècle d'après une page de Joseph Bryennios (ibid. 1, 225–33).

When we pass from Byzantium to other parts of the Christian East, the indigence of medical literature increases. Indeed, to speak of indigence may seem misleading, for there is a complete lack of documents. The author hesitates, however, to accept that lack as final; it may be due to insufficient exploitation of Oriental

[19] Act of foundation, set of regulations, ritual, see Introd. 2, 1114.

archives, and it is certainly due in part to his own ignorance of the Christian languages (outside Greek and Arabic), i.e., the Slavonic, Syriac, Coptic, Aethiopic, Armenian, and Georgian languages. To be safe, he has done his best in every way open to him, but indirect information can never replace the direct, especially with regard to a virgin field. He is well acquainted with Arabic literature, yet has not come across any contemporary Christian medical writings. It is possible that father Cheikho's catalogue (1924) would reveal the existence of some, but this would oblige one to analyze it thoroughly, the indexes being insufficient for that purpose.

The only Oriental Christian who may perhaps be cited in this section is Jacob the Armenian, putative author of one of the most important plague treatises. In two Munich MSS that treatise is entitled Missum regi Bohemiae per Armenium optimum medicorum de pestilentia. It deals with the plague of 1371 in Bohemia and was probably written in Prague; it was soon translated into German. Hence, assuming that Jacob the Armenian was the real author, as he wrote in Latin for the benefit of Western Christendom, it would perhaps have been more appropriate to speak of him in the Bohemian section than in this one.

A similar remark would apply to Guido da Bagnolo, who was physician to Peter I, king of Cyprus. Though that island is located in the Near East, under the Antioche-Lusignan dynasty it was not so much a part of the Christian East as an extension of the Christian West in partibus infidelium. There were other physicians in Cyprus, French, Greek, or Italian, or maybe even of other nationalities, but the only one I can think of at present is Guido da Bagnolo, who was not only a doctor, but also a humanist. The medical history of Cyprus (and for that matter of the Christian East) is still unwritten. There are many fourteenth-century accounts of Cyprus, for the island was often visited by pilgrims going to the Holy Land or on their way home. See the notes on William Boldensele (1333), James of Verona (1335), Ludolf of Sudheim (c. 1340), Sir John Mandeville, Niccolò di Martoni (1394), Ogier d'Anglure (1395), whose Cyprian reminiscences refer to the years indicated between parentheses.[20] Niccolò's account is particularly long, but neither he nor the others have anything to say about medical matters.[21] Though the lords of Cyprus were French, the majority of the people spoke Greek. Says James of Verona, "They understand well the Saracen and Frankish tongues [i.e., Arabic and French] but chiefly use Greek." There were all kinds of Christians in Cyprus, he remarked, not only "true" Christians, but Greeks, Jacobites, Armenians, Georgians, Maronites, Nestorians. He had nothing to say about Muslims, but other observations of his suggest Muslim influences. The pilgrims were impressed by the number of relics and the miracles which occurred in Cyprus;[22] they were even more impressed by the wealth of the island, especially of the cities of Famagusta and Nicosia. That wealth and the indulgence and wickedness associated with it had become fabulous. We hear an echo of that in Dante's Paradiso (XIX, 145–48) and in the commentary of Benvenuto Rambaldi of Imola.

[20] English translations in Claude Delaval Cobham: Excerpta cypria (p. 15–29, Cambridge 1908).

[21] Not even where one would expect it, as in the description by Ogier d'Anglure of the illness and death of his father-in-law, Simon Salebruche (Sarrebruck), in Nicosia, 1396. The physicians are not named.

[22] E.g., Niccolò di Martoni was shown the place (near Famagusta) where St. Catherine of Alexandria was born, and the place where she was betrothed to Christ.

B. *Israel*

Our account of Jewish medicine is divided into six sections: (1) Spain, (2) Catalonia, (3) Provence and Languedoc, (4) Germany, (5) Serbia, and (6) China. This will be followed by a brief note on Samaritan medicine.

B1. *Spain*

Brief reference may be made in the beginning to Joshua ben Joseph II ha-Lorqi, who wrote a treatise on foods and drugs in Arabic. This was soon translated into Hebrew (before 1408), and is known to us only in that Hebrew translation. This Joshua was one of the last Jewish physicians of Spain to use the Arabic language.

His colleagues wrote either in Hebrew or in Spanish or Catalan (but Hebrew script). The second alternative was chosen by Samuel Esperial, who wrote a surgical treatise in Catalan or Spanish; the date of that work is unfortunately very uncertain.

Two other Spanish Jews were concerned with the Qānūn of Ibn Sīnā. Joseph ben Joshua II ha-Lorqi translated a part of it from the Arabic and revised the translation of Nathan ha-Me'ati. He added a Hebrew commentary, and so did Shemṭob Shapruṭ of Tudela.

Meir ben Solomon Alguadez compiled in Spanish a collection of medical recipes, which was increased by his disciple Joseph, and later (much later, 1546) translated into Hebrew.

Physiology and medicine are covered in parts 4 and 5 of the encylopaedia Shebile emunah compiled by Meir ben Aldabi of Toledo.

B2. *Catalonia*

The achievements must be recorded of three physicians called Cabret, all of whom may have belonged to the same family. Jacob ben Judah Cabret translated the medical astrology of Arnold de Villanova, Abraham Cabret wrote a commentary on Hippocrates' Aphorisms, and his son Isaac ben Abraham translated the Expositio of John of Saint Amand. The translations were made from Latin into Hebrew. Thus Spanish Jews were now depending for materia medica, as well as for medical astrology, upon Latin rather than upon Arabic sources.

The last named of the three Cabret is probably identical with Isaac ben Abraham Cabret who flourished in Perpignan from 1409 to 1413. That, however, would not take us away from Catalonian influence. Indeed, Perpignan and the Roussillon were part of the kingdom of Majorca from 1276 to 1344, then taken back by Aragon. The Roussillon suffered many more vicissitudes and was not finally annexed to France until the Treaty of the Pyrenees (1659).

B3. *Provence and Languedoc*

This is by far the largest group, and its members wrote almost exclusively in Hebrew. Let us consider first half a dozen men who are known to us primarily as physicians.

Violas of Rodez discussed the rules of dosage explained by Ibn Rushd;[23] Isaac ben Jacob Lattes has eleven medical tracts to his credit; Isaac ben Ṭodros wrote a treatise on the plague of Avignon (1373), and in another described the distortion

[23] Arabic dosimetry had been put on a new basis by al-Kindī (IX-1). See Léon Gauthier: Antécédents gréco-arabes de la psychophysique (155 p., Beyrouth 1939; Isis 32, 136–38).

of the mouth caused by a stroke of paralysis; Ṭodros de Cavaillon composed an antidotary; Gershon ben Hezekiah, astronomer and grammarian as well as physician, wrote a medical poem Sefer af ḥokmati[24] (5,040 lines) with prose commentary, divided into seven parts, called the seven ears (spica), Shib'ah shibbolim; it includes toward the end a treatise on fevers. Gershon was born before 1374, but this poem (the only writing of his that has survived) was not written until 1419, the author being then locked up in a prison, somewhere in the principality of Orange.[25]

To these medical writers might be added at least one practitioner who did not write, though he was very learned. This is Bendig 'Ain, who knew Arabic, Greek, and Latin as well as Hebrew, and was physician and astrologer to queen Giovanna I of Naples. He was the head of a kind of medical dynasty, three of his daughters having married physicians.

Then we have an imposing group of men who were primarily translators, and but for one partial exception, their translations were made from Latin (not from Arabic) into Hebrew.

The Lilium medicinae of Bernard of Gordon was translated in 1360 by Moses ben Samuel of Roquemaure, then again in 1387 by Jekuthiel ben Solomon of Narbonne. This Moses was himself a medical author, but by a strange compensation, his own writings are known only in Spanish versions. Treatises of Arnold of Villanova (a great favorite of that period) were Hebraicized by Judah ben Solomon Nathan, by Abraham ben Meshullam Abigdor, by Ṭodros ben Moses Yomṭob. The Introductorium juvenum of Gerald de Solo was translated partly by Abraham Abigdor and partly by Leon Joseph of Carcassonne. The same Leon Joseph translated also Gerald's commentary on Nonum Almansoris, books of Jean de Tournemire, and a treatise on astrological medicine falsely ascribed to Hippocrates and to Galen. Ṭodros ben Moses Yomṭob translated a treatise on fever by Mesuë major with the annotations by Peter of Spain; Benjamin ben Isaac of Carcassonne, the plague tract of John of Burgundy; Abraham Abigdor, a collection of recipes taken from the Qānūn by Bernard Alberti, and an abridgment of the Nonum Almansoris.

The only translator who used Arabic originals as well as Latin versions was Judah ben Solomon Nathan, who translated treatises on simples by Abū-l-Ṣalt and by Ibn Wāfid. The others were obliged to derive their knowledge of Arabic medicine from Latin translations.

Philosophers and theologians if they were at all scientific-minded were somewhat acquainted with medical literature, and might even make some contribution to it. Thus, Jacob Ẓarfati of Avignon (presumably identical with the mystical theologian Jacob ben Solomon Ẓarfati)[26] wrote a treatise on vertigo (dizziness or swimming of the head), and the Talmudist and astronomer Profiaṭ Duran annotated the first book of the Qānūn.

B4. *Germany*

Jewish learning was now very largely concentrated in southern France and the Hispanic peninsula, and our accounts of other parts of the Diaspora will not detain us very long. Strangely enough, no evidence of Jewish medicine in Italy has as yet

[24] Also my wisdom (Ecclesiastes 2:9).

[25] Neubauer-Renan (p. 781–83, 1893). Isaac Broydé (JE 5, 639, 1903).

[26] The identification is not certain, for the name Ẓarfati (= Frenchman) is not uncommon; see Cowley (p. 717, 1929).

been collected by me. On the other hand, a very remarkable document has come from Germany. This is the oldest Yiddish MS of some importance, a simple sheet devoted to bloodletting, written in Cologne in 1396.

B5. *Serbia*

The Serbian Talmudist Judah ben Moses Mosconi was a regular Wandering Jew and wandering scholar, who flourished by turns in many islands of the eastern Mediterranean, in Egypt, Morocco, Italy, Majorca, Perpignan. No medical writings of his have come down to us, but his library, the inventory of which was made in Majorca, included the main classics of medicine. We refer to him here faute de mieux as the only representative of Jewish medicine in Eastern Europe.

B6. *China*

The main Jewish colony in Cathay was that of K'ai fêng fu, in Honan, dating from the middle of the twelfth century. The name of a single Jewish physician of that city has come down to us, one Yen Ch'êng, who obtained in 1421 the imperial permission to restore the old synagogue. This suggests that he was a man of importance in the Jewish and also in the Chinese community. His Hebrew name, if he had any, is unknown. It is probable that the Chinese Jews, like the Chinese Muslims, were hardly distinguishable from other Chinese, the only differences being religious and ritualistic (chiefly, the horror of pork, of which the Chinese are on the contrary very fond). It is highly probable that the medicine which Yen Ch'êng practiced was purely Chinese.

C. *Samaritan Medicine*

A separate note must be devoted to the Samaritans (Introd. 1, 151; 2, passim), who did not want to be confused with the Jews, yet were closer to them than to the people of any other faith. There were a number of Samaritan physicians in Damascus and Cairo; we have already dealt with the two outstanding ones, Ṣadaqa ben Munaja' (XIII-1) and Muwaffaq al-dīn (XIII-2). To these may now be added tentatively (for the dating is uncertain) Abū Sa'īd al-'Afīf of Ascalon, who had attained a distinguished position in Cairo, for he was called chief of the physicians (shaykh al-aṭibba'). All these Samaritan doctors wrote in Arabic. Abū Sa'īd al-'Afīf published a collection of extracts from the Qānūn and a treatise on acute diseases entitled Al-lamḥa fī-l-ṭibb.

D. *Islām*

The account of Muslim medicine may be divided into six sections: (1) Andalusia, (2) Ifrīqīya, (3) Mamlūkīya, (4) Yaman, (5) Anatolia (Arabic-Turkish), (6) Īrān (Persian).

D1. *Andalusia*

Accounts of the plague of 1348–49 were written in Arabic by Muḥammad ibn Muḥammad of Almeria, by Ibn al-Khaṭīb of Granada, and by Muḥammad ibn 'Alī of Segura. These treatises were among the first (in any language) to be devoted to the Black Death. Muḥammad ibn 'Alī was the author also of a kind of medical introduction. As to Ibn al-Khaṭīb, though he is chiefly known as a historian, biographer, and humanist, various medical works in prose and verse are ascribed to him. He was one of the outstanding personalities of Andalusia, and later of Morocco, but his writings have not yet received the attention which they seem to deserve.

D2. *Ifrīqīya*

The Algerian man of letters Ibn abī Ḥajala devoted two or three of his abundant compositions to the plague of 1362. I do not know whether these writings, thus far unpublished, are of medical importance, or are simply anecdotic.

The Muqaddama of Ibn Khaldūn, so rich in many respects, is a little disappointing to the historian of medicine. Yet we find in it a brief but impressive description of the Black Death, and in another book of his the earliest reference in any literature to the sleeping sickness. Ibn Khaldūn warned his readers not to attach too much importance to the recipes ascribed to the Prophet. "Prophetic medicine" ('ilm ṭibb al-nabī),[27] he explained, is not a part of the divine revelation.

D3. *Mamlūkīya*

This and the Anatolian (or Turkish) groups are by far the most important; if one took them together, and there would be good reasons for doing so, the intellectual relations between Egypt, Syria, and Turkey having always been close, the combination of the two would completely dominate contemporary Muslim medicine.

The most distinguished physician of the Mamlūk empire was Ṣadaqa ibn Ibrāhīm al-Shādhilī, who was the last of the great Arabic ophthalmologists. Al-Manbijī wrote about the plague of 1373. The zoological encyclopaedia of al-Damīrī contains much medical information; in fact, the indication of the medical properties of each animal is an essential feature of his scheme. In the first article, devoted properly to the lion, king of beasts, al-Damīrī explained his very peculiar views on contagion. Diseases are not naturally contagious, but God can make them so. This was a curious attempt to account for the striking irregularities in the diffusion of plagues. How did it happen that some people, or even some towns, escaped in the midst of disaster? Such irregularities, which could not be denied, tended to reinforce Muslim fatalism (belief in predestination, qadar, taqdīr): "No one can die except by God's permission according to the book that fixeth the term of life" (sūra 3, 139). Not only the Qur'ān and ḥadīth, but the whole of Arabic literature including the Alf laila wa-laila ring the changes upon that central idea.[28] One can never escape it, and hence the notion of contagion, no matter how well it is proved, is doomed to remain secondary and relatively insignificant.

Books dealing with hunting and horsemanship, notably the Ins al-malā bi waḥsh al-falā of Muḥammad ibn Mangalī, include occasional remarks on the medical properties of animals, not to speak of the veterinary advice which constitutes one of the integral parts of such books, whether it be concentrated in a special section or not.

The Ṣubḥ al-a'shā, the great administrative encyclopaedia of al-Qalqashandī, has no chapter specifically devoted to medicine, but it includes one of the two earliest references to the sleeping sickness, the other having been made by Ibn Khaldūn.

[27] See note on al-Dhahabī (XIV-1).
[28] Hughes (p. 472–74, 1885). D. B. Macdonald: Qadar (EI 2, 605, 1924).

One of the leading physicians of Cairo, if not the leading one, was the Samaritan Abū Sa'īd al-'Afīf, of whom we have spoken above in section C. On the other hand, the absence of Jewish-Arabic physicians is very remarkable, if one remembers their preponderance in Cairo in the preceding centuries (Introd. 2, 307, 523, 788). Though the Mamlūk group of physicians was still the most impressive in the Dār al-Islām, it was not comparable to the group of its own predecessors; decadence had definitely set in. Should this be related to the exclusion, or to the absence, of the Jews? Previously, Samaritan doctors had flourished in Damascus (rather than Egypt, which was Jewish territory); did Abū Sa'īd establish himself in Cairo because his Jewish colleagues had been driven out?

Another leader of the medical world of Cairo was the Turk Ḥājjī pāshā, who became chief physician of the Bīmāristān al-Manṣūrī, but returned c. 1380 (or c. 1395) to his native country.

D4. *Yaman*

The single doctor of this time whom we must associate with Yaman illustrates the internationalism of Islām, for he was not a native Yamanī, but a Hindu, perhaps a Bengali. The obligation of the Pilgrimage drew Muslims from everywhere to the sacred cities; they came "on foot and on every fleet camel, arriving by every deep defile" (sūra 22, 28); some of them never returned home, but spent the rest of their life in the Ḥijāz or in southern Arabia. Apparently that is what happened to Muḥammad al-Mahdī, who settled down in Yaman. The capital, Ṣan'ā', was then one of the main cultural centers of Arabia. He wrote an elaborate medical treatise, the Kitāb al-raḥma fī-l-ṭibb wal-ḥikma.

D5. *Anatolia*

It is expedient to consider the physicians writing in Arabic separately from those using the Turkish language. The Arabic writers were only three, Muḥammad ibn Muḥammad al-Āqsarā'ī, Muḥammad ibn Maḥmūd, and Ḥājjī pāshā. The first wrote a commentary on the Mūjiz al-qānūn of Ibn al-Nafīs; the second, a pharmacopoeia, Rauḍat al-'iṭr.

The case of Ḥājjī pāshā is of special interest, as it marks the transition from Arabic to Turkish. Though born and educated in Qonya, he was sent to Cairo for further studies and spent the middle part of his life in that city. Later he returned to his country and completed his main medical work, the Shifā' al-asqām wa dawā' al-ālām, in Ephesus c. 1380. The Shifā' was written, like his other works, in Arabic, but Ḥājjī pāshā came to realize the need of medical books in Turkish, and wrote an abridgment of the Shifā' in that language. It is typical that he found it necessary to apologize for writing in Turkish; indeed, that language was just beginning to be used for scientific purposes. The average Muslim doctor would have thought and said that Arabic was the only language dignified enough for medicine, even as his colleagues of Western Europe would have made the same claim for Latin.

Nevertheless, there was a small but growing number of men who wrote exclusively in Turkish. Thus, Isḥāq ibn Murād of Gerede wrote two medical treatises in 1388/89. Another one is ascribed to the poet Ṣalāḥ al-dīn of Ankara, and a Turkish translation of a Persian book on sexual hygiene bears the same author's name (the laqab Ṣalāḥ al-dīn is not uncommon, hence we should not conclude that these two are but one person). Two more medical works are ascribed to the poet Aḥmedī. The book of falconry written by Maḥmūd ibn Muḥammad al-Bārjīnī is largely devoted to the description of ailments of falcons and the means of curing them. There is in the Topkapı sarayı, Istanbul, an anonymous treatise (in Turkish) on the veterinary art, which was written in the period 1361–1400.[29]

In short, some nine medical treatises were composed in Turkish. There are difficulties concerning the authorship of some of them, and they are not sufficiently available to the Western historian of medicine to enable him to form an opinion of their comparative value. We may safely assume, however, that these Turkish writings were simply reflections of the knowledge published in Arabic, and that they are of greater interest to the student of Turkish philology and of Turkish education than to the historian of medicine.

In conclusion, a few words might be added concerning the famous Turkish MS of the Bibliothèque nationale, Paris (suppt. turc no. 693), entitled Jirrāḥ nameh, a large and richly illustrated treatise on surgery (205 leaves, 26.5 × 18 cm., 163 ill.). There is another MS of the same work in the Fatih library, Istanbul. Both MSS were written and illustrated by the same hand, probably that of the author himself. The text was dedicated in 1465/66 to the sulṭān Muḥammad II al-Fātiḥ. The author, Sharaf al-dīn ibn 'Alī ibn al-Ḥājj Ilyās, better known in local tradition under the Turkish nickname Sabuncuoğlu (son of the soapmonger), was 63 (Muslim) years old at the time of the dedication. He had been physician of the hospital of Amasia for fourteen years. He was born in 1404, began to study medicine in 1421, died after 1468. In 1454, he translated from Persian into Turkish the Dhakhīra-i-khwārizmshāhī of Ismā'īl al-Jurjānī (XII-1), and in 1468 he compiled a collection of recipes entitled The book of experiments, Mücerrebname.

Sharaf al-dīn was a pupil of Burhān al-dīn Aḥmad, who was a pupil of Luqmān al-Khwārizmī, both Turks. Thus he represents an old Turkish tradition, and his works are very important from the point of view of Turkish philology.

He belongs completely to the fifteenth century, but is mentioned here to clear up a misunderstanding. The Paris MS of his illustrated surgery was described by the cataloguer, Edgar Blochet, as a translation of a Persian treatise Jirrāḥīyah khānīyah, composed during the īlkhānī rule of Persia (1256–1349). This was an erroneous interpretation of the title. The treatise is called īlkhānīya simply because the hospital of Amasia, to which the author was attached, was an īlkhānī foundation.[30] As a matter of fact, the text is a literal Turkish version, with some 28 interpolations, of the Taṣrīf of Abū-l-Qāsim al-Zahrāwī (X-2). The figures of surgical instruments are similar to those of the Taṣrīf, but the more elaborate illustrations, which represent physicians and surgeons dealing with their patients, male or female, are original. These illustrations were drawn by Sharaf al-dīn himself, or under his immediate direction.

Edgar Blochet: Catalogue des MSS turcs (2, 34, no. 693, Bibliothèque nationale, Paris 1833), kindly lent by Philip Hitti. A. Süheyl Ünver: Sur un MS médical

[29] It is no. 1695 (67 folii) in the Revan room. A. Süheyl Ünver: Remarks on Turkish as a language for teaching in the Middle Ages (Tedavi kliniği ve laboratuvari vol. 7, no. 27, Istanbul 1937), in Turkish.

[30] Amasia was under the rule of the Saljūq of Rūm from 1077 to 1300, when the Saljūq were conquered by the īl-khān of Persia. The last four Saljūq were merely Mongol governors. Many of the mediaeval foundations of Amasia were due to the last Saljūq ruler, 'Alā al-dīn Kay-Qubād II (1296–1300). The hospital of Amasia, however, was founded a few years later, in 1308.

illustré du XVe siècle (Congrès international d'histoire de la médecine p. 3–7, ill., Bucarest 1932; Isis 25, 535); Kitabül cerrahiyei ilhaniye (48 p., 76 pl., Istanbul 1939), in Turkish with French summary. Laignel-Lavastine (1, 509, 514–15, 522–23, [1936]), for the illustrations and only if Ünver's book is not available. Aydin M. Sayili: Turkish medicine (Isis 26, 403–14, 1937; p. 410). Adnan (p. 37, 1939).

D6. *Īrān*

We need have no hesitation in crediting the following three men to Īrān, for they all wrote in Persian.

Zain al-'Aṭṭār compiled a materia medica in 1366, and revised it a few years later. In 1396, Manṣūr ibn Muḥammad dedicated to a grandson of Tīmūr an illustrated anatomy, and a good many years later he composed a general treatise on medical theory and practice.

One might hesitate to include the third one, al-Ḥasan ibn Muḥammad al-Rāmī, in a history of Persian medicine. He was obviously a Persian, but his connection with medicine is very artificial. His "Lover's companion" is a collection of epithets and similes relative to each part of the body! One wonders whether Persian lovers needed a book like that in order to describe their beloved and write to her (or to him). Let us hope that they did not really need it, or even know of it, but that al-Rāmī indulged his own fancy, which was queer enough.

E. *India*

There is a certain inconsistency in trying to study Hindu writings in chronological order, for the Hindu mind was essentially achronological. Tradition was more important to them than it ever was to Western people, even in mediaeval times. Hence there are good reasons for studying Āyurveda (that is, Hindu medicine) sub specie aeternitatis. The scholar wishing to do this will find abundant references in the two previous volumes (passim), to which might be added such books as those by Paramananda Mariadassou: Moeurs médicales de l'Inde et leurs rapports avec la médecine européenne (178 p., Pondichéry 1906); Le jardin des simples de l'Inde (288 p., Pondichéry 1913); Médecine traditionnelle de l'Inde (3 vols., Pondichéry 1934–35). William Crooke: Baidyā (ERE 2, 332, 1910). Chandra Chakraberty: An interpretation of ancient Hindu medicine (626 p., Calcutta 1923; Isis 7, 266). Dhirendra Nath Ray: The principle of tridoṣa in Āyurveda (376 p., Calcutta 1937; Isis 34, 174–77). Frederick S. Hammett: Ideas of the ancient Hindus concerning man (Isis 28, 57–72, 1938).

In any Hindu work, whether medical or other, the traditional elements are far more numerous and weighty than the novelties, but, come to think of it, could not the same be said of every human work? The historian is always essentially concerned with tradition, but instead of regarding tradition as timeless in the Hindu manner, he realizes that only the immemorial parts of it are really timeless; the rest of it is datable at least in principle. It is extremely interesting to record the traditional accretions, putting each as far as possible in its chronological place, and on that basis to explain the development of tradition. The main difference between the Hindus and us is that their immemorial past is longer than ours, and that instead of trying to shorten it as we do, they lengthen it as much as they can by an unconscious or deliberate suspension of historical memory.

To return to the second half of the fourteenth century, it is well to consider separately the works written in Sanskrit and those written in other languages.

We can cite only two Sanskrit authors, Madanapāla and Merutuṅga. The first was the prince of a little territory north of Delhi. A dictionary of materia medica bears his name. Of course, it does not follow that he was the real author (any more than, say, Theodosius II was the author of the Codex Theodosianus); the chances are that the work was done by others obeying his command. In fact, the compilation has been ascribed to his minister Viśveśvara, but as a code of laws is also ascribed to the same minister, it is probable that the real work was not done by Viśveśvara any more than by the prince himself. At any rate, that dictionary dates from c. 1375.

Merutuṅga was a Jaina alchemist to whom is ascribed the earliest datable rasa treatise. Such a treatise has medical aspects, for it is concerned with means of increasing health, longevity, and sexual vigor. It belongs to the tradition of iatrochemistry.

The non-Sanskrit writings are comparable to the non-Latin ones in Western Christendom, or the non-Arabic ones in Islām. Their aim was to diffuse knowledge already available to scholars and open it up to a new and larger audience.

Maṅgarāja wrote a medical treatise in Canarese, and an unknown author composed the Yoga-ratnākara in Siṅhalese. The sources of the former were Sanskrit; those of the latter, Pāli.

F. *China*

Medical thought and practice of this period is represented by five men, Wang Li, Chia Ming, Tai Ssŭ-kung, Yüan Kung, Chu Hsiao.

Wang Li wrote a treatise on fevers including 397 prescriptions. Chia Ming might be called the Chinese forerunner of Luigi Cornaro; his treatise on diet, a regimen for longevity, was presented by him to the first Ming emperor when he had himself become a centenarian! Various medical treatises are ascribed to Tai Ssŭ-kung, who was said to be the best disciple of Chu Tan-ch'i. Yüan Kung was a physiognomist. Finally, Chu Hsiao, a younger son of the first Ming emperor, compiled an elaborate medical treatise, the P'u-chi fang, c. 1378, and the famous famine herbal Chiu-huang pên-ts'ao in 1406; moreover, he conducted agricultural experiments, being anxious to provide new food resources for his people in times of scarcity.

There is nothing special to report concerning Korea. The new pên ts'ao was of course used in Korea as well as in China, but there was no need of a special Korean edition. Korean doctors were supposed to know Chinese. I am not aware that medical ideas were popularized as early as this in the Korean language. N. H. Bowman: History of Korean medicine (Transactions, Korea branch, Royal Asiatic Society, 6, 1–34, Seoul 1915), very insufficient.

Concerning the presence of Jewish physicians in China, see above, section B6.

G. *Japan*

The Buddhist monk Yūrin compiled a collection of recipes, written in Japanese, but largely derived from Chinese sources. The Japanese school of ophthalmology was founded by Majima Seigan, who died in 1379. The methods were originally Chinese, but gradually modified by the Japanese practitioners, whose tradition remained to a large extent familial and unrecorded, or at any rate unpublished, for a couple of centuries.

By the end of this century Japanese medicine was beginning to emerge out of its Chinese foundation. It was still essentially Chinese, though with a Japanese flavor.

Topical survey

The following sections are meant to supplement the geographical account which precedes and to indicate topic by topic the main directions of medical endeavor. No attempt at completeness is made, for a complete survey would be very long and somewhat futile. This is due not so much to the complexity of the subject as to the perversity of scholars who have devoted themselves to it or have approached it casually. I do not know of any other subject where the disintegration, the pulverization, of knowledge has been carried so far. Our many historico-medical or anecdoto-medical journals contain numberless notes on infinitesimal questions. These notes are often valuable so far as they go, that is, they are often based on original documents and represent new facts, but most of them have too little importance to be considered individually. Such notes were produced not only by dilettanti, or by the kind of scholars who are unable to deal with any but microscopic questions and are incapable of any synthetic effort; bad examples were given, alas! by masters, even the great master, Karl Sudhoff of Leipzig, who published in his AGM innumerable little articles calling attention to a single paragraph or statement in this or that MS. It is a pity that the medical historians, led by Sudhoff, who publish articles or notes with such prodigality are not more patient and forbearing. Instead of publishing separately every chip from their workshop, they would serve the interests of science better by collecting them until enough of any kind had been obtained to justify the writing of a monograph.

The arrangement of the topics is generally the same as in chapter I. Hence the reader interested only in this or that topic can satisfy his curiosity easily by reading the sections dealing with it in chapters I and XV.

1. *Medical astrology and alchemy*

Medical thought continued to be dominated by astrological ideas. These ideas were available in many books of various ages, and they were frequently reasserted by contemporary writers such as the Christians Guy de Chauliac and Bernard of Frankfurt; the Jews Jacob ben Judah Cabret and Solomon Abigdor; the Muslim al-Damīrī.

Chauliac dedicated a special treatise on the subject, Practica astrolabii, to Clement VI. Bernard of Frankfurt developed the astrological explanation of the plague more fully than other authors, but almost every plague treatise was colored by astrological prejudices. One of the most popular teachers of medical astrology was Arnold of Villanova (XIII-2), and his Capitula astrologiae were published in Hebrew by Cabret and by Abigdor. Al-Damīrī discussed astrological ideas in his zoological encyclopaedia. This list might be lengthened considerably.

Astrological medicine may be considered the preparation of the iatromathematical school which became so important in the seventeenth century. It accustomed physicians to dealing with numbers and to searching for physical explanations. Astrology was a crude philosophy of nature which was gradually refined in proportion to the increase of physical knowledge and the concomitant decrease of superstitions; the progress was very slow from the fourteenth century to the sixteenth, and the astrological Weltanschauung remained unchallenged until the time of the new iatromathematicians, Santorio Santorio (1561-1636), Descartes, Giovanni Alfonso Borelli (1608-79), Giorgio Baglivi (1668-1707), etc.

Karl Sudhoff: Iatromathematiker vornehmlich im XV. und XVI. Jahrh. (Abhandlungen zur Geschichte der Medizin 2, 100 p., Breslau 1902). Garrison (p. 257-61, 1929).

In the same way some adumbration of the iatrochemical school may be found in the alchemical writings, and not only in the Latin, Greek, and Arabic ones, but also in the Sanskrit ones of Merutuṅga. The situation was very much the same in both cases. Even as natural philosophy could not emerge out of astrology until the latter had been thoroughly cleaned out, so the iatrochemical doctrines of Paracelsus (1493-1541) and Jean Baptiste van Helmont (1577-1644) could not be formulated until much rubbish had been swept out of alchemy.

2. *Translations and commentaries*

Medicine was very largely book learning, but we should bear in mind that we are necessarily better acquainted with medical authors than with the physicians, however wise and experienced, who did not write, hence our general view is somewhat falsified. It is possible that the most original physicians are unknown to us; however, the tradition of any discovery counts for as much as the discovery itself; a discovery which fails to be transmitted is practically nonexistent.

The transmitters of medical knowledge showed a great deal of respect for the authorities, whom they read, translated, and commented upon. It is interesting to find which authorities arrested their attention.

In order to clear the ground, let us speak first of the Problems of Aristotle, a collection of unknown date, explaining many medical questions from the Peripatetic point of view.[31] This was put in tabulated form by Pietro Tossignano and translated from Latin into French by Evrard de Conty.

Hippocrates was still the great master. We may assume that every physician read some part of the Hippocratic canon. Every medical author referred to him. Abraham Cabret wrote a commentary on the Aphorisms, and Martin de Saint-Gilles translated them from Latin into French. Hippocratic commentaries were composed by Giovanni and Marsiglio da Santa Sofia, by Jacopo della Torre, by Ugo Bènzi, etc.

Next in importance to Hippocrates was Galen, and the two were almost inseparable, for many of the Hippocratic writings were transmitted together with Galen's commentaries. Thus we have commentaries on Galen by the Santa Sofia brothers, Ugo Benzi, Jacopo della Torre, Tommaso del Garbo, Iacopo da Arquà, etc.

Ibn Sīnā was perhaps even more popular than Hippocrates and Galen. The works ascribed to these three men formed the foundation of fourteenth-century medicine. Commentaries on the Qānūn were written by Joannes Jacobi, Jacopo della Torre, Christophorus de Honestis, Tommaso del Garbo, the brothers Santa Sofia, Ugo Benzi, etc. The Qānūn had been translated into Hebrew by Nathan ha-Me'ati (XIII-2) in 1279, and (books I, II) by Zeraḥiah Gracian (XIII-2) about

[31] Very convenient English translation by Edward Seymour Forster (Works of Aristotle vol. 7, Oxford 1927; Isis 11, 155), well indexed.

the same time; Nathan's translation was revised by Joseph ben Joshua II ha-Lorqi before 1402. Notes on the Qānūn were written in Hebrew by Abraham Abigdor, Shemṭob Shapruṭ, and Profiaṭ Duran. We may take it for granted that every Arabic physician was acquainted directly or indirectly[32] with the Qānūn, which was then already acknowledged as the masterpiece of Arabic medicine, while Ibn Sīnā himself was regarded all over the Islamic world as the prince of physicians, al-shaikh al-ra'īs.

The desire to keep Hippocrates, Galen, and Ibn Sīnā together has caused us to overlook the chronological order. At least three earlier Arabic physicians were being studied, to wit Ibn Māsawaih (IX-1) or Mesuë the Elder, al-Rāzī (IX-2), and Māsawaih al-Mārdīnī (XI-1) or Mesuë the Younger. The elder Mesuë was translated from *Latin* into Hebrew by Ṭodros ben Moses; the Antidotarium of the younger one was commented upon by Christophorus de Honestis. In each case, this was an Arabic-Latin tradition. Al-Rāzī was almost as much respected as Ibn Sīnā, especially his Kitāb al-Manṣūrī, and more especially the ninth book of that work, the Nonus Almansoris. Commentaries on the Latin versions of al-Rāzī were composed by Jean de Tournemire, Syllanus de Nigris, Pietro Tossignano, Marsiglio da Santa Sofia, etc.

As to the Arabic physicians posterior to Ibn Sīnā, Ibn Wāfid (XI-1)[32a] and Ibn abī-l-Ṣalt (XII-1) were translated from Arabic into Hebrew by Judah ben Solomon Nathan; Violas of Rodez commented in Hebrew on the posology of Ibn Rushd (XII-2), and al-Āqsarā'ī in Arabic on the Mūjiz al-qānūn of Ibn al-Nafīs (XIII-2).

Let us now consider the original Latin writings. One of the most popular authors was Arnold of Villanova (XIII-2), some of whose writings were put into Hebrew by Judah ben Solomon Nathan, Abraham Abigdor, and Ṭodros ben Moses. John of Saint Amand (XIII-2) was translated by Isaac ben Abraham Cabret, Bernard of Gordon (XIV-1) by Jekuthiel ben Solomon of Narbonne, Gerald de Solo by Abraham Abigdor and Leon Joseph of Carcassonne, Jean de Tournemire by the same Leon Joseph.

All this illustrates the coming of age of Latin medicine. Some of the original Latin writings are beginning to compete with the Arabic and Greek ones. To be sure, their success was favored by social considerations. There might be good reasons (not exclusively scientific) for translating into Hebrew the writings of an influential Montpellier professor like Jean de Tournemire. Yet the main fact is this: Latindom was now fallen heir to the Greek-Arabic tradition and was cultivating that heritage in the proper manner—that is, the physicians of the Christian West did their best to preserve their patrimony and to increase it, however little.[33]

One of the by-products of these translations and discussions was the preparation

[32] E.g., via a commentary, like the Mūjiz al-qānūn of Ibn al-Nafīs (XIII-2). Such a commentary generally included the original text. For a list of commentaries on the Qānūn, abridgments, etc., see Brockelmann (1, 457; suppt. 1, 823).

[32a] A Catalan translation of Ibn Wāfid's Kitāb al-adwiya al-mufrada has been edited by Luis Faraudo de Saint-Germain: El Libre de les medicines particulars (220 p., 2 pl., Barcelona 1943; Isis 37). The translation was made from the Arabic, rather than from the Latin, in the fourteenth century, certainly not later. A copy of it, which I owe to the friendship of professor José Maria Millás i Vallicrosa of Barcelona, reached me just in time to be mentioned in this footnote. War conditions made it impossible for me to know of it more promptly and speak of it in other parts of this work.

[33] They followed Seneca's advice, "Agamus bonum patrem familiae: faciamus ampliora quae accepimus. Maior ista hereditas a me ad posteros transeat" (Introd. 2, 484).

of glossaries ad hoc, like the Clavis sanationis of Simon of Genoa (XIII-2) and the Pandectae medicinae of Matthaeus Sylvaticus (XIV-1). Let us cite two more examples, one Western and one Eastern.

The anonymous Alphita is a medico-botanical glossary which was edited from the Bodleian MS, Selden B 35, by John Lancaster Gough Mowat (Anecdota oxoniensia, Mediaeval series 1, 2, 252 p., Oxford 1887). It is derived mainly from the Antidotarium of Nicholas of Salerno (XII-1), then from Simon of Genoa and other authors, the latest being John Gaddesden (XIV-1). The MS dates from c. 1465, but there is an earlier MS (Sloane 284) in the British Museum. Putting these facts together, the Alphita must be placed in the second half of the fourteenth century, or the beginning of the fifteenth. A new edition was recently published by Rudolf Creutz (Quellen und Studien zur Geschichte der Naturwissenschaften vol. 7, no. 4/5, 80 p., Berlin 1940).

The Oriental example is a glossary of about 200 drug names in Armenian, Arabic (Persian, Turkish), and Latin (Romance), in MS 310 of the Mekhitarist library of Vienna. It is placed at the beginning of a medical encyclopaedia written in Armenian by the scribe Abraham in 1438 and containing three parts: (1) pharmacy; (2) medicine, including extracts from Mekhitar of Her (XII-2); (3) the so-called Book of the sick man. It is largely derived from the Persian work of Abū Manṣūr Muwaffak (X-2), and probably also, but to a much smaller extent, from Ibn al-Baiṭār (XIII-1). The date of the glossary cannot be much earlier than that of the MS, say, the beginning of the fifteenth century. The Armenian work itself may be older, for it is an elaboration of the text of another Armenian MS (in S. Lazzaro, Venice) dating from 1294. Joseph Karst: Das trilingue Medizinalglossar aus MS 310 der Wiener Mekhitaristen-Bibliothek (Zeitschrift für armenische Philologie 2, 112–48, 1903).[34]

3. *Literary and scholastic background*

The more learned physicians, those who had studied in Bologna or Paris, or in other places where they had attended not only medical lectures but also philosophical or legal ones, seemed to think that the best way to distinction and fame was the composition of a general medical treatise along the approved scholastic lines. Quite a few such treatises were composed in this period, such as the Summa medicinalis of Tommaso del Garbo, the Sermones medicinales of Niccolò Falcucci, the Philonium of Valescus de Taranta, the Introductio in practicam of Bernard Alberti, the Breviarium Bartholomei of John of Mirfeld, the Michi competit of Thomas de Sarepta. The same scholastic spirit informed the writings of Ugo Benzi and Sigismondo Polcastro. Other physicians were more literary-minded, and these would be influenced by Petrarca and Boccaccio. Others still, though very few, were clinically minded, or at least were leaning in that direction; good examples of that type were the fin-de-siècle Benzi and Savonarola.

The reading habits of some physicians may be appraised more completely, because inventories of their libraries have come down to us. This is the case for Elia of Venice, Guido da Bagnolo, and Ugolino Montecatini. These early catalogues are more revealing than those of modern scholars, for MSS books were relatively rare and very expensive. Their ownership by a trecento doctor is always

[34] Only 2 volumes of this Zeitschrift were published (Marburg 1903–4), being edited by Abgar Joannissiany, Franz Nikolaus Finck, Esnik Gjandschezian, and Agop Manandian.

significant, whereas the libraries of modern scholars are likely to be cluttered with irrelevant or unused books.

Scholastic tendencies existed also among Jewish doctors, such as Meir ben Isaac Aldabi, and Muslim ones, such as the Egyptian al-Damīrī or the Turk Ḥājjī pāshā. They were often prominent in the commentators dealt with in the preceding section, and indeed the distinction between authors of "original" textbooks and authors of commentaries is rather artificial. An original book might be hardly more than a disguised commentary, and on the other hand a formal commentary might include many original thoughts. A more tangible difference between the commentary and the original "summa" was that the former was derived mainly from the text commented upon, whereas the summa was derived equally from a great many sources. This may remind us of the taunting remark that to copy from one book is called "plagiarism," whereas to copy from many books is sometimes baptized "research." The borrowings of the compilers of medical encyclopaedias might be greater and their initiative smaller than was the case with the commentators.

4. *Anatomy*

The anatomical revival of which Mondino was the protagonist did not develop as one might have expected. On the contrary, the period between Mondino (1316) and the time of Leonardo da Vinci (d. 1519) and Vesalius (1543) saw so little progress that one would almost think of a kind of regression. There was no regression, but the forward movement was very slow. Dissections continued to be made in various places, but they were too rare and in almost every case too perfunctory to impress the students or the doctors who were privileged to attend them. Bologna, where Mondino had taught, continued to be the main center. Mondino's successor was Niccolò Bertruccio (XIV-1), and we know from one of his disciples, Guy de Chauliac, how he proceeded:

"Mon maistre Bertruce," wrote Guy de Chauliac (in the first treatise, Anatomie, of his Grande chirurgie, ed. Nicaise p. 30), "l'a faict plusieurs fois en cette maniere: Ayant situé le corps mort sur vn banc, il en faisoit quatre leçons. En la premiere estoit traicté des membres nutritifs: parce que plustost ils se pourrissent. En la seconde, des membres spirituels. En la troisiesme, des membres animaux. En la quatriesme, on traitoit des extremitez. Et suiuant le commentateur du liure des Sectes [Galien], en chasque membre y auoit neuf choses à voir: c'est à sçauoir, la situation, la substance, la complection, la quantité, le nombre, la figure, la liaison ou alliance, les actions et vtilitez: et quelles sont les maladies qui y peuuent suruenir: desquelles par l'Anatomie, le medecin peut estre secouru et aydé à la connoissance des maux, au prognostic, et à la curation. Nous faisons aussi l'Anatomie és corps desseichez au Soleil, ou consumez en terre, ou fondus en eau courante ou boüillante: nous voions la anatomie au moins des os, cartillages, joinctures, gros nerfs, tendons et ligamens. Par ces deux moyens, on paruient à la connoissance de l'Anatomie és corps des hommes, des cinges, pourceaux, et plusieurs autres animaux: et non par les peintures, comme a fait le susdit Henric,[35] qui auec treize peintures a semblé monstrer l'Anatomie."

The method of Mondino and his successors and imitators is illustrated in the formal dissection scene, a woodcut included in many editions of the Fasciculus

[35] Henri de Mondeville (XIV-1).

medicinae; not in the first, Venice 1491, but in the second (Italian), Venice 1493, and the following. See Charles Singer (1, 36–41, 1925) and Klebs (nos. 573–75). The teacher is sitting in a high cathedra, generally with a book open on his desk, the corpse is stretched out on a table below, the prosector is working, and students stand around him. The value of the dissection depended very much on the prosector's skill and intelligence. Vesalius' achievement was largely due to the fact that he was his own prosector. But we must not anticipate.

As far as the teaching of anatomy is concerned, a distinction should be made between occasional and accidental, even clandestine, dissections and regular ones. Though dissections had taken place not infrequently in Bologna since Mondino's days, they were not officially recognized until 1405. Dissections were organized in Montpellier 1377, in Lerida 1391. The first Viennese dissection was made before 1405 by Galeazzo da Santa Sofia; the first Parisian one, by Jean Le Lièvre in 1407. Under the best conditions, e.g. in Bologna, medical students would witness a dissection once a year; of course, they would not be allowed to do the dissecting themselves, but simply to watch the prosector. The cadavers of criminals would be granted to the universities for such purpose, but only very few, sometimes only one per year, and hence the spectators would be so numerous that few could really profit from the show. As fewer women were condemned to death than men, the opportunity of dissecting female bodies was very rare; a medical student might graduate without having ever witnessed such a dissection.

Additional occasions of obtaining anatomical knowledge were obtained by surgeons and their assistants in the case of accidents and legal autopsies. A post-mortem examination is admirably illustrated in a MS of Guy de Chauliac's surgery (fig. 23),[36] another in the French translation of Bartholomew the Englishman (XIII-1), Lyon 1482, this being the first printed drawing of a dissection scene (Klebs no. 150.1). The most important autopsy of this period was performed by one of Chauliac's disciples, Pietro d'Argelata. Pope Alexander V (Peter of Crete) having died suddenly (in Bologna 1410), it was rumored that he had been poisoned by order of Baldassare Cossa, and Pietro d'Argelata was requested to make a post mortem. Pietro described the autopsy in his Cirurgia (printed Venice 1480; Klebs no. 777). For an English version of that description (taken from the second edition, 1492, lib. V, tract. 12, cap. 3), see Singer (p. 94, 1917).

In spite of their frequent opportunities, surgeons did not materially improve the knowledge of anatomy. For example, the anatomical introductions to the surgical treatises of Henri de Mondeville and Guy de Chauliac are very disappointing. We should bear in mind, however, that the field of surgical intervention was very limited and superficial. The surgeon was restricted to the treatment of fractures and luxations, to amputations, lithotomies, and extractions of teeth, and much of his work was of a kind now entrusted to other doctors, the treatment of wounds, ulcers, abscesses, and skin troubles. Obviously one might spend one's life remedying such complaints, without needing much anatomical knowledge or without increasing the little one knew.

Charles Singer: A study in early Renaissance anatomy, with a new text, the Anathomia of Hieronymo Manfredi, 1490, transcribed and translated by A. Mildred Westland (Studies in the history and method of science 1, 79–164, ill., Oxford

[36] Library of the Montpellier medical school, MS 184 français, fol. 14r. Singer: Studies (vol. 1, pl. xxix, 1917).

Fig. 23. Post-mortem examination. After an incomplete French MS of Chauliac's surgery (Montpellier, MS français 184, fol. 14r), written in 1363 by G. de Caillat, surgeon in Montpellier (Nicaise, p. cxiv). Reproduced from Singer: Studies in the history and method of science (vol. 1, pl. xxix, Oxford 1917). Courtesy of Charles Singer and of the Clarendon Press.

1917). Sudhoff-Singer (1924). C. Singer (1925; 1926). Paul Delaunay: La vie médicale aux XVIe, XVIIe et XVIIIe siècles (556 p., Paris 1935; Isis 25, 298), showing how slowly anatomical teaching developed even after Vesalius.

In the Muslim world conditions were even worse, for surgery had remained under a cloud. It is rather paradoxical that one of the most influential surgical books of the Middle Ages was written by a Muslim, Abū-l-Qāsim al-Zahrāwī (X-2), but that achievement was never surpassed by the Muslims and seldom repeated. The most remarkable Muslim treatise on anatomy of this time was written in Persian by Manṣūr ibn Muḥammad in 1396, for a grandson of Tīmūr Lang.

Note on dwarfs and giants. Considering the tremendous importance given to dwarfs and giants in the literature and folklore of every people, and the attention which men of abnormally high (or low) stature have always attracted, it is curious that early anatomists do not speak of them. As to the traditions, it will suffice to recall Adam, Gog and Magog (Yājūj wa Mājūj), Goliath (Jālūt), the Cyclopes, the Arabian tribe 'Ād, the tutelary giants of many European towns, etc. The people of many nations thought of their ancestors as a race of giants (cf. many examples in Old Testament and classical literature). In his Muqaddama (French ed., 1, 360; 2, 243) Ibn Khaldūn remarked that that was a false notion, partly due to the enormous size of some ancient monuments.

Dwarfs were often used as pages in mediaeval courts. Gilles Aycelin de Montaigut, cardinal of Thérouanne, who died in Avignon 1378, had a dwarf in his service, and so did the antipope Clement VII (ruled 1378–94) and Isabeau of Bavaria (who in 1389 had become the queen of Charles VI of France). Isabeau's dwarf was a woman called dame Aelips. On the other hand, the duke of Burgundy employed a giant (Brun p. 226, 1928).

In spite of this familiarity with real dwarfs and real giants, they aroused no scientific curiosity almost until our own age. This may have been partly caused by the fact that their fabulous importance was so great.

Edward J. Wood: Giants and dwarfs (484 p., London 1868), anecdotes concerning real people. Otto Bollinger: Über Zwerg- und Riesenwuchs (32 p., 3 fig., Berlin 1884), scientific discussion but anterior to the understanding of internal secretions.

For ancient views on giants persisting in the Middle Ages see the curious little book of the Swiss sixteenth-century author Jean Chassanion: De gigantibus, eorumque reliquis atque iis, quae ante annos aliquos nostra aetate in Gallia reperte sunt. Ubi etiam de admirandis prodigiosisque quorundam viribus agitur, qui ad Gigantum naturam proxime videntur accedere. Obiter etiam Ioannis Goropii[37] error perstringitur, qui in sua Gigantomachia nulla Gigantum corpora tanta, quanta dicuntur fuisse, affirmat (85 p., Basel 1580).

For the persistence of ancient views on dwarfs see Paracelsus: De nymphis, sylphis, pygmaeis et salamandris et de caeteris spiritibus. This treatise, written in German (in spite of Latin title), is apocryphal and of unknown date. It was printed in Johannes Huser's edition (9, 45–78, Basel 1591) and in Karl Sudhoff's (Isis 6, 56) edition (14, 115–51, Munich 1933). Englished by Henry E. Sigerist in Four treatises of Paracelsus (p. 215–53, Baltimore 1941; Isis 34, 48). See also

[37] Jan van Gorp, called Goropius Becanus, born in Brabant 1518, died Maestricht 1572. His claim in 1569 that Dutch was the most ancient language, the real mater linguarum, roused considerable discussion. Alphonse Le Roy (Biographie nationale de Belgique 8, 120–23, 1884).

Edward Tyson: A philological essay concerning the pygmies of the ancients, included in his Orang-outang (London 1699). Reprinted with notes by Bertram Coghill Alan Windle (London 1894). M. F. Ashley Montagu: Tyson (Philadelphia 1943; Isis 34, 526).

For mediaeval legends in French literature, see Fritz Wohlgemuth: Riesen und Zwerge in der altfranzösischen erzählenden Dichtung (Diss. Tübingen, 110 p., 1906); in German literature, August Lütjens: Der Zwerg in der deutschen Heldendichtung (Germanistische Abhandlungen 38, 132 p., Breslau 1911). Eugen Mogk (RGA 3, 501, 1916; 4, 597, 1919). Ernst Herwig Ahrendt: Der Riese in der mittelhochdeutschen Epik (Diss. Rostock, 140 p., 1923). John R. Broderius: The giant in Germanic tradition (Chicago thesis, 220 p. typewritten, 1932). Valerie Höttges: Typenverzeichnis der deutschen Riesen- und riesischen Teufelssagen (FF communications no. 122, Academia scientiarum fennica, 288 p., Helsinki 1937).

General discussion of giants by David MacRitchie and W. Scott (ERE 6, 189–97, 1914), and of dwarfs by the former only (ERE 5, 122–26, 1912). For the giant Teutobochus see Henri Grégoire (Renaissance 2, 120–21, 1945).

Mediaeval ideas on giants and dwarfs afford as good an illustration of muddled thinking as could be imagined. The subject was obscured by the confusion of real people with imaginary ones (the latter more in evidence and apparently more alive than the former), and of the genus with the individual, the normal with the exceptional (e.g., dwarfish races with individual dwarfs).

5. *Physiology*

Whatever physiology was combined with anatomy was of very little account, and no wonder. Physiology is the study of the functioning of the body. Now the fabric of the body was very imperfectly known; its most essential parts (such as vessels, nerves, glands) were either unrecognized or misunderstood. Moreover, the explanation of the functions implied physical and chemical knowledge which hardly existed. The fundamental questions could not be stated, let alone solved.

Experimental medicine is based on physiological principles. It was so in the Middle Ages even as today, except that the principles were implied and that the need of them was not even realized. The historian may try, however, to deduce the physiological ideas from their unconscious application to therapeutics. The practice of bloodletting and purgation, and the use of sphygmology and uroscopy for diagnosis (Introd. 2, 75–79), implied some ideas on the blood and digestion, but those ideas were exceedingly vague, jumbled, and mixed with superstition.

As far as uroscopy is concerned, the story told above (p. 1206) about John of Saxony (c. 1392) is typical; hundreds of similar stories could be told, all pointing to the same conclusion, that uroscopy was, like astrology or palmistry, a pseudo science.

In addition to the treatises on urine cited in this volume (e.g., the one written by the Czech doctor Gallus de Strahov), there were others, anonymous, which may be contemporary, e.g., the one included in the Hortus sanitatis of Strassburg 1496 (Klebs 509.2), in the Hortus sanitatis of Venice 1511, or in the Antidotarium Nicolai of Pavia 1478 (Klebs 703.4). The urinoscopic material integrated in the various editions of Joannes de Ketham's Fasciculus medicinae (Klebs 573–75) is also, most if not all of it, of earlier date. Thanks to the facsimile editions provided by Sudhoff and Singer, that material (text and illustrations) is now easily available to every scholar. Comparative data will be found in Ed. Pergens: Eine Urinsschautafel aus Cod. Brux. Nr. 5876 nebst Kommentar (AGM 1, 393–402, 1 pl., 1908), apropos of a French text in a MS written in a fifteenth-century hand.

For bloodletting, see Karl Sudhoff: Lasstafelkunst in Drucken des 15. Jahrh. (AGM 1, 219–88, 1908), very elaborate study; Eine Aderlassanweisung aus dem Ende des 14. Jahrh. (AGM 1, 391, 1908); Ein deutscher diagnostischer Leitfaden zur Aderlassblutschau (AGM 10, 318–19, 1917), German text copied c. 1425.

For the pulse, see Ernest Wickersheimer: Sphygmographie médicale (Communication au premier Congrès de l'art de guérir, 3 p., Anvers 1920; Isis 5, 221), sphygmographic drawings taken out of a fifteenth-century MS, Strassburg, Latin 18.

6. *Embryology and obstetrics*

The following remarks might have been made in chapter I, but it is not too late to offer them here. In order to understand mediaeval ideas on conception, one should remember that the dominating views were those which had been explained by Aristotle (De generatione animalium I, chs. 19, 22)—briefly, the female produces the material for generation, that is, the catamenia which cease to flow out, but that material is informed by the male semen. The same ideas occur in the Wisdom of Solomon (I-1 B.C.) 7:2, in Galen, the Aristotelian Problemata,[38] Ibn Rushd, Albert the Great, etc. Different views, however, which originated perhaps in the Hippocratic περὶ γονῆς (Littré 7, 470–85; p. 476) were clearly expressed by Lucretius (I-1 B.C.), De rerum natura (IV, 1229–33): "Semper enim partus duplici de semine constat." Seed is contributed by both sexes. These views, which we may call Lucretian, can be detected in the writings of al-Rāzī (IX-2), 'Alī ibn 'Abbās al-Majūsī (X-2), Ibn Sīnā (XI-1). Their tradition is more difficult to follow in the Latin West. Not that Lucretius was unknown there; the best proof that he was not is the existence of the two Leiden MSS, MS (A) of the ninth century, formerly in St. Martin's church, Mainz, the seat of Hrabanus Maurus (IX-1), and MS (B) of the tenth century, formerly in the abbey of St. Bertin, near St. Omer (Sandys 1, 631–33, 1903). Moreover, there are evidences of Lucretian knowledge in William of Conches (XII-1). My impression is that the Lucretian tradition in the West was largely underground and silent; as to the Muslim tradition, al-Rāzī, etc., it is unexplainable except as borrowing from Lucretius' own Greek sources. Lucretius did not emerge into full light until 1417, when the De rerum natura was recovered by the Florentine Poggio Bracciolini (1380–1459). It was first printed in Brescia 1473 (Klebs no. 623).

The Aristotelian views prevailed in the West, in the fourteenth century, and they can be recognized not only in the Latin writings, but also in the drawings of the uterus (Singer p. 24, 1925). We have two Latin tracts on the subject written by southern Frenchmen, the De impregnatione mulierum by the Provençal Pierre de Nadilz, and the Regimen de conceptione by the Languedocian Jean Pataran.

The Lucretian views on generation did not appear until the fifteenth century. The two streams of thought continued to flow side by side until modern times; one has to bear that in mind in order to understand the quarrel between the animalculists and the ovists toward the end of the seventeenth century.

For lower creatures the possibility of spontaneous generation had generally been

[38] That apocryphal work enjoyed considerable popularity in the Middle Ages, especially its book IV, dealing with sexual intercourse and generation, which was issued separately, and adapted in such a manner that it became a kind of pornographic publication. Singer has pointed out (p. 28, 1925) that a modification of it circulates clandestinely in England to this day under the title "Aristotle's masterpiece."

accepted, even by Aristotle. In our period, Heinrich von Langenstein gave to that hypothesis a strange astrological twist. Planetary influences not only cause the generation of various kinds of pests, but they also bring into existence other creatures, possibly even new kinds of men. Of course, it was a fundamental principle of astrology that every sexual generation was conditioned and modified by such influences. Men, they might have granted, cannot be born without sexual intercourse of their parents, but the fruits of such intercourse are always qualified by astrological radiations.

They did not grant that absolutely. The possibility of lucina sine concubitu was admitted at least in exceptional cases, and continued to be thus admitted for a long time.[39] There were also occasional doubts concerning the length of pregnancy. For example, we have a document of 1437 wherein bishop Johann II of Würzburg states that a child born to a woman whose husband has been absent for many years may yet be legitimate. The seed may have remained quiescent for some time, as happens to plant seeds, before beginning its normal development.[40]

In the absence of accurate knowledge of impregnation (knowledge which was technically unattainable in those days), such skepticism was permissible. Let us remember that the concept of spontaneous generation could not be driven out except after a series of battles obliging it to retreat into smaller and smaller fields, the battles being fought and won at century intervals by Francesco Redi in 1668, Lazzaro Spallanzani in 1767, and Louis Pasteur in 1861. We are now certain that spontaneous generation could not occur under the conditions with which we are familiar, yet how did life begin?

The skepticism and ignorance were considerably aggravated because of the innumerable superstitions and the rich folklore connected with the procreation of animals, and especially with childbirth. It is impossible to go into that here. See J. A. MacCulloch: Pregnancy (ERE 10, 242–44, 1919). Bernhard Kummer: Empfängnis (HDA 2, 806–14, 1930). P. Saintyves: L'astrologie populaire (p. 194–222, Paris 1937; Isis 30, 387). M. F. Ashley Montagu: Coming into being among the Australian aborigines. A study of the procreative beliefs of the native tribes of Australia (398 p., London 1937; Isis 29, 192–94).

One of the most popular books on obstetrics was probably written in this period, or very soon afterward, the Büchlein wie sich die Schwangeren, Gebärenden und Wöchnerinnen halten sollen, first printed in Ulm c. 1495. Sudhoff (no. 30, 1908); Klebs (no. 716).

Another little treatise, in Latin, including an obstetrical summary for midwives exists in a MS of the medical faculty of Montpellier (no. 597). It is written in a fifteenth-century hand and illustrated. The text and figures were published by Pierre Pansier: Un manuel d'accouchements du XVe siècle (Janus 14, 217–20, 16 fig., 1909). For comparison see Karl Sudhoff: Neue Handschriftenbilder von Kindslagen und der Situs einer Schwangeren vom Jahre 1485 (AGM 1, 310–15, 2 pl., 1908); Die Leipziger Kindslagenbilder mit deutschem Texte (AGM 2, 422–25, 1 pl., 1909). C. Singer (p. 22–28, 1925).

7. *Anatomical (and medical) iconography*

Many of the references given in the corresponding section of chapter I concern the whole century and even overlap it at both ends. The anatomical and surgical

[39] Conway Zirkle: Animals impregnated by the wind (Isis 25, 95–130, 1936; p. 114 f.). Clark Emery: "Sir" John Hill vs. the Royal Society (Isis 34, 16–20, 1942).

[40] Georg Burckhard: Ein merkwürdiges MS aus dem Jahre 1437 (AGM 4, 301–5, 1910).

treatises of the second half of the fourteenth century were often illustrated, and their earliest MSS must be taken into account. The best examples in the West are MSS of Guy de Chauliac's Grande chirurgie (e.g., the Montpellier MS, 184 français) and the Stockholm MS of John Arderne's De arte phisicali et de cirurgia (c. 1420). The best Oriental example is the Persian treatise Tashrīḥ bil-taṣwīr composed in 1396 by Manṣūr ibn Muḥammad and illustrated with five colored schematic drawings. Those five diagrams, however, were but the continuation of a very old tradition.

The dance of death. Representations of skeletons, or of dead or dying people, are often found in the paintings, and in innumerable illustrations of the theme called "the dance of death" (dance macabre, Totentanz). It is difficult to say when that theme originated; it was probably expressed in a literary form before being represented pictorially. The fundamental idea, "memento mori," is of course very old; every philosopher, pagan or Christian, had considered it with more or less emphasis, and poets had rung the changes on it. The idea of "the dance of death" is a mediaeval elaboration. The dead people, or representatives of Death, or Death itself, allure the living, and try to make the latter dance with them. Everybody is taken into the eternal dance, the young as well as the old, the healthy and handsome as well as the sick and ugly, the rich as well as the poor, the saints as well as the sinners. Death is absolutely impartial; it respects nothing; it is the great equalizer, the great leveler. The memento mori and especially that gruesome dance were disturbing to the rich, the powerful, the happy ones, but it afforded some kind of consolation to the great mass of the people, who were poor, despised, hungry, oppressed. The theme of the dance of death may be in some rare instances anterior to the fourteenth century, but its development belongs to that century. It is probable that the Black Death increased its popularity, for it was then almost impossible to escape if not the reality of death, at least the thought, the obsession of it. One of the oldest pictorial representations is the Trionfo della morte, a fresco in the Campo santo of Pisa, generally but wrongly ascribed to Andrea di Cione, called Orcagna (d. 1368);[41] there are a few other fourteenth-century paintings, but the examples became more abundant in the following century. They were among the earliest monuments of xylography and of printing. The theme reached its climax about the middle of the sixteenth century, under the stimulation of Albrecht Dürer (d. 1528) and Hans Holbein the Younger (d. 1543).

It is difficult to say where the theme originated, France or Germany; at any rate, it was very popular in both countries, and also in Italy, Spain, England. The "dance of death," whether expressed in prose or in verse, in Latin or in the vernacular, or by means of the plastic arts or of music, was one of the commonplaces of Western thought from the fourteenth to the sixteenth century.

In the following bibliography I refer only to books which I was able to examine, among others which I also examined but rejected, as being too special or for other reasons.

Hans Ferdinand Massmann: Literatur der Todtentänze. Beytrag zum Jubeljahre der Buchdruckerkunst (reprinted from Serapeum, 135 p., Leipzig 1840). Eustache Hyacinthe Langlois: Essai historique, philosophique et pittoresque sur les Danses des morts (2 vols., 54 pl., ill., Rouen 1851–52), abundant documentation. Georges Kastner: Les danses des morts (folio, 326 p., 20 pl., Paris 1852), followed by Kast-

[41] It was perhaps the work of Francesco Traini (fl. 1341).

ner's Dance macabre, an orchestral partition of 44 p., on words by Edouard Thierry. Hermann Baethcke: Der Lübecker Todtentanz. Ein Versuch zur Herstellung des alten niederdeutschen Textes (Diss. Göttingen, 80 p., Berlin 1873). Pietro Vigo: Le danze macabre in Italia (150 p., Livorno 1878; revised ed., 182 p., 8 pl., Bergamo 1901). Wilhelm Seelmann: Die Totentänze des Mittelalters (Niederdeutsches Jahrbuch 17, 80 p., Norden 1893). Paul Kupka: Über mittelalterliche Totentänze (Gymn. Progr., 36 p., Stendal 1905). Wilhelm Fehse: Der Ursprung der Totentänze, mit dem vierzeiligen oberdeutschen Totentanztext, Cod. Palat. no. 314 (58 p., Halle 1907). Karl Künstle: Die Legende der drei Lebenden und der drei Toten und der Totentanz, nebst einem Exkurs über die Jakobslegende (116 p., 7 pl., 17 fig., Freiburg i.B. 1908). Albert Freybe: Das memento mori in deutscher Sitte, bildlicher Darstellung und Volksglauben, deutscher Sprache, Dichtung und Seelsorge (264 p., Gotha 1909). Wolfgang Stammler: Die Totentänze des Mittelalters (64 p., 17 fig., München 1922). Susan Minns: The dance of death from the twelfth to the twentieth century (American Art Association, New York 1922), sale catalogue of her collection ad hoc, 1,020 items. Gert Buchheit: Der Totentanz (256 p., 58 fig., Berlin 1926). Rudolf Helm: Skelett- und Todesdarstellungen bis zum Auftreten der Totentänze (Studien zur deutschen Kunstgeschichte 255, 80 p., 8 pl., Strassburg 1928). Ellen Breede: Studien zu den lateinischen und deutschsprachlichen Totentanztexten des 13. bis 17. Jahrh. (180 p., Halle 1931). Aldred Scott Warthin: The physician of the dance of death (Annals of medical history vols. 2–3, 1930–31; reprinted with corrections and index, 156 p., 92 fig., New York 1931). Henri Stegemeier: The dance of death in folksong with an introduction on its history (Chicago thesis, 232 p. typewritten, 1939).

8. *Physiognomy*

There is nothing to add concerning the theory of physiognomy to what has been said in chapter I.

The art was practiced in China as well as in the West, witness the books of Yüan Kung and of his son Chung Chê.

The Persian man of letters al-Ḥasan ibn Muḥammad al-Rāmī wrote a book to help lovers name and describe every part of their beloved's body. Whether that book, Anīs al-'ushshāq, deserves to be included in the literature of physiognomy may be discussed. It is a curious book, hard to classify anywhere, except as a literary conceit, or perhaps in the ars amandi.

9. *Surgery*

The progress of surgery continued naturally enough. Indeed, surgery was the only branch of medicine for which the lack of physical or chemical knowledge did not matter so much (at that time) and for which the results of the doctor's activities were sufficiently tangible. Empiricism combined with common sense might open new ways or close unpromising ones. The only drawback to real progress (social progress) was the illiteracy of many surgeons or their inarticulateness. Like other craftsmen, the surgeon found it hard to record his experience in writing; it may be that he was also inhibited, like them, by the need of secrecy. It was more tempting to keep his discoveries for his sons or the young friends who might be apprenticed to him than to broadcast them. The transmission of surgical experience tended to be manual and oral, rather than literary.

In spite of that, a number of surgical treatises were published in the first half of the fourteenth century, and as many in the second half of the fourteenth century. Let us mention first, for the sake of curiosity, the Sefer ha-garaḥot existing in the

Vatican library. It is a surgical treatise written in Catalan but in Hebrew script. There were not many Jewish surgeons, but the author of this treatise, Samuel Esperial, was one, and he dedicated it to another, David of Jaen. The contents of that work are still unknown; further study may oblige us to change our tentative dating of it.

All the other contemporary treatises were written by Christians, and, what is remarkable, most of them were written in Latin. This suggests that the surgeons had become better educated and had risen on the social ladder. The two Frenchmen, however, wrote in French, which had already ceased to be a patois and, thanks to royal patronage and other causes, had become a respectable language. The two Frenchmen were Pierre Fromont and Guy de Chauliac. The Cirurgie of the first received little attention, but it was he who embalmed king Philip VI in 1350. The Chirurgia magna of Guy de Chauliac is one of the classics of medical literature. Chauliac had first written it in Latin, but it was immediately put into French. It remained a standard work until the sixteenth century, when it was superseded by the Dix livres de la chirurgie (Paris 1564) of another Frenchman, Ambroise Paré (1510–90).[42]

The earliest English surgeon of fame was a contemporary of Chauliac, John Arderne, whose superiority was recognized for two centuries, but remained restricted to England, whereas Chauliac's was international. The "Cirurgia Walteri Brit" is wrongly ascribed to the astronomer who flourished in Merton College, Oxford, c. 1390; moreover, it is hardly more than a collection of medical recipes.

The main treatise on surgery composed about that time in Italy is the Cyrurgia ascribed to Pietro da Tossignano, and also to one Giovanni da Milano (or Brescia, a place not very far east of Milano). Another treatise, the Liber in medicina de operacione manuali, bears the name of Jacopo da Prato. The Chirurgia of Pietro d'Argelata is more important than these two and was certainly more influential (witness many printed editions, 1480, etc.), but it was possibly posterior to our period, for Pietro d'Argelata lived until 1423. It was he who made the autopsy of Alexander V in 1410.

None of the surgeons cited in this section was a military surgeon in the same sense as Henri de Mondeville, Jan Yperman, or Ambroise Paré. Yet war, then as ever, was the great teacher of surgery, for it multiplied indefinitely a surgeon's opportunities of learning. In the hand-to-hand fighting of those days, soldiers were often disfigured, e.g., their nose might be cut off, and if they got well again they might wish to recover a human semblance. Thus arose the problems of rhinoplasty (rebuilding of noses), or more generally of plastic surgery.

Rhinoplasty had been practiced by the ancients, the Hindu Suśruta (VI B.C.?), the Roman Celsus (I-1), the Greek Antyllos (II-1), and brief references to it appear in the Byzantine writings. Salernitan surgeons, however, did not speak of it, and the art seemed to have completely vanished, when it suddenly reappeared in southern Italy. The first account of it was written by the historian and humanist Bartolommeo Fazio (d. Naples 1457), according to whom the art was practiced by the Branca family in Catania, Sicily, "Branca pater et Antonius Branca filius Siculi," who must have flourished about the end of the fourteenth century and the beginning of the fifteenth. The father Branca used the skin of forehead and cheek

[42] Francis R. Packard: Life and times of A. Paré (314 p., ill., New York 1921; 2d ed. 1925; Isis 4, 326–27). Janet Doe: Bibliography of the works of A. Paré (285 p., Chicago 1937; Isis 29, 220); Addenda (Chicago 1940).

for transplantation; the son, Antonio, used that of the upper arm; Antonio is said to have corrected defects of lips and ears. He transmitted his method to another Sicilian, Baldassare Pavone, who in his turn transmitted it to the family Vianeo, settled in Maida and Tropaea (two Calabrian localities). Hence the name "magia Tropaeensium" later given to plastic surgery. The best technical account appeared in the Bündt-Ertzney (1460) of Heinrich von Pfolspeundt. This Heinrich was a member of the Teutonic Order, who took part as a surgeon in its campaigns on the eastern marches of Germany; he practiced rhinoplasty, together with his brethren Hans von Tiffen and Heinrich von Baldenstetten. The new art belongs to the fifteenth century, but we must assume that it germinated in Sicily before 1400, if knowledge of it could reach Fazio and Pfolspeundt by 1450. There is no reason to believe that the Sicilian wound surgeons got their knowledge from Byzantine sources, though such sources were more available in southern Italy than in the rest of Western Europe.

Full discussion of this in Gurlt (2, 488–99, 1898). BL (1, 299, 674, 1929).

10. *Eye diseases*

As the Muslim eye doctors were still ahead of the Christians, it is well that the task of making the former's writings available to the latter continued. Joannes Jacobi, professor in Montpellier, translated two ophthalmological treatises from Arabic into Catalan; unfortunately, the treatises which he translated were not by any means the most up-to-date; one of them was that of "Alcoatim" (XII-2), of which the Arabic original is lost (?). This requires further investigation.

New Latin treatises were written by Jean Molinier, De visus debilitate, and by Thomas of Sarepta, De conservatione oculorum. Thomas' treatise, however, is simply a part of his medical treatise Michi competit. This reminds us that eye troubles were discussed in most treatises dealing with medicine in general, or with surgery. Other eye doctors are known to us though no writings are ascribed to them. For example, one Bartolommeo di Guglielmo of Reggio had acquired a high reputation as an eye specialist in Bologna 1391; he was reputed to be a "uomo miracoloso" for the cure of all kinds of eye troubles, and he received from the senate an annual salary of twenty golden florins. At about the same time (1390), Giraldus de Cumba, born in Saint-Flour (Haute Auvergne, dépt. Cantal), was so famous in Lyon that patients came to him from Avignon. In 1383 Giraldus and his wife, Marie de l'Hôpital, tended the plague-stricken people of his native town; in 1390 he was attached to the service of Charles VI (Pansier 6, 110, 1908).[42a]

Jacopo Palmerio da Cingoli (near Iesi, in the march of Ancona) wrote a Libro delle affezioni oculari, largely derived from Benevenutus Grassus (XII-1). The MS of it which belonged to prince Buoncompagni in Rome was written in 1476–80 by Marco Sinzanogio of Sarnano (in the march of Macerata). This Palmerio is unknown; he may have been a century earlier than Sinzanogio. His work has been edited by Giuseppe Albertotti: Il libro delle affezioni oculari (Memorie della R. Accademia vol. 6, 86 p., Modena 1906); Trattamento della cataratta (Beiträge zur Augenheilkunde, Hirschberg Festschrift, 7 p., Leipzig 1905), extract from the Libro.

[42a] During proofreading I found an elaborate note on him under the heading Gérard de Lacombe in Wickersheimer (p. 184, 1936). Gerard died at Chalon-sur-Saône (Burgundy) in 1408 but was buried in Lyon. A Recepta ad oculos (Vatican, MS Lat. 460, fol. 183) by Girardus de Cumis may be ascribed to him. Cumis is probably a variant of Cumba, de Combe, Lacombe.

Two anonymous treatises in a fourteenth-century MS of the Arsenal, Paris (no. 1024), have been edited by Pierre Pansier (6, 122–54, 1908). The first, Tractatus de egritudinibus oculorum ex dictis sapientium veterum compilatis (p. 123–50), in 15 chapters, quotes Hippocrates, Democritos, Jibrīl ibn Bakhtyashū' (IX-1), Sābūr ibn Sahl (IX-2), al-Rāzī (IX-2), Isḥāq al-Isrā'īlī (X-1), and Ibn Sīnā (XI-1), but is derived mainly from the last named. The second, Tractatus de quibusdam dubiis circa dicta oculorum concurrentibus in quo octo queruntur (p. 151–54), quotes Plato, Aristotle, Galen, 'Alī ibn 'Abbās (X-2), Ibn Sīnā, and Ibn Rushd (XII-2). The second text is incomplete; it deals with four questions (out of eight): (1) De definitione oculi; (2) De naturali complexione oculi; (3) De motu oculorum et palpebrarum; (4) De essentia coloris oculorum. In spite of the lateness of the MS, both compilations might have been made in the thirteenth century.

The supreme test of the oculist's expertness was his treatment of the cataract. The sad story of John of Bohemia has already been told (p. 273); if a king could not fare better than that (he ended by being completely blind), what could humbler patients hope for? John's case, however, may have been hopeless. The Benedictine Gilles le Muisit was more fortunate. In 1351, being then 80 years old and blinded by cataracts in both eyes, he was operated by John of Mainz, who was passing through Tournai, and recovered his eyesight, though he was unable to read. The operation was admittedly of great difficulty, to be attempted only by eye surgeons especially trained ad hoc. Some itinerant quacks undertook it, but ran away as soon as they had cashed in. Jean de Tournemire tells us that "Medici cursores curant interdum albuginem cum sit cicatrix magna, et sunt decepti et fugiunt habita pecunia." That is possible, yet John of Mainz was apparently a medicus cursor, and he cured Gilles le Muisit, as much as such an old man could be cured. Quacks were not always as bad as they were painted; we may assume that some of them were pretty skillful and owed their success to their skillfulness. To remove an opaque lens was simply a matter of dexterity, not of learning. Valescus de Taranta's idea was that it was better for the regular surgeons to abandon the operation to the cursores than to risk their own reputation! (Pansier 6, 116).

Spectacles, invented toward the end of the thirteenth century (Introd. 2, 1024–27), were used sparingly in the fourteenth century. Bernard of Gordon was the first physician to speak of them, in his Lilium medicinae (1303). Guy de Chauliac in 1363 advised weak-sighted people to use them "et si ista non valent ad ocularios vitri aut berillorum est recurrendum." Thomas of Sarepta about the same time warned that eyeglasses might weaken the eyesight; this proves that they were actually used and that they were very imperfect. Valescus de Taranta tried vainly to explain their action.

As to the wearers of eyeglasses, we can mention cardinal Ugone di Provenza in 1352 (according to the fresco of Treviso), Petrarca in 1364, Jeanne d'Evreux before 1372 (she was the queen of Charles IV, marrying him in 1324, surviving him 43 years, and dying in 1371). In 1372 her "béricle encerné en manière de lunette" was appraised at 20 francs, a large sum of money; it was probably adorned with jewels. The list might probably be extended, but not very much.

For more than five centuries the Muslim eye doctors had been superior to the Christian ones; their last great textbook, the Kitāb al-'umda al-kuḥlīya fī-l-amrāḍ al-baṣarīya, was written about this time by Ṣadaqa ibn Ibrāhīm al-Shādhilī. This served to embalm Arabic ophthalmology, but had no effect on Western science, as it remained untranslated. Western ophthalmology was the development of the earlier Arabic science (ninth to eleventh centuries); from the twelfth century on, we may say that Arabic and Western ophthalmology developed independently though from the same trunk. The Arabic branches were richer in the thirteenth and fourteenth centuries than the Western, but after that they withered and died out, and from the sixteenth century on, whatever progress there was was purely Western, very slow at first, then faster and faster.

An empirical school of ophthalmology was founded in Japan about the middle of the fourteenth century by Majima Seigan, and the school was called after him the Majima-ryū. Its methods were handed down orally and manually to other members, natural or adopted, of the Majima family, and remained unpublished for two centuries (until 1558).

11. *Various other diseases*

Treatises on the gout were written in French by Jean Le Fèvre and in Latin by Heinrich Thopping, Giovanni da Ravenna (the first), and Giovanni da Noto. Assuming that the last mentioned is identical with Giovanni Aurispa, the two Italian authors were humanists. Gout was ever a disorder of sedentary people. These treatises illustrate the relative prevalence of gout in those days, but we cannot expect to find in them any worth-while knowledge, for the study of arthritism was absolutely beyond the horizon of fourteenth-century science; we are only beginning to understand it in our own days.

Stones in the bladder or the kidneys cause such excruciating pains that the subject could never be ignored, even by people who avoided doctors in almost every other case. No wonder it attracted the attention of many physicians from early days on, cf. Suśruta, Ammonios the Lithotomist (I-2 B.C.)—mark the name!—, Celsus (I-1), etc.; al-Rāzī (IX-2) wrote a treatise ad hoc, and his example was often followed. The subject is dealt with in one of the treatises of the Breslau Salernitan corpus (c. 1160-70; Introd. 2, 434); the Celsus method of operation was practiced even in Iceland, by Rafn Sveinbjörnsson (XIII-1), and it was discussed in every surgical book of the Middle Ages and in many medical ones. Special treatises were written by Jean de Tournemire and Joannes Jacobi.[43]

Jacob Ẓarfati of Avignon wrote a little treatise on vertigo.

The earliest references to the sleeping sickness concern events of the year 1373/74 in the Mandingo country. Accounts of that new sickness (new in medical literature) appear in the writings of Ibn Khaldūn and al-Qalqashandī.

The insanity of Charles VI of France, the Well-beloved, filled his familiars with consternation, and many physicians were consulted, notably Guillaume de Harcigny, but in vain. The madness began on August 1-5, 1392, when he was 24 years of age, and lasted thirty years, until his death in 1422. During those thirty years the king had forty-two remissions or moments of lucidity, but even during those moments he was incapable of attention. He had lost his memory, and the death of his relatives or friends left him completely indifferent. His was a state of utter mental confusion. He was the victim of arthritic heredity on his father's side and

[43] For more details see Ernest Desnos: Histoire de l'urologie (Paris 1914; Isis 2, 466). The frequency of stone troubles in mediaeval times was probably caused by the diet, which was often rich in calcium and always poor in vitamin A. Jack Cecil Drummond and Anne Wilbraham: The Englishman's food (p. 97-99, London 1939; Isis 33, 300).

of vesanic heredity on his mother's side. His mother, Jeanne de Bourbon (1338–78), had a fit of insanity which lasted almost a whole year in 1373. When he was 24 he had typhoid fever, and psychical troubles occurred during his convalescence. It is possible that that fever broke whatever power was still in him to resist a pernicious inheritance. The madness was apparently provoked two months after that illness by a sunstroke. It is not surprising that the physicians called in to heal him were helpless.

J. Saltel: La folie du roi Charles VI (Montpellier thesis no. 732, 66 p., Toulouse 1907), courtesy of Army Medical Library.

12. *Leprosy and cagots*

See chapter I.

13. *Famines*

The end of the fourteenth century was a period of calamity in Hindūstān. In the north, the death of the last sulṭān of the Taghlaqī dynasty (capital Dehlī), Fīrūz Shāh, in September 1388, inaugurated a time of anarchy and confusion. In 1398 Tīmūr-ī-lang crossed the Indus, invaded India, and sacked Dehlī and other cities. It is said that 100,000 prisoners were slain in cold blood. Tīmūr had no intention of remaining in the country, he meant simply to plunder it, and take with him to Samarqand as much booty as possible, as well as useful prisoners, such as desirable women and skilled artisans. He went away via Meerut, Hardwār, and the Panjāb, "leaving anarchy, famine and pestilence behind him."

At that time the Bahmanī dynasty (1347–1526) was ruling the Deccan. In 1396 a terrible famine broke out in Mahārāshtra, and according to the legend lasted twelve years (the same legend obtained concerning the famine of Bombay 1200). As far as can be judged from very incomplete reports, it was one of the most terrible famines of India, even of the world, comparable to the Hindu famines of 1596, 1660–61, 1803–4, 1896–1900. It is traditionally called the famine of Durgā Devī.[44] This happened during the rule of the eighth sulṭān, Tāj al-dīn Firūz Shāh (1397–1421).

There is a considerable literature anent Hindu famines, but the bulk of it concerns modern ones. It does not follow, as some uncritical people have concluded, that the modern famines were worse than the mediaeval ones. They are better known, for they have been actually investigated, whereas the mediaeval calamities are only known in an oblique manner. Nobody then bothered to investigate, and if the old salāṭīn had known the whole truth they would have forbidden the publication of it. On the contrary, with regard to the famines of 1862 and later we have a whole series of official documents, reports by scientific-minded investigators, parliamentary blue books, famine codes, etc. It is impossible to measure the calamity which occurred in 1396 and following years, but it was not for nothing that the Hindu people gave it the grim name of Durgā Devī.

For bibliography, see corresponding note in chapter I. Yao Shan-yu: Flood and drought data in the T'u-shu chi-ch'êng and the Ch'ing shih kao (Harvard journal of Asiatic studies 8, 214–26, 1944; Isis 36, 47), listing Chinese floods from 1368 to

[44] Devī is the mother goddess, the supreme power of the universe from the point of view of Shakta Hinduism. The word Durgā (meaning unattainable) characterizes the goddess in her baleful aspect.

1390 (and from 1518 to 1866) and Chinese droughts from 1368 to 1376 (and from 1515 to 1865).

14. *Veterinary medicine*

The only treatise on veterinary medicine written during this period in the West was the Italian Mascalcia by Dino Dini, completed in 1359. It embodied the experience of three generations of Florentine farriers.

The incunabula treatises on the veterinary art probably represent older Germanic traditions than their date suggests. There are two such treatises, both in German. The first, Arznei der Rosse, is ascribed to "Meister Albrecht keiser Friderichs schmid und marstaller von Constantinopel." If we could accept that statement, the text would go back to the thirteenth century, assuming that Frederick II of Hohenstaufen (XIII-1) is meant, but that ascription is made questionable by its very wording. Sudhoff came across MSS many decades earlier than the princeps; the text might date from the second half of the fourteenth century. At any rate, it was very popular. The princeps (Augsburg 1485) was followed by at least 6 other incunabula editions, Augsburg 1490, Strassburg 1495, Ulm 1498, 1499, 1500, Nürnberg 1500, and it continued to be reprinted until 1666. Sudhoff (nos. 90–95, 1908); Klebs (no. 28). The other text, Pferdearznei-Büchlein, was printed in Erfurt 1500 (Klebs no. 756).

The Muslim traditions of that art were represented by the Arabic treatise Ins al-malā bi-waḥsh al-falā of the Egyptian Muḥammad ibn Mangalī, and no less than three Turkish treatises: (1) A veterinary Turkish treatise written c. 1361–1400 exists in MS in the Topkapı sarayı of Istanbul; (2) another, Baytarname, is in the Qonya museum, ascribed oddly enough to Tīmūr Lang; (3) the treatise on falconry of Maḥmūd ibn Muḥammad al-Bārjīnī contains as usual veterinary chapters.

This abundance of Turkish materials is remarkable but not surprising. By the way, the Arabic treatise itself was probably written by a Turk (of whom there were many in the Mamlūk service), for the name Mangalī is not Arabic, but Turkish (or Persian). The Turkish veterinary treatises constituted the latest wave of Muslim interest in the subject, and their existence naturally coincided with the birth of Turkish literature. The need of new Arabic treatises could not be great, for copies of various excellent ones were available in every private or public library. On the contrary, as the Turks were trying to emancipate themselves from Arabic influences for every nonreligious purpose, it was natural enough that they should want and produce Turkish texts on veterinary medicine, a subject almost as important as medicine itself, yet often abandoned to men less learned than the regular physicians, and less able than these to understand technical explanations in Arabic.

15. *Regimina et consilia*

A complete list of regimina and consilia written in the second half of the fourteenth century would probably be very long. This volume refers to a sufficient number of representative examples, which we shall now briefly enumerate:

The Consilia of Iacopo da Arquà, the Regimen sanitatis of Pietro Tossignano, the Consilia of Antonio Cermisone and of Ugo Benzi and the latter's Trattato utilissimo circa la conservazione della sanità (princeps, Milano 1481), the Consilia of Pierre d'Auxon and Guillaume Boucher, the Regimen for pope Innocent VI of Heinrich Thopping, the clinical observations of Tilmann, the Vitae vivendae ratio of Gallus de Strahov, the very elaborate Regimen sanitatis of Sigismund Albic, the treatise on bloodletting written in Czech by Christian of Prachatice, etc. It is probable that this list might be lengthened without using other volumes than this one.

The Consilia of Taddeo Alderotti, still unpublished in their totality, had inaugurated a new type of medical literature which has been investigated by Dean Putnam Lockwood: Ugo Benzi (Isis 33, 95; 34, 215). Lockwood shows that the redaction of isolated consilia, each discussing the case of a definite patient and prescribing proper care and regimen, led to the publication of collections of consilia selected so as to cover the whole medical field and arranged in systematic order a capite ad calces. Lockwood investigated the consilia of Alderotti (XIII-2), Gentile da Foligno (XIV-1), Ugo Benzi (d. 1439), Antonio Cermisone (d. 1441), Bartolommeo Montagnana (d. c. 1460), Gianmatteo Ferrari da Gradi (d. 1472), Baverio de Baverii (d. 1480). He concluded that Benzi was the first to compile a systematic collection. Such collections attained considerable success and very soon attracted the attention of the early printers. The first editions occurred in the following order: Montagnana, Padua, May 1476 (Klebs no. 689); Cermisone, Brescia, September 1476 (Klebs no. 266); Ferrari da Gradi, Pavia 1480 (Klebs no. 393); Benzi, Bologna 1482 (Klebs no. 1001); Gentile da Foligno, Pavia 1488? (Klebs no. 453). The order is curious; some of the latest collections were printed first, and the earliest, last. The Consilia of Cermisone and Montagnana were printed together in Venice 1497. The vogue of these collections continued in the sixteenth century. The titles of the early editions illustrate the systematic purpose, e.g., the two earliest printed editions; Montagnana's is entitled Opus de omnibus egritudinibus communibus et propriis; Cermisone's, more clearly, Tabula ... contra omnes fere egritudines a capite usque ad pedes consilia (Osler nos. 111, 116, 1923).

Additional information may be found in the following papers:

Karl Sudhoff: Ein Monats-Regimen (AGM 2, 434–36, 1909); Diätetische Verordnung für einen zur Wassersucht Neigenden (mit chronischer Nephritis Befafteten?) ahus dem 15. Jahrh. (AGM 3, 79–80, 1909); Ärztliche Regimina für Land- und Seereisen (AGM 4, 263–81, 1910). Hugh Cameron Gillies: Regimen sanitatis. A Gaelic MS of the early sixteenth century or perhaps older from the vade mecum of the famous Macbeaths, physicians to the lord of Isles and the kings of Scotland for several centuries (140 p., 7 pl., Glasgow 1911); according to Sudhoff (Mitt. 11, 284), this regimen dates from the fifteenth century or even the fourteenth. Hugo Faber: Eine Diätetik aus Montpellier, Sanitatis conservator, dem Ende des 14. Jahrh. entstammend und Tractatus medicus de comestione et digestione vel Regimen sanitatis benannt (Diss. Leipzig, 23 p., 1921; Isis 7, 193). Gerhard Hohlfeld: Ein liber de dietis aus dem Ende des 14. Jahrh. in lateinischen Versen (Diss. Leipzig, 16 p., 1922; Isis 5, 502). Ernest Wickersheimer: Faits cliniques observés à Strasbourg et à Haslach en 1362 et suivis de formules de remèdes (Bull. de la Société française d'histoire de la médecine 33, 69–92, 1939).

One might also consult some incunabula on the use of wine, mead, and beer (Klebs nos. 1038, 1046, 927). Tractatus de vino eius proprietate (Rome? 1480, Italy 1480, Padua 1483, Rome 1495); Von allen Gebrechen des Weines (Erfurt 1497); Spruch von Wein, Met und Bier (Heidelberg 1495).

The mention of a Czech treatise on bloodletting above would justify the mention of many others. (See section 5 on physiology, above.) Here again the line is difficult to draw between a regimen discussing that method incidentally, and a treatise ostensibly devoted to that method yet discussing also the conservation of health in a more general way. Bloodletting was applied universally, by well people to remain healthy and by ill ones to restore their health. Almanacs and regulations were published for that very purpose, witness countless MS copies and early prints such as the Aderlass Büchlein (Strassburg 1473), the Aderlass Regeln (Basel 1470), and various prognostications in Latin, German, French, Dutch, English (Klebs nos. 9, 10, 808). The dial of the great clock of Strassburg cathedral (1352) included a human figure, indicating the time of bloodletting in various parts of the body. There was nothing incongruous in that, for people wanted to know the time to bleed themselves, as well as the time for eating or praying. It is not very surprising that the earliest Yiddish text that has come to us is a short tract on bloodletting; it was written in Cologne 1396.

This reminds us that the Jews shared that idea with the Christians. A treatise on bloodletting was written in Latin by Moses of Roquemaure, and a treatise on foods and drugs, in Arabic, by Joshua ben Joseph II ha-Lorqi. The first of these treatises is available only in Spanish translation, the second in Hebrew.

A Persian treatise on sexual hygiene was translated into Turkish by one Ṣalāḥ al-dīn. Finally, we owe to Chia Ming special advice for the attainment of old age. He preached by deed as well as by precept, for he was already a centenarian when he offered a copy of his book to the Son of Heaven.

16. *Balneology*

The Italian tradition was continued by Giacomo and Giovanni de' Dondi, father and son, who were interested in the hot springs of Abano;[44a] by Francesco da Siena, who studied the baths of Puteoli and many other places; by Pietro da Tossignano, who studied the baths of Bòrmio; by Ugolino da Montecatini, who investigated the baths of Lucca (as had been done before him by Gentile da Foligno) and composed a general survey of the Italian baths, De balneorum Italiae proprietatibus ac virtutibus. We may say that Western balneology is an Italian creation; in this respect at least the Italians were true to their Roman inheritance.

Some Italian spas were already functioning, though the earliest regulations known to me are a bit later. They concern the baths of Aquario, near Reggio nell' Emilia. Karl Sudhoff: Brunnenregeln für Kurärzte einer italienischen Heilquelle aus der Mitte des 15. Jahrh. (Zeitschrift für Balneologie 8, 94–97, Nov. 1915; Mitt. 15, 171).

That Italian tradition was brought to the French people by Richard Eudes, who translated the De balneis puteolanis ascribed to Peter of Eboli (XII-2) into French. As is so often the case, he did not bring the latest fruits of that tradition, but one of the earliest.

A work of an entirely different kind was written by a Languedocian Jew, established in Seville, Moses of Roquemaure alias Juan de Aviñon. Continuing the Hippocratic tradition of climatology, first explained in the *περὶ ἀέρων ὑδάτων τόπων*, he wrote Sevillana medicina, wherein he discussed the different climates of Seville and of the country around. It is curious to note that this point of view appealed especially to Spaniards (or people living in Spain). This may be explained partly by the fact that the Hispanic peninsula is full of geographical and climatic contrasts and paradoxes.

[44a] Theodoric the Great, king of the Ostrogoths from 475 to 526 (Introd. 1, 438), had already taken the trouble to organize the thermae of Abano. See the letter which Cassiodorus (VI-1) wrote in his name to the architect Aloisius. Thomas Hodgkin: The letters of Cassiodorus, being a condensed translation of the Variae epistolae (p. 191–92, London 1886).

17. *Pharmacy*

The most interesting treatise written in the West was probably the De reductione medicamentorum ad actum by Tommaso del Garbo.

Giacomo de' Dondi tried to understand the properties of mineral waters, and he was the first to suggest the extraction of their mineral contents for medical purposes. Gallus de Strahov wrote a treatise on medicinal waters and their properties. It is possible that the incunabula Eaux artificielles (princeps, Vienna before 1485; 9 incunabula ed.; Klebs nos. 358, 150.8) continued that tradition.

Incunabula sheets dealing with special drugs may also be of earlier origin than the printing dates, or the mere fact of being printed, indicate. For example, consider sheets advertising the virtues of oleum de spica (alias balsam Mariae Magdalenae), petroleum, oak mistletoe. Karl Sudhoff: Die heilsamen Eigenschaften des Magdalenenbalsams. Ein Einblattdruck aus den letzten Jahren des 15. Jahrh. (AGM 1, 388–90, 1908), giving the original German text; Zwei deutsche Reklamezettel zur Empfehlung von Arzneimitteln, Petroleum und Eichenmistel, gedruckt um 1500 (AGM 3, 397–402, 1910), German text of both; Handschriftliches vom Eichenmistel (AGM 4, 313–14, 1910), MS text of the fourteenth century concerning mistletoe, the text half Latin half German, "De visco quercino, von dem eichen mistel"; Ein kurzer Traktat über therapeutische Eisen-Anwendung (AGM 6, 80, 1912), De virtute ferri in medicina, out of a fifteenth-century MS, Cod. lat. monacensis 4394.

The sheet advertising petroleum was printed in Geneva 1480, not 1500 (Klebs no. 745). Arnold C. Klebs: Une annonce médicale de pétrole en 1480 (Bull. de la Société française d'histoire de la médecine 16, 391–96, 1922), French original text and facsimile. That mineral oil, which was recommended for internal and external use in all kinds of troubles, came from a mountain called Montesible, belonging to the duke of Ferrara. Italian sources of petroleum were described by Pierre Belon (1517–64): De admirabili operum antiquorum et rerum suspiciendarum praestantia (Paris 1553); one of those sources is called Monte Zibito, and this may be identical with Montesible of the Genevese advertisement, dated 1480.

For pharmaceutical usages see Alexandre Germain: L'apothicairerie à Montpellier (Mémoires de la Société d'archéologie de Montpellier, 72 p., 1882). Hermann Schöppler: Eine Apothekenvisitation zu Regensburg 1392 (Bericht der Deutschen pharmazeutischen Gesellschaft p. 314 f., 1915; Mitt. 15, 70).

Much attention was paid to poisons, not as today for their healing properties in very small doses, but rather for malevolent purposes. Poisons afforded one of the best ways of getting rid of one's enemies, and clever people could do this without falling under suspicion. The poisons might be administered in massive, lethal doses, but the "doctors" had more faith in the frequent repetition of very small doses; the effects then resembled those of natural diseases, and foul play might remain unsuspected. Powerful people, however, who were ready to treat their enemies with poison, were naturally afraid of meeting with foul play themselves. Their fears were so great that when their body was suddenly assailed by violent pains (say, nephritic colics, or acute appendicitis), they were often led to believe that they had been poisoned. It is probable that many people suffered capital punishment because they were accused of having poisoned men whose death or whose pains had been caused, not by any external poison, but by some kind of acute disease. The study of poisons involved the discovery of proper antidotes for each of them.

The most notable poisoner of this time was the Bohemian doctor Jean de Grandville, who was in the service of the king of Hungary, then of the emperor, and finally of Louis II de Bourbon. Treatises on poisons were composed by Francesco Casini, physician to six popes, Christophorus de Honestis, and Guglielmo da Marra.

There are many archaeological witnesses of the criminal use of poisons in the Middle Ages and of the precautions which men in power were obliged to take against that danger. For example, the popes of Avignon[44b] and other great lords used special cups or instruments to try foods and beverages offered to them (this was called the proba or probamentum, preuve). One of those instruments, named in French "languier" or "anguier," might be in the form of a tree in gold or silver, from the branches of which hung various "pierres d'épreuve." The "pierres d'épreuve" most commonly used were the so-called langues de serpent (hence probably the name languier), shark teeth, flint arrow points; strange stones, such as crapaud stone, noble serpentine, pieces of agate or jasper (bloodstone), haematite; pieces of the horn of unicorn or of rhinoceros, etc. When dishes were brought into the dining hall, they were placed on a sideboard near the languier; a chamberlain would dip the touchstones into each dish. It was believed that the presence of poison would cause a change of color in the touchstone and could thus be detected. The dish was then tasted by an official taster and finally brought to the table. It is clear that these precautions were futile, even the tasting, except in the case of poisons meant to cause immediate death. John XXII was very fond of such touchstones, and king Philip V had given him two "languiers," the one in gold, enriched with precious stones, the other in silver, from which eleven serpentine tongues were hanging. The duke of Berry had four horns of unicorn, one of which had been given him by the pope (Brun p. 207, 1928).

The main history of toxicology is Louis Lewin: Die Gifte in der Weltgeschichte (612 p., Berlin 1920; Isis 4, 371–73).

Ṭodros de Cavaillon wrote an antidotary partly in Hebrew, partly in Latin; another Provençal Ṭodros (or is it the same one?), Ṭodros ben Moses Yomṭob, translated into Hebrew the treatise of Arnold of Villanova dealing with digestives and laxatives.

Pharmacopoeias were composed in Persian by Zain al-'Aṭṭār, in Arabic by Muḥammad ibn Maḥmūd al-Shīrwānī, in Sanskrit by Madanapāla, in Japanese by Yūrin.

18. *Medical teaching and profession*

Medical teaching and the medical profession were already so well organized in many places of Western Europe by the middle of the fourteenth century that further progress became a matter of course. The two leading faculties were probably those of Montpellier and of Paris. Montpellier's was already more than two centuries old (Introd. 2, 352), and its very position caused it to be international. It was connected with Aragon and Majorca, with France, with Navarre, and was sufficiently close to Avignon and the comtat Venaissin on the one hand and to Italy on the other. Moreover, Montpellier had succeeded Salerno as a mixing place of

[44b] Not simply the popes of Avignon. As late as 1580 when Montaigne was in Rome he attended a mass celebrated by Gregory XIII and saw him use an instrument (fistola) enabling him to drink from the chalice without fear of poison. Journal de voyage de Montaigne, edited by Louis Lautrey (p. 210, Paris 1906).

Muslim, Jewish, and Christian knowledge. By this time anti-Semitism was strong, but the mixture had been completed. We have already given some idea of the medical teaching available in Montpellier (ch. I, p. 247–48), and there is an abundance of documents illustrating the life of teachers and students,[45] not only in the archives of that university, but in many other European libraries. For example, Wickersheimer found in the municipal library of Lübeck the MSS brought back by one Heinrich Lamme of Lübeck, who had studied medicine in Montpellier at the beginning of the fifteenth century. Lamme had copied with his own hand treatises by Arnold of Villanova, Bernard of Gordon, Gerald de Solo, Joannes Jacobi, Jean de Tournemire—presumably the very texts which he had been expected to con. That collection also included a discourse on medical astrology recited on the occasion of his reception[46] as a bachelor in medicine. Its incipit is a kind of program, "Celum tripliciter influit: motu, lumine, et influentia." Hippocrates, Galen, and Ibn Sīnā are quoted, as well as Aristotle and Boetius, but the tone is scholastic rather than medical. Ernest Wickersheimer: Le discours de réception d'un bachelier en médecine montpelliérain au début du XVe siècle (Bull. de la Société française d'histoire de la médecine 9, 245–51, 1910), with Latin text.

The faculty of medicine of Paris was younger than Montpellier's, less famous, and less important, yet its prestige was growing fast. Rashdall's statement (1, 435, 1936) "It did not attract students from distant lands" is erroneous. The earliest statutes date only from c. 1270–74, but the school was international from the beginning. How could it fail to be so? The university of which it was a part recruited not only its students, but its teachers from everywhere. One of the earliest medical teachers in Paris was an Italian "refugee," Lanfranchi (XIII-2), who had been banished from Milano in 1290 by Matteo Visconti I, il Grande. In 1340, when the lord of Padua, Ubertino da Carrara, fell ill he consulted Gentile da Foligno, professor in Perugia (he did not like to consult local physicians, who might be tempted to poison their beloved duce). Gentile advised Ubertino to send a dozen Paduan students to Paris for medical studies, and this was done. Mind you, there was a medical school in Padua, and two foundations for poor medical students had already been established before 1388. There were also famous physicians in Padua, such as Iacopo da Arquà, Giacomo and Giovanni de' Dondi, Giovanni, Marsiglio, Galeazzo, and Bartolommeo da Santa Sofia, Antonio Cermisone. On the other hand, we have the notebook of a German graduate student, "quidam magister de Almania," who followed the clinical discussions of Guillaume Boucher and Pierre d'Auxon in Paris (c. 1398–1408). These examples might easily be multiplied.

Ernest Wickersheimer: Les secrets et les conseils de maître Guillaume Boucher et de ses confrères. Contribution à l'histoire de la médecine à Paris vers 1400 (Bull. de la Société française d'histoire de la médecine 8, 199–305, 1909). Gustavo Tanfani: Antonio, Uguccione ed Enrigetto da Rio, medici padovani "doctores parisienses" (Rivista di storia delle scienze, anno 30, 49–55, 1939).

[45] Alexandre Germain: La médecine arabe et la médecine grecque à Montpellier (40 p., 1879); L'Ecole de médecine de Montpellier (152 p., 1880), both memoirs reprinted from the Mémoires de la Société archéologique de Montpellier. The same A. Germain (1809–87) began the edition of the Cartulaire de l'Université de Montpellier (quarto, 2 vols., Montpellier 1890–1912). Vol. 1 (800 p., ill.) includes Germain's history of 1880, and documents dating from 1181 to 1400.

[46] Or the reception of a fellow student. The document is neither signed nor dated.

By the middle of the century various efforts were already being made to protect the medical profession against interlopers. For example John II the Good, king of France from 1350 to 1364, published in December 1352 an ordinance against the illicit practice of medicine at Paris (Thorndike, p. 235–36, 1944).

Many of the medical writers of this period are already identified as professors of medicine. Those who adorned the faculty of Padua, the Dondi and the Santa Sofia, have already been named. In Perugia, there were Gentile da Foligno (d. 1348), Franciscus de Gianellis, Tommaso del Garbo, Francesco da Siena. In Pavia, Syllanus de Nigris, Ugo Benzi. In Florence, Francischino de Collignano. In Pisa, Ugolino da Montecatini. In Bologna, Christophorus de Honestis, Pietro da Tossignano, Jacopo della Torre, Pietro d'Argelata. In Montpellier, Bernard Alberti, Joannes Jacobi, Jean de Tournemire. In Paris, Le Lièvre, Guillaume Boucher, Pierre d'Auxon. In Prague, Heinrich Ribbenicz. The same men often taught in many universities, and thus medical ideas and practices were, or at any rate might be, diffused with relative speed.

Other physicians attained some sort of celebrity because of royal patronage. Pierre Fromont was in the service of Jean le Bon; Joannes Jacobi, of Charles V; Guillaume de Harcigny, Guillaume Boucher, Guillaume le Touzé, and Pierre d'Auxon, of Charles VI. Guillaume Boucher also attended the duke of Burgundy; Le Lièvre, the duke of Orléans; Jean de Grandville, the duke of Bourbon; Jean Molinier and Pierre de Nadilz, the king of Navarre; Heinrich Thopping, the count palatine of the Rhine; Thomas of Sarepta, the bishop of Breslau; Niccolò da Udine and Galeazzo da Santa Sofia, the dukes of Austria; Tommaso del Garbo and Marsiglio da Santa Sofia, the Visconti of Milano; Iacopo da Arquà, the king of Hungary; Guido da Bagnolo, the king of Cyprus; Bendig 'Ain, the queen of Naples.

Some of our medical authors were imperial physicians: Gallus de Strahov and Giovanni de' Dondi attended Charles IV; Albic attended Wenzel and Sigismund.

A few others were town physicians, that is, were retained by a town to practice there, given a stipend, and charged with certain municipal duties, especially in time of epidemics. Some such appointment had already been made in favor of Ugo Borgognoni (XIII-1) by the city of Bologna, and that initiative was apparently followed, according to the caprice of circumstances, by other cities of Italy, Germany, and France during the thirteenth and fourteenth centuries. Thus in the second half of the fourteenth century Dionisio II Colle was physician of Belluno, and Ugolini da Montecatini, of Pistoia and Pescia. Such appointments, however, remained very rare until the following century. German medico-historians (Johann Hermann Baas 1876; Theodor Puschmann 1889) have claimed it was the emperor Sigismund (ruled 1410–37) who established the town physician or physicus as a general imperial institution, in 1426. This so-called Reformatio Sigismundi is a myth. The appointment of German physici did not assume any importance before the end of the fifteenth century; their existence at that time is proved by statements occurring in various incunabula.

Karl Sudhoff: Hat Kaiser Sigmund eine Verordnung über die Anstellung von Stadtärzten erlassen? (Mitt. 11, 119–30, 1912). Paul Diepgen: Bemerkung... (Mitt. 13, 309–10, 1914).

For the study of the medical profession in Germany, one may still consult the books of Johann Hermann Baas: Grundriss der Geschichte der Medizin und des heilenden Standes (924 p., ill., Stuttgart 1876), revised edition Englished by Henry Ebenezer Handerson (1180 p., New York 1889); Die geschichtliche Entwicklung des ärztlichen Standes und der medizinischen Wissenschaften (492 p., ill., Berlin 1896). Theodor Puschmann: Geschichte des medizinischen Unterrichts (530 p., Leipzig 1889), Englished by Evan H. Hare (London 1891). Alfons Fischer: Geschichte des deutschen Gesundheitswesens (vol. 1, 364 p., Berlin 1933).

In the monumental work of vicomte Georges d'Avenel: Histoire économique de la propriété, des salaires, des denrées et de tous les prix en général de 1200 à 1800 (7 vols., Paris 1894–1926), we find (4, 54, 1898) a list of thirteen French physicians and surgeons enjoying annual salaries; nine of them were employed by princes, one by a great lady, one by a bishop; only one could be called a town physician; he was retained in 1338 in Marseille to visit the hospital at least once each day. For more information on the medical profession in France, see the same volume, p. 49–61, 1898; 5, 154–97, 1909; very little of it, however, concerns the fourteenth century.

For Italian conditions see Raffaele Ciasca: L'arte dei medici e speziali nella storia e nel commercio fiorentino dal secolo XII al XV (820 p., Florence 1927). The Florentine profession was reorganized in 1349, and somewhat democratized in 1378–82. Ciasca's book, based on a rich documentation, is unfortunately unindexed.[47]

Finally, we shall meet in these pages a good number of papal physicians. To be appointed archiater to a pope was indeed a considerable distinction, medical and social, and to be consulted occasionally by him or members of the curia was a step up on the ladder leading to that appointment. Francesco Casini was employed by six popes, from Urban V to Alexander V. Clement VI was attended by Chauliac; Innocent VI, by Chauliac; Urban V, by Chauliac and Joannes Jacobi; Gregory XI, by Jean de Tournemire and Joannes Jacobi; the antipope Clement VII, by Jean de Tournemire, Joannes Jacobi, and Pierre d'Auxon; Benedict XIII, by the renegade Geronimo de Santa Fé, etc. It was already a distinction to be attached, like Raymond Chalmel de Viviers, to the court of a cardinal.

For more information on papal physicians, see chapter I, page 241, note 1. Marini's work of 1784 could easily be amplified and corrected by means of a number of documents published or calendared since his time. For example, two documents edited by Karl Heinrich Schäfer: Das Testament eines Würzburger Arztes an der päpstlichen Kurie vom Jahre 1348 (AGM 30, 295–300, 1938); Eine römische Chirurgen-Rechnung vom Jahre 1369 (AGM 31, 76–80, 1938). The physicians to whom these documents refer are Albert von Würzburg and Roberto da Senigallia (in Ancona), whom the French called Robert de Chingale. Albert bequeathed some money to the German brotherhood of Avignon and to the Teutonic Knights. Robert was a papal guardsman (serviens armorum pape), barber to Urban V and Gregory XI, surgeon to the latter. According to his account, he had taken charge in 1369 of 13 patients, pilgrims and clerics, at the pope's expense.

The papal, imperial, royal physicians were, then as now, the exception; even the medical authors were, then as now, exceptional. The average physician did not write and, in spite of his merit and devotion, was bound to fall into oblivion. Moreover, there were, then as now, all kinds of physicians, good, bad, and indifferent; some rare ones were devoted to the point of sacrifice; at the other end of the scale, some others were greedy to the point of crime. The student of medical manners and mores will find pertinent details in contemporary literature, e.g., in the French writings of Eustache Deschamps. Archival documents, of which relatively few

[47] The author is indebted for this paragraph and the two preceding ones to Dr. Owsei Temkin, of Baltimore (letter dated July 27, 1943).

have been exploited by medical historians, may reveal more details. The example of Jacopo di Coluccino of Lucca has already been discussed.

As usual, publications relative to the fifteenth century are far more numerous than those relative to the fourteenth, and one may have to consult the former in order to obtain some light on the conditions obtaining at a somewhat earlier time. For example, Sudhoff has published a number of documents wherein physicians advertise their presence in a place in order to draw customers; this touches the field of quackery, though it would be foolish to assume that an itinerant doctor, obliged to announce his arrival in various towns, was necessarily a charlatan, or that a sedentary doctor having a house of his own was necessarily honest. Things are not as simple as that.

Karl Sudhoff: Entwurf zu Reklamezetteln des Meisters Pancratius Sommer von Hirschberg über Augenkuren (AGM 4, 157, 1910), original Latin and German advertisements of the middle of the fifteenth century; Vier Niederlassungsankündigungen von Ärzten aus dem 15. Jahrh. (AGM 6, 309-12, 1912), the first advertisements written in Latin and German c. 1400 by a doctor called Wilhelmus practicus de dei gratia in physice [scientia im]butus, the others a little later by a Franciscan called Bernhard Wittepennig; Kurpfuscher, Ärzte und Stadtbehörden am Ende des 15. Jahrh. (AGM 8, 98-124, 1914).

Forensic documents may throw light on medical ideas and manners. Here are two examples: Karl Sudhoff: Ein Regulativ zur gerichtsärztlichen Begutachtung männlicher Impotenz bei Ehescheidungsklagen aus der Mitte des 15. Jahrh. (AGM 8, 89-97, 1914), Latin text entitled Examen et processus impotentum et frigidorum. Alberto Chiappelli: Di un singolare procedimento medico-legale tenuto in Pistoia nell'anno 1375 per supposizione d'infante (Rivista di storia delle scienze p. 129-35, 1919).

19. *Faith healing*

In the Christian world, sick people, especially those whose illness was apparently incurable, had far more hope in saints than in doctors. There were saints specialized in almost every disease, and among the innumerable places of pilgrimage, there were a good many which attracted patients of a certain kind, say the blind or the lame or the insane. If intelligent physicians had been in attendance in those places they might have collected medical observations, as was done by Greek physicians in the temples dedicated to Asclepios or as is done by modern physicians in Lourdes. Unfortunately such physicians were not available, and the faithful had neither conscious need nor thought of them. One of the most popular healing saints was the Languedocian St. Roch of Montpellier (d. c. 1327), who had become St. Sebastian's powerful assistant in the protection of his suppliants from the plague.[48]

The processes of canonization contain a large number of clinical accounts, the analysis of which would be valuable, if not for the history of medicine, at least for the history of diseases. Consider the case of Pierre de Luxembourg, born at Ligny 1369, a son of Gui I of Luxembourg, count of Ligny; he became a priest, finally bishop of Metz and cardinal. His austerities undermined his health; he was treated by Blaise de Forlivio, and by a Jew called Vital. He died at Villeneuve-lès-Avignon on July 2, 1387, before completing his eighteenth year. Though he had performed no miracles during his lifetime, he performed no end of them for the faithful who

[48] For the understanding of miracles in general see J. A. MacCulloch (ERE 8, 676-90, 1916), and A. Michel (DTC 10, 1798-1859, 1929), defining Catholic doctrine on the subject.

visited his tomb or besought his intercession. By October 4, 1388, 1,964 miracles were already credited to him, but only 178 of them were claimed in his process of beatification, when 90 witnesses gave evidence in his favor. These miraculous interventions were of many kinds—deliverance of captives, protection against bandits, recovery of lost or stolen goods, preservation in shipwreck or fire; a good many are medical. Blessed Pierre of Luxembourg resurrected 13 people (2 who had died suddenly, 4 drowned, 2 asphyxiated, 3 stillborn infants, 2 cases of fever). According to Wickersheimer's analysis, he miraculously cured head wounds, mental diseases, St. John's evil (epilepsy), paralysis (14 cases), eye troubles, deafness, epistaxis (nosebleed), lip and mouth troubles, dumbness, angina, tumor of the breast (remarkable deposition by Jean de Tournemire), haematemesis (blood vomiting), colics, parasitic worms, dropsy, male impotence, barrenness, uterine haemorrhage, hernias (9 cases), fevers, gout, leprosy, St. Anthony's fire (erysipelas or ergotism), scabies (itch), etc.

Acta sanctorum, Julii tomus primus (p. 486–628, Antwerp 1719). Ernest Wickersheimer: Les guérisons miraculeuses du cardinal Pierre de Luxembourg, 1387–90 (Congrès international d'histoire de la médecine p. 371–89, undated reprint received 1923). Wickersheimer (p. 86, 775, 1936).

The practice of incubation (*ἐγκοίμησις*), which the ancient Greeks had inherited from Egypt and had admirably developed,[49] was transmitted to the Middle Ages very largely through the cult of St. Cosmas and St. Damian. It was perhaps more popular among Orthodox than among Catholic populations; it certainly was very popular in the Greek world, where it can be observed to this day. Miss Hamilton gives many examples of mediaeval and modern incubation.[50]

Incubation was practiced also by Jews and probably by Muslims. For a Jewish-Egyptian example concerning Maimonides, see Introd. 2, 373.

20. *Medical deontology*

See chapter I.

21. *Hospitals*

The English hospice of Rome which existed in 1362 has been mentioned in chapter I; that, however, was a hotel, a guest house, rather than a hospital. The line may be difficult to draw, for we must assume that sick pilgrims would receive special attention and medical care. It is probable that the creation of the English hospice was caused by the inconveniences and difficulties suffered by English pilgrims at the time of the jubilee of 1350. That jubilee[51] had been decreed by Clement VI, and in spite of the fact that the pope and curia were seated in Avignon, it was immensely successful. It is said that a million pilgrims visited Rome.

[49] Mary Hamilton: Incubation or the cure of disease in pagan temples and Christian churches (234 p., London 1906). Louis H. Gray (ERE 7, 206–7, 1915). Jamieson B. Hurry: Imhotep (228 p., 26 ill., Oxford 1928; Isis 13, 373–75). F. W. Hasluck: Christianity and Islam under the Sultans (2 vols., 952 p., Oxford 1929).

[50] An example of it, the story of a sick child spending forty days and nights in a church, has been movingly told by the modern Thracian author George T. Bizyenos: *Τὸ ἁμάρτημα τῆς μητρός μου* (*Λογοτεχνικὴ βιβλιοθήκη Φέξη*, Athens 1912). Englished by Demetra Vaka: Modern Greek stories (p. 57–89, New York 1920).

[51] For the earlier jubilee of 1300 see Introd. 2, 823.

There were then in the Eternal City hospices of Aragon, Leon, Flanders, Sweden, Germany, France, etc., but not of England. The English Hospital, or Hospice of the Most Holy Trinity and St. Thomas of Canterbury, was established in or before 1362 on the spot where now stands the Venerable English College (Via Monserrato). In a document of 1364 it was called Universitas sive Societas pauperum Anglorum. In 1396-97 a second English hospice was established on the other side of the Tiber, near the church of St. Chrysogonus. The Trastevere hospice was dedicated to the Holy Trinity and St. Edmund. In 1464, the two hospices were amalgamated.

Cardinal Gasquet: History of the Venerable English College, Rome (304 p., ill., London 1920; p. 26-61).

It would seem that toward the end of the fourteenth century the hospitals existing in the fast-growing cities of northern Italy began to benefit from that growth at the expense of smaller hospices in the countryside. This was the case for the Spedale di Santa Maria Nuova in Florence, founded in 1288. A century later it had become an important institution. We know exactly what it amounted to, materially, in 1376 from the detailed inventory which was drawn up in that year, room by room. This includes, for example, a long list of all the objects contained in the apothecary shop (apoteca spetiarie), shoemaker's shop (chalzolaria), garden, storeroom (guardaspensa), cellar, oil room, etc.

Luigi Chiappelli and Andrea Corsini: Un antico inventario dello spedale di Santa Maria Nuova in Firenze, a. 1376 (Rivista delle biblioteche e degli archivi vol. 32, 37 p., Firenze 1923).

In the meanwhile, St. Bartholomew was growing in London. We have a very definite idea of the medical and theological atmosphere of that famous hospital at this time from the books compiled by John of Mirfeld, and bearing its name, the Breviarium Bartholomei (c. 1387) and Floriarium Bartholomei (c. 1404).

The great importance of Muslim hospitals has been underlined many times (Introd. 2, 246). It is impossible to say how the best of them compared with the best of Christian Europe, for our knowledge of all the hospitals is too vague. Moreover, it is probable that, then as now, the value of each depended very much on the men directing it and the physicians in charge; that value would then fluctuate from time to time as the personnel changed.

Even as Mirfeld's books help us to estimate the knowledge available at Barts, the books of Ḥājjī pāshā render the same service for the Bīmāristān al-Manṣūrī of Cairo, and the surgery of Sharaf al-dīn ibn 'Alī for the hospital of Amasia. The Muslim hospitals were very numerous. According to Aydin Sayili's elaborate study (Harvard doctoral thesis 1941, not yet published), out of 105 hospitals enumerated by him, 12 were in Baghdād, 9 in Cairo, 7 in Damascus, 5 in Qonya; 4 dated from the eighth century, 2 to 4 from the ninth century, 11 or 12 from the tenth century, 9 from the eleventh century, 21 from the twelfth century, 21 from the thirteenth century, 17 from the fourteenth century. More than half (c. 59) of these hospitals were of Turkish foundation. This very large proportion may be due to the fact that one of Sayili's main sources was Turkish, and that he was naturally better acquainted with Turkish hospitals than with those of other Islamic countries, especially those of the Maghrib. It is certain, however, that the Turkish lords were deeply interested in that form of charity and built a large number of hospitals.

List of Fourteenth-Century Muslim Hospitals

(Derived from Sayili 1941)

The name of the place is followed by that of the hospital, if there is a separate name, then the name of the founder and the date. Asterisks designate Turkish foundations.

1. Tabrīz. Ghāzānī, founded by Ghāzān Khān ....ruled 1295–1304
*2. Sulṭānīya. Īlkhānī foundation 1305
*3. Amasia. Īlkhānī foundation 1308
4. Tabrīz. Rashīdī, founded by Rashīd al-dīn[52] ....d. 1318
*5. Ḥusn al-Akrād. Bay Tamir, founded by 'Abdallāh ibn Bay Tamir al-Ashrafī 1319
*6. Sīvās. Dār al-rāhā, founded by Khaṭṭāb and Ḥusain, sons of Kamāl al-dīn Aḥmad ibn Raḥat 1320
*7. Edirne (Adrianople). Lazaretto 1331
8. Al-Ramla. Founded by Muḥammad ibn Faḍlallāh al-Qibṭī 1332
9. Nāblus. Founded by Muḥammad ibn Faḍlallāh al-Qibṭī 1332
*10. Ṣafad. Founded by Taqaz, viceroy of al-Nāṣir Muḥammad ibn Qalā'ūn ruled 1293–94, 1298–1308, 1309–40
*11. Ḥalab. Founded by Arghūn Kāmil 1344, 1355
*12. Al-Karak (east of the Dead Sea in Moab). Sanjar, founded by amīr 'Alam al-dīn Sanjar al-Jawlī ....b. 1256, d. 1345
*13. Ghazza. Named after al-Nāṣir Muḥammad ibn Qalā'ūn .... c. 1345
14. Granada .... c. 1355
15. Salā ....c. 1364
*16. Brusa. Founded by Bāyazīd I ....ruled 1389–1402
17. Tunis .... c. 1395

To the bibliography given in Introd. 2, p. 246, should be added the new Arabic edition of Aḥmad 'Īsā bey: History of the hospitals in Islām (318 p., 22 ill., Damascus 1939; Isis 31, 225). Many of the illustrations refer to epigraphic documents.

22. *Erotics*

Nothing to add to vol. 2, p. 79; vol. 3, p. 296.

XII. HISTORIOGRAPHY

Our account is divided into eight sections: (A) Christendom, (B) Israel, (C) Samaritan, (D) Islām, (E) Ceylon, (F) Java, (G) China and Korea, (H) Japan.

A. *Christendom*

The first of these sections is subdivided into thirteen subsections, as follows: (1) Hispanic peninsula, (2) Italy, (3) France, (4) Ireland, (5) Scotland, (6) England, (7) Belgium, (8) Germany, (9) Bohemia, (10) Poland, (11) Byzantium, (12) Armenia, (13) Egypt.

[52] Rashīd al-dīn (XIV-1) organized hospitals in Tabrīz, Shīrāz, Hamadān.

A1. *Hispanic peninsula*

Historical work was done by a Catalan, an Aragonese, a Basque, a Castilian, and a Portuguese. Ironically enough, the only Castilian in this list was a converted Jew.

Some of the best work was, as it had been for centuries, Catalan. Peter III the Ceremonious continued the noble tradition begun by his great-grandfather. The fact that his chronicle was written under his guidance, rather than by himself, is of little importance. Kings have always had ghost writers at their service. What matters here is not the actual writing, but the royal intention and the royal will to implement it.

The Aragonese version of the Chronicle of Morea, Libro de los fechos e conquistas de la Morea, was completed in 1393 by Juan Fernández de Heredia.[1] This Fernández originated in Munébrega (Calatayud, Zaragoza) c. 1310?; he assumed the habit of the order of St. John of Jerusalem and became finally the grand master of that order. He was in the service of Peter the Ceremonious (= Pedro IV de Aragón), distinguished himself as a diplomat in Avignon, and as a soldier in Crécy-en-Ponthieu (1346) and in an expedition against the Turks at Patras (Morea). The Turks kept him a prisoner for three years (1381). It was probably then that he became interested in the Chronicle of Morea, documented himself, and began his revision. The rest of his life (he died in 1396) was devoted to historical work. He wrote a Gran crónica de España, derived from the Crónica general; La gran crónica de los conquiridores, a collection of romantic biographies, Roman and mediaeval, the latest being those of Chingiz Khān (XIII-1), San Fernando (1199–1252, king of Castile and León), and Jaime I (XIII-2); and the Chronicle of Morea already cited. Juan Fernández de Heredia was a patron of letters as well as a writer. He caused many books to be translated into Aragonese (Catalan).

López de Ayala was a Basque of Vitoria, in Castilian service. He held many offices under four kings, culminating as grand chancellor of Castile. He wrote a chronicle of Castile during the four rules which he had shared (1350–96); hence his work has the value of a contemporary document written, by a witness and actor of the events described, in a critical if not unprejudiced spirit. López de Ayala was one of the outstanding Castilian scholars and writers of his time.

The Castilian Pablo de Santa María (alias Paul of Burgos, alias Solomon ben Isaac ha-Levi) composed a universal history in Spanish verse. Chronicles were written by his brother Alvar García de Santa María, who was an officer of the Castilian court. As the two brothers received baptism only c. 1390, their Christian and Spanish writings may belong to the following century.

The Portuguese historian Fernão Lopes is also a man of the fifteenth century, but as he was born and educated in the fourteenth century, a reference to his extraordinary work may be permitted here. Fernão Lopes was born c. 1380; in 1418 he was appointed keeper of documents (escrituras) in the Torre do Tombo (state archives) of Lisbon, and his task as a royal chronicler of Portugal did not begin until 1434. He was still living but very old and decrepit in 1459. He wrote in Portuguese a chronicle of the early kings of Portugal down to 1415, dealing chiefly with Dom Pedro I o Justiceiro (ruled 1357–67), Dom Fernando I o Formoso (1367–83), and Dom João I de Boa Memória (1383–1433). His art and his science were so good that Robert Southey[2] did not hesitate to claim that he was "the

[1] Hurtado and González Palencia (p. 136, 1932).

[2] As quoted by Bell (p. 3, 1921).

greatest chronicler of any age or nation." Bell does not go so far, yet declares, "He combines with Froissart's picturesqueness moral philosophy, enthusiasm, and high principles, is in fact a Froissart with something of Montaigne added, and easily excels Giovanni Villani or Pero López de Ayala." His chronicles do not belong to our period, but his genius does. Like every great man, Fernão expresses not only his own aspirations, but those of a great people which by the end of the fourteenth century was already poised for immortal deeds.

Aubrey Fitz Gerald Bell: Fernam Lopez (70 p., Oxford 1921); shorter account (p. 81-85, 1922). There are not yet good editions of Lopes' chronicles; for the others (Lisbon 1644, etc.) see Bell.

A2. *Italy*

The Italian group is not as varied and as representative of many historical branches as it was in the first half of the century, hence we need not subdivide it as was done in chapter I. Moreover, it is almost exclusively Florentine.

The excellent chronicle of Giovanni Villani was continued by his brother Matteo, on a somewhat lower level. Giovanni stopped his account in 1346, Matteo extended it to 1363, and his continuation included a description of the plague and of the chaos which that unprecedented calamity had left in its train. The plague did not stop in 1349, but flared up again and again, and Matteo was a victim of it in 1363, even as Giovanni had been in 1348. Matteo's work was continued by his son Filippo, but only for three years, 1363-65. Filippo Villani lacked the scientific detachment which had distinguished his uncle and, to a lesser degree, his own father. He preferred to win fame as a writer rather than as an impartial and humble observer; also his conceit of himself as a humanist led him to abandon Tuscan for Latin. His main work, a collection of Florentine biographies, was produced in that language. That work, however, is forgotten today, except by antiquarians, whereas the Historie fiorentine of his uncle Giovanni will always be considered one of the best mirrors of mediaeval life.

The task which Filippo disdained was performed by another Florentine family, the Capponi. Portentous events happened in Florence in those days, events which would have awakened the true chronicler in Filippo if he had been worthy of his ancestors. The wool carders (ciompi) revolted against the patricians in 1378; Gino Capponi, having participated in their revolt, was exiled, but he came back in 1382 when the Guelphs (in modern parlance, the democrats) were again in power, and thenceforth he was given a share in the government; he was the first Florentine governor of Pisa; he died in 1420. (Filippo Villani had witnessed the main events, for he lived until 1405, but for personal or political reasons his attention was drawn to other matters.) Gino wrote in Italian a masterly account of those labor troubles (il tumulto dei ciompi) and of their long-drawn-out and multifarious consequences (1378-1419). His chronicle was eventually extended to 1456 by his son Neri Capponi, who held leading offices in the Florentine administration and died in 1457. Even as Matteo and Filippo were inferior to Giovanni Villani, so was Neri to Gino Capponi. Yet it is a part of Florence' glory to have given to the world in a single century two masterly historians (no confusion will be caused if we leave out Christian names), Villani and Capponi.

The Capponi chronicle was not as popular as Villani's, and the early printers did not bother about it. Whereas Villani's work was printed in 1537, 1554, the

Capponi had to wait until 1733, when Domenico Maria Manni included their chronicles in his Cronichette antiche di varj scrittori del buon secolo della lingua toscana (Florence 1733; reprinted Milano 1844). Of course, both chronicles will also be found in the collection of Lodovico Antonio Muratori: Rerum italicarum scriptores (18, 1103-1216).

It is not improbable that Filippo Villani had been diverted from his task as a chronicler by the wondrous activities of Petrarca and Boccaccio. The latter was chiefly known in those days, among scholars, for his Latin writings, which were historical books, and, from the point of view of nascent humanism, the true and best kind of historical books. In order to register faithfully the wretched and shabby events happening before his eyes, it was not necessary for the chronicler to be acquainted with Greek and Roman antiquities, he did not even have to know Latin, hence his was a mean besoigne unworthy of a gentleman and a humanist. Boccaccio undertook to provide the historical tools which gentlemen would need. He created no less than four: (1) the lives of illustrious men, (2) the lives of illustrious women, (3) the genealogy of the gods, (4) a dictionary of historical geography. This choice of subjects, as well as his method of treating them, proves that Boccaccio sensed admirably the needs of the new generation of scholars which he was helping to usher in. He was ahead of his own time, together with Petrarca and a few others, but not too far ahead, and therefore his success was considerable. The influence which his four treatises exerted upon the humanities of the Renaissance can hardly be exaggerated. A man trying to understand Roman history, to read intelligently Ovid or Vergil, or to answer the thousand questions which the antiquities scattered throughout the Italian scene were all the time suggesting, could do no better than to study Boccaccio's compendia. To modern readers having at their elbow other tools, incomparably superior and more convenient, Boccaccio's books seem very difficult and clumsy, yet they were the best of their kind and time.

His success was due not only to the value of the tools he was creating, for scholars interested in historical accuracy and anxious, let us say, to identify the places and people of the Aeneid or of the Metamorphoses were few enough; it was due much more to his happy way of meeting the sensibility of his contemporaries. This applies chiefly to his histories of the famous men and of the famous women. The majority of the gentlemen and ladies of the Renaissance would have said (as many people still say today), "We do not care very much for history except in the form of biography. We are anxious to know what happened to individual men and women, especially the famous and romantic ones." That is of course a sound instinct, and history in all ages has tended to be focused on biographies, if it was not restricted to them. Think of Plutarch and of the many Arabic collections of lives. Plutarch's Vitae, however (not to speak of the Arabic ones), were still unknown in Boccaccio's time,[3] hence his own collections, combining scholarship, artistry, romance, and ethics in agreeable measure, were very welcome innovations. Moreover, Boccaccio, following Petrarca's example, liked to insist upon the vicissitudes

[3] A few of Plutarch's Vitae were translated by Leonardo Bruni (1369-1444), Guarino of Verona (1370-1460), Francesco Filelfo (1398-1481). The first complete collection, the Vitae illustrium virorum, edited by Campano, was not known until it was printed (Rome 1470-71). Boccaccio's collections appeared very soon afterward, De claris mulieribus (Ulm 1473), De casibus virorum illustrium (Strassburg c. 1474). As to Petrarca's De viris illustribus, for centuries only Caesar's life was printed (Esslingen 1470, etc.); the first edition of all the Vitae appeared only in 1874-79 (2 vols., Bologna)!

of fortune, and this fascinated his readers, whether they were women or men, fortunate or unfortunate. The moralizing tendencies were equally appreciated by all and sundry. Finally, there was in the De casibus virorum illustrium a kind of superficial comprehensiveness which appealed to the more thoughtful; they were left with the impression of having surveyed the world's history and all its changes, of having seen the wheel of fortune turn, from the creation until their own days. It even included a kind of rudimentary history of industry and learning.[4] No wonder the popularity of Boccaccio's Vitae was as great as was then possible; it increased throughout the Renaissance, witness the number of MSS, printed editions in six languages, and innumerable traces of their influence in contemporary letters and arts.

A sort of compromise between humanism and the early Florentine chronicles was eventually realized by Poggio Bracciolini (c. 1380–1459), who was primarily a humanist, but was appointed the official historiographer of Florence in 1453 and wrote a Latin history of his native city from the origins to 1455.[5] From the point of view of historiography, however, this was a definite retrogression.

The only non-Florentine historian was the Franciscan Michele da Piazza, to whom we owe a chronicle of his native country, Sicily, from 1337 to 1361.

A3. *France*

Though the French group is pitifully small, it is convenient to subdivide it into two, north and south.

Northern France. The Carmelite Jean de Venette wrote a chronicle of France from 1340 to 1368, which forms a startling contrast with the Grandes chroniques de France (or Chroniques de St. Denys), for its inspiration is decidedly popular and democratic. Jean de Venette wrote in Latin; another Carmelite, Jean Golein, translated the Spanish chronicle of Gonzalo de Hinojosa from Latin into French.

A third Jean, the Franciscan Jean Dardel, helped the last king of Armenia, Leon V of Lusignan, to compile a French chronicle of Armenia from Christ to 1384. This brings to our mind the history of another Lusignan, the king of Cyprus, Peter I, and his capture of Alexandria, told by Guillaume de Machaut (XIV-1).[6]

Cardinal Pierre d'Ailly (1350–1420) was primarily a theologian and cosmographer, but toward the end of his busy life he wrote treatises to explain the agreement between astrological predictions, history, and theology. We may call him a theorist of history, but his historical views were singularly backward.

Our respect for contemporary French historiography would be enormously increased if we counted Jean Froissart, perhaps the greatest Christian historian of his time, a Frenchman. This might perhaps be done, but it seemed more natural to count him a "Belgian"; he was a Walloon born in Valenciennes,[7] and he died in Chimay. He was typically a Belgian in his impartiality as between France and England.

4 See in Lydgate version the "comendacion of vertuous besines" (Bergen's ed., book II, lines 2339–2528).

5 The first edition of the Latin text, Historia fiorentina, appeared only in 1715, but an Italian translation by his son, Jacopo Poggio (1441–78), had been printed in 1476. These two editions, curiously enough, were Venetian. The Italian version was reprinted in Florence 1492, 1598.

6 Potthast (p. 563, 1896). Atiya (p. 319–78, 1938).

7 Valenciennes was then a part of the county of Hainaut. It became French only by the treaty of Nijmegen, 1678.

Southern France. Raymond Chalmel de Viviers, physician at the court of Avignon, wrote a treatise on the plague, which is remarkable because of his attempt to estimate mortality rates in 1348 and 1360. His estimates may be compared with those made by Guy de Chauliac. These two men introduced a new point of view, but demographic data and methods were utterly insufficient for their purpose.

Bertran Boysset noted down in his commonplace book a series of papal events in Provence, especially in Arles, from 1365 to 1414. This is a good example of a kind of auxiliary documents which the historian must always be ready to take into account, even if he cannot expect to find much in them.

A4. *Ireland*

Irish annals from 1162 to 1370 were compiled by an enigmatic personality, Christopher Pembridge of Dublin.

A5. *Scotland*

The earliest monument of Scottish literature (that is, Scottish-English, not Gaelic) is the historical poem The Bruce, narrating the deeds of Robert Bruce. It was completed in 1375 by John Barbour. A little later a chronicle of Scotland from Adam to 1406, called Oryginale, was written by Andrew of Wyntoun, who used The Bruce as one of his sources.

In the meanwhile, a Latin chronicle of Scotland was compiled down to 1313 by John Fordun; it was continued to 1437 by Walter Bower.

The Scotsmen were very much like their contemporaries of other countries, in that they attached at least as much importance to fanciful events of the romantic past as to the realities which they or their ancestors had been able to witness. Those realities were more often unpleasant than not, whereas the very calamities of the distant past had lost their sting and retained a kind of glamour. The histories of Troy and of Alexander were translated by Barbour or others. Of course, the Golden Legend was also translated. Thus Scottish people of the fourteenth and fifteenth centuries were able to enjoy the same kind of pabulum as other Christians. What they called history was mostly myth, but that did not worry them. Even the Italian humanists of their age, who could be realistic enough on occasion, were not always able or willing to distinguish between fact and fancy. We may be sure that those early Scots were equally capable of realism with regard to everyday events near in time and space, and of fabulation and glorification with regard to distant days or distant countries.

A6. *England*

The remarks made at the end of the previous subsection apply just as well to England (and other countries) as to Scotland. Historical criticism was utterly undeveloped, and hence educated people (let alone the uneducated ones) were always prone to mistake fables for truth. Thus the most popular historical book was the Brut of England (or the Chronicles of Brute),[8] as is proved by the number of MSS, in French, Latin, and English. Down to the battle of Halidon Hill in 1333, when Edward de Baliol defeated his own countrymen, it is simply a translation of the Brut d'Engleterre, and is more mythical than factual. On that romantic tree, however, were grafted a series of "continuations" which became gradually more

[8] So called because it began with the legendary Brutus and his descendants in Britain.

realistic and more scientific. For the period from 1333 to 1377 (death of Edward III) there is but one continuation, but from 1377 on there are various independent ones. The grand total—early fictions and later realities—was finally called Chronicles of England, or Chronicles of St. Albans because it was edited in that monastery by Thomas Walsingham, or Caxton's chronicles because it was first printed by the English prototypographos, William Caxton (London 1480). Very often reprinted. Critical edition by Friedrich W. D. Brie: The Brut (Early English Text Society, London 1906–8).

C. Gross (no. 1733, 1915). Wells (p. 206, 795, etc.).

A number of Latin chronicles are available for the reigns of Edward III and Richard II. It will suffice to mention the most important in chronological order.

The Chronicon of Geoffrey le Baker narrates English events from 1303 to 1356. In another work, his Chroniculum (to 1336), Baker had the idea of dating each event twice, from Christ and from 1347. This is very curious; it is as if he had been trying to connect the past more directly with the present, as do the modern pedagogues who insist on the necessity of teaching history backward. It is clear that for a man living in 1347, it was more direct and more informative to be told "King Edward died forty years ago" than to be told "King Edward died 1307 years after Christ's birth," and the more so that fourteenth-century people were not by any means as used to the Christian era as we are.[9]

The chronicle of Robert of Avesbury, registrar at the court of Canterbury, extends from 1339 to 1356; that of Henry Knighton, canon of Leicester, extends from the Norman conquest to 1366, and was continued from 1377 to 1395. The chronicle of the archbishops of Canterbury (597–1369), wrongly ascribed to Stephen Birchington, was probably written by John of Reading. The mathematician William Rede, fellow of Merton, wrote a chronicle of popes and emperors to Ludwig of Bavaria, a chronicle of England to 1367, a chronicle of the archbishops of Canterbury to 1374.

The English Benedictines were very active as historians. This paragraph is devoted to no less than five of them. William Thorne wrote a chronicle of his monastery, St. Augustine's in Canterbury, to 1397. Richard of Cirencester, monk at St. Peter's, Westminster, compiled a Speculum historiale de gestibus regum Angliae (447–1066); he is better known, however, because of another work wrongly ascribed to him, De situ Britanniae. That topographical study would have been very valuable indeed if it had been made by Richard or in Richard's time, but it is a forgery of the middle of the eighteenth century. John Malverne, monk in the abbey of Worcester, near Malvern, continued Higden's Polychronicon from 1346 to 1394. Thomas of Burton, abbot of Meaux (or Meux, near Beverley), wrote the chronicle of his abbey from 1150 to 1396. Finally, Thomas Walsingham edited the chronicle of St. Albans from 1376 to 1421.

It is of course difficult to compare these chronicles written in different places, from different angles, and partly derived from different sources. The historian of fourteenth-century England is obliged to take them all into account, plus many others not mentioned here (see C. Gross 1915, or Potthast 1896, p. 1720). Each of

[9] A method similar to Baker's was followed independently in the Encyclopaedia of Chinese biography (Chung kuo jên ming ta tz'ŭ tien) published in Shanghai 1921 (Isis 5, 446–47). All the dates are quoted from a new era, the birth of the Chinese republic (A.D. 1911); hence almost all of them (there are some 40,000 biographies of all times) are negative like our B.C. dates!

them may turn out to be the most valuable for a definite purpose. In spite of their ordinary jejuneness, the historian of culture will find in them occasionally extraordinary bits of information. Take, e.g., the Chronica monasterii de Melsa, compiled by its abbot, Thomas de Burton. Its frankness in criticizing the abuse of indulgences and even the morality of the pope is amazing (Rolls edition by Edward A. Bond, 3, 88-89, 1868). When his confessor would reproach Clement VI for his lack of chastity, the pope would simply answer, "Quando juvenis fuimus hoc usi sumus et quod facimus modo facimus ex consilio medicorum." The same pontiff made fantastic promises to pilgrims who would visit Rome during the jubilee (1350). No reformer would have spoken more boldly than this Benedictine abbot. But here is another story, far more unexpected, and delightful. During the abbacy of Hugh of Leven (fifteenth abbot, 1339-49; Thomas the chronicler was the nineteenth abbot, 1396-99) a new crucifix was ordered for the choir, and, the body having been admirably shaped after a nude model, attracted considerable devotion and was the cause of many miracles.[10] This is the earliest reference in the history of English art to sculpture made from a living model. In 1313, however, William Grenefeld, archbishop of York, had taken fright at the popularity of a statue of the Holy Virgin (Jusserand p. 212, 1884).

Some of the English chronicles were written in French. During his captivity in Edinburgh, Sir Thomas Gray the younger began a chronicle of England from the origins to 1362. The title, Scala cronica, was Latin, but the chronicle itself was composed in French. Then we have the Anonimalle (= anonymous) chronicle (1333-81), written in French at St. Mary's abbey, York, at the end of the century. The earlier part is derived from the Franciscan lost chronicle which was the basis of the Chronicon de Lanercost;[11] from 1338 it uses other sources, and from 1347 on it is independent of any known chronicle. The account of the Peasants' Revolt is particularly full; indeed, half of the work (its most precious part) is devoted to the years 1376-81. It was edited by Vivian Hunter Galbraith (266 p., Manchester University 1927). The chronicle is valuable because York was a center of observation second only to St. Albans. There remains to be named the greatest of all, one of the most important sources for English history, the Chroniques of Jean Froissart (1326-1400), but that work is so famous and its unique value so well appreciated that it must suffice here to evoke it. If you wish to understand the spirit of the fourteenth century, by all means read Froissart!

Though some of the chronicles represented the best kind of historical work, information derived from the sources and often from the very actors or witnesses of the events, contemporaries had more respect for academic compilations like the Polychronicon of Ranulf Higden (XIV-1). This belongs to the preceding period, but it was Englished by John of Trevisa at Berkeley in 1387, and this translation exemplified the growth of a public which was educated enough to want to understand the past, yet found it increasingly difficult to read Latin or French.

When John Gower, however, who could use the three languages equally well, decided to apply himself to historical meditations, he did it in the Latin language. The labor troubles of the eighties, and the evil years which ended Richard's rule and the century, had made a deep impression upon him, and he included his vision of them in his Latin poem, the Vox clamantis. He realized that those social

[10] Rolls ed. (3, 35-36). Unfortunately, the artist is not named.

[11] Lanercost abbey near Carlisle in Cumberland; Augustinian priory. Latin chronicle from 1201 to 1346.

troubles were rooted in the vices of the leaders, lay and clerical, and did not hesitate to denounce them. This is not historiography, but few documents are of greater value to later historians.

A7. *Belgium*

The term "Belgium" may be objected to by topographical purists; it is used here simply to express the fact that the historiographers to be dealt with belonged exclusively to the southern half of the Netherlands, that is, to the territory which corresponds more or less to that of modern Belgium. The fertility in great men of that tiny part of the world is astounding, and it is for that reason that we must consider them in a separate section.

Though one fully expected to find many distinguished historians in Belgium, it is rather surprising that out of seven, only one could be called a Fleming, and that all of them wrote in French, only two in Latin, none in Flemish.

Let us consider the Walloons first and end with the solitary Fleming. The first of the Walloons came from Tournai, and though he could and did write in French, his historical writings were in Latin. They are chronicles of his Benedictine monastery, composed mainly for his brethren. Thus it was natural enough for him to write them in Latin, for a monastery placed in Tournai (Doornik), near the confluence of many countries (Hainaut, Flanders, Artois, Cambrésis, France), would have attracted novices speaking so many different languages or dialects that Latin must have been their easiest means of communication. This Tournaisien was Gilles le Muisit; his chronicles and reminiscences contain so many interesting interpolations that it has been necessary to refer to them repeatedly in this survey.

We now have a group of four Liégeois. Jean Le Bel wrote a chronicle from 1326 to 1341, which was Froissart's main written source. That chronicle, like Froissart's, is typically Belgian in that it took account of events which had happened not only in Belgium proper, but also in France, Germany, and England. Lebel and Froissart were already aware of the fact, more explicitly stated five centuries later by the great historian Henri Pirenne (1862–1935), that Belgium is a microcosm of Europe. The history of Belgium, then, must be to some extent the history of Europe. Whereas Jean Le Bel was a forerunner not only of Froissart but of modern historians, Jean d'Outremeuse continued the old romantic tradition of historical writing. His "mirror of history" is comparable in its spirit and methods to the Brut of England, an indiscriminate and bizarre medley of fact and fancy; his Geste de Liége is a similar composition but restricted to Liége and written in verse; it is a belated chanson de geste with this original feature, that the center of the stage is held not by an individual, but by an impersonated country, Liége! Raoul de Ruisseau (alias Roland of Tongres) wrote a chronicle of the bishops of Liége from 1347 to 1389 (Potthast p. 987, 1896). To Jacques de Hemricourt we owe three other chronicles of Liége, specially devoted to the civil wars raging from 1290 to 1335. In spite of their limited scope, or perhaps because of it, these chronicles are very instructive.

Let us now return to Hainaut, but to Valenciennes instead of Tournai. The two places are close to each other on the same river Escaut (Fl., Schelde; Eng., Scheldt), Valenciennes being some 30 miles higher up. In that city was born one of the greatest historians of Christendom, Jean Froissart. His Chroniques (1326–1400) are one of the masterpieces of mediaeval historiography, as well as a monument of the French language of the fourteenth century.

With John of Ypres we pass to Flanders. He was born at Ypres but spent a great part of his life in St. Omer, being finally the abbot of the Benedictine monastery in that locality. "Long John" was undoubtedly a Fleming, but his writings were in Latin and in French. He wrote a chronicle of St. Bertin, his own abbey, from 590 to 1294, but his fame rests on his collection of travelers' accounts. He has been justly called the "mediaeval Hakluyt"; this title is the best description of his achievement. It was partly thanks to him that the new knowledge of Asia obtained in the thirteenth and fourteenth centuries spread so rapidly in Europe. Whereas the outlook of men like Lebel and Froissart may be called European, that of John of Ypres was international, or supernational. He was a chronicler of geographical adventures and discoveries, that is, he was a historian of science—a historian not of Flanders, or of Europe, but of mankind.

A8. *Germany*

Two remarkable chronicles were composed in Latin and three in German.

The Latin ones are the chronicle of the county of Mark (in Westphalia) from 1000 to 1358, by Levold von Northof, and the chronicle of Limburg on the Lahn (in West Franconia) from 1347 to 1398, by Tilemann Elhen von Wolfhagen. One might think that the scope of these chronicles is too limited to be mentioned in as general a survey as this one, but that would be a misjudgment of their importance. In particular, Tilemann's records are among the most valuable of their kind and time. Tilemann was what one could call today a historian of culture, and because of that tendency, rarer then than now, his chronicle is singularly revealing.

The German chronicles were centered respectively on Nuremberg and on Strassburg, which were then two of the outstanding cities in Germany. The Nuremberg chronicle (from 1349 to 1407) was composed by patrician Ulman Stromer. It was meant as a family chronicle, but, Stromer being deeply interested in economic and industrial matters, such matters are often in the foreground. From that point of view his chronicle is unique. Fritsche Closener and Jacob Twinger were two Alsatians. The first compiled a chronicle of the world leading to the particular history of his own town, Strassburg, to 1362. Jacob Twinger continued that chronicle in the same spirit to 1390, and then to 1415. They were interested in world history, but their world was centered on Strassburg.

A9. *Bohemia*

It so happened that during a good part of this period the king of Bohemia was emperor of Germany. This was Wenceslas, born in Prague 1316, the eldest son of John of Luxemburg. When he was 7 years old he was taken to the court of his uncle Charles IV le Bel, and remained seven years in France. His baptismal name was changed to Charles, and he became as Francophile as his father. He was elected king of the Romans in 1346 in opposition to Louis of Bavaria, and was subservient to Clement VI of Avignon, Louis' enemy. King John and his son fought together at the battle of Crécy (1346), at the end of which the old man was dead and the young man found himself king of Bohemia. He was crowned emperor at Rome in 1355, reorganized the constitution of the Holy Roman Empire (Golden Bull 1356, in force until 1806), but he loved France and, of course, Bohemia much more than Germany. He was called a stepfather of the empire but a true father of Bohemia. The Germans accused him of being always ready to pluck the imperial eagle in order to feather his own Bohemian nest. He founded the University of

Prague (1347)—the first of the empire—and did his best to develop the arts and industries, and to improve the administration of his native country. He died in Prague in 1378.

There would be much more to tell about the emperor Charles IV, but space forbids. The main point was to emphasize his Bohemian interests. He wrote an autobiography which is one of the outstanding mediaeval documents of its kind, encouraged the development of Bohemian (Czech) literature, and did his best to establish the facts concerning the Bohemian past. He first engaged as his secretary and historiographer the Italian explorer Giovanni de' Marignolli (XIV-1), who died in 1359. The Bohemian chronicle of Marignolli was much improved by Charles' second historiographer, Beneš of Weitmil. The latter's chronicle extended from 1283 to 1374. A third historiographer, Přibik son of Dluhý of Radenin, surnamed Pulkava, wrote the history of Bohemia to 1330. The king's interest in these chronicles was not merely passive; he collaborated to some extent with Beneš and Pulkava, providing them with sources of information available to him and perhaps even reading and criticizing their accounts. The collaboration was not one-sided; it would seem that Beneš helped the king to write the reminiscences of his youth, and Pulkava translated them into Czech.

After Charles' death, Bohemian literature and historiography had received such a strong impulse that their development continued in spite of German resistance. Thus Vavřinec z Březowé (= Laurentius de Brezova,[12] or Byzinius), who was born in 1365 and died in 1437, wrote a chronicle of Bohemia for the fateful years 1414 to 1422, which is perhaps the best contemporary record of the Hussite wars. Later, he composed a poem to celebrate the Bohemian victory near Taus (1431). These works were in Latin, but he also wrote various books in Czech, to wit, a dream book for Wácslaw IV (Wenceslas IV, king of Bohemia 1378–1419), a world chronicle, and a translation of John Mandeville's travels.

Text. First complete edition of the Latin writings of Vavřinec, by Constantin v. Höfler: Geschichtsschreiber der husitischen Bewegung in Böhmen (1, 321–527, 596–620, 1856).

Criticism. Potthast (p. 712, 1896). Franz Lützow: History of Bohemian literature (p. 147, 1899).

A10. *Poland*

The chronicle of Poland, the so-called Chronica Cracoviae, was continued to 1384 by Jan Czarnkowski, and to 1395 by another person. That chronicle is very valuable for the history not only of Poland, but also of Prussia, Hungary, and Russia.

A11. *Byzantium*

The Byzantine tradition of ecclesiastical history was continued by Neilos Diassorinos in his summary of the nine oecumenical councils (the ninth being the Palamite council of 1341), composed from the Palamite or Hesychastic point of view.

The same point of view dominated the Byzantine chronicles written by Nicephoros Gregoras (XIV-1) for the period 1204–1359, and by Joannes VI Cantacuzenos for the period 1320–56 (1362). The two chronicles cover partly the same ground

[12] Brezová (birch) is a Slovakian town in the Nitra (or Nyitra) province of Hungary; it is 40 miles northeast of Bratislava.

and should be considered together. Joannes wrote his largely as an apology for the things he had done or left undone during his rule; he wrote it after his abdication (1355), when he was living in monastic retirement. The author's name was, thus, not Joannes Cantacuzenos, but Joseph Christodulos. To these two histories should be added three short chronicles recently edited (or re-edited) by Spyridōn Lampros:[13] (1) from 1204 to 1391, (2) from 1204 to 1425, (3) from 1320 to 1422. These three works are valuable for determining many events of the fourteenth century. The most valuable perhaps is the first, which had been edited previously by J. Müller: Byzantinische Analekten (Sitzungsberichte der Kais. Akad. der Wissenschaften, Wien, phil. Kl., 9, 352 ff., 1852).

Peter Charanis: Les Βραχέα χρονικά comme source historique (Byzantion 13, 335–62, Bruxelles 1938). The three chronicles referred to in my text bear the following numbers in Lampros' posthumous edition: 52, 15, 47.

A12. *Armenia*

The last effective king of Armenia, Leon V of Lusignan (who died in Paris 1393), made it possible for the Franciscan Jean Dardel, his secretary from 1377 to 1384, to write a French chronicle of Armenia from the time of Christ to 1384. That chronicle was necessarily written from the royal and Catholic point of view.

Another story, representing the point of view of the Armenian church, was composed in Armenian by the archimandrite Gregory of Khlath. Unfortunately, that text seems to be lost, and we have only his menology of the Armenian martyrs and various poems, notably one reciting the calamities which overcame his native country from 1386 to 1421.

Thomas of Alovid (or Agovid, in the province of Vaspuragan, around Van) was one of the main disciples of Gregory of Tathev; he became abbot of Medsop in Duruperan. His main work is a story of Tīmūr, dealing chiefly with the latter's invasion of Armenia, to which he added a chronicle of Armenian events down to 1447.

Text. The Armenian text of the history of Tīmūr was edited by G. Schanazarian (Paris 1860). Main parts translated by Félix Nève: Exposé des guerres de Tamerlan et de Schah Rokh d'après la chronique arménienne inédite de Thomas de Medzoph (extrait, s.l., s.a.; Bruxelles 1860?, preface dated Louvain 1858).

Criticism. C. F. Neumann (p. 224, 1836). François Tournebize: Ravages de Timour-Leng en Arménie (Revue de l'Orient chrétien 23, 31–46, 1923).

A13. *Egypt*

Mufaḍḍal ibn abī-l-Faḍā'il, who wrote a chronicle of Egypt from 1260 to 1349, has been grouped with the other Mamlūk historians. He was a Copt, that is, a Christian, but so accustomed to Muslim usages that no great mistake is made in dealing with him together with the Muslim historians of the Near East. Yet he must be mentioned here also, for his chronicle was conceived by him as a sequel to that of al-Makīn Ibn al-'Amīd (XIII-2), and it includes information on the Coptic patriarchate and other Christian matters.

[13] Σπυρίδωνος Λάμπρου Βραχέα χρονικά, ἐκδίδονται ἐπιμελείᾳ K. I. 'Αμάντου ('Ακαδημία 'Αθηνῶν. Μνημεῖα τῆς 'Ελληνικῆς ἱστορίας. Τόμος A', τεῦχος α'. Athens 1932–33).

B. *Israel*

Jewish contributions to historiography were very meager during this period. The most important perhaps is the letter written by Ḥasdai Crescas to the synagogue of Avignon describing the persecutions which occurred in Aragon in 1391, his own son being one of the martyrs. This may stand as a representative of other similar reports, for Jews were persecuted during the last decade of the century not only in Aragon, but also in Seville, Toledo, Valencia, Barcelona, in France, in Prague, and the idea of recording such events for posterity would come to the mind of many people. It is probable that the persecutors would prefer oblivion, but the victims, the parents of the victims, would insist on remembrance. Individual reports, however, are not so much history as documents, materials for history.

Two other Jews, Immanuel Bonfils and Judah Mosconi, both distinguished men in other fields, helped to establish not historical truth, of which they had no clear conception, but rather historical fiction. Their creations belong to that typically mediaeval genre, romances—visions of the past curiously distorted by the imagination of poets. One of the most popular romances, as well as the most international, was the legend of Alexander the Great. That particular legend was told the Jewish public by the Provençal mathematician Immanuel ben Jacob Bonfils. He translated the Historia de proeliis into Hebrew under the title Toledot Alexander (after 1365).

For general introduction and bibliography on that legend, and especially the English forms of it, see Wells (p. 98, 778); for the Hebrew (and Muslim) forms see my note on Bonfils.

While Immanuel Bonfils was thus beguiling himself and his prospective readers in Tarascon, the Serbian (or Yugo-Slavian!) Talmudist Judah ben Moses Mosconi, a typical wandering Jew, was revising the Sefer Yosippon, an olla podrida of Jewish history and romance, reality, fancy, and nonsense.

Some readers might object that the Toledot Alexander and the Sefer Yosippon are equally irrelevant in a survey of historiography. I believe they would be wrong. These "romances" belong to the field of contemporary historiography exactly as much as alchemical fancies belong to that of contemporary chemistry. These things are fictional or nonsensical to us, but they were accepted at their face value in the fourteenth century, and if we wish to understand fourteenth-century thought, we must take them into account at their fourteenth-century valuation.

C. *Samaritan*

A Samaritan chronicle derived from Hebrew, Arabic, and Samaritan books was written in Arabic in 1355 by Abū-l-Fatḥ ibn abī-l-Ḥasan.

D. *Islām*

The Islamic section is almost as important as the Christian one in point of numbers and diversity; it is more important in point of quality. We shall divide it into eight subsections, the first four of which concern the West, the others the East: (1) Granada, (2) Morocco, (3) Algiers, (4) Tunis; (5) Yaman, (6) Mamlūkīya, (7) Turkey, (8) Īrān.

D1. *Granada*

The kingdom of the Banū Naṣr to which Muslim Spain had been reduced was very small indeed, yet it produced a great scholar, Ibn al-Khaṭīb. He was the author of many books on general Islamic history and on the history and biography of Spain. Unfortunately, most of them are still unpublished, yet enough has been revealed by Spanish Arabists to enable us to form an idea of their exceptional value. The most important of his works, the Iḥāṭa bi ta'rīkh Gharnāṭa, is a collection of Spanish Muslim biographies; a critical and well indexed edition of it is one of the desiderata of mediaeval scholarship.

D2. *Morocco*

Ibn Baṭṭūṭa is thought of primarily as a traveler and geographer, yet the historical value of his Riḥla can hardly be exaggerated. His facts are seldom dated, or his dates when he gives them may be incorrect, for he was not chronologically minded, but his work affords a magnificent picture of the Dār al-Islām as it was about the middle of the century, not only in one country or on one continent, but throughout its length and breadth. Thus the Riḥla may be called one of the monuments of fourteenth-century historiography.

D3. *Algiers*

The history of the Banū Ḥafṣ, who were then ruling Tunis, was written by a distinguished Algerian scholar, Ibn al-Qunfūdh. He told the history of that dynasty from 1068 to 1402, and following Muslim tradition put together a collection of biographies of the leading men.

D4. *Tunis*

The Muslim historians of whom we have spoken thus far, Ibn al-Khaṭīb of Granada, Ibn Baṭṭūṭa of Tangiers, Ibn al-Qunfūdh of Constantine, were men of great distinction, but they are completely eclipsed by their Tunisian rivals, the Banū Khaldūn, and especially the elder one.

Let us say something of the younger one first, Yaḥyā ibn Muḥammad. Yaḥyā wrote a history of the Ziyānī dynasty of Tlemcen; he was a good historian and a humanist, more interested in adab than in siyāsa, that is, more interested in belles lettres than in politics (but the connotation of the Arabic terms is somewhat different). On the contrary, 'Abd al-Raḥmān ibn Muḥammad Ibn Khaldūn (or Ibn Khaldūn for short, which means him and nobody else) was a historian, politician, sociologist, economist, a deep student of human affairs, anxious to analyze the past of mankind in order to understand its present and its future. Not only is he the greatest historian of the Middle Ages, towering like a giant over a tribe of pygmies, but one of the first philosophers of history, a forerunner of Machiavelli, Bodin, Vico, Comte, and Cournot. Among Christian historians of the Middle Ages there are but one or two whom we can perhaps compare to him, to wit, Otto von Freising (XII-1)[14] and John of Salisbury (XII-2), and the distance between them and him is great indeed, far greater than the distance between him and Vico. What is equally remarkable, Ibn Khaldūn ventured to speculate on what we should call today the methods of historical research.[15] The vicissitudes of a life spent among the many courts of Muslim Africa had brought him a rich experience; he

[14] For a vindication of Otto von Freising, see George Lincoln Burr: Anent the Middle Ages (American historical review 18, 710–26, 1913); reprinted in the Selections edited by Lois Oliphant Gibbons (p. 378–94, Cornell University 1943; especially p. 383; Isis 35, 147).

[15] In this respect Ibn Khaldūn had Muslim predecessors, such as the great Palestinian biographer al-Ṣafadī (XIV-1), not to speak of the traditionists who were trained from the beginning in the criticism of sources and chains of tradition (isnād), about which see Th. W. Juynboll (EI 2, 189–94, 1914–15).

had witnessed the rise and fall of kingdoms, but all that experience would have been wasted on him but for his scientific curiosity, his philosophical turn of mind, and his genius. In proof of this it will suffice to reflect that there had been no lack of tumults, wars, upsettings, and other catastrophes in Christian Europe; the merciless turning of the wheel of fortune had inspired moralists like Petrarca and Boccaccio, but nobody there had ever attempted a sociological analysis as did Ibn Khaldūn. The idea never occurred to them.

Finally, Ibn Khaldūn deserves the special praise of historians of science for his concern with the sciences and the arts. In this respect, however, he was not an innovator, but the continuer of an ancient Muslim tradition. Witness the Ṭabaqāt al-umam of Qāḍī Ṣā'id al-Andalusī (XI-2),[16] the Ikhbār al-'ulamā' of Ibn al-Qifṭī (XIII-1), and the 'Uyūn al-anbā' of Ibn abī Uṣaibi'a (XIII-1). Ibn Khaldūn was not comparable as a historian of science to the men just named, because his own curiosity was much broader and more diversified, but he did ask himself questions concerning the history and development of science. Such questions naturally invite others on the classification of the sciences and the relations between their several branches. That line of thought rejoined another Greco-Arabic tradition which has been repeatedly discussed in this work. The sixth and last section of Ibn Khaldūn's Muqaddama was devoted to it; he did not add anything new, I believe, to that topic, but kept it alive in the Muslim mind. He was one of the links in the chain which would be forged mainly by Turkish scholars, such as his younger contemporary al-Bisṭāmī (c. 1370–1454) in the latter's lifework Kitāb al-fawā'iḥ al-miskīya fī-l-fawātiḥ al-Mekkīya (an encyclopaedia of a hundred sciences dedicated to Murād II, c. 1440) and his Durrat al-'ulūm wa-jauharat al-funūn (a classification of the sciences), and which would lead after another century to the elaborate classification set forth in the Miftāḥ al-sa'āda of the great encyclopaedist Aḥmad ibn Muṣṭafā' Ṭashköprüzāde (Brusa 1495—Istanbul 1561).[17] In short, Ibn Khaldūn was one of the leaders of thought in the fourteenth century, one of the glories of that age in the light of eternity.

Our division of the Muslim African historians into four groups was made in order to show the vitality of each section, but that division is somewhat artificial, for the men dealt with passed frequently from one into another. Not to speak of Ibn Baṭṭūṭa, who belongs to the whole world of Islām yet managed to end his days in his native land, Ibn al-Khaṭīb lived in Algiers and Morocco as well as in Granada, and he died in Fās; Ibn al-Qunfūdh lived in Spain, Morocco, and Tunis as well as in Algiers, and he died in Tlemcen; Ibn Khaldūn lived all over North Africa and died in Cairo. Moreover, the Algerian historian wrote the history of Tunis, and the Tunisian that of Tlemcen!

So much for the Maghrib, let us now turn to the Mashriq.

D5. *Yaman*

The umarā' of Yaman were historically minded and patronized many scholars whose duty it was to record past events. The annals of al-Janadī (XIV-1) were

[16] Since the publication of my note (Introd. 1, 776), this work has become available to Western readers through the French translation of Régis Blachère (192 p., Paris 1935; Isis 26, 498).

[17] Printed by the Dā'irat al-ma'ārif al-niẓāmīya (2 vols., Haidarābād, Deccan 1911). Brockelmann (2, 425; suppt. 2, 633). Franz Babinger (EI 4, 689, 1929). Ṭashköprüzāde's classification was extended by Ḥājjī Khalīfa (d. 1657) in the muqaddama of his famous Kashf al-ẓunūn (vol. 1, 1835), 307 branches of science being recognized. See outline in Julius Theodor Zenker: Bibliotheca orientalis (p. xviii–xliii, Leipzig 1846).

edited and continued by al-Ḥusain ibn 'Abd al-Raḥmān al-Ahdal (1377–1451) under the title Mukhtaṣar ta'rīkh al-Janadī. In the meanwhile, a new chronicle was composed by Ibn Wahhās, who told the history of Yaman from the beginnings to 1400. All these chronicles, though centered on Ṣan'ā' and Yaman, include valuable information concerning other parts of the Islamic world.

The Yamanī chronicles are of great interest also from the religious point of view, for the a'imma of the Rassī dynasty (893–c. 1300), ruling in Sa'da, belonged to a Shī'a sect, the Zaidīya. The modern dynasty of the a'imma of Ṣan'ā' (1590 ff.) is also Zaidī. Much information on the Zaidī court of the fourteenth century is given in the Ṣubḥ al-a'shā of al-Qalqashandī.[18] See also D. S. Margoliouth (ERE 12, 844–45, 1922) and R. Strothmann (EI 4, 1196–98, 1933).

D6. *Mamlūkīya*

The preponderance of Mamlūk historiography was even greater in the second half of the century than in the first half, for now the Mamlūk historians were more numerous than all the other Muslim historians put together, East and West. Nevertheless, the greatest historian of the century was not a Mamlūk, but a Tunisian, Ibn Khaldūn.

The great works of the first half of the fourteenth century, histories of the Mamālīk, histories of great cities, collections of biographies, historical compendia for civil servants, were continued or rebuilt in a new way. Thus, Mufaḍḍal ibn abī-l-Faḍā'il wrote a chronicle of Mamlūk history from 1260 to 1349, and Ibn Ḥabīb another from 1250 to 1375. Mufaḍḍal was a Copt, and his account contains Christian items which a Muslim would not have thought of recording, but the Muslim items are recorded in the Muslim manner. Ibn Shākir al-Kutubī continued the Wafayāt al-a'yān of Ibn Khallikān, and wrote a history of the Muslim world as seen from Damascus. 'Abd al-Wahhāb al-Subkī collected biographies of the Shāfi'ī theologians and incidentally left us a description of the sack of Baghdād by the Mongols (1258). A general history of the Muslim world (to 1365) was written by Ibn Kathīr on a very large scale. As a contrast we may now take the monograph relative to the siege of Alexandria (1367) by Muḥammad ibn Qāsim al-Nuwairī; would that we could exchange some of the bulky compilations for writings like this one, embodying the report of an eyewitness, but such writings are relatively rare or but few of them have drawn our attention. Ibn al-Furāt explained the development of the Islamic world from the point of view of Egypt; he had the idea of composing it backward, beginning with his own time (1396 to 1107). Another history of Egypt down to 1377 was compiled by Ibn Duqmāq, who also compiled biographical collections and histories of Cairo and of Alexandria. Ibn al-Shiḥna abridged and continued the history of Abū-l-Fidā'; he was, however, primarily a textbook maker, and produced a whole series of them on many subjects (theology, law, medicine, grammar, the life of the Prophet, etc.); and since he wanted his books to be as popular as possible, he wrote them in doggerel verse.

The magnificent tradition of Aḥmad al-Nuwairī and of Ibn Faḍlallāh al-'Umarī was brought to a climax by al-Qalqashandī; the Nihāyat al-arab and the Masālik al-abṣār were succeeded by the Ṣubḥ al-a'shā. These encyclopaedic treatises are so voluminous that a correct estimate of their relative value would require considerable time. It is probable that a detailed analysis of each would reveal the

[18] See the excellent Cairene edition (14 vols., 1913–20), unfortunately not yet indexed. For Yaman, see vol. 5, 1915.

partial superiority of this or that in one field, its partial inferiority in another, and so on. Certain it is that a comparison of sizes would be utterly insufficient; the shortest might well be the most critical and the best. Avoiding premature comparisons, the main point is that Mamlūk administration was so developed and the education of the governing classes so high that such treatises were needed, and that learned authors competed with one another in producing them. There was at that time nothing in the West which was at all comparable to these Arabic encyclopaedias, except perhaps the Specula of Vincent of Beauvais, which were a century older. Al-Qalqashandī's was not the last work of its kind. It will suffice to cite the much smaller but very interesting and practical work, Zubdat kashf al-mamālik fī bayān al-ṭuruq wal-masālik, composed by Khalīl ibn Shāhīn al-Ẓāhirī Ghars al-dīn. The career of this Khalīl al-Ẓāhirī is a typical career of a Mamlūk civil servant; he was born in 1410, was successively ḥākim (governor) of Alexandria, wazīr, amīr al-ḥajj (chief of the pilgrimage), ḥākim of al-Karak, Ṣafad, and Damascus; he died in 1468.

Text. Paul Ravaisse: Zoubdat kachf el-mamālik. Tableau politique et administratif de l'Egypte, de la Syrie et du Ḥidjāz du XIIIe au XVe siècle (158 p., Paris 1894), Arabic text only, no index.
Criticism. Brockelmann (2, 135; suppt. 2, 165).

Khalīl was the youngest of al-Qalqashandī's contemporaries; he was only 8 at the time of the latter's death; four others should be mentioned here, fin-de-siècle historians whose work was done in the following century, yet who grew up in the fourteenth century, to wit al-Maqrīzī, al-'Asqalānī, Ibn Shuhba, and Ibn 'Arabshāh. When al-Qalqashandī died they were respectively 54, 46, 41, and 26 years of age.

Abū-l-'Abbās Aḥmad ibn 'Alī al-Maqrīzī was born in Cairo 1364/65, flourished in Damascus and Cairo, died in Cairo 1442. He was brought up as a Ḥanafī, became a Shāfi'ī with some Ẓāhirī tendencies. His two main works among many others are the Khiṭāṭ, a history and geography of Egypt dealing more especially with the topography of Fusṭāṭ and Cairo, composed c. 1418–37; and the Sulūk, narrating the history of Egypt from 1181 to 1440.

Text. Kitāb al-mawā'iẓ wal i'tibār fī dhikr al-khiṭāṭ wal āthār. Arabic text edited by Gaston Wiet (Mémoires de l'Institut français d'archéologie orientale du Caire, 5 vols., 1911–27). French translation, Livre des admonitions et de l'observation pour l'histoire des quartiers et des monuments, begun by Urbain Bouriant, continued by Paul Casanova (ibid. 1895–1920). There are many partial editions and translations.

Kitāb al-sulūk li ma'rifat duwal al-mulūk. Histoire des sultans Mamlouks (2 vols., Paris 1837–44), Arabic with French translation by E. M. Quatremère.

Criticism. Wüstenfeld (no. 482, 1882). Brockelmann (2, 38–41; suppt. 2, 36–38; EI 3, 175–76, 1929).

A. R. Guest: List of writers, books and other authorities mentioned in the Khiṭāṭ (Journal of the Royal Asiatic Society, 1902, 103–25). Jean Maspero et Gaston Wiet: Matériaux pour servir à la géographie de l'Egypte (295 p., Le Caire 1914–19). Eilhard Wiedemann: Zur Geschichte des Kompasses, usw. (Zeitschrift für Physik 24, 166–68, 1924).

Abū-l-Faḍl Aḥmad ibn 'Alī Ibn Ḥajar Shibāb al-dīn al-'Asqalānī al-Kinānī al-Shāfi'ī was born in Ascalon 1372 and died in Cairo 1449. He was primarily a traditionist, and his vocation was awakened very early. He accomplished the

Pilgrimage for the first time in 1382; in 1391 he traveled to Upper Egypt and Palestine to collect aḥādīth; in 1397 he traveled to Yaman for the same purpose, and in Zabīd (Tihāma of Yaman) became acquainted with the famous lexicographer al-Fīrūzābādī; in 1398 he was again in Mecca, in 1399 he was in Damascus, etc. He settled down in Cairo in 1403 as teacher of ḥadīth and fiqh. He was many times qāḍī-l-quḍāt. He wrote a great many books dealing with tradition, history, biography, notably Al-iṣāba fī tamyīz al-ṣaḥāba (On the contemporaries and followers of the Prophet); Inbā' al-ghumr bi'abnā' al-'umr, political and literary history of Egypt and Syria, 1371–1446; Al-durar al-kāmina fī a'yān al-mi'a al-thāmina (Hidden pearls, biographies of famous men of the fourteenth century, chiefly Syrian and Egyptian); Tahdhīb tahdhīb al-kamāl, biographies of traditionists, for which see the note on al-Dhahabī (XIV-1), one of the most valuable books of its kind; etc.

Text. See Brockelmann.

Criticism. Wüstenfeld (no. 487, 1882). Brockelmann (2, 67–70; suppt. 2, 72–76). C. Van Arendonck (EI 2, 379, 1916).

Abū Bakr ibn Aḥmad Taqī al-dīn ibn qāḍī Shuhba al-Asadī al-Dimashqī al-Shāfi'ī (1377–1448). Professor in the madrasa Amīnīya and in the Iqbālīya; qāḍī and finally chief qāḍī of Damascus, inspector of the Nūrī hospital. He continued the Ta'rīkh al-Islām of al-Dhahabī, under the title Al-i'lām bi ta'rīkh al-Islām, and compiled biographies of Shāfi'ī doctors, the Ṭabaqāt al-Shāfi'īya, in 29 chapters of 20 years each to 1436.

Criticism. Wüstenfeld (no. 486, 1882). Brockelmann (2, 51; suppt. 2, 50).

Abū-l-'Abbās Aḥmad ibn Muḥammad ibn 'Arabshāh Shihāb al-dīn al-Dimashqī al-Ḥanafī (Damascus 1392—Cairo 1450). Historian of Tīmūr. When the latter conquered Damascus, Ibn 'Arabshāh and his family were among the prisoners taken to Samarqand. He studied there with 'Alī ibn Muḥammad al-Jurjānī and Muḥammad ibn Muḥammad al-Jazarī, then traveled to Khaṭā (Mongolia), Khwārizm, Astrakhan, the Crimea, and finally Edirne (Adrianople), where he became secretary to the 'Uthmānlī sulṭān Muḥammad I ibn Bāyazīd. After the latter's death, in 1421, Ibn 'Arabshāh returned to his native place, Damascus. He remained there from 1422 to 1436, then moved to Cairo. He was thrown into prison by the Burjī Mamlūk, al-Ẓāhir Jaqmaq (ruled 1438–53), and died in 1450.

His main work is a history of Tīmūr, completed in 1435, contrasting strikingly with the obsequious eulogies of the Persian historiographers. He showed the beastliness of Tīmūr, but he also showed his great qualities.

For additional information on Ibn 'Arabshāh's work, editions and translations of it, see sections 8 and 9 of the note on Tīmūr.

Criticism. Wüstenfeld (no. 488, 1882). Brockelmann (2, 28–30; suppt. 2, 24). Johannes Pedersen (EI 2, 362, 1916). Browne (3, 355–56, 1920). Franz Babinger: Die Geschichtsschreiber der Osmanen (p. 20–23, Leipzig 1927).

D7. *Turkey*

This section should be considered as closely connected with the previous one, for the only two men to be dealt with, al-'Aiṇī and al-Bisṭāmī, might have been very properly classified with the last group of Mamlūk historians. Both were fin-de-siècle Syrians and Ḥanafī.

Abū Muḥammad Maḥmūd ibn Aḥmad al-'Ainī was born at 'Aintāb (between Aleppo and Antioch) in 1360, and spent most of his life in Cairo; at first a ṣūfī, from 1399 on a civil servant to various Burjī Mamlūk rulers; in 1426 he was chief qāḍī of the Ḥanafī rite; he died in 1451. He had a good knowledge of Turkish and translated into that language the popular Ḥanafī manual of al-Qudūrī[19] for the sulṭān Ṭaṭār (1421), and he was able to translate at sight his own chronicle for the sulṭān al-Ashraf Bars-bey (1422–38). Incidentally, this shows that those Mamlūk rulers did not understand Arabic! The majority of his own works, however, were written in Arabic, not in Turkish. We need mention only his universal chronicle from Adam to 1446, entitled 'Iqd al-jumān fī ta'rīkh ahl al-zamān, and his elaborate and methodical commentary on the Ṣaḥīḥ of al-Bukhārī (IX-1), entitled 'Umdat al-qāri' fī sharḥ al-Bukhārī.

Criticism. Wüstenfeld (no. 489, 1882). Brockelmann (2, 52–53; suppt. 2, 50). Marçais (EI 1, 212–14, 1909).

The other "Turk" has already been referred to as a continuer of Ibn Khaldūn's speculations on the classification of sciences. 'Abd al-Raḥmān ibn Muḥammad al-Bisṭāmī al-Ḥanafī al-Ḥurūfī was born in Antioch c. 1370 (?), studied in Cairo, then established himself in Brusa, where he spent the rest of his life and died in 1454. His encyclopaedia, Al-fawā'iḥ al-miskīya, and his treatise on the classification of sciences, Durrat al-'ulūm, have been named above. He wrote many mystical treatises, some of which discuss the magical properties of letters according to the diacritical signs with them (hence his nickname al-Ḥurūfī). Finally, he compiled a chronicle and collections of biographies. One of these, entitled Durar fī-l-ḥawādīth wal-siyar (or Wafayāt 'alā tartīb al-a'wām), is a collection of biographies (obituaries arranged in the order of death years) of famous men from the Prophet to 1300, dedicated to Murād II in 1431. He wrote exclusively in Arabic.

Criticism. Wüstenfeld (no. 481, 1882). Brockelmann (2, 231; suppt. 2, 323). Franz Babinger: Die Geschichtsschreiber der Osmanen (p. 17–18, Leipzig 1927).

D8. *Īrān*

Inasmuch as reference has been made above to the Arabic biography of Tīmūr, we may mention here his first Persian biographer, Niẓām al-dīn Shāmī, a native of Tabrīz, who was living in Baghdād in 1392 when Tīmūr took that city. In 1401, Tīmūr ordered him to write an account of his rule. The Ẓafar-nāmah (Book of victory), written in Persian, tells Tīmūr's history to 1404.

This history was superseded by another bearing the same title, completed in 1424 by Sharaf al-dīn 'Alī Yazdī (d. 1454).

Still another history of Tīmūr, dealing especially with his invasion of Armenia, was written in Armenian by Thomas of Alovid, who was still living in 1447.

Browne (3, 361–62, 1920). Storey (2, 278–88, 1935).

E. *Ceylon*

Dhammakitti V wrote in Siṅhalese a history of Buddhism from the beginnings down to the fourteenth century, thus covering a period of two millennia. A similar

[19] Mukhtaṣar al-Qudūrī, written by Abū-l-Ḥusain Aḥmad ibn Muḥammad al-Qudūrī al-Baghdādī (972–1036). Brockelmann (1, 174; suppt. 1, 295). The Mukhtaṣar is still in use today; there are many Oriental editions of it in Arabic, Persian, Turkish.

history in Pāli is ascribed to one Dhammakitti, who may be identical with the preceding one.

F. *Java*

A poem written by Prapañca in old Javanese in 1365 is a valuable document for the history and the historical geography of the Mājapāhit empire.

G. *China and Korea*

During this period which witnessed the disaggregation of the Yüan dynasty and, after considerable anarchy, the beginning of the Ming, the historiographers continued their task with admirable imperturbability. The best exemplar of the historiographical tradition about the middle of the century was the Mongol T'o-t'o, who edited the official histories of the Sung, Liao, and Chin dynasties, that is, the twentieth, twenty-first, and twenty-second of the twenty-six histories. As he was not dealing with his own times, but with the years 906-1279, his detachment from the chaos existing around him was perhaps made easier; he was not simply a historian, however, but a civil servant and a minister of state, a victim of the circumstances which he had helped to create; in spite of his devotion to the last Mongol emperor, he was twice driven into banishment and in 1355 he was put to death.

As soon as the Ming dynasty was established, the editing of the records of the overturned dynasty was ordered. The Yüan shih was edited by Sung Lien, Wang Wei, and Li Shan-ch'ang. The best man of that group was probably Sung Lien, whose critical spirit seems to have been unusually developed.

The first task of the Ming historians was to publish the Yüan records; their second task, to compile annals and collect documents which would make the publication of the Ming records possible after the downfall of the new dynasty. Wu Hai was employed by the Ming rulers for the second task. He distinguished himself by his aggressive Confucianism, which was, so to say, the badge of his office. The whole historiographical tradition was essentially and militantly Confucian and of its nature impatient with Buddhist pietism and with Taoist extravagance.

The compilation of gazetteers (discussed in ch. I, p. 204) was closely connected with administration and historiography, and of course with census taking. We know that a nation-wide census was ordered on December 12, 1370, and by a strange hazard a duplicate census blank with its seals was kept for four centuries in the family of a certain Chang Sung. It was published in the gazetteer of P'u-chên (Chehkiang), P'u-chên chi-wên, compiled by Hu Cho c. 1774, a MS copy of which exists in the Library of Congress (see fig. 24). From the description published by Arthur W. Hummel (Report of the Library of Congress for 1940, p. 158-59) we extract the translation of the very strict regulations printed on the blank:

"On December 12, 1370, the Board of Revenue was informed by Imperial edict, that although the country is now at peace, the Government has no clear knowledge of the population. The provincial authorities are therefore instructed to prepare census blanks in duplicate so that a census can be made of the whole Empire. Every revenue official must give notice to the local officials who in turn are to see that all the people under them present to those officials a written statement (without any falsifications) of the number of persons in their households. Each householder is to be given an official blank with a half seal on each stub which can be detached

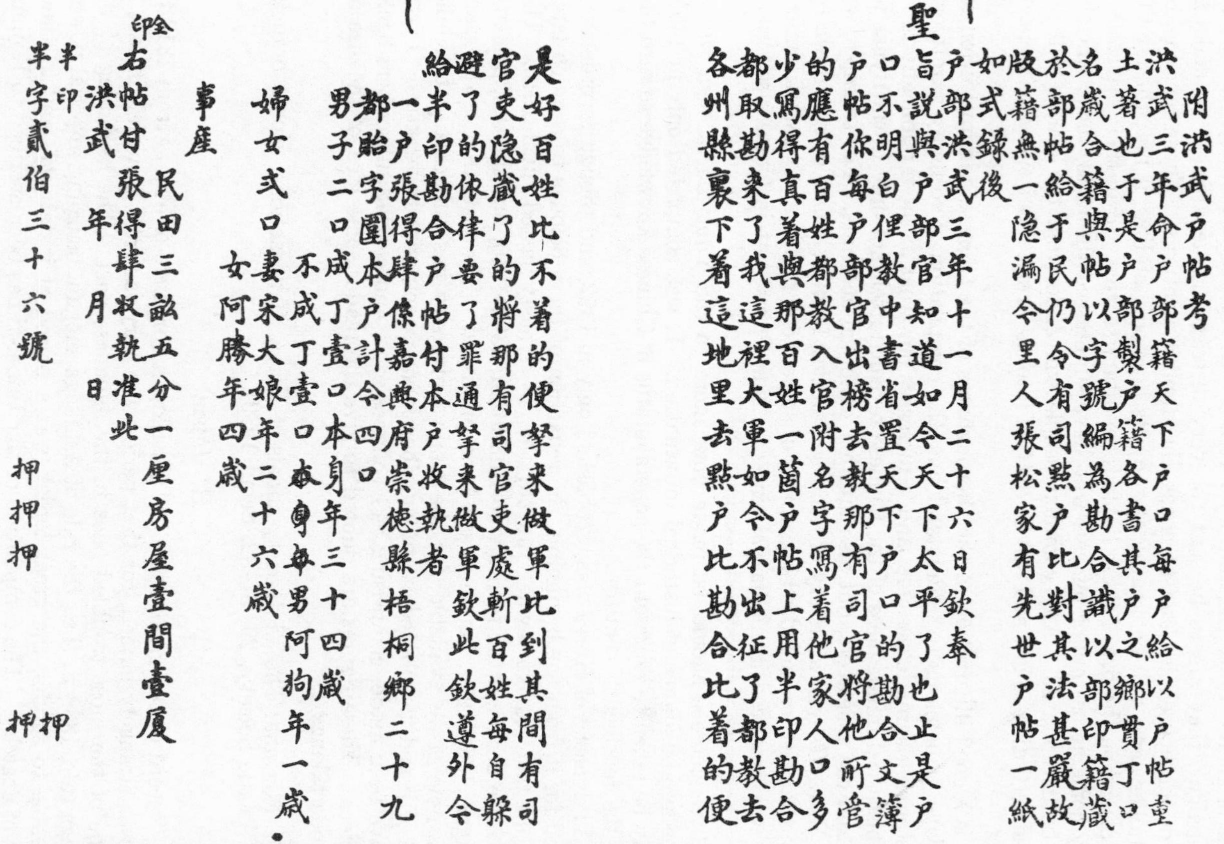

附洪武戶帖考
洪武三年命戶部籍天下戶口每戶給以戶帖壹
土著也于是戶部製戶籍各書其戶之鄉貫丁口
名歲合籍與帖以字號編為勘合識以部印籍藏
於部帖給于民仍令有司點戶比對其法甚嚴故
版籍無一隱漏令里人張松家有先世戶帖一紙
如式錄後
戶部洪武三年十一月二十六日欽奉
聖
旨說與戶部官知道如今天下太平了也止是戶
口不明白俚教中書省置天下戶口的勘合文簿
戶帖你每戶部官出榜去教那有司官將他所管
的應有百姓都教入官附名字寫着他家人口多
少寫得真着與那百姓一箇戶帖上用半印勘合
都取勘來了我這裡大軍如今不出征了都教去
各州縣裏下着這地里去點戶比勘合比着的便
是好百姓比不着的便拏来做軍比到其間有司
官吏隱藏了的將那有司官吏處斬百姓每自躲
避了的依律要了罪通拏来做軍欽此欽遵外令
給半印勘合戶帖付本戶收執者
一戶張得肆係嘉興府崇德縣梧桐鄉二十九
都貽字圍本戶計今四口
男子二口
成丁壹口本身年三十四歲
不成丁壹口[illegible]男阿狗年一歲
婦女弍口
妻宋大娘年二十六歲
女阿勝年四歲
事產
民田三畝五分一厘
房屋壹間壹厦
右帖付張得肆收執准此
全印
洪武 年 月 日
半印
半字貳伯三十六號
押
押
押
押押

FIG. 24. Instructions for the Chinese census of 1370, as printed in the P'u-chên chi-wên. The fragment translated in the text is indicated with brackets at the top. It is written in a rustic vernacular of that time, the peculiarities of which are not reproducible in the translation. Courtesy of Dr. A. W. Hummel and of the Library of Congress.

from the original. Since the military forces of this region are no longer going out on campaigns, they are to be sent to every district and department to make a census of the households and to check the duplicate returns. Those households whose tallies agree will be treated as subjects in good standing; if not, the family will be placed on the list of those liable for military service. If in their search the military come across minor officials who have suppressed the facts, those officials are to be decapitated. Any common people who hide from the census will be punished according to law and will be drafted into the army. Let everyone respect this."

This is a good illustration of the thoroughness of the Chinese administration of those days; it helps us to understand how the compilation of so many gazetteers and histories was made possible, and it increases our trust in those publications.

The historical-mindedness of the Chinese revealed itself not only in the dynastic annals and the gazetteers, but also in other historical accounts. For example, we owe to Hsia Wên-yen a history of Chinese painting from mythical origins down to c. 1365; that history includes biographies of some 1,500 painters. No work similar to this was produced in mediaeval times outside China, but in China itself Hsia Wên-yen had some sixteen predecessors!

Finally, reference should be made once more to the Yung Lo ta tien, which contains an abundance of historical information. It was completed only in 1409, but may be taken to represent the general status of Chinese knowledge toward the end of the fourteenth century.

The Yi dynasty of Korea was established only in 1392, and though records were collected for it from the beginning, the redaction of them belongs to a much later period, in fact, to our own. Indeed, the Yi dynasty lasted until 1910. The annals have been written for its whole duration, 1392–1910, but those of the two last reigns, 1864–1910, have not yet been published. The rest, that is the main part, is now easily available, for the Keijo University has published a facsimile edition of it and distributed it among other Japanese imperial universities. Forty sets have been made, comprising 849 volumes each, and costing subscribers 6,000 yen apiece. These figures are quoted to give the reader some idea of the size of such undertakings.

C. M. McCune: The Yi dynasty annals of Korea (Transactions, Korea branch, Royal Asiatic Society, 29, 57–82, Seoul 1939).

H. *Japan*

The "record of the great peace" (Taihei-ki), a chronicle of events from 1318 to 1368, was strangely named, for that period was very far from peaceful, in fact it was one of the most troubled ones in the Japanese past. The beginning of the Ashikaga rule, 1338 ff. (i.e., the rule of Ashikaga shōgun, usurping imperial power, but unable to subdue the great lords), was a period of instability, and at times almost of anarchy. The compilation of the Taihei-ki has been ascribed to Kojima, a bonze in one of the Hiei-zan monasteries, who died in 1374. In another edition, entitled Taiheiki Sōmoku, the narrative is continued to 1382. In addition to its historical value, this work has had a very considerable influence on Japanese literature.

William George Aston: History of Japanese literature (p. 169–83, Yokohama 1899). Papinot (p. 298, 615, 1909).

XIII. LAW AND SOCIOLOGY

A. *Islām*

A1. *Maghrib*

It seems proper to begin this survey with Islām, for the outstanding sociologist of the age was Ibn Khaldūn. We cannot say that he dominated the age, for he remained practically unknown in the West until the nineteenth century, and it is even probable that his works were not appreciated by Muslims, except the few who got to know him personally. It was, strangely enough, in Turkey that he was first allowed to reach a larger public, and that did not happen before the sixteenth century. This, however, is a common story of universal application. Nobody can be a prophet in his own country and in his own time, unless he be a false prophet and simply the "loud speaker" of his own contemporaries. The true prophet, the man who is ahead of his time and place, is likely to be misunderstood ipso facto.

To us, however, who can see Ibn Khaldūn in his true proportion, he appears like a mountain in the midst of a plain. We might call him the founder of sociology, or say that he was the leading sociologist since Aristotle. It is not necessary to repeat here the justification of such statements given in the relatively long note devoted to him.

As Ibn Khaldūn was a Tunisian, we begin our account of Islām with the Maghrib. This is a curious contrast with the previous half-century, our survey of which was restricted to Eastern Islām. Nor was Ibn Khaldūn the only Maghribī to draw our attention, for something must be said of at least two others.

Mūsā II ibn Ziyān, sulṭān of Tlemcen from 1352 to 1386, wrote a treatise entitled Wāsiṭat al-sulūk fī siyāsat al-mulūk. Though the intention of this book was political, it is very different from, let us say, the Kitāb al-aḥkām al-sulṭānīya of al-Māwardī (XI-2), which remained the standard exposition of political theory and government in Islām.[1] Sulṭān Mūsā was concerned with ethics, or with the ethical foundations of government. His book is comparable to the Latin treatises de eruditione principum. In fact, it was written for the education and direction of his son, being a sort of political testament.

A textbook on law (fiqh = iuris prudentia) was composed in verse by Ibn 'Āṣim of Granada.

These three men, Ibn Khaldūn, Mūsā ibn Ziyān, and Ibn 'Āṣim, belonged to the Mālikī rite, which dominated in Spain and North Africa (west of Egypt). Ibn Khaldūn was not a theologian, that is, he was as little of one as a Muslim doctor could ever be, but he gives us in the Muqaddama (beginning of vol. 3) a brief outline of the different kinds of jurisprudence.

A2. *Mashriq*

Though the Mashriq could boast no Ibn Khaldūn, it produced at this time a number of distinguished jurists, students of government, and administrators. The annals of Ibn Duqmāq have already been mentioned; they contain much information concerning Egyptian society. On the other hand, the great manuals

[1] Al-Māwardī's book is analyzed by Edward J. Jurji: Islamic law in operation (Journal of Semitic languages 57, 32–49, 1940), who then explains the realities of Muslim jurisprudence under three headings, the judge (al-qāḍī), tribunals for appeals (al-naẓar fīl maẓālim), and municipal police (al-ḥisba); the officer in charge of the latter (al-muḥtasib) has been mentioned many times in this volume.

of chancellery, of which the Ṣubḥ al-a'shā of al-Qalqashandī was the latest, are the best source books for the study of Mamlūk government and administration. A number of law books were composed by al-Taftāzānī.

It may seem strange to speak here again of the inhuman "Führer" Tīmūr, but that cannot be helped, if only to discredit his authorship of the Malfūẓāt or Tuzūkāt-i-Tīmūrī. We know that these documents explaining the civil and military institutions of Tīmūr are forgeries of the seventeenth century, definitely posterior to the Bābar-nāma, which inspired their fabrication. Of course, every government, good or bad, deserves analysis, and the analysis is valuable to the sociologist in any case. Though Tīmūr's activities had been largely destructive, he had dreamed of realizing "a new order" in Asia, and he even succeeded in creating it, but only for a very short time. Tīmūr's destructions (e.g., of the flourishing culture of the Near and Middle East) were lasting—they stopped those cultures for centuries; his creations, except for a few monuments in Samarqand and elsewhere, ephemeral.

The Arabic historian of Tīmūr, Ibn 'Arabshāh, was credited with the writing of a "mirror for princes" entitled Fākihat al-khulafā' wa-mufākahat al-ẓurafā', a collection of animal fables mixed with advice to princes. This was probably his work, but it is not original, being largely a translation or adaptation of the Persian Marzubān-nāma by Sa'd al-dīn of Warāmīn (near Ṭihrān), date unknown (Browne 3, 356; EI 2, 363). The translation, having been made toward the end of Ibn 'Arabshāh's life (c. 1448), is outside the scope of this volume.

All these men were probably of the Ḥanafī rite (the earliest and still the most widespread today; the only one completely acceptable within the 'Uthmānlī empire); I am not quite sure about al-Qalqashandī, who, flourishing as he did in Egypt, may have been a Shāfi'ī. As to Tīmūr, he was outwardly a Muslim, possibly a Ḥanafī, certainly a tool of Iblīs. In spite of his generosity to the Naqshbandī darvishes, which was his way of trying to bribe the guardians of heaven, we may be confident that he will never escape from hell—the unanimous hatred of posterity. He is damned forever.

Al-Taftāzānī discussed not only Ḥanafī, but also Mālikī and Shāfi'ī law. It is well to remember that the differences between the four original madhāhib (especially between the three earliest ones, just named) were not great, and it was possible to pass from one madhhab to another (many examples will be found in this volume). The legalistic differences separating one rite from another were much smaller than the temperamental differences existing between their adherents.

B. *Christendom*

Islām continued and united Hebrew and Greco-Roman traditions. Christendom combined Christian with Roman traditions; moreover, it borrowed from Islām a few legal ideas such as limited partnership (qirāḍ) and certain technicalities of commercial law.[2] Muslim influence on the commercial usages of the West is revealed by a number of "business" words in European dialects which are clearly of Arabic origin (tariff, traffic, check, magazine,[3] quintal or kantar, sequin, arratel, oka, etc.).

Let us now consider Christian efforts. Our survey is divided into six sections: (1) Italy, (2) France, (3) Germany, (4) England, (5) the Netherlands, (6) Byzantium.

[2] Edward J. Jurji (p. 33, 1940).

[3] It is rather amusing to note that the Arabic-speaking people of Alexandria are using today to designate a shop the word maghāza, derived from the French magasin, itself derived indirectly from Arabic makhzin, pl. makhāzīn.

B1. *Italy*

The most remarkable constitution of this time, the Constitutiones aegidianae, was promulgated by a Spaniard, Gil Alvarez Carrillo de Albornoz. It is quite proper, however, to speak of cardinal Albornoz in the Italian section, for he had been appointed legate in Italy and his task was the re-establishment of temporal power in the papal states. He organized a kind of totalitarian government which was brutal enough, yet more necessary and less barbaric in the fourteenth century (toutes proportions gardées) than the fascist state in the twentieth century. His code remained in force from 1357 to 1816. It was largely because of his intelligence and activity that the Babylonian captivity was put an end to, and he may be called one of the early artisans of Italian unity.

Juridical learning was admirably continued by Bàrtolo da Sassoferrato and Baldo degli Ubaldi. Bàrtolo, whom his admirers called a new Accorso, was in reality much better, for he represented a higher stage in legal thinking. His field was the whole of law, substantive and adjective, and his teaching, which caused the school of Perugia to eclipse the older one of Bologna, was so constructive and so impressive that it gave as it were a new form and new life to the study of law. The greatest of his immediate disciples was Baldo, who succeeded him in the chair of Perugia and consecrated his influence. Baldo taught law for more than half a century, not only in Perugia, where he spent most of his time, but in five other Italian universities, the last of them being Pavia, where he lived his last decade and where he died in 1400. Between them Bàrtolo and Baldo encompassed the whole century and dominated it. During the following centuries, down to the seventeenth at least, Roman law was the old tradition as interpreted and modified by them. Their views could be discussed, they could not be ignored.

Under stress of mercantilism and urbanization, which were growing particularly fast in northern Italy, Baldo was led to formulate opinions on commercial and financial difficulties (e.g., bills of exchange) which had not been considered by his predecessors.

The financial difficulties were increased by the irresistible expansion of international business. There were then in Italy, notably in Florence, international merchants and bankers like the Bardi and later Francesco Datini. The latter had agencies not only in other Italian cities, but also in Avignon, Barcelona, Majorca, and Valencia, and his activities can be investigated in detail, because the archives of his house have been preserved. One can readily imagine that such activities created new problems and opened new horizons to jurists.

The development of international private law was paralleled by the development of international public law. One of the earliest Western treatises on the latter subject was published in 1360 by a professor of Bologna, Giovanni da Legnano, and dedicated by him to the cardinal Albornoz.[4] Giovanni's treatise De bello was very appropriate, because, then as now, war was an inescapable reality; and it was necessary to define the rights and duties which arose out of it. When and how does war begin? When and how does it end? What are the rights of the victors, of the noncombatants? What are the lawful causes of war, the conditions of armistice and peace? Giovanni da Legnano was as much a theologian as a jurist, and his mind was befogged with astrological fancies; therefore, his De bello is a medley of

[4] Bologna had submitted again to papal power. The history of Bologna in the fourteenth century is very complicated. See Stokvis (3, 879–83, 1893).

theology, astrology, medicine, and law; facts and fancy. Nevertheless, it was one of the first attempts in the West to face such problems and try to solve them in as good a form as possible.

We may note in passing that the discussion of war, if relatively new in Christendom, was old in Islām. In fact, it was discussed by the Prophet himself, and there are frequent references to war (jihād), its causes and duties, etc., in the Qur'ān. Many Arabic treatises are specifically devoted to that very subject, e.g. one by the Berber reformer Ibn Tūmart (XII-1), and the subject is often discussed in treatises on chivalry, such as the Faḍl al-khail of 'Abd al-Mu'min al-Dimyāṭī (XIII-2) and the Kitāb fī-l-jihād wal-furūsīya of Ṭaibughā ibn 'Abdallāh (d. 1394?); it is always discussed in the legal compendia, and there is a long and wistful digression ad hoc in the Muqaddama of Ibn Khaldūn (French ed., 2, 75–91). In short, the moral and legal problems evoked by war conditions were commonplaces of Muslim thought.[5]

It is remarkable that in both cases—Christendom and Islām—the subject, complicated as it was, was often made unnecessarily more so by the attempt to consider not only real war, but also metaphorical war (moral strife, the conflicts within our conscience). The ṣūfī writers distinguished between the greater warfare (al-jihād al-akbar) against our own vices and lusts, and the lesser warfare (al-jihād al-aṣghar) against infidels. In the same way Giovanni speaks of heavenly spiritual war arising from Satan's rebellion, the human spiritual war, which is the same as the jihād akbar of the Muslims, etc. Is that coincidence accidental, or did the Muslim views on jihād reach Giovanni?

There was still another kind of war which was becoming more common in those days: civil war, revolt against a single tyrant, or revolt of ill-treated workmen against their oppressors—political or social revolt. What are the causes of revolt? And how shall the right to revolt be defined and limited? On the other hand, what are the rights of the tyrannus (in modern parlance, the duce or the Führer)? Bàrtolo had already tackled that perilous subject, and Coluccio Salutati came back to it in his De tyranno, written c. 1400, the meditations of a Florentine Guelph irritated by the Milanese imperialists. In that pamphlet Salutati discusses such questions as: (cap. 2) Is it lawful to kill a tyrant? (cap. 4) Was the murder of Julius Caesar justified? The first question cannot be answered absolutely; "just as he who destroys a tyrant in a lawful way is to be loaded with honors, so he who unlawfully slays a ruler deserves the severest penalty." As to the second question, having previously (cap. 3) explained "that Caesar was not a tyrant, seeing that he held his principate in a commonwealth, lawfully and not by abuse of law," he concludes (cap. 5) "that Dante was right in placing Brutus and Cassius in the lowest hell as traitors of the deepest dye."

The right of tyrannicide did not remain the subject of an academic controversy; within a few years a "cause célèbre" placed it in the foreground of actualities. Indeed, on November 23, 1407, Louis of Orléans (brother of the mad king Charles VI and usurper of his power) was murdered by agents of John the Fearless, duke of Burgundy. John's counsellor, Jean Petit,[6] argued that the murder had been a

[5] For general information on jihād, see Hughes (p. 243–48, 1885); D. B. Macdonald (EI 1, 1041, 1913). Majid Khadduri: The law of war and peace in Islam (Chicago thesis, 142 p., London 1940).

[6] Jean Petit (c. 1360–1411) was a very distinguished theologian and publicist, originating in Hesdin (pays de Caux, Normandy). He defended the privileges of the University of Paris and was sent to Rome in 1407 to investigate means of ending the Great Schism. (NBG 39, 705–7, 1862.)

case of legitimate tyrannicide, and a Parisian court gave a judgment in his favor. This enraged his adversaries. Jean Gerson moved heaven and earth to obtain the condemnation of Jean Petit. As is unavoidable in political matters, the question was prejudiced by all kinds of intrigues and personal issues. It was finally submitted to the council of Constance. In 1415, the council condemned tyrannicide in a general way, and it reversed the Parisian judgment on technicalities, but it did not condemn Petit's specific action.[7]

For further discussion see Friedrich Schoenstedt: Tyrannenmord im Spätmittelalter. Studien zur Geschichte des Tyrannenbegriffs und der Tyrannenmordtheorie insbesondere in Frankreich (Berlin 1938), not seen; reviewed in Lychnos (1941, 355–58). Ingvar Andersson: The conception of the tyrant in the Middle Ages and the Renaissance (in Swedish with English summary, Lychnos, Uppsala 1943, 111–29).

Other aspects of the social vicissitudes of those days are given us in the chronicle of Gino Capponi, narrating the revolt of the wool carders of Florence (1378 ff.), in which he had himself participated. That revolt was caused by the industrial development which was disturbing the social equilibrium, and by the greed of operators anxious to get rich as fast as possible; it was an earnest of similar revolts which were to occur in many countries down to our own times.

B2. *France*

Let us first turn to French literature, for literature is always the best mirror of social conditions and to some extent of social thought. Consider the Livre de l'exemple du riche homme et du ladre, an immense poem (some 15,000 lines) composed in 1352 by a canon of La Fère (on the Oise). As the title indicates, the poem is derived from the parable concerning a certain rich man and a certain beggar called Lazarus (Luke 16:19–31); it deals with the seven capital sins, the Lord's prayer, the ten commandments, the seven sacraments, the seven gifts of the Holy Spirit, confession, Sundays and holidays, and reviews the different estates of the world in the following order: pope, cardinals, prelates, monks, secular priests and canons, nuns, kings, princes, judges, lawyers, usurers, notaries and tabellions, false witnesses, murderers, counterfeiters, tavern keepers, soothsayers, soldiers, gamblers, etc. That scheme of precedence is amusing. I do not know how much information on fourteenth-century manners can be obtained from that poem, for it was partly compiled from earlier writings. According to the author's own statement, his main sources were two poems, Roman de charité and Miserere, written by Renclus de Moiliens[8] at the end of the twelfth century.[9]

While the good canon of La Fère was thus engaged in the edification of the people of Picardy, efforts were being made or prepared on a much higher plane by a Norman canon, Nicole Oresme. The latter was a scientifically minded man, who was anxious to provide the French people with the best knowledge available on political matters. That best knowledge was not recent, it had been taught in the Lyceum of Athens seventeen centuries previously! Yet Aristotle's Politics had

[7] Emerton (p. 68–69, 1925). Otto Castellieri: Die Verherrlichung des Tyrannenmordes, in his book Am Hofe der Herzöge von Burgund (p. 37–54, Basel 1926), or in the English translation, The court of Burgundy (p. 36–51, London 1929).

[8] Moiliens or Molliens is probably Molliens-Vidame near Amiens.

[9] Anton Gerard Van Hamel: Li Romans de carité et Miserere du Renclus (= recluse) de Moiliens (2 vols., Paris 1885), critical edition with glossary and notes. Petit de Julleville (2, 200–2, 1896).

been revealed to Latin readers only in 1260 by William of Moerbeke. Since then, St. Thomas and Peter of Auvergne had commented on it, and a small group of doctors and public-spirited men were now fairly well acquainted with the "new" political views. Oresme resolved to divulge these views to a larger audience. He translated into French not only the Politica, but also the Ethica and the Oeconomica, but those views were really too new and too advanced for most educated people, and their popular success was small.

Moreover, Oresme was deeply interested in economic problems; he was one of the earliest students of money (we shall come back to that later on); he has been called the greatest economist of the Middle Ages. It is true, his claim to scientific eminence has been discounted because of his astrological tendencies. This is unfair on two grounds. In the first place, one must remember that astrology dominated contemporary thought to such an extent that it was unavoidable. The mixture of astrology with history and politics is beautifully illustrated in the works of Giovanni da Legnano and Pierre d'Ailly. In the second place, Oresme's astrology was minimal and critical. He escaped from the astrological evil just as much as that was possible for a man of his time.

Humbler views on domestic economy were explained in French in the Ménagier de Paris (c. 1393).

The Babylonish captivity had intensified the dispute between pope and king. That was the old dispute between pope and emperor in a new form. Which prerogative is the highest? Who must bow to the other? The most famous pamphlet ad hoc was the Somnium viridarii or Le songe du vergier, which concluded in the king's favor and enjoyed considerable popularity in both editions (Latin and French). There has been much discussion as to which edition was the original one, and the authorship of either or both has been ascribed to Giovanni da Legnano, Raoul de Presles, Nicole Oresme, Evrart de Trémaugon,[10] and others. It is now believed by many scholars that Philippe de Mézières completed the Latin text c. 1376, and the French text a little later, but the matter is not certain.

The discussions concerning king vs. pope were mild as compared with the controversies caused by the Great Schism. The matter in question now was not simply the relative authority of the pope vs. the emperor or the king, but the authority of the pope vs. the church, and of the church vs. the state. To which society, lay or clerical, did the definition of the perfect society at the beginning of the Politica apply? To be perfect, the society must have means of getting rid of an intolerable ruler. Hence the church could not be a "societas perfecta,"[11] unless it were possible for a council to depose the pope. The question could not be evaded, for when there were two (or three) competing popes, at least one (or two) of them must be illegal. Assuming that God inspired the papal election, he could not inspire the simultaneous rule of two (or three) popes. Unfortunately, the difficulties due to the Schism, pernicious as they were, were complicated and aggravated by all kinds of political and personal jealousies involving all the Christian states of Europe. A review of the books and pamphlets published during that critical half-century (1378–1429), by the defenders of each pope and each king, by the universities (Paris, Toulouse, etc.), by the liberals[12] explaining the conciliar theory and the

[10] Alfred Coville: Evrart de Trémaugon [d. 1386?] et le Songe du vergier (84 p., Paris 1933).

[11] See J. N. Figgis (ERE 11, 650, 1921).

[12] Conrad von Gelnhausen, Heinrich von Langenstein, Pierre d'Ailly, Jean Gerson, Nicolas Clémanges, etc.

conservatives resisting it, would take too much space, but a good many of these writings are cited incidentally in this volume.[13]

Thanks to the application of Aristotelian and Thomist knowledge to these great problems crying for a solution, the theory of government might have made considerable progress. Unhappily, whatever light was produced was obscured or made unavailable because of ungenerous passions. The Great Schism was a great failure from which the church was hardly able to recover; it was one of the distant and not of the least causes of the Reformation.

The political and social education of the French people was made possible by translators, of whom Oresme was the most illustrious, but not the only one. During the rule of Charles V many others were at work. Denis Foulechat translated the Polycratus of John of Salisbury; Raoul de Presles, St. Augustine's City of God and the De utraque potestate of Giles of Rome; Jean Dandin, the De remediis utriusque fortunae of Petrarca and the De eruditione filiorum regalium of Vincent of Beauvais; Jean Golein, the anonymous De informatione principum. Does that mean that there was a large demand for such books? Not necessarily, for royal patronage would suffice to bring them into being. It is probable that the demand was small but growing. The passionate controversies of the age must have helped to promote it.

It is curious that in spite of all that legal and political turmoil, there were at that time no jurists in France who could be compared at all with Bàrtolo da Sassoferrato or Baldo degli Ubaldi, nor even canonists to challenge Gratian's fame. The Corpus iuris canonici had been completed with the Liber septimus (1317) under John XXII. The most distinguished French canonist was perhaps Gilles de Bellemère (c. 1337–1407), who was bishop successively of Lavaur, Puy-en-Vélay, and Avignon, and wrote legal consilia and commentaries on the Decretum. There are good reasons for believing he was the author of the Quinze joies de mariage, a model of French prose, but not exactly the kind of book which one would expect from a doctor of canon law.

The earliest edition of the XV Joyes de mariage has no indication of place or date. Brunet placed it Lyon c. 1480–90, but it may be earlier, for it has a very ancient look (50 leaves, Gothic type, two columns). There is but one copy of it, in the Bibliothèque nationale, Paris. Its text has been almost literally reprinted by Ferdinand Heuckenkamp (84 p., Halle 1901). The authorship has been ascribed to Gilles de Bellemère by Coville, to Antoine de la Salle, to Pierre II de Samer by Pierre Louys, etc.[14] The author was a clerk of Picardy, and the most probable date of composition is the beginning of the fifteenth century.

Alfred Coville: Recherches sur quelques écrivains du XIVe et du XVe siècle (p. 58–174, Paris 1935). Fernand Fleuret: Les quinze joyes de mariage (Paris 1936), text with preface, bibliography, glossary.

B3. *Germany*

The originator of the conciliar theory was not the Frenchman Jean Gerson, as is often repeated, but Conrad von Gelnhausen, a Hessian; he was closely followed

[13] For a well documented and clear review, see Flick (1930).

[14] Antoine de la Salle was born c. 1398, was viguier d'Arles, author of Petit Jehan de Saintré, died c. 1461. Pierre II was abbot of the Benedictine abbey of Samer 1377–78. Samer is near Boulogne. Alfred Coville: Le Petit Jehan de Saintré, recherches complémentaires (153 p., Paris 1937).

by Heinrich von Langenstein. Both were seculars and both alumni of the University of Paris. Therefore, it may be correct to say that the conciliar theory was incubated in Paris. Though it aroused considerable and long-drawn-out opposition, for the whole hierarchy was against it and only a few "liberals" were bold enough at first to defend it, we may recall that it finally triumphed at the council of Constance (1414–18) and made the healing of the Great Schism possible. The Schism, it is now clear enough, could never have been healed otherwise.

Langenstein was interested in economic questions, an interest which he had probably acquired in Paris, where it had been fostered by Buridan and Oresme. He was the first teacher of economics in Vienna. Langenstein might be called Heinrich von Hessen, for he was like Gelnhausen a Hessian, but it is better not to do so, lest he be confused with another and younger Heinrich von Hessen, who taught in Heidelberg, was a Carthusian, and lived until 1427 (Langenstein died in 1397). This younger Heinrich is said to have written a political treatise, Summa de republica (?).

It is curious that the Germans mentioned thus far were all Hessians.[15]

The student of economic history will find much grist for his mill in the family chronicle written by Ulman Stromer of Nuremberg. For example, Stromer explains the conditions governing business transacted by the merchants of Nuremberg with those of other cities of Germany or with other countries.

B4. *England*

A number of literary documents reveal the social fermentation taking place with increasing vigor in the second half of the fourteenth century. About the middle of the century there appeared two visionary poems, the "Parlement of the thre ages" and "Wynnere and Wastoure," both in West Midland dialect. The Parlement (665 alliterative long lines) contains remarkable descriptions of nature. The "three ages" are youth, maturity, and old age, and the intention of the poem is moral; a list of the romantic heroes is given, and the conclusion is "Vanity of vanities!... Death takes all! Go shrive you Youth and Middle Age." The "Tretys and god schorte refreyte by-twixte Wynnere and Wastoure" (503 alliterative long lines) is more to the point. It was written in 1352 in the form of a dream describing a debate held in the presence of Edward III and the Black Prince by the two rival faction leaders, Winner and Waster. It is really an economic pamphlet, satirizing the ugly tendencies of the day, on the one hand the hoarding and profiteering of rich merchants, lawyers, and ecclesiastics, including the pope and the friars, on the other hand the extravagance of the young nobles, especially the Black Prince (Edward, prince of Wales, then 22). The ones are hoarding and the others wasting, while the people starve. Unfortunately, the end of the poem is lost (Wells p. 241–44, 800, etc.).

Both poems influenced a work of far greater importance, Piers Plowman, the popularity of which is attested by the survival of some 50 MSS (against 64 for the Canterbury tales). The first and last versions of it are dated respectively c. 1362 and c. 1393. It is a very effective description of the injustice and misery suffered by the lower classes because of the greed and carelessness of their "betters," also an indictment of governmental and ecclesiastical corruption.

Social unrest was deep in England, deeper even than those poems would suggest,

[15] Dietrich von Niem, who defended the conciliar method in his De modis uniendi et reformandi ecclesiam in concilio universali, wrote that dialogue only in 1410; he was a Westphalian.

for the people who felt it most strongly could neither read nor write. Witness the increasing popularity of the legendary outlaw Robin Hood.[16] The repression was merciless, but such rigor could only retard the explosion and make it more terrible when it finally occurred. English "outlawry," we must remember, was a ferocious conception. Read the Fleta (book 1, ch. 27): "Est enim weyvium[17] quod nullus advocat, et utlagariae aequipollet quoad poenam. Utlagatus et Weyviata capita gerunt lupina, quae ab omnibus impune poterunt amputari; merito enim sine lege perire debent qui secundum legem vivere recusant." The outlaws were not considered human beings; hidden in the forests, they had nothing to lose, everything to gain, by revolting. The life of the poor was so hard that the temptation of outlawry and revolt may have been great and sometimes overwhelming, especially among the most independent and courageous. And yet a real uprising was long delayed. The French Jacquerie (1358) anticipated it but was less serious and was more easily repressed. The English revolt led by Jack Straw, Wat Tyler, John Ball did not occur until 1381. It was a true revolution, involving the burning of manors, the destruction of records of tenures and game parks, the murder of landlords and lawyers, a march on London, etc. The reaction led by Richard II was cruel and apparently efficient, but the liberation of the working classes had definitely begun.

It is remarkable that a historian like the Benedictine Thomas Walsingham, one of the best authorities for the Peasants' Revolt, on the conservative side, ascribed it to the unbelief of the barons.[18] In a sense that was true, but not in the way Thomas understood it. If the barons had practiced the religion which they professed, they would have treated the peasants with more humanity and there would have been no cause for a revolution.

There is of course an abundance of information on social matters in the Canterbury tales, but not of the kind which is found in Piers Plowman. William Langland was very gently on the side of the poor and downtrodden; Geoffrey Chaucer was definitely on the other side, moreover he was first and last a man of letters and a courtier. His qibla was Italy, the home of romance and humanities, the home also of novelties and enterprise. As Coulton wittily observed,[19] "Italy was to Chaucer both what Europe is to a modern American and what America is to a modern European."

The economic organization of England was improving, but far more slowly than that of northern Italy. We may note that bills of exchange were first recognized in English law in 1379; they were probably used a little before that date, but in Italy their use went back to 1161 (Introd. 2, 317).

There was much less interest in civil law and in canon law than in Italy or even in France. As far as canon law is concerned, the Babylonish captivity had increased antipapal tendencies; to be sure, the clergy had to obey it, but the laity was often tempted to resist it, even before the antipapal legislation of Edward III. England drifted so far away from Avignon that it found it difficult to return to

[16] There has been much discussion among scholars about the reality of Robin Hood, and, if he existed at all, about his date. Sidney Lee (DNB 27, 258-61, 1891). That is irrelevant to our argument. The poor people of the fourteenth century did not doubt his reality; they loved him.

[17] A woman could not be outlawed, because she was not in law, but she could be weyved (or waived), which amounted to the same thing.

[18] Historia anglicana (Rolls ed., 2, 12, 1864).

[19] Medieval panorama (p. 329, 1938).

Rome. Yet Wycliffe had frightened the landowners, and many Englishmen, then as now, were so afraid of communism that they preferred a kind of fascism.

The conflict between lay and clerical authorities so well expressed in the Somnium viridarii of Philippe de Mézières was familiar enough in England, even in a form intensified by national antagonism to Avignon; it is possible that the Somnium was read by English clerks and noblemen. John of Trevisa, however, made available to a larger circle of English readers the Dialogue between master and clerk, the Latin original of which was falsely ascribed to William of Occam.

The Regimen principum of Giles of Rome was Englished by John of Trevisa and paraphrased in English verse with the insertion of "lowbrow" materials by Thomas Hoccleve. Hoccleve's poem was astonishingly popular. Indeed, no less than 44 MSS of it have come down to us.[20]

B5. *The Netherlands*

The Netherlands produced two singularly important personalities, Philip of Leiden in the north and Jacques de Hemricourt in the Pays de Liége.

Philip wrote for the count of Holland a Latin treatise on the republic and the prince which contains one of the earliest mediaeval vindications of state rights and unity against feudal vagaries and anarchy. The best-governed country is one in which the utility of the state (regni utilitas, the state being conceived as located in a definite territory) remains uncorrupted without detriment to the individuals who inhabit it. That treatise, completed in 1358, presented imperfect but unique anticipations of many of the ideas to be developed two centuries later in the Principe (1532) of Niccolò Machiavelli and the République (1576) of Jean Bodin.

The Liégeois chronicler Jacques de Hemricourt wrote in 1360–99 in Walloon dialect the Patron de la temporalité, which is a history and description of the civil and ecclesiastical institutions of Liége. It is an extremely interesting document for the constitutional history of Liége, even if one bears in mind that the author was already a little behind the times when he composed it. He was very conservative and often represented things as they ought to be in his opinion, rather than as they actually were. By this time, indeed, the temporal power of the bishops of Liége had been considerably reduced, and much of what remained was formal rather than actual. The last bishop who could behave like an autocrat outside his ecclesiastical field was Henry III of Gelder (1247–74). The industrial progress of Liége in the fourteenth century had increased considerably the power of the popular party; from the end of that century until the end of the principality in 1795, the government of the city was democratic. Nevertheless, the Patron de la temporalité was an excellent description of conditions which were then disappearing but had been real enough not long before, and a record of institutions and precedents which still enjoyed authority in the courts.

B6. *Byzantium*

A speculum regale was composed by Manuel II Palaeologos for his son Joannes after his abdication, during his retirement in the Pantocrator. Manuel, who had traveled in Western Europe in 1399–1402, was presumably well acquainted with Latin literature and Latin ideas. A superficial reading of his Ὑποθῆκαι βασιλικῆς ἀγωγῆς, however, did not reveal to me any explicit reference to Latin writers; the

[20] C. Brown and R. H. Robbins: Index of Middle English verse (p. 737, New York 1943; Isis 34, 443).

only references I noticed were to Greek authors and to the Bible, chiefly the New Testament. The treatise is almost exclusively ethical, not political. It is true, the same could be said of most Latin treatises, but at any rate Vincent of Beauvais' De eruditione filiorum nobilium, which I examined again for the sake of comparison, is far more systematic.[21] Manuel may have been inspired by Latin models, but such hypothesis is unnecessary. The idea of transmitting his experience to his son and successor would occur naturally enough to an aging father, and especially to one who had suffered the vicissitudes of fortune as intensely as had Manuel. In fact, we find some kind of specula regalia in almost every literature.[22]

C. *India*

A new code of law dealing with religious duties and rules of inheritance was edited in Sanskrit c. 1375 by Viśveśvara, minister of prince Madanapāla, who ruled in Kāshṭhā, north of Delhi.

D. *China*

The first emperor of the Ming dynasty, Hung Wu, caused the preparation of a new code, the Ta Ming lü, which was compiled under the direction of Liu Wei-ch'ien. He reorganized the administration, and to some extent the manners and customs, of the empire, following Chinese models, especially those given during the glorious T'ang dynasty, in opposition to the more eclectic methods of the Mongols. Thus, by the end of the century, the isolation and self-sufficiency of the empire were re-established with a vengeance; chauvinism, obscurantism, and lack of toleration of anything foreign were to be aggravated later by the Ch'ing dynasty (1644–1912), which was anxious to approve itself more Chinese than the Chinese, and the total result was the gradual enfeeblement of China, while the Western countries and Japan were getting stronger every day. We may say that that process of excessive conceit, isolation, and debilitation was begun by Hung Wu.

Looking at it from the fourteenth-century point of view, however, Chinese administration, whether Yüan or Ming, was superior in many respects to that of any other country. We have given a curious illustration of it in a previous section dealing with the census of 1370. Chinese self-esteem was justified then, if it can ever be, but such conceit and isolation stupidly continued for over five centuries was bound to have disastrous consequences. It almost destroyed China.

Though we have no political or social writings of this very period, the Chinese annals are full of information on many matters of administration, rites, social and economic life. The same can be said of the great encyclopaedia which was completed during the rule of the third Ming emperor, Yung Lo. Well might the Chinese say, the world has nothing to compare with us in civilization and good manners! By that time, however, they had already been left behind in the field of science, medicine, and technology, but this they did not know, nor was anybody else aware of it. Western science was then like a little plant, insignificant enough as it was, but destined to become the gigantic and pivotal tree of modern life.

[21] See table of contents in the edition by Arpad Steiner (Mediaeval Academy, p. 4–5, Cambridge, Mass. 1938; Isis 31, 150).

[22] For a Chinese example, it is true materially different, but answering the same essential motive, the Jên wu chih of Liu Shao (III-1), see John K. Shryock's edition of it (New Haven 1937; Isis 29, 104–8).

Appendix: Monetary Difficulties and Theory of Money

It has seemed expedient to omit the discussion of these matters from chapter I and to reserve it for this chapter, because the difficulties were essentially the same throughout the century, and their study was completed by Nicole Oresme only c. 1355.

It may be said that political economy (as distinguished from political ethics) began only in the fourteenth century, and its inception was largely due to monetary difficulties. Indeed, those difficulties created problems which were not simply ethical but technical, and which could not be solved with homilies but required technical means.

From this point of view again, the fourteenth century appears as a period of transition, that is, of dissolution of old habits and painful construction of new ones.

In earlier mediaeval days there had been minted a great deal of private money, that is, money which was not guaranteed by the state, but only by the power of feudal lords, big and small. That kind of money was all right for exchanges within the lord's domain, which satisfied most people. The lord could change it, even for his own profit, without creating too much trouble. The "renovatio monetarum" (that is, the withdrawal of money and minting of new money, subject to a minting fee or "seigniorage" which might amount to 10 or 20 per cent) was abused by certain lords, who found it an easy way of taxing their subjects. That evil had at least one good side: it discouraged sterile hoarding, which was then the main form of saving, and encouraged expenditures. At this time some powerful kings, such as the kings of France, were fighting the feudal nobles, and one aspect of their struggle was the gradual diminution of feudal money. A lord's money was declared to be valid only within his own domain; the king's money was good throughout the kingdom. Moreover, the lord's money was generally restricted to low denominations (nummi, bracteati nummi).

Until the middle of the thirteenth century the coinage of Western Christendom was monometallic, silver only. The increasing commerce with the Near East which followed the Crusades made it necessary to create a new kind of money, more precious and compact, gold currency which could be exchanged with the gold currency of Byzantium and Islamic kingdoms. The golden florin was created in Florence 1252; soon afterward the Genoese created the genoviva, and in 1284 Venice began to coin ducats or golden sequins (secchino, from the Arabic sikka, a die or stamp); St. Louis created the écu d'or in imitation of the Muslim dīnār. Thus bimetallism was introduced in France before 1270, in England under Edward I (1272–1307), in Bohemia under Wácslaw II (1283–1305), in Hungary under Charles of Anjou (1308–42), in Germany under Louis IV of Bavaria (1314–47), in Poland under Casimir the Great (1333–70).

In the fourteenth century Western money became very largely national (vs. feudal) and bimetallic. This created new difficulties, for the ratio between gold and silver had to be fixed somehow; in fact, it fluctuated considerably and rapidly from place to place and from time to time. For example, in France that ratio was changed 150 times in a single century. Within ten years it varied as follows:[23]

1303	10.26	1310	15.64
1305	15.90	1311	19.55
1308	14.46	1313	14.37

[23] Ernest Babelon (Grande encyclopédie 24, 111).

No wonder the variation of prices was terrible during the rule of Philippe le Bel, nicknamed "le faux-monnayeur." Obeying the law of Gresham (or Oresme),[24] gold filtered out from one country to another; kings tried not only to prevent this, but also to attract foreign gold. More fluctuations of prices ensued. The confusion of coinage was so great that no transaction was possible without the help of a money-changer, who, even if he were honest, did not work for nothing. Many of these money-changers were Jews, and this did not increase their popularity.

To return to France, where the financial disease was most acute, the aberrations of Philippe le Bel were continued and aggravated by his successors. Chaos reached its climax under Jean II (1350–64), who within ten years changed seventy times the value of the unit "livre tournois."[25] That value oscillated up and down between two extremes, 8 fr. 63 and 1.73, and the gold-silver ratio varied also between the extremes 10 and 2.07! Moreover, large quantities of debased nummi (small coinage) were issued.

No wonder, then, that scholars began to investigate and to try to understand the money tricks. Economic thinking began to shape itself, and we may be sure that money was the ferment. The growth of international business could not help revealing the artificial difficulties caused by the use of discordant systems of coinage, weights, and measures in the different countries or even in different parts or towns of the same country. That was bad enough, but now those difficulties were immeasurably aggravated by wild fluctuations in the currency of each country! There is considerable economic material not only in a book like that of Francesco Pegolotti, where it is of course fully expected, but also in a chronicle like that of Giovanni Villani, or in the theological treatises of the Franciscan François de Meyronnes. The first to discuss clearly the dangers to which the kingdom was exposed by royal interference with money was that very intelligent jurist Pierre Dubois. His reflections were developed and systematized by Jean Buridan and Nicole Oresme.

Buridan (d. 1358) and Oresme (d. 1382) were superior men, among the best minds of their time. There has been some discussion as to which of the two inspired the other. As the necessary documents for the solution of that question of priority are not yet completely available, it is better to waive the question now. Whoever began it, the task was completed by Oresme, whose treatise De origine, natura, jure et mutationibus monetarum (c. 1355) was the first of its kind, and one of the monuments of economic literature. Much of it was old, but the combination was new, a true scientific creation. Oresme's scientific point of view shows itself to advantage in his discussion of the gold-silver ratio, which was one of the roots of financial trouble. He claimed that that ratio should not be changed arbitrarily, but, admitting the possibility of natural changes due to the vicissitudes of mining, he suggested that the legal ratio might have to be modified from time to time to agree with the natural one. He also granted that monetary changes might be justified for the defense of the state (raison d'état), e.g., devaluation might be the simplest way of extricating the state from a situation otherwise hopeless.[26] In

[24] No matter who discovered it, it was an economic law which functioned before it was expressed.

[25] So called because those coins were minted in Tours until the thirteenth century; royal livres continued to be called "tournois," irrespective of their mint.

[26] As was done, to take a modern example, by the United States in 1934 when it devalued the dollar.

any case, such monstrous right can be conceded only to the state (that is, the mass of the people), never to the prince. Even the simple right of coining money, which was traditionally considered one of the prerogatives of ruling princes (monetandi jus ossibus principis adhaeret), belonged, according to Oresme, to the prince only as a representative of the community.

It will interest the historian of science to know that the next important treatise on money was published a little less than two centuries later by the father of modern astronomy, the Pole Nicholas Copernicus. The latter's treatise Monete cudende ratio, written in 1526, is very brief (only 16 printed pages); it seems independent of Oresme, though Copernicus might have known of Oresme's work, which had been printed in French at Bruges (c. 1477) and in Latin at Paris (beginning of sixteenth cent.).[27]

The following references may help the reader to pursue the study of mediaeval monetary questions. Ducange's long articles, in his Glossarium, on moneta and nummus are still very valuable (4, 483–532, 658–59, Paris 1845). Ernest Babelon: Monnaie (Grande encyclopédie 24, 99–147, c. 1899). Joseph Rambaud: Histoire des doctrines économiques (3e éd., Paris 1909). Walter Taeuber: Geld und Kredit im Mittelalter (Berlin 1933). René Gonnard: Histoire des doctrines monétaires (vol. 1, Paris 1935). Albert Despaux: Les dévaluations monétaires dans l'histoire (Paris 1936).

This article is restricted to Western conditions, for I do not know of pertinent studies, comparable to Oresme's, in other parts of the world. Ibn Khaldūn, however, included in his Muqaddama an outline of the history of money in Islām (French text, 2, 55–61), under the title sikka. In another part of the same work (3, 252) he spoke of alchemists' making counterfeit money. That allusion is very interesting. We know that in the West also alchemists owed their welcome in royal courts partly to the hope that their ability might prove useful in producing coins of gold and silver at a lower cost. This would not have been counterfeiting, for the alchemical gold and silver would have been presumably identical with the real metals. I do not know, however, of any examples of alchemists thus employed in the fourteenth century.

A collection of Arabic texts relative to coins and numismatics has been edited by father Anastase Marie de St. Elie (260 p., Baghdād 1939; Isis 34, 69), in Arabic only.

An abundance of facts concerning the realities, not the theories, of prices and moneys in France will be found in Georges d'Avenel: Histoire économique de la propriété, des salaires, des denrées et de tous les prix en général de 1200 à 1800 (7 vols., Paris 1894–1926).

XIV. PHILOLOGY

1. *The Linguistic Situation*

This section is composed exactly in the same way as the corresponding section of chapter I. The numbers given are thus subject to the same restrictions. They should not be considered absolutely, but only in a relative way. If one language happens to be represented by 100 authors and another by 50 authors, it would be

[27] For a discussion of Copernicus' views see the edition of his treatise by Louis Wolowski (Paris 1864); René Gonnard (1, 219–28, 1935).

foolish to conclude that the first was twice as important as the second, but we may assume with some confidence that it was more important. It would be impossible to attain more precision without considerable labor, and even then the truth would elude our grasp, for the items—say, a small but original astronomical treatise in French and a bulky medical compilation in Chinese—cannot be equated; we could only count them. To determine proper coefficients for each of them would be hopelessly complicated. In fact, we do not even count them, but only count the authors, irrespective of their production, as well as possible.

The reader should bear in mind that our comparisons between languages concern only their scientific use, that is, their use as vehicles for the communication of knowledge. Belles lettres as such are not considered at all; it is possible, even probable, that the relations of these languages would be very different if we counted their poetic or dramatic creations.

Throughout this section the numbers given without parentheses refer to the second half of the fourteenth century; those within parentheses, to the first half. Thus are comparisons made easy at every step.

The language most frequently represented is Latin 192(223), and the number of Latin authors considered in this volume is more than twice as large as that of the authors of the language second in importance, Arabic 85(104). We may thus say without fear of error that Latin was by far the most important scientific language in the second half of the fourteenth century. The number of Latin and Arabic authors, however, is smaller than it was in the first half of the century. The explanation of that decrease will appear presently.

Indeed, let us consider the vernaculars of Western Europe. In order of decreasing popularity they are:

1.	French	51(22)	7.	Spanish	4(4)
2.	Italian	30(24)	8.	Norwegian	3(0)
3.	German	15(12)	9.	Icelandic	1(1)
4.	Catalan	14 (7)		Portuguese	1(2)
5.	English	10 (4)		Provençal	1(0)
6.	Dutch	6 (6)		Swedish	1(0)

If the three languages of the Hispanic peninsula and Provençal were grouped together, their coefficient would be 20(13) and they would occupy together the third rank. If the Scandinavian languages were lumped together, 5(1), they would occupy the seventh rank.

The grand total of these vernaculars equals 137(82), against 192(223) for Latin alone. That is, Latin continues to be more important than all the vernaculars of Western Europe put together, yet its supremacy is smaller than it was in the first half of the century. In the first half of the century the Western vernaculars were to Latin in the ratio of 37 to 100, in the second half in the ratio of 71 to 100. The gain made by the vernaculars at the expense of Latin is tremendous; we can almost measure their emancipation.[1]

The most striking fact is the gain of the French vernacular 51(22), which not only beats Italian, but is now far ahead of it, and equals 37 per cent of all the Western vernaculars instead of 27 per cent. It can be said of both the French and the

[1] The gain would be even greater if we counted Czech 8(1) and Polish 0(1), for these two languages were actually competing with Latin. The gain would then be from 38 per cent to 75 per cent (instead of 37 to 71).

Italian that they have now conquered the dignity of languagehood, though, curiously enough, in different ways. Italian (or rather Tuscan) ceased to be a dialect because of the genius of Dante, Petrarca, and Boccaccio; French, because of the unification and prestige of France. There were other causes, of course, but these were predominant, the political one in France, the purely literary one in Italy.

Passing to Eastern Europe and Eastern Christendom, Greek is still and by far the most important language, the other dialects or languages follow far behind:

1. Greek	25(32)		
2. Czech	8 (1)	Slavic [2, 4, 5]	11(3)
3. Armenian	7 (8)		
4. Russian	3 (1)		
5. Polish	0 (1)		
	43(43)		

The relative importance of Greek has diminished like that of Latin, but for different reasons. It has diminished not because of increased competition from the outside, but rather because of a lack of vitality within. The Byzantine world was running down. Czech and Polish, we may recall, were not competing against Greek, but against Latin.

Before we leave Eastern Europe, the singular case of Zyrian must be mentioned. That language of the Finno-Ugrian family, spoken in the northern regions of Russia, was alphabetized by St. Stephen of Perm c. 1372.

The Semitic languages are now reduced to two, Arabic and Hebrew, the two others, Aethiopian and Syriac, being unrepresented. Arabic is still leading 85(104), but its relative importance as compared with Hebrew 63(59) is diminishing, also its world importance. Its climax is passed forever. The Arabic challenge is not met by Hebrew, which is not competing with it, but flourishing in its own (Jewish) domain; it is met by two other Islamic, though non-Semitic, languages, Persian 12(11) and Turkish 10(5).

The following table was compiled for immediate comparison with the one given in chapter I, page 329, the numbers of which are reprinted (between parentheses):

Israel		*W. Christendom*		*E. Christendom*		*Islām*	
Hebrew	63(59)	Latin	192(223)	Greek	25(32)	Arabic	85(104)
		W. vernaculars	137 (82)	Slavic	11 (3)	Persian	12 (11)
				Armenian	7 (8)	Turkish	10 (5)
				Georgian	0 (1)		
				Coptic	0 (1)		
				Aethiopian	0 (2)		
				Syriac	0 (1)		
				Zyrian	1 (0)		
	63(59)		329(305)		44(48)		107(120)

373(353) [W. Christendom + E. Christendom]

This "religious" classification is not to be taken too strictly. For example, among the Hebrew scholars were counted not only Jews, but a few non-Jews; the Latin scholars were not exclusively Christians; Eastern Christendom is a geographical term, not a theological one; the Christianity of the Zyrians cannot be inferred from that of their apostle; etc. Admitting these causes of error, the overwhelming preponderance of Christian authors over Jews or Muslims, or more generally over non-Christians (outside India and Buddhist Asia), is obvious.

The languages of India are represented by writers in Sanskrit 6(3), Pāli 2(3), Gujarātī 2(0), Siṅhalese 2(0), Canarese 2(2), Bengali 1(0), Kashmīrī 1(0), Urdu 1(0), Telugu 0(2); a total of 8(6) Aryan and 9(4) non-Aryan.

Finally, we have 1(0) Tibetan, 1(0) Javanese, 0(1) Mongolian, 26(40) Chinese, and 7(12) Japanese. The material diminution of Chinese and Japanese authors, 33 as compared with 52, is strange.

All the results can be summarized in the following table:

			Totals
Israel		63 (59)	122
W. Christendom	329(305)		
E. Christendom	44 (48)	373(353)	726
Islām		107(120)	227
India and Tibet		18 (10)	28
Far East		34 (53)	87
Totals		595(595)[2]	1,190

The twelve most important languages for scientific communications in the second half of the fourteenth century were as indicated in column II of the following table. For the purpose of comparison, the data relative to the first half of the century and the whole of it, with corresponding ranks, are given in columns I and III.

I. XIV-1	II. XIV-2		III. XIV
1. (223)	1. Latin	192	1. 415
2. (104)	2. Arabic	85	2. 189
3. (59)	3. Hebrew	63	3. 122
7. (22)	4. French	51	4. 73
6. (24)	5. Italian	30	7. 54
4. (40)	6. Chinese	26	5. 66
5. (32)	7. Greek	25	6. 57
8-9.* (12)	8. German	15	8. 27
12. (7)	9. Catalan	14	10. 21
10. (11)	10. Persian	12	9. 23
14.* (4)	11-12. English	10	14.* 14
13.* (5)	11-12. Turkish	10	12-13.* 15

* The double numbers and numbers above 12 in columns I and III are due to the following facts: In XIV-1, Japanese (12) held the 8-9th ranks ex aequo with German, and Armenian (8) the 11th. In XIV-2, Japanese and Armenian were represented each by 7 authors. Therefore the totals for XIV place Japanese, with 19, in the 11th rank, and Armenian, with 15, in the 12-13th rank ex aequo with Turkish.

2. *Latin*

We have described in chapter I how the knowledge of Latin had gradually deteriorated during the Middle Ages even among clerks, in spite of the latter's

[2] The coincidence of these two totals was entirely unexpected, but that accident causes the figures relative to XIV-1 and to XIV-2 to be immediately comparable.

ritual need of that knowledge. In the meanwhile, sundry vernaculars had grown in strength and beauty. About the beginning of the century one might have prophesied the rapid decline and fall of Latin. Yet such a prophecy would have been false. Indeed, a new series of facts, or call it a new spiritual environment, gave Latin a new lease on life. That was the Renaissance then emerging in Italy.

A few glimpses of that renewal have already been given. The main herald was Petrarca, who discovered Ciceronian MSS in 1333 and 1345 and emulated the Latin authors of the silver age. We shall now consider the fruits of that renewal in the second half of the fourteenth century. Our account will be divided into seven subsections, as follows: (i) Humanism in Italy, (ii) Humanism in France, (iii) Humanism in England, (iv) Humanism in Germany, (v) Humanism in the Netherlands, (vi) Books and libraries, (vii) Latin vs. the vernaculars.

i. *Humanism in Italy*

Petrarca was not simply the herald of humanism early in the century, he remained its dominating personality until his death in 1374. Indeed, as he grew older his influence increased, and after his death it continued to increase for a couple of centuries. In the meanwhile, his example had stimulated other men, chiefly one ten years younger than himself, Giovanni Boccaccio, whose activities converged with his and lasted until 1375. During the third quarter of the century these two giants built the foundations of a new temple, nay, they built the temple itself. In particular, they gave the Latin language a new freshness and new prestige. Petrarca had rediscovered MSS of Cicero; Boccaccio discovered the epigrams of the Spaniard Martialis (43–c. 104) and the didactic poems of Ausonius of Bordeaux (IV-2); he was widely acquainted with Latin poetry and prose; he copied many texts with his own hand, giving some of his copies (Cicero and Varro) to Petrarca;[3] he made a complete copy of the comedies of the Carthaginian poet Terentius (194–159 B.C.), the MS exists to this day in the Laurentian library; he was especially interested in Livy and Tacitus; his eagerness in his search for MSS and his love of them is revealed in his moving account of the neglected library of Monte Cassino; this enumeration need not be pursued. Boccaccio, like Petrarca, was one of the early explorers of a half-forgotten paradise, the garden of Latin letters. To complete this aspect of humanism—the search for Latin MSS—we may recall the activities of a third man, Coluccio Salutati, who sought vainly for the lost books of Livy and for complete copies of Curtius and Quintilian; he discovered Cato's De agricultura and the Epistolae ad familiares of Cicero (1392); he obtained many other MSS. In contrast with Boccaccio, whose enthusiasm was uncritical, Salutati was a born critic; he was one of the first to collate Latin MSS (Seneca, St. Augustine) and to try to establish their text as well as possible.

Benvenuto di Rambaldi revived the study of Latin literature in Bologna and Ferrara. Marsiglio of Florence directed a kind of humanistic academy in Santo Spirito; he was familiar with Cicero, Vergil, and Seneca. The first Giovanni da Ravenna (Giovanni di Conversino) taught Latin humanities in a great many Italian cities, and is a prototype of the wandering humanists so frequent in later years. The second Giovanni da Ravenna (not connected with the first) was Petrarca's secretary in Venice, then entered the service of the papal curia; he initiated a new school of Florentine humanists. Domenico di Bandino taught

[3] They did not meet until 1350, in Florence, but the influence of the older man upon the younger one had been exerted for a long time before that.

grammar and letters in Florence; he was far more interested in classical than in barbaric antiquities. Another great teacher was Pietro Paulo Vergerio, il vecchio, who taught various subjects in many places and followed the example of Giovanni di Conversino; he became a secretary of the curia and later of the emperor Sigismund. Thus were the new humanistic ideals carried to Bohemia and Hungary. Vergerio's influence was immortalized in his book De ingenuis moribus et liberalibus studiis (c. 1401), one of the earliest defenses of a classical education.

The following scholars did their main work in the fifteenth century, yet a history of fourteenth-century humanism would be very incomplete if they were left out. We have already spoken twice of Giacomo d'Angelo, who found an illustrated copy of Ptolemy's geography in Constantinople and translated it into Latin (in or before 1406). Gasparino da Barzizza[4] (c. 1370–1431) originated in Barzizza, a village not far from Bergamo, hence his Latin name Gasparinus Pergamensis; he flourished in Pavia, Venice, Padua, Ferrara, and finally in 1418 settled in Milano. He collected Ciceronian MSS, explained the virtues of Cicero's style, especially in the master's letters, which he proposed as examples of perfection. He was "the true apostle of Ciceronianism" (Sabbadini). His own models of easy and familiar letters enjoyed considerable popularity.

Text. Epistolae ad exercitationem accommodatae (Paris 1470); this was the first book printed in France with movable type. Often reprinted, Basel c. 1472, 1474, Louvain 1482, Reutlingen c. 1482, Padua 1483, Deventer c. 1483, 1495?, Strassburg 1486, Basel 1495?, Paris 1498, Basel 1499, Paris 1500?, 1505 (note the international circulation). Orthographia (Paris c. 1470). De eloquentia opusculum, Ciceronis synonymorum libellus (Paris c. 1498). Exempla exordiorum (Padua 1483). Vocabularium (Venice 1516). Gasparini Barzizii Bergomatis et Guiniforti filii opera quorum pleraque ex MSS nunc primum in lucem eruta rec. ac ed. Joseph Alexander Furiettus (quarto, 2 vols. in 1, Rome 1723).

Criticism. Remigio Sabbadini: Storia del ciceronianismo (144 p., Torino 1885). Sandys (2, 23, 1908). Stillwell (p. 75, 1940).

The methods of textual criticism used by Coluccio Salutati were improved by another and younger Florentine, Niccolò de' Niccoli (1363–1437), who carries us to the threshold of the golden age of classical learning in Florence (the reign of Cosimo de' Medici, 1434–64). Niccolò collected Latin (and Greek) MSS, a great many of which are preserved in the Laurentian library; one of them is the Lucretius copied by himself between 1418 and 1434.[5]

Ambrogio Traversari (born in Portico, Romagna, 1386; died in Florence, 1439) is often called Ambrogio Camaldolese, for he assumed the Camaldolite habit (Introd. 2, 154) at Florence in 1400 and became general of his order in 1431. His letters are important documents, but his main title to remembrance is perhaps his Hodoeporicon, a short account of his travels in Italy in 1431–34, as general of his

[4] Not to be confused with his nephew and stepson Cristoforo da Barzizza, who taught medicine at Padua 1434–40. Author of Introductorium sive Janua ad opus practicum medicinae cum eiusdem in nonum Almansoris librum commentariis (Pavia 1494, Augsburg 1518); De febrium cognitione et cura (Lyon 1517). Gurlt (1, 895–96, 1898). Dorothea Waley Singer: Some plague tractates (p. 39, London 1916). Klebs (no. 159).

Two other incunabula bear Cristoforo's name: Grammaticae institutiones (Brescia 1492); De fine oratoris pro Ciceroni et Quintiliani assertione (Brescia 1492). Is this not due to a confusion with Gasparino? Or are there two Cristofori?

[5] Giuseppe Zippel: Niccolò Niccoli (112 p., Firenze 1890), including various documents.

order. He was concerned not only with monastic business, but also with the libraries and antiquities which he came across. He was not as fortunate as Poggio, for he found only one classical MS, Cornelius Nepos, in Padua in 1434.

Text. Epistolae edited by Edmond Martène: Veterum scriptorum . . . collectio (3, 5–694, 1724). New edition with a biography of Traversari by Lorenzo Mehus (2 vols., Florence 1759), valuable documents for the literary history of Florence from c. 1192 to 1440.

Hodoeporicon, edited by Niccolò Bartolini (72 p., Florence 1681), poor edition.

Criticism. Gir. Tiraboschi: Storia della letteratura italiana (2d Modena ed., 6, 157, 204, 808–11). Potthast (p. 1070, 1896). Sandys (2, 34, 44, 1908). Alessandro Dini-Traversari: Ambrogio Traversari e i suoi tempi (Firenze 1912).

It pleases the author exceedingly to be able to say a few words now of the most lovable personality of the early Renaissance, Vittorino da Feltre. How utterly different from those later so-called humanists who distinguished themselves by their boorish manners, their greed, jealousy, vindictiveness, and blackguardism! Vittorino di Ramboldini was born at Feltre (prov. Belluno), near the Piave river, in 1378; he was educated at Padua and flourished there from 1396 to 1415; from 1423 he was established at Mantua, where he died on February 2, 1446. Upon the invitation of Gian Francesco II Gonzaga (lord of Mantua, 1407–44), he organized at Mantua in 1423 a new school, the Joyous House (Casa giocosa, or gioiosa; in Venetian dialect, zoyosa), the most remarkable school of the Renaissance and one of the most remarkable of all times. Vittorino tried to develop simultaneously mind, body, and heart; he taught Latin, Greek, mathematics,[6] and endeavored to combine the highest ideals of classical antiquity with those of Christianity, to harmonize individualism with moral discipline, temperance with piety and joy.

William Harrison Woodward: Vittorino da Feltre and other humanist educators (264 p., Cambridge 1897).

Next we must say something of one of the founders of classical archaeology, Ciriaco, whom Sandys called "the Schliemann of his time." Ciriaco de' Pizzicolli (c. 1391–c. 1450), born in Ancona (hence his Latin name Cyriacus Anconitanus), was endowed with an innate genius for archaeology. He copied inscriptions in Ancona, then in Rome, traveled extensively in Italy, Greece, and the Near East (as far as Damascus) in search of MSS and inscriptions. The inscriptions transcribed by him filled three large volumes, of which only fragments remain. He also made drawings of ancient sculpture; these too are lost, except that some were copied at Padua c. 1466 by the Nuremberg historian and physician Hartmann Schedel (1440–1514). He was perhaps the first man in the modern world (outside of China) to realize the fundamental value of epigraphy and archaeology. He used to relate that one day as he was hunting for antiquities in a church at Vercelli (Piedmont), the priest was suspicious of him and wanted to know his business. Ciriaco answered, "It is sometimes my business to awaken the dead out of their graves; it is an art that I have learnt from the Pythian oracle of Apollo." What did the inquisitive priest think, I wonder, and what did he answer?

Itinerarium nunc primum in lucem erutum. Editionem recensuit, animadversionibus ac praefatione illustravit, nonnullisque Kyriaci epistolis partim editis, partim

[6] Upon the beautiful medal dedicated to him by Pisanello he is called "Victorinus Feltrensis summus mathematicus et omnis humanitatis pater."

ineditis locupletavit Laurentius Mehus (Florence 1742). Fragment in Theodor Preger: De epigrammatis graecis meletemata selecta (p. 43–50, Munich 1889). Christian Huelsen: La Roma antica, disegni inediti del secolo XV (48 p., 18 pl., Roma 1907). Sandys (2, 39–40, 1908).

Let us evoke two more Italian humanists whose youth was spent in the fourteenth century, Guarino Veronese (c. 1370–1460) and Poggio Fiorentino (1380–1459).

Poggio[7] is so famous that we need not say much of him. He was born near Florence in 1380, was apostolic secretary for almost half a century, and died in Florence in 1459. He wrote many books, notably a Latin history of Florence (he was the official historian of the city from 1453), and Latin versions of Xenophon's Cyropaedia and of the histories of Diodoros of Sicily (I-2 B.C.), books I–VI, but his fame is most securely founded upon his extraordinary zeal for the cause of humanism and his diligent search for ancient MSS. While attending the council of Constance in 1414–18, as papal secretary, he explored the monastic libraries of Reichenau, Weingarten, St. Gallen, etc., and he made similar investigations in the course of his frequent travels; thus he discovered MSS of Lucretius, Cicero, Vitruvius, Columella, Frontinus, Manilius, Quintilian, Ammianus Marcellinus, etc. From the point of view of the history of letters, his discoveries of a complete Quintilian (at St. Gallen 1416) and of Cicero's De oratore (at Lodi 1422) were of especial importance. New standards of style and composition were given to the world. This influenced also, indirectly, the development of clear thought and of science. One of Poggio's works, De varietate fortunae, contains the account of Niccolò de' Conti's long stay in India and the Far East, as dictated by Niccolò to Poggio in Rome 1444; it is the most elaborate account of Southern Asia by a Western writer of the quattrocento.[8] The most popular of Poggio's books was unfortunately his Facetiae, a collection of smutty tales, which were relished by many generations of young and old scholars. This illustrates another trait of the early humanists; they had a strong taste for erotics and obscenities, a taste to which the ancient pagan literature could give ample satisfaction. The early humanists, ready to imitate every tendency of classical times, were thus led to publish erotic compositions of their own. Poggio, apostolic secretary, was their guide in this.

Text. Opera (Strassburg 1513, Basel 1538). Epistolae. Editas collegit et emendavit plerasque ex codd. MSS eruit ordine chronologico disposuit notisque illustravit Thomas de Tonellis (3 vols., Florence 1832–61). Vols. 2 and 3 were published posthumously in 1859–61 but soon withdrawn by Tommaso Tonelli's family; they are exceedingly rare. The copy in the Harvard library contains marginal notes by Niccolò Anziani, sometime librarian of the Laurentiana. For other editions of the letters and other works see Potthast (p. 932, 1896).

Niccolò di Conti's account of his journey, taken down by Poggio, disappeared, and when Giambattista Ramusio (1485–1557) was compiling his Navigationi et viaggi (vol. 1, Venice 1550) he was obliged to retranslate it from a Portuguese version. The original Latin appeared only much later, in the fourth book of Poggio's Historiae de varietate fortunae libri IV, edited by the abbé Giovanni Oliva (Paris 1723). English version by Richard Henry Major: India in the fifteenth

[7] Poggius Florentinus. There is no warrant for calling him Gian Francesco. He is often called Poggio Bracciolini, which is correct, though the noble name Bracciolini was added by him to his own only in 1443.

[8] For example, it includes the first description of the magnificent city of Vijayanagar in the Deccan (founded in 1336, destroyed in 1565), to which reference has been made in chapter I (p. 41).

century from Latin, Persian, Russian and Italian sources (Hakluyt Society, London 1857); this includes four accounts, by Kamāl al-dīn 'Abd-al-Razzāq, ambassador from the Tīmūrī sulṭān of Transoxiana, Shāh Rukh (ruled 1404–47), and by Niccolò de' Conti, Athanasius Nikitin of Tver c. 1470, and Girolamo da Santo Stefano, Genoese merchant of the end of the fifteenth century. Mario Longhena: Viaggi in Persia, India e Giava di Niccolò de' Conti, Girolamo Adorno e Girolamo da Santo Stefano (254 p., ill., Milano 1929).

Criticism. William Shepherd: Life of Poggio (London 1802; 2d ed., 472 p., London 1837). Sandys (2, 25–34, 1908). Ernst Walser: Poggius Leben und Werke (575 p., 4 pl., Leipzig 1914). Lynn Thorndike: Medicine vs. law in late medieval and Medicean Florence (Romanic review 17, 8–31, 1926; Isis 9, 155).

Giovanni Battista de' Guarini, born in Verona c. 1370, is generally called Guarino Veronese; he flourished at Constantinople (1403–8), Trent, Verona, Padua, Florence, and from 1429 on at Ferrara, where he died in 1460. In 1408 he brought back from the East more than 50 MSS, in 1419 he discovered at Venice 124 letters of the younger Pliny, and in 1426 at Bologna a MS of Celsus. He translated many works from Greek into Latin, notably the whole of Strabo, some of Plutarch's lives, and his treatise περὶ παίδων ἀγωγῆς (1411).

Text. Strabo: Geographia (Rome 1469, Venice 1472, Rome 1473, Treviso 1480, Venice 1494, 1494/95, etc., Paris 1512, 1652). Klebs (no. 935).

Guarinus Veronensis: De brevibus clarorum hominum inter se contentionibus ex Plutarcho collectis (Brescia 1485). Carmina differentialia (Parma 1492). Regulae grammaticales (Italy c. 1472, Venice 1482, 1485, Florence 1496, Venice 1530).

Ars diphthongandi in Johann Reuchlin's Vocabularius (Basel 1478), often reprinted, see Stillwell (p. 430, 1940).

Erotemata (222 p., Ferrara 1509). Reprinted with the Erotemata of Manuel Chrysoloras (Venice 1517, 1549). Etc.

Epistolario raccolto, ordinato, illustrato da Remigio Sabbadini (3 vols., Venice 1915–19).

Criticism. Carlo de' Rosmini: Vita e disciplina di Guarino e de' suoi discepoli (3 vols. in 1, Brescia 1805–6). Remigio Sabbadini: Guarino e il suo epistolario (82 p., Salerno 1885); La scuola e gli studi di Guarino Guarini (248 p., Catania 1896). W. H. Woodward: Studies in education during the Renaissance (p. 26–47, 1906). Sandys (2, 49–52, 1908). Antonio Favaro: Il carmen de ponderibus di Guarino Veronese (Isis 1, 205–7, 1913), apropos of a Latin poem, 13 lines, on weights and their ratios. Giulio Bertoni: Guarino da Verona fra letterati e cortigiani a Ferrara, 1429–60 (228 p., 5 pl., Geneva 1921).

The excursus devoted to the fin-de-siècle children of the fourteenth century will serve to illustrate the exuberance and many-sidedness of the early Renaissance. It had so many aspects and touched so many interests that it was truly a new conception of life, a new outlook, and inaugurated a new culture. Some of those early humanists, we have seen, were concerned with the search for MSS, others with textual criticism, others with education, others with secretarial work, others with letter-writing in the manner of Cicero and Pliny, others with epigraphy, others with archaeology, others with grammar and rhetoric, others with historiography in the Roman style. It is remarkable that all these men were laymen except Marsiglio Fiorentino, who was an Augustinian, and Ambrogio Traversari, who was a Camaldolite. All of them, however, were Christians in spite of their flirtations with paganism, and some of them, like Vittorino da Feltre, were exemplary Christians. All the virtues and vices of later humanism can already be detected in them.

It requires some imagination to understand their enthusiasm for the Roman classics, because we are so familiar with these from the time of our own childhood that we are denied the joy of discovering them. Indeed, our pleasure is dimmed not only by long familiarity, but more so by the fact that our remembrance of them is inseparable from the remembrance of recitations, examinations, castigations, of long days of penitence in the classrooms, when our bodies were young and restive and the outside world looked so brave and gay. The early humanists, however, discovered many of those classics, and their discoveries of them and of the ancient world were as thrilling to them as are physical or astronomical discoveries to the scientists of today. The classics were new and alive, they acted like ferments accelerating the intellectual metabolism of that age.

It will be a little easier to understand what happened in Italy and to some extent (as we shall see presently) in other countries of Western Europe in the fourteenth century, if we compare European with Chinese experience. The Chinese have venerable classics of their own, but these have been for millennia an intrinsic and unchangeable part of their culture. It took genius for a Chinese really to discover them, that is, to see them in a new light, as we can easily rediscover our own classics after having studied the classics of other nations. With the exception of Buddhist sūtras, to which the majority of scholars remained impervious, the Chinese never experienced the sudden discovery of a new world as different from their own as the Roman one was from the late mediaeval. It is true, some exchanges of ideas with outside nations were permitted to them during the short-lived Yüan dynasty, but at the very time when Italian scholars were exalted and excited by the rediscovery of classical antiquity, the Ming dynasty broke whatever contacts existed with foreign culture, and China was sealed up and condemned to spiritual autarchy and relative sterility for centuries.

Nothing is more certain than that the progress of thought is facilitated by cross-pollination and hybridization and that it is impeded, if not altogether stopped, by self-sufficiency and inbreeding. The proof of this has been given us on a gigantic scale—compare the course of Chinese culture under the Ming and the Ch'ing with that of European culture during the same period. The Chinese are potentially as intelligent as the Europeans, but all men, even the greatest, need some kind of stimulation; without it they become sluggish, stupid, and sterile.

ii. *Humanism in France*

Whatever humanism there was in other countries was very largely colored by the Italian models. It is true that French scholars have claimed that there was a kind of humanism indigenous to France. Their thesis has been brilliantly supported by the Swedish historian Johan Nordström (1929, 1933). The real cradle of humanism, according to them, was not Italy but France. Was not Petrarca educated in Carpentras and Montpellier, did he not spend the most creative years of his life (1337–53) in Vaucluse? It is impossible, however, to deny Petrarca's deep Italianity; it would be absurd to credit his merit to the French account. He was one of the founders not only of Latin humanism, but also of Italian nationality. The issue is somewhat confused by the international prestige of French letters from the thirteenth century on; we are not dealing now with French letters, but with Latin. In fact, the rapid development of French humanism must have impeded to some extent that of the Latin. For example, the translators patronized by Charles the Wise and Jean de Berry made it possible to read many classics in French; could we not say that this tended to discourage their reading in Latin? Does not the law of least effort apply to spiritual matters as well as to material ones?

There were good Latinists in France and lovers of antiquity, but certainly not as many as in Italy. Neither were the French humanists as great and original as their Italian contemporaries. Humanism began somewhat later in France, during the rule of Charles VI (1380–1422). Instead of being as original as Nordström would have it, it was largely a result of Italian stimulation. Not to mention again the great initiators, Petrarca and Boccaccio, other Italians came to France; their purpose was often meretricious, yet they acted as catalyzers. A good example is that of the adventurer Ambrogio de' Migli (Ambrosius de Miliis), who arrived in Paris from Milano c. 1388–90, was appointed secretary to the duke of Orléans, and enjoyed enough popularity to excite the jealousy of French scholars. Not only did he compete successfully with them, but he had the cheek to claim that his understanding of Virgil, Ovid, and Cicero was superior to theirs! We hear amusing echoes of those quarrels in the letters of Nicolas de Clémanges (c. 1360–c. 1434, 1437?) and Jean de Montreuil (c. 1354–1418). The leading French humanists of that time were the two just named, Gontier Col[9] (c. 1351–1418), Laurent de Premierfait (d. 1418), Jacques de Nouvion (d. 1411), Nicolas de Baye (d. 1419), Jean Muret (fl. end XIV). These men were distinguished, but none of them, not even Clémanges, was on a level with the best Italians.[10] They read Cicero, Virgil, Terence, Horace, Sallust, Livy, and even Christian authors like Cyprianus (c. 200–58) and Lactantius (d. c. 325); they read critically and with pleasure. They were breathing in with evident delight the fresh air which came from ancient Rome. Clémanges could express that delight and praise the liberal arts with rare felicity.[11] Curiously enough, their humanism revealed itself in their ability to use scurrilous language and to abuse their rivals with the choicest insults. Witness Jean de Montreuil addressing Ambrogio de' Migli as follows: "canis rabidissime, carnifex vilissime, scelerate et furcifer, garcio impudentissime et denique vipera crudelis ac fera pessima, putredo vilissima, pestis pernicies, litium fabricator, sus luculentissima, spado abjectissime, lenonem parasitumque viscosissimum, pejor serpentibus Afris, scurra, sterquilinium, scortum obscenissimum, olei venditor perniciosissimum, Cayn exsecrabilis, sceleratissime Juda et Nerone neronior. . . ."[12] One would like to know how Ambrogio returned these affectionate greetings. Much of that truculence, it should be remembered, was artificial. A good humanist wanted to show off his art of vituperation; it was a kind of literary exercise, and also a catharsis. After having fired his round of abuse he probably felt a little better and less inimical.

It is not surprising that humanism flourished more luxuriantly in Italy than in France, for the atmosphere of Italian courts was more favorable to it than that of the French ones. There were patrons of rhetoric and poetry in France, like Jean de Berry and Gaston Phoebus, but Italian lords of the same ilk were more numerous, more enthusiastic, they had a greater love of magnificence and dramatization. One would expect them to promote humanism, the new art of expression—not the expression of truth (as the scientist understands it), but the expression of self—

[9] Not Gautier. Gontier = Gontero = Gunther. Gautier = Walther. Col is probably a gallicization of the Italian name Colle. Gontier Col originated in Sens (Yonne).

[10] Nicolas de Clémanges was jealous of Petrarca and tried to belittle Italian merits. He was perhaps the first to defend the independence of French humanism (Coville p. 170, 1934).

[11] Undated letter to cardinal Galeotto Tarlati di Pietramala in the Epistolae edited by Johannes Martinus Lydius (p. 20–24, Leiden 1613; see p. 21). Extract in Coville (p. 100, 1934).

[12] Coville (p. 136, 1934).

poetry, rhetoric, and drama. It is not for nothing that Italy was to be the cradle of opera two centuries later and that Claudio Monteverde was a countryman of Petrarca and Boccaccio.

Humanism was promoted by courts rather than by universities. To be sure, Clémanges and Nouvion were connected with the University of Paris, but the majority of humanists were courtiers rather than magistri. Clémanges, the greatest of them all, is an exceptional and intermediary case. In general, the University of Paris did not produce men like him, but learned doctors like Pierre d'Ailly, Jean Courtecuisse (c. 1350–1423), and Jean Gerson. These were the alumni she was proud of.

The outstanding cenacle of France from the point of view of humanism was the court of Avignon, and that court, it should be noted, attracted Italian as well as French literati. Avignon was French, but it was also international. One of the patrons of humanism in Avignon was the cardinal Galeotto Tarlati di Pietramala, who corresponded with Nicolas de Clémanges, and whose career was typical of the Italian renaissance and of those tumultuous times.[13]

To conclude, French humanism began in the last quarter of the century. It was posterior to Italian humanism and—pace Clémanges and others—subordinated to it.

See the studies of Pierre de Nolhac (1859–1936) on Petrarca. Nordström (1933). Alfred Coville: Gontier et Pierre Col et l'humanisme en France au temps de Charles VI (256 p., Paris 1934); Recherches sur quelques écrivains du XIVe et du XVe siècle (340 p., Paris 1935).

iii. *Humanism in England*

The English situation was complicated by the coexistence of two noble languages and of three kinds of humanism, Latin, French, and English. The clerks, judges, and gentry were protected from the vulgum pecus by two lines of defense; in consequence, each line was a little weaker than it would have been if it had been the only one.

Richard de Bury, godfather of bibliophiles and a humanist of the first generation, had died before the middle of the century. The outstanding Latin humanist of the second half of the century was perhaps John Gower, whose Vox clamantis (begun in 1381) is unlike any poem written on the Continent. He was well acquainted with classical literature and with Boccaccio.

Much of the English work of that time was elementary as compared with the Italian and French efforts. The gradus ad Parnassum was clearly more painful for English boys than for those speaking naturally a Romance language. We have some interesting information concerning the teaching dispensed in Oxford. For example, one Thomas Sampson (fl. 1380) was teaching Latin (and French), explaining how to write letters clearly and elegantly, how to punctuate them, how to observe a rhythmical cursus,[14] how to phrase various documents. In short, he was adapting to the needs of his students the ars dictaminis and the ars notaria. Many

[13] Created cardinal by Urban VI in Rome 1378; in 1386, having been accused of murder, he took refuge with Gian Galeazzo Visconti, lord of Milano, then submitted to the antipope Clement VII of Avignon. Excommunicated by Urban VI, he remained faithful to Clement VII. Hence some people regarded him as a traitor, others as a paragon of faithfulness.

[14] At least, how to obtain the four favored rhythmical endings: planus, medius, tardus, and velox. This use of the term cursus goes back to the De oratore of Cicero (cursus verborum, cursus vocis per omnis sonos).

MSS of his treatises, preserved in English libraries, deal with letter writing, precedents for bills (Hic incipiunt bille secundum novum modum), vocabularies, conveyancing, wills, holding courts, the office of coroner, legal terms, household accounts, heraldry. In short, they explain everything a gentleman should know in order to protect his interests and maintain his position with decorum. This kind of humanism was not disinterested, but on the contrary of a very practical kind, just as necessary as the art of riding or of using arms and armor, a means of personal and class defense; it was the kind of humanism which often tended to dominate the public schools and the older colleges until yesterday. To be sure, the same thing existed in other countries, but in England it was not then compensated and redeemed by the curiosity of a Boccaccio (the Latin Boccaccio), the political spirit of a Salutati, the educational ideals of a Giovanni di Conversino or a Vergerio, the enthusiasm of the MSS hunters, or the sweet reasonableness of a Vittorino da Feltre.

Noël Denholm-Young: The cursus in England, in Oxford essays on medieval history presented to Herbert Edward Salter (p. 68–103, Clarendon Press, Oxford 1934). Henry Gerald Richardson: Business training in medieval Oxford (American historical review 46, 259–80, 1941; Isis 33, 361), with a list of MSS texts on the ars dictaminis in England from the twelfth century to the first half of the fifteenth century.

iv. *Humanism in Germany*

One may wonder whether the ars dictaminis is related to humanism. If humanism is taken in its highest sense, then that ars is hardly related to it, but if it be meant to imply the teaching of Latin, every gradus of it from the ABC to the top, then the ars is certainly an integral part of it. The teaching of Thomas Sampson and of other schoolmasters in England and elsewhere was of a general nature. In addition, collections of letters and formulas were compiled for the use of definite chanceries. To the examples quoted in chapter I (p. 332–33), we may now add the two collections prepared by Dietrich von Niem, who was a notary and abbreviator in the papal service in Avignon, later in Rome; the Liber cancellariae apostolicae (1380) and the Stilus palatii abbreviatus. Both can be easily examined in Georg Erler's edition (1888).

The reader will be tempted to say, these books are not manuals of Latin, but simply manuals of administration. That conclusion would be too hasty. The dictatores, even the most specialized ones, were helping to preserve standards of Latin orthography, grammar, and composition. They did for the notaries and civil servants what civilians did for lawyers, decretalists and theologians for priests, and professors of medicine for physicians. Without them the disintegration of the Latin language would have been far more rapid than it was. It is true they were primarily concerned with administration, but correct and regular administration, faithful to precedents, involved the use of correct language, preserving ancient traditions.

A very different form of humanism was practiced by the Dominican Johann von Dambach. His Consolatio theologiae, obviously inspired by the Consolatio philosophiae, owed much not only to Boetius and fathers of the church, but also to many pagan authors. This is the Christian humanism, which was characteristic of Northern countries and reached its perfection, as we shall see presently, in the Netherlands.

v. *Humanism in the Netherlands*

Under the influence of the German mystics and especially of the Flemish one, Ruysbroeck of Groenendaal, a little band of devoted scholars led by Geert Groote of Deventer and by Gerard Zerbolt of Zutphen introduced a new kind of renaissance, wherein Christian ideals were wisely combined with ancient traditions. While the Italian humanists (with few exceptions, such as Vergerio and Vittorino) tended to revive pagan ideas and feelings, and even to judge Christian writings in a pagan spirit,[15] Groote was anxious to preserve the best of ancient thought yet to subordinate it to Christianity. The moderna devotio produced a masterpiece of religious literature, the Imitation of Christ, and it impregnated for over a century the humanities in the Netherlands, in Germany, and even in northeastern France.

The Christian renaissance which radiated from Deventer and Zwolle in the second half of the fourteenth century was the most promising aspect of Latin humanism. It helped at one and the same time to revivify the teaching of Latin and to purify the Christian faith. It might have prevented the decline of the Latin language and the reformation of the church, but that it was not strong enough and came too late, when the language and the church had already suffered too many abuses. It inspired directly or indirectly many great men, such as Nicholas of Cusa and Erasmus, Martin Luther and St. Ignatius, even Comenius.

vi. *Books and libraries*

The birth of humanism was stimulated by the discovery of ancient MSS, its growth was closely dependent upon the safe-keeping and transmission of those MSS, and of newer ones, and this could only happen if the care and love of books filled the hearts of a sufficient number of men. We have seen that the men appeared first in Italy, then in other countries. The history of humanism is largely the history of their lives and activities. It can be read in such books as Sandys' and in a whole series of other books devoted to special individuals and to special libraries.[16] Of course, this does not concern only Latin humanism, but it may be discussed here, as Latin books were by far the most numerous and the most important books of Western Europe. Schoolbooks were needed in relatively large quantities, and industrial methods had been devised to produce them.[17] Prayerbooks were also in great demand, and their small size caused them to be generally available. The same could perhaps be said of the Gospels, but certainly not of the complete Bibles. These were difficult to obtain; "the average price of a Bible was at least equal to the whole yearly income of a well-to-do priest, and often much greater."[18] It is true the average priest did not use the Bible over much; one sometimes wonders whether he used it at all. It is possible that some Bibles were worn out by use, yet the surviving ones show on the whole very little trace of wear even where one would expect it most, in the Psalms or the Gospels.

[15] For example, they would complain of the bad Latinity of the Vulgate and say it was dangerous for one's taste to read it, or they would use pagan expressions even with regard to sacred matters. Pietro Bembo (1470–1547), papal secretary, called Our Lady "Dea ipsa," appealed to the "Di immortales," etc.

[16] Many are cited in this volume passim. Good introductions to the whole immense subject will be found in Montague Rhodes James: The wanderings and homes of MSS (96 p., London 1919; Isis 3, 470), and James Westfall Thompson (1939).

[17] See, e.g., Jean Destrez: La pecia dans les MSS universitaires du XIIIe et du XIVe siècle (2 vols., Paris 1935; Isis 25, 155–57).

[18] Coulton: Medieval panorama (p. 683, 1938).

The rarity and preciousness of books increased the need of libraries. There were libraries in almost every monastery and nunnery, but in most cases they were exceedingly small, the very largest containing only a few hundred books. There were also libraries in the colleges and cathedrals, the most valuable books being chained[19] or safeguarded in other ways. Collections of MSS were made by individuals—prelates like Richard de Bury, humanists like Boccaccio and Salutati, physicians like Guido da Bagnolo, jurists like Philip of Leiden, etc. (For a complete list of the individual or institutional libraries referred to in this volume, see index s.v. library, collections of MSS.) The richest collections were naturally those made by the kings or great lords, or rather for them, Charles V and Charles VI of France, the duke of Berry, Edward III and Richard II of England. The catalogues of many of those libraries have come down to us, sometimes the books themselves, sometimes the bills and accounts. For example, Edward III bought from Isabel of Lancaster, nun in Amesbury (near Salisbury), a book of romances and paid for it £66.13.4; Richard II bought a French Bible, a Roman de la rose, a Roman de Perceval, paying for the three £28.[20] These were enormous sums of money. We must assume that the books in question were illuminated, luxurious, princely copies, but ordinary copies were already so expensive that a doctor owning, say, a dozen of them was considered a rich collector. We should always bear in mind such limitations when we try to assess mediaeval learning.

vii. *Latin vs. the vernaculars*

The relative importance of Western vernaculars as compared with Latin grew from 38 per cent in the first half of the century to 75 per cent in the second half. This was due to the waxing of many vernaculars (especially French) as well as to the waning of Latin. The field of the latter was steadily narrowing around a permanent core, the ritual needs of the Catholic church. Everything religious, except when written exclusively for laymen or for women, was in Latin. For example, the religious motets of Guillaume de Machaut were worded in Latin, the secular ones in French.

The dangers inherent in such a situation have been explained in chapter I. Latin was gradually divorced from life; it was becoming more and more artificial. This was the case even for priests and monks, not to speak of laymen.[21] The dangers were not simply linguistic, but religious and moral. The church's business tended to become esoteric. Instead of being like a mother welcoming all her children under her mantle, the church tended to become a stepmother who spoke another language.[22]

Two professions, the law and medicine, were to some extent victims of the same policy. The use of Latin made them exclusive, but alienated them from the people. Jurists and physicians spoke Latin among themselves, as well as they could, but they did it less and less fluently and less and less correctly. Pedants took refuge in

[19] Burnett Hillman Streeter: The chained library (390 p., ill., London 1931).

[20] Jusserand (p. 120, 1884). For various catalogues of princely libraries see ch. 15, p. 396.

[21] "In 1473 it was necessary [in Spain] to pass a formal decree providing that no man should be ordained who did not understand the Latin language." James P. R. Lyell: Cardinal Ximenes (p. 17, London 1917).

[22] The situation was well understood and explained a century later by Pietro Bembo (1470–1547), secretary to Leo X. He pointed out that Latin was bound to be superseded by the vernaculars, even as Greek had been ousted from ancient Rome by Latin. He was himself one of the best Latinists of his time (Coulton p. 100, 1940).

Latin, even as today in their own scientific jargon. Happily, the more original minds, trying to express their thoughts as strongly and accurately as possible, were beginning to break their linguistic shackles. They could not help it; it was a fight between expression and repression, and their main concern was to express their message. Latin, however, was still so well entrenched that the liberation from it took many centuries and was not completed until yesterday. At the end of the seventeenth century the Italian anatomist Giorgio Baglivi (1668–1707) could still exclaim, "Reipublicae medicae et litterariae lingua Romana esto.... Quid Gallicâ, quid Anglicâ, quid Germanicâ linguâ medicina sacra in vulgus proferre juvat?"[23]

By 1400 the struggle was still in its initial stage, yet a teacher of Latin, like our Oxford friend Thomas Sampson, might already have lifted his arms high in the air and lamented, "Whereto are we drifting, our boys find it harder and harder to speak and write decent Latin."

The simple truth is that an artificial language can never resist a natural one; its triumph was possible only in artificial surroundings like those of a seminary or a cloister; fighting against life, it was bound to be defeated sooner or later.

3. *Italian*

In the second half of the fourteenth century, the Italian language was used far less than the French for scientific purposes, yet Italian humanism was dominating Europe, being second in importance only to Latin humanism, though very far behind. The reason is simple; the French had nothing to oppose to, or to compare with, the Italian triumvirate—Dante, Petrarca, Boccaccio. Not only that, but Dante had already become the object of a humanistic cult. In 1373, Florence, regretting her lack of justice and generosity to her most illustrious son, had established an annual course of lectures devoted to the Divina commedia, Boccaccio being appointed the first lecturer. Among his successors were the humanist Giovanni da Ravenna the second, who had been for a time Petrarca's secretary, and the chronicler Filippo Villani. In 1375, Bologna imitated Florence's example and established a new Dante lectureship, the first lecturer being Benvenuto di Rambaldi. To this Benvenuto we owe the most elaborate of the early commentaries on the Divina commedia, a commentary which remained the kernel of all the later ones. Thus within a century Dante had been placed on almost as high a pedestal as Homer and Vergil. The language which Dante had used was as it were sanctified and canonized. Italian humanism became a corollary to Latin and Greek humanism; in fact, the same men were often studying the Latin and Italian masterpieces, and even the Greek, as much as they could.

The works which these three giants had written in Italian were composed primarily for the laity. This is obvious as far as the Decamerone is concerned, but is true also of the Canzoniere and the Trionfi and even of the Divina commedia. To these lay classics was now added a purely Catholic one, the Dialogo (1378) of St. Catherine of Siena, a treatise on spiritual life, one of the most ardent ever written

[23] Incomplete quotation taken from Paul Delaunay: La vie médicale aux XVIe, XVIIe et XVIIIe siècles (p. 452, Paris 1935). I was not able to identify it in the Opera omnia of Baglivi (9th ed., Antwerp 1715), but it is plausible. Baglivi's treatise De fibra motrice et morbosa (1700) bears as motto the last paragraph of the Hippocratic Law, "Sacra sacris hominibus communicanda, profanis vero nefas prius quam scientiae mysteriis initiati sint." This was the best motto for the defenders of Latin against the vernaculars.

in mediaeval times. It is an impressive witness of those troubled days, not only because of impassioned visions of the other world and the hereafter, but also because of her clear and sharp criticisms of the corrupted and decadent church. She was the greatest letter writer of her age, next to Petrarca; happily, she wrote not like him in Cicero's language, but in her own idiomatic Tuscan.

Italian was also used for scientific purposes, though much less than French. It was so close to Latin that there was less need of Italian treatises duplicating the Latin ones. We have, however, anonymous texts on arithmetic, algebra, geometry. We may be sure that the bankers of Florence and of other prosperous cities needed arithmetical instructions in Italian for themselves and their employees; they also needed tables to facilitate various commercial computations. No such tables of this period, however, have come down to us in their original form; it is probable that they were worn out. The tables compiled c. 1340 by Francesco Balducci Pegolotti for the Bardi company of Florence have reached us indirectly.

Explanations for painters, sculptors, and craftsmen were composed by Cennino Cennini, Joannes Alcherius, Lorenzo Ghiberti, but these works belong to the fifteenth century rather than to the fourteenth. We may assume that Francesco Landino wrote in Italian, though his favorite language was the international one of music.

Most physicians wrote in Latin; the veterinary treatise of Dino Dini, however, is in Italian; and it is possible that Ugo Benzi himself translated his book on hygiene, originally written in Latin. It was natural enough to publish such a book in the vernacular.

Italian chronicles were written by Matteo Villani, his son Filippo, and Gino Capponi, a curious treatise on chivalry by Gentile degli Mainardi, the geographical poem Dittamondo by Fazio degli Uberti.

It is not always easy to determine the language of a map, but we may safely consider the Este map, the Medicean, Combitis, and Pinelli atlases, and the portolani of Francesco Pizigano Italian productions, even from the purely linguistic point of view.

Finally, mention must be made of the travelers Giorgio Gucci, Leonardo di Frescobaldi, Simone Sigoli, Niccolò and Antonio Zeni, and perhaps of the "alpinist" Rotario d'Asti.

The development of Italian out of Latin, that is, the reconstruction of a noble language out of the wreckage of another one, is of immense interest to the student of natural history and of human history. Its most astonishing feature is its unconsciousness. There is no trace that I could see of deliberate grammatical or lexicographical efforts. The only philologist I came across was Dante, who in his De vulgari eloquentia asked himself pertinent questions about the vernaculars. Nobody was there to heed those questions, let alone answer them. The evolution continued blindly, irresistibly. Though Tuscany was the main spring of the new language, the other regions of Italy contributed to its edification.

Two full centuries had to elapse after Dante before the appearance of the first grammatical essays, the Prose della volgar lingua (Venezia 1525) by cardinal Pietro Bembo (Venezia 1470—Roma 1547). Grammatical consciousness was much increased by various publications of Claudio Tolomei (Siena 1492—Roma 1555), bishop of Curzola (Dalmatia), and the fertile discussions which they kindled. The grammatical landmarks after that were Gian Giorgio Trissino (1478–1550): Grammatichetta (Vicenza 1529);[24] Pier Francesco Giambullari: De la lingua che si parla e scrive in Firenze (402 p., Florence 1551).

As to vocabularies, there are quite a few bilingual ones (Latin-Italian) of the fourteenth and the fifteenth centuries, e.g., the short one compiled c. 1465 by the poet Luigi Pulci of Florence (1432–84) as a help for classical studies. G. Volpi: Il Vocabolista di Luigi Pulci (Rivista delle biblioteche e degli archivi 19, 9–15, 21–28, 1908). There were also purely Italian vocabularies, but none of any importance before the sixteenth century.[25] Among the earliest ones it will suffice to mention Fabricio Luna of Naples: Vocabulario di cinque mila vocabula toschi, non men oscuri che utili e necessarij, del Furioso, Bocaccio, Petrarcha e Dante (Napoli 1536); Francesco Alunno of Ferrara: Della fabrica del mundo libri X ne' quali si contengono le voci di Dante, del Petrarca, del Boccaccio e d'altri buoni authori mediante le quali si possono scriuendo esprimere tutte i concetti dell' huomo di qualcumque cosa creata (Venezia 1546–48), often reprinted. Note that the substance of these vocabularies is very largely of fourteenth-century date and even of the first half of that century, and that they were compiled by non-Tuscans. Luna's was in alphabetical order, Alunno's in methodical order. These and other vocabularies were completely overshadowed by the Vocabolario degli Accademici della Crusca, begun in 1591 and first printed in Venice 1612. The main point is that the vocabularies, even as the grammar, appeared very late.

There are many textbooks dealing with the historic grammar of Italian, but they are of no use for our purpose. We are not concerned with the evolution of Italian grammar or lexicography, but with the birth and development of grammatical consciousness in Italy. I do not know of any book on the subject nor of any adequate treatment of it. I have, however, consulted Policarpo Petrocchi: La lingua e la storia letteraria d'Italia dalle origini fino a Dante (304 p., Roma 1903); Vasco Restori: Dal Latino plebeo all' Italiano illustre (152 p., Mantova 1921). Bearing in mind the fact that from Dante on, every educated Italian was equally familiar with Latin and Italian and must have been aware of grammatical differences, it is astonishing that two centuries were needed for the formulation of Italian grammar. That can be explained only by the assumption of an inferiority complex with regard to Latin for spiritual reasons, and later with regard to French for political ones. Though Dante and Petrarca had lifted the new language to as high a level of beauty and glory as might be desired, many Italian literati continued to be ashamed of it and apologetic about it for centuries.

4. *Castilian* (*Spanish*)

The main defender of Castilian was López de Ayala, who used it for his chronicle of Castile and his book on falconry, and translated many books, ancient and modern (Boccaccio!), from Latin. The Spanish account of Clavijo's journey to Samarqand and his portrait of Tamerlane is one of the best books of its kind, but it was composed only in 1403–6.

As in the first half of the century, some of the work for the defense and diffusion

[24] The Grammatichetta was not available to me, but Giulio Antimaco republished in the Biblioteca rara of G. Daelli, no. 49, Il Castellano di Giangiorgio Trissino ed Il Cesano di Claudio Tolomei, dialoghi intorno alla lingua volgare (130 p., Milano 1864).

[25] Luigi Morandi: Lorenzo il Magnifico, Leonardo da Vinci e la prima grammatica italiana. Leonardo e i primi vocabolari (158 p., Città di Castello 1908).

of Castilian was done by Jews, Meir ben Solomon Alguadez, who wrote Secreta medica in that language, and Solomon ben Isaac ha-Levi (alias Paul of Burgos), who composed a Historia universal in Spanish verse.

The development of grammar and lexicography was almost as slow as in Italy. This, we shall find out, was a general rule. In spite of the fact that educated men using vernaculars had gained some familiarity with grammatical categories in Latin and hence might have been expected to recognize and rediscover examples of them in the common tongue, they did not. This would suggest that they did not take their own vernaculars seriously, or, at least, that they did not think of them as being in the same class as Latin.

In any case, we have to wait until the second half of the fifteenth century for the first grammatical tools. These were finally provided by the great Spanish humanist Elio Antonio de Nebrija (or Lebrija) of Seville (1441–1522). His Spanish grammar, Gramática castellana, printed within his lifetime (Salamanca 1492), is said to have been the first grammar of any vernacular to appear in print. His Spanish-Latin and Latin-Spanish vocabularies printed in the same year (Salamanca 1492) had been preceded by the Universal vocabulario en latin y en romance (Seville 1490) of Alfonso de Palencia (1423–92). The first important dictionary of Spanish alone was the Tesoro de la lengua castellana o española compiled by Sebastián de Covarrubias y Orozco (1539–1613) and published in Madrid 1611, i.e., about the same time as the first dictionary of the Accademia della Crusca (Venice 1612). See Hurtado and González Palencia (p. 202, 275, 730, 1932).

5. *Provençal*

The most remarkable Provençal writings which we came across in the second half of the fourteenth century were put together by Bertran Boysset of Arles. He collected Provençal texts in prose and verse, registered historical and family events in a commonplace book, and wrote a treatise on surveying, the scientific value of which is almost negligible.

To the many texts listed in chapter I (p. 338–41) may still be added the Provençal version of the Dits des philosophes. This was a French abridgment of the Dicta et opiniones philosophorum[26] made by Guillaume de Tignonville, a gentleman in the service of Charles VI, sent by the latter to represent him at the court of Avignon, provost of Paris in 1401, died in 1414.[27] The Dits des philosophes shared the great popularity of the Latin compilation; as many as 38 MSS of it have been listed.[28] One of the copies of the French text was made at Aix-en-Provence in 1402 by Andrivet de Bressé of Saumur, secretary to the king of Jerusalem and Sicily; the Provençal version was made from the French text (but not from that copy).

Inasmuch as the Dicta et opiniones philosophorum have not yet been mentioned in my Introduction, the following information ad hoc may be inserted here. It is of Arabic derivation, the original being the Mukhtār al-ḥikam wa maḥāsin al-kalim composed in 1053–54 by the Egyptian amīr-Abū-l-Wafā' Mubashshir ibn Fātik al-Qā'id.[29] The Arabic text appears also under the titles Manthūr al-ḥikam and

[26] Poor edition of the Latin text by Salvatore de Renzi (3, 68–150, 1854).

[27] Robert Eder: Tignonvillana inedita (Romanische Forschungen 33, 851–1022, Erlangen 1915), including the French text, here entitled Les ditz moraulx.

[28] There is a very beautiful illuminated MS of the fifteenth century in the Pierpont Morgan Library, MS 771. Report for 1930–35 (p. 88).

[29] Brockelmann (1, 459; suppt. 1, 829). Brief reference to it in Introd. 1, 130.

Ādāb al-ḥukamā'; it was itself derived from a collection of wise sayings made by Ḥunain ibn Isḥāq (IX-2).[30] The Arabic text passed into Latin either directly or via a Spanish version, Los bocados de oro.[31] The Latin version may have been made by Giovanni da Procida (XIII-2), or it may have been made a little later by one of the scholars working for Robert of Anjou (king of Naples and Sicily 1309–43). The text was very popular in all its forms, Arabic, Spanish, Latin, French, etc. The French text was twice Englished, first in 1450 by one Stebin Scrope, then by Antony Woodville or Wydville, second earl of Rivers (1442?–83).[32] Woodville had been given a copy of the French version of "Jean de Teonville" to beguile his pilgrimage to Compostella in 1473. His version, Dictes and sayings of the philosophers, was printed by William Caxton in Westminster 1477, this being the first dated book printed in England.

Clovis Brunel: Une traduction provençale des "Dits des philosophes" de Guillaume de Tignonville (Bibliothèque de l'Ecole des chartes 100, 309–28, 1939), Provençal text.

Felibrejado

Some information may be added here about the modern revival of Provençal, and the more so because that revival was caused in part by the rediscovery of the mediaeval literature. The great revivers were the Gascon Jacques Boë, called Jasmin (Agen 1798–1864), Joseph Roumanille (St. Rémy 1818–91), Théodore Aubanel (Avignon 1829–86), above all Frédéric Mistral (Maillane 1830–1914). The poems Li margarideto = The daisies (Avignon 1847) of Roumanille, and Mirèio (Avignon 1859) of Mistral, introduced a procession of masterpieces, chiefly lyrical. Provençal congresses (roumavàgi) took place amid great enthusiasm in Arles 1852, Aix 1853. The new movement was formally created in 1854, May 21 (day of St. Estelle, hence choice of a seven-rayed star, estélo, for the Félibrige emblem) in the little castle of Font-Ségugne, in the Comtat, almost within sight of Petrarca's Vaucluse. The members called themselves felibre and their group felibrejado (in French, félibrige).[33]

One of their purposes was to standardize orthography, phonetics, vocabulary. The felibrejado was divided into seven sections, two of them for the gay science (belles lettres), the others for history, music, sciences, painting, and friendship. The main organ was the Armana prouvençau, containing not only the year's almanac, but plenty of verse, prose, and music. The first number appeared in Avignon for 1855.[34] (Avignon was and remained the capital of the movement.) The popular importance of that almanac may perhaps be compared to that of Franklin's Poor Richard in colonial America, except that the Armana prouvençau was less practical and far more ambitious on the side of the humanities.

[30] Lost in Arabic? Hebrew version by Judah ben Solomon al-Ḥarizi (XIII-1). Early Spanish version, Los buenos proverbios que dixieron los philosophos.

[31] The two Spanish texts, Buenos proverbios and Bocados de oro, have been edited by Hermann Knust: Mittheilungen aus dem Eskurial (686 p., Tübingen 1879).

[32] James Tait (DNB 62, 410–13, 1900).

[33] The meaning of these terms is uncertain. Mistral explained them with reference to an old Provençal song about the child Jesus discussing with the seven doctors of the law (emé li set felibre de la lèi). The founders of the movement were also seven.

[34] There is a complete set of it in the Harvard library! The first volume is entitled Armana prouvençau pèr lou bèl an de Dièu 1855, adouba e publica de la man di felibre (112 p. En Avignoun, Aubanel, 1854).

The Félibrige was reorganized along a more elaborate and ceremonious pattern by Mistral in 1876. Thanks to the latter's genius and prestige, it expanded considerably. Mistral compiled a very rich Provençal-French dictionary, Lou tresor dóu félibrige (Aix 1879–86). The expansion reached other provinces of langue d'oc and almost the whole Latin world at the Fête latine of Montpellier 1878, at which French, Catalan, Italian, Roumanian letters were represented. It even reached foreigners such as the Irishman William Bonaparte Wyse, a grandson of Lucien Bonaparte, author of two collections of Provençal verse (1868, 1882). In 1899, the Museon Arlaten was created by Mistral, and that little museum of Arlesian life and letters was the model of many other provincial museums of great interest to the historian.[35]

It should be noted that Félibrige was the main organism of Provençal letters, but not by any means the only one. Indeed, its solemnity, its conservativeness, and the snobbishness which gathered around it repelled many good men. Political, social, and religious differences caused polemics, recriminations, and schisms.

Gaston Jourdanne: Histoire du félibrige, 1854–1906 (320 p., ill., Avignon 1897). Etienne Cornut (S.J.): Les maîtres du félibrige (331 p., Paris 1897). Emile Ripert: Le félibrige (200 p., coll. Colin, Paris 1924). Marius André: La vie harmonieuse de Mistral (304 p., Paris 1928).

For everything Provençal see the elaborate bibliography compiled by Daniel C. Haskell: Provençal literature and language, including the local history of Southern France (888 p., New York Public Library 1925).

6. *Catalan*

One may say that a new period began in Catalan literature with the middle of the fourteenth century, a glorious period but unfortunately a short one, for the marriage of Isabella of Castile to Ferdinand of Aragon in 1469 presaged its end.[36] The characteristics of the new period were due to the influence of Dante, Petrarca, and Boccaccio and to that of the Consistori de la gaya sciensa created at Toulouse in 1323 and of the poetical competitions which began in the same city in 1324. The combined influences coming from Florence and Toulouse gave a new accent to Catalan letters. "Jocs florals" were established at Barcelona in 1393, but the first celebration took place only in 1395 (Garcia Silvestre p. 170–73, 1932).

The outstanding man of letters was Bernat Metge, who was the main channel through which Boccaccio and Petrarca reached not only Catalonia, but the whole peninsula. He lifted his language up to a higher level.

In the meanwhile, the philological elaboration of the language was continuing, and in this respect Provençal examples predominated. The Leys d'amors inspired Jaume March (born in the kingdom of Valencia c. 1335, died at the beginning of the fifteenth century), who completed in 1371 his dictionary Llibre de concordances de rims, apellat Dictionari. In this he improved on the Provençal achievement,

[35] Concerning the value of regional museums see Isis (8, 492–96, 1926; 16, 114–23, 1931).

[36] In 1474, Isabella succeeded her stepbrother Henry IV (1454–74) on the throne of Castile. In 1478, the Holy Inquisition was established in that happy country, primarily to persecute Marranos (converted Jews). In 1479, Ferdinand II succeeded John II (1458–79) on the throne of Aragon, Catalonia, and Valencia. Thus from 1479 on the dyarchy of the Catholic kings functions. In 1492 Granada is taken, the Jews are expelled from Spain, the Inquisition works overtime. In 1502, the remaining Moors are expelled. Intolerance and obscurantism increase. Castile, Aragon, Catalonia are smothered.

for the academy of Toulouse had failed to provide a dictionary. March's dictionary was a dictionary of rhymes, but that is natural enough. In many nations (e.g., China) such dictionaries have preceded other kinds. After all, the arrangement of words may be made beginning with the tail of their written form or of their sound, just as well as beginning with the head. Another philological work was completed a little later by Lluis d'Aversó of Barcelona (fl. 1410), namely, the Torcimany[37] del gay saber, a prosody followed by a dictionary of rhymes.

Astronomical and astrological treatises and tables were written in Catalan for Pere III el Cerimoniós by Dalmau Ces-Planes and Pere Gilbert; the tables were completed in 1366.

One of the main glories of Catalonia was the Jewish school of cartography established in Majorca. Its masterpiece is the Catalan mappemonde of 1375, and the main cartographers were members of the Cresques family, Abraham Cresques and his son Jahuda, later Gabriel de Vallsecha (related to that family) and Mecia de Viladestes.

In this connection mention should be made of the Visió, a poem (1,328 lines) written by Bernat de So, the only poet given by Roussillon to Catalonia. Bernat de So was lord of Millàs in 1335, and died in 1385. His Visió explains the political geography of Europe in the second half of the fourteenth century; he was much interested in heraldry and describes the arms of the thirteen kings dealt with, the kings of France, England, Portugal, Hungary, Naples, Cyprus, Castile, Aragon, Armenia, Scotland, Sicily, Navarre, and Constantinople. This fact suggests comparison with the Libro del conosçimiento composed by a Castilian Franciscan in 1348. The Visió may be derived from that Libro, or from a common source? (Garcia Silvestre p. 104, 1932).

A treatise on surgery by a Samuel Esperial exists in a Vatican MS written in Hebrew script; it has not yet been analyzed.

The admirable series of Catalan chronicles was concluded with the one bearing the name of Pere III el Cerimoniós, dealing with the period 1300–80. Pere III was a patron of Catalan letters; not only did he write various chronicles or cause them to be written, but he ordered the translation of many books into Catalan and brought together a fine library at Poblet. The Aragonese translation of the Chronicle of Morea was completed in 1393 by Juan Fernández de Heredia, and the same Juan wrote other historical works and continued Pere's patronage of translators (Hurtado and González Palencia p. 136, 1932). Thanks to these two generous men, Pere and Juan, the treasure of Catalan literature was considerably increased. For a summary of other historical works and romances in Catalan, dealing with real facts or with myths, see Joseph Anglade (p. 223–35, 1921). I prefer not to go into more detail, as the distinction between Catalan and Provençal works involves many difficulties.

The richest body of Catalan literature was naturally religious and theological. We can give here only a few glimpses of it. It includes many kinds of books, such as monastic rules, books of devotion and edification, translations such as the Llegenda aurea, that is, a version of the Golden legend of James of Voragine (XIII-2), theological treatises. One of the most important translations from the linguistic point of view is that of the Excitatorium mentis ad Deum. The author of the original, Bernat Oliver (XIV-1), was himself a Catalan; the name of the

[37] Torcimany = Fr. truchement, dragoman, words derived from Arabic, tarjumān; Aramaic, targum.

translator is unknown; he flourished at the end of the fourteenth century or perhaps not until the fifteenth century.

The best religious writings were due to friars, and it is convenient to consider the latter according to their orders. First the Dominicans. The leader was of course St. Vincent Ferrer, the fiery apostle who converted Jews and Muslims by the tens of thousands (!?). His main works are in Latin, but there are also Catalan ones, especially the Quaresma which he preached at Valencia in 1413. The many sermons which he preached to call fidels and infidels to repentance were necessarily delivered in the vernacular, that is, in Catalan. It is probable that more of them will eventually be discovered and edited. Two other Dominicans must be named: Antoni Genebreda of Majorca (born 1332, bishop of Athens from 1382 to his death in 1395), who translated Boetius' Consolation and dedicated it to the prince Jaume de Mallorca (d. 1375), and Antoni Canals of Valencia (d. 1419), disciple of St. Vincent; he composed the Escala de contemplació and many translations (Garcia Silvestre p. 145, 141–44, 1932).

Among the Franciscans were two extraordinary men, En Francesc Eiximènis, author of Lo Crestià and other books, and Anselm Turmeda, who was eventually Islamized, and wrote in Arabic as well as in Catalan.

A brother of St. Vincent, Bonifaci Ferrer (born Valencia 1350, died 1417), assumed the Carthusian habit and became the general of his order. He translated the whole Bible into Catalan; after having been revised by the Dominican Jaume Borrell, the translation was printed at Valencia 1477–78, this being the first vernacular Bible to be printed (Garcia Silvestre p. 265–68, 1932).

Castile and Aragon united in 1479 to thwart Catalan aspirations and outlaw the Catalan language. However, a noble people will not be downed indefinitely. In the nineteenth and twentieth centuries, the Catalans were allowed a renaissance which has caused the whole world to admire them and to love them. That marvelous renaissance was cruelly broken under our own eyes by the fascist government of Spain. The spirit of Catalonia, however, is not dead, it cannot be killed; it has been driven underground by Spanish brutality, but it will revive some day.

For more information on the Catalan language and literature, see V. M. Otto Denk: Einführung in die Geschichte der altcatalanischen Litteratur (548 p., München 1893). Marian Aguiló y Fúster: Catálogo de obras en lengua catalana impresas desde 1474 hasta 1860 (2000 p., Madrid 1923). Josep Calveras (S.J.): La reconstrucció del llenguatge literari català. Estudi d'orientació (334 p., Barcelona 1925), a very interesting contribution to the fundamental problems involved in the revival of any vernacular. A. Griera: Gramática histórica del català antic (157 p., 1931). Garcia Silvestre (1932).

The most valuable study on Catalan mediaeval science is José Millàs Vallicrosa: Assaig d'història de les idees físiques i matemàtiques a la Catalunya medieval (367 p., 20 pl., Barcelona 1931; Isis 18, 203–4). Unfortunately, vol. 1 stops at the twelfth century and the work has not been continued; moreover, it is a study of Latin and Arabic documents of Catalan science, but not of science in Catalan. A large number of excellent and beautiful books have been published in Catalan within the past fifty years; all that is now stopped or rather interrupted. Long live glorious and generous Catalonia!

7. *Portuguese*

A renaissance of Portuguese letters may be said to have begun in 1385, when the battle of Aljubarrota liberated Portugal from Castile,[38] for by the same token

[38] Isis 22, 448.

Portuguese literature became more conscious of its right to independence. The noblest fruit of that renaissance was the chronicle of Fernão Lopes, but it belongs to the following century. Fernão was still a child (5 years of age) at the time of Aljubarrota, and he lived until c. 1459. Among the earlier writers it will suffice to speak of two, Garci Ferrandez de Gerena (c. 1340–c. 1400) and Alfonso Alvarez de Villasandino (c. 1345–c. 1428).

Garci is the Portuguese counterpart of the Catalan Anselm Turmeda. Like Anselm he was a man of great instability, but unlike him he was a poet. Having married one of the dancing girls of Dom João I, he got tired of her, became a hermit near Gerena, got tired of that too, ran away to Malaga, and renounced not only his family but his faith. After having been a Muslim for some time, he returned to Castile and recanted. His type is well known to psychiatrists; it is not incompatible with literary talent.

Alfonso was born in Old Castile, his birthplace, Villasandino, being near Burgos, but he continued the poetic traditions which were Galician, that is, closer to Portuguese than Castilian, and he became the most illustrious troubadour of his time. He is a typical court poet, complacent and ingratiating, the very opposite of poor Garci, who was always in a state of revolt because of his own tortured soul.

These two poets and others keep alive Portuguese poetry. For prose one has to wait until the next century, when the great chronicles of Fernão Lopez established new standards and raised the Portuguese language to a higher level.

In the fourteenth century Portuguese literature was still decidedly inferior to Provençal and Catalan, and even to Castilian, literatures. It was still the least developed of all the Romance literatures of Western Europe.

8. *French*

In spite of a dismal series of political calamities (which began with the Hundred Years' War in 1338 and abated only with Jeanne d'Arc), the high position which the French language held was considerably strengthened during the second half of the fourteenth century; this was due largely to the personal interest which the king and court took in their language. It was a case of French pride, the challenge of French culture, politically conscious of its merit, to the ancients and to the foreigners! The outstanding personality of the French renaissance at this stage was Nicole Oresme, who revealed the political and astronomical writings of Aristotle to the French public. Moreover, Nicole was tutor to the dauphin Charles and remained the latter's adviser after his enthronement as Charles V; we may assume that it was in large measure because of Nicole's influence that the king did so much to patronize translators such as Jean Dandin, Raoul de Presles, Denis Foulechat, Jean Corbechon, Jacques Bauchant, Simon de Hesdin, Nicolas de Gonesse, Jean Golein.

The importance of translations in the spiritual building up of any nation has been emphasized repeatedly in volumes 1 and 2 of this Introduction. It is not only that new texts are thus made available to the readers of a definite language, new spigots of knowledge opened to them, but that the language itself, obliged to adapt itself to the most severe requirements, is thus enabled to develop completely. The conscientious translator must produce in his own language the equivalent of thoughts expressed in another; this obliges him to improve the grammar of his language and to enrich its vocabulary.

This was the task which Oresme and the other translators had to face, and which was sometimes so difficult as to seem hopeless. Raoul de Presles confessed that it was not possible to translate St. Augustine's City of God exactly, but only in a roundabout way (par manière de circonlocucion); Denis Foulechat, trying to translate the Polycratus of John of Salisbury, did not always find a way to produce "quid pro quo" because of the strange grammar (l'estrange gramoire) of the original and its complicated sentences (les sentences suspensives parfondes et obscures). Oresme explained his difficulties and justified the methods to the use of which he had been driven, and the Latin terms he had been obliged to naturalize because they were otherwise untranslatable.

Any boy who has been struggling with Latin versions will readily sympathize with Foulechat, Raoul de Presles, and Oresme, but he should understand that their difficulties were immeasurably worse than his. For his task is simply to translate the thought of one language into another language equally rich and mature; their task was to translate it into a language which was still inadequate. They had to create a new language. For details into which it is impossible to go here, see Petit de Julleville (2, 533–50, 1896); Ferdinand Brunot: Histoire de la langue française (1, 401–547, Paris 1905). The result of their efforts may be summed up in the phrase "Latinization of the French language." The Latinization was natural enough to men translating from Latin, but it was not restricted to them, for we find obvious traces of it in writers like Froissart[39] and even in contemporary romances. Thus was a curious cycle completed. The French language had been born as an unconscious revolt against the Latin, the complexity of which seemed absurd and unbearable to simple people; as those people became more sophisticated and tried to express Latin thoughts in their own language, they were obliged to salvage much of the grammar and of the vocabulary which they had jettisoned.

In the meanwhile the French language developed more naturally in the social intercourse of French people, polite yet innocent of philological problems, and in the creations of literary artists such as Eustache Deschamps and Christine de Pisan.

It was especially for the expression of scientific thoughts that a new terminology was required. As far as mathematics and astronomy are concerned, Nicole Oresme supplied the need; many of the astronomical terms which he introduced have remained an integral part of the language ever since. Treatises on astrology and cosmography were written also by Pèlerin de Prusse and Jean Fusoris.

The creation of the alchemical language occurred somewhat later, for La fontaine des amoureux de science was written by Jean de la Fontaine only in 1413, and the books ascribed to Nicolas Flamel cannot be earlier than the fifteenth century. The technical words used by limners and other craftsmen are necessarily older, for the craftsman must name his tools and tricks as soon as he uses them, yet the earliest writings ad hoc, e.g. those of Jean Le Bègue and Alcherius, are relatively late.

Travel accounts were composed by Jean de Mandeville, Ogier d'Anglure, and

[39] For example, consider the first paragraph of his Chroniques, second redaction (ed. Kervyn de Lettenhove, vol. 2, p. 4, 1867): "Affin que honnourables emprises et nobles aventures et faits d'armes, lesquelles sont avenues par les guerres de France et d'Angleterre, soient notablement registrées et mises en mémoire perpétuel, par quoy les preux aient exemple d'eulx encouragier en bien faisant, je vueil traittier et recorder hystoire et matière de grand louenge. Mais ains que je la commence, je requier au Sauveur de tout le monde, qui de néant créa toutes choses, que il vueille créer et mettre en moy sens et entendement si vertueux que ce livre que j'ai commencié je le puisse continuer et persévérer en telle manière que tous ceulx et celles qui le liront, verront et orront, y puissent prendre esbatement et plaisance, et je encheoir en leur grâce."

Ghillebert de Lannoy. More important, even from the purely linguistic point of view, are the Roman des déduis of Gace de la Bigne, the Miroir de Phoebus of Gaston de Foix, the Bon berger of Jean de Brie, and the books of king Modus and queen Ratio. These writings are full of valuable lore and of precious words.

Medical texts are relatively few in number, as we should expect, for the average physician needed the Latin language to sustain his dignity. His medical opinions, if expressed in the vernacular, would have been considered vulgar and second rate a priori. A man of genius, however, Guy de Chauliac, did not hesitate to publish his work in French. His Chirurgia magna is not only one of the classics of surgery, but also one of the classics of the French language. Another treatise on surgery was written by Pierre Fromont, treatises on the gout by Jean Le Fèvre, on the plague by Jean à la Barbe, and on bloodletting by Jean Le Lièvre, medical translations by Martin de Saint-Gilles, Richard Eudes, and Evrard Conty.

So many historical books were composed in French that the student of history and politics could no longer afford to be ignorant of that language or to be prejudiced against it. We have the chronicle of France by Jean de Venette, the travel books put together by Jean d'Ypres, the great chronicle of Jean Le Bel, the mirror of Jean d'Outremeuse, the books of Jacques de Hemricourt, above all the chronicle of Jean Froissart. This last named is one of the outstanding monuments of mediaeval literature, and it is a French monument.

The international renown of the language is well illustrated by the history of Armenia which the last Armenian king, Leon V of Lusignan, wrote in French with the help of his secretary, Jean Dardel. One may object that the Lusignan family was French; the composition of that chronicle in French rather than in Latin is none the less very remarkable.

There remain to be considered the political and economic writings. The most important by far are those of Nicole Oresme, for his translation of the Aristotelian treatises ad hoc was fundamental. His treatise on money, which he thought necessary to publish in French as well as in Latin, was a landmark in its field. Then behold the Songe du vieil pelerin by Philippe de Mézières, and the Songe du vergier, the moral verse of Gilles Le Muisit, the Livre du chevalier de La Tour, one of the most popular educational books of the Middle Ages, the precepts of Ghillebert de Lannoy, the Ménagier de Paris, and even the cookbook of Guillaume Taillevent. All these books helped the pater familias to regulate his house and to determine his private and public duties.

The great success of the French language is the more remarkable because that language was then very unstable and very imperfect, but languages, like other organisms, owe their success at least as much to outside circumstances as to intrinsic qualities. The age of Middle French (roughly from the beginning of the Valois to the beginning of the Bourbons, 1328–1589) is an age of gestation and indiscipline. Old French had acquired some stability. Middle French never did. The very masters, such as Oresme, Froissart, Gerson, were unable to maintain enough consistency.

It is very curious that in spite of the grammatical difficulties which translators were obliged to face in almost every sentence, no attempt was made *in France* to determine the rules of French grammar until more than a century later. The determination of French lexicography, however, was attempted before the end of the fourteenth century. That attempt took the form of a French adaptation of the famous Latin dictionary, the Catholicon of Giovanni Balbi (XIII-2), completed in 1286. The Latin-French Catholicon, as we may call that anonymous effort, was compiled between 1286 and 1400, probably after 1350, for the earliest MSS date from the end of the fourteenth century. That lexicon was printed in Paris 1485, and again in Geneva 1487. New edition by Mario Roques: Recueil général des lexiques français du Moyen Age (vol. 2, 484 p., Paris 1938).

This Latin-French glossary was rather jejune. For a real French dictionary one had to wait until the publication of the Dictionarium seu Latinae linguae thesaurus . . . cum gallica fere interpretatione (folio, 2 vols., 940 fol., Paris 1531) of Robert I Estienne = Robertus Stephanus (Paris 1503—Geneva 1559), or, better, until the publication of the Thresor de la langue francoyse, tant ancienne que moderne (folio, 678 p., Paris 1606) of Jean Nicot (Nîmes 1530—Paris 1600).[40]

French grammar will be discussed in the following subsection. We may say now in a general way that the French language was constituted on a solid basis only in the sixteenth century. Many grammarians and lexicographers were at work during that century, and their efforts for the defense of the language were implemented by administrative regulations. In 1539, Francis I ordered all public documents to be issued exclusively in the French language of Paris.

Charles Louis Livet: La grammaire française et les grammairiens du XVIe siècle (544 p., Paris 1859). Edmund Stengel: Chronologisches Verzeichnis französischer grammatiken vom Ende des 14. bis zum Ausgange des 18. Jahrhunderts (160 p., Oppeln 1890). Gustav Gröber: Grundriss der romanischen Philologie (vol. 1, Strassburg 1904–6).

French in England

The earliest grammatical efforts were made not in France, but in England. This will not surprise the readers of this Introduction who remember that Greek philology began not in Greece but in Alexandria (II-1 B.C.), Arabic philology not in Arabia but in Baṣra (VIII-2), Hebrew grammar in Sura, 'Irāq (X-1). See Introd. 1, 179, 501, 542, 627. Educated people who speak their native language, and preferably no other, do not need grammars or dictionaries; they have them unformulated, but free from doubts, in their own minds. Foreigners need explanations and short cuts; polyglots are confused and uncertain.

In the thirteenth century, French was still sufficiently known in the English upper classes. Robert Grosseteste (XIII-1) could say that there were but two languages in England, Latin and French. Robert of Gloucester (fl. 1260–1300), he who translated the history of Geoffrey of Monmouth (XII-1) into English, complained that the English were the only people who had lost their own tongue. Matters changed very much, however, in the fourteenth century, and especially after the Black Death. In spite of the fact that the kings of England were probably more familiar with French than with the popular dialect, they had to submit to increasing national pressure. In 1362, upon the request of Parliament, Edward

[40] This Nicot had been ambassador to Lisbon in 1559–61, and had then become acquainted with the plant petum (tobacco); the words Nicotiana, nicotine, etc. are derived from his name. He introduced the plant into France, but the first to write about it was another Frenchman, Jacques Gohory (1520–76), in his Instruction sur l'herbe petum (Paris 1572), for which see Willis Herbert Bowen: The earliest treatise on tobacco (Isis 28, 349–63, 2 fig., 1938). Nicot's prime interest was French lexicography. He had published a Dictionnaire français-latin (771 p., Paris 1584; often reprinted). The Thresor was a posthumous publication.

III ordered that pleadings should take place in English;[41] in the following year the chancellor opened the parliamentary session in English. Still, most of the private and public documents continued to be phrased in French until the following century. It was more elegant for an English gentleman to write in French, but it was more difficult, and it became increasingly more so.

English was dispossessing French; the movement was steady and slow in the English manner; as we know, it was never carried to the extreme, and the legal and royal jargon preserve quaint French phrases to our own days. The general tendency, however, was irresistible, in spite of educational efforts to stem it. John of Trevisa complained (c. 1385) that the children did not know French any more. Of course, that was the very root of the French neglect; French ceased to be natural; it was not yet as artificial as Latin, but was becoming more artificial every day. The remark often repeated, that Chaucer and Lydgate seemed to be translating Latin texts with the help of French versions, proved just that—the English were less unfamiliar with French than with Latin. It was with them as it is with most of us today; we like to use Greek texts with Latin translations, not because our Latin is so strong, but rather because it is stronger than our Greek.

Under these conditions the English needed more helps for the study of French, and it is therefore not at all surprising that French grammar was born in England and for more than a century remained almost exclusively an English business. The earliest book dealing with French grammar is a little book on orthography, including grammatical rules; it was written probably before the middle of the fourteenth century, or not long after. It was edited by Jacob Stürzinger: Orthographia gallica. Ältester Traktat über französische Aussprache und Orthographie (98 p., Heilbronn 1884). The first grammar proper is the "Donait[42] françois pur briefment entroduyr les Anglois en la droit language du Paris et de pais la d'entour fait aux despenses de Johan Barton par pluseurs bons clercs du language avandite."[43] It was written c. 1400 (certainly before 1409) and is remarkably good; of course it was derived from Latin models; it bears comparison with some of the work done in France more than a century later. Revised editions of that Donait were published c. 1410, c. 1415. The next grammar is the "Lytell treatyse for to lerne Englysshe and Frensshe" printed by Wynkyn de Worde (Westminster 1497). This was primarily a vocabulary, and as such had been preceded by the one printed by William Caxton in 1480. To complete this account of incunabula we must still

[41] The statute of 1362 was not very effective, judging from the fact that as late as 1730 "a statute recited that the proceedings in the courts of justice were carried on in a language unknown to those who were summoned and impleaded, and ordered that after March 1733, 'all proceedings . . . shall be in the English tongue and language only, and not in Latin or French.' Since that time more English has crept into the lawyer's vocabulary, but practically all its fundamental and purely technical words are still those for which the statute of 1362 tried to make English lawyers substitute English terms." Quotation culled from G. E. Woodbine: The language of English law (Speculum 18, 395–436, 1943), a most interesting review of that complicated question. Woodbine concludes that "as far as law and government are concerned, the influence which causes French to be used in England as a regularly written language, begins to operate not at the Norman Conquest, but some two hundred years later, following that other French invasion which took place after the marriage of Henry III to Eleanor of Provence [1236]."

[42] So called after the Latin grammarian Donatus (IV-1). Hence the English word donet, meaning a Latin grammar, or by extension any elementary textbook.

[43] Edited by Edmund Stengel (Zeitschrift für neufranzösische Sprache 1, 25–40, Oppeln 1879).

cite the "Good boke to lerne to speke french" printed by R. Pinson c. 1500. (STC nos. 24865-67.)

Reference was made in chapter I (p. 347) to a French-English manual of conversation, Ryght good lernyng, printed by Caxton c. 1483. It was referred to at that place because it was derived from a Flemish example of c. 1340. A similar manual, "La manière de language que enseigne bien à droit parler et escrire doulcz françois," was composed by an Englishman at Bury St. Edmunds in 1396.[44]

As to the teaching of French in the English colleges, we get a pretty good idea of it from the records concerning Thomas Sampson, who was tutoring in Oxford throughout the second half of the fourteenth century. He composed for his students an Orthographia gallica (dealing with French usage as well as spelling), tables of conjugations, vocabularies, French tracts on composition and heraldry, a treatise on epistolary French with examples referring to real people (kings and lords) of his time. He was still living in 1409, being then an octogenarian. It was part of his method to combine the teaching of French and Latin, and to use French for the teaching of other gentlemanly subjects such as heraldry (this was the more justified that the terms of heraldry were French) and accounting.

H. G. Richardson: Business training in medieval Oxford (American historical review 46, 259-80, 1941). Mary Dominica Legge: Anglo-Norman letters and petitions from All Souls MS 182 (Anglo-Norman Text Society no. 3, 520 p., Oxford 1941; Speculum 17, 137-38, 1942), formulary of the period 1390-1410.

It was natural to use the French language for the teaching of arithmetic and thus kill two birds with one stone. An Anglo-Norman algorism of the fourteenth century was edited by Charles N. Staubach, with preface by Louis C. Karpinski (Isis 23, 121-52, 1935). This text of 328 lines occurs in Corpus Christi MS, Oxford (no. 133), together with the Scala cronica of Sir Thomas Gray, begun in 1355.

In spite of the fact that French was gradually losing its hold on English readers, some important books were still written in French, to wit, the Scala cronica wherein Sir Thomas Gray told the history of England from the beginning to 1362, the Anonimalle chronicle dealing with the period 1333-81, and the Speculum meditantis composed by John Gower c. 1379. The last-named work is a very long French poem—long comme un jour sans pain—discussing with painful reiteration the duties of man.

These works were among the last to be written in French by Englishmen. In the fifteenth century French subsisted only as a technical language for legal and administrative purposes; as a literary language it was dead.

By the end of the fourteenth century we may be sure that it could have been said of many gentlemen and ladies as Chaucer said of the Prioress, madame Eglentyne (A Prol. 124):

And Frenssh she spake ful faire and fetisly
After the scole of Stratford atte Bowe,
For Frenssh of Parys was to hire unknowe.

[44] Edited by Paul Meyer: La manière de language qui enseigne à parler et à écrire le français (Revue critique d'histoire, nos. complémentaires de 1870, p. 373-408, Paris 1873), with glossary. New edition (114 p., Bruxelles 1934).

9. *English*

The two parts of section 8 and section 9 should be read together, because they complete one another. They deal with French in France, French in England, English in England. The regress of French meant the progress of English. The two stories are complementary, like the two sides of the same medal. The parliamentary resolutions which introduced or generalized the use of English drove French out (or tried to); considered from one point of view they concern the history of the French language, from another they concern the history of the English language.

It is significant that even the romances which had been read hitherto in French must now be translated into English. For example, Sir Humphrey of Bohun, earl of Hereford (d. 1361), ordered one William to translate the French romance "Guillaume de Palerne"[45] into English; thus originated the poem "William of Palerne" (5,540 alliterative long lines in West Midland dialect; Wells p. 19). About the same time (say, middle of the fourteenth century) another poem, "Joseph of Arimathie" (709 alliterative long lines in West or South West Midland dialect; Wells p. 75), replaced the French Grand Saint Graal. These two poems, William of Palerne and Joseph of Arimathie, are the earliest poems of a kind (alliterative revival; Wells p. 240) which remained very popular for a full century.[46]

Moreover, books were now translated directly from Latin into English without passing through the French (though the translator would be likely to help himself with a French version if any were available).[47] The outstanding translator from Latin into English was John of Trevisa, whose translations are monuments of early English prose. The series of texts which he Englished illustrates his main purpose, the education of gentlemen. They deal with history (Higden), science (Bartholomew the Englishman), military art (Vegetius), ethics (Regimen principum), politics (Dialogus inter militem et clericum). A century earlier the ancestors of those gentlemen would have read the same texts in Latin or in French; they now needed English versions. A similar service was rendered a little later by John Lydgate, whose Fall of princes (c. 1434) made Boccaccio available to English readers. This affords an excellent model of the transmission which was taking place. As the De casibus virorum illustrium became too difficult for people whose Latin was steadily weakening, it was put into French by Laurence de Premierfait. This helped a lot but did not suffice for the English, and Lydgate was obliged to turn Laurence's (second amplified) version from French into English.

We have seen in the preceding section that some teachers like Thomas Sampson were making gallant efforts to defend the fortress of Latin and French, but what could they do against the rising tide? Other schoolmasters were now beginning to teach English—that is, it was realized that English was not or should not be a dialect; it was a language as worthy as Latin or French, but only on condition of

[45] The French romance had itself been translated from the Latin for Yolande, daughter of Baldwin IV, count of Hainaut from 1120 to 1171. The Latin text was probably south Italian or Sicilian, and it incorporated Byzantine elements. It is a love tale including the werewolf theme and other magical elements.

[46] Other examples such as Wynnere and Wastoure, Piers Plowman are referred to in this volume.

[47] That has been done by translators and commentators of every time and clime. They want to translate from the original texts but will use any other text which, being easier to them, may help them to understand the original better.

being studied properly and used decently. Literacy is independent of this or that language; it can be attained in any language, if that language is known sufficiently well. To be sure, the English treasure was still inferior to the Latin and French, but it was growing, and there was no reason preventing it from becoming richer and richer. A good tool is susceptible of indefinite improvements, but at any stage of its own growth its value depends on the skill of the user. English was still immature, but it was potentially on the level of other languages.

The names of two of those pioneer masters of English have come down to us, John Cornwall and his disciple Richard Pencrych, both teaching in Oxford. Here is what John of Trevisa says of them, in his translation of the Polychronicon, 1385: "Thys manere [of translating Latin into French] was moche yused tofore the furste moreyn, and ys sethe somdel ychaunged. For Johan Cornwal, a mayster of gramere, chayngede the lore in gramer-scole, and construccion of Freynsch into Englysch; and Richard Pencrych lurnede that manere techyng of hym, and other men of Pencrych, so that now, the yere of oure Lord a thousond three hondred foure score and fyve, of the seconde kyng Richard after the conquest nyne, in al the gramer-scoles of Engelond childern leveth Frensch and construeth and lurneth an Englysch, and habbeth thereby avanntage in on syde and desavauntage yn another. Ther avauntage ys that they lurneth ther gramer in lesse tyme than childern were i-woned to doo; desavauntage ys that now childern of gramer-scole conneth na more Frensche than can thir lift heele, and that is harme for them an they schulle passe the see and travaille in straunge landes and in many other places."[48] It is curious that we do not know more about these teachers of English, nor about their immediate followers, but we cannot doubt their success, for they were helped by the boys' natural tendencies, they were sailing with wind and tide.

In the first half of the century the English language had been used for the writing of books of edification. Remember Robert Mannyng, Michael of Northgate, Richard Rolle; remember Handlyng synne, the Ayenbite of inwyt, and the Pricke of conscience. By the middle of the century there was already an eager public for such books, and thus it was natural enough for Wycliffe to use the vernacular as well as Latin for the delivery of his message. In fact, Wycliffe's Latinity suggests that he was thinking in English, and some of his Latin sentences must be mentally retranslated into English to be understood. His main title to the gratitude of English scholars is his translation of the Vulgate. He and his disciples produced two such translations, the first of which was completed c. 1383 and the second a little later, before 1401. In the meanwhile, the efforts of Richard Rolle were continued by Walter Hilton and others, and to the Pricke of conscience were added the Scale of perfection and the Cloud of unknowing. English readers wishing food for meditation on life and eternity, God and nature, were now as well provided as their German and Dutch contemporaries. A few years later, c. 1436, was written the Book of Margery Kempe, being the pilgrimages and spiritual autobiography of an extraordinary woman. She was born c. 1373, the daughter of John Burnham, a prosperous burgher of Lynn, and knew no language but English, but she had read the books above mentioned and nourished her soul on their substance. She was neither a nun nor a recluse, but an enthusiast, pilgriming to Rome and Jerusalem. Her book tells the story of her material and spiritual adventures; it is a travel book, but above all an autobiography, the first in English, and one of the most impressive documents of its kind in mediaeval literature.

[48] Leach (p. 196, 1915). Petit de Julleville (2, 526, 1896). There was a Pencrych Hall opposite Merton College; it is probable that John and Richard were teaching there.

The book of Margery Kempe, the text from the unique MS owned by colonel W. Butler-Bowdon edited by Sanford Brown Meech (Early English Text Society no. 212, vol. 1, 510 p., London 1940). Modern version by W. Butler-Bowdon (400 p., London 1936).

Lay books were beginning to appear, and some were of such quality that they have remained permanent sources of joy or of curiosity to English readers. It will suffice to name Piers Plowman, and the Confessio amantis of John Gower. The second work, being a treatise of morality, might have been cited with the religious-ethical books above, but its accent is definitely lay, not clerical or monastic, and John was so much interested in labor problems and betterment that it is natural to speak of his work together with that ascribed to William Langland. The case of Gower is symbolic, for he composed three considerable works, beginning the first in French, 1376, the second in Latin, 1381, the third in English, 1390. His personal evolution characterizes the evolution of his contemporaries. Then came Chaucer, who established English on a solid basis, doing for his own language what Petrarca and Boccaccio had done for theirs. Chaucer did not innovate as much as is often thought, but his genius consecrated the innovations of his people. He made a bold and creative use of the vernacular which generations of Englishmen had beautifully molded and polished. That is the best a great writer can do; if he ventured to create a new language all his own, the result would be disastrous. Chaucer did not create a new language; it is the other way round, an existing vigorous language made his task possible. His success encouraged other writers, chiefly his two disciples, Thomas Hoccleve and John Lydgate, who were both born c. 1370 and died at about the same time, 1450–51.

A few other writings must still be mentioned. The earliest monument of Scottish-English literature, The Bruce, a poem telling the story of Robert Bruce, was completed in 1375 by John Barbour. This was one of the main sources of the Oryginale, a Scottish chronicle from Adam to 1406, by Andrew of Wyntoun. Various romances written in the same dialect date probably from about the same time, late fourteenth and early fifteenth century. Two treatises on the chase date also from the same period, the first being a translation of the Anglo-Norman original composed by William Twici and John Gyfford under Edward II, the translation itself dating probably from the second half of the fourteenth century; the second, entitled The master of game, being the translation of the Miroir de Phoebus by Edward Plantagenet (c. 1406–13). The Boke of St. Albans, dealing with hawking, hunting, fishing, and heraldry, is ascribed to dame Juliana Berners, who flourished at about the same time (beginning of the fifteenth century) near St. Albans in Hertfordshire.

It is clear that at the end of the fourteenth century the English language was fully developed; the struggle with French might have jeopardized it, but English came out stronger and richer than before, with a double vocabulary, the two parts of which completed each other. It is curious that the Englishmen who had been the first to prepare French grammars did not pay as much attention to the structure of their own language, but that was perhaps because they took it for granted and were not sufficiently detached from it to analyze it.

There were vocabularies and glossaries, the purpose of which was at first to explain Latin and French words rather than to enumerate English ones. Many such glossaries, ranging from the tenth to the fifteenth century, have been edited by Thomas Wright: A volume of vocabularies (2 vols., Liverpool 1857–73). A modern collection of fourteenth-century words was compiled by James Orchard Halliwell-

[-Phillips]: A dictionary of archaic and provincial words, obsolete phrases, proverbs and ancient customs from the fourteenth century (2 vols., London 1847; 7th ed., 996 p., London 1924).

The first English lexicographer (as distinguished from a compiler of vocabularies, glossaries, and dialogues) was Geoffrey the Grammarian, alias Starkey (Galfredus Grammaticus, Galfridus Anglicus), of Norfolk, Dominican in Lynn, c. 1440. He compiled an English-Latin dictionary, Promptorium parvulorum clericorum, some 9,000 to 10,000 entries in alphabetic order. First printed in London 1499; often reprinted; modern editions by Albert Way for the Camden Society (3 vols. in 1, London 1843–65), and by Anthony Lawson Mayhew (Early English Text Society no. 102, London 1908). Other lexicographic works, Synonyma, Equivoca, are ascribed to Geoffrey. He may have been the author also of the Ortus (= hortus) vocabulorum, which was the first Latin-English dictionary to be printed in England (London 1500). The Ortus was based upon an earlier work, Medulla grammatice, which may be identical with the Promptorium, called Medulla grammatice in its own colophon.

The word Medulla grammatice should not deceive us. The development of grammatical ideas was exceedingly slow and English grammars did not begin to appear until the end of the sixteenth century. Books like the Elementarie of Richard Mulcaster (London 1582) and the Bref grammar of William Bullokar (London 1586) were largely restricted to orthography and orthophony. The earliest English grammar in my opinion was that of Paul Greaves: Grammatica anglicana praecipuè quatenus à Latina differt, ad unicam P. Rami methodum concinnata (Cambridge 1594). The following grammars appeared only under Charles I, to wit, the English grammar of Charles Butler (Oxford 1633) and the English grammar of Ben Jonson (London 1640). There is room for disagreement as to which grammar was the first, for that depends on one's definition of a grammar. It is certain, however, that Ben Jonson's was not the first in spite of the often repeated assertion to the contrary.

C. L. Kingsford (DNB 21, 145, 1890). M. M. Mathews: Survey of English dictionaries (London 1933).

Modern editions of Mulcaster's Elementarie by Ernest Trafford Campagnac (332 p., Oxford 1925); of Greaves' Grammatica by Otto Funke (92 p., Vienna 1938); of Butler's Grammar by Albert Eichler (166 p., Halle a.S. 1910); of Ben Jonson's by Alice Vinton Waite (162 p., New York 1909). For Butler and Bullokar see Sarton: The feminine monarchie of Charles Butler (Isis 34, 469–72, 6 fig., 1944).

10. *Dutch*

The administrative use of Dutch (Flemish) increased in Flanders during the second half of the century, because count Louis II de Male (rule, 1346–84) was not so Francophile as his father, Louis de Nevers (count from 1322 to his death at the battle of Crécy 1346). Among the 690 documents gathered in Louis de Male's cartulary, 9 are in Latin, 264 in French, 417 in Flemish.

The mystical movement initiated by Jan van Ruysbroeck, who was a "southerner" (that is, a Fleming), blossomed out marvelously in the northern Netherlands. The moderna devotio was born in the diocese of Utrecht. Its founder, Geert Groote, wrote mostly in Latin, but preached in Dutch. The order of the Brothers and Sisters of the Common Life was founded by him in Deventer, but the organization was completed only after his death, by his disciple Florens Radewijns. Though Latin was their ritual language (as it must be for every Catholic), Dutch was the vehicle of mutual edification. The masterpiece of that Christian renaissance, the Imitatio Christi, was published in the first half of the fifteenth century, but it was partly derived from Dutch notes jotted down by Geert Groote in his commonplace book. The soul of that renaissance was Dutch in language as well as in spirit. Moreover, one of the leading brothers, Gerard Zerbolt of Zutphen,[49] vindicated their efforts to translate the Bible into Dutch. In Holland as elsewhere the new spirit derived its sustenance from the vernacular, and it needed the vernacular to be properly preserved and transmitted (Matthew 9:17). In Holland as elsewhere the reactionaries insisted on the sanctity of Latin and the irrelevance and irreverence of the vernaculars. From our privileged point of view at a distance of half a millennium, we see clearly that the merciless repression of Biblical translations into vernaculars was one of the causes of the Reformation. Groote and Zerbolt were not reformers in the Wycliffian sense, they were evangelists. Is it possible to evangelize people and make them repent in any language but their own? Was not the Bible itself, remarked Groote, written in the vernaculars of its times? Their teachings were continued with particular success by Joannes Cele, thanks to whom Zwolle became the main center of the Common Life; we may recall that it was in Zwolle that Thomas a Kempis lived and died.[50] Cele, however, was anxious to spread the Christian renaissance as far as possible and to train clerks and schoolmasters, and therefore it is probable that he attached more importance to the international language, Latin, than to the local one, Dutch.

The only important writer in Flanders was Jan De Weert, representing the tradition of Maerlant. He wrote didactic poems to explain the dictates of theology, religion, and ethics. His satirical remarks help us to picture to ourselves the manners and customs of his time.

Though firmly established at home, the Dutch language did not enjoy the same international diffusion as French or Italian. It was, however, not unknown abroad. For example, a treatise on medicinal plants and their uses ascribed to the great English surgeon John Arderne includes Flemish names as well as French and Irish ones. A fair number of words of Middle Dutch origin bear witness to the influence which the Dutch language exerted upon the English. A list of them may be found in Walter W. Skeat: Etymological dictionary of the English language (new ed., p. 764, Oxford 1910).

By this time the Dutch language was sufficiently developed to serve scientific and philosophic purposes as well as the needs of common life, but it was still free from philological consciousness. The first glimpse of such consciousness may be detected in the Brabantsche yeesten, completed in 1350 by Jan van Boendale. Jan remarks that grammar teaches us to speak well (sie leert ons scone sprake). Yet no grammar or dictionary appeared until much later.

The earliest vocabularies are incunabula, the Teuthonista or Vocabularius der Duytschlender by Gerard de Schueren (Cologne 1477), in the dialect of Cleves; Vocabularius ex quo (Zwolle 1479), Vocabularius copiosus (Louvain c. 1483),

[49] Zutphen was in the duchy of Gelderland, inserted between the eastern and western parts of the bishopric of Utrecht. The moderna devotio spread easily in Gelderland, Cleves, Berg, and Jülich, that is, along the Rhine valley, as well as in the diocese of Utrecht.

[50] Zwolle is only 17 miles distant from Deventer, which was the cradle of the movement.

Gemmula vocabulorum (Antwerp 1484, 1494). More elaborate dictionaries became available only a century later: the Dictionarium, colloquia sive formulae quatuor linguarum, Belgicae, Gallicae, Hispanicae, Italicae (Antwerp 1558);[51] and Plantijn's Thesaurus theutonicae linguae (Antwerp 1573).

As to grammar, the first was composed by a man of Ghent, Josse Lambrecht (d. c. 1556): Nederlandsche spellinghe (Ghent 1549–50); the second, by a man of Brussels, Antoon van T'Sestich (1535–85): De orthographia linguae belgicae, sive de recta dictionum teutonicarum scriptura, secundum Belgarum praesertim Brabantorum pronuntiandi usitatam rationem (Louvain 1576).

Both works stress orthography in their titles. Indeed, orthography was one of the causes of grammatical formulation. As long as the transmission of thought is largely oral, grammar may be overlooked, but as soon as one wishes to write, and to establish a standard orthography, grammatical explanations become indispensable.

One more of the early Dutch philologists may be recalled here, the singular Jan van Gorp, better known under his Latin name Goropius Becanus (born 1518 in Brabant, died 1572 Maestricht), who claimed in his Origines Antverpianae (folio, Antwerp 1569) that Dutch was the original language, the mother of all others. The habit of establishing fantastic etymologies was called after him "goropiser" by Leibniz (Nouveaux essais, livre III, ch. 2).[52]

See Biographie nationale de Belgique for more information on Lambrecht (11, 203–8, 1891), T'Sestich (25, 809–12, 1932), Goropius (8, 120–23, 1884). M. J. Van der Meer: Historische Grammatik der niederländischen Sprache (vol. 1, Heidelberg 1927).

11. *German*

The Nuremberg chronicler Ulman Stromer, being a merchant, was naturally interested in weights and measures. Liquids such as wine and oil were sold in casks (barrels, hogsheads, kegs, butts, pipes), and the determination of the contents of a cask was a difficult problem. It would have been easy to solve it empirically by filling the cask with water and then emptying it into standard containers, but nobody seems to have thought of that; moreover, one might wish to measure a cask without having to empty it. This was done by means of a gauging rod, which the Germans called Visierruthe or Visierstab. The linear dimensions of the cask were measured with the gauging rod, and a formula enabled one to deduce from those dimensions the approximate capacity. The first explanation of that method (Visierkunst) was given by Stromer; he thus opened a tradition which remained exclusively German for over a century.[53] Not only that, but the early texts on Visierkunst were written and printed in German.

Toward the end of the century, a few alchemical and technical texts were also written in that language. For example, one of the MSS of Wimandus' Gloria

[51] The choice of languages is curious: Dutch, French, Spanish, Italian (German and English being left out). The term Belgica to designate Flemish or Dutch is also remarkable. Albert Tiberghien: Lingua belgica (Isis 23, 445, 1935).

[52] C. J. Gerhardt's edition (p. 264, Berlin 1882). The Nouveaux essais sur l'entendement were published only after Leibniz' death (Amsterdam 1765).

[53] As I write this statement derived from my notes, I find it hard to believe it. Let it stand as a challenge which may help to reveal sooner or later the existence of an early gauging art in England or other countries.

mundi is partly in German and partly in Latin. This is rather unexpected, for alchemists were more inclined to secrecy than to popularization. The mythical figure of Swarthy Berthold need not detain us, but some of the early books on military engineering were composed in German, namely, the Streyd-Buch von Pixen, Kriegsrüstung usw., and the Feuerwerksbuch ascribed to Abraham of Memmingen. These texts, however, are somewhat posterior to 1400.

The only travel account in German is the highly entertaining Reisebuch which Hans Schiltberger composed after having been a Turkish prisoner for thirty years (1396–1426).

There are a few medical texts. Two Bohemian doctors, Sulko von Hosstka and Sigismund Albic, used German as well as Latin. Of course, one may always wonder in such cases whether the German texts are not translations (by the author or by someone else) from Latin originals. With Ortolff the Bavarian we are on safer ground with regard to language, but the dating is uncertain. His Arzneibuch and his Büchlein der schwangeren Frauen may be anterior to 1400, but they are more probably somewhat posterior.

Four collections of recipes in Low German are known from their MSS respectively as (1) the Utrecht Arzneibuch, (2) the Wolfenbüttel, (3) the Gotha, (4) the Bremen. The first three are anonymous and date from c. 1400, the fourth was written in 1370–82 by or for Arnoldus Doneldey, a Bremen patrician.

Chronicles were composed in German by Ulman Stromer of Nuremberg, and by Fritsche Closener and Jacob Twinger, both of Strassburg.

Philological elaboration was as slow for German as it was for English and Dutch. As in the case of English, we have a few early glossaries; the earliest, a ninth-century one, has already been mentioned (Introd. 1, 555). Closener compiled a Latin-German vocabulary, and his successor Twinger completed it. The first German grammar was composed only in 1451 (see ch. I, p. 350–51).

12. *Scandinavian*

By 1350 the golden age of Icelandic literature was long past, for the Icelandic republic lasted only until 1261. Its subjugation to Norway gave an advantage to the Norwegian language. The main texts of this period are the accounts of Ivar Bárðarson's residence in Greenland (1341–79) and of the travels of Björn Jórsalafarer to Iceland and Greenland (1385–88). These accounts were written in Norwegian, but the first is known to us only in a Danish version.

The Norwegians were stout adventurers, who thought nothing of sailing to Iceland and Greenland, and who explored the American coast.[54] The main spiritual hero of those days, however, was not a Norwegian but a Swede, and not a sailor but a woman, St. Birgitta. This concerns Swedish letters, for the saint spoke and wrote (that is, dictated) in Swedish, but her letters and visions were immediately translated into Latin. They are chiefly known to us through the Latin texts or translations in other vernaculars, but for her people it was the Swedish text that mattered. The order of Brigittines which she founded at Vadstena in 1346, and the constitution of which was completed by her daughter St. Catherine in 1375, played a fundamental role in the development of Swedish culture and Swedish letters.

[54] For proper understanding of the background see Vilhjalmur Stefansson: Iceland (New York 1939, reprinted 1943); Greenland (New York 1942). Both books reviewed in Isis (34, 379–80, 2 fig.).

13. *Greek*

The amount of Greek writing done in this period, during which the twilight of Byzantine culture set in, was astonishing. As usual, the theologians were the most prolific. Though no attempt is made in this volume to give a complete account of their activities, we have dealt with many of them, Joannes of Cypros, Nicolaos Cabasilas, John VI Cantacuzenos and his son Matthaios, Demetrios Chrysoloras, and Joseph Bryennios on the Orthodox side; Demetrios Cydones and his brother Prochoros, and Manuel Calecas on the Catholic side.

The Catholic theologians were mainly concerned with the diffusion of their religious views, but they were unwittingly accomplishing a transfer of knowledge from West to East. The few Greeks who began to show interest in Latin literature did not always stop at theology, but read other books, such as Boccaccio's. That Latin stream, however, was and remained very small.

Aside from the mathematical and astronomical treatises composed by Nicolaos Cabasilas and Isaac Argyros, the scientific literature was very meager. There are a few medical texts, but the name of no medical author has pierced the gloom. There are a few anonymous chronicles, plus the one edited by John Cantacuzenos. The formulas of Byzantine painting were transmitted to the Orthodox clergy and monks of Russia and the Balkans.

Philological work was not neglected. Neilos Diassorinos wrote a treatise on grammar, rhetoric, and logic; Meliteniotes compiled a glossary of mineralogy. The activities which were most valuable for the defense and diffusion of Greek culture were those of translators and humanists like Symeon Atumanos, Manuel Chrysoloras, Manuel Palaeologos, and Gemistos Pletho. All these men traveled westward and, willingly or not, were missionaries not only of Byzantinism, but of Hellenism as well. To a little vanguard of Latin humanists they opened the doors of the Greek paradise.

Atumanos worked for Urban VI and translated the Bible and Plutarch; Chrysoloras began the translation of Plato's Republic and lectured in Florence. If we were asked, When did Greek humanism begin in the West? the best answer would perhaps be, It began with those lectures in 1397–1400. At about the same time (1399–1402) the ill-starred emperor Manuel Palaeologos visited the courts of Italy, France, and England hoping to obtain help against the Turks; in that he failed, but he succeeded in reviving Western enthusiasm for Greek culture. The Greek renaissance was continued by a small but talented and vigorous band, Gemistos Pletho (c. 1356–1450) and the disciples of Chrysoloras. These disciples were Latins, and the discussion of their work introduces a new subject—Greek knowledge in the West.

Greek in the West

Please note once more the vast difference between Greek and Latin. Greek was a living language, very much alive indeed; when we investigated Greek in the fourteenth century, our first concern was necessarily with genuine native writers. On the contrary, Latin was very much of an artificial language. Greek for non-Greeks is only a small part of our Greek chapter, whereas Latin for non-Latins is the whole of the Latin one.

The first Western scholar of the new age to obtain a competent knowledge of Greek was Boccaccio. He had the privilege of being tutored by the Calabrian

Leonzio Pilato. Pilato's own knowledge was crude but natural and fluent, and this means very much;[55] he was the first teacher of Greek in Florence (1360–62) and probably in Western Europe. According to modern standards his philological training was very imperfect, but he was the initiator; he explained Homer and helped Petrarca to read the Iliad. We have already spoken of Chrysoloras' teaching in the same city a generation later (1397–1400); his teaching was much more scientific, but he was a Greek and we are dealing now with non-Greeks. Niccolò de' Niccoli (1363–1437) collected, collated, and copied Greek MSS as well as Latin ones; he has been called one of the founders of textual criticism, but this could only be said with reference to Latin MSS; indeed, his Greek was weak, and he needed for it the help of Ambrogio Traversari (1386–1439). This Ambrogio, one of Chrysoloras' pupils, was a Camaldolite—the only cleric among all the scholars dealt with in this section; he found his main pleasure in the study of Joannes Chrysostomos (347–407), and translated Diogenes Laertios (III-1). Ciriaco of Ancona (c. 1391–c. 1450) graduated from Dante to Virgil and from Virgil to Homer; he learned Greek in Constantinople and collected Greek MSS, e.g., of Herodotos, Hippocrates, Plato, Aristotle, Plutarch, Ptolemy, Galen. He traveled extensively in Greece and the Greek islands and discovered Greek statues and inscriptions (e.g., the so-called epitaph of Homer in Chios); he was the first Westerner to visit the ruins of Ephesos (1447).[56] He was one of the founders of classical archaeology and epigraphy. More Greek MSS were brought back from the East by Angeli da Scarparia (Homer, Plato, Aristotle, Greek fathers); by Guarino Veronese, who, having spent five years in Chrysoloras' household in Constantinople (1403–8), returned to Venice with more than 50 MSS; by the Sicilian Giovanni Aurispa, who returned to Venice in 1423 with a library of 238 MSS; etc.

It is clear that by the beginning of the fifteenth century Greek humanism was in full swing; almost everything was still to be done, but the will to do it was as strong as it was joyful.

All the men mentioned thus far were Italians. However, a desire for Greek humanities was awakening in France. Philippe de Mézières drew up a plan c. 1384 for schools (écoles de huit langues) where Greek would be taught as well as other Oriental languages. This was of course the continuation of the project examined at the council of Vienne (1311–12); but it was the continuation of a dream rather than of a reality. Chairs were created during the fifteenth century for individual scholars; for example, Greek was taught in Paris from 1458 on by Gregorios Tifernas and his pupil Georgios Hermonymos of Sparta. Among Gregorios' pupils were Reuchlin, Budaeus, and Erasmus (Rashdall 1, 566). There was some Greek teaching in Padua before 1465 (Rashdall 2, 20), and Constantine Lascaris taught in Messina from c. 1465 to his death in 1501 (Sandys 2, 77). A solid tradition of Greek teaching, however, did not begin until the first half of the sixteenth century, when the "trilingual colleges" were organized in Alcalà, Oxford (Corpus Christi), Louvain, etc. Even then serious difficulties occurred. In 1530 the Sorbonne censured the teaching of Greek (and Hebrew) offered at the newly founded Collège de France, declaring it to be scandalous, temerary, heretical, smacking of Lutheranism. Was the Vulgate not sufficient for good Christians?[57]

[55] The first teachers of language should be easygoing and fluent like our mothers, rather than accurate and fastidious like the pedantic masters who tormented our youth.

[56] For later investigations of Ephesos see St. John Ervine: John Turtle Wood, discoverer of the Artemision (Isis 28, 376–84, 4 fig., 1938).

[57] Abel Lefranc: Histoire du Collège de France (p. 122, Paris 1893).

To conclude, a statement made by Ernest Renan must be challenged. In his Avenir de la science (written 1849, printed Paris 1890)[58] he remarked, "Le Moyen âge connut beaucoup de choses de l'antiquité grecque mais rien, absolument rien, de première main" (p. 241). That is unfair. The early humanists like Niccoli and Traversari studied from the very MSS (they could not do otherwise!); Ciriaco learned about inscriptions not in elementary manuals, which did not exist, but in the field; and so on. The mediocrity of their knowledge was not due to secondhandedness, but to the lack of tools and methods. They were pioneers, and pioneers must be satisfied with rough approximations, discomfort, and ignorance.

Nevertheless, it is true that mediaeval Hellenists did not appreciate firsthandedness any more than pioneer farmers appreciate virgin nature. The appreciation of firsthand knowledge grew very slowly in every field of science and learning, and centuries were needed for its gradual refinement, even as centuries were needed for the elaboration of the experimental method. The proper appreciation of firsthand knowledge on the one hand, and of experimental knowledge on the other, constitutes to this very day one of the essential differences between educated and non-educated people. The former have it, the latter are impervious to it.

14. *Slavonic Languages*[58a]

The outstanding Slavonic language was the westernmost one, Bohemian or Czech. Its relative maturity was illustrated in the Chronicle of Dalimil, completed before 1317. Czech thought revived considerably during the second half of the fourteenth century, partly because the king and emperor Charles IV patronized the compilation of national records and the translation of books from Latin into Czech. It is true, the new chronicle of Bohemia (1374) was published by Beneš of Weitmil in Latin, and the emperor's autobiography was edited by Beneš in the same language. They probably wanted to reach an international audience. In the meanwhile, Czech adaptations or translations of Western books were prepared by Flaška z Pardubic and by Vavřinec Březova, medical and mathematical writings were published by Christian Prachatice, and the Latin texts of Gallus de Strahov contained many Czech plant names.

It was in the religious field, however, that the language triumphed. Thomas of Štitný made available to the Czech people the theological ideas and the passionate feelings of St. Augustine, St. Bonaventure, St. Birgitta. A new fervor was brewing under the guidance of Matthew Janow and came to a climax under Jan Hus. Hus' martyrdom in 1415 consecrated the Czech people, its religion and its language. The sufferings of the people were recorded by Vavřinec Březova.

Bohemia was kept in communion with the West of Europe by the Latin priests on the conservative side, and by the Wycliffians on the liberal side. Moreover, Anne of Bohemia, the first queen of Richard II, did as much as she could to increase spiritual communications between her native land and her adopted land, but unfortunately she died of the plague in 1394, at the age of 28.

Russian literature was very meager in comparison with contemporary Czech literature. Pilgrimage accounts were composed by Alexander the Pilgrim, Grethenios, and Ignatius of Smolensk.

[58] G. Sarton: L'avenir de la science (Renaissance 1, 218–37, New York 1943).

[58a] At the time of final proofreading it occurred to me that it would be better to say Slavic than Slavonic, the second term having Balkanic and ecclesiastical connotations. I have kept Slavonic, however, in this section (and perhaps in others) to avoid too many corrections.

The earliest Slavonic grammar, O vosmi chastyakh slova, originated in Serbia in the first half of the fourteenth century. It was adapted to the needs of Bulgarian and hence to the needs of Russian. Constantin the Philosopher (or the Grammarian), who was in the service of the Serbian despotes Stephan Lazarevich (ruled 1389–1427), composed the first Slavonic grammar of known authorship.

I. V. Jagič: Razsuzhdeniya . . . o tserkovno-slavyanskom yazyke (Reflections on the Church-Slavonic language), in Izsledovaniya po russkomu yazyku (Researches on the Russian language, Academy of Sciences, 1, 289–1067, especially p. 364 f., St. Petersburg 1895).

15. *Armenian*

The venerable Armenian language was used chiefly by defenders of the Armenian church, but also by Catholic converts who were trying to lure their brethren into the Roman communion. The main Catholic writer was John Golodik, who wrote commentaries on the Bible, Dionysios the Areopagite, and Peter of Aragon (Dominican of unknown date).

The Armenians who had remained faithful to their own church, that is, the bulk of them, could boast many distinguished authors, most of them theologians and Biblical commentators, but also poets like Arachiel of Sunik. It will suffice here to name John of Orodn, Gregory of Tathev, George of Erseng, Gregory of Khlath, Thomas of Alovid. The last named wrote an Armenian history of Tīmūr, which is of great interest for comparison with the Persian, Arabic, and Western accounts.

Reference must be made here again to the Armenian-Arabic-Latin glossary preserved in the Mekhitarist library of Vienna, dating probably from the beginning of the fifteenth century.

We have already spoken of the "écoles des huit langues," a kind of prototype of the Ecole spéciale des langues orientales vivantes,[59] which Philippe de Mézières dreamt of establishing c. 1384. Armenian was one of the eight languages to be taught, the others being Chaldaean, Arabic, Tatar, Hebrew, etc.[60] Philip's dream was not realized, except in a humbler way by religious orders (chiefly the Dominicans and Franciscans) training missionaries.

16. *Georgian*

See chapter I, page 356.

17. *Syriac*

See chapter I, pages 356–60.

18. *Coptic*

See chapter I, pages 360–62.

19. *Aethiopic*

See chapter I, pages 362–63.

19 bis. *Zyrian*

The number 19 bis is given to Zyrian, not dealt with in chapter I, in order not to disturb our earlier numeration. Zyrian is placed here, at the tail of the Christian

[59] Created by the Convention in 1795.

[60] Etc. covers my ignorance. Abel Lefranc: Histoire du Collège de France (p. 19, Paris 1893) does not name others, nor does Nicolas Iorga: Philippe de Mézières (p. 459, Paris 1896), yet Lefranc calls the schools Ecoles des huit langues.

languages, because it was used mainly for Christian purposes. Our classification is regional and religious rather than linguistic. Zyrian is a Finno-Ugrian language, the only one of its kind to be taken into account in this period.

St. Stephen of Perm invented in 1372 an alphabet which made possible the reduction of that language to a written form. His purpose was to evangelize and educate the Zyrian people, living in the northern part of Russia.

20. *Hebrew*

The number of scholars and scientists writing in Hebrew is too large for detailed analysis, and it will suffice to speak of those who might be called philologists. Nor will it be necessary to speak of them very long, for none was very important, none added anything new or especially precious to the knowledge already available. Hebrew philology was essentially on the same level in 1400 as it was in 1350.

In the West, Pereẓ Trabot compiled a Hebrew dictionary in alphabetical order, giving Arabic, French, and Catalan equivalents. This dictionary, the Maqre dardeqe, enjoyed some popularity and was often imitated. Menahem ben Abraham Bonafos compiled a technical and philosophical glossary, the Miklal yofi, largely based on the Moreh nebukim. Profiaṭ Duran completed in 1403 an elaborate grammar, the Ma'aseh ephod.

In the East we came across a single philologist, Solomon ben Elijah, who flourished in Salonica and Ephesos and wrote a grammatical treatise.

The Samaritan high priest Pineḥas, to whom a Biblical Hebrew-Arabic glossary is ascribed, is probably a later author. This question is full of difficulties. The glossary entitled Melīṣ (or Melīṣa, meaning interpreter) is very elementary; it includes proper names, giving Arabic equivalents in many instances (e.g., Pineḥas = Khiḍr);[61] in several cases the Arabic merely repeats the Hebrew. Many Samaritan high priests bore the name Pineḥas, e.g., Pineḥas V ben Joseph, high priest 1308–65; Pineḥas VI ben Abisha', high priest 1387–1442, patron of the chronicler Abū-l-Fatḥ; Pineḥas ben Ithamar, high priest of the community in Damascus 1390–1430. All these Pineḥas were liturgical poets. Moses Gaster seemed to have identified the author of Melīṣ with Pineḥas VI, but he called him wrongly Pineḥas ben 'Eleazar; this Pineḥas was not the son, but the nephew and successor of 'Eleazar XVII. The earliest extant MS of the Melīṣ is dated 1476; there are two or three other MSS. The glossary covers only the Pentateuch, since that is the only part of the Bible recognized by the Samaritans.

Arthur Ernest Cowley: Samaritan literature (JE 10, 676–81, 1905); Samaritan liturgy (2 vols., Oxford 1909), corpus of liturgical documents known to him, with a long introduction. Moses Gaster: Samaritan literature (suppt. to EI vol. 4, 1925, p. 12). My note on Pineḥas is largely derived from letters kindly written to me by Theodor H. Gaster (New York, May 27, 1942; Ridgefield, Conn., June 17, 1943), who is preparing a corpus of Samaritan literature, except the liturgy, begun by his father, Moses.

Hebrew studies in the West

For the Jews there was but one sacred language, Hebrew; for the Catholics, there were three sacred languages, Hebrew, Greek, and Latin; for the Orthodox

[61] Al-Khiḍr (or al-Khaḍir, the green one) is a mystical personage who has been identified with the prophet Elijah, with St. George, and others (cf. Qur'ān 18, 59–81). Hughes (p. 272, 1885). A. J. Wensinck (EI 2, 861–65, 1925). Sarton (Osiris 2, 459–60, 1936).

(and the Protestants of a later time), there were two sacred languages, Hebrew and Greek. The point is that all would have agreed on at least one language, and that language was Hebrew. Thus Hebrew was extremely important. It is then surprising that so few Christians had enough initiative and perseverance to study it, and that their Hebrew scholarship remained in most cases rudimentary. This is the more surprising that there were enough Jews to tutor them, if their help had been requested. Before judging these fourteenth-century scholars with too much severity, let us remember that even to this day, Christian ministers having a working knowledge of Hebrew are exceptional.

There was no Christian scholar in the second half of the fourteenth century whose Hebrew knowledge equaled that of Nicholas of Lyra, who died in 1349. The best perhaps was the Greek Symeon Atumanos, who prepared for Urban VI a triglot Bible, translating the Old Testament from Hebrew into Greek and Latin, and the New Testament from Greek into Latin and Hebrew. Then we have Pablo de Santa María, whose corrections to the Postilla of Nicholas of Lyra shared the latter's fame. Pablo, however, was a Jewish renegade, and perhaps he should not be counted. His example suggests that the simplest way of forming a Christian Hebraist was to convert a Jew. The Camaldolite Ambrogio Traversari had some knowledge of Hebrew. The same can be said of Heinrich von Langenstein, who wrote a tract De idiomate hebraico (Vienna 1388), wherein, like Roger Bacon a century before, he vindicated the Hebrew language and gave many reasons, good and bad, for its study.

The proper teaching of Hebrew in Christian colleges did not begin before the sixteenth century. It was first organized in the trilingual colleges created at Alcalà, Cambridge, Rome, Oxford, Paris, Louvain, Wittenberg, Vienna, Leipzig, Heidelberg, Ingolstadt.[62] The movement was widespread, and its driving power the realization that a good Christian should master the three sacred languages. As has been pointed out before, this did not succeed without protracted opposition on the part of bigoted defenders of the Vulgate, who affected to consider any preferment of the heretical Greek language or of the Jewish Hebrew as an attack on St. Jerome!

Yiddish

In 1386, the duchy of Lithuania was joined to the kingdom of Poland, when the duke of Lithuania, Jagiełło son of Olgerd, married Jadwiga of Poland, and became king of Poland and Lithuania (later of Moldavia, Wallachia, and Bessarabia) under the name Wladyslaw V Jagiełło (ruled 1386-1434). Lithuania in 1386 was Greek Orthodox, whereas Poland was Catholic. Hence the new king was obliged to make a show and give proofs of religious toleration. For the first time since Constantine the Great (Milano 313?), citizenship was independent of religious confession. In the meanwhile, Jews driven out of Germany, especially after the Black Death, were completing their eastward emigration in Lithuania, where they found an asylum. They had learned to speak German, but their language was Hebraicized, and they wrote it in Hebrew script. Thus developed in Germany and Eastern Europe the language sometimes called Taitsch (= Deutsch), more often Jiddisch or Yiddish (= Jüdisch, Jewish).

[62] The story is told by P. S. Allen: Erasmus. Lectures and wayfaring sketches (p. 138-63, Oxford 1934).

The earliest text of any length is a treatise on bloodletting written in Cologne 1396.

See articles by Salomo Birnbaum in Jüdisches Lexikon (3, 269-78, Berlin 1929) and in EJ (9, 112-27, 1932), and by N. Meisl in EJ (9, 127-80, 1932).

Whether Yiddish is a language or a dialect is a question which need not be discussed here, as it is neither a scientific nor a strictly philological question, but a sociological one.

21. *Arabic*

Throughout the century Arabic was the second language in importance, being surpassed by Latin and followed by Hebrew. Latin, however, had now become more important than Arabic and Hebrew put together.

Let us consider only the few Arabic philologists. By this time the main philological tools, grammars and dictionaries, were already forged, though they were (especially those of the second kind) indefinitely perfectible.

The greatest grammarian and rhetorician of the age was al-Taftāzānī, and his many publications on these subjects were received with considerable favor and have remained popular or rather classical[63] until modern times in the Arabic, Persian, and Turkish world. Al-Āqsarā'ī wrote a commentary on the Īḍāḥ of Khaṭīb Dimashq.

So much for rhetoric. The para-zoological encyclopaedia, Ḥayāt al-ḥayawān, of al-Damīrī might be counted among the dictionaries. It is a thesaurus of literary information relative to every animal known to the author, and is exceedingly rich in names, synonyms, and metaphors. Each article begins with lexicographical information, but the other sections of it are full of examples and proverbs which are of philological interest.

Al-Fīrūzābādī compiled a rich dictionary of Arabic called the Qāmūs, which is the basis of all the Arabic dictionaries published after it. Its name, meaning originally the ocean, is now understood by most people as "dictionary"; in fact, a great many dictionaries are entitled qāmūs (pl. qawāmīs) because of the illustrious precedent which al-Fīrūzābādī had probably established before 1400 (he was still alive then, but in old age).

Note that of the four scholars thus far mentioned, only one was a genuine Arab, namely, al-Damīrī, who was born in Cairo and spent all his life in Egypt or in Arabia. Al-Taftāzānī and al-Āqsarā'ī were Turks, and al-Fīrūzābādī, a Persian.

A study of the development of Arabic philology should include the Arabic equivalent of the Latin dictamen, that is, the art of writing letters, especially official letters, and the methods of secretarial and notarial work. The Arabic dictamen was at least as elaborate as the Latin one; we find it explained in the great manuals prepared for the training of Mamlūk chancellors by Ibn Faḍlallāh al-'Umarī and al-Qalqashandī. No wonder, for dictamen is a natural and pressing need of any sophisticated government, and the Mamlūk government was very sophisticated. Moreover, Arabs, even the poorest, not to speak of the umarā' and the 'ulamā', have always been literary-minded, sensitive to literary values, ready to admire good writing and to despise bad; they were very jealous of their names and genealogies (included in the names), of their titles, dignities, and the honors due to them.

[63] The difference here expressed is that popular books are read, and classics are praised. However, popular books may be praised also, and classics read.

It was, then, very important to teach secretaries and civil servants how to use correct formulas and how to address every person in the proper manner, giving his full name and his titles (of which there was an exuberant variety), and saluting him according to his birthright, rank, and precedence. They had to learn how to announce appointments and discharges, how to make a claim or a grant, how to draft charters of every kind, e.g. for the foundation and endowment of a waqf, and diplomas of investiture, farāmina (pl. of firmān).

There was also the equivalent of cursus (cursus verborum, the rhythmical flow of discourse), except that thanks to the very symmetrical morphology of the Arabic language, rhythmical phrases issued so naturally that a fastidious writer would sometimes take more trouble to eschew assonances than to create them. Poetry (naẓm, shi'r) was often used even for official or semiofficial communications,[64] and prose (nathr) tended to be rhythmical and rhyming (saj'). Proverbs are often like that, also the titles of books. In short, there was no need of teaching cursus, but it was necessary to recommend moderation in its natural use.

There was one essential difference between Latin and Arabic. The language used in the Arabic chancelleries was not artificial in the same degree as Latin was. The Arabic which a king spoke or wrote on formal occasions was only a stilted form, a de luxe edition, of the Arabic which he spoke in the street or in his own ḥarīm, whereas the Western ruler or chancellor spoke one language at court and another in his household. East and West, almost everywhere, good administration was friendly to belles lettres; a sulṭān would appreciate good Arabic secretaries as much as a Western prince or bishop would appreciate good Latin ones. In the Arabic world, however, the royal patronage of literature would bolster up the national language, whereas in the Latin world that patronage would depress it. The main enemies of the European vernaculars were those very secretaries, especially the most sophisticated among them, "the apes of Cicero."[65]

One more difference must be mentioned. In the Latin West charters and diplomas might be well engrossed, but good calligraphy was exceptional, and beautiful calligraphy, rare. On the other hand, the natural beauty of the Arabic script invited calligraphical experiments and efflorescences. For example, an essential element of any charter or firmān was the ṭughrā, a calligraphic emblem of the ruler granting the document. Some of these emblems are very attractive and impressive and give the documents upon which they are drawn an air of beauty. Various examples may be seen in Jean Deny's article (EI 4, 822–26, 38 fig., 1931). Other examples are familiar to almost every reader, for in the course of time the ṭughrā passed from the charters and diplomas to all kinds of documents, official and commercial, even to coins and postage stamps.

A final remark: The Mamlūk rulers who did so much to develop the Arabic ars dictandi were of Turkish origin. The technical words used in this note, firmān and ṭughrā, are Turkish (firmān is really of old Persian ancestry but reached the Arabic world via Turkish channels). Thus we may say that the Turks played a not inconsiderable part in the establishment of the Arabic language.

The study of Arabic had much declined in the West since the time of Ramon Lull.

[64] Even today Arabian princes occasionally send messages written in verse. Ameen Rihani: Arabian peak and desert. Travels in al-Yaman (p. 225, Boston 1930). Partial translation of Amīn al-Riḥānī's Mulūk al-'arab (2 vols., Beirūt 1929).

[65] Phrase coined by Angelo Poliziano (1454–94). Erasmus expressed in scathing language what he thought of those apes, in the dialogue Ciceronianus (1528).

About the year 1400, the outstanding Western Arabist was another Catalan, Anselmo Turmeda, like Ramon a restless spirit. May he rest in peace!

22. *Persian*

As Persian scholars and scientists had to know Arabic, it is not surprising that various Arabic-Persian glossaries were compiled. One is ascribed to the Turkish poet Aḥmad-i Dā'ī, another is found in a MS of the Ikhtiyārāt of the pharmacist Zain al-'Aṭṭār. It is probable, however, that these two works are posterior to 1400. The addition of glossaries to Persian medical books was particularly necessary, even as Arabic-Latin medical glossaries were sometimes added to Latin versions (e.g., of the Qānūn of Ibn Sīnā; Introd. 1, 711).

Persian belles lettres were admirably represented by Ḥāfiẓ, one of the greatest poets of all ages. Another poet, al-Rāmī, may serve to illustrate the main weakness of Persian literature, preciosity or euphuism.

It is probable that the Persian language was strengthened by the ṣūfī and Shī'a holy men who created new orders and generally wrote explanations of their faith. The two outstanding ones were Ni'mat Allāh Walī and Faḍlallāh al-Ḥurūfī. 'Alī ibn Shihāb al-dīn wrote mystical treatises in Persian as well as in Arabic. The main theologians were al-Jurjānī and al-Taftāzānī, jealous rivals who were thrown together in Samarqand. We might call them both Persians, but al-Jurjānī wrote in Arabic and Persian, al-Taftāzānī in Arabic and Turkish. Though no Persian works of the latter have come down to us, it is highly probable that he could speak and write Persian as easily as his rival. Their case is a good example of the futility of making distinctions between Turks and Persians in Central Asia. Let us say that they were two illustrious representatives of Islamic culture in the capital of Tīmūr.

The Arabic lexicographer al-Fīrūzābādī, ṣāḥib al-qāmūs, wrote a life of the Prophet in Persian.

The Arabic knowledge of Persian scientists was apparently so good that their need of Persian technical works was small. We do not know whether Jamshīd ibn Mas'ūd, first director of the Samarqand observatory, wrote in Arabic or Persian. Medical books were composed in Persian by the pharmacist Zain al-'Aṭṭār and the anatomist Manṣūr ibn Muḥammad.

Niẓām al-dīn Shāmī wrote in Persian what might be called the official history of Tīmūr. That is, Tīmūr himself ordered him in 1401 to write it, placing at his disposal all necessary documents (Browne 3, 361-62). It should be noted that Ibn 'Arabshāh, who wrote not long afterward an Arabic (and independent) biography of Tīmūr, was well versed in Persian. Indeed, every Muslim who moved eastward beyond the Dijlah (Tigris) was bound to know that language if he wanted to be independent of interpreters.

23. *Turkish*

The Western Turkish renaissance which began with the fourteenth century continued crescendo throughout that century. After the middle of the century much poetry was written. In 1354, al-Taftāzānī translated the Bustān of Sa'dī. Didactic poems were composed by Ṣalāḥ al-dīn yāzīyī, Aḥmedī, and Aḥmad-i Dā'ī.

Medical books were written in Turkish by Isḥāq ibn Murād of Gerede, Ḥājjī pāshā, and a little later by Sharaf al-dīn ibn 'Alī. There is also a treatise on veterinary medicine dating from c.1361-1400, and a treatise on falconry by Maḥmūd ibn Muḥammad al-Bārjīnī. The relatively large number of early Turkish hospitals must have increased the need of textbooks in the vernacular (as opposed to Arabic ones).

Egypt played an important role in that renaissance. Not only was the country ruled by a Turkish dynasty, but there was probably then even as later an influential Turkish colony. Remember that the first Turkish grammar had been composed in Cairo (by Abū Ḥaiyān 1313), that Aḥmedī and Ḥājjī pāshā had been educated in Cairo, and the latter had become chief physician in the main hospital of that city. The best proof of the Turkishness of the Mamlūk court is given us by the case of al-'Ainī, who had to translate a Ḥanafī manual for the Mamlūk sulṭān Ṭaṭār (1421), and translated his own chronicle at sight for another sulṭān, al-Ashraf Bars-bey (1422-38).

So much for the West. Turkish continued to be spoken in many parts of the Middle East and Central Asia. It was probably Tīmūr's original and best language (East Turkish of course), and the language most used at his court. Ibn 'Arabshāh, who had been abducted by Tīmūr from Damascus to Samarqand, learned Turkish, and was thus able later to translate several Arabic books into Turkish for Muḥammad I ibn Bāyazīd.

The early Mogul emperors of India spoke Turkish. The famous memoirs of the first of them, Ẓahīr al-dīn Bābar (ruled 1526-30), were written by him in Eastern Turkish (Chaghatāi Tūrki). The Tuzūkāt-i-Tīmūrī were probably composed in the same language in imitation of the Bābar-nāma, then translated into Persian. Chaghatāi Tūrki had assimilated a great many Arabic and Persian words, especially since Tīmūr's time, for it was obliged to compete with those languages, which were better equipped for the higher spiritual needs. Though Bābar wrote his memoirs in Tūrki, his poetry was composed in Persian and his prayers in Arabic (see English edition of 1921, 2, 29). The great Akbar (ruled 1556-1605)—whose rule was almost exactly contemporary with queen Elizabeth's (1558-1603)—spoke Tūrki to begin with, then Persian, and in the course of time Persian and Urdū displaced his maternal language. By the way, the name given to the rulers of that Tīmūrī dynasty of India, "Moguls," is very misleading, for those men were of Turkish rather than of Mongol origin.

Finally, it may be remarked that the court language of Persia at the beginning of the Ṣafawī dynasty (1502 ff.) was Turkish, not Persian, because that dynasty was really of Turkish origin.

24. *Mongolian*

There is little to add to what has been said in chapter I (p. 379-81). Various Mongolian documents of the second half of the fourteenth century are quoted by Laufer (p. 193 f., 1907). Ibn 'Arabshāh was reputed to know Mongolian as well as Turkish, Persian, and Arabic. "Tartare" was one of the languages which were to be studied in the écoles des huit langues planned about 1384 by Philippe de Mézières; now tartare (= Tatar) might refer to Mongolian or Turkish. The Western nations had the best of reasons for being on good terms with the great khāns and learning their language.

25. *Manchu*

See chapter I, page 381.

26. *Sanskrit, Pāli, Siṅhalese*

Sanskrit was used by many scholars, the greatest of whom were the two brothers Mādhava and Sāyaṇa; it is possible that these two brothers were only one man, but the mass of their (or his) works is very impressive. It is the outstanding monument of Vedic scholarship in the Middle Ages.

The tradition of Sanskrit mathematics was continued by Nārāyaṇa, of Sanskrit alchemy by Merutuṅga, and of Sanskrit medicine by the same and Madanapāla. A new code was compiled by Viśveśvara.

Pāli and Buddhist letters were represented by Dhammakitti IV and Dhammakitti V. The latter wrote in Siṅhalese as well as in Pāli. His Pāli grammar had a great influence on Siṅhalese scholarship. Siṅhalese, by the way, is an Indo-Aryan language derived from Pāli, but with a strong admixture of Dravidian words; the grammar is close to Pāli grammar and hence the influence of Dhammakitti's Bālāvatāra was natural enough. The Siṅhalese alphabet is a modification of the Pāli one, itself derived from the Sanskrit.

26 bis. *Other Aryan Languages of India*

It is necessary to introduce this section because of the appearance in the second half of the fourteenth century of writings in languages different from the three of the preceding group, yet Indo-Aryan. We shall consider Urdū, Hindī, Kashmirī, Gujarātī, and Bengāli.

Urdū has already been referred to. It is a mixture of Persian with the old Sanskrit stock; politically, it is the result of the Muslim conquest of India. Two mystical treatises were written in Urdū about the end of the century by Banda Nawāz.

Hindī was used by Rāmānanda and his followers in their sermons and writings. It was largely because of their efforts, the purpose of which was purely religious, that Hindī attained the dignity of a literary language and succeeded as well as it did.

Kashmirī, a language related to Sanskrit, was the vehicle in which the poetess Lal Ded expressed her thoughts. She was one of the early prophets of Hindu-Islamic synthesis, of Hindu unity.

The earliest prose works in Gujarātī were written respectively c. 1355 and in 1394. The first is a treatise on Jaina ethics by Taruṇaprabha, the second a Sanskrit grammar by Kulamaṇḍana.

A Bengāli version of the Rāmāyaṇa was composed by Kṛittivāsa, and a Bengāli abridgment of the Mahābhārata by Sañjaya.

27. *Dravidian Languages* (*Canarese*)

The only Dravidian language we have come across in the second half of the fourteenth century is Canarese. Two dictionaries were compiled, ultimately derived from Sanskrit models. The author of the first is unknown; the second was compiled about the end of the century by Abhinava Maṅgarāja, and was called after him Abhinava-nighaṇṭu. Nighaṇṭu is the Sanskrit word for glossary; we find it in the titles of many Sanskrit dictionaries, e.g., those of Hemacandra (XII-2) and of Narahari (XIII-1). Dravidian languages were necessarily dominated by Sanskrit, and their dependence on it increased with their literary development and their spiritual ambitions.

Maṅgarāja I (fl. 1360) wrote a medical treatise, the ultimate source of which was again Sanskrit.

27 bis. *Javanese*

In 1365, Prapañca wrote in Kawi or old Javanese a poem which is an important witness for the historical geography of the Malay Peninsula and Archipelago. Though Kawi is entirely outside the Indo-Aryan family, it includes many words of Sanskrit origin, for the simple reason that the Malay world had been dominated by Hindu culture. The Sanskrit words were legacies of that culture. In the Malay world even as in Hindūstān, there was a mixture of Hindu and Muslim elements, the proportions varying with the vicissitudes of history.

28. *Tibetan*

A reformation of Tibetan monasticism was accomplished c. 1392 by Tsong Kapa, who founded the Ge-lug-pa (virtuous order). Did that reform affect Tibetan letters? For the Tibetan language in general, see chapter I, page 384. Heinrich Laufer: Beiträge zur Kenntnis der Tibetischen Medizin (132 p., Berlin 1900). Max Walleser: Zur Aussprache des Sanskrit und Tibetan (40 p., Heidelberg 1926).

29. *Chinese*

We have seen that Philippe de Mézières, who flourished under Charles VI, dreamed of founding a school for the study of Oriental languages. Philippe's dream was not realized until four centuries later, but while he was dreaming the Ming government did actually create such a school, the Ssŭ-i-kuan, for the study of the languages needed for administrative or spiritual purposes—Mongolian, Turkish, Tibetan, Sanskrit, Persian, Burmese, Siamese.

Continuing a tradition which was then almost eight centuries old, Sung Lien compiled in 1375 a phonetic dictionary classified under 76 rhymes. At about the same time Chao Hui-ch'ien, continuing an even older tradition (twelve and a half centuries), classified all the words according to their written form under 360 radicals (a further reduction of the number of radicals by one-third was accomplished only at the beginning of the seventeenth century).

What might be called Chinese humanism was vindicated by T'ao Tsung-i and Ting Hao-nien, but the supreme flower of it was the great encyclopaedia published c. 1409 by order of the third Ming emperor, Yung Lo. We have been obliged to refer to the Yung Lo ta tien so often in this volume that it is unnecessary to emphasize its importance once more.

30. *Korean*

The remarks made in chapter I (p. 387–89) apply equally well to the second half of the fourteenth century. For example, the main scientific achievement of the new Korean dynasty was the celestial planisphere completed in 1395, but that did not concern the Korean language, for its language and script were purely Chinese. Korean continued to be a popular language, the value of which we do not in any way minimize, but which does not concern the historian of science.

31. *Japanese*

The growth of education was regularized and facilitated by the Ashikaga-gakkō and the Kanazawa-bunko, but that education was largely Chinese. For example, most of the books in the bunko were Chinese; the number of Japanese books was increasing gradually but very, very slowly.

The great teachers of the time, such as Myōō, Gidō Shūshin, and Ryōken, were Zen monks, attaching far more importance to contemplation (dhyāna, ultimate source of the word zen) and intuition than to reading.[66] The Zen recognized no canonic books, yet they did read, and it is said of one of the founders, Eisai (XII-2), that he brought back many books from China. The point is that Buddhists as well as Confucians were obliged to derive their spiritual pabulum almost exclusively from Chinese sources. In fact, the importation of Chinese books reached a new climax after the establishment of the Ashikaga regime in 1338, and the printing of Chinese classics (Confucian, Buddhist, and secular) increased considerably in Japan (see note on early printing in Japan, ch. V, p. 637). Gidō Shūshin compiled an anthology of a thousand Chinese poems (printed in Kyōto in 1388).

The use of the Japanese language was growing. Yūrin published a medical collection which was of course mainly of Chinese origin, but in the Japanese language, or, let us say, adapted to Japanese use. The oculists of the Majima school, if they wrote at all, wrote in Japanese. The chronicle Taihei-ki was composed in Japanese. Yet for the most important monuments of the Japanese language of that time we must look into an entirely different field, that of the drama.

The first literary drama in Japan was the so-called nō (Chinese nêng, meaning ability), derived from more popular forms of performances, dengaku and sarugaku. Dengaku designates music and play connected with the rice-planting festival; sarugaku, acrobatics and jugglery. Out of these games came the formal drama nō, thanks to the genius of two actors, playwrights, producers, Kannami (1333-84) and his more famous son, Seami (1363-1444).[67] The repertoire of nō is guided to this day by Seami's creations.

Poetry, music, dancing were harmoniously blended in the early nō plays, the text being very largely derived from the old romances Ise monogatari (beginning of tenth cent.), Genji monogatari (second half of tenth cent.),[68] Heike monogatari (second half of twelfth cent.), from the poetic anthology Man-yō-shū[69] (Collection of ten thousand leaves, compiled c. 750), and from Buddhist and Shintō legends, Chinese and Japanese folklore.

The success of that literary Japanese revival was made possible by the enlightened and warm patronage of the third Ashikaga shōgun, Yoshimitsu (1358-1408, ruled 1367-95), and because the Zen spirit, hovering over the Japanese people at that time, was encouraging every grace of life—painting, the tea ceremony, gardening, the art of flower arrangement,[70] fanciful dresses. Nō presented the best of Japanese

[66] For a vivid and firsthand account of Zen theory and practice see Emile Steinilber-Oberlin: Les sectes bouddhiques Japonaises (p. 129-96, Paris 1930).

[67] The two are named by Dr. Shio Sakanishi, Kwanze Kwanami Kiyotsuğu and Seami Motokiyo.

[68] Arthur Waley: Tales of the Genji (6 vols., London 1925-33). Complete English translation.

[69] The Manyōshū. One thousand poems (582 p., 5 maps, Nippon gakujutsu shinkōkai, Tōkyō 1940), complete edition in English and romaji. A very elaborate edition in Chinese script, romaji, and English translation, with abundant notes, is in course of publication by Jan Lodewijk Pierson, Jr. (Leyden 1929-).

[70] The ritual of the tea ceremony (cha-no-yu) and of flower arrangement (ikebana) was not stabilized until a century later under Yoshimasa, the eighth Ashikaga shōgun (ruled 1449-74). Edward Sylvester Morse: Japanese homes and their surroundings (Boston 1888; Isis 34, 371-73). Mary Averill: The flower art of Japan (New York 1915). Okakura-Kakuzo (1862-1913): The book of tea (New York 1906). The two subjects, tea and flowers, are often dealt with together as is done by Okakura.

letters and dreams on a ceremonial stage for all to behold and to contemplate. The dreams, explained in the most elegant manner with a beautiful ritual, and informed with yūgen (profundity, mystery), could not be forgotten.

But for nō, the Chinese influences would have been overwhelming. The drama saved Japanese letters and helped to bring out the best of Japanese culture.

There is an abundant literature on nō in Japanese and in Western languages. Here are a few introductory books in English. Ernest Fenollosa and Ezra Pound: Noh or accomplishment (276 p., London 1916), text of plays and music. Arthur Waley: The nō plays of Japan (320 p., London 1921). Beatrice Lane Suzuki: Nōgaku (Wisdom of the East, 124 p., London 1932). Shio Sakanishi, Marion H. Addington, and P. D. Perkins: List of translations of Japanese drama into English, French, and German (American Council of Learned Societies, 98 p., typescript, Washington 1935; Isis 25, 580). Kokusai bunka shinkokai (Society for international cultural relations): The noh drama (66 p., 12 pl., Tōkyō 1937). Jiro Harada: A glimpse of Japanese ideals (p. 155–70, pl. 92–103, Tokyo 1938; Isis 35, 256); the same book contains a chapter on the tea ceremonial, cha-no-yu, "tea's hot water" (p. 195–214, pl. 121–33).

CHAPTER XVI

RELIGIOUS BACKGROUND

(Second Half of the Fourteenth Century)

N.B. For a general survey of the religious background in the second half of the fourteenth century, see section II of chapter XV. In this chapter we deal only with the main personalities; many others are referred to in other chapters, and information relative to them can easily be found by means of the survey and the index.

A. WESTERN CHRISTENDOM

A1. Italy

ST. CATHERINE OF SIENA

Santa Caterina da Siena. Italian mystic, reformer, politician (1347–80).

Contents: (1) Life. (2) Writings. (3) Her disciples and her influence. (4) Text. (5) Early biographies. (6) Criticism.

1. *Life*

Caterina, the last child of twenty-five born to Jacomo Benincasa, a dyer, and Lapa di Puccio Piagenti, in Siena, on March 25, 1347. Her religious and ascetic tendencies appeared when she was still a child (6 or 7 years old); in 1362 she became a mantellata (a Dominican tertiary), and her life was more and more exclusively devoted to devotion, asceticism, and charity. In or about 1366 she was spiritually espoused by Christ, and from that time on she enjoyed visions and revelations which encouraged her to send admonitions to people of all kinds up to kings and popes. From 1370 on she implored Gregory XI to leave Avignon, and he finally did so in 1377, but died the following year.[1] This was the end of the Babylonish captivity, but the beginning of something even worse, the Great Schism.

From 1370 on, an increasing part of Catherine's activity was taken away from pure devotion and given to politics. Her main idea was to bring the pope back to Rome, later to establish him there permanently and defeat his rivals, primarily the antipope, Robert of Geneva (Clement VII, 1378–94). This, however, implied as an indispensable condition the pacification and unification of Italy. From that point of view Catherine should be regarded, as well as Dante and Petrarca, as one of the forerunners of the Italian kingdom. It implied also projects of a new crusade (the best means of consolidating Italy from without) and of a reformation of the church (the best means of consolidating Italy from within). In order to accomplish her great purpose, Catherine was involved in a long series of negotiations, the recital of which would take too much space. One of the most dramatic episodes was the fight between Florence and the Papal State (1376 ff.). Catherine negotiated between Florence, or rather the Parte guelfa, and Avignon, but failed in her peace mission. In 1378 she witnessed il tumulto dei ciompi (outbreak of the wool

[1] In the church of S. Maria Nuova (called S. Francesca since 1608), where Gregory XI is buried, a bas-relief represents him coming back to Rome under St. Catherine's guidance.

carders, i.e., the unskilled workers, the popolo minuto) in Florence. Soon afterward she returned to Siena and dictated the Dialogo.

In 1378 Urban VI called her to Rome, where she spent the rest of her short but intense life. She died there on April 29, 1380, being only 33 years old.

Catherine's native house in the Fontebranda quarter of Siena is preserved, and her incorrupted body lies in the church of Santa Maria sopra Minerva in Rome. The tomb of Fra Angelico of Fiesole is in the same church. Her head is enshrined in a chapel of San Dominico, Siena.

She was canonized in 1461 by Pius II (Aeneas Sylvius Piccolomini).

2. *Writings*

Though Catherine learned to "write" only relatively late in life (c. 1377), her writings (i.e., her dictations) have become classics of Italian literature. She wrote in 1378 her single treatise, the Dialogo (Libro della divina dottrina, Trattato della divina providenza), a treatise on the spiritual life which is divided into six parts: Introduction (cap. 1–8), Trattato della discrezione (cap. 9–64), Trattato dell'orazione (cap. 65–86), Trattato delle lagrime (cap. 87–134), Trattato della divina providenza (cap. 135–53), Trattato dell'obbedienza (cap. 154–67). It is mainly an account of her mystical visions and a passionate defense of the supremacy of love, but the "treatise on tears" includes violent criticisms of the abuses and vices of the clergy, confirming the testimony of Boccaccio and other contemporaries. She conceived the papal power as purely spiritual, at the very time when the pope himself was defending his temporal despotism by all means, fair or foul, pouring Italian blood for the sake of it without any restraint. For example, in 1377 his agent, cardinal Robert of Geneva, ordered the population of Cesena (in Romagna) to be butchered.

Catherine wrote a large number of letters (about 381), addressed to two popes, three kings, the queen of Naples, brethren, and beggars. These letters constitute a valuable source for the historian of those troubled times. They throw light also on her transcendental knowledge of God and the hereafter, as well as on her extraordinary good sense when dealing with practical matters. Next to Petrarca she was the greatest letter writer of her century, but Petrarca wrote in stilted Latin, whereas she wrote with the greatest spontaneity in the purest Tuscan.

Finally, we have from her some 26 prayers. Her book on the Divine providence has been compared with the Divina commedia; it is a sort of mystical counterpart of it, a prose as noble as Dante's verse.

3. *Her disciples and her influence*

However important Catherine's letters, a good part of her great influence was due, not to any writings, but to her own personality. Many were her disciples, so many that only a few of them can be named.

For example, William Flete of Cambridge, who was one of the Augustinian Hermits at Lecceto; Angelo Salvetti, who became general of the Franciscans. I name a few others in chronological order of death years: Barduccio di Piero Canigiani, a Florentine youth (d. 1382). Raimondo da Capua, a descendant of Pier delle Vigne (XIII-1; d. 1249); Gregory XI designated him as her confessor in 1375; he was elected general of the Dominicans soon after her death in 1380; he died at Nuremberg 1399. Neri di Landoccio Pagliaresi, poet of Siena (d. 1406). Stefano di Corrado Maconi, one of her secretaries, who after her death became a Carthusian, then prior of the Certosa of Pavia, later prior general of his order (1347–1424). Finally, the Dominican Tommaso di Antonio Caffarini (d. 1434), who was probably the last of her immediate disciples to survive. These names have not been selected at random, many of them will reappear later. They illustrate how her influence touched not simply members of her own order, but all kinds of men. Indeed, the political and ecclesiastical conflicts caused or revived by the Great Schism were so intense that the old divisions (e.g., Franciscans vs. Dominicans, secular vs. regular) were replaced by new ones (partisans of Urban VI vs. his adversaries, etc.). Catherine of Siena, like Catherine of Sweden, stood in defense of Urban VI, but above all she stood for the peace and unity of the church, and the unification of Italy.

In the history of the Christian church Catherine is one of the greatest among the personalities who help us to understand the development from St. Francis of Assisi to Girolamo Savonarola (d. 1498). In the history of Italian letters, as well as in that of Italian unity, she deserves to be named together with Dante and Petrarca.

4. *Text*

Complete works edited by Girolamo Gigli (1660–1722): L'opere della serafica Santa Caterina da Siena (vol. 1, Siena 1707; vol. 2, Lucca 1721; vol. 3, Siena 1713; vol. 4, Siena 1707; vol. 5, Lucca 1754). Vol. 1 contains the life by Raimondo da Capua translated by Bernardino Pecci; vols. 2 and 3, the letters; vol. 4, the Dialogo; vol. 5, posthumous supplement, the paraphrase of Caffarini's libellus.

For the incunabula see GW (6, 250–57, nos. 6221–26, 1934).

Libro della divina dottrina. First edition, Bologna c. 1475, including Barduccio Canigiani: Epistola della morte di S. Caterina. Second edition, Naples 1478; third, Venice 1494; there are many more editions of the sixteenth century, etc., and still another is included in vol. 4 of Gigli's Opere (Siena 1707, Rome 1866).

Latin translation by Raimundus de Vineis (i.e., fra Raimondo da Capua), first printed in Brescia 1496, then again Cologne 1553, 1601, Ingolstadt 1583. New edition by Matilde Fiorilli (474 p., Bari 1912).

The Latin text was Englished by brother Dane James and printed by Wynkyn de Worde 1519 under the title Orchard of Syon. New English translation by Algar Thorold (London 1896); abridged (London 1907); the abridged edition does not include the offensive part of the Trattato delle lagrime. For a discussion of this, see G. G. Coulton: Five centuries of religion (2, 554–55, Cambridge 1927).

The Dialogus brevis Sanctae Catharinae consummatam continens perfectionem (Lyon 1552) is in all probability apocryphal. The original Italian text, if it existed, is lost. An Italian translation by Alessandro Piccolomini, Trattato della consumata perfettione, is included in Gigli's Opere (4, 327–36, 1707).

The first edition of the letters, printed in Bologna 1492, contains so few letters (only 31) that it is more correct to count the edition of Venice 1500 as the princeps. That Aldine edition, prepared by Bartolommeo da Alzano, contains 368 letters (in reality only 350 because of duplications), together with an address of Aldo Manuzio (1450–1515), the printer, to cardinal Francesco de' Piccolomini (1439–1503; pope Pius III the last month of his life), and a letter written in 1411 by Stefano Maconi, one of Catherine's disciples. It is a small folio of 422 leaves; on fol. 10 verso there is a woodcut representing the saint and a few words printed in italics, this being the earliest example of italics in print. It was reprinted three times, Venice 1548, 1562, 1584, and in vols. 2–3 of Gigli's edition (Lucca 1721, Siena 1713) with notes by Federigo Burlamacchi (373 letters). Modern edition (not sufficiently critical) by Niccolò Tommaseo (4 vols., Florence 1860). Editions by Piero Misciattelli (6 vols., Siena 1913–21) and by Lodovico Ferretti (4 vols., Siena 1918–27).

Vida Dutton Scudder:[2] Saint Catherine of Siena as seen in her letters (362 p., London 1905; reprinted 1906). Convenient edition of selected letters in English with notes.

5. *Early biographies*

The first biography was written soon after her death by fra Raimondo da Capua in Latin (1384–95); this is the Vita or Legenda (eximia legenda, legenda prolixa, in Italian Leggenda maggiore). First edition, Cologne 1553. Edited by the Bollandists in Acta sanctorum, 3d vol. for April (Antwerp 1675, Rome 1866).

The Italian translation begun by Neri di Landoccio Pagliaresi, one of St. Catherine's secretaries, and completed by an anonyme of Piacenza was published (before the original Latin text) at San Jacopo di Ripoli, near Florence, 1477. Another translation, completely made by the anonyme of Piacenza at the request of Stefano Maconi, appeared at Milan 1489. There are many other translations in Italian (in Gigli, vol. 1), French, German, Spanish, and English. There are two English versions, both incomplete, The lyf of St. Katherin of Senis the blessid virgin (Caxton, 1493), and the one by John Fenn (d. 1615) made from the Italian (s.l., 1609).

Processus contestationum super sanctitate et doctrina beatae Catharinae de Senis. Collection of documents edited by fra Tommaso Caffarini (1411–13) plus a few others. Partly edited by Edmond Martène and Ursin Durand: Veterum scriptorum et monumentorum amplissima collectio (vol. 6, Paris 1729).

Tommaso Caffarini: Libellus de supplemento legendae prolixae beatae Catharinae de Senis (written c. 1414; unprinted). Italian paraphrase by Ambrogio Ansano Tantucci in Gigli's Opere (vol. 5, Lucca 1754, Rome 1866).

Tommaso Caffarini: Epitome vitae beatae Caterinae de Senis. Written shortly after 1414, printed in Bonino Mombrizio (c. 1424–c. 1482): Sanctuarium seu vitae sanctorum (vol. 1, Milano 1479). This is the so-called Legenda abbreviata (Ital., Leggenda minore). An Italian translation, La admirabile legenda de la seraphica vergine e del sposo eterno Jesù, was soon made by Stefano Maconi, and printed at Milan (?) before the end of the century. Edited by Francesco Grottanelli (Bologna 1868).

6. *Criticism*

The first elaborate modern biography was the one by cardinal Alfonso Capecelatro (1824–1912): Storia di S. Caterina e del papato del suo tempo (4th ed., 625 p., Siena 1878). Mother Augusta Theodosia Drane (1823–94): The history of St. Catherine and her companions (London 1880; 2d ed., 2 vols., 1887; 3d ed., 2 vols., 1899). French translation of same (2 vols., Paris 1892). Edmund Garratt Gardner: Saint Catherine of Siena, a study of the religion, literature and history of the fourteenth century in Italy (460 p., 9 pl., London 1907); this is a very good account of Catherine's life and thought, partly based on the MSS and including 8 unpublished letters of hers; also a good account of her political and religious background, of the almost inextricable web of intrigues which she had to face. The book, being well indexed, can be used as a dictionary of Catherine's time and world.

Robert Fawtier: Sainte Catherine, essai de critique des sources (2 vols., Paris 1921–30).

For Catherine's influence on art, see Julius Rodenberg: Die heilige Katharina von Siena und ihre Darstellung in der sienesischen Kunst (Heidelberg Diss., 106 p., 1910). P. Lodovico Ferretti: S. Caterina (16 p., 32 pl., Rome 1924).

[2] Miss Scudder (1861–) is one of the glories of Wellesley College in Wellesley, Mass. See her autobiography, On journey (New York 1937).

A2. Catalonia

EYMERIC

Nicholas Eymeric (Nicolás Eimerico). Catalan Dominican and inquisitor (d. 1399).

Eymeric was born at Gerona; he assumed the Dominican habit in 1334. He became inquisitor general for Aragon in 1356, and distinguished himself by his inquisitorial zeal and vigor. He was finally exiled by Juan I of Aragon (ruled 1387-95), but was patronized by the antipopes Clement VII and Benedict XIII.

Among his inquisitorial activities was his leadership of a reaction against Ramon Lull in 1366. He did his best to prove Lull's heterodoxy, but failed. His main work, and the only one to attain some popularity, was his treatise for the guidance of inquisitors, which was far more elaborate than the guide of Bernard Gui (1323), and remained the standard book on the subject as long as the inquisitorial procedure was allowed to continue. The harder instructions published a century later (1484) by the most ferocious of inquisitors, the Dominican Thomas Torquemada of Valladolid (1420-98), were not printed, whereas Eymeric's treatise was printed in 1578 and many times afterward, these editions being produced—be it noted—not for the disinterested needs of historical students, but for inquisitorial use.

Eymeric's Directorium inquisitorum is an enormous work divided into three main parts: (I) definition of the catholic faith; (II) heresies; (III) inquisitorial procedure. The first part is relatively short (about one-ninth of the whole), the two remaining parts much longer and about equal. The second part includes all the relevant Decretales and apostolic letters, followed by glosses and brief accounts of all the heretical tendencies of which inquisitors might have to take cognizance. Some brief chapters deal with superstitions and witchcraft. That part of the book was of course completely superseded later on by the Malleus maleficarum, compiled by two other Dominicans, Jacob Sprenger and Heinrich Kraemer, or Institoris, soon after 1484 (Isis 25, 148).

Other treatises of Eymeric's, unpublished, show that he had paid much attention to the superstitions of his time, as was indeed his inquisitorial duty. While accepting, like all his contemporaries, the fundamental premises of astrology, he condemned the art. He judged alchemy even more severely, forbidding the practice of the alchemical art in accordance with the decretal of John XXII, "Spondent." This helps us to realize that Catholic orthodoxy played a useful part in repressing, or trying to repress, the wild growth of irresponsible superstitions; though it may have discouraged at the same time some legitimate and useful investigations.

Text. The Directorium inquisitorum was printed in Rome 1578-79, 1585, 1587, Venice 1591, 1607; all folio editions. I have seen only the edition of 1587, a bulky folio entitled Directorium inquisitorum cum commentariis Francisci Pegñae. In hac postrema editione iterum emendatum et auctum, et multis litteris apostolicis locupletatum accessit haeresum, rerum et verborum multiplex et copiosissimus index (935 p., Rome 1587), dedicated to Gregory XIII.

Vita antiqua Sancti Raymundi (Raymundiana, part 1, 1898). Eymeric's biography of Raymond of Peñafort (d. 1275), his brother Catalan and Dominican (XIII-1).

Le manuel des inquisiteurs à l'usage des inquisitions d'Espagne et de Portugal, ou Abrégé de . . . Directorium inquisitorum. On y a joint une courte histoire de l'établissement de l'inquisition dans le royaume de Portugal, tirée du latin de Louis a

Paramo[3] (198 p., Lisbonne 1762). This anonymous translation is ascribed to the abbé André Morellet (1727-1819), who had found a copy of the Directorium in Rome and thought that the best way of fighting fanaticism was to show it in action just as it was. See my article on Beccaria (suppt. to Bull. of the history of medicine no. 3, 283-308, Baltimore 1944). Is Lisbonne the real place of publication? Josef Marchena: Manual de inquisidores para uso de las inquisiciones de España y Portugal o compendio de la obra titulada Directorio de inquisidores de Nicolas Eymerico. Traducida del frances en idioma castellano (160 p., Mompeller 1821).

Criticism. Preface to the edition of 1587 by Francisco de Peña (1540-1612). NBG (16, 867, 1856). Henry Charles Lea: History of the Inquisition of the Middle Ages (3 vols., New York 1887). Thorndike (3, 513-15, 1934). Coulton: Medieval panorama (p. 722, 1938). Gertrude Barnes Fiertz: An unusual trial under the Inquisition at Fribourg, Switzerland, in 1399 (Speculum 18, 340-57, 1943; Isis 35, 59).

ST. VINCENT FERRER

San Vicente Ferrer. Catalan Dominican, preacher and wonder-worker (1350-1419).

San Vicente was born in Valencia c. 1350. His parents, Guillermo Ferrer, notary, and Constanza Miquel, belonged to notable Catalan families. A brother of his, Boniface Ferrer, became general of the Carthusians. Vicente was educated in Valencia, assumed the Dominican habit in 1367, and was sent in 1377 to the Toulouse house of the order for the continuation of his studies. From 1379 on he was in the service of Pedro de Luna, cardinal of Aragon (the future Benedict XIII), who was trying to win Aragon to the obedience of the Avignonese popes. In 1385-90 he taught theology in the cathedral school of Valencia. His time and energy were divided between political propaganda for Clement VII and Benedict XIII, and apostolic work. Many conversions were ascribed to him, notably that of Solomon ben Isaac ha-Levi (Paul of Burgos). From 1378 to 1395 he resided in Valencia; from 1395 to 1399 in Avignon. At the end of 1399 Benedict appointed him a legate a latere Christi, and Vincent spent the rest of his life preaching for repentance all over Western Europe. He is said to have converted twenty-five thousand Jews, and many thousand Muslims, but the quality of such wholesale conversions may be justly doubted. He did not attend the council of Constance, and remained faithful to Benedict XIII (d. 1422) until 1416, that is, almost as long as possible, the "union" pope Martin V being elected by the Council in 1417. After the failure of the papal side which he had served so long, he retired to Brittany, and died there, at Vannes on April 5, 1419. He was canonized by Calixtus III in 1455.

During the period of his philosophical and theological studies he composed two philosophical treatises, the one on dialectical suppositions, the other, shorter, on the universals, neither of which seems important. That was the end of his philosophical activities. His other writings, fairly abundant, deal with ecclesiastical politics, edification, homiletics, and prophecies. He wrote a great many sermons (in Latin and Catalan), which enjoyed much popularity, being repeatedly printed from 1475 on.

He was one of the most famous preachers of his time, preaching Jews and Moors

[3] Luis de Páramo (b. 1545), archdeacon in Leon, inquisitor of Spain and Sicily. His main work is the De origine et progressu officii Sanctae Inquisitionis eiusque dignitate et utilitate (folio, 887 p., Madrid 1598).

to conversion, and Christians to repentance. He often spoke of the Last Day, which he believed to be very near (Connolly p. 115, 1928). At the same time he was a political propagandist in the service of the two antipopes Clement VII and Benedict XIII. This is very interesting, as it illustrates the greatest spiritual conflict of that time and the utter confusion of ideas relative to it. For example, in 1380 Vincent addressed a treatise De moderno Ecclesiae schismate to Peter IV of Aragon in order to win him over to Clement's side. In that treatise he claimed not only that Clement was the true pope, but also that no defensor of, or believer in, Urban VI (the Roman pope) could possibly escape hell! (see the edition of Rome 1901, p. 96-100, 180, 197). At the same time another saint, Catherine of Siena, remained deeply loyal to Urban. This was a question of fundamental importance, about which the saints themselves could not agree; what about the non-saints?

Klebs' inclusion of Vincent's De interiori homine in his list of Incunabula scientifica (no. 1035) is unwarranted; that book deals with the "inner man" in the spiritual, not in the material or humorous, sense. It is partly because of the necessity of correcting Klebs' error that I have written this note. To return to the De interiori homine or Tractatus de vita spirituali, as it is more generally called, it was very popular indeed, being represented by a multitude of editions, and by many translations.

Text. Opera omnia, Valencia 1693; this is probably not the first edition.

Oeuvres de Saint Vincent Ferrier, edited by the Dominican father P. H. O. Fages (2 vols., Louvain 1909).

The two philosophical treatises were first edited by Fages in vol. 1 of the Oeuvres (1909).

The Compilacio de interiori homine was first printed in Magdeburg 1493 (Klebs no. 1035.1). The treatise was very frequently reprinted, but under the title Tractatus de vita spirituali (and variants), which seems closer to the original (cf. the common Catalan phrase vida spiritual). It was reprinted in Venice 1500, 1505, thrice in 1510 (Cologne, Paris, and Alcala), etc. A Spanish translation was printed as early as 1510; a French one in Paris 1619, etc. German translation by Heribert Christian Scheeben: Das geistliche Leben (Vechta in Oldenburg 1928).

Albano Sorbelli: Il trattato di S. Vicenzo Ferrer intorno al grande scisma d'Occidente (269 p., Roma 1901; reprinted Bologna 1906).

Many incunabula editions of the Sermons, the bibliography of which is complicated. The earliest were printed in Ulm 1475. Others appeared in Cologne 1482-87 (4 vols.), Strassburg 1485, Milano 1488, Lyon 1490, 1497, 1499, Nuremberg 1492, Venice 1496, Basel 1498. A French translation of sermons was printed at Lyon as early as 1477. There are many sixteenth-century and later editions.

Sermo de S. Vincent martyr predicat en Valencia (12 p., 2d ed. Barcelona 1915).

Quaresma. Predicada a València l'any 1413. Introducció, notes i transcripció per Josep Sanchis Sivera (Barcelona 1927).

Criticism. Marco Antonio Orti: Segundo centenario de los años de la canonizacion del valenciano apostol san Vicente Ferrer (Valencia 1656). Auto de S. Vicente Ferrer . . . (23 p., Lisboa 1854). P. H. O. Fages: Histoire de Saint Vincent Ferrer (2 vols., Paris 1894). Max Droste: Die kirchenpolitische Tätigkeit des hl. Vicente Ferrer (Diss. Freiburg i.Br., 48 p., 1903). Francisco Martínez y Martínez: Algo de bibliografia valenciano-vicentista (Valencia 1919). Sigismund Brettle: San Vicente Ferrer und sein literarischer Nachlass (230 p., Münster i.W. 1924). Matthieu Maxime Gorce: Saint Vincent Ferrer (thèse, Clermont, 2 vols., 360 p., Paris 1923). Long article in EUI (68, 532-40, 1929).

TURMEDA

Anselmo or Anselm Turmeda, Majorcan Franciscan and apostate to Islām, writing in Catalan and Arabic (1352—after 1423).

Anselmo was born in Palma de Majorca in 1352, was educated there, then spent six years in Lerida, where he studied physics and astronomy. He assumed the Franciscan habit in Montblanch (prov. Tarragona). In 1376, he continued his studies in Bologna. He lived there ten years with a venerable priest called Nicholas Myrtil (or Martell); the latter interpreted Jesus' saying "There will come after me a prophet whose name is Paraclet"[4] as a prefiguration of the Prophet Muḥammad, and advised his young friend to become Muslim! (This is Anselmo's own story.) In 1386, he returned to Majorca, where he stayed six months; he then sailed to Sicily, where he spent five months; finally he went to Tunis. Soon after his arrival in that city (1387) he professed Islām before Abū-l-'Abbās Aḥmad II (Ḥafṣī sulṭān 1370–94). He married a Muslim woman, was appointed chief of the customs (or maritime governor), and learned the Arabic language within a year. His Arabic name was 'Abdallāh ibn 'Abdallāh al-Tarjumān al-Māyurqī (= the Majorcan interpreter), and his son was called Muḥammad ibn 'Abdallāh. 'Abdallāh served as interpreter and secretary to Abū-l-'Abbās and to the latter's successor, Abū Fāris 'Abd al-'Azīz (ruled 1394–1433). In 1421, Alphonse V the Magnanimous (king of Aragon 1416–58) tried to obtain his release in exchange of Muslim prisoners, and in 1423 he sent him a safe-conduct.[5] After that we lose track of him. He died in Tunis, where his tomb is venerated to this day.[6] The story of his recantation and Christian martyrdom is a legend dating only from the beginning of the eighteenth century.

All his works were written in Tunis, but all except the last were apparently in Catalan. In 1397 he composed the Llibre de bons amonestaments (Book of good admonitions), in 1398 the Cobles de la divisió del regne de Mallorques, in 1405 the Profecies (poem of 760 very short lines). His two most important books, however, were written somewhat later.

In 1417, he composed in Catalan the Disputa del ase (Dispute of the ass), in which it is shown that man is the king of creation and superior to all animals on account of his moral qualities. The Catalan text is lost, but is known through a French translation of 1544 which made quite a stir in the sixteenth century (it was published four times from 1544 to 1606, and a German translation from the French appeared in Mömpelgard 1606). It had been suspected by Ramón Menéndez y Pelayo (1905) and has been proved by Miguel Asín y Palacios (1914) that Anselmo's Disputa was simply a translation of a part of the Rasā'il ikhwān al-ṣafā' (Introd. 1, 661), written at Baṣra about the end of the tenth century and known in the West not long afterward thanks to Maslama ibn Aḥmad al-Majrīṭī (X-2) or to al-Karmānī (XI-1).

In 1420 'Abdallāh ibn 'Abdallāh wrote in imperfect Arabic a treatise against Christianity, which was superior to other Muslim treatises of the same kind because

[4] In some MSS of Anselmo's autobiography it is written Aḥmad Paraclet; this might be due to a confusion between παράκλητος (comforter, advocatus) and περικλυτός (illustrious), to which Aḥmad is more or less equivalent. In the Barnabas epistles, always popular in North Africa, the Paraclet is also called Aḥmad. See also the Sūrat al-ṣaff (Qur'ān 61, 6).

[5] The two documents of 1421 and 1423 exist in the archives of the kings of Aragon. Facsimiles in Calvet (1914).

[6] It is not the tomb in the Sūq al-sarrājīn reproduced in Revue tunisienne vol. 13, p. 89 (1906), but the one reproduced ibid. p. 292.

of his greater knowledge of the Christian Scriptures and theology. It is entitled Tuḥfat al-'arīb fī-l-radd 'alā ahl al-ṣalīb, and was quite successful among Muslims, witness the number of MSS in Arabic and Turkish. It was given a new vogue at the beginning of the seventeenth century by its republication by Abū-l-Ghaith Muḥammad al-Qashshāsh, who added an introduction and a new title, Taḥīyat al-asrār ta'līf al-aḥjār al-anṣār fī-l-radd 'alā al-Nasārā al-kuffār, and dedicated it to the 'Uthmānlī sulṭān Aḥmad I (ruled 1603–17).

The Tuḥfa is divided into three chapters, of which the first two are autobiographical. The third (more than half of the whole work) is devoted to establishing the truth of Islām against Christendom, full advantage being taken of the Christian Scriptures. In the first chapter 'Abdallāh tells the story of his youth, studies, and conversion to Islām; in the second he describes his experiences in Tunis and praises very warmly the sulṭān Abū Fāris 'Abd al-'Azīz because of his generosity, his endowment of a hospital and of a library in the Jami' al-zaitūna, his refusal to tax immoral trades, etc.

Text. The Arabic text of the Disputa del ase will be found naturally in any edition of the Rasā'il ikhwān al-ṣafā, of which there are many (e.g., Calcutta 1812, 1842, Leipzig 1881, Bombay 1888–89, Cairo 1900, 1928). I have used the last named, where the text is in vol. 2 (out of 4), p. 173 ff. It has been translated into German by Friedrich Dieterici: Der Streit zwischen Mensch und Thier, ein arabisches Mährchen aus den Schriften der lauteren Brüder (304 p., Berlin 1858), and into French by Garcin de Tassy: Allégories, récits poétiques, etc. (p. 73–188, Paris 1876). There are separate Arabic editions of that chapter with Persian glosses (Cawnpore 1894, Lucknow 1899, Cawnpore 1912), without the glosses (Cairo 1900); also Turkish and Hindustani versions. I may repeat on this occasion that a critical English version of all the Rasā'il is very much to be desired; that would be a considerable task requiring much learning.

The Catalan text of Anselmo's version was actually printed, La disputa del ase contra frare Encelm Turmeda sobre la natura e nobleza dels animals (Barcelona 1509). The unique copy in the Columbine Library of Seville has disappeared! A French version of it was printed four times: Lyon 1544, s.a.l., Lyon 1548, Pampelune (i.e., Paris) 1606. The text of the 1544 version was reprinted by Raymond Foulché-Delbosc: Disputation de l'asne contre frère Anselme Turmeda sur la nature et la noblesse des animaulx, faicte et ordonnée par ledict frère Anselme en la cité de Tunicz, l'an 1417 (Revue hispanique 24, 358–479, 1911).

The Tuḥfa has been published many times, but no satisfactory edition is yet available. The first edition appeared in England (192 p., London 1873); it was printed again in Cairo 1895, 1904. The first two editions contain notes by a shaykh 'Abdallāh bey, who cannot be identified. French translation by Jean Spiro, Le présent de l'homme lettré pour réfuter les partisans de la croix (Revue de l'histoire des religions 12, 68–89, 179–201, 278–301, 1885). Chapters 1 and 2 of that translation have been reprinted in the Revue tunisienne (13, 89–103, 1906).

Llibre de bons amonestaments (64 p., Barcelona 1891). Two earlier editions, the first dated Valencia 1688, the other unplaced and undated (end of eighteenth cent.?) have been described by Vicente Castañeda in Revista critica hispanoamericana (5, 7–21, 1919).

Ramon d'Alós: Les Profecies den Turmeda (Revue hispanique 24, 480–96, 1911).

Llibre compost per fra Anselm Turmeda ab la oració de Sant Miquel, etc. (32 p., Cervera s.a.); idem (24 p., Gerona s.a.). Little books of devotion such as are sold in churches.

Criticism. Brockelmann (2, 250, 1902; suppt. 2, 352, 1938). Miguel Asín y Palacios: El original árabe de la Disputa del asno (Revista de filología española 1,

1–51, 1914), reprinted in Asín's Huellas del Islam (Madrid 1941; Isis 33, 539–44). Agustín Calvet: Fray Anselmo Turmeda, heterodoxo español (240 p., 7 pl., Barcelona 1914). J. H. Probst: Turmeda et sa conversion à l'islamisme (Revue hispanique 38, 464–96, 1916). Elaborate article with long bibliography in EUI (65, 412–18, 1929). Garcia Silvestre (p. 116, 250–58, 1932).

A3. Judeo-Spanish Converts

SOLOMON BEN ISAAC HA-LEVI

Paulus (Pablo) de Santa María; Paul of Burgos (c. 1351–1435). Judeo-Spanish Hebraist and theologian. His father, originating in Aragon or Navarre, settled in Burgos in the first half of the fourteenth century. The family was very rich and powerful. Solomon, born at Burgos c. 1351, received a Talmudic education and became a rabbi; he was one of the most learned men of the city as well as the wealthiest. In 1390 (or 1391) he was converted to Christianity and assumed the name Pablo de Santa María.

This baptism was a great event in Burgos, for his two brothers, Pero García de Santa María (or Pedro Suárez) and Alvar García de Santa María, as well as four sisters and some children, were all baptized at that time. His wife Joanna, however, refused to abjure her faith, and died, a Jewess, in 1420.

Solomon, or Paul as we must now call him, was in touch with many Jewish scholars such as Isaac ben Sheshet, Meir Alguadez, Joseph Orabuena, and members of the Lorqi family, and he continued to correspond with them after his conversion.

Paul of Burgos studied in Paris, visited London, became successively archdeacon of Treviño, bishop of Cartagena (1403), keeper of the royal seal (1406) of Henry III of Castile, and after the latter's death (1406) member of the regency of Castile and archbishop of Burgos (1415); he died in 1435.

A few years after his baptism he began the compilation of additions and corrections to the Postilla litteralis of Nicholas of Lyra (XIV-1). These Additiones notabiles ad Postillam, as they were called, were completed in 1429 and shared the fame of Nicholas' work, being frequently printed together with the latter. The apostate's corrections, however, irritated other exegetes, and caused one of them, the German Franciscan Matthias Doering (d. c. 1465) of Erfurt, to write, c. 1434–40, the Correctorium corruptorii Burgensis (Replicae adversus Burgensem) against him. These Replicae are included in some editions of the Postilla, more or less completely. Then the Austrian Benedictine Johann Schlippacher of Melk (Lower Austria) attacked Doering in his Reprehensorium in replicatorem Matthiam Doring contra dominum Paulum episcopum Burgensem (1477). Then the Spanish Dominican Diego Deza (1444–1523) found it necessary to defend St. Thomas Aquinas against Nicholas and Matthias in his Defensorium pro S. Thoma Aquinate contra Nicolaum Liram et invectivas Matthie Dorinck in replicationibus contra Paulum Burgensem (Seville 1491, 1517, etc.), nor was that the end! I have indulged in this digression to illustrate the importance attached in the fifteenth century to the Postilla, and also to illustrate the intensity of theological polemics, which was not a bit inferior in the Christian world to what it was (or had been) in Jewish and Muslim circles. Note also that these theological quarrels were international, for they involved French, German, and Spanish monks, and at least three religious orders: Franciscans, Dominicans, and Benedictines.

Late in life Paul of Burgos composed a Historia universal in Spanish verse.

Like many other converted Jews, he became rabidly anti-Jewish, using his political influence to persecute those whose faith he had shared and nursed so long. He drafted the new law promulgated at Valladolid in 1412 for the forcible conversion of Jews. In 1433, he completed a treatise of Christian apologetics, Dialogus Pauli et Sauli contra Judaeos, sive Scrutinium scripturarum (princeps c. 1470), which enjoyed much popularity and was much used by other anti-Jewish apologists.

The Jew Solomon ben Isaac belongs to the fourteenth century, the Christian Paul of Burgos to the fifteenth. As they cannot be separated, I have spoken of both here.

Paul's brother Alvar García (Burgos 1349-1460?) held high offices in the Castilian court, and wrote various Spanish chronicles. The inventory of his library has been preserved.

Text. Additiones notabiles ad Postillas Nicolae de Lyra in totam Scripturam. Printed in many editions of the Postilla beginning with that of Venice 1481.

The Scrutinium was first printed at Rome, in or before 1471. Many later editions: Strassburg c. 1474, Mantua 1475, Mayence 1478, Burgos 1591, etc.

Criticism. Manuel Martínez Añíbarro y Rives: Intento de un diccionario biográfico y bibliográfico de autores de la provincia de Burgos (p. 237-53, 469-89, Madrid 1889-90). Includes notices on other members of the Santa María family, and the interesting catalogue of Alvar García's library. Paul Albert: Matthias Döring, ein deutscher Minorit des 15. Jahrhunderts (202 p., Stuttgart 1892, see p. 18). Meyer Kayserling (JE 9, 562, 1905). Henri Labrosse: Oeuvres de Nicholas de Lyre (Etudes franciscaines 19, 370-71, 1908). Vera (1, 331-34, 1933), apropos of Alvar García de Santa María, derived from Martínez Añíbarro (1889). Francisco Cantera Burgos: La conversión del célebre talmudista Salomón Levi (Publicaciones de la Sociedad de Menéndez y Pelayo, 32 p., Santander 1933). A. L. Williams (p. 267-76, 1935).

A4. France

MÉZIÈRES

Philippe de Mézières. French moralist and publicist (1327-1405).

Philippe de Mézières (better than Maizières) originated probably in the castle of Mézières in Picardy (dépt. Somme); he was born c. 1327 and was educated in Amiens. Being a younger son of a noble family, he engaged in a life of war and adventure. In 1346, he went to the Near East to take part in the expedition led by Humbert II dauphin of Viennois,[7] and he won his spurs in that very year in Smyrna. After that ill-fated crusade he went to Cyprus and became familiar with a son of Hugues IV, Pierre count of Tripoli. When the latter became king of Cyprus and Jerusalem under the name Pierre I (ruled 1359-69), Philippe was his chancellor. For many years before and after 1369 he traveled considerably all over Europe trying to organize a new crusade. Finally he settled down at the court of Charles V le Sage as councilor. After that king's death (1380) he withdrew to the house of the Celestines in Paris, but without taking their vows. He spent there quietly the rest of his life, dying on May 29, 1405.

Philippe's main idea was the preparation of a new crusade. His life from 1346

[7] Humbert II (1313-55) was the last independent sovereign of Dauphiné. Needing money, he sold his sovereignty to the king of France; his anti-Turkish crusade completed his ruin. He abdicated in 1349 and assumed the Dominican habit. From 1349 on, the title of dauphin was given to the eldest son of the king of France.

to the end was devoted to that single purpose. He realized the precariousness of the Western possessions in the eastern Mediterranean, and of the Christian faith, if the kingdom of Jerusalem were not restored. In order to attain that purpose, new means were needed; he wanted to establish a new military religious order, the order of the Passion of Christ, in order to create a new unity and a new discipline, without which military efforts were doomed to sterility. (The order did not materialize.) Most of his writings deal directly or indirectly with the crusade and with the political, moral, religious preparations which were needed for his purpose. The efforts of 1347, 1362, 1363–64 all failed, and his hopes were finally quashed by the battle of Nicopolis (on the lower Danube), where Sigismund of Hungary and Boucicault, marshal of France, were utterly defeated in 1396 by the 'Uthmānlī sulṭān Bāyazīd I.

One of his first writings was a biography of Peter of Thomas (or Thomasius),[8] who was one of the three promoters of the ill-fated crusade of 1365, and died at Famagusta in 1366. Philippe wrote that biography immediately afterward. His best-known work is the Somnium viridarii, a political pamphlet in the form of a dialogue between a clerk and a knight; the former defending the pope's prerogative, the latter, the king's. The knight wins. That work was ascribed to some nine authors, including Nicole Oresme, Giovanni da Legnano, and Raoul de Presles. The Latin text was completed very probably by Philippe de Mézières, in May 1376. The French text, Le songe du vergier, once thought to be the original, was written later, c. 1376–78, also by Philippe.

We may still cite another curious work of his, the Songe du vieil pelerin (Dream of the old pilgrim), completed in the summer of 1389. It is an allegorical journey. Queen Truth visits the whole of Europe, as well as the known parts of Africa and Asia. It describes contemporary manners and includes political advice to the young king, Charles VI.

Text. The Vita S. Petri Thomasii was printed by Godfrey Henschen in the Acta sanctorum, January 29. Separate edition by the same (Antwerp 1659).

The Somnium viridarii was first printed in French (Lyon 1491), then in Paris (s.a., c. 1500) and in Angers (c. 1500). It was reprinted in Jean Louis Brunet: Traitez des droits et libertez de l'église gallicane (vol. 2, Paris 1731).

The Latin text was first printed under the title Aureus de utraque potestate libellus. Somnium viridarii vulgariter nuncupatus (Paris 1516). It was reprinted by Melchior Goldast: Monarchia sancti romani imperii (vol. 1, Hannover 1611), being ascribed by him to the Bolognese poet Giovanni Filoteo Achillini (1466–1538), author of the Viridario, a poem which has nothing in common with the Somnium viridarii.

Criticism. Nicolas Jorga: Philippe de Mézières et la croisade au XIVe siècle (594 p., Paris 1896), very elaborate study. Karl Young: Philippe de Mézières'

[8] Peter of Thomas, not "St. Peter Thomas." Peter was regarded in Cyprus as a saint, but was not actually canonized. He was born in Salignac de Thomas, Dordogne, about the turn of the century, and assumed the Carmelite habit at Condom (Gers), Gascony. He attained some fame as a teacher of Scotist theology, writing the De conceptu entis and Formalitates (princeps Venice 1515); from 1354, however, his career was that of a prelate and church diplomat. Innocent VI (pope 1352–62) appointed him successively bishop of Patti and Lipari in Sicily, of Coron in Morea, archbishop of Crete, Latin patriarch of Constantinople (Petrus III, 1362–66), apostolic legate to the whole East. He was wounded at the sack of Alexandria in 1365 and died in Famagusta on January 6, 1366. Chevalier (col. 3750, 1907), containing various inaccuracies. Atiya (p. 129–35, 1938).

dramatic office for the presentation of the Virgin (Publications of the Modern Language Association of America 26, 181–234, 1911). Alfred Coville: Evrart de Trémaugon et le Songe du verger (84 p., Paris 1933), ascribing authorship of the Songe, both the Latin text and the free French version, to Evrart de Trémaugon, royal counselor, bishop of Dol, professor in the Faculté de décret, Paris 1369–74; this is not convincing, but one thing is certain, Oresme was not the author (Bibliothèque de l'Ecole des chartes 94, 129–30, 1933). Ilya Golenishchev-Kutuzov: Etude sur le Livre de la vertu du sacrement de mariage et réconfort des dames mariées de Philippe de Mézières, d'après un MS du XIVe siècle de la Bibliothèque nationale à Paris (75 p., Belgrade 1937). That book was written c. 1384–89. Atiya (p. 128–54, 1938). R. E. Pike: St. Thomas Aquinas and the Songe du vergier (Speculum 14, 492, 1939). Philip Ainsworth Means: Newport tower (p. 215–18, New York 1942; Isis 34, 276).

A5. England

WYCLIFFE

John Wycliffe. English theologian and reformer, the "Morning star of the Reformation" (d. 1384).

John Wycliffe (or Wiclif, Wyclif) was born near Richmond, Yorkshire, c. 1324 (for he was 60 when he died). He studied in Oxford, was a master of Balliol by c. 1360, and became a parish priest. In 1366 he was appointed one of the king's chaplains; in 1372, doctor of theology; in 1374, one of the English commissioners to negotiate with the pope's representatives in Bruges.

Wycliffe's antipapal feelings at the beginning were, like those of his countrymen, mainly due to Urban V's insistence upon the payment of the contributions promised by king John in 1213. After 1374 they became more deliberate and violent, and he went so far as to call the pope (Gregory XI) Antichrist. Gregory XI issued five bulls against him and instituted proceedings to condemn him as a follower of the heretics Marsiglio of Padua and John of Jandun. These proceedings and the breaking out of the Great Schism (which seemed to prove that the papal election was not determined by God) completed Wycliffe's conversion into an open enemy of the papacy and of the established church. In 1381 he attacked the church's fundamental doctrine on the Eucharist. The Peasants' Revolt, occurring at that very time (perhaps somewhat influenced by Wycliffe's sermons, but generally due to much deeper causes, e.g., economic ones and the Black Death), turned the English hierarchy (social and religious) more strongly against him.[9] At the synod convoked by the archbishop of Canterbury in 1382[10] his doctrines were condemned, his main heresies being (1) denial of transubstantiation, (2) apostolic poverty, (3) that oral confession is not necessary in articulo mortis, (4) that the English church should be autocephalous like the Orthodox churches. Wycliffe defended himself, showing that his views were not as extreme as that, yet further teaching was forbidden him by order of Richard II, and he withdrew to his rectory at Lutterworth (Leicestershire, near Rugby). He died there on December 31, 1384. The fight against him continued, his writings were suppressed, and the council of Constance ordered that his remains be disinterred and cast out; this order was

[9] It was at that time that the Oxford chancellor and proctors became "ex officio" inquisitores hereticae pravitatis.

[10] Wycliffe called that synod the earthquake council because it took place during the earthquake of 1382, May 21, the center being in Canterbury. Charles Davison: History of British earthquakes (p. 330, Cambridge 1924; Isis 8, 628).

carried out in 1428 by his former disciple Richard Fleming, bishop of Lincoln.[11]

Wycliffe's Latin and English writings are so abundant that we shall not enumerate them. His English works entitle him to be considered the founder of English prose.

He and his associates produced two English versions of the Bible from the Latin Vulgate. The early version was completed toward the end of his lifetime (c. 1382-84); the later version was completed after his death, before the end of the century. It is difficult, if not impossible, to determine his own share in the work. It is probable that the early version of the Old Testament was partly made by Nicholas of Hereford (DNB 40, 418). The later version, at once more accurate and idiomatic than the early one, was largely the work of Wycliffe's faithful disciple John Purvey (1353?-1428?, DNB 47, 51). This was the earliest complete English version. In spite of the ecclesiastical opposition to the English Scriptures which began in 1391, and climaxed in the forbiddance of reading them under pain of excommunication (1406) or under pain of forfeiture of life and property (1414), they were very popular, as is proved by the survival of some 170 MSS.

Wycliffe's other English works include 294 sermons (in addition to 224 Latin ones), a good many controversial writings, also explanations of religious duties, etc. None of these English writings directly concern the historian of science. The Latin writings are more important, e.g., the Logica, and Logicae continuatio, De compositione hominis, XIII Quaestiones logicae et philosophicae, Summa de ente. His main controversial writing was the Trialogus, in which he defended the superiority of Bible over Church, and of individual conscience over public authority. This was his first work to be printed, being edited in 1525 by no less a person than Otto Brunfels (d. 1534), one of the fathers of the botanic renaissance.[12] In the De veritate Sacrae Scripturae Wycliffe insists that the Bible is the true foundation of Christian faith and morality, and should be accepted literally. His abundant controversial writings are devoted to the defense of civil and individual rights against papal and ecclesiastical power.

Wycliffe was a Platonist and a moderate realist of the Scotist type; his views were somewhat modified by Occam's influence, but too sharp a definition of them is irrelevant, for he was not a philosopher, but rather a theologian and a reformer. He was the first great forerunner of the Reformation. General dissatisfaction with the Avignonese popes (not only in England but also on the Continent) had provoked increasing criticism of the pope's temporal power. Wycliffe did not stop there, but criticized the pope's spiritual authority. He was not simply a religious reformer, but also a social one, defending utopian ideas of nonresistance, communism, and anarchy. He was one of the very few mediaeval thinkers, if not the only one, who refused to justify serfdom.[13] These social ideas were spread by the Lollards and naturally challenged opposition. The accession of the duke of Lancaster to the throne in 1399 (Henry IV) marked the beginning of a fierce persecution not only of the Lollards, but also of Wycliffite tendencies of every kind. Thus was the first reformation defeated, together with the social dreams wherewith it was entangled. It should be added that Wycliffe's thoughts were pedantic,

[11] Condemned in 1409 for Wycliffism; bishop of Lincoln 1420; died 1431 (DNB 19, 282). Excommunication of the dead was by no means uncommon or novel, but ecclesiastical opinion as to its legitimacy and expediency varied from time to time; see Henry Charles Lea: Studies in church history (p. 253-55, Philadelphia 1869).

[12] It was printed in March 1525, probably in Basel. Copy in Boston Public Library (More books, May 1944, p. 205).

[13] St. Thomas Aquinas did justify it (Introd. 2, 916).

confused, often contradictory; his power of persuasion was due more to the eagerness of the listeners, that is, to the timeliness of his message, than to his own eloquence. The new ideals were driven underground, but as their social and religious causes continued to act, the ideals themselves were bound to reappear. They were presently reincarnated in Jan Hus and Jerome of Prague and consecrated by their martyrdom (1415, 1416). The Reformation was then finally completed by Martin Luther a century later. Thus ideals which germinated in England were incubated in Bohemia and reached their maturity in Germany.

This requires a word of explanation. How did Wycliffian ideas reach Bohemia? Four groups of facts ought to be taken into account:

(1) Anne of Bohemia, daughter of the emperor Charles IV, became the queen of Richard II in 1382; many Bohemians came to England in her train and eventually returned home loaded with English ideas. It has often been said that Anne herself had been influenced by Wycliffe; there is no proof of that, but she read the Gospels not only in Latin, but also in Czech and German. The remarkably large number of Wycliffian MSS in Vienna and Prague is partly due to her Bohemian entourage. She was born in Prague 1360 and died of the plague at Shene (Richmond) 1394.

(2) Adalbertus Ranco ab Ericinio (Voytěch Raňkův z Ježova), supposed to be one of the most learned Czechs of his time and a friend of Thomas Štitný, studied in Paris, was rector of the university in 1355, studied also in Oxford. He died in 1388, having willed his library to the monastery of Břevnov, and founded scholarships in Paris and Oxford for Bohemian students. Many Bohemian students came to Oxford from Paris; some, like Jerome of Prague (1374-1416),[13a] Hus' disciple, came to Oxford directly from Prague. Robert F. Young: Bohemian scholars and students at the English universities from 1347 to 1750 (English historical review 38, 72-84, 1923).

(3) Wycliffe's books began to circulate in Prague at the beginning of the fifteenth century. The treatise De libris haereticorum legendis which Jan Hus wrote c. 1410 was mainly a defense of Wycliffe. It was dedicated to John Stokes, member of an embassy sent to Bohemia by Henry IV, Bolingbroke (king of England 1399-1413).

(4) The main group of facts concerns Hus' own personality and his peculiar susceptibility to Wycliffian ideals because these existed or were re-created subconsciously in his own mind. There was in him, as in his English predecessor, the same combination of radicalism in religion and politics with realism (Scotism) in philosophy.

Wycliffe referred to an earthquake in 1381 (Op. min. p. 357), "Visus est in Anglia . . . et perceptus est per alia multa loca." This is very probably the earthquake which was felt in England, not in 1381, but May 21-24, 1382.

Text. The earliest book to be printed was the Trialogus or Dialogorum libri quatuor, edited by Otto Brunfels (Basel 1525) and often reprinted. Latest edition by Gotthard Lechler: Trialogus cum supplemento trialogi. Illum recensuit, hoc primum edidit, utrumque commentario critico instruxit (Oxford 1869). The Wyclif Society founded at Oxford in 1882 prepared and published editions of most of the Latin writings; some 35 vols., the last of which appeared in 1922. The Society was dissolved in 1924. James Pounder Whitney: A note on the work of

[13a] Jerome of Prague was at Oxford in 1398 and made copies of Wycliffe's Dialogus and Trialogus (R. F. Young, p. 72).

the Wyclif Society (Essays in history presented to Reginald Lane Poole p. 98–114, Oxford 1927). I quote only the main titles:

Michael Henry Dziewicki: Tractatus de logica (3 vols., London 1893–99); Miscellanea philosophica (2 vols., London 1902–5); De ente librorum duorum excerpta (386 p., London 1909).

Rudolf Buddensieg: De veritate Sacrae Scripturae (3 vols., London 1905–7).

Johann Loserth: Tractatus de potestate papae (472 p., London 1907); Opera minora (522 p., London 1913). Loserth edited all together 13 vols. for the Wyclif Society.

S. Harrison Thomson: Summa de ente, libri primi tractatus primus et secundus (155 p., Oxford 1930; Isis 24, 212).

Passing to the English works, the most important is the English Bible, first edited by Rev. Josiah Forshall and Sir Frederic Madden (4 vols., Oxford 1850).

Thomas Arnold: Select English works (3 vols., Oxford 1869–71). Frederic David Matthew: English works hitherto unprinted (Early English Text Society no. 74, 632 p., London 1880). Herbert E. Winn: Select English writings (Oxford 1929).

Criticism. Walter Waddington Shirley: Catalogue of the original works of Wiclif (Oxford 1865), revised edition by Loserth (London 1924). Henry Legouis: Essai sur le réformation de Wiclef (thèse, Strasbourg 1865). Gotthard Victor Lechler: Wiclif und die Vorgeschichte der Reformation (2 vols., Leipzig 1873), partially Englished by Peter Lorimer (2 vols., London 1878). Poole (1920), ch. X deals with Wycliffe's doctrine of dominion. George Macaulay Trevelyan: England in the age of Wycliffe (London 1899). Hastings Rashdall (DNB 63, 202–23, 1900), one of the longest articles in DNB, 21 p. Josiah Woodward Leeds: Wiclif's anti-war views (12 p., Philadelphia 1901). Dietrich Heine: Wiclif's Lehre vom Güterbesitz (58 p., Gütersloh 1903). John Charles Carrick: Wycliffe and the Lollards (349 p., Edinburgh 1908). Emma Curtiss Tucker: The later version of the Wycliffite Epistle to the Romans compared with the Latin original (Yale studies in English no. 49, 213 p., New Haven 1914). Henry John Wilkins: Was Wycliffe a negligent pluralist? Also John of Trevisa, his life and works (London 1915). Samuel Parkes Cadman: The three religious leaders at Oxford, John Wycliffe, John Wesley, John Henry Newman (614 p., New York 1916).

Johann Loserth: Wicliffs Sendschreiben, Flugschriften und kleinere Werke kirchenpolitischen Inhalts (Akad. der Wissenschaften, phil. Kl., vol. 166, 96 p., Vienna 1910); Wiclif und Guilelmus Peraldus,[13b] Studien zur Geschichte der Entstehung von Wiclifs Summa theologiae (ibid. vol. 180, 101 p., 1916).

Bernard Lord Manning: The people's faith in the time of Wyclif (212 p., Cambridge 1919). Margaret Deanesly: The Lollard Bible and other medieval Biblical versions (Cambridge 1920). Herbert B. Workman (ERE 12, 812–23, 1922); Wyclif. A study of the English medieval church (2 vols., 830 p., Oxford 1926), important. Wells (ch. 12, 1926), consult also many supplements. S. Harrison Thomson: Some Latin works erroneously ascribed to Wyclif (Speculum 3, 382–91, 1928); Three unprinted opuscula (Speculum 3, 248–53, 1928); A lost chapter of Wyclif's Summa de ente (Speculum 4, 339–46, 1929); The order of writing of Wyclif's philosophical works (22 p., Prague 1929). Flick (1, 347–57, 1930). I. H. Stein: Another lost chapter of Wyclif's Summa de ente (Speculum 8, 254–55, 1933); An unpublished fragment of Wyclif's Confessio (Speculum 8, 503–10, 1933). S. Harrison Thomson: Unnoticed MSS and works of Wyclif (Journal of theological

[13b] Guillaume Pérault or Perrault, born in Peyraud, Vivarais (dépt. Ardèche), assumed the Dominican habit in Paris or Lyon, died in 1260. His main work is a Summa virtutum et vitium represented by many MSS, incunabula, and later editions; the exact bibliography is difficult because of confusion with other works bearing similar titles. HL (19, 307–16, 1838). NBG (39, 555, 1862). Chevalier (col. 3573, 1907). Introd. (2, 58, 925, 927).

studies 38, 24–36, 139–48, 1937). Ernest William Talbert: The date of the composition of the English Wyclifite collection of sermons (Speculum 12, 464–74, 1937). Coulton: Medieval panorama (p. 485–92, 1938). Atiya (p. 188, 1938), apropos of Wycliffe's strong opposition to the crusade, which he considered a kind of brigandage. Aubrey Gwynn (S.J.): The English Austin friars in the time of Wyclif (London 1940). Charles C. Butterworth: The literary lineage of the King James Bible, 1340–1611 (406 p., University of Pennsylvania, Philadelphia 1941). Joseph H. Dahmus: Further evidence for the spelling Wyclyf (Speculum 16, 224–25, 1941). S. Harrison Thomson: Cultural relations of Bohemia with Western Europe before the White Mountain, 1620 (Bull. Polish Institute of Arts and Sciences 2, 298–314, New York 1944).

On the Joachimite sources of Wycliffe see Introd. 2, 332–33, and by index; and W. Beveridge (ERE 7, 566–67, 1915).

A6. Germany

GELNHAUSEN

Conrad von Gelnhausen. German publicist (d. 1390).

Gelnhausen is the name of a place in the Wetterau, i.e., the valley of the Wetter, not far from Frankfurt, in the grand duchy of Hesse. Conrad son of Siegfried probably came from that place. Nothing is known of his life until the time of his determinatio (B.A.) in Paris 1344; he obtained the licentia docendi within the same year. Later he was canon in Mainz. About 1368 he went to Bologna to study canon law, and he obtained his doctorate in law there c. 1375. Later he went to Paris, where he celebrated his inceptio (M.A.) in 1378. His main writings were composed in Paris 1379–80. After the death of Charles the Wise (September 16, 1380), the French state more violently defended the Avignonese pope (Clement VII), and the Urbanists or neutrals were obliged to leave the university. Again we lose trace of Gelnhausen, but we find him in Heidelberg 1386, when a new university was founded there by the palsgrave (count palatine) Rupert I. The latter was a partisan of Urban VI. Gelnhausen was at the new university from the very beginning, together with Marsilius van Inghen; Marsilius was its first rector and Gelnhausen its first chancellor (i.e., Urban's representative in the granting of the licentia). Gelnhausen died in Heidelberg on April 13, 1390.

Gelnhausen is important as the first great defender, we might almost call him the founder, of the conciliar theory; one of the main actors of the drama which ended only with the council of Constance in 1414–18. To be sure, he was influenced by earlier men, such as John of Paris, or, nearer to him, Marsiglio of Padua and William Occam.

He wrote a few lectures on the Sentences, questions, a commentary on the Song of Solomon, and a letter dated 1379 to Philippe de Mézières (1327–1405), but he is chiefly remembered because of two treatises wherein he explained his means of healing the Great Schism. The first is the Epistola prima, or brevis (dated August 31, 1379), in which he declared the necessity of a general council as the only means of deciding between Urban and Clement, and cited a number of precedents. The council provides the only way of avoiding a schism. He discussed the composition of the council, the method of convocation, etc. The second is the Epistola concordiae (May 1380), addressed to Charles the Wise; it is a more elaborate treatment of the same question; in fact, the most elaborate defense of what was called later the conciliar theory, except that in his opinion the convocation of a council should be restricted to extraordinary emergencies, such as the coexistence of two popes.

One of these was the true pope, but only by means of a general council, summoned by other authorities, could the true pope be determined and canonic difficulties solved.

Text. The letter to Philippe de Mézières was edited by L. Schmitz: Ein Brief Konrads von Gelnhausen aus dem Jahre 1379 (Römische Quartalschrift für christliche Altertumskunde 9, 185-89, 1895).

Epistola prima. Edited by Hans Kaiser: Der "kurze Brief" (Historische Vierteljahrschrift 3, 379-94, 1900).

Epistola concordiae. Edited by Edm. Martène and Ursinus Durand: Thesaurus novus anecdotorum (2, col. 1200-26, Paris 1717).

Criticism. August Kneer: Die Entstehung der konziliaren Theorie. Zur Geschichte des Schismas und der kirchenpolitischen Schriftsteller Konrad von Gelnhausen und Heinrich von Langenstein (Römische Quartalschrift für christliche Altertumskunde, suppt. no. 1, 145 p., Roma 1893). David E. Culley: Konrad von Gelnhausen. Sein Leben, seine Werke und seine Quellen (Leipzig thesis, 105 p., Halle a.S. 1913). Flick (vol. 1, 1930).

A7. Bohemia

MILIČ

Milič of Kremsier. Bohemian reformer (d. 1374).

Charles IV had, c. 1358, invited Conrad Waldhauser, an Augustinian canon of Upper Austria, who was then preaching in Vienna, to come and preach in Bohemia. Conrad obeyed the king's command and preached in the Teyn church, in Prague, gaining considerable influence over the people who understood German or Latin. His teaching was orthodox, but he became obnoxious to the Dominicans and the Augustinians. After Conrad's death (Prague 1369), his work was continued by a Moravian disciple, Milič, who became rector of the Teyn.

Milič was born at an unknown date of humble parents, probably at Kremsier (in Moravia, not very far from Olmütz on the same river March). He took orders c. 1350, became an archdeacon and canon in St. Vitus, the cathedral of Prague, and was employed in the chancery of Charles IV. Under Conrad's influence, he gave up his prebends and started a campaign of popular preaching in Bohemian, in Bishof-Teinitz and also in Prague. He denounced the corruption of the people, especially of the clerks and monks. The poverty and evils which he witnessed everywhere incensed him to such an extent that he was led to believe in the impending end of the world and apparition of the Antichrist c. 1365-67. Having called Charles IV "antichrist" to his face, he was thrown into prison, then released upon the king's order. In 1367, he traveled to Rome, ahead of Urban V, resumed his comminatory and apocalyptic preachings, and was imprisoned in the Franciscan monastery together with his friend Theodoric the hermit. Soon after his arrival Urban V caused them to be delivered, and they returned to Prague, where Milič continued his missionary and philanthropic activities. In 1374 Milič traveled to Avignon to defend himself before the curia. He died in Avignon, probably in June 1374.

His writings were ordered to be burned by Zbyněk Zajík z Hasenburka, archbishop of Prague from 1403 to 1411, hence only a few of them have come down to us, e.g., the Libellus de Antichristo and the Postilla. The Bohemian work "of the great torments of the Holy Church," often ascribed to him, was written by master John of Přibram.

Text. De praedicatoribus qui revelant Antichristum et de multitudine ipsorum successiva, edited by Konstantin Höfler: Geschichtsschreiber der husitischen Bewegung (2, 40–46, Wien 1865).

Apologia Conradi Waldhauser (ibid. 2, 17–39, 1865).

Criticism. The famous Bohemian Jesuit Aloys Boleslas Balbinus (1621–88) included an impartial biography of Milič in his Miscellanea historica regni Bohemiae (Prague 1679 ff.). My own information is almost exclusively derived from Franz Lützow: History of Bohemian literature (1899; reprinted 1907; p. 59–63).

On Conrad Waldhauser see Reusch (ADB 40, 700, 1896).

MATTHEW OF JANOV

Matthew son of Wenceslav of Janov. Bohemian reformer, precursor of Jan Hus (d. 1393).

Matthias de Janova, magister parisiensis. Matthew originated probably in Janov near Tabor in Bohemia. He was strongly moved by Milič; left Prague before the latter's death (1374), and studied six years in Paris, where he obtained his master's degree. He then traveled to Rome and Nuremberg and returned to Prague. In 1381 he became a canon of St. Vitus, in that city, and continued a canon until his death twelve years later.

He shared Milič's ardent desire for reform, but, the Great Schism (1378) having stultified all hopes of reform from the pope's initiative, he began to entertain more radical views, a return to primitive Christianity. He denounced the excessive cult of images ("idolatry") and of relics, and the belief in the intercession of saints, and even claimed the people's right to read the Bible and to partake of the sacrament frequently in both kinds (sub utraque specie). In 1388 he was condemned by a synod of the archdiocese of Prague, obliged to recant, and suspended from the right to conduct services in his church for six months.

He composed various theological writings, chiefly in Latin but also in Bohemian; the latter were systematically destroyed and none are extant. He collected his Latin works under the title Regulae Veteris et Novi Testamenti. One of them (Regulae, book III end), De abominatione in loco sacro, was formerly ascribed to Wycliffe and also to Hus. Other short writings of his were probably included in the Hus opera. Indeed, he was in many respects a forerunner of Hus, though he lacked the latter's heroism.

Text. De regulis Veteris et Novi Testamenti. The first three books were edited by Vlastimil Kybal in Monumenta reformationis in Bohemia saec. xiv et xv, no. 13 (4 large vols., Innsbrück 1908–13); book IV is edited in the same series by Otakar Odložilík (vol. 5, Czech Academy, Prague 1926); book V (6th and last vol.) was announced for early publication, in 1929 (Speculum 4, 357–58), but work on it was brutally interrupted by German hostilities.

De sacramento altaris ex tractatu de venerabili eukaristia contra Nicolaum de Pelzimov episcopum Taboritarum. Edited by Konstantin Höfler: Geschichtsschreiber der husitischen Bewegung (2, 46, Wien 1865). This is an extract from the Regulae quoted by Jan Příbram in his article against Nicolaus de Pelhrimov.

Criticism. Potthast (p. 780, 1896). Franz Lützow: History of Bohemian literature (p. 79–85, 1899, reprinted 1907). Vlastimil Kybal: Les origines du mouvement hussite en Bohême. Matthias de Ianov (Revue historique 103, 1–31, 1910). Flick (1, 362, 1930). I am indebted to Dr. O. Odložilík for information concerning this note (letter of Nov. 4, 1940).

ŠTITNÝ

Thomas of Štitný. Bohemian moralist, theologian, reformer; one of the fathers of Bohemian literature (c. 1330–1401).

Thomas was born at Štitný in southern Bohemia in 1330 or 1331. He studied at the University of Prague but did not obtain any degree, and about 1360 returned to Štitný, managed the family estate, and married. In 1381, having lost his wife and children (except the daughter Anežka, who survived him), he returned to Prague. He died in 1401. After his death, Anežka may have been in touch with Jan Hus, though it is not necessary to postulate that in order to explain the transmission of Štitný's spirit to his great successor.

Thomas of Štitný's main originality was his use of the Bohemian language instead of Latin for the discussion of lofty subjects, such as ethics or theology. This was quite shocking to the scholastic minds of that time, to whom the use of Bohemian (or any other vernacular) was a kind of desecration of the subject dealt with. Thomas held that the common people should be able to read the Bible in their own language, and he claimed the right and duty to discuss religion in Bohemian, even as St. Paul spoke Hebrew to the Jews and Greek to the Greeks. He was influenced by mystical writings such as the Paradisus animae of Albert the Great, then already available in Bohemian, and by the preaching (also in Bohemian) of Milič of Kremsier. All of which explains the development of his thought, comparable to the contemporary development of the devotio moderna in Holland, and in other respects to the thought of his older contemporary Wycliffe (d. 1384). Indeed, Thomas did not hesitate to denounce the shortcomings of the clergy and to insist upon the urgent need of reform; however, he remained perfectly orthodox. He was, before Hus, the main creator of philosophical and theological terminology in his mother tongue.

His first writings (c. 1370) were translations of St. Augustine and St. Bonaventura. His first great work was the collection of six books on general Christian matters, first completed in 1376, but rewritten four times; the final version, entitled Books of Christian instruction, was completed only a year before his death. The six books treat, respectively, (I) Faith, hope, and love; (II) Virgins, widows, married life. Sexual ethics wisely discussed; of course, virginity was his ideal; (III) The master of a family, the mistress, the household. Domestic ethics and economy. This chapter contains interesting information on the family life of the Bohemian gentry in the fourteenth century; (IV) How the nine orders of people compare with the nine orders of angels; (V) How the devil tempts us; (VI) Purification from our sins.

Thomas' second great work, written under Wenceslas (Wácslaw IV, king of Bohemia 1378–1419), is the Řeči besedni (Learned entertainments), also called Rozmluvy nábožné (Religious conversations), a treatise on God in the form of a dialogue between father and son. It is generally considered his masterpiece. The theology and philosophy are not original, but eclectic, in the spirit of scholastic realism. One of the best parts deals with krása (beauty), that is, "the wisdom of God as it is shown to us in the beauty and splendor of creation." Thomas wrote this treatise in this form in order to enable Bohemian parents better to educate their children.

In 1392, he put together a collection of Discourses for Sundays and fast days. His last work was a translation of St. Birgitta's visions. Birgitta's influence upon him toward the end of his life has been compared by a Bohemian critic to the influence of Christina Ponatovská on Komenský (Joannes Amos Comenius, 1592–1671) a little less than three centuries later.

Text. Critical edition of General Christian matters by Karel Jaromir Erben (1811–1870) in 1852; this includes a biography of Štitný.

First complete edition of the Reči besedni by Martin Hattala in 1897.

Criticism. Franz Lützow: History of Bohemian literature (1899; again 1907; p. 63–79). H. Jelinek: Histoire de la littérature tchèque (Paris 1930).

A8. SWEDEN

ST. BIRGITTA

St. Bridget of Sweden (c. 1303–73). If the form "Bridget" is used it is well to call her St. Bridget of Sweden, to avoid confusion with St. Bridget of Ireland (more correctly Brigid, c. 451–525); we shall call her Birgitta.

Daughter of Birger Persson, lagman (i.e., governor and judge) of Upland and cousin of the reigning king, and of Ingeborg Bengtsdotter, daughter of princess Sigrid the Beautiful. Birger was one of the most important men in Sweden; he codified the laws of his province. Birgitta was born c. 1303; after her mother's death, c. 1315, she went to live with an aunt, wife of the lagman of Öster Götland. In 1316 she was married to Ulf Gudmarsson, who became also a lagman. Birgitta studied theology at the Dominican house of Skeninge. She and Ulf became tertiaries of St. Francis. When king Magnus Ericsson married Blanche of Namur, in 1335, Birgitta was appointed mistress of the household. Ulf and Birgitta went on a pilgrimage to the tomb of St. Olaf Haraldson (995–1030) in Nidaros (Trondhjem), and a little later, in 1341, they accomplished the greater pilgrimage to Santiago de Compostela. On the way back Ulf was taken ill, and he died in 1344 at the Cistercian monastery of Alvastra in Öster Götland. For a time Birgitta returned to Magnus' court, but her religious interests became gradually more and more important. Before long she gave herself entirely to asceticism and devotion. She had visions and Christ made special revelations to her. One of these revelations concerned the constitution of a new order, the Brigittines, for which she received a large endowment in Vadstena from the crown (1346). Vadstena (like Alvastra) is situated on the western shore of Lake Vettern.[14]

In 1349 Birgitta went to Rome with Peter Olafsson of Alvastra and Peter Olafsson of Skeninge and other Swedes. They witnessed the Jubilee of 1350, which had been promised by Clement VI in spite of the fact that the latter resided in Avignon, and took place in spite of the Black Death. Rome was now the center of Birgitta's activities until her death in that city on July 23, 1373. In that same year (or 1372) she had made her last pilgrimage, to the Holy Land. She was canonized by Boniface IX in 1391.

The Vadstena monastery was one of the greatest cultural centers of Scandinavia until the first quarter of the sixteenth century.

Birgitta's letters and revelations. Birgitta wrote to Urban V urging him to return to Rome (he did return in 1367, but not permanently). She also took a deep interest in the political situation in her country, and suffered when Magnus was deposed in 1363. Her main interest, however, was religious. She wrote down

[14] It was my privilege to make a pilgrimage to Vadstena in July 1934. The place is as beautiful as it is holy (Isis 23, 452).

(or dictated) in Swedish the revelations which she received from Christ. They were translated into Latin by her confessor, Peter Olafsson, prior of Alvastra, and by Matthias, canon (later bishop) of Linköping.[15] Later the Liber revelationum was carefully edited by Peter of Alvastra and by Alfonso da Vadaterra.[16] That book attained some popularity in mediaeval times. It was first printed in 1492 and often reprinted.

Here is a curious fact illustrating the mediaeval popularity of Birgitta's visions. Her vision of the Passion is included in an Aethiopic narrative, Dirsan mahyawi (Liber vivificans), for which see August Dillmann's catalogue of Aethiopic MSS in British Museum (no. 40, Add. 16,354). The knowledge of that vision and of others reached Abyssinia possibly through some Coptic channel. My attention was attracted to this fact by M. R. James (p. 150, 152, 1924).

St. Catherine of Sweden[17] (c. 1331–81). Catherina Vastanensis. Ulf and Birgitta had eight children, of whom Catherine (born in 1331 or 1332) was the fourth. Catherine was educated at the convent of Riseberg, and married at the age of 13 or 14 (as her mother had been). While in Rome with her mother, she heard of her husband's death in Sweden, and thenceforth she devoted herself entirely to religion. She accompanied her mother to the Holy Land in 1372/73. In 1374 she brought back her mother's body to Vadstena, the mother house of the Brigittine order, of which she was the first abbess. She obtained new papal confirmations of the order and completed its organization. She remained in Rome from 1375 to 1380, for that purpose and also to obtain her mother's canonization. She died soon after her return to Sweden, on March 24, 1381.

She was canonized in 1484 by Innocent VIII.

The Brigittines. The Order of the Brigittines, or Order of Saint Saviour, was founded by Birgitta at Vadstena in 1346. The organization included adjoining but separate houses for monks and nuns, using the same chapel; the abbess was the temporal head of both houses, but the spiritual direction was naturally wielded by the monk who was confessor general. Reading and study were encouraged. The main purpose was contemplation and devotion. Birgitta obtained a confirmation of the new rule from Urban V in 1370; Catherine obtained other confirmations from Gregory XI in 1377 and from Urban VI in 1379. Catherine was the first abbess or "sovereign" of the order, in 1375. Within a century the Brigittines were spread all over Europe. For further history of the order, e.g., for the creation of the Fratres ordinis Salvatoris novissimi in 1622, see article by Francesca M. Steele (CE 2, 785–87, 1907).

Memories of St. Birgitta and St. Catherine in Rome. When Birgitta first arrived in Rome she lived near S. Lorenzo in Damaso (now within the Palazzo della cancelleria); after her pilgrimage to the Holy Land she occupied a house in the Piazza Farnese, and died there a few months later. She often visited the Poor Clares near S. Lorenzo in Panisperna, and her body was exposed in the church of Panisperna before being translated to Vadstena under the guidance of her daughter Catherine.

When Catherine returned to Rome in 1375 she occupied her mother's cell in the house of the Poor Clares of Panisperna, and Catherine of Siena came to see her there.

[15] At her request Matthias of Linköping also translated the Pentateuch into Swedish.

[16] Alfonso da Vadaterra, sometime bishop of Jaen, was an Augustinian Hermit (d. Genoa 1388). He was Birgitta's confessor, and also a counselor of St. Catherine of Siena.

[17] It is well to add "of Sweden," to distinguish her from her contemporary St. Catherine of Siena (1347–80).

The memory of St. Birgitta is kept alive in other Roman churches, Santa Maria Maggiore, S. Prassede, S. Paolo, the basilica of S. Lorenzo, S. Antonio Abbate, S. Sebastiano, S. Francesco a Ripa.

Text. The bibliography of the early Brigittine publications is very complicated; as far as the incunabula are concerned, a full account will be found in GW (4, 214-34, i.e. nos. 4362-4401, 1930). I give only a few indications.

The first complete editions of the Revelationes appeared in Lübeck 1492[18] and Nürnberg 1500, but extracts had been published in Low German in Lübeck 1478 or before, etc. The two editions of 1492 and 1500 include prefaces by Matthias de Suecia and by Joannes de Turrecremata (John of Torquemada, 1388-1468), and the Vita abbreviata S. Birgittae. The Vita was composed soon after her death in 1373 by Petrus Olavi (Peter Olafsson) confessor vadstenensis and Petrus Olavi alvastrensis. It was as frequently reprinted as the Revelations themselves.

A. Heuser: Revelationes selectae (351 p., Cologne 1851).

Heliga Birgittas uppenbarelser, efter gamla handskrifter utgifna af Gustaf Edvard Klemming (5 vols., Stockholm 1857-84). Robert Geete: Nio kapitel ur H. Birgittas uppenbarelser nedskrifna omkring år 1385 (24 p., Stockholm 1901).

William Patterson Cumming: The revelations of St. Birgitta. Edited from the fifteenth century MS in Princeton (Early English Text Society, 175 p., London 1929; Isis 23, 450-52). This Middle English version, written before 1475, follows closely the Latin text. A life of Birgitta was written in English by Thomas Gascoigne (1403-58); this was edited by John Henry Blunt: The myroure of Oure Ladye (Early English Text Society, p. xlvii-lix, London 1873).

Isak Collijn: Acta et processus canonizacionis beate Birgitte (747 p., Uppsala 1924-31; Isis 23, 450-52). The same scholar has published a facsimile edition of the best MS of these Acta, the Codex holmiensis A 14 (formerly in Vadstena), with an introduction in Swedish and French (Stockholm 1920; Isis 23, 450-52).

Isak Collijn: Iconographia birgittina typographica. Birgitta och Katherina i medeltida bildtryck (2 parts, Stockholm 1915-18; Isis 23, 450-52).

Criticism. J. P. Kirsch (CE 2, 782, 1907; 3, 448, 1908). Knut Bernhard Westman: Birgitta studier (320 p., Uppsala 1911). R. Steffen: Birgitta Birgersdotter (Svenskt biografiskt lexikon 4, 447-62, Stockholm 1924), with elaborate bibliography, p. 459-62. Isak Collijn: Birgittinska gestalter. Forskningar i italienska arkiv och bibliotek (146 p., 5 pl., Stockholm 1929; Isis 23, 450-52). Edith Peacey (a nun of the Brigittine order): Saint Birgitta of Sweden. With a foreword by the countess of Iddesleigh (300 p., 1 pl., 1933; Isis 23, 580), a popular account but well done, with care and moderation. Conrad Bergendoff: A critic of the fourteenth century, St. Birgitta (Mediaeval and historiographical studies in honor of James Westfall Thompson p. 3-18, 1938; Isis 29, 142). Claude H. Christensen: Scandinavian libraries (p. 504 in J. W. Thompson 1939), apropos of the Vadstena library. Johannes Jørgensen: Den hellige Birgitta af Vadstena, vol. 1 (1303-49) (270 p., ill., Copenhagen 1941), in Danish; Swedish review in Lychnos (7, 308, 1942); vol. 2 (1349-73) (304 p., ill., Copenhagen 1943). Swedish translation (2 vols., Stockholm 1944; Lychnos 9, 332-33, 1944-45).

A9. Netherlands

GROOTE

Geert Groote. Dutch father of the "moderna devotio" or "Christian renaissance" (1340-84).

[18] This edition was prepared at the expense of the Vadstena monastery, and two monks were sent to Lübeck to see it through the press (the relations between Sweden and Lübeck were very close). It contains a series of 23 admirable woodcuts. The Morgan library has a copy of it in a contemporary Lübeck binding (pl. xix, p. 79, 83, Pierpont Morgan Library, New York 1941).

Contents: (1) Groote's life. (2) His scientific views. (3) His philosophy and religion. (4) The Brothers and Sisters of the Common Life. (5) The Windesheim Canons. (6) The Imitation of Christ. (7) Groote's influence. The Christian renaissance.

(8) Text. (9) Criticism. (10) The Brothers of the Common Life and the Christian renaissance. (11) Imitatio Christi.

1. *Groote's life*

Gerrit or Geert (our Gerard) Groote or De Groote was born in October 1340, in Deventer, in the princely bishopric of Utrecht. His father was Werner Groote and his mother Heylwig van der Basselen, people of substance. He studied in Aachen, Cologne, Paris (1357–65), and even in Prague (1366). In 1366, he visited the curia in Avignon as a representative of the city of Deventer, and not long afterward he obtained canonries in Utrecht and Aachen. He had become acquainted in Paris with Henry of Calcar;[19] meeting him again in Utrecht, he was deeply influenced by him and was "converted" in 1374. He then resigned his two prebends and gave up the best part of his house to poor women. He spent some time in Monnikhuisen (1377–79) with his friend, but did not assume the Carthusian habit. As early as 1375, he had visited Ruysbroeck (XIV-1) in Groenendaal, and he visited him again various times afterward. Ruysbroeck's influence completed the determination of his life. In 1380, he was ordained deacon (he never became a priest) and obtained his bishop's permission to preach, and he preached all over the Low Countries; speaking in Latin to the clergy and in Dutch to the people. He was a fervent and stirring preacher, a "boetprediker" urging people to repentance. So much so, that he aroused hostility and was finally forbidden to continue (1383). He then withdrew into his house in Deventer, which was already the center of a religious community, and he died there of the plague on August 20, 1384.

2. *His scientific views*

Groote had obtained in Paris a good philosophic and scientific education; there is no evidence that he studied medicine, but he did study astronomy and astrology, and he even dabbled in magic. Soon after his return to Deventer (before his conversion) he fell dangerously ill, and he then renounced magic and nigromancy, and ordered his books on those subjects to be burned. In a letter which he wrote to master Ralph of Enteren he denounced the imposture of astrologers in general, and of Abū Ma'shar (IX-1) in particular. We may assume that his revulsion of feeling against magic was due to religious rather than scientific reasons.

3. *His philosophy and religion*

Though his main interest was religion, he was open-minded enough to appreciate pagan writers, such as Plato and Seneca. He loved books, and sometimes as many

[19] Heinrich Aeger, born in Calcar (in the circle of Cleve, lower Rhine district), studied and taught theology in Paris. Assumed the Carthusian habit in Cologne 1366, and in 1368 became prior of the Carthusian monastery of Monnikhuisen near Arnhem. Later he was prior of other monasteries, and finally visitor of his order in Picardy and Germany, and prior of the Cologne house. He wrote many books, chiefly devotional, and died in Cologne in 1408. Von Slee (ADB 15, 24, 1882). Calcar is familiar to historians of science, because it was the birthplace of Jan Stephan van Calcar (1499–1546), Vesalius' artistic collaborator. M. H. Spielmann: The iconography of Andreas Vesalius (p. 13–16, London 1925).

as five copyists were working for him. He wrote letters and devotional books, but it is not as an author that he is remembered, rather as the founder of a new form of devotion. He was less a reformer than revivalist. However, in his insistence on practical mysticism, on religious freedom, on the value of Scriptures in the vernacular, he anticipated evangelical tendencies. He followed a middle path, which might be called the Augustinian path, between scholasticism on the one hand, either Thomist or Scotist, and theoretical mysticism on the other. He had been influenced by Ruysbroeck, but assimilated only the more practical teachings of that master; he had little use for the German mystics, Eckhart, Tauler, and Suso. He preached a pure and simple Christian life among other men, not in seclusion from them; an active life rather than a contemplative one; contemplation without work, he thought, is only vacuity and delusion. He repeatedly denounced the main monastic evils: sexual immorality, simony, and above all indolence, whether physical or spiritual. This invited conflicts with the monastic orders, chiefly with the mendicant friars; on the other hand, it prepared the reformation of those orders.

Groote's religious and educational ideals were realized in three ways, which we shall consider presently: first, through the Brothers and Sisters of the Common Life; second, through the Augustinian Canons of Windesheim and affiliated communities; last not least, through the Imitation of Christ.

4. *The Brothers and Sisters of the Common Life*

After his conversion in 1374, Groote opened his house in Deventer to some poor women, and five years later drew up rules for them. Thus grew up in his house (Meester Geertshuis) the first community of Sisters of the Common Life. The formal organization of the Brothers and Sisters was completed only after Groote's death, very soon after, by his main disciple, Florens Radewijns.[20] The first real house of Brothers was the "House of Florentius" in 1391 (thus named after Florens, the first rector). The Nova domus or Domus pauperum was created also by Florens, in 1398, for poor clerks.

The Brothers (or Clerks and Brothers) of the Common life (or Lot) constituted a fraternity of clerics and laymen; the members were not obliged to take formal vows, but they lived together, sharing their means. The spirit was devotional and practical, not scholastic; in fact, the whole movement was a healthy reaction against scholasticism. The Brothers were tremendously interested in education: school teaching, the copying of manuscripts, and the promotion of learning by other methods were some of their primary aims. Though mainly restricted to the Trivium, their teaching was as modern as their devotion, for it was permeated by the new humanistic (vs. the scholastic) spirit. They laid great stress on grammar (Donatus, Priscian) and on classical literature (not simply Christian, but pagan as well).

5. *The Windesheim Canons*

As the Brothers and Sisters did not constitute a monastic order, regular monks and friars looked askance at them and sometimes persecuted them. This was one

[20] Florens Radewijns was born in Leerdam, near Utrecht, c. 1350. Studied in Prague, then came under Groote's influence in Deventer and was "converted" by him in 1380. He was a canon in Utrecht, and one of the clerici scriptores in Groote's house. He died in Deventer, March 24/25, 1400. Jan Hendrik Gerretsen: Florentius Radewijns (Utrecht thesis, 154 p., Nijmegen 1891). Brinkerink (Nieuw nederlandsch biografisch woordenboek 5, 556–57, Leiden 1921).

of the reasons which led to the creation of monasteries, having a definite constitution, but sharing the ideals of the Brothers and Sisters of the Common Life. This was recommended by Groote on his deathbed, and he designated Florens Radewijns as his successor. He selected the Augustinian rule because of its moderation. The first house of Augustinian Canons of the new observance[21] was opened in Windesheim, near Zwolle, Overijsel, in 1387. The Canons were mainly recruited from among the Brothers, for the two houses, Windesheim and Deventer, pursued the same purposes. The spirit of the devotio moderna was largely spread by these Canons Regular and others of similar houses, the golden age of their organization being the first half of the fifteenth century. The Canons wrote educational and devotional books, emended the Vulgate, translated parts of it. Their houses were soon considered model communities. They produced a great many manuscripts, some of which were beautifully illuminated. One of the greatest painters of the Netherlands, Hugo van der Goes (d. 1482), was developed in their house of Roodklooster (Rouge-cloître, in the forest of Soignes, near Brussels). One of the greatest canons, after Thomas a Kempis, was Johann Busch (1399–1480),[22] who wrote a chronicle of Windesheim and was one of the chief monastic reformers.

The first house of Canonesses was established at Diepenveen, near Deventer, in 1400, and Diepenveen became a center of monastic reform similar to Windesheim. The Canonesses' relation to the Sisters was very much the same as the Canons' relation to the Brothers. The diffusion of the Christian renaissance was much helped by these parallel movements which reached different groups of people.

6. *The Imitation of Christ*

The outstanding fruit of Groote's teaching and of the teachings of his brethren was the Imitatio Christi, which is one of the most precious books of world literature. There has been much discussion concerning its authorship. It has been ascribed to many doctors of the fifteenth century, including one of the most famous, the Frenchman Jean Gerson (1363–1429).[23] The bulk of the incunabula bear Gerson's name. It was almost certainly written in the period 1380–1424, probably toward the end of it (c. 1416–20), not by a Frenchman or an Italian, but by a Dutchman and by a Canon Regular. The author was a canon in the monastery of the Agnietenberg (Mt. St. Agnes) near Zwolle, named Thomas a Kempis (1380–1471).[24] This is confirmed by contemporary traditions, including an anonymous biography of Thomas written as early as 1488, printed in 1494.

There is no longer any doubt concerning Thomas' authorship, but there is still much discussion concerning the extent of his authorship, or, to put it otherwise, concerning his originality. True originality is obviously out of the question; Thomas would have been the first to deny original intentions. He represented not his views, but those of the new religion, the views of Groote and his disciples.

[21] The Augustinian Canons (Austin Canons, Canons Regular) were established soon after the Lateran Council of 1059; in 1339 Benedict XII centralized their organization (Introd. 1, 748).

[22] Nieuw nederlandsch biografisch woordenboek (6, 236–37, 1924).

[23] For the part played by Gabriel Naudé (1600–53) in that controversy, see James V. Rice: Naudé (p. 40, Baltimore 1939; Isis 35, 232).

[24] Thomas a Kempis, or Thomas Hemerken of Kempen, was born at Kempen, near Crefeld, c. 1380. He came to Deventer in 1392 and visited Radewijns, from whom he received every help, and by 1399 he was in Agnietenberg. He was ordained priest in 1412–13, and elected subprior in 1425. He died there in 1471.

It is probable that Thomas was not simply an editor, but an author, though his book is very likely to contain phrases or fragments due to Groote, Radewijns, Zerbolt, or others.

The Imitatio Christi is not simply one of the best books of Christian literature, but also the most popular, next to the Bible itself. It has been translated into more than fifty languages, and the MSS and editions of it are counted by the thousand. There is a very large collection of these editions in the Harvard library.

Though the author was naturally well acquainted with the religious literature, ancient and mediaeval, available in his days, the Imitatio was nevertheless something new, even as the devotio moderna, the spirit of which it expresses with great simplicity and clearness. It introduced a new spirit in mystical literature—nonscholastic, non-Platonic, practical, moderate, and luminous. These qualifications will be better appreciated if one bears in mind how often mystical writings have the opposite characteristics and are impractical, immoderate, and deliberately obscure.

7. *Groote's influence. The Christian renaissance*

The influence exerted by Groote and his disciples cannot be exaggerated. The Christian revival of which he was certainly the origin was for about a century and a half (say 1380–1520) a cultural stream of enormous importance. The fountainheads were in Deventer and Zwolle, but from them the stream passed to other cities of the Low Countries, and then to cities of other countries, such as Münster in Westphalia. The schools of the Brothers of the Common Life were in a way the first high (or secondary) schools, and hence answered a real need and prospered. By the middle of the fifteenth century, there were already some 150 of them in the Low Countries, Germany, and France. These schools were the best available until the creation of the Jesuit schools, partly modeled upon them, in 1542.

The influence of the Canons was equally great, for they produced a large proportion of the religious and pedagogical books used in the fifteenth and sixteenth centuries, and one of them, the Imitatio Christi, has remained and will always be one of the perennial best sellers of world literature.

As the Brothers had for a long time a kind of monopoly of secondary teaching, they influenced, directly or indirectly, more men of distinction than can be enumerated. Let us mention Nicholas of Cusa (1401–64), Rudolph Agricola (1443–85), the Dutch pope Adrian VI (b. Utrecht 1459, pope 1522–23), Erasmus (1467–1536).

Martin Luther (1483–1546) expressed his indebtedness to Groote and Zerbolt, and St. Ignatius Loyola (1491–1556) placed the Imitation above all other books except the Scriptures. We may say that the Christian renaissance influenced deeply the Counter-Reformation as well as the Reformation itself.

8. *Text*

A complete edition of Groote's works (chiefly letters and sermons) was announced in 1911 as being planned by the Thomas à Kempis Vereeniging. Another edition was begun by George Richard Potter and his wife, but discontinued; they handed over their materials to W. Mulder, of Nijmegen (letter from professor Potter dated Sheffield, Feb. 15, 1938).

Gerardi Magni Epistolae, quas ad fidem codicum recognovit annotavit edidit Willelmus Mulder (414 p., Antwerp 1933). Supersedes previous collections, contains 75 letters of the years 1374–84, 2 of them hitherto unpublished; well indexed.

Frid. Guil. Pistoth. Schoepff: Gerardi Magni sermonis de focaristis et notoriis fornicatoribus pars prior (Aurora, sive Bibliotheca selecta ex scriptis eorum qui ante Lutherum ecclesiae studuerunt restituendae, 5, 42-67, notes 70-76, Dresden 1859).

9. *Criticism*

Thomas a Kempis: Vita Gerardi Magni, earliest printed edition, Nuremberg 1492/94. Critical edition by Henry Sommalius, Antwerp 1600. English translation by J. P. Arthur: The founders of the New Devotion (2, 3-78, London 1905).

Rudolph Dier de Muden:[24a] De magistro Gherardo Grote, domino Florentio et multis aliis devotis fratribus. Vita magistri Gherardi Grote, edited by Gerhard Dumbar: Analecta seu vetera aliquot scripta inedita (1, 1-12, Deventer 1719).

Karl Grube: Gerhard Groot und seine Stiftungen (104 p., Köln 1883). Kühler (Nieuw nederlandsch biografisch woordenboek 1, 995-97, 1911). Henri Pirenne: Histoire de Belgique (3d ed., 2, 462, 485, 488, 1922). M. A. Van Andel: Geert Groote en de kwakzalver (Bijdragen tot de geschiedenis der geneeskunde 13, 212-14, 1933), Dutch translation of a letter written by Groote in 1382 against one Joannes den Heiden "who calls himself a physician." Thorndike (3, 511-12, 1934).

10. *The Brothers of the Common Life and the Christian renaissance*

Samuel Kettlewell: Thomas à Kempis and the Brothers of Common Life (2 vols., New York 1882). S. Harvey Gem (ERE 2, 839-42, 1910). Ernst Barnikol: Die Brüder vom gemeinsamen Leben in Deutschland. Entstehung und Bildung der deutschen Brüderbewegung durch Heinrich von Ahaus[25] (thesis, Marburg 1916). H. Pirenne: Histoire de Belgique (3d ed., 3, 300 ff., 1923). Albert Hyma: The Christian renaissance. A history of the devotio moderna (520 p., Grand Rapids, Mich. 1925), an excellent account. Jean Michel Emile Dols: Bibliographie der moderne devotie (2 vols., Nijmegen 1936-37).

11. *Imitatio Christi*

First edition, Augsburg 1471. At least 25 incunabula editions. Critical edition by Karl Hirsche (Berlin 1874).

One of the various English versions was made by John Wesley: The Christian's pattern (London 1735).

Pierre Edouard Puyol: Descriptions bibliographiques des manuscrits et des principales éditions (496 p., Paris 1898). Walter Arthur Copinger (1847-1910): On the English translations (126 p., Manchester 1900); Handlist of his collection (98 p., London 1909). That collection was acquired by the Harvard library in 1921 and has been considerably increased since.

Rayner Storr: Concordance to the Latin original of the De imitatione Christi given to the world A.D. 1441, by Thomas à Kempis (615 p., London 1910).

Karl Hirsche: Prolegomena zu einer neuen Ausgabe der Imitatio Christi nach dem Autograph des Thomas von Kempen. Zugleich eine Einführung in sämmtliche Schriften des Thomas, sowie ein Versuch zu endgültiger Feststellung der Thatsache dass Thomas und kein anderer der Verfasser der Imitatio ist (3 vols., Berlin 1873-94).

Leonard Abercromby Wheatley: The story of the Imitatio Christi (252 p., London 1891). Bernhard Rosenberg: Die älteste mittelenglische Übersetzung und ihr

[24a] Rudolf Dier van Muiden, born in Muiden, on southern shore of Zuiderzee, northern Holland, in 1384; died in Deventer 1458. Disciple of Radewijns; priest, historian of the brotherhood. Nieuw nederlandsch biografisch woordenboek (8, 392, 1930).

[25] Or Heinrich Ahuys of Münster (d. 1439). He traveled to Deventer in 1400 and brought back to Münster and other places the new Dutch tradition (ADB 1, 163, 1875).

Verhältnis zum Original (thesis, 67 p., Münster 1905). James Edward Geoffrey De Montmorency: Thomas à Kempis (336 p., 22 facs., London 1906). Paul Hagen: Mahnungen zur Innerlichkeit, eine Urschrift des Buchs von der Nachfolge Christi (Lübeck 1926). Connolly (p. 214-23, 1928). Paul Hagen: Untersuchungen über Buch II und III der Imitatio Christi (Verhandelingen der K. Akad. van wetenschappen te Amsterdam, afd. letterkunde, vol. 34, 154 p., Amsterdam 1935). The same author published De Imitatione Christi libri qui dicitur Tractatus secundus et tertius; recognovit et ad auctorem anonymum atque Thomam Kempensem reduxit (198 p., Amsterdam 1935).

Jac. Van Ginneken (S.J.): Die navolging van Christus of het dagboek van Geert Groote in den oorspronkelijken nederlandschen tekst herstelt en met de oudste latijnsche vertaling vergeleken (quarto, 82 p., Brussels 1929). English translation by Joseph Malaise: The following of Christ. The spiritual diary of Gerard Groote (320 p., New York 1937). Van Ginneken tries to identify Groote's lost diary with a part of the Imitation; few scholars have accepted his conclusions. I beg to thank professor Albert Hyma for valuable information with regard to this.

Jac. Van Ginneken: Trois textes pré-kempistes du premier livre de l'Imitation, édités et commentés à l'occasion de l'anniversaire sexcentenaire de Gérard Groote, 1340-1940 (Verhandelingen der K. nederlandsche Akad. van wetenschappen, vol. 44, 156 p., Amsterdam 1940). Alas! this very important edition, the first volume of three announced by the Dutch Academy, appeared at the very time when Dutch neutrality was violated by the German soldiery. What a contrast between the two purposes!

ZERBOLT

Gerard Zerbolt, Gerard van Zutphen. One of the Dutch founders of the moderna devotio (1367-98).

Zerbolt was born in 1367 at Zutphen, where his father seems to have been an alderman (schepen); he was educated in Zutphen and perhaps in Prague (or Paris?). In 1384 he was back in Deventer, where Radewijns persuaded him to join the Brothers of the Common Life. He soon became the leading scholar of that community, and its main exponent and defender. He died at Windesheim of a sudden infection on December 4, 1398.

He wrote many books, the most important of which is a defense of the Brothers against monks. In chapter 7 he justifies their efforts to translate the Bible into the vernacular, and explains which Dutch books laymen may read and which they may not. The Bible was written in the vernaculars of its own times (Hebrew and Greek), not in Latin; why should one be obliged to read it in Latin, and not allowed to read it in one's own vernacular? There can be no objection to the reading of sacred or good books in the vernacular, but only to the reading of bad ones, such as heretical ones.[26]

Another book of Zerbolt, De spiritualibus ascensionibus, partly based on a similar one by Radewijns, is really a course of spiritual exercises, which exerted considerable influence for two centuries at least, in particular upon St. Ignatius of Loyola.

He also wrote a treatise on the Sentences of Peter Lombard (XII-2).

[26] As to the reading of the Scriptures in the vernacular, see my note on Wycliffe. The more liberal views of the Catholic church were expressed by Sir Thomas More (1478-1535) in his Dyaloge (written 1528, printed London 1529). Pertinent extract quoted by G. G. Coulton: Life in the Middle Ages (2d ed., 2, 142-47, Cambridge 1928); Inquisition and liberty (p. 182-91, 1938). Margaret Deanesly: The Lollard Bible and other Biblical versions (Cambridge 1920).

Text. Tractatus de spiritualibus ascensionibus (Lübeck 1490, Antwerp? 1490?, Strassburg? 1495, Basel not after 1498, Montserrat 1499, Cologne 1539, Paris 1510?).

De reformatione virium anime (Basel 1492, 1493, 1535?, Paris 1493, Cologne 1539).

Quaestiones perpulchrae disputabiles super quartum librum Sententiarum (Cologne 1490).

De literis sacris in lingua vulgari legendis et De precibus vernaculis. Partly edited by F. G. P. Schoepff (Aurora 5, 1–34, 68–70, Dresden 1859).

Albert Hyma: Het traktaat Super modo vivendi devotorum hominum simul commorantium (Archief voor de geschiedenis van het aartsbisdom Utrecht 52, 1–100, 1925).

Criticism. Jacobus Revius: Daventria illustrata sive Historia urbis daventriensis (808 p., Leiden 1650–51), includes the texts reprinted by Schoepff in 1859. L. Knappert (Nieuw nederlandsch biografisch woordenboek 5, 1179, 1921). Albert Hyma: The Christian renaissance (p. 66–82, Grand Rapids, Mich. 1924); Christianity, capitalism and communism (ch. 4, Ann Arbor, Mich. 1937).

B. EASTERN CHRISTENDOM

B1. BYZANTIUM

MANUEL CALECAS

Μανουὴλ (Ἐμμανουὴλ) Καλέκας. Byzantine theologian (d. 1410).

Manuel belonged to an eminent family of Constantinople, already made illustrious by Joannes Calecas, patriarch from 1334 to 1347. He entered the Dominican monastery of Pera (a suburb on the north shore of the Golden Horn) and spent his life defending the Catholic philosophy and religion against Byzantine orthodoxy and Hesychasm. He died in Mitylene in 1410.

His main works are: (1) περὶ θείας οὐσίας καὶ θείας ἐνεργείας (De essentia et operatione Dei), not to be confused with the treatise of Prochoros Cydones bearing the same title. (2) A treatise on the procession of the Holy Spirit, ἐκπόρευσις τοῦ ἁγίου πνεύματος, explaining in four books the Latin views as opposed to the Greek ones; including many quotations from the Latin fathers of the church (chiefly Augustine), as well as from the Greek ones far better known to Greek readers. His main purpose was to establish the identity of views of Latin and Greek fathers of the fourth and fifth century on that subject. (3) A large treatise on Christian dogmatics, περὶ πίστεως καὶ περὶ τῶν ἀρχῶν τῆς καθολικῆς πίστεως (de principiis fidei catholicae), discussing Orthodox views on God, Trinity, Incarnation, sacraments, and eschatology, largely derived from the Scriptures and the fathers. There are many smaller writings of his (some of them represented by autographs in the Vatican library). One is a Latin letter, written in Pera 1394/95, wherein he refers to the journey of Manuel Chrysoloras and Demetrios Cydones to Venice. Another is an attack against Joseph Bryennios, monk at the monastery of St. John Baptist of Studion (now Imrahor jami, near the Seven Towers castle in Istanbul).

Text. The three main treatises are available in PG (vol. 152, 1865), but (2) is given only in the early Latin translation by the Italian Camaldolite Ambrogio Traversari (Ambrogio Camaldolese), general of his order in 1431 (1386–1439), first printed in Ingolstadt 1616.

Short texts are given by Mercati.

Criticism. Krumbacher (p. 110, 1897). S. Vailhé (DTC 2, 1332, 1905, reprinted

1923). Giovanni Mercati: Notizie di Procoro e Demetrio Cidone, Manuele Caleca... (p. 85–124, 450–73, Vaticano 1931).

C. ISRAEL

C1. Spain

JOSEPH BEN ELIEZER BONFILS

Joseph ben Eliezer (or Eleazar) ben Joseph ha-Sephardi, called Bonfils or Ṭob-'elem. Hispano-Jewish exegete. Probably identical with Ben Eliezer ha-Sephardi who was dayyan (judge) in Saragossa and compiled calendrical tables in 1355, Luḥot meha tequfot.

In 1370 he was in Damascus and wrote for the nagid David ben Joshua ben Maimon (a descendant of Maimonides, see Introd. 2, 376) a book entitled Ẓafenat pa'neaḥ (The god speaks and he lives; that is, the Egyptian name given to Joseph, Genesis 41: 45), explaining Abraham ben Ezra's commentary on the Torah. Later Joseph traveled to Egypt and to Palestine; he finally settled down in Jerusalem.

Text. An abbreviated edition of the Ẓafenat pa'neaḥ was published under the title Ohel Joseph in the Margalit Ṭoba (Amsterdam 1721), which contains two other contemporary Spanish commentaries on Abraham ben Ezra's Perush ha-Torah, namely the Megillat setarim of Samuel ben Moṭoṭ and the Meqor ḥayyim of Samuel ben Ẓarẓa.

Criticism. Röhricht (p. 89, 1890). M. Zobel (EJ 4, 946, 1929).

C2. Catalonia

NISSIM BEN REUBEN GERONDI

Judeo-Catalan Talmudist. He called himself ha-Gerondi, because he originated in Gerona, Catalonia. He spent most of his adult life, however, in Barcelona, c. 1340–76; he died c. 1376. He was primarily a Talmudist but had some knowledge of medicine and astronomy. Ḥasdai Crescas was one of his pupils.

The Black Death having been seized as a pretext for the persecution of Jews, Nissim Gerondi took up their defense. In 1367, he, Ḥasdai Crescas, and five other Jewish notables were arrested in Barcelona because of an alleged desecration of the Host, but they were later released. He was occasionally consulted by Pedro IV (king of Aragon 1336–87) on Jewish matters.

He wrote many decisions, responsa, and commentaries on the Talmud and on Isaac Alfasi (XI-2), his most important work being his commentary on the tractate Nedarim.[27] His attitude was one of moderation as between the philosophers to the left and the qabbalists to the right. He naturally made considerable use of the writings of his predecessors, this being the very essence of such work. He often quotes Rashi (XI-2), Jacob ben Meïr and Abraham ben Ezra (XII-1), Moses ben Naḥman and Solomon ben Adret (XIII-2), etc., and at least once Levi ben Gerson (XIV-1).

Though his writings hardly concern the historian of science, he deserves to be remembered here because, together with Moses ben Naḥman and Solomon ben Adret, he was one of the main restorers of Talmudic studies south of the Pyrénées.

[27] Dealing with vows. It is one of the seven tractates of the third book of the Talmud, the Seder nashim (women). The Nedarim occurs in the Mishna, Tosefta, and both Talmuds. It is a fantastic elaboration of chapter 30 of the book of Numbers.

Text. There are many editions of his works from the beginning of the sixteenth century on, and his commentary on Nedarim may be found in almost every edition of the Talmud.

Criticism. H. Gross (p. 473, 1897). S. A. Horodezky (EJ 7, 304–7, 1931).

C5. East

ABRAHAM QIRIMI

Crimean rabbi and exegete, born at Qirim[28] near Caffa. The Crimea was then the headquarters of the Qaraites, but Abraham was orthodox. He was much influenced by Abraham ben Ezra, and above all by the Moreh nebukim of Maimonides, and by Shemariah ben Elijah ha-Iqriṭi (XIV-1), whose disciple he may have been and whom he often quotes.

In 1358, he wrote a commentary on the Torah entitled Sefat emet (it is not clear whether the date 1358 given in the introduction is the date of the book or of the author's birth).[29] He wrote the Sefat emet to refute Qaraite opinions in the name of orthodox Talmudism and also of rationalism. Under the influences above mentioned, some of his tendencies were distinctly rationalistic, e.g., he tried occasionally to explain miracles in terms of natural phaenomena, and the sacrifice of the paschal lamb with reference to Egyptian mythology. His interpretations of the words of the Torah, however, were almost always literal and grammatical.

Criticism. I. Markon (EJ 1, 502, 1928).

ELEAZAR BEN NATHAN HA-BABLI

Eleazar Ashkenazi ben Nathan ha-Babli. Jewish exegete who flourished in the Near East, very probably in Egypt, c. 1364.

In that year 1364 he completed a commentary on the Torah entitled Ẓafenat pa'neaḥ, in which he discussed cosmological and philosophical questions. He was acquainted with the Arabic and Coptic languages. His main authority was Abraham ben Ezra. Some of his allegorical interpretations were quite bold, so much so that the scribe, Ephraim ben Shabbethai ha-Melammed, who copied the MS in 1399 deprecated Eleazar's rationalistic tendencies in the margins and even left out some passages which seemed to him particularly objectionable. Eleazar curiously identified the apostle Paul with Abba Saul ben Boṭnit, a Tannaite of the first century.

Criticism. S. A. Horodezky (EJ 6, 433, 1930).

D. ISLAM

D1. Western Islam

'ABD AL-ḤAQQ AL-ISLĀMĪ

Moroccan Jew who flourished in the last quarter of the century, and was converted to Islām.

[28] The name Qirim or better Qrim was first given to the town Sulghat (or Sulkhad), now called Staryi Krim (Old Qrim); later it was given to the whole peninsula, Crimea (EI 2, 1084–85, 1927).

[29] The second alternative is incompatible with his having been the disciple of ha-Iqriṭi, for the latter died not long after 1352.

Abū Muḥammad 'Abd al-Ḥaqq al-Islāmī wrote c. 1393–96, sixteen years after his conversion, a treatise against the Jews entitled Kitāb al-saif al-maḥdūd fīl-radd 'alā-l-Yahūd (The sharpened sword to answer the Jews), using the gematria method in his argument. The dating is based on the assumption that the ruler for whom blessings are invoked at the beginning is the Marīnī Abū-l-Fāris ibn Aḥmad al-Mustanṣir (sulṭān of Morocco 1393–96); the treatise was written for the son of a Marīnī ḥājib (chamberlain) Abū-l-'Abbās Aḥmad al-Qabā'ilī (in charge 1387–93, 1396–1400); it was thus completed probably in 1393 or in 1396.

Text. The text is unpublished. There are five MSS, two in the British Museum, one in Rabat, one in the India Office.

Criticism. M. Perlmann: 'Abd al-Ḥaqq al-Islāmī (Jewish quarterly review 31, 171–91, 1940), including many extracts.

E. INDIA

MĀDHAVA[30]

Mādhava or Mādhavācārya (= master M.), one of the greatest Vedantic scholars of India (fl. 1368–91).

His religious name was Vidyāraṇya (forest of knowledge); he is often called Mādhava Vidyāraṇya. In 1368 he was acting as minister for king Bukka of Vijayanagar,[31] and in 1391 he was presumably an old man, for he then retired from the world and became an ascetic (saṃnyāsin).

Mādhava's best-known work is the (1) Sarvadarśanasaṃgraha, a short summary of all Hindu philosophical systems. It contains discussions of fifteen systems of philosophy or religion (or philology, or science!), arranged roughly in order of smaller to greater truth. It begins with the Cārvāka, followed by Buddhism, Jaina, Rāmānuja (XI-2), various Śaiva schools (nos. 5 to 8), Raseśvara or mercurial system (a kind of alchemy, for which see my note on Merutuṅga), Vaiśeshika, Nyāya, Pūrvamīmāṃsā, the grammatical school of Pāṇini (IV-1 B.C.), Sāṁkhya, and Yoga. The climax is the system of Śaṅkara (IX-1), the "crest-gem of all systems," which is not explained, the author having dealt with it elsewhere (see nos. 4, 5). There is no history in this account, the systems being compared statically as if they were on the same temporal plane, and referred to the Vedānta.

Other works of his are:

2. Nyāyamālāvistara, or Jaiminīyanyāyamālāvistara. Commentary on Pūrvamīmāṃsā.[32]

3. Śaṅkaradigvijaya. Panegyric of Śaṅkara in verse, derived from older poems of the same kind, the author calling himself a "new Kālidāsa" (the greatest poet of Sanskrit literature, who flourished at an unknown time, fourth to sixth centuries). This has no historical value.

4. Pañcadaśi. The most popular explanation of Vedānta in modern India.

[30] This note and the one on Sāyaṇa are complementary and should be read together.

[31] For that dynasty see my note in chapter I, p. 41. Bukkarāya ruled from 1354 to 1379. According to Duff (p. 223, 309, 1899), Mādhava was prime minister not only to Bukka I but also to the latter's predecessor, Harihara I, who ruled from 1339 to 1354; that is, he served under the second and third kings of the first Vijayanagar dynasty.

[32] See my note on Kumārila (VIII-1), who was also a South Indian, having some familiarity with Dravidian languages.

This was composed by Mādhava with the help of Bhāratītīrtha, whom he succeeded as abbot of Śṛiṅgeri.

5. Jīvanmuktiviveka. This is another Vedantic commentary, written by Mādhava in his old age, to explain how the faithful can obtain salvation within their lifetime. It is remarkably eclectic, for it includes extracts from the Bhagavadgītā, the Bhāgavatapurāṇa, and the Yogavāsishṭha.

6. Commentary on the Parāśarasmṛiti, a treatise on dharmaśāstra.

7. Dhātuvṛitti, commentary on Pāṇini's grammar.

Leaving aside difficulties concerning attributions to Mādhava or to his brother (himself?) Sāyaṇa, the list of seven items just given is almost certainly incomplete. To it should be added many Vedic commentaries (Emeneau nos. 465, 490, 511, 549), a treatise on the time proper for religious observances (nos. 2322–23), and at least two other books on religious philosophy (nos. 2782, 2898–99). As it is, my list is sufficient to illustrate the importance of Mādhava's activities in southern India at a time when Hinduism was completely repressed in the rest of Hindūstān by the Muslim conquerors.

Text. Sarvadarśanasaṃgraha. First edited by Tārānātha Tarkavācaspati (Calcutta 1851). Second edition, often mistaken for the first, by Īśwarachandra Vidyāsāgara (Bibliotheca indica, Calcutta 1858). Various other editions: Calcutta 1889, Poona 1906, 1924, 1928.

The text with English translation and notes was published by Edward Byles Cowell and Archibald Edward Gough in the Paṇḍit (Benares 1874–78). Revised edition but without Sanskrit text in Trübner's Oriental series (292 p., London 1882; again 1894). There is also a translation into Bengali (Calcutta 1861; again 1865); translations of ch. 1 into German (Zeitschrift der Deutschen morgenländischen Gesellschaft vol. 14, 1860) and of ch. 2 into French by L. de la Vallée-Poussin (Muséon vols. 2–3, 1901–2).

2. The (Jaiminīya-)nyāyamālāvistara, also called Adhikaraṇaratnamālā or Bhāṭṭasāra, was first edited by Theodor Goldstücker (London 1865–67). Second edition by Edward B. Cowell (London 1878). Third edition (718 p., Calcutta 1889). Fourth in Ānandāśrama series (Poona 1892; again 1916). No translation.

3. Śaṅkaradigvijaya. First (typographic) edition (Bombay 1864). Second edition in the Ānandāśrama series (Poona 1891; reprinted 1915, 1932). No translation.

4. Pañcadaśī. Text and English version by Arthur Venis (Paṇḍit vols. 5–8, Benares 1883–86). Other editions in Sanskrit and English: Srirangam 1912, Bombay 1912. In Sanskrit alone: Ahmadabad 1895. In English alone: Calcutta 1886, 1900.

Editions with Rāmakṛishṇa's commentary: Calcutta 1849, 1882, Bombay 1863, 1905, Poona 1885.

5. Jīvanmuktiviveka. First edition by Vāsudeva Śāstrī Panśīkar (Ānandāśrama series, Poona 1890). Other editions: Benares 1913, Poona 1916. English translation by Manilal N. Dvivedi (208 p., Bombay 1897) with Sanskrit text.

6. The commentary on Parāśarasmṛiti was first edited by Chandrakānta Tarkālankāra (3 vols., Bibliotheca indica, Calcutta 1890–92). Second edition (3 vols., Bombay 1893–1906; 1911).

The chapter on the law of inheritance was published in English before its publication in Sanskrit by A. C. Burnell (72 p., Madras 1868).

7. The commentary on Pāṇini's grammar is unpublished.

Criticism. Duff (p. 223, 309, 1899). Keith (1921). Winternitz (3, 420, 427, 437, 501, 1922). Keith (1928). Dasgupta (1922–40).

SĀYAṆA[33]

Sāyaṇa or Sāyaṇācārya (= master S.) was the greatest Vedic commentator of the Middle Ages (d. 1387).

Sāyaṇa was minister to Saṅgama II[34] and Harihara II of the Vijayanagar dynasty in southern India. From 1331 to 1386 he was abbot of the monastery of Śṛiṅgeri (Kadur district, Mysore).

He was the brother of Mādhava, and, the books of each brother being frequently ascribed to the other, there is considerable confusion. It has been suggested that the two brothers were but one man. I lean to that hypothesis for various reasons, the main one being that at the end of the prologue of the Sarvadarśanasaṃgraha the author calls himself Sāyaṇa-Mādhavaḥ, this double name being followed by a verb not in the dual form. According to Arthur Coke Burnell,[35] Sāyaṇa is a Dravidian name given to a child born after all his siblings have died. Sāyaṇa may refer to the body, Mādhava to the soul.

Whether Sāyaṇa is separate from Mādhava or a part of him, he wrote a great many commentaries on the Ṛigveda, on the Aitareya saṃhitā, brāhmaṇa, and āraṇyaka, on the Taittirīya saṃhitā, brāhmaṇa, and āraṇyaka, etc. The very bulk of these commentaries makes it difficult to believe that he wrote them all personally, and yet immemorial traditions ascribe them to him (or his brother). Let us consider more carefully the Mādhavīyavedārthaprakāśa, as his Ṛigveda commentary is called. Out of 64 adhyāya in the eight ashṭaka of that commentary, 20 refer explicitly to Sāyaṇa's authorship, the others do not. In the very beginning the authorship is ascribed to Mādhava! This is puzzling enough. Moreover, there are many contradictions, the same words in the same contexts being explained differently in different places. Putting all these facts together, one can hardly escape the conclusion that Sāyaṇa was assisted by other scholars, his brother being perhaps one of them. Instead of thinking of him as a single individual, we must think of a school (as we had to do for the great translators from Greek into Arabic or from Arabic into Latin). Further analysis would show that the unit of division of the Ṛigveda among the collaborators was the ashṭaka (or eighth) rather than the māṇḍala (or tenth); it is probable that the grammatical commentary and the exegesis were done by different scholars. The ascription of these enormous commentaries to "Sāyaṇa's school" reduces the interest of the more narrow controversy Sāyaṇa vs. Mādhava.

The earlier Western editors of the Veda relied perhaps too much upon these fourteenth-century commentaries; this was followed by excessive distrust.[35a] The later editors make full use of them, gratefully but critically.

[33] This note and the one on Mādhava are complementary and should be read together.

[34] Saṅgama II was a grandson of Saṅgama I, founder of the dynasty. He flourished c. 1356. Harihara II, son of Bukka I, ruled from 1379 to 1406. For the dynasty as a whole see my note in chapter I, p. 41.

[35] Preface to his edition of the Vaṃśabrāhmaṇa (the 8th Brāhmaṇa of the Sāma Veda), Mangalore 1873.

[35a] Too much confidence in the fourteenth-century commentary was shown by the Englishmen Horace Hayman Wilson and Edward Byles Cowell in their English translation of the Ṛigveda (London 1850–66); too little, by the Germans Rudolf Roth and Herrmann Grassmann. The last named was the mathematician made famous by his Ausdehnungslehre (1844), as well as by his dictionary of the Ṛigveda (1873) and his German translation of it (1876). Sarton: Grassmann (Isis 35, 326–30, 6 fig., 1945).

Text. The editions of the Vedasaṃhitā and Vedabrāhmaṇa cited below are only those including commentaries by Sāyaṇa, hence it is unnecessary to mention that fact for each item. It should be noted that in some of the editions the author of the commentary is called Mādhava, not Sāyaṇa. For other Vedic commentaries ascribed to Mādhava see Emeneau (nos. 465, 490, 511, 549).

The Veda-bhāshya-bhūmikā-saṃgraha (a collection of all available introductions by Sāyaṇa to his Vedic commentaries), edited with notes by Baladeva Upādhyāya (Kāśī series, Benares 1934).

Ṛigveda saṃhitā, edited by F. Max Müller (6 vols., London 1849–74; reprinted in 4 vols., 1890–92). There are various other editions (Emeneau nos. 11–21), e.g., one in 9 vols. (Bombay 1888–90), and another with English translation, by Manmatha Nath Dutt (9 vols. in Sanskrit, 4 in English, Calcutta 1906–12). For partial editions see Emeneau.

Sāmaveda saṃhitā, edited by Satyavrata Sāmaśramī (Bibliotheca indica, 5 vols., Calcutta 1874–78).

Atharvasaṃhitā, edited by Shankar Pāndurang (4 vols., Bombay 1895–98).

Das Aitareya brāhmaṇa, von Theodor Aufrecht (455 p., Bonn 1879). Aitareya brāhmaṇa of the Rig-veda, edited by Satyavrata Sāmaśramī (4 vols., Bibliotheca indica, Calcutta 1895–1906). Other edition in the Ānandāśrama series (Poona 1896).

Daivatabrāhmaṇa and Shaḍviṅśabrāhmaṇa of the Sāmaveda, edited by Jibananda Vidyasagara (2d ed., Calcutta 1881).

Shaḍviṅśabrāhmaṇa, with German translation by Kurt Klemm (94 p., Gütersloh 1894). Other edition by Herman Frederik Eelsingh (270 p., Leiden 1908).

Tāṇḍyamahābrāhmaṇa, edited by Ānandachandra Vedāntavāgīśa (2 vols., Bibliotheca indica, Calcutta 1870–74).

Sāmavidhānabrāhmaṇa (third brāhmaṇa of the Sāmaveda), edited with English translation by A. C. Burnell (vol. 1, 142 p., London 1873). Other Sanskrit edition (Calcutta 1895).

Ārsheyabrāhmaṇa (fourth brāhmaṇa of the Sāmaveda), edited by A. C. Burnell (160 p., Mangalore 1876).

Devatādhyāyabrāhmaṇa (fifth brāhmaṇa of the Sāmaveda), edited by A. C. Burnell (Mangalore 1873).

Mantrabrāhmaṇa, partial editions with German translation by Heinrich Stönner (Halle a.S. 1901) and Hans Jörgensen (Darmstadt 1911).

Vaṃśabrāhmaṇa, edited by A. Weber (Monatsbericht der K. preussischen Akad., p. 493–507, Berlin 1857).

Taittirīyabrāhmaṇa of the Black Yajurveda, edited by Rājendralāla Mitra (3 vols., Bibliotheca indica, Calcutta 1859–90). Other edition in the Ānandāśrama series (3 vols., Poona 1898).

Śatapathabrāhmaṇa of the White Yajurveda, edited by Satyavrata Sāmaśramī (vols. 1–3, 5–7) and Hitavrata Samakantha (vol. 9) (Bibliotheca indica, Calcutta 1900–12).

Aitareyāraṇyaka, edited by Rājendralāla Mitra (Bibliotheca indica, Calcutta 1876). New edition in the Ānandāśrama series (Poona 1898).

Taittirīyāraṇyaka, edited by Rājendralāla Mitra (Bibliotheca indica, Calcutta 1872). New edition (Poona 1898).

Taittirīyasaṃhitā of the Black Yajurveda, edited by E. Röer, E. B. Cowell, etc. (6 vols., Bibliotheca indica, Calcutta 1860–99). New edition in the Ānandāśrama series (9 vols., Poona 1900–8); vol. 9 is an index. English translation by Arthur Berriedale Keith (2 vols., Harvard Oriental series, Cambridge, Mass. 1914).

Criticism. Criticism of Sāyaṇa cannot be separated from Vedic criticism in general. I quote here only a few general sources.

Winternitz (vol. 1, 1907). Paul Masson-Oursel: Bibliographie sommaire de l'Indianisme (Isis 3, 171–218, 1920, chiefly p. 186–90). Arthur Berriedale Keith: Religion and philosophy of the Veda and Upanishads (2 vols., Harvard Oriental series, Cambridge, Mass. 1925). Bhagavad Datta: A history of Vedic literature. Vol. 1, part 2, The commentators (Lahore 1931); vol. 2, The brāhmaṇas and the āraṇyakas (Lahore 1927), in Hindī. Louis Renou: Bibliographie védique (340 p., Paris 1931). Emeneau (1935).

Maurice Bloomfield: A Vedic concordance (Harvard Oriental series, 1100 p., 1906). Arthur Anthony Macdonell: Vedic index of names and subjects (2 vols., London 1912).

P. D. Gune: Sāyaṇa's commentary, its composition (Sir Asutosh Mookerjee silver jubilee volumes, vol. 3, part 3, 467–76, Calcutta 1927).

DHAMMAKITTI IV

Siṅhalese Buddhist writing in Pāli (fl. third quarter of fourteenth century).

There were at least five Siṅhalese friars named Dhammakitti who held high positions in the Buddhist order. The first flourished at the end of the twelfth century,[36] the second and third in the thirteenth, the fourth and fifth in the fourteenth.

Dhammakitti IV lived at the Gaḍalādeṇivihāra (i.e., the monastery in the village of Gaḍalādeṇi, Ceylon) during the rules of Parākramabāhu V (1348–60) and Vikramabāhu III (1347–75), became head of the Buddhist church (saṅgharāja), held a great convocation of monks in 1369, and effected reforms of the order.

He wrote a Pāli poem entitled Pāramīmahāsataka, dealing with the ten Buddhist perfections or transcendental virtues (pāramit). It consists of 100 verses divided into ten sections. The materials of it are naturally derived from the Jātaka and the Cariyā-piṭaka (collections of Buddhist stories, undatable, the second derived from the former).

Criticism. Don M. de Z. Wickremasinghe: The several Pali and Sinhalese authors known as Dhammakitti (Journal of the Royal Asiatic Society, 1896, 200–3). G. P. Malalasekera: The Pāli literature of Ceylon (p. 240–42, Royal Asiatic Society 1928).

DHAMMAKITTI V

Siṅhalese Buddhist writing in Siṅhalese and in Pāli (fl. c. 1360–97).

Dhammakitti V flourished in the Gaḍalādeṇivihāra, was a disciple of Dhammakitti IV, and succeeded him as saṅgharāja. He lived in the reigns of Bhuvanekabāhu V (1360–91) and Vīrabāhu II (1391–97). Like his predecessor, he held a synod and effected reforms of his order.

Among the various works ascribed to him it will suffice to mention the following:

1. Saddharmālaṅkāra, a Siṅhalese compilation of Buddhist legends. It is largely a free translation or adaptation of the Rasavāhinī of Vedeha thera (XIV-1). Out of 24 chapters, the last 21 are derived from the Rasavāhinī.

2. Nikāyasaṅgraha. A history of Buddhism from the days of Buddha until twenty centuries later. This contains valuable information on the church, especially for the thirteenth and fourteenth centuries. This is also written in Siṅhalese.

[36] Dhammakitti I wrote c. 1211 the well known Pāli poem Dāṭhāvaṃsa, on the tooth relic of the Buddha. Dhammakitti II (fl. 1240–75) was probably identical with the author of the first section of the Cūlavaṃsa, for which see my note on Siṅhalese chronicles (XIV-1).

3. Bālāvatāra. A very short treatise on Pāli grammar, extensively used in Ceylon. It is naturally derived from Kaccāyana, but is arranged differently. The section on syntax (kāraka) marks a great improvement upon the older grammars. The Bālāvatāra is the basis of a number of Siṅhalese works on Pāli grammar, the best-known of which, Gaḍalādeṇi sanne (or paraphrase by a member of the Gaḍalādeṇi vihāra), is generally ascribed to Dhammakitti himself.

4. Saddhammasaṅgaha. History of Buddhism in Pāli, including a list of the books written from the earliest times down to the second half of the twelfth century. The ascription to *this* Dhammakitti is uncertain. The author is perhaps a Hindu (not Siṅhalese) called Dhammakitti Mahāsāmi, who spent some time in the Gaḍalādeṇivihāra under Dhammakitti IV or V and returned to India after having obtained the highest ordination.

Text. Bālāvatāra, edited by Andris de Silva Baṭuvantuḍāve (82 p., Colombo 1869), in Siṅhalese script. Edition and translation by Satischandra Vidyābhusana and Samaṇa Puṇṇānanda Swāmi (168 p., University of Calcutta 1916).

Saddhammasaṅgaha, edited by Nedimāle Saddhānanda (Journal of the Pāli Text Society, 1890, p. 21–90).

Criticism. G. P. Malalasekera: Pāli literature of Ceylon (London 1928).

F. TIBET

TSONG KAPA

Tsoṅ-k'a-pa (the man from the land of the onions). Reformer of Tibetan Buddhism, founder of the sect of Yellow Hats.

He was born in 1357 at Kumbum,[37] province of Amdō, in northeastern Tibet; he died in 1419. A Hindu monk Atīsha, who visited Tibet in 1038, had realized the need of reforming Lamaism, that is, the form of Buddhism established by Padmasambhava (VIII-2), who arrived in Tibet in 747. Atīsha created the new sect called Kah-dam-pa (those bound by commandments), and died in 1053. This effort was unsuccessful, but Tsong Kapa renewed it and succeeded. The sect founded by him c. 1392, called Ge-lug-pa (the virtuous order), was less ascetic and more highly ritualistic, and its success was rapid and enormous. The reformed lamas are known as Yellow Hats (S'a-ser), as opposed to the Red Hats (S'a-mar), who represent the older, unreformed body. They are forbidden to marry and to drink wine. Being powerfully organized, the Yellow-Hats soon eclipsed all other sects, and within the space of five generations not only became the established church of Tibet, but gained control of the temporal government of the country.

Tsong Kapa wrote many religious books, the main one being entitled Lām-rim (The gradual way). He founded two large lamaseries at Ganden and Sera, near Lhasa. These two monasteries are still extant, and together with a third, the Drepung monastery (also near Lhasa), are the three most powerful religious bodies in Tibet; they are called Den-sa sum (the three pillars of the state).

He was succeeded by his nephew Gedun-ḍub (Geden-tub-pa, Ganden Truppa), who was born in 1389 or 1391, founded the Tashi-lhünpo monastery in 1445, and died in 1473/74. This Gedun-ḍub was the first Dalai Lāma (or Grand Lama; the Tibetan pope).

[37] Kumbum (or Gumbum) is about 50 miles east of lake Koko-Nor, in the Chinese province of Kansuh. The name means (in Tibetan) "ten thousand images," with reference to a sacred tree the leaves of which bear Tibetan characters. Father Huc saw the tree and described it (2, 113–15, 1850).

Criticism. Evariste Régis Huc (1813-60): Souvenirs d'un voyage dans la Tartarie, le Thibet et la Chine pendant les années 1844, 1845 et 1846 (2 vols., Paris 1850; vol. 2, p. 61, 104-13, 377). Father Huc's account of the long journey which he undertook with his brother Lazarist Joseph Gabet is one of the outstanding books of its kind in world literature; his firsthand description of Tibetan religion and customs is extremely interesting. Sarat Chandra Das: Life and legend of Tsongkhapa or Lossang-tag-pa (Journal of the Asiatic Society of Bengal, 1882). Lawrence Austine Waddell: Buddhism of Tibet (London 1895). Sir Charles Bell: Tibet (p. 33, Oxford 1924). Alexandra David-Neel: Mystiques et magiciens du Tibet (312 p., Paris 1929; Isis 14, 441-44); Initiations lamaïques (250 p., Paris 1930). A. D. Howell Smith: The so-called devil dances of Tibet (Indian art and letters 15, 95-99, 1941).

Wilhelm Filchner: Beitrag zur Geschichte des Klosters Kumbum (180 p., ill., 40 pl., 4 maps, Berlin 1906); Kumbum Dschamba ling, Das Kloster der hunderttausend Bilder Maitreyás (quarto, 572 p., ill., Leipzig 1933; p. 171-95, 437-48). Eugène Obermiller: Tson-kha-pa le pandit (Mélanges chinois et bouddhiques 3, 319-38, 1935; Isis 35, 227).

CHAPTER XVII

THE TRANSLATORS

(Second Half of the Fourteenth Century)

N.B. The reader should bear in mind that only the main translators, or rather the men whose main activity was translating, are dealt with in this chapter. For a general survey of all the translations, see section III of chapter XV. More information on the additional translators and their translations may easily be obtained by means of the index.

1a. TRANSLATIONS FROM ARABIC INTO HEBREW

JOSEPH BEN JOSHUA I HA-LORQI

Judeo-Spanish physician and scholar. Also called Ibn Vives (Vivas, Bibas). He or his ancestors originated in Lorca near Murcia, hence the name Lorqi. He died before 1372.

He revised the Hebrew translation, Millot ha higgayon, of Maimonides' Maqālat fī ṣinā'at al-manṭiq (1151) made by Moses ibn Tibbon (XIII-2) in 1254, and dedicated his revision (or new translation) to his pupil Ezra ben Solomon ben Gatigno, who flourished c. 1356–72 in Saragossa and Agramunt (Lerida). That text was for a long time the main textbook of logic in Jewish circles, but its influence was felt mainly through the early translation of Moses ibn Tibbon and subsidiarily through that of Aḥiṭub ben Isaac (XIII-2).

He wrote a philosophical treatise on the elements (Sefer ha-yesodot).

He was probably the father of Joshua ben Joseph ibn Vives Lorqi and the grandfather of Joseph ben Joshua Lorqi II.

Criticism. Steinschneider (p. 436, 1893). B. Suler (EJ 10, 1116, 1934).

JOSEPH BEN JOSHUA II HA-LORQI

Joseph ben Joshua ibn Vives al-Lorqi. Judeo-Murcian physician and translator from Arabic into Hebrew (d. before 1408). Probably related (grandson?) to Joseph ben Joshua I ha-Lorqi.

He translated a part of the Qānūn of Ibn Sīnā before 1402, revised the translation of Nathan ha-Me'ati (XIII-2), and added a commentary. The part translated by him included at least the first book and the first treatise of the second book. His translation was appreciated and finally printed (1491), and his commentary was included in the commentary of Shemṭob ben Isaac ben Shapruṭ of Tudela.

Text. Hebrew version of the Qānūn by Joseph Lorqi and Nathan ha-Me'ati (Naples 1491–92). Facsimile of 2 pages in Osiris (5, 109, 148–49, 1938).

Criticism. Steinschneider (p. 681, 762, 1893). B. Suler (EJ 10, 1116, 1934), only a few lines.

DAVID IBN YA'ĪSH

David ben Solomon Ibn Ya'īsh of Seville. Translator from Arabic into Hebrew who flourished probably in the second half of the fourteenth century (c. 1373?). Possibly the son of Solomon ibn Ya'īsh (XIV-1).

David translated the Arabic version of a Greek treatise on domestic economy, the οἰκονομικός (λόγος) of the neo-Pythagorean "Bryson." That treatise is lost in Greek, but extant in Arabic, Hebrew, and Latin, and through these versions, especially the Arabic, it exerted some influence upon mediaeval thought. The Hebrew title reads Seder hanhagat ha-adam bebaithu, the Arabic one Kitāb Brūsun fī tadbīr al-rajul limanzilihi. The management of a house involves four essential factors: money, servants, wife, children, which are discussed in that order.

Text. The Hebrew as well as the Arabic and Latin versions were edited by Martin Plessner (1928).

The Latin version abridged from the Arabic by Armengaud son of Blaise (XIII-2), entitled Yconomica and ascribed to Galen, had been edited previously by Theodor Trotz: Der Inhalt der Dresdener lateinischen Galenhandschrift aus dem Anfange des 15. Jahrhunderts. Erster Abdruck der Oeconomica Galeni (14 p., Leipzig 1921; Isis 4, 398).

Criticism. Steinschneider (p. 228, 1893). Plessner (1928). According to Plessner, the date of the activity of David Ibn Ya'īsh cannot be determined (p. 20), nevertheless the one which we have tentatively adopted is very plausible.

JUDAH BEN SOLOMON NATHAN

Called in Provençal Maestro Bongodas, En Bongodas, Bongoes. Judeo-Provençal physician, philosopher, and translator from Arabic and Latin into Hebrew. He was born in the first fifth of the century, probably at Avignon (or in Montpellier, or Arles), and apparently was still living in 1377; his latest dated work was completed in 1362.

Five translations were made by him in the following order:

1. Umaiya ibn abī-l-Ṣalt (XII-1): Kitāb al-adwiya al-mufrada. This was perhaps Judah's first translation into Hebrew. The same work had been translated into Latin, Simplicia, by Arnold of Villanova (XIII-2). Judah's very literal translation was revised with the assistance of his uncle, Nathan ben Shelemiah. It is entitled Kelal qaẓer meha-samim ha-nifradim.

2. Al-Ghazzālī (XI-2): Maqāṣid al-falāsifa. This had been translated into Latin by John of Seville (XII-1) and into Hebrew by Isaac Albalag (XIII-2). Judah's new translation, entitled Kawwenot ha-filosofim (Tendencies of the philosophers), was made before 1340, on the request of his uncle, Nathan ben Shelemiah. Judging by the number of MSS, it was relatively popular. For the preparation of it Judah used the Kitāb al-shifā' and the Kitāb al-najāt of Ibn Sīnā, the Kitāb al-mabāḥith al-sharqīya of Fakhr al-dīn al-Rāzī (XII-1), and the Tahāfut al-tahāfut of Ibn Rushd, and he added a long introduction. His purpose was different from that of his predecessor Isaac Albalag, for the latter translated the Maqāṣid to defend philosophy, whereas Judah's object was protection against it. Qur'ānic quotations are replaced in the translation by Biblical ones.

3. Ibn Wāfid (XI-1): Kitāb al-wisād (Book of the pillow, Liber de cervicalibus capitis), a treatise on simples. The translation, Mera'ashot ha-rosh, divided into 27 chapters, was completed in 1352. Judah added notes taken from Ibn Sīnā, and from Latin authors, such as Gilbert the Englishman (XIII-1) and John of Saint Amand (XIII-2). A copy of this MS (Parma) was made in 1391 by Abraham ben Reuben Amilabi (i.e., ha-Milabi, of Milhau, near Nîmes), who added the Hebrew equivalents of some Arabic terms which Judah had left untranslated.

4. Arnold of Villanova (XIII-2): De vino (sive vinis). Abridged translation completed in 1358, Ha-dibur be-yenot, treatise on wines and their medical uses.

5. Treatise on fevers. Compilation dated 1362, derived for the most part from Gilbert the Englishman (XIII-1) and Bernard of Gordon (XIV-1). It is divided into 8 sections: (1) fevers in general, (2) diseases in general, (3–8) particular diseases from head to foot. It quotes Ibn Sīnā, the Circa instans of Matthaeus Platearius (XII-1), Roger of Salerno (XII-2), Theodoric of Cervia (XIII-1), the 'Aleh ha-refu'ah of Abraham ben David Caslari (XIV-1), Maestro Vidal de Bourian, Giles of Arles. In one MS the book is called Gordon qaẓer (The abridged Gordon).

Finally, he wrote an epistle (iggeret) wherein he vindicated the study of philosophy against the Talmudists (this seems to contradict what I said under no. 2 above, but it is a matter of degree which is difficult to appraise).

The treatise Sod ha-sodot (Mystery of mysteries), an orderless collection of medical recipes ascribed to him, is apocryphal: it was composed in Spain, probably by a relative or disciple of his. The following authors are mentioned in it: Bongodas Nathan Crescas, Maestro Vidal de Bourian, Constantine the African, and the Circa instans. A Latin treatise on obstetrics ascribed to one Bongodas Cohen may be his (though the Hebrew written forms Cohen and Nathan are not easy to confuse).

Criticism. H. Gross (p. 8, 344, passim, 1897). Steinschneider (p. 306, 735, 738, 781, 798, 1893). Neubauer-Renan (p. 574–80, 700, 1893). Isaac Broydé (JE 9, 183, 1905). Wickersheimer (p. 3, 91, 1936).

JACOB CARSONO

Jacob ben abi Abraham Isaac ben al-Carsono (or Carsi; Corsono), in Hebrew writing al-Qorsono (one samak, three waw). Hispano-Jewish astronomer, and translator from Latin and Arabic into Hebrew (fl. 1375–78).

He wrote an Arabic treatise on the astrolabe at Seville in 1375–76, and translated it into Hebrew at Barcelona 1378, Bi'ur 'asiyot ha-aẓṭurlab (Explanation of the construction of the astrolabe), divided into 8 chapters.

As the Alphonsine tables became insufficient, Pedro IV[1] the Ceremonious, king of Aragon from 1336 to 1387, ordered the compilation of new ones. This work, begun by Pere Engelbert, was completed (1366) after the latter's death by his associate and pupil Dalmau Ces-Planes. The tables were somewhat modified[2] by Carsono, who seems to have also translated them into Hebrew (the tables and almanac of Engelbert and Dalmau being presumably in Latin or Catalan).

Criticism. M. Steinschneider: Notice sur les tables astronomiques attribuées à Pierre III d'Aragon (Bullettino di bibliografia e di storia delle scienze matematiche 13, 413–36, 1880); includes Latin and Hebrew texts of the king's preface to the Canones super tabulis regis Petri tertii (i.e., our Peter IV). Andreu Balaguer y Merino: La veu del Monserrat (vol. 5, 1882); not seen. Steinschneider (p. 596, 638, 1893); Die Mathematik bei den Juden (BM 13, 38, 1899); (p. 170, 1902). Moritz Kayserling (JE 3, 593, 1902). Rubió y Lluch (1, 190, 199, 280, 298, 1908; 2, 139–42, 1921). B. Suler (EJ 5, 61, 1930), very short note containing nothing new.

SAMUEL IBN MOṬOṬ

Samuel ben Sa'adia ibn Moṭoṭ. Flourished in Guadalajara, new Castile, about 1370–92. Judeo-Castilian exegete, theologian, and translator from Arabic into Hebrew.

[1] Also called Pedro III, which is confusing. We call Pedro III the king, Peter the Great, who ruled from 1276 to 1285; this one is then Pedro IV.

[2] I do not understand the real nature of the transformation, very badly explained by Steinschneider in Boncompagni's Bullettino (13, 415). The computations were made with reference to the eighth sphere instead of the ninth.

His best-known work, the Megillat setarim, is a commentary on the Firush ha-Torah of Abraham ben Ezra (XII-1), written about 1380 probably in Guadalajara. It is based on many Talmudic, philosophic, and qabbalistic sources. His main authorities were Abraham ben Ezra for astrology, and Moses ben Naḥman for philosophy and exegesis.

He wrote other commentaries on the Torah, the daily prayers, the Haggadot, and the Sefer yeẓirah (Introd. 2, 367–68). The last-named one, entitled Meshobeb netibot (Restorer of the paths), was written at Guadalajara in 1370. It is divided into three parts, including 6 chapters each: (I) numbers, intelligence, etc., by way of introduction; (II) commentary on the Yeẓirah; (III) appendixes.

He translated the following books:

1. 'Abdallāh ibn Muḥammad al-Baṭalyūsī (XII-1): Kitāb al-ḥadā'iq (The orchard). Lost in Arabic, but known in Hebrew through the translation made by Moses ibn Tibbon (XIII-2) and the incomplete one (chs. 1–4) made by Samuel ibn Moṭoṭ and included by him in his Meshobeb netibot (1370).

2. Abraham ben David ha-Levi (XII-2): Kitāb al-'aqīdah al-rafī'ah (The sublime faith). Translated by Samuel in 1392 for Isaac ben Sheshet (Valencia 1326—Algiers 1408)[3] under the title Emunah nissa'ah. That translation was superseded by another, on the whole more correct, entitled Emunah ramah, made soon afterward by Solomon ben Labi.

3. Pseudo Abraham ben Ezra: Sefer ha-'eẓemim (Book of substances). Arabic text lost. Fragments quoted in Hebrew by Samuel ibn Sanah ibn Ẓarẓa of Valencia, and also by Samuel ibn Moṭoṭ. The book is divided into six chapters: (1) first cause; (2) influence of the highest world (the separate intellect) upon the subordinate worlds; (3) on a special path (Sabians? Nabataeans?); (4) souls; (5) animals; (6) spheres. It is an astrological and occultist composition.

Text. The Megillat setarim was first published at Venice 1554. Abridged edition by Jekuthiel ben Nahum Lazi in the Sefer margaliot ṭobah, a collection of commentaries on Abraham ben Ezra's Firush ha-Torah (Amsterdam 1721).

David Kaufmann: Die Spuren des al-Batlajusis in der jüdischen Religionsphilosophie (Budapest 1880). Includes Samuel's translation of the Ḥadā'iq, together with Moses ibn Tibbon's translation and an introduction.

The Emunah nissa'ah is unpublished, but the Emunah ramah was edited in Hebrew and German by Samson Weil (243 p., Francfort a.M. 1852).

The Sefer ha-'eẓemim was edited by Menasseh Grossberg (London 1901). This edition includes also two letters of Isaac Abarbanel (1437–1508) and some responsa.

Criticism. Steinschneider (p. 287, 370, 449, 1893). Max Schloessinger (JE 9, 99, 1905).

SOLOMON BEN LABI

Judeo-Aragonese translator from Arabic into Hebrew, who flourished probably at Ixar or Ijar (?), Aragon, toward the end of the fourteenth century.

He translated the Kitāb al-'aqīdah al-rafī'ah (The sublime faith), a philosophical treatise, of Abraham ben David ha-Levi of Toledo (XII-2), under the title Emunah ramah. That translation superseded another one made by Samuel ibn Moṭoṭ at about the same time (1392).

[3] A famous rabbi who emigrated from Spain at the time of the persecutions of 1391 and became even more famous in Algiers, where his tomb is venerated to this day and is the center of a pilgrimage.

There is a possibility that this Solomon ben Labi may be identical with Judah ben Solomon ibn Labi (Benveniste della Caballeria), who died in 1411, or may be related to him.

Text. The Sefer ha-emunah ha-ramah was edited with a German translation by Samson Weil (Francfort a.M. 1852).

Criticism. Steinschneider (p. 370, 1893). B. Suler (EJ 10, 540, 1934).

JUDAH BEN SOLOMON IBN LABI

Benveniste ben Solomon ibn Labi; Benveniste della Caballeria. Jewish financier and patron of learning; he was a man of great importance at the Aragonese court, chiefly during the years 1380–1403; he flourished mainly in Saragossa, then in Alcañiz, where he died in 1411, full of honors.

We mention him here because he patronized the work of at least three Jewish scholars. He helped

(1) Meir Alguadez to translate the Nicomachean Ethics from Latin into Hebrew.

(2) Zerahiah ben Isaac ha-Levi (called Saladin), a pupil of Ḥasdai Crescas, to translate the Kitāb tahāfut al-falāsifa of al-Ghazzālī from Arabic into Hebrew under the title Happalat ha-filosofim. This Zerahiah should not be confused with two others: Zerahiah ben Isaac ha-Levi Gerondi, Talmudist and Arabist, who was a disciple of Moses ben Joseph Qimḥi of Narbonne (XII-2); and Zerahiah ben Isaac ben Shealtiel Gracian, translator from Arabic into Hebrew (XIII-2).

(3) Joshua ben Joseph Lorqi II to compile an Arabic treatise on the powers and qualities of various foods and of simple and composite drugs. That treatise is lost, but exists in a Hebrew version, Gerem ha-ma'alot, made by Benveniste's son, Joseph Vidal, in or before 1408.

Besides the scholars already mentioned, Benveniste was acquainted with many others, such as Ḥasdai Crescas, Isaac ben Sheshet, the apostate Astruc Rimok in Aragon, and Joseph Orabuena in Navarre.

Criticism. Steinschneider (p. 112, 211, 328, 762, 1893). Moritz Kayserling (JE 3, 42, 1902), short and erroneous. Josef Heller (EJ 4, 155, 1929).

2a. TRANSLATIONS FROM GREEK INTO LATIN

LEONZIO PILATO

Leontius Pilatus (Πιλάτος), Calabrian humanist and translator from Greek into Latin. Like his teacher Barlaam, he had removed to Constantinople, where he had improved his knowledge of Greek and become Orthodox. Upon Leontius' return from the East and arrival in Venice on his way to Avignon in the winter 1359–60, Petrarca became acquainted with him, persuaded him to undertake a translation of the Iliad, and passed him on to Boccaccio. The latter invited him to come and teach Greek in Florence, obtained for him a position in the Studio, and gave him the hospitality of his own home for almost three years (until October 1362). Leontius was the first public teacher of Greek in Florence, and most probably in Europe. He was very uncouth and ignorant, his knowledge of Greek being on a low empirical level. He and Boccaccio read and discussed Homer together; his bald Latin translation was made available to Petrarca.

Sometime after 1362, Leontius went back to Constantinople in search of Greek MSS; when he returned, at the end of 1366 (or the very beginning of 1367), he was struck by lightning in the course of a tempest in the Adriatic, and died. See two long undated letters addressed by Petrarca to Boccaccio from Venice (Epistolae rerum senilium, lib. III, 5; lib. VI, 1). In the second, January 27 [1367], Petrarca tells the story of Leontius' tragic death.

Text. Il primo canto dell' Iliade tradotto da Leonzio Pilato, edited by Attilio Hortis (Studj sulle opere latine del Boccaccio p. 543–61, Trieste 1879). Il primo canto dell' Odissea, edited by the same (ibid. p. 562–76).

Criticism. Pierre de Nolhac: Pétrarque et l'humanisme (new ed., 2 vols., Paris 1907; by index, chiefly 2, 156–65). Henri Hauvette: Boccace (361–66, Paris 1914). Vasiliev (2, 425–27, 1932).

2b. TRANSLATIONS FROM GREEK INTO HEBREW

SOLOMON BEN ELIJAH

Greco-Jewish astronomer and translator from Greek and Arabic into Hebrew, who flourished c. 1374–86 in Salonica and Ephesus. He called himself Sharbiṭ ha-zahab (the golden scepter; Esther 4:11). Steinschneider suggests that this name was possibly selected as an equivalent to Χρυσοκόκκης.

In Salonica 1374, Solomon compiled Hebrew astronomical tables, Mahalak ha-kokabim (Course of the stars), after the method of the Almagest, then after the method of the "Persians." These tables are preceded by an introduction in 12 chapters, explaining the calendar, eclipses, etc. It is not clear to what extent these tables are original, and to what extent a translation or adaptation of the tables of Georgios Chrysococces (XIV-1), whom the mention of a "Persian method" at once evokes.

Solomon translated into Hebrew the treatise on the astrolabe ascribed to Ptolemy, and an additional chapter explaining the lines of the astrolabe. The translation, supposedly made from the Greek, bewrays an Arabic source. We may assume from his places of residence that Solomon was acquainted with both languages (Greek and Arabic). Is that Hebrew Iggeret ha-aẓṭurlab the same text as the treatise translated into Latin in London 1147 by Robert of Chester (XII-1)?

He also wrote a grammatical treatise, Ḥesheq Solomon, a commentary on the Sefer ha-shem of Abraham ben Ezra (this was done in Ephesus), liturgical poems, and a commentary on the Torah wherein he attacked the Qaraites. The latter were defended against him in the Iggeret ha-ẓom (On fasting) by Elijah ben Moses Beshiẓi (or Bashyazi) of Adrianople (1420–90).

Text. An investigation of the text of Solomon's translations, and a comparison with the relevant Arabic, Greek, and Latin texts, is very desirable. In the meanwhile this note is necessarily tentative.

Criticism. Steinschneider (p. 536, 630, 1893); Die Mathematik bei den Juden (BM 13, 40, 1899). Isaac Broydé (JE 11, 451, 1905; 2, 574–75, 1902).

3a. TRANSLATIONS FROM LATIN INTO HEBREW

MOSES OF ROQUEMAURE

Moses ben Samuel of Roquemaure (Gard). Judeo-Languedocian physician and translator from Latin into Hebrew. He flourished in Avignon, Toledo (?), and Seville. About the year 1358 he was converted to Christianity and called Jean d'Avignon (Juan de Aviñón).

Before his conversion he wrote in Toledo (?) a poem of 62 lines against the eccentric and Messianic theologian Shemariah ben Elijah ha-Iqriṭi (XIV-1).

In 1359-60, being in Seville, he translated the Lilium medicinae of Bernard of Gordon under the title Peraḥ ha-refu'ot (The bud or sprout of health). He changed the order of the Lilium somewhat, and his translation differs in other ways from the one made in 1387 by Jekuthiel ben Solomon.

He wrote two medical works in Latin, both of which seem to be lost in the original but are preserved in Spanish versions. The first of these is a treatise on blood-letting, Phlebotomiae institutio. The other, a treatise entitled Sevillana medicina, deals with the medical climatology of Seville, hygiene, physiology, psychology, mortality. As far as medical topography and climatology are concerned, the Sevillana medicina is the third Spanish effort of its kind, being preceded by a medical discussion of the climate of Zaragoza by Benjamin of Tudela (XII-2) and by the anonymous Medicina castellana regia.[4]

The Sevillana medicina is divided into 69 chapters, wherein Juan discusses such subjects as: the air in general, the air of Seville, climatic differences between various districts of the city, kinds of food available, then many of the topics usually dealt with in a regimen sanitatis, purgation, clysters, coitus, whether a virgin can conceive without it, whether sons are created by the male semen and girls by the female semen, regimen of salvation (del regimiento de la salud), mortality, epidemics in Seville from 1391 to 1419. Juan's medical climatology is naturally mixed up with astrology.

Text. Tratado de flebotomia. Traducido por Juan Lorenzo Carnicer (Zaragoza 1533). This Carnicer, who flourished in Zaragoza in the first half of the sixteenth century, was also the Spanish translator of Guy de Chauliac (1533-54).

Sevillana medicina, que trata el modo conservativo y curativo de los que habitan en la muy insigne ciudad de Sevilla, la cual sirve y aprovecha para cualquiera otro lugar de estos reinos: obra antigua y digna de ser leida. This is the Spanish translation by Nicolás Monardes of Seville (1493-1588), printed Seville 1545. Reprinted for the Sociedad de bibliofilos andaluces (358 p., Seville 1885).

Criticism. Antonio Hernández Morejón: Historia bibliográfica de la medicina española (1, 286-88, Madrid 1842). Steinschneider (p. 785, 1893). Neubauer-Renan (p. 651-53, 1893). H. Gross (p. 629, 1897). Wickersheimer (p. 356, 1936). H. J. Paoli: Juan de Aviñón (Rivista di storia delle scienze, anno 30, 1-25, 234, 1939; Isis 31, 153).

LEON JOSEPH OF CARCASSONNE

Judeo-Languedocian physician and translator of medical books from Latin into Hebrew, who flourished at Carcassonne, Montpellier, Avignon, etc. about 1384-1402.

He translated the following books:

1. Gerald de Solo (XIV-1): Commentary in nonum Almansoris (al-Rāzī, IX-2). He began this translation in Carcassonne 1394, revised it in 1402. In his long preface, he explains the need of better medical books in Hebrew, the available translations from the Arabic and the Latin being insufficient. As examples of insufficiency, he cites the translation of Ibn Sīnā's Qānūn by Nathan ha-Me'ati

[4] That work was written by an unknown physician—Jewish?—who flourished in Toledo at the end of the thirteenth century. Indeed, he was called to treat the *young* Fernando, son of Sancho IV (Fernando was born in 1285, and was king of Castile and Leon from 1295 to 1312). It is divided into an introduction and ten treatises (Escorial MS). Analysis of it in Morejón (1, 86-90, 1842).

(XIII-2) revised by Joseph ben Joshua II ha-Lorqi (though he praised the latter), and the translations of the Lilium medicinae and the De prognosticis of Bernard of Gordon (XIV-1). He had great difficulty in obtaining the Latin texts of Gerald de Solo and Jean de Tournemire, which he was anxious to translate, as the Montpellier doctors had threatened to anathematize anyone selling such books to a Jew.

An abridged Hebrew translation of the same commentary in nonum Almansoris was made at about the same time in the same country by another Jew, Abraham Abigdor. Leon Joseph added many notes to his translation, which was apparently his first work.

2. Gerald de Solo: Introductorium juvenum sive de regimine corporis humani. Translated under the title Mayshir ha-mathilim, after the translation of Gerald's commentary in nonum Almansoris, hence after 1394, perhaps after 1402.

3. Jean de Tournemire: Treatise on urine, being a part of the Libellus isagogicus (sive Introductorium) ad practicam medicinae.

4. Jean de Tournemire: Clarificatorium in nonum Almansoris. The translation is variously entitled Sefer ha-zikkuk, Zikkuk meleket ha-refu'ah, etc. Its ascription to Leon Joseph is uncertain.

5. Pseudo-Hippocratic: De esse aegrotorum secundum Lunam, equivalent to pseudo-Galenic Prognostica de decubitu ex mathematica scientia. An Arabic (?) treatise on astrological medicine which enjoyed some popularity. It was translated at least twice into Latin, by William of Moerbeke and Peter of Abano. Leon Joseph's Hebrew version was entitled Ḥibbur be-ḥokmat ha-ḥizayon; another Hebrew version was made in Italy 1406 by Tanḥum ben Moses of Beaucaire, under the title Fanim le fanim (Face to face).

Criticism. Neubauer-Renan (p. 719, 770–78, 786, 1893); including long extracts from the Hebrew texts. Steinschneider (p. 666, 694, 794–97, 834, 1893). H. Gross (p. 616, 1897). Isaac Broydé (JE 8, 4, 1904). M. Zobel (EJ 10, 791, 1934).

JEKUTHIEL BEN SOLOMON

Jekuthiel ben Solomon of Narbonne. Also called Maestro Bonsenior Salomon. Judeo-Languedocian physician and translator from Latin into Hebrew.

In 1387, he made a new translation of the Lilium medicinae of Bernard of Gordon, entitling it Shoshan ha-refuah (same meaning as Latin title).

Criticism. Steinschneider (p. 785, 1893). Neubauer-Renan (p. 732, 1893). H. Gross (p. 429, 1897). Josef Heller (EJ 8, 1068, 1931).

ABRAHAM ABIGDOR

Abraham ben Meshullam ben Solomon Abigdor. Also called Abraham Bonet (written Boneṭ) Abigdor, of the well known Jewish family of the Abigdorim. Born at Arles, Provence, 1350/51, studied medicine and philosophy in Montpellier, where he spent all together twelve years (c. 1367–79), then established himself at Arles, where he practiced medicine; he was still living there in 1399.

Provençal-Jewish physician and philosopher but primarily translator from Latin into Hebrew. He wrote the following works:

1. Sefer segullat melakim (Treasure of kings). This was his only original work and also his earliest work, for he began it at the age of 17 in 1367, when he was a student in Montpellier (according to another MS it was completed in 1377). It was written in rhymed prose, divided into 4 chapters, and derived from al-Ghazzālī's

Maqāṣid al-falāsifa, which had been translated into Latin by John of Seville (XII-1) and into Hebrew, in 1292 or later, by Isaac Albalag (XIII-2).[4a] The author remarks that many students of physics and metaphysics are deficient in logical knowledge, which is as essential for those studies as grammar for the language. He then explains the main ideas of Aristotelian logic. In addition to being rhymed, his account was different from those of al-Ghazzālī and Ibn Rushd; he also refers to al-Fārābī and Maimonides. His treatment of physics and theology is very brief. He points out that logical errors lead to misunderstandings and are thus a cause of heterodoxy.

Nos. 2 to 7 are translations:

2. Mabo bi-melekeh (Introduction into the art [of medicine]). Translation of the Introductorium in practicam pro provectis in theorica, a collection of recipes derived from Ibn Sīnā's Qānūn (IV, fen i) by Bernard Alberti of Montpellier in 1358. The Hebrew translation was made by Abraham for a friend of his, in all probability during his stay in Montpellier c. 1367–79; it was thus made very soon after the composition of the original text. The latter was printed, under the title Recepte, under the name of Gentile da Foligno (XIV-1) in Venice c. 1490.

In the preface to his translation Abraham explains that he went to Montpellier to study under Christian teachers; he has found many useful medical books available in Latin and is planning to translate some of them into Hebrew. These words would suggest that this was his first translation, and that its date would thus be close to 1367.

3. Pereqe Arnauṭ. Translation of the Medicationis parabolae, or Regulae generales, which Arnold of Villanova dedicated to Philip the Fair in Montpellier 1300 (Introd. 2, 894). The translation is dated 1348 (?!), which should probably be read 1378.

4. Sefer mabo ha-ne'arim (Introduction for the young). Partial translation of the Introductorium juvenum, sive de regimine corporis humani, etc., a textbook for the students of Montpellier composed by Gerald de Solo (XIV-1). Abraham translated only the part dealing with fevers, in Montpellier (or Arles) 1379, the rest being translated later by Leon Joseph of Carcassonne c. 1402. It is not quite clear to me whether this treatise De febribus must be considered a part of the Introductorium or a separate work, but Abraham translated it under the title Mabo ha-ne'arim.

5. Megillah. Translation of the Digestiva et purgantia of Arnold of Villanova, in 9 chapters, made in Arles 1381. The same text was retranslated in 1394 by Ṭodros ben Moses Yom-ṭob (Bondia). The Latin original seems to be lost.

6. Almanẓori. Abridged translation of the ninth book of the Kitāb al-Manṣūrī of al-Rāzī, from the Latin (it had been translated into Latin by Gerard of Cremona) together with Gerald de Solo's commentary, Almansoris liber nonus cum expositione Geraldi de Solo.

7. Ṭraṭaṭo or Higgaion (Meditation). Translation of the Summulae logicales of Peter of Spain. There are other Hebrew translations of the same treatise, whose mediaeval fame was considerable (Introd. 2, 890).

8. Commentary on Ibn Rushd's talkhīṣ on the first three parts of the Organon: the Isagoge, the Categories, and the Interpretation. Of course this was done on the basis of a translation, for there is nothing to suggest that Abraham knew Arabic.

[4a] It is not superfluous to mention both translations. Indeed, it is probable that Abraham used the Latin text rather than the Hebrew one.

9. In Arles 1399 (not 1393) he helped his son Solomon to translate the De judiciis astronomiae of Arnold of Villanova.

Text. Nothing printed.

Criticism. Steinschneider (1893, by index). Neubauer-Renan (p. 717–21, 1893). H. Gross (p. 333, 1897). S. Kahn (JE 1, 58, 1901). I. M. Salkind (EJ 1, 305–7, 1928). Wickersheimer (p. 3, 1936).

SOLOMON ABIGDOR

Solomon ben Abraham Abigdor. Provençal-Jewish translator from Latin into Hebrew. Born presumably at Arles 1384 (or 1378?). Two translations bear his name:

1. Panim ba-mishpaṭ (Methods of judgment; see Deuteronomy 1:17, where the meaning is different). In 17 chapters. Translation of the Capitula astrologiae of Arnold of Villanova. He made that translation with his father's help at the age of 15 in 1399 (hence his birth year 1384). In Introd. 2, 897, I gave the date 1393 (hence the birth year 1378), but according to Salkind the correct date is 1399.[5] The same work had been previously but imperfectly Hebraicized by Jacob ben Judah Cabret (Qabriṭ) in 1381.

2. Sefer mareh ha-ofanim (Indicator of the wheels; allusion to Ezekiel's vision, Ezekiel 1:16, "the appearance of the wheels . . . and their appearance and their work was as it were a wheel in the middle of a wheel." The wheels represent here the astronomical spheres). Translation of the Sphaera mundi composed by Sacrobosco c. 1233, one of the most popular astronomical books of the Middle Ages. Solomon completed his Hebrew version in February 1399. There are various Hebrew MSS, some of which, bearing other titles, may represent other versions; there are also Hebrew commentaries by Mattithiah ben Solomon Delacrut (Delaquṭ, d. c. 1552?), Moses ben Baruch Almosnino (c. 1546), etc.

Text. The Mareh was printed under the title Sefer ha-esfera, together with the Ẓurat ha-ereẓ of Abraham bar Ḥiyya (Offenbach 1720).

Criticism. Neubauer-Renan (p. 721, 1893). Steinschneider (p. 643, 782, 1893); Die Mathematik bei den Juden (BM 13, 97, 1899).

SOLOMON BEN NATHAN CRESCAS

Also called Solomon Orgier or Nathan Orgier. Jewish-Provençal physician and translator from Latin into Hebrew. Born or/and educated in Aix, he flourished in Marseille c. 1388–1414. In 1396, he was appointed town physician.

He translated from Latin into Hebrew a magical book of Apollonios of Tyana (d. 97/8) (Introd. 1, 320), under the title Meleket muskelet (Intellectual art).

Criticism. L. Barthélemy: Les médecins à Marseille avant et pendant le moyen âge (37 p., Marseille 1883; see Revue des études juives 7, 292–94, 1883). Steinschneider (p. 848, 1893). H. Gross (p. 28, 1897). Ad. Crémieux: Les Juifs de Marseille au Moyen-âge (Revue des études juives vol. 46, 1903; see p. 39). J. Heller (EJ 5, 709, 1930), very short note. Wickersheimer (p. 728, 1936).

SOLOMON BEN DAVID DAVIN

Judeo-Provençal astronomer and translator from Latin into Hebrew, who originated or/and flourished in Rodez, Rouergue, in the last quarter of the four-

[5] EJ 1, 307. That statement is contradicted, however, in the same work a few columns farther, 311.

teenth century. Perhaps identical with the Solomon Davin who was in 1385 at Noves, near Avignon. He was a disciple of Immanuel Bonfils, who taught at least until 1377.

He translated from Latin into Hebrew:

1. The astronomical tables of Paris. These tables were a modification of the Alphonsine, compiled c. 1368 for the Paris meridian. Davin's glosses were much criticized by Moses Farissol Botarel[6] a century later.

2. Ibn abī-l-Rijāl (XI-1): Kitāb al-bāri'. Translated from Arabic into Spanish by Judah ben Moses ha-Kohen in 1256, then from Spanish into Latin by Aegidius de Thebaldis of Parma and Petrus de Regio (Pedro del Real). Davin's translation was made from this Latin version; it was thus thrice removed from the original. It was entitled Sefer mishpeṭe ha-kokabim (Judgments of stars; judicial astrology). He added many glosses complaining of the corruption and obscurity of the text.

Criticism. Neubauer-Renan (p. 763–66, 1893). Steinschneider (p. 579, 647, 1893); Die Mathematik bei den Juden (BM 13, 1–2, 1899). H. Gross (p. 389, 626, 1897). Isaac Broydé (JE 4, 473, 1903). J. Heller (EJ 5, 880, 1930), very short note, nothing new.

BENJAMIN BEN ISAAC OF CARCASSONNE

Judeo-Languedocian translator from Latin into Hebrew. He translated the treatise on the corruption of the air and the plague written at Liége in 1362 or 1365 by John of Burgundy (Joannes ad Barbam, for whom see my note on Sir John Mandeville). The contemporary Hebrew version is entitled 'Ezer Elah (God's help), and begins with the words Eli Eli (my God, my God); it is also called Be-'ippush ha-awir veha-deber (The corruption of the air and the plague).

Text. Texts edited by Reuben Levy and translated by him into English in Dorothea Waley Singer and Reuben Levy: Plague tractates (Annals of medical history 1, 400–11, 1917).

Criticism. Neubauer-Renan (p. 723–25, 1893). Steinschneider (p. 803, 1893). H. Gross (p. 617, 1897). Josef Heller (EJ 4, 121, 1929).

JACOB BEN JUDAH CABRET

Cabret or Cabrit. The name is said to be derived from a Spanish locality, but I have not been able to find such a locality, except the island Cabrita (little goat), off Cadiz, and the places called Cabrera in Leon and in the Balearic Islands. The Hebrew spelling of the name is Qabriṭ.

Judeo-Catalan translator from Latin into Hebrew (fl. c. 1355–81). In 1381, being in Barcelona, he translated and abridged Arnold de Villanova's treatise on medical astrology (De judiciis astronomiae, or Capitula astrologiae). A more complete translation of the same work was made a little later (in 1399) by the young Solomon Abigdor helped by his father.

Two other Jewish scholars named Cabret, and possibly of the same family, may be mentioned here.

[6] This Botarel (written with ṭeth), an astronomer who flourished in the second half of the fifteenth century, should not be confused with the Qabbalist Moses Botarel of Cisneros (fl. 1409–14), nor with Moses ben Leon Botarel who lived in Constantinople in the second half of the sixteenth century and wrote a Hebrew paraphrase of Nostradamus' Centuries (JE 9, 63, 1905).

Abraham Cabret, who flourished in the second half of the fourteenth century, wrote a commentary on Hippocrates' Aphorisms.

His son Isaac ben Abraham Cabret translated in 1403, from Latin into Hebrew, the Expositio sive additio super antidotarium Nicolai of John of Saint Amand (XIII-2). This Isaac is probably the same as Isaac ben Abraham Cabret who flourished in Perpignan 1409-13. This takes us into the fifteenth century, but it seemed hardly worth while to separate this Cabret from the two others.

Criticism. Isidore Loeb: Liste nominative des Juifs de Barcelone en 1392 (Revue des études juives 4, 57-77, 1882; p. 61, 71), refers to one Moses Cabret. Steinschneider (p. 783, 1893). Neubauer-Renan (p. 721, 1893). H. Gross (p. 474, 1897). Isaac Broydé (JE 3, 480, 1902). Rubió y Lluch (2, 111, 1921), quotes a document of king Peter III dated Perpignan 1355, referring to a "judeus cirurgicus Barchinone vocatus magister Boniuha Cabrit" who is probably identical with Jacob ben Judah Cabret. S. Posener (EJ 4, 1243, 1929).

MEIR ALGUADEZ

Meir ben Solomon Alguadez. Hispano-Jewish physician and translator from Latin into Hebrew. He was physician and adviser to Henry III, king of Castile from 1390 to 1406. The story told by the Franciscan Alfonso de Spina in his anti-Semitic treatise Fortalitium fidei (1459-61), that Don Meir was tortured to death in 1410 because of an alleged desecration of the Host, is otherwise unknown. Toward the end of the fourteenth century Don Meir was a man of great influence in Castile. Among his literary friends and correspondents were the Castilian apostate Paul of Burgos; in Aragon, Judah ben Solomon ibn Labi, Ḥasdai Crescas, Profiaṭ Duran, the poet Solomon ben Meshullam Dapiera; in Navarre, the chief rabbi Joseph Orabuena.

Alguadez did not believe that Aristotelian and other Greek knowledge was of Jewish origin, but he considered it worth while to examine the conclusions to which Greek sages had been independently led without being enlightened by the Torah. He translated the Nicomachean Ethics from the Latin into Hebrew under the title Sefer ha-midot, and was planning to translate also the Aristotelian Economics and Politics as soon as he should find the necessary commentaries. His translation of the Ethics was based upon the Latin version of one Boetius, presumably made from the Arabic. That Boetius is unknown; Steinschneider, following Amable Jourdain, speaks of a Boetius of Dalmatia, whom he confuses with Boetius of Dacia (i.e., Denmark). See BM (5, 113, 1891) and my Introduction (2, 970). Alguadez' translation was patronized by Judah ben Solomon ibn Labi, who was a powerful person at the Aragonese court c. 1380-1403 (that is, at the very time when Alguadez was so much in favor at the Castilian court).

Alguadez compiled in Spanish a collection of medical recipes, Secreta medica, to which a disciple of his, named Joseph, added others. That collection was translated from Spanish into Hebrew in Genoa 1546, under the title Meqiẓ nirdamim (The awakener of sleepers), by the historian Joseph ben Joshua ha-Kohen (b. Avignon 1496, d. in or after 1577). Joseph ha-Kohen added to the collection a few Hebrew-Latin recipes against the "French disease."

Text. The Sefer ha-midot was published with a Hebrew commentary by Isaac ben Moses Satanow (Berlin 1790-91). That edition is incorrect and does not contain the translator's interesting preface.

Criticism. Steinschneider (p. 209–12, 775, 1893). Moritz Kayserling (JE 1, 387, 1901). Fritz Baer (EJ 2, 308, 1928).

SHEMṬOB SHAPRUṬ

Shemṭob ben Isaac (ibn) Shapruṭ (or Shafruṭ) of Tudela. Judeo-Navarrese physician, translator from Latin into Hebrew, exegete, Talmudist, and Jewish apologist. He was born in Tudela (Navarra) and flourished about the end of the fourteenth century; he was in Pamplona in 1375, practiced medicine in Tarazona, Aragon in 1380–85, and was in Lucena in 1400.

He wrote a Hebrew commentary on the first book of the Qānūn of Ibn Sīnā, entitled 'Ain kol (The eye of everything). That commentary includes those of Solomon ibn Ya'īsh (XIV-1), Joseph ben Joshua II ha-Lorqi, and one Abū-l-Kātib (or Khāṭib, Khaṭīb?). He quoted Galen, the Kitāb al-shifā' of Ibn Sīnā, and the treatise (or fragment) on music of Moses ben Joseph Abulafia, alias Abū 'Imrān (or 'Amrān) Mūsā ibn al-Lawī (d. 1283?). Much of this was available in Hebrew; he actually mentioned the translation of Nathan ha-Me'ati. He criticized Lorqi severely.

He translated parts of the four Gospels (the whole of Matthew) from Latin into Hebrew.

In Pamplona 1375 he took part in a public disputation on the subject of original sin and redemption with Pedro de Luna (afterward antipope Benedict XIII, 1394–1417) in the presence of many theologians.

He composed one of the most comprehensive mediaeval books in defense of Judaism, under the title Eben boḥan (A tried stone, Isaiah 28:16), a treatise directed against baptized Jews, in the form of a dialogue. This book is represented by many divergent MSS but was never published. The original version consisted of twelve books; a revision including two more was completed at Tarazona 1385, a fifteenth book was added at Lucena 1400, and two more were interpolated later still.

The Eben boḥan is divided as follows: (I) principles of the Jewish faith; (II–X) discussion of Old Testament passages which are interpreted differently by Jews and Christians; these nine books are largely based on the Milḥamot ha-shem (Wars of the Lord) of Jacob bar Reuben,[7] which he ascribes to Joseph ben Isaac Qimḥi (XII-2); (XI) discussion of Talmudic haggadot understood differently by Jews and Christians; (XII) translation of Matthew; (XIII) resurrection; (XIV) Messiah; (XV) refutation of the Milḥamot Adonai of Alfonso of Valladolid (Abner of Burgos, XIV-1). Later still Shemṭob wrote another treatise against Christian theology, based on the Kelimmat ha-goyim composed in 1397 by Profiaṭ Duran. In some MSS that treatise is inserted before and after the translation of Matthew. Then chapters XII and XIII–XV become respectively XIII and XV–XVII. According to JE (6, 540), chapter XIII contains a fragment by a fourteenth-century Schopenhauer, who wrote under the pseudonym Lamas (Samal, Samuel?).

Shemṭob wrote a commentary, Ẓafnat pa'aneaḥ (i.e., Joseph's Egyptian name, Genesis 41:45), on Abraham ben Ezra's commentary on the Torah, and he explained difficult Talmudic stories under the title Pardes rimonim (Garden of pomegranates) 'al haggadot ha-Talmud (this may be identical with book XI of Eben boḥan).

[7] We know nothing about this Jacob bar Reuben. He is different from Jacob ben Reuben the Qaraite, who flourished in Constantinople in the twelfth century, visited his Qaraite brethren in many countries, and wrote a Biblical commentary called Sefer ha-'osher (Book of riches); he is also different from Jacob ben Reuben who flourished in the thirteenth century and translated Marbode's lapidary into Hebrew, also under the title Sefer ha-'osher (Introd. 2, 48).

Beware of confusing this Shemṭob ben Isaac of Tudela with Shemṭob ben Isaac of Tortosa (XIII-2).

Text. Pardes rimonim (Sabbioneta 1554). Second edition (Zhitomir 1866).

Besorat Mattai. Hebrew versions of Matthew were first published by Sebastian Münster (Basel 1537, 1557, 1582) and by J. du Tillet (Paris 1555). It was assumed by Richard Simon (1638–1712) that these sixteenth-century editors reproduced Shemṭob's version, and that error was inexcusably repeated by a modern editor, Adolf Herbst: Des Schemtob ben Schaprut hebräische Übersetzung des Evangeliums Matthäi nach den Drucken des S. Münster und J. du Tillet-Mercier neu herausgegeben (Göttingen 1879). In reality Shemṭob's version is still unpublished.

Criticism. Steinschneider (p. 689, 957, 1893); (p. 162, 1902). Meyer Kayserling (JE 6, 539, 1904). Alexander Marx: The polemical MSS in the library of the Jewish Theological Seminary of America (A. S. Freidus memorial volume, New York 1929; Isis 15, 282); discussing on p. 265–70 the divergencies between the MSS of Eben boḥan, and on p. 270–75 the different Hebrew versions of Matthew.

3b. TRANSLATIONS FROM LATIN INTO GREEK

PROCHOROS CYDONES

Πρόχορος ὁ Κυδώνης. Byzantine theologian and translator from Latin into Greek (d. 1368/69).

Prochoros was a member of an old Salonican family. The father died early, and the family was ruined by the revolutionary events which upset Salonica in 1346 and following years. His elder brother Demetrios was befriended by John Cantacuzenos; Prochoros retired early into the great lavra of Mt. Athos and became a monk and priest. There he spent the rest of his life except for a short visit to his brother Demetrios. Yet his Latin sympathies were bound to cause trouble for him in that hotbed of Hesychasm and extreme anti-Catholic orthodoxy. At the synod of April 1368, Philotheos (patriarch 1354–55, 1364–76) canonized Gregorios Palamas (XIV-1; d. c. 1360) and anathematized Prochoros. The latter died soon afterward (1368/69), being still relatively young, in extreme disgrace, without having been given the extreme unction, without funeral, and without burial in a consecrated tomb.

His main work is the treatise (1) *περὶ οὐσίας καὶ ἐνεργείας* previously ascribed to Gregorios Acindynos (XIV-1). That treatise is divided into six books, but no complete MS of it has come down to us. We have parts of books III and V; books I, II, and VI are entirely known, the latter dealing exclusively with the moot question of the Uncreated Light of Mt. Tabor and being sometimes considered a separate work. The whole treatise is very largely derived, often verbatim, from the writings of St. Thomas Aquinas, chiefly from the Summa contra Gentiles (De veritate catholicae fidei), but also from the Summa theologica and the Quaestiones disputatae. It would seem that Prochoros did not use the translation of the Summa contra Gentiles completed by his brother Demetrios in 1354, but used either the Latin text or another translation. In any case it is extremely interesting to witness the diffusion of St. Thomas' writings in the Greek world at this time; judging from the rarity of MSS, however, that diffusion was very restricted.

Prochoros' anathematization is understandable if one bears in mind that the Hesychastic movement was at least in part a revolt against the Occidental scholasticism which he was trying to introduce. The main issue was not between monks and non-monks within the Orthodox church, but rather between Orthodoxy and mysticism on the one hand, and the moderate intellectualism of the Western doctors, chiefly St. Thomas, on the other.

Prochoros wrote at least three other theological treatises against the Hesychasts or Palamites: (2) περὶ τῆς ἐν τῷ Θεῷ πατρότητος καὶ υἱότητος (Fathership and sonship in God), also ascribed to his contemporary Joannes of Cypros; (3) a treatise against the Palamites of the Holy Mountain on the main points of contention, such as the light of Tabor, divine operation, etc.; (4) περὶ καταφατικοῦ καὶ ἀποφατικοῦ τρόπου ἐπὶ τῆς θεολογίας καὶ περὶ τῆς ἐν τῷ ὄρει τοῦ Κυρίου θεοφανείας (The affirmative and the negative on theology and on the theophany [or epiphany] of the Lord on the mountain). Toward the end of his life he composed a strongly worded apology for his life and doctrine, which he addressed to the patriarch Philotheos after having been condemned by him (April 1368). In one of the MSS that apology is ascribed to his brother Demetrios, but he is more likely to have written it himself.

More important than all these are Prochoros' translations from Latin into Greek: (1) St. Jerome's preface to the Vulgate (IV-2); (2) various writings of St. Augustine (V-1); (3) books I and II of the De differentiis topicis of Boetius (VI-1), περὶ διαλεκτικῆς πραγματείας τινά; (4) three texts of St. Thomas Aquinas (XIII-2), De mundi aeternitate, 82 articles taken from the third part of the Summa theologica, preface to his commentary on Aristotle's metaphysics. The choice of these texts is significant; it is clear that Prochoros was anxious to take soundings in Occidental metaphysics and theology.

Text. Two books of the περὶ οὐσίας καὶ ἐνεργείας were edited in Greek by the Jesuit Jacob Gretser (or Gretscher, 1562–1625) of Ingolstadt, who ascribed the work to Acindynos, ascription repeated by every later writer until 1931. The title reads Gregorii Acindyni libri duo De essentia et operatione Dei, olim adversus inscitiam quorundum Graecorum conscripti jam vero contra calvinianam imperitiam Conradi Vorstii et Vorstianorum graece publicati (Ingolstadt 1616). Reprinted with Gretser's preface and Latin translation in PG (151, 1187–1242, Paris 1865). Father Gretser's preface is a virulent attack against the reformer Conrad Vorstius (1569–1622); it does not refer at all to St. Thomas.

Criticism. Krumbacher (p. 102, 106, 110, 1897), very short and insufficient. Giovanni Mercati: Notizie di Procorio e Demetrio Cidone . . . (p. 1–61, Vaticano 1931), including unpublished extracts from the περὶ οὐσίας, books III, V, VI, and the anathemas which were recited in Salonica in the fifteenth century against Demetrios and Prochoros Cydones.

DEMETRIOS CYDONES

Δημήτριος ὁ Κυδώνης. Byzantine theologian, and translator from Latin into Greek (d. c. 1400).

He was probably born at Salonica in the first quarter of the century. He flourished in that city, which was then a cultural center (a second Athens!), then later in Constantinople. His great talents brought him into contact with the most famous men of letters and theologians of his time. He was befriended by John VI Cantacuzenos, and at the time of the latter's deposition (1355) followed him into monastic retirement, though without taking orders. Later he went to Milano, where he continued his studies of Latin theology and language. After his return he lived in Constantinople, Salonica, and Crete (?). It is said that he died in a monastery of that island at the end of the century; it is more probable that he died in Venice at the end of 1399.

In addition to his literary distinction, his importance lies in his being one of the first translators from Latin into Greek, and one of the first interpreters of Catholic theology to the Orthodox theologians. He was on good terms with many of the latter, e.g., the Hesychast Nicolaos Cabasilas, in spite of his being naturally anti-Hesychastic.

He wrote treatises against Gregorios Palamas, and on that highly controversial subject, the procession of the Holy Spirit;[8] two deliberative speeches (συμβουλευτικοί) discussing the growing Turkish danger and the need of concerted action of Greeks and Latins against the common enemy; one of these treatises was written in 1369 while John V Palaeologos was traveling in Italy to obtain assistance (Ῥωμαίοις συμβουλευτικός), the other at the time when Murād ('Uthmānlī sulṭān 1360–89) was trying to obtain the town of Callipolis (Gallipoli), advising against that concession (Συμβουλευτικὸς ἕτερος περὶ Καλλιπόλεως αἰτήσαντος τοῦ Μουράτου); an ode on the victims of the peasant insurrection which broke out in Salonica 1345 (μονῳδία ἐπὶ τοῖς ἐν Θεσσαλονίκῃ πεσοῦσιν); a treatise on the contempt of death (περὶ τοῦ καταφρονεῖν τὸν θάνατον) which was read by many for centuries; and more than 450 letters addressed to John Cantacuzenos, Manuel II, and the intellectual elite of his time. A part of his correspondence is valuable for the history of humanism, e.g., it includes a letter addressed to Cydones in 1396 by Coluccio Salutati.

Cydones' most important writings, however, are his translations from Latin into Greek, to wit, a mass of the Ambrosian rite, writings of St. Augustine (V-1), Fulgentius (d. 533), St. Anselm (XI-2), the Confutatio Alcorani of Ricoldo di Monte Croce (XIII-2), and, most important of all, the Summa contra Gentiles of St. Thomas Aquinas. Cydones admired St. Thomas exceedingly; he completed the translation of the Summa after a year's work, in 1354, December 24. The date is significant, for it shows that he knew enough Latin for that great task before going to Milano.

It is possible that Demetrios' translation of St. Thomas was preceded by another made c. 1300 by the French Dominican Guillaume Bernard of Gaillac (XIV-1), but in any case a translation into Greek by a scholar having but an artificial knowledge of that language would be very inferior to one made by a Greek having but an artificial knowledge of Latin.

Text. Many of the treatises were published in PG (vol. 154, 1866). The translation of the Confutatio Alcorani had been published before by Theodore Bibliander (d. 1564) in his anti-Islamic folio (Basel 1543).

The Opusculum de contemnenda morte was published many times, the princeps by Raphael Seiler (Basel 1553). Others, 1559, 1577, 1586, 1786, 1866 (in PG), 1901. I have seen the edition of Christianus Theophilus Kuinoel (Christian Gottlieb Kühnöl, 1768–1841) in Greek and Latin with abundant notes (160 p., Leipzig 1786), and the latest one, by Henry Deckelmann (60 p., Leipzig 1901), in Greek only.

Correspondance, texte inédit, établi et traduit par Giuseppe Cammelli (264 p., Paris 1913). Chronological list and summary of all the letters, edition of fifty hitherto unpublished ones (Byzantinische Zeitschrift 35, 100–4, 1935).

Giovanni Mercati: Notizie di Procoro e Demetrio Cidone, Manuele Caleca e Teodore Meliteniota ed altri appunti per la storia della teologia e della letteratura bizantina del secolo XIV (560 p., 12 pl., Città del Vaticano 1931; Byzantinische Zeitschrift 35, 92–100, 1935). Including many unpublished texts (p. 283–450).

[8] One of the treatises on that subject formerly ascribed to him is now ascribed (by G. Mercati) to one of his disciples, Manuel Calecas (Μανουὴλ Καλέκας), Dominican in Pera, who died in Mytilene 1410 (Krumbacher p. 110).

Criticism. Krumbacher (chiefly p. 102–3, 487–89, 1897). A. Palmieri (DTC 3, 2454–58, 1907). E. Bouvy: St. Thomas, ses traducteurs byzantins (Revue augustinienne 16, 407–8, 1910), not seen. Tafrali (342 p., 1912). Mercati (1931). Vasiliev (2, 399–401, 1932). Peter Charanis: The Greek historical sources of the second half of the fourteenth century (Bull. Polish Institute 2, 406–12, New York 1944), a plea for the publication of Cydones' complete works.

3c. TRANSLATIONS FROM LATIN INTO FRENCH

JEAN DE SY

French translator of the Bible (fl. 1348–55).

Jean de Sy or Joannes de Siaco is probably identical with a friar who lectured on the Sentences at the University of Paris in 1348–50. Sy is a locality in the diocese of Reims (dépt. Ardennes). Jean de Sy is the author of a very remarkable French translation of the Bible which king John the Good ordered to be made at the expense of the Jews. The text which has come down to us (Bibliothèque nationale) extends from Genesis 8 to the end of Deuteronomy, and includes many glosses. It is dated 1355. The translation was probably interrupted in 1356, when the Black Prince defeated king John at Maupertuis, near Poitiers, and made him prisoner. Sy's translation was independent of the earlier thirteenth-century translation. It was continued by many other writers, and illustrated by sundry limners working for Louis and Charles d'Orléans; king John's Bible, as it was called, was not yet completed in 1410.

A translation into French verse of Boetius' Consolation ascribed to him is probably not his; it has also been ascribed to one Jean de Cis, who seems to be different from Jean de Sy (Cis-la-Commune is in the Aisne department). I have already explained (Introd. 2, 932–34) the great importance attached in mediaeval times to the Consolation; there are an abundance of translations of it, beginning with the Anglo-Saxon one by king Alfred (IX-2), a Provençal one (end of eleventh century), and a whole series of French ones (first, in latter part of twelfth century).

Criticism. Samuel Berger: La Bible française au moyen âge. Etude sur les plus anciennes versions de la Bible écrites en prose de langue d'oïl (p. 238–43, Paris 1884), including extract. A. Thomas: Jean de Sy et Jean de Cis (Romania 21, 612–15, 1892).

MARTIN DE SAINT-GILLES

French physician and translator (fl. 1362).

There are many localities called Saint-Gilles in France, e.g., one near Nîmes which may have been Martin's native or familial place, for he was flourishing in Avignon in 1362. He undertook there a French translation, probably from the Latin, of the Aphorisms of Hippocrates with Galen's commentary, Livre des amphorismes Ypocras en medecine avecques les commens de Galien.

Martin had studied theology as well as medicine, both in Paris, and was in the service of the dauphine Jeanne de Bourbon (wife of Charles duke of Normandy, later Charles V).

Text. The translation of the Aphorisms is unpublished. MS fr. 24,246, Bibliothèque nationale, Paris.

Criticism. Wickersheimer (p. 543, 1936).

JEAN CORBECHON

French translator from Latin into French, who flourished in 1372.

In that year he translated for Charles V the De proprietatibus rerum of Bartholomew the Englishman (XIII-1), Livre des proprietez des choses.

Criticism. HL (24, 184, 1862).

FOULECHAT

Denis Foulechat. French translator from Latin into French (fl. 1372).

Franciscan in Paris. He translated for Charles the Wise (king 1364–80) in 1372 the Polycratus of John of Salisbury (XII-2). His is a very poor translation; he did not always understand the text, and left many passages untranslated; he apologized to the king for having spent so much time on that difficult task; he humbly realized his limitations.

Criticism. Petit de Julleville (2, 265, 1896).

PRESLES

Raoul or Rodolphe de Presles. French translator from Latin into French (d. c. 1382).

He was born c. 1314 in Paris, being the son of Raoul de Presles, secretary of Philippe le Bel, thrown into prison by Louis X, died 1331. He became a lawyer, and was "maître des requêtes" from 1373. He died in Paris in 1382 (or 1383).

He was one of the best translators employed by Charles the Wise (king 1364–80). He began the translation of the Bible ordered by the king, this being simply a revision of the thirteenth-century translation. In 1375, he completed the translation of St. Augustine's Civitas Dei. He had also translated for the king a political treatise by Giles of Rome, De utraque potestate.

His translation of the Civitas Dei was not literal, but free (par maniere de circonlocucion), and he added various remarks (additions ou declaracions) to the text.

He wrote the Compendieux moral de la chose publique, La muse, and Croniques en françois (chronicles from the beginning of the world, of no special value).

The Somnium viridarii was wrongly ascribed to him. The Latin text was written very probably by Philippe de Mézières and completed in May 1376; the French text, Le songe du vergier, once thought to be the original, was written later, c. 1376–78, Raoul de Presles or Philippe himself being the translator.

Text. Raoul's translation of the Civitas Dei was printed in Abbeville 1486, then again in Paris 1531, each edition in two volumes.

Criticism. P. Paris: Nouvelles recherches sur le véritable auteur du Songe du vergier (Mémoires de l'Académie des inscriptions 15, 336–68, 1842; p. 354 ff.). Adolphe Franck: Réformateurs et publicistes de l'Europe (p. 219–50, Paris 1864); a chapter of that book is devoted to Raoul de Presles, or, more exactly, to the Songe du vergier, on the assumption that Raoul wrote it. Samuel Berger: La Bible française au Moyen âge (p. 244–58, Paris 1884). Petit de Julleville (2, 264, 1896).

JEAN DANDIN

French translator from Latin into French. He was one of the translators employed by Charles V the Wise, and translated for him the De remediis utriusque fortunae composed by Petrarca, and the De eruditione filiorum regalium which Vincent of Beauvais had written (c. 1254–60) by order of St. Louis.

Criticism. HL (24, 181, 190, 575, 1862).

HESDIN

Simon de Hesdin. Translator from Latin into French, flourished under Charles the Wise (king 1364–80).

Simon originated probably in the town of Hesdin (in Artois; dépt. Pas-de-Calais). He was a master in theology and a knight of St. John of Jerusalem (a Hospitaler), and began for Charles V a French translation of the Facta et dicta memorabilia of Valerius Maximus (under Tiberius, emperor 14–37), a work which enjoyed considerable popularity in mediaeval times. The Facta are divided into nine books; Simon's translation extended only as far as the seventh book; the final books were translated in 1401 by Nicolas de Gonesse, master in arts and theology, for Jean duke of Berry. Nicolas humbly remarks that his part of the translation is not so perfect as Simon's.

Text. The French translation of Simon and Nicolas was printed in 1476, 2 vols. folio, no place mentioned. Second edition, Lyon 1485; third edition, Lyon 1489, etc.

Criticism. Emile Van Arenbergh (Biographie nationale de Belgique 9, 312–14, 1887).

EUDES

Richard Eudes. French physician and translator from Latin into French fl. 1379–85).

We may assume that he was a Norman, for he is first mentioned as a subdeacon in the diocese of Avranches, and in 1379 he was a master of arts and a fourth-year medical student of the Norman nation at the University of Paris. In 1385, being a master of medicine, he joined in Auxerre Mary of Blois, queen of Naples, and followed in her train to Provence.

He translated into French verse the Latin poem of Peter of Eboli (XII-2) on the mineral waters of Pozzuoli (near Naples).

Criticism. Wickersheimer (p. 700, 1936).

JACQUES BAUCHANT

French bibliophile and translator from Latin into French (d. 1396).

He was born in Saint-Quentin (Vermandois; dépt. Aisne). He formed a collection of books which attracted the attention of Charles V (king 1364–80), who was then beginning to form his own "librairie" in the Louvre. The king appointed him his sergeant at arms and ordered him to translate Latin classics for him. Bauchant translated the De remediis fortuitorum of Seneca. After his death many MSS gathered by him were bought by Louis duke of Orléans, brother of Charles VI, and are now in the Bibliothèque nationale, Paris.

Bauchant's translation is important because it was the first French version of a book of Seneca, except for the letters to Lucilius, translated into French c. 1308–10 by an anonymous south Italian for Bartolommeo Siginulfo,[9] a favorite of Charles II

[9] Siginulfo was not the translator as I put it wrongly in chapter I, but the patron of the anonymous translator. The latter declares in his prologue that he did his work as well as he could at the request of "misire Bartholomy Singuilerfe [sic], conte de Caserte, etc." MS in Paris, Bibliothèque nationale, fr. 12,235 fol. 1 (HL 35, 633, 1921).

of Anjou, king of Naples. This earlier translation was soon retranslated into Catalan, and there is also an early Sicilian translation which may have been made from the Latin or from the French, for Siginulfo spent the last years of his life, 1310–c. 1316, in exile in Sicily.

Criticism. Charles Desmaze: Jacques Bauchant, sergent d'armes, bibliophile saint-quentinois (Bull. de la Société des antiquaires de Picardie 10, 226–34, Amiens 1870; reprinted Saint-Quentin 1873). Articles by Antoine Thomas in Grande encyclopédie (5, 849) and HL (35, 633–35, 1921).

GOLEIN

Jean Golein. French translator from Latin into French (d. 1403).

Jean Golein or Goulain was born in Blacqueville, Normandy, c. 1320? He assumed the Carmelite habit in Rouen; at the chapter of Perpignan 1354 he was selected by his order to teach theology in Paris, and he soon became a distinguished professor in the university of that city. Later he was elected provincial of France. He was one of the translators selected by Charles V the Wise (king 1364–80), and as such attained some prestige, which was lost during the sad rule of Charles VI. He died in Paris 1403.

Golein was one of the most active translators (if not the most active) of that period. He was praised by Christine de Pisan. The main works translated by him are:

1. Joannes Cassianus Eremita (c. 360–c. 435): Collationes patrum. Translation dedicated to Charles V in 1370. Cassianus was one of the founders of monasticism in the West, a semi-Pelagian. His works are included in PL (vols. 49–50, 1846). The Collationes are dialogues of the Egyptian fathers. Cassianus had been educated in Bethlehem, had spent many years with the ascetics of Egypt, had been ordained deacon in Constantinople and priest in Rome. After 410 he founded a convent for nuns and the abbey of St. Victor in Marseille, hence he is often called John of Marseille, Joannes Massiliensis.

2. De informatione principum, treatise written by a Dominican after 1297 and before 1314, and often confused with the Regimen principum of Giles of Rome (XIII-2). Golein translated the anonymous treatise (Introd. 2, 925).

3. William Durand "Speculator" (XIII-2): Rationale divinorum officiorum. The French version omits parts of the original text and adds novelties; it is interesting for the history of French liturgy.

4. Bernard Gui (XIV-1): Translation of various works, presented to the king in 1369.

5. Gonzalo de Hinojosa (1260–1327). Chronicae ab origine mundi. Work generally called "Chronicle of Spain" or "Chronicle of Burgos." The author was bishop of Burgos from 1313 to 1327, and it was during that time that he composed his very long chronicle. Golein translated it into French c. 1370–73; that was his longest work.

Text. Le mirouer exemplaire . . . selon la compillation de Gilles de Romme . . . du regime et gouvernement des roys . . . (Paris 1517). This is Golein's French translation of no. 2.

Criticism. Cosmas de Villiers: Biblioteca carmelitana (1, 854–57, Orléans 1752; reprint of Rome 1927). Léopold Delisle: Auteur du Liber de informatione principum (HL 31, 35–47, 1893). Auguste Castan: Les chroniques de Burgos traduites pour Charles V en partie retrouvées à la bibliothèque de Besançon (Bibliothèque de l'Ecole des chartes 44, 265–83, Paris 1883), includes extracts from Golein's translation. Vera (2, 15–16, 1934), for Hinojosa.

EVRARD DE CONTY

Evrard de Conty (de Contis, de Contiaco), *not* de Coucy. (Conty is not far from Amiens in Picardie; Coucy not far from Laon in the Ile-de-France.) French priest, physician, and translator from Latin into French (d. 1405).

He translated the Problems ascribed to Aristotle (Livre des problèmes), probably from the Greco-Latin version of Bartholomew of Messina (XIII-2). Evrard's translation is represented by many MSS, one of which (in the Paris Bibliothèque nationale) is said to be holograph.

In 1357 he was a master regent of the medical faculty of Paris, and continued so until at least 1379; he was physician to Charles V and to queen Blanche of Navarre (widow of Philip VI); thanks to Blanche's influence, he was appointed in 1363 curate of Daubeuf-en-Vexin. His jubilee was celebrated by the medical faculty of Paris in 1403, during his absence; he died in 1405.

Criticism. Wickersheimer (p. 146, 1936).

3e. TRANSLATIONS FROM LATIN INTO ENGLISH

TREVISA

John of Trevisa. English translator from Latin into English (d. 1402).

John belonged to a Cornish family. The date and place of his birth are uncertain. As to the place, it was in Cornwall, perhaps at Crocadon or Caradok in the parish of St. Mellion in Hundred of East (near Trevisa[10] in St. Enedor; near Saltash); the dates run from 1322 to 1342. He went to Oxford for study, entering Exeter College in 1362; later he became a fellow of Queen's. At some time before 1387 (perhaps a long time before), he was appointed domestic chaplain to the lord of Berkeley; later, vicar of Berkeley (Gloucestershire). He spent the best part of his active life there, traveled in Germany and Savoy, and died at Berkeley in 1402 (not 1412).

His activity as a translator from Latin into English is significant because it illustrates the growing importance of English vs. French. His translations are examples of early English prose. He translated the following works:

1. The Polychronicon of Ranulf Higden, continued to 1357. The translation was completed at Berkeley in 1387. It was revised by William Caxton, who added an introduction and a continuation to 1460, forming the eighth book, and printed it in 1482.

2. De proprietatibus rerum, by Bartholomew the Englishman (XIII-1), written c. 1230. That translation was completed at Berkeley in 1397–98 (princeps c. 1495).

3. The Gospel of Nicodemos (Νικόδημος), De passione Christi. "The passyoun of oure Lord ihesu translated by mayster John Treuysa" (James p. 94–146, 1924).

4. De re militari of Vegetius (IV-2). Translation completed in 1408 at Berkeley. This does not tally with Trevisa's newly found death date, 1402 (instead of 1412). It seems apocryphal.

[10] The name Trevisa seems Italian, but is Cornish. Trevisa is the lower town, as opposed to Trewhella, the upper town; both names occur in St. Enedor.

5. De regimine principum, by Giles of Rome (XIII-2), composed c. 1285. The translation is more usually ascribed to Thomas Hoccleve,[11] but this may be due to a misunderstanding, for Hoccleve's wretched English poem De regimine principum (5,488 lines, written in 1411–12) is derived not only from Giles of Rome, but also from the Secretum secretorum and from the game of chess moralized (De moribus hominum et de officiis nobilium super ludo scaccorum) by Jacques de Cessoles.[12]

6. Dialogus inter militem et clericum, ascribed to William Occam and also to Pierre Dubois.

7. Defensio curatorum, by Richard Fitzralph, archbishop of Armagh (d. 1360), for whom see R. L. Poole (DNB 19, 194–98, 1889). This is one of the sermons preached by Richard in defense of the seculars and against the clerical duty of evangelical poverty. It was delivered in Avignon 1357.

8. The translation of Methodius, The begynnyng of the world and the ende of worldes, is doubly apocryphal. That is, the translation ascribed to Trevisa is apocryphal, and the text itself, ascribed to Methodios (presumably Methodios the Confessor, Ὁμολογητής, patriarch of Constantinople, d. 847), is also apocryphal. Itis a pseudo-Methodios translated by a pseudo-Trevisa.

Text. 1. Polychronicon. First printed by William Caxton (Westminster 1482). Second edition by Wynkyn de Worde (Westminster 1495). De Worde's edition was reprinted by Peter Treveris (Southwerke 1527). A part of the work, entitled The description of England, was printed separately by Caxton in 1480 and by de Worde in 1498.

Complete edition together with the Latin text in the Rolls series (9 vols., 1865–86).

2. The translation of Bartholomew was first printed by Wynkyn de Worde (Westminster c. 1495); then again by T. Berthelet (London 1535). The third edition was rearranged by Stephen Batman (d. 1584), printed by T. East (London 1582). Selections edited by Robert Steele: Mediaeval lore from Bartholomaeus Anglicus, with preface by William Morris (London 1893; reprinted 1907). The first edition, of c. 1495, contains among other illustrations (10 woodcuts) a drawing of a dissection scene, the earliest to appear in a book printed in England or in an English book.

3. The treatys of Nychodemus gospell. First printed by Julyan Notary (London 1507). Later editions 1509, 1511, 1512, 1518, 1529, 1532, 1537? Text and translation edited by J. Warren (Rouen 1620).

6, 7, 8. Dialogus inter militem et clericum, Defensio curatorum, The bygynnyng of the world and the ende of worldes, edited by Aaron Jenkins Perry (Early English Text Society no. 167, 272 p., London 1925).

For the printed editions of the Latin texts, see Perry's introduction (p. liii–lv).

Criticism. C. L. Kingsford (DNB 57, 212, 1899), out of date. Bernhard Pfeffer: Die Sprache des Polychronicons John Trevisa's (Diss. Bonn, 151 p., 1912). Murray (p. 537–45, 1913). Henry John Wilkins: Was John Wycliffe a negligent pluralist? Also John of Trevisa, his life and work (London 1915); Appendix (18 p., Bristol 1916). Wells (p. 204, 438, 1926). George A. Plimpton: The education of Chaucer (p. 34, London 1935).

4. TRANSLATIONS FROM HEBREW INTO GREEK AND LATIN

ATUMANOS

Symeon Atumanos, Συμεὼν τοῦ Ἀτουμάνου. Simon of Constantinople. Byzantine translator of the Bible (d. 1383–87).

[11] Thomas Hoccleve or Occleve (1370?–1450?), English poet and clerk in the privy seal office. F. G. Fotheringham (DNB 27, 56–57, 1891).

[12] For Jacques de Cessoles see the note on Jean de Vignai (XIV-1).

The name Atumanos is spelled and misspelled in many ways, e.g., Athomanus, Atumaeus, Iatomeus. Symeon was born in Constantinople and became a monk in the Basilian monastery of St. John of Studion (now Imrahor mosque, near the Seven Towers castle). It is possible that he became a disciple of Barlaam and followed the latter to Italy. It is certain that he succeeded Barlaam as bishop of Gerace (Reggio di Calabria) in 1348, and continued in that bishopric until 1366, when he was appointed archbishop of Thebes, Boeotia. During the Catalan invasion (1380–83) he was reduced to poverty and finally went to Rome, where he spent the rest of his life but for a short visit to Constantinople. He died between 1383 and 1387.

He undertook to translate for Urban VI (pope 1378–89) the Old Testament from Hebrew into Greek and Latin; it is said that he also translated or planned to translate the New Testament from Greek into Latin and into Hebrew. He thus produced a triglot Bible, or at least a part of it. The famous MS Graecus venetus (Marcianus graecus VII) of the Old Testament is Atumanos' new Greek version from the Hebrew. Atumanos was a good Hellenist, but a poor Latinist. His translation from Greek into Latin of Plutarchos' treatise on anger (De remediis irae or De cohibenda ira) was severely criticized by Coluccio Salutati, who called its language semi-Greek and rewrote it in a more elegant Latin. Atumanos owned a MS of the tragedies of Sophocles and Euripides (now Laurentianus graecus XXXII, 2), and had added various marginal notes to it.

During his Roman residence Atumanos was also a teacher of Greek, one of his pupils being Radulphus de Rivo (also called Raoul de Ruisseau, Roland of Breda or of Tongres), born in Breda, canon of Tongres, rector of the University of Cologne in 1397, died in Tongres 1403. Radulphus was Atumanos' pupil in 1381–83. He was a good all-around scholar, if not a creative one. His main work is a chronicle of the bishops of Liége from 1347 to 1389. In the course of his travels he acquired many MSS, which he bequeathed to churches of Liége, Breda, and Tongres, notably a Greek text of the New Testament used by Erasmus. The chronicle was edited by John Chapeauville (canon of Liége, d. 1617): Qui gesta pontificum tungrensium, traiectensium et leodiensium scripserunt... (3, 1–58, Liége 1618). Sylv. Balau (Biographie nationale de Belgique 18, 548–51, 1905).

Text. Oscar Gebhardt: Graecus venetus. Pentateuchi Proverbiorum Ruth Cantici Ecclesiastae Threnorum Danielis versio graeca (602 p., Leipzig 1875).

Criticism. Giovanni Mercati: Se la versione dall' ebraico del codice veneto greco VII sia di Simone Atumano (67 p., 2 pl., Rome 1916), including biography and documents. J. W. Thompson (p. 436, 1939).

7. TRANSLATIONS FROM SANSKRIT INTO BENGĀLI

KRITTIVĀSA

Bengāli poet (b. 1346).

The two greatest monuments of ancient Sanskrit poetry, the Mahābhārata, "edited" by the mythical Vyāsa (the arranger), and the Rāmāyaṇa of Vālmīki,[13]

[13] The Mahābhārata contains more than 100,000 śloka, and the Rāmāyaṇa about 24,000. The śloka equals 2 lines of 16 syllables each, or 4 lines of 8 syllables. For comparison, let us recall that the Iliad contains 15,693 lines, and the Odyssey 12,110, together 27,803 lines. Hence the Mahābhārata alone is more than eight times longer than the whole of Homer! For a general account of the Mahābhārata see E. Washburn Hopkins (ERE 8, 325–27, 1916), and for the Rāmāyana see A. A. MacDonell (ERE 10, 574–78, 1919).

both of great antiquity, have made a very deep impress upon all the people submitted to Hindu influences, not only in their original Sanskrit form, but also in countless translations and adaptations in the many vernaculars of India, southeastern Asia, and the East Indies. In many cases these translations and adaptations are among the earliest and outstanding monuments of those vernaculars, and must be dealt with in any account of the cultures which these vernaculars represent.

Thus, one of the earliest landmarks of Bengāli literature is the translation of the Rāmāyaṇa ascribed to Kṛittivāsa. That Bengāli text has not come to us in its original state, but only after having been modified in many ways. As it is, it has remained throughout the centuries one of the most popular books of Bengal, being used throughout the Gangetic valley as a kind of Bible.

Kṛittivāsa (b. 1346) belonged to an illustrious Brāhmin family. He wrote his translation of the Rāmāyaṇa at the request of the king of Gauḍa (Bengal).

A Bengāli summary of the Mahābhārata was composed by another Brāhmin poet, Sañjaya, at about the same time. Thus by the end of the fourteenth century the two great Sanskrit epics were available to the people of Bengal.

Text. There are many Bengāli editions of the Rāmāyaṇa in the version ascribed to "Kirtee Bass" (Serampore 1802) or "Krittee-Bas" (Serampore 1830-34), etc. There are also editions in Sanskrit and Bengāli. The most elaborate Bengāli edition, Sapta-kāṇḍa kṛitti-vāsa-rāmāyaṇa, was prepared by Pūrṇachandra De, Kavi-bhūshaṇa (824 p., 46 pl., Calcutta 1926).

For other Bengāli editions, complete or partial, of the Rāmāyaṇa, and also of the Mahābhārata, see J. F. Blumhardt: Catalogue of Bengāli books in British Museum (London 1886) and the two supplementary volumes (London 1910, 1939).

Criticism. Dinesh Chandra Sen: History of Bengāli language and literature (1044 p., Calcutta 1911; chiefly p. 170-85, 570-72, 196-220). Winternitz (3, 593, 1922), only a few lines.

CHAPTER XVIII

EDUCATION

(Second Half of the Fourteenth Century)

N.B. Only the main notes relative to education are published in this chapter. Many men who may be called educators but were primarily something else—philosophers, historians, etc.—are dealt with in other chapters. For a general survey of education, see section IV of chapter XV. More information on the educators named in that section may easily be obtained by means of the index.

A. CHRISTENDOM

1. Creation of New Universities

Ten universities were created during the first half of the fourteenth century, and about the same number (eleven) in the second half of the fourteenth century The essential information concerning each of these new foundations follows.

References to Rashdall will enable the reader to obtain more information should he desire it. He should also refer to Stephen d'Irsay (1933–35), consulting for each university d'Irsay's own index.

Huesca (1354)

Huesca in Aragon is the ancient Osca, where Q. Sertorius had established a short-lived school c. 77 A.D. In 1354, Pedro IV[1] created a new university at Huesca for his Aragonese subjects, the older University of Lerida (founded 1300; Introd. 2, 862) being supposed to meet primarily Catalan needs. The competition of Lerida was too strong for it, however, and the new school never amounted to much. Toward the end of his rule, in 1394, Juan I (= Joan I el Caçador; king 1387–95) projected the establishment of a department of Lemosin[2] studies; the project was realized by his successor, Martin (king 1395–1410). According to Rashdall (2, 98–100, 1936), this was "probably the earliest recognition of the modern humanities as a branch of university education." The Catalan people rightly call that king Marti l'Humà.

Pavia (1361)

A school of law existed in Pavia before the school of Bologna had become famous. It was established as early as 825 by Lothair. That school declined, but had somewhat revived by the beginning of the fourteenth century, so much so that Giovanni d'Andrea (XIV-1) could speak of it as one of the famous schools of Italy, the others being Padua, Perugia, and of course Bologna. It was established as a studium generale (with the same privileges as Paris, Bologna, Oxford, Orléans, and Montpellier) in 1361 by the emperor Charles IV; in 1389 the foundation was renewed by the pope Boniface IX, who ignored the imperial charter.

[1] King of Aragon 1336–87; he was also king of Catalonia under the name Pere III el Cerimoniós, and duke of Athens 1382–87. Thus in English he may be called Peter III or Peter IV.

[2] I.e., langue d'oc. See my notes on Provençal and Catalan, p. 338–43, 1302–6.

A plague caused a migration to Piacenza (founded 1248; Introd. 2, 571), and the University of Pavia seems to have been merged with that of Piacenza in 1398. The restoration of the Pavia university was attempted in 1412 and completed by 1421. Pavia became the university town of the duchy of Milan, even as Pisa (1343) was the university town of Florence, and Padua (1222) of Venice. (Rashdall 2, 51–53, 1936.)

Cracow (1364, 1397)

A university was founded in Cracow 1364 by Casimir the Great (king of Poland 1333–70), and the foundation was confirmed in the same year by Urban V. The plans, however, do not seem to have materialized, so much so that it was necessary for the first king of the Jagello dynasty, Ladislaus (Wladyslaw V Jagiello, king 1386–1434), to resurrect the university in 1397 by means of a new charter obtained from Boniface IX (Roman pope 1389–1404). This new foundation was very successful, but its history belongs to the fifteenth century and later. (Rashdall 2, 289–94, 1936.)

Orange (1365)

This "university," if it may be so called, is mentioned here in spite of its unimportance, because it is a curious mediaeval equivalent to the wretched diploma mills which have sometimes assumed the name of university in modern times.

Orange, in the Rhône valley, 20 km. north of Avignon, was a principality enclaved in the comtat Venaissin and enfeoffed to the Empire.[3] A school of law and grammar existed there in 1268. In 1365, Urban V gave it a charter as a privileged studium particulare; in June of the same year, when Charles IV came to Arles to be crowned, he issued a new charter recognizing a studium generale, which could grant the ius ubique docendi. The bull of Charles IV was confirmed in 1379 by Clement VII.

The situation was not clear, however, and the Orange teachers and students did nothing to improve it. In 1475, Sixtus IV suppressed the right of giving degrees in favor of Avignon; in 1485, Charles VIII, king of France, took a similar measure in favor of Montpellier. Yet a shadowy institution continued to function until the eighteenth century. (Rashdall 2, 184–86, 1936.)

Vienna (1365)

A cathedral school, St. Stephen's, had existed in Vienna since the end of the twelfth century. That nucleus was developed for political purposes by Rudolf IV (duke of Austria 1356–65), in a charter dated March 12, 1365, into a university modeled upon Athens, Rome, and Paris! The real model was Paris. The charter was confirmed by Urban V within the same year, except that the pope did not accredit the theological faculty. The students were divided into four nations: (1) Austria, (2) Saxony, (3) Bohemia, (4) Hungary.

The first rector, in 1366, was the famous Albert of Saxony, to be discussed in the next chapter. The university vegetated until 1383, when duke Albert III obtained the collaboration of Heinrich Langenstein, who had just been driven out of the University of Paris. In 1384 Urban VI authorized the theological faculty, and in

[3] It is traced back to Charlemagne; from c. 1180 to 1393 it belonged to the family of Baux, one of the oldest noble families of Provence. In 1530, it fell to the share of the house of Nassau, whence Louis XIV took it in 1673. The present dynasty of the kingdom of the Netherlands is styled house of Orange and Nassau.

1388–89 new statutes were established. The nations were redefined: (1) the Austrian (including Italy), (2) the Rhenish (with western Germany and western Europe), (3) the Hungarian (including the Slavonic people), (4) the Saxon (including northern and eastern Germany, Scandinavia, the British Isles). This example has been given to illustrate the laxity general in the naming of "nations" and the danger of drawing conclusions as to the nationality of a student from his presence in this or that nation (e.g., discussions about Copernic).

Nationalistic and religious troubles in Prague caused the emigration of German students, especially in 1409 and later, much to the advantage of Vienna and of the new German universities to be dealt with presently. (Rashdall 2, 234–45, 1936.)

Pécs or Fünfkirchen (1367)

The first Hungarian university was founded in 1360 by Nagy Lajos I (Louis the Great, king of Hungary 1342–82) in Pécs = Fünfkirchen, the see of a bishop in the province of Barânya (in the angle made by the Drave and the Danube). The bull completing the foundation was granted by Urban V only in 1367. A Bolognese doctor, Gabranus Bettinus, was called to teach canon law at the expense of the bishopric. The latest document concerning that university is dated 1376, hence we may conclude that it miscarried. (Rashdall 2, 294–95, 1936.)

Erfurt (1379, 1392)

The first university in Germany proper was established in Erfurt (Thuringia), where grammar schools of unusual importance had flourished since the twelfth century, if not earlier. By the end of the thirteenth century the four principal schools of Erfurt, i.e., schools connected with the four main churches, were placed under the supervision of a rector superior. In 1362, the then rector, Heinrich Totting, applied vainly for a charter to Urban V. The studium generale was finally established by a bull of the Avignonese antipope Clement VII in September 1379, but this did not satisfy everybody, and in 1389 a new bull was received from the Roman pope Urban VI. The first rector was elected only in 1392, after the foundation of two other German universities in Heidelberg and Cologne. The institution was successful, just as soon as it began to function, because plenty of students and teachers were ready for it; it grew considerably after 1409 at the expense of Prague. By the middle of the fifteenth century it had become famous, thanks especially to the teaching of Johann Rucherath, better known under the name Johann von Wesel (or Vesalia; d. 1481), one of the forerunners of the Reformation.[4] Martin Luther graduated in Erfurt as master of theology, 1505.

The earliest college, Collegium maius, for masters of art, dates from the end of the fourteenth century; the Collegium amplonianum, or Porta caeli, for jurists came a little later, 1412 ff. It was named after one of its alumni and rectors, Amplonius von Berka (1363–1435),[5] immortalized by the Amplonian collection of MSS preserved in Erfurt, the most comprehensive early collection of mediaeval MSS in Germany.

The university was suppressed in 1816. (Rashdall 2, 245–50, 1936.)

[4] ADB (29, 439–44, 1889). Not to be confused with Johannes Wessel (Gansfort; Wesselius), who was born in Groningen c. 1419 and died there in 1489; he flourished with the Brothers of the Common Life in Zwolle, was a Greek scholar and a forerunner of Luther. Note that the first Johann von Wesel was born not in Wesel (near Cleve), the place whence the famous anatomist Vesalius derived his name, but in Oberwesel, higher up in the Rhine valley near the rocks of Lorelei.

[5] ADB (45, 772–74, 1900).

Heidelberg (1385)

The University of Heidelberg was founded by the count palatine Rupert I, a bull ad hoc being issued by the Roman pope Urban VI in 1385. The first rector was a Dutch refugee from Paris, Marsilius van Inghen (q.v.); and the university was organized on the Parisian pattern.

It was immediately successful, many students being attracted to it.

Various colleges had to be established promptly in order to accommodate them: (1) the Cistercian Collegium jacobiticum, by Rupert I in 1389; (2) the Collegium artistarum on the model of the Sorbonne, by the first chancellor, Conrad von Gelnhausen, in 1390; it was located in the confiscated houses of Jews; (3) the Contubernium dionysianum, for poor scholars, by Gerlach von Homburg in 1396.

The nominalistic tendencies were even stronger in Heidelberg than in Erfurt, this being due to Marsilius' rectorship and even more to the hatred of Wycliffe and Hus, of Prague and Bohemia. However, after the council of Constance (1414-18), in spite of its formal condemnation of Wycliffism and execution of Hus, realism found more and more vindicators among orthodox churchmen. By the middle of the century (c. 1455) the faculty of arts was obliged to accommodate both tendencies; it organized separate lectures and examinations for the via antiqua and for the via moderna. (Rashdall 2, 250-54, 1936.)

Cologne (1388)

Cologne had been for many centuries a great center of pilgrimages and of learning. Its cathedral school was famous; its Dominican school was the leading one in Germany and had been made illustrious by the teaching of Albert the Great and the presence of Thomas Aquinas; Duns Scot spent the last year of his life (1308) in its Franciscan school. The university was created at the town's own request by the Roman pope Urban VI on December 22, 1388. It began well, but could not compete with Heidelberg or even Erfurt.

It ceased to exist during the French Revolution. (Rashdall 2, 254-57, 1936.)

Buda (1389, 1395)

The university of Buda was created by Sigismund of Luxemburg (king of Hungary 1387-1437), who obtained a bull from the Roman pope Boniface IX in 1389. Constitutional changes were made in new bulls issued by the same pope in 1395, and by John XXIII in 1410. The university never acquired any importance and hardly survived its founder, who died in 1437. (Rashdall 2, 295-96, 1936.)

Ferrara (1391)

The University of Ferrara was founded at the request of the marchese Alberto d'Este (ruler of Ferrara and Modena 1388-93). In 1391, he obtained from his liege lord the Roman pope Boniface IX a bull creating a studium generale with the same privileges as Bologna and Paris. The university did not have much success until its reorganization in 1430, when it enjoyed a modicum of popularity. (Rashdall 2, 53-55, 1936.)

Of the eleven universities created in the second half of the fourteenth century, only five were of great and lasting importance, to wit, Pavia, Cracow, Vienna, Erfurt, Heidelberg. The first two had no real importance until the fifteenth century; the last three enjoyed a modicum of success before the end of the fourteenth. These three were German universities, and therefore we may say that this period (XIV-2) is remarkable for having witnessed the auspicious beginnings of university life in German lands. The success of those universities was largely due to the fact that they were created in scholarly environments. The mediaeval universitas was essentially, as the name indicates, a corporation—a guild of scholars. It could prosper only if a sufficient number of scholars were ready and eager to enlist. Of course, then as now, many students came less to learn than to obtain valuable diplomas, yet, then as now, the diploma mill could not function if there was not a sufficient body of earnest teachers and students, desiring learning for its own sake, or for religious, philosophical, or political reasons, not for selfish reasons only. The necessary atmosphere for a successful university could not be found everywhere; it could not be created by a papal bull, but only by the people of the localities concerned.

A great many documents concerning university life from the twelfth to the seventeenth century were published by Thorndike in 1944. Sixty-nine of those 176 documents deal with the fourteenth century. As that book was not available to me until May 1945, I could not use it in part I of my own book, already proof-read. For example, Thorndike includes extracts from the writings of Pierre Dubois and Alvaro Pelayo to which I should have liked to refer in the articles devoted to those men. One of the most interesting texts edited by Thorndike in Latin and English (p. 201-35, 409-33, 1944) is the De commendatione cleri (Vatican Palatine MS 1252, fol. 99-109), written by a German cleric who studied in Paris. It explains educational ideals and practice about the middle of the fourteenth century.

2. English Colleges

Oxford

The main event in the University of Oxford was the "slaughter" of 1355, a frightful battle between town and gown which originated at the Mermaid Tavern, at Quatervois. Many people were killed on both sides. As a consequence, both the university and the town had to surrender all their privileges and charters, and lay for more than a year under an interdict. The final outcome was more privileges to the university and less to the town. (Rashdall 3, 96-102, 1936.)

Three colleges had been created in Oxford during the first half of the century, Exeter, Oriel, and Queen's. Two new ones were added during the second half, Canterbury and New College.

Canterbury (1361). Canterbury Hall was founded in 1361 by Simon Islip (d. 1366), archbishop of Canterbury, for the accommodation of regulars and seculars. Refer to my note on the perennial conflicts between regulars and seculars (Introd. 2, 823) to appreciate the difficulties involved. The first warden was a monk; the second, a secular, John Wyclif, who has been identified, though not convincingly, with the reformer. In 1371, the new archbishop, Simon Langham (d. 1376), who was himself a Benedictine, awarded not only the wardenship but the whole college to the Benedictine order. It continued under these auspices until the dissolution (1539). The Canterbury Gate and quadrangle of Christ Church[6] are so named as a memorial to Canterbury Hall. (Rashdall 3, 210-13, 1936.)

New College (1379). New College was founded in 1379 by Wliliam of Wakeham (1324-1404), bishop of Winchester and chancellor of England. It was originally

[6] Founded in 1524 by cardinal Wolsey (1475?-1530).

called "S. Marie Colledge of Winchester in Oxford." The magnificent buildings which were prepared for it and can be admired to this day were ready in 1387. The chapel is the earliest building in England entirely in the perpendicular style. The seventy scholars for whom accommodation was provided were chosen exclusively (and continued to be so chosen until 1854) from the Winchester school, created a few years previously by the same benefactor.

Wykeham's foundation, or rather his double foundation, was unique up to that time in its magnitude and splendor. He may be called the creator of English collegiate architecture. New College was not simply an endowed boarding house, but a community comparable to the monastic establishments, and the "warden" (as its head was called) lived like an abbot in a house of his own within the college walls. (Rashdall 3, 213–23, 1936.)

Between 1379, when New College was born, and 1500, only three more colleges were founded in Oxford, all of them within the second quarter of the fifteenth century, Lincoln in 1429, All Souls in 1438, and Magdalen in 1448.

Cambridge

Six colleges date from the first half of the century, to wit, King's Hall, Michaelhouse, Clare, Pembroke, Gonville, and Trinity. To these only one was added in the second half, Corpus Christi.

Corpus Christi (1352). The creation of this college was partly inspired by the Black Death. Indeed, it was founded in 1352 by a charitable society, the guild "of Corpus Christi and the Blessed Mary," and established near the church of St. Benet (= Benedict), hence it was often called St. Benet's college. The master and fellows were chaplains to the guild. (Rashdall 3, 310–12, 1936.)

Between the foundation of Corpus Christi, in 1352, and 1500, five more colleges were established in Cambridge. The first of these, however, was founded only after an interval of almost a century; that was Godshouse in 1439 or 1441–42,[7] followed by King's in 1441, Queens' in 1448, St. Catherine's in 1475, and Jesus in 1497.

3. English Schools

Winchester (1378)

William of Wykeham, referred to above as the founder of New College, was also the founder of a preparatory school for New College. This school, Winchester College, was established in Winchester, Hampshire, the see of William's bishopric, the foundation being solemnized in a bull dated June 1, 1378 of the Roman pope Urban VI. The buildings specially prepared for it, and existing to this day, were taken possession of in 1394.

The idea of associating a grammar school or preparatory school with a college was not new; it had been realized in Merton and Queen's, Oxford, and in Navarre, Paris. The novelty was to have the preparatory school in another locality with its own endowment and government.

The creation of New College and Winchester was partly caused by the Black Death, the Secunda pestis of 1361, and the third of 1367, William of Wykeham himself giving as reason for his double foundation "the cure of the common disease of the clerical army, which we have seen grievously wounded by lack of clerks, due to plagues, wars and other miseries" (Leach p. 203, 1915).

[7] In 1505, absorbed in the Lady Margaret's foundation of Christ's College.

Winchester was created for the accommodation of seventy *poor* scholars. By what strange perversion did the charity school become the earliest "public" school of England?[8] Poor did not mean then what it means now. The really poor, the ascripti glebae, were altogether out of the picture; they were not supposed to need or deserve any kind of education, and they were punishable if they presumed to send their children to school. As a matter of fact, the scholars from the very beginning were recruited from the aristocracy and the middle class, but they had to take a vow of poverty.[9]

The first master, John Melton, was appointed by Wykeham himself. The second, Thomas of Romsey, was appointed in 1394.

There were many other grammar schools—cathedral, chantry, or guild schools—in England in the second half of the fourteenth century, and the success of Winchester encouraged the creation of others. See Leach (p. 201–12, 1915).

Register of William of Wykeham, bishop of Winchester, 1367–1404, edited by Thomas Frederick Kirby (Hampshire Record Society, 2 vols., London 1896–99).

Robert Lowth: The life of Wykeham (2d ed., London 1759). M. E. C. Walcott: Wykeham and his colleges (514 p., Winchester 1852). W. A. Spooner: Wykeham (London 1909). Douglas Knoop and Gwilym Peredur Jones: The mediaeval mason (p. 24–27, Manchester 1933; Isis 35, 73). Robert Fitzgibbon Young: "Poor and needy" in the statutes of Winchester and Eton (Journal of education p. 438, Sept. 1944).

To return to the "poor" students of Wykeham and elsewhere, it is certain that many were poor or broke, as the majority of students have ever been, even when their parents were not. They were often endowed with a spirit of friary or Bohemianism, and occasionally acted like beggars and truants. In order to beg, however, they must have a letter identifying them as students, or be punished.[10]

The education given in the grammar schools, even in Winchester, even in the colleges of Oxford and Cambridge, was often rudimentary in the extreme. Plenty of illustrations of this may be found in Leach (1915), in Coulton (1940), or in Coulton's previous works. A single one must suffice here. In 1356/57, the bishop of Exeter[11] issued a pastoral letter in which he complained that many scholars were so ignorant that they recited their prayers and other ritual texts without understanding their meaning. He concluded:

[8] The "public schools" of England are endowed institutions, expensive and exclusive, which give a liberal education or prepare for the universities. Winchester 1379 was the first of them. The others best known among the earlier ones are Eton, founded by Henry VI in 1440, Rugby by Laurence Sheriff (d. 1567), Harrow by John Lyon in 1572.

[9] "Every scholar had to swear: 'I N. (Name), admitted to the college of St. Mary near Winchester, swear that I have nothing whereby I know I can spend beyond five marks a year.' Five marks was the limit of value of church livings for exemption from paying taxes to the Pope or for the support of Papal nuncios. In the diocese of Winchester there were sixty-seven livings below that value. It meant £3 6s. 8d. a year, whereas the pay of a skilled artisan was £1 6s. 8d. a year at the outside" (Leach p. 207, 1915).

[10] "Et qe les clers des universitées qi vont ensy mendinantz eient lettres de tesmoigne de lour chanceller sur mesme la peyne," 12 Richard II (1399), ch. VII (Jusserand p. 157, 1884).

[11] John Grandison (1292?–1369), bishop from 1328 on. He was largely responsible for the building of the Exeter cathedral, completing the nave in 1367 (DNB 22, 371–72, 1890). His sister, Catharine, married William Montacute (1301–44), first earl of Salisbury. The story of "honi soit qui mal y pense" is often but wrongly connected with her (DNB 38, 213, 1899). The only sure fact is that Edward III created the Order of the Garter in 1349. Later fictions were invented to justify its motto (the same happened for the Golden Fleece, created in 1429).

"We, therefore, willing to eradicate so horrible and foolish an abuse, already too deeprooted in our diocese, by all means and methods in our power, do now commit and depute to each of you the duty of warning and enjoining all masters and instructors whatsoever that preside over Grammar Schools within the limits of his arch deaconry . . . that they should not, as hitherto, teach the boys whom they receive as Grammar pupils only to read or learn by heart; but rather that, postponing all else, they should make them construe and understand the Lord's Prayer, the Ave Maria, the Creed, the Mattins and Hours of the Blessed Virgin, and decline and parse the words therein, before permitting them to pass on to other books. Moreover, we proclaim that we purpose to confer clerical orders henceforth on no boys but upon such as may be found to have learnt after this method."[12]

This question has already been discussed above, apropos of Latin, in chapter I (p. 333–35), for the educational weakness of the Middle Ages was largely due to the necessity of teaching and studying in a language which was divorced from life. "Communication" between teacher and student was doomed to remain incomplete and precarious as long as it occurred in a language which was artificial almost always to the latter, and sometimes even to the former. Similar reflections might apply to other countries as well as to England, but the difficulties increased together with the distance between Latin and the vernacular of each country. They were obviously smaller for an Italian than for an Englishman. In any case, that fundamental artificialness imprisoned mediaeval teaching in a cloud of unreality.

4. Education in France

The University of Paris

The origins of the University of Paris were dealt with in volume 2 (p. 351); they can be traced back to the end of the twelfth century. We must speak of that university again, because its absolute and relative importance increased during the thirteenth and fourteenth centuries. Moreover, it offers the best illustration of the fact that universities were extensively used to promote orthodoxy and were primarily political instruments. Their other function, to create expert professional men and to educate servants for the state and church, was decidedly subordinated to the needs of orthodoxy and propaganda.

In 1366, the University of Paris was forced to accept new statutes by the papal legates, the cardinals Gilles de Montaigu and Jean de Blandy. These statutes determined not only the curriculum, but even the very books to be used in teaching. The list included, for grammar, the Graecismus of Eberhard of Bethune (XIII-1), the Doctrinale puerorum of Alexandre de Villedieu (XIII-1); for logic, the Organon, the Topics of Boetius (VI-1), etc., then many other parts of the Aristotelian corpus, De anima, Physica, De generatione et corruptione, De caelo et mundo, Parva naturalia, Metaphysica. The course of instruction of the artists was divided into three stages, the requirements being:

For B.A.: grammar, logic, psychology.

For the License in arts: natural philosophy and metaphysics.

For M.A.: moral philosophy (the Ethics) and natural philosophy. (Rashdall 1, 443, 1936.)

In exchange for its docility to papal instructions, the university gained con-

[12] Quoted by Coulton: Life in the Middle Ages (2, 113–14, 1928).

siderable authority, and as the students and teachers were recruited from everywhere, that authority became almost as oecumenical as the church itself.

This applies particularly to the faculty of theology, which was sometimes obliged to arbitrate between the Franciscan and Dominican theologians. These theologians were members of the faculty, yet subordinated to the generals of their respective orders. Here is a remarkable example of the triangular conflicts which could thus originate. The official philosophy of the university might be said to be Aristotelianism as modified by St. Thomas; this gave the Dominicans a great advantage. With regard to the burning controversy of the day on the Immaculate Conception, however, the general feeling was in favor of its acceptance, that is, with the Franciscans and against the Dominicans (see Introd. 2, 968 and by index). In 1387, the Dominican Juan de Monzón,[13] who resisted the incipient dogma, was condemned by his bishop; having appealed to the Avignonese curia, where Pierre d'Ailly represented the university against him, he was excommunicated and took refuge in Aragon with the Urbanists. The Paris Dominicans, having refused to accept his condemnation, were expelled from the university and stayed out sixteen years. When they finally recanted and submitted in 1403, they were degraded to the lowest place in the university procession. Toward the end of the century a Dominican preacher stirred up trouble again, and thereupon in 1497 candidates for theological degrees in Paris were obliged to take an oath to defend the Immaculate Conception. (The dogma was established only in 1854.) In other cases, the faculty of theology took sides against the Franciscans, or rather against the left wing of their order, the Spirituals or Fraticelli.

In short, the faculty of theology of the university, and the university itself, acted as a supreme court of theology, the necessity of which increased during the Great Schism (1378–1429). A consequence of this will be often noticed in this volume: as scholars were expelled from the University of Paris or were unable to stick it out there any longer for theological and political reasons, they moved to other universities and other countries. Thus were Parisian ideas disseminated throughout Western Europe.

Parisian Colleges

The vitality of the University of Paris is illustrated by the number of colleges which were gradually associated with it. Two were created in the twelfth century, seventeen in the thirteenth century, thirty-eight in the fourteenth, a dozen more in the fifteenth. All together some sixty-nine, many of which, it is true, were short-lived or small. Among the eleven colleges which originated in the second half of the fourteenth century there is not a single one which rings a bell in my memory (see list in Rashdall 1, 539, 1936). It is probable that too many colleges were founded; some of the older ones, however, such as Montaigu and Navarre, continued to play a dominant part not only in the university, but in the kingdom as well.

Foundation and location of colleges at Paris in the later Middle Ages (Thorndike p. 433–48, maps, 1944).

Education in the Provinces

As no scholar has done for France what Leach (1915) did for England, I have no clear and general view of the schools and colleges outside Paris. Of course, every

[13] Born at Monzón (prov. Huesca, Aragon) c. 1350, died there 1412. Assumed the Dominican habit probably in Valencia and obtained his Th.M. in Paris 1386 (EUI 36, 835).

cathedral would have its own school, if it were only a chantry one, and numerous classes would be conducted all over the country in monastic houses. Then the universities would have, of necessity, preparatory schools in their neighborhood. This applies to Montpellier, Chartres, Orléans, Angers, Toulouse, Avignon, Cahors, Grenoble, Orange. About provincial colleges comparable to the larger Parisian ones I know nothing.

On account of its proximity to the curia, the University of Avignon might have assumed international significance, but its development was thwarted by the competition of Montpellier and Paris. Colleges were established in the neighborhood at Saint Germain de Calberte, near Mende; at Orange; at Trets,[14] near Aix. Urban V is said to have sent some 180 students to the last-named one; he was supporting over a thousand students all over Europe.

The pontifical library in Avignon was larger than the royal library in the Louvre. We have a catalogue of the former made for Urban V in 1369 by Jean Surrei, and a catalogue of the latter made for Charles V in 1373. There were 1,239 books in the Paris library as against 2,102 in the Avignon one (Brun p. 268, 1928).

LA TOUR-LANDRY

French educator (d. after 1389).

Geoffroy de la Tour-Landry originated in a place situated between Cholet and Vezins in Anjou (Maine-et-Loire). The ruins of the feudal castle, dating from the twelfth century, are still visible. Geoffroy's birth date is unknown, but he was present at the siege of Aguillon in 1346; by 1371 he was a widower with five children, in 1383 he was still in active service, and he married a second time in 1389. After this the curtain falls.

In 1371–72, he wrote in French for the sake of his three motherless daughters, with the assistance of two priests and two clerks, a treatise on the domestic education of women, Le livre du chevalier de la Tour, which was one of the most popular educational books of the Middle Ages. According to his own declaration ("Et pour ce . . . ay-je fait deux livres, l'un pour mes filz, et l'autre pour mes filles pour apprendre à rommancier"), he had written before that time a similar book for his sons. The book written for his sons is lost, the book written for his daughters enjoyed much popularity. It is divided into 144 chapters, and deals outspokenly with the education of gentlewomen, the dangers to which they are exposed, etc. The ethical level is not high, but that is hardly surprising, considering the rudeness of those times, the boorishness of the men, and the complete subordination of the women to them.

The book was twice translated into English, the first time by an anonymous translator about the middle of the fifteenth century, the second time in 1483 by William Caxton, who printed it in the following year. Caxton's English edition of 1484 was the first printed edition in any language. A German translation was published in 1493 by Marquard vom Stein, who was then a governor of the count of Württemberg in Mömpelgart (Montbéliard, dépt. Doubs).[15] That translation was even more popular than the original or the English version.

[14] Marius Chaillan: Le studium papal de Trets au XIVe siècle (Mémoires de l'Académie d'Aix 17, 113–256, Aix-en-Provence 1897). Derived from the MS account kept by the rector of that studium, Déodat Jordan, Rationes scholarum de Tritis 1364–66 (Vatican archives).

[15] Indeed, the principality of Montbéliard was from 1397 a Württembergian enclave in Franche-Comté. It was annexed to France only in 1786. Thus was the French naturalist Georges Cuvier born in Germany (Montbéliard 1769).

Text. Le Livre du chevalier de la Tour was first printed by Guillaume Eustace (Paris 1514). A second edition by another Parisian printer appeared soon afterward. The third edition was a critical one by Anatole de Montaiglon (Bibliothèque elzévirienne, 368 p., Paris 1854), with elaborate introduction.

The first English edition, The booke of thenseygnementes and techynge that the knyght of the Towre made to his doughters, was printed by William Caxton in Westminster 1484. This was not reprinted until 1902, when Gertrude Burford Rawlings edited selected chapters from it, a little more than half of the original, with illustrations, brief introduction, glossary (London 1902). The earlier English translation was printed for the first time by Thomas Wright: The book of the Knight of La Tour-Landry (Early English Text Society no. 33, 257 p., London 1868; revised edition, 304 p., 1906). The text of that first translation was incomplete, though superior in other respects; it was completed in Wright's edition with fragments taken out of Caxton's translation; notes, glossary, index. Modernized English edition by D. B. Wyndham Lewis (322 p., London 1930).

The German translation, Der Ritter vom Turn, von den Exempeln der Gotsforcht und Erberkeit, was first printed in Basel 1493. It was reprinted in Basel 1513, Augsburg 1495, 1498, Strassburg 1519, 1538, Frankfurt 1569, 1572, 1593, Nürnberg 1680, 1682, etc. Modernized edition by O. L. B. Wolff, Leipzig 1850.

Criticism. Montaiglon's introduction (1854) and Wright's (1868). Rudolf Kautzsch: Die Holzschnitte zum Ritter vom Turn, Basel 1493 (24 p., 48 pl., Strassburg 1903). Alexander Kehrmann: Die deutsche Übersetzung der Novellen des Ritters vom Turn (Diss. Marburg, 77 p., 1905). Louis Poulain: Der Ritter vom Turn von Marquart vom Stein (Diss. Basel, 1906). Peter Stolingwa: Zum Livre du chevalier de la Tour-Landry. Die Breslauer Hs. des Textes (Diss., 160 p., Breslau 1911).

5. Italy

GIOVANNI DA RAVENNA (I)

Giovanni di Conversino (1343–1408). Italian humanist, one of the greatest educators of his time. His father, born in Frignano (Modena), was physician to Louis d'Anjou[16] (king of Hungary 1342–82), and hence Giovanni was born in Buda 1343. He was brought back as a baby to Ravenna, where he received his first education from Donato degli Albanzani. Later he studied law in Bologna, and obtained the diploma of notary in 1362. He taught in Bologna (1364), Ferrara, Treviso, Firenze (1368, Studio pubblico), Conegliano, Belluno, Udine, Venezia (three different periods), Padova (Università), finally in Muggia nell'Istria; he died in Venice in the summer of 1408. During his life he also acted as chancellor to the republic of Ragusa (Dalmatia) and to Francesco I da Carrara and his son Francesco II Novello, lords of Padova, and as their ambassador. A true wandering scholar, anticipating in his restlessness as well as in love of learning many scholars of a later time.

He had known Boccaccio in his early youth in Donato's house; he became acquainted with Petrarca in Venice (1363). He was a great teacher, insisting on the use of friendly persuasion rather than coercion, the need of developing the intelligence rather than the memory, the value of cooperation between home and school. Among his pupils were such illustrious humanists as Pietro Paolo Vergerio (c. 1370–c. 1444), Guarino da Verona (c. 1370–1460), Vittorino da Feltre (1378–1446).

Sabbadini enumerates 18 writings of his, all unpublished and unimportant,

[16] Nagy Lajos I (Louis I the Great).

except the Rationarium vite, an autobiographical document of remarkable candor. The Conventio inter podagram et araneam (1407) is simply a literary amusement; it reminds us that the author suffered from the gout.

Text and criticism. Remigio Sabbadini: Giovanni da Ravenna, insigne figura d'umanista (270 p., Como 1924). This includes the list of earlier sources, most of which are difficult to use because of the constant confusion between two different Giovanni da Ravenna, confusion natural enough, as they not only were contemporary, but had many other things in common. Sabbadini's book also includes a series of extracts from Giovanni's writings (p. 127–240).

6. Netherlands

CELE

Joannes Cele. Dutch schoolmaster (d. 1417).

Though Cele left no writings, except letters, he deserves to be dealt with in this Introduction, because he was one of the greatest schoolmasters of all time, and one of the founders of the "devotio moderna," or Christian renaissance, originated by Groote.

He was born in Zwolle about 1347, was educated in his native city, then at the University of Prague, whence he returned c. 1374. He was soon appointed rector of the high school of Zwolle. In 1375 he accompanied Groote to Groenendael (to see Ruysbroeck) and to Paris. As Thomas a Kempis put it, they were two men of a single soul and mind. Cele was rector of the Zwolle school for some forty years (1375–1417), and under his rule the school became famous, attracting pupils from all over the Low Countries, the duchy of Cleve, and other German lands. It is largely thanks to him that Zwolle became a center of the new culture comparable to Deventer. He insisted that work and active goodness are more important than knowledge and talk. He died in Zwolle on May 9, 1417, at the age of about 70, and was buried in his beloved monastery of Windesheim.

His successors at the head of the Zwolle school were Livinius of Middelburg, Herman Kerstken, and in 1432 John van Dalen, who ushered in a second period of prosperity. One of his main assistants was John Busch (1399–1480), who became the chronicler of Windesheim and was ordered by cardinal Nicholas of Cusa in 1451 to reform the monasteries of the Augustinian Canons in Germany.

Criticism. Zuidema (Nieuw nederlandsch biografisch woordenboek 4, 407, Leiden 1918). Hyma (1924).

D. JAPAN

THE ASHIKAGA-GAKKŌ

The Ashikaga-gakkō is a famous school, the origin of which is traced back to Ashikaga Yoshikane (1147–96) or even to Ono no Takamura (802–52), but which did not become important until the middle of the fourteenth century. In 1350, Ashikaga Motouji (1304–67) enlarged it, and in 1394, Nagao Kagehisa moved it to Ashikaga in the province of Shimotsuke. Later still, in 1439, the great statesman and patron of learning Uesugi Norizane (d. 1466) gave it a considerable endowment. The Ashikaga-gakkō then became the most important center of Chinese learning in Japan until the end of the sixteenth century; after that, that is, under the Tokugawa shogunate, it declined gradually.

Criticism. Papinot (p. 39, 714, 1909).

CHAPTER XIX

PHILOSOPHICAL AND CULTURAL BACKGROUND

(Second Half of the Fourteenth Century)

N.B. Only the main notes are published in this chapter. Many men who may be called philosophers, or have influenced—sometimes deeply—the intellectual climate of their time, are dealt with in other chapters, because they were primarily something else, e.g., mathematicians or physicians. For a general survey of the philosophical or cultural background read section V of chapter XV. More information on the men dealt with in that survey can then easily be obtained by means of the index.

A. WESTERN CHRISTENDOM

A1. Italy

DOMENICO DI BANDINO

Italian encyclopaedist and humanist (d. 1418).

Ser Domenico son of maestro Bandino Bianco, Dominicus Bandinus, was born in Arezzo c. 1335. He was a notary and teacher, and spent a good part of his life in Florence teaching grammar and the arts. He died at the end of August 1418.

He undertook in 1374 and completed at the beginning of the fifteenth century an encyclopaedic treatise entitled De mundi fabrica, or Fons memorabilium universi (mundi).

It is divided into five parts in honor of Christ's five wounds. Part I is subdivided into 4 books: God, the angels, the soul, hell and its demons; part II into 5 books: the universe, heavens, stars, planets, seasons; part III into 8 books: the elements in general, fire, air, meteorology, birds, seas; rivers, lakes, and fountains; fish; part IV into 12 books: provinces, islands, cities, notable buildings, peoples and customs, mountains, trees, herbs, quadrupeds, reptiles, stones, metals; part V into 5 books: illustrious men, philosophical sects, heresies, virtues, famous women. More roughly: part I deals with theology, II with cosmology, III with the elements and natural history, IV with geography and natural history, V with history. The biographies illustrate the author's greater interest in antiquity and the new Tuscan culture than in the Middle Ages. His astronomical knowledge may be judged from the fact that he predicted solar eclipses for 1399–1419 and lunar eclipses for 1396–1417 (Vatican 3121, fol. 40v and fol. 50v; Thorndike 3, 563).

In spite of his comparative neglect of mediaeval writers, it is clear that much of his knowledge was derived from them, e.g., from Matthaeus Platearius, Gervase of Tilbury, Michael Scot, Albert the Great. He obtained much information, however, from relatively recent Italian writers such as Giovanni Campano, Guido Bonatti, Pietro dei Crescenzi, Cecco d'Ascoli, Andalò di Negro. He referred to the Genoese expedition of 1341 to the Canary Islands, also described by Boccaccio (q.v.).

One of the best parts of the Fons memorabilium is the botanical one. Domenico deals with 265 herbs in alphabetical order, listing their virtues and sometimes adding agricultural hints.

Criticism. Sabbadini (2, 179-80, 1914). Thorndike (3, 196, 560-67, 759-61, 1934). Thorndike has examined a number of MSS of the Fons memorabilium universi, which is still unpublished.

A2. Catalonia

FRANCESC EIXIMÈNIS

Catalan theologian and educator, writing in Catalan and Latin (c. 1349-c. 1410).

Fra Francesc Eiximènis (called in Spanish Francesco Eximenis or Ximenis, Ximenez; in Latin Franciscus Ximenes) was born in Gerona, county of Barcelona, c. 1349; he assumed the Franciscan habit very early, and studied philosophy and theology in Valencia. He traveled for further studies, visiting Cologne, Paris, Oxford, perhaps also Rome. About 1374, already bearing the title of master in theology, he established himself in Barcelona; from 1383 to 1408 he resided mostly in Valencia, this being his period of greatest activity. He was a member of the commission appointed by Valencia and Majorca to fight the pirates who were then molesting sailors navigating along the coast or to the Balearic Islands. He was elected patriarch of Jerusalem in 1408, administrator of the bishopric of Elna, and cardinal priest of St. Lorenzo in Lucina.

He composed, chiefly in Catalan, a good many treatises dealing with theology, ethics, government, education. His main work was a sort of religious and educational encyclopaedia called Lo Crestià (The Christian), planned to extend to thirteen books; of these only four survive, and it is possible that the others remained unwritten. Other books of his are entitled Regiment de la cosa pública, Llibre dels angels, Llibre de les dones, etc. These books attained considerable success and were among the first books printed in the peninsula. Incunabula editions appeared not only in Catalan, but also in Spanish and French.

Text. The incunabula editions available in America are, according to Stillwell (p. 523, 1940): Primer libre appellat Crestia (Valencia 1483). Dotzen libre del Crestia (Valencia 1484). Le livre des saints anges (Geneva 1478). Libro de los sanctos angelos (Burgos 1490). Pastoral (Barcelona 1495). Primer volumen de la vida de Christo (Granada 1496). Regiment de la cosa publica (Valencia 1499). Scala Dei (Barcelona 1494). De les dones (Barcelona 1495).

Criticism. EUI (70, 570, 1930). Garcia Silvestre (p. 135-40, 1932). E. Allison Peers: Catalonia infelix (p. 49, London 1937).

A3. France

DESCHAMPS

Eustache Deschamps. French (Champenois) poet (c. 1346-c. 1406).

Eustache Deschamps or Des Champs, also called Morel, perhaps because of his dark complexion. Born at Vertus (Champagne, dépt. Marne), probably in 1346. Though Deschamps was the most fertile French writer of the century, he would not deserve to be mentioned here except that some of his innumerable verses deal with medicine. He studied law in Orléans and then became an officer of the crown, messenger of Charles V (king 1364-80), bailiff, forest master, castellan of Fismes (near Reims) under Charles VI (king 1380-1422). He died in 1406 or 1407, more probably in 1406.

He was influenced by Jean de Meung (XIII-2) and by Guillaume de Machaut (XIV-1). He rhymed all the time and apropos of everything, but was not in any real sense a poet. He was a lover of food and drink, of merry gatherings, a jolly fellow. He loved comfort and property, loved his country, especially the plain people who are made to bear everybody's burdens. He hated women and their ways, courtiers, financiers, and was always grumbling about one thing or another. Within these limitations—bourgeois epicurism and jovial vulgarity mixed with peevishness—his verses afford us an excellent mirror of his time.

It would take too long to enumerate his works. One may find in them information about almost every aspect of social life in France in the fourteenth century, e.g., on medical practice. He is more indulgent to physicians than John of Meung. For him medicine consists mainly in bloodletting, cupping, and purging. He is fond of giving hygienic advice and rules for preserving oneself from plagues. From 1376 on he suffered from arthritis, and from then on spoke many times of his gout and the treatment which he followed. He made a distinction between hot gout and cold gout (rheumatism?). He refers to the epidemics of 1379, 1387, 1388, 1399; being a victim to some extent of the two middle ones. He speaks of many other diseases, naming each of them almost always, as was the custom in those days, after the saint called upon for its cure, e.g., mal saint Côme, glands; mal saint Espoint, bellyache; mal saint Flour, deafness; mal saint Matthieu, ulcers; mal saint Maur, gout; mal saint Riquier, fevers.

The majority of his writings are in French, but he also wrote a few in Latin. He translated a few works from Latin into French, e.g., his own Complainte de l'Eglise, Frenchified for Philip the Bold, duke of Burgundy from 1363 to 1404, and the De contemptu mundi of Innocent III (pope 1198–1216), abridged under the title Le double lai de fragilité humaine, dedicated to king Charles VI, 1383.

Among Deschamps' French writings I may still cite the Demonstracions contre sortileges, written in prose, wherein he denounces the use of magic and gives many examples of the violent deaths meted out to princes who used magic or witchcraft. In his youth he had studied and practiced astrology ("Ptolemy's theory"); later he continued to believe in it and tried to reconcile the use of horoscopes with the Christian dogma of free will and free agency. Finally he seems to have accepted the ecclesiastical prohibition of what he calls the "art of Toledo," the art of unveiling the future.

His Art de dictier et de fere chançons, which he completed in 1392, is the oldest extant treatise on French prosody (the chapter on rhymes in the Archiloge Sophie of Jacques Legrand[1] was written a little before 1405). Before discussing the problems of prosody, Deschamps gives a general account of the trivium and quadrivium, placing prosody within the last part of the latter, i.e., music. In this he followed John of Garland (XIII-1), connecting prosody with music, not with rhetoric.

The "Dolente et piteuse compleinte de l'Eglise moult désolée au jour d'ui," is one of the many lamentations brought forth by the Great Schism. It seems to have been inspired by Pedro de Luna (Benedict XIII, antipope 1394–1417). Deschamps wrote it first in Latin, then translated it into French as indicated above.

[1] Jacques Legrand (or Jacobus Magnus), French Augustinian, born at Toulouse, flourished in Paris about the beginning of the fifteenth century. Moralist and preacher. The Archiloge Sophie was the French translation made by him for the duke of Orleans of his own Sophologium ex antiquorum poetarum oratorum atque philosophorum gravibus sententiis collectum, an anthology which enjoyed considerable popularity (14 incunabula editions, Klebs no. 595) (NBG 30, 419–21, 1859).

Text. It will suffice to indicate the opera omnia edited for the Société des anciens textes français by the marquis de Queux de Saint-Hilaire and Gaston Raynaud (10 vols., Paris 1878–1901).

Criticism. The main work on Deschamps was published by the same Société and forms vol. 11 of the Oeuvres complètes. That volume was prepared by G. Raynaud (380 p., Paris 1903). It includes a biography of Deschamps, notices on the MSS and early editions, an elaborate study on the form, substance, and sources of his writings, and many additional documents. Unfortunately there is no index.

Amédée Sarradin: Etude sur Eustache Deschamps (Paris thesis, 336 p., Versailles 1878). Ernst Hoepffner: Eustache Deschamps, Leben und Werke (240 p., Strassburg 1904). Jan Gerard Bruins: Observations sur la langue de Deschamps et de Christine de Pisan (Amsterdam thesis, 144 p., Dordrecht 1925). Franz Frese: Allegorische und mythologische Gestalten in den Dichtungen Deschamps' (Münster thesis, 90 p., 1934). Arnold Dickmann: Deschamps als Schilderer der Sitten seiner Zeit (Münster thesis, 190 p., 1935). Wickersheimer (p. 145, 1936).

John Livingston Lowes: The Chaucerian "Merciles beauté" and three poems of Deschamps (Modern language review 5, 33–39, 1910); Chaucer and the Miroir de mariage (Modern philology 8, 52 p., 1910–1911); Illustrations of Chaucer. Drawn chiefly from Deschamps (Romanic review 2, 113–28, 1911). The Miroir de mariage is one of Deschamps' poems, more than 12,000 lines long, on the popular subject "wiles of women"; Deschamps composed it about 1381–89; it is largely derived from earlier writings.

A4. England

STRODE

Ralph Strode. English logician (fl. c. 1360). Educated at Merton College, Oxford, where he became a fellow before 1360.

He attained fame as a teacher of logic, and as a logician trying to follow a middle road between the nominalists and the realists (somewhat like Albert the Great, St. Bonaventura, and St. Thomas before him). Two of his logical treatises remain, entitled Consequentiae and Obligationes, which appeared in print before the end of the fifteenth century. The Consequentiae is a collection of rules for syllogistic reasoning, and the Obligationes (or Scholastica militia) contains more rules and exercises ad hoc.

Strode had known John Wycliffe (d. 1384) in Oxford and engaged in a gentle polemic against him, which is known only through Wycliffe's friendly answer, Responsiones ad Rodolphum Strodum. Strode apparently took the side of ecclesiastical conservatism, against adventurous ideas such as radical reforms of the church and apostolic poverty.

In an old Merton list he is mentioned as having flourished under Edward III (king 1327–77) and described as "poeta nobilis qui carmine elegiaco librum fecit, qui vocatur Fantasma Randulphi." One Radulphus Strode is also mentioned as a lawyer, and common serjeant of the city of London between 1375 and 1385, dying in 1387. It is not certain whether the logician was identical with the poet, or the lawyer, or both.

Chaucer praised Strode together with John Gower:

> O moral Gower this book I directe
> to thee, and to the philosophical Strode

(Troylus and Cryseyde 5, l. 1856–57; poem written between 1372 and 1386).

Text. The Consequentiae were printed together with William of Heytesbury: Regulae solvendi sophismata, in Padua 1481 (Klebs 512). Consequentiae et obligationes cum commentis (Venice 1493).

DNB cites editions of 1477 and 1507; Prantl (4, 45) cites editions of 1488 and 1507.

Alexandri Sermonete cum Dubiis Paulii Pergulensis nec non Gaetani de Thienis quibusdam Declarativis in Consequentias Strodi commentariolum (Venice 1488). This contains the text of Strode's Consequentiae plus commentaries by three fifteenth-century nominalists: Alexander Sermoneta of Siena; Paul of Pergola (d. 1451), an Augustinian Hermit who flourished in Venice; Gaetano da Thiene (d. 1465), who flourished at Padua.

Consequentiae Strodi cum commento Alexandri Sermonete, Declarationes Gaetani in easdem Consequentias, Dubia Pauli Pergulensis, Obligationes eiusdem Strodi, Consequentiae Ricardi de Ferabrich, Expositio Gaetani super easdem (Venice 1507). Richard Ferabrich or Feribrigus was a contemporary of Strode (according to Prantl 4, 56).

Tractatus insolubilium et obligationum Davidis Cranston de novo recognitus per Guillermum Mandreston et Anthonium Silvestri eius discipulos, cum Obligationibus Strodi nunquam prius citra montes impressis (s.a.l.; Paris?); David Cranstoun (fl. Paris 1509-26; DNB 13, 31); William Manderstown (fl. Paris 1515-40; DNB 36, 20); Antonius Silvester (d. 1515).

Criticism. Prantl (4, 45-56, 1870). Israel Gollancz (DNB 55, 57-59, 1898). R. T. Gunther (2, 43, 1923), simple reference.

"LANGLAND"

William Langland. English poet and reformer (c. 1332—after 1399).

William Langland originated somewhere in the western Midlands and was well educated; he had probably taken minor orders[2] and was married; he spent a good part of his life in London; his literary activity extended from 1362 to 1399.

The biographical data given above are derived from the assumption that William was the sole author of Piers Plowman, an assumption accepted by Walter William Skeat, Jean Jules Jusserand, and others. In 1906 and following years a new theory was developed by John Matthews Manly, according to which Piers Plowman was produced not by one author, but by many, even by as many as five. This caused discussions, which will probably continue forever, even as similar discussions concerning Homer, for neither side can prove its case completely. A good summary of them will be found in Wells (p. 244-70 and suppts.).

In what follows, the words "William Langland" stand for "the main author of Piers Plowman." Let us consider the work itself. "The vision of William concerning Piers the Plowman, together with Vita de Dowel, Dobet et Dobest,[3] secundum wit and resoun" (Visio Willi de Petro Plouhman) is the greatest poem in Middle English after the Canterbury tales, and one of the most important poems of mediaeval literature. It is, as the title indicates, a "vision," but a vision based upon realities observed by an enthusiastic, imaginative, and generous poet. Allegory is always mixed with realism. To that extent the poem is comparable to the

[2] The minor orders are four, to wit, doorkeeper, reader or anagnost, exorcist, and acolyte. These orders were generally given together, and the man who had received them was called a clerk or acolyte. The major or holy orders are three, to wit, subdeacon, deacon, and priest. Sometimes the bishopric is considered an eighth order. The minor and major orders are somewhat different in the Orthodox and Anglican churches; e.g., the order of bishop is always included by them.

[3] Bet is the old comparative of well; "better" is pleonastic as would be "worser." In text B, ch. XIII, 136 ff., Langland explains that learn does well, teach does better, and love does best, which he sums up with the three Latin words disce, doce, dilige. A beautiful conceit.

Divina commedia. It is written in the old English meter, in unrhymed irregular alliterative lines including generally four accented syllables.

It exists in three versions, called A, B, and C. The A version, in 12 passus or cantos, 2,567 lines, was completed c. 1362, and is represented by 10 MSS. The B text, in 20 passus, 7,242 lines, was completed in 1376-77 and is represented by 14 MSS. The C text, in 23 passus, 7,357 lines, was completed c. 1393 (or 1393-99) and is represented by 17 MSS. There are at least 7 more mixed MSS, hence a total of at least 48 MSS, which prove the great popularity of the poem.

The author refers to many ancient and mediaeval writings, but his allusions are vague and superficial. The true sources of his inspiration were deeper, in life itself rather than in books. He had an intense sympathy for the lower classes, whose condition was terrible indeed. He describes the life of the poor, the development of the commons; the rapacity of the friars, the abuses of church and state, denouncing those evils with bitter sarcasm and passion, yet not without charity. As a social satire, Piers Plowman is comparable to the second part of the Roman de la rose,[4] but it is more effective. Indeed, it constitutes the most adequate representation of the many evils of that time. It should be noted that though William had been influenced by Wycliffe, he was not a revolutionary; he was rather conservative, but in the good sense. He would not conserve the abuses, the sufferings, the miseries which were crying to heaven.

It is interesting to compare Langland with Chaucer: the first, a man of the people, gregarious and moralizing; the second, a wealthy and leisured man, a fastidious courtier. It is even more interesting to compare Langland with Carlyle, each endowed with a violent inferiority complex (Coulton p. 539, 1938b).

William Langland's poem is digressive and formless, yet he manages to touch in the imaginative manner of a true poet all the problems of social life as they stood in his day, problems many of which are not solved yet, though the conditions obtaining now are incomparably less cruel than those which he witnessed. The Vision of Piers Plowman is a document of the very first order for the history of political and social circumstances, and even for the history of political and social ideas.

There are various other poems in Middle English of the same kind as Piers Plowman, which were in all probability evoked by the latter's popularity. It will suffice to mention two of them, as the later ones are probably posterior to the fourteenth century.

Pierce the Ploughmans crede is a poem of 850 alliterative long lines written by a Wycliffite c. 1394. It is derived from Piers Plowman, particularly from the prologue to Vita de Dowel.

Richard the Redeless is a poem of 857 alliterative long lines divided into four passus (ending abruptly in the single MS). It describes the misrule and deposition of Richard II (king 1377-99). If it was written by William Langland, the latter resided in Bristol in 1399.

Text. First printed c. 1530 and many times reprinted in the sixteenth century and later. It will suffice to mention here the critical edition in 5 volumes prepared by Walter William Skeat (1835-1912) for the Early English Text Society (4 parts in 5 vols., London 1867-77), also another edition prepared by him for the Oxford Press (2 vols., Oxford 1886) and many times reprinted. A new critical edition is

[4] It is uncertain whether William could read French. The Roman de la rose and other French compositions were well known in England in his time.

being prepared for the Early English Text Society; see report by J. H. G. Grattan dated June 27, 1945 (Speculum 20, 482–83, 1945).

There are various editions in modernized English prose or verse, by Kate M. Warren (London 1895, revised 1899), by Skeat (London 1905, reprinted 1907, 1910, 1922), by Arthur Burrell (Everyman's, London 1912), by Henry W. Wells (London 1935).

Piers Plowman. The Huntington Library MS reproduced in photostat. With an introduction by Raymond Wilson Chambers and technical examination by R. B. Haselden and H. C. Schulz (San Marino, Calif. 1936).

Criticism. J. W. Hales' article in DNB (32, 104–8, 1892) is out of date, as are most publications anterior to the Manly controversy. Jean Jules Jusserand: Les Anglais au Moyen age. L'épopée mystique de William Langland (275 p., Paris 1893); Englished under the title: Piers Plowman, a contribution to the history of English mysticism (265 p., London 1894). John Matthews Manly: Piers the Plowman and its sequence (reprinted from the Cambridge history of English literature, 58 p., Cambridge 1908). Jean Jules Jusserand: The Piers Plowman controversy (Early English Text Society no. 139, 4 parts bound together, 194 p., London 1910). Henry Bradley: The authorship of Piers the Plowman (Modern language review, Cambridge 1910). Heinrich Gebhard: Langlands und Gowers Kritik der kirchlichen Verhältnisse ihrer Zeit (Strassburg Diss., 193 p., 1911). Dorothy L. Owen: Piers Plowman, a comparison with some earlier and contemporary French allegories (London thesis, 183 p., 1912). Dorothy Chadwick: Social life in the days of Piers Plowman (137 p., Cambridge 1922). Ikuzo Iijima: Langland and Chaucer (256 p., Boston 1925). Allan H. Bright: New light on Piers Plowman (94 p., London 1928). Francis Anthony R. Carnegy: The relations between the social and divine order in William's Vision (Sprache und Kultur der germanischen und romanischen Völker, A, vol. 12, 48 p., Breslau 1934). Heinrich Wiehe: Piers Plowman und die sozialen Fragen seiner Zeit (Münster Diss., 1935). Werner Klett: The vision of William . . . unter dem Titel Peter der Pflüger ins Deutsche übersetzt (80 p., Bonn 1935). Thomas Patrick Dunning: Piers Plowman, an interpretation of the A-text (224 p., New York 1937). Greta Hort: Piers Plowman and contemporary religious thought (Society for Promoting Christian Knowledge, London 1937). Coulton: Mediaeval panorama (1938); one of the best chapters in this admirable work, The peasant saint (p. 534–54), is devoted to Piers Plowman. R. W. Chambers: Man's unconquerable mind (15, 88–171, London 1939). Morton W. Bloomfield: Present state of Piers Plowman studies (Speculum 14, 215–32, 1939; Isis 31, 521).

HILTON

Walter Hilton. English mystic (d. 1396).

Walter Hilton (or Hylton) was an Austin Canon in Thurgarton, near Newark, Nottinghamshire; he died on the eve of the Annunciation 1395 (March 24, 1396).

A number of mystical and devotional books written in English and available in English or Latin are ascribed to him. In many cases these ascriptions are largely due to his popularity. Even the Imitation of Christ has been attributed to him, and that baseless claim is interesting as a witness to his prestige. His mysticism is typically English (as opposed to the contemporary German Dominican mysticism) in that it is concerned far more with devotional practice than with theology.

His main work is the Scale (or ladder) of perfection, extant in many MSS. It is divided into two books of 93 and 46 chapters. The general purpose is to lead the soul toward perfection, that is, union with God. It discusses various kinds of contemplation, and the aids to it, humility, faith, hope, prayer, meditation, how to eschew temptations and reform the soul. The number of MSS proves that that "manual for contemplatives" enjoyed much popularity. It was soon translated into Latin by the Carmelite Thomas Fyslawe (early fifteenth century). It was especially esteemed by Carthusians. By the middle of the fifteenth century Cecily, duchess of York, mother of Edward IV, caused it to be read aloud in the refectories together with the books of St. Bonaventure, St. Catherine of Siena, and St. Birgitta. In 1494, the lady Margaret, Henry VII's mother, caused it to be printed by Wynkyn de Worde, and it was many times reprinted.

Among the other devotional works ascribed to Hilton, the following are probably his: "An epistle on mixed life" (c. 7,500 words), discussing the active and the contemplative life, the nature and scope of each, and the need of mixing them as Christ did; "Of angels' songs" (2,000 words); "Proper will" (1,000 words), etc. Hilton recommended reading the Gospels, but only in Latin.

Text. The first edition of the Scale of perfection was the first book printed by Wynkyn de Worde; it was printed in 1494. Reprinted 1507, 1523, 1525, 1533. A modernized edition was prepared by the Benedictine Dom Augustine Baker (1575–1641) and published by the latter's disciple Dom Serenus Cressy (London 1659). New edition by Dom R. E. Guy (London 1869) and the Oratorian John Dobree (Bernard) Dalgairns (London 1870). Frequently reprinted in Catholic collections.

Dorothy Jones: Minor works of Walter Hilton (300 p., London 1929). Including (1) Mixed life, (2) A treatise necessary for men that give themselves to perfection, (3) Qui habitat, (4) Bonum est, (5) Benedictus. In spite of their Latin titles, which are simply the first words of the scriptural lessons, the last three treatises are also in English.

Evelyn Underhill: A book of contemplation which is called the Cloud of unknowing, in which a soul is oned with God (315 p., London 1912). Wrongly ascribed to Hilton and also to the Cambridge Carthusian William Exmew or Exmeuse (1507?–35) (DNB 18, 97). See following article.

Criticism. C. Trice Martin (DNB 26, 435, 1891). R. M. Jones: Studies in mystical religion (p. 338, London 1919). Wells (p. 460–63, 840, 1926).

The Cloud of Unknowing

This is perhaps the best place to say a few words of a series of seven English treatises, probably written by the same author, once believed to be Hilton. They are probably a little anterior, to be placed between Rolle (XIV-1) and Hilton; indeed, the latter's Scale of perfection contains reminiscences of the Cloud.

The outstanding work of that collection is (1) the Cloud of unknowing, to which we shall come back presently. The others are (2) the Epistle of privy council, a sort of appendix to the Cloud; (3) Dionise hid divinity, a free version of the mystical theology of "Dionysios the Areopagite" (V-2);[5] (4) Benjamin, an adaptation of the De praeparatione animi ad contemplationem seu Liber dictus Benjamin minor by Richard of Saint Victor;[6] (5) Epistle of prayer; (6) Epistle of discretion; (7) Of discerning of spirits.

The "Book of contemplation, the which is called the cloud of unknowing, in the

[5] A Christianized version of the theology of Proclos (V-2). It was ascribed to Dionysios the Areopagite (mentioned in Acts 17:34) to give it a kind of apostolic authority, and enjoyed immense popularity throughout the Middle Ages (Isis 29, 423–28).

[6] Richard of Saint Victor was born in Scotland. He became a canon in the abbey of St. Victor, Paris, and was the pupil and successor of Hugh of Saint Victor (XII-1). He died c. 1173. Main works in PL (vol. 196, 1855), with prolegomena by abbé Hugonin. DNB (48, 18[illegible]).

which a soul is oned with God" is a short treatise, divided into 75 chapters, beautifully and forcefully written in the northern Midland dialect (i.e., Chaucer's dialect). The author is entirely unknown. The text is represented by many MSS of the fifteenth century and by at least one of the late fourteenth century (in Cambridge University). The main sources are the pseudo-Dionysius in the translation of John Sarrazin (XII-2) and the paraphrase (extractio) and commentary of Thomas of Vercelli (or Thomas of Saint Victor, d. 1246), St. Augustine, Richard of Saint Victor. The purpose of the book is to explain to a young man the meaning of the contemplative life and the means of preparing oneself for it. Considering the limitations of the human mind and the infinite transcendence of God, the best approach to divine knowledge is through the cloud (the darkness) of ignorance and through a progressive abstraction from sensible things, discursive thought being replaced by an act of will and by love. Prayers should be brief, and thinking restricted to simple, even monosyllabic, words such as God or Love (cf. Hindu and Buddhist parallels to this).

In chapter 4 of the Cloud there is a reference to atoms of time, which suggests the division of an hour into 22,560 atoms explained by Bartholomew the Englishman (XIII-1).

The Cloud was translated into Latin, Nubes ignorandi, by Richard Methley, Carthusian of Mount Grace in Yorkshire, toward the end of the fifteenth century.

Text. First edition of the Cloud, under the title The divine cloud, by Henry Collins (London 1871). Second edition from an earlier fifteenth-century MS by Evelyn Underhill (London 1912; again 1922, 1934). Third edition by Justin McCann (London 1924). Dom Justin's book includes first editions of (2), (3), and of a commentary on the Cloud by the Benedictine father Augustine Baker, written in Cambrai 1629.

The other texts, (4), (5), (6), (7), were edited by Edmund Garratt Gardner: Cell of self-knowledge, seven early English mystical treatises printed by Henry Pepwell in 1521 (162 p., London 1910).

Criticism. Wells (p. 455, 839, 984, 1020, 1129, 1221, 1314, 1408, 1463, 1514, 1629, etc.).

CHAUCER

Geoffrey Chaucer (c. 1340–1400). English poet, translator from Latin and French into English, author of an English treatise on the astrolabe.

Contents: **(1) Life. (2) Influences received by him. (3) His works. (4) His scientific knowledge. (5) A note about cats in early English literature. (6) Chaucer's influence. (6 bis) The testament of love.**

(7) Text. (8) Bibliographies. (9) Concordance. (10) Biographies and general criticism. (11) Special criticism. (12) Scientific criticism. (13) Iconography.

1. *Life*

Geoffrey Chaucer was born c. 1340, probably in London, where his father, John Chaucer, was a prominent vintner. He was very well educated, and in 1357 was a page in the household of Elizabeth, wife of Lionel of Antwerp, third son of Edward III. This detail is given to indicate his social standing. He spent a good part of his life as a courtier at the king's court and other courts of England. In 1359–60 he took part in a military expedition to France, was taken prisoner near Reims and

ransomed. He returned to France on other occasions and was at least twice in Italy (1372–73, Genoa, Florence; 1378, Milan), on diplomatic or secret missions. About 1366 he married one Philippa (Roet?), who died in 1387; his wife was for a time in the queen's service. After 1386 his position was less fortunate, and he suffered financial and other difficulties. He died in Westminster on October 25, 1400, and was buried in Westminster Abbey.

2. *Influences received by him*

Thanks to his excellent education, he early obtained a good knowledge of Latin and French. He was well acquainted with the Latin poets, chiefly Ovid, Vergil, Statius, Juvenal, and less well with Cicero and Seneca. He had also a good knowledge of mediaeval Latin literature: Macrobius, Boetius, the Megacosmos of Bernard Silvester of Tours, the Anticlaudianus of Alan of Lille, the Labyrinthus of Eberhard of Bethune, the Historia destructionis Troiae of Guido delle Colonne of Messina (fl. second half of thirteenth century), the Legenda aurea of Jacobus de Voragine, the Annales of Nicholas Trevet, Thomas Bradwardine.

From the time of his military service in France to 1372, he was also submitted to French influences, and it was then that he thought of translating the Roman de la rose and perhaps did a part of the translation.

From 1372 to 1386 he was deeply influenced by the three Italians: Dante, Petrarca, and Boccaccio.

3. *His works*

Chaucer was first and last a poet, and most of his works are purely literary creations which do not concern us. A complete list of his works would thus be irrelevant, but the following deserve consideration:

1. Romaunt of the rose. Chaucer contemplated a translation of the Roman de la rose, and he certainly studied the French original (q.v., Introd. 2, 932–34). There is a partial translation into Middle English (single MS, Glasgow), but the ascription of it to Chaucer is uncertain. Maybe Chaucer wrote a part of it? However that may be, that text is almost always included in Chaucer's works, as well as in the concordance. Chaucer's efforts in this field were probably his first literary efforts; they certainly belong to the period anterior to 1370.

2. English translation of the De consolatione philosophiae of Boetius. This translation, written by Chaucer about 1382, was probably inspired by the Roman de la rose (a paraphrase of the Consolation being included in the latter) or by the French translation which John of Meung made of it after the completion of the Roman de la rose (Introd. 2, 933). Chaucer was acquainted with the commentary on the Consolation by Nicholas Trevet (XIV-1), as well as with John's French translation. His own translation is very imperfect.

3. The Canterbury tales, Chaucer's masterpiece, deserves consideration on the same basis as Boccaccio's Decamerone. Its importance in English literature is at least equal to the Decamerone's importance in the history of Italian letters. It confirmed the establishment of the English language and of English letters on an equal footing with the Latin and the French.

It cannot be proved that Chaucer was acquainted with the Decamerone, though he was familiar with Boccaccio's Latin writings. The general scheme of the Canterbury tales is superior in dramatic quality to that of the Decamerone, and the narrators created by the English artist are far more living than the Italian ones;

FIG. 25. Portrait of Geoffrey Chaucer. The so-called Seddon portrait, now in the Harvard University Library. It is painted in oils on a panel $19\frac{1}{8}$ by $15\frac{3}{16}$ inches. See note on Chaucer's iconography in the text. Courtesy of Harvard Library and Fogg Museum, Cambridge, Massachusetts.

we remember the former, while the latter are forgotten. The framework of the Tales is as follows: On April 16 a number of pilgrims are assembled at the Tabard Inn in Southwark (London), preparing for a pilgrimage to the shrine of St. Thomas à Becket in Canterbury. They resolve to tell stories, each in turn; each is to tell two stories on the journey to Canterbury (which occupied usually three days and a half), and two more on the way back. This called for a total of 120 tales, but the number of tales actually told is considerably smaller (25).

The general scheme was conceived by Chaucer c. 1387, when the Prologue was written, but some of the tales are anterior, such as the Knightes tales (Palamon and Arcite), the Second nonnes tale (Lyf of Seynt Cecyle), and the Monkes tale. The collection as we have it now was largely completed by 1393–94, but Chaucer continued to work on it almost to the end of his life.

4. Tretis of the astrolabie (Treatise on the astrolabe). Chaucer wrote this treatise in 1391 (or somewhat earlier), for a little boy, Lewis, then 10 years old, who was his own son or the son of a friend. It is the oldest English treatise on the subject, professedly an elementary one written for a small boy, with the purpose of teaching him not only the construction and use of that instrument, but also the principles of astronomy and mathematical geography and the rules of astrology. The treatise was written for the year 1391 and the latitude of Oxford.

Chaucer was aware of the existence of similar treatises in Greek, Arabic, Hebrew, and Latin, and quoted as his main authorities Ptolemy and Alcabitius (al-Qabīṣī, X-2),[7] but his work is largely, if not exclusively and slavishly, derived from the Compositio et operatio astrolabii of Māshāllāh (VIII-2).[8]

According to its own account, the Tretis was meant to be divided into five parts, whereof only the first two were completed: (1) Bread and milk for children (introductory), (2) Use of the astrolabe, (3) astronomical and geographical tables, according to the calendars of the friars John Somer (1367) and Nicholas Lenne (or Lynn, 1387), (4) planetary tables and theories, (5) general rules of astrology. Chaucer illustrated his text with a number of diagrams (as many as 62 in the more complete MSS) and insisted that little Lewis should study it with a real astrolabe in hand.

4. *His scientific knowledge*

Chaucer's treatise on the astrolabe is a real scientific treatise, which, as far as can be judged from the two parts available, was a sound textbook, without originality, but implying an earnest study of the subject. On that subject we know exactly the extent of his knowledge; with regard to other scientific subjects we can only guess.

In addition to astronomy and astrology, he was sufficiently familiar with the medical and other scientific theories of his day, and with its superstitions, to be able to refer to them more or less casually in his writings. For example, he was acquainted with the theory of humors and temperaments, with physiognomy, metoposcopy (divination by means of the marks on the forehead), geomancy, alchemy, oneirology. It is impossible to say in each case whether he shared a

[7] Chaucer cites many Muslim astrologers; but not Abū Ma'shar (IX-1). This is curious, for according to his younger contemporary John Lydgate, "Albumasar [first] fond astronomye" (Fall of princes, ii, l. 2489; p. 270, 1923).

[8] The Arabic text of that treatise is apparently lost, no MS being mentioned by Brockelmann (suppt. 1, 392, 1937). The Latin translator is unknown (Introd. 1, 531).

definite belief or superstition, and to what extent he shared it; my impression is that he shared them all "more poetico." Indeed, he was first and last a literary artist, making use of scientific details as of any others suitable to his artistic purpose. His selection of scientific or pseudo-scientific details was very intelligent; he used them with admirable restraint, just enough to suggest the intellectual background of his characters.

Therefore the study of Chaucer's scientific knowledge is important not so much from the point of view of the history of science stricto sensu, but rather for the understanding of the popular diffusion of scientific ideas in his time.

Apparently he accepted the common views of his age concerning the virtues of the signs of the zodiac and of the houses, the sympathetic relations between the stars and parts of the human body, the rule of the planets over the days and the hours; he believed in judicial astrology like the majority of his contemporaries, yet was obliged to condemn it or at least to mitigate it because astrological fatalism did not harmonize with the Christian faith in the freedom of the will. His hostility to judicial astrology was thus due to religious rather than scientific reasons.

In the Chanouns Yemannes tale he inserted a violent satire against alchemists; it does not follow that he was entirely opposed to alchemy, but it shows that he had investigated the subject and knew what tempting opportunities it offered to charlatans.

The sources of his scientific ideas are difficult to determine; they cannot be deduced with any certainty from the names which he manages to introduce here and there: Hippocrates, Galen, Constantine the African, etc. These ideas were commonplace in his time and might have been obtained by him from many authors, old or new, or from oral tradition.

On the basis of a few lines (113–17) in the Parlement of foules:

> Cytherea! [i.e., Venus] . . .
> As wisly as I sey thee north north west

it has been claimed that Chaucer had some knowledge of magnetic declination. The position of Venus indicated by him must be understood as a magnetic azimuth; the misplacement of Venus (NNW instead of NW) corresponds to an error of about 23½°, tallying sufficiently well with the extrapolated value of the declination in London 1380. The argument seems very far-fetched to me.

Hugo Lange: Hat Chaucer den Kompass gekannt und benutzt? (Anglia 58, 333–44, 1934). H. Lange and A. Nippoldt: Die Deklination am 20. Mai 1380 in London (Quellen und Studien zur Geschichte der Naturwissenschaften und der Medizin 5, 38–56, 1936; Isis 28, 368).

5. *A note about cats in early English literature*

It is generally believed that Chaucer was the first to speak of cats in English literature. The best example is in the Manciple's tale, l. 175, but there are many others; see "cat" and "cats" in John S. P. Tatlock and Arthur G. Kennedy: Chaucer concordance (Washington 1927; Isis 10, 134). There is, however, an earlier mention of cats in the Ancren riwle, "the most significant piece of earlier Middle English prose," also existing in French and Latin (regulae inclusarum). That is a collection of rules for nuns, and one of the rules reads, "Ye shall not possess any beast, my dear sisters, except only a cat." It is ascribed to Simon of Ghent, bishop of Salisbury 1297–1315, who addressed it to anchoresses at Tarrant Kainston (Dorsetshire), and also more plausibly to Richard Poor, who was an earlier bishop of Salisbury 1217–28 (then of Durham 1228–37) and founded a small house for Cistercian nuns at Tarrant Kainston. It is more probable that the rules were written by the founder of that nunnery, and the language is of the early thirteenth rather than of the following century. H. E. D. Blakiston (DNB 46, 106–9, 1896). Wells (p. 361–65 and suppts.).

Speaking of cats, they make a professional appearance in the contemporary codes of maritime law, such as the Llibre del consolat de mar. They are supposed to be kept on board a ship, or else the managing owner of the ship ought to make compensation for the goods destroyed by rats. See Sir Travers Twiss: The Black book of the Admiralty. Appendix, part III (p. 99, London 1874).

6. *Chaucer's influence*

Chaucer's influence was mainly, if not exclusively, of the literary kind; he is one of the creators of the English language, and his susceptibility to foreign influences (chiefly French and Italian), combined with his poetic genius, enabled him to enrich considerably the traditions of his own country. The poet John Lydgate (1370?–1451?) called himself Chaucer's disciple[9] and continued the latter's teaching.

As to Chaucer's scientific influence, it is negligible; he was simply a mirror of the common scientific thought of his time, nothing more. Even his treatise on the astrolabe is unimportant, though the existence of some 18 MSS shows that it enjoyed some popularity.

6 bis. *The testament of love*

This is a prose composition which follows closely (sometimes verbatim) Chaucer's translation of the De consolatione philosophiae. It is divided into three books, and the third is largely derived from St. Anselm (XI-2): De concordia praescientiae et praedestinationis nec non gratiae Dei cum liberio arbitrio (PL vol. 158). The title means "the witnessing of heavenly love." The author is in prison hoping for a change of fortune and praying for aid to Margaret, the grace of God. Heavenly love comes to succor him. . . . The composition is obscure and disjointed, and lacks unity of matter and form.

It occupied 145 pages in the first complete edition of Chaucer, prepared by William Thynne (London 1532). From that time until 1844 it was regarded as an authentic work of Chaucer's and was even used to ascertain details of the latter's biography. It is now admitted that the author was Thomas Usk.[10] This Thomas was a confidential clerk of John de Northampton (fl. 1376–90), lord mayor of London during a critical period; Thomas betrayed his master and was executed on March 4, 1388. The Testament of love was probably written during the incarceration preceding his execution.

Henry Bradley (DNB 58, 60–62, 1899). Wells (p. 370–71). George Sanderlin: Usk's Testament of love and St. Anselm (Speculum 17, 69–73, 1942).

7. *Text*

The number of Chaucerian editions is so considerable that we can only cite the most important:

[9] Fall of princes. Prologue (l. 246 f.), "My maistir Chaucer. . . . "

[10] Not related to Adam of Usk (c. 1362–c. 1430), author of a Latin chronicle of English history from 1377 to 1404, wherein the execution of Thomas Usk is mentioned (DNB 1, 83, 1885). Adam came from Usk (Monmouthshire), Thomas was a Londoner.

Collected works. The first (incomplete) edition was published by the printer Richard Pynson (d. 1530) in London 1526; three parts, in black letter. The first complete edition was that of William Thynne (d. 1546), in London 1532, also black letter. It was reproduced in facsimile by the Oxford Press in 1905, with an introduction (44 p.) by Walter W. Skeat.

The foundation of the Chaucer Society by Frederick James Furnivall (1825–1910) with the collaboration of the Harvard professor Francis James Child (1825–96) and others led to the preparation and publication of many studies, and mainly of a new collected edition, the so-called "Oxford Chaucer," edited by W. W. Skeat (6 vols., Oxford 1894; suppt. vol. 7, Oxford 1897). This text was reproduced with but few variations in the sumptuous edition of F. S. Ellis, with 87 woodcuts designed under Burne-Jones' direction, admirably printed by William Morris (Kelmscott Press, Hammersmith 1896), one of the finest books of our time.

Of later editions, we shall mention only the "Globe edition," by Alfred W. Pollard and others (1 vol., London 1898), and the one prepared by Fred Norris Robinson (1174 p., Boston 1933). Robinson's critical edition is more conservative than either Skeat's or Pollard's (Speculum 9, 459–64).

Romaunt of the rose. First printed in Thynne's Chaucer (1532), and in all subsequent collected editions.

Separate edition with the French original by Max Kaluza (Chaucer Society, London 1891).

Boetius. First printed by William Caxton before 1479, then by Thynne (1532), and in subsequent collected editions.

Canterbury tales. First edition by Caxton, c. 1478, then again c. 1484. Pynson, c. 1492. Wynkyn de Worde, 1495, 1498.

Edition begun by Thomas Morell (1 vol., London 1737), containing only the Prologue and the Knight's tale; no more published. First complete critical edition by Thomas Tyrwhitt (5 vols., London 1775–78). Monumental edition by John Matthews Manly, Edith Rickert, and others: The text of the Canterbury tales studied on the basis of all known MSS (8 vols., University of Chicago 1940). Innumerable other editions, for scholars, students, or children; complete or selected, textual or modernized. Translations into German, French, and Italian (all modern).

Treatise on the astrolabe. First printed in Thynne (1532), and reprinted in many collected editions. Edited by Andrew Edmund Brae (114 p., London 1870), in appendix, The astronomy of Chaucer in the Canterbury tales (p. 63–108). New edition by W. W. Skeat (Early English Text Society, London 1872). More complete edition by Robert Theodore Gunther: Chaucer and Messahalla on the astrolabe (242 p., 73 fig., Oxford 1929; Isis 14, 233–35); including Chaucer's treatise, the Latin texts of Māshāllāh's De compositione astrolabii, De operatione vel utilitate astrolabii, and English translations of the same. P. Pintelon (1914–39): Chaucer's Treatise on the astrolabe MS 4862–4869 of the Royal Library in Brussels (Publications of the Faculty of philosophy and letters of the University of Ghent, no. 89, 144 p., plus facsimile of the MSS, Antwerp 1940; Isis 37). This posthumous publication is not a new edition, but it gives the MS itself in facsimile plus abundant variants and other notes, study of all the MSS, etc.; the MS reproduced dates from c. 1400.

8. *Bibliographies*

Eleanor Prescott Hammond: Chaucer, a bibliographical manual (589 p., New York 1908), a rich collection of Chauceriana, including elaborate descriptions of the editions, information on the students of Chaucer, etc. Dudley David Griffith: A bibliography of Chaucer, 1908–1924 (148 p., Seattle 1926), a supplement to Hammond. Willard E. Martin, jr.: A Chaucer bibliography, 1925–33 (Durham, N. C. 1935).

Caroline Frances Eleanor Spurgeon: Chaucer devant la critique en Angleterre et en France depuis son temps jusqu'à nos jours (430 p., Paris 1911); Five hundred years of Chaucer criticism and allusion, 1357–1900 (7 parts, Chaucer Society, London, issues for 1908–17, "publisht" in 1904–24); new edition in 3 vols., illustrated (Cambridge 1925). Wells (1916, etc.)

9. *Concordance*

John Strong Perry Tatlock and Arthur Garfield Kennedy: A concordance to the complete works of Geoffrey Chaucer and to the Romaunt of the rose (1125 p., Carnegie Institution, Washington 1927; Isis 10, 134), based on the Globe text.

10. *Biographies and general criticism*

The first critical biography was written by Sir Nicholas Harris Nicolas, by way of preface to the Aldine Chaucer (London 1845). Chaucer Society: Life records of Chaucer (4 parts, London 1875–1900); index to them by E. P. Kuhl (Modern philology 10, 527–52, 1913). For other publications of the Chaucer Society see E. P. Hammond (p. 522–41, 1908). George Gordon Coulton: Chaucer and his England (London 1908; 2d ed., 1910; 3d, 342 p., 12 pl., 1921). Emile Legouis: Geoffroy Chaucer (268 p., Paris 1910); Englished by Louis Lailavoix (256 p., London 1913). Robert Dudley French: A Chaucer handbook (406 p., New York 1927; 4th printing 1935). Gilbert Keith Chesterton: Chaucer (302 p., London 1932). John Livingston Lowes: Chaucer and the development of his genius (302 p., Boston 1934), lectures delivered at Swarthmore College in 1932. Vincent B. and Lilian J. Redstone: The Heyrons of London, a study in the social origins of Chaucer (Speculum 12, 182–95, 1937). Coulton: Mediaeval panorama (p. 248–57, 1938). Howard Rollin Patch: On rereading Chaucer (280 p., Harvard University 1939). Percy Van Dyke Shelly: The living Chaucer (340 p., University of Pennsylvania, Philadelphia 1940).

11. *Special criticism*

Francis James Child: Observations on the language of Chaucer (Memoirs of the American Academy 1863). Bernhard Ten Brink (1841–92): Chaucer. Studien zur Geschichte seiner Entwicklung und zur Chronologie seiner Schriften (Münster 1870), part 1, no more published. Thomas Raynesford Lounsbury: Studies in Chaucer, his life and writings (3 vols., New York 1892). Max Kaluza: Chaucer und der Rosenroman (253 p., Berlin 1893). W. W. Skeat: The Chaucer canon (178 p., Oxford 1900); Evolution of the Canterbury tales (37 p., London 1907). Hubertis Maurice Cummings: The indebtedness of Chaucer's works to Boccaccio (206 p., Menasha, Wis. 1916). Bernard Levi Jefferson: Chaucer and Boethius (174 p., Princeton 1917). George Lyman Kittredge: Chaucer's Lollius (Harvard studies in classical philology 28, 47–134, 1917). Albert Stanburrough Cook: Chaucerian papers (Transactions of the Connecticut Academy vol. 23, 1919). Aage Brusendorff: The Chaucer tradition (London 1925). John Matthews Manly: Some new light on Chaucer. Lectures delivered at the Lowell Institute (317 p., New York 1926), adventurous. John Livingston Lowes: The art of G. Chaucer (Proceedings of the British Academy 16, 297–326, 1930). Germaine Dempster: Dramatic irony in Chaucer (102 p., University ser., Language and literature, vol. 4, no. 3, Stanford University 1932). James B. Herrick: Why I read Chaucer at seventy (Annals of medical history 5, 62–72, 1933). Sir William McCormick and Janet E. Heseltine: The MSS of the Canterbury tales (593 p., Oxford 1933). Bartlett Jere Whiting: Chaucer's use of proverbs (310 p., Harvard University 1934). Ruth Crosby: Oral delivery in the Middle Ages (Speculum 11, 88–110, 1936; 13, 413–32, 1938; Isis 25, 561). Mary Ernestine Whitmore: Medieval English domestic life and amusements in Chaucer (290 p., Catholic University,

Washington 1937). Joseph Mersand: Chaucer's Romance vocabulary (175 p., New York 1937). Stephen J. Herben, jr.: Arms and armor in Chaucer (Speculum 12, 475–87, 1937). Joe Horrell: Chaucer's symbolic plowman (Speculum 14, 82–92, 1939). William Frank Bryan and Germaine Dempster: Sources and analogues of Chaucer's Canterbury tales (782 p., University of Chicago 1941; Speculum 17, 274–83). Clair C. Olson: Chaucer and the music of the XIVth century (Speculum 16, 64–91, 1941). Hans J. Epstein: The identity of Chaucer's Lollius (Modern language quarterly 3, 391–400, 1942). Jonathan Burke Severs: Literary relationships of the Clerkes tale (Yale studies in English no. 96, 340 p., 1 pl., New Haven 1942; Speculum 17, 577–82). Florence R. Scott: Chaucer and the parliament of 1386 (Speculum 18, 80–86, 1943). Karl Young: Chaucer's appeal to the Platonic deity (Speculum 19, 1–13, 1944).

12. *Scientific criticism*

L. C. Karpinski: Augrim stones (Modern language notes, Nov. 1912). John Strong Perry Tatlock: Astrology and magic in Chaucer's Franklin's tale (Anniversary papers to G. L. Kittredge p. 339–50, 1913). Florence Marie Grimm: Astronomical lore in Chaucer (University of Nebraska, Studies in language 2, 96 p., Lincoln 1919). Wedel (1920). R. T. Gunther (2, 202–4, 1920). Walter Clyde Curry: Chaucer and the mediaeval sciences (290 p., New York 1926), analysis of the scientific and pseudo-scientific ideas suggested in the Canterbury tales, divided into 9 chapters each of which is devoted to one or two of the Chaucerian characters, as the Wife of Bath with her horoscope, the Summoner and the Cook, etc. George A. Plimpton: The education of Chaucer illustrated from the schoolbooks in use in his time (176 p., abundantly ill., Oxford Press 1935; Isis 26, 251). J. D. Rolleston: Chaucer and mediaeval medicine (Comptes rendus du IXe Congrès international d'histoire de la médecine, 12 p., Bukarest 1935). H. Lange and A. Nippoldt: Die Deklination am 20. Mai 1380 in London (Quellen und Studien zur Geschichte der Naturwissenschaften 5, part 4, 38–56, Berlin 1936; Isis 27, 368). Julius Ruska: Chaucer und das Buch Senior (Anglia 49, 136–37, 1937; Isis 29, 488). Walter B. Veazie: Chaucer's textbook of astronomy, Joannes de Sacrobosco (University of Colorado studies, ser. B, 1, 169–82, Boulder 1940). Marie P. Hamilton: The clerical status of Chaucer's alchemist (Speculum 16, 103–8, 5 pl., 1941). Leo J. Henkin: The Pardoner's sheep-bone and lapidary lore (Bull. history of medicine 10, 504–12, Baltimore 1941).

13. *Iconography*

The portraits of Chaucer have been investigated by Marion Harry Spielmann and the results published by the Chaucer Society (2d ser., no. 31, London 1900); also under the title Chaucer memorial lectures read before the Royal Society of Literature, edited by Percy W. Ames (London 1900). In this collection Spielmann's essay is printed on pp. 111–41, 10 pl. See also note in E. P. Hammond's bibliography (p. 49, 1908).

Spielmann concludes that the so-called Hoccleve (or Occleve) portrait is the sole authentic one. That portrait in colors occurs in the margin of Thomas Hoccleve's (1370?–1450?) De regimine principum, Harleian MS 4866, British Museum, written in 1411–12. It represents Chaucer half length. It is no. I in Spielmann's list of the ten principal portraits. No. VII in the same list is the so-called Seddon portrait, from one of its last owners, the architect John P. Seddon. Seddon sold it to Fairfax Murray, who sold it to Charles Eliot Norton. Norton bequeathed it to the Harvard University Library in 1908. It bears a close resemblance to the Hoccleve portrait. Spielmann concludes, "It is not possible to claim for it any positive authority in spite of its evident antiquity and its claim to a measure of respect." We publish it here (fig. 25) with kind permission of the Harvard Library, because it is really impressive, sufficiently plausible, and especially dear to Harvard men.

GOWER

English didactic poet and moralist writing in French, Latin, and English (d. 1408).

John Gower was born of a good Kentish family at an unknown place and time (he called himself senex in 1400). It is probable that he spent a few years of his youth in France, but most of his life was passed in Kent. In his old age he resided in the priory of St. Mary Overies,[11] Southwark. He died there in 1408 and was buried in the church, where his beautiful altar-tomb, with a recumbent effigy of himself, can still be seen. He wrote many poems, chiefly didactic, but a few lyrical, in three languages. It will suffice to mention the three main ones.

1. Speculum hominis (or, meditantis). A French poem of almost 30,000 lines, long believed to be lost, but identified in 1895 with the Mirour de l'omme. It is a didactic poem, written c. 1376–79, dealing with vices and virtues, man's moral and religious life; in short, it is a moral treatise, very prolix and very tedious.

2. The Vox clamantis is a Latin elegiac and didactic poem in seven books, begun in 1381 and completed before the end of the century. It is dedicated to archbishop Arundel, i.e., Thomas Arundel (1353–1414), who became archbishop of York in 1388 and of Canterbury in 1396. The first and longest book (one-quarter of the whole) contains an allegorical account of the labor troubles which occurred in Kent in the spring of 1381 down to the death of Wat Tyler in the same year. Book II deals with religious faith; books III and IV, with the vices of the clergy and the need of reformation (Gower was not a Lollard, but rather conservative); book V, with the need of a good army; book VI, with the shortcomings of lawyers, the need of good councilors, peace, morality, and low taxation; book VII, with the evils of the government of Richard II (king of England 1377–99). By 1386 the king's worthlessness was generally recognized. He abdicated in 1399, being succeeded by Henry of Lancaster, Henry IV (1399–1413). The story of the last evil years of Richard II and of his abdication is told by Gower himself in a sort of appendix called Chronica tripartita (three books in Latin verse).

3. The Confessio amantis is an English didactic poem of great prolixity (c. 30,000 lines), completed in 1390, revised in 1393. First meant for Richard II, it was finally dedicated to Henry of Lancaster. It is divided into eight books plus a prologue. It is a treatise on morality, containing some 112 stories, derived from many ancient and mediaeval sources and badly arranged. In book VII there is a summary of popular lore, much of which is borrowed from the Secretum secretorum (Introd. 1, 556; vol. 2 by index).

"Moral Gower" (as Chaucer called him) was well acquainted with Latin literature, ancient and mediaeval, also with Dante and Boccaccio; Chaucer and he were friends. As a poet he is distinctly inferior to Chaucer, and his scientific knowledge is also very inferior to Chaucer's. He had some interest in alchemy, astrology, and the theory of the microcosm, but his knowledge remained superficial and vulgar. A comparative study of his writings and Chaucer's enables us to estimate the scientific lore available in England in the second half of the fourteenth century, at two very different levels. His long poems are so tedious that they are almost unreadable, but they are not more tedious than the great majority of didactic

[11] Or Overy. That is, St. Mary of the Ferry, or over the rie (water). Now Saviour's Church, Southwark cathedral.

poems of the Middle Ages. They answered the taste of their times, and enjoyed some popularity, witness the number of extant MSS. For example, there are 49 MSS of the Confessio amantis, that is, almost as many as of Piers Plowman. C. Brown and R. H. Robbins: Index of Middle English verse (p. 737, New York 1943; Isis 34, 443).

Text. The complete works of John Gower, edited from the MSS with introductions, notes and glossaries by George Campbell Macaulay (4 vols., Oxford 1899-1902). Vol. 1, 1899, contains the French works; vols. 2 and 3, 1901, the English ones; vol. 4, 1902, the Latin ones. Macaulay's edition of the Speculum meditantis (Mirour de l'omme) in 1899 was the first edition of that text identified by himself.

Poema quod dicitur Vox clamantis necnon Chronica tripartita. First edition by Henry Octavius Coxe (Roxburghe Club, 490 p., London 1850).

The Confessio amantis was first printed by Caxton (London 1483); the colophon is wrongly dated 1493. It was reprinted in London 1532 and again in 1554. New edition by Reinhold Pauli (3 vols., London 1857).

An extract from book IV is included in Elias Ashmole (1617-92): Theatrum chemicum britannicum (p. 368-73, London 1652).

Confision del amante por Joan Goer. Spanische Übersetzung von Gowers Confessio amantis aus dem Vermächtnis von Hermann Knust nach der Handschrift im Escorial hrg. von Adolf Birch-Hirschfeld (584 p., Leipzig 1909). The first version (1390) of the Confessio amantis was soon translated into Portuguese by one Roberto Payn or Payna (Robert Payne), canon of Lisbon, and the Portuguese text was translated into Castilian by Juan de Cuenca of Huete; the MS of Juan's translation edited by Birch-Hirschfeld dates from c. 1400. These two versions were thus very early indeed.

Criticism. Sidney Lee (DNB 22, 299-304, 1890). Rachel Elfreda Fowler: Une source française des poèmes de Gower (thèse, 212 p., Paris 1905). William George Dodd: Courtly love in Chaucer and Gower (thesis, 265 p., Boston 1913). John Livingston Lowes: Spenser and the Mirour de l'omme (Modern Language Association publications vol. 29, 388-452, Cambridge, Mass. 1914). Wedel (p. 132-56, 1920). George Gillespie Fox: The mediaeval sciences in the works of John Gower (thesis, 164 p., Princeton 1931).

A5. Germany

ALBERT OF SAXONY

German philosopher (1316?-1390). Aristotelian commentator, expositor of the new (Occamist) logic, mechanician. Transmitter of Parisian science to Vienna.

Also called Albertus de Helmstede, Albertus de Saxonia, Albertus de Ricmestorp (Riggensdorf). Albertutius, Albertus novus (as opposed to Albertus Magnus).

P. Duhem refused to admit the identity of Albert of Saxony with Albert of Ricmestorp. That identity has been proved independently by M. Jullien (1910) and A. Dyroff (1913).

He was born at an unknown date (1316?) at Ricmestorp or Helmstedt in Lower Saxony. It may be that Ricmestorp is his family name. His parents were peasants, his father was called Bernard (Bernhard Rike?). It is possible that he began his higher studies at the University of Prague (created in 1347); he obtained his master's degree in Paris 1351, under Albert of Bohemia. He occupied various offices in the English nation of the University of Paris, being successively procurator, examinator, rector, receptor. The last record of him in the Paris archives is dated 1362. In 1364/65 he was instrumental in the creation of the University of

Vienna, being the intermediary between the Viennese scholars and the curia (Urban V); he was the first rector of that university in 1366.

Early editors called him a Franciscan, a Dominican, or an Augustinian Hermit, according to their own affiliations; in reality he was not a regular, but a secular priest. He was for a time vicar of Laa (35 miles north of Vienna), then in 1366 canon of Hildesheim; in the same year he was appointed bishop of Halberstadt (in Saxony, 29 miles from Magdeburg). He remained in that office until the end of his life. He died on July 8, 1390, "in bona senectute" (the birth date 1316 is thus plausible), and was buried in the cathedral of Halberstadt.

His activities will be considered under the following headings: logic, Aristotelian commentaries, mechanics and physics, astronomy, mathematics, geology, ethics, other writings.

Logic. Six works of his reveal his deep interest in logic:

1. Logica Albertutii (1522).
2. Sophismata Alberti de Saxonia (1489).
3. Commentarius in Posteriora Aristotelis (1497).
4. Quaestiones in Occami logicam (1496).
5. Tractatus obligationum (1490).
6. Insolubilia (1490).

The dates following the titles are those of the first printed editions; they illustrate the relative popularity of these treatises, all of which (except the first) were printed in the fifteenth century. Treatises 2 to 6 are represented by at least a dozen different incunabula editions, that is, if one counts as different the editions of treatises 2, 5, 6 in the same volumes (Paris 1490, 1495, c. 1496/98).

Albert represented the new logic (the via moderna of the Occamists nominales, terministae) against the old logic (via antiqua) of the Thomists and Scotists. He was partly responsible for the diffusion of the new logic from Paris to the German universities.

Aristotelian commentaries. Albert composed a number of commentaries on Aristotle's works, as follows:

3. Commentarius in Posteriora (1497), already mentioned.
7. Quaestiones super octo libros Physicorum (1500?).
8. Quaestiones in libros de Coelo et mundo (1481).
9. Quaestiones de Generatione et corruptione (1504).
10. Quaestiones super totalem librum de Sensu et sensato (unpublished).
11. Conclusiones et auctoritates supra Parva naturalia (written in Prague 1378, unpublished).
12. Expositio super decem libros Ethicorum (unpublished). I shall come back to this presently.
13. Dicta super Yconomicam (unpublished).

Mechanics and physics. Albert's physical views are scattered in his commentaries on Aristotelian physics (items 7, 8, 9) and in the second part of his Tractatus proportionum (item 16). For example, in (7) he rejected the Aristotelian concept of the impossibility of a vacuum.

It is his mechanical ideas which have attracted most attention; in that field he continued Buridan's investigations, and similar tendencies appear in the activities of Nicole Oresme and of Albert's own disciple Themon son of the Jew.

He stated that in every heavy body there is a well determined point, the center of gravity, which tends to be as near as possible to the center of the universe, the common center of all heavy bodies. This may be considered an adumbration of Galileo's and Torricelli's principle of statical equilibrium: a system of heavy bodies is in statical equilibrium when the center of gravity cannot descend any lower (Evangelista Torricelli, De motu gravium naturaliter descendentium, in his Opera geometrica, Firenze 1644).

Under the influence of Bradwardine and Buridan, he tried to precise the notion of accelerated speed, in particular the notion of speed with constant acceleration (uniformiter difformis). He accounted for the acceleration of a falling body by an accumulation of impetus. He said that the speed of a falling body was proportional to the time, and also that it was proportional to the space, without being able to choose between these two contradictory hypotheses. If anything, he seems to have preferred the second, that is, the wrong one. So did Galileo in his youth, but Galileo later gave a final proof of the first hypothesis. Albert seems to have rejected both hypotheses on the ground that according to either the speed would increase beyond any limit with the length of fall. He was thus led to introduce the notion of resistance, not only the resistance of the medium, but also a kind of internal resistance (resistentia intrinseca); this suggested to him a third hypothesis implying a speed limit caused by an increasing resistance.

Albert assimilated the impetus to a gravitas accidentalis, a something which increases in proportion to the motion itself. Like Buridan, he assumed the existence of an impetus for celestial bodies as well as for sublunar ones. He was unable to explain the nature of that impetus or gravitas, even in his own scholastic language—as to whether it was a substance or an accident, a quality or a quantity.

Astronomy. His astronomy was Ptolemaic rather than Alpetragian, yet he used ten spheres, one of them being needed to account for the trepidation of the equinoxes.

Albert wrote a commentary on Sacrobosco's treatise on the sphere: (14) Questiones super spheram Johannis de Sacrobosco (unpublished).

Mathematics. His mathematical writings are:

15. Tractatus de latitudinibus formarum (according to Cantor; apocryphal?).

16. Tractatus (liber) proportionum. Divided into two parts, the first of which deals with proportions considered arithmetically and geometrically, and the second with speeds and other mechanical problems. This book was quite popular. At least 11 editions appeared between 1477? and 1506. Its popularity as late as the beginning of the sixteenth century is attested by the abridgment of it made by the Milanese Dominican Isidoro Isolani (d. c. 1528): Epithoma in proportiones fratris Alberti de Saxonia (princeps 1513). Moreover, a commentary was devoted to it by Benedetto Vittori (born at Faenza in the last quarter of the fifteenth century; taught in Bologna from 1503 on; died in 1561), in or soon before 1506.

17. Demonstrationes de quadratura circuli. Scholastic and sterile discussion of the subject. Albert ends, like Giovanni Campano (XIII-2), in a practical conclusion equivalent to $\pi = 3\frac{1}{7}$.

18. Quaestio de proportione diametri quadrati ad costam ejusdem. Sterile discussion of irrationality (proportio irrationalis). Duhem does not accept the ascription of this treatise to Albert (Etudes 1, 341–44, 1906). It should be ascribed to Oresme.

Geology. Albert explained more completely than Ibn Sīnā and others the geological action of water. If no other action interfered, thanks to continued erosion the ocean would finally cover the whole earth. But there is an antagonistic action, a steady uplifting of continents, conceived as a means of compensating the disruption of statical equilibrium due to erosion. Erosion and local uplifting succeed and compensate each other periodically.

Ethics. Albert's ethical views were explained in his commentaries on the Nicomachean Ethics and the Economics. The former had been translated into Latin by Robert Grosseteste c. 1240–43; the latter by William of Moerbeke, a generation or two later. During the fourteenth century there developed a great interest in the Ethics, witness the university programs, witness also the commentary composed before 1329 by the Franciscan Geraldus Odonis (d. 1349), then a series of other commentaries by the Carmelite John Baconthorpe (d. 1346), by Walter Burley c. 1340, by Buridan, by Albert of Saxony, and the French translation made by Oresme (in 1370).

In his commentary, Albert quotes Boetius, Eustratios of Nicaea (c. 1050–c. 1120), the "Commentator" (Ibn Rushd), Robert Grosseteste, Albertus Magnus, Thomas Aquinas, but he never mentions Burley, from whose commentary his own was slavishly derived.

Other writings. To complete the list of Albert's works, it will suffice to mention his (19) Quaestiones philosophicae disputatae Parisiis, and (20) Quaestiones Ocham interminabiles—two unpublished works which have not yet been investigated.

Text. 1. Logica Albertutii (Venice 1522).

2. Sophismata (Paris 1489, 1490, 1495, c. 1496/98).

3. Commentarius in Posteriora (Milano 1497, Venice 1497).

4. Quaestiones in Occami logicam. Printed together with Occam's Expositio aurea (Bologna 1496).

5. Tractatus obligationum (Lyon c. 1493, 1498, Paris 1490, 1495, c. 1496/98).

6. Insolubilia (Paris 1490, 1495, c. 1496/98). The editions of Paris 1490, 1495, c. 1496/98 contain items 2, 5, and 6 in a single volume.

7. Quaestiones super octo libros Physicorum (Venice 1500?, 1504, 1516, Paris 1516, 1518).

8. Quaestiones in libros de Coelo et mundo (Pavia 1481, Venice 1492, 1497, 1520, Paris 1516, 1518).

9. Quaestiones de Generatione et corruptione. First printed with the commentaries of Giles of Rome (XIII-2) and Marsilius of Inghen (Venice 1504, 1505, 1518), also separately (Venice 1515, 1520, 1568, Paris 1516).

15. Tractatus de latitudinibus formarum (?). Printed in 1505 according to Cantor.

16. Tractatus proportionum. (Padua 1477?, 1482, 1484, 1487, Paris c. 1485, 1500?, Rouen c. 1493, Venice 1487, 1494, Bologna 1502, 1506). The edition of 1506 contains the commentary by Benedetto Vittori. Epithoma in proportiones by Isidoro Isolani (Pavia 1513, 1522, Lyon 1580).

17. De quadratura circuli. Edited by Heinrich Suter (Zeitschrift für Mathematik 29, hist. Abt., 81–101, 1884).

18. De proportione diametri quadrati ad costam ejusdem. Edited by the same (ibid., 32, 41–56, 1887).

Criticism. Ferdinando Jacoli: Intorno ad un comento di Benedetto Vittori medico faentino al Tractatus proportionum (Boncompagni's Bullettino 4, 493–97, Roma 1871). B. Boncompagni: Intorno al Tractatus proportionum (ibid. p. 498–511, 1871), elaborate bibliography. Cantor (2d ed., 2, 143–49, 1899).

It is well to group P. Duhem's abundant writings on Albert of Saxony. Origines de la statique (2, 1–185, 336, 1906), on gravity, center of gravity; Etudes (vol. 1, passim, 1906), a great part of that volume is devoted to Albert; ibid. (vol. 2, 1909), p. 78–82 on plurality of worlds, 82–90 on actio in distans, 327–32 on geology, 367 on bibliography; ibid. (vol. 3, 1913), p. 3-6, 23-34, 309-14 on gravity, 54-112 on dynamics, 302-9 on kinematics, 399-405 on latitudines; Système (4, 151-57, 1916), astronomy.

M. Jullien: Un scolastique de la décadence, Albert de Saxe (Revue augustinienne vol. 16, 1910), not seen. Adolf Dyroff: Über Albertus von Sachsen (Beitr. zur Gesch. der Philosophie des Mittelalters, Supplementband, Clemens Baeumker Festgabe, p. 319-46, Münster i.W. 1913). Georg Heidingsfelder: Albert von Sachsen. Sein Lebensgang und sein Kommentar zur Nikomachischen Ethik (same collection, vol. 22, parts 3-4, 168 p., Münster i.W. 1921; Isis 5, 219). Eduard Jan Dijksterhuis: Val en worp (p. 78-88, Groningen 1924; Isis 8, 378-79), largely derived from Duhem. Michalski (p. 113, 1925a);(p. 144-49, 1927). Ernst Borchert: Die Lehre von der Bewegung bei Nicolaus Oresme (p. 39, 43, Münster i.W. 1934; Isis 25, 534). Benjamin Ginzburg: Duhem and Jordanus Nemorarius (Isis 25, 341-62, 1936), a very useful warning against Duhem's exaggerations.

HENRY OF OYTA

German schoolman, born c. 1330, died in Vienna 1397. Heinrich Totting of Oyta (that word is spelled in many different ways). Totting was his family name, Oyta the place of his birth or origin. Oyta is not identified, but it was in the diocese of Osnabrück (Hanover). Henry was not a Carmelite, but a secular priest.

He was among the first students of the University of Prague (founded in 1347). In 1355 he was already M.A.; he taught in Prague, became a priest before 1367; in 1373 he was called to the curia in Avignon to defend himself against imputations made by the Prague theologian Adalbert Ranconis de Ericinio,[12] and was acquitted; in 1377-81 he was in Paris, where he became master in theology (1381). After 1378 many masters left the University of Paris in order to avoid the difficulties caused by the Great Schism; there were openings for them in the new German universities. In 1381-84 Henry was in Prague, and from 1384 to 1397 in Vienna. He died in that city on May 20, 1397, and was buried near his great friend Heinrich von Langenstein in the Stephanskirche.

He wrote commentaries on Aristotle and on the Sentences of Peter the Lombard, and abbreviated (c. 1373-77) the commentary on the Sentences by Adam Wodeham. He may thus be regarded as one of the Occamists. He wrote also a number of Biblical commentaries, sermons, and dissertations on theological questions of his day.

Text. A. Goddam super quattuor libros sententiarum (Paris 1512). There are two variants of that edition. Though bearing Goddam's name, it is really Henry's abbreviation of Goddam's (Wodeham's) work.

Criticism. Michalski (p. 48, 85, 1925a). Albert Lang: Heinrich Totting von Oyta. Ein Beitrag zur Entstehungsgeschichte der ersten deutschen Universitäten und zur Problemgeschichte der Spätscholastik (Beiträge zur Geschichte der Philosophie und Theologie des Mittelalters vol. 33, no. 4-5, 268 p., Münster i.W. 1937), very elaborate study based on the MSS.

DINKELSBÜHL

Nicholas of Dinkelsbühl. German philosopher and scientist (c. 1360-1433).

Nicholas was born, probably in Dinkelsbühl, Swabia, c. 1360. He studied at the University of Vienna, where he obtained his bachelor's degree in 1385 and his

[12] M.A. Paris 1348, and rector of the Paris university in 1355. In 1364 went to Prague, and became "Domscholasticus" (cathedral teacher) there in 1367.

master's degree in the faculty of arts in 1389. He gave many scientific courses there from 1390 to 1405. He was a canon of St. Stephen's, rector of the university in 1405–6, doctor in theology 1409, thrice dean of the faculty of theology. He took part in the council of Constance (1414–18) as a representative of the duke of Austria, Albert V, and upon the arrival of the emperor Sigismund he addressed him in the name of the assembly. He also addressed the new pope Martin V (1417) in the name of the Austrian duke. After the council he returned to Vienna and devoted himself to his university duties. When the council of Basel was summoned (1431), Nicholas and his younger colleague Thomas Ebendorfer[13] were charged by the university to redact its recommendations for ecclesiastical reform. He died in Vienna (not in Maria Zell) in 1433 and was buried in St. Stephen's.

He wrote a commentary on Aristotle's Physics and a great many theological books and Biblical commentaries. Though his career extended to the end of the first third of the fifteenth century, his scientific activities belong very largely to the fourteenth century. In 1391/92 he lectured on latitudines formarum; in 1393/94 on Euclid I–V; in 1394/95 on Sacrobosco's Sphaera; in 1395/96 on perspectiva communis (i.e., optics, meteorology), presumably on the basis of the treatise of John Peckham (XIII-2); in 1405 on the Theoretica planetarum (on the work of Gerard of Sabbioneta?, XIII-2).

His philosophical tendencies were probably similar to those of his older and more famous colleague in the University of Vienna, Henry of Langenstein (d. 1397), that is, he was one of the "moderns," a moderate nominalist. Hence his predilection for scientific topics. In the proceedings against Jan Hus and Jerome of Prague he seems to have been moved by philosophical as well as by national antipathies. Indeed, Hus, following Wycliffe, was a realist of the Scotist type.

Nicholas did not belong to the Augustinian order; the fact that he was elected rector of the university is sufficient proof of that, for no monk would be elected to that office.

Text. None of Nicholas' scientific writings have thus far been published.

Criticism. Stanonik (ADB 23, 622–23, 1886). S. Günther (p. 198, 1887). Hans Künssberg: Nikolaus von Dinkelsbühl. Alt-Dinkelsbühl. Mitteilungen aus der Geschichte Dinkelsbühls und seiner Umgebung. Beilage zum Wörnitz-Boten (6. Jahrg., nr. 3 to 6, no date, c. 1919). Not seen; known only through Günther's summary in Mitteilungen zur Geschichte der Medizin (18, 195, 1919).

DAMBACH

John of Dambach. Alsatian Dominican, author of the Consolatio theologiae (d. 1372).

Joannes de Tambaco Teutonicus. Born about 1289, assumed the Dominican habit about 1308, was teaching theology in Prague 1347, that is, in the Dominican monastery and studium. (By the middle of the century theological teaching was organized in colleges affiliated with the University of Prague, by the Dominicans, the Franciscans, the Cistercians, and the Augustinians.) He was in Strassburg in 1356 and 1370; he probably was there from 1356 (or before) to his death on January 2, 1372.

He wrote a number of treatises on moral and theological questions, e.g., on paradise, guilt and grace, property rights of mendicant orders, indulgences, interdict,

[13] Thomas Ebendorfer of Haselbach (on the Enns; 1387–1464). Austrian chronicler, theologian, eminent professor in the University of Vienna (ADB 5, 526–28, 1877).

simony, etc. In 1348 he addressed an exhortation to Charles IV of Luxemburg on the subject of excommunication and interdict.

By far his most important work is the De consolatione theologiae, completed in 1366. I have given many examples in previous volumes of the very great influence exerted by the Consolatio philosophiae of Boetius (VI-1). That influence is proved throughout the Middle Ages by an abundance of MSS, of translations, commentaries, and imitations. Dambach's Consolatio theologiae is one of the most remarkable of those imitations, and the title is significant. The book, he declares in the prologue, was written "ad consolationem omnium hominum praecipue autem illorum qui pie volunt vivere in Christo et ob hoc . . . persecutionem . . . patiuntur." And the source of inspiration is acknowledged a little farther on: "Sicut olim insignis ille Boëthius dum regis Theodorici favere tyrannidi recusaret, missus in exilio . . . de consolatione philosophiae librum edidit."

Dambach's Consolatio is divided into fifteen books, the contents of which are not easy to specify, as the work is not well divided and is somewhat discursive. The following indications are correct grosso modo: (1) true and false happiness, and unhappiness, taedium vitae; (2) other causes of unhappiness and misery; (3) various kinds of suffering, including a chapter on parturition; (4-7) consideration of one's fellow beings; (8) various relationships, such as friendship, family, marriage; (9, 10) physical pleasures; (11) discipline; (12) "psychoanalysis"; discussion of psychical troubles, as ligamen intricatae conscientiae, defectus melancholicae complexionis, etc.; (13) physical pains, containing passages of medical interest; (14) varia; (15) firmness of character, spiritual peace.

Dambach was much influenced not only by Boetius and fathers of the church, but also by pagan writers, chiefly Aristotle, Theophrastos, Cicero, Valerius Maximus, and Seneca. Thus Dambach continues the Boetian tradition, the use of pagan wisdom to reinforce Christian consolation.

The Consolatio theologiae being a compilation, its intrinsic importance is small, yet it exerted a not inconsiderable influence in the fourteenth and fifteenth centuries, either directly or by means of extracts and anthologies (deflorationes), which appeared under various titles (in addition to the original one) such as Consolatorium theologicum, Speculum sapientiae, Speculum patientiae, Consolatio philosophiae, Speculum humanae vitae.

Text. On account of the various forms of the text of the Consolatio theologiae, complete or abbreviated in various ways, the bibliography of the MSS and printed editions is very complicated. For details, see Auer (1928). I give only a few indications.

Consolatorium theologium (Basel 1492, reprinted 1502, 1506, 1509; Paris 1493).
Speculum patientiae (Nürnberg 1509).
De spegel der sammitticheyt (s.l., c. 1484-87, Rostock 1507).
The remedy against the troubles of temptacyons (Wynkyn de Worde, London 1519).

Criticism. Albert Auer (O.S.B.): Johannes von Dambach und die Trostbücher vom 11. bis zum 16. Jahrhundert (Beiträge zur Geschichte der Philosophie und Theologie des Mittelalters vol. 27, no. 1-2, 406 p., Münster i.W. 1928; Isis 13, 492).

A6. Netherlands

MARSILIUS VAN INGHEN

Dutch philosopher, astronomer, physicist, commentator on Aristotle and Peter the Lombard (d. 1396).

Contents: (1) Life. (2) Philosophy. (3) Works. (4) Mathematics and physics. (5) Astronomy. (6) Marsilius' library.
(7) Text. (8) Criticism.

1. *Life*

Marsilius de Inghen (Ingen, Inguem) de Novimagio. According to his Dutch biographer (J. Fruytier, and for such biographical details countrymen are likely to be better informed), Marsilius was born not in Nijmegen, Gelderland, as his Latin name suggests, but in the village of Ingen (now Lienden in de Betuwe), bishopric of Utrecht. According to Gustav Toepke and Gerhard Ritter, however, the name Inghen is a family, not a local, name, and Marsilius was actually born near Nijmegen in an unknown parish of the Utrecht diocese. The date of his birth is unknown; the first mention of him appears in the records of the English nation of the University of Paris, under the date 1362, September 27, when he gave his inaugural lecture as magister. He was a very popular regens artium at that university (special steps had to be taken to accommodate the students flocking to hear him); in 1367 and 1371 he was rector, in 1362, 1373–75, proctor of the English nation; in 1368 and 1376 he represented the university at the court of Avignon. After his second visit, 1376, he accompanied Gregory XI to Rome, and he was present in that city in 1378, when Urban VI was elected and the Great Schism began. He was a strong defender of Urban VI. His long term of service at the University of Paris (at least twenty years) ended sometime afterward (before 1382). The growing unrest due to the Schism was probably the cause of his departure; many other scholars left the university during that critical period (1378–83); they thus weakened it irremediably, but on the other hand extended its influence to other countries. The University of Heidelberg had been founded by Urban VI in 1386; Marsilius was its first rector in 1386, and was re-elected six times. In 1389 he returned ad limina apostolorum to extend the homage and explain the needs of the young university to the new pope Boniface IX. His life of work and austerity ended in Heidelberg on August 20, 1396.

2. *Philosophy*

Marsilius continued the traditions of Occam and Bradwardine (both d. 1349), of Buridan (d. 1358), and to a less extent of Oresme (d. 1382). Even as Albert of Saxony carried them to Vienna in 1366, he carried them to Heidelberg twenty years later. He tempered Occam's conceptualism, inclining even more than his master to realism, and like Buridan he took pains to subordinate in every case his reason to his faith.

3. *Works*

Marsilius wrote a commentary on the Book of sentences of Peter the Lombard, and on various parts of the Aristotelian corpus: Prior analytics, Dialectics, De generatione et corruptione, Physics.

At least a part of his commentaries on the Organon was translated into Hebrew by Abraham Shalom ben Isaac (Catalan philosopher, d. 1492), under the title Questions and answers (Sheelot ve teshubot). Some 78 questions are dealt with in the Hebrew translation (list given by Jellinek 1859).

As to the dating of his writings, we can only say that the commentary on the De generatione was composed before 1385, and probably a few years before 1385, during his stay in Paris. Indeed, the printed edition of 1518 and probably also earlier ones contain commentaries not only by Marsilius, but also by Giles of Rome and Albert of Saxony, to which has been added a table of all the questions dealt with by those three commentators. Now the list is dated April 13, 1385. This suggests that Marsilius composed the other Aristotelian commentaries also during his stay in Paris, and perhaps before 1376, for after that date much of his attention was taken up by the papal disputes.

The commentary on the Sentences was certainly written in Heidelberg; it may date from the beginning of his stay there, c. 1386.

4. *Mathematics and physics*

It is not necessary to deal as lengthily with the scientific views of Marsilius as with those of his contemporaries, because they are less original.

He adopted the theory of latitudes and longitudes explained by Oresme, and the mechanical views of Buridan and Albert of Saxony.

How are the water and land spheres of the earth situated with regard to the center of gravity of the world? Marsilius showed that that question was related to the following, Why is the earth's surface partly covered with water and partly uncovered? Nicholas of Lyra had tried to account for that by assuming that the water and land spheres were slightly eccentric. Marsilius maintains that both spheres have the same center (the center of gravity of the world), but that the so-called land sphere is not a sphere, but has an irregular shape; hence some parts of it are immersed while others emerge.

He discussed gravity as elaborately as his predecessors, but without introducing new ideas. He continued to maintain the Aristotelian doctrine of the impossibility of a vacuum.

5. *Astronomy*

His astronomical theories were partly derived from Bernard of Verdun and Giles of Rome (d. 1316). The movements of the stars are accounted for by the three outermost spheres—the tenth causing the diurnal motion, the ninth the trepidation, and the eighth the precession. The other spheres serve for the planets; they constitute seven concentric cavities within which are seven rings included in the thickness of the zodiac. The planets move within these rings.

6. *Marsilius' library*

Marsilius' large collection of books was bequeathed by him to the library of the University of Heidelberg, of which he deserves more than anybody else to be called the founder. See Friedrich Wilken: Geschichte der Bildung, Beraubung und Vernichtung der alten Heidelbergischen Büchersammlungen (p. 34 f., Heidelberg 1817). A list of Marsilius' books may be found in Gustav Toepke: Die Matrikel der Universität Heidelberg von 1386 bis 1662 (1, 678–85, Heidelberg 1884). According to a letter kindly written to me by Dr. Karl Preisendanz, director of the Heidelberg University Library (July 16, 1937), some of the MSS which belonged to Marsilius may still exist; if so, they would not be in Heidelberg, but in the Palatina collection of the Vatican library.

7. *Text*

Quaestiones super quatuor libros Sententiarum (Hagenau 1497, Strassburg 1501).

Egidii Romani in libros Priorum analeticorum expositio et interpretatio. Questiones Marsilii in eosdem . . . (Venice 1516, 1522).

The preface to the Hebrew translation of the commentary on the Organon by Abraham Shalom ben Isaac was edited by Adolph (or Aaron) Jellinek in his Marsilius ab Inghen (Leipzig 1859), together with a list of the questions dealt with in the translation.

Textus dialectices de suppositionibus, ampliationibus, appellationibus, restrictionibus, alienationibus et consequentiarum partibus pro communi omnium utilitate noviter abbreviatus (undated incunabulum, Cracow).

Compendiarius parvorum logicalium liber continens . . . Petri Hispani tractatus priores sex et . . . Marsilii dialectices documenta . . . (Vienna 1512, 1516).

Commentum novum in primum et quartum tractatus Petri Hispani cum commento parvorum logicalium Marsilii (Basel 1487).

Commentarium secundum modernam doctrinam in tractatus logices Petri Hispani I et IV. Item commentarium in tractatus parvorum logicalium Marsilii (Hagenau 1503).

Suppositiones prodierunt sub nomine Marsilii parisiensis (edited by F. A. Zuccarini, Torino 1792).

Questiones subtilissime super octo libros Physicorum secundum nominalium viam (Lyon 1518). A later edition, Venice 1617, ascribed these questions wrongly to Duns Scot, and they were then reprinted in the latter's Opera omnia of 1639. On the other hand, Duns Scot's own questions on the Physics appeared in Paris 1513 under the name of Marsilius of Inghen.

Abbreviationes libri Physicorum (Paris? 1480?, Venice c. 1490, 1521).

Questiones super libris De generatione et corruptione (Padoa 1476?, 1480, Venice 1493, 1500, 1504, 1505, 1518, 1567, Strassburg 1501). Some at least of these editions include other commentaries, e.g. by Giles of Rome.

Marsilii rationes cur Urbano pontifici electo adhaerandum (edited by G. Ritter, p. 199–204, 1921).

Anonymous commentary on the treatise De confusionibus ascribed to Marsilius (edited by G. Ritter, p. 204–6, 1921).

8. *Criticism.*

Steinschneider (p. 469–70, 1893), includes analysis of Abraham Shalom's interesting preface. Duhem: Origines (2, 53–57, 1906); Etudes (3, 401–5, 1913); Système (4, 164–68, 1916). Gerard Ritter: Marsilius von Inghen und die okkamistische Schule in Deutschland (Sitzungsberichte der Heidelberger Akad., phil. Kl., 210 p., 1921), very elaborate study dealing with the biography of Marsilius, his views on logic, theory of knowledge, physics, metaphysics and theology, and the bibliography of his writings. Michalski (p. 82–84, 1925a). J. Fruytier (Nieuw nederlandsch biografisch woordenboek 8, 908–9, 1930).

JAN DE WEERT

Flemish surgeon and didactic poet (d. 1362?).

The De Weert were members of the guild of drapers in Ypres. Jan called himself "clerc in surgyen," meaning something like master surgeon. Compare my notes on two other contemporary Flemish surgeons, Jan Yperman of Ypres (d. c. 1330) and Thomas Scellinck of Thienen (fl. 1343). We know nothing about him as a surgeon. He died in 1362 (?).

Under the influence of Maerlant (XIII-2) he wrote c. 1351 a didactic poem, the Niwe doctrinael (New doctrinal), dealing with the seven deadly sins and the ten commandments (2,670 lines). It is also called Spieghel der sonden (Mirror of sins). The first title, Niwe doctrinael, was probably suggested by the Dietsche doctrinael (Flemish doctrinal), completed by Jan van Boendale at Antwerp 1346.

The aim is primarily ethical, but De Weert's poem contains satirical descriptions and interesting references to the manners and customs of his time.

Another poem of his in the form of a dialogue, somewhat like Maerlant's Martijn (Introd. 2, 947), is entitled Een dispitacie van Rogiere ende van Janne (A disputation between Roger and John). It deals with the problem of grace and free will, and is more stilted than the Niwe doctrinael, probably because of the difficulty of the subject.

Text. Die niwe doctrinael, edited by Philips Blommaert in the latter's Oudvlaemsche gedichten (3, 75–105, 149–57, Gent 1851). New edition, which I did not see, by J. H. Jacobs (Groningen 1915).

The Dispitacie was edited by Eduard von Kausler in his Altniederländische Gedichte (2, 14–82, Leipzig 1866).

Criticism. J. Stecher (Biographie nationale de Belgique 5, 905–7, 1876). W. J. A. Jonckbloet: Geschiedenis der nederlandsche letterkunde in de middeleeuwen (2, 183–93, Groningen 1889). Jan Te Winkel: De ontwikkelingsgang der nederlandsche letterkunde (1, 72–74; 5, 25, Haarlem 1908–21).

B. EASTERN CHRISTENDOM

B1. Byzantium

JOHN OF CYPROS

Ἰωάννης Κυπαρισσιώτης ὁ σοφός. Byzantine theologian (d. after 1359).

Adversary of Gregorios Palamas, second in importance only to Nicephoros Gregoras, who died in 1359 and whom he survived. He wrote a number of treatises against the Palamites and against Neilos Cabasilas (archbishop of Salonica 1360–61), a treatise on heresies (περὶ αἱρέσεων), and a treatise on Orthodox theology written on the model of Occidental dogmatics, Ἔκθεσις στοιχειώδης ῥήσεων θεολογικῶν (Elementary exposition of theological texts). It consists essentially of a long array of quotations arranged in systematic order (definitions, affirmations, negations, discussions, reconciliations, etc.) after the manner of Western scholastics. The main sources are Athanasios of Alexandria (c. 293–373), John Chrysostom (c. 345–407), Cyril of Alexandria (376–444), Dionysios the Areopagite (V-2), John of Damascus (VIII-1).

Text. The Ἔκθεσις was published only in Latin, being translated and annotated by the Spanish Jesuit Francisco Torres (Turrianus, c. 1509–84), Ioannis Sapientis Cyparissioti Expositio materiarum quae de Deo a theologis dicuntur in decem decades partita (309 p., Rome 1581). Books 1 and 4 τῶν Παλαματικῶν παραβάσεων first edited by the French Dominican François Combéfis (1605–79) in the Auctarium novissimum (2, 68–105, 1672). All of which is reprinted in PG (vol. 152, 1865), Palamiticarum transgressionum libri I et IV (col. 663–738), De Deo expositio materiaria decades 1–10 (col. 741–992).

Criticism. Krumbacher (p. 106, 1897). Eleutheroudakis encyclopaedia (8, 307, 1930). Giovanni Mercati: Notizie di Procoro e Demetrio Cidone . . . (passim, Vaticano 1931).

CABASILAS

Nicolaos Cabasilas, Νικόλαος ὁ Καβάσιλας. Byzantine Hesychast and astronomer (c. 1290–1371).

He was born in Salonica c. 1290, his original name being Χαμαετός, and went to

Constantinople to continue his studies c. 1310. He first emerges from obscurity in the office of a court bursar (σακελλάριος). He took part in the civil war between John V Palaeologos and John VI Cantacuzenos on the side of the latter and of the patriarch John XIV Aprenos, both of whom entrusted various missions to him. When Cantacuzenos withdrew to the monastery τῶν Μαγγάνων,[14] Demetrios Cydones and Cabasilas accompanied him; in 1361 the latter succeeded his uncle Neilos Cabasilas (Νεῖλος ὁ Καβάσιλας) in the see of Salonica,[15] and he died there in 1371.

Nicolaos Cabasilas wrote abundantly on theological and ecclesiastical subjects. His two main works are the Περὶ τῆς ἐν Χριστῷ ζωῆς (Life in Christ) in seven books, and the Ἑρμηνεία τῆς θείας λειτουργίας (Explanation of the sacred liturgy), both of which are mystical interpretations of Christian life and of the sacraments. He had absorbed the teachings of Dionysios the Areopagite (V-2),[16] and, thanks to Maximos Confessor (VII-1), had succeeded in harmonizing them completely with Orthodox theology. His correspondence is important for the study of contemporary altercations.

He attempted to reconstruct the commentary on book III of the Almagest by Theon of Alexandria (IV-2), and Theon's commentary on that book, dealing with the length of the year, was unknown in any other form until canon Rome rediscovered (in 1924) Theon's own text in a tenth-century MS (Med. 28.18, Florence).

A contemporary portrait of Nicolaos is said to exist in the church of the Protaton in Caryes (Mt. Athos).[17]

Text. For the mystical writings see PG (vol. 150, 1865). The main writings of Neilos Cabasilas are available in the same collection (vol. 149, 1865).

W. Gass: Die Mystik vom Leben in Christo (Leipzig 1899), Greek text with commentary. S. Broussaleux: La vie en Jesus-Christ (238 p., Irénikon, Amay sur Meuse, before 1936), French translation of Nicolaos' main work.

Nicolaos' restitution of Theon's commentary on the Almagest III is included in the Greek princeps of the Almagest (folio, Basel 1538), which is also the princeps of Theon's commentary. It is entitled: Νικολάου τοῦ Καβάσιλλα (sic) εἰς τρίτον τῆς μαθηματικῆς συντάξεως τοῦ Πτολεμαίου περὶ τῆς μεγέθους τοῦ ἐνιαυσίου χρόνου. It is a long text, covering in that edition 64 closely printed folio pages (p. 131–94).

Criticism. Krumbacher (p. 158–60, 623, 1897). Tafrali (1912). A. Rome: Le troisième livre des commentaires sur l'Almageste par Théon et Hypatie (Annales de la Société scientifique de Bruxelles vol. 46, 14 p., 1926; Isis 9, 499), announcing and discussing his discovery of Theon's commentary on Almagest III. Eleutheroudakis encyclopaedia (7, 10, 1929). Rodolphe Guilland: La correspondance inédite de Nicolas Cabasilas (Byzantinische Zeitschrift 30, 96–102, 1929–30); Le traité inédit sur l'usure (Εἰς μνήμην Σπυρίδωνος Λάμπρου p. 269–77, Athens 1935), apropos of the treatise περὶ τόκου addressed by Cabasilas c. 1347 to Anne of Savoy, widow of Andronicos III. M. Lot-Borodine: La grâce déifiante des sacrements d'après Cabasilas (Revue des sciences philosophiques et théologiques 25, 290–330, 1936).

[14] St. George of the Mangana, not far from Hagia Sophia.

[15] We have seen that Gregorios Palamas was consecrated archbishop of Salonica in 1349. According to Krumbacher (p. 109), Neilos succeeded him in 1360. Neilos wrote various books against the Latins from the extreme Orthodox, Hesychastic, point of view.

[16] That is, a Christian adaptation of Proclos (V-2), as proved by Hugo Koch (1900; Isis 29, 425).

[17] Robert Byron: The station (p. 66, London 1928). If that portrait is authentic, it cannot be "early fourteenth century" as written on the plate reproducing it, for it represents an old man. Gabriel Millet: Les monuments de l'Athos. I. Les peintures (pl. 57, Paris 1927). Millet gives the date 1526, but it is not clear whether that refers to the portrait itself or to the chapel, "Chapelle du Précurseur (1526)," wherein it is kept.

PETER OF CRETE

Greek schoolman and pope (Alexander V, d. 1410). Πέτρος Φίλαργος (Φιλάργης, Φιλάρετος). Πάπας 'Αλέξανδρος Ε'. Petros Philarges, Petrus Cretensis. Born in Crete[18] c. 1340, of Greek stock; assumed the Franciscan habit in his native island; educated in Padua, Oxford, and Paris (c. 1378-80). He then became chancellor to Gian Galeazzo Visconti (1347-1402), duke of Milan, and, probably thanks to Visconti patronage, obtained the bishopric of Piacenza (1386), then of Vicenza and Novara. In 1402 he became archbishop of Milan, and three years later was made a cardinal by Innocent VII (pope 1404-6).

Since the beginning of the Great Schism (1378-1417) there had been two competing popes, the one in Rome, the other in Avignon. By 1406 the two popes were: in Avignon Benedict XIII (the Aragonese Pedro de Luna, c. 1328-1422/23, pope 1394-1417), and in Rome Innocent VII's successor Gregory XII (the Venetian Angelo Corraro, or Corrér, pope 1406-15). In order to put an end to that lamentable situation, the council of Pisa in 1409 declared the two pontiffs to be heretics, deposed them, and on June 26, 1409, elected Peter of Crete the new pope, under the name Alexander V. This only increased the confusion, for there were now three popes instead of two, and ecclesiastical intrigues were hopelessly mixed with military and dynastic ones. The new pope was well meaning and could not be accused of nepotism, for (as he himself remarked) he had never known his father, mother, brother, sister, or nephew, but he was badly advised by the cardinal legate of Bologna, the condottiere Baldassarre Cossa, and died suddenly on May 3, 1410. Cossa was elected in his place by the cardinals at Bologna a fortnight later, and ruled under the name John XXIII until he was obliged to abdicate by the council of Constance in 1415.

That story had to be told, if only in bare outline, because it is an intrinsic part of Peter's biography, but Peter's scientific work is much anterior to it. It was probably over by 1381. His writings include four principia (1378-79) or inaugural lectures and a commentary on the Books of the sentences (chiefly books I and II) which was completed in 1380. He was said to have translated books from Greek into Latin. His philosophy is not yet sufficiently known, but whatever its intrinsic value, it derives some extrinsic importance from the strangeness of his personality and the vicissitudes of his life. His commentary is also interesting because of the light it throws on the philosophical rivalries of that time. It is somewhat flippant and ironical. According to cardinal Ehrle, his general point of view is a kind of nominalism tinged with Scotism or Scotism tinged with nominalism.

It is interesting to note that Uberto Decembrio, father of the two humanists Angelo and Pier Candido, was secretary and later chancellor to Peter of Crete; his connection with the latter began in 1390 or earlier.

Text. Peter's writings are still unpublished.

Criticism. Franz Ehrle: Der Sentenzenkommentar Peters von Candia. Ein Beitrag zur Scheidung der Schulen in der Scholastik des vierzehnten Jahrhunderts und zur Geschichte des Wegestreites (Franziskanische Studien, Beiheft 9, 375 p., Münster i.W. 1925), very elaborate study (Isis 29, 488). Michalski (p. 225-26, 231, 1925b). De Wulf (2, 196-98, 1926). Eleutheroudakis encyclopaedia (1, 746, 1927). Am. Teetaert (DTC 12, 1890-95, Paris 1935). Mary Niven Alston: Attitude of the church toward dissection before 1500 (Bull. of the history of medi-

[18] This seems proved. However, an inscription on the wall of via Saragozza 62, Bologna, claims that he was born in that house!

cine 16, 221–38, 1944), quoting (p. 235) procès-verbal of the embalming of Alexander V.

B2. Armenia

JOHN OF ORODN

Armenian theologian of the Gregorian Armenian church, philosopher (d. 1388).

John of Orodn, Hovhannes Vorotnetsi or Orodnetsi. His surname was Gakhig, and he was the son of Ivan prince of the castle of Valant (or Wachant) in the province of Orodn. He was a nephew of Sarkis (bishop of Sunik in 1337) and a disciple of Isaiah of Nik (in Persian Armenia), archimandrite of Klazor in Sunik; then he moved to the monastery of Abragún (Tathev), of which he became the archimandrite in succession to his uncle Sarkis. He became metropolitan of Sunik, but was never a bishop. He obtained a great reputation as a teacher and had many pupils, the most famous being Gregory of Tathev. He led the opposition against the United Brethren, i.e., the party favoring union with the church of Rome and the study of Latin letters.

He wrote commentaries on the Gospel of St. John, the epistles of St. Paul, explanations of the Categories and the περὶ ἑρμηνείας, a summary of homilies of Philon the Jew (I-1), and some homilies of his own.

Criticism. Somal (p. 132–33, 1829). Neumann (p. 214, 1836). Dwight (p. 274, 1853). Patcanian (p. 84, 1860).

GREGORY OF TATHEV

Armenian theologian of the Gregorian Armenian church (1346–1410).

Gregory of Tathev (or Dathev); Kürikor Datevatsi, Grigor Tathevatsi. Born in 1346 in the province of Vajotzor; he was the main disciple of John of Orodn and became abbot of the monastery of St. Eustathios in Tathev, hence his name. He was the leader of the opposition against the United Brethren (i.e., the Armenians converted to Catholicism) and thus was as strongly hated by these as he was praised by the orthodox Armenians. The latter gave him a posthumous name of honor, equivalent (in Armenian) to trismegistos. Under his guidance, the monastery of Tathev became the focus of the anti-Roman, anti-Latin reaction. He died in 1410.

His main work, written in 1397, is the Book of questions (and answers), which is a theological treatise mainly devoted to the refutation of the errors of Jews, Manichaeans, Muslims, and Christian heretics. It explains the orthodox Armenian point of view on fundamental topics such as the creation, the incarnation, the end of the world, and the last judgment. The completion of this great Armenian summa in 1397 is the more remarkable when one remembers that Tīmūr Lang had just devastated the whole country (1387). How could the scholarly life of Gregory and his disciples continue in Tathev in the midst of such calamities? Judging from the number of MSS and later testimonies, the Book of questions enjoyed considerable popularity in orthodox Armenian circles.

In addition, Gregory composed Biblical commentaries, a list and discussion of profane literature (1383), a commentary on St. Cyril of Alexandria (archbishop 412–44), written in 1391 at the request of his friend the theologian and ritualist George of Erseng (Erzinghensis), i.e., George of Erzinjān (in the plain between Erzerum and Sīwās).

Text. The Book of questions was published in Constantinople (folio, 1729–30), but without the chapter against the Tājik or Muslims. That chapter has been edited by Mgr. Babgén Episkopos Kuleserian (= Guleserian), sometime chief librarian of the Armenian library of Istanbul, in a work on Islām in Armenian literature (vol. 1, 240 p., Mekhitarist press, Vienna 1930). Mgr. Babgén (or Papken) Guleserian was later archbishop of the Armenian monastery of Jerusalem and adjunct catholicos of the Armenians in Syria, representing Sis.

A collection of sermons was printed in Constantinople (2 vols., 1740–41).

Criticism. Somal (p. 132–37, 139, 142, 1829). Neumann (p. 215–17, 1836). Dwight (p. 275, 1853). Patcanian (p. 85, 1860). Frédéric Macler: L'Islam dans la littérature arménienne d'après la publication récente du Livre des questions de Tathewatsi (Revue des études islamiques 4, 493–522, 1932; Isis 22, 338), apropos of Mgr. Babgén's work. Lootfy Levonian: Krikor Datewatzy and his treatise against Moslems (Amicitiae corolla, essays presented to James Rendel Harris, p. 184–202, London 1933). M. A. van den Oudenrijn: Un florilège arménien de sentences attribuées à Albert le Grand (Orientalia 7, 118–26, Rome 1938); Armenian writers beginning with Gregory have assumed that the Compendium theologicae veritatis was a genuine work of Albert the Great; it was actually written by Hugh (Ripelin) of Strassburg, a Dominican who flourished at the end of the thirteenth century. Arthur Jeffery: Gregory of Tathew's contra Mohammedanos (Moslem world 32, 219–35, 1942).

Archag Tchobanian: La roseraie d'Arménie (1, 7, Paris 1918). This first volume is entirely devoted to the great Armenian poet Arakel (or Arachiel) of Sunik, nephew of Gregory of Tathev and his successor as archimandrite of Tathev and metropolitan of Sunik, bishop c. 1401. Arakel's main work is a poem on Adam composed in 1403; he also wrote various mystical poems which may be read in French in Tchobanian's book.

C. ISRAEL

C1. Spain

MEIR BEN ALDABI

Meir ben Isaac ibn al-Dabi. Hispano-Jewish encyclopaedist. Born in Toledo in the first quarter of the fourteenth century, of a noble family: he was a grandson of Asher ben Jehiel, and his father was a Talmudist nicknamed ha-ḥassid (the pious one). He was obliged to leave Toledo and Spain at an unknown time. The place of his later residence is strangely unknown. It has been claimed[19] that he spent some time in Jerusalem, but this cannot be proved.

Before leaving Toledo he conceived the plan of a treatise of encyclopaedic scope, the purpose of which was to put together all the wisdom and knowledge of his people. Much of that knowledge was generally assumed to be of Greek origin, but he thought that the Greek writings were ultimately derived from Hebrew ones.[20] For one nursing such a belief, the restitution of all that knowledge and wisdom to their Jewish originators was undoubtedly a great purpose. This work, entitled Shebile emunah (The paths of faith), was completed in 1360. It is not an encyclopaedia in the proper sense, for it is not an organic synthesis, but a juxtaposition of extracts, compiled in the same spirit as the Chinese encyclopaedias or the Speculum

[19] See also his own statement at the end of the Shebile emunah.

[20] That belief was not peculiar to him; it was not uncommon in mediaeval times, being shared not only by Jews, but also by Christians, e.g. Roger Bacon (see Introd. 2, 962).

of Vincent of Beauvais. To call him a plagiarist is hardly fair; he was more like the editor of an anthology or source book, except that he sometimes forgot to quote his sources. He seems to have had some knowledge of Arabic (e.g., to have consulted the Arabic text of the thirteen articles of the Jewish faith in Maimonides' Kitāb al-sirāj) and claims in his preface to have obtained much information from foreign languages, yet his knowledge was almost entirely derived from Hebrew writings.

As the Shebile emunah is a good illustration of Jewish knowledge in the middle of the fourteenth century, we shall analyze it and consider its sources.

It is divided into ten "paths" or sections: (I) Theology. Belief in God, his unity, explanation of his name and attributes. (II) Creation of the world: (1) Biblical account and Naḥmanides' theory of it, (2) shape of the earth and of the inhabited part of it, geographical positions of various localities, climata (nof), (3) celestial spheres, their stars and courses; the names of the planets are given in Arabic as well as in Hebrew, (4) spheres of the sun and moon, their movements and eclipses. This second section is thus a summary of astronomy and mathematical geography. (III) Creation of man. This is followed by two essays on married life, the second being simply the famous Iggeret ha-qodesh (On the holiness of marriage) of Moses ben Naḥman (who is not named). (IV) Embryology, physiology, and purposes of the organs. This includes therapeutic indications. (V) Hygiene and dietetic rules. (VI) Psychology. Souls and their qualities. Their immortality is insured by their intellectual perfection, but in an impersonal manner as Maimonides explained it. (VII) Their salvation is insured by the strict observation of religious duties. (VIII) Summary of the tradition down to the time of the compilation of the Mishna and Talmud. Interpretation of haggadot in the moderately rationalistic manner of Solomon ben Adret. (IX) Retribution. Paradise and hell, transmigration of souls, etc. (X) Messianism and resurrection of the dead.

This plan was remarkably comprehensive and original, as will be more apparent when it is summarized: (I) God, (II) world, (III–V) man; marriage, anatomy and physiology, hygiene, (VI, VII) psychology, (VIII) tradition, (IX, X) eschatology. Meir's point of view was that of orthodox Talmudism, but not intransigent; his leanings were to the right rather than to the left, i.e., toward qabbalism rather than rationalism.

The sources of the scientific part (section II) were primarily: al-Farghānī (IX-1) probably in Jacob Anaṭoli's translation, Abraham bar Ḥiyya (XII-1), Isaac Israeli (XIV-1). The sources of the rest were primarily: Ibn Gabirol (XI-1), the Ḥobot ha-lebabot of Baḥya ben Joseph (XII-1), who is not mentioned, Maimonides (XII-2), Isaac ben Abraham ben Laṭīf of Toledo (XIII-1), Moses ben Naḥman, Hillel ben Samuel of Verona, Solomon ben Adret, and Gershon ben Solomon (XIII-2). Gershon's Sha'ar ha-shamayim was perhaps the source which he exploited most thoroughly, especially in section IV.

Text. The Shebile emunah was first printed at Riva di Trento 1558. Later editions, Amsterdam 1627, 1708. There is at least one later edition without place or date (1810?). A critical edition with English translation and commentary is much to be desired.

Criticism. David Kaufmann: Die Sinne. Beiträge zur Geschichte der Physiologie und Psychologie im Mittelalter aus hebräischen und arabischen Quellen (200 p., Leipzig 1884), includes many extracts from Aldabi. Steinschneider (p. 16, 24–27,

1893); Die Mathematik bei den Juden (BM 12, 37, 1898). Joseph L. Sossnitz and Kaufmann Kohler (JE 1, 334, 1901). I. Sonne (EJ 2, 162–65, 1928).

IBN MALKAH

Judah ben Nissim Ibn Malkah (or Melkah). Jewish Neoplatonic philosopher who flourished in Spain or North Africa c. 1365.

In that year he completed in Arabic a commentary on the Sefer yeẓirah and on the Pirqe rabbi Eli'ezer (i.e., Eliezer ben Hyrcanus ha-gadol, leading tanna of the second generation, who flourished in the first and second centuries in Jerusalem, Jabneh, Lydda, and finally Caesarea, where he died. The Pirqe bearing his name are apocryphal and relatively late, certainly post-Talmudic).

This commentary is divided into three parts: (1) Anīs al-gharīb (Companion of the stranger), introduction to the Yeẓirah in the form of dialogues between the author and his soul, and between a pupil and his master, in ten chapters dealing with the achievement of perfect knowledge; (2) Tafsīr sefer yeẓirah; (3) Tafsīr pirqe rabbi Eli'ezer.

Ibn Malkah's views are similar in many respects to those of Ibn Gabirol (XI-1). He does not quote the latter, however, and there is no proof that he knew the Yanbū' al-ḥayāt. Avicebronian ideas could reach him along various other channels.

The commentary on the Yeẓirah was translated into Hebrew by an unknown scholar.

Criticism. Munk (p. 301, 1859). Steinschneider (p. 405, 1893; p. 170, 1902). Max Seligsohn (JE 6, 536, 1904).

MENAHEM BEN ZERAḤ

Menahem ben Aaron ben Zeraḥ. Judeo-Navarrese theologian and codifier. The Zeraḥ family was of French origin; at the time of the exile in 1306 they moved to Estella (Navarre), where Menahem was probably born. During the pogrom which occurred in Estella in 1328, Menahem's family was almost completely destroyed, but he escaped. He studied in Toledo, then in Alcala (Castile), where he became rabbi c. 1350. After the civil war and the riots of 1368–69, having lost everything, he continued his work under the protection of Don Samuel Abravanel (alias John of Seville). He died in Toledo August 1385.

During the dark years of persecution and contumely he composed the Ẓedah la-derek (Provision for the road), a summary of the Jewish commandments, and c. 1374 he dedicated it to John of Seville. It is divided into five parts (372 sections): (1) ritual rules, (2) food, (3) women, (4) sabbath and holy days, (5) fast days. It is simply written without references and subtilities; sometimes the rules are justified, and theological and ethical questions discussed. Mysticism is avoided. Chapter 2 of part 4 deals with the calendar and the calculation of the intercalation, and explains two astronomical tables (not included in the printed editions).

Text. Ẓedah la-derek. First edition by Abraham Usque (Ferrara 1554). Second, by Vicenzo Conti (Sabbioneta, s.a., c. 1568). To this second edition is appended an astronomical table by one Israel Zifroni, from 5055 to 6000 (1294 to 2239).

Criticism. Neubauer-Renan (p. 707–10, 1893). Steinschneider: Die Mathematik bei den Juden (BM 13, 8, 1899). Louis Ginzberg (JE 8, 466, 1904).

IBN AL-NAQAWA

Rabbi Israel ben Joseph Ibn al-Naqawa of Toledo. (Also spelled Alnaqua, Alnequa, Aluncawi, Ankava, Ankoa. In Hebrew it is written al-Naqawah with aleph in the middle.) Castilian-Jewish moralist who belonged to an old Toledan family, flourished in Toledo, and died there a martyr, together with Judah ben Asher II and others, during the persecutions of 1391. The date of his birth is unknown, but his father, rabbi Joseph ben Samuel, died in 1349.

Israel's son, Ephraim, fled to Africa in 1391 and flourished in Tlemcen, where he gained fame as a rabbi and miracle worker. He died in Tlemcen in 1442 and became a legendary figure, "the Rab." He was not the founder of the Jewish community of Tlemcen, which is considerably older, but its restorer. The synagogue which he founded exists to this day, bearing his name, and his tomb is a center of pilgrimage for North African Jews. The present tombstone was placed in 1842, at the time of the fourth centenary of the Rab's death. Dúring my stay in Tlemcen in June 1932 I visited the synagogue, tomb, and fountain of the Rab. See Alfred Bel: Tlemcen et ses environs (2d ed., Toulouse, no date, received in 1932; p. 36, 51, 133).

To return to rabbi Israel, during the dark years (1369–91) which preceded the final calamities of 1391,[21] he devoted himself to the composition of a book which would contain the ethical and ritual traditions of the Jewish people. It is entitled Menorat ha-maor (Candelabrum of light) and divided into 20 chapters: (1) charity, (2) prayer, (3) repentance, (4) humility, (5) fixed hours of study, (6) commandments and their fulfillment, (7) acts of mercy, (8) observance of sabbath and holydays, (9) honoring of parents, (10) marriage, (11) education of children, (12) upright conduct in business, (13) proper administration of justice, (14) contentment, (15) equanimity, (16) avoidance of flattery and deception, (17) love of comrades and their considerate treatment, (18) cleanness of speech, (19) keeping a friend's secret, (20) good manners.

It is largely made up of Midrashic and Talmudic stories, and quotations from older writings some of which are lost. It includes valuable data for the study of Jewish customs and folklore. The author's main purpose was to emphasize the ethical side of religion in opposition to the philosophical and mystical (qabbalistic) sides. He was not irrational, and quoted occasionally such critical writers as Maimonides and Jacob Anaṭoli, yet the spirit of Moses ben Naḥman was more congenial to him.

The Menorat ha-maor is historically important because it contributed indirectly more than any other contemporary book to the diffusion of Talmudic traditions among Jewish folks of all kinds. I say indirectly because its fortune was strange—a good illustration of that uncertainty of fate which was a commonplace of rabbinic teaching. It was almost forgotten, and is represented today by a single Bodleian MS, most of which was written in Spain in 1441. At some time in the fifteenth century, however, the substance of that book was incorporated in another book bearing the same title, Menorat ha-maor, attributed to one rabbi Isaac Aboab; this new book was not as well arranged as the first one, but it became one of the most popular books of Hebrew literature (first edition 1514).

[21] The Jews had been well treated in Castile under Alfonso XI (1312–50) and Pedro the Cruel (1350–69), but anti-Semitism could no longer be restrained after Pedro's death. The defeat of Pedro at Montiel in 1369 was the defeat of the Jews of Castile (Graetz), and the massacres and devastations of 1391 marked the end of Jewish prosperity in Castile, especially in Toledo.

Leopold (Yomṭob Lipmann) Zunz (1859), followed by other scholars, believed this second Menorat ha-maor to be the original composition, and he postulated the existence of one Isaac Aboab I, living at the end of the thirteenth century or the beginning of the fourteenth, as the author. According to the editor of Ibn al-Naqawa, the latter was the real author, and the popular Menorat ha-maor was derived from Ibn al-Naqawa's forgotten book. If Enelow's conclusion is correct (and it apparently is), Isaac Aboab senior did not exist and my note on him (Introd. 2, 878) should be canceled! The Isaac Aboab to whom the second Menorat ha-maor is ascribed is unknown; if he existed at all, he must have existed after Ibn al-Naqawa, probably in the fifteenth century.

Of course the matter of supreme importance is not the authorship but the book itself, which, humble as it is, is one of the significant Jewish books of the Middle Ages. Nevertheless, nothing can give the historian more pleasure than to help in rehabilitating a forgotten scholar, as in this case when it is our privilege to replace Ibn al-Naqawa among the noble men of his time.

Text. The second Menorat ha-maor, ascribed to Isaac Aboab, was first printed in Constantinople 1514. Many later editions: Venice 1544, Mantua 1563, Venice 1595–1602, 1623, Frankfurt a.M. 1687, Amsterdam 1700, 1708, 1722, 1739, etc.

Hebrew text with Spaniol (Ladino) translation by Jacob ben Samuel Ḥagiz (Livorno 1657, reprinted Amsterdam 1708).

Hebrew text with Yiddish translation by Moses Frankfurter (Amsterdam 1700).

Hebrew text with German translation by Raphael Jacob Fürstenthal and Benzion Behrend (3 parts, Krotoschin 1848). Etc.

The Ibn al-Naqawa text was first printed in 1578. An abridgment entitled Menorat zahab kullah (Candelabrum wholly of gold) was printed in Cracow c. 1593. Yiddish extracts in Johann Christof Wagenseil: Belehrung der jüdisch-teutschen Red- und Schreibart (Königsberg 1699).

Monumental edition by Hyman Gerson Enelow (1876–1934): Menorat ha-maor, by R. Israel ibn al-Nakawa. From a unique MS in the Bodleian library (4 vols., over 2100 p., New York 1929–32), Hebrew text with English translation and notes.

Ephraim ben Israel Ibn al-Naqawa: Sha'ar kebod Adonai (The gate of God's glory). This book by Israel's son, the Rab of Tlemcen, was published in Tunis 1902.

Criticism. Introd. 2, 878. L. Zunz: Die Ritus des synagogalen Gottesdienstes (p. 204–10, Berlin 1859). Moses Buttenwieser (JE 1, 437, 1901). Introductions to the 4 vols. of Enelow's edition (1929–32).

C2. Catalonia and Aragon

Ḥasdai Crescas

Ḥasdai (or Ḥisdai) ben Abraham Crescas (I write Crescas because this is really a word of Latin origin, and it is generally written that way, but in Hebrew it is spelled with two qof, or sometimes with two kaf, and two sin, Qresqas or Kreskas). Judeo-Catalan philosopher, born in Barcelona c. 1340, died in Saragossa c. 1411.

He was a leader of the community in Barcelona. In 1367, he, Isaac ben Sheshet, Nissim ben Reuben Gerondi, and others were held responsible for a desecration of the Host and imprisoned, but they were soon released. He negotiated with Pedro IV of Aragon (king 1336–87) in behalf of the Jewish community, and was a favorite at the court of Juan I (king 1387–95). About 1390 he moved to Saragossa, being appointed rabbi instead of Isaac ben Sheshet sometime after the latter's departure for Valencia. During the pogrom of 1391, Ḥasdai's son died a martyr. In and after 1393 Ḥasdai was one of the Jewish notables entrusted with the work of pacification and reconstruction. In 1401–2, at the request of Charles III the Noble (king of Navarre 1387–1425), he spent some months in Pamplona. The end of his life was spent in Saragossa.

He tried to liberate Jewish thought from the bondage of Aristotelianism, and thus was led to criticize Aristotle and Maimonides in about the same way as al-Ghazzālī had criticized the Muslim peripatetics. That is, he did not condemn reason, as earlier theologians had done, but on the contrary made use of it to expose its very limitations. He had, however, no understanding of experimental methods.

As against the Aristotelian conception of one finite universe, he conceived an infinite space within which more than one world might be floating. As against the Aristotelian doctrine of the essential difference between the sublunar and the translunar worlds, he postulated that matter and law are the same everywhere. Thus "form" is not a principle of actualization, but a kind of accident. His unification of the forces of nature was extended to magnetic attraction in spite of the Aristotelian principle according to which every efficient cause of motion must be moved itself while producing motion in something else. Crescas' philosophy is historically important because he was a pioneer in his criticism of Aristotle and in his revival of the views of pre-Aristotelian Greek philosophers, and incidentally he adumbrated a new conception of the universe. Indeed, he anticipated Giordano Bruno to some extent, and he deeply influenced Spinoza. His direct disciples were but few, the most important being Joseph Albo, and Zechariah ben Isaac ha-Levi, who translated al-Ghazzālī's Tahāfut al-falāsifa into Hebrew.

Three works of his have come down to us:

1. A letter to the Avignon community wherein he describes the persecution of the Jews which occurred in Aragon in 1391, in the course of which his son was killed.

2. Refutation of Christianity and apology for Judaism, written in Spanish (Tratado) in 1396 or 1398. The original text is lost, but we have a free and incomplete version in Hebrew made by Joseph ben Shemṭob in Alcalá de Henares 1451, under the title Biṭṭul 'iqqere ha-Noẓerim (Refutation of the principles of the Christians).

3. Or Adonai (Light of the Lord). This was by far his most important work. It was completed only toward the end of his life, in 1410, and thus might be superficially considered as belonging to the fifteenth century rather than to the fourteenth. It is clear, however, that the author devoted to it a good many years of his life, and that much of it was published by means of lectures to students long before its formal completion. Ḥasdai had planned a second part, to be called Ner Adonai (Lamp of the Lord)—or perhaps that was meant as the title of the whole work, the second part being then entitled Ner miẓwa (Light of commandment). At any rate, that second part was meant to bear the same relation to the first part as Maimonides' Yad ha-Ḥazaqah to the Moreh nebukim, but it remained unwritten.

The Or Adonai is divided into four main divisions: (1) discussion of the 25 propositions by means of which Maimonides had summarized Aristotelian philosophy (in his introduction to the second part of the Dalālat al-ḥā'irīn), in order to prove the existence, unity, and incorporeality of God; Crescas' object "was to show that the Aristotelian explanation of the universe as outlined by Maimonides in his propositions was false and that the proofs of the existence of God which they were supposed to establish were groundless" (Wolfson, p. 3, 1929); (2) fundamental doctrines of the Jewish faith; (3) less fundamental doctrines; (4) philosophical questions.

Crescas knew Aristotle almost as well as his Bible and Talmud, in spite of the fact that his knowledge was necessarily secondhand, as he could read neither Greek nor Arabic. His Aristotelian knowledge was derived mainly from excellent Hebrew translations of Ibn Rushd's middle commentaries; he used also some of the longer commentaries. He was also acquainted with the commentaries of Levi ben Gerson, and with various commentaries on Maimonides' Moreh nebukim, mainly one by Muḥammad ibn Muḥammad al-Tabrīzī (XIII-2) which had been translated into Hebrew in Majorca c. 1347 by Isaac ben Nathan (XIV-1), and the one by Moses ben Joshua of Narbonne (XIV-1) completed at Soria 1362. Finally, he often drew on the Maqāṣid al-falāsifa of al-Ghazzālī (XI-2), translated into Hebrew by Isaac Albalag (XIII-2) and by Judah ben Solomon Nathan before 1340 under the title Kawwenot ha-filosofim, and on the Kitāb al-'aqīdah al-rafī'ah of Abraham ben David ha-Levi (XII-2), twice Hebraicized before the end of the fourteenth century, and well known to the Jews under the title Emunah ramah. On the other hand, it does not appear that he knew the Tahāfut or the Tahāfut al-tahāfut, for his Algazellian knowledge may have been derived exclusively from the Maqāṣid, and his Averroistic, from the commentaries.

The Or Adonai was an important work containing bold views, but it remained far less known than Albo's Sefer ha-'iqqarim, since Albo's work, though distinctly inferior, was more systematic and written with greater care. On the other hand, some Christian critics of Aristotle made use of Crescas' treatise, notably Gianfrancesco Pico della Mirandola (1470-1533), nephew of the more famous Giovanni Pico (1463-94), in his Examen doctrinae vanitatis gentium, 1520.

Text. 1. Letter to the Avignon congregation edited by Meir Wiener in appendix to his edition of the Shebeṭ Jehudah of Solomon ben Verga (Hannover 1855-56).

2. Biṭṭul. First edition s.a.l. (Salonica 1860?). Reprinted by Ephraim Deinard (Kearny, New York 1904). Steinschneider had prepared a critical edition but could not finish it.

3. Or Adonai. First edition, Ferrara 1555-56. Second, Vienna 1859. Third, Johannesburg 1861. Other partial editions. Modern edition by Solomon Gottlieb Stern (Vienna 1859), imperfect.

Criticism. Manuel Joël: Don Chasdai Creskas' religionsphilosophische Lehren (Breslau 1866); Zur Genesis der Lehre Spinoza's (Breslau 1871). Emil G. Hirsch (JE 4, 350-53, 1903). Julius Wolfsohn: Der Einfluss Gazalis auf Chisdai Crescas (Leipzig 1905). Julius Guttmann: Creskas als Kritiker der aristotelischen Physik (Festschrift zum 70. Geburtstage Jacob Guttmanns, Leipzig 1915). Harry Austryn Wolfson: Crescas on the problem of divine attributes (Jewish quarterly vol. 7, 1916); Crescas' definition of time (ibid. vol. 10, 17 p., 1919). Duhem: Système (5, 229-32, 1917), suggesting that Crescas was influenced by Christian schoolmen, for example by Oresme; but he could obtain all he needed from Hebrew sources. Husik (p. 388-408, 1916). Meyer Waxman: The philosophy of Don Hasdai Crescas (174 p., New York 1920; Isis 4, 587; first published in the Jewish quarterly, vols. 8-10, 1917-20). Harry Austryn Wolfson: Crescas' critique of Aristotle (776 p., Harvard University, Cambridge 1929; Isis 14, 240-44), fundamental; includes the text and translation of the 25 propositions of part 1 of book 1 of the Or Adonai, and elaborate notes and indexes. José M. Millàs i Vallicrosa: Crescas' critique of Aristotle (8 p., Madrid 1930), criticism of Wolfson's work. J. Gordin (EJ 5, 696-708, 1930). H. A. Wolfson: Studies in Crescas (Proceedings of the American Academy for Jewish Research 5, 155-75, Philadelphia 1934).

C3. Provence

JACOB BEN SOLOMON ẒARFATI

The name Ẓarfati or Ẓarphathi, meaning the Frenchman, was given to various French Jews, for example, to some of the exiles in Provence, Catalonia, and Spain.

Jacob ben Solomon was one of those exiles who took refuge in the South, probably in Avignon. He flourished in the second half of the fourteenth century, and was a theologian and physician.

His main work, entitled Sefer mishkenot Ya'aqob (Jacob's tabernacles; Numbers 24:5), is a treatise on mystical theology, divided into four parts: (1) Bet Ya'aqob (Jacob's house), allegorical interpretation of a few passages of the Torah; (2) Yeshu'ot Ya'aqob (Jacob's salvations), dealing with the ten plagues of Egypt; (3) Qehillat Ya'aqob (Jacob's community), on the laws given on Mt. Sinai in addition to the ten commandments; the observance of the law is more important than theological doctrine; defense of the idea of creatio ex nihilo; (4) account of the sorrowful events (bereavements) which happened in his family 1382–95; a great plague raged in the South in 1395.

Jacob Ẓarfati d'Avignon, presumably identical with the theologian, wrote a short medical treatise (8 chapters) de vertigine (written in Hebrew verṭigine), that is, about the ailment called vertigo. The author states that he is a contemporary of Gilbert, physician to the king of France, whom I cannot identify.

Criticism. Adolf Neubauer: Catalogue of Hebrew MSS in the Bodleian (vol. 1, no. 2583, 1886), apropos of the medical text. Neubauer-Renan (p. 710–13, 1893). Isaac Broydé (JE 12, 637, 1906), short note, containing nothing new.

BONSENIOR BEN YAḤYA

The following note might be excluded on scientific grounds (chess is an art, not science!), or on chronological grounds, for Bonsenior's time is uncertain; I have included it partly for the sake of curiosity, and partly as a sort of addition to my note on Abraham ben Ezra (XII-1), to whom the earliest Hebrew writing on chess is ascribed.[22] It is every reader's privilege to consider it "non avenu."

Bonsenior ben Yaḥya flourished in southern France or in Spain in the fourteenth or fifteenth century. My placing him in the second half of the fourteenth century is thus arbitrary and tentative. He composed a description of the game of chess in rhymed Hebrew prose, entitled Meliẓat seḥoq ha-ishqaqi (Discourse on the game of chess). This was not the first mention of the game, or even description of it, in Hebrew. Aside from uncertain allusions in the Talmud (the games there mentioned are probably different from chess), the earliest Jewish reference to chess was made by the great Persian physician, of Jewish ancestry, 'Alī ibn Sahl Rabbān al-Ṭabarī (IX-1),[22a] al-Rāzī's teacher; after this come the mention included in the Disciplina clericalis of Petrus Alphonsi (XII-1) and the poem ascribed to Abraham ben Ezra.

According to that poem, the Hebrew tradition of chess was somewhat different from the Arabic tradition.

[22] My failure to speak of that writing in my note on Rabbi ben Ezra (Introd. 2, 187–89) may be explained by the fact that I am not a chess player. There are, however, a few other references to chess in my Introduction: 1, 451 Chinese chess, 705 Firdawsī; 2, 217 al-Khāzinī, 839 Alfonso el Sabio; and hence that excuse is unacceptable.

[22a] In his Firdaws al-ḥikma, completed in 849/50. See the edition by M. Z. Siddiqi (Berlin 1928; Isis 16, 6–54). At the end (p. 601–10) there are "chessboard-like figures" for the composition of remedies (Isis 16, 46).

Text. The Meliẓat seḥoq ha-ishqaqi was first printed together with the Mishle shu'alim of Berakya ha-Naqdan (XII-2) in Mantua 1557 (some copies dated 1559). Then in Thomas Hyde: De ludis orientalibus (part 2, Oxford 1694), together with Abraham ben Ezra's poem, and a third Hebrew writing, Ma'adane melek, ascribed to Jedaiah ben Abraham ha-Bedersi (XIV-1), the three texts in Hebrew and Latin. Reprinted under the title De historia shahiludii tria scripta hebraica (Oxford 1702). Again reprinted in Syntagma dissertationum quas olim Th. Hyde separatim edidit (vol. 2, Oxford 1767).

Bonsenior's text was also edited together with Abraham ben Ezra's poem Melizat or Ḥaruzim 'al sheḥoq shah-mat and with the Ma'adane melek by Asher Anschel (Frankfurt a.M. 1726, 1728), and with Abraham ben Ezra's Sefat yeter, by Me'ir Letteris (Pressburg 1838).

L. Hollaenderski: Délices royales ou le jeu des échecs (2 parts, Paris 1864), Hebrew and French.

Criticism. M. Steinschneider: Schach bei den Juden, in Antonius van der Linde: Geschichte und Litteratur des Schachspiels (2 vols., Berlin 1874). A. Porter: Chess (JE 4, 16–20, 1903). Murray (1913), the Jewish part of the subject has been somewhat neglected in this monumental work (see p. 446–47, 526–28), Bonsenior's treatise being overlooked. Josef Heller (EJ 4, 954, 1929). Félix M. Pareja Casañas: Libro del ajedrez, de sus problemas y sutilezas de autor árabe desconocido (2 vols., Madrid 1935; Isis 25, 199), Arabic text of 1257 with translation and commentary, for comparison.

C4. East

ISAIAH BEN JOSEPH OF TABRĪZ

Judeo-Persian qabbalist who composed in 1351, near Tabrīz, Ādharbaijān, a qabbalistic treatise entitled Eẓ ḥayyim (The tree of life). He quotes the encyclopaedia of Judah ben Solomon ha-Kohen (XIII-1). He discusses the ten celestial spheres and identifies them with the ten emanations or sefirot.[23]

Further investigation of the Ez ḥayyim is desirable, though it may be disappointing.

Criticism. M. Steinschneider: Die Mathematik bei den Juden (BM 12, 33, 1898).

JUDAH BEN MOSES MOSCONI

Judah (or Leon) ben Moses Mosconi. Judeo-Serbian Talmudist. Born in 1328 at Okhrida (or Ohrid) on the Lake of Okhrida west of Monástir (now Yugoslavia), he traveled extensively; we find him not only in various places of the Near East—Chios, Cyprus, Negropont 1345, Egypt—but also in Morocco 1360, Italy, Majorca, Perpignan c. 1362.

In Negropont (i.e., Euboea) or in Crete (?) he was the pupil of Shemariah ben Elijah ha-Iqriṭi; in Egypt he found the man whom he described as his most influential teacher, Obadiah Miẓri, otherwise unknown to me; in Perpignan he was in touch with Moses ben Joshua of Narbonne and with David Bongoron (ben Yom-ṭob).

He wrote a supercommentary on Abraham ben Ezra's commentary on the Torah, entitled Eben ha-'ezer (Stone of help). This was perhaps one of a series of four or twelve works entitled Arba'ah ṭurim (Four rows, Exodus 28:17) or Mizbeaḥ obnayim (Altar of wheels).

He quotes a large number of authors, most of them Jewish, but some of them

[23] See Introd. 2, 606 and by index.

Arabic and Greek. He was somewhat acquainted with the Arabic language, but his knowledge of Arabic and Greek writings was derived from Hebrew translations.

He insisted on the fundamental importance of grammatical studies, and began a grammar called Ṭa'ame ha-mibṭa (Quick decisions), and at least two other treatises which he was unable to complete because of the vicissitudes of his life.

Mosconi had a large library, the inventory of which was made by his widow, Muna. It included a good many scientific books, such as books by Hippocrates, Aristotle, Ptolemy (Almagest in Hebrew and in Arabic), Galen, Ibn Sīnā, Abraham ben Ezra, Maimonides, Ibn Rushd, Samuel ben Judah Ibn Tibbon; a few romances like Barlaam and Ioasaph, and of course many theological treatises.

He revised the Sefer Yosippon and wrote a preface to it. The Sefer Yosippon (or pseudo Josephus) is a history of the Jews from 539 B.C. to A.D. 70, written in Hebrew, the author of which, whose name is given as Josippon or Yosippon the Greek, was wrongly identified with Flavius Josephus (I-2). It is a worthless and sometimes ludicrous compilation chiefly derived from Flavius Josephus. The real author, whom we may call the "Hebrew" or "lesser Josephus," "Joseph ben Gorion" ("Josephus Gorionides"), was probably a Jew of southern Italy, living in the first half of the tenth century. The book is certainly anterior to c. 950, but there may have been a Byzantine prototype dating back to sometime in the fourth to sixth centuries.

The tradition of that text is very complicated and interesting. It was copied in Hebrew MSS, and also in Arabic ones written in Hebrew script. There is also an early Slavonic version. The Arabic version was made by Zechariah ben Sa'īd al-Yamānī (i.e., the Yemenite), who flourished at an unknown time (tenth to thirteenth century, eleventh century?). The Arabic text, somewhat different from the Hebrew, was translated into Aethiopian, perhaps as early as the fourteenth century, and attained much popularity in that language, witness the existence of no less than twelve Aethiopian MSS in European libraries.

The first edition of the Sefer ben Gorion was published by Abraham ben Solomon Conat (Mantua c. 1476–79); this text was reproduced with a Latin translation by Sebastian Münster (Basel 1541). A more elaborate edition was prepared by Tam ben David ibn Yaḥya (Constantinople 1510). There are many later editions in Hebrew, Latin, Yiddish, Spaniol (Ladino, Judaeo-Spanish), French, etc. The difficulty of the bibliography is further increased by the existence of a Hebrew compendium of the original text appended to the Sefer ha-qabbalah of Abraham ben David ha-Levi (XII-2) and printed in the editions of that book beginning with the princeps (Mantua 1513/14), also in the editions with Latin translation by Sebastian Münster (Worms 1529, Basel 1559). From the Latin version were derived two German ones (1530, 1557, etc.) and an English one by Peter Morwyng (London 1561, 1575–79, 1608), revised by James Howell (London 1653, 1669). A part of the Arabic version by Zechariah ben Sa'īd, Kitāb al-Maqābiyīn wa huwa al-thānī, Liber Machabaeorum secundus, was edited with a Latin version by Gabriel Sionita in the polyglot Bibles (1645, 1657). Complete but imperfect Arabic edition (334 p., Beirūt 1872). Chapters 18–28 of the 4th book translated from Hebrew into Arabic by Mas'ūd al-Dahhān (54 p., in Hebrew characters, Livorno 1886). Julius Wellhausen: Der arabische Josippus (Abhandlungen der K. Gesellschaft der Wissenschaften zu Göttingen, phil. Cl., vol. 1, no. 4, 50 p., 1897), abridged German translation of the Arabic text. Critical edition of the Aethiopian text with glossary and indexes, by Murad Kamil (382 p., 12 pl., New York 1938; Isis 31, 223; D. S. Margoliouth in JRAS p. 137, 1939). The French version of François de Belleforest was made from the Latin and included in Gilbert Génébrard: Histoire de Flavius Josèphe (2, 417, 1609). I may also mention the Judaeo-Spanish edition (Constantinople 1743). Many other editions are listed by Cowley (p. 331–32, 1929). See also Steinschneider (p. 598, 1893; no. 71, p. 114, 1902), Max Schloessinger (JE 7, 259–60, 1904), Umberto Cassuto (EJ 9, 420–25, 1932).

Text. The preface to Eben ha-'ezer was edited by Abraham Berliner (Oẓar ṭob 1, 1–10, Berlin 1878). Mosconi's preface to Yosippon was edited by the same (ibid. p. 17–23).

Criticism. M. Steinschneider: Jehuda Mosconi (Magazin für die Wissenschaft des Judentums vol. 3, 1876); reprinted in his Gesammelte Schriften (1, 536–74, 1876). H. Gross (p. 469, 1897). Israël Lévi: L'inventaire du mobilier et de la bibliothèque d'un médecin juif de Majorque (Revue des études juives 39, 242–60, 1899). Max Seligsohn (JE 9, 39, 1905).

JOSEPH BEN MOSES HA-KILTI

Joseph ben Moses ha-Kilti (Kalti or Kelti); also called ha-Yewani (the Greek) and therefore confused with Joseph ben David ha-Yewani (XIV-1).

Judeo-Greek philosopher and mathematician who flourished at the end of the fourteenth century and the beginning of the fifteenth. He composed an account of the Aristotelian Organon in the form of Hippocrates' Aphorisms, under the title Minḥat Judah (Judah's gift), divided into six parts: isagoge, categories, hermeneutics, syllogism, demonstration and topics, sophistics, rhetorics, poetics. He dedicated the Minḥah to Judah ben Jacob ibn 'Aṭṭar, a Talmudist who flourished in Spain probably about the end of the century (JE 2, 291, 1902). He wrote a commentary on the mathematics of Abraham ben Ezra (XII-1).

Steinschneider (p. 499, 1893); Die Mathematik bei den Juden (BM 13, 39, 1899). M. Zobel (EJ 9, 1232, 1932).

D. ISLĀM

D1. Granada

IBN 'ABBĀD

Abū 'Abdallāh Muḥammad ibn Ibrāhīm ibn 'Abbād al-Nafzī al-Rundī. Hispano-Muslim mystic of the Shādhilīya sect (1332–90).

Ibn 'Abbād was born in Ronda, Andalusia, 1332 and was educated in that city. He belonged to an illustrious family which had ruled in Seville in the eleventh century ('Abbādī dynasty, 1023–91). His father, Ibrāhīm, was a theologian and preacher, and his uncle 'Abdallāh al-Fārisī was qāḍī of Ronda. Ibn 'Abbād completed his theological studies in Fez, Tlemcen, Salé, and Tangiers. He established himself in Salé and finally in Fez, where he was imām and khaṭīb and was much honored by the Marīnī sulṭān Abū-l-'Abbās (1374–84). He died in Fez 1390, and was buried there near the Bāb al-futūḥ.

He was deeply influenced by a mystical treatise enjoying much popularity in Islām, namely the Qūt al-qulūb (Qūt al-qulūb fī mu'āmalat al-maḥbūb wa waṣf ṭarīq al-murīd ilā maqām al-tawḥīd) by Abū Ṭālib Muḥammad ibn 'Alī al-Makkī (d. 996), a book which was also one of the main sources of the Iḥyā of al-Ghazzālī.

At some unknown time he was initiated into the Shādhilīya fraternity.[24] His main work is a commentary on one of the outstanding books of that ṣūfī sect, the Kitāb al-ḥikam al-'Aṭā'īya by Abū-l-Faḍl Aḥmad ibn Muḥammad ibn 'Aṭā'allāh al-Iskandarī al-Shādhilī (d. Cairo 1309). That commentary, Sharḥ al-ḥikam or Ghaith al-mawāhib al-'alīya, is used as a textbook of mystical philosophy in Muslim schools to this day, e.g., in the Jāmi' al-zaitūna of Tunis. According to Miguel Asín, who made a special study of it, the Sharḥ al-ḥikam profoundly influenced Christian mystics of the Carmelite order, chiefly the Castilian San Juan de la Cruz (1542–91) (Introd. 2, 549).

Ibn 'Abbād also left a collection of spiritual letters (al rasā'il al-kubra, and others), wherein he discusses the Qūt al-qulūb and other mystical questions.

Text. The Ghaith al-mawāhib al-'alīya was printed together with Al-ḥikam al-'Aṭa'īya, in Būlāq 1869, and Cairo 1871–72.

Criticism. Brockelmann (2, 118, 265, 1902; suppt. 2, 146, 358, 1938). Miguel Asín y Palacios: Un precursor hispanomusulmán de San Juan de la Cruz (Al-Andalus 1, 7–79, Madrid 1933; Isis 21, 366), elaborate study including long extracts in Spanish from the Sharḥ ḥikam (p. 37–79). Reprinted in Asín's Huellas del Islam (p. 235–304, Madrid 1941; Isis 33, 539–44).

IBN 'ĀṢIM

Abū Bakr Muḥammad ibn Muḥammad Ibn 'Āṣim al-Mālikī al-Qaisī al-Gharnāṭī. Spanish Muslim theologian of the Mālikī school (1359–1427).

The nisba Qaisī refers probably to the north Arabian tribe Qais-'Ailān (EI 2, 652–57). Ibn 'Āṣim was born in April 1359, and flourished in Granada, being wazīr under Yūsuf II (Naṣrī ruler of Granada 1391/92); he died in August 1427.

His best-known work is a poem (rajaz) on the principles of jurisprudence, Tuḥfat al-ḥukkām fī nakth al-'uqūd wal-aḥkām, often commented upon. He dedicated to Yūsuf II a collection of anecdotes called Ḥadā'iq al-azāhir.

Text. Octave Houdas and F. Martel: Traité de droit musulman. La Tohfat d'Ebn Acem (928 p., Alger 1882–93), Arabic text with French translation and notes. There are also various Moroccan and Algerian editions of the Arabic text and of some commentaries.

Ḥadā'iq al-azāhir. Lithographic ed., Fās (s.a.).

Criticism. Brockelmann (2, 264, 1902; suppt. 2, 375, 1938).

D3. Mamlūkīya

'ABD AL-RAḤĪM IBN AL-ḤASAN AL-ISNAWĪ

'Abd al-Raḥīm ibn al-Ḥasan Jamāl al-dīn al-Isnawī al-Qurashī al-Shāfi'ī. Egyptian theologian (1305–70).

'Abd al-Raḥīm was born at Isna (or Esna, Latopolis) on the upper Nile (33 miles south of Luxor) in July 1305. He went to Cairo c. 1321 to study under Muḥammad ibn 'Abd al-Ṣamad al-Sanbāṭī (d. 1322), Taqī al-dīn 'Alī al-Subkī (XIV-1), Abū Ḥaiyān (XIV-1). From 1327 on he was a teacher in various madāris of Cairo, and explained the Qur'ān in the mosque of Ibn Ṭūlūn. For a time (1358–61) he held the position of muḥtasib. He died on December 8, 1370.

[24] A ṭarīqa named after its founder, Abū-l-Ḥasan 'Alī ibn 'Abdallāh al-Zarwīlī al-Shādhilī, born in 1196, probably in Morocco, died in Upper Egypt 1258 (EI 4, 246–49, 1926).

He wrote various books on Shāfi'ī law, a collection of biographies of Shāfi'ī doctors, Ṭabaqāt al-Shāfi'īya (begun 1349, completed 1368), and a book concerning hermaphrodites, Aḥkām al-khunthā, derived from two earlier works on the same subject. His last work, completed in 1368, dealt with a number of legal difficulties, Ṭirāz al-maḥāfil fī alghāz al-masā'il.

In 1354–58, he wrote a pamphlet against the Christians entitled Al-kalimāt al-muhimma fī mubāsharat ahl al-dhimma (Earnest appeal against the employment of non-Muslim subject people); this was directed against the Copts, who had obtained considerable importance in the Mamlūk state because of their financial and administrative abilities.

Criticism. Wüstenfeld (no. 432, p. 15, 1882). Brockelmann (2, 90, 1902; suppt. 2, 107, 1938). M Perlmann: Notes on anti-Christian propaganda in the Mamlūk empire (Bull. of the London School of Oriental Studies 10, 843–61, 1942), discussion of the Kalimāt.

'UMAR IBN ISḤĀQ AL-HINDĪ

Hindu theologian of the Ḥanafī school, flourishing in Egypt (1314–72).

The nisba Hindī connects him with India, others with Ghazna, with Dawlatābād in Jibāl. He is also called al-Shiblī after the village Shiblīya in the Ushrūsanah province, Transoxiana, but the name Shiblī is not uncommon. We are perhaps not justified in calling him Hindu, but he hailed certainly from the East, whether from Ghazna or from farther east beyond the river Indus.

He was born in 1314, studied law and tradition at the feet of many teachers, made the Pilgrimage, and c. 1339 established himself in Egypt. He was appointed qāḍī al-'askar and later (1367) qāḍī al-quḍāt. He died in January 1372.

He wrote the Zubdat al-aḥkām fī ikhtilāf al-a'imma al-a'lām, explaining the points on which the four schools of religious law agree and disagree. Most of his writings are in the form of commentaries on earlier ones, which I cite here in the chronological order of their writers:

1. The Ziyādāt of Muḥammad ibn al-Ḥasan al-Shaibānī (749–804).
2. 'Aqīdat ahl al-sunna wal-jamā'a (or Muqaddama fī uṣūl al-dīn) of Aḥmad ibn Muḥammad al-Ṭaḥāwī (843–933).
3. Hidāya of al-Marghīnānī (XII-2). 'Umar al-Hindī wrote two commentaries on this work.
4. Naẓm al-sulūk of Ibn al-Fāriḍ (XIII-1). This illustrates 'Umar's interest in mysticism; he himself wrote a treatise on the subject.
5. Badī' al-niẓām fī uṣūl al fiqh of Aḥmad ibn 'Alī Ibn al-Sā'ātī (d. 1296).
6. Al-mughnī fī uṣūl al fiqh of 'Umar ibn Muḥammad al-Khabbāzī (d. 1292).
7. Manār al-anwār fī uṣūl al fiqh of al-Nasafī (XIII-2).
8. Al-mukhtār lil-fatāwā of 'Abdallāh ibn Maḥmūd al-Buldajī (1202–84).
9. Mystic verses of al-Yāfi'ī (XIV-1), the commentary itself being called Lawā'iḥ al-anwār fī-l radd 'alā man ankara 'alā 'ārifīn laṭā'if al-asrār. Discussion of fate, revelation, etc.
10. Jam' al-jawāmi' fī-l-uṣūl of 'Abd al-Wahhāb al-Subkī.

This list is probably incomplete, but is sufficient to give an idea of 'Umar's efforts to explain the thought of the great Ḥanafī doctors and also, by way of comparison, the thought of other doctors (as in the Zubdat al-aḥkām), the mystical point of view (Ibn al-Fāriḍ), or the Shāfi'ī one (al-Yāfi'ī and al-Subkī both belonged to the Shāfi'ī school).

Many religious decisions (fatāwā) of his were collected by Muḥammad ibn 'Abdallāh al-Timirtāshī al-Ḥanafī (d. 1595/96).

Criticism. Brockelmann (2, 80, 1902; suppt. 2, 89, 1938). Joseph Schacht (EI 4, 361, 1926).

SĪDĪ KHALĪL

Khalīl ibn Isḥāq Ibn al-Jundī, called (in Algeria, where his popularity is greatest) Sīdī Khalīl. Egyptian Mālikī theologian and jurist (d. 1365 or later).

Khalīl's father, Isḥāq ibn Mūsā, was a Ḥanafī theologian, but Khalīl, who studied theology and law under various teachers in Cairo, became a Mālikī under their influence. About 1348 he began to teach at the Shaikhūnīya school and became muftī. He died in 1365 or 1374.

On his way to or from the Pilgrimage he sojourned some time in Madīna, otherwise he lived in Cairo, and the end of his life was spent in retirement. His main work is a textbook of Mālikī law, the Mukhtaṣar, which is important because of its great popularity, especially in Egypt, Algeria, and West Africa. It is very concise, often to the point of obscurity, but has been expanded and variously explained in a number of commentaries. Sīdī Khalīl had been influenced himself by an older Mālikī teacher, Ibn al-Ḥājib (XIII-1), whose tendencies he continued, that is, the combination of Egyptian and Maghribī ideas, also the coloring of Mālikī doctrines with Shāfi'ī views. He devoted twenty-five years to the elaboration of his Mukhtaṣar, and at the time of his death was engaged in the preparation of a final MS of it which he had no time to continue beyond the chapter on sexual intercourse.

Text. The Mukhtaṣar has often been printed, Paris 1855, 1883, then again by Gaétan Delphin in 1900; Fez 1883, 1900, 1904, Būlāq 1876, 1886, 1891, Constantine 1878.

French translation by Nicolas Perron (6 vols., in Exploration scientifique de l'Algérie, Sciences historiques, vols. 10–15, Paris 1848–52; tables, 1854. Reprinted Paris 1877). This translation is said to be imperfect; it was abbreviated in English by F. H. Ruxton for the government of Nigeria (436 p., London 1916).

Italian translation by Ignazio Guidi and David Santillana (2 vols., Milano 1919; Isis 13, 435).

Separate parts translated into French by Edmond Fagnan: Le djihād ou la guerre sainte (Alger 1908); Mariage et répudiation (Alger 1909).

Manual of the law of marriage in Arabic and English by Alexander David Russell and 'Abdallāh al-Ma'mūn Suhrawardy (365 p., London s.a.).

Criticism. Edmond Fagnan: Concordances du manuel de droit de Sidi Khalil (375 p., Alger 1889). Brockelmann (2, 83–85, 1902; suppt. 2, 96–99, 1938). Carra de Vaux (3, 320, 340, 360–63, 1923). Moh. ben Cheneb (EI 2, 888, 1925).

MUḤAMMAD IBN MUḤAMMAD AL-JAZARĪ

Syrian traditionist and student of the Qur'ān (1350–1429).

Shams al-dīn Abū-l-Khair Muḥammad ibn Muḥammad al-Jazarī al-Qurashī. His nisba Jazarī is derived from the place Jazīrat ibn 'Umar (on middle Tigris). He was born on November 26, 1350 in Damascus; studied theology and tradition, made the Pilgrimage in 1367, then went to Cairo. In 1391 he was qāḍī in Damascus. In 1395 his fortune was lost or confiscated in Egypt and he betook himself to the court of Bāyazīd in Brusa; when Bāyazīd was defeated in 1402, Muḥammad was deported by Tīmūr to Samarqand. After Tīmūr's death (1405), Muḥammad settled down in Shīrāz, where he died on December 3, 1429.

He wrote extensively (some 28 items) in prose and verse, on ḥadīth, the proper ways of reading the Qur'ān and intoning it, biographies of Qur'ānic readers and teachers, etc. Some of these writings have been repeatedly commented upon.

One of his poems has some historical interest; it is the Dhāt al-shifā' fī sīrat al-nabī wal-khulafā, a poem in rajaz written at the request of sulṭān Muḥammad of Shīrāz a few days after the victory of Nicopolis 1396 (Atiya p. 543, 1938). As the title indicates, it deals with the lives of the Prophet and the four orthodox caliphs, but it extends to the time of Bāyazīd Yildirim.

Traditionists would call him simply al-Jazarī; but it is better for historians of science, or even for historians of art, not to do so, as the name evokes to them another man, Ismā'īl ibn al-Razzāz al-Jazarī (XIII-1), author of a book on mechanical contrivances represented in many museums by automata miniatures.

Text. Al-nashr fī l-qirā'āt al-'ashr (Damascus 1345 H.), dealing with the different ways of reading the Qur'ān.

Ghāyat al-nihāya fī asmā' rijāl al-qirā'āt. Edition begun by Gotthelf Bergstraesser (1886–1933), continued by Otto Pretzl (2 vols., Bibliotheca islamica, Leipzig 1933–35). Indexes by Pretzl (ibid., 252 p., Leipzig 1935). Biographies of "readers," a collection which has the same importance for the student wishing to appreciate the relative values of different methods of reading the Qur'ān that biographies of traditionists have for the student of tradition.

Criticism. Brockelmann (2, 201-3, 1902; suppt. 2, 274-78, 1938). Johann Fück (Orientalistische Literaturzeitung 40, 742–44, 1937; 42, 169, 1939).

D4. Īrān

Ḥāfiẓ

Shams al-dīn Muḥammad Ḥāfiẓ al-Shīrāzī. The greatest poet of Persia and one of the greatest of the world (c. 1320–89).

Though Ḥāfiẓ was simply a lyrical poet, not deliberately didactic, we must speak of him even as we had to speak of Vergil, of Firdawsī, or of Dante. He is one of the greatest personalities of his time, and deeply influenced the spiritual life of Persia, Turkey, and other Muslim countries.

He was born c. 1320 in Shīrāz. His father, Bahā' al-dīn, had moved from Iṣfahān to Shīrāz, had made a fortune in business, then lost it, and after his death his family was poor. Muḥammad was a precocious poet; he was well educated in theology and mystical literature, and though he wrote only in Persian, he had necessarily a deep knowledge of Arabic. His takhalluṣ (nom de plume) Ḥāfiẓ is the name commonly bestowed upon those who know the whole Qur'ān by heart and are able to recite it. When he became famous other honorific names were given to him, as Lisān al-ghaib or Tarjumān al-asrār (voice of the unseen or interpreter of secrets).

He spent the greatest part of his life in his native city and died there in 1389. During his lifetime Shīrāz suffered terrible vicissitudes of fortune, but Ḥāfiẓ remained, obtaining the patronage of many princes. Other princes tried to attract him to India, but he refused. He often spoke of the beauty of Shīrāz, of its lovely river Ruknābād and of the rose gardens of Muṣallā'.

It should be noted that in spite of wars and calamities Shīrāz was then an intellectual center of great importance, to which leading thinkers and artists were attracted by the loveliness of the place as well as by the patronage of sophisticated princes. For example, shāh Shujā' (the Muẓafarrī king of Fārs 1357–84) had given a chair to al-Jurjānī in the Dār al-shifā', and it is highly probable that Ḥāfiẓ and al-Jurjānī came together and confabulated. It would seem that Ḥāfiẓ' period of greatest poetical activity occurred during the rule of this prince, Jalāl al-dīn shāh Shujā'. When Shīrāz was conquered by Tīmūr in 1387, it is possible that Ḥāfiẓ met the conqueror, but in any case he was then close to the end of his own life.

Ḥāfiẓ brought to its perfection the Persian ode (ghazal). His dīwān includes 693 separate poems, 573 of which are odes (ghazalīyāt), and 69, quatrains (rubā'īyāt). The latter make one think naturally of 'Umar al-Khayyām (XI-2), but there are deep differences between the two poets. 'Umar Khayyām was an agnostic, somewhat also of a rationalist, suggesting comparisons with Lucretius and Voltaire. Ḥāfiẓ is not deeper, but he is sweeter, as well as softer and subtler; he is primarily a poet of love, human and divine love, mysticism (taṣawwuf). He is the foremost interpreter of unquenchable mystical desire and of the happiness and torments which such desire causes; he knows how to express the joy of the soul appeased by her union with the beloved—God (al-nafs muṭma'inna, Qur'ān 89, 27). There has been considerable discussion, East and West, as to whether the hedonistic and erotic poems of Ḥāfiẓ should be understood literally or given allegorical interpretations. Such discussion is of its nature endless.

The first edition of Ḥāfiẓ' dīwān was prepared after his death by his friend Muḥammad Gulandām. There are many commentaries in Persian and Turkish, the best being the one composed in the latter language by Sūdī.[25] Sūdī's interpretations are literal rather than allegorical; being a Sunnī, he omitted a few poems which reveal Shī'a feelings. To illustrate Ḥāfiẓ' influence on the Turks, I must mention also the dīwān of Muḥammad ibn Sulaimān al-Fuẓūlī, a Kurdish poet who was born in Baghdād and died in 1556 or 1562; he wrote in Ādharbāijānī Turkī and was called the Turkish Ḥāfiẓ (EI 2, 124, 1914).

The influence of Ḥāfiẓ is also very noticeable in Urdū; it is naturally considerable in Persian literature. There has been much discussion as to his orthodoxy; that discussion is but another form of the one relative to the real meaning of his poems. If they are to be taken literally, then Ḥāfiẓ was an infidel and a pagan; if they are to be taken allegorically, you can suit yourself. In spite of the hatred of the fanatic defenders of orthodoxy, the tomb of Ḥāfiẓ in Shīrāz soon became, like that of Sa'dī (XIII-2), which is about a mile farther north, the object of a pilgrimage. It is surrounded by the tombs of many men who wanted to lie near him.[26] Ḥāfiẓ' prestige in his native country is evidenced by the fact that his dīwān is commonly used for taking an augury (tafā'ul), even as the Qur'ān itself. Oriental editions of the Dīwān generally include special tables, called fāl-nāma, which facilitate that operation and give it a more scientific appearance. Remember that the ancient Romans used Vergil's poems in the same way (sortes vergilianae) and that

[25] A Turkish man of letters of Bosniac origin. He flourished in Constantinople, translated books from Arabic into Turkish, commented on many Persian poems, and died in Constantinople, c. 1596–97 (Guy p. xxxiv, 1927). In order to judge his method, see W. H. Lowe: Twelve odes of Ḥāfiẓ done literally into English together with the corresponding portion of the Turkish commentary of Sūdī for the first time translated (80 p., Cambridge 1877).

[26] The tomb of 'Umar Khayyām was comparatively neglected, but it has now been beautifully restored; see my article on the subject (Isis 29, 15–19, 1 fig., 1938).

Christians applied the same superstition to the Bible. See the article sortes sanctorum in Ducange: Glossarium (6, 304–5, Paris 1846); other examples in the articles on divination (ERE 4, 1912).

Ḥāfiẓ also exerted some influence on Western literatures (e.g., through Goethe), though less than his two great rivals 'Umar Khayyām and Sa'dī.

Text. Collections of poems are liable to suffer omissions or to receive apocryphal additions, hence the Persian MSS vary considerably. The first important edition was that of Abū Ṭālib Khān of Iṣfahān (Calcutta 1791), containing 725 poems, but careless. First critical edition, derived from the text accepted by Sūdī, by Hermann Brockhaus (692 poems, Leipzig 1854–63). A better edition was produced by Vincenz von Rosenzweig-Schwannau: Der Diwan im persischen Original herausgegeben, ins Deutsche übersetzt und mit Anmerkungen versehen (3 vols., Wien 1858, 1863, 1864). This is a kind of standard according to which the poems are generally numbered.

Many other editions have been published in Persia, Turkey, Muslim India, and other countries, and new ones appear every year. There are also many Western editions.

Hāfiẓ was first revealed to the Western world in the Latin translation of François de Mesgnien Meninski (1680). Other Latin translations were made by Thomas Hyde (1767) and count Charles Rewiczki (212 p., Vienna 1771). Sir William Jones translated some poems into English verse (1792) and into French (1799). These translations are known to me only indirectly, and I do not vouch for their publication, except that of Rewiczki.

There are at least three complete translations into Western languages, two in German and the third in English: by Joseph von Hammer-Purgstall (2 vols., Stuttgart 1812–13); by Rosenzweig-Schwannau (3 vols., Wien 1858–64); by Henry Wilberforce Clarke (2 vols., 1011 p., Calcutta 1891). Clarke's work includes a biography and abundant notes. His translation of the 'Awārif al-ma'ārif of 'Umar ibn 'Abdallāh al-Suhrawardī (XII-2), an important mystical book, was published as a companion piece to the Dīwān, which it helped to explain (174 p., Calcutta 1891).

I must still mention four partial translations into English verse: by Herman Bicknell (404 p., London 1875); by Gertrude Lowthian Bell (London 1897; reprinted 1928); by Walter Leaf (76 p., London 1898); by John Payne (3 vols., Villon Society, London 1901). These versions vary materially, as has been shown by Browne in his lecture on the Literature of Persia (Persia Society, London 1912) and in his Literary history of Persia (3, 304–11, 1920). Miss Bell's version is a poetical re-creation comparable to Edward Fitzgerald's version of 'Umar Khayyām (1859), though far less appreciated.

Arthur Guy: Les poèmes érotiques de Ḥāfiẓ en calque rhythmique et avec rime à la persane (vol. 1, 316 p., Paris 1927), including 175 poems.

Criticism. Harald Rasmussen: Studier over Ḥāfiẓ (235 p., Copenhagen 1892). A. V. Williams Jackson: Persia past and present (p. 328–32, New York 1906). K. Süssheim (EI 2, 210–12, 1915). Browne (3, 271–319, 1920, again 1928). Carra de Vaux (4, 277–92, 1923).

'ALĪ IBN SHIHĀB AL-DĪN

'Alī ibn Shihāb al-dīn al-Ḥusainī al-Hamadhānī al-Amīr al-kabīr. Persian ṣūfī writing in Arabic and in Persian (1314–83).

He was born in October 1314, became a darwīsh, and founded a new ṭarīqa. He probably spent the main part of his life in Hamadhān or its vicinity; in 1379 the arrival of Tīmūr caused him to move with seven hundred young men from Hamadhān to Kashmīr. He died in 1383 and is buried in the land of Badakshān (east of Balkh, south of the Oxus in a bend of the river).

He wrote a number of ṣūfī treatises in Arabic and apparently also in Persian. That is, some of them are available in Persian. One of them is a commentary on the Fuṣūṣ al-ḥikam of Ibn 'Arabī (XIII-1).

Text. Aurād fatḥīya (Book of prayers). Printed Lucknow 1841, 1872, Cawnpore 1876. These editions include Persian translations and notes.

Dhakhīrat al-mulūk (Treasure of kings). Extract concerning conditions imposed by the caliph 'Umar on non-Muslim conquered subjects, published in Arabic and Latin by E. F. C. Rosenmüller: Analecta arabica (part 1, Leipzig 1825). Same extract translated into French by Charles Solvet: Instituts du droit mahométan sur la guerre avec les infidèles (Paris 1829).

Criticism. Brockelmann (2, 221, 1902; suppt. 2, 311, 1938).

'ABD AL-KARĪM AL-JĪLĪ

Quṭb al-dīn 'Abd al-Karīm ibn Ibrāhīm ibn Sibṭ 'Abd al-Qādir al-Jīlī al-Ṣūfī (1365–1428). Persian theologian and mystic, writing in Arabic.

As his name indicates, he was a descendant of 'Abd al-Qādir al-Jīlī (XII-1), reputed founder of the ṭarīqa of dervishes called Qādirīya. The nisba Jīlī (or Jīlānī) refers to the country Jīl (or Jīlān), delta lands southwest of the Caspian Sea.

He wrote many books on theology in the mystical way. Two of them at least are commentaries on two works, the Kitāb al-asfār and Al-futūḥāt al-Makkīya, of Ibn 'Arabī (XIII-1).

Criticism. Brockelmann (2, 205, 1902; suppt. 2, 283, 1938).

NI'MAT ALLĀH WALĪ

Persian ṣūfī, writing in Persian (1330–1431).

The Sayyid (or "shāh") Ni'matu'llāh ibn 'Abdallāh was a descendant of the fifth imām of the Shī'a, Bākir. He was born in Aleppo 1330/31, traveled to 'Irāq and later (1354) to Mecca, where he became the disciple and khalīfa of the shaykh al-Yāfi'ī (XIV-1). After the latter's death (1367) he went to Samarqand, Herāt, Yazd, and finally (c. 1406) settled in Māhān, near Kirmān. He died April 5, 1431, in Māhān, where a monastery of his order perpetuates his memory. His tomb in that monastery is a center of pilgrimage.

The darwīsh order founded by him and called after him Ni'mat Allāhī was protected by various rulers, chiefly Tīmūr's son Shāhrukh. He wrote a dīwān of mystic verse and a great many (c. 100) ṣūfī treatises. His fame, however, is rather that of a saint and wonder-worker than that of a poet or philosopher. He was a follower of al-Yāfi'ī, that is, indirectly of the Spaniard Ibn 'Arabī (XIII-1). This is a good example of the way doctrines spread from the West to the East via Mecca.

Criticism. Browne (3, 463–71, 1920), examples of his poetry. E. Berthels (EI 3, 922, 1935).

FAḌLALLĀH AL-ḤURŪFĪ

Persian founder of a mystic sect which flourished mostly in Turkey (1339–93).

Faḍlallāh ibn Abī Muḥammad of Tabrīz was born in Astarābādh (in Jurjān, near the southeast corner of the Caspian Sea); he made the great Pilgrimage in 1373 and was put to death by order of Tīmūr in 1393/94 or in 1401/2.

Under the influence of Qarmaṭī doctrines,[27] that is, an Islamic (Shī'a) development of Hermetism, Neo-Platonism, Neo-Pythagoreanism, Sabeanism, he explained a new mystical philosophy wherein considerable stress was laid on the numerical values of the Arabic-Persian alphabet. Hence his name Ḥurūfī (ḥarf, pl. ḥurūf, means letters of the alphabet in Arabic), and the name of his sect, Ḥurūfīya. Similar aberrations have often been encountered in our previous volumes, e.g., apropos of the qabbala and gematria (Introd. 2, 881); they are found in one form or another in almost every mediaeval literature.

Faḍlallāh's main work is the Jāwidān-i kabīr (The great eternal), written in a strange mixture of Arabic, Persian, and the (Persian) dialect of Astarābādh. The propaganda of these ideas was cut short by Tīmūr, and they did not flourish considerably in Persia, but strangely enough they were carried by a disciple, 'Alī al-A'lā, to Turkey and were adopted by the Baktāshī dervishes and developed by them. They constitute an essential part of Baktāshī mysticism. Thus did a Shī'a doctrine manage to flourish almost exclusively in a Sunnī country! For example, two of the greatest early Turkish poets belong to the Ḥurūfī school, namely, Saiyid Imām al-dīn Nasīmī (put to death for his heresy, Aleppo 1417/18) and the latter's disciple Rafī'ī (fl. 1409). Of the other writings of the Hurūfīya sect, some are in Persian and some in 'Uthmānlī Turkish.

Hasluck (1929) tended to consider Faḍlallāh the real founder of the Baktāshī order and to doubt the historicity of Ḥājjī Baktāsh (or Baqtāsh) except as a tribal eponym, but Birge, summarizing the investigations of modern Turkish scholars, reaches different conclusions. He shows that the Baktāshī and Ḥurūfī systems, however congenial, were and remained different and separate. Both systems are syncretic and badly defined, and they have many ideas in common; it was always possible but not necessary to be a Baktāshī and a Ḥurūfī at one and the same time. As to Ḥājjī Baktāsh Walī, he was a real person who came from Nīshāpūr to Anatolia in the thirteenth century, attained popularity as a saint, and created a new ṭarīqa. When the sulṭān Urkhān (ruled 1326–60) created the new 'Uthmānlī infantry yeñi-čerik (janissaries), that military body was intimately connected from the very beginning with the Baktāshī order, and that connection continued until the suppression of the janissaries, on June 10, 1826. The Baktāshī order thus gained considerable power. We are more interested, however, in the kind of prestige which accrued to it because of its consistent devotion to the Turkish language and literature (against the Arabic predilection of the 'ulamā' and the Persian tendencies of the courtesans and literati) and because of its fidelity to the pre-Islamic elements of Anatolian life. The Baktāshī darwīsh expressed Turkish national ideas in addition to (or even against) Islamic internationalism; he expressed the freedom of poetry and mysticism against Islamic scholasticism.

Faḍlallāh al-Ḥurūfī should not be confused with Mawlānā Faḍlallāh, also of Tabrīz, who was Tīmūr's physician and attended the latter at the time of his death (1405).

Text. Clément Huart: Textes persans relatifs à la secte des Houroufis, publiés, traduits et annotés, suivis d'une étude sur la religion des Houroufis par Riẓā Tevfīq, connu sous le nom de Feylesouf Riẓā (Gibb memorial series vol. 9, Leiden 1909). Riḍā-Tawfīq is a Turkish politician and philosopher, fl. 1909.

[27] For a good account of them, see L. Massignon (EI 2, 767–72, 1925). For Qarmaṭī influence on chemistry see Introd. 2, 1044.

Criticism. Gibb (1, 336–88, 1900). Tschudi: Bektāsh (EI 1, 691–92, 1911). Cl. Huart: Faḍlallāh Ḥurūfī (EI 2, 37, 1913). H. Lammens: Ḥurūfī (EI 2, 338–39, 1916). Browne (3, 365–74, 449–52, 479, 1920). Cl. Huart: Janissaries (EI 2, 572–74, 1921). Brown (1927). Frederick William Hasluck: Christianity and Islam under the sultans (Oxford Press, 1929). Birge (1937). For purposes of comparison, Vincent F. Hopper: Medieval number symbolism (254 p., New York 1938; Isis 31, 101–3).

AL-JURJĀNĪ

Persian philosopher, astronomer, theologian, and grammarian who wrote mostly in Arabic, but also in Persian (1340–1413).

'Alī ibn Muḥammad al-Jurjānī al-Saiyid al-Sharīf was born near Astarābād (in the Jurjān province, southeast of the Caspian) in February 1340; he studied in Herāt, Kirmān, and Egypt; in 1377 he returned eastward via Istanbul. In that same year al-Taftāzānī introduced him to shāh Shujā' (Muẓaffarī ruler of Persia 1357–84), who gave him a chair in the Dār al-shifā' of Shīrāz. After the conquest of Shīrāz by Tīmūr (1387), the latter took al-Jurjānī to Samarqand, where he was al-Taftāzānī's successful rival. After Tīmūr's death, in 1405, al-Jurjānī returned to Shīrāz, where he died in July 1413.

Al-Jurjānī wrote a great many works in Arabic (some 44) and at least three in Persian. The majority of his works are commentaries or supercommentaries on works of philosophy, Qur'ānic exegesis, law, or logic by such men as al-Zamakhsharī (XII-1), al-Sajāwandī (end of twelfth century), al-Sakkākī (XIII-1), al-Ījī (XIV-1), and his great rival al-Taftāzānī. He also wrote commentaries on two astronomical treatises, the Tadhkira fī 'ilm al-hai'a of Nāṣir al-dīn al-Ṭūsī (XIII-2), and Al-mulakhkhaṣ fī-l-hai'a of al-Jaghmīnī (XIV-1).

His own works were primarily devoted to the classification of sciences (Risāla fī taqsīm al-'ulūm), to definitions (Ta'rīfāt) of technical terms, especially ṣūfī terms, and to similar subjects: Maqālīd al-'ulūm fī-l-ḥudūd wal-rusūm, a book of definitions concerning 21 branches of science. Music is one of the sciences dealt with, but this is not sufficient to justify the ascription to him of an elaborate commentary on the Kitāb al-adwār (Musical modes) of Ṣafī al-dīn (XIII-2). In the British Museum MS (Or. 2361) that commentary is entitled Sharḥ mawlānā mubārak shāh bar adwār, which Farmer suggests should be understood as a reference to (the blessed) shāh Shujā' (the real author according to Farmer being al-Jurjānī). Mubārak shāh, however, is a known Arabic name; it may refer to a definite person, to wit, Shams al-dīn Mīrak Muḥammad ibn Mubārakshāh (XIV-1).

Text. The Kitāb al-ta'rīfāt was first edited by Gustav Flügel, together with a similar work by Muḥammad ibn 'Alī Ibn 'Arabī (XIII-1): Definitiones (374 p., Leipzig 1845). Other editions, Cairo 1866, Constantinople 1883, etc.

For Jurjānī's commentaries see authors commented upon, or Brockelmann.

Baron Rodolphe d'Erlanger: Les commentaires de Mawlānā Mubārak Shāh sur le Kitāb al-adwār de Ṣāfiyu-d-dīn (La musique arabe 3, 185–609, Paris 1938; Isis 30, 334), French translation of that very long text, with notes.

Criticism. Suter (no. 424, 1900). Brockelmann (2, 216–17, 1902; suppt. 2, 305–6, 1938); (EI 1, 1066, 1913). Browne (3, 355, 1920). Carra de Vaux (4, 187, 1923). H. P. J. Renaud (Isis 18, 174, 1932). Farmer (nos. 241, 242, p. 56, 1940).

D5. Anatolia

AL-TAFTĀZĀNĪ

One of the greatest Persian (or Turkish) scholars of the fourteenth century, writing mostly in Arabic, but also in Turkish (1322–90).

Sa'd al-dīn Mas'ūd ibn 'Umar al-Taftāzānī was born in Taftāzān, near Nasā, Khurāsān, in 1322; he studied under 'Abd al-Raḥmān ibn Aḥmad al-Ījī (XIV-1) and Muḥammad ibn Muḥammad al-Taḥtānī (XIV-1). In 1338 he was in Fariyūmad and in 1347 in Herāt, but soon afterward he left Khurāsān, and we find him in 1355 in Ghujduwān, near Bukhārā. For a time he was at the court of Jānī Beg Maḥmūd, khān from 1340 to 1357 of the Blue horde of western Qipčaq, then at the court of the shāh Shujā' ibn Muḥammad (ruler of Fārs 1357–84) in Shīrāz (he introduced al-Jurjānī to that shāh in 1377). In 1379 Tīmūr allowed him to establish himself at the court of Sarakhs in his native Khurāsān, but later he ordered him to proceed to his own court in Samarqand and treated him there with great honor. After 1387 al-Jurjānī flourished at the same court, and there was much jealousy between him and al-Taftāzānī. The latter died in Samarqand in 1390.

He composed some twenty works, most of them in the form of commentaries upon earlier ones. We shall enumerate only the most important or best known, after having arranged them by subjects and then as far as possible in chronological order.

Logic and theology. 1(21).[28] Sharḥ īsāghūjī. Commentary on the Isagoge of Porphyrios (III-2).

2(9). Sharḥ al-risāla al-shamsīya. Commentary on the logic of 'Alī ibn 'Umar al-Kātibī (XIII-2), completed in 1360.

3(10). Kitāb al-maqāṣid al-ṭālibīn fī uṣūl al-dīn (fī-l-kalām), or Maqāṣid al-kalām fī 'aqā'id al-in'ām. Samarqand 1383 (or 1356?).

4(1). Tahdhīb al-manṭiq wal-kalām (ghāyat tahdhīb al-kalām fī taḥrīr al-manṭiq). Samarqand 1386/87. The second part may be an abridgment of the Maqāṣid. This is his most important work. Judging from the number of MSS, commentaries, adaptations, summaries, translations, editions, its influence must have been considerable. One would think that every Muslim doctor would have come across this work in one form or another.

Mystic philosophy. 5(16). Fāḍiḥat al-mulḥidīn (Confusion of the heretics). Criticism of erroneous views in the Fuṣūṣ al-ḥikam of Ibn 'Arabī (XIII-1).

Explanation of the Qur'ān. 6(2). Sharḥ al-kashshāf. Samarqand 1387. Commentary on the famous book of Maḥmūd ibn 'Umar al-Zamakhsharī (XII-1).

Law and theology. 7(15). Al-talwīḥ ilā' kashf ḥaqā'iq al-tanqīḥ. Gulistān 1357. Commentary on the Tanqīḥ al-uṣūl of Ṣadr al-Sharī'a al-thānī (XIV-1).

8(1). Sharḥ al-'aqā'id al-nasafīya. Khwārizm 1367. Commentary on the Ḥanafī catechism of 'Umar ibn Muḥammad al-Nasafī (XII-1).

9(14). Sharḥ sharḥ al-mukhtaṣar fī-l-uṣūl. Khwārizm 1369. Commentary on the Muntahā, the treatise on Mālikī law of 'Uthmān ibn 'Umar Ibn al-Ḥājib (XIII-1).

10(13). Sharḥ al-miftāḥ. Compendium of Shāfi'ī law. Sarakhs 1370 or 1376.

11(20). Sharḥ talkhīṣ al-jāmi' al-kabīr. Sarakhs 1383. Commentary on Ḥanafī law on the basis of the Jāmi' kabīr of Muḥammad ibn al-Ḥasan al-Shaibānī (749—after 804), a pupil of Abū Ḥanīfa (VIII-1).

[28] The numbers in parentheses are those given by Brockelmann.

Note that he discussed not only Ḥanafī law, but also Mālikī and Shāfi'ī law.

Grammar. 12(2). Sharḥ taṣrīf al-Zanjānī. Commentary on the book on declensions and conjugations by 'Abd al-wahhāb ibn Ibrāhīm al-Zanjānī (fl. Baghdād 1254). He wrote this at the age of 16 in Fariyūmad, Khurāsān, 1338.

13(3). Irshād al-hādī. Grammatical guide written for his son in Khwārizm 1372 or 1376. This work was often commented upon.

14(4). Al-tarkīb al-jalīl. On syntax.

15(5). Tarkīb gharīb wa tartīb 'ajīb. On syntax.

Rhetoric. 16, 17(7). Sharḥ talkhīṣ al-miftāḥ. Herāt 1347; extract Ghujduwān 1355. The most famous treatise on Arabic rhetoric was the Miftāḥ al-'ulūm of Yūsuf ibn abī Bakr al-Sakkākī (XIII-1); Muḥammad ibn 'Abd al-Raḥmān Khaṭīb Dimashq (XIV-1) wrote a summary of it, Talkhīṣ al-miftāḥ, which was itself the basis of many commentaries, notably these two. The first of Taftāzānī's commentaries (1347) is derived from another commentary called Muṭawwal and is called Sharḥ (al-talkhīṣ) al-muṭawwal; the second (1355) is called Mukhtaṣar al-ma'ānī.

18(8). Sharḥ al-qism al-thālith min al-miftāḥ. Samarqand 1385 or 1387. Commentary devoted more specially to the third (rhetorical) part of the same Miftāh; the first two parts being a grammatical introduction (Introd. 2, 701).

Proverbs. 19(17). Sharḥ nawābigh al-kilam. Commentary on the collection of proverbs made by al-Zamakhsharī (XII-1).

All his numerous publications were in Arabic, except one in Turkish; none, strangely enough, in Persian (this is subject to correction; there are of course Persian editions of some of his works). The Turkish one is a versified translation of the Bustān of Sa'dī (XIII-2), made in 1354, one of the earliest monuments of Turkish poetry.

His contemporary fame must have been considerable, witness the rivalry of many courts for his services and Tīmūr's final decision to keep and honor him in his own court. Ibn Khaldūn spoke very highly of him (Muqaddama 3, 92). That fame has grown to such an extent that Eastern people often consider him the dividing line between the "ancient" scholars and the "modern" ones. It is evidenced by the number of MSS, and Oriental editions, many of which are used as textbooks in the madāris of the East.

Text. For the many editions, practically all Oriental, see Brockelmann or Storey.

Criticism. Gibb (1, 202–3, 1900). Browne (3, 353–54, 458, 1920). C. A. Storey (EI 4, 604–7, 1928). Brockelmann (2, 215–16, 1902; suppt. 2, 301–4, 1938).

Dr. Luṭfī M. Sa'di, of Detroit, Michigan, honored me on March 20 and June 1, 1942 with two Arabic letters wherein he referred to a passage of the Tahdhīb al-manṭiq (edition Cairo 1330 = 1912, p. 41–43) and pointed out similarities with the views of Planck and Einstein! Such comparisons are of course irrelevant, but it is interesting that they could be made at all. The physical views of al-Taftāzānī would seem to deserve deeper investigation than I can devote to them at present.

It would seem worth while to examine al-Taftāzānī's writings and particularly his commentary on al-Nasafī's 'Aqā'id for the study of Muslim atomism. Both al-Nasafī and al-Taftāzānī were atomists for curious anti-materialistic reasons. See B. Carra de Vaux: Djawhar (EI 1, 1027, 1913) and D. B. Macdonald: Continuous re-creation and atomic time in Muslim scholastic theology (Isis 9, 326–44,

1927). Apropos of this I should like to remark that the idea of atomic time may be found in the Etymologiae of Isidore of Seville (VII-1), book XIII, ch. 2, also in the De divisionibus temporum of Baeda Venerabilis (VIII-1), etc. Kurd Lasswitz: Geschichte der Atomistik vom Mittelalter bis Newton (1, 31–34, Hamburg 1890). Ernest Brehaut: An encyclopedist of the dark ages (p. 235, New York 1912).

ṢALĀḤ AL-DĪN

Turkish didactic poet who wrote in Turkish and flourished under Yildirim Bāyazīd (ruled 1389–1402) and later.

He is called al-Kātib (or yāzījī), the scribe, and was patronized by Ḥājjī pāshā. He is said to have come from Būlī (ancient Claudiopolis; in Qizil Aḥmadlī), but spent most of his life in Ankara; he seems to have lived at least for a time in Qāḍī Köyi, where his eldest son, Meḥmed, was born. Two of his sons became famous Turkish poets and mystics, the elder being Yāzījī-oghlu Meḥmed (d. Gallipoli 1451) and the younger Yāzījī-oghlu Aḥmad (called Aḥmad Bījān because he was so thin, d. Gallipoli c. 1456).

To return to Ṣalāḥ al-dīn, whose own dates of birth and death are unknown, he wrote in Turkish books on mysticism and medicine (?) and a curious poem called Shamsīya, i.e., The solar (poem). The Shamsīya was completed in 1408/9 and dedicated to one Qaṣṣāb 'Alī ('Alī the butcher). It is a kind of astrological calendar in 5,000 couplets, giving prognostics to be derived from meteorological phaenomena such as eclipses, halos, rainbows, and shooting stars. His sources are Noah, Daniel, Luqmān, and Plato (the first three being legendary ones connected with Biblical and, as concerns Luqmān, with old Arabic and Qur'ānic traditions). The Shamsīya is also called Mulhima (Revelation). It was rewritten and modernized by the poet Jawrī in 1635. There are many MSS, though more of the second version than of the earlier one.

If this Ṣalāḥ al-dīn really came from Būlī, he was probably identical with the shaikh Ṣalāḥ al-dīn named (by Ṭāshköprüzāde) as a friend and disciple of Ḥājjī Bairām,[29] who was the teacher also of another Turkish poet, the oldest Shaikhī. This helps us to realize that Ankara was then an important literary and religious center.

This Ṣalāḥ al-dīn may be identical also with the one to whom is ascribed an early Turkish translation of the Persian treatise on sexual hygiene by Nāṣir al-dīn al-Ṭūsī (XIII-2), the Bāb-nāma-i shāhī, which is probably the Kitāb al-bāb al-bāhīya mentioned in my volume 2, page 1010. There are many copies of the Turkish translation in the Istanbul libraries.

Criticism. Joseph von Hammer-Purgstall: Geschichte der osmanischen Dichtkunst (1, 73–89, Pesth 1836), including analysis of the Shamsīya. Gibb (1, 388–91, 1900). Franz Babinger (EI 4, 1171, 1933). I. Hakkı Uzunçarşılıoğlu: Anadolu beylikleri (p. 84, Ankara 1937), Anatolian states, in Turkish.

AḤMEDĪ

Aḥmedī (c. 1334–1413) is one of the most famous Turkish poets of the fourteenth century and of great importance to us, because he was one of the first to diffuse scientific knowledge by means of the Turkish language and prosody. That is, he

[29] Ḥājjī Bairām was a famous ṣūfī saint and "pīr," founder of the order of dervishes called after him Bairāmīya. He died in Ankara 1429/30, and is buried there near the Monumentum ancyranum (EI 1, 595, 1911).

did for the Turks something like what Jean de Meung (XIII-2) did for the French and Jacob van Maerlant (XIII-2) for the Dutch.

Tāj al-dīn Aḥmad ibn Ibrāhīm al-Aḥmedī was born before 1334 in Germiyān (district in the center of Anatolia corresponding roughly to ancient Phrygia); according to others he was born in Sīwās (in eastern Anatolia, on the upper course of the Halys or "red river," Kızıl-ırmak). He studied in Cairo, where he was deeply influenced by his illustrious countrymen Ḥājjī pāshā and Muḥammad ibn Ḥamza al-Fanārī. Then he returned home and entered the service of Mīr Sulmān, ruler of Germiyān, as tutor (khūjā). Sometime after 1390 he moved to Amasia (in eastern Anatolia); he was there with Tīmūr after the battle of Ankara (1402, when Tīmūr defeated Bāyazīd and made him prisoner). Later still, probably after Tīmūr's death (1405), Aḥmedī fled to the court of Bāyazīd's eldest son, Sulaimān, in Adrianople (later in Brusa), and wrote many poems for him. Sulaimān, having fallen into disgrace, fled to the court of Manuel II in Constantinople, and died in 1410. Aḥmedī returned to Amasia, where he died in 1413.

His most famous work is the Turkish epic Iskandar-nāma, describing in 8,250 couplets the deeds of Alexander the Great and his conquests from Morocco to Japan! It is a didactic poem as well as an epic one, for it contains a large amount of scientific knowledge (psychology, medicine, mathematics, astronomy, etc.) put into the mouths of various philosophers, chiefly Aristotle and Plato. Aristotle explains prophetically the events that happened after Alexander's days and his own. The arrangement is modeled upon that of the Alexandrian story in Firdawsī. The work was completed on March 19, 1390 and dedicated to Mīr Sulmān; but supplements were added extending the historical part to 1410/11.

Two medical works are ascribed to Aḥmedī: the Tarwīḥ al-arwāḥ, dealing with medicine and hygiene, dedicated to Bāyazīd I ('Uthmānlī sulṭān 1389–1402); and the Muntakhab al-shifā'. It should be noted that a work bearing the second title, and presumably in Turkish, is also ascribed to Ḥājjī pāshā (are these two treatises not perhaps a single work ascribed to two contemporary Turkish authors?). As to the first title, it is given to an Arabic work, Tarwīḥ al-arwāḥ lī taṣḥīḥ al-ashbāḥ, on diet and hygiene, written by 'Alā al-dīn 'Alī ibn al-Ḥusain al-Baihaqī in 1506; this is probably a mere coincidence, though it is curious that both Tarwīḥ deal with hygiene.

It is also possible that the author of these medical works or of one of them is not Aḥmedī, but a contemporary Turkish poet, Aḥmad-i Dā'ī (he who calls and prays for, "missionary"), who flourished with Aḥmedī at the court of the amīr Sulaimān. Aḥmad-i Dā'ī was not only a poet, he wrote a book on the art of correspondence ('ilm al-tarassul) and, it is said, another on Persian and Arabic lexicography ('Uqūd al-jawāhir).

Criticism. Gibb (1, 260–98, 1900), including long extracts in English from the Iskandar-nāma. Karl Süssheim (EI 1, 205 1909). Franz Babinger: Die Geschichtsschreiber der Osmanen (p. 11–14, Leipzig 1927). Süheyl Ünver: Sur l'histoire de la médecine et de l'hygiène en Turquie (Türk tıb tarihi arkivi, no. 1, 1935). I. Hakkı Uzunçarşılıoğlu: Anadolu beylikleri (p. 80–81, Ankara 1937; Isis 32), in Turkish. Adnan (p. 19, 1939).

AL-FANĀRĪ

Mawlānā Shams al-dīn Muḥammad ibn Ḥamza al-Fanārī al-Ḥanafī. Turkish theologian and encyclopaedist writing in Arabic (1350–1431).

He was born in April 1350. He studied in his own country and in Egypt. During the rules of Yildirim Bāyazīd (1389–1402) and Muḥammad I (1402–21) he obtained great repute as a teacher in Brusa and became one of the leading 'ulamā' of the 'Uthmānlī nation. He was thrown into prison by order of Tīmūr. In 1425 he was appointed qāḍī of Brusa by Murād II. Having lost his eyesight, then recovered it, he made a second pilgrimage to Mecca in 1430 as an act of thanksgiving. He died soon after his return in March 1431.

He wrote books on logic, on philosophical and theological questions. His importance lies apparently less in these books than in his being one of the early great educators of his country.

It is told of him that, meditating on the ḥadīth "the earth does not digest the flesh of holy men," he caused the tomb of his master Qara 'Alā al-dīn (a famous teacher under Urkhān, 'Uthmānlī sulṭān 1326–60) to be opened by way of experiment; the body was found to have been preserved. It is interesting to note that that Muslim tradition agrees with the Roman Catholic tradition but not with the Athonite tradition.[30]

Al-Fanārī's son, Muḥammad shāh Čelebī (ibn Muḥammad al-Fanārī), was a teacher in the madrasa sulṭānīya in Brusa and died in 1435/36 (or not until 1454/55). He wrote the Anmūdhaj al-'ulūm ṭibāqan limafhūm (Model of the sciences), an encyclopaedia dealing with a hundred sciences, derived from the Persian encyclopaedia Ḥadā'iq al-anwār of Fakhr al-dīn al-Rāzī (XII-2). It is said that the Anmūdhaj was taken to Samarqand by the great Turkish scholar Qāḍī Zāde al-Rūmī, who was born in Brusa but flourished in Samarqand, where he was the second director of Ulūgh Beg's observatory and where he died c. 1436–46. To complete the history of the al-Fanārī family, a son of Muḥammad shāh Čelebī, called al-Ḥasan Čelebī ibn Muḥammad shāh al-Fanārī (1436–81), was professor of theology in Adrianople, Iznīq, Istanbul, and spent the end of his life in Brusa.

Text. I cite only a few books available in print.

Tafsīr surat al-fātiḥa (Istanbul 1326).

Sharḥ īsāghūjī (Istanbul 1263, 1274, Delhi 1288), commentary on the Isagoge of Porphyry (III-2), printed with other commentaries on the same work.

Fuṣūl al-badā'i' fi uṣūl al-sharā'i' (Istanbul 1289).

Kitāb al-manṭiq (Istanbul 1304).

Criticism. Gibb (1, 261, 1900). Brockelmann (2, 233, 1902; suppt. 2, 328, 1938). Sarkis (col. 1460–61, 1930), in Arabic. Adnan (p. 11, 30, 1939), confusing father and son.

[30] From the Athonite point of view, the uncorruptedness of a body is "a sure sign of a wicked life and an evil death." R. M. Dawkins: The monks of Athos (p. 305, London 1936). It should be noted that the Athonite (Balkanic?) view is a singularity in the Orthodox church, which as a whole shares the Catholic tradition in this matter. Witness many bodies (or parts of bodies) of Orthodox saints which were exhibited in churches or monasteries. It is remarkable that the Orthodox tradition has been followed in Russia by the anticlerical Bolshevists with regard to Lenin's body! On the incorruptibility of saintly bodies see also Saintyves (p. 282–325, 528–33, 1930). When George Bernard Shaw and the Astors visited Russia, he was taken to visit the anti-religious museum established in the Vasili Blazhennyi church, Moscow. He was shown two peasant bodies admirably preserved from decay, and his girl guide told him this exhibit was arranged to counteract the priestly claim that incorruptibility was a miracle vouchsafed only to saints. Shaw objected, "How do you know that these two were not saints?" Hesketh Pearson: G. B. S. (p. 327, New York 1942).

D6. The Destroyer

TĪMŪR LANG

Conqueror of Asia (1336–1405).

Though this book is primarily devoted to creators, spiritual creators, not to destroyers, Tīmūr destroyed on such a fantastic scale that we must speak of him, even as we spoke of his greatest predecessors, Alexander the Great (IV-2 B.C.) and Chingiz Khān (XIII-1), and of the Black Death.

Contents: (1) Life and conquests. (2) Tīmūr's character. (3) The destruction caused by Tīmūr. (4) Samarqand. (5) Gūr-i-Mīr, Tīmūr's mausoleum. A problem in jade archaeology. (6) The so-called Memoirs and Institutes of Tīmūr. (7) Tīmūr's court and influence. (8) The historians of Tīmūr. (9) Criticism.

1. *Life and conquests*

Tīmūr Lang means Tīmūr the Lame (Tamerlane). Tīmūr itself means, in Turkish, iron (cf. Stalin, steel). He was born near Kish in Sughd (some 50 miles south of Samarqand) in the very year, 736 H., when the dynasty of the Mongol īl-khān of Persia, founded by Hūlāgū, virtually ended with the death of Abu Sa'īd. Abu Sa'īd died on November 30, 1335; Tīmūr was born on April 8, 1336. His father, Tārāghāi, was the head of a Turkish tribe, and one of his ancestors had been a high officer in the army of Chagatāy, son of Chingiz Khān. Tīmūr started fighting in his early youth, but like Chingiz he did not begin to conquer in earnest until he was in his forties. In the meanwhile he had ascended the throne of Balkh in 1370, as a successor to Chagatāy and Chingiz. From that time on his life was but a long series of raids (ghazw; ghazā, pl. ghazawāt) and wars, conducted with incredible energy and ferocity. A complete enumeration would be tedious. It will suffice to indicate the main ones.

He conquered, destroyed, decimated many of the leading cities of his time, Herāt, Iṣfahān (1387), Edessa, Takrīt, Mārdīn, Amīd, Moscow (1395), Delhi (1398), Sīwās, Aleppo, Damascus, Baghdād (1401), Brusa, Smyrna (1402). In many places he built pyramids of human skulls to serve as warnings.

His most important victories perhaps were the one over Maḥmūd II (Taghlaqī sulṭān of Delhi) in 1398–99, which increased the communications between India and Persia, and that over Bāyazīd in Ankara 1402, which gave a breathing spell to the Byzantine empire. Remember that Bāyazīd's victory over Sigismund of Hungary at Nicopolis (on the Danube) in 1396, the commercial rivalry of Venice and Genoa and their perfidies, etc., had increased the dangers of that empire considerably. Manuel II Palaeologos (emperor 1391–1425) was traveling in Europe to obtain help against the Turks. He failed to obtain it there, but Tīmūr unwittingly gave it; after Ankara, Manuel could return to his throne in peace and the empire was granted a reprieve of half a century.

The princes of Europe appreciated the situation. Henry IV of England and Charles VI of France congratulated Tīmūr on his victory over Bāyazīd, and Henry III of Castile[31] sent him a special envoy, Ruy González de Clavijo, to whom we owe an excellent account of Tīmūr and his court and administration.

[31] Henry III had been in touch with Tīmūr before Ankara. Two "military attachés" of his, Pelayo de Sotomayor and Fernando de Palazuelos, witnessed the Ankara battle on the Mongol side. Tīmūr presented them with two Christian women, one Angelica (or Angelina),

By the end of his life Tīmūr had conquered a great part of the world, from the eastern part of Russia, across Asia Minor, Armenia, Georgia, Syria, 'Irāq, Persia, Khurāsān, Khwārizm, Transoxiana, Afghanistān, the northern part of India to the latitude of Delhi; but he was not satisfied, and undertook the conquest of China (end of 1404). He died on the way, at Utrār, on the right bank of the Sīr Daryā (Saiḥūn), in February 1405. His body was brought back to Samarqand by his grandson Ulūgh Beg and buried in a splendid monument, the Gūr-i-Mīr (or Gūr-i-Amīr), which still exists today (see section 5 below).

Tīmūr never assumed an imperial title, but called himself "the amīr Tīmūr" or "the amīr," and it was under that simple name that Asia knew him and knows him still. He was not of noble birth, but many of his children were, for he married (among other women) two Chinese princesses, the Great Queen and the Little Queen (al-malika al-kubrā, al-malika al-ṣughrā). After his death his empire was soon divided into two parts, the western going to his son Mīrānshāh and the latter's sons, the eastern (i.e., Khurāsān, Transoxiana) to his son Shāhrukh. The latter was a patron of science and arts, and even more so was Shāhrukh's son Ulūgh Beg, the astronomer-king (born 1393, put to death by his own son 1449). Many parts of the empire were reduced to a state of endemic war and anarchy; this was especially true of India, where chaos obtained until its conquest by the Mongol Bābar, a descendant of Tīmūr in the fifth generation, and founder of the Mongol (or Mogul) dynasty which lasted from 1525 to 1857 (Bābar 1921).

2. *Tīmūr's character*

Tīmūr was a real leader or "Führer," aggressive, fearless, able to inspire absolute devotion in his followers, autocratic, impatient, always cruel, but ruthless in anger. He was a strategist and tactician of genius, who fully knew the value of speed, great strength immediately applied, dissimulation. He was also a great organizer, able to think of the common good as soon as he himself was satisfied, and to protect the common men against lesser gangsters than himself. He was capable of justice, when it could be carried out at the expense of other people, especially of his enemies. He could be generous with ostentation in the Oriental manner; that is, an amīr must be generous, even to the point of extravagance, in order to advertise his own power, wealth, and "nobility."

His ferocity was truly that of a barbarian unrestrained by any tradition or any code. As specimens may be quoted (from Browne, p. 181): "his massacre of the people of Sīstán in 1383–4, when he caused some two thousand prisoners to be built up in a wall; his cold-blooded slaughter of a hundred thousand captive Indians near Dihlī in December 1398; his burying alive of four thousand Armenians in 1400–1, and the twenty towers of skulls erected by him at Aleppo and Damascus in the same year; and his massacre of 70,000 of the inhabitants of Iṣfahán in November 1387."

Apparently he knew no Arabic, beyond the elementary Islamic vocabulary, but he had some knowledge of Persian, Turkish, and Mongol. He was probably illiterate, but that does not matter much for a man as intelligent as he was, and one

---

of Greek parentage, the other Maria, a granddaughter of the king of Hungary, found captives in the harem of Bāyazīd, and probably taken by the latter at Nicopolis. After their arrival in Castile, Maria the Hungarian married Pelayo de Sotomayor, and Angelica, Diego González de Contreras, afterward regidor of Segovia. Both women are mentioned in contemporary Spanish ballads.

who could always command the services of readers and writers. Many books on history were read to him and, it is said, he could often detect the reader's omissions or mistakes.

He honored learned men, theologians, astrologers, and physicians, but did not so well appreciate actors and poets.

He was a great chess player, and always played the greater game (al-shaṭranj al-kabīr), in which there are 110 squares (instead of 64) and there is a greater variety of chessmen, including camels, giraffes, etc! His son Shāhrukh and the city Shāhrukhīya on the river Sayḥūn were named after a technicality of chess; he had just given shāh-rukh (check-rook) and won when the birth of the former and the completion of the latter were announced to him. There were famous chess experts at his court, the most important being 'Alā' al-dīn al-Tabrīzī (or 'Alī al-Shaṭranjī), who wrote a treatise on the subject. A problem of chess is ascribed to Tīmūr himself. Finally, a passion for chess remained a passion of the Tīmūrī, and later of the Mogul, princes. This information is derived from Ibn 'Arabshāh, chiefly his last chapter (many MSS of it include diagrams of Tīmūr's chessboard), and from Murray (p. 167, 171, 182, 204–6, 331, 1913). The same book contains a description of the "great chess" or Tīmūr chess and of other similar extensions of the ordinary game (p. 344–51).

As opposed to Chingiz, who remained a pagan, Tīmūr was brought up as a Muslim, and he gave proofs of Islamic sympathy and devotion. For example, he favored dervishes of the Naqshbandī order (see my note ad hoc in chapter XV). Yet one suspects that his religion was neither very deep, nor very high, but rather on the level of superstition. He was perhaps a little less cruel to Muslims than to Christians, but his religion could not restrain the beast in him. Looking at it from the point of view of jurisprudence, he followed the laws of Chingiz Khān rather than those of the Prophet.

To complete this character sketch, Tīmūr's motto was "rāstī rastī" (which may be translated "truth is safety"), and his "brand" was composed of three rings in triangular position like the three Medici rings!

3. *The destruction caused by Tīmūr*

The destruction of the Islamic East begun by Chingiz Khān in the first half of the thirteenth century was completed by Tīmūr a century and a half later. In the meanwhile considerable additional damage had been wrought by the īl-khān of Persia, that is, a provincial line of Mongol rulers. For example, Baghdād was taken and plundered by the first īl-khān, Hūlāgū, in 1258, but he did not destroy it as completely as other towns; the destruction was completed and the population nearly exterminated by Tīmūr in 1401. We may say that the eastern Islamic world never recovered from his destructiveness.

Therefore his appearance is a definite "cut" in the history of every country which he "visited" (like a plague); we must speak of it as it was before Tīmūr, and after Tīmūr.

Tīmūr's raids finished the destruction of the irrigation system which had made the Mesopotamia of earlier days a paradise. It is said that in Sassanian times (before the Muslim conquest) a squirrel could travel from Seleucia to the Persian Gulf without ever having to come to ground. The canals and ditches without which the earth lost its fertility were neglected, destroyed, neglected again, and so on, and gradually disappeared. Tīmūr completed the job.

Of the three Mongol invasions, by Chingiz Khān, Hūlāgū, and Tīmūr, the third was certainly the most terrible. It was also the last, and hence it not only completed but to some extent canceled the previous ones. Tīmūr was not able to preserve his own empire, which could hardly continue without him. The Tīmūrī culture of the fifteenth century, and the Mogul culture of India (1525–1857), are very different from his own imperial dreams.

4. *Samarqand*

To Tīmūr's credit must be placed the development of Samarqand, one of the two main cities of Sughd (Sogdiana, Transoxiana), the other being Bukhārā. It was an ancient city admirably situated on the south bank of the river Sughd; so ancient that it had been occupied by Alexander the Great. To illustrate its cultural importance, it will suffice to recall that it was the first place outside of China where paper was used (650) and made (757).[32] It always was extremely cosmopolitan; a natural rendezvous for all the peoples of Central Asia and a strong magnet for a great variety of other people. Tīmūr made of it his favorite capital and embellished it with the loot of the world. When Ibn Baṭṭūṭa saw it, about the middle of the century, he spoke of it as one of the most beautiful cities of the world, yet half ruined; from 1369 on, Tīmūr revived and restored it, built new bazaars, mosques, libraries, a menagerie, an observatory,[33] palaces surrounded with magnificent gardens. From the conquered cities of Syria, Anatolia, Persia, and India, he took with him to Samarqand not only loot but learned men and craftsmen, such as weavers, tailors, gem cutters, goldsmiths, carpenters, farriers and furriers, limners, bowmakers, gardeners, falconers, chess players, and leeches. He built in a few years an immense memorial mosque for his favorite wife, Bībī Khānum, but little of it has been preserved. The most impressive remainder of the old city is the Rīgistān, his own mausoleum, and the collection of royal tombs near by, Shāh-i-Zinda, whose mosaics and turquoise-colored tiles are astounding, and whose general aspect is one of incredible and unforgettable beauty.

Samarqand was conquered by the Russians in 1868. It is now the capital of the Uzbek Soviet Republic. Tīmūr was so anxious to develop his city that he often built too fast for permanence; it would seem that the Russians are making the same mistake. The development of modern Samarqand is enormous, especially with regard to schools of every kind; it suggests comparison with some of our own Middle Western university towns; but good observers think that the speed is too great for safety and soundness.

There is a considerable literature on Samarqand. For first orientation see H. H. Schaeder (EI 4, 129–31, 1925), and the accounts of Ibn 'Arabshāh and Clavijo, the Bābar-nāma, etc. Among travel books I would quote Stephen Graham: Through Russian central Asia (New York 1916), recording pre-war impressions, and Rosita Forbes: Forbidden road. Kabul to Samarqand (London 1937), describing Soviet experiments. Gustav Krist: Alone through the forbidden land. Journeys in disguise through Soviet Asia (New York 1938).

[32] After Carter (1925, 1931).

[33] Of course a far more elaborate and famous observatory was established near Samarqand by his grandson Ulūgh Beg in 1420–21, and used for the preparation of new tables, Zīj Ulūgh Beg, c. 1437–38.

5. *Gūr-i-Mīr, Tīmūr's mausoleum. A problem in jade archaeology*

Inside this very beautiful monument is the tomb of the conqueror,[34] covered with an enormous block of green jade (nephrite), 1.92 m. long, 0.37 m wide, split in the middle. This is the largest jade *object* in the world. According to Mr. Herbert P. Whitlock (letters dated New York, Feb. 14 and 21, 1940), it weighs about 2,250 pounds. His estimate is derived from the dimensions quoted above (found in the Russian Granat encyclopaedia, vol. 37, s.v. Samarqand), from a figure in Krist's volume (fig. 30, 1938), and from the assumption of maximal specific gravity (3). There are in the American Museum of Natural History, New York, two specimens of jade (nephrite) which are heavier than the Samarqand one. The first was found by George Frederick Kunz in 1899, in a mine at Jordansmühl near Breslau, Silesia, and weighs 4,710 pounds.[35] The other is a jade boulder found in New Zealand in 1902; it probably came from the west coast of the South Island, at Milford Sound. It measures 7 feet long by 4 feet wide, and must weigh about 7,000 pounds. The Kunz specimen is described in Annals of the New York Academy of Sciences (12, 671, 1899–1900); see also G. F. Kunz: Curious lore of precious stones (p. 250, Philadelphia 1913). The New Zealand boulder is described in the American Museum journal (11, 57, New York 1911).

The Kunz specimen is the largest specimen of jade ever mined, the New Zealand one is the largest boulder, the Samarqand one is the largest jade object. It must have been cut from a boulder which was considerably larger (see following note on "jade mountains," however).

Since writing the above I have had the opportunity of obtaining more information on the Samarqand jade slab from the sumptuous catalogue of the Bishop collection, entitled Investigations and studies in jade (elephant folio, 2 vols., New York 1906; only 100 copies privately printed and distributed; see vol. 1, 7, 172, 183, 249; vol. 2, 26). The Bishop collection is now in the Metropolitan Museum, but I found a copy of its catalogue in the Boston Museum. The Samarqand monument was first figured by Heinrich Fischer in Archiv für Anthropologie (12, 469, 1880), then more fully described by W. von Beck and J. W. von Muschketow in Transactions of the Imperial Mineralogical Society of St. Petersburg (18, 38–50, 2 pl., St. Petersburg 1882). It is deep-green nephrite, the kind called in Chinese pi yü, length 192 cm., breadth 36.75 cm., thickness 30 cm., density 2.926. The origin is eastern Turkestan, either from the neighborhood of Khotan, or from Manas, Sungaria, on the northern slope of the T'ien shan (celestial mountains), or from the valley of the Yarkand river (the so-called jade mountains, Kāsh Tāg in Turki, Yü shan in Chinese). This last-named site was already known to Benedict Goes in 1602; it has always been one of the main sources of pi yü in China.

There is a fragment of the Samarqand monument in the American Museum of Natural History, New York, from the collection of Heinrich Fischer, and there is a tiny part (a little more than one gram) of that fragment in the Metropolitan, described in the Bishop catalogue (item 77, vol. 2, p. 26).

[34] There is an old Bukhārā tradition according to which Tīmūr is not buried in that tomb, but in an oasis in the desert (?).

[35] Kunz detached that block himself from the floor of the quarry, situated in a locality where Hermann Traube had discovered small pieces of jade in 1884. The existence of this enormous specimen suggests that prehistoric jade objects found in Europe are not necessarily of Asiatic origin.

"Jade mountains" in Peiping. Long after I had written the previous note on jade, my Harvard colleague Langdon Warner drew my attention (letter Nov. 8, 1943) to the book of John Andrew Goette: Jade lore (330 p., ill., New York 1937), wherein are described (p. 180–89) three so-called "jade mountains" preserved in the Imperial City. They are three very large jade blocks which have been carved to look like mountains or hills, a subject dear to the Chinese heart because of Shan shui, the cult of mountain and water. Two of these three are certainly, and the third is probably, heavier than Tīmūr's tomb. The largest, called "jade mountain pagoda," is an exquisitely carved shaft 7 × 3 × 3 feet, weighing at least 7 tons; it is kept in the Lo shou t'ang (pavilion of longevity and happiness); the original boulder from which it was carved was given by the governor of Chinese Turkestan to Ch'ien Lung in 1778; the carving was completed ten years later. The second in size is the Shou shan (mountain of longevity), preserved in the same pavilion. It measures 57½ × 41 × 30 inches, must weigh about 3 tons, and is dated 1781.[36] These two monuments have very much the same color, a grayish white with green streaks. The Shou shan has been carved to represent "a sloping hillside dotted with cypress trees from which peep a round pavilion below, and a storied palace and pagoda above. Two figures are seen crossing a wooden bridge over a spring while herds of deer appear elsewhere." The third monument, also in the Forbidden City, stands in front of the jade throne in the Chai kung (hall of abstinence); it is gray-green with gray and green lines; it rises 4 feet and is 3 feet round at the bottom, but tapers off gradually to a short peak. Estimated weight, 1½ ton.

A fourth specimen, dated 1784, much smaller (640 pounds), was looted from the Forbidden City in 1860 and is now in the Walker Art Galleries, Minneapolis, Minnesota. It is remarkable that the four monuments all date from the reign of Ch'ien Lung (1736–96).

The Chicago Natural History Museum received in 1944 a nephrite jade boulder of 2,490 pounds, probably the second largest piece yet discovered in the United States; it was found in an area about 50 miles southwest of Lander, Wyoming. A small section, about half a square foot in area, has been cut from one end and polished so as to bring out the rich dark green color and variegated markings of the specimen.

6. *The so-called Memoirs and Institutes of Tīmūr*

In the eighteenth century and the beginning of the nineteenth, many scholars formed a more favorable impression of Tīmūr's character than we do now, because they were deceived by the "Memoirs" (Malfūẓāt) and "Institutes" (Tuzūkāt-i-Tīmūrī) ascribed to him. These documents are now proved to be apocryphal. They were produced in Persian under Shāh-Jahān (great Mogul, 1628–59) by one Abū Ṭālib al-Ḥusainī, who claimed to have translated them from a Turkī original discovered by him in the library of Ja'far pāshā, governor of Yamàn. That original has never been seen by anybody else. It is probable that the work was written by Abū Ṭālib himself in imitation of the Bābar-nāma, i.e., the memoirs of Bābar (the first Great Mogul, 1525–30).

Persian text of the Tuzūkāt and English translation edited by William Davy and Joseph White (520 p., Oxford 1783) for the East India Company. Reprint,

[36] In the imperial inscription of 1781 this monument is named "the spring terrace for the understanding of alchemy."

Calcutta 1785. French translation by Louis Mathieu Langlès: Instituts politiques et militaires de Tamerlan (Paris 1787). English translation of the Malfūẓāt by Charles Stewart (London 1830). Bābar (p. xxiii f., 1921).

Fifteen letters exchanged by Tīmūr and Bāyazīd were edited by Aḥmad Firīdūn al-Tawqī'ī in the middle of the sixteenth century. The text will be found in the collection of Turkish state papers Munsha'āt-i-Firīdūn bey (1, 118–42, Constantinople 1858). Analysis in Browne (3, 204–6).

7. *Tīmūr's court and influence*

Thanks to Tīmūr's power and his destruction of many of the most important cultural centers of Asia, Samarqand became for a short time the main, if not the unique, center of cultural influence, eclipsing Tabrīz and Baghdād. During his rule communications between India and Samarqand increased, and hence Samarqand could relay Hindu influences toward the West. Little is yet known about that, however.

It is not clear to me which was the main language of Tīmūr's government. Probably Persian, but they used also Arabic, Uighūr (that is, Turkish), and Mongol.

Tīmūr had attracted to his court, or more exactly commandeered, a number of learned men and craftsmen. Ibn 'Arabshāh mentions many of them, as the theologians al-Jurjānī and al-Taftāzānī, the physicians Faḍlallāh of Tabrīz and Jamāl al-dīn, chief physician in Syria; the astronomer Aḥmad Ṭabīb al-Naḥḥās Mustakhrij (?), who had drawn up astronomical tables for 200 years (he said so in 1406); the musician 'Abd al-Qādir ibn Ghaibī. Many other men made that period illustrious, above all Ḥāfiẓ—whose interview with the conqueror is probably apocryphal—and Ḥāfiẓ' rival, 'Imād al-dīn al-Faqīh of Kirmān (d. 1371/72); 'Imād al-dīn had taught his cat to make the ritual prostrations of Islām with him!

Tīmūr had noticed the bulbous shape of a tower of Damascus before its destruction, and it is said that that was his fundamental inspiration for the Tīmūrī style of architecture, well exemplified in the Gūr-i-mīr. This in its turn was the origin of the Mogul style, as developed in the Tāj Maḥall, and of the many bulbs surmounting Russian churches. Other characteristics of the Tīmūrī buildings were their massiveness and the abundant use of tiles, especially blue tiles, for their decoration.

Whatever art and culture began to grow at the court of Tīmūr was developed chiefly by his son Shāhrukh (1404–47), peaceful and art-loving; by the latter's son, the astronomer Ulūgh Beg (1447–49); and by one of Ulūgh's protégés, Ḥusain ibn Manṣūr ibn Bayqarā, who ruled Herāt for 38 years (1468–1506) and made of that city one of the main intellectual centers of Persia. In the meanwhile Samarqand had been captured by Bābar (1497), and its decadence had set in. It was soon eclipsed by Herāt and Bukhārā and sank into gradual isolation and oblivion.

8. *The historians of Tīmūr*

Tīmūr's deeds are relatively well known because of the testimony of various witnesses. A biography of him, the Ẓafar-nāma, was written in Persian upon his own order by Niẓām al-dīn al-Shāmī and completed before his death, in 1403–4. Another official biography, written in Turkī verse and Uighūr script, is lost. The Ẓafar-nāma was superseded by another Persian work bearing the same title, by Sharaf al-dīn 'Alī Yazdī (d. 1454). These accounts are balanced by the Arabic one, 'Ajā'ib al-maqdūr fī nawā'ib Tīmūr, completed in 1435 by the Syrian Ibn 'Arabshāh (c. 1390–1450). The latter has been accused of unfairness; he seems fair enough to me, for he praises Tīmūr whenever he can, but there was more to damn than to praise in that "scourge of God."[37] Later Persian historians need not be mentioned here.

An excellent account of Tīmūr's court and administration was given by the Spanish ambassador Ruy González de Clavijo (d. 1412), who saw Tīmūr shortly before the latter's death. Some information was also transmitted by two men made prisoners by the Turks at Nicopolis 1396, Jean de Boucicault, marshal of France (d. 1421), and the German traveler Hans Schiltberger, who spent thirty-two years of slavery and adventure in the East (d. c. 1440).

9. *Criticism*

The Ẓafar-nāma of Sharaf al-dīn was edited in the Bibliotheca indica (nos. 82–83, Calcutta 1887–88). Translated into French by François Pétis de la Croix (1653–1713): Histoire de Timur-Bec, connu sous le nom de Grand Tamerlan (4 vols., Paris 1722), and by François Bernard Charmoy (2 vols., St. Pétersbourg 1868–75). Translated from French into English by John Darby (London 1723).

The 'Ajā'ib al-maqdūr was edited and translated into Latin by Jacob Golius (448 p., Leiden 1636). Later editions by Jacob Meyer (Oxford 1703–4) and by Samuel Heinrich Manger (2 vols., Leeuwarden 1767–72). There are also many Oriental editions, printed in Calcutta and Cairo. French translation by Pierre Vattier (2 vols., Paris 1658). English translation by John Herne Sanders (360 p., London 1936), poorly edited.

Ruy González de Clavijo: Historia del gran Tamorlan. First edition by Gonçalo Argote de Molina (Seville 1582). Many other editions and translations. English translations by Sir Clements Markham (Hakluyt Society, 260 p., London 1859) and by Guy le Strange (390 p., London 1927).

Browne (3, 159–61, 180–208, 1920). Harold Lamb: Tamerlane, the earth shaker (New York 1928), popular account often reprinted, and translated into French. W. A. Wigram: The Assyrians and their neighbours (p. 48, 142–47, London 1929). L. Bouvat (EI 4, 777–79, 1930). Atiya (p. 257–59, 1938).

A. Süheil Ünver: Was Tīmūr a veterinary doctor? (in Turkish; Türk tıb tarihi arkivi 4, no. 14, 49–58, Istanbul 1939). Article dealing with the composite Turkish veterinary MS 2838, Baytarname, in the Qonya museum; the MS is a late copy, A.D. 1842, but contains old materials some of which may date back to Mamlūk days, when hippiatric literature was highly developed in the Muslim East. It is stated in that MS (relevant passages are reproduced in facsimile) that Tīmūr was a hippiatric expert and that he owed his early rise partly to that; this is not implausible, as in those days, when cavalry provided the best means of speedy warfare, a good knowledge of horses would be of great benefit to any commander.

E. INDIA

TARUṆAPRABHA

Gujarātī-Jaina author (fl. 1355).

Taruṇaprabha is the first author of merit in Gujarātī prose. He wrote a vigorous and graceful language. In 1355 he composed the Parikramaṇabālāvabodha[38] in order to illustrate Jaina ethics.

The second book in Gujarātī prose deserving mention is the Mugdhāvabodha,[39] a Sanskrit grammar with explanations in Gujarātī written in 1394 by Kulamaṇḍana.

[37] Title given to Attila, king of the Huns (d. 453), but deserved by Tīmūr even more.

[38] Or Prati- instead of Pari-.

[39] Not to be confused with another Sanskrit grammar, the Mugdhabodha of Vopadeva (XIII-2).

Gujarātī is one of the Aryan vernaculars of India spoken along the western coast near Bombay (Gujarāta territory). The great majority of its users are Hindus; but it is used also by minorities of Jains, Muslims, and Parsis. In fact, subdialects have developed which might be called Muslim Gujarātī and Parsi Gujarātī. The Gujarāta region has become famous in our time as the home of Mahātmā Gandhi, the best modern incarnation of Hindu dharma.

Criticism. Kanaiyalal M. Munshi: Gujarāta and its literature (p. 86, 92, Bombay 1935), excellent work.

LAL DED

Lal Ded, or Lal Dīdī, or Māī Lal Dīddī (all of which means "granny Lal"); in Sanskrit Lallā Yōgīshwarī (Lallā the mistress of yōga ascesis). Kashmirian poetess and mystic (fl. c. 1380).

Lallā was a poet and Śaiva yōginī who wandered about in a seminude state, dancing and singing in an ecstatic frenzy as did the Hebrew prophets and the modern darāwīsh. A great many legends have clustered about her name in the folklore of Kashmīr, but she seems to have been a real person who flourished in that country at the same time as the Muslim apostle of Kashmīr, al-Sayyid 'Alī al-Hamadhānī (c. 1380–85), a member of the Naqshbandī order (for which see chapter XV and my note on Tīmūr).

Many of her verses have been transmitted orally, and their collection is commonly called Lallā-vākyāni (Lallā's wise sayings). They represent a popular form of Hinduist philosophy, Śaiva yōga. The purpose of yōga is to emancipate the human soul (purusha) from its bondage to the material universe (prakṛiti). That purpose is not essentially different from that of Christian mysticism and Muslim taṣawwuf, but it is attained by highly original methods, physical and mental. The form of yōga professed by Lal Ded was the one connected with the cult of Śiva, Śaiva (one of the two great divisions of Hinduism, the other being the cult of Vishṇu, Vaishṇava). In addition she was influenced by other Hinduist ideas, by the Bhagavadgītā, and by convergent ideas in Islām, witness the story of her meeting with the Muslim saint mentioned above.

Lallā is not interesting only in herself. She was the contemporary of Rāmānanda (XIV-1) of Allāhābād, who introduced into northern India the qualified monism (viśishṭa advaita) of the southern philosopher Rāmāṇuja (XI-2). Indeed, though Rāmānanda was born at the end of the thirteenth century he lived to a very old age. She is truly the forerunner of his great disciple the weaver of Benares Kabīr (fl. 1440–1518), and the latter's disciple Nānak (1469–1538). Kabīr was the founder of a sect (the Kabīr panth) syncretizing to some extent the ideas of India and Islām, and counting to this day a good many members (not far short of a million) in northern and central India. Nānak was the founder or first teacher (guru) of the Sikh religion, and his writings are included in the Sikh Bible, Ādi granth (The first book), which was canonized sometime after the death of the tenth and last guru, Govind Singh (assassinated in 1708). Nānak continued the syncretizing tendencies of Kabīr.[40] The same stream of thought can be followed in other Hindu efforts, for example, in the organization of the Brāhma-Samāj (1828), etc.

Please note that Rāmānuja and Rāmānanda wrote in Sanskrit, Lallā sang in

[40] Nānak's friendliness to the Muslims was gradually forgotten and the Sikh people have become more and more anti-Muslim; they are often difficult to distinguish from orthodox Hindus.

Kashmīrī, and Kabīr in Hindī. As to the Sikh Bible, it is written mainly in old Panjābī, but it includes not only Sanskrit (as we should expect), but Hindī, Marathī, Persian, Arabic, and even some peculiar words which cannot be ascribed to any known language.[41]

Text. Sir George Grierson and Lionel D. Barnett: Lallā-vākyāni, edited with translation, notes, and vocabulary (Asiatic Society monographs no. 17, 233 p., London 1920). Edition of the Kashmīrī text derived from the oral tradition and from collateral materials in Hindī and Sanskrit.

Sir Richard Carnac Temple: The words of Lallā the prophetess, being the sayings of Lal Ded, done in English verse and annotated (308 p., Cambridge 1924).

Criticism. Sir George's edition and Sir Richard's contain much information. Winternitz (p. 586–92, 1922).

G. H. Westcott: Kabir and the Kabir panth (192 p., 3 ill., Cawnpore 1907). Rabindranath Tagore: One hundred poems of Kabir translated, with introduction by Evelyn Underhill (94 p., India Society, London 1914). Sir Richard Burn: Kabīr, Kabīrpanthīs (ERE 7, 632–34, 1915). F. E. Keay: Kabīr and his followers (Religious life of India, 194 p., 14 ill., Calcutta 1931).

For everything pertaining to the Sikh religion the standard work is Max Arthur Macauliffe: The Sikh religion, its gurus, sacred writings and authors (6 vols., Clarendon Press, Oxford 1909). H. A. Rose: Granth (ERE 6, 389–90, 1914); Sikhs (ERE 11, 507–11, 1921). J. W. Youngson: Nānak (ERE 9, 181–84, 1917). John Clark Archer: The Sikhs in relation to Hindus, Moslems, Christians and Ahmadiyyas (365 p., 12 ill., Princeton University 1946).

Sivanath Sastri: History of the Brahmo Samaj (2 vols., Calcutta 1911–12; Isis 3, 428–29).

Kashmīrī is an Aryan language, but after the Muslim conquest in the fourteenth century it absorbed a great number of Persian words, and indirectly of Arabic ones.

BANDA NAWĀZ

Hindu mystic writing in Urdū (fl. end of fourteenth century).

Al-Sayyid Muḥammad Banda Nawāz, also called Gīsū Darāz or Khwaja Banda Nawāz, belonged to the famous Chishti family, so named after a quarter in Sinjār (in Jazīra, west of Mūṣul; a Yazīdī district). The first illustrious member of that family was Mu'īn al-dīn Chishti Aftab-i-Mulk-i-Hind (sun of the realm of India), who died in 1235 and is buried in Ajmer.[42] Banda Nawāz is said to have been born in 1321, and to have died in 1422. He came to the Deccan in 1397/98 and to Gulbarga during the rule of Fīrūz Shāh[43] in 1413; the king's brother built a madrasa for him near the city, and a shrine (dargah) was erected to his memory (c. 1460) not far from the tombs of the Bahmanī kings. Some of Banda's descendants are living near his shrine to this day.

Banda Nawāz wrote two short treatises in prose, both dealing with Islamic mysticism (taṣawwuf), the Mi'rāj al-'āshiqīn (Ascension of the lovers)[44] and the

[41] The most common name of the Sikh scriptures, Granth ṣāḥib, is typical of the polyglottism involved, for granth is a Hindī word derived from the Sanskrit grantha (book), and ṣāḥib is an Arabic one, meaning companion, lord, here strangely given the connotation of holy!

[42] In the British district Ajmer-Merwara, right in the center of Rajputana.

[43] This Fīrūz Shāh was the eighth sulṭān of the Bahmanī dynasty of the Deccan (1347–1526); he ruled from 1397 to 1422. Gulbarga (or Kulbargā, now in the Nizam's dominions, Hyderabad) was the capital of that dynasty until 1428, when it was abandoned in favor of Bidar.

[44] For Muslims mi'rāj is not any ascension, but the ascension of the Prophet to heaven. See the Sūrat al-isrā in the Qur'ān. Thus the title implies a play on words.

Hidāya nāma (Gift book).[45] The first is about 19 pages long. These two books are important as the earliest examples of Urdū prose.

The Urdū language is of great historical interest as a witness of the tremendous impact of Islām on India, especially in this period. Urdū is a derivative of the Western Hindī, itself a descendant of Sanskrit via a Prākrit dialect. While "High" Hindī reverted more and more to its origins, excluding foreign words and replacing them by Sanskrit ones, Urdū was created by the impact of Persian (and secondarily Arabic and Turkish) on the Prākrit dialect. Urdū originated in the Dūāb,[46] and more particularly in Dihlī (Delhi), which was the Muslim capital. The name urdū is Turkish, meaning camp, army. The ahl-i urdū were the "people of the camp," who mixed Persian and Hindī and thus created a new language. To complete the contrast, Urdū is written mostly in the Persian script (with a few additional signs), whereas Hindī uses the same scripts as Sanskrit, preferably the Devanāgarī; Urdū is rather a Muslim language, and Hindī is rather a Hinduist one.

It is remarkable that the development of Urdū literature took place, not in the upper Gangetic region where the language was born, but in the Deccan, and that it was connected with the growth of Muslim mysticism. Even as the Buddha spoke Pāli[47] instead of Sanskrit, the ṣūfī missionary learned to speak the new Urdū dialect rather than Persian or Arabic, because in both cases they wanted to reach the masses of the people. The main center of Urdū culture today is Hyderabad.

The term Hindūstānī is often used for Urdū. That is misleading, for both terms have not the same extension. The word Hindūstānī serves to designate many dialects of India, e.g., Eastern Hindī, Western Hindī, Rājasthānī. Consider, for example, the following definitions of Urdū and Hindī: Urdū is the Persianized Hindūstānī of educated Muslims, Hindī is the Sanskritized Hindūstānī of educated Hindus. It is clear that when we deal with the particular language or literature called by its own people Urdū, we should never use the European and ambiguous term Hindūstānī.

Text. The Mi'rāj al-'ashiqīn was edited by Abdul Haq (Hyderabad 1900). Not listed in Emeneau (1935), whose Urdū bibliography is very meager indeed.

Criticism. Ram Babu Saksena: History of Urdu literature (Allahabad 1927), does not speak of Banda Nawāz. Thomas Grahame Bailey: History of Urdu literature (Heritage of India series, p. 16, Calcutta 1932), work completed in 1929. Abdul Haq: Urdū (EI 4, 1023–29, 1932).

F. CHINA

HSIEH YING-FANG

Chinese scholar (d. after 1384).

Hsieh Ying-fang was born at Wu-chin in Kiangsu and became famous for his learning. In 1341, while he was living in his cottage called the "tortoise nest,"

[45] These two titles would read almost exactly alike in Arabic and in Persian.

[46] Dūāb is the Persian equivalent of the Greek word Mesopotamia, land of two rivers; specifically, the land between the Ganges and the Jumna down to their confluence near Allahabad. That land constitutes the western side of the United Provinces (Meerut, Agra, and Allahabad divisions). Delhi is on the Jumna, just at the western edge of that region.

[47] To be correct, the Buddha spoke the Prākrit dialect of Kosala or Magadha. The language which we now call Pāli was formerly called Māgadhī. The term Pāli is relatively late, as late as Buddhaghosha (V-1), and at first it referred not to language, but to content, i.e., to the text (vs. commentaries) of the Buddhist writings. What Europeans and modern Buddhist doctors of Ceylon, Burma, and Siam call Pāli is the language of the Buddhist canon. See introduction to B. C. Law (1933).

Kuei ch'ao, he was appointed director of education in his native place. During the troubled period marking the end of the Yüan dynasty he withdrew from the service, and in 1364, being over 70, he established himself in a mountain hermitage of his province. He edited the local topography. He died at the age of 96, that is, c. 1384-90.

His main work is a treatise against the abundant superstitions of his time, Pien-huo p'ien. They are described under fifteen heads: life and death, pestilence, spiritual powers, sacrifices, illicit sacrifices, elfish monstrosities, witchcraft, divination, mourning observances, selection of tombs, physiognomy, fortune-telling, positions, times and days, strange doctrines.

Text. The Library of Congress has the Pien-huo p'ien in vol. 74 of the Shuo fu; in vol. 55 of the Shou shan ko ts'ung shu; and in vol. 83 of the Ch'ing chao t'ang ts'ung shu.

Criticism. Wylie (p. 87, 1902). Giles (no. 746, 1898). Wieger (p. 388, 515, 1920).

G. KOREA

CHÊNG MÊNG CHOU

Korean Confucianist and man of letters (1337-92).

Chêng Mêng Chou, better known under his pen name Pu yin. One of the leading Korean statesmen and philosophers, canonized in 1517 by the inclusion of his tablet in the western shrine of the Confucian temple.

He was a servant of the Koryu dynasty, being sent on diplomatic missions to Japan in 1377 and to China in 1382. He took so much pains teaching Confucianism as explained by Chu Hsi (XII-2) and fighting Buddhistic superstitions that he was called, rather inaptly, the grandfather of metaphysics. He left few, if any, philosophical writings, but an abundance of essays and poems, which were admired and enjoyed considerable popularity not only in his own country, but also in China and Japan.

According to Korean sources, he was a very able statesman who remained calm and masterful in times of national crises. He established village schools in order to sow Confucian seeds in the people's minds, he provided granaries to relieve the poor, and established water stations to facilitate the transportation of the royal grain.

His fame is due partly to his active life as a statesman, partly to his writings, but above all to his death as a martyr. Even as it had been his destiny to witness the fall of the Yüan dynasty (in 1369, when he was 32) and the beginning of the Ming, it was his dire fate twenty-three years later to see the end of the Koryu kings whom he had served. He refused to swear allegiance to the Li conquerors and was killed in 1392 in the old capital Songdo, on the "bridge of the bamboo of excellence," Shan chu ch'iao, where stains of his blood are still visible! There is a collegiate chapel or shu yüan to his memory where his portrait is exhibited. His tomb is in a remote place near Su-won.

There was a galaxy of Korean literati toward the end of the Koryu dynasty. Li Ch'i-hsien (XIV-1), who died in 1367, was in a way their master. Pu yin, with whom we have just dealt, was the leader of his generation. With him were associated Li Ch'ung Jên (1347-97), known as T'ao yin; Li Sê (1328-96), known as Mu yin; and the patriot Chi Tsai, named Yeh yin. The first three are often called the three yin, and sometimes the four of them are called the four yin. The last named was more of a patriot than a scholar, and left but few writings; on the other hand, Mu yin was a prolific author, his works filling 25 volumes. To these men may still be added a younger one, Ch'üan Chin (1352–1409), named Yang Ts'un, who worked in the service of the Li dynasty and whose fame and writings spread to China.

Texts. There are many editions of Chinese writings of Pu yin and of his contemporaries, but as they concern Chinese-Korean literature, rather than science and philosophy, we shall not attempt to enumerate them.

Criticism. Courant (1894–1901). A. W. Hummel: Report of the Library of Congress (p. 301–6, 1928). Trollope (p. 46–53, 1932), includes Pu yin's portrait facing p. 46.

CHAPTER XX

MATHEMATICS AND ASTRONOMY

(Second Half of the Fourteenth Century)

N.B. Only the main notes are published in this chapter. The mathematical and astronomical contributions of many other men, whose main work was done in other fields, are discussed in other chapters. For a general survey of mathematics and astronomy in the second half of the fourteenth century, see section VI of chapter XV. More information on the men referred to in that survey may then easily be found by means of the index.

A. WESTERN CHRISTENDOM

A1. Italy

THOMAS DE PISAN

Italian astrologer (c. 1320–c. 1384).

Thomas de Pisan is so called because he was the son of Benvenuto da Pizzano (a place in the hills near Bologna); the French form of his name is due to the fact that he flourished mainly in Paris; it was crystallized by his illustrious daughter Christine de Pisan. Thomas is also called Thomas of Bologna because he was born in (or near) that city. There he became master of medicine in 1343, and later lecturer in astrology.

He gained so much repute in Bologna as an astrologer that both the king of Hungary, Nagy Lajos I (Louis le Grand, 1342–82), and the king of France, Charles V the Wise (1364–80), tried to attach him to their courts. Sometime between the years 1364 and 1368 he became physician and astrologer to king Charles; he prepared for him horoscopes, philters, and magical operations and gave him astrological advice on important matters such as royal marriages. He was also in the service of Charles VI. One loses track of him after 1384, and we have it from his daughter Christine that he did not survive Charles V very long, hence he died in 1384 or soon afterward.

He exchanged letters on alchemy with Bernard of Treves, a mysterious alchemist, whose nationality and time are equally uncertain.[1] The letter of Thomas to Bernard on the philosopher's stone seems to be genuine and to have been written at a time when Thomas was treating the king of France and the duke of Burgundy (i.e., before 1378) or perhaps a little later; in that case, Bernard of Treves would decidedly belong to the second half of the fourteenth century, being a mature alchemist by 1384 or earlier.

Thomas' letter and Bernard's very long answer (1385?) deal with alchemy in the rhetorical and occult manner, that is, they are equally intangible and useless.

[1] He is called Bernardus Trevisanus and connected with Treviso and Padua (1406–90?), or Trevirensis and connected with Treves (Trier). Thorndike leans toward the second hypothesis. The dates given above (1406–90) are inconsistent with the correspondence with Thomas de Pisan. Many alchemical books appeared under the name of Bernardus Trevisanus. Ferguson (1, 100–4; 2, 466, 1906). Tenney L. Davis: The text of alchemy and the Songe verd (The monist 30, 70–106, 1920; Isis 4, 588). Thorndike (3, 618–27).

Thomas was in Venice in 1357 and married there and then, or soon afterward, the daughter of Thomas of Mondino, counselor of the Venetian republic. Of that marriage was born in Venice 1363 or 1364 a girl, Christine. In 1368 Thomas' wife and their daughter Christine joined him in Paris. Christine spent the rest of her life (she died c. 1430) in France and was one of the leading writers of her time, the first professional woman of letters in France. Her writings belong to the fifteenth century, otherwise we should be obliged to discuss them, for they have considerable documentary value for the study of her time and "milieu," and they deal with such subjects as history, cosmography, morality, and defense of feminine rights. Thomas was one of the most famous astrologers of his time; he is almost completely forgotten today except as the father of Christine de Pisan.

Text. Thomas' letter on alchemy is unprinted, but Thorndike has given an elaborate analysis of it. For Bernard's writings see Ferguson (1906).

Criticism. Marie Josèphe Pinet: Christine de Pisan 1364–1430 (Lyon thesis, 490 p., Paris 1927; Isis 13, 164). Thorndike (2, 801, 1923; 3, 32, 611–27, 1934). Wickersheimer (p. 764, 1936). S. Solente: Le livre des fais et bonnes meurs du sage roy Charles V par Christine de Pisan (Société de l'histoire de France; vol. 1, introduction, Paris 1936).

MONTULMO

Antonio da Montulmo. Italian astrologer (fl. 1384–96).

Antonius de Montulmo (or Monte Ulmo, Monte Olmo, in Macerata, Marche) was a doctor of arts and of medicine who flourished in Bologna c. 1384–90. He taught astrology at the university from 1387 to 1389. He was in Mantua in 1394 and made an astronomical observation in 1396. The dates of his birth and death are unknown.

He was an astrologer and magician of the cheaper kind, yet must be mentioned because he attracted Regiomontanus' attention, and his main astrological work, being printed in 1540, may have influenced other scientists and pseudo scientists.

He wrote two treatises, the one on the judgments of nativities, De iudiciis nativitatum, completed at Mantua in 1394, and the other on occult and manifest arts, De occultis et manifestis, undated.

The first treatise, divided into 11 chapters, is a regular textbook of astrology, explaining how to make horoscopes for various occasions. It is derived from Ptolemy and Dorotheus;[2] from Arabic authorities like Omar (perhaps Abū Ma'shar, IX-1), Alcabitius ('Abd al-'Azīz al-Qabīṣī, X-2), or Haly (probably 'Alī ibn abī-l-Rijāl, XI-1); and from recent Latin ones such as the Astrologia de urina non visa of William the Englishman (XIII-1), the books of Guido Bonatti (XIII-2) and Leopold of Austria (XIII-2), the Speculum astronomiae ascribed to Albert the Great (XIII-2), and the recent Summa medicinalis of Tommaso del Garbo.

The second treatise deals with magic and necromancy. We need not consider it. Regiomontanus prepared additions to the astrological treatise and referred in a letter of 1465 to what seems to be another astrological treatise by Montulmo.

[2] Unidentified ancient astrologer also quoted in the Liber novem judicum in judiciis astrorum, said to have been compiled by order of Frederick II (Introd. 2, 577). Symon de Phares writing at the end of the fifteenth century calls Dorothée "souverain philozophe et grant astrologien" and gives fantastic information. See his Recueil des plus célèbres astrologues, edited by Ernest Wickersheimer (chiefly p. 134, Paris 1929; Isis 13, 167).

Text. De iudiciis nativitatum liber praeclarissimus (Nuremberg 1540). This includes additions by Regiomontanus, and is sometimes bound with another treatise on nativities by the papal astrologer Luca Gaurico (Giffoni near Salerno 1475—Rome 1558).

An almanack and prognosticacion for 1555 by master Antonino de Montulmo, an Italian doctoure of physicke and astronomy (London 1555). Presumably derived from the edition of 1540.

The De occultis et manifestis is unpublished.

Criticism. Riccardi (p. 38, 1887). Max Curtze: Regiomontans Briefwechsel (Abhandlungen zur Geschichte der mathematischen Wissenschaften no. 12, p. 306, 1902). Thorndike (3, 602–10, 1934).

GENTILE DEGLI MAINARDI

Italian writer on chivalry and astrology who flourished probably in the third quarter of the fourteenth century.

He wrote after 1348 a treatise on chivalry, in Italian, entitled Gentil milicia, wherein he names himself Gentile d'Odoardo degli Mainardi d'Ascoli (Ascoli in the Marche?). The book is dedicated to one Cecco d'Arcone degli Arconi of Rome. It exists in a unique MS (British Museum, Egerton MS 3149). It refers to a fight near Ascoli in 1348 and to a Giovanni d'Ascoli who may be the canonist who flourished in Bologna 1360. The connection with Ascoli is well established, as well as the approximate date.

Gentil milicia is divided into three books: (I) seven degrees of friendship ranged under the seven planets, (II) ceremonies, incidents, and virtues of knighthood, (III) nobility. The most curious feature is the combination of the virtues and characteristics of various kinds of friendship with astrology.

The author was well read, especially in ancient Latin literature. He quotes chiefly Valerius Maximus, a historian and anecdotist of the age of Tiberius, who enjoyed considerable popularity in the Middle Ages. He also refers to Cicero; Vergil, Ovid, Sallust, Livy; Lucan, Statius, Frontinus; Suetonius; Vegetius the tactician. Among mediaeval writers he mentions Giles of Rome (XIII-2), Giovanni del Vergilio, Onesto da Bologna, Dante (XIV-1), Cino da Pistoia (XIV-1), Giovanni Villani (XIV-1).

It would be interesting to compare this treatise with Arabic-Mamlūk treatises on chivalry.

Criticism. R. Flower: An Italian treatise on chivalry (British Museum quarterly 13, 50–52, 1939).

ANDREA DA SOMMERIA

Andreas Summarius. Italian astrologer (fl. 1389).

In or about the year 1389 Andrea composed an astrological treatise on the stars and their motions (De stellis et motu earum), bearing on the flyleaf of the Vatican MS "quod astrologia non possit scire." He begins by saying that he does not know whether the movement of stars is knowable, but that he is certain it is not yet known. The rest of the treatise, however, is devoted to an explanation of the conventional astrological doctrines of those days.

Nothing is known about the author, but he was twice quoted in the Disputationes in astrologiam, book IX, by Giovanni Pico della Mirandola (1463–94), and also by the latter's nephew Gian Francesco Pico (1470–1533), Examen vanitatis doctrinae gentium (Mirandola 1520).

Criticism. Thorndike (3, 597–98, 1934).

GUARIMBERTUS

Matthaeus Guarimbertus of Parma. Italian astrologer (d. before 1412).

This Matthew became a doctor of arts at Padua 1370, and when Petrarch died, in 1374, succeeded him as archdeacon of Parma. Matthew died after 1400 and before 1412. He wrote a treatise on human felicity, and another on astrology, De directione et proiectione radiorum. This second treatise is divided into eight chapters, the fourth of which (De diversis modis dirigendi et proiciendi radios et aspectus positis ab auctoribus secundum diversas eorum opiniones circa hoc) takes up more than one-third of the whole. The fifth chapter introduces the astronomical tables which are indispensable to the astrologer. That treatise had the distinction of attracting the attention of Regiomontanus, who discussed it in the De directionibus contra archidiaconum parmensem (i.e., Guarimbertum).

Text. The De directione et proiectione radiorum was printed at Nürnberg 1534/35 with a Greek-Latin edition of Ptolemy's Quadripartitum, and at Rome 1557 with an astronomical work by Luca Gaurico (1475–1558). Thus Thorndike; I have failed to identify that second edition. It is not in Riccardi nor in the catalogues available to me.

Criticism. Max Curtze: Regiomontans Briefwechsel (Abhandlungen zur Geschichte der mathematischen Wissenschaften no. 12, p. 295; no. 13, preface, 1902). Thorndike (3, 598, 768–70, 1934), includes table of contents of the astrological treatise.

EARLY ARITHMETIC

In one of the MSS of the queen of Sweden in the Vatican (no. 1285, 164 leaves folio), containing a number of treatises on the astrolabe, astronomy, and astrology, there is also a curious arithmetical treatise, Introductorius liber qui et pulveris dicitur in mathematicam disciplinam (fol. 14r–20v.). The MS dates from the second half of the fourteenth century, but the text itself cannot be dated.

It begins "Quisquis in quatuor matheseos disciplinis"; it ends with a short chapter on subtraction, a table of grades, and a table of multiplication. The word pulvis in the title suggests immediately the Arabic term ghubār (Introd. 1, 648, 649, 663, 670; 2, 4, 748, 998) used by the Moors to designate Hindu numerals. The text, however, is not a translation from the Arabic, but represents rather an original attempt to explain the new arithmetic; it might thus date from the thirteenth century, as well as from the fourteenth. It explains the new numerals and the principle of position; the division of numbers used in finger symbolism, digits and articles;[3] the six operations (addition, subtraction, duplication, dimidiation, multiplication, division); fractions, their multiplication and division; extraction of square roots; division of the unit into twelve ounces and of the ounces into duodecimal parts. These Roman fractions are sufficient to prove the originality of the treatise with respect to Arabic traditions.

[3] This is still found in Robert Recorde's Ground of artes (London c. 1542), even in an edition of it as late as London 1668, for which see D. E. Smith (p. 217–21, 1908) and Florence A. Yeldham: The teaching of arithmetic through four hundred years, 1535–1935 (p. 33, London 1936; Isis 27, 92–94).

The fact that this MS was owned by queen Christina of Sweden (1626–89) does not help us to determine its provenance. She collected the bulk of her MSS in Rome, but had obtained many before settling in that city. We list this text with the Italian texts for the sake of convenience.

Criticism. Henri Narducci: Sur un MS du Vatican du XIVe siècle contenant un traité de calcul emprunté à la méthode gobāri (Bulletin des sciences mathématiques 7. 247–56, 1883). Cantor (2, 154–56, 1899).

ITALIAN COMPUTUS OF 1393

MS in the Plimpton collection (Columbia University), 69 leaves 222 × 296 mm. The first 54 leaves contain the computus; leaves 55 to 63, miscellanea cosmographica; the final leaves, 64 to 69, are blank. The introduction begins, "Dio padre nel principio della creatione del mondo, sichome dicie Moisè nel principio del primo libro della Bibia chessi chiama Genesi . . . ." The computus itself begins, "Questo sichiama i libro del chonputo, cioè chorso di sole e di luna secondo l'ordine. Conputo è una scienzia per sapere ciertifichare del tempo secondo il corso del sole et della luna sechondo che all'uso della chiesa s'apartiene. Conputo in gramaticha à tanto a dire quanto in volghare anoverare . . . ."

The anonymous author was Florentine or at least Tuscan. His elaborate account was analyzed by father Giuseppe Boffito: Un ignoto calendarista del secolo XIV (Bibliofilia 7, 1–5, Firenze 1905). Facsimile of p. 1 in D. E. Smith (p. 445, 1908).

ALCUNE COSE DI ABACO

An Italian treatise on arithmetic and algebra first mentioned by Libri (2, 214, 1838; 3, 302–49, 1840), who owned it, dates probably from the second half of the fourteenth century; it cannot be much earlier. It begins, "Essendo io pregato di dovere scrivere alcune cose di abaco necessarie a' mercatanti, da tale che i preghi suoi mi sono comandamenti, non come prosuntuoso ma per ubbidire mi sforzero . . . ." The mercantile intention is thus clear; many such books were written in Italy for merchants rather than for scholars, and therefore they were written in Italian; they anticipate the early printed commercial arithmetics.[4] The author, however, whoever he was, did not restrict himself to commercial problems such as problems of interest (merito) and compound interest. He was a born algebraist. This illustrates once more the ambiguity of the term abaco;[5] it might occasionally apply not only to the new arithmetic, but even as in this case to algebra.

The author of this "abaco" dealt with equations, the constant quantities of which are called numero; the unknown and its powers up to the fifth are called cosa, quadrato (censo), (censo) cubo, censo di censo, censo di cubo. Cf. census, res, radix as used by Gherard of Cremona (XII-2) and Leonardo da Pisa (XIII-1).

[4] David Eugene Smith: The first printed arithmetic, Treviso 1478 (Isis 6, 311–31, 2 fig., 1924); The first great commercial arithmetic, Venice 1484 (Isis 8, 41–49, 1926); (p. 3–7, 16–22, 1908).

[5] Introd. 1, 756; 2, 4, 167, 169, 210. Remember the rich contents of the Liber abaci (1202) of Leonardo of Pisa (XIII-1).

Negative numbers (meno —) are used as well as positive ones. Only one solution of a quadratic equation is considered.

$$\sqrt{10} - \sqrt{4 \cdot \frac{4}{9}} = \sqrt{1\frac{1}{9}} \qquad \sqrt[5]{5153632} = 22$$

$$x^3 = \frac{16}{27}x^2 + \frac{5}{27}x \qquad x = \frac{8}{27} + \sqrt{\frac{199}{729}}$$

$$x^4 + 20 = 9x^2 \qquad x^2 = \frac{9}{2} - \sqrt{\frac{81}{4} - 20} = 4$$

$$ax^5 + bx^4 + cx^3 + dx^2 + ex = k$$

$$x = \sqrt[5]{\frac{cd}{ab} + \frac{k}{a}} - \sqrt[3]{\frac{e}{b}}$$

which works out well in a particular case (of course the equations are not written, but a verbal equivalent of them). It is clear that this algebraist solved equations up to the fifth degree, according to certain rules, but the rules are not stated. He was a very clever calculator, but generalized too easily. He also dealt with such geometrical problems as these: Inscribe within a circle, triangle, or square a given number of circles, or equilateral triangles, or squares such that the total of their areas be as high as possible. Inscribe within a cube the bulkiest tetrahedron possible. Cantor (2, 157–63, 1899.)

A2. Spain

DALMAU CES-PLANES AND PERE ENGELBERT

It is convenient to consider these two Catalan astronomers (or astrologers) together, as their activities cannot be completely separated. They appear together in most of the documents.

There are many variants to their names: Dalmau Ces-Planes, çes-Planes, Sesplanes, or Planes; in Latin, Dalmatius Planes de Propeniani. Pere Engelbert or Pere Gilbert; in Latin, Petrus Engisberti de Rucherna (or de Conchena).

Toward the end of the year 1359, Pere IV (also called Pere or Peter III), king of Aragon from 1336 to 1387, had summoned Pere Engelbert, master of arts, and his pupil Dalmau to come to Barcelona and prepare new planetary tables. In a document dated Cervera (Gerona), October 24, 1359 (Rubió 1, 190), Dalmau was permitted to use all the astronomical books in the royal library except those of 'Alī ibn abī-l-Rijāl al-Maghribī (XI-1). In another letter, written the same day, the king showed his anxiousness to obtain *their* own book as soon as possible (Rubió 1, 191). He made it possible for them to build themselves large and elaborate instruments (spheres, armillae, some of which were 16 cubits and more in diameter). In 1362 he gave an order to pay whatever was due for an astronomical sphere in Barcelona (Rubió 1, 199). Other payments were made by him for astronomical instruments (Rubió 2, 118), and we have a long account of Dalmau's expenditures for a sphere (Rubió 2, 139–42).

They started their astronomical work together on January 1, 1360. Pere

Gilbert died early in 1362. On March 24, 1362, the king ordered his veguer (vicarius, royal judge) in Barcelona to investigate whether Dalmau was guilty of Pere Gilbert's death (Rubió 2, 142). Dalmau was accused of having appropriated his associate's belongings.

Dalmau was apparently exculpated and permitted to continue his astronomical work. The tables were completed by him toward the end of 1366. In the introduction he says that they covered some sixty years to 1433, and were computed for Barcelona, the position of which he quotes as lat. 41, long. 33 (the correct latitude is 41°22′). These planetary tables were apparently elaborate; Dalmau realized that the Alphonsine tables, not to speak of the older Toledo tables, contained many errors.

Gilbert and Dalmau began together and the latter completed an astrological treatise (art d'astrologia).

In or before 1379, Dalmau composed a treatise on eclipses (Rubió 1, 280). He was still active as king Pere's astrologer at the very end of 1381 (Rubió 1, 290, 298).

Text. Lynn Thorndike: Introduction and canon by Dalmatius for the years 1361–1433 (Isis 26, 310–25, 1937). Text edited on the Berne MS 227, a fifteenth-century MS.

Criticism. Massó y Torrents wrote a paper on these astrologers, imperfectly quoted by Rubió, and not yet available to me.

Antoni Rubió y Lluch (1908–1921), by index and as cited above. Lynn Thorndike: Other astronomical tables beginning in 1361 (Isis 34, 6, 410, 1942); Dalmatius again (Isis 36, 158, 1946).

A3. France

ORESME

Nicole Oresme (c. 1323–82). One of the greatest men of science of the fourteenth century. One of the greatest mathematicians, mechanicians, and economists of the Middle Ages; one of the founders of the French scientific language and of French prose in general.

Contents: (1) Biography. (2) Mathematics. (3) Mechanics. (4) Astronomy. (5) Astrology. (6) Magic and superstition. (7) Psychology. (8) Natural philosophy. (9) Commentaries on Aristotle. (10) French works and translations. (11) Theory of money.
(12) Text. (13) General criticism.

1. *Biography*

Nicole (not Nicolas) Oresme (or Orem, Oren, Horen) was born in the early twenties, near Caen, probably in the town of Allemagne. He entered the College of Navarre in Paris 1348, with a fellowship in theology; in 1356, he became the principal of that college with the title of Grand maître (this implies that he had already obtained his doctorate in theology); he remained connected with the college until the end of 1361. In 1362 he was canon in Rouen, in 1363–64 canon in Paris. On December 24, 1363, he preached before Urban V in Avignon on the abuses and dangers of the church. From 1364 to 1377 he was dean of the chapter of Rouen. In 1377 he was appointed bishop of Lisieux; he died in his see on July 11, 1382. Thus his whole life was spent either in his native Normandy or in Paris.

From c. 1360 on he was associated with the dauphin Charles (b. 1337), who was king of France from 1364 to 1380, under the name of Charles V the Wise, but was already in charge of affairs by 1356. Oresme was the dauphin's tutor, not the king's, but he was one of the king's advisers on spiritual matters, and one of the scholars employed by him for the translation of important ancient works into French.

2. *Mathematics*

Oresme's main mathematical works are: (1) Tractatus de latitudinibus formarum (first printed in 1482 and often reprinted); (2) Tractatus de uniformitate et difformitate intensionum, written before 1371 (partly published in 1914); (3) Tractatus proportionum (printed in 1505); (4) Algorismus proportionum, written in or before 1359 (printed in 1868). The dates of composition of 1, 2, 3 are uncertain.

The first two deal with the mediaeval theory of latitudes and longitudes, i.e., the application of these geographical ideas to the study of functions and their graphical representation. The notion of graph is much older than Oresme, witness the occurrence of a tenth-century example in a Macrobius MS of Munich.[6] Oresme uses the words longitudo and latitudo with the meaning abscissa and ordinate. On the other hand, he does not use auxiliary lines as was occasionally done by Archimedes and Apollonios. He may be credited with a twofold idea: (1) more systematic use of coordinates, (2) more systematic use of graphs to represent the growth of a function. This may have made the later discovery of analytic geometry easier (even as Archimedes and Apollonios prepared the way for that discovery in another and deeper way). It cannot be called an anticipation of that discovery. Even today there are many people who understand graphs, and various peculiarities of graphs, but have no knowledge whatever of analytic geometry (i.e., a method of enabling one to pass from equations to curves and vice versa without ambiguity).

Oresme had the intuition that the least amount of change occurs near the highest or lowest points of a curve. This is an adumbration of the modern theory of maxima and minima.

The second treatise, Tractatus de uniformitate et difformitate intensionum,[7] contains (part 1, ch. 4) the earliest mediaeval reference to four dimensions, the notion being rejected. There is but one possible earlier reference, and that a disputable one, namely, in the commentary to Aristotle's De caelo by Simplicios (VI-1). See Isis (7, 486–89). The same treatise shows that Oresme knew the number of combinations of six objects, taken 1, 2, 3, 4, or 5 at a time.

The third treatise, Tractatus proportionum, deals with proportions somewhat in the manner of Jordanus Nemorarius (XIII-1) in the fifth book of his Arithmetica.

The fourth treatise, Algorismus proportionum, is very important, as it contains an anticipation of fractional exponents and the main rules governing them, but with a clumsy notation. Like Jordanus, however, he used letters to represent generalized numbers.

Unfortunately, as contrasted with the Tractatus de latitudinibus formarum, which was four times printed before 1516 and must have been well known to sixteenth-century mathematicians,[8] the Algorismus proportionum remained prac-

[6] H. Gray Funkhouser: A note on a tenth century graph (Osiris 1, 260–62, 1 fig., 1936; Isis 25, 529).

[7] For alternative titles see below under "Text."

[8] Also to Descartes as early as 1618 (though Descartes derived his main inspiration for his Géométrie from the Greeks); and perhaps even to Galileo as early as 1604. See Wieleitner (BM 14, 241–43).

tically unknown (there are, however, at least five early MSS, one dated 1359, another dated 1401, two more of the fifteenth century, and one of the sixteenth).

Mathematical criticism. Abbé Picard: Dissertation sur un traité philosophique de N. Oresme (Précis analytiques des travaux de l'Académie . . . de Rouen, 1851–52, p. 456–75). Maximilian Curtze: Die mathematischen Schriften des N. Oresme. Ein mathematisch-bibliographischer Versuch (20 p., Berlin 1870). Siegmund Günther: Die Anfänge und Entwicklungsstadien des Coordinatenprincips (Abhandlungen der Naturhistorischen Gesellschaft zu Nürnberg, 1877, also in Italian translation in Boncompagni's Bullettino 10, 363–406, 1877). Cantor (2d ed., 2, 128–37, 1899). J. Timtchenko: Sur un point du Tractatus de latitudinibus formarum (BM 1, 515, 1900). Federico Amodeo: Riproduzione delle questioni sul trattato de latitudinibus formarum fatto da Biagio Pelacani (Annali dell'Istituto tecnico, 27 p., Napoli 1909). Adolf Krazer: Zur Geschichte der graphischen Darstellung von Funktionen (Jahresbericht der Deutschen Mathematiker-Vereinigung 24, 340–63, 1915, i.e. 1916; Isis 4, 138). Florian Cajori: History of mathematical notations (1, 123, 129, 308, 333, Chicago 1928; Isis 12, 332–36). H. Gray Funkhouser: Historical development of the graphical representation of statistical data (Osiris 3, 269–404, 1937; chiefly p. 274–77, facsimile). Julian Coolidge: History of geometrical methods (p. 118, Oxford 1940; Isis 33, 347–50).

Heinrich Wieleitner: Der Tractatus de latitudinibus formarum (BM 13, 115–45, 1913), elaborate analysis of that treatise; Über den Funktionsbegriff und die graphische Darstellung bei Oresme (BM 14, 193–243, 1914); Oresme und die graphische Darstellung der Spätscholastik (Natur und Kultur, 14. Jahrg., 529–36, 1917); Zur Geschichte der gebrochenen Exponenten (Isis 6, 509–21, 1924; 7, 490–91, 1925); Zur Frühgeschichte der Räume von mehr als drei Dimensionen (Isis 7, 486–89, 1925). Wieleitner's articles are quoted separately, out of the chronological order, because of their importance.

3. *Mechanics*

Oresme's views on mechanics are to be found in his mathematical writings, primarily the Tractatus de latitudinibus formarum, and in his Aristotelian commentaries, primarily the French commentary on the De caelo et mundo. I say his "views," for we are not given a complete theory, but only fragments of one, in the most abstruse scholastic manner.

According to Oresme, (absolute) motion can be defined only with reference to an immovable infinite space, placed beyond the fixed stars, and identified with the infinity of God. The gravity of an element together with its forma substantialis are the causa efficiens (sc. immanens) of its local movement. Movement may be natural or violent (contre nature); it may be simple (circular and infinite, or rectilinear and finite) or complex. Terrestrial motions are always dependent on celestial ones. This theory of movement is the Aristotelian, with the sole restriction that movement may be conceived as a forma fluens (or fluxus formae). The impetus is the quality of the moved body. Oresme's theory of impetus was not invented by him, it was simply the development of a theory which can be traced back to Peter Olivi (XIII-2) and even to John Philoponos (VI-1). It is at best but a vague anticipation of the theory of inertia. Oresme discusses the continuity of space, motion, and time.

In the Tractatus de latitudinibus formarum (pars 3, cap. 7) he foresaw the relation between distance and time with regard to the motion of a body having a constant acceleration. That is, he remarks that when a body moves during a certain time with uniformly accelerated speed, the length of its path is equal to that which it would cover during the same time if its speed were constant and equal to the middle speed (Omnis qualitas, si fuerit uniformiter difformis, secundum gradum puncti medii ipsa est tanta quanta qualitas eiusdem subiecti). This is an anticipation of Galileo, but we find it also in Buridan and Albert of Saxony. On the other hand, he reintroduced a serious Aristotelian error, which Buridan and Albert of Saxony had the wisdom to abandon: he believed that the speed of a projectile continues to increase for a little while after its departure. That error influenced Leonardo da Vinci, Cardano, and others.

According to his theory of gravity, probably derived from the Timaeos, it is not necessary to postulate the existence of a fixed center of attraction in the center of the world. This was another step toward the Copernican system, and perhaps a bigger one than his argument for the earth's diurnal rotation, to be mentioned in our astronomical section. His attitude of mind, however, was too abstract and too theological to enable him to anticipate Copernicus, or for that matter Galileo.

Mechanical criticism. Duhem: Origines (2, 336–37, 1906), on gravity; Etudes (3, 346–405, 481–92, 1913). H. Wieleitner: Das Gesetz vom freien Falle in der Scholastik, bei Descartes und Galilei (Zeitschrift für mathematischen und naturwissenschaftlichen Unterricht 45, 209–28, 1914); Über die Begriffe der Geschwindigkeit und Beschleunigung in der Scholastik (Das Weltall, 17. Jahrg., 49–55, 1916/17). Eduard Jan Dijksterhuis: Val en worp (p. 88–114, Groningen 1924; Isis 8, 378–79). Ernst Borchert: Die Lehre von der Bewegung bei Oresme (Beiträge zur Geschichte der Philosophie und Theologie des Mittelalters vol. 31, no. 3, 128 p., Münster i.W. 1934; Isis 25, 534), elaborate study.

Duhem was a pioneer in these investigations, but he lacked impartiality and thoroughness. This is proved by Borchert and also by Benjamin Ginzburg: Duhem and Jordanus Nemorarius (Isis 25, 341–62, 1936). Duhem's works should be used with caution.

4. *Astronomy*

Oresme's most remarkable astronomical work is the one entitled De commensurabilitate (sive proportionalitate, sive incommensurabilitate) motuum coelestium, wherein he argues that if the celestial movements are incommensurable, which may be the case, the existence of cycles (such as the Platonic great year) is inconceivable, and the possibility of astronomical and astrological predictions falls to the ground. That idea may be traced back to the Jew Hagin Deulacres (XIII-2), who translated Rabbi ben Ezra's astrological tracts from Hebrew into French, and to Henry Bate's (XIII-2) Latin translation of the same tracts. The argument is somewhat specious, for approximate predictions might still be possible. It is very interesting, however, in the first place because it illustrates Oresme's determination to use every means to fight astrology, and in the second place because it may be regarded as an adumbration of one of the most remarkable controversies in the history of celestial mechanics. I am referring to the magnificent tournament between Laplace and Lagrange concerning the "great inequality" of Jupiter and Saturn. In 1788, Laplace was finally able to prove that the cause of that "great inequality" was found in the near approach to commensurability of their mean motions.[9]

To his French translation of the De coelo et mundo, to which we shall return presently, Oresme added a commentary which includes a very clear argument in

[9] Théorie de Jupiter et de Saturne, published in the Mémoires de l'Académie royale des sciences de Paris, année 1785, 1788, and in the Oeuvres complètes (11, 95–239, 1895).

favor of the diurnal rotation of the earth (an idea which cropped out repeatedly in ancient and mediaeval times). He remained faithful, however, to the Ptolemaic system. It is not quite correct to call him a forerunner of Copernicus, but he prepared the way for the Copernican revolution. Oresme's argument, written in French for the king, must have been well known in France, but this very fact decreased its availability to foreigners.

Oresme wrote in French a treatise on the sphere, Traicté de l'espère. This is an original work, not a translation of Sacrobosco's famous treatise on the subject, but it does not seem to be essentially different from it. It was written after 1361 and before 1377. It is divided into 50 chapters and deals with the elements of mathematical geography.

In one of his works he mentions parhelia, that is, mock suns which are sometimes seen on the parhelic circle (a circle parallel to the horizon at the altitude of the sun); a kind of halo.

Astronomical criticism. Ernest de Fréville: Mémoire sur la cosmographie du Moyen âge, le traité de la sphère par Oresme et les découvertes maritimes des Normands (Revue des sociétés savantes des départements, 2d ser., 2, 705–29, chiefly 717–25, Paris 1859). P. Duhem: Un précurseur français de Copernic: Nicole Oresme, 1377 (Revue générale des sciences 20, 866–73, 1909; erratum p. 1028), includes the whole text of Oresme's argument for the diurnal motion of the earth; Système du monde (4, 157–64, 1916). Ernst Zinner: Geschichte der Sternkunde (p. 386, Berlin 1931; Isis 16, 161–67), bare statement about parhelia, no details being given, no source quoted. Grant McColley: The theory of the diurnal rotation of the earth (Isis 26, 392–402, 1937).

5. *Astrology*

Oresme was very much interested in astrology, but in a negative way. Various books of his were deliberately written against astrologers, and anti-astrological warnings are found passim in his other writings, e.g., in the conclusion of his Traicté de l'espère. According to him, astrological research is both vain and wicked. His antagonism was a consequence of his own strong scientific tendencies, and perhaps also of the king's astrological tendencies. Charles V had a rich collection of astrological books in his library; Oresme had been his tutor and remained his adviser; the king's astrological fancies would naturally stiffen the honest tutor's aversion from them.

Among his writings against astrology we may quote the short Tractatus contra astrologos (incipit: Multi principes et magnates noxia curiositate solliciti vanis nituntur artibus occulta perquirere et investigare futura . . .) in 7 chapters, wherein he reviews the pros as well as the cons but concludes against astrology; then the French tract Des divinations (December 1361), which was later translated into Latin, Tractatus contra iudiciarios astronomos et principes se in talibus occupantes (this Latin translation was possibly by another hand); and the Questio contra divinatores horoscopios, written in 1370, this being his most elaborate discussion of the subject, in the worst scholastic style. He was very well acquainted with the anti-astrological literature, could quote Aristotle, Cicero, Seneca, St. Augustine, Ibn Sīnā, Ibn Rushd, John of Salisbury, knew all the stock arguments against astrology, but the main source of his strength was his own scientific experience and common sense. He never tired of denouncing the tricks and deceits of astrologers and of explaining how their predictions could be justified either by the events or by their own sophisms and evasions. He realized, however, that there might be a nucleus of truth in astrology: revolutions and conjunctions might have a *general* influence; in any case, astrological judgments became more and more uncertain as they were more special, as for instance in astrological medicine. He also insisted that meteorological (or sublunar, inferior) influences might be more effective than astrological (superior) ones.

Considering the experimental knowledge available in his days, Oresme's antagonism to an almost universal delusion was as strong as it could be without unwarranted dogmatism. In fact, he was considerably ahead of the majority of his contemporaries. This explains why his influence was relatively small. It was exerted mainly through the intermediary of Giovanni Pico della Mirandola (1463–94), whose Disputationes adversus astrologiam divinatricam (Bologna 1495) appeared more than a century after Oresme's death, and were still ahead of their time.

Criticism. Charles Jourdain: Nicolas Oresme et les astrologues de la cour de Charles V (Revue des questions historiques, 28 p., 1875, reprinted in Excursions historiques et philosophiques à travers le moyen âge, p. 561–85, Paris 1888). Wedel (p. 96, 118, 1920). Lynn Thorndike: Vatican Latin manuscripts (Isis 13, 84, 1929); History of magic (3, 398–423, 1934). Wedel and Thorndike agree in criticizing Oresme because his condemnation of astrology was not absolute; that is hardly fair. Oresme went as far as it was possible to go in his time, and he cannot be praised too highly for his courage and moderation.

6. *Magic and superstition*

Oresme's attitude toward other superstitions was consistent with his attitude toward astrology. The few restrictions which had still to be made with regard to the latter, however, need not be made at all with regard to geomancy and other mancies. Even chiromancy (a part of physiognomy), though it may suggest useful observations, has no prophetic value. His views on the subject are included in the French and Latin De divinationibus, in the Questio of 1370, in the very long Quodlibeta later annexed to it, also passim in other books such as his De configuratione qualitatum (written before 1370). There are two kinds of magic, he explains, one of which is good, and the other is bad (nigromancy). He tries to show that many magical or marvelous things can be accounted for in rational terms, either mechanically or by illusions or misleading sensual perceptions (such as the optical illusions described by Witelo, XIII-2) or by psychological errors. Thus "magical" effects can be produced by physical means, by special diets and fasts, intoxications, the use of drugs. He quotes similar arguments made by William of Auvergne (XIII-1). He realizes that it is not yet possible to explain everything rationally; instead of accepting marvels uncritically, however, it is safer to be always on the lookout against the deceptions of magicians, charlatans, and even theologians. By the way, his reference to the famous rope trick (climbing up a rope thrown into the air without visible support) is perhaps the earliest in European literature (in his Quodlibeta, Thorndike 3, 454).

The treatise on fascination (Tractatus de fastinacione) ascribed to him is a somewhat earlier composition; indeed, it was written by Engelbert of Admont (XIV-1).

7. *Psychology*

Oresme's analysis of various magical problems reveals a remarkable appreciation of psychological difficulties. He is, however, generally unable to formulate these clearly, let alone solve them. He discusses sound (which may be nothing but motion) and hearing, light and vision; the nature of the soul; dreams; etc. He admits the possibility of thought transference, but rejects the suggestion made by Ibn Sīnā and al-Ghazzālī that a man's thought can move exterior objects without material contact. He is also aware of many problems of pathological psychology.

8. *Natural philosophy*

Oresme's study of nature, of "marvels," and of psychological facts and delusions led him to a scientific philosophy which is remarkably rational. He realizes the infinite physical and psychological diversities between men, the infinite complexities of causes and qualities. He accepts the old doctrine of four elements and four qualities, but wonders whether the fundamental qualities which are generally accepted are really the most fundamental. Are not light and local motion more fundamental, since either causes heat? He is groping for the idea that some special combinations of elements and qualities may be exceptionally important. He sees clearly that small causes may have immense effects, or that small differences in the causes may be immeasurably multiplied in the consequences. One must prepare oneself to penetrate far behind the appearances, and unravel the natural or artificial illusions which hide reality. One must always bear in mind that man's understanding of nature may be jeopardized at any time by errors of his senses or of his judgment (e.g., post hoc ergo propter hoc), by his lack of criticism and his love of the marvelous.

His final attitude is one of vigilant criticism and skepticism, "Ideo quidem nichil scio nisi quia scio me nichil scire," which reminds one of that of the wisest men of science of our own days, and is the more praiseworthy because his positive knowledge was immeasurably smaller and cruder than theirs. Indeed, it takes much knowledge and wisdom to realize one's ignorance.

Criticism. For the three preceding sections, on magic, psychology, and natural philosophy, see Lynn Thorndike: History of magic (3, 424–71, 1934); Coelestinus' summary of Nicholas Oresme on marvels (Osiris 1, 629–35, 1936), apropos of a treatise written by one Coelestinus in 1478, and edited by Oronce Finé in 1542. That treatise, De his quae mundo mirabiliter eveniunt, is a clear abridgment of Oresme's Quodlibeta, but it is typical that Coelestinus and, we must assume, Finé were not as radical in their rationalism as Oresme had dared to be, more than a century before them.

N.B. The original MS of sections 9 to 11 was mysteriously lost in my office, the loss being detected on November 10, 1936, at the time of typing them. Unfortunately the accumulated notes upon which I had based these chapters were then already destroyed, and I had to rewrite them from scratch. I must ask for the reader's indulgence.

9. *Commentaries on Aristotle*

As we shall see in the following section, Oresme translated the Ethica, Politica, and Oeconomica of Aristotle, as well as the De coelo et mundo. These translations included commentaries. It is not necessary, however, to deal with the commentaries apart from the translations. Oresme's importance as a commentator is insignificant; his importance as a translator is very great.

10. *French works and translations*

We have already spoken of two treatises written by Oresme in French, to wit his Traicté de l'espère, written after 1361 and before 1377, and his treatise Des divinations, written in December 1361, and later translated (probably by himself) into Latin. His Traicté de l'espère was the first vehicle of many of the astronomical and geographical terms used in the French language to this day.

The fact that he wrote these two treatises in French is very remarkable. Perhaps he was obliged to do so because of his relations with the future Charles V. He himself admits that it was more difficult for him to write in French than in Latin, and that is indeed what we should expect. His first translation (as well as his first work in French) was perhaps that of Ptolemy's Quadripartitum, made before 1364. In his Aristotelian translations, which we shall consider presently, he was very apologetic about his language, the imperfections of which he keenly realized.

His treatise on money was originally composed by him in Latin (c. 1355), then revised in Latin (1357/58), then translated into French before 1360. The French texts which have come down to us contain interpolations and have been so much interfered with that the tracing of the French traditions raises very difficult problems.

Oresme's fame depends largely upon his translations of various Aristotelian treatises from Latin into French, these being the earliest translations of their kind into any vernacular. They were made at the request of Charles V. He translated the Ethica Nicomachea (Les Ethiques d'Aristote à son fils Nicomachus) in 1370, upon the Greco-Latin translation (c. 1240–43) of Robert Grosseteste, using also Robert's translations of various commentaries, and perhaps other translations. In 1372–74, he translated the Politica and the Oeconomica; the first, upon the Greco-Latin translation of William of Moerbeke (1260); the second, upon the Greco-Latin translation revised in 1295 by Durand d'Auvergne. Finally in 1377 he translated the De coelo et mundo mainly upon the Greco-Latin version of it and of Simplicios' commentary ascribed to William of Moerbeke.

The first three of these works formed a trilogy in mediaeval tradition: the Ethica dealing with individual morality, the Oeconomica with familial morality, and the Politica with civic morality. In mediaeval usage, however, the Oeconomica was always placed at the end. Two manuscripts of Oresme's translation of that trilogy were prepared for the king, a large copy for the library, and a smaller one for travel. There is in the municipal library of Rouen a magnificent illustrated manuscript of it made for the aldermen of that city, the Ethica early in the fifteenth century, the two other parts about the year 1454; the three parts were bound together by Gillet de Bolbec in 1455. Emile van Moé: Les Ethiques, Politiques et Economiques, traduites par Nicole Oresme, Mns. de la Bibliothèque de la ville de Rouen (Trésors des bibliothèques de France 3, 1–15, 5 pl., Paris 1929).

Oresme is said to have translated Vegetius' L'art de chevalerie, but that translation seems apocryphal, and the same is probably true of various other translations ascribed to him. For example, the translation of Petrarca's De remediis utriusque fortunae was made not by him, but by his contemporary Jean Dandin, canon in the Sainte Chapelle; the French translation of the Bible ordered by Charles V[10] was not made by Oresme, but by Raoul de Presles. Neither had Oresme anything to

[10] This must be added because another French translation was composed a century earlier (c. 1291) by Guiard des Moulins, canon of Aire. Guiard's translation was the one printed under Charles VIII (king 1483–98).

do with the translation of the Somnium viridarii (Songe du vergier). That political dialogue between a clerk and a knight was written for Charles V by Philippe of Mézières, chancellor to Peter of Lusignan (king of Cyprus), and from 1374 on counselor to Charles V. Philippe wrote his treatise in Latin, then in French.

Oresme was the most distinguished of the many translators who worked for Charles the Wise. He was fully aware of the difficulties of his task, was obliged to coin new terms and new phrases, and added glossaries to his translations. He took pains to revise his translations twice or thrice, and was so engaged at the time of his death in 1382. He is responsible for the creation of a good part of the French scientific vocabulary, and also for the gradual Latinization of the French language which set in at that time and continued through the Renaissance. That Latinization was partly evil, and partly good; in particular, Oresme's style introduced into the French language a concision and firmness which had been thus far alien to it.

See the appendixes on Oresme's grammar and glossary in Meunier: Essai sur la vie et les ouvrages d'Oresme (p. 143–205, Paris 1857). Petit de Julleville (vol. 2, 1896). Sybil Douglas Wingate: The mediaeval Latin versions of the Aristotelian scientific corpus (London 1931; Isis 18, 202). Albert D. Menut: Oresme's first work in French (Romanic review 26, 12–17, 1935).

11. *Theory of money*

Oresme is best known in the world today because of his treatise on money, De origine, natura, jure et mutationibus monetarum. The first Latin form of it (in 23 chapters) goes back to c. 1355; the second Latin form (in 26 chapters) was written in 1357/58. We have indicated above the difficulty of studying the Latin and French traditions of that treatise, and hence of determining exactly Oresme's personal contributions.

Upon the "rediscovery" of that treatise in 1863 by Wilhelm Roscher, and its re-editing in Latin and French by Louis Wolowski in the following year, Oresme was hailed as the greatest economist of the Middle Ages. Later a deeper study of mediaeval economic thought (by Charles Jourdain 1869 and others) revealed that Oresme's treatise was far less original than had been previously believed, and hence less important. It must be conceded, however, that his treatise was the first independent monograph on the subject, not simply a paragraph or a chapter in a summa, but a full treatise, a comprehensive and well built synthesis, which must be regarded as one of the main landmarks in early economic literature.

Taken individually, most of his views can be traced back to earlier writers. He was very well acquainted with the main mediaeval authorities, such as John of Salisbury, Albert the Great, St. Thomas, Giles of Rome, Walter Burley, with the writings of the civilians and canonists, and with ancient literature. One of the sources of his superiority was his deep knowledge of the Aristotelian texts and commentaries. He borrowed widely but not slavishly from all these sources. Thus we find in his treatise clear statements concerning such subjects as the condemnation of usury and speculative money changing, the theory of value (value is based not only on rarity but on intrinsic qualities), origin, utility, and sterility of money, the function of specie, etc. Little of that is completely new, but the synthesis is. Other views of his are more novel, at least in their intensity, e.g., his insistence on the necessity of monetary stability, the description of the qualities necessary to good money, the account of the variations in value of precious metals, the determination of the ratio of gold to silver and of the value of alloys. He criticized feudal monetary uses or abuses with great vigor. He emphasized the economic rights of the community against the prince (the nucleus of these thoughts is of course Aristotelian): the prince is a trustee of the community, he derives his sovereignty from God but only in so far as he acts for the common good, in particular he has no right to change the value of money. Starting from Aristotelian premises, Oresme reached an almost opposite conclusion with regard to the nature of money; Aristotle conceived money as a sign or measure of value; Oresme, as merchandise, a medium of exchange having a value of its own.

The fundamental novelties of his work are, in the first place, its independence of philosophy and theology, and, in the second place, its experimental nature. Oresme was primarily an economist, not a philosopher, and he is perhaps the first writer in that field about whom such a statement can be made. He was well acquainted not only with the theories of his time, but also with the practice, which mattered more, and he was all the time concerned with the applications of his views, not only with their formulation. His book was written under the pressure of the terrible economic and monetary difficulties which it was his sad privilege to witness.[11] It is not an academic treatise, but a pamphlet answering the needs of his days, such as might have been written by an educated financier.

In our final assessment of a treatise written about the middle of the fourteenth century, it is well to remember that our own views on money are still very confused and that our monetary practice is still so imperfect as to be the cause of considerable sufferings all over the world.

It has been claimed that Oresme derived his economic ideas from his older contemporary Buridan (d. 1358); according to other scholars, the borrowing was done in the other direction. See my note on Buridan (XIV-1).

Oresme has been credited with the discovery of Gresham's law,[12] to wit, that the worst form of currency in circulation regulates the value of the whole currency and drives out all other forms ("bad money drives out good"). This requires a double qualification. In the first place, Oresme's Latin text is not sufficiently explicit[13] and the French text (end of the prologue) is a later interpolation. In the second place, it is certain that Gresham's law is anterior to Gresham; if Oresme did not formulate it, the author of that interpolation formulated it a little later. That law summarizes experimental facts which must have been observed long before Oresme, whenever money was debased. For example, there is a remark pointing in that direction in Aristophanes' Frogs.[14]

Economic criticism. Wilhelm Roscher: Ein grosser Nationalökonom des 14. Jahrhunderts (Zeitschrift für die gesamte Staatswissenschaft vol. 19, 1863). Charles Jourdain: Mémoire sur les commencements de l'économie politique dans les écoles du Moyen âge (Mémoires de l'Académie des inscriptions vol. 28, 1874;

[11] Elaborate accounts and discussions of them will be found in Bridrey's book (1906), or Gonnard's (1935).

[12] So called after Sir Thomas Gresham (1519?–79), founder of the Royal Exchange, by Henry Dunning Macleod (1821–1902). According to Macleod, writing three centuries later, Gresham formulated that law about the time of Elizabeth's accession (1558). Among the forerunners of Gresham are not only Oresme, but also Copernicus (first half of sixteenth century).

[13] E.g., Homines enim conantur suam monetam portare ad loca ubi eam credunt magis valere. That is *not* the equivalent of Gresham's law.

[14] Edited and translated by Benjamin B. Rogers: The comedies of Aristophanes (5, 109–11, London 1902).

reprinted in his Excursions historiques, p. 423–62, 1888). Henry Hertrich: Les théories monétaires du XIVe siècle, Oresme (thesis, Lyon 1899). Emile Bridrey: La théorie de la monnaie au XIVe siècle, N. Oresme: Etude historique des doctrines et des faits économiques (781 p., Paris 1906), very important study, including abundant documents. Thomas Willing Balch: The law of Oresme, Copernicus and Gresham (21 p., Philadelphia 1908). Adolphe Landry: Notes critiques sur le N. Oresme de M. Bridrey (Le moyen âge 22, 145–78, 1909). Henry Laurent: La loi de Gresham au Moyen âge; essai sur la circulation monétaire entre la Flandre et le Brabant à la fin du XIVe siècle (217 p., Bruxelles 1933); Le problème des traductions françaises du Traité des monnaies dans les Pays Bas bourguignons (Revue d'histoire économique et sociale 21, 13–24, 1933). René Gonnard: Histoire des doctrines monétaires dans ses rapports avec l'histoire des monnaies (vol. 1, Paris 1935).

12. *Text*

Tractatus de latitudinibus formarum. First published Padua 1482. Later editions: Padua 1486, Venice 1505, Vienna 1515.

Tractatus proportionum Nicholai Oren. First printed Paris? c. 1500, then Venice 1505 with the previous item. Reprinted Paris c. 1510 together with treatises bearing the same title by Albert of Saxony and Thomas Bradwardine. In this edition the author is named Nicholas Horen.

Algorismus proportionum. E. L. W. M. Curtze: Der Algorismus proportionum zum ersten Male nach der Lesart der Handschrift R 4°.2 des K. Gymnasium zu Thorn herausgegeben (32 p., 2 pl., Berlin 1868). Fragments edited by the same in the Literaturzeitung der Zeitschrift für Mathematik und Physik (13, 101–4, 1868).

The Tractatus de uniformitate et difformitate intensionum (alias: Tractatus de figuratione potentiarum et mensurarum sive Tractatus de configuracionibus qualitatum) is unpublished, but there is an analysis of it with abundant extracts in Wieleitner's paper of 1914 cited below.

Traicté de l'espère. Two editions were printed in Paris by the same printer, Simon Dubois, the first without date, at the beginning of the sixteenth century, the second in 1508. A critical edition of it is being prepared by A. D. Menut to appear eventually in Osiris.

Critical edition of the Traité du ciel et du monde by Albert D. Menut and Alexander J. Denomy, C.S.B. (Mediaeval studies 3, 185–281; 4, 159–297, 46 figs.; 5, 167–333, Toronto 1941–43; Isis 34, 244; 35, 227), with long introduction and elaborate glossary.

Tractatus contra astrologos, edited by Hubert Pruckner: Studien zu den astrologischen Schriften des Heinrich von Langenstein (p. 227–50, Leipzig 1933; Isis 23, 452–54).

Oresme's French translations of Aristotle were printed by Antoine Vérard in Paris, the Ethics in 1488 (1 folio vol.), the Politics and Economics in 1489 (2 folio vols.). Albert Douglas Menut: Le livre de éthiques. Published from the text of Brussels MS 2902 with a critical introduction and notes (560 p., 20 pl., New York 1940), elaborate critical edition (Isis 33, 68–71).

Dandin's translation of Petrarca: Des remèdes de l'une et de l'autre fortune prospère et adverse was printed by Galliot du Pré in Paris 1523.

The French treatise on money, Traictie de la première invention des monnoies, was the first to be printed, namely by Colard Mansion, Bruges c. 1477 (exceedingly rare). The Latin treatise, De origine . . . monetarum, was printed by Thomas Keet in Paris, s.a., at the beginning of the sixteenth century, then again in Lyon 1605, and in the Maxima bibliotheca veterum patrum (26, 226–34, Lyon 1677).

Both Latin and French texts have been reprinted by Louis Wolowski (294 p., Paris 1864). This edition includes notes and commentary and also Copernicus' treatise, Monete cudende ratio (1526), with French translation.

The Latin text of Oresme's treatise was also appended to William Cunningham: The growth of English industry and commerce (p. 556–79, 1890).

Fragments of an early English version of Oresme's treatise are printed in Bridrey's book (p. 687–97, 1906) after a MS of Trinity College in Cambridge.

Sermo coram papa Urbano V et cardinalibus habitus. Printed in Flacius Illyricus: Catalogus testium veritatis (Basel 1556), and many times reprinted. A contemporary satirical document, the Epistola Luciferi ad malos principes ecclesiasticos, has been ascribed to Oresme on the very insufficient basis of this Sermo. It was printed in Strasbourg 1507 and many times reprinted. Extracts in French in HL (24, 34–35, 1862).

13. *General criticism*

Francis Meunier: Essai sur la vie et les ouvrages de Nicole Oresme (208 p., Paris 1857). This is the only general study exclusively devoted to Oresme; it is still serviceable but very insufficient. Abbé Pierre Feret: La faculté de théologie de Paris et ses docteurs les plus célèbres (Moyen âge 2, 224, Paris 1895; 3, 289–304, 1896). Michalski (p. 150–55, 1927). Hugo Dingler: Über die Stellung von Oresme in der Geschichte der Wissenschaften (Archeion 11, xv–xxii, 1929; Philosophisches Jahrbuch der Görres Gesellschaft 45, 58–64, 1932). Dana B. Durand: Oresme and the mediaeval origins of modern science (Speculum 16, 167–85, 1941). Many of the studies cited above apropos of special topics also contain generalities. That is specially true of Bridrey (1906), Thorndike (1934), Borchert (1934).

The Oresme note was read by Dana B. Durand and Albert Douglas Menut, each of whom kindly suggested a few emendations.

JEAN FUSORIS

French (Ardennais) maker of clocks and astrolabes, astronomer and astrologer, writing in French and Latin (c. 1365–1436).

His name may be construed John son of the founder (in metals). Indeed, his father was a pewterer in Giraumont (Ardennes, then county of Rethel), where John was born c. 1365. John studied in Mézières, then in Paris, where he was B.A. in 1379. After having obtained his master's degree he returned for a while to Giraumont and learned his father's craft. He went back to Paris c. 1391 and was master of medicine in 1396, one of the masters regents of the faculty until 1400.

He made an astrolabe for Juan I (king of Aragon 1387–95), and sold two clocks to the duke of Orleans in 1398. In Bologna 1410 he gave a sphere and astrolabe to John XXIII (pope 1410–15). In 1423 he built an astronomical clock for the cathedral of Bourges (Berry).

He seems to have resided mostly in Paris until 1415, and had opened a school. In 1414 he became acquainted in Paris with Richard of Courtenay, bishop of Norwich and at that time British envoy to France. In the meanwhile he had become bachelor in theology and had accumulated various canonries and other preferments, and in June 1415 he was a member of the French embassy to England. After his return he was suspected of treason, and interned in the Petit-Châtelet (1415–16), then released but restricted to remain in Mézières, later Reims. He died in 1436.

He wrote (1) a Latin treatise on the use of the astrolabe for Peter of Navarre, son of Charles II the Bad (king of Navarre 1349–87); also in French?; (2) tables of chords, Tabule cordarum arcuum; (3) a Traité de cosmographie, written for the chapter of Metz in 1432. The last-named item is in French; it includes a description of one of his clocks.

Criticism. Léon Mirot: Le procès de maître Jean Fusoris, chanoine de Notre Dame de Paris, 1415–16. Episode des négociations franco-anglaises durant la guerre de cent ans (Mémoires de la Société d'histoire de Paris 27, 137–72, 1900; documents p. 173–279, 1901). Wickersheimer (p. 403, 1936).

PÈLERIN DE PRUSSE

Author of two French books on astrology dated 1361–62.

Pèlerin de Prusse (Pruce, Pousse?) wrote a French treatise on astrology, divided into three parts, and dedicated it on July 11, 1361 to the dauphin Charles (Charles V, 1364–80). It is derived (if not simply translated) from the Latin version of al-Qabīṣī's (X-2) astrological introduction by John of Seville (XII-1). On May 9, 1362 he wrote a French treatise on the use of the astrolabe. His purpose was to provide for the dauphin in the French language a complete and self-sufficient textbook on astrology.

The influence of John of Seville's Libellus ysagogicus Abdilazi (i.e., 'Abd al-'Azīz al-Qabīṣī) at that very time is proved also by the commentary (Scriptum sur Alkabicium) made in 1359 by John of Stendal, Dominican in Magdeburg, for the masters and students of Erfurt.

Text. MS in St. Johns College, Oxford, no. 164.
Criticism. Thorndike (3, 223, 586, 1934).

BERTRAN BOYSSET

Author of a Provençal treatise on land measuring (c. 1345–c. 1414).

Bertrand Boisset (to use the French form of his name) was the son of a fisherman, Jacques Boisset, and of Bertrande; he was born at Arles c. 1345, was married there in 1372, and had many children. He was a sworn surveyor and died in or after 1414.

He seems to have received a fairly good education, yet his knowledge of Latin was rudimentary and his knowledge of Provençal mediocre; he was a practical surveyor, probably unacquainted with the writings of the agrimensores but continuing local traditions.

All his writings are in Provençal and are represented by autograph MSS plus copies of these. They may be divided into three groups:

1. Chronique. Chronicle of papal events and events in Arles and Provence, with many items concerning himself or his family. That is, it is a combination of chronicle and commonplace book (livre de raison). It was begun c. 1389 and extends from 1365 to 1400, 1372–1414. Two autograph MSS, the one in Genoa, the other in Paris (BN fr. 5728).

2. Collection of Provençal texts in prose and verse. MS autograph of 71 leaves in private ownership (Paul Arbaud, Aix-en-Provence). These texts were simply copied by him (1372–75), but some of them would have been lost to us otherwise. The collection includes the romance of Sidrach (XIII-1), the story of the good child (Enfant sage, a dialogue between Adrian and Epictetos), the Roman d'Arles, the life of St. Mary Magdalene, the life of St. Trophimus (an Arlesian saint).

3. (This is the most important item, justifying my note.) Syensa de destrar e d'atermenar. Treatise on surveying, or, more literally, on measuring land and delimiting it (arpentage et bornage). The autograph MS (Carpentras)[15] covers 316 folios and contains many quaint and naïve illustrations, drawn and colored by

[15] Bibliothèque inguimbertine, Carpentras (Vaucluse), no. 323. The MS was a part of the library of Thomassin de Mazaugues, bought in Aix in 1745 by Mgr. d'Inguimbert. It may have been previously in the library of N. C. Fabri de Peiresc (1580–Aix 1637), see Isis 22, 348.

Bertran himself. The treatise is written without order, and as far as I could see (for only parts of the text were available to me) without mathematics. It includes technicalities, e.g., concerning the local measures (a standard of length equal to the Avignon standard, authenticated by Anthoni Lucian and Bertran Boysset, was inserted in the wall of the royal palace in Arles). It deals with legal questions such as riparian rights on new alluvia or new river islands. The text is repeatedly ascribed to Arnold of Villanova (XIII-2), who is said to have written it in 1312 under the dictation of Robert, king of Naples (1309–43), count of Provence. Arnold died in 1311; the ascription is not plausible; it was probably made because Arnold was the most illustrious Catalan author known to Bertran. It may be that the real author, if not Bertran, was one Arnaut del Puey (Arnaudus de Podio), confused with the more illustrious Arnold of Villanova? The treatise as we have it was written in many installments (the only dates appearing in it are the terminal dates 1404–5). The author or editor had a very high idea of its value, bequeathing it to Arles or to king Louis of Provence.[16] We may assume that Boysset was the real author of that treatise, wherein he had recorded from time to time the main results of his long professional experience. It is more valuable from the linguistic than from the technical point of view.

Boysset's memory was sufficiently green in Provence to be celebrated by Frederi Mistral (1830–1914) in Nerte (IV Lou lioun).

Text. 1. The Chronique was edited by the abbé Bonemant in Le Musée, revue arlésienne (Arles 1876–77). Again by Franz Ehrle, S.J., in Archiv für Litteratur und Kirchengeschichte des Mittelalters (7, 311–420; article published in 1893, whole vol. dated 1900). See Romania (22, 126).

3. The treatise on surveying was analyzed by Paul Meyer (Romania 22, 96–126, 1893) and partly edited by Pierre Pansier (Annales d'Avignon et du Comtat 1926). Pansier's paper not available to me.

Criticism. Camille Chabaneau: Le roman d'Arles (Revue des langues romanes 32, 473–542, 1888). Francesco Novati: Le livre de raisons de B. Boysset d'après le MS des Trinitaires d'Arles actuellement conservé à Gênes (Romania 21, 528–56, 1892). Paul Meyer: Les manuscrits de B. Boysset (Romania 21, 557–80, 1892; 22, 87–126, 1893). Nicola Zingarelli: Le roman de Saint Trophime (Annales du Midi, année 13, 297–345, 1901). Robert Caillet: Le traité d'arpentage de Boisset (Trésors des bibliothèques de France 5, 140–46, 3 pl., 1935), illustrated.

A4. England

REDE

William Rede. English mathematician and astronomer (d. 1385).

William Rede (or Reed, Read, Reade) was born in the diocese of Exeter, and was already studying in Oxford before 1337. He studied in Exeter College, later in Merton. In 1344, he was M.A. and fellow of Merton, in 1352–53 bursar, later he returned to Exeter. He was curate of Buttermere, Wiltshire, in 1361; later provost of Wingham, Kent; he became bishop of Chichester, Sussex, on September 23, 1368, and traveled to Avignon for his consecration. He died on August 18, 1385 and was buried in the church of Selsey,[17] near Chichester.

William of Chichester must have been a rich man. He built himself a castle in

[16] I suppose Louis II, count of Provence (1384–1417), is meant.

[17] The explanation of this is that Selsey (seal's island) was the earlier see of the diocese. It was in Selsey that St. Wilfrid established Christianity among the southern Saxons in 681. The see was transferred from Selsey to Chichester by William the Conqueror.

Amberley, and in 1377 received license to crenelate it. In 1379 he lent 100 l. to the king, and by his will dated 1382 he bequeathed a relatively large amount of money and books to Merton College, and made a number of smaller bequests to Balliol, Oriel, Queen's, Exeter, and New College.

His main title to immortality perhaps is his creation of the library of Merton College, a beautiful little building which is still one of the delights of Oxford. He was himself a distinguished mathematician and astrologer, and the patron of the Merton, and other Oxford, mathematicians. Before speaking of his works we may add that he determined the latitude of Oxford, 51°50′ (instead of 51°46′), and its longitude, a little more than 15°.

Astronomical writings:

1. Almanak solis pro 4 annis, 1337–1340 calculata et scripta.
2. Tabulae astronomicae. Almanak sive tabulae solis pro 4 annis 1341–1344.
3. Canones tabularum ad meridiem Oxon. This is also ascribed to Nicholas of Lynn, a contemporary Oxford Carmelite. The library of Robert Recorde (1510?–58) included a copy of Rede's Tabulae astronomicae et canones in easdem, which may be identical with items 1 to 3.
4. Pronosticationes eclipseos Lunae 1345. W. Rede calculavit, Joh. Ashenden pronosticavit.
5. Calculations concerning the conjunction of Saturn and Jupiter in October 1365, made in Oxford 1357.

Historical writings:

6. Chronica a Christo de papis et imperatoribus ad Ludovicum Bavariae. The lives of the earlier popes were written by Richard of Cluny (i.e., Richard de Poitiers, Benedictine in Cluny, 1171), those of the later ones, from Honorius III (1216–27) to Gregory XI (1370–78), by Rede. Thus he wrote this Chronica after 1370.
7. De archiepiscopis cantuariensibus ad Whittlesey. Rede had known Simon Islip, fellow of Merton, archbishop of Canterbury from 1349 to 1366, and probably also the latter's nephew, William Whittlesey, archbishop from 1368 to 1374.
8. Chronica a Bruto usque ad 1367. For the Roman de Brut, see Introd. 2, 453.

Two other documents concerning Rede must still be mentioned: (9) a collection of Questiones given to him by his tutor, Nicholas de Sandwych; (10) a letter addressed in 1367 to Rede by Reginald Lambourne (or Lamborn), who studied under him at Merton, and then became successively a Benedictine and a Franciscan (DNB 32, 21, 1892). The letter deals with the conjunctions of Saturn, Jupiter, and Mars and the subsequent evils to occur in 1368–74.

Criticism. C. L. Kingsford (DNB 47, 374–76, 1896). J. L. E. Dreyer: On the original form of the Alfonsine tables (Monthly notices of the Royal Astronomical Society 80, 243–62, 1920; Isis 4, 137). R. T. Gunther (1, 96, 108, 315; 2, 44, 53, 56–59, 66, 381–85, 1923), includes the catalogue (2, 381–85) of Rede's rich library.

BRIT

Walter Brit (or Britte, Brytte). English astronomer, fellow of Merton College, Oxford, c. 1390.

This notice on Brit is included for the sake of reference only, as the various books formerly ascribed to him are now generally ascribed to others. For example, the Theorica planetarum, apropos of which John Bale (d. 1563) said of him "Gualtherus Brit astronomus qui theoricam fecit omnium planetarum" and placed him "sub Ricardo?" (i.e., 1377–99), is now credited to Gherardo da Sabbioneta (XIII-2).

Another Theorica is assigned to Bredon; the Theoremata planetarum to John of Sacrobosco (XIII-1). The Cirurgia Walteri Brit is a collection of medical recipes.

A drawing of a quadrant to illustrate an earlier (thirteenth-century) text in a Bodleian MS (Digby 98, fol. 162) may have been made by Brit in 1395?

Finally, it has been suggested that Brit was identical with Walter Brute, a lay follower of Wycliffe in the diocese of Hereford, author of a tract De auferendis clero possessionibus, who was tried before John Trevenant, bishop of Hereford in 1391.

Criticism. R. L. Poole (DNB 6, 358, 1886). R. T. Gunther (2, 43, 66, 160, 1923).

NICHOLAS OF LYNN

Nicholas of Lynn (or Lynne), Nicolaus de Linea (there are various places called Lynn in Norfolk); English Carmelite astronomer (fl. 1386).

He was lecturer in theology to the Carmelites of Oxford, and in 1386 (this being the only dated event of his life) he compiled at the request of John of Gaunt, duke of Lancaster (Ghent 1340-99), a calendar adjusted to the coordinates of Oxford for the years 1386 to 1462, Kalendarium ad latitudinem et longitudinem civitatis Oxoniae compositum pro quatuor cyclis decennovenalibus immediate sequentibus annum 1386. That calendar as well as John Somer's was mentioned by Chaucer in the preface to his Treatise on the astrolabe ("the calendars of the reverend scholars, friar John Somer and friar Nicholas Lenne").

Nicholas of Lynn was unwarrantedly identified by Hakluyt with an unnamed Oxford Franciscan and mathematician, mentioned by Gerard Mercator (1512-94) and John Dee (1527-1608), who is said by them to have traveled to the arctic regions in 1360, described the places visited by him, and measured their latitudes with an astrolabe. According to John Dee, that Oxford traveler of 1360 wrote a Latin account of his journey, entitled Inventio fortunata (aliter fortunae) qui liber incipit a gradu 54 usque ad polum, which he gave to the king of England. That account is lost. Whether the traveler was Nicholas of Lynn, or Hugh of Ireland, or somebody else, the account of his journey is plausible, and his book may have been one of the sources of information concerning arctic regions the tradition of which may be detected in the works of Claudius Clavus (1388—after 1424) and Martin Behaim (d. 1507).

Criticism. Richard Hakluyt: The principal navigations, voyages, traffiques, and discoveries of the English nation (first printed London 1589; I quote from the Hakluyt Society edition, extra series, 1, 301-4, Glasgow 1903).

A. G. Little (DNB 40, 418, 1894). Nansen (vol. 2, 1911). R. T. Gunther (2, 60, 62, 1923). Sarton: The mysterious arctic traveller of 1360. Nicholas of Lynn (query no. 74, Isis 29, 98-99, 1938). Hennig (3, 261-67, 1938). Martin Frobisher: The three voyages, edited by Vilhjalmur Stefansson (2 vols., London 1938; Isis 30, 284-89), Stefansson's introduction proves that geographical knowledge of northern regions was continuously available from the twelfth century onward. Aubrey Diller: Answer to query no. 74 (Isis 30, 277-78, 1939).

SOMER

John Somer (or Semur, Somerarius). English Franciscan astronomer; in Oxford in 1380.

He was a member of the Franciscan monastery at Bridgwater, Somerset. At the request of his provincial, Thomas Kingsbury,[18] he computed a calendar with astronomical tables, Tertium opusculum kalendarii, for Joan, princess of Wales, mother of Richard II. The MSS of it are dated variously 1380, 1384, 1372, and the period covered is 1387 to 1462, or 1405 to 1481. John is said to have written also a "Castigation of former calendars collected from many sources," beginning "Corruptio calendarii horribilis est . . . ."

The calendars of John Somer and Nicholas Lenne (Nicholas of Lynn) were both mentioned by Chaucer in the preface to his treatise on the astrolabe.

Criticism. Andrew George Little: The Grey friars in Oxford (p. 244–46, Oxford 1892). Miss Bateson (DNB 53, 218, 1898). R. T. Gunther (2, 60–62, 1923).

A5. Netherlands

JAN DE HEUSDEN

Flemish physician and astronomer (d. 1401).

Master of arts and medicine. Physician from 1363 on to Louis II de Mâle (count of Flanders 1346–84), later to Philippe le Hardi[19] (duke of Burgundy 1363–1404). He was a witness to Louis de Mâle's will in St. Omer 1384. He was canon of St. Donatien, Bruges, canon of Courtrai, provost of Notre-Dame, Bruges (1383).

He studied astronomy and built a sphere wherewith to demonstrate the motions of stars (and planets?). He died in Bruges on February 20, 1401, and was buried in Notre-Dame, his tomb being covered with a brass plate bearing a long epitaph.

Criticism. Alphonse Wauters (Biographie nationale de Belgique 10, 408, 1888–89). Wickersheimer (p. 469, 1936).

A6. Germany

LANGENSTEIN

Heinrich von Langenstein. German mathematician, astronomer, philosopher, reformer (d. 1397).

Contents: (1) Life. (2) Heinrich von Hessen der Jüngere. (3) Langenstein's writings. (4) Philosophy. (5) Mathematics. (6) Astronomy. (7) Physics. (8) Alchemy. (9) Biology. (10) Medicine. (11) Mysticism. (12) Religious reform. (13) Economics. (14) Study of Hebrew.

(15) Text. (16) Criticism. (17) Scientific criticism (astronomy and physics).

1. *Life*

Henricus Hembuche (Hainbuche) de Hassia dictus de Langenstein. Heinrich von Hessen der Aeltere. Henricus Hessianus. Born at Hainbuch, Langenstein, near Marburg (Hesse-Nassau), in 1325 (or 1340?). He was perhaps of noble family but certainly very poor. He was already in Paris in 1363, teaching and studying; he was licentiate in theology in 1375 and doctor in the following year; he was a member of the Sorbonne, and before 1381 vice-chancellor. The political difficulties

[18] Or Thomas Kyngesbury (Kynbury), provincial of the English Minorites, 1380–90; patron of scientific studies (DNB 31, 360).

[19] Philippe le Hardi had married the daughter of Louis de Mâle, Marguerite of Flanders, in Ghent 1369. Marguerite III ruled Flanders with Philippe from 1384 to 1405, and through her Flanders became a part of Burgundy.

created by the Schism obliged him to leave Paris in 1383, for, having taken sides with Urban VI, the Roman pope, he found himself in opposition to the French king, who protected the pope of Avignon, Clement VII. Together with other Germans he returned to Germany with the purpose of establishing a new university. He stopped for a while at the Cistercian monastery of Eberbach,[20] though he was himself a secular. Then he proceeded with Heinrich von Oyta and Gerhard von Kalkar to Vienna. He was one of the founders of the University of Vienna; irrespective of his services as a teacher and adviser to the archduke Albert III (ruled 1365–95), it was probably he who obtained from the Roman pope the bull of foundation (Dum generosos 1384) and the permission to establish a faculty of theology. The rest of his life was spent in that city. He died there on February 11, 1397, and was buried in the church of St. Stephen.

2. *Heinrich von Hessen der Jüngere*

If our Henry is called Henry of Hessen, one should add "the Elder" to distinguish him from Henry of Hessen the Younger. The two men have often been confused, and the works of the one wrongly ascribed to the other.

Henry of Hessen the Younger taught philosophy and theology in the University of Heidelberg at the end of the fourteenth century and the beginning of the fifteenth. He was canon in Neuhausen, near Worms. In 1414, he assumed the Carthusian habit; he died on August 12, 1427, being the prior of the Carthusian monastery Monikhusen near Arnhem in Gelderland.

He wrote commentaries on the Bible, and on the Books of sentences, a treatise on politics entitled Summa de republica (?), a treatise for confessors Tractatus ad eruditionem confessorum (incipit: Tibi dabo claves . . .), first printed at Memmingen 1483, and reprinted at Esslingen before the end of the century with another writing of his (?), Regulae ad cognoscendam differentiam inter peccatum mortale et veniale. (Stanonik, ADB 11, 637, 1880.)

3. *Langenstein's writings*

To return to Henry of Hessen the Elder, his writings were very abundant. They are too many, and most of them too irrelevant to our purpose, to be enumerated here. In the list compiled by F. W. E. Roth in 1888, they are divided into 10 groups: (I) astronomical, 7, (II) historico-political, 18, (III) theologico-polemical, 7, (IV) exegetical, 4, (V) dogmatic, 17, (VI) edifying, 50, (VII) sermons, not numbered, (VIII) occasional writings and letters, 12, (IX) prophecies, 2, (X) medical, 2?; a total of more than 119 writings, to which are added 12 apocryphal ones. Those of special interest to our readers will be dealt with in the following sections. Roth's classification is insufficient and misleading (e.g., one of Langenstein's main astronomical works is his commentary on Genesis), but his list gives one an idea of the variety of Langenstein's activities.

4. *Philosophy*

As Langenstein's main philosophical work, his Questiones super quatuor libros Sententiarum, is still unpublished and unexplored, it is difficult to define his philosophy with precision, but he was one of the "moderni," one of the followers of the

[20] Near Wiesbaden. In the best hock district, near the Steinberg vineyard, and not far from Johannisberg.

via nova as opposed to the via antiqua of the Scotists and Thomists. He was an Occamist, though probably a very moderate one.

5. *Mathematics*

Though no mathematical writings are ascribed to him, he deserves to be mentioned in the history of mathematics, as the introducer of mathematics in Vienna, whence it radiated throughout Germany; that is, he was the beginner of a tradition which proved to be of great importance. See statements made by Georg Tannstetter (c. 1480–1530) in 1514 (Duhem, Etudes 3, 14) and by Pierre de la Ramée (1515–72) a little later (Cantor 2, 150).

6. *Astronomy*

Our interest in Langenstein is largely due to his astronomical writings; to begin with, the first book of his enormous Commentary on Genesis 1–3, wherein astronomical theories are discussed; then the treatise De improbatione epicyclorum et concentricorum; then several others which are remarkable because of their anti-astrological tendencies.

The earliest dated one is the Quaestio de cometa, relative to the comet of 1368, and directed against the astrological treatise of Giovanni da Legnano on the same subject. The burden of it is that prognostications based on comets are worthless. The fact that Langenstein was still accepting Aristotelian views on the nature of comets and conceiving them as exhalations of terrestrial origin does not detract much from the value of his healthy and vigorous skepticism. Thorndike (3, 493) pays a great compliment to him by comparing his short treatise to the writings of Pierre Bayle (1647–1706), composed mainly apropos of the comet of 1680, more than three centuries later,[21] for it took considerably more vision and more courage to defend rationalistic views in the fourteenth century than in Newton's time.

Before 1373 Langenstein wrote two other treatises, Tractatus physicus de reductione effectuum specialium in virtutes communes (according to Roth apocryphal?) and De habitudine causarum et influxu naturae communis respectu inferiorum. In the last-named one, he argues that God does not act through the agency of stars or spheres, but immediately; inferior nature is not controlled by the celestial spheres, but immanently by Himself. Astrological influences are, if not entirely irrelevant, at least secondary. Yet he conceives all beings and bodies as partaking of a common nature (natura communis), and this leads him to the concept of an almost mechanistic universe. Whatever influence the stars may have is independent of their relative positions.

In the De reductione effectuum, Langenstein admits that the "common and general philosophy" may be insufficient to explain unusual and hitherto inexplicable phaenomena; there may be some need of a natural metaphysics, but not of any kind of occultism. The doctrine of four elements, of the four primary qualities, their derivatives, and their endless variations is sufficient to account for the infinite complexity of nature and its unlimited potentialities. He rejects the Aristotelian theory that the superlunar world is essentially different from the sublunar one. Even if the radiations of stars have some definite influence, it would be difficult to

[21] Lettre . . . où il est prouvé par plusieurs raisons tirées de la philosophie et de la théologie que les comètes ne sont point le présage d'aucun malheur (574 p., Cologne 1682). Pensées diverses écrites . . . à l'occasion de la comète qui parut au mois de décembre 1680 (2 vols., Rotterdam 1683). Many times republished; 6th ed., 4 vols., Amsterdam 1749.

localize it, as those radiations are reflected and diffused in a number of ways.

The many astrological predictions evoked by the conjunction of Saturn and Mars in March 1373 caused Langenstein to reiterate his attack against the astrologers in his Tractatus contra astrologos coniunctionistas de eventibus futurorum, written in 1373. It is divided into three books: (1) discussion of the theory of conjunctions (17 chapters), (2) even if conjunctions were influential, the special results of their influences could not be predicted (8 chapters), (3) calamities, such as famines, pestilences, floods, can be explained without astrological influences (4 chapters). This is a well thought-out anti-astrological treatise, as convincing as was possible in the physical ignorance of those days. Moreover, Langenstein denounced the disingenuous methods of astrologers, for example, their habit of going back to old astronomical phaenomena for the explanation of present calamities.

In short, Langenstein's tendency was to explain phaenomena in rational terms, without appeal to magic or occultism. His main concession to astrology was his acceptance of a theory of radiation which reminds me of Bacon's idea of radiation and "multiplication of species" (Introd. 2, 956–57). A true astrologer, according to him, would be a man knowing all the physical conditions of a problem and thus able to offer a rational explanation of it; such an astrologer of course would come very close to our modern conception of the "natural philosopher"; it is typical of the times that the word "astrologer" could admit of such extension.[22]

Much in his arguments is similar to those used by his greater contemporary Oresme. The latter was somewhat his senior, and Oresme's writings were on the whole anterior to his own. It is not necessary, however, to imply that the one influenced the other. It is probably more correct to consider them both as representative of the more advanced contemporary thinking concerning superstition in general, and astrological predictions in particular. Oresme and Langenstein were the rationalistic vanguard of their times. Note that they both belonged to the Parisian circle and that Langenstein's main anti-astrological writings were completed before he left Paris.

It would not be difficult to find inconsistencies and crudities in those treatises, but it would be very unfair to judge the authors too severely on account of them. On the contrary, those treatises help us to realize how hopeless it was to try to explain the operations of nature in rational terms, at a time when hardly any single function was isolated and properly understood. It is much to the glory of Langenstein and Oresme that they preferred skepticism to superstition, and ignorance to occultism.

Another aspect of astrology is revealed by one of Langenstein's later writings, the Liber adversus Thelesphori eremitae vaticinia de ultimis temporibus (c. 1392). Fra Telesforo of Cosenza (in Calabria) had dedicated his prophecies to Antoniotto Adorno, doge of Genoa, in 1386; they were said to camouflage French propaganda for the annexation of Genoa. The Great Schism was then an unfailing source of spiritual violence, of exaltation and rancor, and the pamphleteers on both sides used astrological arguments in order to vindicate their claims, and to prove, as it were, that heaven itself was in their favor. Apropos of Hildegard's (XII-2) visions, however, Langenstein was ready (on another occasion) to concede their soundness. All this takes us away from science proper, but illustrates his common sense. The disinterested visions of a saint are one thing, the astrological prophecies of a partisan quite another.

[22] Contra coniunctionistas II, 2; p. 172–73 in Pruckner's edition.

7. *Physics*

It is clear from the concrete examples often quoted by him that Langenstein had deeply meditated on physical phaenomena. Apropos of vacuum he remarked that when two flat objects were pressed very closely together it was more difficult to separate them than if there was some air between them; thus, when a flat object was placed upon the surface of water it was possible to raise that surface a little by lifting the object (in De habitudine causarum as quoted by Thorndike 3, 759). He seemed on his way to abandoning the Aristotelian idea of the logical impossibility of vacuum.

Some questions on the Perspectiva communis of John Peckham (XIII-2) are ascribed to him in an edition of 1503 (they have also been ascribed to Oresme). They include a discussion of the rainbow suggesting comparison with that given at the beginning of the century by Dietrich of Freiberg.

In the Contra coniunctionistas (1373)[23] Langenstein remarked that the magnetic attraction of iron varies from place to place in Norway. It does not follow that he was acquainted with magnetic declination, but simply that magnetic irregularities, which might be due in that country to local attraction of magnetic iron ore, had been reported to him. There is, however, nothing improbable in his having some knowledge of magnetic declination, for such declination could be observed with sufficient ease as soon as it was large enough; a similar knowledge has also been ascribed (though on grounds which are hardly better) to his contemporary Chaucer.

8. *Alchemy*

Langenstein was so used to thinking of the infinite possibilities inherent in the endless complexity of nature that he was very indulgent to the claims of the alchemists. They might even be able to make gold under certain circumstances, why not? Alchemy, however, should not be mixed with occultism.

He conceived gases different from air—he calls them exhalations—which partake of the nature of the substances whence they emerge.[24]

9. *Biology*

The De habitudine causarum and the De reductione effectuum (as quoted from the MSS by Thorndike, 3, 479–86) contain some strange biological ideas, which we must briefly indicate. He tries to account for spontaneous generation (of mice, worms, vermin) out of putrefying matter by the interactions of qualities under superlunar influences. Such is the complexity of nature that new combinations may always arise; thus have new species of plants and animals been created in the past, and thus will new ones appear in the future. New diseases may occur in the same manner, as well as new remedies to cure them. He goes so far as to suggest that there might be different kinds of men. The boldness of that idea, its almost heretical nature, will appear more clearly if one bears in mind the principle of orthodox Christian anthropology, as set forth, e.g., by St. Augustine (Introd. 2, 45–46).

10. *Medicine*

The same two treatises also contain medical ideas. We have already indicated one: the possibility of new diseases' originating by the mere shuffling of pathological

[23] I, 15; p. 163 in Pruckner's edition.
[24] Contra coniunctionistas III, 3; p. 198 in Pruckner's edition.

causes into new combinations. On the other hand, it is clear that Langenstein, in spite of his incipient rationalism, could not shake off the arguments and implications of astrological medicine. He tried also to explain disease and cure by the application of the ideas of intension, proportion, latitude, configuration, etc., but that was not very helpful.

In a text which may be apocryphal, Queritur utrum secundum naturalem philosophiam sint alique substantie separate preter motores orbium celestium (Vatican 9369, 26r–40r; Thorndike 3, 505), he suggests a pathological interpretation of dreams and hallucinations.

Two medical treatises are ascribed to him (Munich MSS; Roth p. 19), Tractatus de medicinis simplicibus, and Medicamentorum compositiones Heinrici de Hassia et aliorum (including recipes in Latin and German). The genuineness of these texts is very doubtful.

11. *Mysticism*

Langenstein was obliged as a theologian to discuss the fundamental questions concerning spirits, angels, demons, etc. In his treatise De discretione spirituum he distinguishes twelve kinds of spirit, five intrinsic and seven extrinsic (all of which is simply a psychological discussion of qualities and tendencies); then again four kinds, his own soul (as discussed before), the Holy Spirit, good and bad angels. This is a strange mixture of natural psychology and metapsychology, which was hardly avoidable.

He wrote many books of edification, asceticism, and practical mysticism; the only one which I know is the Speculum animae (alias Speculum animae peccatricis, De animae conditionibus, De anima contemplativa, De contemplatione, etc.). This is said to be his masterpiece in that field. It is a short manual for the inner life, composed in the form of a soliloquy to his soul (incipit: Novi, anima mea, quod curiosa sis . . .), wherein the reader is taught to withdraw "ab exterioribus ad interiora" then "ab interioribus ad superiora" (from the world to self, and from self to God). Each man's soul is truly God's mirror (hence the title), even as it is his only means of approach to God. This little golden book enjoyed some popularity, as witnessed by the abundance of MSS, though nothing comparable to the success obtained less than half a century later by the Imitatio Christi.[25]

12. *Religious reform*

As was indicated in section 1, Langenstein was one of the small group of German scholars whom political difficulties obliged to leave Paris and who became thus the disseminators of the ideas of the Parisian university in the German countries. The great Western Schism had occurred on September 20, 1378; Langenstein and other Germans remained faithful to the Roman pope Urban VI, while Clement VII of Avignon was supported by the French king and state. In June 1379, being still in Paris, Langenstein wrote his first political treatise, Epistola pacis, wherein the Schism is discussed in the form of a dialogue in 88 parts between an Urbanist and a Clementine. He advised Clement not to prop himself on a "reed" like king Charles V, and declared the invalidity of his election. In order to put an end to the schism, he suggested appealing to the mediation of the University of Paris, or of a commission of fifteen to twenty members made up of Urbanists, Clementines, and

[25] For the Imitatio Christi see my note on Geert Groote.

neutrals, or, better still, of a general council having sovereign power over the popes as well as over the rest of Christendom.

These conciliar ideas continued to ferment in his mind, and at the end of May 1381 he wrote a second tract, Epistola concilii pacis (20 chapters in 5 parts), wherein the general council is strongly recommended as the means not only of healing the schism, but of cleansing and reforming the church. It is a very vigorous pamphlet, partly based on the writings of Conrad of Gelnhausen (c. 1320–90), but more radical. It throws a lurid light on the evils of the church and society of that time.

He was obliged to leave Paris in 1383. During his stay at the abbey of Eberbach in the same year, he addressed to the bishop of Worms the Epistola de futuris periculis ecclesiae, largely derived from Hildegard's writings (a saint and prophet of that very region, XII-2). During the rest of his life, spent in Vienna, he wrote other treatises on the subject, to wit, the Invectiva contra monstrum Babylonis (1393), the Epistola de cathedra Petri addressed in 1395 to Berthold, bishop of Freising, and many others. The last named was a clear summary of his conciliar theory.

On the basis of these writings Langenstein must be counted among the few wise men who saw the dangers ahead, but whose advice unfortunately was not heeded in time. If the church had listened to them, not only would the Western Schism have been abridged, but the greater schism of the sixteenth century might have been avoided.

13. *Economics*

During his stay in Vienna Langenstein also took some interest in economic subjects, and wrote his Tractatus de contractibus (questiones de emptione et venditione et de simonia), and his Tractatus de contractibus inter ementes et vendentes (Epistola de contractibus emptionis et venditionis ad consules viennenses). In these writings he also touched on ecclesiastical questions, criticized one of the greatest ecclesiastical evils of the time (simony), and exposed the dangers of excessive property in mortmain.

14. *Study of Hebrew*

Langenstein had obtained some knowledge of Hebrew, and in Vienna 1388 he wrote a treatise de idiomate hebraico. The first part (12 chapters) deals with philological questions such as script in general and problems of transliteration, value of the study of Hebrew for a better knowledge of the Old Testament and better polemics against the Jews, particularities of Hebrew script, e.g. its direction from right to left, the writing of numbers by means of letters. The second part is devoted to the mysteries of the Hebrew alphabet, such as the tetragrammaton, or such as were developed in the gematria of the qabbalists. Langenstein's knowledge of Hebrew was very probably insufficient to obtain such information directly from qabbalistic writings, but he could easily get it from converted Jews. Langenstein should not be blamed for indulging in such fantastic ideas. It is well to bear in mind that the divine origin of the Hebrew characters was generally accepted, and if that premise was right, then their investigation (as we should investigate nature) was not unsound.[26]

[26] For the sake of comparison, allow me to recall that as late as 1687, it was discussed in a thesis before Harvard University whether the Hebrew vowel points were of divine origin as well as the letters themselves! (Isis 25, 515). The affirmative was defended by Gurdon Saltonstall (1666–1724), later governor of Connecticut.

15. *Text*

Langenstein's two main anti-astrological treatises, Questio de cometa and Tractatus contra astrologos coniunctionistas, are edited in Pruckner's book cited below (p. 89–206, Berlin 1933).

Contra fratrem Telesphorum was edited by Bernhard Pez: Thesaurus anecd. novissimus (1, part 2, 507–64, 1721), being wrongly ascribed to Henry of Hessen junior.

The doubtful questions on the Perspectiva communis of John Peckham were printed in a composite Mathematicarum opus (Valencia 1503), together with Bradwardine's arithmetic and geometry.

De spiritibus eorumque discretione libri duo, prior Henrici a Vrimaria, posterior Henrici ab Hassia dicti de Langhensteyn (216 p., Antwerp 1652). Langenstein's treatise is on pp. 123–72. The author of the other treatise was Heinrich von Friemar (Brimaria, Vrimaria, Vrimach, etc.), an Augustinian Hermit, originating in Friemar, near Gotha, who died in Erfurt 1354 (Stanonik, ADB 11, 633–36, 1880).

Speculum animae. Two printings in the fifteenth century: one in Cologne 1470? and another without place or date. Other editions: Strassburg 1507, Basel 1555. The Strassburg text has been reprinted by father Watrigant: La méditation fondamentale avant St. Ignace (p. 116–39), not seen.

French translation with notes by Emmanuel Mistiaen (S.J.): Le miroir de l'âme (Museum lessianum, section ascétique, no. 9, 90 p., Bruges 1923).

Other mystical or edifying books have been printed, even in the fifteenth century, e.g. Secreta sacerdotum (at least 4 incunabula editions); Expositio super dominicam orationem, etc.

Om Klosterlefverne. Swedish translation edited by F. A. Dahlgren: Skrifter till läsning för klosterfolk (p. 1–26, Stockholm 1875).

For the political writings, see Potthast (p. 580–81, 1895–96), and the books of Kneer (1893) and Valois (1896–1902) cited below.

The Tractatus de contractibus was published among the Opera of Jean Gerson (4, 188, Strassburg 1488), not seen.

16. *Criticism*

Otto Hartwig: Henricus de Langenstein dictus de Hassia (60 p., Marburg 1857). Von Schulte (ADB 17, 672, 1883). F. W. E. Roth: Zur Bibliographie des Henricus Hembuche de Hassia (Beihefte zum Centralblatt für Bibliothekswesen 1, 97–118, 26 p., Leipzig 1888). August Kneer: Die Entstehung der konziliaren Theorie (Römische Quartalschrift für christliche Altertumskunde, Supplementheft 1, 145 p., Roma 1893), including text of the Invectiva and of the Epistola de cathedra Petri and analyses of other relevant texts. Noël Valois: La France et le grand schisme d'Occident (4 vols., Paris 1896–1902). Bernhard Walde: Christliche Hebraisten Deutschlands am Ausgang des Mittelalters (p. 8–30, Münster i.W. 1916), including analysis of and extracts from De idiomate hebraico. Langenstein is the earliest of the German Christian Hebraists studied by Walde. Michalski (p. 156, 1927). Karl Grossmann: Die Frühzeit des Humanismus in Wien (Jahrbuch für Landeskunde von Niederoesterreich 22, 150–325, 1929). Flick (1, 295–99, 1930).

17. *Scientific criticism (astronomy and physics)*

Cantor (2, 149, 1899). Duhem: Etudes (3, 15, 1913). Hubert Pruckner: Studien zu den astrologischen Schriften des Heinrich von Langenstein (Studien der Bibliothek Warburg, 286 p., Berlin 1933; Isis 23, 452–54). Thorndike (3, 472–510, 751–59, 1934). A. Crichton Mitchell: The discovery of the magnetic declination (Terrestrial magnetism and atmospheric electricity 42, 241–280, 1937; p. 245; Isis 29, 261). Lynn Thorndike: A hitherto unnoticed criticism of astrology (Isis

31, 68-78, 1939; Isis 32), apropos of the Liber de reprobatione iudiciorum astrologiae ascribable to Oresme or Langenstein; the text is analyzed and discussed.

EVNO

Evno (Eyno, Enno). German (Bavarian) meteorologist (fl. 1331-55).

Evno flourished in Würzburg, Lower Franconia, and wrote a treatise on astrological meteorology and geography entitled Iudicia de impressionibus quae fiunt in aere. It is divided into 18 chapters dealing with the influence of particular signs (houses) and planets, four seasons, seven climes, geographical regions corresponding to each sign, causes of various kinds of weather, aurora borealis. It is largely based on Abu Ma'shar (IX-1). Though the work is theoretical (not a plain record of observations like Merle's), it contains many mentions of meteorological events from 1331 to 1355, the events being cited by the author to justify his predictions and vindicate his astrological theories. The latest fact cited is the price of grain in Franconia 1355, when Saturn was in the sign of the Bull.

Criticism. Thorndike (3, 145-46, 1934).

JOHN OF LIVANIA

German astrologer who flourished in Treves in 1374, that is, according to the Chronicon hirsaugiense of John Trithemius (1462-1516).

John was a canon in St. Simeon, Treves. He wrote books against Occam (XIV-1) and against the alchemist Rupescissa. He composed astrological treatises, and may have been the author of a horoscope of Urban VI at the time of the latter's coronation (1378).

He is said to have been a native of the Moselle district, but the place name, Livania, cannot be identified. Perhaps it should be read Livonia, name of a Baltic region, and John was a German Balt established in Treves?

Criticism. Thorndike (3, 512, 1934).

A7. Poland

HERMANN DE PRZEWORSKO

Polish physician and astrologer (fl. 1368-80), who originated probably in Przeworsko, a small place northwest of Przemýsl in Galicia.

He wrote a short astrological treatise concerning the comet of 1368, De cometa modicum.

There are in the Jagellonian library of Cracow MS tables of syzygies for the meridian of Cracow and the years 1379-80. The unnamed author of those tables was possibly Hermann de Przeworsko, who was soon afterward physician in ordinary at the court of king Władysław V Jagiełło (ruled 1386-1434). The tables prove that the geographical position of Cracow was fairly well determined in the last quarter of the fourteenth century and that mechanical clocks were not of uncommon use in Poland.

Text. MS no. 813, fol. 173-74, University library of Cracow. For tables, MS no. 805 folio, same library.

Criticism. Ludwik Birkenmajer: Krakowskie tablice syzygjów na r. 1379 i 1380 (Bull. of Academy of Sciences, Cracow, Nov. 1890). Hubert Pruckner: Studien zu den astrologischen Schriften des Heinrich von Langenstein (p. 75, Berlin 1933; Isis 23, 452-54).

B. EASTERN CHRISTENDOM

Byzantium

ISAAC ARGYROS

Ἰσαὰκ ὁ Ἀργυρός. Byzantine mathematician, astronomer, and theologian who flourished about the middle of the fourteenth century. He was in his boyhood in 1318, and was still living in 1372. He is described as being a monk and as a disciple of Nicephoros Gregoras (XIV-1; 1295–1359), hence he flourished probably in Constantinople.

He is said to have written astronomical works derived from the Persian sources which had been revealed to Byzantine scientists in 1323 and following years, Πραγματεία *νέων κανονίων συνοδικῶν τε καὶ πανσεληνιακῶν* and Παράδοσις *εἰς τοὺς περσικοὺς προχείρους κανόνας τῆς ἀστρονομίας.*

There are many MSS of the Παράδοσις, most of which are anonymous; in one the work is ascribed to Georgios Chrysococces (XIV-1; fl. Trebizond 1335–46). Argyros might be the author of the Παράδοσις, but that is unproved. On the other hand, the Παράδοσις and the *Ἀστρονομικὴ τρίβιβλος* compiled by Theodoros Meliteniotes c. 1361 have very much in common. Both works date obviously from the same time and are derived from the same Persian sources; in addition, it is possible that the author of the Παράδοσις took advantage of the Τρίβιβλος or vice versa. The Τρίβιβλος is supposed to have been composed c. 1361, the Παράδοσις, which by the way is much shorter, in 1371.

With regard to other mathematical works ascribed to Argyros, we are on safer ground. They are many, and represented by a good many MSS: scholia to the first six books of Euclid and to Ptolemy; a geodesy ("method of geodesy or the measurement of surfaces, exact and shortened") addressed to one Colybos[27] and entirely derived from Heron of Alexandria; notes to Rhabdas' edition of Planudes' arithmetic; a treatise on the astrolabe (dated 1367); and another on the extraction of square roots. The latter is followed by a table of the square roots of all numbers from 1 to 102 in sexagesimal fractions, e.g., $\sqrt{2} = 1\ 24'\ 51''\ 48'''$.

Argyros wrote in 1372 an ecclesiastical computus for one Andronicos Oinaiotes (*Οἰναιώτης*), wherein he recalls having witnessed more than fifty years before in the theme of Thrace, before beginning mathematical studies, an interval of 32 days between the Jewish Passover (March 20) and the Christian Easter (April 23). Now this can only refer to the year 1318, whence we may deduce that he was born probably in the first decade of the century. A second computus, dated 1377, has been ascribed to Argyros by the Jesuit Denis Petau of Orléans (Petavius, 1583–1652) without authority. The method explained in that computus for the determination of Easter is the same as Rhabdas' method.

The introduction to arithmetic (*Εἰσαγωγὴ ἀριθμητική*) of Nicomachos of Gerasa (I-2) was commented upon by Proclos (V-2) and by Philoponos (VI-1). A new edition of that commentary was revised by Argyros.

Finally, he composed three theological treatises against the Palamites: (1) *Ὁ περὶ τῆς τοῦ Θεοῦ μετοχῆς λόγος*, beginning *Ἰσαὰκ μοναχοῦ περὶ διακρίσεως μετοχῆς Θεοῦ ἐν τέσσαρσι τρόποις*, (2) *Λύσις ἀπορίας τινὸς Παλαμητικῆς*, (3) *Τῷ μοναχῷ κῦρ Γεδεὼν τῷ Ζωγράφῳ περὶ τοῦ κατὰ τὴν μεταμόρφωσιν τοῦ σωτῆρος φωτός* (I cannot identify the monk Gideon Zographos). The last treatise discusses with great objectivity the Hesychastic theory concerning the uncreated light which the disciples saw above

[27] Or Colybas (Κολυβᾶς)?

Christ at the time of his transfiguration on Mt. Tabor (see my note on Barlaam, XIV-1). He does not name his adversaries; it is probable that one of them was Joannes Cantacuzenos, who wrote a long treatise against Argyros.

Text. The apocryphal computus was edited by Dionysius Petavius: Uranologion sive systema variorum authorum qui de sphaera ac sideribus eorumque motibus graece commentati sunt . . . (folio, Paris 1630). The two compoti are in PG (vol. 19, 1857, see also vol. 148, 80), Computus ecclesiasticus (col. 1279–1316), computus alius (col. 1315–30). The theological treatises are unpublished except some extracts given by Mercati.

Περὶ εὑρέσεως τῶν τετραγωνικῶν πλευρῶν τῶν μὴ ῥητῶν τετραγώνων ἀριθμῶν. Table of contents of the treatise, and complete table of square roots following it, edited by J. L. Heiberg: Byzantinische Analekten (Abhandlungen zur Geschichte der Mathematik no. 9, dedicated to Moritz Cantor, p. 169–72, Leipzig 1899).

Variations of the commentary on book I of Nicomachos' introduction were edited by Richard Hoche: *Ἰωάννου γραμματικοῦ Ἀλεξανδρέως (τοῦ Φιλοπόνου) ἐξήγησις εἰς τὸ πρῶτον τῆς Νικομάχου ἀριθμητικῆς εἰσαγωγῆς* (Progr. Gymnasium, Wesel, 3 parts, 1864, 1865, 1867). For book II, see Armand Delatte: Commentaire de Proclus-Philopon à l'Introduction arithmétique, *Ἀρχὴ τῆς ἐξηγήσεως τῆς εἰς τὸ δεύτερον τῶν ἀριθμητικῶν ἃ ἐξηγεῖται ὁ Φιλόπονος* (in Anecdota atheniensia 2, 129–87, 1939).

The treatise on the astrolabe, *Μέθοδος κατασκευῆς ἀστρολαβικοῦ ὀργάνου, ἔτι δὲ καὶ ἀπόδειξις λογικὴ τῶν ἐν αὐτῷ καταγραφομένων μεταφορικῶς ἀπὸ τῶν ἐν τῇ σφαιρικῇ ἐπιφανείᾳ εἰς ἐπίπεδον* was edited by Delatte in the same book (2, 236–53, 4 fig., 1939), together with four other treatises on the astrolabe, the last of which is an anonymous one on the Persian astrolabe, *Ἐκ τῆς ἐξηγήσεως τοῦ περσικοῦ ἀστρολάβου* (p. 263–71). This text, derived from a Paris MS (Coislin 338) of the fifteenth century, is probably contemporary with Argyros, or not much later. It is an additional witness to the Persian influences impinging on Byzantine astronomy after 1323.

Criticism. Krumbacher (p. 623, 1897), only 6 lines. Louis H. Gray: Zu den byzantinischen Angaben über den altiranischen Kalender (Byzantinische Zeitschrift 11, 468–72, 1902). Joseph Heeg: Codices vaticani (Catalogus 5, part iii, p. 65, 67, 1910). Heath (2, 555, 1921). Giovanni Mercati: Notizie di Procoro . . . ed altri appunti per la storia della teologia e della letteratura bizantina del secolo XIV (p. 174–75, 229–42, Vaticano 1931), includes (p. 270–75) extracts from Argyros' theological treatises and from Cantacuzenos' treatise against Argyros.

THEODOROS MELITENIOTES

Θεόδωρος ὁ Μελιτηνιώτης. Byzantine astronomer who flourished in Constantinople c. 1360–88.

In the years 1360–88, Theodoros was chief bursar of the great church, archdeacon, and teacher of the teachers, i.e. director of the patriarchal academy in Constantinople (*ὁ μέγας σακελλάριος τῆς ἁγιωτάτης τοῦ Θεοῦ μεγάλης ἐκκλησίας διδάσκαλος τῶν διδασκάλων καὶ ἀρχιδιάκονος τοῦ εὐαγοῦς βασιλικοῦ κλήρου Θεοδώρητος ὁ Μελητινιώτης*). The form *Μελητινιώτης* is probably the original one, but *Μελιτηνιώτης* appears in the fourteenth century and is more frequently used. The dates of his birth and death are unknown.

He wrote c. 1361 an elaborate astronomical treatise entitled *Ἀστρονομικὴ τρίβιβλος*, which is the largest Byzantine treatise on the subject. It is based partly on translations from Persian works, which had become available in his time thanks to the anonymous translation of 1323 (see my note on Shams al-dīn Mīrak Muḥammad al-Bukhārī, XIV-1) and to efforts of Gregorios Chioniades (XIV-1) and the school of Trebizond, but also on Ptolemy and Theon of Alexandria (IV-2). Theodoros' book was very learned, but it does not seem to have been popular, for it is represented today by a single MS (Cod. Vaticanus graecus 1059).

Theodoros' Tribiblos and the Paradosis ascribed to Argyros have much in common; this may be due to plagiarism in the one direction or the other, or to the use and abuse of common sources. This question is discussed more fully in my note on Isaac Argyros.

Theodoros composed a kind of diatessaron, an enormous commentary on the four Gospels, divided into nine parts, a triple triad, *Εἰς τριάδα τριπλῆν ἐξηγήσεις τοῦ διὰ τεσσάρων ἁγίου εὐαγγελίου*, each of which includes nine treatises (*διαλέξεις*); the commentary was based primarily on the Gospel of Luke. As far as can be judged from the remains, for we have only parts IV and V, the whole work must have covered over 2,500 leaves. It was largely derived, and often copied verbatim, from the commentaries of the Greek fathers Basil the Great (IV-2), John Chrysostom, Gregory of Nyssa, Cyril of Alexandria, and John of Damascus (VIII-1).

A long allegorical poem dedicated to a wonderful virgin, impersonating the quality Prudence, *Εἰς τὴν σωφροσύνην* (*ἐρωτικὴ διήγησις* . . .), in 3,060 political verses of fifteen syllables, is often called after its author Meliteniotes, but it is not certain that the author was the same Theodoros who wrote the Tribiblos. It is a fantastic, pedantic, and highly heterogeneous composition containing all kinds of strange ingredients, e.g., what might be called a glossary of mineralogy. It is possible that the author of that monstrous compilation in verse was inspired by the Amorosa visione which Boccaccio composed c. 1342? This would open new horizons concerning the exchange of influences between Italian and Byzantine humanists. We generally think only of the westward stream of influence; there was also undoubtedly an eastward stream. For example, the Teseide of Boccaccio was translated into Greek verse![28] Whether the eastward stream began as early as the middle of the fourteenth century is another question.

It is possible that the Codex genevensis 44, one of the best MSS of the Iliad (Henri Estienne's MS), including a valuable collection of scholia, was written by Theodoros Meliteniotes, or for him; it was certainly owned by him and contains various notes concerning the history of his own family, e.g., the premature death of his father Joannes in 1333; of his brother Nicolas in 1338 at the age of 20, etc.

Text. The commentary on the Gospels is included in PG (149, 881–988, 1865). The introduction to the Tribiblos is edited there (p. 987–1002). Other extracts in Usener (1876), Heeg (1910), and Mercati (1931).

Εἰς τὴν σωφροσύνην. Poème allégorique publié d'après un MS de la Bibliothèque impériale par Emmanuel Miller (Académie des inscriptions 19, part 2, 1–138, Paris 1858).

Criticism. Leone Allacci (Leon Allatios of Chios, 1586–1669): Diatribae, in Angelo Mai's Novae patrum bibliotheca (6, 191–93, Rome 1853). Reprinted in PG (149, 877–80). Hermann Usener: Ad historiam astronomiae symbola (Bonn 1876). Jules Nicole: Les scolies genevoises de l'Iliade (1, xix–xxii, Paris 1891). Krumbacher (chiefly p. 135, 623, 782, 870, 1897). Joseph Heeg: Codices vaticani (Catalogus 5, part iii, p. 68, 133–47, 1910). Giovanni Mercati: Notizie di Procoro e Demetrio Cidone, Manuele Caleca e Teodoro Meliteniota (p. 172–89, Vaticano 1931; Byzantinische Zeitschrift 35, 92–100, 1935). Franz Dölger: Die Abfassungs-

[28] The translation was made soon after the publication of the Italian text (Ferrara 1475), *Θησέος καὶ γάμοι τῆς Ἐμηλίας* (sic) (Venice 1529). John Schmitt: La Théséide de Boccace et la Théséide grecque, in the Etudes de philologie néo-grecque edited by Jean Psichari (p. 279–345, Paris 1892), including long extracts from the Greek text.

zeit des Gedichtes des Meliteniotes Auf die Enthaltsamkeit (Annuaire de l'Institut de philologie et d'histoire orientales vol. 2, Mélanges Bidez, p. 315–30, Bruxelles 1934), concluding that that poem was written very probably by Theodoros Meliteniotes between c. 1355 and 1395.

C. ISRAEL

C1. Spain

JOSEPH BEN ISAAC IBN WAQAR

Joseph ben Isaac ben Moses ibn Waqar of Seville. Judeo-Andalusian astronomer, who flourished c. 1357–95, in Seville and Toledo.

In 1357–58, he compiled astronomical tables in Arabic for the period 720–840 H. = A.D. 1320–1437 and the latitude of Toledo, making them shorter than the much used tables of Ibn al-Kammād (see note below). In 1395–96 he translated these tables himself into Hebrew. Both versions (Arabic and Hebrew) are preceded by an introduction (canones) explaining the construction and use of such tables and the technical terms.

Another member of the same Ibn Waqar family is known to us through the Escorial MS Arabic 873 (Renaud p. 82, 84, 1941). It is a composite astronomical-medical MS containing eleven items, the fifth being an abridgment of the Qānūn of Ibn Sīnā (XI-1) and the eleventh a collection of extracts from the Ḥāwī of al-Rāzī (IX-2) by one wazīr Abū-l-Ḥasan Yahūda ibn abī Isḥāq ibn Istīlja (?). These two items were copied by Yahūda ibn Solomon ibn Waqqār al-Isrā'īlī, at Guadalajara, Castile, respectively in 1333 (?) and 1387.

Criticism. Steinschneider: Hebraeische Übersetzungen (p. 598, 1893); Die hebraeischen Handschriften der Bibliothek in München (2d ed., p. 247, 1895); Die Mathematik bei den Juden (BM 12, 36, 1898); Arabische Literatur der Juden (p. 169, 1902). The Munich catalogue contains an analysis of the Canones. Braunmühl (1, 103, 1900), very brief mention. Melchior M. Antuña: Una versión árabe compendiada de la Estoria de España de Alfonso el Sabio (Andalus 1, 105–54, 1933; p. 107).

Note on Ibn al-Kammād (XII-2?)

This is in all probability Abū-l-'Abbās (?) Aḥmad ibn Yūsuf Ibn al-Kammād,[29] a Spanish (Sevillian?)[30] or Moroccan astronomer who compiled astronomical tables based upon those of al-Zarqālī (XI-2). I did not speak of him in volume 2 because his time is too uncertain; all that one can say is that he is posterior to al-Zarqālī and anterior to al-Ḥasan ibn 'Alī al-Marrākushī (XIII-1), who quotes him; the former died c. 1087, the latter c. 1262.

He compiled three tables: (1) Al-kaur 'alā-l-daur (this is difficult to translate, the words having been chosen for the rhyme rather than for the sense; it refers to a circular movement). (2) Al-amad 'alā-l abad (The purpose for eternity). This table was praised by al-Marrākushī for its correctness. (3) Al-muqtabas (The borrowed [table]). Probably so called because it was derived from the other two tables. He also wrote an astrological treatise, Miftāḥ al-asrār (Key to the secrets).

[29] Variants: Kamād, Jammād, Ḥammād. All these forms are possible, the last mentioned being the most pleasant; it means he who is always praising God.

[30] He is called Ishbilī by W. Ahlwardt in the Berlin catalogue of MSS (5, 219, 1893). Ahlwardt adds that he died in 1194–95 (?).

Ibn al-Kammād is mentioned by Ibn Khaldūn (Quatremère's ed., 3, 107, 1858; translation, 3, 148), but the French editor, misled by Ḥājjī Khalīfa—whose information is contradictory—has confused Ibn al-Kammād with the Tunisian Abū-l-'Abbās (?) Aḥmad ibn 'Alī Ibn Isḥāq al-Tamīmī. This Ibn Isḥāq, who lived in the first half of the thirteenth century, was also a compiler of astronomical tables much used in the Maghrib; he communicated accurate observations made by a Jewish astronomer in Sicily. According to Ibn Khaldūn (whose data are not always correct), the Kitāb minhāj al-ṭālib li ta'dīl al-kawākib of Ibn al-Bannā' (XIII-2; d. c. 1321) was abstracted from the tables of Ibn Isḥāq. According to Quatremère (op. cit. 3, 148), Ibn Isḥāq quoted the date 1280–81 in his tables. The two statements are not irreconcilable. Suter (p. 142, 196, 1900). Sarton: Introd. (2, 999).

ISAAC ALḤADIB[31]

Isaac ben Solomon ben Ẓaddiq ibn al-Ḥadib (or al-Aḥdab; ḥadib and aḥdab mean hunchback in Arabic). Hispano-Jewish astronomer who flourished probably in Castile before 1391 and Aragon before 1396; he was in Syracuse in 1396 and probably in Palermo in 1426.

He was a disciple of Judah ben Asher II, who flourished in Burgos and Toledo and died in 1391; and a correspondent of Samuel ben Ẓarẓa, alias Ibn Sana (or Seneh), who flourished in Valencia in the second half of the fourteenth century; he composed a poem in honor of Isaac ben Sheshet Barfat (Valencia 1326—Algiers 1408). His relation with the last two suggests that he may have spent some time in Aragon before proceeding to Sicily.

He wrote:

1. Oraḥ selulah (Leveled path). Astronomical tables, for the determination of seasons and leap years, based upon the tables commonly used in Tunis of Ibn al-Raqqām, together with four additional tables derived from al-Battānī (IX-2) and a fifth after Ibn al-Kammād.[32] The tables include Canones, divided into 9 chapters. Their date is c. 1381. Their preface contains criticism of the previous tables of Jacob ben David Bonet (Perpignan 1361) and Immanuel ben Jacob Bonfils (Tarascon 1340, 1365). They are represented by many MSS.

2. Keli ḥemda (Precious instruments). Dealing with a kind of astrolabe invented by Alḥadib in Syracuse 1396, which he claimed was superior to the ṣafīḥa of al-Zarqālī (XI-2).

3. Keli ha-memuẓẓa' (Intermediate instrument). Apropos of an astronomical instrument intermediate between the astrolabe and the quadrant, easier to manufacture than the former, easier to handle than the latter. The description is divided into two parts, the first of these subdivided into 26 chapters. The instrument is made for the latitude 36° or 37° (the Hebrew letters waw and zain, representing the figures 6 and 7, can easily be confused). The latitude of Syracuse is 37°3 N.

4. Leshon zahab (Wedge of gold, see Joshua 72:1). On Biblical weights and measures. Lost.

5. Luḥot (Tables). Dated Palermo 1426.

6. He completed the poem written by Moses Ḥandali at the beginning of his

[31] I write this name in one word, because it is a Jewish name. No Jew would have called him Ḥadib or Aḥdab.

[32] I do not know anything about Ibn al-Raqqām (better I think than Rakkām). For Ibn al-Kammād see note above.

(Moses') commentary on the Hebrew translation of the elements of astronomy of al-Farghānī (IX-1), made by Jacob Anaṭoli (XIII-1) c. 1233.

Isaac wrote notes on the treatise on the astrolabe of Jacob ben Maḥir ibn Tibbon (XIII-2) and on the tables of Isaac Israeli the Younger (XIV-1).

Text. Alḥadib's letter to Samuel ben Ẓarẓa is included in the latter's Meqor ḥayyim, a philosophical commentary on the Torah, printed in Mantua 1559.

Criticism. M. Steinschneider: Hebraeische Übersetzungen (p. 550, 556, 1893); Die Mathematik bei den Juden (BM 13, 3–7, 37, 1899). Richard Gottheil (JE 1, 387, 1901). M. E. Jernenski (EJ 2, 136, 1928), very short note.

C2. Catalonia

JACOB BONET

Jacob ben David ben Yom-ṭob (or in Provençal, Bonjorn, Bongodon, Bongoron). Sen Bonet (Boniat). Also Jacob Po'el or ha-Po'el (the maker of tables?). Catalan-Jewish astronomer who flourished at Perpignan c. 1361. His son David was baptized forcibly.

Jacob compiled in 1361 Hebrew astronomical tables (luḥot) for the latitude of Perpignan. They constituted a kind of perpetual lunar calendar, involving a cycle of 31 years. The tables were based upon Abraham bar Ḥiyya and Jābir ibn Aflaḥ (XII-1), Maimonides (XII-2), the Alphonsine tables (XIII-2), and Levi ben Gerson (XIV-1). It should be noted that the Iṣlāḥ al-majisṭī of Jābir ibn Aflaḥ had been available in Hebrew since 1274 and that there were at least two Hebrew translations of it (by Moses ibn Tibbon and by Jacob ben Maḥir), yet very few writers quoted the Hebrew version; as to the Alphonsine tables, they were not available in Hebrew until much later—c. 1460—when Moses ben Abraham Ya'ari of Nîmes translated them. Bonet's tables were preceded by an introduction explaining their use and bewraying their sources.

Judging from the number of MSS in Hebrew, or Latin, or in both languages, these tables were very popular. They were translated into Latin, Tabulae Jacobi filii David Bonaediei, as well as their canones, in the fourteenth or fifteenth century, by an unknown author, and the Latin version was retranslated into Hebrew before the end of the fifteenth century. There are also Hebrew commentaries upon them, by Samuel Kansi, by Joseph ben Saul Qimḥi (unknown time), and by Samuel Foto of Mistra (in Laconia) about the middle of the fifteenth century. They were criticized by Isaac Alḥadib and Abraham ben Samuel Zacuto (1450–c. 1515).

Jacob Bonet wrote geometrical notes (on the cone) to the tables of Jacob ben Maḥir.

Criticism. Neubauer-Renan (p. 591, 701, 1893). M. Steinschneider: Hebraeische Übersetzungen (p. 614–16, 1893); Verzeichnis der hebraeischen Handschriften der K. Bibliothek in Berlin (pt. 2, p. 150, 1897); Die Mathematik bei den Juden (BM 12, 39–40, 1898). H. Gross (p. 470, 1897). Isaac Broydé (JE 3, 305, 1902). Alexander Marx: Recent donations to the library of the Jewish Theological Seminary (United Synagogue recorder p. 13, 1929), apropos of a MS of Foto's commentary written after 1465 by his pupil Joseph. B. Suler (EJ 4, 941, 1929).

Lynn Thorndike: Other astronomical tables beginning in the year 1361 (Isis 34, 6–7, 1942). Notes by J. Ma. Millàs Vallicrosa and Alexander Marx (Isis 34, 410, 1943).

C3. Provence

IMMANUEL BONFILS

Immanuel ben Jacob Bonfils of Tarascon. Judeo-Provençal mathematician, astronomer, astrologer, and translator from Latin into Hebrew. He flourished c. 1340–77, mainly in Tarascon, also in Avignon and Orange; he made astronomical observations and taught mathematics in 1377.

Of his many publications, one had such an extraordinary fortune that we shall deal with it first. That is the Kanfe nesharim (Wings of eagles; allusion to Exodus 19:4), astronomical tables divided into six parts, hence better known under the title Shesh kenafayim (Six wings, allusion to the six wings of the seraphim in Isaiah 6:2); their author is often called Ba'al kenafayim (master of the wings). The tables were completed at Tarascon in 1365, but there was possibly an earlier redaction (radix 1340). The main purpose was to help in determining the Jewish calendar. The six "wings" deal respectively with (a, b) conjunctions and oppositions of the seven planets, (c) determination of time and limits of eclipses, (d) lunar eclipses, (e, f) solar eclipses.

The popularity of these tables is evidenced by the existence of many Hebrew MSS, in some of which there are additional astrological tables and the calculations are continued for later periods. For example, there is one wherein they have been extended to 1480 or 1490 by one Uzziel and entitled Ammude sekel (The pillars of intellect). The text was translated into Latin in 1406 by a physician named Johannes Lucae e Camerino? (= Giovanni del maestro Lucha dell' abaco); that translation was used by Pico della Mirandola (1463–94). What is most remarkable of all, the Six wings were commented upon in Greek by Michael Chrysococces in 1435 under the title *Ἔκδοσις εἰς τὸ ἰουδαϊκὸν ἑξαπτέρυγον*. There were also many Hebrew commentaries, the most interesting being probably those written by Qaraites, with notes indicating how to adjust the Tarascon tables for use in Constantinople and the Crimea.

There must be some connection between the fact that Immanuel's tables were known to the Qaraites and the fact that they were one of the very few mediaeval Hebrew writings which penetrated into the Greek world. Indeed, many Qaraites were conversant with the Greek language, and the Qaraite community was thus a natural link between Israel and Byzantium.

We may now deal more rapidly with Immanuel's other writings. His works may be divided into four groups: astronomy, arithmetic, astrology, Alexandrian legend. I put the astronomical writings in the first group, simply because I have already dealt with one of them, which we may thus leave at the top of the list.

Astronomy. 1. Kanfe nesharim, see above.

2. Bi'ur mi-luḥot le-ḥishuv maqumot ha-kokabim (Treatise with tables for the calculation of the positions of stars). Composed in Tarascon not before 1340.

3. Table to compute the sun's declination based upon the Eben ha-'ezer (Stone of help) ascribed to Abraham bar Ḥiyya. The tables are compiled for Tarascon and Avignon.

4. Luaḥ mattanah ṭobah (Tables of good gift). Tables of Venus and Mercury from 1300 to 1357, according to cycles of 8 and 46 years.

5. Bi'ur 'assiyat ha-aẓṭorlab (On the making of the astrolabe). The latitudes of Arles, Tarascon, and Avignon are mentioned.

6. Note on cycles? (tequfot).

7. Ma'amar 'erek ha-ḥilluf (Value of the inequality). Dealing with inequalities in the motions of sun and moon, which must be taken into account for the accurate determination of eclipses. Together with a criticism of a passage of the Ẓurat al-ereẓ of Abraham bar Ḥiyya (XII-1) concerning lunar eclipses. Computations made with reference to Tarascon 1365.

Arithmetic. 8. Computation of the ratio of the diameter to the circumference. Result, 21,600:67,861. Followed by other arithmetical rules (extraction of square root).

9. Arithmetical rules concerning division, square root, etc.

10. Derek ḥilluq (Way of division). Note on decimal fractions. This short treatise is extremely important, for it contains an anticipation of the exponential calculus as we find it more than a century later in Nicholas Chuquet (1484), and also an anticipation of the decimal calculus developed by Elijah ben Abraham Mizraḥi (d. c. 1525) and others and finally completed by Simon Stevin (1585). Immanuel divides numbers into three classes: integers, fractions, and unit integers. He uses no symbols whatsoever, but his tripartition amounts to this: the "unit integers" are the numbers 1 to 9; "integers" and "fractions," the numbers $a.10^n$ when n is respectively positive or negative. Older mathematicians gave to the units the degree 1, to the tens the degree 2, etc.; using the same language, we should say that Immanuel gives to the units the degree 0, to the tens the degree 1, etc.; this introduction of the exponent 0 (as we should put it, but Immanuel did not) was a necessary condition for the possibility of the exponential calculus. He is aware of the main rules of that calculus,[33]

$$a^m \times a^n = a^{m+n} \quad \text{and} \quad a^m/a^n = a^{m-n},$$

and applies them to decimal multiples and submultiples. In the course of his explanation, however, he relapses into the use of the sexagesimal terminology. He explains the decimal magnification of numbers for root extraction; this was no novelty, it can be traced back at least to the eleventh century.[34]

Immanuel's main scientific sources were al-Battānī (IX-2)—there was no Hebrew translation of his work, but it was available to non-Arabic-reading Jews in the Latin translation of Plato of Tivoli (XII-1); also Abraham ben Ezra and Abraham bar Ḥiyya (XII-1), and Levi ben Gerson (XIV-1). Even if Immanuel did not use Plato's translation, Albategnian astronomy was largely available to him through Abraham bar Ḥiyya.

[33] The first of these rules was implicitly known to Archimedes (witness his Sand reckoner), and the second was implicitly known to Euclid (Elements IX, 11), but both rules were obscured by their wrong conception of the ordering of the decimal numbers. According to the ancient mathematicians, indeed, the units constituted the first degree, the tens the second, etc. This led them to a formula which we should express $a^m.a^n = a^{m+n-1}$. Thus the degree of 100 is 3, of 1,000, 4; 100 × 1,000 = 100,000, the degree of which is 6 (= 3+4−1). This misunderstanding was continued throughout a good part of the Middle Ages; we find it still in the Liber algorismi de practica arismetrice (p. 116) of John of Seville (XII-1), in Abraham bar Ḥiyya (XII-1), and even in Jean de Meurs (XIV-1). The first to express the rule correctly was al-Karkhī (XI-1) in his Kitāb al-kāfī fī-l-ḥisāb (II, ii, ch. 37), but this was done by him with reference to sexagesimal fractions. Immanuel re-explained the correct rule and applied it to the decimal fractions. After that no further progress was possible until a proper symbolism had been invented. For further details on the early history of the exponential calculus, see Gandz' paper of 1936.

[34] G. Sarton: First explanation of decimal fractions, etc. (Isis 23, 168–70, 1935).

Astrology. 11. Treatise on seven constellations.

12. Bi'ur 'al mozne ḥanok. Commentary on the scales of Enoch (or Hermes), which are mentioned in the book of nativities of Abraham ben Ezra.

13. Note on nine comets, ascribed to Ptolemy.

14. Commentary on Abraham ben Ezra's interpretation of the tetragrammaton (i.e., the quadriliteral name of God, yhwh).[35] Includes data concerning 26 conjunctions of five planets.

Alexandrian legend. 15. Toledot[36] Alexander. Under this title Immanuel translated from Latin into Hebrew the Historia de proeliis, the legendary story of Alexander. The translation was made after the Shesh kenafayim (1365), and may have been his last work or one of the last.

But for a general reference in Introd. 1 (p. 127), and other brief allusions passim, I have not dealt with the Alexandrian romance because it belongs to the history of literature and the history of human fancies. It is not too late, however, to remark that since its crystallization in Egypt by the pseudo-Callisthenes[36a] (about second century) it had gradually captured the imagination of all the peoples of the West and of the East as far as and including India. Forms of it are found in almost every language of those countries. There are various traditions (and groups of traditions) in these stories, some of which have been unraveled and thus help us to understand the intellectual linkages connecting in a hundred ways the peoples of the world.

For the Muslim tradition, which began in the Qur'ān (18, 59, Alexander being confused with Moses), see Iskandar-nāma in EI (2, 535, 1921). Emilio García Gómez: Un texto árabe occidental de la leyenda de Alejandro (Madrid 1929; Isis 13, 494), includes a discussion of the two main Arabic traditions—Eastern and Western, i.e., Greek-Arabic and Latin-Arabic. For the Jewish tradition, see Israel Lévi (JE 1, 341–43, 1901); Jehoshua Gutmann (EJ 2, 205–6, 1928).

An archpriest of Naples, called Leo, who went to Constantinople c. 942, brought back a Greek text which he translated into Latin. Leo's version (Nativitas et victoriae Alexandri magni, and other titles, such as later Historia de proeliis) triumphed over all others in the West, and not only in the Western languages, for it was translated into Hebrew and into Arabic, and also from Arabic into Hebrew. Its success was established by the princeps, Strasbourg 1486.

We cannot dwell upon that extremely complicated story, the mere outline of which would fill a large volume: indeed, it would be a cross section of the literary background of the whole civilized world from the Atlantic to Hindūstān, during more than two millennia. Before abandoning it, however, I wish to point out that even such a fantastic collection of legends and marvels as the Alexandrian romance is may be of interest to the historian of science. For example, it includes stories concerning Alexander's descent into the sea. These stories (text and MS illustra-

[35] Ludwig Blau (JE 12, 118–20, 1906).

[36] The word toledot originally meant genealogies, but, genealogies being often accompanied by tales, the meaning changed to history, legend. Solomon Gandz: Dawn of literature (Osiris 7, 437, 1939).

[36a] The pseudo-Callisthenes was probably an Egyptian Greek who flourished before 300. Wilhelm Kroll (PW 20, 1707–26, 1919). The original Callisthenes was born in Olynthos, Macedonia, c. 360 and died in 327 B.C. He was a relation and pupil of Aristotle and a companion of Alexander. He wrote an account of Alexander's expedition, a history of Greece from 387 to 357, etc. His writings are lost, except fragments. Felix Jacoby (PW 20, 1674–1707, 1919).

tions) have been considered by William Beebe in Half mile down (p. 33–41, New York 1934; Isis 24, 236), one of the most fascinating books of the scientific literature of our own time.

Text. The Hebrew text of Shesh kenafayim was published by Naḥmu Bibowiẓ in his edition of the Sefer or ha-Lebana of the Qaraite Isaac ben Solomon (Zhitomir 1872). The text of the Shesh kenafayim, covering 24 pages, was corrected by the famous Ḥayyim Selig Slonimski (1810–1904). Zhitomir is in southwestern Russia, west of Kiev; a great center of Jewish printing. Isaac ben Solomon is otherwise unknown to me.

Immanuel's translation of the Historia de proeliis is unpublished, but another Hebrew translation of the same version done from an Arabic version was edited by Israel Lévi: Le roman d'Alexandre, texte hébreu anonyme (98 p., Paris 1887). The same author published still another Hebrew text, representing another tradition of the same romance, in the Festschrift dedicated to Moritz Steinschneider (p. 142 of Hebrew part, Leipzig 1895).

Solomon Gandz: The invention of the decimal fractions and the application of the exponential calculus by Immanuel Bonfils (Isis 25, 16–45, 1936), first edition of the Hebrew text, with English translation, glossary, and introduction.

Criticism. Neubauer-Renan (p. 692–99, 706, 781, 1893). H. Gross (p. 250, 1897). M. Steinschneider: Hebraeische Übersetzungen (p. 615, 624, 629, 904, 1893); Die Mathematik bei den Juden (BM 12, 79–87, 1898); Die mathematischen Wissenschaften bei den Juden (BM 2, 71, 1901). Isaac Broydé (JE 3, 306, 1902). B. Suler (EJ 4, 944–46, 1929). Alexander Marx: Register Jewish Theological Seminary (p. 184, New York 1930–31), apropos of a Qaraite MS of the Shesh kenafayim, including three commentaries, two of which are by Qaraites; one of these Qaraites was Elijah Shubshi ben Judah Gibbor. George Sarton: The views of Immanuel Bonfils on decimal fractions? (Isis 25, 132–33, 1936), query no. 58, apropos of the Derek ḥilluq. Alexander Marx: The scientific work of some outstanding mediaeval Jewish scholars (Essays in memory of Linda R. Miller p. 165–66, New York 1938).

SAMUEL BEN SIMEON KANSI

Samuel (or Samiel) Astruc d'Escola (Dascola, Dascala). Kansi, derived from keneset (society, school), is the Hebrew equivalent of d'Escola. There are variants in the Hebrew spelling of the name d'Escola, but it is always written with sin and qof. Provençal-Jewish astronomer who flourished probably in the last third of the fourteenth century.

He wrote an abridgment of the Shesh kenafayim of Immanuel Bonfils, with tables derived from Bonfils' work, beginning with the year 1370.

Assuming him to be identical with Samuel ha-Nasi d'Escola, he explained the astronomical tables of Jacob Bonet. He may also be identical with Astruc Samiel d'Escola, who copied the Mishneh Torah of Maimonides in Avignon 1406.

Criticism. Neubauer-Renan (p. 705–6, 1893). H. Gross (p. 146, 1897). Isaac Broydé (JE 7, 433, 1904).

PROFIAṬ DURAN

Isaac ben Moses ha-Levi. Better known under one of his Provençal names, Profiat[37] Duran, Maestre Profiat, En Profet Duran. In Latin: Enprophiath

[37] Endless variants of Profiat: Periphot, Prifoth, Parfait, Pourphet, Propheta. In Hebrew script, final ṭeth.

Duran Hispanus, Peripetus Durant, etc. Literary name: Isaac Efodi, hence Latin Ephodaeus.

Judeo-Catalan philosopher, astronomer, physician, grammarian, defender of Israel. He was born at Perpignan or at Melgueil (Mauguio), near Montpellier; studied in a yeshivah, perhaps in a German one (?); was tutor in the house of Ḥasdai Crescas or of other members of the Crescas family; during the persecutions of 1391 he was converted to Christianity or pretended to be converted, but soon afterward he planned a pilgrimage to Palestine in order to atone for his apostasy and return to his ancestral faith; he was accompanied by David Bonet Bonjorn, who had also been forcibly converted,[38] but who soon abandoned him, probably under the influence of Paul of Burgos, and preferred to remain a Christian. Whether he accomplished the pilgrimage or not, and whatever was the date of his recantation, Profiaṭ Duran was certainly an orthodox Jew at the time of publication of his grammar in 1403. There are no more traces of him after that time.

Talmudic studies did not satisfy him very long, and he turned his attention to philosophy and science (i.e., astronomy, medicine, and grammar). He studied particularly the Sefer ha-kuzari of Judah ha-Levi (XII-1) and the Moreh nebukim (I give the titles of the Hebrew versions, for it was those versions which he read, not the Arabic originals); he was an enthusiastic defender of Maimonides.

His writings were exclusively in Hebrew. A list of them, approximately in chronological order (as in Renan), follows. The most important items are 8, 9, 10, 11, and 13.

1. Remarks on various passages of Abraham ben Ezra (XII-1). One of these concerns the number seven.

2. Astronomical observations written by a pupil. Notes on Ibn Rushd's summary of the Almagest as translated by Jacob Anaṭoli in 1231. Discussion of the astronomical day and of the length of day and night according to season and latitude.

3. Notes on the first book of Ibn Sīnā's Qānūn.

4. Answer to astrological queries concerning the real and middle conjunctions made by Shealtiel Gracian (or Ḥen), a Catalan rabbi, who flourished c. 1383 in Barcelona. See Joseph Heller (EJ 7, 635, 1931).

5, 6. Five letters to Meir Crescas on Biblical questions. One of them deals with the number ten, with references to Abraham ben Ezra and Levi ben Gerson. Another, with the immortality of the soul. A third, with the views on the soul in the Sefer ha tamar (Palm tree, date palm) of Abū Aflaḥ.

Abū Aflaḥ[39] ha-Saraqosṭi (i.e., of Syracuse, not Saragossa) is a mysterious Arabic (?) writer who wrote the book on the palm tree ascribed to king Solomon, at the request of one Abū (or ibn) Mas'ūd of Seville, then head of a Moroccan madrasa. That magical book is known only in Hebrew, Sefer ha-tamar (or ha-tamarim). Another book of his (alchemical) is entitled in the Hebrew version (no other text being extant) Em ha-melek (Mother of the king). The Sefer ha-tamarim was edited by Gerhard Scholem, together with extracts from the Em ha-melek (Qiryat

[38] This David Bonet Bonjorn was probably the son of the astronomer Jacob Bonet. His Christian name was Maestro Astruc Francisco Dios Carna. This according to B. Suler (EJ 4, 950, 1929).

[39] The name Aflaḥ is Arabic. It designates one with a slit underlip. It occurs in the name of the great astronomer Jābir ibn Aflaḥ (XII-1). It does not follow from this Arabic name that the original author wrote in Arabic, even if the Hebrew text includes Arabicisms.

sefer, Jerusalem 1926). Scholem has also edited the Tamar with a German translation (Hannover 1927). See also Steinschneider (p. 849, 1893). J. Kaufmann (EJ 1, 614, 1928).

Additional note on the Sefer ha-tamar kindly supplied to me by Solomon Gandz (letter of July 30, 1935): The Sefer ha-tamar has nothing to say about the sex of palm trees. Its burden is how to prepare out of a paste of dates an artificial or magic bird which will supply oracular answers to questions. Contents: mysticism, magic, sorcery, alchemy, spiritualism (ḥikmah ruḥaniyut), pneumatology, etc. The book was apparently written before the Norman conquest (1071–91), since reference is made to the Arab rulers of the island. In reality it was written much later. Ibn Rushd is quoted. We may conclude that it was actually written in the thirteenth or fourteenth century.

7. Letter of condolence addressed in 1393 to En Joseph Abraham, son of Don Abraham ben Isaac ha-Levi, rabbi of Gerona, apropos of the latter's death.

*8. Ḥesheb ha-ephod (The ephod's girdle), a treatise on the Jewish calendar and its astronomical basis, composed in 1395. Divided into 29 chapters, the 23d of which, on conjunctions and intercalations, is written in verse for mnemonic reasons.

*9. Al tehi ka aboteka (Be not like thy fathers), written in answer to David Bonet Bonjorn, c. 1396, when the latter refused to continue with him to Jerusalem and recant his apostasy. It is a satire on Christianity written in such shrewd manner that Christians mistook it at first for a panegyric. They called it Alteca boteca and used it for their own propaganda, until they realized their mistake and caused the book to be destroyed in autos-da-fé. Having been communicated to Don Meir Alguadez, physician to the king of Castile, it was soon very well known among the Jews of Spain. It was commented upon by the Castilian Joseph ben Shem-ṭob Ibn Shem-ṭob (d. 1480) and others.

*10. Ma'aseh ephod (The ephod's work). Completed in 1403. Divided into 33 chapters with a remarkable introduction. This is an elaborate Hebrew grammar wherein he explains the principles and the religious importance of grammar (Hebrew being the divine language). Jewish learned men may be divided into three groups: talmudists, philosophers, and qabbalists, all of whom are backward in their Biblical studies because of their grammatical ignorance. Strangely enough, in his remarks on the qabbala Profiaṭ speaks only of the Sefer ha-tagin, not of the Sefer yeẓirah and the Bahir, nor even of the Zohar.[40] According to him, the calamities of 1391 may have been partly caused by the Biblical backwardness due to grammatical ignorance. He gives fifteen excellent rules for the improvement of individual studies (see Neubauer-Renan p. 748). He deplores the degeneration of the Hebrew language. His principles were those of the old grammarians such as Ḥayyuj (X-2) and Ibn Janāḥ (XI-1), as against the novelties of Abraham ben Ezra (XII-1) and the empiricism of David Qimḥi (XII-2). He realized that the nif'al is not simply the passive of qal, but is reflexive. His grammar was very popular, and influenced many later grammarians, Christian as well as Jewish.

*11. Kelimmat ha-goyim (Disgrace of nations) or Sefer ha-kelimma. A treatise against Christianity, in 12 chapters, written probably in 1397, dedicated to Ḥasdai Crescas. Profiaṭ was well acquainted with the New Testament, which he had read in Latin, as well as with patristic literature. He controverted the anticipations

[40] For the Sefer yeẓirah see Introd. 2, 367; for the Bahir, 2, 366; for the Zohar, 2, 878. For the Sefer ha-tagin, book of crowns (of the Hebrew letters) and their mystical meanings and virtues, see Judah David Eisenstein (JE 11, 666–67, 1905).

of the New Testament which Christian apologists claim to find in the Old Testament. The Kelimma was used by Shem-ṭob ben Isaac ben Shapruṭ in his Eben boḥan, and more extensively by Simeon ben Ẓemaḥ Duran (1361–1444) in his Qeshet u-magen, without reference to the author.

12. Synoptic commentary on the Moreh nebukim. There are also many references to the same work in his Ma'aseh ephod. At least a part of this commentary was translated into Arabic.

*13. Ma'amar zikron ha-shemadot (Remembrance of the persecutions). A history of persecutions of the Jews down to his own time. It is lost except for extracts preserved in the Yeshu'ot meshiḥo (Victories of his Messiah) of Isaac ben Judah Abravanel (1437–1508), and in other chronicles.

14. Teshubat ephod, answer to the Or 'olam of Joseph ben Joseph Naḥmias (XIV–1).

Text. I cite only the editions of the main publications.

8. Ḥesheb ha-ephod, partly published in the Vienna edition of Ma'aseh ephod (1865).

9. Al tehi ka aboteka. First edition by Isaac 'Aqrish (Constantinople c. 1577). Including commentaries by Joseph ben Shem-ṭob, Astruc Rimok, Solomon Bonfed, Isaac Tarphon, Solomon Duran, Nathan Nagar, Joseph ben Sheshet, Simeon Duran, Joseph ben Yaḥya, Jehiel ben Asher. Later editions; the text only in Abraham Geiger: Melo ḥofnayim (Berlin 1840); text with various commentaries (Breslau 1844); text with various commentaries, notes, and Yiddish translation in Phinehas Heilpern: Eben boḥan (part 2, Frankfurt a.M. 1846). German translations by A. Geiger (Wissenschaftliche Zeitschrift für jüdische Theologie vol. 4, 1839) and by Bertha Badt-Strauss (Berlin, recent, not seen).

10. Ma'aseh ephod. Einleitung in das Studium und Grammatik der hebräischen Sprache. Edited by Joseph Friedländer, Joseph Kohen-Ẓedeq, and Samuel David Luzzatto (Vienna 1865). This edition contains other texts by Profiaṭ Duran.

See also Elisha ben Abraham ben Mattithiah: Magen David (Constantinople 1517), a defense of David Qimḥi against Profiaṭ Duran and David ben Yaḥya.

Short extract from the Ma'aseh (ch. 8) entitled The definition of the science of language and its branches, in Benzion Halper: Postbiblical Hebrew literature (2 vols., Philadelphia 1921), in Hebrew and English.

11. Kelimmat ha-goyim, edited by Adolf (or Ze'eb) Poznański in the periodical Ha-ẓofe me-ereẓ Hagar (Budapest 1913–14).

12. The commentary on the Moreh nebukim is included in various editions of that work, e.g., the folio edition of Venice 1551.

Criticism. Wilhelm Bacher: Die hebräische Sprachwissenschaft vom 10. bis zum 16. Jahrhundert (Trier 1892). Neubauer-Renan (p. 741–53, 1893). M. Steinschneider: Die Mathematik bei den Juden (BM 13, 42–45, 1899). H. Gross (p. 355, 358, 472, 1897). Meyer Kayserling (JE 5, 16, 1893). B. Suler (EJ 6, 123–28, 1930).

D. ISLĀM

D1. Maghrib

'ALĪ IBN ABĪ 'ALĪ AL-QUSṬANṬĪNĪ

Abū-l-Ḥasan 'Alī ibn abī 'Alī al-Qusṭanṭīnī al-Gharnāṭī. Spanish Muslim astronomer (fl. c. 1360).

The nisba Qusṭanṭīnī may refer to Constantina between Seville and Cordova, or to Constantine in Algiers. He wrote an astronomical poem with tables for Abū Sālim Ibrāhīm al-Musta'īn (Marīnī ruler of Morocco 1359–61).

Criticism. Suter (no. 371, 1900), dated c. 1255. H. P. J. Renaud: Additions à Suter (Isis 18, 172, 1932). Brockelmann (suppt. 2, 364, 1938).

AL-JĀDARĪ

Abū Zaid 'Abd al-Raḥmān ibn abī Ghālib al-Jādarī al-Madyūnī. Arabic (Iraqian?) astronomer (fl. 1391).

He was born c. 1375, became timekeeper (muwaqqit) at the great mosque (masjid al-Qarawīyīn) of Fās, and died in that city sometime between 1415 and 1435.

He wrote in 1391/92 a treatise on the determination of time day and night, Rauḍat al-azhār fī 'ilm waqt al-lail wal-nahār, which was commented upon by himself under the title Iqtiṭāf al-anwār (Picking of flowers). He also wrote a treatise on the calendar, Tanbīh al-ānām, and a commentary on a similar treatise by Abū Muqri' (XIV-1).

Criticism. Suter (no. 424a, 1900). Brockelmann (2, 168, 1902; suppt. 2, 217, 1938). H. P. J. Renaud: Additions à Suter (Isis 18, 175, 1932); Déterminations marocaines de l'obliquité de l'écliptique (Bull. de l'Enseignement public du Maroc, 16 p., oct.–déc. 1941), apropos of two unpublished commentaries on the Rauḍat al-azhār; discussing various determinations of the obliquity of the ecliptic by Moroccan astronomers.

D3. Mamlukīyā

AL-BAHĀNIQĪ

Shihāb al-dīn Aḥmad ibn Muḥammad al-Ḥanafī al-Azharī al-Bahāniqī Ibn al-Mu'īnī. Egyptian astronomer (b. 1355).

Author of a treatise on the use of the sufficient quadrant, Risāla fī-l-'amal bil-rub' al-mughnī. I know him only through Brockelmann (suppt. 2, 158, 1938), who says he was born in 1355 (the date of birth is generally the least-known date concerning an unknown person). I do not understand the nisba Bahāniqī; Azharī refers to the college al-Azhar in Cairo.

IBN AL-SHĀṬIR

'Alā al-dīn 'Alī ibn Ibrāhīm Ibn al-Shāṭir al-Muwaqqit. Syrian astronomer (1306–75).

He was born in March 1306, flourished in Damascus, where he was muwaqqit at the great mosque (jāmi' al-Umawī), that is, he was responsible for the determination of the exact times of prayer. He died, presumably in Damascus, in 1375/76.

Like other members of his profession, he was a maker of astronomical instruments, and wrote various treatises explaining their structure and use; but unlike them, he invented new types of instrument and, what is more remarkable, he made valuable astronomical observations and criticized the accepted astronomical theories. He must be counted one of the outstanding astronomers of his time.

He made astronomical observations and wrote perhaps a special treatise, Raṣd ibn Shāṭir, concerning them; at any rate, we gather from his other writings that he fully realized the need of continued and precise observations if one would discover the true motions of heavenly bodies. He determined the obliquity of the ecliptic, at Damascus in 1363/64, 23°31′ (the correct value extrapolated from the present one is 23°31′19″.8).

He invented two new types of quadrant, one of which was called after him al-

'Alā'ī and was described in 1332/33 in his treatise Nuzhat al-sāmi' fī-l-'amal bil-rub' al-jāmi' (Delight of the listener concerning the use of the universal quadrant). The other was called the perfect quadrant (al-rub' al-tāmm) and was described in his treatise Al-naf' al-āmm fī-l-'amal bil-rub' al-tāmm. Other writings of his deal with instruments, Risālat al-iṣṭarlāb, Mukhtaṣar fī-l-'amal bil-iṣṭarlāb . . . , Īḍāḥ al-mughaiyab fī-l-'amal bil-rub' al-mujaiyab, etc.

A model of the 'alā'ī quadrant is preserved to this day in the Bibliothèque nationale, Paris. Ibn al-Shāṭir made it in 1337 for the shaikh 'Alī ibn Muḥammad al-Darbandī. It is told of him that he had constructed a very large and elaborate astrolabe.

In addition to many treatises describing the construction and use of instruments, he wrote others dealing with astronomical problems and theories. The best known is the table bearing his name, Zīj ibn al-Shāṭir, or called the new table, Al-zīj al-jadīd, which was compiled by order of Murād I, 'Uthmānlī sulṭān from 1360 to 1389. Not only are those tables represented by many MSS, but there are also many abbreviations and commentaries. Two of the abbreviations (or commentaries) were made by men holding positions like the author's, that of muwaqqit (which confirms the impression that the muwaqqit of the mosque was likely to be the astronomer and astrologer of a Muslim community). To wit, Al rauḍ al-'āṭir (The perfumed garden), by Ibn Zuraiq al-Khairī, muwaqqit at the Omayyad mosque in Damascus; and the Nuzhat al-nāẓir (Delight of the beholder), by Aḥmad ibn Ghulāmallāh al-Kūm al-Rīshī (d. 1432), muwaqqit in the mosque of al-Mu'ayyad (or al-Aḥmar) in Cairo.

In the introduction to the Zīj, Ibn al-Shāṭir mentions his sources: Maslama ibn Aḥmad al-Majrīṭī (X-2), Ibn al-Haitham (XI-1), Muḥammad ibn al-Ḥusain of Granada (d. 1192), Nāṣir al-dīn al-Ṭūsī (XIII-2), Mu'ayyad al-dīn al-'Urḍī (XIII-2), Muḥyī al-dīn al-Maghribī (XIII-2), Quṭb al-dīn al-Shīrāzī (XIII-2). Thus he was well acquainted with Ptolemaic[41] and Arabic astronomy.

In that introduction and in other theoretical works, such as Ta'līq al-arṣād (Supplement to the observations), Nihāyat al-su'ūl fī taṣḥīḥ al-uṣūl (Final wish in the rectification of the principles), Nihāyat al-ghāyāt fī a'māl al-falakīyāt (Final goal in astronomical operations), he ventures to discuss Ptolemaic astronomy on the basis of new observations. Much as he admires it, he cannot overlook discrepancies. He thus continues the Arabic stream of astronomical criticism exemplified before by such men as Jābir ibn Aflaḥ (XII-1) and Nāṣir al-dīn al-Ṭūsī (XIII-2). He was strongly criticized for that by Muḥammad ibn Ma'rūf Taqī al-dīn (1525–85), who was a decimalist before Stevin yet a Ptolemaist after Copernicus (Isis 23, 171).

Finally, he wrote a treatise dealing with the sexagesimal ratio (bi-l-nisba al-sittīnīya), that is, I assume, with sexagesimal fractions?

Ibn al-Shāṭir might have been placed in the first half of the century, for he was precocious enough to carry on a correspondence concerning the quadrant with Aḥmad ibn al-Sarrāj (d. c. 1326);[42] yet his main work, the Zīj jadīd, was completed after 1360, and he lived until 1375. It is thus better to place him in the second half of the century.

[41] All the sources quoted were Ptolemaic, the main one being Nāṣir al-dīn, who had edited the Almagest (Introd. 2, 1008, no. 34). In the Nihāyat al-su'ūl, Ibn al-Shāṭir quoted the Hypothesis of Ptolemy, which he knew in the Arabic translation of Thābit ibn Qurra (IX-2)—we ourselves do not know the second part of it otherwise.

[42] Shihāb al-dīn Aḥmad ibn al Sarrāj al-Ḥamawī was then in Cairo. He wrote treatises on the astrolabe and the quadrant, and died in Aleppo c. 1326. See Brockelmann (2, 126; suppt 2, 156). Suter (no. 508) places him much later.

Text. The texts are unpublished, but an extract from Al-rauḍ al-'āṭir giving the longitude, latitude, and inḥirāf of the qibla[43] for about a hundred places was edited by Carl Schoy: Abhandlungen von Al-Faḍl ibn Ḥātim al-Nairīzī über die Richtung der Qibla (Sitzungsberichte der K. bayerischen Akad. der Wissenschaften, math. Kl., p. 55–68, Munich 1922; Isis 5, 209).

Criticism. Ḥājjī Khalīfa (2, no. 6460, p. 465–69; no. 6462, no. 6934, p. 557, 1842), unusually long articles on the 'ilm al-raṣd and the 'ilm al-zīj. Suter (p. 168, 1900; p. 177, 1902). Brockelmann (2, 126, 1902; suppt. 2, 157, 1938). Eilhard Wiedemann: Ibn al-Shāṭir (Beiträge 79; Erlangen Sitzungsberichte 60, 317–26, 1928, Erlangen 1929), this was his last Beitrag, published posthumously; he died in 1928. Schmalzl (p. 100–8, 1929).

IBN ZURAIQ

Syrian astronomer (flourished at end of fourteenth century and beginning of fifteenth).

Muḥammad ibn 'Alī Ibn Zuraiq (better reading than Zarīq) al-Khairī al-Jabartī[44] al-Shāfi'ī was muwaqqit at the Omayyad mosque in Damascus.

He wrote (1) a summary (talkhīṣ), Al-rauḍ al-'āṭir (The perfumed garden), of the astronomical tables of his predecessor Ibn al-Shāṭir; (2) Risāla al-nashr al-muṭaiyab fī-l-'amal bil-rub' al-mujaiyab (The pleasant smell concerning the use of the sine quadrant); (3) Talkhīṣ al-'ibārāt wa īḍāḥ al-ishārāt (on binomial and ἀποτομή).

Criticism. Suter (p. 173, 1900). Eilhard Wiedemann: Ibn al-Shāṭir (Beiträge 79, p. 324, Erlangen 1929). H. P. J. Renaud: Additions à Suter (Isis 18, 175, 1932). Brockelmann (suppt. 2, 157, 1938).

AL-KHALĪLĪ

Shams al-dīn Abū 'Abdallāh Muḥammad ibn Muḥammad al-Khalīlī. Syrian astronomer (fl. 1378–1408).

He was mu'adhdhin in the Omayyad mosque in Damascus toward the end of the century. He compiled c. 1378 elaborate tables after the pattern of the tables of al-Ḥasan al-Marrākushī (XIII-1), serving for the determination of time, qibla, etc. The title Al-jadwal āl-āfāqī refers to the whole work or to a part of it. Another table of his, dated 1408, is entitled Jadwal faḍl al-dā'ir wa'amal al-lail wal-nahār; it is calculated for the latitude 33°31′ (the latitude of Damascus is 33°30′). "Faḍl al-dā'ir" is the hour angle (or its supplement); this is thus a table (jadwal) giving the hour angles of sun and stars, for use in the day or at night.

He also wrote treatises on the use of various kinds of quadrants: Risāla fīl-'amal bil-jaib al-ghā'ib (with the hidden sine); Risāla fīl-'amal bil-murabba'; Al-nujūm al-zāhira, on the use of the sine quadrant. The last-named title (Brilliant stars) was given to similar writings by other writers, 'Abdallāh ibn Muḥammad al-Wafā'ī, also time keeper (muwaqqit) in the Omayyad mosque (d. 1469), and Sibṭ al-Māridīnī (d. c. 1494 or 1506).

One of these quadrant treatises is perhaps identical with the treatise on the sine quadrant translated into Hebrew by Moses Galliano ben Judah.

[43] Azimuth of the place with reference to the direction Mecca-Madīna. See C. Schoy: Qibla (EI 2, 985–89, 1927).

[44] This nisba refers to a Muslim Abyssinian origin, but the reading of it is uncertain. It may be Jabarī, Jibritī, Jizī, or Ḥarīrī?

Another Khalīlī who was probably also a mu'adhdhin or muwaqqit flourished at the same time, to wit, Sharaf al-dīn Abū 'Imrān Mūsā ibn Muḥammad al-Khalīlī, who wrote c. 1402 a treatise on the determination of the times of prayers and of the direction of the qibla, Talkhīṣ fī ma'rifat awqāt al-ṣalāt wajihat al-qibla 'inda 'adam al-ālāt; he also wrote a treatise on the astrolabe and its use for the determination of time, Risāla fī-l-aṣṭarlāb wa ma'rifat al-awqāt. The nisba Khalīlī refers probably in both cases to the place Khalīl = Hebron in southern Palestine, so called after the friend (khalīl) of God, Abraham.

Criticism. Steinschneider (p. 575, 1893). Suter (p. 169, 1900). Brockelmann (2, 127, 1902; suppt. 2, 157, 1938). Schmalzl (1929).

For the second Khalīlī, see Suter (p. 173, 1900). Brockelmann (2, 127, 1902; suppt. 2, 158, 1938).

TAQĪ AL-DĪN AL-ḤANBALĪ

Taqī al-dīn ibn 'Izz al-dīn al-Ḥanbalī. Egyptian or Syrian mathematician (fl. before 1409).

He wrote a treatise on arithmetic called Ḥāwī al-lubāb min 'ilm al-ḥisāb, the MS of which (Paris, Bibliothèque nationale, 2469) is dated 1409/10. We place him tentatively in the second half of the fourteenth century.

The treatise includes a discussion of arithmetical proofs (mīzān, or imtiḥān) by casting out of sevens, eights, nines, and elevens.

Criticism. Carra de Vaux: Sur l'histoire de l'arithmétique arabe, 2. De la preuve par 7, 8, 9 ou 11 (BM 13, 33–36, 1899). Suter (no. 502, p. 199, 1900). Brockelmann (suppt. 2, 156, 1938).

IBN AL-HĀ'IM

Egyptian mathematician (1352/55–1412).

Shihāb al-dīn Abū-l-'Abbās Aḥmad ibn Muḥammad Ibn al-Hā'im al-Faraḍī was born in Cairo in 1352 or 1355, and was for a long time professor in the madrasa Ṣalāḥīya (founded by Ṣalāḥ al-dīn in 1188) in Jerusalem. He died in that city in 1412.

He wrote many books dealing with arithmetic, inheritance problems, algebra. Suter enumerates ten, Brockelmann eighteen. He seems to have been the mediaeval equivalent of the successful writer of elementary textbooks today. His textbooks were frequently republished with new commentaries. For example (the numbers are Brockelmann's):

1. Murshid al-ṭālib ilā' asnā'-l-maṭālib, on arithmetic, commented upon six times and also many times abridged, the abridgments being the basis of new commentaries.

2. Kitāb al-luma' fī 'ilm al-ḥisāb. Arithmetic with special reference to inheritance problems. Thrice commented upon.

3. Al-muqni'. Short algebraic poem. Commented upon by the Syro-Egyptian mathematician, astronomer, and instrument maker Sibṭ al-Māridīnī (1423–1506), who was even more prolific and successful as a textbook producer than Ibn al-Hā'im, and who commented upon other writings of his (e.g., nos. 4, 7 below).

4. Targhīb al-rā'iḍ fī 'ilm al-farā'iḍ.

7. Al-ma'ūna fī 'ilm al-hawā'ī, on mental computation. Abridgment entitled Al-wasīla.

10. Ghāyat al-su'ūl fī-l-iqrār bil-majhūl.

15. Sharḥ al-arjūza al-Yāsmīnīya. Commentary on the algebraic poem of the Moroccan Ibn al-Yāsmīnī (XII-2).

Shihāb al-dīn Abū-l-'Abbās Aḥmad ibn Muḥammad ibn al-Hā'im should not be confused with an Egyptian poet who bore exactly the same name but who was born in al-Manṣūra, Egypt, in 1396, flourished in Cairo, and died there in 1482 (Brockelmann 2, 19).

Criticism. Suter (p. 171, 1900; p. 178, 1902). Brockelmann (2, 125, 1902; suppt. 2, 154–55, 1938).

Some information on Ibn al-Hā'im will be found in the Kitāb ins (or anīs) al-jalīl bi ta'rīkh al-Quds wal-Khalīl, a chronicle of Jerusalem and Hebron to 1494 written by 'Abd al-Raḥmān ibn Muḥammad Mujīr al-dīn al-'Ulaimī al-Ḥanbalī (1456–1521). Printed in Arabic (2 vols., 712 p., Cairo 1866), extracts in French by Henry Sauvaire: Histoire de Jérusalem et d'Hébron (346 p., Paris 1876). Brockelmann (2, 43, 1902; suppt. 2, 41, 1938). Tūqān (p. 222–24, 1941).

IBN AL-MAJDĪ

Egyptian astronomer and mathematician (1358?–1447).

Shihāb al-dīn Abū-l-'Abbās Aḥmad ibn Rajab ibn Ṭībughā, called Ibn al-Majdī. He was born in 1358/59 (or 1365?), flourished in Egypt, and died on January 27, 1447.

He wrote many treatises on the use of quadrants, astronomical observations and tables, etc. Brockelmann enumerates 26, but this includes probably many duplications. I shall cite most of them, classifying them as well as possible, but keeping Brockelmann's numbers for the student's convenience in finding MSS.

Use of quadrants. 1. Khulāṣat al-aqwāl fī ma'rifat al-waqt wa-ru'yat al-hilāl (Choice words concerning the determination of time and the discovery of the new moon as soon as it appears), explaining use of the sine quadrant.

17. Al-manhal al-'adhb al-zulāl fī taqwīm al-kawākib wa ru'yat al-hilāl. May possibly be identical with no. 1?

2. Irshād al-ḥā'ir ilā takhṭīṭ faḍl al-dā'ir (Guide of the perplexed concerning the drawing of sine lines on the quadrant or dial).

11. Zād al-musāfir fī (ma'rifat) rasm khuṭūṭ faḍl al-dā'ir (The traveler's viaticum concerning the drawing of sine lines on the quadrant). This is an extract from no. 2.

4. Risāla fī-l-'amal bi rub' al-muqanṭarāt al-maqtū'. On the use of a special kind of quadrant bearing projections of almucantars or parallels of altitude.

19, 22. Irshād al-sā'il ilā uṣūl (or aḥwāl) al-masā'il. Commentary on the Al-durr (or al-lu'lu') al-manthūr fī-l-'amal bi rub' al-dastūr, a treatise by 'Abdallāh ibn Khalīl al-Māridīnī on the use of the dastūr quadrant. That quadrant is a full circle like an astrolabe, but with one of its quadrants fully delineated.

26. Al-rauḍ al-azhar (The brilliant garden), on the use of a special kind of quadrant called mushaṭṭaḥ (drunken, ṣūfī term) or musattar (hidden).

Determination of the qibla. 3. Tuḥfat al-aḥbāb fī naṣb al-bādhahanj wal-miḥrāb (Gift of friends on the erection of the bādhahanj [?][44a] and the miḥrāb).

Almanacs and tables. 6. Al-jāmi' al-mufīd fī-l-kashf 'an-uṣūl masā'il al-taqwīm wal-mawālīd (On the principles of almanacs and nativities).

[44a] Probably misreading for the Persian word bād-āhanj, ventilating window. Compare the two other Persian words bādkash, punkah, and bād-gīr, airy house, funnel for the admission of air.

8, 9. Al-durr al-yatīm fī tashīl ṣinā'at al-taqwīm (The unique pearl, to facilitate the compilation of the calendar). That book is lost, but there is a commentary by the author explaining how to use it, Risāla fī 'amal kitābihi musammā al-durr . . . , and a table of Saturn, Ta'dīl zuḥal, extracted from it.

12. Al-tashīl wal-taqrīb fī bayān ṭuruq al-ḥall wal-tarkīb, on methods of explanation and composition of tables.

13. Ghunyat al-fahīm wal-ṭarīq ilā ḥall al-taqwīm, method of explanation of the calendar.

14. Al-kawākib al-muḍī'a fīl-'amal bil-masā'il al-daurīya (Brilliant stars concerning periodic motions?).

23. Majmū' maḥlūlāt fī 'ilm al-nujūm. Collection of problems concerning the stars.

25. Jadāwil al-sumūt. Table of azimuths. (The words azimuth and zenith are both derived from the Arabic samt, pl. sumūt).

Sun and moon. 15, 16. Dastūr al-nayyirain (Tables of the sun and moon). Probably the same as Zīj al-shams wal-qamar.

18. 'Iqd al-durar fīl-'amal bil-qamar (Pearl necklace, tables of the moon).

24. Taqdīr al-qamar (or ta'ādīl al-qamar). Tables of the moon.

Arithmetic. 10. Kashf al-ḥaqā'iq fī ḥisāb al-daraj wal-daqā'iq (Unveiling of the truth concerning the calculation of degrees and minutes), on sexagesimal fractions.

(Suter no. 7). Al-muftakarāt al-ḥisābīya (Reflections on computation). This is available in an Escorial MS with a commentary by Nūr al-dīn 'Alī al-Faraḍī dated 1461.

Inheritance problems. 20. Ibrāz laṭā'if al-ghawāmiḍ wa iḥrāz ṣinā'at al-farā'iḍ. Extracted from his Kāfī fī mīrāth al-umma, dated 1434.

21. Sharḥ (commentary on the) Naẓm al-la'ālī fīl-farā'iḍ of Ṣāliḥ ibn Thāmir al-Ja'barī (1223–1306), a Shāfi'ī treatise on inheritance.

Text. None of these texts has been published.

Criticism. Suter (p. 175–77, 1900; p. 178, 1902). Brockelmann (2, 128, 1902; suppt. 2, 158, 1938). Schmalzl (1929).

IBRĀHĪM AL-ḤĀSIB

Ibrāhīm al-Ḥāsib al-Mālikī al-Manṣūrī al-Naṣīrī. Egyptian astrologer (fl. 1358). He wrote in Cairo 1358 commentaries on (or extracts from) the Kitāb al-ulūf wal-adwār, the Kitāb al-qirānāt, and the Kitāb al-amthāl of Abū Ma'shar (IX-1).

Criticism. Not in Suter. Brockelmann (suppt. 2, 157, 1938).

D5. Farther East

'AṬĀ' IBN AḤMAD

Abū Muḥammad 'Aṭā' ibn Aḥmad ibn Muḥammad ibn Khwāja Ghāzī al-Samarqandī. Persian astronomer, writing in Arabic (fl. 1362).

In 1362, 'Aṭā ibn Aḥmad wrote an astronomical treatise with lunar tables for a Mongol prince of the Yüan dynasty, Tchenn-hsi-wou-tsing (?).[45] The original autograph MS (Bibliothèque nationale, Paris, MS arabe 6040, 58 leaves) bears

[45] I copy the name as given by Blochet, hence spelled in the French way. Blochet does not give the Chinese characters.

annotations in Mongol and a Chinese title.[46] This text would deserve to be investigated.

Criticism. E. Blochet: Catalogue des MSS arabes (p. 169, Paris 1925), giving full name and genealogy of the Yüan prince, but without Chinese characters; the part of it which is transcribed above would probably read in our transliteration Chên hsi wu ching. The Chinese-Arabic title, which we reproduce for the sake of curiosity (fig. 26), does not throw any light on this point; it is not really a title, but a bibliographer's or cataloguer's note, including the mention "59" (leaves).

'ABD AL-WĀḤID IBN MUḤAMMAD

Muslim astronomer (fl. 1394).

He wrote (1) in the year 1394/95 an Arabic commentary on Risāla-i-sī faṣl (a Persian treatise on the calendar in thirty chapters) of Nāṣir al-dīn al-Ṭūsī (XIII-2); (2) a commentary on Al-mulakhkhaṣ fī-l-hai'a (Quintessence of astronomy) of al-Jaghmīnī (XIV-1); (3) a poem (manẓūma) on the use of the astrolabe, for his disciple Muḥammad Shāh al-Fanārī.

This 'Abd al-Wāḥid ibn Muḥammad should not be confused with 'Abd al-Wāḥid ibn Muḥammad, abū 'Ubaid al-Juzjānī,[47] who was the favorite pupil of Ibn Sīnā (XI-1) and completed the latter's autobiography. A treatise on astronomy, Kaifīya tarkīb al-aflāk, and an appendix to Ibn Sīnā's Kitāb al-najāh are ascribed to al-Juzjānī.

Criticism. Suter (no. 425, 1900). Brockelmann (1, 512, 1898; suppt. 1, 931, 1937).

'ABDALLĀH IBN KHALĪL AL-MĀRIDĪNĪ

Iraqian mathematician (d. 1406/7).

I think it would be better to read the nisba Mārdīnī, for it is connected with the city generally called Mārdīn (Māridīn in Arabic, Marde in Syriac) in Upper Mesopotamia (EI 3, 273–77). We have come across another mathematician bearing the same nisba, Ismā'īl ibn Ibrāhīm al-Māridīnī (XIII-1), and there is a third one, 'Abdallāh's grandson, Muḥammad ibn Muḥammad (1423–1506) called Sibṭ al-Māridīnī (sibṭ = ibn bint, son of the daughter). Since this third one, who flourished in Cairo, was the more famous, writings of his grandfather are ascribed to him.[47a]

'Abdallāh was the caller to prayer (mu'adhdhin) in the Omayyad mosque in Damascus (not in Cairo, as is sometimes said because of confusion with his grandson). He wrote treatises on the use of quadrants and on trigonometry. The following are numbered as in Brockelmann.

1. Al-durr (or al-lu'lu') al-manthūr fī-l-'amal bi rub' al-dastūr (The dispersed pearls on the use of the dastūr quadrant). Also called al-sittīnīya because it is divided into 60 chapters. There is a commentary by Ibn al-Majdī.

2. Al-waraqāt, or Risāla fī 'amal bi rub' al-dā'ira al-mawḍū' fīhi-l-muqanṭarāt,

[46] I have a complete film of that MS.

[47] In Introd. 1, p. 711, I called him Zuzajānī. That is simply another plausible vocalization of the same name.

[47a] For Sibṭ al-Māridīnī see Karl Schoy: Sonnenuhren der spätarabischen Astronomie (Isis 6, 332–60, 1924). Suter (no. 445, p. 182, 1900; p. 179, 1902). Brockelmann (2, 167–68, 1902; suppt. 2, 215–17, 1938).

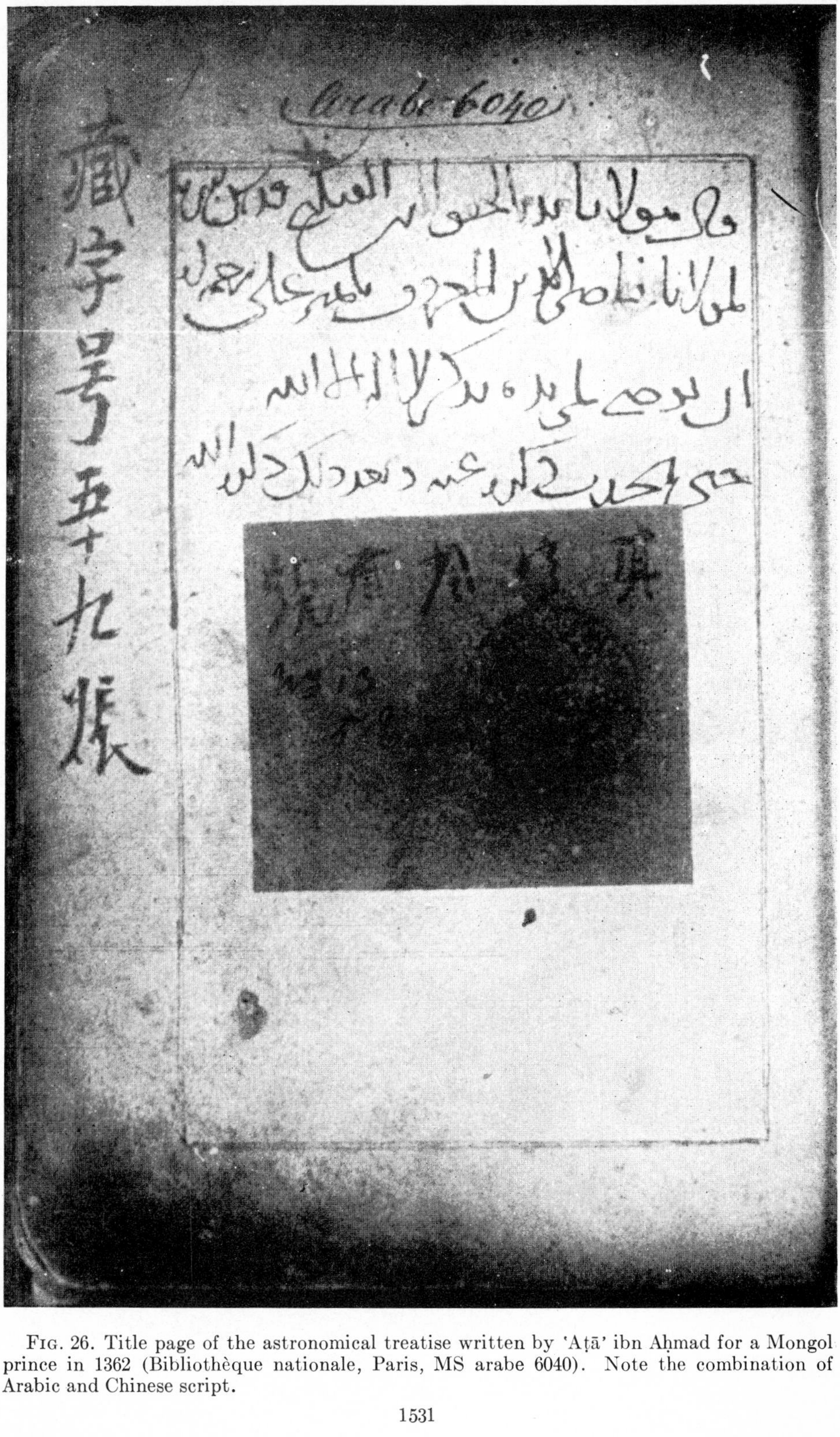

FIG. 26. Title page of the astronomical treatise written by 'Aṭā' ibn Aḥmad for a Mongol prince in 1362 (Bibliothèque nationale, Paris, MS arabe 6040). Note the combination of Arabic and Chinese script.

on the use of a quadrant bearing "almucantars" or parallels of altitude (circles of equal altitude). This was commented upon by al-Ḥasan ibn Khalīl al-Karādīsī al-Ṭubnī (Algerian mathematician who flourished in Cairo, 1420–82) and abbreviated by Sibṭ al-Māridīnī and others.

3. Risāla fī-l-'amal bil-rub' al-mujaiyab, or Mujmalat al-maṭlūb fī'amal al-juyūb. Use of the sine quadrant.

4. Al-shabaka (The network), trigonometrical and astronomical tables.

6. Ghāyat al-intifā'. On the sine quadrant.

Criticism. Suter (p. 170, 1900; p. 177, 1902). Brockelmann (2, 169, 1902; suppt. 2, 218, 1938). Schmalzl (1929). Martin Plessner (EI 3, 294, 1930). H. P. J. Renaud: Additions à Suter (Isis 18, 173, 1932). H. G. Farmer (nos. 240, 240a, 1940), ascribing to this Māridīnī two musical treatises, Muqaddama fī 'ilm qawānīn al-anghām (on the canons of melodies), Arjūza fī sharḥ al-naghamāt (poem on melodies). W. H. Worrell and W. Carl Rufus: Maridini's introduction to the use of the quadrant (Scripta mathematica 10, 170–80, 1944), contains translation of the introduction to item 1.

D6. Islam (Undetermined)

'ABD AL-QĀDIR IBN 'ALĪ

Muḥyī al-dīn 'Abd al-Qādir ibn 'Alī ibn Sha'bān al-Ṣūfī. Muslim author of a treatise on finger reckoning, who flourished in the last quarter of the fourteenth century or later.

The treatise is a commentary (sharḥ) on another text on the same subject, a poem (manẓūma) of 54 lines, fī ḥisāb al-yad (finger reckoning), ascribed to one Abū-l-Ḥasan 'Alī called Ibn al-Maghribī (this suggests that that 'Alī was of Western origin but lived in the East or in Egypt, for he would not be called a Maghribī in the Maghrib); the author of the manẓūma is also called Ibn Shu'lah. The dating of the commentary is very uncertain, a terminus post quem being provided by a reference in it to a treatise on archery, Ghunyat al-ṭullāb fī ma'rifat al-ramy bil-nushshāb, which may be the poem (arjūza) bearing that very title composed by Ṭaibughā al-Ashrafī al-Baklamishī al-Yūnānī (d. c. 1394).

All this is very unsatisfactory, and the manẓūma and its commentary would not have been mentioned here at all, but for their exceptional interest. For they are the earliest Arabic texts dealing with finger reckoning, and they are probably not earlier than the fourteenth century. There is a tradition, however, that some kind of such reckoning (ḥisāb al-'uqūd) was already practiced by companions of the Prophet (Ḥājjī Khalīfa 3, 64), and thus I should not be surprised if earlier texts than these came to light. Indeed, I know of one text by title (no MSS are thus far available), the Kitāb al-ḥisāb bilā takht bal bil-yad (Computation without writing board with the hand), by Abū-l-Qāsim 'Alī ibn Aḥmad al-Mujtabā al-Anṭāqī (from Antioch), who flourished in Baghdād under the Buwayhī sulṭān 'Adūd al-dawla (949–82) and died in 987. Suter (no. 140, 1900). Ṣāliḥ Zekī (1911).

The earliest Western text on finger reckoning is the De loquela per gestum digitorum of Bede (VIII-1), who speaks of flexus and inflexiones digitorum, but does not make the distinction between digiti (digits, numbers under ten) and higher numbers, articuli. That distinction was first made by Abbo of Fleury

(X-2), as explained by his pupil Byrhtferth of Ramsey (XI-1).[48] The Arabic texts just mentioned have no terms for digiti vs. articuli, but speak only of flexion or knots ('aqd, 'uqūd).

Text. Text of the sharḥ including the manẓūma edited by Julius Ruska: Arabische Texte über Fingerrechnen (Der Islam 10, 87–119, 1920; Isis 3, 456).

Commentary. Brockelmann (2, 135, 1902; suppt. 2, 167, 1938), for Ṭaibughā. Florence A. Yeldham: The story of reckoning in the Middle Ages (London 1926; Isis 10, 259), deals only with Western Christendom.

Other Oriental Texts on Finger Reckoning

There are at least two other texts, the one in Persian, the other in Arabic; the second may be anterior to that of 'Abd al-Qādir ibn 'Alī, the first is certainly posterior. In any case the three texts represent similar traditions and should be investigated together.

Gul-Chīn: To the editor (Asiatic journal 6, 337–47, London 1818), undated Persian text with translation. Gul-Chīn (whoever that may be) first copied it from an old Persian MS dictionary, afterward destroyed, then found it again in the Farhang-i Jahāngīrī, the dictionary compiled by Jamāl al-dīn Ḥusain Injū (lithographed, Lucknow 1876). Silvestre de Sacy: De la manière de compter au moyen des jointures des doigts, usitée dans l'Orient (Journal asiatique 3, 65–71, 1823), French translation of the same text as given in the Jahāngīrī. Aristide Marre: Manière de compter des anciens avec les doigts des mains d'après un petit poème inédit arabe de Chems-eddin el-Mossouli et le Tratado de mathematicas de Juan Perez de Moya imprimé à Alcala de Henares en 1573 (Boncompagni's Bullettino 1, 309–18, Roma 1868). This poem was written by Shams al-dīn Abū 'Abdallāh Muḥammad ibn Aḥmad al-Mawṣilī al-Ḥanbalī, whom I cannot identify with certainty; he may be identical with one mentioned by Brockelmann (1, 409, §12) who died in 1258 (?).

See also for further comparison the article 'ilm al-ḥisāb in Ḥājjī Khalīfa (3, 60, 1842), especially ḥisāb al-'uqūd (p. 64). Heinrich Suter: Ḥisāb (EI 2, 315–16, 1916).

E. INDIA

NĀRĀYAṆA

Hindu mathematician (fl. 1356).

The name Nārāyaṇa is not uncommon in Sanskrit literature, but the earliest and most important of the men of science bearing it is the mathematician Nārāyaṇa

[48] The continued use of finger reckoning in the West is illustrated by a reference to it in Frederick II (XIII-1): De arte venandi cum avibus (book II, ch. 42). English translation by Casey A. Wood (p. 143, 1943; Isis 35, 182–84). That reference is particularly impressive because of its casualness; the emperor would not have made it if it had not been perfectly clear to his readers. J. G. Schneider's explanation, quoted by Wood (p. 143, n. 1), that the monks used finger reckoning because they were sworn to silence, is silly.

Florian Cajori: Comparison of methods of determining calendar dates by finger reckoning (Archeion 9, 31–42, 5 figs., 1928; Isis 11, 529). The earliest example of calendar reckoning by hand was found by Cajori in an Italian portolano prepared for the period 1384–1434, once owned by the Venetian family Pinelli, now in the British Museum.

For the history of finger reckoning in Israel see Solomon Gandz: The hall of reckoning in Jerusalem (Jewish quarterly review 31, 383–404, 1941; Isis 33, 390).

son of Nṛisiṃha (or Narasiṃha). His place of origin is unknown. In order to appreciate the importance of his achievements it is well to bear in mind that Hindu (vs. Muslim) culture and science was then in a decadent, if not moribund, stage because of the cultural oppression of the Muslim conquerors.

From the single date in Nārāyaṇa's life (1356) we conclude that he was fortunate enough to outlive the cruel and disastrous rule of Muḥammad ibn Taghlaq (ruled 1325–51) and to enjoy that of Fīrūz Shāh (ruled 1351–88), who was perhaps the best emperor of his dynasty.

Nārāyaṇa wrote two or three mathematical works: (1) Gaṇita-pāṭi-kaumudī, or simply Gaṇita-kaumudī (Elucidation of arithmetic), and (2) Bīja-gaṇitāvataṃsa (Ornament of algebras). According to the MS, the first of these works was completed in Śaka 1278 = A.D. 1356; the date of the second is unknown, the only MS extant (no. 2298 in Sanskrit College, Benares) breaking off abruptly in the middle. The third work, (3) Karma-pradīpikā, is a commentary on the Līlāvatī of Bhāskara. Though it bears Nārāyaṇa's name in the MS (Government Library, Madras, no. 13484), the ascription to this Nārāyaṇa is uncertain.

The arithmetical text does not seem to contain any important novelties as compared with earlier Sanskrit ones. For example, he follows his predecessors Āryabhaṭa (V-2), Mahāvīra (IX-1), Bhāskara (XII-1) in naming the decimal places (eka, unit; daśa, ten; śata, hundred; etc. Mahāvīra gives 24 such names, i.e., up to 10^{23}), but some of the names used by him are different; that is, he uses synonyms.

The algebra is more important and better known. It is divided into two parts, discussing the following items: (I) salutation, laws of signs, operations with zero, operations with unknown, surds, pulverizer (indeterminate analysis of first degree), square-nature (so-called Pellian equations), cyclic method, approximate value of surds; (II) salutation, four kinds of analysis, simple equations (five rules are given, and one example, then the text breaks off abruptly). The Bīja-gaṇitāvataṃsa, in the incomplete form extant, contains 95 rules illustrated with 46 examples.

Following the example of Bhāskara and in some cases of earlier Hindu mathematicians, he represented the unknown quantities by means of (1) letters of the alphabet, or (2) names of colors. He added a few more names, and suggested the additional use of names of flavors, such as madhura (sweet). He said that only the initial letters of positive numbers and unknowns should be written in order to indicate them, those of negative numbers must be marked with superposed dots; this rule was given by Bhāskara and is probably older still.

He does not quote the sources of his algebra, but it is certain that he used the Bījagaṇita of Bhāskara[49] (XII-1). He was often referred to by the Hindu mathematicians of the sixteenth century, such as Jñānarāja (1503), Sūryadāsa (1540), Gaṇeśa (1545).

Text. An edition of the Gaṇita-kaumudī by Padmakara Dvivedi was announced in 1933 as being published by the Sanskrit College, Benares. I have not seen it.

Criticism. Bibhutibhusan Datta: Nārāyaṇa's method for finding approximate value of a surd (Bull. Calcutta Mathematical Society 23, 187–94, 1931); The algebra of Nārāyaṇa (Isis 19, 472–85, 1933); History of Hindu mathematics, with Avadhesh Narayan Singh (vols. 1, 2, passim, Lahore 1935–38; Isis 25, 478–88).

[49] In my note on Bhāskara (Introd. 2, 212–14), I call that work wrongly Vījagaṇita.

F. CHINA

TING CHÜ

Chinese mathematician (fl. 1355).

Ting Chü composed in 1355 a collection of arithmetical problems, called Ting Chü suan fa. But few rules are given, and no order is apparent.

Another collection of the same kind and time (?), but containing more minute explanations, is entitled T'ou-lien hsi-ts'ao, without author's name.

Text. Both collections are partly published in the Chih pu tsu chai ts'ung shu, available in the Library of Congress. Both are also included in chüan 16343–4 of the Yung Lo ta tien, available in the University Library of Cambridge.

Criticism. A. Wylie (p. 118, 1902). Wieger (p. 436, 533, 1920).

YEN KUNG

Chinese mathematician (fl. 1372).

Yen Kung was a native of Soochow, Kiangsu. In 1372, he wrote the treatise T'ung yüan suan fa, published with a preface by Chao Yu of Ch'ao Chou, Kuangtung. That treatise contains some problems on congruence equations, which are partly solved; that is, the author was satisfied by the finding of one particular solution; he did not try to find all of them. It should be noted that Chinese mathematicians had begun the study of such equations very early; some such may already be found in the Suan ching of Sun-Tzŭ (III-1?).

Text. Text included in the Yung Lo ta tien, chüan 16343–4. Copy in the University Library of Cambridge.

Criticism. Dickson (2, 57–64, 1920).

In addition to the mathematical texts already mentioned in my notes on Ting Chü and Yen Kung, the same chüan of the Yung Lo ta tien contain a few other texts which may belong to the same period, to wit:

Ch'üan nêng chi, by Chia t'ung; Hsiang ming suan fa, by An chih chai; Chin nang ch'i mêng, anonymous.

See Li Yen's[49a] study on the mathematical works in Yung Lo ta tien (Gesammelte Abhandlungen über die Geschichte der chinesischen Mathematik 2, 83–91, Commercial press, Shanghai 1931), in Chinese.

LIU CHI

Chinese astronomer (1311–75).

Liu Chi, styled Po wên, was born in Ch'ing-t'ien, Chehkiang, and obtained his chin shih degree in 1330. He was a soldier and a poet, as well as an astronomer or astrologer. He threw in his lot with the party rebelling against the Mongols and became familiar with the leader Chu Yüan-chang, who assumed imperial power in 1368. The emperor always called him teacher, Hsien shêng, and rewarded him with various honors; Liu fell a victim to palace intrigues, however, and was poisoned

[49a] Li Yen (1880–1945) was a railroad engineer, and a prominent member of the Science Society of China and of the Chinese Engineering Society. He was one of the outstanding authorities on the history of Chinese mathematics and his library ad hoc was the best in China. He wrote many books and articles on that subject, the last being his History of Chinese mathematics (Commercial press, Shanghai 1937). Information kindly sent to me by Dr. A. Kaiming Chiu (April 15, 1946). The Chinese titles of Li Yen's main works are given by Hummel (p. 540, 1943).

by the new favorite, with the emperor's connivance, in 1375. He was canonized as Wên ch'êng in 1514.

He was ordered to prepare the first Ming calendar, Ta-t'ung li, which was compiled for the year 1370. It is interesting to note that another calendar was prepared for that same year by the Uighūr mathematician whose Chinese name was Chêng A-li. This second calendar, entitled Hui-hui li, was established by means of the Hindu-Arabic methods. The simultaneous publication of these two calendars is a good symbol of the ending of the Mongol and the beginning of the Ming dynasty (1368).

A short treatise on geomancy, K'an-yü man-hsing, dated 1368, is also ascribed to Liu Chi. In 1361, he wrote a preface to the Ling ch'i ching, an ancient (third century?) treatise on divination, of unknown authorship.

Text. Both calendars are given in the Ming shih, chs. 32–39. The Library of Congress has two copies of the Ming shih, each in 332 chüan, but the one is bound in 56 vols., the other in 80 vols. Both copies were printed in 1877.

Most of Liu Chi's writings are included in the Ch'êng i po wên chi, in 20 chüan.

The Ling ch'i ching for which Liu Chi wrote a preface in 1361 is known to me through the Korean edition listed by Courant (no. 2415, 1896).

Criticism. Giles (no. 1282, 1898). Wieger (p. 251, 353, 417, 508–9, 1920).

For Chinese divination see note on Kuo P'o (IV-1), and Edwin Joshua Dukes: Fêng shui (ERE 5, 833–35, 1912).

G. KOREA

KOREAN ASTRONOMY AT THE END OF THE FOURTEENTH CENTURY

In 1392, the Korean dynasty of Koryu or Kao Li (918–1392) came to an end, and a new dynasty was founded by king Li Ch'êng kuei, who established his capital in Seoul. That date, 1392, is often considered the opening date of "modern" Korea, for the new dynasty, the Li, continued in power until the annexation of that kingdom by Japan in 1910.

Li dismissed the astronomers of the fallen dynasty and established a new astronomical board, Shu Yün kuan. A new set of astronomical, astrological, and geomantic tables was compiled in 1394. One of the computers, Chin Shu, was discharged in 1398 because his prediction of an eclipse of the moon was inaccurate. Arrangements were made in the same year to give the people of Seoul a standard of time.

The main achievement of the new board was the production of a celestial planisphere, completed in December 1395. The work was directed by Ch'üan chin, the computations were supervised by Liu Fang Tsê, and the characters inscribed by Hsieh Ch'ing Shou. The following astronomers took part in the investigations: Ch'üan chung ho, Lu I chün, Ch'ih ch'ên yüan, T'ien jun ch'üan, Chin Hou, Ts'ui Jung, Yin Jên Lung, Chin Tui, Chin Tzŭ Sui.

A handwritten copy of the chart was prepared by Hsieh Ch'ang-shou, brother of Hsieh Ch'ing Shou, and signed by him in June 1395; he died in 1399. The final copy, completed in December 1395, was engraved on stone. The original engraving being worn out, the map was engraved again without any change c. 1687, on a new stone. The two stones used to be preserved in the bureau of astrology of Seoul; they are now in the government museum, Chang-duk palace, in that city. Rubbings of it are available in various places, e.g., in the Paris Observatory. This particular copy is 145 cm. high and 90 cm. wide. Another celestial map originating from the astrological bureau of Seoul is preserved in the Paris Observatory; it measures 165 cm. square.

The map of 1395 was derived from a Chinese one engraved on stone kept at Pyeng Yang, Korea, and lost in the Tai-tong river when Ko-gu-ryu[50] fell in 672. The Korean astronomers copied it as it was, and hence the astronomical date of their map cannot be later than 672. According to Rufus, the position of Polaris suggests a much earlier date, perhaps as early as the beginning of the Former Han dynasty, second century B.C. The chart includes 1,464 stars and 306 names.

Criticism. Courant (3, nos. 2366, 2367, pl. iii, 1896). W. Carl Rufus: The celestial planisphere of king Yi Tai-jo[51] (Transactions, Korea branch, R. Asiatic Society 4, part 3, 23–72, Seoul 1913); Astronomy in Korea (ibid. vol. 26, 52 p., 17 pl., Seoul 1936; Isis 28, 239; 30, 167). Rufus' first description is very elaborate and includes many illustrations. The best illustration of the whole planisphere is in Courant. W. Carl Rufus and Celia Chao: A Korean star map (Isis 35, 316–26, 1 pl., 1944), with five tables giving Chinese characters of 306 identified constellations or single stars.

[50] One of the three kingdoms (san han) of which the old Korea was constituted (Introd. 1, 364). Chinese name, Kao k'o li; Japanese name, Koma or Kōrai (hence Korea). That Japanese name was for a time applied to the whole country, but in 1392 was replaced by Chōsen.

[51] That is, Li Ch'êng kuei, when read in Chinese.

CHAPTER XXI

PHYSICS, TECHNOLOGY, AND MUSIC

(Second Half of the Fourteenth Century)

N.B. Only the main notes are published in this chapter. The physical and musical contributions of many other men, whose main work was done in other fields, are discussed in other chapters. For a general survey of physics, technology, and music in the second half of the fourteenth century, see section VII of chapter XV. More information on the men referred to in that survey may then easily be found by means of the index.

1. OPTICS AND OPTICAL METEOROLOGY

THEMON SON OF THE JEW

Themo Judaei. German (Westphalian) commentator on Aristotle, physicist. He originated, or spent part of his youth, in Münster, Westphalia, then proceeded to Paris. It is not known when he was baptized. He studied at the Sorbonne and passed his final examinations in 1349 under the presidency of Domenico da Chivasso (XIV-1). He was a man of some means. He was thrice elected proctor of the English nation, in 1353, 1355, 1356, and treasurer of it from 1357 to October 1361, when he was replaced by Albert of Saxony. He was a famous teacher who trained many students. In 1359 he was sent to Avignon as an emissary of his nation to Innocent VI, and he was sent again in 1360, this time as representative of the whole university, to celebrate the return of king Jean II le Bon to Paris after his liberation by the English at the peace of Brétigny. It is not known what happened to Themon after 1361.

He was a disciple of Albert of Saxony, and wrote a commentary on Aristotle's Meteorologica, in the same form as Albert's commentaries on the Physica, the De coelo, and the De generatione et corruptione. In fact, there is so much similarity between these commentaries, not simply in the form but in the leading thoughts, that a later commentator, Agostino Nifo (d. 1538 or 1545), ascribed them all to Albert. According to him, Themon was simply the editor of the commentary on the Meteorologica, the real author being Albert of Saxony. This is contradicted by the text as edited in 1516 and 1518.

A commentary on the Meteorologica implies naturally the discussion of a great many topics. We must restrict our examination to a few. Does the center of gravity of the universe coincide with the center of gravity of earth and water, or with the center of gravity of water only? Themon hesitates. He rejects the theory of Nicholas of Lyra according to which the sphere of the earth and the sphere of the ocean are both eccentric to the center of gravity of the world. He seems to conclude that that center of gravity C coincides with the center of gravity C_1 of the earth and with the center of gravity C_2 of the waters. C_2 is also the geometrical center of the watery sphere, but C_1 is not the geometrical center of the earth sphere, the shape of which is very irregular.

Themon rejects the old idea, still held by Thomas Bradwardine, according to which the densities of the four elements increase in geometrical progression of ratio

10: fire, air, water, earth. His merit will be better appreciated if one bears in mind that that fantastic doctrine continued to obtain some currency down to the sixteenth century. A consequence of it was that the elements were believed to be placed around the center of the world in the order of their densities, the earth sphere being the nearest to it, the fire sphere the most distant. Hence the general level of the waters would be above the land level. Following Giovanni Campano (XIII-2), Themon claimed that the water level was generally inferior to the land one. Again, in his discussion of springs he introduces the principle that water cannot move higher up than its source; hence springs cannot be due to upward infiltration of subterranean waters, but are more probably due to downward infiltration of rain water.

Themon's theory of tides is very strange; he tries to account for the well known influences of sun and moon by assuming that the waters are vaporized by the sun and reliquefied by the moon, and that these processes cause the tidal motions.

He refers to Roger Bacon's theory of vision. His discussion of the rainbow is very elaborate, comparable to that given at the beginning of the century by Dietrich von Freiberg (XIV-1) and superior to that given by Marco Antonio de Dominis considerably later (1611).[1]

Many of these ideas may be found in the MSS of Leonardo da Vinci and his treatise Del moto e misura dell' acqua. It is quite possible that Leonardo consulted Themon's commentaries and made use of them. As to post-Leonardo physicists, when similar ideas are found in their writings it is simpler to assume that they read the commentaries of Themon and of Albert of Saxony rather than Leonardo's notes, which were not available to them, or hardly so.

It is rather difficult to get hold of Themon's ideas because he generally introduces more than one explanation, each being followed by criticisms, and objections to these criticisms, and he frequently contradicts himself or seems to do so. Similar remarks apply to Leonardo's notebooks (of course it is perfectly natural for any man to contradict himself in a notebook the writing of which is spaced out over a sufficient interval of time).

Text. Quaestiones IV librorum meteorologicorum, Pavia c. 1480 (Klebs no. 959). The commentary on the Meteorologica was printed together with the text of that work and notes and memoirs by Gaetano da Thiene (1387–1465) in an early sixteenth-century edition (s.a.l., c. 1505?). Reprinted Venice 1522.

Themon's commentary was re-edited, together with commentaries of Albert of Saxony and Buridan, by George Lokert under the title Quaestiones et decisiones physicales insignium virorum (Paris 1516, 1518).

Criticism. Duhem: Origines (vol. 2, 1906); Etudes (vols. 1–3, 1906–13). Duhem's most elaborate study is in the Etudes (1, 159–220, 1906), this being a reprint of his memoir Thémon le fils du Juif et Léonard de Vinci (Bulletin italien 6, 97–124, 185–218, 1906).

I could find no information on Themon in Jewish sources.

4. MECHANICAL CLOCKS

We have seen in chapter VII that mechanical clocks, that is, clocks equipped with a weight drive setting a train of wheels in motion and with a simple oscillatory escapement, were probably made and used in the first half of the fourteenth century,

[1] R. E. Ockenden: Marco Antonio de Dominis and his explanation of the rainbow (Isis 26, 40–49, 2 fig., 1936).

though we were not able to clinch the argument by means of a single example completely authenticated by tallying documents and monuments. Let us examine now the literary and archaeological evidence relative to the second half of the century.

1352 (or 1354?), Strassburg cathedral. This is the earliest public clock definitely known on the European continent outside Italy. The account of its construction by one Jehan Boernave, who had studied with the Arabs, is legendary. The builder is unknown, but he worked at it for two years. The dial included many figures, as the Three Kings bowing and a crowing cock; there was a carillon and a human figure upon which proper times for bloodletting in various parts of the body were indicated. This connection of the great mechanical novelty with bloodletting confirms the popularity of the latter. Nothing remains of that old clock except the rooster, preserved in the Frauenhaus, Strassburg. This clock has nothing to do with the greater one built in the sixteenth century by Conrad Dasypodius (d. 1600) and others for the same cathedral; completed in 1574, it is in use to this day, but was rebuilt in 1838.

To return to the clock of 1352, it enjoyed considerable fame and originated the popular craze for clocks adorned with all kinds of jacks, specimens of which are found in many European cities. That fashion has continued to our own days, witness the beautiful clock in Herald Square, New York City, dating from 1895.

Alfred Ungerer: L'horloge astronomique de la cathédrale de Strasbourg (Comptes rendus du Congrès international des mathématiciens de Strasbourg p. 656-63, 1920; Isis 5, 567). Feldhaus (col. 1200, 1204, 1914). Ungerer (p. 161-78, 1931), see bibliography in chapter VII, p. 717-22.

1353, Genoa. Striking clock (Robertson p. 34, 1931).

1353, Avignon. Domus horologii in the pontifical palace (see note ad hoc under 1343 in chapter VII).

1356, Bologna. Striking clock in a tower (Muratori: Rerum italicarum scriptores 18, 444).

1359. A house clock was made for king Jean while he was prisoner in London (Robertson p. 44).

1354-60. Public clocks in Geneva, Florence, Bologna, Siena, Frankenburg, Nürnberg (Baillie p. 41, 1929a).

1356-61, Marienkapelle (Frauenkirche), Nürnberg. Famous clock called Männleinlaufen built to commemorate the Golden Bull granted by Charles IV of Luxemburg in 1356, transforming the German empire into an aristocratic federation. The clock represented the emperor and the seven electors. The mechanism was completely repaired in 1506-9, again in 1880, and in 1904; the figures were replaced in 1823 (Feldhaus col. 1205).

1362, Brussels (Baillie p. 41).

1364, Pavia. Clock built by Giovanni de' Dondi. It was an elaborate clock and orrery in brass and copper, the construction of which occupied him for sixteen years (1348-64). Giovanni wrote a description of it in his Planetarium. He sold it to Gian Galeazzo Visconti, who placed it in the castle of Pavia. Nothing remains of it. See my note on Giovanni de' Dondi; Thorndike (3, 386-97, 1934).

1366, Toledo (Baillie p. 40).

1368, Westminster. Edward III invited three craftsmen, "Johannem Vrieman, Willielmum Vrieman et Johannem Lietuyt de Delft, orologiers, veniendo in regnum nostrum." This should perhaps be connected with his building a clock tower of stone in Westminster 1365–66. There is a record of a clock keeper in 1371 (HG p. 272; Baillie p. 40).

1368, Breslau. Tower clock striking the hours from 1 to 24 (Feldhaus col. 1235).

1370, Paris, Royal Palace (Palais de justice). Charles V invited Heinrich von Wiek (Henri de Vic, Henry de Vick) to come to build a public clock. Heinrich worked at it from 1362 to 1370. The clock was described by Froissart in his poem Li orloge amoureus (edited by Aug. Scheler, Oeuvres de Froissart, Poésies, 1, 53–86, Bruxelles 1870), 1,174 lines including many technical details. A later description by Julien Le Roy (d. 1759), first published by Louis Moinet: Nouveau traité . . . d'horlogerie (vol. 1, Paris 1848), is less reliable, for it was not based on the original mechanism, but on the mechanism modified by many restorations. The original clock was made to strike the hours from 1 to 24.

Henri de Vic was replaced as royal clock maker by Petrus de Sancta Beata, already referred to in chapter VII. We know nothing more about Henri, except that a clock established in Metz 1391 is ascribed to him.

The clock of 1370 gave its name to the "quai de l'horloge." It has been wrongly stated (e.g., by Feldhaus col. 1235) that it was that clock which gave the signal in the night of August 23/24, 1572 for the massacre of the Protestants; no, the signal of the St. Barthélemy "purge" was given by the bells of the church of St. Germain l'Auxerrois.

1373. A monk of Malmesbury, Wiltshire, records "Hoc anno horologia distinguentia 24 horas primo inventa sunt" (Scriptores rerum brit., Eulogium, Chronicon ab orbe condito usque ad 1366 a monacho quodam malmesburiensi exaratum, edited by Frank Scott Haydon, 3, 336, London 1863). Our summary shows that the monk was wrong, yet he testifies to the novelty of that invention.

1372–77. During these years various belfry clocks were established in Flemish cities, Courtrai, Maestricht, Malines, Ypres, Termonde; also in Mons (Baillie p. 40). A striking clock was put in the belfry of Ghent within the years 1370–78 (Robertson p. 39).

1377–78. Various accounts paid by Charles V of France to his clock maker, Pierre de Sainte Béate, and to the bell founder Jehan Jouvence (the same who had cast the bell for Henri de Vic's clock). These accounts refer to small portable clocks (orloge portative). This, however, should not suggest to our mind too small a clock, for even as late as 1481, the "portable" clock made for Louis XI had to be packed in a case and carried on a horse; a horse and driver were used for that purpose only. The clocks which belonged to Charles V are briefly described in the inventory made at the time of his death, 1380 (Baillie p. 44; Robertson p. 44).

1381, Louvain. Tower clock constructed by Jan van Hingene of Alost for the collegiate church of St. Peter in Louvain. The town paid a very large sum of money for the mechanism. A gigantic jack, called Meester Jan, struck the hours on two bells. The clock was destroyed in a fire, 1485 (Biographie nationale de Belgique 10, 409, 1888–89).

1382, Courtrai. Philip the Bold, duke of Burgundy, caused the mechanical clock of Courtrai to be dismantled and carried to Dijon. It was a clock that struck the 24 hours of day and night (Froissart, ed. Kervyn de Lettenhove, 10, 188, 1870).

c. 1390, St. Albans, Hertfordshire. Clock completed during the abbacy of Thomas de la Mare. See my note on the clock of 1326–35 in chapter VII. It had a 24-hour dial (HG p. 271).

1392, Nuremberg. Mechanical clock now in the Germanisches Museum, but

FIG. 27. Ancient works of the Wells Cathedral clock. They were in use at the cathedral from c. 1392 to 1835, and are now preserved in the Science Museum, South Kensington, London. Reproduced by permission of the dean and chapter of Wells Cathedral. Photograph kindly given by the Science Museum.

FIG. 28. Interior dial of Wells Cathedral clock. Notice the division of the circle into 24 parts (see p. 717, 1542, 1546). Courtesy of the dean and chapter of Wells Cathedral.

previously in the church of St. Sebald. It is only 16 inches high, without striking mechanism, but with a device to release an alarm at the hour. It was used to warn the watchman, who then struck the hour on the bell. It is important, because it is one of the very earliest pieces of clock mechanism which have come down to us (Feldhaus col. 1223, fig. 775; Baillie p. 45). It may be later than 1392 yet anterior to the fifteenth century.

c. 1392, Cathedral of Wells, Somerset. It was formerly believed that this clock was the one built for Glastonbury abbey in 1323–34 by Peter Lightfoot, and moved to Wells at the time of the Reformation. That legend has been discussed in chapter VII. The clock of Wells is perhaps anterior to 1392, but not much, and it may be a little later; it is mentioned in the accounts of the dean and chapter for 1392/93.

The (interior) dial plate (fig. 28) is 6 feet 4 inches in diameter, contained in a square frame in the corners of which are angels holding the four winds. The outer circle is divided into 24 parts. A large star (the sun) moving around that circle indicates the hour; a smaller star moving around an inner circle indicates the minutes. A third circle gives the days of the lunar month. Etc. On a platform above the dial a few jacks (four charging horsemen) can be seen moving every hour. There is also an outside dial with two jacks of its own.

The mechanism (fig. 27) continued in use until c. 1835, when it was replaced by a modern one and put in the crypt of the cathedral. It is now in the Science Museum, London, where it can be seen in working order. Originally, it was controlled by a verge escapement with a foliot balance, but sometime after the introduction of the pendulum, in the second half of the seventeenth century, an anchor escapement and pendulum were substituted. The framing and wheels are of wrought iron and the framework is fastened together by mortises, tenons, and cotters. The striking part is driven by separate weights and is of the locking-plate type still used in tower clocks; it strikes the hours and quarters.

The Wells mechanism measures about 5 feet cube, that is, it is considerably larger than the Dover one, but it has been subject to deeper modifications (chiefly the replacement of the foliot by a pendulum).

My description of the mechanism is taken from R. P. Howgrave-Graham: Peter Lightfoot and the old clock at Wells (Glastonbury 1922). More detailed description by same in 1927 (p. 289–95), with abundant illustrations. See also Baillie (p. 35).

It was my great privilege to visit Wells Cathedral in August 1936; the mechanism of the clock I have seen many times in the Science Museum.

c. 1396, Rouen. The belfry of Rouen was destroyed in 1382 by order of Charles VI. Soon afterward the commune asked for permission to rebuild it in order to establish in it a public clock. The work lasted from 1389 to 1398. The clock was begun by Jourdain Delestre, continued and completed by Jehan de Felains (de Felanis); it was already in use in 1396. This so-called "Grosse horloge" was one of the earliest public clocks striking every quarter of the hour. In the first half of the sixteenth century the clock was placed not in the belfry, but in another building close to it bridging the street, connecting the belfry with the town hall. In 1713, its foliot was replaced by a pendulum (Ungerer p. 144–49, 5 fig., 1931).

1390–1400, Dover. The clock of Dover Castle, traditionally dated 1348, and therefore discussed in chapter VII (p. 721, fig. 13), may date only from the end of the fourteenth century.

To conclude, it is clear that tower clocks became frequent in the second half of the fourteenth century. The new contrivance did not serve practical needs only; it was one of the symbols of municipal pride, and was considered a necessary adornment to the town's belfry or cathedral. We have good descriptions of the clock completed by Giovanni de' Dondi in 1364 and established soon afterward in the castle of Pavia, and of the one built by Heinrich von Wiek in 1370 for the royal palace in Paris. What is equally important, we have at least three clock mechanisms dating back to the end of the century, to wit, the Dover, Wells, and Nuremberg clocks. Hence the story of mechanical clocks, which began somewhat vaguely in the middle of the thirteenth century, is become by the end of the fourteenth century a subject capable of concrete and detailed discussion.

These clocks introduced regular hours instead of canonical ones, but in most cases the dials were still divided into 24 parts, instead of 12. The division into 12 parts must seem to us an obvious mechanical simplification, but obvious things are often difficult to see. In this connection it is amusing to recall that in relatively recent times (nineteenth and twentieth centuries) watches with a 24-hour dial were again put in circulation in Europe; this was done for the sake of the idiots who were put out by continental railroad tables giving times on a 24-hour basis. The new dials were supposed to help them in adjusting themselves to railroad usage, but made adjustments to other usages more difficult; that was not very helpful.

The workmanship of these clocks was rough and hence the clocks were relatively large; the history of house clocks, of small size, does not begin before the fifteenth century; the history of pocket watches, not before the sixteenth century.

These early clocks lacked precision and needed the daily attendance of a clock maker (we know this from the communal or cathedral accounts). For greater precision it is probable that clepsydrae continued to be used. It is rather puzzling to hear Geoffroy of Meaux state that the total lunar eclipse of March 18, 1345 lasted $3^h29^m54^s$. How could he measure the time as accurately as that? His contemporary, John of Ashendon, gives the duration of the same eclipse as 3^h42^m, which is some 12^m more!? (Thorndike 3, 290, 1934). As a matter of fact, these numbers were the results not of measurements, but of computations. According to Oppolzer (1887), the duration of that particular eclipse was 3^h38^m.[2] Even with the best clepsydra the time of an event could not be determined with greater precision than a quarter of an hour, or say half of that. For a better appreciation of the difficulties involved in exact time measurement even a century later, see the very elaborate study of Ernst Zinner on Regiomontanus (München 1938; Isis 30, 109-11).

To complete this account of clocks, I may add that mechanical clocks were not discovered independently in the Far East. The Chinese (and Japanese) were of course familiar from early days with sundials, they had obtained some knowledge of clepsydrae (from the Roman West?), and they had learned also to measure time with burning tapers or candles; they never thought of mechanical clocks until some were shown to them by missionaries. St. Francis Xavier presented a clock to the Japanese ruler in 1550, in the name of the Portuguese viceroy of India.

The application of the clock to Far Eastern usage implied some difficulty, because

[2] That is, duration from beginning of partial phase to end of partial phase. The experimental determination of that duration is full of difficulties. Note that Oppolzer does not go beyond the minutes. Even the simplest computations can easily lead to complicated fractions, and produce a false appearance of precision; novices do that and deceive other novices.

the Chinese (and the Japanese) did not divide the day into twice twelve equal hours, but into two unequal periods (day and night), each divided into six equal divisions. Six consecutive divisions were marked by strokes on the temple bell in descending order from 9 to 4 (midnight to noon). The twelve hours from dusk to dusk were associated with the signs of the zodiac, as follows (read the first column, then the second):

Night	*Day*
6 cock (dusk)	6 hare (dawn)
5 dog	5 dragon
4 boar	4 serpent
9 rat (midnight)	9 horse (midday)
8 ox	8 sheep
7 tiger	7 monkey

The hours of each column are equal between themselves, but different from those of the other column (Robertson p. 197–99).

Each zodiacal sign corresponds really to the middle of the double hour which it names. For example, the horse hour begins at 11 A.M. and ends at 1 P.M. (our time). There is a combination of three arrangements: (1) two unequal groups of six consecutive equal hours, dusk to dawn and dawn to dusk, (2) six hours numbered from 9 to 4 (midnight to midday), (3) a series of twelve hours named after the twelve earthly branches, generally in the order rat (tzŭ) to boar (hai). Hence the introduction of mechanical clocks necessarily created a deeper disruption of ancient usage in the Far East than in the Christian West. The fact that the Chinese (and the Japanese) did not invent them need not surprise us; it is more remarkable that they adopted them at all. This can be explained only by the necessity of adapting their ways to the Western ways forced upon them.

5. ARMS, ARMOR, DINANDERIE

ARMS

It has been explained in chapter VII that firearms were invented and first used in the second quarter of the fourteenth century. There is abundant evidence of the making and use of cannon in the second half of the same century. A complete enumeration of all the items would be very long and tedious. I shall mention only a few which attracted my attention. The list can be easily increased, though not completed, by the use of Feldhaus (1914) and Rathgen (1928).

The "race of armaments" was already on by the middle of the century, though it remained slow at first. England was behind the continent, Flanders and Germany, where the arts of metal had been very much developed. See my note on dinanderie and monumental brasses (XIV-1). Yet we hear of William of Aldgate (in London), brazier and gunfounder, 1353–60; and of one John Byker, artillator regis, who was making and repairing springalds in the same period. He was also styled "balistarius domini regis infra turrim Londoniarum"; he was succeeded in 1360 by Patrick Byker, and in 1370, by William Byker. In 1382–88, William was making crossbows as well as cannon. This illustrates the persistence of the old arms, explainable only by the relative inefficiency of the new ones.

Other makers of guns were at work in England (Tout p. 248–51, 1911; see bibliography in ch. VII, p. 726). The following comparison of prices in 1375 with those of five centuries later (1865) is interesting (ffoulkes p. 12, 1937):

	Price per lb., 1375			*Price per lb., 1865*		
	£	s.	d.	£	s.	d.
Iron	2	10	0	0	0	$1\frac{1}{2}$
Steel	4	0	0	0	0	9
"Gun metal"	8	0	0	0	1	0
Lead	4	0	0	0	0	2
Gunpowder	50	0	0	0	0	7

In 1378, St. Malo was besieged by the English with 400 cannon (Froissart); many of these were probably small mortars.

In 1382, 73 guns were cast in London by William Woodward, of which one, a multi-barreled gun, weighed 737 pounds and cost £12.5.8 (ffoulkes p. 105).

The fashion of gigantic guns began to spread, though often the dates traditionally given to them have been proved to be too early. For example, the great bombard of the Rijksmuseum, Amsterdam, 50 cm. caliber, dated 1377, is probably later (Rathgen p. 707). Another bombard of about the same size (56 cm.) was made in 1377 in Châlons by an artillerist from Majorca (?). The big gun which I know by far the best, the "Dulle Griet" (Mad Meg), still to be seen near the Vrijdagmarkt in Ghent, was supposed to have been made in 1382, but it dates only from the following century. What is certain is that cannon became relatively common in the last quarter of the century. Their fabrication was simple, and hence they were often of local manufacture and could be multiplied almost indefinitely. Some men could produce them in larger quantities, e.g., William Woodward cited above, and William the Founder, who in 1385 cast twelve cannon for Dover's castle, at the order of Richard II.

Nevertheless the number of early guns that have come down to us is very small; the others were probably destroyed by men or nature, and the metal used for other purposes. Rathgen (p. 514–15, 1928) gives in tabular form many data relative to six big iron guns, the earliest extant, all of the fifteenth century. A few of these data are reprinted here, in simplified manner, that is, without indicating small divergences between authorities. For example, the guns were not weighed, but their weight was estimated after ascribing to the metal a definite specific gravity, which may vary from one author to another.

	Gun	*Date*	*Length* (*cm.*)	*Caliber* (*cm.*)	*Approx. weight* (*kg.*)
1	English guns in Mt. St. Michel	before 1423	364	48	150
2			353	36	75
3	Mons Meg	before 1460	400	50	147
4	Mad Meg	after 1430	502	64	340
5	Burgundian guns in Basel	1426–30	273	35	48
6		1474	227	23	12

Mad Meg is by far the largest. The other Margaret, Mons Meg, kept to this day in the castle of Edinburgh, comes next; it is so called because it was formerly believed to have been cast in Mons, county of Hainaut (annexed to Burgundy in 1433).

In the meanwhile, the Chinese, who had invented gunpowder, had never thought of using it for destructive purposes. According to Chinese chronicles, firearms were first used by the Ming general Chang Fu in 1407, when he thereby defeated the

Annamites in a great battle (Giles no. 52, 1898). A small gun (35.7 cm. long) in bronze dated year 19 of the Ming emperor Yung Lo (= 1421) is kept in the Museum für Völkerkunde in Berlin. This is the oldest bronze barrel of a hand firearm thus far known. F. M. Feldhaus: Eine chinesische Stangenbüchse von 1421 (Zeitschrift für historische Waffenkunde 4, 256, 1906–8).

The same emperor ordered the compilation of an immense encyclopaedia called after him the Yung Lo ta tien, the largest effort of its kind ever made anywhere,[3] completed in 1409. Considering the existence of the record of 1407 and the gun of 1421, one might expect the Yung Lo ta tien to include an account of gunpowder and firearms, but the volumes which have come down to us do not contain it. For further discussion of Chinese gunpowder and guns, see Paul Pelliot (T'oung pao 21, 432–34, 1922).

In the Shansi Provincial Museum at T'ai-yüan there is an iron gun cast in Shansi in the tenth (not eleventh) year of Ming Hung Wu (= 1377, not 1378). There are several hundred cannon in the Peking Historical Museum dating from the time of Hung Wu and later times down to the middle of the following century. The only cannon of earlier date are from a find of 500 of assorted sizes said to have been manufactured for the anti-Mongol rebel Chang Shih-ch'êng (d. 1367), who set himself up as emperor in 1354–57 under the title Chou T'ien-yu (Giles no. 103). Two of them, weighing respectively 666 and 466 pounds, are dated 1356 and 1357. A general bureau of gunpowder artillery (?) was set up in Korea in 1377, and the gunpowder and weapons were formally inspected in 1381.

Sarton: A Chinese gun of 1378? (query 105, Isis 35, 177, 1944). L. Carrington Goodrich: Note on a few early Chinese bombards (Isis 35, 211, 5 figs., 1944); Early development of fire arms in China (Isis 36, 114–23, 4 figs., 1946). This paper is a new general review for the period 1000–1403, based upon contemporary documents, some of which have only recently become available; I did not avail myself of it in my own summary.

After the preceding note had been added, another paper on the same subject, The invention and use of gunpowder and firearms in China, by Wang Ling, member of the Academia Sinica, in Lichuang, Ssŭch'uan, was brought to me from China by Joseph Needham for publication in Isis. Though I accepted the Goodrich MS on August 25, 1944 and Wang's on February 23, 1945, it does not follow that the second was written later than the first. The American and Chinese scholars worked independently, and as they covered the same ground, they used to some extent the same sources.

Western firearms were very inefficient and continued to be so for centuries. As late as 1776, the wise Benjamin Franklin[4] could still advocate the use of pikes,

[3] It comprised originally 22,937 chüan, forming 11,095 volumes (60 of them containing the index). These 11,095 volumes, standing nearly 20 inches high and 1 foot deep, would occupy about one-seventh of a mile of shelf space. On account of its bulk it was never printed (Walter T. Swingle, Report of the Library of Congress for 1923, p. 187–95; Isis 7, 260). The only existing copy, in the Han-lin Academy, Peking, was destroyed by fire in 1900, but many volumes were rescued by "foreign devils" and scattered all over the world. No one knows exactly how many volumes were thus saved. About 368 volumes are known to exist, 41 of which are in the Library of Congress (Report for 1940, p. 157). Some 280 lost Chinese works have already been extracted from that enormous collection; it is proposed to publish them in a series to be called Yung Lo ta tien ts'ung shu, comprising about a hundred volumes, as soon as possible.

[4] Writing to Charles Lee, Philadelphia, Feb. 11, 1776. Writings of B. Franklin, ed. by Albert Henry Smyth (6, 438–39, New York 1907).

bows and arrows! He gave six arguments in their favor and strangely enough quoted Polydore Vergil (d. 1555?),[5] one of the earliest historians of science, to support his views! This shows once more how little industrial progress was made between the Middle Ages and the nineteenth century, and yet one should not exaggerate that impression. The technical progress may have been slow and small, nevertheless immense efforts were made under the stress of recurrent war needs.

TREATISES ON MILITARY TECHNOLOGY

During the fifteenth century there appeared a long series of treatises or simply collections of drawings with brief explanations illustrating the problems of military engineering, the construction of fortifications and other defenses, the preparation of gunpowder and rockets, the making of harquebuses, guns, and other weapons, and their use. These military MSS are a typical product of the fifteenth century. The printing of most of them was considerably delayed or never occurred,[6] probably because secrecy rather than publicity was desired or because the public interested in such technicalities was too small. That public was unlearned, if not illiterate, and this explains why these military MSS contain more drawings than reading matter. See analyses in Jähns (1889) and Romocki (1895); complete references in chapter VII, p. 726.

As these writings reflect the technical thought of the fourteenth century, I shall enumerate them briefly in chronological order. A deeper investigation of them is out of the question here, as it concerns the student of the fifteenth century. They should be studied in conjunction with two "war books" of the first half of the fourteenth century, less technical in nature, to wit, the Liber secretorum completed in 1313 by Marino Sanudo il Vecchio (XIV-1), and the Thesaurus acquisitionis Terre sancte written in 1335 by Guido da Vigevano (XIV-1).

The first of these technical military writers and the originator of a new tradition, Konrad Kyeser, was a man of the fourteenth century, and he began his work in 1396. Though he did not complete it until ten years later, it is worth while to consider it here, together with other fruits of the same tradition.

1. Konrad Kyeser (born at Eichstädt, Franconia, 1366, still living in 1405 in Bohemia). He began in 1396 and completed in 1405 a work entitled Bellifortis, the earliest of that series of illustrated handbooks on military engineering. It is written in Latin verse and prose and is divided into ten books, as follows: war chariots, siege engines, hydraulic engines, ladders and hoisting machinery, ballistics, fortifications, secret means, use of fire as a weapon, peaceful use of fire, tools. Its influence can be traced in MSS for a century and a half. It contains an illustration of the earliest type of portable firearm (Stangenbüchse) and of a ship with paddle wheels.

Main MS in the University of Göttingen (Cod. phil. 63), 140 parchment leaves with 243 written pages. Later MS (c. 1410) in the library of the prince of Fürstenberg in Donaueschingen, with additional material.

[5] John Ferguson: Notes on the work of Polydore Vergil, De inventoribus rerum (Isis 17, 71–93, 1 pl., 1932). I had already referred to Franklin's astounding proposition (Introd. 2, 767). John F. Fulton: Handlist of editions of Polydore Vergil's De inventoribus rerum (15 p. typescript, New Haven 1944; Isis 36, 29).

[6] With the exception of Roberto Valturio's Res militaris, already printed thrice in Verona before the end of the century.

The Göttingen MS includes a portrait of the author which has the earmarks of a genuine portrait, and if we date it 1405, it is the oldest portrait of a German known to us.

Jähns (p. 248–56). Romocki (p. 133–78). Feldhaus (col. 594, 423, 23, 1914), also in ADB (52, 768, 1906). Carl von Klinckowstroem: Kyeser (Waldenburger Schriften für 1928, p. 115–21, 2 ill.; Isis 13, 437).

2. Streyd-Buch von Pixen, Kriegsrüstung, Sturmzeuch und Feurwerckh. Illustrated manual in verse for the master gunner, dating from the beginning of the fifteenth century. MS in the art collection of the Kaiserhaus in Vienna, cod. 5135.

Jähns (p. 382–89). Feldhaus (col. 22, 1914).

3. Giovanni de' Fontana (Venetian, professor at Padua and rector of the faculty of arts 1418–19). He wrote c. 1410–20 a treatise on military engineering less elaborate than Kyeser's but equally interesting, for it contains information on technicalities not dealt with by Kyeser (rocket torpedoes, rolling rockets, etc.). It is essentially a collection of drawings entitled Bellicorum instrumentorum liber cum figuris et ficticiis literis conscriptus.

Cod. icon. 242, Hofbibliothek, München. Latin MS, 70 parchment leaves, written in cipher. Graf von Klinckowstroem of Munich made a German translation of it, unpublished.

Jähns (p. 276). Romocki (p. 231–40). Feldhaus (col. 334). Chr. Huelsen: Der Liber instrumentorum des Giovanni Fontana (Festgabe für Hugo Blümner p. 507–14, 1 pl., Zürich 1914; Isis 8, 338). G. Sarton: Giovanni de' Fontana (query 3, Isis 7, 105, 1925). Lynn Thorndike (Isis 13, 103, 1929; 14, 221, 1930).

4. Feuerwerksbuch. This treatise dates from c. 1422. It is perhaps the most important, even as it was the most popular, of all similar treatises, and a great many MSS of it have been registered, yet it did not appear in print until more than a century later (Augsburg 1529). Its author may be considered the inventor of a practical nitro explosive substance, of a process of manufacture of sulphuric acid, of a kind of shrapnel, etc. The Feuerwerksbuch has been ascribed, though without sufficient reason, to one Abraham of Memmingen, a master gunner who was c. 1422 in the service of duke Frederick IV of Austria.

Jähns (p. 392–408). Romocki (p. 179–230). F. M. Feldhaus: Verfasste Abraham von Memmingen das Feuerwerksbuch? (Zeitschrift für historische Waffenkunde 5, 27, c. 1909). M. Ginsburger: Les Juifs et l'art militaire au Moyen-âge (Revue des études juives 88, 156–66, 1929; Isis 25, 204), referring to a MS of the Feuerwerksbuch written in Hebrew script, and to a Jew named Typsiles, who invented gunpowder in Augsburg 1353 (?).

5. Anonymous of the Hussite Wars (c. 1430). The author was probably a German who took part in the Hussite Wars (1420–33). Technical drawings covering 48 p. of the Cod. lat. 197, Hofbibliothek, Munich. All kinds of machines are represented.

Marcellin Berthelot: Pour l'histoire des arts mécaniques et de l'artillerie au Moyen-âge (Annales de chimie 24, 433–521, 66 fig., 1891). Jähns (p. 275). Feldhaus (col. 23, 1914).

6. Weimar MS 328 (c. 1430). This is perhaps the most comprehensive of this series of illustrated MSS; 329 parchment leaves quarto. It is largely derived from Kyeser's Bellifortis. From sheet 98 on it represents scenes of court life, and that part was drawn later (c. 1520).

Jähns (p. 274). Feldhaus (col. 22).

7. Jacopo Mariano Taccola (Jacopo Mariano, Marianus Taccola or Archimede). Italian engineer of Siena, who flourished c. 1438–49. Various collections of technical drawings made and annotated by him are extant and are of great value for the study of early technology. One, dated 1438, is in Munich (Cod. lat. 197); another, entitled De machinis libri X, dated 1449, with a preface by Santino, is in San Marco, Venice (Cod. lat. XIX, 5); the so-called Constantinople MS, admirably illustrated, is in Paris (Bibliothèque nationale, Cod. 7239); a fourth MS, in Vienna, is a copy. The Munich MS contains among other things the earliest illustration of a dam to keep up a body of water, with movable door. Other illustrations represent a ship with paddle wheel, diver with diver's dress, etc.

M. Berthelot (article of 1891 cited above). Feldhaus (col. 687). Hugo Th. Horwitz: Mariano und Valturio (Geschichtsblätter der Technik 9, 38–40, 1922; Isis 5, 220). Comte A. de Laborde: Un MS de Marianus Taccola, revenu de Constantinople (Mélanges Schlumberger p. 494–505, Paris 1924; Isis 10, 139).

This Mariano of Siena should not be confused with a namesake and contemporary, Mariano di Nanni da Siena, rector of San Pietro a Uvile, who pilgrimed to the Holy Land in 1431 and wrote an account of his journey. First edition by Domenico Moreni (298 p., Florence 1822). Often reprinted: Parma 1843, Florence 1862, Parma 1865. Röhricht (p. 108, 1890). Potthast (p. 766, 1896).

8. Roberto Valturio (born at Rimini, died there after 1482). Engineer and technical adviser to Sigismondo Malatesta, lord of Rimini, he composed c. 1460 his De re militari in 12 books, of which many illustrated MSS are extant. The first edition (Verona 1472), with many full-page woodcuts,[7] was the earliest technical work to appear in print.

The text of the princeps (Verona 1472) was improved for the second edition (Verona 1483) by Paolo Ramusio,[8] who also translated it into Italian (Verona 1483). See Klebs (nos. 1014, 1015), Stillwell (p. 509). The Latin text was often reprinted in the sixteenth century, Paris 1532, 1534, 1535, 1555.

Criticism. Jähns (p. 358–62). Hugo Th. Horwitz (1922, cited above). William M. Ivins, jr.: Valturius' De re militari (Bull. Metropolitan Museum p. 267, 1926).

9. Critobulos. As there are but few mediaeval accounts of gun founding, it is worth while to mention the one given in the history of Muḥammad II al-Fātiḥ

[7] The woodcuts were not printed at the same time as the letterpress, but inserted later. It is the third Italian illustrated book, preceded only by an early Venetian block book and by the Meditations of cardinal Torquemada (Rome 1467), the illustrations of which are very crude. The Valturio woodcuts were reproduced in the German translation of the Epitoma rei militaris of Flavius Renatus Vegetius (IV-2), printed in Augsburg 1476, the first technical book to appear in German (Introd. 1, 368).

[8] This Ramusio, like Valturio, was a son of Rimini; born c. 1443, he was a jurist in Venice and died in Bergamo 1506. He was the earliest prominent member of the noble Ramusio family and the father of its most illustrious scion, Giambattista Ramusio (1485–1557), the editor of the Navigationi et viaggi (3 vols., Venice 1550–59).

('Uthmānlī sulṭān 1451–81) written in Greek after 1467 by Critobulos (Κριτόβουλος) of Imbros. Text partly published by Carl Müller: Fragmenta historicorum graecorum (5, 40–161, Paris 1870), with Latin translation, De rebus gestis Mechemetis II, 1451–1467. In book 1, ch. 29, p. 76–78, Critobulos describes the founding of a large gun in situ for the siege of Constantinople, 1453. English version by ffoulkes (p. 13, 1937; see bibliography in ch. VII, p. 726). In his edition of Critobulos, Müller refers (p. 62, 70) to another great gun, bombarda maxima, built at Adrianople by Orbanus Hungarus; that bombarda is described by the two contemporary Byzantine historians Laonicos Chalcondyles and Ducas.

These texts are interesting because they reintroduce unexpectedly into our summary both the Greeks and the Muslims, who were pioneers in pyrotechnics. The so-called Dardanelles gun, dated 1463/64, kept at the Tower of London, was cast in the same way as the gun of 1453 described by Critobulos. For further discussion of this see ffoulkes (p. 8–19).

10. Martin Mercz (Mertz, Merz). German blunderbuss maker of the Palatinate, who flourished at Amberg and died there in 1501. His tombstone in the church of Amberg, bearing his likeness in low relief, is still extant, being the earliest such monument of interest to the historian of technology. Martin had lost his right eye, probably in the course of his work, and the monument shows him wearing an eye shield. He composed in 1471, in German, an illustrated work on harquebusery, Kunst aus Büchsen zu schiessen.

MS of 1471 in the library of the prince of Liechtenstein. MS of 1475 in the Munich library.

Jähns (p. 409–11). F. M. Feldhaus: Ruhmesblätter der Technik (p. 28, ill., Leipzig 1910); (col. 703, 1914).

11. "Mittelalterliches Hausbuch" (c. 1480). Anonymous album compiled in southern Germany (Heidelberg, Speyer?) by an unknown harquebus maker. Magnificent MS in the library of the princes of Waldburg-Wolfegg-Waldsee, in the Wolfegg castle, Württemberg. The MS is well known to historians of art; the draftsman is identical with the "Master of the Amsterdam cabinet." It includes many technical drawings, not simply of arms, but of machines and tools of various kinds, e.g. a spinning wheel. It is a sort of iconographic encyclopaedia and a very important source for the history not only of mediaeval technology, but also of mediaeval life.

Poor edition, Leipzig 1866. New editions by August von Essenwein (Frankfurt 1887) and by Helmuth Th. Bossert and Willy F. Storck (Leipzig 1912).

Jähns (p. 269–70). Feldhaus (col. 516, 1061, 1914). Bernhard Neumann: Minen- und Gasangriffe vor 500 Jahren (Chemiker-Zeitung p. 253, 1918); Die ältesten Zeichnungen eines mittelalterlichen Hüttenwerkes und die ältesten Angaben über den deutschen Kupferhüttenprozess (Metall und Erz p. 333–39, 353–61, 17 ill., 1920). E. O. von Lippmann: Technologisches aus dem "Mittelalterlichen Hausbuch" (Chemiker-Zeitung p. 341–42, 346–47, 1922; Isis 5, 220), reprinted in his Beiträge zur Geschichte der Naturwissenschaften (p. 200–10, Berlin 1923; Isis 6, 116–19), important study.

12. Ulreuch Bessnitzer (1489). German military engineer, born in Landshut, composed in 1489 an illustrated work on weapons and machines entitled Der Gezewg mit seiner Zugehörunge.

MS in Heidelberg University library (Cod. palat. germ. 130).
Jähns (p. 412). Feldhaus (col. 82).

13. Philip Mönch (1496). German mechanician and blunderbuss maker. Born in the Palatinate. He composed in 1496 in German an illustrated treatise on harquebusery, Buch der stryt und buchssen, containing many mechanical drawings. He made considerable use of iron in his contrivances. One of the machines elaborately drawn is a gun borer moved by horse power.

The MS is in the Heidelberg University library (Cod. palat. germ. 126). The author's portrait is on the title page.
Feldhaus (p. 29–30, 132, 1910, cited above); (col. 717, 1914).

14. Ludwig von Eybe zum Hartenstein.[9] Military engineer who flourished in various parts of Germany in the second half of the fifteenth century and the beginning of the sixteenth. He composed at Amberg[10] in 1500 an illustrated treatise on the military art, Kriegsbuch, which is one of the most elaborate of its kind.

MS in University library, Erlangen (no. 1390).
Jähns (p. 272–74). Feldhaus (col. 270, 1914).

Rereading the description of these fourteen items, one is startled by the fact that although no. 9, really three items in one, refers to Greek sources and three items are Italian, all others, ten in number, are of German origin. This may be partly due to a deeper investigation of German archives, but the main reason is that there were more mechanicians and military engineers in the fifteenth century in Germany than anywhere else. This seems to bear out general Rathgen's contentions (Isis 13, 127). We may not accept his statement that "Die Waffe ist der Ausgangspunkt aller Kultur"; arms are not the beginning of every culture, but they seem to be the origin of German culture.

These technical writings of the fourteenth and fifteenth centuries help us to understand the military and technical efforts of Leonardo da Vinci (1452–1519). He was undoubtedly a great mechanician and engineer, but his inventions are not by any means as original as many people think. Like the rest of his thinking, they are rooted in the Middle Ages.

For more elaborate studies on the manufacture and use of guns, and related subjects such as the making of gunpowder and range finding, one has to wait until the first half of the sixteenth century, when the field was dominated not by Germans, but by two Italians, Vannoccio Biringuccio of Siena (1480–1539) and Niccolò Tartaglia of Brescia (c. 1506–59).

Biringuccio published his treatise De la pirotechnia in Venice 1540; Tartaglia, his Nova scientia in Venice 1537, including discussion of ballistic problems, and the Quesiti et inventioni diverse in Venice 1546. These books were often reprinted in Italian and other languages, and were extensively used, both text and illustrations, by later writers to the end of the eighteenth century. The De re metallica of Georgius Agricola should not be mentioned in this connection, not only because it

[9] Called Ludwig von Eybe the Younger to distinguish him from his father, Ludwig von Eybe the Elder (1417–1502), famous statesman (ADB 6, 449–51).

[10] Where Martin Mercz lived and wrote a similar book in 1471 (see our no. 10 above). Hence, there seems to have been a definite technical tradition in that center.

was decidedly later (Basel 1556), but also because it does not deal with gunpowder, arms, armor.[11]

ARMOR

Our knowledge of fourteenth-century armor was much increased by excavations carried out in 1905, 1912, 1928–30 near Visby. The people of Gotland (largest Swedish island in the Baltic) had been defeated by the Danish king Valdimarr V Atterdag (ruled 1340–75) on July 27, 1361. A memorial cross was erected on the battlefield near the southern gate of the Visby wall, where it can be seen to this day.[12] It is said that 1,800 soldiers were killed in the battle and buried near the place where they fought and died. The three common graves thus far excavated have yielded the remains of 1,185 men, together with a large quantity of armor. An exemplary study of the bodies and armor was published by Bengt Thordeman, in collaboration with Poul Nörlund and Bo E. Ingelmark: Armour from the battle of Wisby 1361 (quarto, 2 vols.; vol. 1, text, 494 p.; vol. 2, 145 pl.; Kungl. vitterhets historie och antikvitets akademien, Stockholm 1939–40). Thordeman's book includes elaborate descriptions of the armor and gauntlets, as well as histories of lamellar armor and of coat of plates. Ellis H. Minns: The Wisby armour (Antiquity 18, 197–200, 1944).

After the study of Thordeman's work I applied for additional information to Stephen Vincent Grancsay, curator of the department of arms and armor in the Metropolitan Museum, New York, who allowed me to examine the fourteenth-century bits of armor in his keeping and explained technical points in the armory workshop. Armor was difficult to make because casting was out of the question; every piece had to be created in its proper shape by hammering; for example, a helmet was hammered out of a single piece of iron. Shapes were nicely calculated to obtain the maximum deviation of any impact from the bodies to be protected.

Though the Visby finds constitute the largest collection of authentic armor the date of which is undoubtedly anterior to 1362, there are a few other finds of fourteenth-century armor which were kindly listed for me by Mr. Grancsay (letter New York, June 12, 1941):

"1. Armor unearthed in the ruins of Küssnach Castle, Canton Schwytz, Switzerland, now in the Swiss National Museum at Zürich. (Thordeman refers to this in his bibliography under the author E. A. Gessler.)

"2. The castle of Tannenberg which was razed by Ruprecht von der Pfalz and his allies in 1399. The excavation of the ruins ordered by the Grand Duke of Hesse in 1849 brought to light considerable material, including a brass cannon with full charge of powder and lead, very large and heavy stone cannon balls, arrows and crossbow bolts, swords and daggers, war hammer, lance heads, rowel spurs, stirrups, bits, basinet, helm, plates of brigandines, shoulder plates, a short-cuffed gauntlet, buckles . . . . This material is now preserved in the Hessisches Landesmuseum in Darmstadt. (Thordeman refers to these in his bibliography under the authors J. H. v. Hefner-Alteneck and H. Müller-Hickler.)

[11] Biringuccio's work is now available to English readers because of the translation prepared by Cyril Stanley Smith and Martha Teach Gnudi: The Pirotechnia (502 p., ill., American Institute of Mining Engineers, New York 1942; Isis 34, 514–16). Agricola's De re metallica was Englished by Herbert Clark Hoover (later president of the United States) and his wife Lou Henry Hoover (folio, 672 p., Mining magazine, London 1912; Isis 13, 113–16).

[12] I saw it in July 1934, when it was my privilege to spend a few weeks in that island so beautiful and so rich in memories (Isis 23, 320). The great commercial importance of Visby has been pointed out in Introd. 2, 1063.

"3. Armor from the castle ruins of Alt-Titschein in Moravia. (See Thordeman's bibliography under R. Prihoda.)

"4. Armor from Castle Helfenstein. (See Thordeman's bibliography under Werner Fleischhauer.)

"In addition to these there is an important collection of armor from the Castle of Chalcis which was captured by the Turks from the Venetians in 1470. The armor found there dates from the middle of the fourteenth century to about 1470. Some of it is in the Metropolitan.[13] The following articles describe and illustrate it: Charles ffoulkes: Italian Armour from Chalcis in the Ethnological Museum at Athens (Archaeologia, 1911, vol. 62, pp. 381–390). Carl Otto v. Kienbusch and Stephen V. Grancsay: The Bashford Dean Collection of Arms and Armor in The Metropolitan Museum of Art (Portland, Maine, 1933).

"There is some fourteenth-century armor which is still in its ancient surroundings: The achievements of Edward, Prince of Wales, the 'Black Prince,' in the Cathedral Church of Canterbury. W. H. St. John Hope: The achievements of Edward (Vetusta monumenta, 1895, vol. 7, pp. 13–22). The armor of a Vogt of Matsch in the Castle of Churburg. The Armoury of the Castle of Churburg by Oswald Graf Trapp, translated with a preface by James G. Mann (London, 1929, p. 19). The heraldic shields in the St. Elizabeth Church in Marburg. Die mittelalterlichen heraldischen Kampfschilde in der St. Elizabeth-Kirche zu Marburg by F. Warnecke (Berlin, 1884).

"Sir Guy Francis Laking includes illustrations of elements of fourteenth-century armor, particularly helmets, in his Record of European Armour and Arms through Seven Centuries (5 vols. London 1920–22)."

Moreover, information on fourteenth-century armor may be derived from contemporary monuments. I shall refer only to two monuments with which I am very familiar, both anterior to the middle of the century. They are good examples of a class which became far more numerous in the second half of the century and later.

The first is a brass (see note on monumental brasses in chapter VII) preserved in the Archaeological Museum of Ghent, commemorating Willem Wenemaer (slain 1325). Wenemaer is represented fully armed. The second is the "Steenen man" (Stone Man), dating from 1338, formerly in the Belfry of Ghent, now preserved in the abbey of St. Bavon of the same city. The "Stone Man" is a rude but very impressive statue. It represents a man wearing "a basinet (helmet) of steel; a row of staples follows the lower border and over these passes a wide leather band to which is sewed the aventail (face, neck, and shoulder defense of mail). The arm defenses are of steel plates. Over the body armor (impossible to tell whether of plate armor or mail) is worn the surcoat. The leg defenses are of mail.

"The 'stone man' has been described in detail, and I am sending you the references herewith: Napoléon de Pauw: L'homme du Beffroi (Inventaire archéologique de Gand. Ser. 1, 1897–1901, Feb. 10, 1897). Hermann van Duyse: Le costume de l'homme du Beffroi (Inventaire archéologique de Gand. Ser. 1, 1897–1901, June 26, 1897).

"The Ghent brass has also been described several times. Here are two references: Hermann van Duyse: Dalle tumulaire de Guillaume Wenemaer (Inventaire archéologique de Gand. Ser. 1, 1897–1901, June 26, 1897). Albert Way: Notices

[13] Among specimens in the Metropolitan is a splendid basinet, that is, a steel helmet, probably Italian. It is 14 inches high and made in one piece. It seems very early, say, c. 1350.

FIG. 29. Brass plate to the memory of Willem Wenemaer, slain July 5, 1325, and of his wife, Margriet Sbrunen. Formerly placed in the hospital founded by him in Ghent, it is now in the Archaeological Museum of that city.

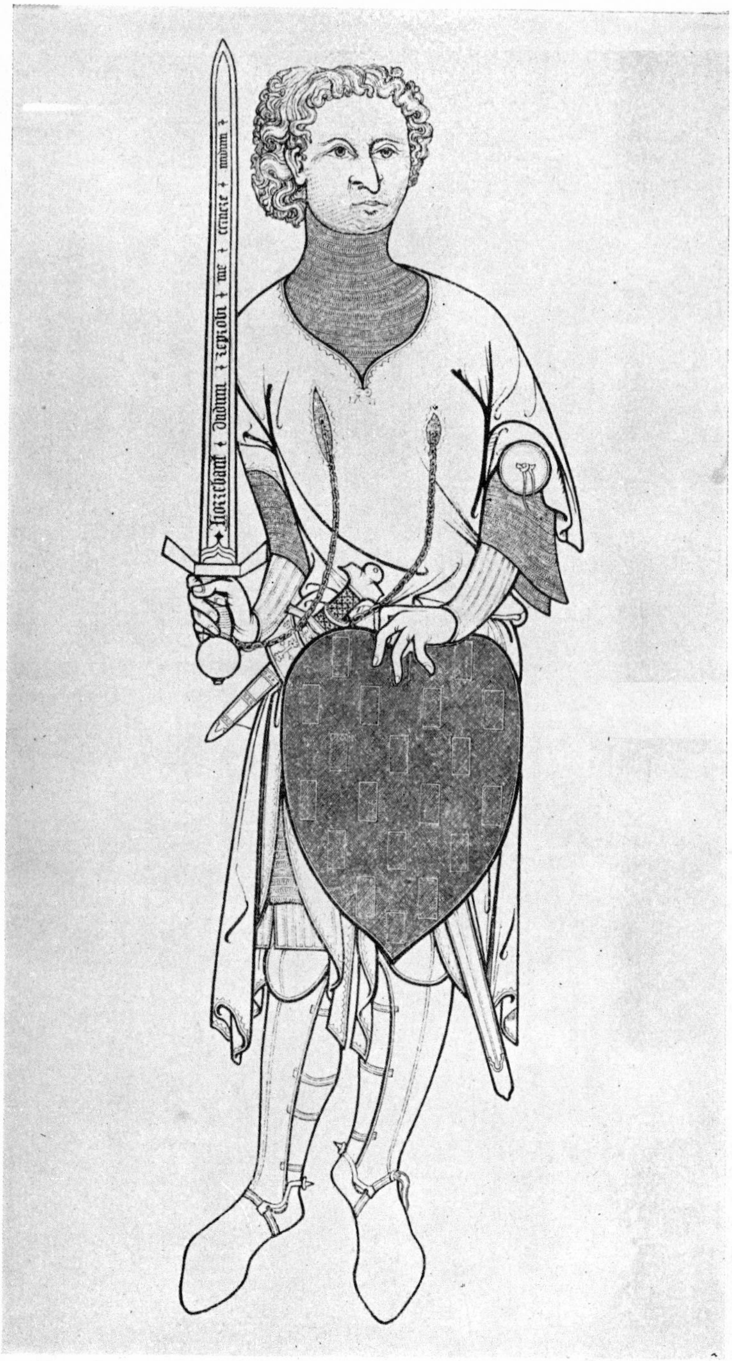

Fig. 30. Drawing of the Wenemaer brass showing the details of his armor. From Archaeological journal (7, 287, London 1850).

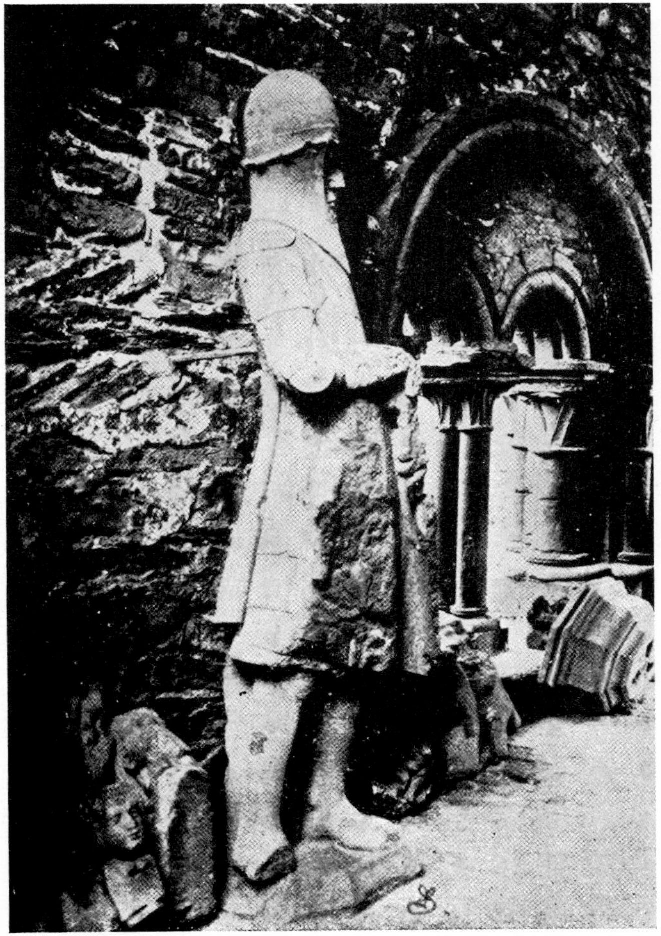

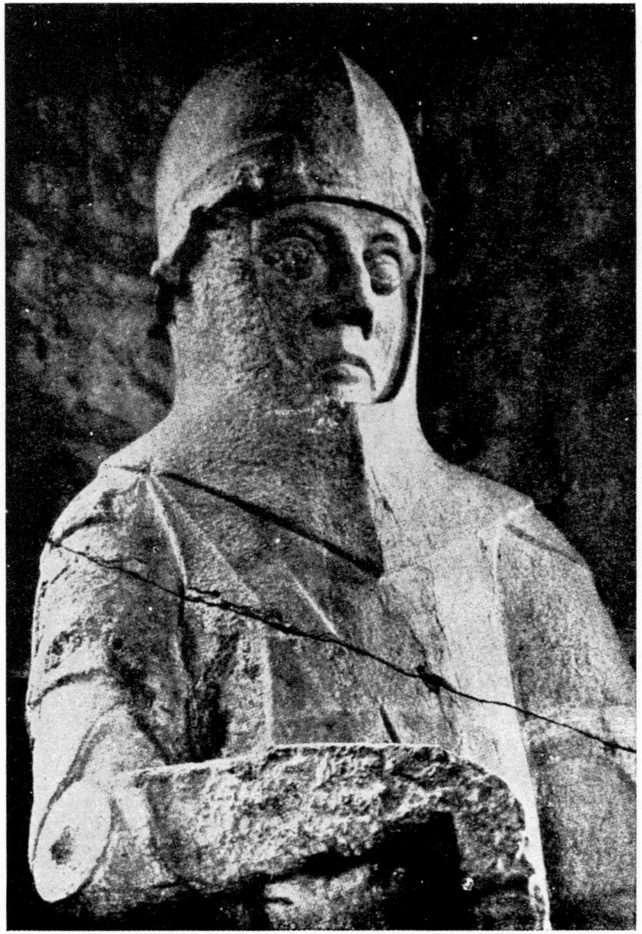

FIGS. 31, 32. The "Stone Man" of Ghent, dated 1338. Formerly in the Belfry, it is now preserved in the ruins of the abbey of St. Bavon, used as a lapidary museum. Figure 32 shows details of his armor.

of foreign sepulchral brasses (Archaeological Journal, London, 1850, vol. 7, pp. 283-291, ill. opp. p. 287)." (Letter from S. V. Grancsay, New York, Nov. 29, 1941.) Other monuments are illustrated in Thordeman (1939–40).

For the comparative study of Chinese armor, see Berthold Laufer: Chinese clay figures (Field Museum Publ. 177, Anthropological ser. vol. 13, no. 2; Chicago 1914); of Japanese arms and armor, see Bashford Dean: Handbook of arms and armor (4th ed., p. 254–91, Metropolitan Museum, New York 1930); of Korean arms and armor, John L. Boots: Korean weapons and armor (Trans. Korea branch, R. Asiatic Society, vol. 23, part 2, 37 p., 41 pl., Seoul 1934).

DINANDERIE

There is not much to add to the article on dinanderie in chapter VII, except if one were trying to compile a list of remarkable bells or other monuments dated or datable before 1401. This is hardly necessary; a few examples must suffice.

1. Equestrian statue of St. George and the Dragon cast in bronze by Martin and George of Kolozsvár in 1373. It was restored in 1562 and now stands in the courtyard of the Hradčany (citadel) at Prague. J. Tavenor Perry: Dinanderie (pl. 3, p. 66, London 1910).

2. Dragon serving as weathercock at the top of the belfry of Ghent. It is 3.70 m. long. It was long believed to have been brought back by the Crusaders, when the count of Flanders, Baldwin IX, helped to sack Constantinople and became its first Latin emperor, Baldwin I (1204–5). The study of communal accounts has proved that the dragon was made in Ghent in 1377–78. Julius Vuylsteke: Inventaire archéologique de Gand (1st ser., p. 26, Ghent, May 30, 1897).

3. Two bells in the steeple of the halles at Damme (near Bruges) were cast by the brothers Harlebeke and dated 1392 (Tavenor Perry p. 208).

4. Bronze sculpture in the royal tombs, Westminster Abbey (cire perdue process). Effigies of Henry III (king 1216–72) and his queen, Eleanor of Provence (d. 1291), made by William Torel, a London goldsmith, in 1391. Effigy of Edward III (king 1327–77) made by John Orchard, a "latoner" (= lattener, a worker in latten or brass). Effigies of Richard II (king 1377–99) and his queen, Anne of Bohemia (1366–94). Molds were made in 1394 and a contract entered into for two gilt images with Godfrey Prest and Nicholas Broker, coppersmiths in London. The beautiful effigy of Edward the Black Prince (1330–76) in Canterbury was probably made by John Orchard, though the enamels on the coronet and sword belt might be Limousin (?) (Tavenor Perry p. 91).

During the war it was necessary to remove the Westminster effigies to a place of safety. Before their re-establishment in Westminster they were exhibited in the Victoria and Albert Museum, where they could be examined in detail and photographed under excellent conditions. See handbook published by that Museum and article in The Connoisseur (London, Dec. 1945, p. 124–25, 5 fig.).

These examples show that work in brass or copper had reached a very high standard of excellence before the end of the century. Our knowledge of the technique involved, however, is very meager, and these and other examples are more interesting to the historian of art than to the historian of technology.

6. PRINTING, EAST AND WEST

FAR EAST

The art of printing was continued in the Far East with increasing vigor, but without material improvement. A list of the main publications of that period would thus be of bibliographical rather than of technical interest. The best sources of information are Kawase's book of 1937, in Japanese, and the T'ieh ch'in tung chien lou Sung Chin Yüan pen shu ying (1922), in Chinese, cited at the end of the note on printing in chapter VII.

In Japan printing was largely restricted to Chinese texts and to Buddhist sūtra; this was so from the beginning of printing[13a] to the end of the Kamakura period (1338). From 1400 on, Japanese editions, imitating Sung or Yüan ones, began to be issued, which are called Gozan-han or Kōya-han after the monasteries where they were printed. These editions were xylographic.

In China and Korea the early typographic printing was followed by a return to the old method, then back to typography. This was due to the fact that the economy of labor and money effected by typography was not sufficient and tended to vanish when illustrations were included in the text. The cost of a Chinese font of cast bronze and copper type was naturally very large, and there might be temptations to use the valuable metal for other purposes. Wood blocks were less expensive, less attractive as loot, yet easier to replace if stolen or lost.

A renaissance of typography began in Korea with the new Li dynasty (1392), when a special officer was appointed to take charge of casting type and printing books. No work was done, however, until 1403, when Tai tsung, Korea's greatest king, ordered the casting of type in metal. The Korean annals (Kao li shih) and the postfaces to early Korean books prove that the use of metal type was at once recognized as a great invention. Within a few months after the king's order several hundred thousand type had been cast. Improvements and with them new fonts of type followed one another rapidly. Between 1403 and 1544 no less than eleven royal decrees deal with the casting of type and the printing of books by means of such type. At least three fonts were cast before the invention of typography in Europe—in 1403, 1420, 1434—enormous quantities of type being produced and large numbers of books printed (the earliest extant dated 1409). New fonts were cast in 1455, 1465, and finally in 1484. During the rule of Chuang Hsien Wang (king 1419–50), a Korean alphabet was invented, a phonetic alphabet derived from Sanskrit, but strange to say the Koreans[14] failed to see the almost obvious relation between alphabet and typography (i.e., that the economy of the latter is in inverse proportion to the number of different types), and their invention instead of simplifying printing made it more complicated. Indeed, each Chinese character with its Korean phonetic equivalent formed one type, but as some characters have more than one phonetic equivalent, it became necessary to have more type than there are characters.[15] If the Koreans failed to complete and fructify their invention of the alphabet, it cannot be denied that their invention of typography was, outside of that, almost complete. They invented the type mold but did not make it sufficiently uniform, and various mechanical devices were necessary to keep the type firmly in place. The museum of Seoul treasures specimens of the earlier fonts

[13a] The earliest printed document which has come down to us is a Buddhist charm, printed, not in China but in Japan, by order of Shōtoku-tennō c. 770 (Introd. 1, 451, 529). Of course printing had begun long before that time in China and somewhat before it in Japan. See chapter VII, p. 729–32.

[14] Like the Uighūr of an earlier time, see note on Wang Chên (XIV-1).

[15] The same aberration obtains in Japan. The Japanese have a syllabary of fifty symbols, but the Chinese characters and the Japanese kana are on the same piece of type. Thus a Japanese newspaper requires a larger font than a Chinese newspaper (c. 20,000 different characters).

(1403, 1416, 1420, 1434, etc.) and some specimens may be seen in many other museums, e.g., in the American Museum of Natural History in New York. The use of the Korean metal type spread gradually to China (end of fifteenth century) and to Japan (1596). In Korea itself it was completely stopped from 1544 to 1770. On account of the enormous fonts required in China, Korea, and Japan, it is not surprising that in all those countries block printing, and later lithography and photography, have continued to vie with typography until our own days.

For more information see Courant (1894), chiefly p. xliv ff. of the admirable introduction. William George Aston: Writing, printing and the alphabet in Corea (Journal Royal Asiatic Society, 1895, 505–11). James Scarth Gale: The Korean alphabet (Trans. Korea branch, R. Asiatic Society, 4, 13–61, Seoul 1912). Carter (p. 169–79, 1925). Judson Daland (1931; see bibliography in ch. VII) for the chemical analysis of early Korean type. Mark Napier Trollope: Book production and printing in Korea (Trans. Korea branch, R. Asiatic Society, 25, 103–7, 1936).

The Korean edition of the Analects (c. 1317) has been discussed in chapter VII. We cannot prove the existence of Korean typography in the first half of the fourteenth century; on the other hand, the date of the revival 1403 is sure; typography was thus practiced in Korea on a gigantic scale, a full generation before Gutenberg.

WEST

After the long story of Oriental printing told in volume 1 and in chapters VII and XXI of this one, we may now pass to the consideration of Western printing. It will suffice to say that Western xylography did not begin before the last quarter or last third of the fourteenth century. The "Bois Protat," so called because it belongs to Jules Protat, printer in Mâcon, is a block of walnut wood representing in reverse a fragment of a Crucifixion; it was much used for printing and is dated by experts c. 1370–80.[16] Playing cards were printed c. 1392 for the mad king Charles VI.[17] Various xylographic documents are dated from the end of the fourteenth century and the beginning of the following one. Block books continued to be produced throughout the incunabula age and even beyond.

Consult histories of engraving, of playing cards, of art. Henri Bouchot: Un ancêtre de la gravure sur bois. Etudes sur un xylographe taillé en Bourgogne vers 1370 (144 p., Paris 1902); La gravure et l'estampe in André Michel: Histoire de

[16] The fragmentary Bois Protat is so large (60 cm. high) that the whole of it must have exceeded any size of vellum or of paper available in those days. Hence it must have been used for printing on textiles or on a wall surface, and that is another story. The use of blocks for printing patterns on textiles (printing not with ink but with a resist or mordant, also "dry printing") was developed early in many parts of the world, India, Japan, Egypt. Some specimens of about the sixth century, resist prints on cotton, have been excavated in Egypt. The earliest European example of printed fabric was found in the tomb of St. Caesarius, bishop of Arles 502–43; it is probably Oriental. Carter (p. 145–49, 246–49, 1925).

[17] Were they printed or drawn? The origin of playing cards is very dark. Did they originate in Egypt, in India, or in China? Were they brought West by Crusaders? What is certain is that they do not emerge from obscurity in the West until the last quarter of the fourteenth century. William Hughes Willshire: Descriptive catalogue of playing and other cards in the British Museum. Supplement (2 vols., ill., London 1876–77). Mrs. John King Van Rensselaer: The devil's picture books (New York 1890). Henry René d'Allemagne: Les cartes à jouer du XIVe au XXe siècle (2 vols., 3200 ill., Paris 1906). Note that Allemagne begins his exhaustive study in the fourteenth century.

l'art (3, part 1, 327–42, Paris 1907). There are facsimile reproductions of many block books or xylographs, catalogues raisonnés and other descriptive literature, but that concerns the fifteenth century almost exclusively. E.g., Paul André Lemoisne: Les xylographies du XIVe et du XVe siècle au Cabinet des estampes de la Bibliothèque nationale (folio, 2 vols., Paris 1927–30), 350 p. of text plus 107 colored and 34 black plates. Elizabeth Mongan and Carl O. Schniewind: The first century of printmaking 1400–1500. An exhibition at the Art Institute (152 p., ill., Chicago 1941), catalogue of 138 items, all of the fifteenth century, except the first, which is a printed textile, silver and black on yellow silk, ascribed to the twelfth or thirteenth century, lent by the Brooklyn Museum; it is probably South German (upper Rhine).

As to Western typography, it was not invented until sometime before 1450, and in all probability that invention was independent of the Eastern one. Its embryonic development may have occurred in more than one place; the commercial stage was probably reached in Mainz c. 1440. The inventor, Johann Gutenberg or whoever else he was, seems to have found almost immediately something superior to the Eastern invention in at least two respects: (1) a better casting method, controlling more exactly the dimensions of the type, (2) a new kind of ink better adapted to printing purposes. That ink was oily, and its discovery was probably derived from the technique of oil painting, which can be traced back in the West at least to Theophilus the Priest (XII-1) and is discussed by Peter of Saint Omer (XIII-2). The painters had found the value of linseed oil, well boiled down, for producing a varnish; that varnish was the necessary basis for printing, as against writing, ink. The development of oil painting, however, as well as the Western invention of typography, are outside the scope of this volume.

Frank Bestow Wiborg: Printing ink (319 p., 10 ill., New York 1926; Isis 9, 134–38). Pierce Butler: The origin of printing in Europe (172 p., Chicago 1940; Isis 33, 95).

9. MECHANICAL THEORIES

PELACANI

Biagio Pelacani of Parma. Italian mechanician, physicist, commentator on Aristotle, and astrologer (d. 1416).

Contents: (1) Life. (2) Writings. (3) Statics and hydrostatics. (4) Astrology. (5) Text. (6) Criticism.

1. *Life*

Biagio da Parma, Biagio Pelacani da Parma, Blasius Parmensis. Nothing is known of him before 1377, when he was on the faculty of arts of Pavia. He is said, however, to have obtained his doctorate in the same university in 1374. In 1379–80 and following years he was teaching logic, philosophy, and astrology in Bologna; in 1384–85, he was teaching in Padua; then again in Pavia, etc. By 1389 he was already famous in his country, being called in Il paradiso degli Alberti, written about that year (Thorndike 4, 67, 1934), the most universal philosopher and mathematician of his time. In 1396, his orthodoxy was questioned by his bishop, but he avoided further trouble. He spent some time in Paris, but we do not know when. In 1407, he finally returned to Padua, where he continued to teach until 1411. He went back to his native city, Parma, where he died on April 23, 1416.

He seems to have been an unpopular teacher. It may be that his unpopularity was greatest during the final years, when he had probably become a vain, greedy, cross-grained, and cantankerous old man. They spoke of him as "aut diabolus est, aut Blasius Parmensis." His most famous pupil was the mathematician Prosdocimo de' Beldomandi (d. 1428). Vittorino da Feltre (1378–1446), who was to become one of the greatest educators of the Italian Renaissance, was very badly treated by him; and the Pavian physician Antonio Guainerio (d. c. 1445) spoke ill of him. On the other hand, Luca Pacioli recognized his indebtedness to him in his Summa (princeps, Venice 1494), and Niccolò Burzio of Parma (1450–1518) in his Bononia illustrata (Bologna 1494) counted him one of the four greatest men of their native city, the three others being Cassius Parmensis (one of the murderers of Caesar in 44 B.C.), Cassius the poet (Cassius Etruscus?), and Macrobius (V-1). All this takes us well out of the fourteenth century. Indeed, Pelacani was one of the "fin-de-siècle" authors who belong to the two centuries.

His son Francesco Pelacani received the doctorate in Pavia 1422, and he taught logic and natural philosophy there until 1448 or later.

2. *Writings*

Pelacani composed a number of Aristotelian commentaries, to wit, on the Organon, De anima, De coelo et mundo, De generatione et corruptione, Meteora, two sets of questions on the Physica. He also commented upon the Sphere of John of Sacrobosco (XIII-1), the logic of Peter of Spain (XIII-2), the Perspectiva communis of John Peckham (XIII-2); he arranged questions of John Buridan (XIV-1); he discussed the theory of proportions, intension and remission, latitudes of forms, etc., of Thomas Bradwardine, Richard Swineshead, and Nicole Oresme. Finally, he wrote a Tractatus de ponderibus, which is a kind of commentary on the auctores de ponderibus, and to which we shall come back presently.

His commentary on the Perspectiva communis, though restricted to 24 questions, was so elaborate that it exceeded the whole work in length. He tried to explain some prodigious appearances in the sky by the reflection of light from the clouds.

There are many MSS of these writings, some of them contemporary or not much later. By the end of the fifteenth century, however, his fame was already waning, and the only work of his to be printed in that century was the commentary on Oresme's Latitudines formarum (1482, 1486).

3. *Statics and hydrostatics*

Pelacani's main interests were apparently mechanical. In addition to the mechanical discussions which are probably included in the Aristotelian commentaries above mentioned, he wrote a treatise De motu iuxta mentem Aristotelis, a query Utrum duo vel plura corpora dura possint se tangere et ab invicem equidistanter elevari. His capital work in that field is the Tractatus de ponderibus, available in a MS copied in Naples 1476 by Arnald of Brussels.[18]

The Tractatus de ponderibus is a development of the mechanical views already expressed by the school of Jordanus Nemorarius (XIII-1), that is, the author of the De ratione ponderis, whom Duhem called "the Forerunner of Leonardo" (Introd. 2, 614); by other unknown "authores de ponderibus," as the authors of the Liber Euclidis de ponderibus and of the De canonio; finally, by Albert of Saxony (d. 1390).

[18] With regard to that famous scientific scribe and printer see W. J. Wilson: An alchemical manuscript by Arnaldus de Bruxella (Osiris 2, 220–405, 1936), chiefly p. 229–238.

Pelacani's Tractatus is divided into three parts, the first two of which deal with statics, the third with hydrostatics.

In his statics Pelacani develops the Jordanian notion of gravitas secundum situm (or gravitas situalis). He remarks that when the beam of an equal-armed balance is removed from the center of the world, the weights suspended to it seem to increase with their distance from that center because the direction along which they tend to fall is nearer to the vertical. This argument was eventually repeated by Roberval and Etienne Pascal in their controversy with Fermat, also by Descartes and Mersenne. He discusses the inclined plane, wondering why a body sliding along one plane can equilibrate a heavier one sliding along another plane less steep. He considers passive resistances and makes a weak attempt to take them into account in the study of statical equilibrium.

His hydrostatics (third part of the Tractatus) is derived from Archimedes, from the pseudo-Archimedean De ponderibus, from Albert of Saxony, and from the Carmen de ponderibus ascribed to the Roman grammarian Priscianus (VI-1). It is from that Carmen that he derived the idea of the areometer or hydrometer of constant weight.

Pelacani had imagination, but he lacked mental vigor and could not put his ideas together for their mutual clarification. Thus he invented nothing, and his influence was almost negligible, but his treatise was one of the channels through which mediaeval mechanics reached Leonardo da Vinci and Cardano.

4. *Astrology*

Pelacani was a teacher of astrology and he was called upon (e.g., in 1386) to make astrological predictions. He wrote at least two astronomical treatises, his commentary on Sacrobosco and the Theorica planetarum (of course, this may be purely astrological), and a Iudicium anni 1405 (Iudicium revolutionis anni 1405, 11 martii cum horis et fractionibus). In that Iudicium he foresees all kinds of troubles, which were likely enough to happen in those troubled days, but prefaces them with warnings lest Christian dogmas be undermined. Astrological influences cannot nullify God's will but can be nullified by it at any time; they cannot suppress free will. A rational man can resist those influences if he wills it. These warnings may have been added by him to forestall charges of heresy (he had been under suspicion in 1396), or he may have been completely honest. A conditional belief in astrology, within the frame of orthodoxy, seems to have been common in those days, for it was equally impossible to evade the commandments of Christian dogmatics and the universally accepted assumptions and implications of judicial astrology.

5. *Text*

Quaestiones de latitudinibus formarum. Printed Padua 1482 (Klebs 739.1). Reprinted in the second edition of Oresme's Latitudines formarum, Padua 1486 (Klebs 713.2). Reprinted a third time in Venice 1505. This third edition also contains Pelacani's question Utrum duo vel plura corpora dura possint se tangere....

6. *Criticism*

Ireneo Affò: Memorie degli scrittori e letterati parmigiani (2, 112, Parma 1789). Libri (2, 208, 1838). J. Timtchenko: [Pelacani on latitudes] (BM 1, 504, 1900). Federico Amodeo: Riproduzione della questione sul trattato de latitudinibus formarum fatto da Biagio Pelacani (Atti dell' Istituto tecnico, 27 p., Napoli 1909); Appunti su Biagio Pelacani da Parma (Atti del IV Congresso internazionale dei matematici, Roma 1908, 3, 549–53, Roma 1909). Duhem: Origines (1, 147–55, 1905; 2, 57, 341–43, 1906); Système (4, 278–80, 1916). Heinrich Wieleitner: Der Tractatus de latitudinibus formarum des Oresme (BM 13, 115–45, 1913). Adolf Krazer: Zur Geschichte der graphischen Darstellung von Funktionen (Jahresbericht der deutschen Mathematiker-Vereinigung 24, 340–63, Leipzig 1915–16; Isis 4, 138). Lynn Thorndike: Blasius of Parma (Archeion 9, 177–90, 1928; Isis 13, 436); article revised and elaborated in his History of magic (4, 65–79, 652–62, 1934); Blasius' recantation in 1396 (p. 258, 1944), apropos of his temporary difficulties with his bishop in that year. Wickersheimer (p. 86, 1936).

12. MUSICAL THEORIES

LANDINO

Francesco Landino, Francescus de Florentia. Italian musician (1325–97).

Francesco was born in Fiesole, near Florence, in 1325, and became blind in childhood as a result of smallpox, hence his Latin name Franciscus Caecus.

He was for a time in Verona during the rule of Martino della Scala (ruled 1329–51), and we find him in Venice 1364, but the best part of his life was spent in Florence. According to his grandnephew Cristoforo Landino (1424–1504), professor of rhetoric and poetry in that city, Francisco had some knowledge of philosophy and astrology, but a deep one of music. He was the only Occamist in the Florentine circle. Vivid impressions of him are given in Il paradiso degli Alberti, written in 1389 by Giovanni da Prato. That novel, though less known than the Decamerone, is superior to it in its description of the Florentine circle wherein the new music was performed.

He devoted himself to music, playing many instruments (guitar, lute, organ, clavier). He invented a new kind of clavier, the serena serenorum. He was a famous composer and organist. Many of his compositions are still extant; they constitute over one-third of the Italian music of the fourteenth century which has come down to us. Francesco did not contribute to musical theory, but is included here for the sake of completeness, because he was the main Italian representative of the ars nova in the fourteenth century. He was organist in San Lorenzo, and when he died, in Florence on September 2, 1397, he was buried in that church. A monument was soon built to his memory there, representing him in bas-relief with a small organ. That monument has often been reproduced in illustrated histories of music.

He was crowned with laurels by the king of Cyprus in 1364 at the end of a musical tournament in Venice, Petrarca being a member of the jury.

Text. Leonard Ellinwood: The works of Francesco Landini (360 p., Mediaeval Academy, Cambridge, Mass. 1939; Isis 31, 521; Speculum 15, 503–7).

Criticism. Giosuè Carducci: Musica e poesia nel mondo elegante italiano del secolo XIV (Studi letterarii, 2d ed., p. 369–441, Livorno 1880), first published 1870. Johannes Wolf: Florenz in der Musikgeschichte des 14. Jahrhunderts (Sammelbände der internationalen Musikgesellschaft 3, 599–646, 1902). Short note by E. van der Straeten in Grove (3, 85, 1927). Leonard Ellinwood (1939). W. Thomas Marrocco: Fourteenth century Italian cacce (104 p., 5 pl., Cambridge, Mass. 1942; Isis 34, 244).

TUNSTED

Simon Tunsted. English Franciscan, mathematician, physicist, and musician (d. 1369).

Simon Tunsted (or Tunstede, Tunstude, Donostadius) was born at Norwich, but his father hailed from Tunstead in the same county (Norfolk). Simon assumed the Franciscan habit in Norwich, eventually became doctor of theology, warden of the Norwich monastery, in 1351 regent master of the Oxford Minorites, and c. 1360 provincial of the English province. He died in 1369 and was buried in the nunnery of Bruisyard, Suffolk.

He improved the Albion of Richard Wallingford, both the instrument and the description of it.

His fame rests on a musical treatise the ascription of which to him is not quite certain. It is entitled De quattuor principalibus musices (also De musica continua et discreta cum diagrammatibus). This is one of the best and most elaborate treatises of that time, comparable to that of Tunsted's older contemporary, the Benedictine Walter Odington (XIV-1). It is clear and practical. The four divisions of the Quattuor principalia deal respectively with (I) generalities, (II) elements of music, construction of the monochord and intervals, (III) notation and plain song, (IV) mensural music (musica mensurabilis). This Quartum principale was the most novel part of the book and the most important. According to the colophon of a Bodleian MS ascribing it to "Simon de Tunstude doctor sacre theologie qui in musica pollebat etiam in septem artibus liberalibus," it was completed in August 1351; another Bodleian MS gives the same name and date.

Tunsted extravagantly praised Philip of Vitry (XIV-1), "qui fuit flos totius mundi musicorum." This may be due simply to the fact that he had obtained from Vitry his own musical enlightenment. The ultimate source of the new musical theory was al-Fārābī (X-1), who had been building on Greek foundations (Isis 20, 280–83).

The commentary on Aristotle's Meteorology formerly ascribed to Duns Scot (XIII-2) was credited by the English Franciscan Luke Wadding (1588–1657) in his edition of it (1639) to Simon Tunsted, and that new ascription has been generally accepted. Duhem, however, opposed it in 1906. Though agreeing that the author was an Englishman or had lived in England, he saw no reason to identify him with Tunsted. He found many resemblances between this commentary and the one composed by Tunsted's contemporary Themon son of the Jew, so many that he considered it a sort of abridgment of Themon's commentary. That abridgment was again abridged by Nicole Oresme. In conclusion, the commentary was certainly not written by Duns Scot; Tunsted may have been the author, but that is doubtful. It is a sort of transition between that of Themon and that of Oresme. In one of its forms it influenced Leonardo da Vinci.

Whoever the author was, it must be a work of about the middle of the fourteenth century. It contains the usual discussion on such topics as the shape of the earth and of the waters, and their centers (or common center) of figure and of gravity. Do the volumes of the four elements form a geometrical progression? The author concludes that the volume of waters must be inferior to the volume of earth, otherwise the latter would be completely submerged. He explains the theory of the eccentricity of the earth and water spheres, which he wrongly ascribes to Giovanni Campano (XIII-2).

Text. Quattuor principalia musices, edited by Coussemaker (4, 201–98, 1876). The last section of the book had already been included by him, without author's name, in his vol. 3, 334–64.

Meteorologicorum libri quattuor. First edition by Luke Wadding in the Joannis Duns Scoti Opera omnia (vol. 3, Lyon 1639). Reprinted in Joannis Duns Scoti Opera omnia, editio nova (4, 1–263, Ludovicus Vives, Paris 1891). I have seen only the reprint which includes Wadding's censura, not the original edition.

Criticism. Henry Davey (DNB 57, 317, 1899). Duhem: Origines (2, 326–35, 1906). R. T. Gunther (2, 50, 70, 1923). A. Hughes-Hughes in Grove (5, 408, 1928)

THEINRED

English Benedictine and musician (fl. 1371).

Theinred or Thinred (the Christian name David is apocryphal) flourished in the Benedictine monastery of Dover, where he was precentor; he died and was buried there.

In 1371, he dedicated to one Alured of Canterbury a musical treatise De legitimis ordinibus pentachordorum et tetrachordorum, divided into three books: (I) De proportionibus musicorum sonorum, de comatis; (II) De consonantiis musicorum sonorum; (III) includes various diagrams and scales in the old letter notation. Theinred was quoted and praised by English antiquarians, John Boston of Bury (Boston Buriensis, fl. 1410), John Bale (1495–1563), and John Pits (1560–1616), the second going so far as to call him musicorum sui temporis phoenix, yet his work is practically unknown.

Text. Theinred's treatise, represented by a unique Bodleian MS, was announced for publication in Coussemaker's fourth volume, but that project did not materialize.

Criticism. François Joseph Fétis: Biographie des musiciens (8, 211, Paris 1870). Henry Davey (DNB 56, 109, 1898).

ACOUSTIC VASES

The reading of a book on the antiquities of Cyprus called our attention to the acoustic vases which were found embedded in the vaults of St. Mary of Carmel of Famagusta, built c. 1360. The ceramic vases were built in in such a manner that only their openings were visible, their purpose being to improve the acoustics of the hall. This was not by any means a novelty, but the Cypriot examples were the first to arrest our attention; we should have spoken of the subject earlier, but "mieux vaut tard que jamais."

The idea is Greek according to Vitruvius (I-2 B.C.), who uses the word ἠχεῖα to designate resonators placed in the Greek theaters, volumes of enclosed air responding to tones in the neighborhood of the audience. Ἠχεῖον is a drum or gong; according to the latest edition of Liddell and Scott (1940), ἠχεῖα in the meaning just indicated is used only by Vitruvius (De architectura I, 1), "Vasa aerea, quae in cellis sub gradibus mathematica ratione conlocantur sonituum ad discrimina, quae graeci ἠχεῖα appellant . . . ." Vitruvius devoted the whole chapter 5 of book V, De theatri vasis, to their description. No Greek or Roman examples have yet been discovered, but according to Enlart (p. 797), such acoustic vases have been found in many French churches dating from the eleventh to the seventeenth centuries. The earliest example referred to by him is in Pommiers (Loire), eleventh century. There are also examples in England (Ipswich and Norwich), the Low Countries, Poland, Denmark, Sweden, and Italy.

Acoustic vases were included in the Chartreuse of Villeneuve (the town built opposite Avignon, across the Rhône, in Languedoc), in the chapel built by Innocent VI (pope 1352–62). Three of these vases are 78 cm. long, that is, larger than the earlier vases found in Lyon (thirteenth century), Arles (thirteenth), and perhaps Cahors (fourteenth). Brun (p. 126, 1928).

For Vitruvius, the most convenient edition is the Latin-French one by Auguste Choisy (4 vols., Paris 1909). Vol. 1, Analyse (p. 201–2); vols. 2, 3, text; vol. 4, plates. See vol. 2 (p. 10, 233–38).

G. W. W. Minns: Acoustic pottery (Norfolk archaeology 7, 93–101, 1872), discussing Norwich examples. Camille Enlart: Manuel d'archéologie française. I. Architecture religieuse (2d ed., p. 797–99, Paris 1920), with photograph of Famagusta vases. Hope Bagenal and Alex. Wood: Planning for good acoustics (464 p., 236 ill., New York 1933; p. 338–48), excellent discussion of the acoustical problem. We need more information concerning the "vases" themselves in ancient and mediaeval times.

There is a reference to the ancient acoustic vases in the Epistle dedicatory of Sir Thomas Browne's Hydriotaphia (London 1658). A French traveler of a century ago observed a large number of acoustic vases fitted in the walls of the church of Cydonia (Asiatic coast opposite Mitylene); they amplified the preacher's voice remarkably well. Ambroise Firmin Didot: Notes d'un voyage fait dans le Levant en 1816 et 1817 (p. 401, Paris 1826).

It would seem that the Japanese used ceramic vases for acoustical purposes in the theaters devoted to the nō drama. Jiro Harada: A glimpse of Japanese ideals (p. 159, Tokyo 1938; Isis 35, 256).

I do not understand how these acoustic vessels would work, for such resonators would not amplify all the sounds equally and hence would cause distortions.

'ABD AL-QĀDIR IBN GHAIBĪ

One of the greatest Persian writers on the theory of music; writing in Arabic (d. 1435).

'Abd al-Qādir was born about the middle of the century in Marāgha, then the capital of Ādharbāijān and a center of Persian-Mongol culture.[19] Indeed, he was a musician at the court of Ḥusain (Jalāirī sulṭān of that part of Persia, 1374–82), and in 1379 he composed a new piece of music for each day of Ramaḍān. He continued at the court of Ḥusain's successor, sulṭān Aḥmad, then for a time at the court of Yildirim Bāyazīd ('Uthmānlī, 1389–1402). When Tīmūr conquered Baghdād (1393), he ordered 'Abd al-Qādir and other artists to go to Samarqand. At the end of the century 'Abd al-Qādir was in Tabrīz with Tīmūr's intractable son Mīrānshāh; Tīmūr wanted to kill him, but he escaped and returned to the court of sulṭān Aḥmad in Baghdād. When Tīmūr recaptured Baghdād in 1401, 'Abd al-Qādir fell into his hands again, but was forgiven. He spent the rest of his life at the Tīmūrī court in Samarqand, except for a visit to Murād II ('Uthmānlī, 1421–51) in Brusa. He was a victim of the great plague of Herāt and died there in March 1435.

[19] See my article on Nāṣir al-dīn al-Ṭūsī (XIII-2; Introd. 2, 1004) for the observatory and library of that city. According to Ibn Baṭṭūṭa (1, 171), Marāgha was called the "little Damascus."

Though he was already famous as an artist in the seventies of the fourteenth century, his theoretical works written in Arabic[20] were completed only in the fifteenth. They place him in the history of music almost on the same level as Ṣafī al-dīn 'Abd al-Mu'min (XIII-2), who like himself originated in Ādharbāijān. His main works are: (1) Jāmi' al-alḥān (Compiler of melodies), 1405; he revised it later and also summarized it. (2) Maqāṣid al-alḥān (Purports of melodies), 1418. (3) Kanz al-alḥān (Treasure of melodies). (4) Sharḥ al-adwār (Explanation of modes).

These works contain not only musical theories, but descriptions of instruments. Item 3, unfortunately lost, was a collection of his own melodies; according to tradition, he was a great composer and a distinguished lute player, and he was praised also for his poetry, painting, and calligraphy. In the fourteenth century the favorite kind of composition was the nauba, a "petite suite" including four movements called qaul, ghazal, tarāna, and furū dāsht (or firo-dast?); in 1379 'Abd al-Qādir added a fifth movement, the mustazād. In his books he quotes from the standard musical treatises available in Arabic, to wit, al-Fārābī (X-1), Ṣafī al-dīn (XIII-2), and Quṭb al-dīn al-Shīrāzī (XIII-2).

His musical talent continued to flourish in his family, for other musical treatises are ascribed to his son 'Abd al-'Azīz and to his grandson Maḥmūd. 'Abd al-'Azīz dedicated the Naqāwat al-adwār (Selection of modes) to Muḥammad II al-Fātiḥ ('Uthmānlī, 1451–81); Maḥmūd dedicated the Maqāṣid al-alḥan (Purports of melodies) to Bāyazīd II ('Uthmānlī, 1481–1512).

Criticism. Raphael Georg Kiesewetter: Die Musik der Araber nach Originalquellen dargestellt (quarto, 116 p., 6 fig., 24 p. of music, Leipzig 1842). Browne (3, 191, 384, 1920, reprinted 1928). Henry George Farmer: History of Arabian music (p. 198–200, 203, London 1929; Isis 13, 375–76); Historical facts for the Arabian musical influence (London 1930; Isis 15, 370–72); (EI suppt. 4–5, 1934).

[20] According to Farmer (p. 200, 1929), the only musical treatises in Persian are (1) the one included in the encyclopaedia Jawāmi' al-'ulūm of Fakhr al-dīn al-Rāzī (XII-2), (2) the Bahjat al-rūḥ of 'Abd al-Mu'min ibn Ṣafī al-dīn, who flourished in Afghānistān under Mu'izz al-dīn Muḥammad Ghūrī (ruled 1173–1205). Note that these are two twelfth-century texts; later mediaeval treatises by Persian musicians were in Arabic. This illustrates once more the supremacy of the Arabic language, even in a field where one might have expected that supremacy to be challenged.

CHAPTER XXII

CHEMISTRY

(Second Half of the Fourteenth Century)

N.B. Only the main notes are published in this chapter. The chemical contributions of many other men, whose main work was done in other fields, are discussed in other chapters. For a general survey of chemistry in the second half of the fourteenth century, see section VIII of chapter XV. More information on the men referred to in that survey may then easily be found by means of the index.

A. CHRISTENDOM

A1. Catalonia

RUPESCISSA

John of Rupescissa or Roquetaillade. Catalan Franciscan, alchemist and visionary (d. after 1356).

Joannes de Rupescissa (Ruppecissa). Juan de Peratallada, (Ribatallada, Roccatagliada, Rupetagliata, Rochatallada). Jean de Roquetaillade (Rochetaillade). There is a place called Peratallada in the province of Gerona, Catalonia, and our John may have originated there. The theory of his Catalan (vs. French) origin is based not only on his name, but also on the existence of many Catalan MSS, and on the frequent confusion of his works with those of two other Catalan authors, Arnold of Villanova and Raymond Lull. There is, however, no formal proof that he was a Catalan, only the circumstantial evidence just mentioned.

John of Rupescissa studied philosophy in Toulouse, then entered the Franciscan order; he flourished for a time at the Franciscan monastery of Aurillac (in Auvergne; dépt. Cantal). In 1345 he was imprisoned in the monastery of Figeac (Quercy; dépt. Lot) by order of the Franciscan provincial of Aquitaine. He was again thrown into prison in 1346, 1349, 1356. The latest imprisonment was by order of Innocent VI (pope 1352–62). The circumstances of his life after 1356 are unknown; some say that he died in prison, others that he was burned to death in 1362 (this is unlikely), others that he was released in 1378 by Urban VI (pope 1378–89), and that he was buried in the monastery of his order in Villefranche-sur-Saône (not far from Lyon).

He spent at least seven years of his life in prison. As no archives concerning his imprisonments have yet been brought to light, their causes are unknown. He indulged in reckless prophecies; he did not actually claim to be a prophet, but to have received from God the understanding of apocalyptic secrets and of other Biblical prophecies. He vehemently denounced clerical vices; criticized the wealth of the church, and reproached temporal and ecclesiastical rulers for their oppression of the common people. He may have been punished for ill-timed prophecies, or for radicalism and demagogism, or for occultism, or for restlessness; or he may have given his superiors other opportunities for putting him out of their way.

His works include prophecies which do not concern us, e.g., one written in prison 1349, and the Vademecum in tribulatione, written in 1356. We are more interested in his other works, dealing with alchemy and medicine. His most important works of that kind are the De consideratione quintae essentiae rerum omnium and the Liber lucis. The following have also been ascribed to him: Thesaurus mundi; De aqua vite rectificata; Abbreviatio quedam de secretis pauperum (written by one Joannes pauperum?); finally the medical book Decretorium simplicium electorum.

The Liber de consideratione quintae essentiae (also called Liber de famulatu philosophiae) exists in different forms, MS and printed, more or less amplified.[1] It is divided into two books, subdivided, the first into canons, the second into remedies. The number of canons varies from one MS or printed edition to another, from 6 to 15. The main purpose of the work seems to be medical rather than alchemical stricto sensu. The quintessence is thought of as an elixir of youth rather than a stone of transmutation, that is, as a method of staving off corruption and putrefaction. This quintessence is aqua ardens or aqua vite, but of course not the ordinary kind! Other quintessences may be extracted from human blood, from roots, herbs, from minerals, in short from every thing. Indeed, there is a quintessence in each thing, and the discovery and control of it is the chief goal of the alchemical art. See Thorndike's account of the quintessence of antimony (3, 359, 1934). The second book is largely a rearrangement of the materials of the first under medical headings, or the application of alchemical and astrological knowledge to the solution of medical problems, as how to cure this or that disease, etc. The magnetic needle and the tides are quoted as examples of astrological influence.

The Liber lucis, or Liber de confectione veri lapidis philosophorum, is much shorter than the treatise on the quintessence. It describes the seven operations or stages leading gradually to the complete transmutation, and explains in a final (eighth) part the construction of an alchemical furnace. The main tool is sulphuric acid (Roman vitriol), which makes it possible to release the very spirit of sulphur and cause it to react upon mercury, saltpeter, sal ammoniac, etc. The fourth operation is called expressing the milk of the virgin (lac virginis); at that stage the four elements are already separated. The author does not claim to have invented these operations, but simply to reveal secret knowledge. He quotes "Hermes," "Alfidius," "Rosarius," Geber, Ibn Sīnā, Arnold of Villanova.

To return to the De consideratione quintae essentiae, the original text was expanded and amalgamated with other occult theories, especially of the Lullian school. This process was carried very far before the end of the fourteenth century, when the treatise was already ascribed to Ramon Lull. Because of the syncretic and secretive tendencies of occult writers it is always difficult, if not hopeless, to disentangle the many threads capriciously interwoven in their compositions.

Text. The treatise De consideratione quintae essentiae was first printed in its Lullian form, under Lull's name and the title De secretis nature, together with the Consilia of Gianmatteo Ferrari da Gradi, in Venice 1514. It was reprinted separately in Venice 1518 and Augsburg 1518. The earliest edition seen by me is the French translation, La vertu et propriété de la quinte essence de toutes choses. Faite en Latin par Ioannes de Rupescissa et mise en François par Antoine du Moulin Masconnois (i.e., of the pays of Mâcon), valet de chambre de la Royne de Navarre (155 p., 16 cm. high, Lyon 1549). Reprinted in a small pocket edition by the same printer, Jean de Tournes (170 p., 12 cm. high, Lyon 1581). Later Latin editions in the collection of Guglielmo Gratarolo: Verae alchemiae (Basel 1561), in Zetzner (3, 359–485, 1659).

[1] My direct knowledge is restricted to the sixteenth-century French translation cited below. For the text of the MS tradition, I follow Thorndike.

The Liber lucis is found in Gratarolo's collection (1561), in Daniel van Broekhuizen: Secreta alchimiae magnalia (Basel 1598; Leiden 1612), in Zetzner (3, 284, 1659), in Manget (vol. 2, 1702).

Thesaurus mundi, Ein Büchlein welches genandt wird ein Schatz der Welt, edited by Theophilus Neander: Heptas alchymica (p. 294, Leipzig 1621).

Edward Brown: Fasciculus rerum expetendarum et fugiendarum (vol. 2, London 1690). The Fasciculus rerum is a collection of tracts concerning the council of Basel (1431–45), edited by Orthvinus Gratius (folio, Cologne 1535). Edward Brown, rector of Sundridge, Kent, prepared a new edition of it (2 vols. folio), with an appendix containing writings "of ancient authors who condemned the abuses and errors of the church and insisted on the urgent necessity of correcting them." That appendix includes two of Rupescissa's prophetic writings.

Criticism. Pierre Bayle: Dictionnaire historique (5th ed., 4, 74–75, Amsterdam 1740). Ferguson (2, 305–6, 1906), with many references to earlier writings which I have not used except Bayle. Carbonelli (1925). Thorndike (3, 347–69, 722–40; 4, 38 etc., 1934). Wickersheimer (p. 473, 1936). Wilson (p. 707, 1939). Millàs Vallicrosa (p. 82, MS xvi, 1942).

TÁRREGA

Ramon de Tárrega. Catalan theologian and alchemist (d. 1371).

Ramon or Raimundo was a Jew of Tárrega, a place in the bishopric of Vich, province of Lerida, Catalonia. He became a Christian at the age of 10 and later assumed the Dominican habit. His philosophical and theological innovations attracted the attention of the Holy Office, and he was prosecuted by the general inquisitor of Aragon, the Dominican Nicholas Eymeric, who ordered his imprisonment c. 1368, in the Barcelona monastery. The process of inquisition was delayed because Ramon refused to admit heresy and to retract his views. In 1371 Gregory XI decided to submit Ramon's writings to a commission of thirty theologians meeting in Avignon. In the meanwhile Ramon died in the cell wherein he was detained in Barcelona, on September 20, 1371.

His theological writings are not important to us, but he must be mentioned here because of the alchemical writings ascribed to him. It has been claimed that some of the Lullian alchemical treatises (these are very numerous, and most of them, if not all, apocryphal; Introd. 2, 909) were actually written by Ramon de Tárrega. This may be true, or it may be due to a confusion. For, in the first place, Ramon de Tárrega was also called Ramon Lull de Tárrega; I do not know whether this was simply a mistake or whether his name was really Lull. In the second place, Eymeric had taken a special interest in the prosecution of alchemy and astrology. Neither of these facts is convincing. Ramon de Tárrega may be the author of alchemical writings, but there is nothing yet to prove it.

The bibliography of the Lullian alchemical writings is too complicated to be attempted here. It is a waste of time to compile it before all the MSS have been examined and compared, a considerable task which remains to be done.

Criticism. Not included in Quétif-Echard. Felix Torres Amat: Memorias para ayudar a formar un diccionario critico de los escritores catalanes (p. 615–16, Barcelona 1836). Thorndike (2, 864, 1923; 4, 15, 1934). Millàs Vallicrosa (p. 83, MS xvi, 1942).

SEDACER

Guillem Sedacer. Catalan Carmelite, d. 1382–83.
Guillelmus Sedacerius, Sedacianus, Sedaciensis.

He composed c. 1378 a treatise on alchemy entitled Sedacina totius alchimiae, or Summa sedacina. If he be identical with Guillelmus Sadacius, he wrote another treatise De lapide philosophico, in four books.

The Sedacina was meant to include four books (which suggests that the De lapide philosophico might be simply the same work under a different title), but only two are extant in the MSS examined by Thorndike. The author was apparently very well read in Greek, Arabic, and Christian alchemy, for he quotes many of the standard authors who were available to him in Latin.

The first book is divided into 36 chapters. It is devoted to generalities concerning alchemy, methods, nature and properties of metals. Alchemy is defined as a secret art concerning not only the transmutation of base metals into gold, but also the restoration of health and youth. "Nine precepts laid down for its practitioners which we may note are fear of God, knowledge of the natures of things and of modes of operating, perseverance, the superiority of experience to meditation, the proper proportioning of ingredients by measure and weight, continued study and incessant reading, knowing the right time to operate, which is from March to September, having a suitable and secret laboratory with associates and assistants who can be trusted, and not revealing the secret to the uninitiated" (Thorndike 3, 630). Then special chapters are devoted to lead, antimony, tin, iron, gold, copper, sandarac (realgar, AsS), silver, alloys, calcination, talc, gypsum, coral, crystal, glass, hematites, magnet, bloodstone, ocher, vitriol, spirits, mercury, sal ammoniac, sulphur, arsenic, etc. Each of these chapters includes recipes leading to transmutation.

The second book is divided into 19 chapters, most of which deal with special substances, such as alums and other salts, borax (referring to its Saracenic origin; cf. Arabic būraq), oils. The last 3 chapters deal with man (minor mundus), the tortoise, and the cock. Alchemy is compared with astrology; it is an "inferior astrology," that is, an astrology relative to the sublunar world.

There are many points of contact between the Summa sedacina and an anonymous Greek text περὶ μεταλλικῆς τέχνης edited by C. O. Zuretti (1930; Isis 15, 410). According to Zuretti, the Greek text is probably somewhat anterior to the Summa. See my note on Byzantine alchemy (XIV-1).

Cosma de Villiers: Bibliotheca carmelitana (1, 607, Aurelianis 1752). Torres Amat (p. 596, 1836). Rubió i Lluch (1, 299, 1908; 2, 265, 1921). Rovira i Virgili (6, 113, 1931). Thorndike (3, 176, 628–32, 1934).

A3. France

"ORTOLANUS"

Mysterious French (?) alchemist about whom nothing is known with any certainty, not even his name, Richardus or Martinus Ortholanus, Hortolanus, Hortulanus; Martin Ortolan or Lortholain. According to some, he flourished c. 1040; others confused him with John of Garland (XIII-1), and the Compendium alchemiae wrongly ascribed to the latter was also ascribed to the former. The confusion is increased by the fact that the titles or names Hortulanus, Hortulus, Hortus were much in favor among alchemists.

Still another opinion, which I accept tentatively, is that Ortolanus practiced alchemy in Paris and completed an alchemical Practica in that city in 1358. For that reason we place him in the second half of the fourteenth century and call him "French," but without conviction.

The writings ascribed to him include a commentary on the Tabula smaragdina, the Practica already mentioned, which was developed in 1386 by John Dombelay, the Rosarius minor, and the Textus alkimie (dated 1325?). Each of these attributions raises difficult questions; we are nowhere on solid ground.

The commentary on the Emerald table is preceded by a short text on the fifth essence identical with the Potestas divitiarum ascribed to Raymond Lull (in Manget 1, 866–68, 1702), and is followed by another short text on putrefaction as the mother of all things, ascribed to one Alphidius (Alphiatus? Alfred of Sareshel?). Like the Tabula smaragdina itself (or Verba secretorum Hermetis Trismegisti), this commentary belongs to the kind of alchemy which may be called mystical and cosmological.

As the Practica is known only through Dombelay's adaptation, we shall speak of it in the article on Dombelay below.

The Rosarius minor is a discussion of the transmutation of metals in the form of allegories concerning perfect white and red roses. It is also called Rosarius novus, possibly to differentiate it from the Rosarius philosophorum of Arnold of Villanova (XIII-2; Introd. 2, 896). It was commented upon in the fifteenth century or before by one Pratearius of Pisa.

The Textus alkimie (alias, Liber de magni lapidis compositione, incipit Studio namque florenti) has been ascribed to Ortolanus, John of Florence, Valentinus, Honorius Philadelphus, all of which names are equally mysterious. It begins with a defense of alchemy, an explanation of its usefulness to clerics and rulers alike, and an account of the qualities required for good alchemical work. The author insists on the need of practice vs. reading, the more so that alchemical books are deliberately obscure. Alchemical reactions are produced by one kind of mercury and three kinds of sulphur; the four main reactions are called after the four seasons, winter, spring, summer, and autumn. He quotes the Lilium and the Summa perfectionis magisterii of Geber, and treatises of Albert the Great and Arnold of Villanova. It is clear from his text that he had made experiments with his own hands, though without any advantage to himself or at any rate to his readers.

Text. Hortulani philosophi ab hortis maritimis commentariolus in Tabulam smaragdinam. Published first in the collection Alchemia (p. 364, Nürnberg 1541) and many times afterward, being included in various alchemical collections. The latest edition is in Julius Ruska: Tabula smaragdina (p. 180–86, Heidelberg 1926).

For the Practica of 1358, see my note on Dombelay.

Rosarius minor is included in the collection Alchemia (p. 309, Nürnberg 1541), in Guglielmo Gratarolo: Verae alchemiae . . . doctrina (1, 222, Basel 1561), in Zetzner (2, 406–23, 1659).

Textus alkimie in Zetzner (4, 941–54, 1659).

Criticism. Ferguson (1, 421–23; 2, 157, 1906). Julius Ruska: Tabula smaragdina (Heidelberg 1926; Isis 9, 375–77), my review in Isis contains the Latin text of the Tabula smaragdina. Thorndike (3, 176–90, 686–92, 1934); A study in the analysis of complex scientific MSS, Sloane 3457, an important alchemical MS (Isis 29, 377–92, 1938). Wilson (p. 706. 1939).

FLAMEL

Nicolas Flamel. French business man to whom alchemical writings have been falsely ascribed (d. 1418).

Nicolas Flamel was born in Pontoise (?) in the second quarter of the fourteenth century; died in Paris, March 22, 1418. He began his career as a scrivener-bookseller in Paris, but soon realized the possibility of earning more money in other ways. A rich marriage (c. 1370) enabled him to extend his financial activities. He became wealthy, and his wealth, greatly exaggerated in the legendary tradition, was ascribed to his having discovered the secret of gold making (c. 1382). His secret, however, had nothing to do with alchemy; it was simply the art developed by many successful "realtors," promoters, and financiers, before and after him, the art of extracting gold, not from base metals, but from the pockets of other people. Nicolas and his wife Pernelle (d. 1397) were generous to the poor and the sick and anxious to be as successful in the hereafter as in their lifetime. They gave money to churches, hospitals, and houses for the poor. Being childless, he bequeathed his fortune to St. Jacques la Boucherie and to other churches and foundations. He prepared his own tombstone in St. Jacques (now in the Cluny museum).

Various alchemical treatises were ascribed to him in later times, obviously for the sake of capitalizing his legendary fame as a successful alchemist. It is probable that an analysis of these writings would make it possible to determine termini post quos; they are certainly not contemporary.

Flamel does not belong at all to the history of science, except by mistake; that mistake must be taken into account, however, if only for its own refutation.

Texts (apocryphal). Le livre des figures hiéroglyphiques de Nicolas Flamel, ainsi qu'elles sont en la quatrième arche du Cymetière des innocents à Paris, entrant par la grande porte de la ruë saint Denis devers la main droite, avec l'explication d'icelles par le dit Flamel, traittant de la transmutation métallique, non jamais imprimé. Included in Pierre Arnauld: Trois traictez de la philosophie naturelle, non encore imprimez (Paris 1612). According to Arnauld, this was translated by him from Latin into French. The remaining copies of this edition were sold in 1659 with a new title page (Paris 1659). The two other treatises in Arnauld's collection were those ascribed to "Artephius" (XII-1; Introd. 2, 219) and to Synesios (V-1; Introd. 1, 388). This explains the title page of a later edition (or resale of the remainders with new preface and supplement) of Arnauld's collection, Philosophie naturelle de trois anciens philosophes renommez Artephius, Flamel et Synesius traitant de l'art occulte et de la transmutation métallique. Dernière edition. Augmentée d'un petit traité du mercure et de la pierre des philosophes de G. Ripleus (106 p., Paris 1682). G. Ripleus is George Ripley (d. Boston 1490). The colophon of 1612 still reappears in this "third" edition (p. 98).

Exposition of the hieroglyphical figures concerning both the theory and practice of the philosophers' stone, Englished by Eirenaeus Orandus (London 1624), reprinted with introduction by W. W. Wescott (London 1889).

The "hieroglyphic figures" reproduced in these books are not all alchemical symbols, but portraits of God and saints with various attributes, which decorated Flamel's building at the Cimetière des innocents. The building itself no longer exists.

Des berühmten Philosophi Nicolai Flamelli chymische Werke (290 p., Wien 1751). There are earlier editions (1673? 1681? 1730?).

Annotata quaedam ex Flamello, edited by Gerard Dorn, in Trevisanus de Chymico miraculo (Basel 1583, again 1600), in Zetzner (1, 748, 1659), in Manget (2, 350, 1702).

Sommaire philosophique. Printed in a book entitled De la transformation métallique (Paris 1561); in Jean Maugin de Richebourg's Bibliothèque des philosophes chimiques (Paris 1672; nouvelle éd., 2, 263, Paris 1740); in Guillaume de Lorris: Le roman de la rose (4, 205–42, 1814). The original text (Latin?) is supposed to have been written c. 1395 (?). There are at least six editions of the Latin text, Summarium philosophicum, in various collections (1612, 1619, 1702, 1704, 1743, 1749). Englished, Summary of philosophy, in Aurifontina chymica (London 1680).

Le grand éclaircissement de la pierre philosophale pour la transmutation de tous les métaux. Edited by P. Beraud (Paris 1628, Amsterdam 1782).

Le livre des lavures ("Cy commence la vraye pratique de la noble science de philosophie"). MS copy by Albert Poisson (q.v., below) from a MS in St. Germain des Prés (Harvard Library).

This list, however incomplete, is sufficient to show the extent of the Flamellian apocryphal literature.

Criticism. Abbé Etienne François Villain: Histoire critique de Nicolas Flamel et de Pernelle sa femme. Recueillie d'actes anciens qui justifient l'origine et la médiocrité de leur fortune contre les imputations des alchimistes (416 p., Paris 1761). Vallet de Viriville (NBG 17, 817–23, 1856). Albert Poisson: Nicolas Flamel. Sa vie, ses fondations, ses oeuvres. Suivi de la réimpression du livre des figures hiéroglyphiques et de la lettre de Dom Pernety à l'abbé Villain (252 p., Bibliothèque Chacornac, Paris 1893). Article by H. Monin (Grande encyclopédie 17, 558). Schelenz (p. 231, 1904). Ferguson (1, 279–81, 1906). La plus vieille maison de Paris (Gazette médicale de Paris, 28 août 1912); that is Flamel's house, built in 1407; see a view of it in l'Illustration française (12 août 1911).

A4. England

DOMBELAY

John Dombelay. English alchemist (fl. c. 1384–86).

John Dombelay or Joannes Dumbeleius de Anglia is presumably identical with John Bombelen or Bumbeles. Though he is not quite so mysterious as Ortolanus, our knowledge of him is exceedingly meager. His works should be studied in connection with those of Ortolanus.

Three alchemical works are ascribed to him, the Hortus amoris, the Stella alchimie 1384, and the commentary on Ortolanus' Practica 1386.

The Hortus amoris (or Ortum amoris), liber de arte alchymiae, was dedicated to the archbishop of Trier, Cuno of Falkenstein; Cuno was archbishop from 1362 to his death in 1388. It is divided into 12 chapters, the first 8 dealing with theory, the 4 others with practice. The Rosarius of Arnold of Villanova is quoted.

The Stella alchimie was dedicated to an unknown bishop in 1384. It is also divided into 12 chapters, 12 being a sacred number to astrologers. Arnold's Rosarius is referred to many times. The purpose of the Stella is to guide would-be alchemists (like the star which guided the Magi) to the perfect mastery of the secret art. It is largely mystical, though there are references to alchemical instruments (cucurbita, scutella, alembic) and operations, which have the earmarks of experience in the laboratory.

Finally, Dombelay's commentary on Ortolanus' Practica was written in 1386 for the same archbishop of Trier to whom the Hortus amoris was dedicated at an earlier time. Dombelay quotes not only Ortolanus' treatise of 1358, but many other traditional sources, such as Hermes, Geber, Alphidius (?), the Turba philosophorum,[2] and Arnold of Villanova. The treatise begins with the statement that for the making of the elixir four substances are needed, mercury, sulphur, vitriol, and saltpeter. Ortolanus' experiments with arsenic and sulphur are

[2] Probably an Arabic (Egyptian) work of the ninth or tenth century. Julius Ruska: Turba philosophorum (Berlin 1931; Isis 20, 302–5).

related; Ortolanus completed his first operation in seven days, but could hardly repeat it in eighty days and then worked fruitlessly for seven years. The procedure seems matter-of-fact, and there is less hocus-pocus than in other alchemical treatises, yet we come across the usual comparisons of alchemical operations with the seasons of the year or the seven planets, etc. Indeed, no alchemical operation can be completed without astrological concurrence and divine grace.

Text. Hortus amoris edited by Joannes Rhenanus (or Rheinland, fl. first half of seventeenth century) in the Harmoniae imperscrutabilis chimico-philosophiae (p. 3-79, Francfort 1625).

Practica vera alkimica Parisiis probata et experta sub A.D. 1358. Edited by Lazarus Zetzner in the Theatrum chemicum (Ursel 1602). In the 3d edition (Strassburg 1659-61) it will be found in vol. 4, p. 912-34.

Criticism. Thorndike (3, 179, 188, 633-37, 770, 1934); A study in the analysis of complex scientific MSS, Sloane 3457, an important alchemical MS (Isis 29, 377-92, 1938; p. 389).

A5. Germany

WIMANDUS

Wimandus (or Wynandus, Weigandus, etc.) de Ruffo Clipeo (Rothschild). German alchemist who flourished probably about the end of the fourteenth century or the beginning of the next one.

He wrote two or three alchemical treatises, entitled Gloria mundi, Expositiones omnium rerum mineralium, Operationes omnes. The main one is Gloria mundi, represented by many fifteenth-century MSS, one of them (S. Marco) written partly in German, partly in Latin. He quotes Albert the Great but not Arnold of Villanova; on the other hand, he refers to a letter written by Bernard of Treves to Thomas of Bologna (d. 1384; see my note on Thomas de Pisan).

The Gloria mundi is an alchemical treatise of the most occult type. For example, it explains the triple art based on the use of the Greek names and alphabet, Hebrew names and alphabet, and Latin names and alphabet (the third not so good as the other two). The author claims as usual that he has tested experimentally everything he speaks of, but his experiments are intangible.

Criticism. Thorndike (4, 336-38, 691-92, 1934), including list of MSS of Gloria mundi.

STROMER

Ulman Stromer (1329-1407). Nuremberg patrician, merchant, and chronicler writing in German.

He was born in Nuremberg on January 6, 1329, the son of the alderman Heinrich Stromer and of Margaretha, daughter of the Schultheiss (village mayor) Heinrich Geuschmied. He spent all his life in his native city, where he held many important offices, and where he died on April 13, 1407.

He was in charge of many public affairs, was sent on political or diplomatic missions, and his importance was recognized not only in Nuremberg, but outside, e.g., at the court of the duke of Bavaria.

In 1360, he began the redaction of a family chronicle entitled Püchel von mein Geslechet und von Abentewr, extending from 1349 to 1407. Apart from his genealogy and other details concerning his family, the chronicle is very valuable because of the light it throws on the events of his lifetime, especially in Nuremberg, and on the peaceful or warlike relations of Nuremberg with other sovereignties. It speaks of the persecutions of the Jews in 1349 and 1385, and of the cancellation of debts due to them all over southwestern Germany in 1390. The most interesting facts are those relating to economic and industrial matters. For example, Ulman Stromer names a number of cities in Germany, Flanders, Burgundy, Switzerland with which Nuremberg had contracts for the free exchange of goods. He gives information on the weights, measures, currencies, tariffs, tolls, commissions, and consignments in various places. Finally, he explains the use of the Visierruthe, to determine the contents of casks.

Though linen paper may have been made in Germany before the middle of the fourteenth century, Stromer was the first to produce it on what might be called an industrial scale. In 1390 he founded a paper mill near Nuremberg. His chief helpers were the Italian brothers Franciscus and Marcus de Marchia. He first established two wheels which set eighteen stampers in motion; later he tried to add a third wheel, but this caused labor trouble. The workers were imprisoned, then released. In 1394, Stromer leased the mill equipped with three wheels to one Jörg Tyrman, for four years. The mill founded in 1390 by Stromer and described by him in his autobiography marks the beginning of paper manufacture in Germany; the circumstances of the foundation prove that the art was introduced from Italy.

Text. Autograph MS in the Germanic Museum, Nuremberg. Edited by Karl Hegel in Chroniken der deutschen Städte. Die Chroniken der fränkischen Städte. Nürnberg 1. Band (Leipzig 1862), with many additional documents.

Criticism. Mummenhoff (ADB 36, 617–18, 1893). Potthast (p. 1036, 1896). Dard Hunter: Paper making through eighteen centuries (ch. 1, New York 1930), with facsimile of the Stromer MS. Blum (p. 32, 1935).

Note on the Visierruthe and the Visierkunst

Stromer's account of how to ascertain the capacity of a cask or of a similar vessel is the earliest known to me. This method developed into a special art, Visierkunst (gauging), which attained much popularity in Germany in the sixteenth century, judging by its representation in various arithmetical treatises or even in separate books. Next to Stromer's account, the earliest known to me occurs in a Latin MS written in a German hand c. 1450–75 (Plimpton collection); the text is copied in another Latin MS written in Germany c. 1500 (same collection) (D. E. Smith p. 468, 480, 1908). The first printed text is Ein Fisierbüchlein auf allerhand Eich by Hanns Briefmaler of Nuremberg (also called Hanns Buchdrucker, Hanns Sporer),[3] printed in Regensburg 1485 and in Bamberg 1487; the author was a contemporary of the printer. This text explains how to find the contents of a barrel whether full or not; the Visierruthe was introduced through the bunghole to find the level of the liquid.

It is interesting to name a few of the other texts on gauging known to me, in chronological order. Calling Stromer's text no. 1, the two Plimpton MSS are nos. 2, 3, and Briefmaler's Fisierbüchlein of 1485 is no. 4.

5. Jacob Köbel of Heidelberg (1470–1533): Ein new geordnet Vysirbuch (princeps, 32 l., Oppenheim 1515), with woodcut illustrating the Visierruthe or Vysirstab. Often reprinted in the sixteenth century (Smith p. 106, 113, 1908).

6. Henricus Grammateus (Heinrich Schreiber of Erfurt, b. end of fifteenth

[3] According to Cantor (2, 237, 1900). Klebs no. 1042 (under Visierbüchlein). Not in Stillwell (1940).

century): Ayn new künstlich Buch. Preface dated Vienna 1518; first printed Nuremberg 1518. Often reprinted (Smith p. 123–26, 1908).

7. Erhart Helm: Visirbuch, attached to the arithmetic of Adam Riese (princeps 1522). The Visirbüchlin is included in the edition of 1533 and many following; I do not know whether it is included in anterior editions. At least 40 editions of that arithmetic were printed in the sixteenth century, and several more in the seventeenth century (Smith p. 138–43, 1908).

8. Petrus Apianus (1495–1552): Liber de mensuratione vasorum cum artificiali partis vacuae inventione. Lost text quoted by Cantor (2, 404, 1900).

9. Johann Frey of Nuremberg: Ein new Visierbüchlein (36 l., Nuremberg 1543). Single edition (Smith p. 221, 1908).

10. Burchard Mithob (1504–65): Visierkunst, published by him in his Stereometria, ars docens certas dimensiones corporum ratione mathematica et virga stereometrica, cum dimensore, aequatorioque desuper (Francfort 1544) (Cantor 2, 449, 1900).

This list is probably incomplete, yet conclusions may already be drawn from it. It is interesting to note that all these texts originated in Germany, and that most of them are in the German language, the others being in Latin (nos. 2, 3, 8, 10). According to Smith (p. 221, 1908), the art of gauging was less common in England than in Germany; for example, it was not represented in the comprehensive editions of Robert Recorde's Ground of artes published from 1542 on throughout the sixteenth and seventeenth centuries. It existed in England, however, witness the two following quotations taken from OED under gauge §3: "[1353 Act 27 Edw. III, Stat. I. c. 8, Que tous vins . . soient bient & loialment gaugez par le Gaugeour le Roi ou son depute.] 1483 Act I Rich. III, c. 13, All the Vessels of Wine . . shall . . be well and truly gauged by the King's Gauger." How accurate that gauging was, we have no way of knowing; it was probably sufficient for rough comparisons.

Gauging is explained in the early American arithmetics down to the middle of the nineteenth century.

"BERTHOLD DER SCHWARZE"

Bertholdus Niger. Legendary inventor of gunpowder and firearms.

There is no agreement among the many data concerning him; a full discussion of them would be very long and sterile. Was he a Cistercian monk? Or a Franciscan who flourished in Freiburg im Breisgau in the thirteenth or fourteenth century? (A statue was dedicated to him, as inventor of gunpowder, in Freiburg in 1854!) Was his original name Constantin Ancklitzen? In a fifteenth-century document he is called "ein meister aus Kriechenland," which exemplifies the lasting fame of Marcus Graecus (XIII-2).

He is credited with the invention of gunpowder and of the earlier guns or mortars. The most probable date for the devilish invention is 1380, and it is said that he was executed in 1388 because of it. By that time, however, firearms, not to speak of gunpowder, had already been invented. He may have introduced some improvement, for example, the casting of mortars or guns in bronze? We know nothing, and this note is printed here merely for the sake of indicating the legendary nature of the reports concerning Black Berthold.

The invention of gunpowder was discussed in volume 2 (p. 1036–38). It took place probably before the end of the thirteenth century, but nobody as yet understood its implications. The use of the explosive power of gunpowder for the propulsion of projectiles, the invention of guns and mortars provided with locks, was probably made in the third decade of the fourteenth century. We do not know where it originated. It was probably in Germany. The idea was in the air and the invention may have occurred at about the same time in various places. Many German chroniclers speak of the invention as having been made in their district, but that claim is natural enough, as they would be better acquainted with local achievements than with foreign ones, and is thus unconvincing. Furthermore, the invention of firearms was susceptible of infinite improvements (it is not yet completed!), and thus it was possible to speak in good faith of many inventors.

Criticism. Good article by E. G. in NBG (43, 604–5, 1864).

Franz Maria Feldhaus: Was wissen wir vom schwarzen Berthold? (Zeitschrift für historische Waffenkunde p. 65–69, 113–18, 1906); Die ältesten Nachrichten über Berthold (Chemiker-Zeitung no. 68, 1907); Der Pulvermönch Berthold 1313 oder 1393? (Mitt. 7, 250–51, 1908), the date 1313 in the Memorieboek in the Ghent archives stands for 1393 (ibid. p. 528); Wer war der schwarze Berthold (Die Welt der Technik, 1908); Nochmals der schwarze Berthold (Mitt. 8, 228–30, 1909); Die Technik der Vorzeit (p. 78–80, 1914); Die Technik der Antike (p. 324, 351, 1931).

Oscar Guttmann: Monumenta pulveris pyrii (London 1906), an iconographic collection (fig. 5–16 deal with Berthold; they include caricatures, wherein Berthold is represented with the Devil, the invention of gunpowder being presumably diabolical); Der Pulvermönch Berthold (Mitt. 7, 425–27, 1908).

Henry W. L. Hime (1915), repeats many old errors. Rathgen (3, 18, 163, 476, 677, 1928), considers Berthold legendary, but claims, on the basis of many archival documents, that firearms were invented in Germany.

LEONARD OF MAURPERG

Austrian alchemist (fl. 1394).

The place Maurperg may be identified with Mailberg, in lower Austria, near the Austrian-Moravian boundary.

In the year 1394, this Leonard compiled a collection of alchemical recipes included with other alchemical texts in MS Lat. 14005 (fol. 119–31), Bibliothèque nationale, Paris: "A.D. 1394 ego Leonardus has infrascriptas vias cum magna difficultate inter doctos homines fui assecutus, plurimis fatigis previis pariter et expensis," etc. The collection is interesting, because most of the recipes bear the names of their authors, who constitute a very cosmopolitan group. One gathers the impression that alchemists were often restless individuals, traveling from one country to another and finding almost everywhere congenial spirits, with whom they could discuss their alchemical fancies and sometimes drive a bargain. They might sell recipes or buy them. Leonard was generally a naïve "buyer," in modern parlance a sucker. In Calabra, master Anthony of Toledo sold him a recipe which had been formerly bequeathed by Petrarca to the cardinal of Bologna. Another recipe was sold to him as coming from Albert the Great. In Posen, Poland, he spent a lot of money with Liphard of Tuscany. He bought an operatio from Daniel de Roucliffe, a notary to the king of Navarre. He worked ten months in Montpellier with the alchemist James the German. Leonard was also in Sicily, went to Cologne and to Rome, and if we may believe him traveled as far as Persia.

In 1394, he left Maurperg with a priest, Bartholomew of Prague, to visit master Demetrius in Cracow. The latter advised them to go to Jerusalem, where they arrived three months later. From Jerusalem, they went to Tabrīz, and ten days later finally reached the "Greek school," where they found the masters Florus,

Alexander, and Olympus, to whom they delivered Demetrius' letter. These masters could not divulge the secret, but gave our two travelers money for the homeward journey. Leonard and Bartholomew returned to Jerusalem, where they fell in with another alchemist, Pierre de Bretagne, who took them to Rhodes.

Criticism. James Corbett: L'alchimiste Léonard de Maurperg (Bibliothèque de l'Ecole des chartes 97, 131–41, 1936), with Latin text of Leonard's journey to Tabrīz. See also Corbett (no. 52, p. 173–75, 1939).

A6. Russia

INTRODUCTION OF THE BYZANTINE TECHNIQUE OF PAINTING INTO RUSSIA

The main literary source for the Byzantine technique is the Ἑρμηνεία τῆς ζωγραφικῆς (Painter's guide) discovered by Didron in Mt. Athos, 1839, and discussed in chapter I.

There were two early schools of Byzantine painting, represented respectively by Manuel Panselinos of Salonica and by Theophanes the Cretan. The author of the Ἑρμηνεία, Dionysios of Phurna, Διονύσιος ὁ ἐξ Ἀγράφων, claimed to be a follower of Panselinos. The school of Theophanes or Cretan school is far better known, witness frescoes in many churches of Mt. Athos, all of the sixteenth century it is true, but continuing older traditions. In the fourteenth century, the Cretan school was already displacing the Macedonian one in Greece, Serbia, and Russia. Consider the wonderful frescoes in the Peribleptos church of Mistra, those painted by one Caliergis (1315) in the church Hagios Christos in Verria (not far from Salonica), those painted by Eutychios (1317) in Nagoritchino, "the most precious frescoes of Serbian art." The Russian protagonist was Theophanes the Greek, who decorated the church of the Transfiguration in Novgorod (1378), and worked in Moscow from 1395 to 1405. In that last year he was helped by his most famous disciple, Andrei Rublev; they painted together the frescoes of the church of the Annunciation in Moscow. In 1408, Rublev decorated the church of the Dormition in Vladimir. All the frescoes which I have enumerated continue the tradition of the Peribleptos. Diehl (p. 790, 792, 836–38, 868, 1926).

This is very important in a more general way, for it proves the extent of Byzantine influences in Serbia and Russia in the fourteenth century. These influences, we may be sure, were not restricted to painting, for they were ecclesiastical and hence permeated the whole of Russian life. The frescoes as well as the church music are the most tangible and beautiful symptoms of the situation.

Additional information will be found in books dealing with the beginnings of Russian art and with icons. Pavel Pavlovich Muratov: Les icones russes (Paris 1927). Nikodim Pavlovich Kondakov: Russian icons (252 p., 66 pl., Clarendon Press, Oxford 1927); The Russian icon (folio, 4 vols., Prague 1928–33), in Russian. Philipp Schweinfurth: Geschichte der russischen Malerei im Mittelalter (518 p., 8 pl., 169 ill., The Hague 1930). Michael Farbman (editor): Masterpieces of Russian painting (folio, 60 pl., London 1930). See also catalogues of exhibitions of icons, e.g., that of the USSR in Boston Museum of Fine Arts (Boston 1930), and collection of George R. Hann (Carnegie Institute, Pittsburgh 1944).

For the sake of comparison, we may mention a unique Icelandic text concerning the painting of saints, dating possibly from the thirteenth century, included in the Alfraeði islenzk, a mediaeval Icelandic encyclopaedia (edited by Kristian Kålund, 148 p., Copenhagen 1908).

It is probable that these early texts deal less with the technique of painting than with purely iconographic questions (how should each saint be represented, with what kind of attributes?). Iconographic and iconometric regulations were not peculiar to Byzantine artists. In particular, a canon of proportions of the human body was established by the artists and iconologists of many countries. For Egypt, see Jean Capart: L'art égyptien. Etudes et histoire (1, 142–44, Bruxelles 1924). For Greece, see Gisela M. A. Richter: Sculpture and sculptors of the Greeks (p. 117, New Haven 1929). For India, Jitendra Nath Banerjea: Development of Hindu iconography (University of Calcutta 1941), including text and translation of the Bṛhatsaṃhitā (ch. 57, verses 1–29, 49–52), a kind of astrological encyclopaedia by Varāhamihira (VI-1), and of the Pratimāmānalakshaṇa. This last-named treatise was edited in Sanskrit, Tibetan, and English by Phanindra Nath Bose (74 p., Lahore 1929). For the Renaissance see the drawings and commentaries of Leonardo da Vinci and Albrecht Dürer.

C. INDIA

MERUTUṄGA

Jaina[4] alchemist and physician (fl. 1386). He is the author of the earliest datable treatise on rasa (metallic, chiefly mercurial, preparations). Indeed, he wrote in 1386 a commentary on the Rasādhyāya.

There is an abundant Sanskrit literature on the subject, most of which is not only undated but undatable. These writings deal with rasa and with the "prince of rasa" (rasendra, raseśvara), which is the alchemical essence (like al-iksīr, elixir, of the Arabic alchemists) supposed to give health, longevity, sexual vigor, etc. One of these writings is ascribed by Chinese tradition to the Buddhist patriarch Nāgārjuna (III-1), but it may be that the author was another Nāgārjuna who according to Ray flourished in the seventh or eighth century, and according to al-Bīrūnī (XI-1)[5] was "a native of fort Daihak near Somanāth who lived nearly a hundred years before our time," i.e., fl. c. 930. Al-Bīrūnī spoke with contempt of that peculiar alchemy, or rasāyana; he quoted that very term, tracing it back as the name of a method of liberation to Patañjali (II-2 B.C.). A whole chapter (ch. 9) of the Sarvadarśanasaṃgraha of Mādhava is devoted to the mercurial system, raseśvaradarśana, the mercury itself being called pārada[6] and rasa; Mādhava quotes from the treatises Rasārṇava, Raseśvarasiddhānta, Rasasiddhānta, Rasahṛidaya, which thus cannot be later than the fourteenth century and are probably earlier. According to Ray, who edited it, the Rasārṇava, an elaborate treatise in verse in 18 sections (paṭala), dates from the twelfth century. It is quoted in two other works, the Rasaratnākara of Nityanātha and the Rasendracintāmaṇi of Rāmacandra, but that is not very helpful as I cannot identify these two authors. Finally, there is the Rasaratnasamuccaya ascribed to one Vāgbhaṭa son of Siṃhagupta (but also in other MSS to Nityanātha or Aśvinīkumāra), who may be identical with the

[4] For indications on Jaina religion and Jaina physics see my note on Mahāvīra (VI B.C.). Helmuth von Glasenapp: Der Jainismus, eine indische Erlösungsreligion (520 p., 31 pl., Berlin 1925). Walther Schubring: Die Lehre des Jainas nach den alten Quellen (Berlin 1935). Jagmandar-lāl Jainī (d. 1927): Outlines of Jainism (200 p., 2 tables, Cambridge 1940). This is a corrected reprint of the book of 1916, published by the Jain Literature Society (founded in Cambridge 1935).

[5] Edward C. Sachau: Alberuni's India (1, 188, London 1910). Arabic text in Sachau's edition (p. 92, London 1887).

[6] The word pārada was already used by Suśruta (VI B.C.).

physician Vāgbhaṭa (VII-1). Indeed, in some MSS of the Ashṭāṅgasaṃgraha and of the Ashṭāṅgahṛidayasaṃhitā the author is called Vāgbhaṭa son of Siṃhagupta son of Vāgbhaṭa. The difficulty is increased by the fact that the first of these two medical works is sometimes ascribed to Vṛiddha Vāgbhaṭa (Vāgbhaṭa the Elder) and the other to Vāgbhaṭa. In short, there are a good many alchemical writings in Sanskrit, some of which are certainly anterior to the eleventh century, and probably much earlier still; others date from the period eleventh to fourteenth centuries.

The alchemist Merutuṅga should not be confused with another Jaina bearing the same name and of the same century, author of a collection of historical and fanciful anecdotes entitled Prabandhacintāmaṇi (Wishing stone of stories), completed in Saṁvat 1362 = A.D. 1306. Winternitz (2, 332; 3, 142, 352). Keith (p. 293, 344 note 3, 1928).

Text. The Rasādhyāya with a commentary edited by Ramkrishna Sharma (Kāśī Sanscrit series, Benares 1930).

The Rasārṇava, or the Ocean of mercury and other metals and minerals, edited by Praphulla Chandra Ray and Hariśchandra Kaviratna (Bibliotheca indica, no. 175 in 3 parts, Asiatic Society, Calcutta 1908–10). Another Rasārṇava was edited by Amaranātha Jhā (The Paṇḍit vol. 42, nos. 4–12, 53 p., 1920).

Rasaratnasamuccaya of Vāgbhaṭa, edited by Kṛishṇarāva Śarman Bāpaṭa (Ānandāśrama series, Poona 1890; reprinted 1905).

Many correlated Sanskrit texts have been edited by Praphulla Chandra Ray in his History of Hindu chemistry (2 vols., Calcutta 1903–9).

The Prabandhacintāmaṇi of the other Merutuṅga was edited by Rāmacandra Dīnānātha (Bombay 1888). English translation by Charles Henry Tawney (256 p., Bibliotheca indica, no. 141 in 3 parts, Asiatic Society, Calcutta 1901), including indexes.

Criticism. Duff (p. 210, 222, 229, 253, 1899). Julius Jolly: Medizin (Grundriss der indo-arischen Philologie vol. 3, no. 10, p. 3, 9, 1901). Ray (1903–9). Winternitz (3, 553, 1922). Keith (p. 512, 1928). Dasgupta (2, 357–66, 1932), dealing with the theory of rasas and their chemistry but containing little information pertinent to our purpose; it is valuable for the study of philosophical implications.

D. CHINA

T'AO TSUNG-I

Chinese man of letters (fl. c. 1368).

T'ao Tsung-i, style Chiu Ch'êng, was born in Huang-yen, Chehkiang. Having failed to obtain his chin shih degree, he retired into private life, meditating and writing. In 1368 he published a collection of essays in 30 books entitled Cho keng lu. This contains valuable information on the decadence of the Yüan dynasty and a variety of other subjects, poetry, painting, ceramics, etc. For example, it includes a long list of ink manufacturers from the T'ang to the Yüan dynasty, and an article on "precious stones of the Muslims," Hui-hui shih t'ou, wherein it is suggested that most of the precious stones sold in Peking were brought into China from abroad, chiefly when Western Asia was plundered by the Mongols.

In the Cho keng lu there is a mention of small balls, p'an chih, the very term used for the balls of the suan p'an (Chinese form of abacus). This raises the question, When did the Chinese begin to use that instrument? Mei Wên ting (1633–1721)[7] in his Li suan ch'üan shu suggested that they began only in the first

[7] A distinguished mathematician and astronomer (Giles no. 1510, 1898; Hummel p. 570–71, 1943).

years of the Ming dynasty. Some modern writers, as Li Yen in his Chu suan chih tu k'ao,[8] accept that conclusion. On the other hand, Ch'ien Ta hsin[9] in his Shih chia chai yang hsin lu said that the suan p'an was already used during the Yüan dynasty. I am inclined to believe that its use is considerably older. For example, Hsü Yüeh (II-2) speaks of chu suan or ball arithmetic, which seems to imply the use of some kind of abacus. Various treatises on the suan p'an were apparently written in the eleventh and twelfth centuries (Introd. 1, 756). See also my note on Ch'in Chiu-shao (XIII-1). Of course the form of that abacus may have changed through the ages, but that is a secondary matter.

T'ao also wrote the Kuo fêng tsun ching and a literary anthology, Shuo fu.

Text. The Library of Congress has the Cho keng lu in the Ch'ing chao t'ang ts'ung shu, vols. 67–72.

Criticism. E. Bretschneider (1, 173–76, 1888), no Chinese characters. Giles (no. 1899, 1898). Wylie (p. 189, 1902). B. Laufer in Frank B. Wiborg: Printing ink (p. 19, New York 1926; Isis 9, 134).

For history of the suan p'an, reference may also be made to A. Terrien de La Couperie: The old numerals, the counting rods and the swan-pan in China (Numismatic chronicle 3, 297–40, reprint 44 p., London 1883). Cargill G. Knott: The abacus in its historic and scientific aspects (Transactions Asiatic Society of Japan 14, 18–71, 1886). A. Vissière: Recherches sur l'origine de l'abaque chinoise (Bull. de géographie, 28 p., Paris 1892). Other titles quoted by Cordier (2, col. 1442, 1905–6; 5, col. 3815, 1922).

Note on Chinese Muslims

T'ao's memoir on the precious stones of the Muslims, Hui-hui shih t'ou, gives me a welcome opportunity to explain the difficult questions relative to the Hui-hui or Chinese Muslims. These questions have been complicated by the fact of having been discussed either by Sinologists knowing no Arabic, or by Arabists knowing no Chinese. Let us try to clear them up.

To begin with, how can we account for that strange name Hui-hui? The word hui means to come back, to return.[10] Giles (p. 640, 1912) suggests that the Muslim meaning of the word was due to assimilation with the Arabic akhī (my brother), a word often used by Muslims (did Chinese Muslims actually use it, I wonder?). That is improbable. Dabry de Thiersant had suggested before (his vol. 1, p. 2, 1878) that hui was the Chinese equivalent of the Arabic Islām, Muslim, mu'min, etc., expressing the idea of return and submission to God. That seems rather far-fetched. The explanation given by the foremost Chinese Muslim scholar,

[8] Included in his Collected memoirs concerning the history of Chinese mathematics (3, 37–57, Commercial Press, Shanghai 1931), in Chinese. For Li Yen see footnote 49a in chapter XX, p. 1536.

[9] Famous Ch'ing historian and geographer (1728–1804) (Giles no. 366, 1898; Hummel p. 152–55, 1943).

[10] This is taken literally by those among the Chinese who do not like their Muslim neighbors. In the admirable book of Mildred Cable and Francesca French: The Gobi desert (p. 246, London 1942; Isis 35, 74): "The Chinese call them Huei-huei, which can be translated 'Returners,' and when a Chinese is asked the meaning of that term he has but one answer: 'Their ancestors came to this land unwanted and promised to return again to their own place, but they never did so. Therefore we call them "Huei-huei"—Returners.' "

Liu chih,[11] seems preferable (fig. 33). According to him, many of the Muslims came from Central Asia and were no other than the Turkish Uighūr, of whom we have spoken so often in volumes 1 and 2. Now, the Chinese transcription of Uighūr was Hui-ho. Later when the Uighūr Muslims disappeared (many of the Uighūr became Buddhists) or were superseded by other Muslims, the term Hui-ho, becoming meaningless, was replaced by Hui-hui, to which Chinese Muslim doctors gave fancy interpretations flattering to their pride. Liu chih recalls one of them. The character hui is the duplication of the character k'ou = mouth, a mouth within a mouth, recalling the two fundamental commandments of Islām, both relative to the mouth: "Thou shalt praise no one but God"; "Thou shalt eat nothing impure" (especially no pork as the other Chinese do!). All considered, the derivation of Hui-hui from Hui-ho seems the best explanation. We shall appreciate that more fully if we consider the history of Chinese Islām.

The earliest Muslims to reach China were probably Arabic or Persian sailors, who gradually dominated the maritime trade of Asia. They were already much in evidence in the ninth century, witness the lost Akhbār al-Ṣīn wal-Hind of Ibn Wahb, who visited the Chinese court in 870 and whose account was used by Abū Zaid (X-1). These Arabic sailors may have settled in the harbors such as Canton and Hangchow, but in small numbers; they did not create Muslim colonies. The tomb of the mythical Sa'd Ibn abī Waqqās (alias Wahb abū Kabsha) in Canton perpetuates that tradition. Larger bodies of Muslims came from Central Asia. Muslim soldiers were already established in Shansi in 757; and in 801 more than 20,000 were counted in a single army in Yünnan (d'Ollone p. 433, 437, 1911). In 1070, many Muslims came from Bukhārā and settled in Yünnan. Among them was the ancestor of the leading Muslim chief al-Sayyid al-Ajall Shams al-dīn 'Umar, who eventually entered into the military service of Chingiz Khān (XIII-1). This sayyid founded the most important Muslim family of China, represented by his descendants to this day; he, and even more perhaps his son Nāṣir al-dīn, established Muslim prestige in that country. Indeed, Nāṣir al-dīn became imperial governor in Yünnan, and when he died in 1292 was succeeded by his brother Ḥusain. In the meanwhile, the Mongol dynasty had come into power, and their period (1280–1368) marked the climax of Muslim prestige. We have often referred to Muslim engineers and scholars who entered the service of the Yüan rulers. Whatever Arabic and Muslim influences can be detected in Chinese science (mathematics, astronomy, etc.) date probably from the Yüan dynasty.

In 1335, a descendant of the sayyid Ajall (bearing the same name) obtained from the emperor a ruling that Islām should be called officially "the true and pure religion" (ching chên chiao). Muslim influence was strong enough to survive the Yüan dynasty, and another descendant of the sayyid Ajall was ordered by the Ming emperor in 1420 to build mosques in the capitals Si-an-fu and Nanking.

[11] Liu chih flourished in Nanking about 1710. He is the main Muslim writer of China and is called by his brethren "the apostle of religion." He was well learned in Arabic theology and wrote many Chinese books, which constitute the best part of Muslim Chinese literature. See Dabry de Thiersant (2, 365–68, 1878). His discourse on the Muslims, Hui-hui shuo, was printed in the Chu t'ien ta tsan chi chieh, a Chinese Muslim compilation by Ma An-li, "descendant of the Arabs," fl. c. 1878. All the other studies in that book are by one A jih fu. The work explains that Arabia and not China is the center of the world, and that the Chinese wise men of antiquity were really of Muslim origin! It pays due attention to the Chinese classics, which are frequently quoted.

The Muslim settlements were not religious in purpose; the Muslims came from Central Asia to Cathay in order to improve their condition as soldiers, farmers, or

附回回說 金陵劉介廉先生著 先生諱智國初康熙時人
清眞教人。天方稱穆民穆士。蓋謂從穆罕默德聖人
之教者也。夫吾道之自西而東也。經回紇國而來。回
紇乃中國之邊譯。亦天方之邊譯也。行天方之教。教
類相似。則以吾人亦稱回紇。至宋元天方學人大至。
視回紇二字無謂。而改爲回回。聲音相近而義理頗
深。或曰回者邪也。稱名不美。吾人不當自居其稱。此
舉一廢百之說也。夫回之一字訓義不同。其說如訓
避。訓返。訓迴轉環繞。避則避世避色。返則返本還原。
迴轉環繞。則包括周徧。皆美義也。稱名亦不一。其人
況天方大聖 卷一
敬畏堂周氏藏板

FIG. 33. Example of Muslim Chinese publication. Page of the Chu t'ien ta tsan chi chieh, containing Liu chih's explanation of the term Hui-hui used to designate Muslims (passage between brackets, lines 4 to 8 counting from the right). From d'Ollone (p. 405, 422, 1911). The two identical characters transcribed Hui-hui (a small square within a larger one) can be seen in the central part of the text.

The date of this edition (1 chüan, 41 leaves) is difficult to determine. The copy described by commandant d'Ollone contains two prefaces, the first of which, dated 1878, is by the author; the second, dated 1863, by a religious dignitary; the plates were engraved in 1897.

merchants. This helps to explain the lateness of Muslim printing in China; though the retardation may have been partly due to Muslim prejudices against printing (see ch. I, p. 145) and to linguistic difficulties. The great bulk of Chinese

Muslims were of Chinese race, without linguistic contact with the sources of Islām; their few doctors who knew enough Arabic were seldom able to write in Chinese.[12] In any case, the earliest Islamic book in Chinese appeared only in 1642, that is, the Chêng chiao chên ch'üan (Veritable explanation of the true religion), by Wang Tai-yü (fl. c. 1642), nicknamed Chên hui lao yên (the genuine Muslim elder). It is analyzed by A. Vissière in the d'Ollone book (p. 393-94). There are all together some three dozens of Chinese Muslim books.[12a] One of them, written by Liu chih in 1710, may be mentioned here and then I must stop; that is the T'ien-fang tzŭ mu chieh i, wherein the meaning of Arabic letters is explained. That is, I believe, the earliest book of Arabic philology in a Far Eastern language (Vissière no. 36, p. 416-17 of d'Ollone's book). The reader will not be surprised to hear that these Muslim Chinese books contain many Confucian ideas; this could easily be done without Islamic disloyalty.

The main studies on Chinese Islām are Philibert Dabry de Thiersant: Le mahométisme en Chine (2 vols., Paris 1878). Bretschneider (1, 364-74, 1888). Marshall Broomhall: Islam in China (Shanghai 1910). Greg. Arnáiz and Max van Berchem: Mémoire sur les antiquités musulmanes de Ts'iuan-tcheou[13] (T'oung pao 12, 677-727, 1911). According to the Spanish Dominican and his Islamic interpreter, the earliest Arabic inscription extant in China is dated 710 H. = 1310/11, in a mosque of Ch'üan chou founded in 1009/10; the inscription in the mosque of Canton is later, September 1350. Commandant d'Ollone and others (1911). Couling (p. 378, 1917). Martin Hartmann: Zur Geschichte des Islam in China (Leipzig 1921), also rich summary by same in EI (1, 839-54, 1912) and ERE (8, 888-95, 1916). Wilhelm Filchner: Hui-hui, Asiens Islamkämpfe (424 p., ill., Berlin 1928). F. G. Onley: Literature in Chinese for Moslems (Moslem world 31, 421-22, 1941), dealing with the Christian anti-Muslim literature in Chinese; its relative abundance testifies to the importance of Islām in China. Hummel (p. 1087, index s.v. Mohammedan, 1944).

To encourage the study of Mohammedan culture, the Ministry of Education has ordered the National Central University, the National Northwest University, and the National Yünnan University to establish chairs of the Arabic language and literature. The National Yünnan University has already offered the chair to professor Sha Kuo-chen, and the chairs in the other two universities will be established during the next academic year (Quarterly bulletin of Chinese bibliography 1, 148, 1940). According to a statement made by the Chinese ambassador in London, Dr. V. K. Wellington Koo, to the Mustami'a 'arabī (vol. 3, no. 6, June 21, 1942), the number of Chinese Muslims is about 48,000,000.

The great majority belong to the Ḥanafī rite, a minority to the Shāfi'ī. Claude L. Pickens: The Moslem population of China (Friends of Moslems vol. 10, 1936),

[12] This statement applies to our own days. There are many millions of Muslims in China today who are anthropologically indistinguishable from their neighbors. They speak Chinese only, and behave like their neighbors in every respect except rites; e.g., they do not eat pork.

[12a] Not counting books published in our own time. It is highly probable that the Chinese Muslims are now publishing many books and pamphlets, because they are engaged in a battle of propaganda with men of other faiths. About the year 1940 there were being published in China 100 Muslim periodicals (very probably all of them in Chinese), as against 740 Christian periodicals, 155 Buddhist, 41 Taoist, 21 Confucian, and 36 Jewish. Rudolf Löwenthal: The religious periodical press in China (300 p., 7 maps, 16 charts, Synodal commission, Peking 1940; Isis 33, 388).

[13] That is, Ch'üan chou, in Fuhkien; Polo's Zayton (Introd. 2, 645, 1055).

reprinted in William Charles White: Chinese Jews (1, 200-3, Toronto 1942; Isis 35, 257).

SHÊN CHI-SUN

Chinese ink manufacturer (fl. 1398).

Shên Chi-sun wrote an elementary treatise on the fabrication of ink cakes, entitled Mo fa chi yao, the preface of which is dated by him 1398. It is very detailed and practical, and is illustrated with 27 woodcuts showing various stages in the process of manufacture. It deals with such topics as how to produce lamp-black and sift it, how to prepare glue, how to mold the balls or cakes, how to test the ink, etc. Earlier treatises on the subject, written by literati, devoted much attention to the history of ink manufacture and to literary references. As is shown in his own preface, the author is aware of that but prefers to restrict himself to technical matters, or more strictly to his own experience as a manufacturer together with some information received by him from a Buddhist priest.

Among earlier treatises I shall mention only the elaborate Mo ching,[14] the ink classic, written under the Sung by Ch'ao Kuan-chih, style Chi-i, reprinted in the T'u shu encyclopaedia.

This "technical" treatise is a singularity among Chinese mediaeval writings. That singularity is partly explained by the fact that ink, which is used only for literary purposes, has almost a sacred character. Paper is not considered by the Chinese with the same respect because it is used for other purposes as well. The names and marks of ink manufacturers have been preserved, and there are many (Chinese) collections of ink cakes.

Text. The Library of Congress has the Mo fa chi yao in the Wu ying tien chü chen pan ts'ung shu. It is found in vol. 268 of the Fuhkien edition, and in vol. 529 of the Kuangtung edition.

Russian translation of the Mo fa by I. Goshkevich in the Reports of the Russian Mission in Peking (vol. 1, 1852). French translation with reproduction of the woodcuts by Maurice Jametel: L'encre de Chine, son histoire et sa fabrication d'après des documents chinois (Bibliothèque orientale elzévirienne, 124 p., small size, Paris 1882), with historical introduction; Chinese characters in appendix.

Criticism. B. Laufer in Frank B. Wiborg: Printing ink (p. 19-20, New York 1926; Isis 9, 134). Laufer seems to be in error when he calls the author of the Sung Mo ching Ch'ao Shuo-chih. This Ch'ao Shuo-chih was a brother of Ch'ao Kuan-chih, and the latter, not the former, was the author of the Mo ching.

For Chinese ink, Couling (p. 250, 1917); Hummel (p. 1083, index s.v. ink, 1944).

[14] The non-Sinologist should not confuse this treatise with another one bearing apparently the same title, Mo ching, the famous treatise on the pulse by Wang Shu-ho (III-2). See Introd. 1, 342; 2, 76; Isis 15, 202, 1931. These two words "mo," though pronounced with the same intonation, represent two different characters, mo meaning pulse and mo meaning ink, respectively characters 8011 and 8022 in Giles' Dictionary (1912).

CHAPTER XXIII

GEOGRAPHY

(Second Half of the Fourteenth Century)

N.B. Only the main notes are published in this chapter. The geographical contributions of many other men, whose main work was done in other fields, are discussed in other chapters. For a general survey of geography in the second half of the fourteenth century, see section IX of chapter XV. More information on the men referred to in that survey may then easily be found by means of the index.

CATALONIA

CATALAN MAPPEMONDE 1375

This mappa mundi was made in 1375 for Charles V of France, and it is now preserved in the Bibliothèque nationale, Paris. It consists of six parchment leaves mounted in atlas form, each double page measuring 62 × 49 cm.

It is called Catalan because of its language; for example, the title reads "Mapa mondi vol dir aytant con ymage del mon y delos diversas etats del mon e de los regions qui son sus la terra, de diversas maneras de gens qui en la habitan." It refers to the year 1375 and bears the arms of Aragon (in 1343/44 the kingdom of Majorca had reverted to Aragon).

The mappemonde covers the whole world from north to south, and from west, i.e., from the Azores Islands, to the Far East. It has been considered the masterpiece of mediaeval cartography. It incorporated more fully than the previous portolani the results of overland exploration in Central and Eastern Asia. It contains the first satisfactory exhibition of the peninsular shape of India. The discoveries made in West Africa in 1346 are also recorded. The Mediterranean is dealt with in the usual portolano style.

The author of the Catalan atlas is unknown. It may have been the contemporary Majorcan cartographer Abraham Cresques (d. 1387); that identification has some plausibility but is unproved.

Another anonymous Catalan map of the end of the fourteenth century or beginning of the fifteenth is preserved in the national library of Florence. It measures 118 × 92 cm. and its terminology is Catalan. It covers Europe and the Mediterranean region and extends eastward to the Caspian and the Persian Gulf. It includes many legends, some of them filling many lines.

Text and criticism. J. A. C. Buchon: Un atlas en langue catalane de l'an 1374 (Notices et extraits des MSS vol. 13 (2), 144 p., 1838), with facsimiles. J. A. C. Buchon and J. Tastu: Un atlas en langue catalane de l'an 1375 (ibid. vol. 14 (2), 152 p., 1841), with facsimiles. Choix de documents géographiques publiés par la Bibliothèque nationale (pl. ix–xx, Paris 1883), excellent reproduction. E. T. Hamy: Cresques lo Juheu (Bull. de géographie historique p. 218–22, Paris 1891). H. Cordier: L'extrême orient dans l'atlas catalan (Bull. de géographie historique, 1895). Nordenskiöld (pl. xi–xiv, 1897).

Beazley (3, 525–27, 1906). Kretschmer (p. 122–24, 126, 1909). Edward

Luther Stevenson: Portolan charts, their origin and characteristics, with a descriptive list of those belonging to the Hispanic Society (76 p., ill., New York 1911), describing 32 portolani, ranging from the end of the fifteenth cent. to 1650. Yule (1, 299-310, 1915). Kimble (1938).

The Catalan map of 1375 should be compared with a later Catalan map, the so-called Este map, dating from about the middle of the fifteenth century. It is preserved in the R. Biblioteca Estense at Modena. Though inferior in many respects to the map of 1375, it contains some information not available to the earlier map maker. It is largely derived from the Libro del conosçimiento (XIV-1), and includes some of the results of recent Portuguese exploration along the west coast of Africa. The latest discovery registered is that of Cape Roxo (1446), and the Cape Verde islands (discovered in 1456) are not recorded; this dates the Este map. Comparisons should also be made with a Catalan map of c. 1440, with the Andrea Bianco maps of 1436 and 1448, with the Borgia map of c. 1450, and with the Fra Mauro planisphere of 1459.

Facsimiles of the Este map were published in Italy, Mappamondo catalana della Estense (natural size, 1075 × 1097 mm., Modena bef. 1921), and England, by George H. Kimble: The Catalan world map of the R. Bibl. Estense (Reproductions of early MS maps, 2, 10 p. fol. and map, Royal Geographical Society, London 1934). Oscar Peschel: Fac-simile dell'atlante di Andrea Bianco 1436, R. Bibl. Marciana, Venezia (10 pl., Venezia 1871). Theobald Fischer: Fac-simile della carta nautica di Andrea Bianco 1448, R. Bibl. Ambrosiana, Milano (4 pl., Venezia 1881).

SOLERI

William Soleri, Majorcan cartographer (fl. 1385).

This Soleri is known only through two portolani:

1. The first bears the dated title "Guillelmus Solerij ciuis maioricarum me fecit 1385." It measures 100 × 62 cm. and is kept in the state archives, Florence. It is restricted to the Mediterranean basin and the Atlantic coast to the British Isles and Jutland. It shows some of the legendary islands of the Atlantic, e.g., insula de brazir. The empty space of the hinterlands contains views of the Holy Sepulcher, Rome, Venice, etc. The terminology of the map (names and a few legends) is Latin.

2. The second portolano bears the same author's name but no date. It very much resembles the first map and hence dates from about the same time. It measures 105 × 64 cm. and is kept in the Bibliothèque nationale, Paris. It covers very much the same ground: Europe from Jutland on southward to North Africa and eastward to the Black Sea.

Gabriel Marcel: Choix de cartes et de mappemondes des XIVe et XVe siècles (Recueil de voyages et de documents, 3, Paris 1896), facsimile of the portolano of 1385. Nordenskiöld (pl. xviii, 1897). Kretschmer (p. 124, 1909). William H. Babcock: Legendary islands of the Atlantic (New York 1922; Isis 5, 167-70), for Brazil and other islands, no mention of Soleri.

ABRAHAM CRESQUES

Cresques lo Juheu (the Jew), lo Jueu buscolor (the map Jew), el Judio de las brujulas (the compass Jew). Catalan Jewish cartographer. Flourished at Palma de Mallorca, died in 1387.

He was one of the greatest cartographers of his age and the founder of the Jewish cartographical school of Majorca. He was in the service of the infante John of Aragon in the quality of a master of maps and compasses (magister mapamundorum et buxolarum), and made for him in 1381 a mapa mundi which was sent to Charles VI of France (king 1380–1422). In the same year the infante authorized him to establish public baths in Palma. In the following year, 1382, Peter IV of Aragon (king 1336–87) ordered the payment to him of one hundred and fifty golden florins for his "tabulas in quibus est figura mundi."

He was probably the author of the famous "Atlas Catalan" made for Charles V in 1375—one of the greatest cartographical achievements of the Middle Ages—but there is no archival proof of this.

JAHUDA CRESQUES

Jaffuda or Judah was the son of Abraham, and he lived and worked with him in Majorca. It is impossible to dissociate their activities completely. At the time of the persecutions of 1391 he was forcibly converted to Christianity, and thereafter called Jayme Ribes.

He was in the service of the kings of Aragon Juan I (king 1387–95) and Martin (king 1395–1410). He completed for Juan I al-Cazadór in 1387 a mapa mundi begun by his father, and was called in 1399 "magister cartarum navigandi." The date of his death is unknown.

It has been claimed, but not yet proved, that he was identical with one Jacme de Majorca in the service of Henry the Navigator.

Criticism. E. T. Hamy: Cresques lo Juheu (in his Etudes historiques et géographiques, Paris 1896; first published in Bull. de géographie historique p. 218–22, Paris 1891). Joseph Jacobs (JE 3, 679, 1902; 4, 354, 1903), short notes, father and son are confused. Pullé (p. 110–39, 1905). Rubió y Lluch (1, 295, 345, 346, 373, 1908; 2, 245, 253, 255, 1921). La Roncière (vol. 1, 1925), a whole section, p. 121–60, deals with the cartographical school of Majorca. Fritz Baer (EJ 5, 711, 1930). Gonçal de Reparaz, fill: Catalunya a les mars (Barcelona 1930; Isis 16, 173); "Mestre Jacome de Malhorca" cartógrafo do Infante (55 p., Coimbra 1930; Isis 17, 490), claiming that Jacme de Malhorca and Judah Cresques are identical. Paul Borchardt (EJ 9, 1014–17, 1932).

A. CHRISTENDOM

A2. Italy

"THE BROTHERS ZENI"

Niccolò Zeno and his brother Antonio are two Venetian adventurers alleged to have traveled among the islands of the North Atlantic, c. 1380–1400.

Before dealing with that story it is well to remark that there was a famous Zeno family in Venice; and there were at about that time two brothers Niccolò and Antonio Zeno. The latter is practically unknown (d. in or before 1403), but Niccolò was a Venetian sailor who traveled considerably in the Mediterranean region. In 1370, he sailed in charge of a fleet to Trebizond; in 1379, during the war between Venice and Genoa, he was in charge of a galley in the Levant; in 1380, he was "savio per la guerra" (something like secretary of war); in 1387, castellan in Modone and Corone (in Messenia, Peloponnesus); in 1389, chief of a galley fleet;

in 1396, he was condemned to pay a heavy fine and excluded from public office because of his malversations during his castellanship. He made his will in Venice in 1400, and died before 1403.

In 1558, a member of the same family, Niccolò Zeno the younger (1515–65), published an account of travels of the elder Niccolò Zeno and Antonio Zeno, as well as of those of Caterino Zeno, Venetian ambassador to Persia c. 1471. According to that account, the elder Niccolò, being shipwrecked in 1380 on the island of Frisland (Faroe Islands?), was taken into the service of Zichmni (?), lord of the Orkneys, who was trying to conquer Greenland. Later Antonio joined his brother and served with him four years. Then Niccolò died and Antonio succeeded him, and remained in Zichmni's service thirteen years longer. He finally went back to Frisland; he was never allowed to return to Venice, but wrote to his brother Carlo the story of their adventures.

There are no means of testing completely the narrative which was published in 1558 together with a map (carta da navegar). We have seen that the elder Niccolò Zeno is a real personality, but one whose achievements were very different from and incompatible with those ascribed to him. Either the whole story was invented by the younger Niccolò, or else, whatever documents may have come to him from his ancestors, they were edited by him in the light of the knowledge available in his time and recast to the extent of leaving no trace of their original state. The carta da navegar is obviously based on other maps of the late fifteenth and sixteenth centuries. In either case, the narrative has no value as far as the study of fourteenth-century geography is concerned, but it must be taken into account in any study of geography in the second half of the sixteenth century. The narrative of 1558 had a great and evil influence upon the cartography of a whole century or more, introducing two new islands (Estotiland and Drogio), shifting others widely into new positions, etc.

Text. Dei commentarii del viaggio in Persia di M. Caterino Zeno il k.[1] & delle guerre fatte nell' imperio persiano dal tempo di Vssuncassano[2] in quà, libri due, et dello scoprimento dell'isole Frislanda, Eslanda, Engrouelanda, Estotilanda et Icaria fatto sotto il Polo Artico da due fratelli Zeni, M. Niccolò il k. & M. Antonio, libro uno con un disegno particolare di tutte le dette parte di Tramontana da lor scoperte (Venice 1558). Facsimile of the general preface and of the second part (Dello scoprimento etc., p. 45–58) in Lucas (1898). Reprinted in Giambattista Ramusio: Navigationi (2d ed., vol. 2, fol. 222–25, 1574). First English version in Richard Hakluyt: Diverse voyages (signatures D4–E, 1584); facsimile in Lucas (1898).

New edition of Italian and English texts by Richard Henry Major: The voyages of the Venetian brothers, Niccolò and Antonio Zeno to the northern seas in the fourteenth century, comprising the latest known accounts of the lost colony of Greenland, and of the Northmen in America before Columbus (Hakluyt Society, 166 p., 4 maps, London 1873).

Criticism. Joachim Lelewel: Tavola di navicare de Nicolo et Antonio Zeni et les cartes des régions septentrionales à l'époque de sa publication en 1558, in his Géographie du Moyen âge (4, 77–108, Bruxelles 1852). Major's long introduction (102 p.) to his edition of 1873 is a defense of the genuineness of the narrative.

[1] The initial M. stands for messire and the small k. for cavaliere. The same remark applies to other words in the same title. I do not understand the use of k rather than c.

[2] Uzun Ḥasan, the Turkoman chief of the White sheep (Āq-quyunlī), who superseded the Black sheep (Qarā-quyunlī) in 1469.

Adolf Erik Nordenskiöld: Studien und Forschungen veranlasst durch meine Reisen im hohen Norden (Leipzig 1885). Frederic William Lucas: The annals of the voyages of the brothers Zeni . . . and the claim founded thereon to a Venetian discovery of America (quarto, 247 p., 18 large maps, many smaller ones and other ill., London 1898), very elaborate indictment of the genuineness, with corpus of all relevant documents in facsimile, translation, etc., and a list of some 400 maps and books bearing upon the subject; Lucas was able to take advantage of various maps and other documents not available to Major in 1873. Miller Christy: The silver map of the world, a contemporary medallion of Drake's great voyage (1577–80), including some remarks on the Zeno narrative and chart of 1558 (83 p., London 1900). William H. Babcock: Legendary islands of the Atlantic (p. 124–43, New York 1922; Isis 5, 167–70), excellent summary with a map concluding against the genuineness of the narrative in its present state. A. Da Mosto: I navigatori Zeni (Miscellanea Luzio, Florence 1935). Hennig (3, 317–24, 1936).

GUCCI

Giorgio Gucci; Giorgio son of Guccio di Dino Gucci. Ambassador and civil servant of the signoria of Florence, he accompanied Frescobaldi and others on their pilgrimage to the Near East in 1384–85, and wrote in Italian an account of their visit to the Holy Land.

Text. First published by Carlo Gargiolli: Viaggio ai luoghi santi, in his Viaggi in Terra santa (p. 271–438, Firenze 1862).

Criticism. Röhricht (p. 91, 1890).

FRESCOBALDI

Florentine traveler to the Near East in 1384–85.

Leonardo di Niccolò Frescobaldi. He visited Egypt and the Holy Land in 1384; on his return in 1385, he was appointed podestà of Città di Castello; in 1390, he took possession of Montepulciano in the name of the signoria of Florence; in 1398, he was Florentine ambassador to pope Boniface IX in Rome; he distinguished himself at the siege of Pisa, in 1405, this being the latest reference to him on record.

He left Florence on August 10, 1384, with Simone di Gentile Sigoli, Giorgio Gucci, and others; they went to Venice, whence they sailed to Alexandria. They visited Cairo, then proceeded to Mt. Sinai, Gaza, the Holy Land, Damascus, Beirut. They sailed from Beirut in May 1385 for Venice. Frescobaldi left a detailed account of the journey in Italian, which contains some very valuable information, e.g., on the immense amount of navigation on the Nile, and on the social and economic life of the countries traversed by him. He carried with him letters of credit from the Portinari bank in Florence, which had branches in Alexandria and Damascus.

Text. First edition by Guglielmo Manzi: Viaggio di Lionardo Frescobaldi in Egitto e in Terra santa, con un discorso sopra il commercio degl' Italiani nel secolo XIV (198 p., Rome 1818). Reprinted by Lorenzo Magalotti (224 p., Parma 1845). Also in Carlo Gargiolli: Viaggi in Terra santa del secolo XIV (p. 3–149, 11 cm. high, Firenze 1862).

Criticism. C. Defrémery and B. R. Sanguinetti: Voyages d'Ibn Batoutah (vol. 1, 1853; p. xxxv–xlvi in reprint 1874). Röhricht (p. 91, 1890). Beazley (3, 489, 1906). Sapegno (p. 585–87, 1934). Atiya (p. 173, 1938).

SIGOLI

Simone Sigoli. Noble Florentine who accompanied Frescobaldi to the Near East in 1384–85, and wrote in 1390 a detailed account, in Italian, of their journey under the misleading title Viaggio al Monte Sinai. He and his companions visited Mt. Sinai, but that was only a part of their journey. The account covers about a hundred octavo printed pages.

He makes an interesting reference (p. 45 of first edition) to Presto Giovanni ("Prester John," XII-2; Introd. 2, 416–17), a powerful sovereign living in India, to whom the sultan of Egypt pays homage, because he (John) commands the sources of the Nile. This shows that the confusion of ideas with regard to Abyssinia and India was not yet cleared up. It is true enough, of course, that the floods of the Nile are controlled in the Abyssinian highlands.

Text. First edition, Viaggio al Monte Sinai di Simone Sigoli. Testo di lingua (348 p., Florence 1829), with two introductory lectures by Luigi Fiacchi and Francesco Poggi, and abundant notes by the latter (p. 103–276). Eighth edition in Carlo Gargiolli: Viaggi in Terra santa (p. 153–268, Firenze 1862). Later editions, Parma 1865, Torino 1873, Florence 1883.

Criticism. Röhricht (p. 92, 1890). Potthast (p. 1019, 1896). Beazley (3, 403, 1906).

NICCOLÒ DI MARTONI

Niccolò di Martoni (de Marthono), Italian pilgrim to Jerusalem in 1394.

Niccolò was a notary in Carinola near Calvi in the Campagna. He sailed on June 17, 1394 from Gaeta to Rhodes, then to Alexandria, then proceeded to Cairo, Mt. Sinai, the Holy Land, and returned via Cyprus, Rhodes, Greece, arriving home at the end of May 1395. He was a simple pilgrim, naïve and ignorant, ill prepared for the many adventures which he met, lacking courage, but bolstered up by his piety and his hope of "merit." As he remarked, "dulcia non meruit qui non gustavit amara." He kept a diary, which he rewrote later under the title Liber peregrinationis ad loca sancta. By loca sancta are meant not only the conventional Holy Places, but also all the places connected with St. Catherine of Alexandria, for whom he professed a special devotion. The account is fairly long (93 p. in the printed text), sincere, and accurate for everything which the author witnessed, but not so truthful for the stories which he accepted too credulously.

He noticed the incubators for chickens in Alexandria (these were an old Egyptian invention),[3] the lizards, etc. The most interesting part of his book is his description

[3] The artificial incubation of chickens as it is practiced to this day, especially in the Faiyūm, goes back probably to early times. There is no inherent difficulty in the invention, which might be suggested to any intelligent husbandman by the incubation of other eggs, such as turtle eggs, in the sand without maternal heat. Aristotle was aware that such incubation was possible, De generatione animalium 752 b 30; Pliny refers to it in his Historia naturalis, book X, ch. 75 (54). As far as the incubation of *chicken* eggs is concerned, however, the Egyptian invention must be posterior to the Persian conquest (525 B.C.), for there were probably no chickens in Egypt before that time! (PW 8, 2522 s.v. Huhn). As for eggs of other domesticated birds, geese, ducks, etc., their representation is extremely rare. See Adolf Erman, Hermann Ranke: Aegypten (p. 268, Tübingen 1923). Apparently the eating of eggs was considered sinful. I owe much of this note to the kindness of Mr. Dows Dunham, curator of Egyptian antiquities in the Boston Museum of Fine Arts, who concludes his letter (Jan. 19, 1943) with the words, "I know of no evidence, pictorial or otherwise, pointing to artificial incubation" (in ancient Egypt). After Martoni, many visitors to Egypt described the artificial incubation

of Greece, where circumstances obliged him to travel considerably. He had an eye for antiquities (this was very rare in his time), and described or mentioned many. There are exceedingly few descriptions of mediaeval Athens, and his is one of them. For example, he describes "Hadrian's palace" (the temple of Zeus Olympios) and the Church of St. Mary (the Parthenon). He also recorded traditions, e.g., one concerning Hippocrates of Cos.

Text. The Liber peregrinationis was edited by Léon Le Grand (Revue de l'Orient latin 3, 566-669, 1895).

Criticism. Röhricht (p. 94, 1890), "1394. Nicolaus de Marchono." C. Enlart: Notes sur le voyage de Nicolas de Martoni en Chypre (Revue de l'Orient latin 4, 623-32, 1896). Atiya (p. 175, 1938).

THE MEDICEAN ATLAS, 1351

The atlas is called Medicean or Laurentian, both names being justified by the fact that it is preserved in the R. Biblioteca Medicea Lorenziana in Florence. It contains 8 leaves (56 × 42 cm.).

The first leaf is devoted to a lunar calendar for the year 1351, and the dating of the whole atlas is based on that circumstance. The validity of that conclusion has been denied, however, on the ground that the cartographer might have copied an old calendar. Franz von Wieser claims that the Medicean atlas is not anterior (and is possibly posterior) to the mappemonde of Albertin de Virga, dating from about 1415. His claim is based on his recognition in both works of the first traces of Ptolemaic influences in mediaeval cartography; now Ptolemy's geography became available to the Latin world only in 1409 through the Latin translation made by Giacomo d'Angelo (Jacobus Angelus) and dedicated by him in that year to pope Alexander V (pope 1409-10). It is simpler to assume that the date 1351 is correct but that interpolations and changes were introduced into the atlas sometime after 1415.

Leaf 2. Mappemonde of remarkable amplitude. It covers the whole of Europe, Asia to the western part of India, and an Africa far extended to the south. It is possible that the more modern features of the map are later interpolations?

Leaf 3. Adriatic. Also a part of the Caspian Sea.

Leaf 4. Spanish peninsula with parts of the French and African coasts.

Leaf 5. Western Europe, including the Baltic, and the British Isles. Spain extends southward to Segura, Italy is entirely outlined, also the Greek-Albanian coast. (The map was left uncompleted.)

Leaf 6. Eastern Mediterranean extending far enough westward to include Sicily and the greater part of Italy.

Leaf 7. Archipelago.

Leaf 8. Black Sea.

The author is entirely unknown, but his vocabulary suggests that he might be Genoese, or at any rate Ligurian. The scales of the maps vary from 1:30,000,000 for the world map to 1:2,400,000 for the map of the Archipelago. All the maps are

---

of chickens, and Olivier de Serres (1539-1619) tried to introduce it into France. The practice was improved by Réaumur (1750) and Bonnemain (1780 or 1816).

According to the history of China published by father Juan Gonzalez de Mendoza (first edition, Spanish, Rome 1585; many other editions in Spanish, Italian, French, Latin, English), the Chinese practiced artificial incubation of duck eggs.

of the portolano or marine type, but on the mappemonde the hinterlands are colored and include various cosmographic legends.

Apropos of this atlas Beazley remarked (p. 523–25, without footnotes):

"In the world map, the general shape of Africa, the southern projection of the Dark Continent towards the Cape, and especially the great line of the Gulf of Guinea, are represented with such an approach to reality, that we cannot believe the designer was merely guessing at the truth. In particular, the shore-line between our Sierra Leone and Cameroons must have been here laid down with some help from actual knowledge. Again, in the western section of the detailed four-sheet portolan, the Atlantic islands appear (the Azores for the first time) with the fullness and accuracy of a pilot-chart or at least of a work immediately derived from pilot-charts. Among other features of this atlas (some to be found in the general map of the Western World, others in the detailed sheets which follow) is the near approach of Scotland to Norway; separated only by a narrow strait, these northern lands almost make of the German Ocean another Euxine. Again, in Asia, where several traces of Polo influence occur, the beginnings of an Indian peninsula may be deduced from the contour of South Asia at the extreme east of the design. The lake- and river-system of Europe is realized, at least in some particulars, with uncommon clearness; no earlier designer has given us so good a shape for the Red Sea and the Caspian; and even if the Somali peninsula is practically wanting to the Dark Continent; if a western Nile, rising in close neighbourhood to the White, is drawn half-way across Africa to the Atlantic; if the Persian and Cambayan Gulfs, like the north coasts of Britain, are badly distorted; and if the Baltic, though less exaggerated than of old, is still misdirected, these are but the typical shortcomings of the best map-science of the time." (Beazley's judgment is based on the whole of the atlas with later interpolations.)

Text and criticism. Teobaldo Fischer: Facsimile del portolano Laurenziano-Gaddiano (Venezia 1881). Beazley (3, 523–25, 1906). Kretschmer (p. 119–21, 1909). George H. T. Kimble: The Laurentian world map with special reference to its portrayal of Africa (Imago mundi 1, 29–33, facsim., Berlin 1935; Isis 26, 251), defending the compromise adopted in my note above; the date 1351 is correct, but the "prophetic" features of the African map, otherwise unaccountable, are interpolations posterior to 1415 and even to 1450.

Albertin de Virga was a Venetian cartographer about whom nothing is known except that he drew his famous map of the world in 1415.[4] That map is very important, because it was the first to combine the newly reconquered Ptolemaic knowledge with the knowledge accumulated during the Middle Ages. It represents the dawn of a new cartographic age.

A complete and full-sized facsimile of it was published with introduction by Franz R. von Wieser: Die Weltkarte des Albertin de Virga (Innsbruck 1912).

Roberto Almagià: Il mappamondo di Albertin da Virga (Rivista geografica italiana 21, 92–96, 1914). Kimble (p. 115–17, 1938).

PIZIGANO

Francesco Pizigano (Pizzigano, Picigano). Venetian cartographer (fl. 1367–73). Two cartographical monuments bearing his name have come down to us:

[4] It is drawn on a full skin of vellum, measures about 70 × 44 cm., and bears the inscription "A. 1415: Albirtin. divirga me fezit in vinexia." It is in the Albrecht Figdor collection in Vienna.

1. A portolano dated Venice 1367. It is one of the largest portolani extant, measuring 134 × 90 cm. It is now preserved in the Biblioteca reale of Parma. It represents the Mediterranean world, the northwest of Europe, and North Africa.

2. An atlas now preserved in the Ambrosiana, Milano (probably identical with the atlas formerly seen in San Michele, Murano). It includes nine sheets of small size (25 × 15 cm.), folded in two (12.5 × 15 cm.), the first of which bears the author's name, Francescho Picigano, and the date Venice 1373.

Five of these sheets, the odd-numbered ones, are Pizigano's work and may be assumed to have been done in that year 1373. Contents: (1) Black Sea, (3) eastern Mediterranean, (5) central Mediterranean, (7) western Mediterranean, (9) Western Europe including the Jutland peninsula and the British Isles.

The four other sheets inserted between Pizigano's, thus even-numbered, are by another hand, and somewhat later. Theobald Fischer would date them on palaeographical grounds as late as the sixteenth century. One of them, however, refers to the naval battle of Chioggia in the southern part of the Venice lagoon (Genoese fleet destroyed by the Venetians in 1380) and bears the date 1381. Kretschmer concludes that these interpolated maps and charts are not much younger than Pizigano's and belong to the fourteenth century. Contents: (2) trajectories of the planets, sun, and moon, with views of Venice and Genoa in the middle, (4) four elements, moon phases; in the center, views of Paradise and of its four rivers, (6) Aegaean Sea, (8) Adriatic.

Kretschmer (p. 121–22, 1909), including references to previous literature. La Roncière (vol. 1, pl. viii, 1925). Bovill (p. 74, 137, 1933).

TWO ANONYMOUS ITALIAN PORTOLANI DATING PROBABLY FROM THE LAST QUARTER OF THE FOURTEENTH CENTURY

Two anonymous portolani apparently posterior to the Catalan atlas (1375) deserve to be briefly described here. They are the Combitis atlas and the Pinelli atlas.

1. Combitis atlas. Atlas of four sheets 38 × 30 cm., preserved in the San Marco library. It bears the inscription "Haec tabula ex testamento domini Nicolai de Combitis devenit in monasterio Cartusiae florentinae." The name Nicolaus de Combitis is strange. This Nicolaus bequeathed his atlas to the Carthusian monastery of Florence; it does not follow that he was Florentine or Carthusian. He may be the author (or copyist) of this atlas or not; if he were, however, he would have probably made a statement to that effect. The date is uncertain. According to Theobald Fischer the atlas is posterior to the Catalan atlas and may be anterior to the fifteenth century. Contents: (1) eastern Mediterranean, (2) middle Mediterranean, (3) western Mediterranean, (4) coasts of Spain and North Africa.

2. Pinelli atlas. Atlas of six sheets bearing the name of the Venetian family, Pinelli, which once owned it. It is now in the British Museum. It is probably a Genoese (?) work of before or about 1384. The dating is based on the presence on leaf 1 of a calendar for the half-century 1384–1434. Contents: (1) on one half, the calendar already mentioned; on the other, coast of Spain and northwest Africa to Cape Bojador (26°7′N.), discovered by Jaime Ferrer in 1346; (2) Western Europe to the British Isles and Jutland; coasts of France and Spain as far as Savona (near Genoa), and of North Africa to Cape Bojador; (3) middle Mediterranean from the mouth of the Rhône eastward; including the whole of Italy, the western Balkanic coast to the island of Cerigo (just south of Greece), and the corresponding African

coast; (4) eastern Mediterranean from Greece on to the Black Sea; (5) enlargement of the Adriatic part of map 3; (6) enlargement of the Archipelago to the Dardanelles and to Candia. Maps 5 and 6 are by another hand than maps 1 to 4.

For the first atlas see Theobald Fischer: Sammlung mittelalterlicher Welt- und Seekarten (p. 151–52, Venice 1886). For both see Kretschmer (p. 125–26, 1909), describing many more portolani of the fifteenth century (nos. 22–75, p. 126–48).

The first *printed* portolano was the Isolario of Bartolommeo dalli Sonetti, fl. 1477–85 (Venice c. 1485; Klebs no. 158), containing 48 woodcut charts depicting the islands of the Aegean Sea, together with descriptive sonnets. Copy in Boston Public library. Discussion by Zoltán Haraszti (More books, March 1943, p. 108–14).

FAZIO DEGLI UBERTI

Florentine didactic and lyric poet (d. c. 1368).

Fazio (short for Bonifazio) was a member of an illustrious Florentine and Ghibelline family, the Uberti, made famous in the previous century by Manente degli Uberti, detto Farinata (fl. 1260). Fazio was born, probably in Pisa, between 1305 and 1309. He was born in exile, and the whole of his life was spent in exile and errantry. It is possible that Filippo Villani exaggerated when he said of him "per guadagno frequentava le corti dei tiranni e adulava la vita e i costumi dei potenti." At any rate, he traveled considerably in upper Italy; perhaps also in France (there are a few Provençal lines in his Dittamondo). He spent some time at the court of the Scaligeri in Verona and at that of Luchino Visconti, tyrant of Milano (1339–49). It would seem that he died soon after 1367.

He wrote a number of lyrical poems (at least 16 canzoni and 13 sonetti), some of which deal with political matters, e.g., his canzone addressed in 1343 to Ludwig V of Bavaria, appealing to the emperor for vengeance, and another addressed in 1355 to Charles IV of Luxemburg, wherein he expresses the anger of the disappointed Ghibellines. In other poems he complains of his poverty, solitude, and lack of home, or sings the praise of Ghidola Malaspina, wife of Feltrino da Montefeltro. In these poems he reveals himself a true poet, if a minor one.

His main work, as far as we are concerned, is a very long didactic poem, entitled Dittamondo (dicta mundi), which he composed between 1348 and 1360, 1367. It is written, in imitation of the Divina commedia, in terzine. Though the form is Dantesque, the inspiration is very different. It is clear and sometimes elegant, and on the whole superior to the Acerba of Cecco d'Ascoli (XIV-1; d. 1327) and the Dottrinale of Iacopo Alighieri (XIV-1; d. 1348). Fazio tries to describe the real world even as Dante had explained the world of ideas.

The Dittamondo may be called a geographical poem, a treatise in verse for the popularization of knowledge on the arrangement and beauty of the world. It begins with an account of the glory and decadence of Rome. Then the poet sets out on his travels guided by Solinus (III-2)—a pale imitation of Dante's Virgil. Under Solinus' guidance he visits Italy, Greece, Germany, France, Spain, Northern Europe, the known parts of Africa and Asia. We are told many of the legends concerning those countries. In addition to Solinus, Uberti's main sources are Pomponius Mela (I-1), Pliny the Elder (I-2), and Isidore of Seville (VII-1); in other words, his geography is not by any means up-to-date, but rather archaeological or retrospective, and legendary. (This should not cause too much surprise, if one remembers that the conception of geography as a natural science is relatively new;

until almost yesterday, geography and history were somewhat confused in European universities; that is, one was taught to think of geography very largely in historical terms.) Yet there are some good descriptions, e.g., in book III, ch. 9, the view from Alvernia in Casentino (a mount in the Apennines from which one dominates Tuscany and Umbria, already consecrated by St. Francis and Dante).

Text. Dittamondo. First edition, Vicenza 1474 (Klebs no. 996). Second edition, Venice 1501 (267 fol.). Il Dittamondo, ridotto a buona lezione colle correzioni pubblicate dal cav. Vincenzo Monti nella proposta e con piu altre (536 p., Milano 1826).

Rodolfo Renier: Liriche edite ed inedite (632 p., Florence 1883), elaborate critical edition with long introduction (372 p.) but no index.

Criticism. Giusto Grion: Intorno alla famiglia e alla vita di Fazio degli Uberti (38 p., s.l., 1861). Victor Le Clerc (HL 24, 576, 1862). Renier's introduction (1883). Theodor Paur: Fazio degli Uberti, ein Epigone Dantes (Neues lausitzisches Magazin vol. 67, 20 p., Görlitz 1891). Achille Pellizzari: Il Dittamondo e la Divina commedia, saggio sulle fonti del Dittamondo e sulla imitazione dantesca nel secolo XIV (140 p., Pisa 1905). Pullé (p. 75–77, 1905). Giuseppe Corsi: Appunti sul Dittamondo (172 p., Fabriano 1917). Sapegno (p. 129–31, 478–84, 1934).

A3. France

ANGLURE

Ogier VIII of Anglure (Champagne; dépt. Marne), pilgrim to the Holy Land in 1395.

Ogier VIII was a descendant of Ogier lord of Saint Chéron (near Anglure), who took part in two crusades (1190, 1199), was on the first occasion generously freed by Ṣalāḥ al-dīn in spite of his inability to pay for his ransom,[5] and died in Champagne in or after 1213. Ogier VIII was lord of Anglure and avoué[6] of Thérouanne (near St. Omer, Pas-de-Calais). The pilgrimage headed by him included his father-in-law, Simon of Sarrebruck (died at Nicosia, Cyprus, 1396), an Artesian knight Pierre de Nortquelmes (or Morquelines), and the clerk who wrote the account which has come down to us.

The pilgrims left Anglure on July 16, 1395, went to Pavia, Venice, Padua, Corfu, Rhodes, Beirut (where St. George killed the dragon), Jerusalem. They visited the Holy Sepulcher on October 5. The account, written in French, gives much information on the Holy Land, which the pilgrims visited very conscientiously. Then they traveled across the desert to St. Catherine in the Sinai peninsula, then to Egypt. They sailed from Alexandria on December 21, returning home via Cyprus, Rhodes, Venice, arriving at Anglure on June 22, 1396. The account of the journey covers about a hundred printed pages. It is even more detailed concerning Egypt than concerning the Holy Land. The pilgrims were allowed to travel a little way up the Nile, though most foreigners were forbidden to do so lest they discover the secret of the Indian trade route. They visited the Coptic monasteries of St. Anthony and

[5] For the complete story or legend relative to that, see Bonnardot's edition (p. xxxi, 1878).

[6] Avoué = advocatus was originally a champion ready to fight for those who could not fight for themselves (cripples, women, institutions); later it meant the protector of, say, a church or an abbey; also its official representative before a law court. See Ducange s.v. advocator. Henry Charles Lea: Superstition and force (4th ed., p. 198, Philadelphia 1892). In England the word advocatus meant patron, a patron enjoying various rights, one of which is perpetuated by the word and alas! the practice of advowson.

St. Paul in the eastern desert between the Nile and the Red Sea. The description of them is unique in contemporary literature.[7]

Text. First edition, Troyes 1621, wherein the text is ascribed to Simon of Sarrebruck, baron of Anglure. Second edition by the abbé Michon in the Bibliothèque catholique de voyages et de romans edited by the abbé Domenech (222 p., small size, Paris 1858). Critical edition for the Société des anciens textes français, by François Bonnardot et Auguste Longnon: Le saint voyage de Jherusalem du seigneur d'Anglure (258 p., Paris 1878).

Criticism. Prefaces to the editions. Röhricht (p. 94, 1890). Atiya (p. 178–84, 1938). G. Levi Della Vida: "Chrestiens de la saincture" (Modern language notes, Nov. 1944, 484–87; Isis 36, 27).

A4. England

MANDEVILLE

Joannes de Mandeuil, Jehan de Mandeville, Sir John Mandeville.

An English nobleman and physician who practiced medicine in Liége, where he was buried in 1372. According to his own account, he was born in St. Albans, and was forced to flee in 1322 because he had killed a man of high rank. Thus he began the long series of journeys which he described in his famous Travels. Isaac Jackson claims that John was not born in St. Albans, but might have been the Sir John Mandeville of Donnahir who killed William de Burgh, earl of Ulster, in 1333 and who disappeared immediately. The date 1322 was given by John in the Travels to provide an alibi if he were ever caught. It has also been proved that the book was written c. 1365 (the oldest MS is dated 1371), and not in 1355, the date given by himself. The original redaction was probably French. John's stories were believed to be genuine, and their success was phenomenal. They were translated into Latin c. 1390, into German between 1369 and 1398, and into Dutch, English, Italian, Spanish, and Czech at very early dates.

According to some writers, notably the late professor Hamelius, Jean d'Outremeuse, a friend of Mandeville, was probably the real author of the Travels. His conclusion is based on the following facts: (1) there is considerable similarity between the Mirror of histories written by Outremeuse and the Travels; (2) various peculiar mistakes of fact are common to the two; (3) Outremeuse says in the Mirror that he will not describe Tartary because he has described it in another work; this description does not appear in his Trésorier de philosophie naturelle, but is in the Travels; (4) the Travels contain a number of definite attacks on the papacy and show the author to have strong Wycliffite tendencies, therefore it would be advisable to issue such a work under a false name; (5) the style of writing is very similar in the two works, the author, or authors, imitating closely the conventions of the minstrels; (6) the two works have practically identical sources.

Even if John of Mandeville did compose the Travels, the book was largely a compilation of passages taken from older works and not the account of his own journeys. The book is divided into two main parts. Part I (15 chapters) describes a journey to the Holy Land and the various routes to it, together with Egypt and Sinai. If any of his material was drawn from personal knowledge and observation, it is to be found only in these first 15 chapters. Some of his facts come from the

[7] Alfred Joshua Butler: Ancient Coptic churches in Egypt (1, 341–48, Oxford 1884). The Dair Mār Būlus is not dedicated to Paul the apostle, but to St. Anthony's friend and fellow anchorite, Paul of Thebes.

History of the First Crusade written by Albert of Aix (after 1121; Introd. 2, 253), and a great deal from William Boldensele (XIV-1); to a lesser extent from Pliny the Elder, Solinus, Peter Comestor, Jacques de Vitry, Brunetto Latini, Hayton the Armenian, and others. Much of the earlier material, however, was probably taken from the Historiale of Vincent of Beauvais (XIII-2) instead of directly from the original works. Part II deals with travels farther East, from Trebizond to Ormuz, India, the Indian Archipelago, and China, and back again to Western Asia. Most of this part is taken bodily from the De rebus incognitis of Odoric of Pordenone (XIV-1), also some from the Liber Tartarorum of Giovanni del Pian del Càrpine (XIII-1), from Hayton the Armenian (XIV-1), and others. Here again the earlier authorities were probably read only in Vincent of Beauvais. The compiler's own interpolations are generally extravagant, but he tells the story of a man who traveling continually eastward came back to his own country (ch. xxi, Hamelius' ed., 1, 122; see also index s.v. circumnavigation). That whole chapter xxi deals with the sphericity of the earth and various consequences thereof.

One of Mandeville's sources, as mentioned above, was Odoric of Pordenone (XIV-1). The latter described cormorant fishing, but in some MSS cormorant fishing is curiously replaced by otter fishing (also practiced in China). Mandeville got hold of the otter story and popularized it in his own composition. E. W. Gudger: Fishing with the otter (American naturalist 61, 193–225, 1927; Isis 12, 425; 35, 178, 331).

In the Travels Mandeville says that he met a Jean à la Barbe in Cairo, and later was his patient at Liége in 1356. It is more than probable that Mandeville and Jean à la Barbe are one and the same person. Thus it was Mandeville who wrote one or more treatises on the plague, the main one appearing in 1365 under the name of Jean à la Barbe (Joannes ad Barbam), and Jean de Bourgogne or Bourgoyne (Joannes de Burgundia). This was probably written first in Latin and then translated into French. His astrological introduction gives the remote causes of the plague. This is followed by a personal introduction in which he says he is a physician of Liége and is called Jean à la Barbe and Jehan de Bourgoigne. He says that he has written several plague treatises and that this one is a general summary written for the layman. The main part of the treatise (section III) begins with a discussion of prophylactic measures for the prevention of the plague, such as the proper diet, disinfection of houses etc., aromatic and herbal remedies, bloodletting. Section IV contains his pathological theory; a description of the way in which the disease works when it does take hold of a person. Section V is on therapeutic measures; bloodletting, drugs, diet, etc. Section VI, an astrological epilogue, explains that the epidemic of 1365 was not caused by the recent conjunction of Jupiter and Saturn, but by the "vestigia" of one which occurred twenty years before. Section VII is a postscript giving the reasons for the composition of this work; another discussion of drugs and bloodletting, and a list of medical writers such as Hippocrates, Galen, Dioscorides, etc. The whole postscript may have been taken from some earlier work. Section VIII is a brief Explicit. A sixteenth-century medical MS entitled Thesaurus pauperum contains an English translation of this plague tract.

Another treatise on the plague, which is very similar to the one written in 1365, is ascribed to a certain John of Bordeaux (Burdeus, Burdigalensis). Many copies of this redaction are dated 1390. Some authorities have claimed that John of Bordeaux is the same person as John of Burgundy, Jean à la Barbe, and Mandeville.

Mrs. Singer, however, says that John of Bordeaux was probably another person, living at a little later time, who reorganized and changed slightly the 1365 treatise of John of Burgundy. The name John of Bordeaux may have been the name of this later compiler or it may have been merely a corruption of the name John of Burgundy.

The Lapidary ascribed to Mandeville was probably not written by him. Like his Travels, however, it is not an original work, but copied principally from Marbode (XI-2).

A consilium and one of the plague treatises ascribed to Mandeville were translated into Hebrew. The plague treatise was translated by Benjamin ben Isaac of Carcassonne.

Some brief writings have often been ascribed to John of Burgundy, John à la Barbe, John of Bordeaux, or Sir John Mandeville; Pulvers in das Grosse Kunst Buch, also some collections of medicinal recipes, are found in various libraries. There is also a treatise on herbs ascribed to Joannes ad Barbam (1357).

According to Mrs. Singer (1916), the Regimen sanitatis ascribed to Jean de Bordeaux (British Museum, Sloane 989) is identical with the Governayle of helthe printed by Caxton in 1489, and also by Wynkyn de Worde (s.a.).

Text. A. *Travels, early editions.* The earliest printed edition of Mandeville's Travels is probably the Dutch version of 1470 (?). Other Dutch editions, by Govaerdt Back, Antwerp 1494, 1677; by Jan Bouman, Amsterdam 1650, 1742; by Jacob de Bodt, Amsterdam 1677; by Jan Gimblet, Ghent 1780, etc.

Probably the first German edition was that of the translation by Otto von Diemeringen printed Basel? c. 1475; later editions of this translation, Strassburg 1483, 1484, 1488, 1499, 1507, Frankfurt-am-Main 1580, 1584, Cologne 1600, etc. The German translation by Michelfeld was printed in Augsburg 1481, 1482.

French translations, Lyon 1480, 1487, 1490. The earliest Paris editions are without date, also 1487, c. 1521, c. 1550, c. 1560.

Italian translations, Milan 1480, 1517, Bologna 1488, 1492, 1497, Venice by Nicolaus de Ferrariis 1491, by Manfredo da Montferato da Streno de Bonello 1496, 1504, 1505, 1521, 1534, 1537, 1567, Florence by Lorenzo de Morgiani and Giovanni da Maganza 1492, by Piero da Pescia c. 1512.

The first Latin editions are undated; one of these was printed c. 1480, Zwolle 1483, another Antwerp 1485, 1564.

Czech translations, Pilsen 1510, 1513, Prag 1576, 1610, 1797, 1811.

Spanish translations, Valencia 1515, 1521, 1540, Alcalà de Henares 1547.

Probably the first English translation was the one printed by Richard Pynson, no date, but between 1493 and 1499. Another printed by Wynkyn de Worde, London 1499, 1503, both with woodcuts. Again by Thomas East, London 1568, by Thomas Snodham, London 1612, by Thomas Stansby 1618, by J. Woodman and D. Lyon, London 1725, and many later editions. (Klebs nos. 548–52.)

B. *Travels, modern editions.* Reprint of the 1568 edition, Oxford 1932. This reprint includes a passage over 20 p. long which the early translator had omitted. The missing passage was restored from the Cotton MS as edited in 1725. Reprint of the edition of 1725 by J. O. Halliwell, with notes and glossary (344 p., London 1839). Thomas Wright: Early travels in Palestine (p. 127–282, London 1848). John Ashton: The voiage and travayle of Sir John Maundeville . . . , edited, annotated and illustrated in facsimile (314 p., London 1887), reprint of Pynson's edition of c. 1496. Sir George F. Warner: The buke of John Maundeville, edited from Egerton MS 1982 British Museum, with 28 miniatures from Additional MS 24,189 (Roxburghe Club, 278 p., Westminster 1889), with abundant notes, elaborate introduction, and the French text. Arthur Layard: The marvellous adventures of Sir John Maundavile (444 p., profusely illustrated, Westminster 1895). Alfred W. Pollard: Version of Cotton MS in modern spelling with three narratives, in illustration of it, from Hakluyt's Navigations (405 p., London 1900, again 1915). Paul Hamelius: Mandeville's Travels, edited from MS Cotton Titus c. xvi British Museum, translated from the French of Jean d'Outremeuse (Early English Text Society nos. 153, 154, 2 vols., London 1919–23), vol. 1, 232 p., text; vol. 2, 198 p., introduction and notes. Francesco Zambrini: I viaggi. Volgarizzamento antico toscano ora ridotto a buona lezione coll' aiuto di due testi a penna (2 vols., Bologna 1870). Markus Lorenzen: Mandevilles rejse i gammeldansk oversaettelse tillige med en vejleder for pilgrimme (300 p., Copenhagen 1882). Sven Martinsson: Itinerarium orientale. Mandeville's Reisebeschreibung in mittelniederdeutscher Uebersetzung mit Einleitung, Varianten und Glossar (197 p., Lund 1918).

C. *Treatises on the plague.* Georg Guttmann: Die Pestschrift des Jean à la Barbe 1370. Zum ersten Male hrg. übersetzt und erklärt (Giessen Diss., 30 p., Berlin 1903). French version edited by Dorothea Waley Singer: Some plague tractates (reprint from Proceedings of the Royal Society of Medicine 9, 42–54, London 1916).

Plague tracts of John of Burgundy and John of Bordeaux, edited by Karl Sudhoff: Pestschriften nach der Epidemie des "schwarzen Todes" 1348 (AGM 5, 58–75, 1911).

D. *The spurious lapidary.* Le lapidaire en françoys, Lyon? 1531, Paris 1561, this last edition republished with notes by Is. del Sotto: Le lapidaire du XIVe siècle (240 p., 2 pl., Vienne 1862). Klebs (p. 216, 1938).

Criticism. A. *Mandeville's biography and geographical criticism.* Johann Vogels: Das Verhältnis der italienischen Version Mandeville's zum Original (Festschrift dem Gymnasium Adolfinum zu Moers, Crefeld, p. 37–45, Bonn 1882); Die ungedruckten lateinischen Versionen Mandevilles (Progr., 23 p., Crefeld 1886); Handschriftliche Untersuchungen über die englische Version Mandeville's (52 p., Crefeld 1891). Albert Bovenschen: Untersuchungen über Johann von Mandeville und die Quellen seiner Reisebeschreibung (Zeitschrift der Gesellschaft für Erdkunde 23, 177–306, Berlin 1888). Cordier: Bibliotheca sinica (3, 2022–45, 1906–7; 5, 4014, 1922), extensive bibliography of the editions of the Travels; Jean de Mandeville (T'oung pao vol. 2, 38 p., 1891).

Röhricht (p. 79–85, 1890). George F. Warner: Sir John Mandeville (DNB 36, 23–29, 1893). Francis Edward Sandbach: Handschriftliche Untersuchungen über Otto von Diemeringen's deutsche Bearbeitung der Reisebeschreibung Mandeville's (Diss. Strassburg, 56 p., 1899). Robert Herndon Fife, jr.: Der Wortschatz des englischen Maundeville nach der Version der Cotton Handschrift (Diss., 292 p., Leipzig 1902). Beazley (3, 319–23, 1906). Godefroid Kurth: Etude critique sur Jean d'Outremeuse (Mémoires, Académie royale de Belgique, vol. 7, 105 p., Brussels 1910). E. W. B. Nicholson and Sir Henry Yule: Sir John Mandeville (Encyclopedia britannica, 11th ed., 17, 560–64, 1911). August Gebhart: Das Erlanger Mandeville Bruchstück und die Entstehungszeit der Diemeringschen Verdeutschung (Münchener Museum 2, 191–204, 1915). Otto de Dymerenges died in 1398; his German version is not anterior to 1369. Wells (p. 433–37, 1926). Isaac Jackson: Who was Sir John Mandeville? A fresh clue (Modern language review 23, 466–68, 1928). Hindrikus Johannes van der Meer: Main facts concerning the syntax of Mandeville's Travels (178 p., Utrecht 1929). Dorothy Everett: Middle English (The year's work in English studies 9, 112–13, 1930). Arpad Steiner: The date of composition of Mandeville's Travels (Speculum 9, 144–47, 1934; Isis 23, 501). Kenneth Walter Cameron: A discovery in John de Mandevilles (Speculum 11, 351–59, 1936). Hennig (3, 161–64, 1938).

B. *Medical treatises.* Emile van Avenberg: Jean à la Barbe (Biographie nationale de Belgique 10, 359, 1889). David Murray: John de Burdeus or John de Burgundia, otherwise Sir John Mandeville and the pestilence (34 p., London 1891). Karl Sudhoff: Pestschriften nach der Epidemie des "schwarzen Todes" 1348 (AGM 5, 71, 1911), Sudhoff does not believe that John Mandeville, John of Burgundy, and John of Bordeaux are identical. Dorothea Waley Singer: Some plague tractates (fourteenth and fifteenth centuries) (reprint from Proceedings of the Royal Society of Medicine 9, 3–14, 1916). Dorothea Waley Singer and Reuben Levy: Plague tractates (Annals of medical history 1, 394–411, 1917). Wickersheimer (p. 367, 369–70, 1936).

C. *Lapidary.* Léopold Pannier: Les lapidaires français du moyen âge (p. 189–204, Paris 1882). Joan Evans: Magical jewels of the Middle Ages and the Renaissance (p. 65–68, Oxford 1922).

THOMAS SWINBURNE

Thomas Swinburne (or Swynburne). English pilgrim to Jerusalem in 1392.

Thomas was the son of Robert Swinburne, lord of the manor of Horkesley (Essex), who died in 1391. He was appointed castellan of Guines (Pas-de-Calais) by Richard II in 1390, and was permitted to perform the pilgrimage in 1392. After his return he became mayor of Bordeaux (1402) and admiral of the English fleet in that city; in 1408 he was castellan of Fronsac (on the Dordogne, Gironde). He died in 1415; there are French epitaphs dedicated to his father and to him in the church of Little Horkesley.

An account of his pilgrimage, Itinerarium in Terram sanctam Domini Thomae de Swynburne, was written by one of his companions, Thomas Brygg (or Brigg). The account is brief but clear and businesslike, and ends with an itemized list of the expenditures for the journey, which lasted 159 days.

Swinburne and Brigg left Guines on August 6, 1392, arrived in Venice on September 2, and sailed on the following day with a group of other pilgrims coming from Germany and Bohemia. They landed in Alexandria, traveled to Cairo, where they admired the Pyramids (granaria famosa), elephants, giraffes, and the Coptic Church of Our Lady, then to the monastery of St. Catherine in Sinai, Gaza, Hebron, Bethlehem, Jerusalem (8 days), Damascus, Beirut, finally Rhodes, whence they sailed homeward.

Text. The Itinerarium was edited by count Paul Riant in Archives de l'Orient Latin (vol. 2, documents p. 380–88, 1884).

Criticism. Atiya (p. 176, 1938).

A5. NETHERLANDS

HESE

Johannes de Hese. Dutch author of a fantastic tale of travel in Asia (fl. c. 1389).

Johannes Witte de Hese (Hesse, Helt) was a priest in the diocese of Utrecht; he originated probably in the village Hees in Gelderland. He wrote an account of an imaginary journey which must be mentioned because of its great popularity, witness the number of MSS and early editions. It represents the geographical lore of that time and became in its turn a source of geographical information (or misinformation) concerning the Near East, Abyssinia, 'Irāq, and India. Many of the stock tales of mediaeval travel in Western literature or in the Arabian Nights are found in Hese's story, e.g., the giant fish mistaken for an isle, pygmies, cyclopes, magnetic mountain; and it was one of the main sources for the legends concerning "Prester John"

(XII-2; Introd. 2, 416–17). In fact, the earliest edition of Prester John's letter of c. 1165 appeared in Hese's book, Itinerarius ad Jerusalem per diversas mundi partes (1499 etc.).

John Hese claims to have visited Jerusalem and the Holy Places near by in the spring of 1389 (not 1489, not 889). In May he proceeded to the River Jordan and the Red Sea, where he saw a great number of flying fishes; to Hermipolis, capital of Egypt; to the Sinai and St. Catherina's monastery; to Chaldaea, then back to the Nile and down the river to Damiad (this very itinerary is sufficient to show that John had never traveled to the East himself); to Aethiopia by sea; to Andronopolis in India, where many Christians of St. Thomas lived and where king Brandicanus (the great khān) ruled in Prester John's name. A month later he sailed to Beliad and Gadda, then to Edessa on the Tigris (!), the capital of Prester John, lord of eleven Christian and seven pagan kings. He describes Prester John's palaces. Then to Hulna (or Ulua) in Mesopotamia to visit the tomb of St. Thomas the Apostle. As he proceeds his tale grows taller and taller, for he reaches the very wall of Paradise, visits Purgatory, and hears the shrieks of the damned, etc. He finally comes back to Jerusalem, which ends his account.

John's travels are fictitious, yet one can recognize in his account a great many twisted and mixed facts obtained from the tales of genuine travelers, and traditions derived from the letter of Prester John incorporated in the text, as well as the Tractatus de decem nationibus Christianorum, Liber de infantia Mariae, and De adventu patriarchae Indorum ad urbem sub Calixto papa secundo (pope 1119–24).

John's account was soon translated into Dutch by an unknown translator (Voet in the Dutch text is a corruption of Witte, not the translator's name).

Text. Itinerarius per diversas mundi partes. Klebs enumerates 8 incunabula editions (nos. 558.1–8), Cologne 1490, Deventer 1499, 1500, Antwerp 1500, Cologne 1500, 1500, 1500, Paris before 1505. Later editions, Deventer 1504; Peregrinatio Joannis Hesei, Antwerp 1565.

Gustav Oppert: Der Presbyter Johannes in Sage und Geschichte (Berlin 1864; revised ed., p. 167, 180–93, Berlin 1870).

Friedrich Zarncke: Priester Johannes (Abhandlungen der Sächsischen Gesellschaft der Wissenschaften, phil.-hist. Cl., p. 159–71, Leipzig 1876).

The early Dutch version was edited by M. de Vries (Verslagen en berichten der Vereeniging voor oude nederlandsche letterkunde 2, 5–32, Leiden 1845).

Criticism. Jan Te Winkel: Geschiedenis der nederlandsche letterkunde (1, 569–72, Haarlem 1887). Röhricht (p. 92, 95, 160, 1890). Victor Hantsch (ADB 50, 271–72, 1905). Maj. H. J. A. Ruys (Nieuw nederlandsch biografisch woordenboek 4, 728, Leiden 1918).

A7. Scandinavia

IVAR BÁRÐARSON

Ivar the Greenlander. In modern Norwegian, his name would be written Baardsson. The form Bárdsson is a compound of the old and modern forms.

Norwegian priest who was sent in 1341 (or 1349?) by Hákon, bishop of Bergen, to Greenland. For many years he was steward of the bishop's residence at Gardar, and he seems to have visited the Western Settlement, which was then already abandoned. He dwelt in Greenland until 1379. There is a Danish description of the fjords of Greenland, chiefly of the Eastern (i.e., southwestern) Settlement, which claims to be derived from Ivar's account. The original text is lost.

Grönlands historiske Mindesmaerker (3, 258, 1838–45). F. Jónsson: Grönlands gamle Topografi efter Kilderne (Meddelelser om Grönland 20, 328, Copenhagen 1899).

The Danish text referred to above was edited together with Latin and English translation by Richard Henry Major: The voyages of the Venetian brothers, Niccolò and Antonio Zeno, to the northern seas in the fourteenth century (Hakluyt Society, p. 39–54, London 1873).

Beazley (3, 495, 1906). Nansen (2, 107–111, 1911). See this volume p. 195.

BJÖRN JÓRSALAFARER

Björn Einarsson Jórsalafarer.[8] Norwegian sailor. In the course of a voyage to Iceland in 1385, he was driven out of his course to the "Eastern" Settlement of Greenland, with four ships. He remained in Greenland until 1387, when he returned safely to Iceland. He rescued two young Eskimos (whom he calls "trolls"), brother and sister, who lived with him until he left Greenland. The account of his voyage is very uncritical and full of extravagances, but there can be no doubt of his residence in Greenland or of his intimate contact with Eskimos, i.e., Skraelings of the "Eastern" Settlement. When Björn and his companions returned from Iceland to Bergen in 1388, they were prosecuted for illegal trading with Greenland, the regular trade being a royal monopoly, but they pleaded not guilty on account of the necessity of circumstances and were acquitted (1389).

It would seem that the adventures of Björn Jórsalafarer have been confused in later MSS with the adventures of another Björn, called the Rich, who was driven to Greenland in 1446, spent the following winter there, and returned to Iceland in 1447. Björn the Rich may have brought the news and complaints which were transmitted probably by the bishops of Skalholt and Holar (in Iceland) to the Holy See. These complaints are referred to in the letter written by pope Nicholas V in 1448, directly to the bishops of Iceland (not to their superior, the archbishop of Norway).

Text. Björn's account was included in the Annals of Greenland compiled by Björn Jónsson of Skardsá (1574–1656). Published in the Grönlands historiske Mindesmaerker (vol. 1, Copenhagen 1838), also in Gustav Storm: Islandske Annaler indtil 1578 (Christiania 1888).

Criticism. Nansen (2, 82, 106, 112, 1911). Vilhjalmur Stefansson: Greenland (p. 214–16, New York 1942; Isis 34, 379), quoting the pope's letter of 1448 in English translation.

SCANDINAVIAN EXPLORATION OF NORTH AMERICA

The Scandinavian discovery of the eastern coast of North America has been discussed in volume 1 (p. 724–25) and referred to again in chapter I of this volume (p. 194). The reality of that discovery is generally admitted, but there is no certain knowledge concerning the territories which Leif Ericsson discovered in 1000, or where Thorfin Karlsefni settled in 1003–6. Those territories were called Helluland (slateland), Markland (forestland), and Vinland (vine- or wineland); they were located along the eastern coast somewhere between Labrador in the north and the Chesapeake Bay in the south. Vinland has often been identified with the coast of southern New England, or more specially with the coast east of the Hudson River to Cape Cod and the islands south of the cape.

[8] Jórsalafarer or Jórsalafari means (in Icelandic) a pilgrim to Jerusalem; suðrfari means a pilgrim to the south, chiefly Rome.

Though the settlement of 1003–6 was short-lived, lasting only until c. 1030, it does not follow that no Vikings remained in America or that none came back after that year. On the contrary, as the road Iceland, Greenland, Vinland was now well established, it is likely that other sailors followed it. A knowledge of it was kept alive by the Descriptio insularum aquilonis of Adam of Bremen (XI-2), written c. 1075, and by the sagas, by merchants, by missionaries and clerics reporting to the heads of their orders or to their bishops. The sagas to be considered are the Hauksbók of Haukr Erlendsson (XIV-1), the Saga of Eric the Red, c. 1400 (Codex Arnamagnaeanus AM 557, 4to, University of Copenhagen) and the Tale of Eric the Red, the Tale of the Greenlanders, and both parts of the Flateyjarbók (MS no. 1005 fol., Royal Library, Copenhagen) written by two priests, Magnus Thórhallsson and Jón Thórdarson, for Jón Hakonarson and completed c. 1390.

Arthur Middleton Reeves: The finding of Wineland the Good (quarto, 214 p., London 1890), facsimiles of the MSS, original texts, and translations. G. M. Gathorne-Hardy: The Norse discovery of America. The Wineland sagas translated and discussed (304 p., Clarendon Press, Oxford 1921; Isis 4, 505–8). Einar Haugen: Voyages to Vinland. The first American saga newly translated, illustrated by Frederick Trench Chapman (214 p., New York 1942; Isis 34, 443).

There are good reasons for believing that relations between America and Greenland continued. For one thing, the colonists of Greenland needed timber, and it was much easier and quicker to obtain it from southern Labrador than from Norway. Then the church wanted to continue its proselytism in the new world. In 1112 Eric Gnupsson was appointed bishop of Greenland and Vinland in partibus infidelium by Paschal II (pope 1099–1118); bishop Eric is said to have visited Vinland in 1121.

Greenland was an Icelandic colony, but the Icelandic republic founded c. 930 ceased to exist in 1262, submitting to Norway. In 1380, Norway having itself submitted to Denmark, Iceland became a Danish colony; it continued to be Danish after the separation of the two kingdoms (Norway, Denmark) in 1814. From 1262 to 1380 Vinland was probably a subsidiary and secret colony of Norway; there is a curious reference to that in one of the writings of Philippe de Mézières.[9]

In 1347 a ship arrived in Iceland with seventeen Greenland sailors who had sailed to Markland and been driven away by a storm; in the following years these men proceeded to Bergen (then the capital of Norway). They must have brought with them some knowledge of America. In 1354 Magnus, king of Norway, Sweden, and Skaane, sent a mission to Greenland headed by Poul Knutsson. The mission was absent from 1355 to 1364; its purpose was mainly religious, the defense of Christianity in peril in the colonies. Now, considering the long absence of that mission (ten years), it is probable that they included Vinland in their survey.

That hypothesis has received a strange confirmation from the discovery made in the summer of 1898 by a farmer of western Minnesota, called Olof Ohman. In the village of Kensington (Douglas county), he found under and between the roots of an old aspen a stone (79 × 41 × 15 cm.) bearing a runic inscription (220 characters plus 62 double dots to separate words).[10] Various Teutonic and Scandinavian peoples used a runic alphabet (often called fu*þ*ork after its six first letters, just as we say abc for ours) from the third century on at least until late into the Middle Ages.[11] It was gradually replaced by our alphabet, introduced into Scandinavia

[9] As quoted by P. A. Means: Newport tower (p. 215–17, New York 1942).

[10] The stone is now preserved in Alexandria, the seat of Douglas county, Minnesota.

[11] The outstanding student of runes today is Helmut Arntz (b. 1912): Handbuch der Runen-

together with the Latin language about the eleventh century or earlier, yet it continued to be used more or less long afterward. According to the archbishop of Uppsala Olaus Magnus (1490–1558) in his Historia de gentibus septentrionalibus (Rome 1555), runes were still commonly used in his time for calendric purposes. The traditions of learned people as well as popular lore and superstition extended their occasional use in some parts of Scandinavia (e.g., Telemark in southern Norway, Gotland and Dalecarlia in Sweden) until modern times.

The Kensington inscription being translated reads:

"8 Goths and 22 Norwegians on exploration from Vinland through the West, camped by a lake with 2 skerries one day journey from this stone. We were [out] and fished one day. After we came home [we] found 10 [of our] men red with blood and dead. AVM [= Ave Maria, or Ave Virgo Maria].

"[We] have 10 of [our party] by the sea to look after our ship 14 days-journey from this island [in] year 1362."

Runic numbers, by the way, are very clear and unequivocal; on the Kensington stone they are written on a decimal basis, just as we write 1362. Decimal numbers had been introduced into the Icelandic world at the beginning of the fourteenth century if not before, witness their use in the Hauksbók of Haukr Erlendsson (XIV-1), written c. 1320.[12] Various forms of runic numbers may be seen in the table here reproduced (fig. 34) from the Fasti danici of Ole Worm[13] (p. 52, Copenhagen 1633), wherein columns 1 and 2 show runic letters having the values indicated in the last column; columns 3 and 4 show ordinary runic numerals, column 5 other runic numerals; the basis is obviously decimal with Roman reminiscences. The table extends to 19, the golden number, the ancient Metonic cycle,[14] important for the determination of Easter.

The discovery of that inscription and its decipherment caused endless controversies. The script is very similar to that of the Codex runicus (a code of law, Skånske lov), written probably in the first half of the fourteenth century. The inscription is plausible and the suggestion that it may be a late forgery is, all considered, implausible.[15]

Whether Poul Knutsson and his party came to Vinland c. 1360 or not, other Greenlanders, Icelanders, or even Norwegians did probably come. After having reached the American coast, the most adventurous might be tempted to do what their ancestors, such as Naddod the Viking and Gardar Svavarsson, did c. 865

---

kunde (346 p., 15 pl., Halle a.d.S. 1935); Bibliographie der Runenkunde (308 p., Leipzig 1937); Die Runenschrift. Ihre Geschichte und ihre Denkmäler (122 p., 31 pl., Halle 1938), introductory textbook; Berichte zur Runenforschung (Leipzig 1939 ff.), I have seen only part 1 of vol. 1, 1939; Gesamtausgabe der älteren Runendenkmäler, vol. 1 with Hans Zeiss, Die einheimischen Runendenkmäler des Festlands (536 p., 44 pl., 1 map, Leipzig 1939). For briefer account, see Jensen (p. 178–85, 1925; p. 376–95, 1935).

[12] Decimal numbers occur in the earliest Icelandic books with reference to foreign matters; a duodecimal system was used for other purposes. The earliest Icelandic writings are of the beginning of the twelfth century (Halldór Hermannsson, in letter dated Ithaca, N. Y., Feb. 10, 1943).

[13] Olaus Worm (1588–1654): Fasti danici universam tempora computandi rationem antiquitus in Dania et vicinis regionibus observatam libris tribus exhibentes (Hafniae 1633).

[14] Cycle of Meton (V B.C.), based upon the observation that 19 solar years approximate 235 lunar months (Introd. 1, 94, 141, 409).

[15] Vilhjalmur Stefansson, whom I consulted on this moot question, kindly wrote (New York, Feb. 9, 1943) that the scholars who have investigated it are almost equally divided "but my feeling is that there is something better than an even chance for those to be right who favor authenticity."

when they reached Iceland; they circumnavigated the island in order to obtain some idea of its size. A party of them may have sailed around the coast of Labrador, around Hudson Bay, then down the Nelson River, Lake Winnipeg, etc.; they might have been the victims of the event described on the Kensington Stone of 1362.[16]

NUMERORUM AUREORUM FIGURÆ. VALOR.

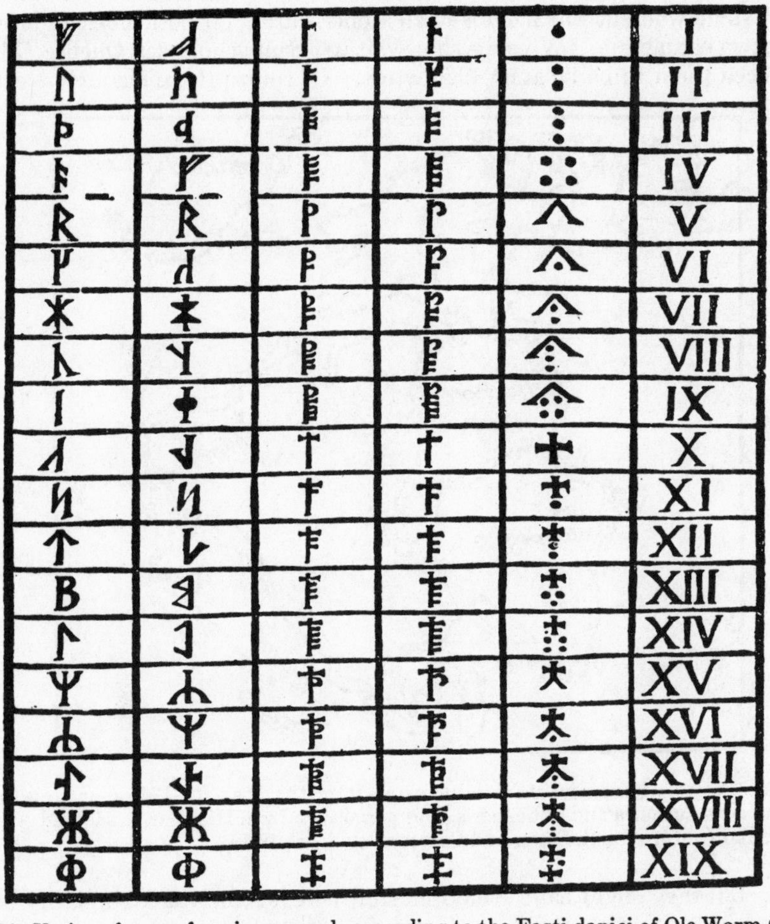

FIG. 34. Various forms of runic numerals according to the Fasti danici of Ole Worm (Copenhagen 1633).

See the sketch map (fig. 35) borrowed from Hjalmar R. Holand's book (p. 141, 1940).

What puzzles me most is that this runic inscription is unique in America. Why should the party which traveled so deeply into our continent have waited until it

[16] Philip Ainsworth Means, whom I also consulted, does not doubt the authenticity of the Kensington stone, but believes that the Norsemen reached Kensington in a different manner, e.g., that they traveled from Vinland to Duluth or to Green Bay, Wisconsin, where they left their boats and continued overland (letter dated Pomfret, Conn., Feb. 17, 1943).

reached Minnesota to make an inscription? Or if they made others, how did all the other inscriptions disappear?

There is no reference to any other inscription, except one which is doubtful. When the Swedish traveler Per Kalm (1716–79) visited Quebec in 1749, he came across Pierre Gaultier de Varennes, sieur de La Vérendrye (1685–1749), the first white explorer of the Minnesota and Dakota plains since 1362.[17] In 1738 La Vérendrye had traveled through the Mandan territory (North Dakota) and seen a pillar of stone wherein was fixed a small stone bearing on both sides an inscription in unknown characters. When he showed it to Jesuit scholars in Quebec 1743, they pronounced them to be "Tatar" characters. Of course those characters could not

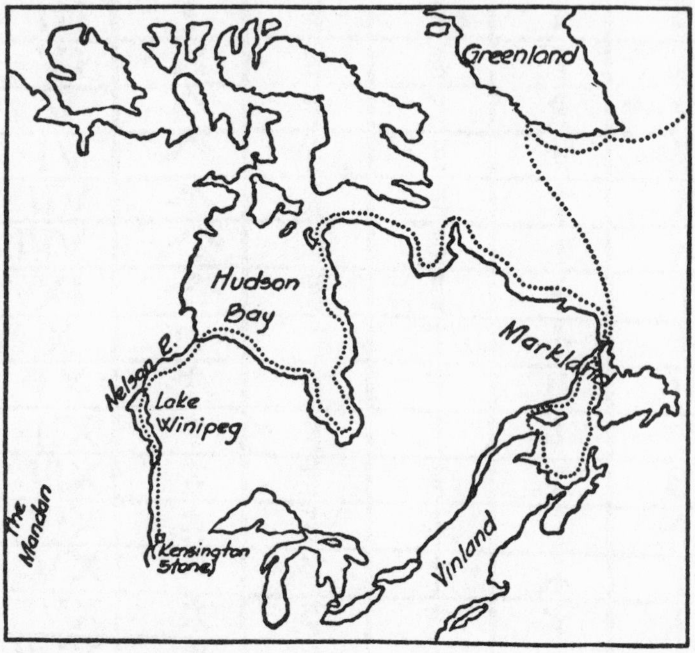

FIG. 35. Possible itinerary of Scandinavians from the coast of Labrador to Minnesota. Reprinted with author's and publisher's kind permission from Hjalmar R. Holand: Westward from Vinland (p. 141, Duell, Sloan and Pearce, New York 1940).

be Tatar, but they might have been runic, for there is some vague similarity between runes and, say, Siberian script.

The Indian tribe called Mandan was so different from others in many respects that it has been many times assumed[18] they had some white ancestors. As they lived in the territory which the authors of the Kensington inscription traversed, and as these authors disappeared, it is not impossible that they were amalgamated with that tribe.

Various weapons and implements have been found in that region (south of Lake Winnipeg) which are very similar to the Viking implements kept in Scandinavian

[17] Peter Kalm's Travels in North America. English version of 1770. Revised by Adolph B. Benson (p. 440-42, New York 1937).

[18] Sarton: George Catlin (Isis 22, 77–94, 1934; p. 84).

museums. Many of these American-Scandinavian implements may be examined in the museums of Milwaukee and Toronto.

The best introduction to these intricate and problematic questions has been given by Hjalmar Rued Holand: The Kensington stone. A study in pre-Columbian American history (324 p., 34 ill., Ephraim, Wis. 1932); Westward from Vinland. An account of Norse discoveries and explorations in America, 982–1362 (364 p., 17 fig., New York 1940). The second volume is an amplification of the first and supersedes it. It includes an elaborate bibliography (p. 318–34). Hennig (3, 268–99, 1938). Allan Nevins: The gateway to history (p. 128, Boston 1938).

The theory has been advanced that the Newport Tower (in Newport, Rhode Island) is the surviving part of a round church built by Norsemen in the period twelfth to fourteenth century. Such round churches exist in many parts of Europe, the original pattern being the Holy Sepulcher rotunda in Jerusalem. The original pattern itself might have been observed by Scandinavians such as Sigurd of Norway (XII-1) and his followers, who traveled to the Holy Land in 1107–11. The Newport "church" might have been built at the time of bishop Eric Gnupsson c. 1121 or later, or at the time of Poul Knutsson c. 1360. In any case, it would be the earliest Christian building in the New World. The question might perhaps be settled by careful excavations made immediately around the church, and it is to be hoped that the Newport aediles will encourage such excavations instead of forbidding them.

Elaborate but tantalizing discussion by Philip Ainsworth Means: Newport tower (368 p., 141 ill., New York 1942; Isis 34, 276), with long bibliography.

A8. Russia and Byzantium

IGNATIUS OF SMOLENSK

Russian pilgrim to the Holy Land (fl. 1389–1405). He started from Moscow in 1389 in the train of Pimen, metropolitan of Russia, and of Michael, bishop of Smolensk. He wrote an elaborate account in Russian, represented by at least five MSS.

The party traveled from Moscow down the rivers Moskva, Oka, and Don. Near the mouth of the Don in the Sea of Azov they were ill treated by the Franks and Germans holding that port (Azov or Tana). They then crossed the Black Sea. Before reaching Constantinople they heard of the famous battle of Kossowo Polje (Turkish Qoṣowa) June 20, 1389, during which the Serbians and their allies had been completely defeated by the third 'Uthmānlī sulṭān, Murād I (Amurath), who lost his own life. Pimen died soon afterward and was succeeded as metropolitan, in Constantinople, by Cyprian of Kiev, who returned to Moscow.

Ignatius describes the religious wonders of the Byzantine Rome, the political troubles which followed the defeat of the Serbians, the coronation (in 1391) of Manuel II. He visited Salonica and the Holy Mountain, and his account, the main points of which are still recognizable to the visitor of today, is the earliest Russian account of the Athonite community. The work ends with his pilgrimage to Jerusalem, and includes the usual description of the Holy Places.

Text. The Russian text was edited by Ivan Petrovich Sakharov in his Narrations of the Russian people (2, 97–107, St. Petersburg 1849). French translation by Mme B. de Khitrowo: Itinéraires russes en Orient (p. 129–57, Genève 1889).

Criticism. Röhricht (p. 93, 1890). Beazley (3, 405–7, 1906). Robert Byron: The station (p. 193, London 1928).

ALEXANDER THE PILGRIM

Russian scribe and pilgrim who visited Constantinople "during the time of the patriarch Antonios and the emperor Manuel." This must refer to Manuel II (1391–1425) and Antonios IV (1389–90, 1391–97), hence his visit occurred during the period 1391–97. He gave a short account of the holy places of Constantinople in the Russian language, which may be compared with a similar one written somewhat earlier by Stephen of Novgorod. He states that the purpose of his journey was merchant's business, but says nothing more about that.

Text. The Russian text was edited by Ivan Petrovich Sakharov in his Narrations of the Russian people (2, 72, St. Petersburg 1849). French translation by Mme B. de Khitrowo: Itinéraires russes en Orient (p. 161–64, Genève 1889).

GRETHENIOS

Russian (or Greek) archimandrite of the monastery of the Holy Virgin (in Moscow?) who went on a pilgrimage to the Holy Land c. 1400 and wrote a short account of it in Russian.

The first town named in his itinerary is Moscow. The way followed was via Constantinople, then Dardanelles, Lemnos, Mitylene, Chios, Rhodes, Cyprus, Jaffa. The itinerary is very brief, but is followed by a much longer description of the Holy Places, especially of the Holy Sepulcher.

Text. French translation by Mme B. de Khitrowo in her Itinéraïres russes en Orient (p. 165–91, Genève 1889).

Criticism. Röhricht (p. 102, 1890).

C. ISLĀM

C1. MAGHRIB

IBN BAṬṬŪṬA

Ibn Baṭṭūṭa. The greatest traveler of Islām, and the greatest, not excepting Marco Polo, in mediaeval times (1304–77).

Contents: (1) Life. (2) Travels. (3) The Riḥla. (4) Veracity. (5) Other traits. (6) Dār al-Islām. (7) Muslim diaspora. (8) Scientific information. (9) Natural history. (10) Anthropology. (11) Varia. (12) Medicine. (13) Economics.
(14) Text. (15) Criticism.

1. *Life*

Abū 'Abdallāh Muḥammad ibn 'Abdallāh ibn Muḥammad al-Lawātī al-Tanjī Ibn Baṭṭūṭa was born in Tangiers on February 24, 1304. He belonged to the Berber tribe of the Lawāta, whose territory extended at various times from western Egypt to the Maghrib (EI 3, 19, 1928). His father lived in Tangiers; there were many qūḍā (judges) in the family. After having completed his literary and religious education, Ibn Baṭṭūṭa left Tangiers on June 14, 1325 to accomplish the Pilgrimage. He returned only in 1349, but left soon afterward for a new journey in the West, and came back in 1354. He then dictated an account of his travels. He was appointed a qāḍī in one of the Moroccan towns (probably Fez) and died there in

1377/78. While in India he was often called (3, 392)[19] Mawlānā Badr al-dīn (the first word, meaning "our master," is a title which Muslim Hindus often gave to their teachers).

It is interesting to realize that the greatest travelers respectively of Islam and of Christendom, though belonging to different generations, were contemporaries. Marco Polo (XIII-2) died in 1324, and at that time Ibn Baṭṭūṭa was 20 years old and ready to begin his adventurous career. Their works, however, are separated by a period of over half a century (1299, 1355).

2. *Travels*

His travels were so extensive that to give a complete account of them would take too long; it must suffice to indicate their general scope (the four maps included in Gibb's translation 1929 will be useful for a quick survey). He traveled from Tangiers via North Africa to Alexandria, Cairo, up the Nile as far as Edfu, across the desert to 'Aidhāb on the Red Sea coast (then terminal port of Yaman and India trade; declined at the end of the fourteenth century and sank into oblivion), back to Cairo, Gaza, Jerusalem, Ḥamāh, Aleppo, Damascus (1326). There he joined the Syrian caravan to Madīna and Mecca. Back to Madīna, then to Mashhad 'Alī al-Riḍā in Khurāsān (here ends vol. 1).

To Baṣra, travel in Persia, back to 'Irāq: Kūfā, Baghdād, Mūṣul, Diyār Bakr district (all this traveling was done to occupy his time before the season of the next pilgrimage), return to Baghdād and Mecca, where he spent three years (1328–30). To Yaman, East African coast (Zeila, Mogdishu, Mombasa, Quiloa or Kilwa, c. 9°S. lat.). Back to Yaman, 'Umān, Hurmuz (eastern Persian Gulf), Lār (in Fārs), Baḥrain islands. New pilgrimage to Mecca (1332), then via Egypt and Syria to Lhādhiqīya, whence he sailed in a Genoese ship to 'Alāyā (Candelor) in Turkish territory (south Anatolian coast). Travel inland around the Anatolian peninsula, ending in Ṣanūb (Sinope on the Black Sea), whence he sailed on a Greek ship to Caffa (where the Genoese had their main Black Sea factory) and across the Sea of Azov to the steppes of the Qipchaq (see EI 2, 1022) in southern Russia, then ruled by Ūzbeg (khān of the Golden horde, 1312–40). The excursion to Bulghār (near the junction of the Volga and Kama rivers, c. 55°N.) seems to be an interpolation derived from hearsay. Return to Astrakhan. Here he was invited to escort a Greek princess, married to the sultan Ūzbeg, to Constantinople in order that she might be delivered in her father's home. He visited Constantinople, then ruled by Andronicos III (1328–41), and met the latter's father, Andronicos II (1282–1328), who was spending the last years of his life (1328–32) in monkish retirement. He called the emperor Takfūr (from Armenian tagavor, king), and his father George, probably Andronicos II's monkish name. From Constantinople Ibn Baṭṭūṭa proceeded to Sarā (probably new Sarā, on the lower Volga) to rejoin Ūzbeg Khān (here ends vol. 2).

From Sarā to Khwārizm, Bukhārā, Samarqand, Balkh, Herāt, Ṭūs, Nīsābūr, the Hindū Kūsh mountains, Ghazna, Kābul, reaching Sind, i.e. the lower Indus valley, on September 12, 1333 (here ends the first part of Ibn Baṭṭūṭa's travels; 3, 92).

[19] This reference and similar ones below are to the Defrémery-Sanguinetti edition. I have given it in only a few cases, for in most cases the elaborate index of that edition (vol. 5) and the tables of contents of vols. 1 to 4 make it possible to determine without difficulty the text relative to any statement.

Travels in India. From Sind to Dihlī (Delhi), where he spent some seven years at the court of Muḥammad II ibn Taghlaq (sulṭān 1324-51). Ibn Baṭṭūṭa gives long accounts of the latter's character, administration, etc. Muḥammad had appointed him Mālikī qāḍī of Delhi, and finally ordered him to head a special mission to the emperor of China (end of vol. 3).

One would expect the succeeding chapters of his narrative to be devoted to China, but soon after his departure from Delhi (July 22, 1342) his real Indian adventures began, for he was made prisoner by infidels (i.e., non-Muslims) at Jalālī (near Aligarh), gave up the embassy, traveled across western India via Gwalior, Ujjain, Daulatabad, Cambay, then down the Malabar coast (Calicut) to the Maldive Islands, where he became a qāḍī and spent eighteen months; to Ceylon for a pilgrimage to its highest peak, the Foot of Adam; the lower Coromandel coast, back to Malabar and the Maldives. More adventures in that region, whence he sailed from Mahal (one of the Maldive Islands) to Bengal, after a navigation of 43 days. To Sumatra, finally to Zaitūn, the greatest Chinese harbor of those days (Introd. 2, 1055). He visited many Chinese cities, such as Canton and Peking, and gives an elaborate description of Chinese arts and manners. Return to Sumatra, Kawlam (i.e., Quilon, lower Malabar coast) in January 1347, Calicut, Ẓafār in southern Yaman, Masqaṭ (in 'Umān), Shīrāz, Baṣra, Baghdād, Palmyra, Damascus (1348), Jerusalem, Cairo, one more pilgrimage (the sixth?) to Mecca and Madīna. Return to Cairo; sailing in a Tunisian ship to the island of Jerba (1349). Tunis, Sardinia, Tenes, Mostaganem, Tlemcen, Tāzā, Fez (November 13, 1349), Tangiers, where he stayed only a very short time.

Travel to Andalusia. Gibraltar, Malaga, Granada, Ronda, etc., then return to Morocco.

Travel in Morocco and western Sūdān. Sijilmāsa, Taghāzā, Iyūālāten, Māllī district, the river Niger (which he always calls Nile). He spent eight months in Māllī. Timbuktū, Tagaddā (1353), Tawāt, land of Haggār, Sijilmāsa, Fez (beginning of 1354). Here ends the fourth and last volume.

In spite of my trying to give as brief an account of Ibn Baṭṭūṭa's travels as possible, it turns out to be long, and no wonder, for those travels were continued for thirty years. It was estimated (by Sir Henry Yule, 1820-89) that he traveled by land and sea about 75,000 miles, that is, considerably more than Marco Polo or than any other traveler before the age of steam and speed. He had visited all the Islamic lands, and in most cases met their rulers, and was recognized before his death as the Muslim traveler par excellence (4, 449). Moreover, he had visited many non-Muslim countries, such as Caffa, Constantinople, parts of Hinduist India, Ceylon, China.

By the way, it is much easier to give an idea of the immensity of his travels by enumerating (as I have done) his main stopping places than by drawing a map, for his account contains not a few ambiguities and discontinuities, and in some cases it is impossible to say, even roughly, how he went from one place to another.

His point of view was never that of a geographer or of a historian; nevertheless, his account has considerable geographical and historical value. For example, he often names the salāṭīn and umarā who ruled the districts he was visiting, and tells their vicissitudes. In many cases he is the earliest authority sufficiently to describe a country. For example, he is the only Arabic traveler who gave a sufficient description of 'Omān. His account of Asia Minor reveals the many principalities into which the Saljūq empire of Rūm (1077-1300) had been broken, under Mongol and Turkish pressure, and the beginning of 'Uthmānlī power (1299 ff.). His description of the

Qipchaq country (southern Russia) is full of interest. His relation of Constantinople is superior to those of contemporary Christian travelers, and completes them from a new angle; of course he did not always appreciate what he saw, for he did not understand the Greek language and traditions, or was curiously inhibited (he did not go inside of Hagia Sophia). He is quick in noticing the salient points, e.g., the cosmopolitanism of Sarā, 'Aden, and Caffa; the cisterns and abundant shipping of 'Aden. The description of the court and administration of Delhi is the most elaborate of its kind and time; his history of Hindu rules and revolutions contains many errors, but that was almost unavoidable considering its endless complexities and the fact that he never tried any kind of historical synthesis, but gave the information as he stumbled upon it. He observed the use of millenary stones near Delhi (4, 42); the organization of the governmental postal services (barīd). The many pages devoted to the Maldive archipelago are the earliest of their kind (except for brief references). Though Ceylon had been often mentioned by Arabic writers (under the name Sarandīb), Ibn Baṭṭūṭa was first to make and narrate his pilgrimage to Adam's Peak (a pilgrimage for Muslims as well as for Hinduists, Buddhists, and Christians). The Chinese section is full of valuable details: various kinds of ships and how they are built (4, 91), old-age pensions (4, 288), porcelain, chicken, paper money (4, 259), artistic abilities, portraits made of strangers like himself and published on the walls of cities (4, 262), registration of ship cargoes, customs (douane), elaborate inspection of trade and traders (4, 265), careful treatment of travelers, organization of trade, etc. On his return to Morocco, Ibn Baṭṭūṭa compared his native country with the many foreign ones he had visited, and found it superior in many respects. This was partly due to innate patriotism, partly to his desire to propitiate the Marīnī sulṭān Abū 'Inān (1348–58).

He was the first to give a detailed personal narrative of the western Sūdān, that is, the country south of Morocco across the Sahara desert, inhabited by Negroes, irrigated by the Niger. His use of the word Nile for the Sudanese Nile (Niger) and the Egyptian one does not imply that he considered the two great rivers as one; he did not raise the question (the word Nile was occasionally used also for the Indus).[20] He speaks of the salt mines of Taghāzā, of the veiled men (ahl al-lithām) (4, 430), of the copper mines of Tagaddā (4, 440), of the Negro empire of Māllī (which remained powerful until the beginning of the sixteenth century and petered out about the middle of the following century), of Negro (Mandingo)[21] and Berber characteristics and customs. He noticed that the people of Tagaddā trafficked with Egypt across the desert. All this, and much more, is extremely interesting in the mouth of a witness of the middle of the fourteenth century.

3. *The Riḥla*

After Ibn Baṭṭūṭa's return and settlement in the Marīnī capital, Fez, in 1354, the sulṭān Abū 'Inān Fāris ordered his secretary Ibn Juzayy to edit the account which the traveler dictated. That account, entitled (4, 448) Tuḥfat al-nuẓẓār fī

[20] According to the Arabic-French dictionary of A. de Biberstein Kazimirski (2, 1376, 1860), source not quoted. Apparently Ibn Baṭṭūṭa took for granted the identity of the two Niles, for in his chapter on the Nīl Miṣr (the Egyptian Nile, 1, 77) he enumerates the ten largest rivers of the world: (1) Nile, (2) Euphrates, (3) Tigris, (4) Sayḥūn (Jaxartes), (5) Jayḥūn (Oxus). Then (6) river of Sind called Benjāb (five rivers), Indus, (7) Ganges, (8) Jumna, (9) Volga, (10) Yellow River. Nile stands for Nile and Niger, whereas Ganges and Jumna are considered two separate rivers.

[21] For orientation on this, see H. Labouret (EI 3, 203, 239–42, 1929), the earliest sources quoted being Ibn Baṭṭūṭa and Ibn Khaldūn.

gharā'ib al-amṣār wa 'ajā'ib al-asfār (Gift to the observers dealing with the curiosities of cities and the wonders of journeys), but generally called Riḥlat ibn Baṭṭūṭa or Riḥla (Journey), was completed by Ibn Juzayy on December 13, 1355, and the MS was transcribed by him in February 1356 (the second part of the autograph is extant in the Bibliothèque nationale, Paris).

This secretary, called Abū 'Abdallāh Muḥammad ibn Muḥammad Ibn Juzayy al-Kalbī al-Gharnāṭī, belonged to the Syrian-Arabic tribe of Kalb and was born in Granada; he died in 1356. His interpolations into the text are always easily recognizable and generally of no importance, being purely literary developments, poetic quotations. In addition, it is possible that the large borrowings from Ibn Jubair (XII-2), concerning Syria and Arabia, were made by the editor to complete the text dictated to him. The same doubt arises with regard to the Bulghār episode (2, 398–402), which seems to be an interpolation made by the traveler or by his editor. On the other hand, the pedantic accuracy in the vocalization of proper names may also be ascribed to either.

4. *Veracity*

This raises the question of the truthfulness of the Riḥla and of the honesty of its author (and editor). The account contains various difficulties of chronology and itinerary, but this is not surprising considering the extent and duration (almost thirty years) of his journeys. In particular, when a traveler has passed many times through the same places, his reminiscences of various sojourns may become confused. Did Ibn Baṭṭūṭa bring back a diary or notes? It has been suggested that he did not; the fact that he lost some notes referring to epitaphs copied by him in Bukhārā (3, 28) does not prove that he lost all his notes; it proves that he took notes. He quotes an inscription of 783/84 copied by him in the main mosque of Mecca (1, 307). Making full allowance for the better memories of people in that age of oral tradition, as compared with ours, the remembrance of such a long and complex narrative without the support of notes is almost unthinkable. It is probable, however, that Ibn Baṭṭūṭa's notes were incomplete and scanty, and this would explain his omissions and inconsistencies.

It is noteworthy that Ibn Khaldūn expressed some credulity regarding Ibn Baṭṭūṭa's account of India but was reproved by the wazīr Fāris ibn Wadrār (3, 464–67; also Prolégomènes 1, 370–72; Arabic text 1, 327–29). The same thing happened to Marco Polo (Introd. 2, 1057–59); both were telling truths which were stranger than fiction. We may conclude that apart from the miraculous stories which Ibn Baṭṭūṭa accepted too readily, and from occasional lapses of memory or judgment, he is generally veracious and honest.

5. *Other traits*

The Riḥla is instinct with life; when reading it one can almost evoke Ibn Baṭṭūṭa's strong if commonplace personality. He was not interested in nature, but very much so in men and women. There are many facts of anthropological interest in his work, some of which appear in it for the first time, but his descriptions of nature are very poor, and more often than not nonexistent. Whenever he reached a city, his first concern was to visit the learned men and the religious men, whom he often enumerates; then the people in authority, whose vicissitudes he describes. He may also discuss social conditions, organization of government, manners and customs, etc. He paid little attention to landscape, climate, or monuments. For example, he visited Ba'albek, but does not say a word of its magnificent ruins (1, 185–87); he twice visited (1, 107; 2, 253) the tomb of the saint Abū-l-Ḥajjāj al-Uqṣurī (d. 1244) in the great temple of Amun, Luxor, yet says not a word of those astounding monuments! On the other hand, he twice visited the pharos of Alexandria, in 1326 and 1349 (1, 29); in 1326 it was in ruins, by 1349 the destruction was complete.[22] One of his very few references to antiquities concerns a place called Tārnā, near Lāharī (3, 113), where he saw an innumerable quantity of sculptured stones representing men, animals, plants, and the remains of a ruined city.[23]

In his study of women he had the advantage of being able to marry them, and he was very uxorious indeed throughout his travels. In addition he bought concubines, and had thus the best opportunities for becoming familiar with the characteristics of women of various races.

Next to his simple humanity or curiosity concerning men and women, his main trait was his deep religiousness. He was a hard-boiled Muslim devotee of the Mālikī rite. He was credulous like most pilgrims, and tells a great many pious anecdotes, accounts of miracles, etc. For example, read the healing of people sick of the palsy in Mashhad 'Alī (1, 417). Yet he could remain critical in certain cases (2, 12).

His interest in miracles and occult events was largely due to his ṣūfī tendencies. Being a Moroccan, he was naturally inclined to saint worship and mysticism. He approved the obligatory attendance at the mosque in Khwārizm (3, 4), and the obligatory study of the Qur'ān in the Sūdān, Negro children being kept in irons until they knew it (4, 422). He was afraid of compromising himself with heretics (2, 360). He was relatively tolerant, yet showed anger against a Jewish physician who presumed to sit above the readers of the Qur'ān (2, 305); remember that he was a Moroccan.

6. *Dār al-Islām*

The Riḥla is of special interest in that it gives us a very concrete image of the immensity of the Islamic world of that time, and of its remarkable unity, except for the division between Sunni and Shī'a. Ibn Baṭṭūṭa visited a great many Muslim countries which differed in various ways, yet he found himself at home everywhere because of religious and linguistic bonds which those differences seemed to tighten rather than to loosen. The main trade roads of that time, both in Africa and in Asia, were largely in Muslim hands, and hence the Muslim traveler was privileged. Yet the Dār al-Islām was already decadent, and the Riḥla gives us many illustrations of its disintegration, to such an extent that a full understanding of it implies an elaborate study of Muslim history all over the world in the first half of the fourteenth century and before.

Ibn Baṭṭūṭa gives us a good general picture of religious usage in various countries, and especially of the development of Muslim traditions. In Tustar, Khūzistān, he witnessed a kind of religious revival (2, 27). In Damascus (1326) he studied

[22] This is confirmed by al-Qalqashandī, who states that the destruction was begun by the Greeks early in the eighth century, and that it was completed by the middle of the fourteenth.

[23] Is this a reference to the royal cemeteries and ruins of Tatta in Sind, 55 miles north of Karachi? Yet Ibn Baṭṭūṭa defines Tārnā as being 7 miles away from Lāharī (Larry-Bender). For Tatta see Sir John Cumming: Revealing India's past (p. 82–84, India Society, London 1939; Isis 34, 67). Dr. J. Ph. Vogel, of Leiden, whom I consulted, wrote me a long and kind letter (Aug. 24, 1939), wherein he rejects the hypothesis Tatta and suggests that the name misunderstood by Ibn Baṭṭūṭa may have been the Sanskrit sthāna, meaning place.

under many teachers and received from them the ījāza 'āmma (general permission, venia docendi); he gives a list of them (2, 248–53), twelve men and two women, and in some cases explains their traditions, their own spiritual ancestry, back to the ninth century! He received another ījāza in Iṣfahān, 1327 (2, 48). Learning was transmitted not so much by books as by living men, and its soundness was proved by enumerating and criticizing the human links through whom the transmission had taken place.

7. *Muslim diaspora*

Not only did the Muslims govern a great part of the world, but Muslim communities were found in non-Muslim countries, such as China, ready to welcome their Muslim brethren. The necessities of the pilgrimage, as well as the size of the Dār al-Islām, the needs of Muslim trade, the realities of Islamic brotherhood, and the roving habits of Arabic people, caused a very wide dispersion of them, which is frequently reflected in the Riḥla. In Alexandria he met a man who had a friend in Sind, another in India, a third in China, and who engaged him to visit them all (1, 38). In Turkey, India, and China he met doctors and merchants who came from Egypt or the Maghrib; on the other hand, he came across Easterners in Granada, and an Egyptian in Timbuktū.

8. *Scientific information*

Though Ibn Baṭṭūṭa's curiosity was purely human or religious, not in the least scientific, his account contains many items of interest to the historian of science.

He saw a map of Gibraltar or a model in relief of the town and its approaches (4, 359).

Apropos of the pyramids of Egypt, he refers to Hermes the ancient (Hermes al-awwal), who invented all the sciences known before the flood[24] (1, 80), and was called Khunūkh (cf. Idrīs, Enoch). In the Biqā' (Coelesyria) he stopped in Kerak Nūḥ to visit the tomb of Abū Ya'qūb Yūsuf (1, 134–37), who could transform copper into gold by means of al-iksīr (elixir).

9. *Natural history*

He was not interested in plants or animals except when they were of special use (or danger) to man. For example, he may enumerate fruits or cereals of a country, but never mentions ornamental plants. He describes betel and coconut (2, 204–11), incense (2, 214), all of which he observed in southern Arabia; the use of ḥashīsh in Sinope on the Black Sea (2, 351); the famous melons of Khwārizm, better even than those of Iṣfahān (3, 15); the prunes of Wafkend near Bukhārā (3, 21); he gives a long list of the trees, fruits, and eatable plants of India (3, 125–33). Apropos of his stay on the Malabar coast, he describes pepper (4, 76–77), cinnamon, and brazilwood (4, 99). He names the trees of the Maldive Islands (4, 113). In Sumatra (4, 240) he finds benzoin or benjamin (lubān), camphor, aloe, clove; in the western Sūdān (4, 435), not far from Timbuktū, delicious cucumbers.

As to the animal realm, he speaks of the pearl fisheries in the Baḥrain Islands (2, 244), where he was led to believe that some divers could stay an hour or two

[24] This passage dealing with the origins of science is taken verbatim from the Ṭabaqāt al-umam of Ṣā'id al-Andalusī (XI-2, Introd. 1, 776). See French translation of that text by Régis Blachère (Paris 1935; Isis 26, 498).

under water; when he was in southern Russia he drank kumiss (2, 392); he gives accounts of the rhinoceros (3, 100), the rukhkh (4, 305); in the western Sūdān he notices extraordinary scorpions (4, 439) and the use of grasshoppers as food by the natives (4, 447). In Ceylon he observes a white elephant, precious stones, monkeys, and flying leeches (4, 173–79).

In Birgī, western Anatolia, the sulṭān showed him a meteorite and they tried vainly to break it (2, 306). It was probably a siderite. Ibn Baṭṭūṭa's reference to a meteorite is valuable because definite references of that kind are very rare. Only two have thus far been recorded in my Introduction, namely, the reference by Anaxagoras (V B.C.) to a meteorite which fell in 468–67 in the Aegos Potamoi, and that by Shēn Kua (XI-2) to one which fell in 1064. There may be others. The stones (al-ḥajar al-aswad, al-ḥajar al-as'ad) in the Ka'ba, Mecca, may be meteorites, but there is nothing to prove it except perhaps the immemorial reverence paid to them. The earliest meteorite the fall of which was recorded and fragments of which are still available (e.g., in the Chicago Museum of Natural History) is the one which fell near Einsisheim, Upper Alsace, on November 16, 1492 at 11:30 P.M. (127 kg.). There is a contemporary printed record of it by Sebastian Brant (Basel 1492), facsimile in Osiris (5, fig. 49, p. 119, 1938).

In the Hindū Kūsh mountains, after he had washed himself with the water of a hot spring his skin was excoriated and he suffered much (3, 85).

10. *Anthropology*

It would take too long to list his anthropological and ethnological observations. Here are a few: the people of Ẓafār in Yaman have many points in common with those of the Maghrib (2, 201); notes on the slave girls whom he bought in various places and their erotic characteristics; suttee, cremation of widows in India (3, 136); annular vaginal orifice (2, 390); notes on yogis (whom he calls jūkiya, 4, 35–39) and their tricks, such as feats of levitation and the rope trick (4, 291); use of letters of introduction (1, 108); use of seals printed on the arms of people to identify them in Damietta (1, 60); local tabu against the number 10, the people say 9 + 1 (1, 146).

11. *Varia*

Ibn Baṭṭūṭa saw the tomb of Sa'dī near Shīrāz in 1327 (2, 87) and the house of Galen (whom he calls Plato!) in Pergamon (2, 315).

According to tradition, Arabic grammar was founded by Abū-l-Aswad (VII-2), who flourished in Baṣra, yet at the time of Ibn Baṭṭūṭa's passage through that city there was not a single preacher who could speak Arabic grammatically (2, 11). In Anatolia there were places where nobody knew Arabic (2, 327). Turkish sentences noted by Ibn Baṭṭūṭa, not only in Anatolia but also in southern Russia and Turkistān, are many times quoted in the Riḥla (e.g., 3, 33); they may be of value for the study of the evolution of that language.

12. *Medicine*

Remarks of medical interest are infrequent. He witnessed the Black Death in Damascus 1348, when Muslims, Jews, and Christians united in their public prayers (1, 227); later while he was in Aleppo he received reports of the destruction caused by the plague in the Near East (4, 319, 323), and later still while in Tāzā (1349) he learned that his own mother had died from the plague (4, 332). In Ẓafār he noticed the great frequency of elephantiasis and hernias (2, 199).[25]

13. *Economics*

We should expect an earth-bound simple-minded ṣūfī like Ibn Baṭṭūṭa to pay due attention to prices and costs; he did. He many times compares the prices of commodities, including slave girls, in various countries, or simply in the East vs. the West (3, 372; 4, 211, 334); he refers to the use of cowries (wuda'a) for money (e.g., 4, 121). In Sermīn, Syria, he notices the fabrication of soap and cotton goods which are exported to Damascus and Cairo (1, 145). In 1328, pilgrims distributed such an abundance of alms that the price of gold fell in Mecca! (1, 403). Pitch sources near the Tigris, also between Kūfa and Baṣra (2, 133). Business by barter and ermine trade in southern Russia (2, 401). Government postal service (barīd) in Muslim India (3, 95); Hindu money counted in lacs, that is, in hundred thousands (4, 106).

14. *Text*

There are many MSS of the Riḥla, five of them in the Bibliothèque nationale of Paris, not to speak of others. One of these Parisian MSS (no. 907), discovered a century ago in Constantine, is Ibn Juzayy's own autograph, completed in February 1356.

The first publication of this text was Samuel Lee's abbreviated English edition (London 1829). The second, a Portuguese version by J. de Santo Antonio Moura: Viagens extensas e dilatadas do celebre Arabe . . . Ben Batuta (Lisbon 1840–55).

First edition of the complete Arabic text by Charles Defrémery and B. R. Sanguinetti: Voyages d'Ibn Batoutah (5 vols., Société asiatique, Paris 1853–59), Arabic text with French translation, relatively few notes but elaborate index (vol. 5, 91 p., 1859). Various reprints; dates of the copy used by me, vol. 1, 1874, vol. 2, 1877, vol. 3, 1877, vol. 4, 1879. There are also Oriental reprints of the Arabic text of the Paris edition (2 vols., Cairo 1870–71). I have one in 2 vols. dated Cairo 1904–5. Annotated extracts in Blachère (p. 348–69, 1932).

Partial German translation by Hans von Mžik: Die Reisen des Ibn Baṭūṭa durch Indien und China (490 p., Hamburg 1911; Der Islam 4, 433–38). German extracts in Hennig (3, 165–76, 256–60, 1938).

French extracts in Ferrand (2, 426–58, 1914).

H. A. R. Gibb: Ibn Battūta. Travels in Asia and Africa 1325–54. Translated and selected with introduction and notes (406 p., 4 pl., 4 maps, London 1929; reprinted 1939). Gibb is preparing a complete translation for the Hakluyt Society.

15. *Criticism*

E. H. F. Meyer (3, 309–25, 1856). Ernest Renan: Mélanges d'histoire (p. 291–303, Paris 1890). Brockelmann (2, 256, 1902; suppt. 2, 365–66, 1938); (EI 2, 368, 1916). Beazley (3, 535–38, 1906). Yule: Cathay (4, 1–166, 1916). A. Fischer: Baṭṭūṭa nicht Baṭūṭa (Zeitschrift der Deutschen morgenländischen Gesellschaft 72, 289, 1918). William Boulting: Four pilgrims (p. 89–162, London 1921), popular. Eilhard Wiedemann: Eine Sonnenfinsternis, usw. (Weltall 20, 154, 1920; Isis 4, 432), apropos of a meteorite. La Roncière (1, 99–102, 1925).

[25] This is Ẓafār in southeastern Arabia, not the older Ḥimyarī city in Yaman. Jaroslaus Tkatsch (EI 4, 1185–90, 1933). A medical missionary of our own days has also observed the frequency of hernias in southeastern Arabia, see Paul W. Harrison: Doctor in Arabia (p. 149, New York 1940; Isis 33, 392). Dr. Harrison has practiced in the 'Omān district.

Kammerer (1, 68–72, 1929). Stephen Janicsek: Ibn Battuta's journey to Bulghar (Journal of the R. Asiatic Society, 1929, 791–800; Isis 14, 482). Bovill (1933). Agha Mahdi Husain: Le gouvernement du sultanat de Delhi, étude critique d'Ibn Battuta et des historiens indiens du 14ᵉ siècle (Paris thesis, 110 p., 1936); The rise and fall of Muḥammad bin Tughluq (300 p., 2 maps, 5 ill., London 1938). Mohd. A. R. Khan: A siderite of the fourteenth century (Nature 154, 464, 1944), apropos of the meteorite which Ibn Baṭṭūṭa saw in Birgī.

C2. Mashriq

AḤMAD IBN MUḤAMMAD AL-MAQDISĪ

Aḥmad ibn Muḥammad Ibn Hilāl al-Maqdisī al-Shāfi'ī (1314–64). Author of a pilgrim book for Jerusalem.

He was a teacher in the Tunguzīya madrasa in Jerusalem, and died in Cairo 1364. On October 15, 1351 he completed a book concerning the blessings of the pilgrimage to Jerusalem and Syria, Muthīr al-gharām ilā ziyārat al-Quds wal-Shām, which was abbreviated at the end of the century by Muḥammad ibn 'Ammār al-Mālikī (1368–1440). It is divided into two parts, dealing respectively with generalities on Syria and Palestine, and with the Ḥaram of Jerusalem and personalities connected with it.

Another book of his, entitled Kitāb al-miṣbāḥ fī-l-jam' bain al-adhkār wal-ṣilāḥ, is derived from al-Nawawī (XIII-2) and Muḥammad ibn Muḥammad Ibn Humām of Cairo (d. 1344).

Criticism. Wüstenfeld (no. 425, p. 12, 1882). C. König: Der Kitāb muthīr (Diss. Leipzig 1896), not seen. Brockelmann (2, 130, 1902; suppt. 2, 162, 1938).

AL-BĀKUWĪ

Caucasian Muslim geographer (fl. end of fourteenth century and beginning of fifteenth).

'Abd al-Rashīd ibn Ṣāliḥ ibn Nūrī al-Bākuwī. The nisba refers to Bākuh, modern Baku, on the western coast of the Caspian Sea (EI 1, 609, 1911). The dates of his birth and death are unknown, but his father died in 1403.

About 1397, 1403, or 1413 he compiled an Arabic summary of the geography of al-Qazwīnī (XIII-2), under the title Talkhīṣ al-athār wa 'ajā'ib al-malik al-qahhār (General view of the monuments and marvels of the omnipotent king). Al-Bākuwī frequently adds the latitude and longitude, lacking in al-Qazwīnī; his origin of longitudes is in the Canaries. His book is really a dictionary including 465 articles arranged in seven alphabetical series, one for each climate. Brief as they are, his descriptions contain fables as well as facts. For each country he indicates its main products (minerals, plants, animals). In the preface he explains that minerals are each found in certain kinds of country and not in others. For example, gold is found only in deserts and certain mountains; silver, copper, and iron in earthly stones; sulphur in fiery ones, etc. He also gives some broad indications concerning plant and animal distribution.

Text. Joseph de Guignes: Exposition de ce qu'il y a de plus remarquable (sur la terre) et des merveilles du roi tout puissant (Notices et extraits des MSS 2, 386–545, 1789). Abbreviated translation of the Talkhīṣ, containing many inaccuracies, being based on a single late MS (Bibliothèque nationale, Paris, Arabic MS 585, 148 p. quarto, dated 1614) and made at a time when Arabic geography was still very imperfectly known.

Criticism. Ḥājjī Khalīfa (2, 399, no. 3529, 1837). Brockelmann (1, 481, 1898; 2, 213, 1902). M. Streck (EI 2, 843, 1925). Sarton: Introd. (2, 869).

D. JAVA

NĀGARAKṚITĀGAMA

The Nāgarakṛitāgama is a poem written in the Kawi[26] or Old Javanese language by a court poet named Prapañca in honor of his sovereign, Hayam Wuruk, or Rajasanagara, the greatest ruler of Mājapāhit (1350–89). It was written in the year Śaka 1287 = A.D. 1365, and includes 98 short canti.

In order to appreciate the importance of this poem, one must have some idea of the very complicated mediaeval vicissitudes of the Malay peninsula and archipelago. The Hindu Sumatra empire of Śrīvijaya[27] dominated various parts of that area from the beginning of our era until the last quarter of the thirteenth century. In the meanwhile various principalities developed in Java and Farther India. The growing chaos was brought to a climax by the expedition of Kublai Khān (XIII-2) to Java in 1293. Out of that chaos emerged the new Javanese empire of Mājapāhit, thus named after its capital in the northeastern part of Java. This empire was culturally Hindu but Buddhist in religion. It gradually dominated Java, Sumatra, eastern Indonesia, parts of the Malay peninsula. It reached its climax under Hayam Wuruk (1350–89); the last remains of the Śrīvijaya empire were destroyed in Sumatra in 1377. The new empire lasted two centuries, the fourteenth and fifteenth.

From 1368 on, there were active commercial (and cultural?) relations between China and Mājapāhit. By this time, however, India was dominated by Muslims, and the sea trade was largely Muslim too. Thus in the fourteenth century, and even more in the fifteenth, Java was gradually impregnated with Muslim influences driving out the Hindu ones. About 1520 the empire of Mājapāhit was destroyed by a coalition of Muslim princes. From that time on Java and Sumatra were predominantly Muslim. Buddhism was driven out, and replaced by Islām (with a Hindu substructure), except, strangely enough, in the little island of Bāli (east of Java), where it was replaced by Hinduism.

To return to the Nāgarakṛitāgama, its main interest to us lies in the data relative to the historical geography of the Malay peninsula and archipelago. It gives us a clear idea of the amount of geographical knowledge which the Javanese had obtained of their part of the world by the middle of the fourteenth century. That knowledge is definite but bare, for the poet does hardly more than enumerate all the countries which concern his lord.

Text. Jan Brandes (1857–?): Nāgara Krĕtāgama (Verhandelingen van het Bataviaasch genootschap van kunsten en wetenschappen vol. 54, part 1, Batavia 1902), edition in Bāli character without transcription.

The transcription was given together with an annotated Dutch translation by Hendrik Kern (1833–1917), published in Bijdragen tot de taal-, land-, en volkenkunde van Nederlandsch-Indië (vols. 61, 63, 65–69, 's-Gravenhage 1908–14).

[26] Kawi is one of the Austronesian languages of the Malayo-Javanese group. It is a literary language, the "language of poetry"; it includes a good many words of Sanskrit origin.

[27] Or Jāvaka, transcribed in Arabic Zābaj and in Chinese Shê po. See the articles Sayābija and Zābaj by Gabriel Ferrand (EI 4, 200–1, 1926; 1182–83, 1933), and Śrī Vijaya by K. A. Nilakanta Sastri (Bull. de l'Ecole française d'Extrême Orient 40, 239–313, 9 pl., Hanoi 1941).

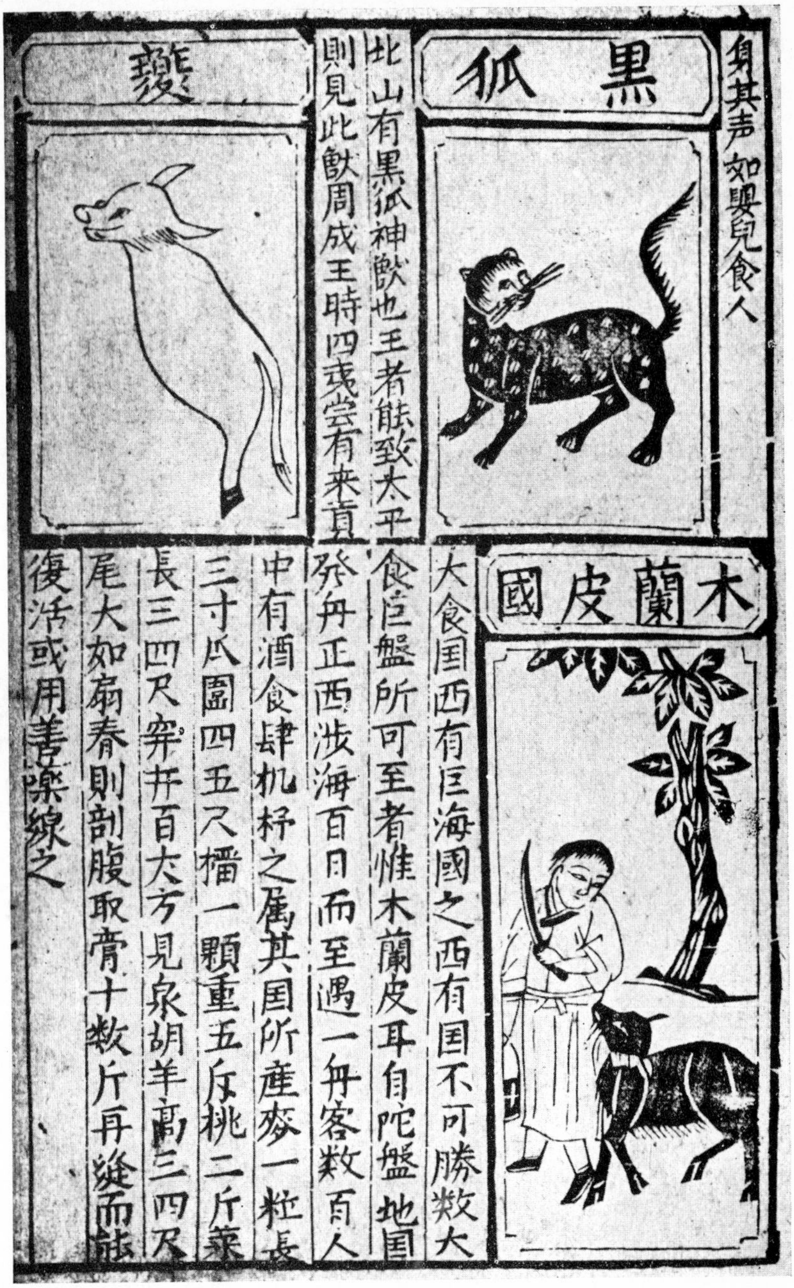
身其声如嬰兒食人
黑狐
此山有黑狐神獸也王者能致太平
則見此獸周成王時四夷嘗有來貢
夔
木蘭皮國
大食国西有巨海國之西有国不可勝數大
食巨盤所可至者惟木蘭皮耳自陀盤地国
發舟正西涉海百日而至遇一舟容數百人
中有酒食肆机杼之屬其国所產麥一粒長
三寸瓜圍四五尺榴一顆重五斤桃二斤菉
長三四尺井百丈方見泉胡羊高三四尺
尾大如扇春則剖腹取膏十數斤再縫而能
復活或用善藥線之

Fig. 36. Page of the Ming encyclopaedia of 1609, reproducing the I-yü t'u-chih in the lower part. The upper part relates to the Shan-hai ching, the Hill and water classic, a book of great antiquity which Kuo P'o (IV-1) edited. The picture at the bottom bears the title Mu-lan-p'i kuo, referring to the Muslim Maghrib. The name is a phonetic transcription of Murābiṭ, name of the dynasty (anglice, the Almoravides) which ruled Morocco, part of Algeria, and Spain from 1056 to 1147. That region was first referred to in the Ling wai tai ta, which Chou Ch'ü-fei completed in 1178 (Introd. 2, 646). The picture represents a man with sword and sheep; the text close to it is probably taken from the Chu fan chih, written by Chao Ju-kua (XIII-1) c. 1225. See F. Hirth and W. W. Rockhill: Chao Ju Kua (p. 142, St. Petersburg 1911).

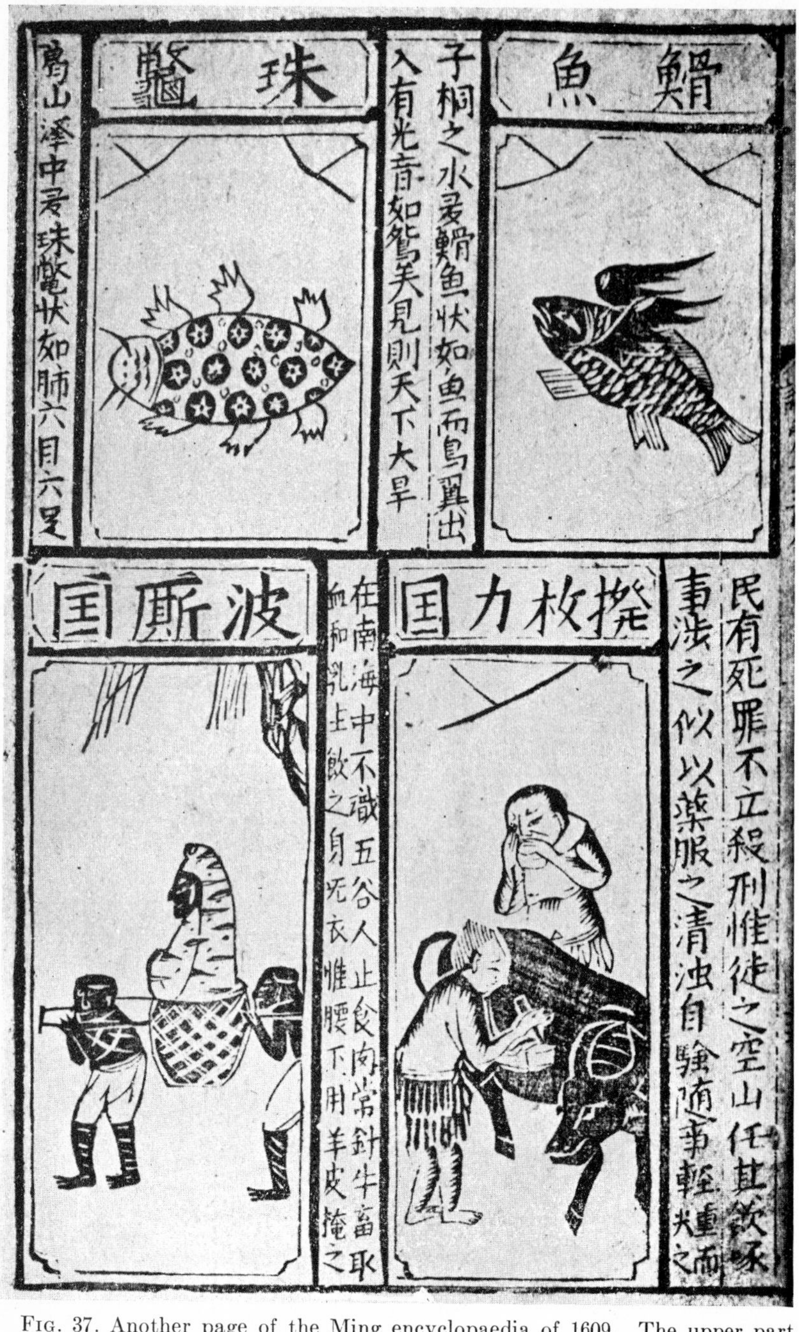

FIG. 37. Another page of the Ming encyclopaedia of 1609. The upper part relates to the Shan-hai ching. Consider the picture in the lower right corner, representing a cow and two men. It bears at the top the words Po-mei-li kuo, name of an unidentified region in the South Seas. The description to the left of the picture reads: "These people in the South Seas are not acquainted with the five cereal crops. They eat only meat, and are accustomed to pierce their cattle for blood, and this they drink unboiled with milk. They do not wear clothes, but use sheepskins to cover their lower extremities."

The courtesy of Dr. A. W. Hummel and of the Library of Congress is acknowledged for figures 36 and 37.

An English analysis of this masterpiece of the old Javanese literature is much to be desired.

Criticism. Hendrik Kern: Een oud Javaansch geschiedkundig gedicht uit het bloeitijdperk van Madjapahit (De indische gids, 25th year, 1, 341–60, Amsterdam 1903); Eenige plaatsen uit de Nāgarakrĕtāgama betreffende Hayam Wuruk (Bijdragen tot de taal-, land-, en volkenkunde van Nederlandsch-Indië 58, 357–63, 1905). G. P. Rouffaer: Encyclopaedie van Nederlandsch-Indië (4, 384–85, 's-Gravenhage 1905). G. E. Gerini: The Nagarakretagama list of countries on the Indo-Chinese mainland, circa 1380 A.D.[28] (Journal of the R. Asiatic Society, 1905, 485–511). Charles Otto Blagden: Notes on Malay history (Journal, Straits branch, R. Asiatic Society 53, 145–53, 1909). Ferrand (2, 651–65, 1914). R. A. Kern: De reis van koning Hajam Woeroek door Lamadjang in 1359 (Tijdschrift van het Kon. nederlandsch aardrijkskundig genootschap 44, 613–24, 1927). Grousset (p. 154–61, 1929). Bernard H. M. Vlekke: Nusantara (p. 45, 53, 60, 65, Cambridge, Mass. 1943; Isis 35, 77).

E. CHINA

CHINESE KNOWLEDGE OF GEOGRAPHY AND ZOOLOGY AT THE END OF THE FOURTEENTH CENTURY OR THE BEGINNING OF THE FIFTEENTH

An interesting glimpse of that knowledge is given to us by an anonymous book in the Wade collection in Cambridge, the I-yü t'u-chih, which might be translated Pictures and descriptions of strange nations. It is a collection of 90 leaves measuring 31 × 19 cm., each printed from a block, surrounded by a heavy black line and a finer inner one measuring 26 cm. in height and 33 cm. (the two pages) in width.

The book contains illustrations of 168 countries or places, each accompanied by the name of the place or a note about it. The main value of the book lies in drawings of a great many animals, including such rare ones as zebra, giraffe, oryx, hornbill, each being named.

The I-yü t'u-chih was compiled sometime in the Ming dynasty between 1392 and 1430, and was printed in 1489 by Chin Hsien. It is not clear whether the Cambridge book is an earlier print or a later one.

A. C. Moule: An introduction to the I yü t'u chih (T'oung pao 27, 179–88, 1930; Isis 21, 366).

The Cambridge copy of the I-yü t'u-chih is the only one known, but the pictures and text have been reproduced, somewhat reduced, in a very rare encyclopaedia printed about 1609, the Wan yung chêng-tsung pu-ch'iu-jên ch'üan-pien (The "ask no questions" complete handbook for general use), in 12 volumes. See detailed descriptions of it by A. W. Hummel (Library of Congress, Report for 1940, p. 165–67). The illustrations and explanations correspond in every detail to the Cambridge copy, and there can be no doubt that this encyclopaedia has reproduced the I-yü t'u-chih. The Cambridge copy has 168 illustrations of strange peoples and animals, but the Library of Congress copy of the encyclopaedia has only 129, because the last few pages are missing. See our facsimiles (figs. 36, 37).[29] The pictures at the top relate to the Shan-hai ching (Hill and water classic) by Kuo P'o (IV-1), and only those at the bottom to the I-yü t'u-chih.

[28] That date is incorrect; the correct date, as indicated above, is 1365.

[29] We owe the necessary photostats from the Library of Congress copy of that rare encyclopaedia to Dr. A. W. Hummel; the explanations relative to it were kindly given by him in his letter of Oct. 22, 1940.

CHAPTER XXIV

NATURAL HISTORY

(Second Half of the Fourteenth Century)

N.B. Only the main notes are published in this chapter. The contributions of many other men, whose main work was done in other fields, are discussed in other chapters. For a general survey of natural history in the second half of the fourteenth century, see section X of chapter XV. More information on the men referred to in that survey may then easily be found by means of the index.

A. CHRISTENDOM

A2. ITALY

ROTARIO D'ASTI

Bonifacio Rotario d'Asti. Italian "alpinist" (fl. 1358).

Legendary personality. According to some, while Rotario was in the Holy Land with the Crusaders he was made prisoner by Muslims and promised the Virgin Mary that if he recovered his freedom he would return to Piedmont and climb to the top of the Rocciamelone,[1] which be believed to be the highest Alp. He succeeded in doing that on September 1, 1358, and deposited on the top a bronze triptych representing the Virgin, St. George, and St. Joseph. That triptych still exists; it is said to be a Flemish (?) monument of the fourteenth century, and it does bear the inscription "Hic me aportauit bonefacius rotarius ciuis astensis in honore dni nri yhu Xi et beate marie virginis ano dni mccc.Lviii die p.mo septembr." There is no early document confirming the story. According to another tradition, Rotario was not a Crusader and never left his own country, but for some other reason he made a vow to the Virgin, etc. The triptych was kept for centuries in the cathedral San Giusto of Susa in the valley below the mountain; it has recently been placed in a new chapel on the Rocciamelone. There was already a chapel there in 1549 and probably earlier, and a special holiday and procession to the Madonna delle Neve (Our Lady of the Snows) is also an ancient institution (it became a holiday for the whole Catholic church under Pius V, 1566–72, but it was probably a local holiday long before that time).

If Rotario d'Asti reached the summit of Rocciamelone in 1358 bearing that triptych, that would be a very remarkable achievement indeed. It is not impossible, but very implausible.

Criticism. Mario Esposito: Contributi alla storia dell' alpinismo. I. Il Rocciamelone attraverso i secoli (Archivio storico italiano ser. 7, vol. 20, 3–48, 1933).

[1] In the Cottian Alps, north of the river Dora Riparia. Its height is only 3,538 m., but its white pyramid rises majestically above the Valle di Susa. The Mont Blanc is 4,810 m. high, but it would have been impossible in those days to measure or even estimate the real heights of the two mountains. Of course, the impression which they make depends not on the absolute height, but rather on the height above the surrounding country. Florian Cajori: History of determinations of heights of mountains (Isis 12, 482–514, 13 ill., 1929).

A3. France

GASTON PHOEBUS

Gaston III count of Foix, viscount of Béarn, called Phoebus (1331–91). Author of a French book on the chase, one of the best and most popular of its kind in the Middle Ages.

Gaston III was born in 1331, the son of Gaston II count of Foix and of Eleonora of Comminges; at the age of 16 he was appointed lieutenant general of Languedoc by the king; in 1348 he married Agnes, daughter of the king of Navarre, Philip of Evreux. He was one of the greatest feudal lords of southern France and one of the most famous soldiers of his time. An outline of his very complicated military and political career would take too much space; sometimes he would be fighting with the English, sometimes with the French, sometimes he remained neutral. He was a celebrated huntsman, had the reputation of being a perfect knight, and was much admired by Froissart. It is true he was greedy, a cruel voluptuary, he had strangled his only son with his own hands and he had many other crimes and treacheries on his conscience, but he must be judged in comparison with other members of his class and time. He was perhaps a good deal better than his contemporaries the count of Armagnac and the duke Jean de Berry. He died of a stroke at Orthez (Béarn; dépt. Basses-Pyrénées) in 1391.

We should not deal with him at all but for the fact that he was a patron of arts and letters and the author of a valuable book on the chase. He accumulated a fine library, and many MSS limned for him are extant.

He began in 1387 the composition of a great treatise on hunting, in French, entitled "Le miroir de Phoebus des déduiz de la chasse, des bestes sauvaiges et des oiseaulx de proye," which was very much esteemed in the fifteenth century, that is, in the limited circle of the aristocracy (hunting being one of their most cherished privileges); witness the relatively large number of MSS (40 at least), some of which are beautifully illustrated. Two of these MSS are of outstanding importance. The first was prepared, perhaps under Gaston's own eyes, for his friend Philippe le Hardi (1342–1404), duke of Burgundy; it was kept in the Escorial library but disappeared from it in 1809; the other is one of the most valuable MSS of the Bibliothèque nationale in Paris (MS fr. 616), because it contains an admirable series of 87 miniatures by one of the greatest, if unknown, limners of the beginning of the fifteenth century. Many of these miniatures represent hounds and beasts of venery or of the chase.

To return to the text, it begins with a prologue wherein the author dwells on the ethical value of the chase, e.g., it enables gentlemen to avoid idleness and sinfulness, and gives them opportunities for physical exercise. Then there is a series of chapters dealing with the hare and her nature, the hart and his nature, etc., the other animals being the buck, roe, wild boar, wolf, fox, badger, wildcat, and otter. What might be called the second part treats of the manners, habits, and conditions of hounds; their sicknesses and corruptions; their various kinds, such as greyhounds, spaniels, mastiffs; how to keep the kennels, how to lead the hounds, etc. A third part deals with hunting itself and the qualities of a good veneur. This contains some teaching of woodcraft; how to recognize a hart by his trace, or fumes, etc.; how to hunt at night or in various kinds of country, etc.

This treatise was written in a clear and lively style, because the author was tremendously interested in the subject and knew it very well. It was not a rhetorical exercise, but a scientific composition written con amore by an expert for the sake of his brother huntsmen. To appreciate its full meaning one must bear in mind the immense social importance of hunting in mediaeval times. It was not an idle sport as today; it was an essential part of a gentleman's education; it was one of the most tangible symbols of lordship and knightship. Hence all the ceremonial and ritual of venery (i.e., the hunting of the "five beasts of venery," hart, hind, hare, boar, and wolf) and of the chase.

The social aspect does not concern us here, but we must bear in mind that treatises on hunting (text and illustrations) constitute our best source for the study of mediaeval zoology. In fact, they contain a good amount of information on various kinds of game and their habits, the animals used for hunting, and the means of breeding, training, and keeping them in good health. Gaston was interested only in hounds; it is said he kept 1,600 of them.

Gaston's treatise is partly derived from the books of Bartholomew the Englishman (XIII-1) and Vincent of Beauvais (XIII-2), and from earlier treatises of its own kind, chiefly the regulations of Sancho VI el Sabio (XII-2), and the De arte venandi cum avibus of Frederick II of Hohenstaufen (XIII-1); it should be noted, however, that these two books deal with falconry, not with hunting with hounds.

Did Gaston know the French poem Le roman des oiseaux (Roman de déduits) written by Gace de la Bigne (or Vigne), chaplain to Jean le Bon? Gace began it at Hertford in 1359 for his king during the latter's captivity in England; he finished it in Paris. As to Sancho's Paramientos de la caza of 1180, mentioned above, this was the first code of regulations relative to hunting; considering Gaston's family relationship with the king of Navarre, he could not possibly be ignorant of it. A similar code was not promulgated in France until a little later, in 1396, being perhaps inspired by Gaston's treatise.

The main source of Gaston's knowledge was his own experience, which was deep and varied. He had even hunted reindeer in Scandinavia.

Gaston's French book was soon translated into English, c. 1406–13, by Edward Plantagenet (or Edward of Norwich, 1373?—Agincourt 1415), second duke of York, grandson of Edward III, master of the game to his cousin Henry IV. His translation, entitled The master of game, is the second oldest English book on the subject.[2] It is divided into 36 chapters, 5 of which are original. There are also interpolations which are valuable for the study of English conditions.

Text. Phébus, des déduiz de la chasse des bestes sauvaiges et des oyseaux de proye (Vérard, Paris c. 1507). There are two other early Parisian editions, undated.

La chasse de Gaston Phoebus, avec des notes et sa vie par Joseph Lavallée, édité par Léon Bertrand (356 p., Paris 1854). La chasse de Gaston Phoebus (448 p., Paris 1897). Le livre de la chasse transcrit en français moderne par André et Robert Bossuat, known to me only through a long review in Larousse mensuel (p. 149, July 1932).

Reproduction réduite des 87 miniatures du MS français 616 de la Bibliothèque nationale. Edited by Camille Couderc (35 p., 90 pl., Paris 1909).

[2] Another treatise on hunting was written in England before this one, but in Anglo-Norman. That is the treatise written by William Twici (or Twety) and John Gyfford for Edward II (king 1307–27). There is an English version of it which is somewhat anterior to the Master of game (say, second half of fourteenth cent.) and is the oldest English book on hunting. It was edited in French and English by Sir T. Phillipps: Le art de venerie par Guyllame Twici (private press, Middle Hill 1840), again in both languages by H. Dryden: The art of hunting (private press, Daventry 1843), only 25 copies. Paul Maximilian Sahlender: Der Jagdtraktat Twici's (Leipzig thesis, 60 p., 1904). Wells (p. 427, 832, 1926).

The master of game. Edited by Wm. A. and F. Baillie-Grohman, with a foreword by Theodore Roosevelt (folio, 340 p., 52 pl., London 1904). Contains the old translation by Edward second duke of York, together with a version in modern English, elaborate introduction, bibliography, glossary, and a dictionary of the chase. The beautiful full-page illustrations are selected from the French MS 616. In the English text the original parts (i.e., those not found in the French text) are printed in italics. Edition de luxe of which only 600 copies were published.

Le livre des oraisons de Gaston Phébus, publié pour la première fois par l'abbé de Madaune (41 p., Paris 1893). Livre des prières, 1385. Publié par La Brière, 2e édition (215 p., Paris 1899).

Criticism. Jean Michel de Madaune: Gaston Phébus, comte de Foix et souverain de Béarn (335 p., Pau 1864), local semipopular publication. Harting (p. 73, 111, 166, 1891). Justin Bellanger: Gaston Phébus (18 p., Paris 1896), reprint from an unnamed journal. Moulé (part 3, p. 67, 1900). A. Molinier (Grande encyclopédie 18, 589). Paul Mylo: Das Verhältnis der Handschriften des mittelenglischen Jagdbuches Maistre of game (Diss. Würzburg, 56 p., 1908).

JEHAN DE BRIE

Jean de Brie, the "good shepherd" (fl. 1379).

Jean de Brie wrote in 1379 for king Charles V a treatise on shepherdy in French, which contains valuable information for the study of husbandry in that time. All that we know of the author is told by himself in his first chapter, but I feel we may trust him.

He originated in Villers-sur-Rognon near Coulommiers (pays de Brie; Seine-et-Marne), and at the age of 8 was already employed to watch the geese and other farmyard birds; half a year later he became a pigherd in the neighboring town Nolongue, then a cowherd. Having been wounded by one of the animals, he was put in charge of the lambs. It was perhaps then that he improved his comparative leisure and began to teach himself the art of letters. After having spent so much time with sheep and lambs that he had become "licencié et maistre en ceste science de bergerie, et qu'il estoit digne de lire en la rue au Feurre,[3] auprès la cresche aux veaulx ou soubz l'ombre d'ung ourmel ou tilleul derrière les brebis"—meaning, he had become a master of shepherdy worthy to lecture on the subject at the university, or near the calves' manger or in the shade of an elm or linden tree behind the ewes—he moved to Paris and was in the domestic service of the treasurer, later of a canon, of the Sainte Chapelle. His literary education was probably continued during that time preceding the year 1379, when he wrote his book "Le bon berger ou le vray régime et gouvernement des bergers et bergères, traitant de l'état, science et pratique de l'art de bergerie et de garder ouailles et bêtes à laine."

The text is divided into 47 chapters: (1) autobiography; (2) usefulness of this treatise; (3) the shepherd's honor, the dignity of his labor (de l'honneur du berger, et comment l'estat de bergerie est grand et honnorable); (4) general rules for shepherds; (5–7) meteorological: how to know the coming weather from the observation of birds, or other animals, or from other signs; different kinds of wind; (8) the shepherd's life; (9–20) 12 chapters explaining the shepherd's duties month by month (the shepherd's calendar); (21–32) 12 chapters dealing with the sheep's

[3] Feurre should be read Fouarre. The rue de Fouarre and the rue Garlande were the original streets of the Latin Quarter when the University of Paris began to move to the left bank of the Seine at the beginning of the thirteenth century. I have given a rather long quotation to illustrate Jean's naïve and pleasant language and his rustic wit.

ailments; (33–44) 12 chapters dealing with remedies; (45) bloodletting; (46) castration; (47) the sheep dog. Final poem (40 lines).

Aside from its importance for the history of mediaeval husbandry and veterinary art, the book is also valuable for the history of the French language.

Text. There are three early editions of Jean de Brie's Bon berger. Two undated ones date from the beginning of the sixteenth century; the third was published in Paris 1541. Paul Lacroix reprinted the third edition, though it is not so good as the previous ones, uncritically (182 p., 14 cm. high, Paris 1879). A critical edition is much to be desired.

Criticism. Paul Meyer (Romania 8, 450–54, 1879), criticizing Lacroix's edition, and giving samples of Jean's vocabulary.

TAILLEVENT

Guillaume Tirel, dit Taillevent. French royal cook (d. 1395).

Born about 1315, for in 1326 he was "enfant de cuisine" to Jeanne, queen of Philippe d'Evreux king of Navarre; from 1346 to 1349 he was "queu"[3a] to Philippe VI de Valois; "écuyer de l'hôtel" to mgr. le dauphin de Viennois, then "queu" to him in 1355; "queu" to the duke of Normandy in 1359–61; "queu et sergent d'armes" to Charles V in 1368, "premier queu" to same in 1373 and 1377; "écuyer de cuisine" to Charles VI in 1381, "premier écuyer de cuisine" to the same in 1388, "maitre des garnisons de cuisine" to the same in 1392. He died probably in 1395; he had built himself a tomb, representing him between his two wives, in a chapel founded by him, at the priory of Our Lady of Hennemont near St. Germain-en-Laye. The remains of that monument, mutilated during the Revolution, are preserved in the museum of that city.

This curriculum is interesting as an example of the career of a royal cook. Taillevent composed a cookbook which is one of the first books of its kind in the French language. The only earlier one I know of is a brief one which was probably written in the first quarter of the fourteenth century, for it is found in a composite MS of about that time including Henri de Mondeville's Cyrurgia. It is also one of the very earliest outside the pure Apician tradition (for "Apicius" see Introd. 1, 340).

Taillevent called his book "Le viandier" (i.e., he who deals with viands) and composed it between 1373 and 1381, probably before 1380. It was very popular, not only before the invention of printing but after (at least 15 printed editions before 1605). There are great differences between the text of the MSS and that of the printed editions, which is not very surprising, as such a subject would naturally call for additions.

A more ambitious compilation entitled Le ménagier de Paris, put together c. 1393, borrowed considerably from Le viandier for its chapters on cookery, but it dealt with many other subjects. Le ménagier de Paris is a treatise on domestic ethics and economy. It is divided into three "distinctions": (I) respective duties of husband and wife (it is especially written for the latter); (II) domestic economy; gardening, how to choose and rule servants, cookbook, arrangement of dinners; (III) hunting, chiefly hawking; how to train sparrow hawks and hunt with them in various seasons; diseases of hawks and other birds of prey and their cure.

Such books as the anonymous French cookbook of the first quarter of the four-

[3a] Queu, derived from the Latin coquus (see Du Cange). In modern French it is written queux and generally used in the phrase maître queux, to mean a good chef or an experienced cook.

teenth century, Taillevent's Viandier, and Le ménagier de Paris are of value to the historian of science and culture in many ways. They contain information on domestic manners and customs, husbandry, economics, perhaps chemistry and technology. It would be worth while to make a comparative study of them from those points of view.

Texts. Le viandier. The early editions are undated; at least 2 are incunabula (Klebs no. 949). Pichon enumerates 15 editions anterior to his own, of which the 12th is the first dated one (Lyon 1545). Then follow the editions of Lyon 1580, 1603, 1604.

Critical edition by the baron Jérôme Pichon and Georges Vicaire: Le viandier de Guillaume Tirel dit Taillevent. This includes the text of the oldest MS as well as the first printed text, with an elaborate introduction, original documents, and index (365 p., ill., Paris 1892).

L. Douet-d'Arcq: Un petit traité de cuisine écrit en français au commencement du XIVe siècle (Bibliothèque de l'Ecole des chartes 1 (5), 209–27, Paris 1860). This early text was reprinted in Pichon's edition (p. 115–28, 1892).

[Jérôme Pichon]: Le ménagier de Paris. Traité de morale et d'économie domestique composé vers 1393 par un bourgeois parisien. Contenant des préceptes moraux, quelques faits historiques, des instructions sur l'art de diriger une maison, des renseignements sur la consommation du roi, des princes et de la ville de Paris à la fin du quatorzième siècle, des conseils sur le jardinage et sur le choix des chevaux, un traité de cuisine fort étendu, et un autre non moins complet sur la chasse à l'épervier. Ensemble: l'histoire de Grisélidis, Mélibée et Prudence par Albertan de Brescia (1246) traduit par frère Renault de Louens, et le Chemin de povreté et de richesse poème composé en 1342 par Jean Bruyant, notaire au Châtelet de Paris. Publié pour la première fois par la Société des bibliophiles françois[4] (2 vols., Paris 1846).

Criticism. See introduction to the editions above mentioned. Emile Littré: Anonyme auteur d'un traité de cuisine (HL 27, 26–29, 1877) apropos of the treatise first edited by Douet-d'Arcq in 1860.

"CYBO OF HYÈRES"

The British Museum owns three fragments of an illuminated MS of Ligurian origin, Add. MSS 27695, 28841, and Egerton MS 3127, acquired respectively in 1867, 1871, and 1934. The size of the pages is about $6\frac{1}{2} \times 4$ inches. The extraordinarily interesting illustrations are ascribed to one Cybo "the monk of Hyères" (or one of the Hyères islands, Var, Provence). This Cybo was very probably a member of the famous Cibo or Cybò family of Genoa; he was probably born in Genoa and flourished toward the end of the fourteenth century. We know practically nothing about him, and it is not even certain that the illustrations ascribed to him are all by the same hand.

The original book contained two Latin texts, the one, in prose, being a treatise

[4] The title is reproduced verbatim. For Albertano da Brescia (XIII-1) see Introd. 2, 697. For Renault de Louens, see Aimé Vayssière: Renaut de Louens, poète franc-comtois du XIVe siècle (L'année dominicaine p. 141–54; undated reprint, c. 1873). F. Nagel: Die altfranzösische Übersetzung der Consolatio philosophiae des Boëthius von Renaut von Louhans (Zeitschrift für romanische Philologie 15, 1–23, 1891), adversely criticized by Gaston Paris (Romania 20, 329, 1891). The Dominican father Raynaud de Louens or better Louhans (in Burgundy; Saône-et-Loire) is one of the early French translators of Boethius' Consolation. He completed his translation in Poligny (Jura), 1336. Many extracts from it are quoted by Vayssière and by Nagel.

on the vices, the other, in loose rhythmical verse, dealing with the history of Sicily under Frederick II of Hohenstaufen (XIII-1). Both texts were written by a member of the Cocharelli family of Genoa, who obtained part of his information (for both) from his grandfather Pelegrino Cocharelli (de Cocharellis vir nobilis nomine dictus Pelegrinus).

The text, however, is insignificant as compared with the miniatures and borders illuminating the leaves and including naturalistic drawings of various plants and animals, birds, insects, mollusks, etc. Similar drawings are used for line fillings. This is a very valuable document concerning the observation of nature in Liguria or Provence at the end of the fourteenth century. One astonishing feature is the artist's predilection for insects, such as bees, grasshoppers, beetles, spiders, and not only imagoes but caterpillars as well. This interest in insects is exceedingly rare in the Western tradition, but there are Arabic MSS containing admirable entomological illustrations, and the Chinese and Japanese showed from early times a deep curiosity about insects (see chapter XV, p. 1188).

Cybo may have been influenced in his entomological tastes by Oriental models, for his limning shows other proofs of Oriental influence; for example, his illustration of the vice of gluttony represents a Tatar khan, and another representing a hawking scene reveals Oriental traits. This is easy to account for, considering the vast Oriental trade of Genoa.

Text. Two leaves were reproduced in the Facsimiles of the Palaeographical Society of London (1, 149, 150, 1873). Two leaves were reproduced also in the British Museum reproductions from illustrated MSS (ser. IV, London 1928). In September 1934, thanks to Mr. Eric Millar's kind assistance, I was able to examine the three MSS leisurely, and I had a set of photographs made which are now in my archives and available to any qualified investigator. Miniatures and borders attributed to Cybo, the "monk of Hyères" (6 pictorial cards printed in colors, British Museum set B.69, London c. 1935).

Criticism. Girolamo Tiraboschi: Storia della letteratura italiana (5, 483, 1789). John A. Herbert: Illuminated manuscripts (Connoisseur's library, p. 263, London 1911). Ulrich Thieme: Allgemeines Lexikon der bildenden Künstler (8, 234, 1913). R. Flower: Two leaves from the book of "the monk of Hyères" (British Museum quarterly 8, 128–30, 1 pl., London 1934), apropos of the acquisition of the Egerton MS 3127.

B. ISRAEL

GATIGNO

Name of a Jewish family of Aragonese origin. The name is spelled variously in Hebrew (but always with ṭeth) or Latin script: Gatigno, Gatinho, Gatenyo. Gateyn.

En Solomon Astruc (Gatigno) ha-qadosh. Hispano-Jewish exegete and physician who flourished in Barcelona in the second half of the fourteenth century and wrote a commentary on the Torah entitled Midreshe ha-Torah, sometime after 1376. He gave an account of a locust plague which occurred in 1359, when he was already middle-aged. The epithet "qadosh," usually given to martyrs, suggests that he may have been the victim of some persecution, possibly in 1391? The date of his death is unknown.

Ezra ben Solomon Gatigno was probably the son of En Solomon Astruc; the two are often confused. Ezra lived in Saragossa and Agramunt (near Lerida) and completed in 1372 the Sefer ha-zikronot, being the first part of a commentary on the

Firush ha-Torah of Abraham ben Ezra (XII-1). The Sefer ha-zikronot deals with Abraham's simple explanations (pashuṭim), taking advantage of earlier works such as those of Joseph Kaspi (XIV-1). The second part of this supercommentary, Sod Adonai, deals with Abraham's esoteric explanations.

Text. Solomon Astruc: Midreshe ha-Torah, edited by Simeon Eppenstein in the collection Meqiẓe nirdamim (Berlin 1899).

Criticism. H. Brody (EJ 7, 108–11, 1931).

C. ISLĀM

C1. Maghrib

IBN HUDHAIL

'Alī ibn 'Abd al-Raḥmān Ibn Hudhail al-Fazārī al-Andalusī al-Gharnāṭī. Spanish Muslim writer on horses, flourished in Granada in the second half of the fourteenth century, and perhaps also in the beginning of the fifteenth century.

He was a disciple of 'Abdallāh Ibn Juzayy, and is not mentioned in the Iḥāṭa probably because he was still too young when that work was composed by Ibn al-Khaṭīb (c. 1363). He wrote three works dealing with horses:

1. Kitāb al-fawā'id al-musaṭṭara fī 'ilm al-baiṭara. Treatise on hippiatry dedicated to the Naṣrī king Muḥammad V (ruled Granada 1354–59, 1362–91). This is the treatise to which Ibn Juzayy referred. It is derived from Greek sources and early Arabic traditions.

2. Tuḥfat al-anfās wa shi'ār sukkān al-Andalus. Treatise on horses divided into two parts, dealing respectively, the first with military art (jihād and ribāṭ), the second with hippology, equitation, and the handling of arms on horseback. Dedicated to the same king.

3. Ḥilyat al-fursān wa shi'ār al-shuj'ān, dedicated to the Naṣrī king Muḥammad VII (ruled Granada 1392–1407). This is an abridgment and adaptation of the Tuḥfat al-anfās, that is, of its second part only, the part dealing with jihād and ribāṭ being left out completely. It is divided into 20 chapters dealing roughly with (1) creation of the horse, its domestication and diffusion, (2) its mysterious virtues, (3) recommendations concerning its care, (4) names of its different parts, (5) qualities to be looked for in those parts, (6) particularities of its coat, (7) characteristics and names of noble horses, (8) natural and acquired vices, (9) how to test horses; their physiognomy, (10) horse riding, (11) races and bets, (12) names of the horses of the Prophet and of other famous horses, (13) terms relative to horses, (14) poetic quotations, (15) sword, (16) spear, (17) bow and arrow, (18) armor, (19) shields, (20) arms and equipment in general. The Ḥilyat al-fursān is anonymous, but probably by the same author as the Tuḥfat al-anfās rather than a plagiarism by another author.

Text. Louis Mercier: La parure des cavaliers et l'insigne des preux (102 p., Paris 1922); Traduction française précédée d'une étude sur les sources des hippiatres arabes et accompagnée d'appendices critiques sur l'histoire du pur-sang, de l'équitation et des sports hippiques arabes, en Maghreb et en Orient (600 p., 34 ill., Paris 1924; Isis 8, 346–49, 541; 9, 504).

Louis Mercier: L'ornement des âmes et la devise des habitants d'al-Andalus. Traité de guerre sainte islamique. Reproduction du MS de M. Nehlil revu et corrigé (108 p., Paris 1936; JRAS, 1938, 625–26); the same author is preparing a French translation.

Criticism. Louis Mercier: La chasse et les sports chez les Arabes (256 p., Paris 1927; Isis 10, 511–13). H. Ritter: La parure des cavaliers und die Literatur über die ritterlichen Künste (Der Islam 18, 116–54, 1929). Georges S. Colin: Un nouveau traité grenadin d'hippologie (Islamica 6, 335, 1934). Brockelmann (suppt. 2, 379, 1938).

The student of Arabic hippology may obtain valuable information from Carl R. Raswan: Vocabulary of Bedouin words concerning horses (Journal of Near Eastern studies 4, 97–129, 1945), 1,050 terms given in Arabic script and transcription, and explained. He will obtain more information in Lady Wentworth: The authentic Arabian horse and his descendants. Three voices concerning the horses of Arabia. Tradition (Nejd, Inner East), romantic fable (Islam), the outside world of the West (400 p., 291 pl., 28½ × 23 cm., London 1945).

IBN JUZAYY

Abū Muḥammad 'Abdallāh ibn Muḥammad ibn Juzayy of Granada. Spanish Muslim writer on horses (fl. third quarter of fourteenth century).

He was the son of Abū-l-Qāsim Muḥammad ibn Juzayy al-Kalbī al-Gharnāṭī, who was one of the teachers of Ibn al-Khaṭīb. He was the brother of Abū 'Abdallāh Muḥammad ibn Muḥammad al-Juzayy, who is mentioned in our note on Ibn Baṭṭūṭa as the editor of the latter's Riḥla in 1354.

'Abdallāh ibn Juzayy wrote a treatise on hippology entitled Kitāb maṭli' al-yumn wal-iqbāl fī intiqā' kitāb al-iḥtifāl wa istidrāk mā fātahu min al-maqāl, and dedicated to the Naṣrī king Muḥammad V (ruled Granada 1354–59, 1362–91). The date of composition would seem to fall between 1369 and 1391. As the title indicates, the treatise is an adaptation of an earlier one, which is (as stated in the introduction) the Kitāb al-iḥtifāl fī-istifā taṣnīf mā lil-khail min al-aḥwāl written by Muḥammad ibn Riḍwān Ibn Arqam (d. 1259) of Cadiz and dedicated by him to the first Naṣrī king, Muḥammad I (ruled 1232–73).

The older treatise, the Kitāb al-iḥtifāl, describes the qualities, colors, shapes, names, and other peculiarities of horses and ends with a summary of the art of horsemanship. Ibn Juzayy's revision of the older work consisted in suppressing a great many technical terms borrowed from the early lexicographers al-Aṣma'ī and Abū 'Ubaida (both VIII-2), and in adding chapters dealing with the intelligence of horses and other animals, anecdotes on the hoopoe (hudhud), and other anecdotes concerning Andalusia. In the chapter on dawā'ir ("tourbillons de poils") Ibn Juzayy repeats a reference of Ibn Arqam to a Hindu writer Jull al-Hindī (?). Veterinary considerations are left out, the author referring for them to the work of one of his disciples, Ibn Hudhail.

In short, the Maṭli' al-yumn (Levant of happiness) is not a zoological or veterinary work, but a literary one written for lovers of horse riding or chevalerie (furūsīya) and jihād.

Criticism. Georges S. Colin: Un nouveau traité grenadin d'hippologie (Islamica 6, 332–37, 1934).

The Kitāb al-iḥtifāl was ascribed by Casiri (1, 321, no. 897, 1760) to Abū Muḥammad 'Abdallāh al-Lakhmī of Cordova and dated as of the rule of the Naṣrī Muḥammad III (1303–9). That error has been repeated by Moulé (part 2, p. 37, Paris 1896). A biography of Ibn Arqam is included in the Iḥāṭa of Ibn al-Khaṭīb (Cairo ed., 2, 101–21).

C2. Arabia

AL-'ABBĀS AL-RASŪLĪ

Al-Malik al-Afḍal al-'Abbās ibn 'Alī. Sixth Rasūlī sulṭān of Yaman, son of the fifth sulṭān, al-Mujāhid 'Alī (XIV-1). Al-'Abbās ruled from 1362/63 to 1376. He continued the learned traditions of his family and wrote a remarkable treatise on agriculture.

That treatise, entitled Bughyat al-fallāḥīn fī-l-ashjār al-muthmira wal-rayāḥīn (The desired book of peasants on useful trees and aromatic plants), is divided into 17 chapters: (1) soils; (2) fertilizers; (3) waters; (4) amelioration of land; (5) seasons; (6) growing from seeds (grains: sorgho, spelt, barley, millet, rice, etc.); (7) pulses (chick-peas, lentils, mungo beans, fenugreek, etc.); (8) cucumber plants (melons, vegetable marrow, brinjal[4a] or eggplant), onions, turnips, carrots, etc.; (9) spices; (10) perfumes; (11) fruit trees, beginning with a very long section (20 p. folio) on the date palm, then vine, fig tree, pomegranate, apple, pear, olive tree, coconut, areca nut, banana, sugar cane, citrus trees, cotton, etc.; (12) cutting of trees; (13) grafting, with description and primitive pictures of instruments (17 p.); (14) specific qualities of plants; (15) prevention of damage to plants, references to Cassianos Bassos (VI-2) and to Ibn Waḥshīya (X-1); (16) varia, including an enumeration of medicinal plants growing in Yaman, mostly from notes by the author's father; and a mention of the latter's discovery of iron ore in Yaman in 1333/34; (17) weights and measures; exposition of the seven climates.

According to the author's own preface, his sources were the Greek and Nabataean books on husbandry (referred to above), but also the knowledge traditionally accumulated in his own family. He often mentions written records by his father (bi-khaṭṭ wālidī), who had obtained his knowledge from his own father and grandfather. He mentions a book of the latter, the third Rasūlī sulṭān al-Ashraf 'Umar ibn Yūsuf (ruled 1295–97), who wrote the Milḥ al-milāḥa fī ma'rifat al-falāḥa (The salt of saltiness on the knowledge of agriculture) and a treatise on the astrolabe, Mu'īn al-ṭullāb 'alā 'amal al-aṣṭurlab. In his introduction he also quotes other writers such as Plato, Aristotle, the grammarian Khalīl ibn Aḥmad (VIII-2), and later in the text one Ibn al-Baṣṣāl.[5] Apparently he was not acquainted with the Kitāb al-falāḥa of the Sevillan Ibn al-Awwām (XII-2), a fact which shows that agricultural books did not travel as fast from West to East as theological ones—but that is not surprising.

Text. The text is included in MS 155 Zirā'a (agriculture) in the Egyptian library in Cairo. An edition and translation of it is highly to be desired. It has been examined for me by my friend Dr. Max Meyerhof, of Cairo, to whose letter of Oct. 13, 1939 I owe the substance of this note and to whom I express once more my gratitude. Dr. Meyerhof's MS copy of the original text covers almost 6,000 lines.

Criticism. The main source for the early history of the Rasūlī salāṭīn is the 'Uqūd lu'lu'īya of Ibn Wahhās al-Khazrajī. For the third Rasūlī sulṭān, 'Umar

[4a] The Anglo-Indian word brinjal or brinjaul is derived, via the Portuguese bringella, from the Persian bādinjān or bādingān, Arabic bādhinjān. Hobson-Jobson (p. 115–16, 1903).

[5] Abū 'Abdallāh Muḥammad ibn Ibrāhīm Ibn al-Baṣṣāl flourished probably in Toledo under the Banū Dhī-l-Nūn (ruled 1035–85). His book on agriculture, often referred to by Ibn al-'Awwām (XII-2), is lost in Arabic, but Millàs has found a Castilian translation of it, which he is planning to edit, in an early fifteenth-century MS of the Cathedral of Toledo. Millàs Vallicrosa (p. 91–103, 1942).

ibn Yūsuf (d. 1296/97), omitted from Introd. vol. 2, see Suter (no. 394, p. 160, 1900; suppt. p. 177, 1902). Carlo A. Nallino (Rivista degli studi orientali 2, 480, 1909). Max Meyerhof: Sur un traité d'agriculture composé par un sultan yéménite du XIVe siècle (Bulletin de l'Institut d'Egypte 25, 55–63, 1943; 26, 51–65, 1944; Isis 36, 181), elaborate study prepared in Cairo during the war and kindly communicated to me after the war and Dr. Meyerhof's death (in 1945) by his widow.

C3. 'Irāq and Mamlūkīya

IBN AL-DURAIHIM

Tāj al-dīn 'Alī ibn Muḥammad ibn 'Abd al-'Azīz Ibn al-Duraihim al-Tha'labī al-Shāfi'ī al-Mawṣilī. 'Irāqī zoologist (1312–60).

Ibn al-Duraihim was born in Mūṣul, December 1312; he studied in his native city. He had inherited a fortune from his father, but it was so badly administered that he received only a part of it at the time of his majority. He traveled to Damascus and Cairo; in 1348 he went to Aleppo, then returned to Damascus, where he was appointed professor in the mosque of the Banū Umayya. In 1359 he moved to Cairo. Soon afterward the Mamlūk sulṭān al-Nāṣir Ḥasan sent him on a diplomatic mission to Abyssinia, but he died on the way thither, at Qūṣ on the upper Nile, December 1360.

His father, Muḥammad ibn 'Abd al-'Azīz Ibn Duraihim, wrote a treatise in verse on secret writing, Urjūza fī-l-mutarjam.

As to Tāj al-dīn, he wrote a treatise Ghāyat al-maghnam fī-l-ism al-a'ẓam, dealing with the exalted name of God (Hughes p. 220, 1885), and a treatise on the properties of animals, Kitāb manāfi' al-ḥayawān, not to be confused with other treatises bearing the same title, notably those ascribed (1) to 'Alī ibn 'Īsā ibn 'Alī, pupil of Isḥāq ibn Ḥunain (IX-2) and physician to the caliph al-Mu'tamid (ruled 870–92), (2) to 'Ubaidallāh ibn Jibrīl ibn Bakhtyashū' (XI-1). It is possible, however, that these three treatises dealing with the same subject are related like different editions of one text.

The treatise bearing the name of Ibn al-Duraihim was composed or edited in or before 1354, for it is represented by a magnificent MS in the Escorial (no. 898) dated 3 rabī' I 755 = 28 March 1354, and collated with the original text. That MS is one of the most beautiful Arabic MSS in the Escorial. It includes some 250 miniatures painted on a gold background, representing animals with great accuracy. It is written in eastern script (154 leaves, 13 lines to a page, 18 × 26 cm.). The beginning is lost, the remaining text starts in the middle of the description of man, dealing with liquids and secretions of the body. Then follow descriptions of domestic and wild animals, domestic and wild birds, fishes, reptiles, worms, insects, etc.

Criticism. Leclerc (2, 277, 1876). Brockelmann (1, 233, 236, 483, 1898; 2, 165, 1902; suppt. 2, 213, 1938). Renaud (p. 115–16, 1941).

Iconography of Animals (and Plants)

There are other illustrated MSS entitled Manāfi' al-ḥayawān in public and private collections, showing that this was a favorite subject for Muslim limners. I examined such MSS or isolated miniatures from them in the Freer collection, Washington, the Boston Museum of Fine Arts, the Metropolitan, the John Pierpont Morgan Library in New York, etc. (Introd. 2, 61, 1073). Many of these MSS are said to be of the thirteenth century or earlier, and hence Ibn al-Duraihim's authorship or editorship is excluded so far as they are concerned. The text of these MSS is generally very short; they are rather collections of zoological images with explanatory legends. Their interest for the history of zoological (and botanical) iconography is great.

To the references given in Introd. 2, 1073 add Edouard Blochet: Musulman painting (London 1929), including reproductions of some of the Pierpont Morgan miniatures (pl. xli–xliii, Tabrīz 1295), and many other images of horses, camels, monkeys, hares, birds, etc. reproduced from other Muslim MSS such as Kalīla wa-Dimna. Other books on Muslim art would yield similar documents.

AL-DAMĪRĪ

Egyptian theologian and encyclopaedic writer on animals (1344–1405).

Abū-l-Baqā Kamāl al-dīn Muḥammad ibn Mūsā al-Damīrī. The nisba is derived from the town Damīra near Samannūd in the Delta. He was born in Cairo in 1344 (rather than 1349) and was educated in al-Azhar; later he was himself a teacher in that famous school. Between 1360 and 1379 he made the Great Pilgrimage five times, and he resided in Mecca from 1379 to 1399. He then returned to Cairo, where he died in October 1405. He was a Shāfi'ī and also a ṣūfī affiliated with the Khānqāh brotherhood near Cairo.

He wrote various treatises in prose and verse on theological subjects, e.g., Al-jauhar al-farīd fī 'ilm al-tawḥīd (on the unity of God). The most important of these theological works is probably his elaborate commentary in four volumes, Al-najm al-wihāj fī sharḥ al-minhāj, on the Minhāj al-ṭālibīn, a popular manual of Shāfi'ī law by al-Nawawī (XIII-2).

His main work, however, and the only one by which he is remembered, is the Kitāb ḥayāt al-ḥayawān (The lives of animals), which was completed by him in the beginning of 1372. It is a large para-zoological encyclopaedia, dealing with a great many animals, real and imaginary, in alphabetical order. There are 1,069 articles, but on account of duplications the number of animals dealt with is somewhat smaller. The only exception to the alphabetical order is that the first animal dealt with is al-asad (the lion), because he is the king. Among the imaginary animals we find, e.g., al-burāq, the flying beast upon which the Prophet accomplished his ascent (mi'rāj) to heaven. I call the book para-zoological because the vast amount of information given apropos of each animal is not zoological, as we understand it, but chiefly nonzoological. The articles vary greatly in length; some are as large as treatises, others are restricted to a few lines.

The order followed for the articles is generally this: (1) name of the animal and its lexicographical and grammatical peculiarities (broken plurals, etc.) after al-Jāḥiẓ (IX-2), al-Jauharī (X-2), Ibn Sīda (XI-2), etc.; (2) description of the animal, after Aristotle and Jāḥiẓ (this comes closer to zoology proper); (3) traditions (ḥawādith) concerning the animals according to the six canonical collections (al-kutub al-sitta, list in EI 2, 192) and other sources; (4) legal questions; licit or illicit use of each animal for food or other purposes, according not only to the Shāfi'ī school but also to the three other schools of law, and to the opinions of theologians such as al-Ghazzālī; (5) proverbs relative to each animal, chiefly after the Majma' al-amthāl of al-Maidānī (XII-1); (6) medical and other properties (khawāṣṣ) of different parts of animals, their secretions and excretions, chiefly after Aristotle, al-Jāḥiẓ (IX-2), Ḥunain ibn Isḥāq (IX-2), 'Ubaidallāh ibn Bakhtyashū' (XI-1)

Ibn Sīnā (XI-1), Ibn Zuhr (XII-1), al-Qazwīnī (XIII-2); (7) interpretation (ta'bīr) of dreams concerning each animal; in most cases the interpretation implies reference to the Qur'ān. It is only for the most important animals that the information is completely given according to this scheme; sections 6 and 7 are often omitted.

If al-Damīrī had restricted himself to the program indicated, his collection would already have been considerable, and the more so that he was excessively learned. His work is full of references to some 807 authors and to many books the authorship of which cannot be determined. All the literature referred to is in Arabic, but it includes translations, e.g., from the following Greek authors: Hermes, Democritos of Abdera and Hippocrates, Plato, Aristotle, Galen, and Artemidoros Daldianos (II-2). The collection is considerably increased because of the author's discursiveness; he is always ready to fly off on a tangent apropos of a proverb or other quotation. For example, in the first article (on the lion) he indulges in a discussion of contagion, concluding that diseases are not naturally contagious but that God can make them so; further, a discussion of theology compared with astrology, the study of which may be permissible, indifferent, or blamable. The longest digression of the book occurs in the article on the goose (iwazz), 72 full pages devoted to the history of the caliphate (and two other subjects by way of subdigressions!) derived from 35 sources. Apropos of the scorpion ('aqrab) we are given an account of the games of shaṭranj (chess) and nard (backgammon); apropos of leeches ('alaq), the history of the child Moses; apropos of pigs (khinzīr), Arabic accounts of Christ, etc. In order to illustrate the lengths to which the philological section could be carried because of the very luxuriance of the Arabic language, we may recall with the author that there are in Arabic 630 names (or metaphors) used to describe the lion; happily al-Damīrī does not mention them all, but only the best known, about thirty.

The Ḥayāt al-ḥayawān is a treasure of Muslim folklore which is almost inexhaustible and has not yet been exploited as much as it deserves. A part of the information collected in it appears also in another form in the Alf laila wa-laila (the Arabian nights). Al-Damīrī's work enjoyed much popularity, being circulated in three recensions (like the commentaries of Ibn Rushd! see my remarks ad hoc, Introd. 2, 356), the large one (al-kubrā), the middle one (al-wusṭā), and the small one (al-ṣughrā). Moreover, there are abridged editions (all or some of the digressions being omitted), adaptations,[6] translations into Persian and into Turkish. Poetical extracts, Dīwān al-ḥayawān, made by the Egyptian polygraph al-Suyūṭī (d. 1505) were translated into Latin by the Maronite Abraham Ecchellensis (d. Italy 1664), and much of it was incorporated into the Hierozoicon of the French Protestant Samuel Bochart of Caen (1599–1667). The Hierozoicon (folio, 2 vols., London 1663) is an enormous collection of histories concerning the animals mentioned in the Bible, a sort of counterpart to the Ḥayāt al-ḥayawān devoted to the animals mentioned in the Qur'ān and the Islamic traditions. Thus did Islamic ideas on animals penetrate the West in the seventeenth century.

Text. The largest text of the Ḥayāt al-ḥayawān was first printed in Cairo (Būlāq 1858–59), then again in 1867–78 and 1887–99. I have used the last of these editions (2 vols.), containing the 'Ajā'ib al-makhlūqāt of al-Qazwīnī (XIII-2) in the margin. It was reprinted in Cairo 1891–92, 1911–12 (1383 p.).

There is also a lithographic edition with small drawings in the margins, printed

[6] **One of these adaptations or imitations, the Bulūgh al-murād min al-ḥayawān wal-nabāt wal-jamād, was composed by Ibn Ḥijjah of Ḥamāh (1366–1434), referred to in my note on al-Qalqashandī.**

in Persia (Teheran? 1869), probably derived from the first or second Egyptian edition.

English translation by the retired lieutenant colonel A. S. G. Jayakar (vol. 1, vol. 2 part 1; a total of 1498 p., Bombay 1906–8). Vol. 1 has English and Arabic indexes; not so vol. 2, which was left incomplete presumably because of the editor's death. The translation extends to Abū-l-Firās, a name of the lion; it is about three-quarters of the total, some digressions having been omitted. The revision and completion of that work is very desirable.

Extracts have been translated into French by A. J. Silvestre de Sacy in his French edition of Oppianos II: La chasse (Strasbourg 1787). For Oppianos II of Syria (fl. 214), author of the *Κυνηγετικά*, as well as for Oppianos of Cilicia (fl. 177), author of the *'Αλιευτικά*, both of whom were unfortunately omitted from Introd. vol. 1, see notes by Joseph Needham (Isis 11, 413–14, 1928). Other extracts concerning camels, cattle, sheep, elephants, translated with notes in A. Perron: Le Nacéri, la perfection des deux arts (3, 425–73, Paris 1860).

Criticism. Leclerc (2, 278–79, 1876). Sándor Kégl: A critical examination of Damīrī's work (35 p., Budapest 1889), in Hungarian. Brockelmann (2, 138, 1902; suppt. 2, 170, 1938). D. B. Macdonald (EI 1, 912, 1912). J. Stephenson: The zoological section of the Nuzhatu'l-qulūb (Isis 11, 303, 1928). Bodenheimer (1, 131–48, 1928), extracts relative to insects. H. A. Winkler: Eine Zusammenstellung christlicher Geschichten im Artikel über das Schwein in Damīrī's Tierbuch (Der Islam 18, 285–93, 1929).

Joseph de Somogyi: Index des sources de la Ḥayāt al-ḥayawān (Journal asiatique 213, 5–128, 1928), very elaborate study listing 807 authors divided into 23 categories, well indexed; Die Chalifengeschichte in Damīrī's Ḥayāt al-ḥayawān (Der Islam 18, 154–58, 1929); A history of the caliphate, etc. (Bull. of the School of Oriental Studies 8, 143–55, London 1935); The interpretation of dreams in Damīrī (Journal of the R. Asiatic Society, 1940, 1–20).

MUḤAMMAD IBN MANGALĪ

Muḥammad ibn Mangalī (or Manglī; the g stands for the Persian kāf) al-Nāṣirī. Chief of the guard of al-Ashraf Sha'bān (Mamlūk sulṭān 1363–76). Egyptian author of books on hunting and horsemanship.

His best-known work is a treatise on hunting, Ins al-malā bi-waḥsh al-falā; he wrote at least two other books dealing with hunting and equitation in peace and war.

The Ins al-malā is so comprehensive that it is worth while to indicate briefly its main contents. It begins properly with a discussion of the religious duties of hunting men, the things which are permitted or forbidden to them. The flesh of a piece of game recently killed by a lynx, or even by the hunter's own dogs, may not be eaten; the eating of it is lawful only if the hunter has killed the animal himself by cutting its throat. No game killed by means of a blunt instrument may be eaten. Then the author discusses other duties of sportsmen in general, and especially of princes, while on the chase or on the way to it or from it; how to use hunting weapons (bows of different kinds, lances, stones, clubs, javelins, swords and daggers). Hunting gazelles, lions, elephants, tigers, hyaenas, wolves, boars, cheetahs (how to catch them alive, domesticate them, and train them for the chase), various kinds of leopards, lynxes, and caracals. The most valuable kind of leopard is the one which has been trained to hunt in concert with a falcon. Training of hounds. Use of birdlime (history of that use). On various kinds of hawks (ṣaqr), falcons (bāz, pl. buzā), eagles ('uqāb, pl. 'uqbān), etc., and their qualities. Males of the hunting birds (always weaker than the females). Crows, owls, zummaj (pl. zamāmij) =

Falco halioetus. History of falconry. Training of falcons and their care (Syrian methods). Hunting of ostriches with ṣaqr. Eagles (nasr, nusūr) and their qualities. Anūq = ? pygargus,[7] a kind of hunting bird. Hunting with nets and traps. Catching hares with traps. Various presages for the determination of favorable hunting days. Lucky names. How to drive noxious animals out of plantations and vineyards (crows, grasshoppers, moles, rats, ants). Precautions against snakes. Peacocks (ṭā'ūs, ṭawāwīs). Crocodiles (timsāḥ, tamāsīḥ). Saqanqūr (a kind of lizard), tortoise, hippopotamus, and beaver (qundus). In spite of its relatively small size (154 printed pages), the book contains a large amount and a great variety of information. For example, there are many indications concerning the medical properties of various parts of animals. The account is lightly and pleasantly written; it includes vivid descriptions and amusing anecdotes.

Text. Florian Pharaon: Sid Mohamed el Mangali. Traité de vénerie, avec une introduction par le marquis G. de Cherville (308 p., Paris 1880), Arabic text of the Ins al-malā' plus incomplete and hasty translation into French. Only 300 copies printed, one of which was kindly lent to me by the Cleveland Public Library. The editor and translator of this work was dragoman of the French army in Algiers; his father and grandfather had been dragomans, the latter being Bonaparte's own dragoman in Egypt. We need a critical edition of this text together with an annotated translation, well documented and well indexed. Pharaon's work is only a rough approximation.

Criticism. James Edmund Harting: Essay on sport and natural history (p. 362–70, London 1883); Bibliotheca accipitraria (p. 103, 205, 1891). Brockelmann (2, 136, 1902; suppt. 2, 167, 1938). Louis Mercier: La parure des cavaliers (p. xiii, 400, 409, 457, Paris 1924; Isis 8, 346–49; 9, 504). Atiya (p. 544, 1938), wherein Mangalī is spelled Minkalī.

MUḤAMMAD IBN LĀJĪN

Muḥammad ibn Lājīn al-Ḥusāmī al-Ṭarābulusī al-Rammāḥ (the lancer of Tripoli). Syrian writer on chivalry, cavalry tactics, etc. (fl. 1379).

In December 1378 or January 1379 he wrote for amīr Ashiktīmūr Saif al-dīn al-Māridīnī, Mamlūk governor of Aleppo (d. 1388/89), a treatise on cavalry tactics, entitled Bughyat al-qāṣidīn bil-'amal fī-l-mayādīn. Three other treatises of the same kind are ascribed to him, though some of these may be identical in spite of different titles.

His father, Lājīn ibn 'Abdallāh al-Dhahabī Ḥusām al-dīn al-Ṭarābulusī (d. 1337), had also written a book on the same subject, Tuḥfat al-mujāhidīn fī-l-'amal bil-mayādīn.

Criticism. Brockelmann (2, 135–36, 1902; suppt. 2, 166–67, 1938).

The Mamlūk empire in Egypt and Syria was very prosperous throughout the fourteenth and fifteenth centuries and until the Ottoman conquest in 1517; in fact,

[7] It is difficult if not impossible to say whether the words anūq and pygargus refer to the same bird. Circus pygargus is a hawk, one of the marsh harriers. "It was named binomially by Linnaeus in 1758 who based his description on the older works of John Ray and Eleazar Albin, both of whom simply called the bird 'The Pygargus.' The English vernacular name today is 'Montagu's Harrier.' This bird is an old world species breeding in England and through northern Europe and Asia to Turkestan, the Altai and northwestern Mongolia, south to Spain, northwestern Africa, Italy, Rumania, and northern Iran. It winters from Palestine to South Africa and also in India, Ceylon, and Assam. Its principal food is taken alive and consists of small mammals, birds, reptiles, and amphibians." (Information kindly given me by James Lee Peters, curator of birds, Harvard Museum, in a letter dated Oct. 19, 1945.)

it was during that period one of the most prosperous countries, and its military organization, chiefly in the form of cavalry, was excellent. As a result there is an abundant Arabic Mamlūk literature on the art of war, especially cavalry tactics, horsemanship, veterinary art, furūsīya, jarīd (a kind of racing), fantasia, jihād (holy war), swordsmanship, use of lances, bows and arrows, war engines, Greek fire and other inflammable substances, falconry, etc. Many of these writings are cited by me in various places, but I did not attempt to cover that field completely. Lists of such books will be found in Louis Mercier: La parure des cavaliers et l'insigne des preux (p. 431–59, Paris 1924; Isis 8, 346–49; 9, 504). Hellmut Ritter: La parure des cavaliers und die Literatur über die ritterlichen Künste (Der Islam 18, 116–54, 1929).

ṬAIBUGHĀ

Ṭaibughā ibn 'Abdallāh al-Ashrafī al-Baklamishī al-Yūnānī. Turkish-Greek writer on the art of war and cavalry tactics, writing in Arabic (d. 1394?).

He wrote for al-Ashraf Sha'bān (Baḥrī Mamlūk 1363–76) a qaṣīda on shooting with bow and arrows, Bughyat al-marām wa ghāyat al-gharām (or Ghunyat al-rāmī wa ghāyat al-marām). Other treatises of his on similar subjects: Ghunyat al-ṭullāb fī ma'rifat al-ramy bil-nushshāb; Kitāb fī-l-jihād wal-furūsīya wa funūn al-ādāb al-ḥarbīya.

Criticism. Brockelmann (2, 135, 1902; suppt. 2, 167, 1938). Louis Mercier: Parure des cavaliers (p. 251, 387, Paris 1924). Hellmut Ritter (Der Islam 18, 137, 1929).

C4. Turkey

MAḤMŪD IBN MUḤAMMAD AL-BĀRJĪNĪ

Turkish author of a book on falconry, entitled Bāz-nāma, written in Turkish in the third quarter of the fourteenth century. The nisba Bārjīnī refers to the town Bārjīn (or Bārčīn) in the vicinity of Milas (ancient Mylasa, southwestern Anatolia).

According to the author (in his preface), the Bāz-nāma was first written in "a civilized language" (Greek?), then translated into Arabic, from Arabic into Persian, and finally by him from Persian into Turkish. It is not clear whether it is a plain translation of one text, or an adaptation derived from many texts; it is not clear either whether references (in the Turkish text) to personal observations were contributed by the translator or were simply translated by him. Such questions could be solved only by collation of all the texts involved, and we have only the Turkish one.

It is divided into 155 chapters, many of which are very brief, for the whole Turkish text covers only 95 pages, or about 1,900 lines. In the preface and first chapter the author discusses the purpose of the book and tells a largely mythical history of falconry. According to him, the first to hunt with falcons was king Demetrios. Of course there were kings of that name in Macedonia and Syria, and falconry originated probably in the Near East, but I wonder whether the Demetrios legend is not derived from the fact that the earliest Greek treatise on falconry was composed by Demetrios Pepagomenos (XIII-2), physician to the emperor Michael Palaeologos c. 1270. In the following chapter Maḥmūd describes and discusses the different kinds of hunting birds, how to recognize the best ones, their classes, colors, qualities; the qualities required of falconers, the differences between different kinds of hunting birds, how to feed and train them. The greatest part of the Bāz-nāma (chs. 30–155) is devoted to a description of ailments to which hawks and falcons are liable, and methods of curing them. The names of birds are given not only in Turkish, but also in Arabic and Persian.

In the preface the author cites a number of earlier books on the subject, some of which I could not identify. To wit, (1) one by Jamālī Muḥammad Ganja of the Sāsān family, written in Akhlāṭ (western shore of Lake Van, Armenia) in 1145; (2) one by Nicetas Sacatophoros,[8] written for the emperor in Constantinople in 1175; (3) the book of the great Turkish king Khāqān[8a] and of the king of India, by 'Izz al-dīn Muḥammad al-Bālāsāghunī, written in Damascus 1181 (there is a place called Bālāsāghun in Turkistān); (4) a book written by Abū-l-Qāsim in Alexandria 1194; (5) the book of Nūshirwān the Just by 'Imād al-dīn of Iṣfahān, written in Ba'albek 1195; (6) the book of Mawlānā Badr al-dīn Muḥammad of Balkh, written in Aleppo in 1174 (items 3, 5, and 6 were mentioned in Introd. 2, 425); (7) a *new* book composed for 'Alī Kāma of Khurāsān by Sharaf al-dīn Ālp Arslān Qarābalī, written in Erzerum (Armenia) in 1195. I quote the dates as given in the Turkish text; they seem to involve contradictions and may be erroneous. It is remarkable that they are restricted to the twelfth century; thus this text may belong to the thirteenth century, though we should hardly expect it in its Turkish form before the fourteenth. According to a recent Turkish source, the Turkish translation was made by order of Menteşe Oğlu Mehmed (that is, the Muḥammad who ruled the Menteshe territory in southwestern Anatolia c. 1354–75);[9] see also p. 3v of Turkish text; by the way, the town of Bārjīn, with which the translator was connected, was then the seat of government of the Menteshe Oghullari.

Text. The Turkish text of the Bāz-nāma was edited by Jos. von Hammer-Purgstall in his Falkner Klee (Pesth 1840), together with a German translation. That book is rare, only 300 copies having been published; apparently the only copy available in America is in the Cleveland Public Library, which kindly communicated it to me. The title Falkner Klee (Falconer's trefoil) is due to the fact that the same book contains two other texts, namely, an anonymous Byzantine text Ἱερακοσόφιον (see Introd. 2, 1095) and the Handschrift über Falknerey of the emperor Maximilian (ruled 1493–1519).

Criticism. Harting (p. 54, 193, 1891), criticizing Hammer-Purgstall's translation, particularly the wrong names given to the different hunting birds. I. Hakkı Uzunçarşılıoğlu: Anadolu beylikleri (p. 84, Ankara 1937; Isis 32), Turkish study on the mediaeval Anatolian states; the author of the Bāz-nāma is called Muhammed oğlu Mahmud, but such inversions are not uncommon in Oriental names.

D. CHINA

CHU HSIAO

Chinese physician and botanist (d. 1425).

Chu Hsiao was the fifth son of the first Ming emperor, Hung Wu (ruled 1368–98). He received from him in 1378 the title of honor Chou Wang (meaning prince Chou). Sometime later he fell under suspicion, was forbidden to use the title, and was obliged to spend a good part of his life in banishment and disgrace. He was honored, however, by his brother, the third emperor, Yung Lo (ruled 1403–25), who restored

[8] Spelled Sqṭūfrūs in the Turkish text. Saqāṭ (Ar.) means very sharp sword.

[8a] Khāqān is not a name, but a Turkish title meaning khān khānān, lord of lords. See Yule's Marco Polo (vol. 1, *10*, 1926). Cordier's Notes (p. 3, 1920). Hobson-Jobson (p. 479, 1903).

[9] Zambaur (p. 153, 1927).

the title Chou Wang to him at the time of his own accession. Therefore, he is generally called Chou Wang Hsiao (see Ming shih, ch'üan 116).

From 1382 to 1400 he lived on his estates near Kai-fêng-fu, Honan, and he created there not only a botanical garden, but also an experimental garden for the acclimatization of wild plants which might be used in times of famine. He is said to have obtained some 400 plants from farmers and hermits for his experiments. He died in 1425 and received the posthumous name Chou Ting Wang, which is perhaps more commonly used by Chinese scholars to designate him than any other.

Herbal. He wrote a herbal called the Chiu huang pên ts'ao, meaning "Famine herbal" or "Herbal to relieve famine"; this was completed in 1406, date of the preface by his friend and collaborator Pien T'ung, and presumably date of the first edition. It was, however, the fruit of many years of research, and hence it may be considered in our survey of the fourteenth century.

The Chiu huang pên ts'ao contains descriptions and illustrations of 414 species of plants, of which only 138 had been discussed in earlier herbals, 276 being described for the first time. What is even more remarkable, the descriptions and drawings were based on the specimens cultivated in his own garden. The Chinese pên ts'ao, like the Western herbals, were generally concerned with herbs or drugs, rather than with food plants;[10] on the contrary, the Chiu huang pên ts'ao was largely devoted to plants to be eaten, especially those from which additional food could be obtained in times of scarcity. Herbs were not neglected (some 245 are mentioned), but an unusually large number of other plants were described.

The work is divided into two books, called shang "upper" and hsia "lower," and each book is divided into two parts, ch'ien "leading" and hou "following," paged separately. These four parts are designated in the earliest edition (1406?) by the four characters yüan, hêng, li, chên, which are the first four characters of the Book of changes, I-ching, here used symbolically (as 1, 2, 3, 4). This explains why in later editions the work is divided into four books.

The 414 plants are divided as follows. In book I there are descriptions and figures of 173 herbs, only 40 of which had been dealt with in earlier works. Book II describes 241 plants classified under trees, grains, fruits, vegetables, and of these only 98 had been mentioned before. The amount of new materials is very large indeed.

According to Li Shih-chên in the Pên ts'ao kang mu, the Chiu huang pên ts'ao was compiled by prince Chou Hsien, a son of Chou Wang Hsiao, during the Hung Wu period (1368–98), but that ascription is very doubtful, as it involves chronological difficulties.

Botanical iconography. The illustrations are particularly remarkable, and, assuming the earliest printed edition to have the date of its preface (1406), the woodcuts adorning it antedate by seventy years the earliest ones of the West, i.e., those included in the princeps of the Buch der Natur of Conrad von Megenberg (Augsburg 1475). The first Latin herbal, Herbarium Apulei, appeared in Rome 1481; the first Herbarius in Mainz 1484, the Herbarius zu deutsch in Mainz 1485 (Klebs nos. 505–10, 1938; Sarton p. 111, 118, fig. 48, 1938).

One need not quarrel about the date of the first edition of this particular herbal, for there are many printed editions of other Chinese herbals which are considerably earlier—more than four centuries earlier. The earliest printed Chinese herbal

[10] The term Shih wu pên ts'ao or "Food herbal" does not mean herbal dealing with food plants, but rather treatise on diet or household medicine.

dates from 973. It was overlooked in our volume 1, the earliest printed herbal to be cited by us (Introd. 2, 442) being the T'u ching pên ts'ao by Su Sung, style Tzŭ-jung, who died in 1101, aged 82 (Wong and Wu p. 93, 1936). It was compiled by imperial order and published in 1061. It is probable that the woodcuts of the "Famine herbal" continued the iconographic traditions of that Sung herbal, for the latter is mentioned in Pien T'ung's preface.

Unfortunately no printed copies of the T'u ching pên ts'ao of 1061 have yet been traced, nor even of another Sung herbal published a century later, in 1159, the Shao hsing chiao tung ching shih chêng lei pei chi pên ts'ao, compiled by Wang Chi-hsien, Chang Hsiao-chih, Ch'ai Yüan, and Kao Shao-kung, but manuscript copies of the second herbal are available and there are also manuscript copies of some illustrations of the first. The iconographic tradition is also confirmed by Japanese editions or MSS derived from the Chinese originals (Report of the Library of Congress for 1927, p. 254–59).

To return to the early Ming edition of the Chiu huang pên ts'ao, its plant illustrations (see fig. 38) are relatively large (the largest being framed in a space 18 × 12 cm.) and they are remarkably free and strong. It is said that prince Chu Hsiao employed artists to draw these illustrations from the living specimens available in his garden. Knowing the excellence of Chinese artistic traditions, it is not surprising that their plant illustrations are so pleasing. They compare very favorably with the Western illustrations. In this case, however, we cannot claim, as we did for the printed illustrations, that the Chinese are earlier. That is, it is extremely difficult to date the beginning of MS plant illustrations, either East or West. Western ones have been traced back to the first century B.C., but there are many solutions of continuity;[11] the Chinese tradition is probably as old if not older, but the complete story has not yet been told.

P'u-chi fang. Another work ascribed to Chu Hsiao is a large treatise on medicine entitled P'u-chi fang, compiled c. 1378?, in 168 chüan. It was the most elaborate of its kind thus far produced, including 1,960 discourses on 2,175 different subjects with 778 rules, 61,739 prescriptions, and 239 diagrams (Wylie).

Text. The original edition of the Chiu huang pên ts'ao, preface dated 1406 and published presumably in the same year or soon afterward, was printed in Kai-fêng-fu, Honan, on the author's estate. In 1526, it was reprinted by Li Lien, Shansi; in 1555 it was again reprinted in Wei, northern Honan and southern Shansi. This third edition included another similar work, the Yeh ts'ai p'u, by Wang P'an, style Hung-chien, first published under Chêng-tê (emperor 1506–22), describing and illustrating 60 plants that could be used for food especially during a famine.

Other editions of the Chiu huang appeared in Ssŭch'uan 1562; in Yünnan 1566; in 1639, etc. A reprint of it was published in 1640 at the end of the famous treatise on agriculture, Nung chêng ch'üan shu (60 chüan), by Hsü Kuang-ch'i (1562–1633),[12] minister of state under Wan Li (Ming emperor 1573–1620), disciple of Matteo Ricci and baptized under the name Paul Hsü at Nanking.

The edition included in the Ssŭ k'u chüan shu is a reprint of the 1555 edition with a preface by Lu Tung.

The first Japanese edition of it was prepared and punctuated by the herbalist Matsuoka Gentatsu (literary name Joan), and printed by Yoshinoya Gonbei (8

[11] Charles Singer: The herbal in antiquity (Journal of Hellenic studies vol. 47, 1927; Isis 10, 519–21). Introd. 2, 54.

[12] The date of death 1634 given by Giles (no. 779) is incorrect. The third centenary of Hsü's death was celebrated at Zikawei, near Shanghai, in 1933 (Isis 24, 122–23, 1935). Hummel (p. 316–19, 1943).

Fig. 38. Illustration from the Famine herbal (Chiu huang pên ts'ao), first edition (c. 1406). It is taken from a section designated Shang-hou, p. 28, and represents the Ch'ang-p'u = Acorus calamus, sweet flag, an herb of the arum family (Araceae). According to Giles' dictionary (no. 434, 1912), leaves of that herb are hung on door lintels in the shape of a sword on the fifth day of the fifth moon, the Dragon festival, to ward off evil influences. Courtesy of Dr. A. W. Hummel and of the Library of Congress.

vols., Kyōto 1716). This was reprinted about the middle of the eighteenth century, without date. These two Japanese editions include also the Yeh ts'ai p'u (here called Chiu huang yeh p'u) and its supplement, pu-i. The Japanese editor, Matsuoka Gentatsu, added prefaces wherein he discussed famine relief in China and the nature of true wealth, and added to the text explanations in Japanese katakana.[13] The Japanese editions contain the same text and figures as the Chinese ones, with minor differences, but the illustrations are not quite so good as the early Chinese woodcuts.

Criticism. Wylie (p. 99, 1902). Hübotter (p. 66, 1924). The date of publication of the P'u-chi fang, 1378, is given by Wong and Wu (p. 237, 1936) without any explanation. Report of the Library of Congress for 1925 (p. 265) and for 1935 (p. 193–202), elaborate description by Walter T. Swingle of the early Ming edition, and briefer ones of the other Chinese and Japanese editions. For comparison, A. W. Hummel: The printed herbal of 1249 (Isis 33, 439–42, 1941).

[13] Introd. 1, 519, 553.

CHAPTER XXV

MEDICINE

(Second Half of the Fourteenth Century)

N.B. Only the main notes are published in this chapter. The medical contributions of many other men, whose main work was done in other fields, are discussed in other chapters. For a general survey of medicine in the second half of the fourteenth century, see section XI of chapter XV. More information on the men referred to in that survey may then easily be found by means of the index.

PLAGUES

THE BLACK DEATH

The epidemic of bubonic plague which began in 1348 was perhaps the most terrible calamity in the recorded annals of mankind. Since it was as sharp and sudden in its initial stages as it was frightful, it constitutes a real "cut"[1] in the past, a solution of continuity, perhaps the best example of such a solution that one could cite, because it concerned a very large part of the civilized world.

It was not the first considerable epidemic to be recorded, though one cannot be sure that the earlier ones were caused by the same disease. The plague of Athens (430–425 B.C.) described by Thucydides (V B.C.) was certainly something else.[2] The earliest description of the real plague is (or may be) in the medical collection of Oribasios (IV-2), wherein it appears under the title *Περὶ βουβῶνος ἐκ τῶν Ῥούφου*,[3] On the bubo, taken from Rufus of Ephesus (II-1). The so-called plague of Justinian, lasting from 542 to 594, was almost certainly the bubonic plague; it began in Egypt 542, reached Constantinople, and then spread across Europe; it was described by Procopios (VI-2), Evagrios (VI-2), Gregory of Tours (VI-2).[4] The pest of Cadwalader[5] which ravaged Great Britain in 664–84 and was described by Bede (VIII-1) was probably also bubonic, for a pestis inguinaria was recorded in Rome shortly afterward (690).

Other plagues were described in Arabic by Ibn al-Jazzār (X-2) and 'Abd al-Laṭīf (XIII-1), the latter dealing with the plague of Egypt, 1200. A reference to the plague of 1286 is found in the Latin chronicle of fra Salimbene (XIII-2). Other examples in Sticker (1, 34–41, 1908).

The plague of 1348 was infinitely more disastrous than the preceding ones, perhaps because the increase of international trade by land and sea had considerably multiplied the chances of contagion, while the means of defense had remained as rudimentary as before. There can be no doubt as to its nature. It was the true

[1] Taking the word in its mathematical acception.

[2] For the latest discussion of this see John H. Finley, jr.: Thucydides (p. 158–59, Harvard University, Cambridge, Mass. 1942). Finley is tempted to favor the hypothesis of ergotism, though George Barger discountenanced it in his excellent monograph Ergot and ergotism (p. 42, London 1931).

[3] Book 44, ch. 17. Bussemaker et Daremberg: Oeuvres d'Oribase (3, 607, Paris 1858).

[4] Edward Gibbon, ch. 43 (in J. B. Bury's illustrated ed., 4, 465–69, 1925).

[5] Cadwalader or Caedwalla, king of Wessex 659?–89; died in Rome 689 after having been baptized by Sergius I (pope 687–701).

Oriental plague, whether bubonic or pulmonary. Indeed, axillary, inguinal, and pulmonary lesions were witnessed and duly recorded.

As nearly as can be ascertained, that plague began in Muttra (on the Jumna, between Delhi and Agra) in 1332, that being the time of a great pilgrimage occurring every twelfth year. We have an account of the Muttra plague in Ibn Baṭṭūṭa (4, 200–2). The pilgrims distributed the sickness far and wide; it spread out eastward as far as Farther India until 1351. Epidemics occurring in Russia in 1341 and in Styria in 1342 may have been the first Western forerunners of the greater calamity generally known as the Black Death.

By 1346 the plague had done its worst in Asia and it was moving steadily westward. It reached Constantinople in 1347 and soon afterward the main parts of Southern Europe; for example, that same year 1347 saw it already in Sicily, Naples, and Genoa. Venice was visited by the pestilence at the beginning of 1348. From that great emporium it spread rapidly in many directions. The Mediterranean countries seem to have been visited first, the climax of the plague occurring there in 1348; in Central Europe and England the climax did not occur until the following year, and in Russia not until 1352. The journey of the pestilence through the whole of Europe seems to have been, in the main, horseshoe-shaped, beginning with Constantinople, proceeding south of Europe as far west as the Atlantic, then north, and finally returning to Asia along a northern course.

The climax in each place lasted from about four to six months, very seldom more or less. Where and when the disease began during the winter, it assumed the pulmonary form and kept it or became of the bubonic type in the spring. We now know that the infection is spread by fleas and rats, but nobody suspected that, and hence the prophylaxy was irrelevant, except in so far as cleanliness tended to keep down every kind of parasite, and segregation restricted the contagion. The onslaught of the disease was always sudden and violent, and the initial mortality high, but the course of the epidemic, in this as in other cases, or in the case of conflagrations, was often capricious. Some localities suffered considerably more, while others in the same neighborhood were mysteriously spared. This seemed to confirm the ancient theory of airs and climates, some airs being naturally more healthful than others. Of course, climatic peculiarities might cause deflections of the pestilence, but we may assume that most of the deflections were accidental or that their causes were too complex for analysis.

There is no point in explaining here in greater detail the progress of the disease; the complete story would be very long and to be properly understood should be illustrated with tables, maps, and diagrams. The information available is exceedingly abundant and varied. Not only do we have a collection of special plague treatises, to be listed below, but a great many accounts are spread in the annals and belles-lettres of many nations. A few examples will suffice.

To begin with Arabic sources, Ibn Baṭṭūṭa referred not only to the Muttra episode, but to others. He witnessed the plague in Damascus 1348 (1, 227–29), in Cairo and Fusṭāṭ (1, 229), in Ghazza, Ḥomṣ, Jerusalem (4, 320 f.). Ibn Khaldūn tells us in his autobiography written eleven years before his death that his father died in Tunis of the plague of 749 (= 1348/49), and he gives us in his Muqaddama an account of that calamity which is so brief and forceful that we may be allowed to give a free translation of it (De Slane, Arabic, 1, 51):

"In the middle of the eighth [i.e. fourteenth] century a plague visited the countries of the East and the West, decimated the peoples, carried off a good part of this generation, folded up and wiped off many of the amenities of civilized life. That calamity shook nations which were in their old age and had reached the end of their career; it restricted their power, weakened their sovereignty, and precipitated their disintegration and their ruin. Husbandry was curtailed because of the lack of men, cities were devastated, palaces tumbled to pieces, landmarks were obliterated, houses and settlements deserted. Nations and tribes were enfeebled, and the life of the people changed. The same thing happened in the East and in the West, causing damages in proportion to the culture of each part. It is as if the voice of nature had called the world to repentance and humiliation and the world has hastened to comply; truly God is the heir of the earth and of all that it bears. When such a profound upheaval occurs, as if nature were radically transformed and a new creation were shaping itself, there is need for a historian who will describe the condition of the world, of the countries, and of the peoples, and the changes in manners and creeds, do again what al-Mas'ūdī did in his own time, and thus serve as an example and a guide to his successors. . . ."

This statement of Ibn Khaldūn is remarkable on many grounds. It bears witness to the fact that the Black Death was a universal calamity and that well informed contemporaries were aware of its extent. In addition, Ibn Khaldūn realized that it was a solution of continuity in human affairs and that as such it set for the historian a new task, and imposed upon him new duties. His belief that the calamity had been so destructive because it coincided with the senility of nations was of course a false generalization of his experience of the decadent Islamic world.

Among Western writers the best-remembered is probably Boccaccio, who described the pest as an introduction to his Decamerone. Other descriptions were given by such diverse persons as the Florentine historian Matteo Villani; a Belgian cleric who was at the court of Avignon early in 1348 and wrote a letter home; the French surgeon Guy de Chauliac; the French poet and musician Guillaume de Machaut, etc. Then there are formal documents, the most important of which is probably the statement prepared in October 1348 by the faculty of medicine of the University of Paris upon the request of king Philippe VI le Bien fortuné.[6]

Greek accounts of the plague may be found in the chronicles of Nicephoros Gregoras and Joannes Cantacuzenos, and there are also Hebrew ones, e.g., in the 'Emeq refa'im[7] of Ḥayyim ben Abraham (ibn) Galipapa.[8] The 'Emeq refa'im is really a commentary on Semaḥot,[9] but it includes descriptions of the sufferings of the Jews in Catalonia and Provence c. 1347–50, sufferings due to the pestilence and to persecutions. The text of the 'Emeq refa'im is preserved in the 'Emeq ha-baka (The balsam vale) of the French historian and physician Joseph ha-Kohen.[10]

[6] Compendium de epidemia per Collegium facultatis medicorum Parisius ordinatum. The first complete edition was published by Hippolyte Emile Rebouis: Etude historique et critique sur la peste (p. 70–144, Paris 1888), with French translation. There are many early MSS of that text in Latin and French. Sudhoff: Pestschriften, no. 263 (AGM 17, 65–76, 1925). Alfred Coville (HL 37, 336–59, 1938).

[7] Valley of Rephaim, meaning of ghosts or of giants (2 Samuel 5:22), southwest of Jerusalem, now called Baq'a.

[8] This Galipapa was born in Monzon (Huesca, Aragon) c. 1310, died 1380. He was rabbi in Huesca, later in Pamplona. JE (5, 555, 1903). EJ (7, 60, 1931).

[9] Semaḥot (joys), nickname of the treatise Ebel rabbati, dealing with the mourning for the dead, in the Babylonian Talmud. It is appended to the fourth order, Neziqim (injuries), of the Mishnah.

[10] Joseph ben Joshua ha-Kohen, born in Avignon 1496, died in Genoa c. 1577. JE (7, 266, 1904). EJ (9, 349–52, 1932). The 'Emeq ha-baka was edited by Max Letteris (Vienna 1852) and translated into German by Me'ir Wiener (Leipzig 1858).

The Black Death is generally dated 1348, but, as we have seen, it began a few years before, and it lasted until 1352. The mortality in Europe was highest during the years 1348 to 1352, and highest of all in 1348. Moreover, the plague did not stop completely in 1352. It apparently died out then, like a conflagration when everything that could easily burn has been burned, but one knows that the fire is smoldering under the embers, ready to flare up from time to time. The same thing happened with the plague. It stopped in 1352 when all the people that were susceptible to it had been killed off or tried out. It flared up again in various places in 1356, 1357, 1358, 1359, 1360, 1361, 1362, 1363, 1364, 1365, 1366, 1367, 1368, 1369, 1370, 1371, 1372, 1374, 1375, 1377, 1378, 1379, 1380, 1381, 1382, etc. In short, between 1348 and 1400 there was scarcely a year when the bubonic plague was not raging somewhere. Nor did it end with the fourteenth century; it reappeared at irregular intervals until our own days. Every English reader knows of the great pest of London which lasted from 1629 to 1664, reaching its climax in 1636–37 and lower maxima in 1640–42 and 1646–47. An epidemic spreading from Hong Kong in 1894 might have been as terrible as the Black Death but that the defenses against it were immeasurably improved. The plague flared up ominously in San Francisco 1907–8. It is only in relatively recent times that the etiology of the disease has been understood and hence a scientific prophylaxy has become possible. The bacillus of the plague was discovered by Shibasaburo Kitasato and Alexander Yersin in 1894.[11]

To return to the epidemic of 1348, it is impossible to say with any precision how many people were its victims. It has been estimated that one-fourth of the population of the civilized world was destroyed, the proportion of mortality being considerably higher in certain districts. Indeed, some villages were practically depopulated. The economic, political, and social consequences of such radical depletion can be imagined; they are so easy to imagine that one must be very careful when reading accounts of the plague to draw the line between such imaginations and factual knowledge. Even contemporaries may be led to exaggerate. For example, when we read in William Dene,[12] "So great was the want of labourers and workmen of every art and craft" in those days "that a third part and more of the land throughout the entire kingdom remained uncultivated. Labourers and skilled workmen became so rebellious that neither the King, nor the law, nor the justices, the guardians of the law, were able to punish them," we realize that such a statement, being an induction from gossip, should not be taken literally.

In any attempt to draw conclusions from the comparison of estimated populations, say in 1340 and 1380, one must bear in mind two great causes of confusion. The population of certain countries was decimated by war as well as by the plague. In France, the Hundred Years' War (1337–1453) caused directly and indirectly a good many deaths. Then the plague casualties varied materially from one district to another, e.g., from one diocese to the next one.[13] Local chroniclers would naturally be tempted to generalize their own experience.

We may assume that the mortality of the poor tended everywhere to be greater than that of the rich and powerful, because the poor were more exposed to contagion and could not escape it as easily if they chose. The result was a depletion of

[11] William Bulloch: History of bacteriology (p. 237, Oxford 1938; Isis 31, 480–82).

[12] Chronicler fl. 1350, notary public to Haymo, bishop of Rochester, probably author of Annales roffenses, history of Rochester from 1314 to 1350 (DNB 14, 341). The passage quoted is taken from Gasquet (p. 199, 1893).

[13] Coulton: Medieval panorama (p. 496, 1938).

laborers and a premium on labor. Thousands of acres remained uncultivated. Prices rose; this was certainly the case in England for such commodities as iron, salt, clothing, even fish. The humble herring became a luxury. Wages rose in spite of protracted efforts to keep them down. The frequent reiteration of royal commands forbidding masters to offer or pay higher wages and laborers to demand or accept them is in itself a proof that wages were raised. On the other hand, rents were decreased and the tenure of land deeply modified. The laborers' and the tenants' gains were defended by sundry trade unions which are designated in a statute against them as "alliances, covines, congregations, chapters, ordinances, and oaths" (Gasquet p. 200). The people were awakening and realizing their power. Labor troubles were brewing. It will suffice to recall the Jacquerie (1358) in France and the Peasants' Revolt (1381) in England; the plague was not by any means the only cause nor even the main cause of those revolts, but it helped to precipitate them. It may also be said that the Black Death facilitated the downfall of chivalry, but it was only one cause of that downfall among many, and probably not the most important.

The moral and religious consequences of the plague are even more difficult to appraise and to assess than the material consequences. The fear of contagion revealed the existence of many selfish and cowardly people, but many others were sufficiently brave and loving to overcome that fear and risk their life for their relatives or their neighbors. Family and social ties were often loosened or broken. The faith of some men was intensified, while others lapsed into pessimism and cynicism, and lost grace and courage. Adversity is the best touchstone. It hardened the heart of some men and opened up the heart of many others. It is hardly possible to say what happened in each case, and quite impossible to generalize.

It is difficult to say whether on the whole faith was increased or not, but it is certain that superstitions were multiplied. The astrological mentality, which obtained in various degrees everywhere, favored the growth of superstitions. The plain people might be resigned to accept the plague as a divine punishment for their sins; the more sophisticated ones wanted a more scientific explanation, and that explanation was almost always astrological. There were also strong tendencies to establish causal nexus between this calamity and others, such as volcanic eruptions or earthquakes, or between the plague and mysterious portents such as comets, eclipses, or other conjunctions. Innocent practices, such as the veneration of relics and images, were necessarily multiplied. Special prayers and incantations were devised.[14] Unfortunately, the history of such fallacies is singularly barren. We can hardly count them, for their name is legion, and they are essentially similar. It is a waste of time to try to analyze them.

There are other ways of measuring the harm done to the people's religion. So many shepherds were killed that the flocks must have been neglected. This is something tangible and measurable. Ecclesiastical annalists have revealed many pertinent facts. Out of 27 or 28 cardinals in office, 8 or 9 died in 1348/49; out of 69 metropolitans, 25 died; out of 575 bishops, 207 died (Campbell p. 136 f., 1931). The mortality was much higher among the lower clergy, who, if they did their duty (and we may assume that most of them did),[15] were frequently exposed to contagion.

[14] For a good example, see G. Del Guerra: Per la storia degli amuleti, una preghiera contra la peste del 1400 (Rivista di storia delle scienze, anno 24, 15, 49–53, 1933).

[15] That is my guess, but Coulton has reached a very different conclusion (Medieval panorama p. 500, 1938): "Briefly we have the judgment of 22 chroniclers, English and foreign, upon the

Says Coulton (Medieval panorama p. 497), "It seems now quite certain that nearly half of the beneficed clergy [of England] died during these plague months."

According to Dom Francis Aidan Gasquet (p. 162 f., 1893), who made a special study of English conditions (but they would not be very different in other plague-stricken countries), many monasteries were emptied or decimated, and so many livings were suddenly vacated that it was impossible to appoint new incumbents having the necessary qualifications. Bishops were obliged "to institute young and inexperienced, if not entirely uneducated clerics, to the vacant livings, and this cannot but have had its effect upon succeeding generations." And he quotes the chronicler Knighton saying, "At that time there was everywhere such a dearth of priests that many churches were left without the divine offices, mass, matins, vespers, sacraments, and sacramentals. One could hardly get a chaplain to serve a church for less than £10, or 10 marks. And whereas before the pestilence, when there were plenty of priests, anyone could get a chaplain for 5 or even 4 marks, or for 2 marks and his board, at this time there was hardly a soul who would accept a vicarage for £20, or 20 marks. In a short time after, however, a large number of those whose wives had died in the pestilence came up to receive orders. Of these many were illiterate and mere laics, except in so far as they knew in a way how to read, although they did not understand" what they read. Ordinations were accelerated, and other irregularities overlooked. The worst is that many of the new clerics were completely ignorant, even concerning their own prayers and rites. One wonders whether the lapses from duty and devotion noted by contemporary chroniclers and summarized by Coulton were not mainly due to these hasty ordinations of poor devils.

Sacred buildings the creation of which had been begun before the plague remained unfinished, e.g., St. Nicholas in Great Yarmouth (Norfolk), the church of Tideswell (Derbyshire), or in another country the duomo of Siena. On the other hand, the immense duomo of Milano was begun after the plague (in 1386) and may be considered a monument of the reviving faith.[16] The plague seems to have created a break in the tradition of stained-glass manufacture (Gasquet p. 203).

---

behaviour of the clergy during the pestilence. Of the eight least unfavourable, one only is entirely favourable; but he speaks only for his own neighbourhood (Catania). The two next best, while praising the friars or the nurses, contrast these with the negligent behaviour of the parish priests. The remainder are frankly, and sometimes violently, unfavourable. It would be difficult to find any historical question, involving so directly and so deeply the reputation of an enormously numerous and influential body, with exceptional facilities for self-defence and self-advertisement, in which the evidence is so overwhelming against them. Even though all these chroniclers had been mistaken as to the facts (though, as we have seen, the official documents go far to support them), there would still remain the plain consideration that, whatever the priests had actually done, public opinion did judge them to have fallen, as a body, far below the height of their sacred office. That belief, in itself, would go far to explain Lollardy and the Reformation."

[16] The cathedral replaced an earlier one destroyed when Frederick Barbarossa ruined Milano in 1166. It was largely the ambitious conception of Gian Galeazzo Visconti (1347–1402, ruler 1374–1402) and was dedicated to Maria Nascens (to the birth of the Virgin). The name of the first architect is unknown, but many architects Italian and foreign are mentioned in connection with it. Among the Italians were Andrea degli Organi of Modena (c. 1387) and his son Filippino, Simone Orsenigo (ingeniere alla fabbrica), and many "maestri campionesi," i.e., maîtres d'oeuvre coming from Campione (Lago di Lugano, Lombardia), a famous nursery of architects, builders, sculptors, such as Marco da Campione, etc. Among the Germans were Heinrich Arler (or Parler) von Gmünd = Enrico da Gamodia, or Gamundia, fl. Milano 1391–92 (ADB 25, 180, 1887), Johann von Fernach. In 1388 the Parisian geometer Nicolas de Bona-

One particularly hideous consequence of the plague was the fact that a great many people, integrating their superstitious fears with their anti-Semitism, threw the responsibility of the common miseries upon the Jews, whom they accused of having poisoned wells in order to destroy the Christians. This terrible delusion became very prevalent in Central Europe, especially in Germany. In some cases, it was connected with the old blood accusation.[17] In every case, it was the cause or became the pretext for persecuting the Jews. A great many of them were killed, and their goods stolen or ruined. By the end of the fifteenth century, there were only three considerable Jewish communities left in the whole of Germany. There is no need of narrating all these horrors, which remained unsurpassed, even in Germany, until our own days. Summary by Joseph Jacobs (JE 3, 233–36, 1902), with list of places where persecutions occurred in 1348–49 and a map which we reproduce with kind permission (fig. 39); see also article on the blood accusation by the same (JE 3, 260–67).

It is a relief to turn one's attention from those unspeakable crimes to the courage shown by pope Clement VI, who was then ruling in Avignon (his papacy lasted from 1342 to 1352). He showed the absurdity of the accusation made against the Jews, for the plague raged everywhere irrespective of their presence or absence, and he took them under his protection. He also refused to persecute the friars at the request of the secular clergy, who were jealous of their success.

Ernest Wickersheimer: Les accusations d'empoisonnement portées pendant la première moitié du XIVe siècle contre les lépreux et les Juifs; leur relations avec les épidémies de peste (4e Congrès international d'histoire de la médecine, Bruxelles, avril 1923; 8 p., Anvers 1927). Flick (1, 72, 1930). Coulton: Inquisition (p. 288 f., 1938).

On the occasion of other plagues (Geneva 1542–45, Milano 1630) some people, not necessarily Jews, were accused of having spread the disease maliciously by means of ointments. The tragic fate of the "untori" of 1630 has been discussed in my article on Beccaria (Bull. of the history of medicine, suppt. no. 3, 286, 301–3, Baltimore 1944). I am not aware that that particular accusation was made against the Jews in 1348–49. The change of the accusation from "poisoning wells" to "besmearing with poisonous ointments" illustrates the gamut of futile variations which one may expect in the annals of superstition.

The influence of the Black Death on education was of the same kind as its influence on religion. The mortality among teachers and students jeopardized the functioning, and sometimes the very existence, of universities and colleges. The claim that students and scholars were demoralized by the plague is as difficult to substantiate as the similar accusation made against the clergy. It is easy to cite

---

venture was called in and competed with Jacopo da Campione for the great window of the apse; the executed design was Nicolas'. Italian jealousy, however, drove Nicolas out, and duke Gian Galeazzo called in his place in 1399 another Frenchman, Jean Mignot (c. 1346–c. 1410), who built the vestry on the south side. Mignot got into trouble with the Italian architects such as Bartolino da Novara, partly because he claimed that the fabric was insecure; he was dismissed in 1402. He it was who said, Ars sine scientia nihil (Ananda Coomaraswamy, Catholic art quarterly vol. 6, 5 p., 1943). NBG (6, 552, 1855; 35, 491, 1861).

[17] The accusation that Jews, or some Jews, employed Christian blood for their rites was first formulated by the Alexandrian grammarian Apion of Oasis (Ἀπίων ὁ Ὀασιτικός) and was refuted by his younger contemporary Josephus (I-2).

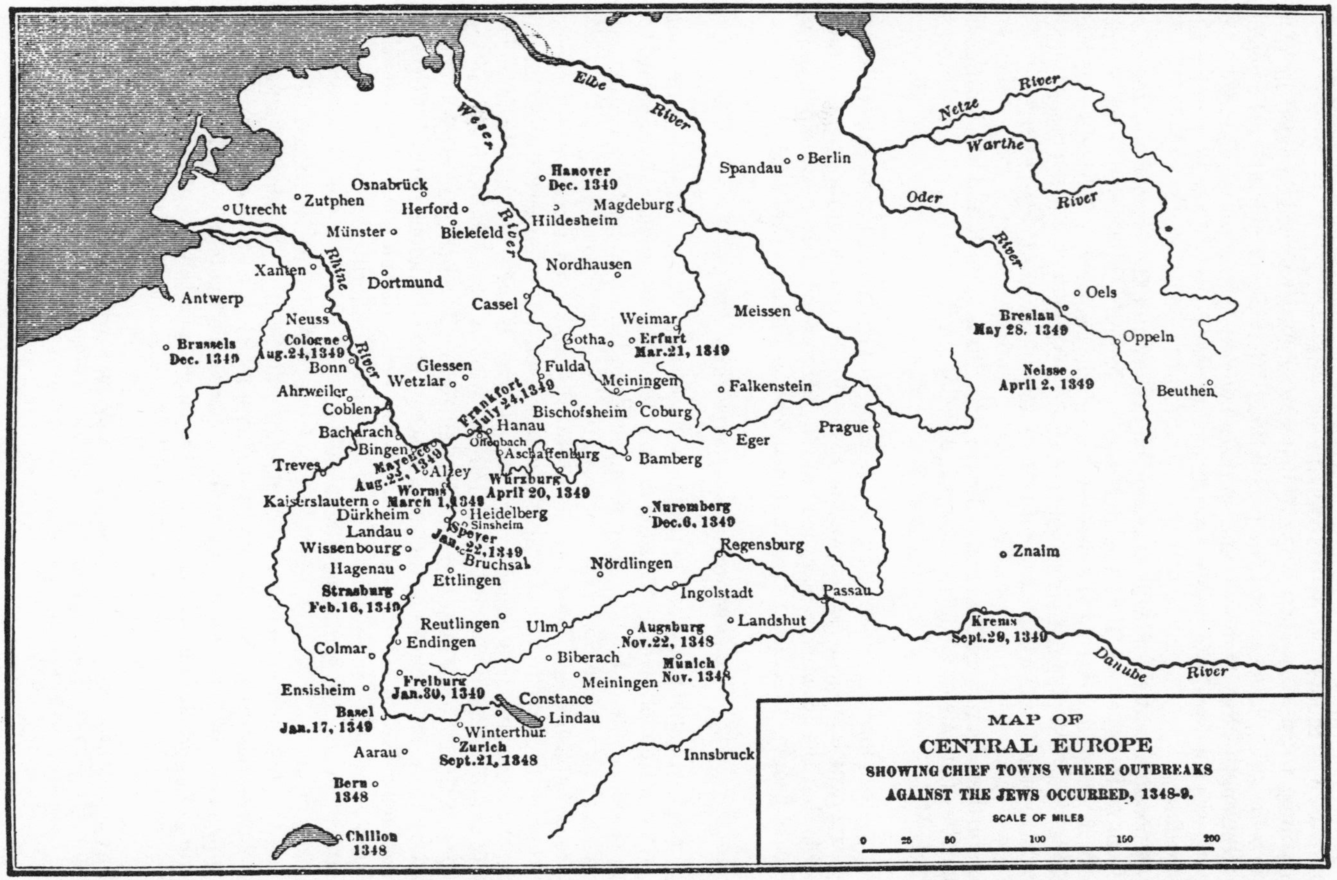

FIG. 39. Map of Central Europe showing chief towns where outbreaks against the Jews occurred, 1348–49. From Jewish encyclopedia (3, 235, 1902). Courtesy of Funk and Wagnalls, New York.

examples of demoralization, but were they caused by the plague, or by contemporary miseries such as the war, or by individual accursedness?

According to Matteo Villani, the University of Florence was founded in 1349, partly with a view to increasing the population of that city, depleted by the plague, and to strengthening its morale and spirit, weakened by the same calamity. The purpose was good and the method excellent, but the success of the new university was mediocre.

It is possible that the plague favored the diffusion of the European vernaculars vs. Latin. It is certain that the diffusion of English (in England) vs. French increased materially during the second half of the century. It is possible, even probable, that the plague had something to do with that, for it delivered such a formidable blow to the whole of society that everything was affected by it.

For further details see Stephen d'Irsay: The Black Death and the mediaeval universities (Annals of medical history 7, 220–25, 1925) and Campbell's elaborate study (1931).

The destruction of the Icelandic settlements in Greenland has been ascribed to the plague which swept over Norway in 1348–49, but that is unproved; it is more probable that the Icelanders marooned in Greenland were gradually assimilated by the native people. See discussion of that subject in chapter I (p. 196).

Development of Public Sanitation

The most valuable result of the plague was the organization of public sanitation, that is, the introduction of various regulations to avoid contagion and safeguard the health of the people. There was no scientific definition of contagion; for that, one had to wait at least two centuries longer, until Gerolamo Fracastoro (c. 1478–1553) of Verona published his De contagione (1546),[18] and even three centuries more until the age of Pasteur and the birth of bacteriology. An empirical awareness of contagion, however, was ancient. It can be traced back to the Pentateuch,[19] wherein are to be read the earliest prophylactic measures. Throughout the ages people sensed that it was safer to avoid the sick, especially when many were suddenly visited by the same sickness in the same place. The contagious nature of leprosy, of the plague, and of a few other diseases was realized, and the best precaution, which unfortunately could be taken only by a small minority, was to go away and stay away (Fuge cito, vade longe, rede tarde).

Andrea Dandolo (XIV-1), doge of Venice from 1343 to 1354, organized what was perhaps the first municipal commission of public health. Similar organizations were soon established in Florence, Foligno, Ragusa, Lucca, Pistoia, etc. An analysis and comparison of their several ordinances cannot be made here and now. The stationing of some kind of sanitary cordon around places to prevent the entrance of afflicted people must have occurred often (the trouble is that they could not always

[18] Hieronymus Fracastorius (1478–1553): De contagione et contagiosis morbis et eorum curatione libri III (Venice 1546). Handy edition of the Latin text with English translation by Wilmer Cave Wright (New York Academy of Medicine, New York 1930; Isis 16, 138–41). See also the bibliography of Fracastoro's other work, Syphilis (Verona 1530) by Leona Baumgartner and John F. Fulton (158 p., 9 fig., New Haven 1935; Isis 24, 437–39).

[19] Maurice Bear Gordon: Medicine among the ancient Hebrews (Isis 33, 454–85, 1941), with abundant references. The Jewish regulations were probably derived from early Babylonian ones.

tell who the afflicted were), and the guarding of walled cities was apparently easy. The first more complete attempt at prophylactic isolation[20] was probably made by Ragusa (1348), plague-stricken people being sent to the neighboring island Zuppana.[21] According to Guy de Chauliac, Avignon was protected by a sanitary cordon in 1348 and 1360. Barnabò Visconti, lord of Milano from 1354 to 1385, in a letter dated January 17, 1374 ordered the isolation of suspicious people for ten days and had the audacity to forbid religious processions in times of epidemics. A new regulation issued in Ragusa, 1377, ordered the isolation of afflicted or suspicious people for thirty days (that was the trentina). Six years later, Marseille extended the period of probation to forty days, the quarantaine. The number forty was chosen arbitrarily, perhaps with some remembrance of the conventional use of that number from early days (e.g., Old Testament) and of the mystical value sometimes attached to it. The Marseille regulation of 1383 is the origin of the modern quarantine.[22] It is not surprising that quarantine regulations originated in sea harbors (Venice, Ragusa, Marseille), where the danger of sudden epidemic invasions was considerably greater. In 1385, Venice had already created a competent administration, the magistrato della sanità.

Because of the ignorance of the true nature of contagion and of the etiology of infectious diseases, these regulations, wisely meant, were very inefficient. Therefore, it was not possible to prove their superiority over other methods of prophylaxy, such as processions, pilgrimages, kissing of reliquaries, etc., which were positively dangerous. The favorite tutelary saints against the plague were two Languedocians, St. Sebastian (born in Narbonne c. 256, martyred Rome 288; feast, January 20) and St. Roch (born and died Montpellier, c. 1293–c. 1327; feast, August 16). Raymond Crawfurd in Plague and pestilence (p. 99, Oxford 1914) and Henry Ernest Sigerist in The historical aspect of art and medicine (Bull. of the Institute of the History of Medicine 4, 271–97, 1936) have argued that St. Sebastian in his role as intercessor in times of pestilence is the Christian avatar of Apollo. In any case, St. Sebastian has been as great an inspiration to Christian artists wishing to reproduce a beautiful male body as Apollo was to the pagan sculptors.

The cult of St. Roch is represented by curious incunabula including stories of miraculous cures and hence having possibly some medical interest. Klebs (nos. 335, 852–54, 1938), Sarton (p. 51, 184, 1938). Similarly, there are early printed plague sheets featuring St. Sebastian. For example, a very early one (c. 1450–60), a combination of woodcut and xylographic Latin text, shows the saint being shot by Diocletian's soldiers with their crossbows; the text is a deprecation against the plague. That unique print was probably made in Upper Germany. It is reproduced in Elizabeth Mongan and Carl O. Schniewind: The first century of printmaking (p. 21–22, Chicago 1941).

Plague Treatises

In addition to the accounts of the plague written by annalists, historians, and men of letters, and to the abundant references to it scattered in every literature of

[20] An earlier regulation may be that of Venice 1127, cited by F. G. Clemow: The origin of quarantine (British medical journal 1, 122, 1929).

[21] For this and a few following facts I am indebted to J. W. S. Johnsson (1868–1929): La peste de 1763 en Dalmatie (Isis 11, 343–63, 1 pl., 1928; 12, 47–85, 255–86, 1929; see 11, 357 f.), documents of 1374 and 1377 quoted in extenso.

[22] The English word quarantine was soon used to mean a period of prophylactic segregation not necessarily restricted to 40 days. Thus Pepys refers in his diary (26 Nov. 1663) to a "quarantine for thirty days" (OED).

the fourteenth-fifteenth century, there were also special treatises written by physicians for the use of other physicians or of laymen. These treatises are generally divided as follows: (I) discussion of the causes of the plague (largely astrological), (II) prophylaxis, (III) treatment. There might be an epilogue, wherein the astrological arguments of the first part would probably be repeated. The pathological descriptions are generally of the most meager kind.

These treatises are very numerous; most of them are written in Latin, others are written in several vernaculars, in Arabic, and in Hebrew. The first scholar to undertake a comparative study of them was Karl Sudhoff, who proved himself a pioneer in this field as well as in almost every other field of medical history. In the Archiv für Geschichte der Medizin (vol. 1, 1908), published by the Puschmann-Stiftung[23] of the University of Leipzig and directed by him, he edited many such treatises, beginning with Ein deutsches Pest-Regiment aus dem 14. Jahrh. (AGM 2, 379–83, 1909), Ein weiteres deutsches Pest-Regiment aus dem 14. Jahrh. und seine lateinische Vorlage, das Prager Sendschreiben "Missum imperatori" vom Jahre 1371 (AGM 3, 144–53, 1909), Epistola et regimen Alphontii Cordubensis de pestilentia (AGM 3, 223–26, 1909). In the meanwhile, Sudhoff had been collecting photographs of a large number of MSS, and in the following year he was able to start the publication of an ambitious series entitled Pestschriften aus den ersten 150 Jahren nach der Epidemie des "schwarzen Todes" 1348 (AGM vols. 4–17, 1910–25). In that collection he dealt with so many texts (some 281!) that it would take too much space to enumerate them here. A complete list with indexes and table of incipits will be found in AGM (17, 266–91, 1925). Moreover, the majority of these texts belong to the fifteenth century; as to the fourteenth-century ones, many are referred to in the notes of this volume devoted to their authors. Many of these texts, however, were anonymous, and for those the reader is invited to consult the Sudhoff series.

The following generalities may be mentioned: Of the 281 texts investigated by Sudhoff, 141 came from Germany, 77 from Italy, 21 from France, 9 from Spain, 9 from England, 17 from unknown places. The fact that half are of German origin is accidental, Sudhoff having naturally been able to explore the German collections of MSS more thoroughly than the collections of other countries. The large number of texts of Italian origin (almost one-third) may be explained in a similar way, Sudhoff having explored the Italian archives more methodically than those of other countries foreign to him. Of the 141 texts of German provenience, 70 are in Latin, 63 in German, 2 translated from French, 2 translated from Latin, 4 in German and Latin. Of the 281 texts, 155 can be ascribed to definite authors, the others are anonymous. The fourteenth-century texts are 77 in number, originating 26 in Germany, 29 in Italy, 10 in France, 2 in Spain, 3 in England, 7 in unknown places.

We owe similar surveys, more modest in scope but of equal merit, to Dorothea Waley Singer: Some plague treatises (Proceedings of the Royal Society of Medicine, hist. sec., 9, 159–212, London 1916; Isis 3, 327) and to Alfred Coville: Ecrits contemporains sur la peste de 1348 à 1350 (HL 37, 325–90, 1938).

Mrs. Singer's study, like Sudhoff's, covers the fifteenth century as well as the fourteenth, but it is centered on the tractate composed in 1365 by John of Burgundy. She deals with 22 texts, 10 of which are of the fourteenth century.

[23] This foundation devoted to the history of medicine was established by the Silesian physician Theodor Puschmann (1847–99), the same who organized the great treatise on the history of medicine, Handbuch der Geschichte der Medizin, edited by Max Neuburger and Julius Pagel (vol. 1, Jena 1902; vol. 2, 1903; vol. 3, 1905).

Coville restricts himself to early texts, the most valuable being the treatise published in October 1348 by the medical faculty of Paris and already referred to. He deals not only with medical texts, but also with poems, letters, and liturgical documents. See also Ernest Wickersheimer: Zeitgenossen über den Schwarzen Tod (AGM 3, 348–49, 1909), apropos of two interpolations relative to the plague of 1348 in MSS of Richard of Saint Victor;[24] La peste noire à Strasbourg et le régime des cinq médecins strasbourgeois (3e Congrès de l'histoire de l'art de guérir, Londres 1922, 7 p., Anvers 1923; Isis 7, 195).

Finally, one should consult as usual the plague incunabula. This has been made easy by the elaborate studies of Paul Heitz: Pestblätter des XV. Jahrh. (20 p., 40 pl., Strassburg 1901), and Arnold C. Klebs: Remedies against the plague. The earliest French tracts printed in the fifteenth century, facsimiles, notes and list of all the incunabula on the plague (96 p., Paris 1925); Die ersten gedruckten Pestschriften (München 1926; Isis 9, 430–33). The first of Klebs' books was also published under a French title; the first book was prepared with Eugénie Droz, the second with Karl Sudhoff.

All the surveys thus far named left out the Arabic texts; information about the latter will be found under the names of the respective authors. Investigations will be facilitated by the following alphabetic list of all the fourteenth-century "plague" authors dealt with in my Introduction.

List of Plague Treatises

This list of the plague treatises, or remarks concerning the plague, referred to in this volume is possibly incomplete. The places and dates are no more than first indications; they may refer to the plague or to writings about the plague. More information may be obtained by means of the general index.

'Abd al-Raḥmān b. Khaldūn (XIV-2) 1348
Abner of Burgos (XIV-1)
Agramont, see James
Aḥmad b. 'Alī b. Khātimah (XIV-1) .... Almeria 1348/49
Aḥmad b. Yaḥyā b. a. Ḥajala (XIV-2) 1362
Albert, master 1348
Albert of Parma (XIV-1) .... Strassburg 1349
Albic, see Sigismund
Almeria, see Muḥammad b. Muḥammad
Alphonso of Cordova (XIV-1) .... Montpellier 1348
Aurispa, Giovanni (b. Noto, Sicily, c. 1370; d. 1459), may be identical with John da Noto, below .... 1398?
Benjamin b. Isaac of Carcassonne (XIV-2) .... after 1362
Bernard of Frankfurt (XIV-2) 1381
Boccaccio, see John
Burgo, see Nicholas
Burgos, see Abner
Carcassonne, see Benjamin b. Isaac
Cardo of Milano (XIV-2) 1378
Casini, see Francesco
Chalmel de Viviers, see Raymond
Colle, see Dionisio

[24] Richard of Saint Victor (d. 1173?), Scotch mystical theologian, canon and later prior in the abbey of St. Victor, Paris (DNB 48, 188).

Collignano, see Franciscchino
Conrad of Megenberg (XIV-1)
Cordova, see Alphonso
Couvin, see Simon
Damouzy, see Peter
Dionisio II Colle (XIV-2) .... after 1350
Dondi, see John
Foligno, see Gentile
Frankfurt, see Bernard
Francesco Casini (XIV-2) .... c. 1370
Francischino de Collignano (XIV-2) 1382
Franciscus de Gianellis (XIV-2) .... after 1351
Gallus de Strahov (XIV-2)
Garbo, see Tommaso
Gentile da Foligno (XIV-1) .... Genoa 1348
Geoffroi de Meaux (XIV-1) 1348
Gianellis, see Franciscus
Glogau, see John
b. a. Ḥajala, see Aḥmad b. Yaḥyā
Hake, see John
Henry Knighton (XIV-2) 1348
Henry Ribbenicz (XIV-2)
Isaac b. Ṭodros (XIV-2) .... Avignon 1373
Jacob the Armenian (XIV-2) .... Bohemia 1371
Jacobi, see John
James d'Agramont (XIV-1) .... Lerida, April 24, 1348
John Boccaccio (XIV-2) .... Florence 1348
John de' Dondi (XIV-2) .... before 1371
John of Glogau (XIV-2) 1371–73
John Hake (XIV-1) .... Avignon 1348/49
John Jacobi (XIV-2) 1373
John Mandeville (XIV-2) 1365
John da Noto (XIV-2) .... Bologna 1398
John della Penna (XIV-1) .... Naples 1348
John da Santa Sofia (XIV-2)
John of Saxony (fl. Strassburg 1409)
John de Tournemire (XIV-2) .... Montpellier 1378–82
b. Khaldūn, see 'Abd al-Raḥmān
b. al-Khaṭīb, see Muḥammad b. 'Abdallāh
b. Khātimah, see Aḥmad b. 'Alī
Knighton, see Henry
Maino de Maineri (XIV-1) 1360
Manbijī, see Muḥammad b. Muḥammad
Mandeville, see John
Matteo Villani .... Florence 1348
Meaux, see Geoffroi
Megenberg, see Conrad
Michele da Piazza (XIV-2) .... Messina 1347
Milano, see Cardo
Montpellier, anonymous .... May 19, 1349
Muḥammad b. 'Abdallāh b. al-Khaṭīb (XIV-2) 1348
Muḥammad b. 'Alī al-Shaqūrī (XIV-2) 1348
Muḥammad b. Muḥammad of Almeria (XIV-2)
Muḥammad b. Muḥammad al-Manbijī (XIV-2) 1373

Nicholas of Burgo (XIV-2)....1382
Nicholas of Udine (XIV-2)....Vienna 1390
Noto, see John
Paris, faculty of medicine....October 1348
Parma, see Albert
Penna, see John
Peter of Damouzy (XIV-1)....August 16, 1348
Peter of Tossignano (XIV-2)....1397–98
Piazza, see Michele
Raymond Chalmel de Viviers (XIV-2)....Avignon 1382
Ribbenicz, see Henry
Santa Sofia, see John
Saxony, see John
Shaqūrī, see Muḥammad b. 'Alī
Siena, see Francesco Casini
Sigismund Albic (XIV-2)
Simon de Couvin (XIV-1)....1348, Paris 1350
Strahov, see Gallus
Strassburg, five physicians....July–October 1349
Taranta, see Valescus
Ṭodros, see Isaac
Tommaso del Garbo (XIV-2)....after 1348
Tossignano, see Peter
Tournemire, see John
Udine, see Nicholas
Valescus de Taranta (fl. Montpellier from 1382, still living 1418)....1401
Villani, see Matteo

Bibliography (in addition to references already given in this article). The standard treatise is that of Georg Sticker: Die Pest (Abhandlungen aus der Seuchengeschichte und Seuchenlehre vol. 1; 2 vols., Giessen 1908–10), vol. 1 contains the history of the plague down to 1908, with bibliography and 12 maps.

L. A. Joseph Michon: Documents inédits sur la grande peste de 1348 (thesis, Paris 1860). Robert Hoeniger: Der Schwarze Tod in Deutschland (186 p., Berlin 1882). Karl Lechner: Das grosse Sterben in Deutschland 1348 bis 1351 und die folgenden Pestepidemien bis zum Schlusse des 14. Jahrh. (172 p., Innsbruck 1884). J. F. K. Hecker: The Black Death (47 p., New York 1885). Francis Aidan Gasquet: The great pestilence (264 p., London 1893), new edition under the title The Black Death of 1348–49 (298 p., London 1908). Edmund Alfred Wesley: The Black Death (Proceedings of the Literary Society of Liverpool no. 60, 24 p., 1907). Raymond Crawfurd: Plague and pestilence in literature and art (230 p., Oxford 1914). Peter George Mode: Influence of the Black Death on the English monasteries (diss., 108 p., Chicago 1916). Johannes Nohl: Der Schwarze Tod, eine Chronik der Pest (374 p., Potsdam 1924; Isis 9, 380–82), also available in English translation (London 1926), mediocre anecdotic book, badly arranged, with interesting illustrations. Koenraad Oege Meinsma: De Zwarte Dood, 1347–52 (487 p., Zutphen 1924; Isis 8, 542). Herman B. Allyn: The Black Death, its social and economic results (Annals of medical history 7, 226–36, 1925). Stephen d'Irsay: Defense reactions during the Black Death (Annals of medical history 9, 169–79, 1927). Anna Montgomery Campbell: The Black Death and men of learning (222 p., New York 1931; Isis 18, 195–97). Charles Verlinden: La grande peste de 1348 en Espagne (Revue belge de philologie 17, 103–46, 1938).

George Gordon Coulton: Five centuries (2, 392, 394, 397, 663, 1927); The Black Death (79 p., London 1928); Medieval panorama (p. 493–506, 1938).

Wu Lien-teh (= tê): A treatise on pneumonic plague (480 p., League of Nations, Geneva 1926). There is a long chapter (118 p.) on the history of pneumonic plague, but except for 8 introductory pages it is entirely devoted to the present pandemic.

OTHER EPIDEMICS

The people who suffered from the Black Death realized that that visitation was but one, to be sure the worst one, among many. In the Lilium medicinae Bernard of Gordon (XIV-1) enumerated eight contagious diseases, to wit, acute fevers, tuberculosis, scabies, erysipelas, epilepsy, anthrax, trachoma or ophthalmic gonorrhea, leprosy. The Latin text is given in the note on Bernard of Gordon. That list was incorrect in that epilepsy is not contagious, and the plague itself was not explicitly included,[25] but it illustrates mediaeval appreciation of epidemic dangers.

There are other lists similar to Bernard's and enumerating five, nine, or eleven diseases. Here are two of them; the first is anterior to 1300 (Leipzig MS 1119):

Hii sunt morbi contagiosi, id est inficientes alios
Febris acuta, ptysis, scabies, pedicon, sacer ignis
Cancer, lippa, lepra, frenesis, squinancia, antras.

The second line is the same as Bernard's first; the third might be translated cancer, trachoma, leprosy, typhus (and cerebrospinal meningitis), diphtheria (and croup), anthrax (and glanders).

Another example may be found in a Breslau MS (III fol. 20) of the second half of the fourteenth century:

Nota quinque sunt morbi contagiosi unde versus:
Lepra, febris, lippa, scabies, morbusque caducus
Corporibus nostris transicione nocent.

The morbus caducus in line two is the same as pedicon in the previous example, i.e., erysipelas or perhaps impetigo. The same MS indicates three ways in which the air can be corrupted and the disease thus transmitted: "Nota aer corrumpitur tripliciter, primo modo propter malam constellacionem, secundo modo propter putredinem cadaverum, tercio modo ex fetido, id est racione anhelitus fetidi." Observe that the first cause is astrological.

The two texts have been published by Karl Sudhoff: Elf ansteckende Krankheiten vor 1300 (Mitt. 16, 132–34, 1917; Isis 3, 326); Fünf ansteckende Krankheiten (ibid. 14, 405, 1915; Isis 3, 328). In his commentaries Sudhoff refers to other examples. It is thus certain that the people of the thirteenth and fourteenth centuries (notably Pietro da Tossignano) were aware of the possibility of contagion, even if their conception of its mechanism was wrong. See also Sudhoff: Welche Menschen man fliehen soll (AGM 8, 221, 1914).

Cholera

The reader may wonder how it is that cholera is not mentioned in these lists, for that epidemic seems to be very old. Its name, χολέρα (derived from χολή = gall bile), occurs often in the Hippocratic collection[26] and in the later Greek medical writings. That name, however, covered several diseases characterized by violent

[25] Bernard's Lilium was completed in 1303.
[26] The references are too numerous to be listed here. See index to Littré's edition (10, 524).

diarrhoea and various syndromes. According to a classification made in 1830, there are three main kinds of choleras: (1) cholera morbus, indigena, endemica, sporadica, aestivalis; cholera nostras, europaea, choléra simple (Laveran), hot-weather diarrhoea (Buchanan), etc.; (2) cholera infantum (Rush 1789); (3) cholera asiatica, indica. The ancient and mediaeval descriptions concerned the first two kinds, some of which were contagious but not epidemic. The dreaded Asiatic cholera was unknown in Europe before the nineteenth century. There may be references to it in ancient Asiatic literatures, Sanskrit, Tibetan, Chinese, but these references are unclear and uncertain. The first recorded epidemics occurred in India, to wit in Ganjam, Madras 1780; Hardwar (Hari-dwára or Ganga-dwára), Saráhanpur, U. P. 1783; Jessor, Bengal 1817. The last-named (Bengal) epidemic spread over the whole of Hindūstān, reached the Caucasus and the Volga basin in 1823, and menaced Europe. It now became the world epidemic which caused as many fears, if not quite as much destruction, as the Black Death.

The unambiguous definition of these ailments became possible only after the discovery and sufficient development of bacteriology. The infectious kinds of cholera may be clinically alike in many respects; they are scientifically defined and distinguished from one another by the bacteria causing them. Thus, the cholera asiatica is defined by the presence in a sick organism of the cholera vibrio (Vibrio comma, Spirillum cholerae asiaticae), discovered by Robert Koch in 1883. The discovery was not generally accepted except after long discussions due to the instability of that vibrio and the strange irregularities in its behavior (e.g., it may be quiescent, and its virulence may vary considerably from time to time or from place to place).

Asiatic cholera is endemic in Asia, but its main home is in India. It broke out many times in Europe, 1831–32, 1837, 1847, 1853, 1865–66, etc. One of the main causes of its westward propagation was the Muslim Pilgrimage; Mecca was a great center of diffusion. From 1866 on the international organization of quarantine became chiefly concerned with the defense against cholera, and this implied in the first place the sanitation of the Pilgrimage. A good account of this has been given by Firmin Duguet: Le pèlerinage de la Mecque (Paris 1932; Isis 20, 499–503).[26a]

The standard book on the history of cholera is Georg Sticker: Die Cholera (Abhandlungen aus der Seuchengeschichte und Seuchenlehre vol. 2, 596 p., Giessen 1912).

The Dancing Mania

During the last quarter of the fourteenth century there spread through German lands a curious epidemic which was called variously the dance of St. John or the dance of St. Vitus (chorea Sancti Viti), because its climax occurred each year about the time of the festivals of those saints in June.[27] The patients used to dance wildly until they were exhausted.

The earliest known occurrence of St. John's dance was in Aix-la-Chapelle (Aachen) in 1374. Soon afterward it appeared in neighboring places, Liége, Tongres, Utrecht,

[26a] Pilgrimages in general were excellent means of diffusing epidemic diseases. The Muslim pilgrimages to Mecca and Medina were less dangerous than they might have been because the sacred cities were surrounded by deserts. Yet many of the pilgrims died or disappeared, as many as 25 per cent in good times and 40 per cent in bad ones (Isis 20, 500–1).

[27] The feast of SS. Vitus, Modestus, and Crescentia is on June 15; they suffered martyrdom under Diocletian, c. 303. The feast of St. John the Baptist is on June 24.

Cologne, and all along the Rhine, Metz, etc. Strassburg was visited by the dancing plague in 1418. As the disease was there associated with St. Vitus, the churches named after that saint, in Zabern (Saverne) and Rotestein, became centers of pilgrimages to the afflicted and probably centers of diffusion of the affliction. St. Vitus cured some patients, however, as might be expected from a saint counted as one of the fourteen "helpers" (Nothhelfer, Apotheker).[28]

Such dancing manias had appeared before; not to speak of the ancient Bacchanalia and Liberalia, various isolated occurrences are recorded in 1237 (Erfurt), 1278 (Utrecht), etc.; but the epidemic extending over large parts of the country and recurring year after year seems to have begun in 1374 and to have continued intermittently and sporadically yet frequently throughout the fifteenth and sixteenth centuries. It was probably an aftermath of the Black Death, floods, and famines in western Germany, an explosive mass reaction after years of privation and suffering. There are numerous references to the dancing mania in the chronicles of the countries or localities concerned, but the earliest scientific account was written by Paracelsus (d. 1541) in his tract Von den krankheiten, so die Vernunfft berauben. .[29] Before Paracelsus' time the disease was considered a demoniacal one which it was only in the power of priests, not of physicians, to avert and cure. Paracelsus' own cures were psychological as well as physical.

The mediaeval dancing mania as described by contemporaries was a mental epidemic. It may have found ready victims among people suffering from nervous disorders such as epilepsy or hysteria, but it was independent of those disorders and often seized people who were apparently in good health. It was primarily mental and highly contagious, especially among people whose minds had been unhinged by physical or spiritual pains. The only definite physical symptom, outside the dancing itself, was tympanites[30] (a distention of the abdomen due to air or gases); a kind of hysterical tympanites is known to the physicians of our own time.

A similar mania had developed in Italy but under different auspices, that is, tarantism, which was thought for a long time to be caused by the bite of a venomous spider, the tarantula. It was ancient, but became epidemic at about the same time as the dancing mania of Germany. It was cured by exhausting dancing to appropriate music, various kinds of tarantella.[31] Patients in Italy as well as in Germany were also very sensitive to colors, some of which increased their fury while others decreased it. The colors varied from country to country.

[28] The word Apotheker in this sense seems to be a corruption of ἀποτρόπαιος = averruncus. The fourteen saints to whose churches pilgrimages are still made (e.g., a series of churches between Coburg and Bamberg) are George the Martyr, Blase of Sebaste (in Armenia), Erasmus of Antioch, Vitus (Guy) of Italy, Pantaleon of Nicomedia, Christopher of Antioch, Dionysius (Denis) of Paris, Cyriacus of Rome, Achatius of Constantinople, Eustachius of Nicaea, Aegidius (Giles) of Greece (?), Margaret of Antioch, Catherine of Alexandria, and Barbara. Most of them, if not all, are martyrs of the third or fourth century; most of them are Easterners. The cult of these ἀποτρόπαιοι saints is thus very ancient.

[29] First printed Basel 1567. English translation by Gregory Zilboorg in Henry E. Sigerist: Four treatises of Paracelsus (p. 127–212, Baltimore 1941; Isis 34, 48).

[30] According to Alban (p. 20, 1872), tympanites was characteristic only of the epidemic of 1374.

[31] As late as 1695 the illustrious Dalmatian physician Giorgio Baglivi (1668–1707) wrote a treatise De anatome morsu et effectibus tarantulae, wherein he analyzed the disease, ascribed it to the tarantula, whose anatomy and generation were explained, discussed eight cases, and concluded that dancing and music were the best remedies. Baglivi was a Baconian experimentalist and he has been likened to Sydenham. He was less than 40 when he died. That treatise may be read in his Opera omnia medico-practica et anatomica (9th ed., p. 599–640, Antwerp 1715, with map of the southernmost part of Italy).

There is no doubt that wherever it occurred, the epidemic was unconsciously increased by ill-balanced people and consciously by ill-mannered or ill-minded ones, minstrels and impostors, people who found sexual excitement or monetary profits in these orgies.

It is interesting to compare the mediaeval mania with a similar one which still prevailed a century ago, together with other mediaeval conditions, in the Tigré district of Abyssinia. That is the tigretier, witnessed by Nathaniel Pearce (1779–1820), and described by him in his Life and adventures during a residence in Abyssinia from 1810 to 1819 (1, 290–96, London 1831). Other comparisons might be made with dancing manias developed by religious sects in Europe and America in the eighteenth and nineteenth centuries.

The study of the original St. Vitus dance has been obscured by the ascription of the same name (St. Vitus' dance, dance de Saint Gui) to disorders which have nothing in common with it beyond the occurrence in the patients of uncontrollable dancing or jerking. The various kinds of chorea described by modern physicians are nervous disorders rather than mental ones, continuous rather than periodical or seasonal, hereditary not epidemic, individual not social. Moreover, the physical symptoms, outside the jerking or dancing motions, are very different. For example,[32] (1) the acute chorea (or Sydenham's chorea,[33] misleadingly called St. Vitus' dance) affects children rather than adults and has a remarkable liability to acute endocarditis; it is frequently associated with rheumatic fever; (2) the chronic hereditary chorea, described by George Huntington in 1872 (often called Huntington's chorea), is hereditary (never skips a generation), and the age of onset does not appear to vary much (c. 35 to 38). It leads to increasing instability of temper, depression, and sometimes dementia. Of course, it is possible that some of the dancing maniacs of the fourteenth and fifteenth centuries suffered from ailments which modern physicians would label Sydenham's chorea or Huntington's chorea, but the majority of the patients were simply the victims of mass psychoses to which the mediaeval climate, permeated with fears and magic, was peculiarly favorable.

Brief bibliography. Paracelsus' book of 1567 has already been cited. For tarantism see Athanasius Kircher: Magnes sive De arte magnetica (folio, 3d rev. ed., p. 586–95, Roma 1654), with examples of various modes of tarantèlla,[34] music for the cure of the afflicted. Justus Friedrich Karl Hecker: Die Tanzwut, eine Volkskrankheit im Mittelalter nach den Quellen bearbeitet (Berlin 1832), French translation in Annales d'hygiène et de médecine légale (12, 213–63, 1834), English translation by Benjamin Guy Babington: Epidemics of the Middle Ages (p. 79–174, London 1844), excellent account very well documented. Emilien Louis Alban: La danse de Saint-Guy du XIVe au XVIIe siècle (Paris med. thesis, 46 p., 1872), the historical part is almost exclusively taken from Hecker without sufficient acknowledgment. I owe communication of this thesis to the Army Medical Library, Washington, and other information to Dr. C. F. Mayer (Jan. 16, 1942). Raymond W. Thorp and Weldon D. Woodson: Black widow. America's most poisonous spider (Chapel Hill, N. C. 1945), brief chapter on tarantism, p. 14–20.

The famous Dancing procession celebrated every Whit-Tuesday at Echternach (Grand Duchy of Luxembourg) may be a vestige of the epidemics of 1374 and

[32] The two examples following are taken from Sir William Osler: Principles and practice of medicine (10th ed., p. 1095–1102, 960, 1926).

[33] After Thomas Sydenham (1624–89), who described it in his Schedula monitoria de novae febris ingressu (London 1686).

[34] The word tarantèlla is used for the music, the dance, and the disease.

following years. Echternach was founded in 698 by St. Willibrord (VIII-1), and the abbey of St. Willibrord in that town contains the saint's relics. The popular success of the procession is due to healing powers traditionally ascribed to him. Camille Meillac: La procession dansante d'Echternach (Larousse mensuel p. 110, mai 1938).

The chorea Sancti Viti should not be confused with the ignis sacer, ignis infernalis, or St. Anthony fire, which was first heard of in Xanten (in the Rhine district, not far from Cleve) in 857. Many epidemics of it are recorded in France from 944 to 1129; after that they became rarer, yet the disease reappeared from time to time for centuries. It was a form of gangrenous ergotism, but its symptoms were often confused with those of erysipelas, gangrene, and bubonic plague. Garrison (p. 187, 202, 1929). Many studies have been devoted to it by Henry Chaumartin, the first being L'Abbaye de Saint Antoine de Viennois et le feu Saint Antoine (Lyon thesis, 228 p., 8 pl., Vienne 1926; Isis 9, 600); the latest, Le mal des ardents, is now (July 1945) announced for publication.

A. CHRISTENDOM

A1. Italy

DIONISIO II COLLE

Dionysius secundus Colle. Physician of Belluno (on the Piave, in the Venetia montana) who belonged to a famous medical family of that city. He flourished about the middle of the fourteenth century.

The first Dionisio was a knight of Frederick II in 1236; the second Dionisio, son of Manfred, was the grandson of Dionisio I. The son of Dionisio II, Dionisio III, was practicing medicine c. 1380; it was the grandson of Dionisio III, Tiziano Colle, who preserved the treatise of his great-grandfather. Tiziano Colle was elected to the council of Belluno in 1441. Many other members of the Colle family were physicians, and especially epidemiologists; Dionisio II studied the plague of 1348–49, Vivenzio and Bernardo Colle continued his studies c. 1440, Avanzio Colle and his son Giorgio c. 1513, Giorgio alone c. 1537. Giorgio's son, Giovanni Colle, the most illustrious member of the family, also an epidemiologist, was born at Belluno in 1558 and died in Padua 1630. We have followed one Italian family for more than four centuries!

To return to Dionysius secundus, he wrote a treatise on the plague of 1348–50 sometime after it had subsided, De pestilentia 1348–1350 et peripneumonia pestilentiali et maligna simul, divided into seven chapters. It is a clinical account, describing the remedies and methods used by the author himself or by his colleagues, and the results of their use. He had himself been a victim of the plague before being able to treat other victims. Many of the remedies used by the author were folk remedies, some of them disgusting compounds such as occur in the folklore of every country. The treatise of Dionisio II is the only one of the early plague treatises which describes such remedies. One can easily imagine that during the panic induced by the plague, all kinds of remedies were tried, and that the disgusting folk medicine may have cured (or seemed to cure) some of the patients.

Text. The De pestilentia 1348–1350 was edited by Giovanni Colle (1558–1631) in the latter's plague collection, Medicina practica sive nova methodus cognoscendorum pariter et curandorum omnium corpus humanum infestari et grassari passim solitorum praeter naturam effectuum malignorum et pestilentium (p. 570–76, Pisa 1617).

Criticism. Campbell (p. 28–30, 1931).

FRANCISCUS DE GIANELLIS

Franciscus son of Petrus de Gianellis (or Zanellis, Canellis), Francis of Bologna. Italian physician (d. after 1351).

This Franciscus obtained his M.D. in Bologna in 1347, and became professor of medicine in Perugia 1351. Sometime after his appointment he presented to the University of Perugia a Consilium ad evitandum pestilencie periculum. It is divided into three parts, the third of which is written against the physician Giovanni de Penna of Naples (XIV-1). It was translated into Hebrew by one Joshua of Bologna.

A quaestio medica and an appendix to the Regimen acutorum of Arnold of Villanova are also ascribed to him.

Criticism. Steinschneider (p. 790, 1893). Wickersheimer (p. 153, 1936).

DINO DINI

Dino di Pietro Dini of Florence. Italian veterinarian (fl. 1352–59).

He began on January 19, 1352 and completed on December 29, 1359 an Italian treatise on the veterinary art, largely derived from the Mulomedicina of Vegetius (IV-2); he also quotes Aristotle, Theodoric Borgognoni (XIII-1), Giordano Ruffo (XIII-2), etc. He had considerable familial experience, for he was the representative of the third generation of a family of Florentine veterinarians. His grandfather Dino di Pietro Dini was a marshal, and so were the latter's three sons Cristofano, Pietro, and Agostino; the second named was Dino's own father, and thus was the ancestral name Dino di Pietro Dini repeated. Moreover, he refers to many other marshals not otherwise known, which suggests that veterinarian traditions were partly, perhaps largely, unwritten (that is just what we should expect). For example, he refers to Minuccio of Arezzo, marshal to Guido, bishop of that city; to Pietro of Cortone, a specialist in the gelding of horses; to Guglielmo Lucci dalla Scarperia of Florence, who was an expert in horseshoeing especially interested in difficult cases, etc.

Text. The Mascalcia of Dino di Pietro Dini is unpublished. There are at least two MSS, one in the Bibliothèque nationale, Paris, the other in the Riccardiana, Florence.

Criticism. Pietro Delprato: La mascalcia di Lorenzo Rusio (2, 59–66, Bologna 1867). Moulé (3, 39–41, 1900).

GIACOMO DE' DONDI

Jacopo de' Dondi; Jacobus Dondus, de Dondis.

Italian physician, mechanician, astronomer. One of the founders of balneology. He was born at Padua before 1293, not in 1298, and died in 1359. He was elected municipal physician of Chioggia in 1313. By 1342 he was teaching medicine at Padua.

Giacomo designed a mechanical clock, which was executed by Antonio da Padua, and placed in the entrance tower of the Carrara palace at Padua in 1344 by Ubertino of Carrara, lord of the city from 1338 on. It was a complicated automatic clock which probably struck the hours. It attracted so much attention that its author was called Giacomo dall' Orologio, a name which was handed down to his descendants. It should not be confused with another clock constructed a little later by his son Giovanni (q.v.), and installed in Pavia. The old Padua clock was destroyed by the Milanese in 1390; it was certainly one of the earliest tower clocks on record (this was discussed above).

Giacomo's most extensive work was the Aggregatio medicamentorum, or Promptuarium medicinae, a work which contains a large collection of medical recipes based largely on Greek and Arabic sources. It is divided into four main sections: (1) impostumes (37 chapters), (2) contusions and fractures (8 chapters), (3) wounds (12 chapters), (4) ulcers and abscesses (20 chapters). This work was completed after 1358. It is sometimes called (as well as the author himself) Aggregator paduanus, or more fully Aggregator paduanus de medicinis simplicibus, probably after the Aggregator brixiensis of William Corvi (XIII-2).

Giacomo also wrote a work entitled Planetarium, a set of astronomical tables based on the Alphonsine ones but presented in a simpler form and computed for the meridian of Padua. This work must not be confused with one by his son Giovanni which has the same title. Giacomo's tables have some importance because of the Canones de motibus corporum supercoelestium which Prosdocimo de' Beldomandi (c. 1375–1428) derived from them in 1424.

Giacomo wrote a brief tract in four parts called Tractatus de causa salsedinis aquarum, et modo conficiendi salis ex eis (or ex aquis calidis aponensibus, or ex aquis calidis fontium Aponi): (1) the different substances in water, (2) the cause of salt in water, (3) the method of extracting salt from water, (4) the purity of the salt in the springs near Padua (probably at Abano). Giacomo was apparently the first to recommend the extraction of salts from mineral waters for medicinal purposes.

Giacomo wrote a treatise on tides, de fluxu et refluxu maris, wherein they are ascribed to the influence of heavenly bodies, not only the sun and moon, but also Venus or Jupiter when these planets are near enough to the sun and moon. In a natural day there are four points at which the tidal influence is minimal: noon, sunset, midnight, and dawn; it is maximal at points halfway between these. The variations in the tides are explained by the variations in the relative positions of sun and moon; smaller variations may be caused by geographical or meteorological conditions. For example, tides are smaller and less regular in the Mediterranean because that sea is almost completely shut off from the ocean.

Text. Aggregatio medicamentorum, or Promptuarium medicinae, Strassburg? c. 1470–81, Venice 1481, 1543, 1576. The editions of 1543 and 1576 are illustrated by Venetian woodcuts made in 1499. An Italian translation appeared under the title Herbolario volgare, Venice 1536, 1540. The edition of Venice 1481 may be the first; it is the first in Klebs' list (no. 349).

Tractatus de causa salsedinis aquarum et modo conficiendi salis ex eis, in De balneis, Venice 1553, probably also with the De fluxu in Venice 1571.

De fluxu et refluxu maris, probably in Venice 1571; new edition by Paolo Revelli: Il trattato della marea (Rivista geografica italiana 19, 238–54, 1912), with Italian translation (p. 255–70); the text is preceded by a long discussion of Dondi's work (p. 200–37), and followed by a study of other early writings on tides, either published or unpublished (p. 271–83).

Criticism. Francesco Maria Colle: Storia scientifico-letteraria dello studio di Padova (3, 174–81, Padua 1825). Haeser (1, 705, 1875). Andrea Gloria: Monumenti della Università di Padova, 1222–1318 (Memorie del R. Istituto veneto di scienze, lettere, ed arti vol. 22, 1884); Monumenti della Università di Padova, 1318–1405 (Univ. Studi vols. 1–2, Padua 1888); I due orologi meravigliosi inventati da Jacopo e Giovanni Dondi (Atti del R. Istituto veneto di scienze, lettere, ed arti 7, 675–736, 1896); L'orologio inventato da Jacopo Dondi (ibid. 7, 1000–17, 1897). Roberto Almagià: La dottrina della marea nell' antichità e nel medioevo (Memorie della R. Accad. dei Lincei, sci. fis., ser. 5, vol. 5, 375–513, 1905; p. 477). Vittorio Lazzarini: I libri, gli argenti, le vesti di Giovanni Dondi dall'Orologio (Boll. del Museo civico di Padova, 28, 1925). Giovanni Astegiano: La cittadinanza veneta a Jacopo de Dondi (Rivista di storia delle scienze 7, 317–26, 1925; Isis 8, 744), poor paper containing nothing new and rehearsing exploded errors. Lynn Thorndike: The clocks of Jacopo and Giovanni de' Dondi (Isis 10, 360–62, 1928); History of magic (3, 386–97, 1934). Gustavo Tanfani: Jacopo Dondi, medico padovano del trecento, ed il suo metodo di estrazione del sale dalle acque termali (Rivista di storia delle scienze 17, 8–23, 3 fig., 1935). Lynn Thorndike: Milan MSS of . . . Jacopo de Dondi's discussion of tides (Archeion 18, 308–17, 1937). Loren C. MacKinney: Medieval medical dictionaries and glossaries (Medieval essays in honor of J. W. Thompson p. 240–68, Chicago 1938; p. 249; Isis 29, 244).

MARRA

William de Marra of Padua. Italian physician, probable author of a treatise on poisons (fl. 1362?). He studied in Padua and was probably in Avignon c. 1362.

The Sertum papale de venenis (Papal garland concerning poisons) is ascribed in one MS to Gulielmus de Marra; in another, to Gaspar of Sarnana. According to Thorndike the first ascription is more plausible, and we accept it. The garland was apparently addressed to Urban V at the very beginning of his pontificate, that is, in 1362. We should bear in mind that in those troubled days men in power had good reason to fear being poisoned,[35] and hence a book on poisons was to them a very acceptable gift.

The garland is divided into three parts, dealing respectively with prophylaxy and diagnosis, treatment, and various problems. The author quotes Galen, Ibn Sīnā, and uses Peter of Abano's treatise on the same subject. He classifies the poisons in various ways (occult or not; hot, dry, cold, moist; mineral, vegetable, animal) and discusses their modalities. He devotes special attention to the herb tormentil, a remedy against the poison of snakes and scorpions discovered and experimented with by the semplicista Benedict of Mantua (Marra had witnessed some of those experiments in Padua). He discusses the circulation of poisons in the body. A large amount of space is given to the consideration of hydrophobia, and the author tries to explain why the victims of it shun water. In all these discussions, and even more in the queries filling the third part, we can hardly follow the author in his fantastic musings. We must remember, however, that the problems to the solution of which he addressed himself were urgent problems clamoring for some kind of solution, and yet that neither he nor anybody else in that time had the means of analyzing them rationally, to say nothing of solving them.

William of Marra may be identical with one William de Mirica who dedicated to Clement VI (1342–52) a commentary on the pseudo-Aristotelian physiognomonica.

[35] To illustrate, when Columbus returned from his first voyage, the grand cardinal of Spain, Don Pero González de Mendoza, invited him to a banquet, and (Las Casas remarks) this was the first time that Columbus was served in a covered dish and his food tested first for poison. Greatness in mediaeval times implied the risk of being poisoned and was thus acknowledged by the ceremony of testing food for poison! Salvador de Madariaga: Columbus (p. 245, 475, New York 1940; Isis 32).

Criticism. My information on Marra is exclusively derived from Lynn Thondike, who first spoke of him in his Vatican Latin MSS (Isis 13, 53–102, 1929; p. 92). That short reference may now be disregarded. He gave a long account of Marra's treatise in his History of magic (3, 526–34, 1934). The whole chapter entitled Works on poisons (p. 525–45) should be read for the sake of comparing Marra's treatise with contemporary Italian treatises.

GUIDO DA BAGNOLO

Italian physician who flourished in Cyprus (d. 1370).

Guido da Bagnolo (Guido de Bagnolo de Reggio) was the son of Filippino degli Scopoli da Bagnolo and of the daughter of Guido Gazzata. He was born in Bagnolo in Piano, near Reggio nell' Emilia,[36] at an unknown date (c. 1320–25). He flourished in Reggio, Venice, and Cyprus. He was a member of the medical fraternity (Confraternità di Santa Maria della Carità) of Venice in 1353, and by 1360 had rendered sufficient services to that city to be granted the honor of citizenship. By that time he was already physician to the king of Cyprus, Peter I of Lusignan (1359–69). He wrote a will in Reggio 1349, and another in Nicosia 1362. He was a friend of Petrarca, who referred to him in the De ipsius et aliorum ignorantia (1366).

He was not only king Peter's physician, but also his counselor, and signed one of his charters in 1363 together with Philippe de Mézières and others. In 1365, the king sent him on a mission to Genoa to obtain Genoese help in a crusade which led in the same year to the taking of Alexandria. Apparently Guido did not return to Cyprus; he died in Venice in 1370.

We have the inventory of his library drawn in 1380. It included 60 volumes valued at "ducati 266 e soldi 10." These volumes were not only medical, but philosophical, mathematical, astrological, and literary. Their owner was a learned physician and a humanist. It is especially because of the existence of this catalogue that Guido da Bagnolo is dealt with in this volume. It is interesting to compare Guido's library (or what remained of it ten years after his death) with another trecento library, that of Elia of Venice, including 59 volumes. There is a catalogue of it with prices, dated 1326.

Criticism. My note is derived from the elaborate memoir of Ridolfo Livi: Guido da Bagnolo medico del re di Cipro (Atti e memorie della R. deputazione di storia per le provincie modenesi 11, 45–91, Modena 1918); this part appeared in 1916, the volume is dated 1918. Includes the catalogue of Guido's library, and also a list of catalogues of other Italian libraries from 1326 to 1477, six in all (p. 80).

The catalogue of the library of Elia of Venice was edited by Bartolomeo Cecchetti: Per la storia della medicina in Venezia (Venezia 1886).

TOMMASO DEL GARBO

Famous Florentine physician (d. 1370).

Tommaso was the son of Dino del Garbo (XIV-1), who died in 1327. He was strongly influenced by the ideas of Taddeo Alderotti (XIII-2), and the teaching of Dino. Tommaso taught for a while in Perugia. Later he succeeded his father as a professor of medicine in Bologna. According to the records of the University of Florence, Tommaso was teaching there in 1364. Galeazzo Visconti called him to

[36] **Reggio is on the road from Milano to Modena, 15 miles from Modena. Bagnolo is 5 miles from Reggio on the road to Guastalla.**

Milan in 1368 to attend him during an attack of the gout. Tommaso died on the 8th of August 1370.

Tommaso was a friend of Petrarca and carried on an interesting correspondence with him. Although Petrarca usually had only unkind words for the medical profession, he praised Tommaso extravagantly (Epistulae rerum senilium VIII, 3). Tommaso was also praised by Filippo Villani.

Tommaso's principal work is the Summa medicinalis, which is a good summary of the medical knowledge and controversies of that time. His treatment of all questions is philosophic as well as practical. He based many of his statements on the theories of his father and Taddeo. This work may be defined as a general pathology; it is divided into two books, (1) De rebus naturalibus et de eis annexis humano corpori pertinentibus, (2) De rebus non naturalibus appellatis ab extra inevitabiliter humano corpori occurrentibus. These are the only books that Tommaso finished, but in the introduction he said that he meant to write a third, entitled De rebus praeter naturam humanam corpus accidentaliter corrumpentibus.

Tommaso's plague treatise, Tractatus super ordinem regiminis preservationis a pestilentia, servans per homines in sanitate vigentes, addressed to the people of Florence, was a very popular work. It was probably written sometime after the plague of 1348, after the doctors had had time to consider carefully all the problems of the plague. Only the Italian version of this treatise has been printed; the manuscripts of the Latin edition appear to be extremely scarce. There are a number of important variations among the different versions, chapters being added to some and left out of others.

Tommaso sums up very adequately and after careful consideration the best ways of living during an epidemic. One should always leave a stricken district if possible. The streets should be fumigated, and the houses thoroughly cleaned. Everyone should guard against eating heavy foods, avoid crowds, and have a good time. It is well to drink wine, but not too much nor too strong; malvagia (malmsey) and vernaccia (a white Sardinian wine) are recommended for occasional, not everyday, use. Many recipes for pills and medicinal draughts are given.

Two other brief works which are often printed with the Summa, De restauratione humidi radicalis and De reductione medicamentorum ad actum, deal with the ways in which medicines should be made, the proper proportions, etc.

Tommaso wrote a number of commentaries on the works of Aristotle, Galen, and Ibn Sīnā. The Expositio super capitulo de generatione embryonis, tertii canonis, fen xxv Avicennae, and the Commentaria in libros Galeni de febrium differentiis have both been printed a number of times. These commentaries are well written and give very clear explanations of these works. Tommaso also wrote a commentary on the De anima of Aristotle which was never finished and has not been printed. Among the books listed in the inventory of Ugolino da Montecatini is mentioned (49) a work entitled Tommaso del Garbo sopra tegni.

Text. Summa medicinalis, Venice 1506, 1521, 1529, 1531, Lyon 1529.

De reductione medicinarum ad actum, Venice 1506, 1521, 1531 (with Summa). Printed with other works, by Paulus Meietus: Opuscula illustrium medicorum de dosibus, Lyon 1584. Also Pavia 1556, Padua 1564.

De restauratione humidi radicalis, Venice 1506, 1521, 1529, 1531, Lyon 1529.

Expositio super capitulo de generatione embryonis, tertii canonis, fen xxv Avicennae, Venice 1502, Lyon 1514.

Commentaria in libros Galeni de febrium differentiis, Lyon 1514, Pavia 1519, Venice 1521.

Ordine e reggimento, che si debbe osservare nel tempo di pistolenza, massimamente per bene e salute degli uomini, che abitano nella città di Firenze, printed with the Consiglio of Marsilio Ficino, Siena 1522, Florence 1522, 1523, 1571, Venice 1556. New edition edited by Pietro Ferrato: Scelta di curiosità letterarie inedite o rare dal secolo XIII al XVII (vol. 74, 59 p., Bologna 1866). This edition contains the De' vestimenti, which is not in the other editions.

Criticism. Filippo Villani: Liber de civitatis florentiae famosis civibus (edited by Gustavo C. Galletti, p. 29, Florence 1848). A. W. E. Th. Henschel: Berühmte Wundärzte und Aerzte des XIII. und XIV. Jahrhunderts (Janus vol. 2, 1852). Puccinotti (2, part 2, 346–52, 498–99, 1859). Haeser (1, 702–3, 1875). Alessandro Gherardi: Statuti della università e studio fiorentino (p. 299, Florence 1881). Giovanni Calò: Filippo Villani e il "Liber de origine civitatis florentiae et eiusdem famosis civibus" (p. 112, 136, 161, 238, Rocca S. Casciano 1904). Karl Sudhoff: Das Concilium de modo vivendi in tempore pestilentiae (AGM 5, 348–51, 1911). Neuburger (2, 484, 1911). Justus Niedling: Die mittelalterlichen und frühneuzeitlichen Kommentare zur Techne des Galenos (Diss., p. 15, Paderborn 1924). Arturo Castiglioni: Il libro della pestilenza di Giovanni de Albertis (p. 10–12, Trieste 1924; Isis 7, 539). Karl Sudhoff: Der lateinische Pesttext des Tommaso del Garbo (AGM 16, 134–35, 1925). Thorndike (3, 220, 604; 4, 342, 1934).

CARDO OF MILAN

Cardo or Cardone. Milanese physician (fl. second half of fourteenth century). Nothing is known about him except that in 1378 he wrote an elaborate plague regimen containing all the prophylactic measures used in those days.

I wonder whether this Cardone of Milan is not identical with one Cordone or Cardone of Pavia, who wrote a Pratticola, of which there is a Hebrew translation. See Steinschneider (p. 790, 1893).

Cardo's plague tract is entitled Regimen in pestilencia, and is based primarily on the works of Galen, Abū Ma'shar, al-Rāzī, Ibn Sīnā, and Albert the Great. It is a fairly brief but well organized and clearly stated treatise. He, like all the best writers, discusses the methods of disinfecting putrid air and water, and of cleansing the houses. He gives a list of foods that one should avoid as well as a fairly comprehensive list of those which are good for people. He warns against taking public baths and overexercising. Quite a number of prescriptions for pills and medicinal drinks are included. Several paragraphs deal with the cause and treatment of impostumes. The outstanding fact about this tract is its complete freedom from any supernatural ideas concerning the causes or cures of plagues.

Text. Regimen in pestilencia, edited by Karl Sudhoff: Pestschriften (AGM 6, 318–28, 1913).

NICCOLÒ DI BURGO

Florentine physician who composed a plague treatise in 1382. This work is longer than many contemporary ones, and although Niccolò has practically the same theories concerning the plague as the other authors, he discusses the prevention and cure of the disease in a more detailed manner and with more rational suggestions. The first (and by far the largest) part of the treatise deals with various methods of warding off the disease, the second with possible cures for those who have already contracted it. For those who are not able to leave an infected district, Niccolò advised that the air in the towns be purified by burning sweet-smelling plants in the streets and that all filth be removed. Likewise the houses should be cleansed and in summer the doors and windows should be left open unless it were too hot, or cloudy, or very windy. In winter the houses should be purified by burning aromatic boughs or pieces of apples (the burning peelings of apples are still used as deodorants). One must not overexert himself, nor worry, nor have too great a dread of the plague and of death, nor lose too much sleep. He advocated frequent bathing in tepid water or in sulphur, provided the water was not taken from an infected district. Everyone should be very careful about his diet; he should not eat too much, nor any foods that are hard to digest, nor any that give little nourishment. Wine must not be used in excess, nor should turbid water be drunk. Everyone should eat vegetables, good bread, some cheese, fresh fish, meat that was not more than a day old, and fruits; but everything in moderation. Niccolò also advocated bloodletting, scarification, and purging pills (for which he gives a number of recipes) as preventive measures.

According to this treatise there are three main methods of aiding one stricken with the plague, "diet, medicinal draughts, and surgery," and Niccolò discusses each of these points very briefly, adding a few remarks to what he has already said on these three points in the first part of his work.

Text. Consilium illatum contra pestilentiam, 1382, edited by Karl Sudhoff: Pestschriften (AGM 5, 354–65, 1911).

FRANCISCHINO DE COLLIGNANO

Florentine physician, who wrote a plague treatise in 1382. If he be identical with Francischi de Conigrano, Francesco da Collegrano, he was a doctor of medicine in the University of Florence between 1364 and 1368, and taught philosophy.

His treatise on the plague is elaborate and somewhat scholastic in form, since every question is punctiliously debated. Nevertheless it is based on personal experience and is very detailed.

Like most writers on the plague, Francischino begins with a discussion of the causes; such as eclipses, comets, and conjunctions of planets (quoting from Galen and Ibn Sīnā). Humid and hot seasons also help to cause the pestilence. He disagrees with other writers who say that the autumn is the season when most plagues start, since cold, dry air is not unhealthful. People will take the disease more readily if they eat bad food, herbs, fruits, and similar things (quoting from Galen and Ibn Zuhr). In his discussion of the proper place to live to escape the plague, he disagrees with most authorities in claiming that it is not best to live on high mountains. He says it is far better to stay in underground places or in the valleys, or on very small hills, because the movements of the heavenly bodies can infect the air of the mountains more easily than the lower places.

Francischino gives a long list of things that might be used for the fumigation of towns; also preventive drinks and aromatic mixtures that could be held in the hand and breathed by the person, who would then be able to live safely in infected air. He also gives many recipes for pills and draughts. He describes in minute detail the various apostemae which might appear during the course of the disease. He advises the use of bloodletting, exercise, and plenty of sleep, and the putting aside of fear and worry. This work contains some interesting remarks on changing therapeutic methods, e.g. he complains of the physical degeneration of his contemporaries; they have become so weak that they can no longer stand the medical doses used by the ancients.

Text. Leve consilium de pestilentia, edited by Karl Sudhoff: Pestschriften (AGM 5, 365–84, 1911).

Criticism. Alessandro Gherardi: Statuti della università e studio fiorentino (p. 299–340, Florence 1881). Arturo Castiglioni: Il libro della pestilenza di Giovanni de Albertis da Capodistria (p. 14, Bologna 1924).

IACOPO DA ARQUÀ

Iacopo Paradisi de Arquada. Italian physician originating in Arquà (now Arquà Petrarca; 22.5 km. from Padua). Master of arts of Paris, doctor of medicine of Padua 1351. An ambassador of Louis I the Great (king of Hungary and Poland 1342–82) to Padua was cured of his leprosy in 1372 by Iacopo by means of snake flesh (?). Thereafter Iacopo had the title of physician to that king. I do not know whether he ever went to the Hungarian court or not. He established a foundation at the University of Padua for the sake of poor medical students; this was the second foundation of its kind in Padua; it is still in force. He made his testament on September 27, 1385, and died not long afterward (before 1388).

He wrote Commentaria on the De alimentis of Galen, and consilia.

He should not be confused with another Iacopo of Padua, who in 1342 was already master of arts and medicine, a member of the Sorbonne, became a canon of Padua, and was a member of the theological faculty of Paris (c. 1349–53); nor with one Iacobus de Sanatis de Padua who wrote a commentary on the fourth fen of the first canon of Avicenna (MS in Prague library, no. 599).

Text. A few consilia were edited by Manfred Schreiber (Leipzig thesis, only partly published, 12 p., 1923; Isis 7, 194).

Criticism. Girolamo Tiraboschi: Storia della letteratura italiana (2d ed., 5, 68, Modena 1789). Wickersheimer (p. 334, 1936).

For the two other Iacopo de Padua mentioned at the end of my note, see Ch. V. Langlois (HL 36, 424–32, 1927).

GIOVANNI DE' DONDI

Italian physician, mechanician, astronomer. He was born at Chioggia in 1318, the son of Giacomo de' Dondi, q.v. Giovanni was chosen in 1349 as a personal physician of Charles IV, emperor 1347–78. The next year, 1350, he was teaching astronomy at Padua. By c. 1367–70 he was lecturing on medicine at Florence; in 1379–88 he was connected with the University of Pavia. He died at Genoa in 1389.

Giovanni did not simply design like his father, but constructed with his own hands a very elaborate clock and orrery in brass and copper. The mechanism was far more complicated than that devised by his father; he worked at it for sixteen years (1348–64), and a few years later sold it to Gian Galeazzo Visconti (1347–1402), who had it placed in the castle of Pavia. The clock has disappeared, but we have a detailed description of it in Giovanni's Planetarium, and it was praised by two contemporaries, Philippe de Mézières in Le songe du vieil pélerin (c. 1389), and Giovanni Manzini, podestà of Pisa in 1405. Thus there can be no doubt as to the reality of that clock.

In his Planetarium Giovanni explains with the help of many diagrams how to build common clocks, and his account was the earliest full account of its kind. He then gives elaborate directions concerning his own clock and orrery (Thorndike 3, 390–92).

He also wrote a plague tract, De modo vivendi tempore pestilentiali, probably before 1371. It is brief and deals mostly with diet.

His treatise on the hot springs near Padua, De fontibus calidis agri Patavini, was written after 1372. His account is more complete than the one written by his father. The treatise is based partly on earlier authorities. It is divided into eight parts: (1) properties of the waters; (2) causes of their heat according to the authorities; (3) Giovanni opposes the explanation that hot mineral springs are caused by subterranean waters flowing over veins of sulphur; (4) gives his own explanation: that celestial rays and the stars cause subterranean fires and gases which in turn heat the mineral springs; (5) sets forth the objections to his views given by other writers; (6) answers these objections; (7) explains other phaenomena connected with the hot springs; (8) describes the medical properties of these waters. The treatise includes a detailed description of the hot baths of Abano (near Padua), of the methods of salt extraction, etc. It is an interesting, if ineffectual, attempt to deal with a geological problem of great complexity. It must be said to his credit that he realized the infinite difficulties or "marvels" (mirabilia) which were involved.

He also wrote a work entitled Quaestiones aliquae in physica et medica, which has not yet been printed.

In 1370 Petrarca addressed to him (Ioanni patavino physico insigni) two very long letters (two treatises) De quibusdam consiliis medicinae, wherein he criticized the Arabic tendencies and the medical pedantism and superstitions of their time. The two letters form the whole of book XII of the Epistolae rerum senilium (Basel ed. 1581, p. 897–914, 18 long folio pages). Giovanni's friendship with Petrarca was natural enough, for he was a true humanist, sharing with him and with Cola di Rienzi a deep interest in the ruins of ancient Rome; he and Cola recorded some inscriptions. The famous Petrarca Vergil MS (now in the Ambrosiana, Milano) belonged to Giovanni de' Dondi after Petrarca's death.

Text. De modo vivendi tempore pestilentiali, edited by Karl Sudhoff (AGM 5, 351–54, 1911).

De fontibus calidis agri Patavini consideratio ad magistrum Vicentinum, in De balneis (fol. 94r–108v, Venice 1553).

Criticism. Francesco Maria Colle: Storia scientifico-letteraria dello studio di Padova (3, 181–91, Padua 1825). Haeser (1, 705–6, 1875). Giovanni Urbani de Gheltof: Un amico di Francesco Petrarca, Giov. Dondi (Bull. d'arti p. 58–68, Venezia 1880–81). Andrea Gloria: Monumenti della Università di Padova, 1222–1318 (Memorie del R. Istituto veneto di scienze, lettere, ed arti vol. 22, 1884); Monumenti della Università di Padova, 1318–1405 (Univ. Studi vols. 1–2, Padua 1888); I due orologi meravigliosi inventati dà Jacopo e Giovanni Dondi (Atti del R. Istituto veneto di scienze, lettere, ed arti 7, 675–736, 1896). Vittorio Lazzarini: I libri, gli argenti, le vesti di Giovanni Dondi dall'Orologio (Boll. del Museo civico di Padova, 28, 1925). Lynn Thorndike: The clocks of Jacopo and Giovanni de' Dondi (Isis 10, 360–62, 1928); History of magic (3, 386–97, 740, 1934); Milan MSS of Giovanni de' Dondi's astronomical clock . . . (Archeion 18, 308–17, 1936).

GIOVANNI DA SANTA SOFIA

Joannes de Sancta Sophia. Italian physician and philosopher (d. Padua 1389). He was the son of Niccolò (XIV-1) and the elder brother of Marsiglio da Santa Sofia. He received his medical degree in 1353, and then taught in Padua. He taught both philosophy and medicine, and became very popular and famous as a teacher and a practitioner. Giovanni wrote particularly intelligent commentaries on the works of Hippocrates, Galen, and Ibn Sīnā. In 1388 he was invited to teach in Bologna, but returned to Padua in 1389, the year of his death.

He wrote a Practica medicina in 180 chapters, and a plague tract entitled Consilium ad pestilentiam. The latter is probably identical with the Modus praeservandi, atque tuendi corpora a peste quantum medico est possibile, which is ascribed to Giovanni.

This Consilium is more sensible and gives more rational advice than many written by his contemporaries. He advised the town council of Udine (Veneto) to have various plants and herbs burned in the streets to purify the air; the houses should be cleansed by washing with rose water and vinegar. The best part of the article deals with the proper diet to use in preventing sickness and to use if one has contracted it. Also the citizens must not take too much exercise, must not worry or get too little sleep. There are a few recipes for pills, adopted principally from the Taisīr of Ibn Zuhr (XII-1). Giovanni himself tested the efficacy of these pills in a plague in Perugia. His instructions concerning bloodletting are very sensible; the doctor must not resort to this method if the patient is weak or if the disease is too far advanced.

Giovanni had a very acrimonious and involved argument with Albertino Rainoldi de Salso on Galen's ideas in his treatise De corpore aegro simpliciter; Giovanni attacking Galen's theories and Albertino upholding them. This debate was later (1376) compiled by Albertino and written down by a medical student in Padua. According to Albertino, the three questions were: (1) Utrum ordines omnes omnium corporum de quibus determinavit G. sint solum sex. (2) Utrum corpora senum et puerorum sint neutra. (3) Quare neutrum senilis decidentie, et convalescentie, secundum rei veritatem non comprehendatur sub latitudine sanitatis nec egritudinis, etc.

Text. Commentarium universum, Venice 1531.

Consilium ad pestilentiam excellentissimi arcium et medicinae monarchae, scriptum ad Utinenses, edited by K. Sudhoff: Ein Pestkonsilium des Giovanni Santa Sofia an den Rat der Stadt Udine (AGM 6, 344–49, 1913).

Criticism. G. Tiraboschi: Storia della letteratura italiana (5, 269, Modena 1789). Francesco Maria Colle: Storia scientifico-letteraria dello studio di Padova (3, 197–200, Padua 1825). Puccinotti (2, part 1, CXXXVII, 1855). Andrea Gloria: Monumenti della Università di Padova 1318–1405 (1, 379–81, Padua 1888). Gustavo Tànfani: Una illustre famiglia di medici padovani nel medio evo (Rivista di storia delle scienze 15, 97–112, Siena 1933).

NICHOLAS OF UDINE

Nicolaus de Utzimo, Utino. There are a district and a place called Udine in Friuli (Veneto).

Physician who flourished in Vienna in the second half of the fourteenth century. In 1390 he wrote in Vienna a treatise on the plague for his patron Albert III, duke of Austria from 1365 to 1395. From his treatise one can believe that Nicholas was a well educated physician who had had a good deal of experience.

His Regimen contra pestilenciam is well organized and more detailed than many contemporary ones. He lists the usual causes of a plague, such as infected air and water, but is more definite in his descriptions of the places where they would be found. He understood the necessity of boiling water when the source might be contaminated, an unusual idea in his period. He goes into great detail concerning the proper foods and drinks to preserve one's health. The usual remedies are recommended, such as correct amounts of sleep and exercise, bloodletting, and medicines.

Quite a number of recipes for pills and medicinal draughts are given. He thought that the Italian prescriptions and drugs were too weak for the rugged Viennese constitutions.

Text. Regimen contra pestilenciam pro serenissimo principe domino Alberto, duce Austriae, per egregium doctorem magistrum Nycolaum de Utino, edited by Karl Sudhoff: Pestschriften (AGM 6, 361–69, 1913).

CHRISTOPHORUS DE HONESTIS

Cristoforo di Domenico Onesti, Cristoforo degli Onesti, Christophorus Georgius Honestis.

Italian physician (d. 1392). Born in Bologna according to some, in Florence according to others, at the beginning of the fourteenth century. In 1367, he received his doctorate in Bologna, where he had studied medicine under the direction of Tommaso del Garbo. He mentions this professor many times in his Expositio on the antidotary of Mesuë the Younger (XI-1).

He taught logic, philosophy, and medicine in Bologna, and his name is mentioned many times in the Chartularium of that university between the years 1371 and 1384. The names of Matthew, Bartholomeus, and Peter Varignana and Jacob of Montecalvo appear with that of Honestis.

Christophorus may have taught for a while in Perugia about 1380. Between 1385 and 1389 he taught in Florence, then he returned to Bologna, where he died in 1392 and was buried in the church of San Domenico.

Christophorus' best-known work, written probably in Florence c. 1386, is his commentary on the Antidotarium of Mesuë the Younger (XI-1). Honestis begins his discussion with explanations of the words antidotarium and grabadin, then continues with a list of the best authorities, giving very fulsome praise to Nicholas of Salerno (XII-1). His notes consist, principally, of descriptions of the plants from which the medicinal drugs are obtained and where they come from, what they are like, and in what forms they are used, i.e. in plasters, pills, drinks, etc. He also gives the proportions to use in each case, and the best methods for taking these medicines. He tells which prescriptions are no longer in use; in some cases because the ingredients are no longer obtainable, in others because better prescriptions have been found.

In some editions, e.g. the edition of Lyon 1525, there are "Additiones" to almost all the paragraphs which have evidently been added by a later writer.

A number of his works have not been printed. One of the most important of these is the De venenis, dealing with various problems concerning the nature of poison, its attraction to the heart, pestilential airs, venomous animals, plants, and minerals. Other unpublished works are: Sermo Christophori de Onestis in scholaris, De viribus medicamentorum (in Italian), De regimine sanitatis (in Italian), and Hypocrates. The Quaestiones super prima, et secunda fen primi canonis Avicennae, are notes on his lectures written by a student, called Thomas, in Bologna.

The treatise on poisons was plagiarized by Giovanni Martini de' Ferrarii of Parma, who flourished about the middle of the fifteenth century, in the latter's De venenis evitandis et eorum remediis libellus, and it was used, in preference to other contemporary Italian treatises, by Sante Ardoino of Pesaro when he compiled his elaborate Opus de venenis c. 1425 (first edition, Venice 1492).

Text. Expositio super antidotario Mesuë, cum De saccelis caputpurgiis epithimatibus et clysteribus; Tractatulus utilis de aqua ordei et de modo faciendi ptisanam secundum communionem modum practicantum; Modus faciendi ptisanam ordei. First edition, Ferrara, March 1488; second, Bologna, April 1488 (Klebs no. 709). Moreover, the three last incunabula editions of Mesuë's Grabadin included Christophorus' Expositio (Venice 1491, 1495, 1497; Klebs 680.13–15). Later editions, Lyon 1525; Venice 1527, 1562; Bologna 1640. These editions have not been collated; they may or may not contain the smaller treatises enumerated above after the Expositio.

De cognitione, et cura febrium, Basel s.a.

Introductorium, sive Janua ad omne opus practicum medicinae, Augsburg 1518. These two last titles are quoted after Fantuzzi.

Criticism. Giovanni Fantuzzi: Notizie degli scrittori bolognesi (6, 179–81, Bologna 1788). Serafino Mazzetti: Memorie storiche sopra l'università e l'istituto delle scienze di Bologna (p. 378, Bologna 1840). Sarti and Fattorini: De claris archigymnasii bononiensis professoribus (2, 299, Bologna 1888–96). Schelenz (p. 330, 1904). Lodovico Frati: Chartularium studii bononiensis (4, 100–2, passim, Bologna 1919). Thorndike (3, 530–31, 538–40, 1934).

SYLLANUS DE NIGRIS

Syllanus (or Sillanus, Gillanus) de Nigris. Physician of Cremona (fl. c. end of fourteenth century); professor of medicine in the University of Pavia.

He wrote a commentary on the ninth book of the Kitāb al-Manṣūrī of al-Rāzī (IX-2), of which there are four incunabula editions. That ninth book, "Nonus Almansoris," it should be remembered, was a treatise of practical medicine, De curatione aegritudinum a capite usque ad pedes.

Text. Expositio noni libri Almansoris. First edition Padua 1476. Then Venice 1483, 1490, 1497 (Klebs no. 946).

De medicina practica (Venice 1518). Is this not simply another edition of the Expositio? the title would be natural enough.

Criticism. Francesco Arisi: Cremona literata (1, 247, Parma 1702). Osler (no. 110, ed. of 1476, pl. xi, 1923).

BARTOLOMMEO DA PISA

Italian Franciscan physician (d. 1401).

Bartolommeo de' Albizzi (Bartholomaeus Pisanus) was a centenarian at the time of his death 1401. He wrote a Quadragesimale de contemptu mundi (that is, a sermon delivered in Lent on the contempt of the world) and a summary of medicine, Epitoma medicinae.

This Bartolommeo da Pisa should not be confused (as was done, e.g., by Marie Pellechet) with another Bartolommeo da Pisa, Bartolommeo dei Granchi, Bartolomaeus de San Concordio, a Dominican born in Pisa c. 1250, died Pisa 1347, who wrote a very popular Summa de casibus conscientiae.

Text. The Quadragesimale was printed in Milano 1498.

The Epitoma medicinae was first printed in Venice after 1500. It is wrongly included in Klebs' list (no. 157). It is preceded by a preface to Piero Soderini of Florence (1452–1522), elected gonfaloniere a vita in 1502.

The Summa of Bartolomaeus de San Concordio was first printed in Italy 1473. Later incunabula editions, Cologne 1474, Paris c. 1475, Augsburg 1475, Albi 1478, Speyer not after 1479, Venice 1481. Spanish edition, Zamora c. 1482.

MARSIGLIO DA SANTA SOFIA

Marsilius de Sancta Sophia.

Italian physician. Died about 1405, although one unpublished chronicle says 1411. He was the most illustrious member of the Santa Sofia family (see my note on his father, Niccolò, XIV-1). He taught logic and medicine at Padua from 1367 to 1381. He was also one of the physicians of Gian Galeazzo Visconti (1347–1402) and was banished with him from Padua in 1390. Although his possessions had been restored to him by 1392, Marsiglio soon went to Pavia to teach, and from there to Piacenza; he was also in Bologna, but by 1400 had returned to Pavia.

Marsiglio wrote commentaries on some of the works of Hippocrates, Galen, al-Rāzī, and Ibn Sīnā, as well as a few independent works.

There are a number of manuscript copies of brief works of Marsiglio, some of which may have been notes on his lectures taken by his students; for instance, Quaestio de elementis; Quaestio de sensatione; Quaestio de melancholia; Recollectio super Tegni Galieni; Scholae de Techna Galieni; Praelectiones de medicinis et morbis in studio papiensi institutae; Pilule.

Text. Luculenta expositio in divi Hippocratis particulam tertiam, Lyon 1507, Venice 1514.

Quaestiones in Aphorismos Hippocratis, Pavia 1485, Venice 1490, 1514, Lyon 1507.

Expositio in particulam tertiam et septimam Aphorismorum Hippocratis, Padua c. 1480, Pavia 1484, Venice 1490, 1495, 1508, 1520.

Celeberrimus tractatus de febribus, Lyon 1507, 1517, Venice 1514.

Rescripte super quarta fen primi Avicenne de febribus, Venice 1517, 1524.

Commentarius super [librum ad] Almansorem (al-Rāzī), Hagenau 1533, 1583.

De omnium modorum fluxu ventris, Lyon 1517.

De febre pestilentiali, Lyon 1517.

Criticism. G. Tiraboschi: Storia della letteratura italiana (5, 267–69, Modena 1789). Francesco Maria Colle: Storia scientifico-letteraria dello studio di Padova (3, 192–97, Padua 1825). Andrea Gloria: Monumenti della Università di Padova 1318–1405 (1, 390–395, Padua 1888). Neuburger (2, 487, 1911). Justus Niedling: Die mittelalterlichen und frühneuzeitlichen Kommentare zur Techne des Galenos (Leipzig Diss., p. 15, Paderborn 1924). Gustavo Tànfani: Una illustre famiglia di medici padovani nel medio evo (Rivista di storia delle scienze 15, 97–112, Siena 1933).

PIETRO DA TOSSIGNANO

Petrus de Tausignano or Tussignano, Petrus Albergheti de Curialtis de Tausignanis, Pietro Curialti da Tossignano, Piero de Tausignano, Tusignano, Tuxignano, etc.

North Italian physician (b. first half of fourteenth century, d. c. 1407). He was a member of an illustrious family, the Curialti of Tossignano near Imola. His father's name was Zeto or Gepto, or Alberghetto dei Curialti. Pietro married Caterina Ruffini in 1372, and had at least two sons, Antonio a lawyer, Alberto a doctor, and one daugher Lippa or Filippa.

Pietro studied medicine and surgery in Padua. By 1364 he was mentioned as a professor of medicine in Bologna, where he was a contemporary of Christophorus de Honestis and Tommaso del Garbo. In 1386 the Council of Four Hundred of Bologna bestowed citizenship on him and his descendants. But later, when Pietro accepted the invitation from Francesco di Carrara to teach medicine in Padua, his property in Bologna was confiscated (in 1390). In 1396, however, he returned to Bologna and, his property being restored, lived there until his death c. 1407.

Before Mazzini's elaborate study of Pietro and his work, most authorities thought that there were three or at least two men by the name of Pietro da Tossignano whose writings are extant. But according to Mazzini all these writings belong to the Pietro da Tossignano who lived in the second half of the fourteenth century. He wrote various medical treatises, of which the best known is one on the plague of 1397, which forms an important part of the Fasciculus medicinae, a famous collection of medical texts, edited by John of Ketham (fl. Vienna c. 1460).

This treatise, entitled Consilium pro peste evitanda, was written about 1398 and dedicated to Giovanni Galeazzo Visconti. It is divided into four parts and fifty chapters: (I) deals with the astrological causes, eclipses of the sun and moon, conjunctions of planets, and corrupt air, etc.; discusses not only the plague, but also smallpox and measles; (II) gives a prophylactic regimen, treats not only of the plague, but also paralysis, apoplexy, and epilepsy; (III) presents and answers eleven questions concerning the disease and various preventive measures; (IV) describes therapeutic measures. Although Pietro discusses the usual astrological causes of the disease, he is more advanced than most of his contemporaries, since he recognizes other methods of contagion, such as contact with infected persons or places; he calls the homes of the plague victims "contagious houses." He says it is safer to live in places which have not been visited by the plague. He warned doctors to be careful when treating the impostumes, since the discharge is highly infectious. His emphasis on infection, versus miasma, thus helped to pave the way for the work of Gerolamo Fracastoro. He indicates clearly that the plague had entered Europe through the ports where ships arrived from the East, and then spread from country to country. Throughout he insists far more on preventive measures than on treatment. This plague treatise was translated into Hebrew by an anonymous author.

Another work by him, entitled De regimine sanitatis, is a compendium of hygienic and dietetic rules for preserving health. It is a discussion of the six "nonnatural" things which are necessary to human life: (I) air, one must live in places where the air is pure, far from marshes and all stagnant water; (II) food and drink, one should use moderation in both; should also regulate the diet according to one's temperament, sanguine, choleric, phlegmatic, or melancholic; (III) sleep, plenty of it, and never too soon after meals; (IV) de repletione et inanitione, poor health comes from poor mastication, lingering too long at table, drinking too much and too frequently; one should eat only a few times a day and never to satiety; should remain sober from morning until night; (V) mental hygiene, avoid anger, sadness, fear, have a good time, enjoy music, read history, etc.; (VI) observe the changing of the seasons by a change of diet, exercise, and general methods of living; the proper times for bloodletting and purgation.

The work which gave him the greatest repute in his own time was his Receptae super nonum Almansoris, which is a textbook of therapeutics and materia medica. It is divided into nine parts: (1) de digestione humorum; (2) de solutivis; (3) de digerentibus et solventibus simul; (4) de dosibus solutivorum simplicium primo; (5) de praeparatione medicinarum simplicium praedictarum; (6) de medicinis simplicibus; (7) de medicinis evacuantibus; (8) de medicinis confortantibus; (9) de cura aegritudinum particularium a capite usque ad pedes secundum Rhazem. Pietro follows the order of the Kitāb al-Manṣūrī (Liber Almansoris) of al-Rāzī (IX-2), and presents a quantity of different medical recipes. The material is well organized within the various divisions, according to different diseases. This work also appeared in some printed editions under the title De medicamentorum formulis (Venice 1518), and again under the title Compositiones et remedia ad plerosque omnes affectus morbosque sanandos (Lyon 1587, etc.).

Pietro's Liber de balneis Burmi, although very brief, is an important treatise on the therapeutic value of the waters of the Bagni di Bòrmio in the Valtellina, northeast of the lake of Como. He says that the waters are good for catarrh, gout, skin diseases, arthritis, and many internal disorders. These few folios are full of personal observations and important clinical discussions and theories. The tract was soon translated into German and became very popular throughout Germany.

Pietro found that Aristotle's Problemata was such a useful guide in making his own observations and in teaching that he composed a Tabula super Problemata Aristotelis, in which he arranged in alphabetical order the most important observations of Aristotle.

The Additiones Petri de Tusciano ad Thesaurum pauperum Magistri Petri Yspani are criticisms and corrections added to the Thesaurus pauperum of Peter of Spain (XIII-2). It is difficult to tell which are Pietro's words because the comments of Bernard of Gordon (XIV-1) on this same work are intermingled with his.

Pietro may have been the author of a surgical treatise, Cyrurgia, which is sometimes ascribed to him and sometimes to a John of Milan, also called John de Ptraccia, Prattia, or Braccia (Brescia?). The Cyrurgia contains many references to authorities such as Galen, Ibn Sīnā, "Almansor" (i.e., Rāzī), Abū-l-Qāsim, Roger of Salerno, Bruno da Longoburgo, to unnamed "modern practitioners," or to the author's experience. Sometimes old facts are cited by him as if derived from his own experience. The author, whoever he was, insists upon the fundamental need of surgical practice, e.g. for the art of incision, or the binding up of wounds. He realizes the difficulties and length of medical studies, which should include astrological knowledge. He is strongly opposed to mere empirics, such as barber-surgeons and herbalists, and tells examples of fatal accidents caused by their ignorance. According to him, cancer can be cured only if treated in its initial stage, but the early diagnosis is very difficult and requires considerable experience. He was very conservative in his intervention, being equally reluctant to use knife or cautery; he preferred to use less drastic means, such as dietetic regulations, ruptories, caustic waters, binding with silk thread, and the like.

Two other works are ascribed to him: De variis morbis et remediis and De modo dosandi, which may have been compiled from his own writings by someone else.

Text. Tractatus de peste (1398), or Consilium pro peste evitanda, Venice c. 1475; with the editions of Ketham's Fasciculus, in Latin Venice 1491, 1495, 1500, 1501 etc., Pavia 1501; in Italian Venice 1493, Milan 1509. The Latin edition of Venice 1491 has been reproduced in facsimile by Charles Singer: The Fasciculus medicinae of Johannes de Ketham (Milan 1924; Isis 6, 547–49). The Consilium is a sort of appendix to the Fasciculus printed right at the end (after the colophon) in smaller type. The Italian edition of Venice 1493 has also been reproduced in facsimile by Dr. Singer: The Fasciculo di medicina Venice 1493 (part 2, Florence 1925; Isis 8, 350). Pietro's treatise is now an integral part of the work, printed in the middle of it, in the same type as the rest.

De regimine sanitatis, Paris 1536, 1539, 1540.

Recepte super nonum Almansoris, Venice 1483, 1490, 1497, 1517, 1518, Salamanca 1496; under the title De medicamentorum formulis, Venice 1518; under the title

Compositiones et remedia ad plerosque omnes affectus morbosque sanandos, Lyon 1587, 1597.

Liber de balneis Burmi in quo non solum aquarum vires et medicinae sed earum quoque exhibendarum canones explicantur, edited in De balneis omnia quae extant apud Graecos, Latinos et Arabos, Venice 1553, Lyon 1587.

Problemata Aristotelis . . . cum expositionibus Petri Aponi. Tabula secundum Petrum de Tussignano per alphabetum, Mantua 1473, Venice 1501, 1505, 1518, 1519, Paris s.a.

Additiones Petri de Tusciano ad Thesaurum pauperum Magistri Petri Yspani, Antwerp 1497.

Criticism. Francesco Maria Colle: Storia scientifico-letteraria dello studio di Padova (3, 208–13, Padua 1824/25). A. W. E. Th. Henschel: Berühmte Wundärzte und Aerzte des XIII. und XIV. Jahrhunderts (Janus 2, 419–21, 1853). Andrea Gloria: Monumenti della Università di Padova 1318–1405 (1, 406–7, Padua 1888). Steinschneider (p. 818, 1893). Piero Giacosa: Documents sur deux épidémies de peste en Italie en 1387 et en 1448 (Janus 4, 130–31, 1899). Karl Sudhoff: Pestschriften (AGM 5, 390–95, 1911; 16, 131, 1925; 17, 40–43, 244, passim, 1925); Beiträge (2, 421–24, 1918). Neuburger (2, 485, 1911). Dorothy W. Singer: Some plague tractates (Proceedings R. Society of Medicine, hist. sec., p. 29–31, London 1916). Riccardo Simonini: La peste negli stati estensi dal 1000 al 1400 (Rivista di storia delle scienze vol. 6, p. 5, 10, 16, 1924). Charles Singer (1, 29–30, 1925). Klebs and Sudhoff (p. 52, 110–13, 1926). Giuseppe Mazzini: Vita e opera di Maestro Pietro da Tossignano (181 p., Rome 1926; portrait of Pietro dated 1629, p. 37; Isis 9, 504). Lynn Thorndike: Science and thought in the fifteenth century (p. 81–108, New York 1929; Isis 14, 235–40), apropos of the Practica cirurgie, which is analyzed and fragments of which are translated.

FRANCESCO CASINI

Francesco Casini, papal archiater (b. c. 1349, d. after 1415).

Francesco was the son of Bartolommeo of the noble Casini family of Siena. He was born in Siena at an unknown time (c. 1345–49), and he is last heard of in the first days of 1416, when he was a member of a Sienese embassy to one king James. He was archiater to six popes, to wit Urban V, Gregory XI, Urban VI, Innocent VII, Gregory XII, and Alexander V (popes from 1362 to 1410). While he was in Avignon he became acquainted with Petrarca, who wrote two letters to him;[37] he was also in touch with Caterina of Siena. His functions were not only medical, but diplomatic; he was an important link between Siena and the curia.

The date of his death, 1390, given by Marini is wrong, also the date 1374 given by others; he died after 1415. His was a medical family, for his father, Bartolommeo, was a doctor, and so was his only brother, Giovanni. He had three sons, Antonio, who became cardinal (d. 1429), Tommé (born 1388), and Bartolommeo, bishop of Pesaro in 1409. He was employed by Malatesta in Pesaro 1398–1401, at an annual salary of 500 florins.

There has been some confusion concerning his writings because he was called Francesco da Siena (Franciscus de Senis), a name which might properly be applied to contemporary physicians. We know at least two other physicians called Francesco da Siena, the one Francesco di Marco, cousin of Ugo Benzi, and the other Ugo's own son, Francesco di Ugo. The second, however, hardly comes into this

[37] Epistolae de rebus senilibus (XVI, 2, 3). The letters are dated Padua March 22, and Arquà May 1; they are distant in time, the year of the second being probably 1374.

account, for he was not born until 1409, and was driven out to Florence because of the Sienese vexations to his family.

While Francesco was at the court of Avignon in 1375 he wrote a Tractatus de balneis dedicated to the duke of Milano, and a Tractatus de venenis dedicated to Philippe d'Alençon, then patriarch of Jerusalem and administrator of the diocese of Auch (Gascony). He may be the author also of a Consilium de balneo written for the bishop of Pavia and ascribed (in the Giuntine edition of 1553) to Franciscus de Senis. The plague treatises in Italian and Latin are probably apocryphal; the author is probably another Francesco da Siena, who may be a contemporary. The importance of Francesco di Bartolommeo, however, does not lie so much in his writings as in his activities as an agent of Siena and a papal physician and adviser. In the field of medical learning he was completely eclipsed by his younger townsman, Ugo Benzi, or Ugo da Siena (c. 1370–1439).

He deserves some attention as one of the early writers on medical balneology (Introd. 2, 96) together with Giacomo and Giovanni de' Dondi and Ugolino da Montecatini. The Tractatus de balneis written in 1375 was dedicated (or rededicated) in 1399 to Gian Galeazzo, duke of Milan (sole ruler 1385–1402). In this work Francesco describes the baths of Puteoli (Pozzuoli), and those in the vicinity of Siena, Pisa, Viterbo, in the papal states, Naples, and other places.

The Tractatus de venenis (1375) is divided into two parts. In the first part (5 chapters) Francesco deals with the general nature of poisons and their remedies; this is followed by a list of all poisons and a table of the weights and measures which he is using. In the second part he discusses 142 poisons in 139 chapters, classifying them under three headings, mineral, vegetable, and animal poisons. His principal authorities are Ibn Sīnā and his older contemporary William de Marra.

The Consiglio optimo contro lo morbo pistolenziale (1370?), whatever its authorship, is a plague treatise of some originality. It describes the great speed with which the plague spread straight to the heart, just like the venom of a snake, and then to the liver or brain and other parts of the body. The remedies were bloodletting, followed by strengthening electuaries and pills, and a suitable diet. The main authorities are Dioscorides, Galen, al-Rāzī, Constantine the African, and Ibn Sīnā.

As to the Latin Consilium, according to a MS of it in the Riccardiana, Florence, it was addressed "ad Bernardum Torium med. Flor. qui vivebat anno 1485." That date is of course far too late for our author, and even for his namesake, son of Ugo Benzi.

Text. Dicta de balneo Petrioli, printed with the De balneis of Gentile da Foligno, Padua 1473 (Klebs no. 444). Consilium de balneis in the Collectio de balneis, Venice 1553; the whole text covers less than a single page, reproduced in facsimile in Garosi (p. 306, 1935).

Consiglio contra pestilenza, Venice 1475, Cagli 1476? (Klebs no. 421).

The main treatises of 1375 are unpublished.

Criticism. Gaetano Marini (1742–1815): Degli archiatri pontificj (2 vols., Rome 1784). A. W. E. Th. Henschel: Berühmte Wundärzte und Aerzte des XIII. und XIV. Jahrhunderts (Janus 2, 418–19, 1853). Julius Pagel: Geschichte der Heilkunde im Mittelalter (Puschmann's Handbuch 1, 683, Jena 1902). Pierre Pansier: Les médecins des papes d'Avignon, 1308–1403 (Janus 14, 415, 1909). Osler (nos. 43, 79, 89, 1923). Karl Sudhoff: Franciscus de Senis, Consiglio contro il morbo pestilenziale (AGM 16, 148, 1925; 17, 248, 1925). Klebs and Sudhoff (p. 30, 112, 131–32, 1926). Thorndike (3, 534–38, 1934). A. Garosi: La vita e l'opera di Francesco Casini archiatro di sei papi (Bull. senese di storia patria 6, 277–378, 1935), elaborate study based on archival documents and correcting all the earlier biographies. Wickersheimer (p. 152, 1936), out of date.

UGOLINO DA MONTECATINI

Italian physician, one of the earliest balneologists (c. 1345–1425).

Ugolino was the son of Giovanni de' Caccini of Montecatini, a Tuscan watering place about halfway between Lucca and Florence. The date of his birth is uncertain, but he obtained his doctorate in medicine in Bologna on April 12, 1367. He was town physician in Pistoia, then in Pescia; teacher of medicine in Pisa for some 25 years, then in Florence from 1393 to 1395. Later we find him practicing or teaching medicine or doing both in Pisa, Lucca, Pesaro, Perugia. In his old age he returned to Florence, where he died on October 10, 1425, and was buried in Santa Maria Novella.

His most important work is the De balneorum Italiae (Etruriae) proprietatibus ac virtutibus, which is one of the earliest balneological treatises. We have already mentioned a treatise by Gentile da Foligno (XIV-1) dealing also with the mineral baths of the Lucca region, but less experimental. The treatise upon which Ugolino's fame is based was not written until the beginning of the fifteenth century.

He wrote a consilium for Averardo de' Medici, a commentary on the sixteenth fen of the third book of the Qānūn of Ibn Sīnā, a treatise on the plague (lost), etc. He had a rich library, chiefly medical, the catalogue of which (113 items) has been preserved.

Text. The De balneorum proprietatibus was printed in the Collectio de balneis (p. 47–57, Venice 1553).

F. Baldasseroni and G. Degli Azzi: Consiglio medico ad Averardo de' Medici (Archivio storico italiano 38, 140–52, 1906).

Criticism. Francesco Novati: Ugolino ed il suo trattato de' bagni termali in Italia (Memorie dell'Istituto lombardo 20, 143–66, 1896). Walter Bombe: Hausinventar und Bibliothek Ugolinos, mit Anmerkungen von Karl Sudhoff (AGM 5, 225–39, 1911). Karl Sudhoff: Die Pestschrift des Ugolino, in Pestschriften (AGM 5, 395, 1911; 16, 140, 1925). Domenico Barduzzi: Ugolino (82 p., 7 pl., Firenze 1915; Isis 3, 99). Mario Battistini: Contributo alla vita di Ugolino (Rivista di storia delle scienze, anno 14, vol. 5, 125–47, 1923), including various archival documents (Isis 6, 150). BL (5, 672, 1934).

JACOPO DA PRATO

Jacobus de Prato. Italian physician (fl. second half of fourteenth century). He originated in Prato, between Florence and Pistoia.

The treatise, Liber in medicina de operacione manuali, bearing his name is a discussion of the pathology and therapeutics of external diseases for the information of surgeons. Chapter I, the introduction, gives the reason for writing this work. Students were finding many difficulties in reading the Greek and Arabic authorities, so Jacopo wished to sum up in a clear and concise manner all that was necessary for them to know about certain external diseases. In chapter II he says that they must know anatomy thoroughly before attempting any surgery. They must also have plenty of instruments in good condition, medicines, plasters, etc. Later chapters, of which Sudhoff prints only the titles, deal with various kinds of abscesses, ulcers, erysipelas, carbuncles, scrofula, cancer, scabies, smallpox, and other diseases of a similar nature; their causes and cures. These diseases were generally classified as skin diseases and as such abandoned by physicians to the care of surgeons.

Text. Liber in medicina de operatione manuali, chs. I, II edited by Karl Sudhoff: Beiträge (2, 425–28, 1918).

Two brief fragments of other writings of Jacopo are also printed by Sudhoff (ibid. p. 425).

A2. Hispanic Peninsula

JOANNES JACOBI

Joannes Jacobi, Jean or Jehan Jaume, Joan Jacme or Jasme. John son of James.

Catalan physician, and translator from Arabic into Catalan, professor of medicine in Montpellier. His birthplace is unknown, but it was possibly Lleida (Lerida on the Segre), and he may have studied in the university of that city. He was mentioned as early as 1360 in a contested election for the chancellorship of the University of Montpellier, was finally elected to that position in 1364, and retained it until his death in 1384. He was consulting physician to several popes and kings: he attended pope Urban V (1362–70); in 1370 he was called to Avignon to aid pope Gregory XI (1370–78); in 1378 he was appointed physician to Charles V the Wise, king of France 1364–80; in 1384 he attended the antipope Clement VII (1378–94) in Avignon.

Joannes wrote a number of medical treatises, notably the Tractatus de pestilentia, the Secretarium practicae medicinae, and the Tractatus de calculis in vesica.

The first of these was probably the first to be composed, about 1373. Judging by the number of early printed editions, Joannes' treatise on the plague was by far the most popular work of its kind. More than 30 editions of it appeared before 1501 (more than 25 under the name of Canutus) in French, Latin, English, and Portuguese.

The ascription of most editions of this plague treatise to one Canutus (Kanutus, Kamintus, Ramintus) episcopus Arusiensis raises a difficult problem. Who was this Canutus? Arusiensis may refer to two distinct localities, Aarhus in Denmark and Vesterås in Sweden. There was no Danish bishop called Canutus (Knut). The only bishop who might be identified with the plagiarist of Joannes' treatise is Bengt Knutsson (Benedictus Canuti), bishop of Vesterås, near Stockholm, in 1461, who died in 1462. But there is no evidence whatever that this Bengt Knutsson ever published a plague treatise or any medical work. It is thus safer to assume that the ascription of this treatise by early printers to one Canutus episcopus was either an error or a deliberate falsification for commercial purposes.

His plague treatise is divided into three parts, dealing with the cause of the pestilence, the proper regimen for avoiding it, and the treatment. In part I he says that the plague may be caused by infections coming from bad sanitation, foul stagnant water, corrupt air. The two signs of the disease are fever and apostumes. Various questions concerning the susceptibilities of different people are debated. Part II deals with the precautions against the disease which everyone should take. Suitable dwelling places and proper living conditions are described; methods of fumigation, proper diet and exercise are advised. Bloodletting is to be used with caution. In part III the methods of treatment are discussed; these are purgation, bloodletting, and strengthening drugs.

His Secretarium practicae medicinae (or Thesaurarium) was written about 1378. In the introduction he says that he was requested by Charles V, king of France, "to write a brief and useful summary of medicine from many books." This work is based on the writings of Galen, Alexander of Tralles, al-Rāzī, Ibn Sīnā, and Gariopontus. Joannes says that he does not follow the organization of the Qānūn of Ibn Sīnā, but of the Passionarius of Gariopontus (XI-1), a medical encyclopaedia, "sometimes subtracting, sometimes adding things which are more appropriate and useful." The Secretarium is divided into six books, which in turn are divided into sections and chapters. Book I deals with diseases of the head, such as megrim, vertigo, frenzy, melancholia, etc., also of the eyes, ears, nose, teeth, and mouth. Book II discusses the diseases "from the head to the diaphragm," including chapters on the lungs, stomach, and liver. Book III deals with the spleen, the belly, kidneys, etc. Book IV deals with sciatica, gout, etc., and book V with spasm, tremor, dropsy, paralysis, etc. In book VI there is a long and detailed discussion of all kinds of fevers. The whole work shows a great dependence on the Passionarius. The Secretarium was translated into Hebrew at least once.

Joannes also wrote a Tractatus de calculis in vesica which is briefer and more to the point than a similar work by John of Tornamira, a contemporary. Joannes Jacobi did not take much of his material directly from Arab writers, but depended mainly on the works of Gilbert the Englishman, Bernard Gordon, John Gaddesden, and others. His therapeutic measures are simpler than theirs, he does not advise so many obnoxious medicines or magical charms as the others. This treatise is divided into three parts: (I) the causes; certain foods and drinks such as cheese, beef, new wine, turbid water cause indigestion, thick humors, and thence stones; (II) the symptoms of the disease; (III) the cure; Joannes gives a detailed regimen, with a number of medicines.

Joannes also wrote a Recepte super quarto canonis Avicenne de febribus, which has not been published. A Tractatus ad anathomicam compositionem oculorum intelligendam, recently found in the cathedral of Zaragoza, has also been ascribed to him.

The same Zaragoza MS contains two ophthalmological texts translated by Joannes from the Arabic into Catalan. The first of these is Alcoatim (XII-2), Libre de la figura del uyl; the second, much shorter, is entitled Rúbrica de les letres que Galien trames a Coris el maestre de les malalties dels uyls e de les cures. There is no reason to doubt Joannes' authorship of these translations. explicitly stated in the incipit.

Text. Plague tracts that appear under the name of Jean Jasme or Jacobi: a brief poem in French on the plague, Le regime de l'épidémie et remede contre icelle (24 fol., Lyon c. 1476). There are other incunabula editions, all in Paris (c. 1485, c. 1489, c. 1490, c. 1500).

Tractatus de pestilentia, Augsburg c. 1480, Besançon 1487, new edition by Karl Sudhoff: Der Pesttraktat des Magister Johannes Jacobi zu Montpellier (1373) und seine spätere Überarbeitung (AGM 17, 16–32, 1925).

Preservatio pestilentie, and Ordinacio utilis et commodiosa abreviacio super epidimia que multociens invadit in hac vita degentes, two brief plague regimes edited by E. Wickersheimer (Archivio di storia della scienza 6, 105–12, 1925).

Editions appearing under the name of Canutus are: Paris c. 1480, Nuremberg 1482, Antwerp c. 1483 (2), before 1484, 1485 (2), c. 1486, c. 1487, Cologne c. 1490 (2), Leipzig 1492, 1493, 1494, Freiburg c. 1495, Paris c. 1498 (2), Cologne c. 1500 (6).

To these must be added the English and Portuguese translations, all under the name of Canutus. Three editions of the "Little book for the pestilence" were printed by William of Malines, London c. 1485. This is said to be the first medical book printed in England and the first English book with a separate title page. One of these English editions was reproduced in facsimile by the John Rylands Library (Manchester 1910) with an introduction by Guthrie Vine.

The Portuguese translation, Regimento proueytoso contra ha pestenença, by "Raminto," was printed at Lisbon c. 1495. This Portuguese edition is the only one bearing the names of place and printer and the date.

Regimen calculosorum, edited by Ernest Wickersheimer: Johannes Jacobis Steintraktat (AGM 3, 41–62, 1909).

The translations from Arabic into Catalan have been edited as follows:

Alcoatí, Libre de la figura del uyl. Text català traduït de l'àrab per Mestre Joan Jacme i conservat en un manuscrit del XIV^{n} segle a la Biblioteca capitular de la Seu de Saragossa, ara exhumat i presentat per Lluis Deztany amb una Notícia històrico-medical del Dr. Josef M. Simon de Guilleuma (246 p., Barcelona 1933; Isis 27, 123).

Deztany's volume contains translations not only of Alcoatim's treatise, but of the shorter one, entitled in Catalan Les letres que Galien trames a Coris el maestre de les malalties dels uyls e de les cures (p. xc ff.). This shorter text, the Arabic original and authorship of which are unknown, was translated into Latin by the late Pierre Pansier: Littere Galieni ad Corisium de morbis oculorum et eorum curis translate de arabico in linguam Catalaunie per Magistrum Johannem Jacobi circa annum 1350 et nunc de lingua Catalaunie in latinam (Collectio ophthalmologica fasc. vii, 211–21, 1933). The same volume also contains (p. xcix–cii) the Tractatus ad anathomicam compositionem oculorum intelligendam ascribed to Joannes Jacobi.

Criticism. Steinschneider (p. 804–5, 1893). Neubauer-Renan (p. 787, 1893). Pierre Pansier: Maîtres de la faculté de médecine de Montpellier (Janus 9, 600–2, 1904); Les médecins des papes d'Avignon, 1308–1403 (Janus 14, 406–7, 421–22, 1909). J. W. S. Johnsson: Liber ecclesiae Sancti Lucii Roskildensis (Dansk Kliniks Festskrift til Prof. Julius Petersens p. 121–43, Copenhagen 1910). Karl Sudhoff: Die Identität des Regimen contra pestilentiam des Kanutus mit der Pestschrift des Johann Jacobi (AGM 5, 56–58, 1911); Der Pesttraktat des Mag. Johann Jacobi zu Montpellier, 1373, und seine spätere Überarbeitung (AGM 17, 16–32, 1925), containing the original text of John's treatise; "Kamintus" englisch (AGM 17, 132, 1925).

Dorothea Waley Singer: Some plague tractates (Proceedings of the R. Society of Medicine, sec. hist. med., 9, 179–85, or p. 21–27 of reprint, 1916). Fr. Hallager: Bishop Knuds Bog om Pesten (Copenhagen 1919), untrustworthy. André Barbot: Traité de la Peste composé en 1376 par Jean Jaume (diss., 40 p., Montpellier 1923). August Bloedner: Das Secretarium practicae medicinae des Johannes Jacobi (diss., 35 p., 1926; Isis 10, 133). Klebs and Sudhoff (p. 19–26, 33–35, 145–49, passim, 1926). Lynn Thorndike: Vatican Latin manuscripts (Isis 13, 77, no. 51, 1929). Sonoma Cooper: The medical school of Montpellier in the fourteenth century (Annals of medical history 2, 184–85, 1930). For the examination of Scandinavian documents on the Canutus question, I am indebted to J. W. S. Johnsson, of Copenhagen, and O. T. Hult, librarian of the Svenska Läkaresällskapet in Stockholm. Wickersheimer (p. 422–24, 1936). James F. Ballard: Catalogue of the medieval and renaissance MSS (p. 111, Boston 1944; Isis 35, 218), apropos of an undescribed copy of the Remède très utile contre fièvre pestilencieuse (Klebs no. 543.1), and of the Tractatus de pestilentia (Klebs no. 542.1).

A3. France

FROMONT

Pierre Fromont (or Fourment). French royal surgeon (fl. Paris about the middle of the fourteenth century).

He was surgeon to Jean, duke of Normandy, later Jean II le Bon, from 1348 to 1352; sworn surgeon in the Châtelet of Paris, 1352–56 (the Châtelet was then the court of royal justice). He wrote a Cirurgie in French, beginning Comme entre toutes.

In 1350 it was he who embalmed the body of king Philippe VI le Bien fortuné.

Text. La Cirurgie maistre Pierre Fromont is still unpublished. MS in Bibliothèque nationale, Paris. Léopold Delisle: Le cabinet des manuscripts (3, 152, no. 829, Paris 1881).

Criticism. Wickersheimer (p. 634, 1936).

BERNARD ALBERTI

Bernart Albert, Albert Brouat. Physician who studied and taught at the University of Montpellier between 1339 and 1358. His principal work, compiled c. 1358, was a collection of prescriptions, Introductorium in practicam pro provectis in theorica, based on the first fen of the fourth qānūn of Ibn Sīnā, dealing with fevers. According to Steinschneider, this work was printed by Antony Cermison, Venice c. 1490, and falsely ascribed to Gentile de Foligno (XIV-1) in some manuscripts and to Bernard of Gordon (XIV-1) in others. A Hebrew translation, Mabo bi-melekeh (Introduction in the art), was made by Abraham Abigdor in Montpellier, c. 1367–79.

Another title attributed to Bernard, Tractatus de febribus, is probably the same as the Introductorium.

A work De judicio urine is ascribed to him by Pansier.

Text. Recepte, edited by Anthony Cermison, Consilia Gentilis. Recepte Gentilis [de Foligno] de febribus. Venice (s.a., 1490?), falsely attributed here to Gentile de Foligno.

Criticism. Moritz Steinschneider: Bernard Alberti, Pseudo-Gentilis de Fulgineo (Deutsches Archiv für Geschichte der Medicin 1, 123–26, 1878); Hebraeische Uebersetzungen (p. 777, 791, 1893). Pierre Pansier: Les maîtres de la faculté de médecine de Montpellier au moyen âge (Janus 9, 539, 1904). Wickersheimer (p. 71, 1936).

GUY DE CHAULIAC

Guigo de Chaulhaco, Guido de Cauliaco, de Caillat, de Chaulhac. French physician and surgeon (d. c. 1368).

Guy was born in the latter part of the thirteenth century in the village of Chauliac in Gévaudan, diocese of Mende, department of Lozère. His family were of peasant stock, but Guy was aided by the lords of Mercoeur. He studied medicine first in Toulouse, then in Montpellier under Raymond of Molières (XIV-1; chancellor in 1334). Later he studied anatomy under Niccolò Bertruccio (XIV-1) in Bologna and surgery under a certain Alberto of Bologna.[38] From 1315 to 1320 Guy was in Paris. He practiced medicine for a long time in Lyon, where he also was a canon and prévôt of St. Just. He was a canon of Reims by 1353, and of Mende in 1367. Guy spent a great deal of his time, however, in Avignon, where he was physician to three popes, Clement VI (1342–52), Innocent VI (1352–62), and Urban V (1362–70). He died in or near Lyon about 1368.

[38] Boccaccio in 1348 (1st day, novella X) mentions a medical man, well known in Bologna, called Alberto, who was probably Alberto Zancari (XIV-1; d. after 1348); could this be the Alberto mentioned by Guy?

Guy de Chauliac was one of the most influential surgeons of the fourteenth century. At the end of his career he wrote his Inventorium sive collectorium in parte chirurgicali medicine. It was finished in 1363 in Avignon. This treatise on surgery remained a standard work in Western Europe up to the time of Ambroise Paré (died 1590), and is very systematic, comprehensive, and based on much learning and experience. It is also known under the shorter titles Chirurgia and Chirurgia magna (Grande chirurgie).

This work is a collection of the best medical ideas extant in the time of Guy, but he himself adds very little that is new. He shows, however, an unusually broad understanding of the earlier literature and is often critical, basing his criticisms on his own experience. He himself says that it is a compilation from almost every previous author. Guy has thus carried out the plan which Henri de Mondeville (XIV-1) had proposed: the scientific presentation of the surgery of his time.

Although he cites in all 88 authorities, Guy depends heavily on the writings of Galen (cited 890 times), Abū-l-Qāsim (175 times), Alī ibn 'Abbās (149 times), and Ibn Sīnā (661 times). As Guy himself says, it was fortunate for him that he had the new translations of Galen's works made by Niccolò da Reggio in the first half of the fourteenth century.

His work was immediately popular and was soon translated into other languages—French, Provençal, Catalan, Italian, English, Dutch, Hebrew, and Irish. The English translation was quite popular, judging by the number of (fifteenth-century) MSS, but it remained unprinted except for the extracts contained in the Questyonary of cyrurgyens, translated from the French by Robert Copland (fl. 1508–47) and printed in London 1542.

The Chirurgia magna consists of seven tractates, which in turn are divided into "doctrinae" and these into chapters. It was probably written first in Latin, but was immediately translated into French. The whole work is preceded by a Capitulum singulare, explaining certain general facts every surgeon should know concerning the liberal arts, diet, surgical instruments, and the manner of conducting operations; and, most important of all, including an interesting history of medicine and surgery in the form of brief notes on earlier physicians and surgeons.

Tractatus I is a brief treatise on anatomy based largely on Galen's De usu partium corporis humani, and on the teachings of Guy's master Bertruccio. Guy strongly advocates the study of anatomy, saying that the "surgeon who is ignorant of anatomy carves the human body as a blind man carves wood" (Nicaise ed., p. 29). This chapter is more detailed than the treatise of Mondino, and is free from teleological explanations. In fact, he avoids discussions concerning the functions and "raisons d'être" of the organs, stating "et cecy est une mer, en laquelle n'est permis au Medecin de naviguer" (Nicaise p. 32).

Tractatus II deals with carbuncles, abscesses, tumors, etc. He says that cancer must be cut out at an early stage, but even then there is slight hope for recovery if it is a real cancerous ulcer and not just an ordinary one which can be cured by various medicaments. Apropos of buboes in the armpits, Guy describes the plagues of 1348 and of 1360 at Avignon. Since he was in Avignon during both epidemics, and was himself ill with the disease for six weeks during the year 1348, his account is particularly valuable. He describes the prevalence of the disease in Asia and Europe and points out the difference between the pneumonic and the bubonic types. He blames the disease on the Jews who wished to poison the world, and on certain conjunctions of the planets. He recognizes the contagious nature of the plague and recommends venesections, purification of the air, and a good diet for patients.

Tractatus III deals with various kinds of wounds; diets for wounded persons; the various diseases which may attack a wounded person; and the treatments for wounds. He recommends a low diet for the patient. He is a reactionary, however, in the treatment of wounds, refusing to follow the teaching of Mondeville and advocating the use of salves and ointments. He knew how to use five different kinds of sutures. One of the best discussions in this tractate is that dealing with fractures of the skull (Nicaise p. 252 ff.). Among other things he noted the escape of the cerebrospinal fluid and the effect of pressure on the respiration. He gives very exact indications for trephining. Contrary to the practice of Galen and Ibn Sīnā, Guy closed chest wounds unless there was effusion to be removed.

He divided wounds of the abdomen into two kinds: those which perforate the abdominal wall and those which do not. He recognized the absolute fatality of wounds in the abdomen in which the intestines were opened, if they were not treated, and describes two methods of suturing wounds of the intestines, quoting from Paulos Aegineta (VII-1) and Abū-l-Qāsim (X-2). Guy noted accurately that contact with the air could have bad consequences.

Tractatus IV is concerned with the general nature of ulcers, and then with ulcers which appear in various parts of the body.

Tractatus V contains general discussions concerning fractures and dislocations. On these subjects Guy adds very little that is new, with the exception of his instructions for arranging the position of a fractured femur. He advises the suspension of fractured limbs in a sort of cradle, and treated fractures of the thigh with splints and pulleys and weights.

Tractatus VI deals with local pathology from the surgical point of view. He includes chapters on sciatica, leprosy, etc. Also he discusses diseases of various parts of the body, of the eyes, ears, etc. His chapters on these diseases are well organized but do not add anything new. In connection with dentistry he gives an interesting description of the dental instruments used in that time.

In his discussion of stone he follows the theory of Galen that it should be broken up by the administration of drugs. If medical treatment fails, however, though it is very dangerous, stone should be cut out of the bladder. But for renal calculus no operation should be attempted.

Tractatus VII is an especially comprehensive antidotary in which Guy named about 750 medical substances.

Although Guy often criticizes the use of occult methods in medicine, in his Chirurgia he sometimes advocates the use of charms. He also wrote a treatise on astrology, Practica astrolabii, sometimes called De astronomia. It was dedicated to Clement VI. In this work he discusses the astrological aspects of medicine.

Guy wrote two other works which are now lost. The first, De ruptura, was a short treatise on hernia. The other, De subtilianti diaeta, was a treatise on cataract and a regimen for the patient. It was written for king John of Bohemia, probably in 1340, since that was the date of John's expedition to Montpellier to seek aid for his blindness.

A Chirurgia parva is often ascribed to him, but this is only a poor compendium of some parts of his Chirurgia magna, made by a student or another physician. The Chirurgia parva was translated into Hebrew by Asher ben Moses Valabrègue in Arles 1468. The Hebrew translation of the Chirurgia magna, mentioned above, is anonymous and incompletely preserved.

Various portraits of Chauliac have been published, but none can be regarded as authentic (Nicaise p. xcii). One of the illustrations of the earliest French MS (Montpellier 1363) is reproduced in our figure 23.

Text. Klebs (nos. 494-97). The first edition of the Inventorium sive collectorium in parte chirurgicali medicine was published in French under the title De la pratique de cyrurgie, collated with the Latin text by Nicolas Panis, Lyon 1478 (not Paris) (Osiris 5, 112, fig. 35), Lyon 1490, reprinted 1498/99 with woodcuts; other editions Lyon 1503, 1520, 1534.

First Latin edition: Venice 1498; other editions Venice 1499, 1500, 1519, 1546, Lyon 1537, 1559, 1572, 1585, etc.

Italian translations: Venice 1480, 1493, 1505, 1513, 1521, etc.

Dutch translations: Antwerp 1500, Leiden 1507, Amsterdam 1646.

Catalan and Spanish translations: Barcelona 1492, Seville 1493, 1498.

There are many other editions. The latest is the French translation edited by Edouard Nicaise: La grande chirurgie de Guy de Chauliac (938 p., Paris 1890), with a long critical introduction, elaborate bibliography, and glossaries. The text edited by Nicaise is an early (fifteenth-century) French translation very close to the Latin original.

Various parts of the Chirurgia have been printed separately:

Capitulum singulare, edited by Jean Canappe, Lyon 1542.

The questyonary of cyrurgyens with the formulary of lytel Guydo in Cyrurgie. English translation from the French of parts of the Chirurgia made by Robert Copland, London 1542, reprinted London 1579.

Part of tractatus II, Of the apostems of the chest, translated by Ralph H. Major: Classic descriptions of disease (p. 74-76, Baltimore 1932; Isis 19, 518-20).

Tractatus III translated by William Augustine Brennan: Guy de Chauliac. Wounds and fractures (164 p., Chicago 1923).

Criticism. Steinschneider (p. 802, 1893). Gurlt (2, 77-107, 1898). J. A. Nixon: Guy de Chauliac, a new MS including the Practica astrolabii (Janus 12, 1-6, 1907). Ernest Wickersheimer: Une version en bas-allemand de Guy de Chauliac (Janus 14, 486-90, 1909). Pierre Pansier: Les médecins des papes d'Avignon 1308-1403 (Janus 14, 416-17, 1909). Neuburger (2, 495-501, 1911). J. A. Nixon: A new Guy de Chauliac MS (Congrès périodique international des sciences médicales, 17th session, sec. 23, 419-24, London 1913). Edward Clark Streeter: A fourteenth century English MS of Guy de Chauliac (Proceedings of the Charaka Club 4, 107-11, New York 1916), description of an English MS owned by him. Charles Singer: The figures of the Bristol Chauliac MS, c. 1430 (Proceedings of the R. Society of Medicine vol. 10, hist. sec., 71-90, 1917). Sudhoff: Beiträge (2, 472-79, 500, 517, 1918). Walter von Brunn: Die Stellung des Guy de Chauliac in der Chirurgie des Mittelalters (AGM 12, 85-100, 1920; 13, 65-106, 1921). Charles Singer: Sur un manuscrit attribué à Chauliac (Comptes rendus du 2e Congrès international d'histoire de la médecine, Paris 1921, p. 167-76, Evreux 1922; Isis 31, 153). Oskar Schwind: Zahnärztliches bei den italienischen Chirurgen des 13. Jahrhunderts und bei Guy de Chauliac (Diss., p. 29-43, Leipzig 1924). Karl Sudhoff: Guy de Chauliac: Transgressio de mortalitate 1363 (AGM vol. 17, p. 15, 1925). J. G. De Lint: Afbeeldingen uit de handschriften van Guy de Chauliac (Bijdragen tot de geschiedenis der geneeskunde 6, 25-36, 5 fig., 1926); Instrumentenafbeeldingen in handschriften van Guy de Chauliac (ibid. 7, 117-42, 32 fig., 1927); Representations in the Utrecht MS of Guy de Chauliac of instruments for the reduction of the uvula (Annals of medical history 9, 408-10, 1927). Arthur Ernest Cowley: The Magna chirurgia of Guy de Chauliac (Essay in history presented to Reginald Lane Poole p. 1-4, Oxford 1927; Isis 11, 177), fragments of a Portuguese translation in Hebrew characters c. 1450. Campbell (p. 2-3, 29,

108–10, 1931). Thorndike (3, 518–20, 1934). Wickersheimer (p. 214, 1936). Sarton: Early English version of Chauliac's surgery (Isis 35, p. 30, 2 pl., 1944), apropos of the early fifteenth-century MS in New York Academy of Medicine, formerly owned by E. C. Streeter (see above).

PIERRE DE NADILZ

Pierre de Nadilz (de Nadillis or Nandillis). Provençal physician (fl. 1369–74).

This Peter flourished mainly in Montpellier, but he was physician to Charles II the Bad (king of Navarre 1349–87), and traveled with him as far as Paris and Normandy (1369–70) or Navarre (1374). He wrote a treatise De impregnatione mulierum.

Criticism. Wickersheimer (p. 652, 1936).

PATARAN

Jean Pataran. Languedocian physician (fl. 1375–82).

He flourished as a physician in Lunel (Languedoc; dépt. Hérault) in 1375–76, and was syndic of that town in 1382. He wrote a Regimen de conceptione.

Criticism. Wickersheimer (p. 460, 1936).

RAYMOND CHALMEL DE VIVIERS

Raymundus Chalmellus de Vivario, Raymundus Raynaldi de Vinario, incorrectly spelled Chalin de Vinario. French physician born at Viviers in Vivarais (dépt. Ardèche) about 1334.

He studied in Montpellier and by 1373, at least, he was at the papal court in Avignon. In 1379 he is mentioned as the physician of cardinal Anglic de Grimoard (d. 1388), brother of Urban V. He completed at Avignon in 1382 an important treatise on the plague, dealing with the epidemics of 1348, 1360, 1372, and 1382. Although he was probably an eyewitness of all these, his description of the plague of 1382 is particularly accurate.

The first part of the work deals with the causes of the plague, which according to him are mainly astrological. There are many citations from the works of Aristotle, Ptolemy, Abū Ma'shar, Ibn Sīnā, Ibn Zuhr, and others. Then he discusses in detail and with unusual clearness the symptoms of the disease, of which he was able to note more than the usual number. Two types of the plague are mentioned, the first with fever and boils, the second with fever alone.

In the second part he deals with methods of warding off the disease, and in the third with curative measures. He is careful to state that the disease is highly infectious and the doctors are very uncertain on the subject of cures; that many cases are really incurable. He used phlebotomy only when the patient was particularly strong, otherwise cupping or leeches.

It is interesting to compare Chalmel's estimate of the mortality rate of the plagues of 1348, 1360–61 with that of Guy de Chauliac. According to Chalmel, in 1348 about one-third of the population were ill and practically all of these died; in 1360 less than one-half were stricken and very few recovered; in 1372 less than one-tenth took the disease but many recovered; whereas in 1382 about one-twentieth were ill and most of them survived (rather a contradiction of the statement that the disease was practically incurable). The estimate made by Guy de Chauliac was that in 1348 three-quarters had it and practically all of them died; in 1360/61 about one-half had it and most of them died.

Chalmel probably wrote another treatise called De curandis morbis, which he cites in De peste.

Text. De peste libri tres. According to Nicaise it was edited by Guillaume Lothier, surgeon in Montpellier, Lyon 1542.

A free rendering and elaboration of the text in classical Latin by Jacques Dalechamp, Lyon 1552.

The first book has been transcribed from a fifteenth-century MS in Danzig (Allerheiligen Bibliothek des Marienstiftes vol. 200, folio), by Robert Hoeniger: Der schwarze Tod in Deutschland (p. 159–77, Berlin 1882).

Brief but important selections have been edited by Karl Sudhoff: Pestschriften (AGM 17, 37–39, 1925).

The late Pierre Pansier (1864–1934) had promised a critical edition of the whole work.

Criticism. A. W. E. Th. Henschel: Biographisch-literarische Notizen (in second Janus 2, 403, 1853). Haeser (3, 95–97, 130, 185, 1882). Edouard Nicaise: La grande chirurgie de Guy de Chauliac (p. 168, Paris 1890). Hermann Grauert: Meister Johann von Toledo (Sitzungsberichte der K. bayerischen Akad., phil. Cl., 1901, 111–325; p. 275). Pierre Pansier: Les maîtres de la faculté de médecine de Montpellier au moyen âge (Janus vol. 10, p. 7, 1905); Les médecins des papes d'Avignon, 1308–1403 (Janus 14, 406, 428–30, 1909), new material superseding earlier biographies. Neuburger (2, 425, 477, 501, 1911). Karl Sudhoff: Eine italienische Pest-Kompilation in 3 Traktaten, namentlich aus "Raimundus" (AGM 16, 150, 1925); Das Pestwerkchen des Raymundus Chalin de Vinario, 1382 (AGM 17, 35–39, 1925), Pestschrift no. 50. Sonoma Cooper: The medical school of Montpellier in the fourteenth century (Annals of medical history 2, 185–87, 1930). Wickersheimer (p. 674, 1936).

JEAN LE FÈVRE

French physician originating in Metz, in Lorraine, but established in Montpellier. Toward the end of the fourteenth century one Jean d'Aix (or d'Esch) (probably the one who was an alderman of Metz in 1373 and died before 1398) suffering from the gout wrote his fellow townsman asking for advice. In answer to that consultation Jean Le Fèvre wrote a little treatise on gout, in the French language (Metz dialect). As he had not seen his patient, he declared that the gout might have a hot cause or a cold one; these two kinds of gout would require different treatments. He gives his own treatment on the assumption that Jean d'Aix is suffering from the "hot" gout. The advice contained in this little treatise seems wise and conservative; there is but little superstition and astrology in it. Much importance is attached to the diet, the doctor indicating many kinds of food which should be avoided, then others which are more appropriate to that particular ailment. He finally advises his patient to consult a good local physician.

Wickersheimer mentions two other Jean Le Fèvre and one Jean Le Feron who were surgeons in the fourteenth century in Paris and Rouen. This is not very surprising, as there were a great many surgeons and the name Jean Le Fèvre (like our John Smith) was fairly common.

Text. The text was edited by Paul Meyer: Notice d'un MS messin, Montpellier 164 et Libri 96 (Romania 15, 161–91, 1886; p. 178–87). English translation of the text by Hymen Saye (Bull. of the Institute of the History of Medicine 2, 112–22,

Baltimore 1934; Isis 23, 501). There are more notes, even medical ones, in the Meyer edition than in the Saye one.

Criticism. Brief notes on this and the other Jean Le Fèvre in Wickersheimer (p. 433, 1936).

HARCIGNY

Guillaume de Harcigny. French royal physician and naturalist (d. 1393).

Guillaume de Harcigny (or Harselly, Harsinis); Wille de Hersignies. Guillaume's family orginated in Harcigny (dépt. Aisne), but he was born at Laon (same dépt.) c. 1300. He was educated in Laon, then in Paris, where he obtained his master's degree in medicine. He traveled to Syria and Egypt, attended Italian universities, and returned to his country. He practiced medicine in Laon and Noyon.

According to Froissart, Guillaume was called to Creil in 1392 to try to cure the incipient demency of Charles VI. He refused to remain in the king's service because of his old age, and was richly recompensed. He was already wealthy. He died at Laon on July 10, 1393. The monument placed on his tomb (a wasted corpse) is preserved in the museum of that city.

Guillaume was apparently an important physician. Therefore it is surprising that none of his writings are extant except perhaps a few medical recipes. It is said that he wrote an account of his journey to the Near East, a treatise on anatomy in Latin (Frenchified by himself in 1368), another on precious stones, another still on mineral waters.

Criticism. Wickersheimer (p. 246, 1936).

JEAN DE TOURNEMIRE

Johannes de Tornamira. French physician and later chancellor of the University of Montpellier (d. c. 1390–96).

Jean was born about 1329 in Pouzols, diocese of Albi, and studied in the University of Montpellier. He began to practice medicine in 1348, practicing both in Montpellier and in Avignon. In 1364 he was the opponent of Joannes Jacobi in a contest for the appointment as chancellor of the University of Montpellier. Jacobi received the appointment at this time, but at his death, 1384, Jean was finally appointed chancellor.

Jean was one of the physicians of Gregory XI (pope 1370–78) and resided in Avignon from 1372 to 1376, when Gregory left that city; after Gregory's death, he was a physician of Clement VII (1378–94). Valescus of Taranta was one of his most famous students.

Jean's best-known work is the Clarificatorium partis practice medicine super nono Almansoris cum textu ipsius Rasis. This is a brief compendium of medicine in the form of a commentary on the ninth book of al-Rāzī's Kitāb al-Manṣūrī. The Clarificatorium was written in Montpellier in 1365 and was probably the course of lectures which Jean gave as an introduction to the study of al-Rāzī's ninth book, entitled De omnibus egritudinibus que accidunt a capite usque ad pedes. He never hesitated to point out the errors of al-Rāzī. There are 96 chapters, the first entitled De cephalea et emigranea[38a] et de eorum cura, and the last De doloribus exteriorum membrorum. The text of al-Rāzī is given first, then that of Tournemire in the

[38a] Cephalea from κεφαλαλγία means dolor capitis qui multum tempus tenet (Du Cange). Emigranea, French migraine, English megrim are all derived from ἡμικρανία, a pain in half of the skull, dolor medii imo et totius capitis (Du Cange, under hemigranea).

form of glosses. The Clarificatorium was translated into Hebrew, probably by Leon Joseph of Carcassonne.

Second in importance is Jean's Introductorium (sive Isagogicus libellus) ad practicam medicinae, a short introduction to medical practice written for young medical students. This treatise is also found under the title Breve compendium and ascribed to Bernard of Gordon (XIV-1). The Breve compendium found in the MSS under the name of Tornamira is actually by Gordon. One chapter of the Introduction, the De urina, is sometimes found as a separate tract. The De urina was translated into Hebrew by Leon Joseph of Carcassonne.

Jean experienced the plague of 1348 but did not write his tract, Praeservatio et cura apostematum antrosorum pestilentialium, or De epydemia, until 1372 or 1382 during a sojourn in Montpellier. This work begins with a good description of the general condition and symptoms of plague patients. The rest of this rather brief tract deals with various remedies, concoctions, bloodletting, and diet. He stresses the fact that the strength of the heart must be constantly guarded.

The Consilium on the plague which he wrote for Henry of Castile[38b] exists in a Latin MS and also in a Spanish translation, of which there is a MS in Hebrew script at the University of Leeuwarden (Neubauer-Renan p. 787, 1893). There is also an adaptation of the De pestilentia in German verse (printed on German incunabula broadsheets).

In 1387 Jean was called from Avignon to his home in Montpellier to treat his daughter, who was suffering from a cancer of the breast. He predicted that she would die in about a year and a half. Later he sent her a relic of Peter of Luxemburg, which cured her. He wrote an account of this cancer in a letter on the subject of the canonization of Peter.

His work on fevers, De febribus, sums up all the contemporary medical knowledge on this subject.

Wickersheimer mentions two other works of Jean de Tournemire which are still unpublished: the Tractatus de ingenio sanitatis, begun in 1369 (Bibliothèque nationale, Paris), and a Regimen sanitatis addressed to a cardinal (Vienna).

Jean de Tournemire seems to have been liberal to Jews, but the majority of the Montpellier doctors were not. See my note on Leon Joseph of Carcassonne.

Text. Klebs (nos. 984–85). Clarificatorium in nonum ad Almansorem, Lyon 1490 (princeps), 1500, 1501, 1506, Venice 1507, 1521.

Introductorium ad practicam medicine, Lyon 1490, 1500, 1516, 1526, Venice 1502, 1589, etc. (with Valescus de Taranta's Philonium).

Tractatus de febribus (with the Clarificatorium), Lyon 1501, Venice 1507, 1521.

Praeservatio et cura apostematum antrosorum pestilentialium or De epidemia (written 1372 or 1382), edited by Karl Sudhoff (AGM 5, 47–53; 17, 32–34, 1925).

Margareta, filia Johannis de Tournumirá . . . in villa Montispessulani comorans, Latin edition, Processus de B. Petro de Luxemburgo (Acta sanctorum, July, 1, 598–99, 1746). Also edited in Latin and translated into French by Pierre Pansier: Jean de Tournemire (Mémoires de l'Académie de Vaucluse 4, 98–102, 1904).

Criticism. Haeser (1, 712, 1875). Steinschneider (p. 833, 1893). Neubauer-Renan (p. 786, 1893). Gurlt (2, 107, 1898). Julius Pagel: Geschichte der Heilkunde im Mittelalter (Puschmann's Handbuch 1, 695, Jena 1902). Pierre Pansier: Jean de Tournemire 1329–1396 (Mémoires de l'Académie de Vaucluse 4, 84–102, Avignon 1904), contains the translation of Jean's account of his daughter's cancer

[38b] This might be Enrique II de Trastamara, el Bastardo, king of Castile from 1369 to 1379, or Enrique III, el Doliente, who ruled from 1390 to 1406.

1387; Les maîtres de la faculté de médecine de Montpellier au moyen âge (Janus 10, 2–3, 1905); Les médecins des papes d'Avignon, 1308–1403 (Janus 14, 424–25, 1909). Ernest Wickersheimer: Johannes Jacobis Steintraktat (AGM 3, 41–44, 1909), comparing the Clarificatorium with the Regimen calculosorum of Joannes Jacobi. Neuburger (2, 423, 501, 1911). Ernest Wickersheimer: Les guérisons miraculeuses du cardinal Pierre de Luxembourg (Congrès international d'histoire de la médecine p. 371–89, undated reprint received in 1923), apropos of Tournemire's clinical account of a tumor at the breast. Erna Kollert: Zwei Compendien "De neutralitatibus decidenciae" von Bernhard Gordon und Johann Tornamira (Diss., 31 p., Leipzig 1924; Isis 7, 539), the treatise ascribed to Jean seems to be an elaboration of Gordon's. Karl Sudhoff: Pestschriften (AGM 17, 32–35, 1925). Wickersheimer (p. 494–95, 1936).

MOLINIER

Jean Molinier. French royal physician (fl. 1385–97).

Jean Molinier, Joannes Molinerius. Physician to Charles the Bad, king of Navarre 1349–87. He wrote in 1397 a treatise on weakness of sight, De visus debilitate.

Text. The treatise is unpublished. Vatican MS, Reg. Suev. 1847 fol. 128r–135v.

Criticism. Lynn Thorndike: Vatican Latin MSS (Isis 13, 79, 1929). Wickersheimer (p. 452, 1936).

BOUCHER

Guillaume Boucher. French royal physician (d. 1410).

Guillaume Boucher (or Bouchier), Guilelmus Carnificis. Born near Gonesse (Ile-de-France; dépt. Seine-et-Oise). In 1362 he was already a master of arts, and applied for a canonry in St. Bartholomew of Beauvais; in 1365, he applied for one in St. Germain l'Auxerrois in Paris. In 1367 he was procurator of the French nation, and in 1368 rector of the University of Paris. In 1375 he was master in medicine and was authorized by Gregory XI to be a regent of the faculty in spite of his being married. He remained a member of the Parisian faculty until his death in 1410.

He was in the service of the duke of Orléans and treated one of the latter's sons in 1396. In 1398 he was already physician to king Charles VI, and continued to be until 1409. He was consulted by Philip the Bold, duke of Burgundy in 1402, and had probably been of medical service to him at least six years earlier.

He is dealt with here because a book of consultations compiled by an unknown German magister in Paris contains many consilia credited to him. Such consilia are more important than the medical theories of that time, largely contaminated with astrology, because they provided a sound experimental basis for the development of medicine. The consilia collected by the German master date from the very end of the fourteenth or the first years of the following century (in or after 1398, before 1410, perhaps before 1408). Few authorities are quoted: Hippocrates, Mesuë, Ibn Sīnā, Ibn Rushd, Simon of Genoa, Bruno da Longoburgo. Very few theories are mentioned, among them the Galenic one according to which pregnancies of seven months are natural though less favorable than those of nine months. For treatment, dietary rules are prescribed as well as a great variety of drugs, many of which are fantastic. Much use is made of enemas and bloodletting. Most of the consultations were held, no longer in Notre Dame, but in the church of the Mathurins (i.e., Trinitarians; Introd. 2, 334).

Text. Ernest Wickersheimer: Les secrets et les conseils de maître Boucher et de ses confrères. Contribution à l'histoire de la médecine à Paris vers 1400 (Bull. de la Société française d'histoire de la médecine 8, 199–305, Paris 1909). The text proper, Tituli secretorum et consiliorum Carnificis et Danszon [i.e., Pierre d'Auxon], medici [sic] de medicis regis . . . , covers p. 211–305.

Criticism. Wickersheimer's introduction to his edition (1909). See also his Dictionnaire (p. 229, 1936).

AUXON

Pierre d'Auxon. French papal and royal physician (d. 1410).

Pierre d'Auxon (Ausson), Petrus de Ausonno (Aversonone, etc.). Originated in Auxon in Saint-Brancher (Yonne); clerk of the diocese of Autun (Burgundy; dépt. Saône-et-Loire). In 1379 he was already a M.A. of Paris and bachelor of medicine of Montpellier and applied for a canonry in his diocese. In 1389 he was master in medicine and canon in Rouen. Regent of the medical faculty of Paris from 1393 to his death on August 29, 1410. Canon of St. Merri from 1392, physician to the antipope Clement VII, and to king Charles VI c. 1405–9. He was buried in his native country, at Pontaubert (Yonne). He bequeathed to the Paris faculty of medicine a MS of Galen's De utilitate particularum.

He is often quoted in the Secreta et consilia compiled by an unknown German physician in Paris c. 1400. See my note on Guillaume Boucher, and Wickersheimer (p. 614, 1936).

JEAN LE LIÈVRE

Joannes Leporis, Jehan Le Lièvre. French physician and anatomist (d. 1418, not 1408).

Jean was born in Semur, Côte d'Or, later was a cleric in the diocese of Autun. He must not be confused with Jehan Liefray of the diocese of Limoges. By 1392 he was master regent of the medical faculty of the University of Paris, and in 1394–95 he was dean of the same faculty. He was physician to the theologian Nicolas de Clamanges (c. 1360–c. 1434), also to duke Louis d'Orléans and his son Charles; and he attended Louis's widow, Valentina Visconti, in 1408 during her last illness.

In 1407 Jean presided over the earliest recorded anatomical dissection made in Paris. This was a real autopsy, and he discussed it with great accuracy and detail. This dissection was probably made for the instruction of the barbers in Paris, since Jean was also the first teacher of these barber-surgeons.

Jean wrote three medical works of no special importance, two in Latin and one in French. Only one, the Traité de la saignée, has yet been published. It is a poor compilation based on the works of al-Rāzī, Ibn Sīnā, and Lanfranchi of Milan. Since it is in French, it was probably written only for the use of the barbers.

The other two works are entitled: Instructio secundum communia instrumenta practice maxime experta (book on therapeutics), and Regimen contra epidemiam.

Text. Traité de la saignée, or Petit traictié sur le fait du nombre de la declairacion des vaynes qui sont assises sur le corps de la personne, edited by Ernest Wickersheimer: Le traité de la saignée de Jehan Le Lièvre (Mélanges offerts à Emile Picot 1, 14–19, Paris 1913).

Criticism. Ernest Wickersheimer: Les premières dissections à la faculté de médecine de Paris (Bull. de la société de l'histoire de Paris 37, 159–69, 1910). P. Delaunay: Un médecin de Charles d'Orléans (France médicale p. 442, 1913). Karl Sudhoff: Pestschriften (AGM 17, 92, 1925), brief note. Wickersheimer (p. 434, 1936).

A4. England

JOHN ARDERNE

John Arderne or Arden. The earliest great English surgeon (1307–77 or after).

He was born in 1307, a member of the family of Arderne or Arden, claiming descent from Saxon times. He took part in the Hundred Years' War, serving as a surgeon under two dukes of Lancaster; he was probably at Antwerp in 1338, at Algeciras (Spain) in 1343 (when Greek fire was used, and gunpowder is said to have been employed for the first time), at Bergerac (Aquitania) in 1347. He practiced medicine in Wiltshire; then from 1349 to 1370 he practiced at Newark-upon-Trent (Nottinghamshire); in 1370 he moved to London; he was still living in 1377. His literary activity took place mainly if not exclusively during his residence in London.

Apparently he had received no medical training, but he was not an uneducated man; he wrote a tolerable Latin, quoted Cato and Boetius. He was a man of wide experience, sound judgment, and independent thought. His medical ideas were those of his time, but he was a surgeon of genius. He had fully grasped three fundamental ideas in surgery, ideas which were then somewhat revolutionary: first, to cut boldly if necessary without fear of bleeding; second, to keep the instruments and wounds as clean as possible, and to obtain healing with a minimum of suppuration; third, to use light dressings, causing a minimum of irritation, and to change them as few times as possible (see similar ideas in Mondeville).

The therapeutic measures which he suggested are usually simple and rational, although he added some charms and other superstitious practices (having taken many of them from the old Saxon traditions). His writings contain valuable case histories.

His most important work is the Practica de fistula in ano, written in 1376, one of the outstanding medical works of the Middle Ages. It is full of original details derived from his own experience. His method of operating the fistula was an original modification of the method of Abū-l-Qāsim al-Zahrāwī (X-2); its principles still hold good today. Moreover, he recognized ischiorectal abscesses and their etiological relation to fistula in ano.

According to an early English version, A tretis extracte of Maistre Iohn Arden of fistula in ano and of fistula in other places, etc., that famous treatise is divided as follows: Fistula in ano, 6 chapters, the first of which contains autobiographical and other historical facts of great interest, deontological considerations, generalities on curable and incurable fistulae, on the instruments needed for their treatment, etc.; (chs. 7–13) fistula in the limbs; (ch. 14) mormales (bad ulcers); (ch. 15) piles; (ch. 16) tenesmus; (ch. 17) prolapse; (ch. 18) clysters; (chs.19–27) powders (vitriol, alum, verdigris, arsenic, orpiment, pulvis sine pari, pulvis sanguis veneris salus populi, . . .); (chs. 28–40) oils and waters (Syriac oil, Arabic unguent, Greek powder, oil of roses, violets, . . .); (chs. 41–44) valences (valence of scabious, wormwood; sleeping powders). Many authorities are quoted, sometimes verbatim, but subordinated to the subject.

Other writings: De arte phisicali et de cirurgia, a collection of cases and recipes covering a wide field. An extraordinary MS of that text was found in Skåne in 1756–58 by the Swedish archaeologist N. Wessman and has been ever since one of the treasures of the Royal Library in Stockholm.[39] It is a roll of parchment about

[39] Thanks to the courtesy of Dr. Isak Collijn it was my privilege to examine it there in the summer of 1934 (July 13).

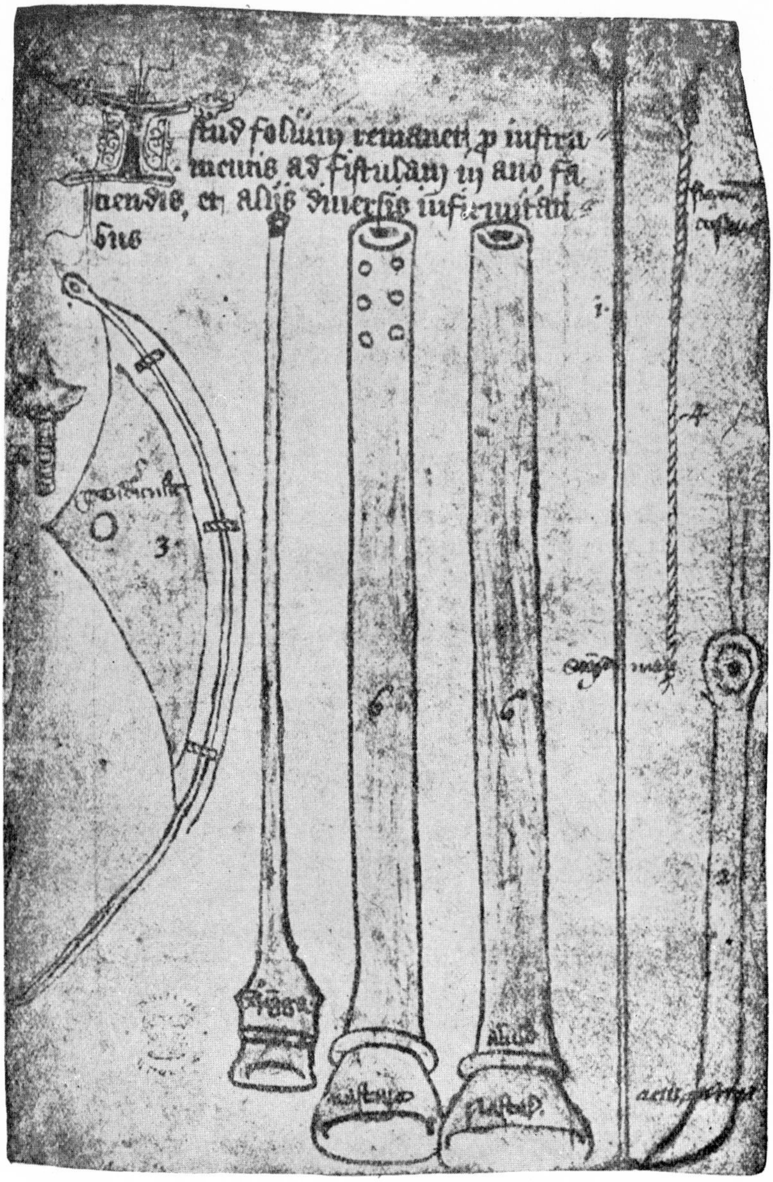

FIG. 40. Instruments used by John Arderne in the cure of fistula. (1) The probe—sequere me; (2) the snouted needle—acus rostrata; (3) the dilator—tendiculum; (4) the strong thread—fraenum Caesaris; (5) the peg—vertile—fitting into the hole in the wide part of the tendiculum; (6) the syringe in general use, with lateral openings; (6a) Arderne's modification of the syringe, with a terminal opening only. From Sloane MS 2002, leaf 24. Reprinted with kind permission of the Early English Text Society, from Treatises of fistula in ano, haemorrhoids, and clysters, edited by D'Arcy Power (p. 10, London 1910).

5½ m. long and about 37 cm. wide; the text is written parallel to the width in two or three columns, and there are over a hundred quaint anatomical and medical illustrations also arranged in three columns. In addition to Arderne's treatise, this MS contains extracts from other treatises. It was probably written in England about 1420. It may have been prepared as a gift for Philippa, daughter of Henry IV of England, who had become the queen of Erik VIII of Pomerania (king of the three Scandinavian countries 1396–1439). It was not unusual for medical MSS to be specially composed or copied for queens or princesses as part of their trousseau or later (e.g., the Régime du corps written by Aldobrandin of Siena c. 1256 for Beatrice of Savoy).

De cura oculorum, 1377.

Speculum phlebotomiae, a practical work on the best methods and seasons for bloodletting. Including many quotations from Ptolemy, Galen, al-Rāzī, Ibn Sīnā.

On medicinal plants and their uses, including foreign (French, Flemish, Irish) names of plants.

On gout. Rather detailed account of it, the treatment being mainly derived from the Compendium of Gilbert the Englishman.

On clysters.

Liber medicinarum sive receptorum, liber medicinalium. Commonplace-book containing various recipes and case histories.

Scala sanitatis contra plagas.

On colic, including a careful distinction between passio iliaca and other forms of colic.

A formula for making Greek fire (in French).

Regimen for nephritics.

On haemorrhage, gonorrhea, scabies, some veterinary remedies, treatment of wounds, rabies, diseases of women, etc.

On purging pellets. This is mainly an abstract from the antidotary of Lanfranchi of Milan (XIII-2).

A commentary on the De judiciis urinarum of Giles of Corbeil (XII-2) is probably apocryphal. It was not Arderne's manner to write commentaries.

Many of Arderne's works are still unpublished. Some of them may be parts or variants of others.

Three pharmaceutical preparations invented by him appear in the second issue of the first Pharmacopoeia of 1618, and some of them were certainly in use as late as 1733 (D'Arcy Power p. viii, 1922).

To return to his surgery, John Arderne was well read on the subject: he quotes Gilbert the Englishman (XIII-1) and Guy de Chauliac, "Master Gilbertyn" and "Master Guy," and was probably acquainted with Bernard of Gordon, Henri de Mondeville, and John of Gaddesden (all XIV-1). Yet he remains independent of their opinions, having more confidence in his experience and common sense. He is the first conspicuous military surgeon in English history.

His Latin writings were soon translated into English (the Tretis mentioned above being available at the beginning of the fifteenth century if not before; the Stockholm Practice in 1412), and their popularity is proved by the number of MSS (at least 18 in the British Museum alone). Some of these MSS are illustrated, showing crude pictures of lesions, drawings of plants and of surgical instruments. What is more remarkable, they continued to be copied until the seventeenth century. There are at least five MSS of that time, one of them having been copied by the royal physician and chemist Sir Theodore Turquet de Mayerne (1573–1655).[40] In spite of that popularity, there was only one early printed edition, and that relatively late, the treatise on fistulas translated by John Read of Gloucester[41] (1588).

Text. Franciscus Arcaeus: A most excellent and compendious method of curing woundes in the head . . . translated into English by John Read, chirurgion: Whereunto is added the exact cure of the caruncle, never before set foorth in the English toung. With a treatise of the fistulae in the fundament, and other places of the body, translated out of Johannes Ardern (London 1588). Francisco Arceo was a Spanish surgeon, born in 1493, died in or after 1573; the English surgeon John Read practiced in Gloucester, and from 1588 in London.

D'Arcy Power: Treatises of fistula in ano, haemorrhoids, and clysters, from an early fifteenth century manuscript translation (Early English Text Society no. 139, 194 p., 4 pl., London 1910). Careful edition, with good introduction (30 p.) and notes (31 p.) but no glossary. One of the illustrations is reproduced in our figure 40.

De arte phisicali et de cirurgia of Master John Arderne, surgeon of Newark, dated 1412. Translated by Sir D'Arcy Power, from a transcript made by Eric Millar (Wellcome Museum, Research studies no. 1, 72 p., 14 pl., London 1922). Based on Stockholm MS. Less carefully edited than the first text.

The Stockholm MS was completely reproduced full size, in photolithography, with introduction by Oscar Wiesselgren: Utländska medeltida handskrifter utgivna i ljustryck. I. John Arderne, De arte phisicali et de cirurgia (Kungl. Biblioteket, Stockholm 1929). Only 100 copies; the introduction is in Swedish but there is an English summary. This facsimile was published at the request of the famous Swedish explorer Sven Hedin for the sake of his friend the American brain surgeon Harvey Cushing (1869–1939), who received a hand-colored copy of it. This publication thus unites in our remembrance a great English surgeon of the fourteenth century, a famous American one of the twentieth century, and the Swedish Marco Polo! Dr. Isak Collijn kindly gave me a copy of it.

Criticism. Albert A. Gore: Maister John Arderne. Some account of an old MS presented to the Royal College of Surgeons in Ireland (Journal of the Medical Society 76, 269–97, Dublin 1883). J. F. Payne: Arderne (DNB 2, 76–77, 1885). Edward T. Withington: Medical history (p. 400–1, London 1894). Gurlt (2, 167–68, 1898). Karl Sudhoff: Weitere Beiträge zur Geschichte der Anatomie im Mittelalter (AGM 8, 135–39, 1914). Choulant (1920), Arderne is not mentioned but the illustrations of the Stockholm MS are discussed on p. 61. D'Arcy Power: The lesser writings of John Arderne (17th International Congress of Medicine, sec. 23, 107–33, London 1914); Epoch-making books in British surgery. 1. "A system of surgery" by Master John Arderne (London 1927). Alfred Brown: John Arderne, surgeon of early England (Annals of medical history 10, 402–8, 3 fig., 1928), apropos of Arderne and Sir Thomas Browne. M. C. Welborn: The long tradition, a study in fourteenth century medical deontology (Medieval essays in honor of James Westfall Thompson p. 344–57, Chicago 1938; Isis 29, 213).

JOHN OF MIRFELD

Johannes Marifeldus, de Mirfeld, Meryfeld, John Mirfield. English writer on medical and theological subjects (d. 1407).

A member of the important family of Mirfeld of Yorkshire. The date of his birth is uncertain; he may have been born in Mirfield in Yorkshire, or in London. His precise relation to the priory and hospital of St. Bartholomew is uncertain,

[40] Norman Moore (DNB 37, 150–52, 1894).
[41] D'Arcy Power (DNB 47, 351, 1896).

but he was probably an unbeneficed priest who resided in the priory which governed the hospital.

It has been claimed that he was a skilled physician, and that he studied in Oxford under Nicholas Tyngewich (one of the physicians of Edward I), but these statements have been denied by his latest biographers. His knowledge of medicine was purely academic and bookish.

His two books, Breviarium Bartholomei and Floriarium Bartholomei, are very scholastic and not in the least original. Their importance lies in the fact that they are the first to be connected with any English hospital, and that they show the state of medical and theological knowledge in London in the second half of the fourteenth century.

The Breviarium was written between 1380 and 1395. It is an extensive encyclopaedia of Greek, Arabic, and contemporary medical knowledge, superstitions, and incantations. It deals primarily with the remedies for innumerable diseases, and shows practically no knowledge of anatomy, very little medical theory, and only very brief statements concerning symptoms. The Breviarium is divided into fifteen parts. Part I deals with fevers, and a great deal of it is based on the writings of Galen. John foretells the coming of fever epidemics by astrological means, and uses incantations to banish fever. The chapter on pestilential fevers is based on the Lilium of Bernard of Gordon (XIV-1), his main authority, and to a lesser degree on actual observation. There is also a chapter On the signs of evil portent in feverish and other types of patients (De signis malis), but this is found only in MS. Since this separate copy contains some additional material, it is often listed as another treatise. Part II deals with affections of the whole body. Leprosy is discussed at some length; it is declared to be an incurable disease although drugs sometimes give temporary relief. John gives a diet regimen for such patients. Much of the material on this disease is taken from Platearius the Younger (XI-2). In this part he also deals with such ailments as gout, chronic rheumatism, scrofula, makes some original observations concerning smallpox, and discusses other diseases of a similar nature. Part III deals with diseases of the head, with chapters on epilepsy, apoplexy, etc., based largely on the Rosa of John of Gaddesden (XIV-1). Parts IV to IX deal respectively with the neck and throat, the chest, abdomen, pelvic organs, legs, boils, wounds and contusions. Part X treats of fractures and dislocations. John told how long each fracture would normally take for complete union (ribs, 2 days; a humerus or femur, 40, etc.). He also noted that union is more difficult in the aged. An instrument called "tornellus" (English wyndas) was used to reduce certain dislocations. Part XI has to do with the joints. Parts XII and XIII deal with simple and compound medicines. In these John describes drugs, and gives many prescriptions. Part XIV is on purgatives, and XV is a regimen of health which is based largely on the Regimen sanitatis salernitanum. The Breviarium is followed by a Sinonoma Bartholomei which is a glossary of the Latin medical and medicobotanical terms used in the Breviarium. The Breviarium is mainly a compilation made from the writings of al-Rāzī, Ibn Sīnā, the Macer floridus, Constantine the African, Gilbert the Englishman, Arnold of Villanova, Lanfranchi of Milan, Bernard of Gordon, John of Gaddesden, and many others. These borrowed ideas, however, are occasionally interspersed with some original observations which John had made in the hospital of St. Bartholomew. His therapeutic measures are sometimes quite rational.

John's Florarium, completed about 1404, is primarily a theological work consisting of a prologue, 175 chapters, and an epilogue. It is a collection of passages from the Scriptures and the church fathers. One chapter deals with medical deontology, showing that John's ethical standards were of a high order, and also with general rules for diet and exercise to preserve health. The whole work shows that he had read extensively in the works of Horace, Vergil, Ovid, St. Augustine, Boetius, Isidore of Seville, Thomas Aquinas, and many others.

Text. There is no edition of the whole Breviarium, but Sir Norman Moore has published various extracts from it in his Progress of medicine at St. Bartholomew's Hospital (34 p., London 1888) and his other publications. The following sections have been printed and translated by Hartley and Aldridge: Proemium, De signis malis, De ptisi, Pulvis pro instrumento bellico, Emplastrum Bartholomei, De ponderibus et mensuris, Epilogue (p. 46–95, Cambridge 1936).

The Sinonoma Bartholomei was edited by John Lancaster G. Mowat: Anecdota oxoniensia (1, 1–46, Oxford 1882).

Three parts of the Florarium Bartholomei have been edited and translated into English by Hartley and Aldridge: Proemium, De medicis et eorum medicinis, Epilogue (p. 114–63, Cambridge 1936).

Criticism. Norman Moore: John Mirfeld (DNB 38, 50, 1894); Mirfeld and medical study in London during the Middle Ages (British medical journal, Nov. 18, 1905); The history of the study of medicine in the British Isles (p. 25–49, Oxford 1908); The history of St. Bartholomew's Hospital (1, 608–14, London 1918). Neuburger (2, 423, 502, 1911). Percival Horton-Smith Hartley and Harold Richard Aldridge: Johannes de Mirfeld of St. Bartholomew's, Smithfield, his life and works (xiii+191 p., University Press, Cambridge 1936; Isis 26, 458–60). Loren C. MacKinney: Medieval medical dictionaries and glossaries (Medieval essays in honor of J. W. Thompson p. 240–68, Chicago 1938; Isis 29, 244). Mary Catherine Welborn: The long tradition (ibid. p. 344–57; p. 355; Isis 29, 213).

A5. Germany

THOPPING

Heinrich Thopping of Sinsheim (an der Elsenz, Baden, 13 miles from Heidelberg). German magister and physician (fl. 1353).

He was physician to Rodolph II of Bavaria, count of the Lower (Rhine) Palatinate (d. 1353), and wrote a regimen for Innocent VI (pope 1353–1362), who was suffering from gout. The date of it is February 24, 1353.

Text. The regimen was edited by Walter Brand (Leipzig thesis, 10 p., 1924).
Criticism. Wickersheimer (p. 288, 1936).

TILMANN

Tilmannus Henrici, dictus Sure de Syberg. Priest and physician of the diocese of Cologne (fl. 1362).

He originated in Siegburg (not very far from Cologne; on the Sieg, an eastern affluent of the Rhine). He was a bachelor of arts and medicine of Montpellier, vicary of St. John Baptist in Vilich (near Bonn), applied for ecclesiastical benefices to the chapter of Bonn in 1362 and of Strassburg in 1363.

The facts that he was a medical graduate, and that Amplonius called him practicus artis medicine eruditissimus, give plausibility to the ascription to him of a medical MS (Amplonian coll., Erfurt, Q. 193, fol. 91–98) written by an anonymous author who left Siegburg in 1362, going to Strassburg.

The text of that MS contains (I) a series of fourteen clinical observations, most of them made in Strassburg, comparable to the Italian "consilia" (Introd. 2, 94, 1086, 1088; Introd. 3, by index); (II) a collection of popular remedies for men and beasts. Everything is written in Latin, but there are German terms in the second part.

The author of part I was undoubtedly a practical physician; he was also a learned one, for he quotes the Aphorisms of Hippocrates, the Pantegni, i.e. the translation of the Kitāb al-malikī of 'Alī ibn 'Abbās (X-2) by Constantine the African (XI-2), the Viaticum, i.e. the translation of the Zād al-musāfir of Ibn al-Jazzār (X-2) by the same, the Canon of Ibn Sīnā (XI-1), and Mondino de' Luzzi (XIV-1).

Text. The medical text was edited by Ernest Wickersheimer: Faits cliniques observés à Strasbourg et à Haslach en 1362 et suivi de formules de remèdes (Bull. de la Société française d'histoire de la médecine 33, 69–92, 1939).

Criticism. Wickersheimer (p. 769, 1936).

JOHN OF GLOGAU

Joannes physicus. Johannes Glogaviensis. Silesian physician and clergyman (d. 1377 or after).

John was born about 1300–10. In 1354 he was canon of Glogau (on the Oder; duchy of Silesia), archdeacon in 1377, dean in 1379; later played a part in the struggle for the bishopric of Breslau, which remained vacant from 1376 to 1382.

About 1371–73 he wrote a plague treatise entitled Causae et signa pestilentiae et summa remedia contra ipsam. It is similar to that of Heinrich Ribbenicz, a contemporary, showing some of the same astrological and scholastic tendencies. John's work, however, contains many practical recommendations, especially concerning the causes of the disease and the proper diet for everyone, well or sick.

The treatise is in five parts: (I) Scientia stellarum ex te et illis est, deals briefly with the causes of the plague: (a) air that is corrupt either in quality or in substance; for instance, the air may be infected by foul vapors from the earth, which sometimes are not entirely absorbed by the sun; (b) vapors from infected areas, blown by strong winds into uninfected places; (c) infected waters, which are used either for drinking or for bathing. (II) Causae pestilenciae. Infected vapors are caused by the conjunctions of planets and the movements of stars. The conjunction of Saturn, Jupiter, and Mars is especially ominous. Also certain persons are more susceptible to the disease than others; for instance, some people have more corrupt humors in their bodies than others; and others have large pores. These people should not bathe too often. (III) Signa pestilenciae generalia. Astronomical phaenomena, cloudy and damp weather (especially in September and October). (IV) Signa pestilenciae specialia. General signs of ill health in certain individuals, who should be given a good health regime by their physicians to regulate their food, rest, and exercise. (V) De praeservatione pestilenciae. Various remarks on the best food and medicines to take during the plague. But in the last sentence he admits that the best remedy is to get away from infected places as soon as possible.

His principal authorities are Ptolemy, Galen, Ibn Sīnā, and Gentile da Foligno.

He also wrote a health regime entitled Nova vinea seu sanitatis custodia.

This John of Glogau must not be confused with a namesake who obtained his M.A. at Cracow in or before 1430, taught mathematics and philosophy in that city, and died in 1507.

Text. Causae et signa pestilentiae et summa remedia contra ipsam, edited by Karl Sudhoff: Pestschriften (AGM 9, 65–78, 1915).

Criticism. A. W. E. Th. Henschel: Schlesiens wissenschaftliche Zustände im 14. Jahrhundert (p. 78–82, Breslau 1850). Johann Heyne: Dokumentirte Geschichte des Bisthums Breslau (2, 208–21, Breslau 1864). The medical writings of John Glogau are dealt with in the biography of Johann von Neumarkt, bishop of Olmütz (1364–80), and ascribed to the latter. Aleksander Birkenmajer: Silesian astronomers and astrologers in the Middle Ages (p. 17, Katowitz 1937), in Polish.

THOMAS OF SAREPTA

Thomas of Breslau. Silesian (i.e., German or Polish) physician and botanist (1297–c. 1378).

Thomas was born in 1297 in Silesia (which he always called Polonia). He became a master in medicine, traveled extensively, and practiced medicine in various countries; he showed some knowledge of conditions in Bohemia, Germany, even England; he visited southern France and perhaps Italy and Catalonia. After his return to his homeland he entered the service of Henry VI prince of Breslau. That was probably before 1334. In 1336 he was definitely established in Breslau, and he assumed the Premonstratensian habit in that city. He lived at the St. Vincent monastery of that order near Breslau, and continued his medical practice there. His religious name was Peter, "Petrus physicus." In 1352, he was appointed bishop in partibus infidelium of Sarepta (Zarephath, Ṣarafend, on the Palestinian coast, 8 miles south of Sidon), and he then resumed his name Thomas, which is the only name under which he is remembered. He died in or after 1378, probably in Breslau.

He wrote two long medical works. The first, called from its incipit Michi competit, was begun in 1360. Thomas started with these words because, although he was not sure that his work would satisfy others, it satisfied him. It is divided into four parts, each having its own title, which has been a cause of confusion, as many MSS are incomplete. (I) Regimen sanitatis, concerning the conservation of health; (II) Aggregatum, dealing with simples, their qualities and degrees; (III) Antidotarium, dealing with compound drugs; (IV) Practica, dealing with therapeutic methods partly derived from his own experience. The name Practica (or Practica medicinalis) was given erroneously to the whole work.

The Tractatus de conservatione oculorum is chapter 13 of part IV of the Michi competit. Its authorities are Alphanus of Salerno (XI-1), Roger of Salerno (XII-2), Gilbert the Englishman (XIII-1), and William of Saliceto (XIII-2). It is perhaps the earliest text containing the statement that the use of glasses weakens the eyesight, "consuetudo videndi per oculos vitreos vel lancerneos [lanterneos?] ingrossat aciem oculorum." That statement is doubly interesting: because it suggests that eyeglasses were not uncommonly used c. 1360, and because it is still accepted by many people today.[41a] It was far more justified then than now, for on account of the lack of optometry the selection of glasses was then very much of a gamble, and of course the use of wrong glasses may and did hurt the eyesight.

The second work, called Collectorium secundum alphabetum, or Alphabetum, or Adversaria, or De differentia affectionum variorum, is a collection of medical facts

[41a] The distrust of glasses has been rationalized and their avoidance systematized by the American optician Dr. William Horatio Bates (1860–1931): The cure of imperfect sight by treatment without glasses (334 p., New York 1920) and his disciple Dr. Margaret Darst Corbett: How to improve your eyes (95 p., Los Angeles 1938). See also Cecil Stanley Price: The improvement of sight by natural methods (240 p., London 1934) and Aldous Huxley: The art of seeing (152 p., London 1942).

arranged in alphabetical order. This includes also, as we should expect, astrological facts under such headings as astrum et astronomia, augmentum lunae, tempora anni, praenosticatio. His astrological tendencies, however, were not immoderate, and he was opposed to alchemy and uroscopy.

Other medical works are ascribed to him, to wit, De flebotomia sive judiciis cruoris; De urinis; De prognosticatione temporum anni. A treatise of astrological medicine to which he himself refers, the Noli errare, is lost.

The most remarkable feature of his personality was his knowledge of botany. In his youth he had collected plants and prepared a herbarium, containing some English specimens mentioned in the Michi competit.

Thomas was a well educated physician. He was well read and often quoted such men as Gilbert the Englishman (XIII-1) or his own contemporaries Gentile da Foligno, John of Gaddesden, Bernard of Gordon (all XIV-1), etc. Moreover, he had obtained considerable experience in many countries; he was a good observer and sober in his judgments. He tried to regulate the dispensation of drugs under medical control.

Text. Only fragments of the Michi competit have been printed: the introduction and ch. 1 in Julius Pagel: Miscellanea zum Theil aus handschriftlichen Quellen (Janus 1, 372–74, 1896/97); chs. 21–25, concerning the diseases of the teeth and mouth, by Johannes Köhler: Zahnärztliches bei Thomas von Sarepta (Diss., p. 4–13, Leipzig 1924; Isis 7, 193); ch. 3, De febre pestilenciali, by Karl Sudhoff: Pestschriften (AGM 9, 57–59, 1915).

Criticism. A. W. E. Th. Henschel: Schlesiens wissenschaftliche Zustände im 14. Jahrhundert (p. 83–104, Breslau 1850). Johann Heyne: Dokumentirte Geschichte des Bisthums Breslau (2, 202–7, Breslau 1864). Haeser (1, 727, 1875). Schelenz (p. 321, 342, 1904). Neuburger (2, 503, 1911). Wickersheimer (p. 766, 1936). Aleksander Birkenmajer: Silesian astronomy and astrology in the Middle Ages (p. 15–17, Katowitz 1937), in Polish.

BERNARD OF FRANKFURT

A German physician who was probably educated in Italy. He practiced medicine in Frankfurt and Trier (Treves), where he flourished c. 1381.

A certain Bernardo di Alemagna was employed as a plague physician in the Este dominion (Ferrara and Modena) in 1463–64. It has been suggested that Bernard of Frankfurt and Bernardo di Alemagna were identical, but that is hardly plausible if the dates of the one (fl. 1381) and of the other (fl. 1463) are correct. Bernard (Bernhard) is a common name in Germany.

Bernard of Frankfurt wrote a plague tract, probably in Trier 1381. The copy printed by Sudhoff, according to its own explicit, is merely an abstract of a longer work. Bernard gives more astrological reasons for the causes of a plague than do many of his contemporaries. He states the methods he uses for determining in advance the appearance of a pestilence. He then explains that the corrupt air which the people breathe is mixed with the humors of their bodies and thus produces apostemae and fevers. The consumption of putrid and indigestible foods and drinks is harmful, and their evil effects spread into the flesh but not into the veins! Thus this fever is harder to cure than others because it is harder to draw off poisons which accumulate in the flesh than in the veins.

His methods of curing the plague are similar to those used by many other physicians. Before the patient has taken the disease, he should use a protecting regimen, taking purging pills, for which a number of recipes are given, and avoiding fogs, common baths, cold and dampness, cold and watery foods and drinks. A patient suffering from the plague who has many apostemae should be given hot wine and medicinal drinks to drive out the evil humors and thus reduce the apostemae.

Text. Consilium contra pestem; this is an abstract, "Abbreviatio huius consilii," made in 1484 of a longer work by Bernard; edited by Karl Sudhoff: Pestschriften (AGM 8, 244–52, 1915).

Criticism. Karl Sudhoff: Pestschriften (AGM 11, 143, 156, 1919; 17, 244, 1925). Riccardo Simonini: La peste negli stati estensi dal 1000 al 1400 (Rivista di storia critica delle scienze, anno 1924, p. 1–28; see p. 19).

HEINRICH RIBBENICZ

Henricus de Bremis, or de Rybbenicz, Henricus de Rybinitz, Reibnitz, Heinrich Rybinitz, Hinricus Rybbinis de Wartislavia.

German physician (d. after 1397). He received his bachelor's degree in 1381 from the University of Prague, and by 1392 was rector in that university.

About 1370 he wrote a Tractatus de praeservationibus et remediis pestilentiarum in the form of a letter to the people of Breslau. In that tract he foretold on astrological grounds a new outbreak of the plague. His prediction was realized and the plague did ravage Silesia, Bohemia, and the eastern provinces in 1371 and 1372. This work suggests comparison with the famous Missum imperatori of 1371 (see Jacob the Armenian). It is probable that the author of the Missum knew Heinrich or his work. The most interesting feature of Ribbenicz' treatise is the suggestion that the plague may have been caused by the Jews, using a poisonous plant, napellus (Aconitum napellus, monkshood), growing near Milan. This is the earliest trace (or one of the earliest) of that terrible suspicion, which caused calamities even greater than the plague itself.

Heinrich's work is not as original as many of those written by his contemporaries. His causes and signs of the plague are mostly astrological and are based on the writings of Hippocrates, Aristotle, Galen, al-Rāzī, and Ibn Sīnā. Most of the treatise deals with these causes and signs, and various drugs which should be used, but the reader feels that the author had not been an eyewitness of an epidemic.

Text. Tractatus de praeservationibus et remediis pestilentiarum, edited by Karl Sudhoff (AGM 4, 209–22, 1910); another redaction edited by Sudhoff (AGM 7, 82–89, 1913).

Criticism. Karl Sudhoff: Pestschriften (AGM 4, 205–8, 1910); Die Schrift des Magister Johannes, Archidiakon zu Glogau und der Pesttraktat Meister Heinrichs von Ribbenitz (AGM 9, 65–68, 1915).

LOW GERMAN MEDICAL WRITINGS OF THE SECOND HALF OF THE FOURTEENTH CENTURY

There are a number of composite medical treatises written in High and Low German which are very interesting for two reasons:

(1) They enable us to study the diffusion of scientific knowledge in German lands. Most of them are derived directly or indirectly from Latin sources, but they contain (or may contain) popular interpolations. That is, they represent the knowledge attained by educated people, a knowledge different from, and (though not necessarily) somewhat lower than, that of the learned class. Putting it otherwise, they represent a sort of compromise between scientific knowledge and folklore.

(2) They are important documents for the study of the development of the German competitive dialects.

The second of these reasons does not concern us; the first does, but only to a limited extent, as this work is devoted to the study of the progress of science, rather than to the study of its diffusion.

We shall consider here four Low German medical collections, which are called after the main MSS (1) the Utrecht Arzneibuch, (II) the Wolfenbüttel one, (III) the Gotha one, (IV) the Bremen (or Doneldey) one.

I. The Utrecht Arzneibuch. MS written at the end of the fourteenth century or the beginning of the fifteenth, found in 1884 by J. H. Gallée and given by him to the University Library of Utrecht. It is written in Low German, but is at least partly derived from High German sources, mainly Meister Bartholomaeus, and from the Macer floridus.

J. H. Gallée: Mittelniederdeutsches Arzneibuch (Jahrbuch des Vereins für niederdeutsche Sprachforschung, Jahrg. 1889, 15, 105–49, Norden 1890).

II. The Wolfenbüttel[42] Arzneibuch. Compilation in Low German derived from the Macer floridus, the Arzneibuch of Bartholomaeus, and a theory of the twelve months. For bibliography see next item.

III. The Gotha[43] Arzneibuch. MS dating from c. 1400, in Low German. It includes two main parts: (A) Düdesche Arstedie (Dutch medicine), collection of medical indications arranged a capite ad calcem; this purely medical work is followed by an astrological work, dealing with various prognoses, theory of twelve months, unlucky days of the month, bloodletting, dietetic rules, prognoses concerning the character of unborn children, etc.; (B) the Low German Bartholomaeus, a more learned work than A, describing many diseases identified by their Latin names and indicating remedies, many of which are pharmaceutical ones ("dat vindestu in der apoteken"). Both texts A and B contain a good many Latin words or phrases mixed with the Low German.

Karl Regel: Das mittelniederdeutsche Gothaer Arzneibuch und seine Pflanzennamen (Progr., Gotha 1872–73); Zwei mittelniederdeutsche Arzneibücher, Cod. chart. Gotha 980 und Cod. Wolfenbüttel 23,3 (Jahrbuch des Vereins für niederdeutsche Sprachforschung, Jahrg. 1878, p. 5–26, Bremen 1879). Felix von Oefele: Angebliche Practica des Bartholomaeus von Salerno, ein zeilengetreuer Abdruck von Bl. 85–104 der Gothaer Hs. (Neuenrath 1894). Sven Norrbom: Das Gothaer mittelniederdeutsche Arzneibuch und seine Sippe (240 p., Hamburg 1921), elaborate edition, with notes and glossary, forming vol. 1 of the Mittelniederdeutsche Arzneibücher edited by Conrad Borchling. It would be advisable to begin one's study of Low German medicine with Norrbom's book.

IV. The Bremen (or Arnoldus Doneldey's) Arzneibuch. This medical collection was written in Low German in 1370 and following years, and completed in 1382. It bears in fine the name of Arnoldus Doneldey. There is no reason to believe that Doneldey was the author; it is far more probable that the collection was compiled and copied by somebody else for his use. Arnoldus Doneldey was a member of a patrician family of Bremen, many members of which were burgomasters or councilmen in the thirteenth and fourteenth centuries. His father, Albero, was many times burgomaster. Arnoldus was born c. 1342; he became a trustee of St. Jürgen hospital; he died between 1387 and 1398.

[42] Wolfenbüttel, small town near Brunswick, famous for its library. Lessing was for a time (1770–81) its librarian.

[43] Capital of the Duchy of Saxe-Coburg Gotha. Not far from Erfurt.

Arnoldus' Liber medicinalis is difficult to analyze, as it is not well composed, but its contents can be divided roughly as follows: (I) extract from the High German Arzneibuch of Meister Bartholomaeus; (II) theory of complexions, brain diseases, fevers, various recipes; (III) special diseases and recipes put together without order; this includes fragments originating from Bartholomaeus; (IV) more Bartholomaeus material; (V) on the devil's power, deprecation against worms; (VI) two little treatises on urine; (VII) herbs, healing draughts, and salves; (VIII) advice relative to each of the twelve months; (IX) medico-calendrical materials, Egyptian days (unlucky days), prediction of weather.

This compilation is sometimes derived from Low German sources, but far more often from High German ones, and above all from Meister Bartholomaeus. Of course the High German writings are themselves derived from Latin ones, with perhaps a few folklore interpolations.

Franz Willeke: Das Arzneibuch des Arnoldus Doneldey (Diss., 72 p., Münster i.W. 1912).

Ernst Windler: Das Bremer mittelniederdeutsche Arzneibuch des Arnoldus Doneldey (Niederdeutsche Denkmäler vol. 7, 100 p., Neumünster 1932; Isis 21, 366), edition of the text with commentary and glossary.

Paul Diepgen: Deutsche Volksmedizin. Wissenschaftliche Heilkunde und Kultur (144 p., Stuttgart 1935; p. 46–47; Isis 24, 285).

A6. Bohemia

GALLUS DE STRAHOV

Mistr Havel, Gallus de Hradecz Reginae, Gallus de Sumo, de Monte Syon, Gallus Havel de Strahov.

Bohemian physician. About 1350–60, he taught astronomy and medicine at the University of Prague. He was one of the physicians of Charles IV, emperor 1355–78. Gallus was also a canon in Strahov, a Premonstratensian abbey in Prague.

He wrote a Vitae vivendae ratio addressed to Charles IV. It deals with the quality and quantity of spices and drinks one should use, the proper amount of sleep everyone should have, the way one should regulate his activities during the day in order to maintain good health.

His treatise on various kinds of medicinal waters and their properties, entitled Aquae infrascriptae et eorum virtutes, contains Czechish plant names.

In a number of copies of the Missum imperatori of 1371 (see Jacob the Armenian), Gallus is cited as the author, but there is no definite proof that he was alive in 1371. Another very brief plague treatise, however, Medicina contra pestilenciam ex dictis magistrorum Galieni, Avicennae, Ypocratis medicorum graecorum experta, written by Gallus, by its similarity seems to indicate the same authorship for both. He wrote still another very short but substantial treatise on this subject, Remedium quando apostema aliquem invadit in pestilencia, dealing with baths, bloodletting, and diet; and a short Tractatus urinarum.

Text. Vitae vivendae ratio in gratiam Caroli IV, edited by Friedrich Müller (Prague 1819), very poor edition.

Medicina contra pestilenciam ex dictis magistrorum Galieni, Avicennae, Ypocratis medicorum graecorum experta, edited by Karl Sudhoff: Pestschriften (AGM 7, 70, 1913).

Remedium quando apostema aliquem invadit in pestilencia, edited by Karl Sudhoff (AGM 7, 71–72, 1913).

The Missum imperatori was edited by Sudhoff (AGM 3, 149–50, 1909; 4, 194–95, 1911).

Criticism. Jos. Ritter von Hasner: Die älteste Medizin in Böhmen (Prager Vierteljahresschrift vol. 90, p. 13 ff., 1866). Neuburger (2, 504, 1911). Karl Sudhoff: Pestschriften (AGM 4, 194–203, 1910; 7, 68–73, 1913).

JEAN DE GRANDVILLE

Bohemian physician and poisoner (d. in or after 1397).

This Joannes de Grandi Villa was, according to his own testimony, born in Grantville (Grossdorf?) in the diocese of Prague, being the son of Peter, lord of that place. He studied in Prague, then in Padua, under Iacopo da Arquà, physician to the king of Hungary. He himself became physician to the emperor and traveled with him to Rome. After a while he returned to Bohemia, and was physician to the duke of Austria, etc. Later we find him in Montpellier, Toulouse, Marseille, the Barbary coast, Savoy, Auvergne . . . .

About 1391 he was in the service of Louis II of Bourbon (d. 1410).[44] At the request of Bonne de Bourbon[45] he is said to have poisoned her son Amedeo VII, the "Red Count" of Savoy (1383–91). Being interrogated by officers of the duke of Berry in Chalon-sur-Saône 1393, he admitted having given the "Red Count" at Bonne's request an ointment which paralyzed and killed him; he also provided Bonne with a powder wherewith to kill two of her enemies.

He wrote his will in 1397, requesting that a red stone of his "qui nuncupatur lapis Philippi" be given to the treasurer of the pays of Forez for the duke of Bourbon, and that he be buried in the church of Notre Dame d'Espérance in Montbrison (capital of Forez, now dépt. Loire) under the portrait of the blessed Urban V (pope 1362–70).

Criticism. Wickersheimer (p. 412, 1936). Arthur Piaget: Oton de Grandson, sa vie et ses poésies (Mémoires publiés par la Société d'histoire de la Suisse romande, 412 p., Lausanne 1941). Not available to me, but should contain some information on Grandville, whom Othon III de Grandson protected; so much so that Othon was accused of complicity in the murder of the "Red Count," was obliged to flee to England, and his possessions were confiscated. Having been rehabilitated by the king of France, Othon returned to the pays de Vaud. Soon afterward the accusations against him were revived by other noblemen; he was challenged to a judicial duel and killed at Bourg-en-Bresse, August 7, 1397 (Dictionnaire historique de la Suisse 3, 531, Neuchâtel 1926).

SIGISMUND ALBIC

Sigmund Albich, Sigismund Albikus, Albericy de Praga. Bohemian physician (of German-Czech parentage), born in Unčov (Mährisch-Neustadt, near Olmütz, Moravia), about the middle of the fourteenth century. He is said to have been

[44] Louis II of Bourbon having married in 1371 Anne, duchess of Auvergne and countess of Forez, the pays of Forez (western part of the Lyonnais) was a Bourbon possession from that year on until 1522. It was then adjudged to Louise of Savoy, and after her death in 1531 passed to her son Francis I; it has remained since then a part of France.

[45] Bonne of Bourbon was the daughter of Peter I, second duke of Bourbon (1310–56), and the sister of Louis II, the third duke. She married Amedeo VI, count of Savoy, and died in 1382.

born c. 1347, but he took his bachelor's degree in Prague only in 1382, and this would suggest a later birth date. He died in 1427.

Sigismund studied law in Prague, then took his doctorate in law at the University of Padua. It is not certain where he studied medicine, but it was probably in Prague. By 1394 he had been made personal physician to king Wenzel IV (1378–1419). For a few months in 1411–12 he was archbishop of Prague, then he was made archbishop of Caesarea in partibus infidelium, but also remained the physician and adviser of the king. As the Hussite troubles increased he fled first to Olmütz, then to Hungary, where he was a physician of the emperor Sigismund (1368–1437) until his own death in 1427.

Albic was the main representative of pre-Renaissance medicine in Bohemia. Many of his ideas were taken from the writings of Arnold of Villanova (XIII-2), but he did not blindly accept statements of authorities without checking them by his own observations and experience. He was well educated and knew the principal Greek and Arabic writings from Hippocrates to his own period.

Albic distinguished himself during the Prague epidemy of Black Death (1379–80) and the persecution of Jews which followed. Many of his writings deal with the prevention and cure of this disease.

His principal work, Regimen sanitatis, sometimes incorrectly divided into three separate works entitled respectively Praxis medendi, Regimen hominis sive Vetularius, and Regimen pestilentiae, is a collection of macrobiotic regulations for king Wenzel IV. In this he deals with such subjects as diet, exercise, work, the necessity of avoiding too many spices, and the general mode of living, as methods for securing good health. The last part deals with the proper diets and methods of living to adopt during the time of a plague.

Two brief plague tracts, Regimen tempore pestilenciae, and a Regimen (in a Germanic dialect), are very similar as to content and discuss the question of diet, the signs of death in a plague-stricken patient, the types of "apostemae" to be found on patients and how best to treat them.

Another brief work, the Medicinale, is a series of questions, without logical arrangement, which deal with paralysis, plague, diseases of women and children, dietetics, diseases of the eyes, and general therapy.

Two much longer plague treatises, a Collectorium maius and a Collectorium minus, are probably by Sigismund. According to Sudhoff, the Maius might have been written first, c. 1406/7, the Minus soon afterward. They deal with the plague of 1406 in Bohemia.

In the Maius, Sigismund discusses at great length the first symptoms of the plague, basing his remarks not only on his own observations, but also on the works of Hippocrates, Aristotle, Galen, Ibn Sīnā, and Arnold of Villanova. Before attempting to cure a patient, the doctor must be careful to find out the type of fever and apply only the remedies which are suitable to it. The principal methods of treatment are bloodletting, purging, and diet. Sigismund includes many recipes for purging pills and medicinal draughts. The proper diet for patients is discussed at some length, in this and in other writings of Sigismund, both the foods one should eat and those one should avoid. One should eat often and in moderate amounts (a method often advised today). Frequent baths are recommended, but should be taken in one's own home and not in the public baths, since the plague could easily be spread in the latter.

In the Collectorium minus, Sigismund stresses some of the same points made in the Maius, but goes into greater detail concerning the causes of plagues. The main cause is infected air, which is caused by certain conjunctions of planets, eclipses, and other astrological phaenomena, by the damp vapors coming from the earth, and by the breath of infected persons. Some of the reasons why certain people take the disease are: they follow unhealthful regimes, they eat too many "humid" foods and those which are not easily digested, they worry too much, and do not get enough sleep. The remedies given in the work are: proper food, disinfected cities and homes, private baths, purging pills (for which he gives many recipes), bloodletting, and plenty of rest.

A number of the works of Albic have not yet been printed but can be found in quite a few manuscript copies (especially in Prague). There is a group of Receptae on various subjects; Pro sompno (1398); Remedia contra tussim; Recepta ad coitum et contra coitum superfluum; Contra dolorem dentium; Experimenta; Recepta et experimenta. He wrote in 1416 in Buda a treatise entitled Medicina contra paralysim quam Albicus ante agonem mortis suae domino regi fecit (Sigismund of Luxemburg, emperor 1410–37), also, for the same emperor, a Regimen corporis, consilium ad Sigismundum. Other unprinted works include: Tractatus de crisi; Quaestio solemnis, utrum terminum acutarum aegritudinum sit dies quarta decima? videtur quod non; Reportata ex lectionibus, Febris est calor extraneus: Formulae medicales; a brief Practica; and a Půch der erczney (in German).

Text. His principal work, the Regimen sanitatis, printed by Marcus Brant, Leipzig 1484, was incorrectly divided by Hain into three works (Praxis medendi, Regimen hominis sive Vetularius, Regimen pestilentiae).

Regimen contra reumata, quod misit ante obitum suum Sigismundo Romanorum regi, Latin with a Czech translation edited by Andreas Schrutz (Časopisu lékařův Českých'-Roč no. 1, 24 p., 1909).

Collectorium minus (1406), edited by Karl Sudhoff: Pestschriften (AGM 9, 119–37, 1915).

Collectorium maius, edited by K. Sudhoff (AGM 9, 138–56, 1915). This work is probably by Albic.

Regimen tempore pestilenciae, edited by K. Sudhoff: Pestschriften (AGM 7, 92–94, 1913).

Regimen (also concerning the plague, in German), edited by K. Sudhoff (AGM 7, 94–97, 1913).

Criticism. Neuburger (2, 504–5, 1911). Karl Sudhoff: Ein spätmittelalterliches Epileptikerheim zu Rufach im Oberelsass (AGM 6, 454–55, 1913); Sigmund Albich über die Pest (AGM 7, 89–99, 104, 1913). Friedel Pick: Prag und Montpellier (AGM 17, 161–64, 1925). Gerhard Eis: Das Deutschtum des Arztes Albich (Zeitschrift für deutsche Philologie 65, 174–209, 1939; Mitt. 39, 135).

A8. Christian East

JACOB THE ARMENIAN

A physician by this name was established in Frankfurt about 1385. He may be the physician to whom two MS copies of the famous plague treatise Missum imperatori, of 1371, are ascribed. These copies, both in Munich, are entitled Missum regi Bohemiae per Armenium optimum medicorum de pestilentia.

This plague regimen is in the form of an open letter to the emperor Charles IV (1355–78). It deals with the plague of 1371 in Bohemia, and was probably written in the University of Prague; Charles IV was one of the great patrons of this university. In this tract the discussion centers mainly upon the different places where apostemae may appear on the body, and their treatment by bloodletting. If the apostema appears in the armpit, the median vein of the same arm is to be opened. If, however, it appears near the glands or behind the ears, then the part of the cephalic vein which is between the thumb and index finger is opened. The author also discusses briefly methods of fumigating houses and towns; foods which are to be avoided; and emphasizes the fact that public bathing is a menace to health. According to the author, this tract is based primarily on the works of Hippocrates, Galen, and Ibn Sīnā.

There are several German translations, one of which is printed by Sudhoff.

Text. Georg Ludwig Kriegk: Deutsches Bürgerthum im Mittelalter (1, 37, Frankfurt a.M. 1868). Karl Sudhoff: Ein weiteres deutsches Pest-Regiment aus dem 14. Jahrhundert und seine lateinische Vorlage, das Prager Sendschreiben "Missum imperatori" vom Jahre 1371 (AGM 3, 144–53, 1909; 4, 194–203, 1910; 8, 252, 1914).

B. ISRAEL

B1–2. Spain

JOSHUA BEN JOSEPH II HA-LORQI

Joshua ben Joseph ibn Vives ha-Lorqi, Judeo-Aragonese physician (fl. second half of fourteenth century in Alcañiz, Aragon). At the request of Judah (or Benveniste) ben Solomon ibn Labi he compiled an Arabic treatise on the powers and qualities of various foods and of simple and compound drugs. That treatise is lost in its Arabic form, but preserved in a Hebrew version, Gerem ha-ma'alot, made by Benveniste's son Joseph Vidal[46] in or before 1408.

He may be identical, or not, with one or two contemporary homonyms. The first of these wrote a virulent letter to Solomon ben Isaac ha-Levi after the latter's conversion to Christianity and baptism under the name Paul of Burgos. That letter sums up the Jewish arguments against the Messianic nature of Christ.

The second (who may or may not be identical with the first) himself became a Christian under the name Hieronymus a Sancta Fide (Geronimo de Santa Fé), the "apostle of Tortosa," and was physician to Benedict XIII in Avignon (antipope 1394–1417). It was possibly on his advice that that pope organized the Christian-Jewish disputations of Tortosa (in Aragon, near the mouth of the Ebro) in 1413–14. Later the pope sent him to Alcañiz and other cities in order to encourage the apostasy of other Jews.

Hieronymus wrote two anti-Jewish treatises: (1) Contra perfidiam Judaeorum (sive Ad convincendum perfidiam Judaeorum), defending the Messianic nature of Christ; (2) De judaicis erroribus ex Talmuth. In the edition of 1677 (p. 554), it is stated that they were first published in 1412 (plausible date) "sine contradictione." They were eventually answered, however, by Vidal Benveniste in his Qodesh ha-qodashim and by Isaac ben Qalonymos Nathan in his Tokaḥat maṭ'eh (Rebuke of the deceiver).[47]

[46] Joseph ibn Vidal Labi or Joseph Vidal ibn Labi. He flourished at Saragossa and was one of the twenty-odd rabbis who were ordered by Benedict XIII to take part in the Christian-Jewish disputation of Tortosa, 1413–14. Dates of birth and death unknown (JE 7, 589, 1904).

[47] Vidal ben Labi Benveniste was chief of the Jewish community in Saragossa and delegated to take part in the disputation at Tortosa in 1414. He may be identical with Don Ferrer of Gerona, but is certainly not identical with Vidal ben Labi de la Caballeria, nor with the Aragonese poet Vidal Beneviste who flourished like himself in the fourteenth and fifteenth centuries (EJ 4, 158, 1929).

Isaac ben Qalonymos Nathan flourished in Arles and Avignon in the fourteenth and fifteenth

Hieronymus died in or before 1419. His son, Francesco de Santa Fé, a marrano living in Saragossa, was accused of plotting against the inquisitor and thrown into prison, where he committed suicide in 1486. Other members of the Santa Fé family were burned at the stake for marranism in 1497 and 1499.

Text. The Gerem ha-ma'alot is unpublished.

Joshua's Iggeret to Paul of Burgos is included by Eliezer Ashkenazi II in the Sefer dibre ḥakamim (Metz 1849), together with other writings of the same kind. New edition with German translation by L. Landau (Antwerp 1906).

The two Latin treatises by Hieronymus a Sancta Fide are included in the Bibliotheca maxima veterum patrum (folio, 26, 528–54, Lyon 1677) and other collections. The De judaicis erroribus was printed also in Zürich 1552, and Hamburg 1654.

Criticism. Steinschneider: Hebraeische Übersetzungen (p. 762, 1893); Arabische Literatur der Juden (p. 170, 1902). Meyer Kayserling (JE 6, 551–52, 1904). B. Suler (EJ 10, 1116–18, 1934). Williams (p. 261–66, 1935), apropos of Geronimo de Santa Fé.

SAMUEL ESPERIAL

Judeo-Spanish physician who flourished in Cordova in the fourteenth or fifteenth century. I place him tentatively in the second half of the fourteenth century.

He dedicated to the surgeon (ha-garaḥ) rabbi David of Jaen a treatise on surgery, Sefer ha-garaḥot, written in the Catalan or Spanish language but in Hebrew script. (The word garaḥot is derived from the Arabic jirāḥa, meaning surgery.) This MS is in the Vatican Library, and I know nothing of it but what is said in Assemani's old catalogus (Rome 1756, p. 347, no. 372), "R. Samuelis Asperelli, Medici Cordubensis, Sepher Hagarchoth, Liber Chirurgicus de vulneribus curandis, lingua Catalonica sed characteribus Rabbinicis descriptus R. Davidi de Gain Chirurgo nuncupatus . . . ." The MS was apparently written in the fifteenth century. It contains two other medical texts. The Sefer ha-garaḥot covers 88 folios. An investigation of this text is very desirable.

Criticism. Josef Heller (EJ 6, 780, 1930), only 11 lines.

According to information kindly sent me by mgr. Eugène Tisserant (Vatican, Nov. 22, 1935), the MS Vat. heb. 372 has not yet been properly investigated, though it was consulted by Berliner in 1885, by A. Neubauer in 1886, and by A. Freimann in 1913.

Antonio Cardoner Planas: El médico judio Šelomó Caravida y algunos aspectos de la medicina de su época (Sefarad 3, 377–92, 1943). This study based on archival documents concerns a Judeo-Spanish physician whom I had overlooked. He was physician to Pedro IV of Aragon (ruled 1336–87).

B3. Provence and Languedoc

VIOLAS OF RODEZ

Mordecai ben Joshua of Rodez. Maestro Violas (or Biolas) of Rodez (or Rhodez), Aveyron or Rouergue in Guyenne. Judeo-French physician and astrologer.

---

centuries; he was probably the grandson of the translator Judah ben Solomon Nathan (Maestro Bongodas) and is famous as the author of Meïr netib (or Or netib, Light of the path), earliest Hebrew concordance to the Old Testament, first printed Venice 1523/24; new edition by Johannes I Buxtorf, Basel 1632 (Neubauer-Renan p. 583, 1893; EJ 6, 628, 1904).

He made an astrological observation in 1355 and he wrote a medical treatise entitled Bi'ur taksise ha-harkeb 'al da'at bin Rushd (Commentary on the rules of dosage according to Ibn Rushd).

Criticism. Neubauer-Renan (p. 651 and by index, 1893). Gross (p. 627, 897).

ISAAC BEN JACOB LATTES

Isaac ben Jacob ben Isaac Lattes. Judeo-Languedocian historian, exegete, traditionist, and physician. He flourished in the country between Béziers and Montpellier about 1372. He was a grandson of Isaac ben Judah Lattes (XIV-1) and a disciple of Nissim ben Reuben Gerondi, who died c. 1376; he must therefore have spent at least some time in Barcelona.

He composed in 1372 a historical work entitled Qiryat sefer (City of the book),[48] divided into two parts: Sha'are Ẓion (The gates of Zion) and Toledot Isaac (History of Isaac). The first part is divided into 16 chapters: (1) history of tradition, (2–4) bibliography of Mishna, (5) bibliography of Tosephta, (6, 7) the Mishneh Torah of Maimonides, (8) commandments to be observed by women, (9) commandments to be observed by everybody, (10) rules received by Moses on Sinai; chronological notes on the doctors of the Mishna and Talmud, etc. Other chapters deal with Abraham ben Ezra, Maimonides, Moses ben Jacob of Coucy (XIII-1), and Isaac ben Joseph of Corbeil (fl. 1277). It might be called a history of Jewish literature, and contains valuable information on Provençal authors of his century, the rest being largely derived from earlier writings. The second part, Toledot Isaac, is a commentary on the Torah.

His medical writings are (1) a treatise on fevers, without title, (2) a shorter treatise on indigestion (maamar ha-beqi'ah), and perhaps (3) a treatise on aliments (sefer ha-maakalim). The treatise on fevers includes recipes in Latin and Provençal written in Hebrew script; it is divided into eleven parts: (1–7) various kinds of fevers, respectively sanguine, choleric, phlegmatic, melancholic, epidemic, composed, hectic, (8) concomitant accidents such as sweating, (9) diseases in the lungs and ribs, (10) ulcers, (11) prophylactic advice to physicians.

Text. The medical writings are unpublished.

The first chapter of Sha'are Ẓion was edited by Henri Gross in the Magazin für die Wissenschaft des Judenthums (4, 54–77, 1877–78). New edition by Solomon Buber: Schaaré Zion. Beitrag zur Geschichte des Judenthums bis 1372 (Jaroslaw 1885).

Criticism. Neubauer-Renan (p. 682–91, 1893). H. Gross (p. 266, 1897). B. Suler (EJ 10, 676, 1934).

ISAAC BEN ṬODROS

Isaac ben Ṭodros of Avignon. Judeo-Provençal physician who originated in Avignon and flourished there. He studied there c. 1373 mathematics and astronomy under Immanuel Bonfils of Tarascon; he also studied philosophy in the Moreh nebukim, astrology, and of course medicine.

[48] So named from a city in the hills of Judah, near Hebron, also called "Qiryat sannah, which is Debir" (Joshua 15:49); translated in the Septuagint πόλις γραμμάτων, αὕτη ἐστὶν Δαβίρ. Hence a number of puns, the city of the book, or of the books, the library city, etc. The same title was chosen in 1924 for the quarterly bibliographical review of the Jewish National and University Library in Jerusalem, a bibliography of all Palestinian prints, and of all Hebraica and Judaica.

He witnessed the plague of 1377 in Avignon and devoted a treatise to it entitled Be'er laḥai (Well of the living; reference to Genesis 16:14), containing two introductions dealing with the air, and three chapters on diet and remedies. He mentions a number of physicians: Hippocrates, Galen, Rāzī, Isaac Israeli I, Ibn Zuhr, Ibn Rushd, Maimonides, also contemporaries like Moses ben Joshua of Narbonne (XIV-1), his master Immanuel Bonfils, Judah ben Solomon Nathan, Jean de Tournemire, and Joannes Jacobi.

He also wrote a little treatise on the distortion of the mouth caused by paralysis, Maamer belaqwah (i.e., the Arabic word laqwa, meaning that very distortion) or 'Iwot ha-fanim (Distortion of the face).

Text. The Be'er laḥai was edited by David von Günzburg in the Jubelschrift zum 90. Geburtstag des Dr. Leopold Zunz (p. 91 ff., Berlin 1884). An English translation of it is desirable, as well as the edition and translation of the other treatise. The translation of the Be'er laḥai should take into account the Bodleian MS of it, which baron von Günzburg did not know of; he thought his own MS was unique.

Criticism. Neubauer-Renan (p. 699–700, 1903). H. Gross (p. 7–8, 1897). Richard Gottheil (JE 6, 633, 1904). Jacob Klatzkin (EJ 8, 559, 1931). Wickersheimer (p. 311, 1936).

ṬODROS DE CAVAILLON

Judeo-Provençal physician who flourished toward the end of the fourteenth century in Cavaillon (Vaucluse, old comtat Venaissin),[49] not far from Avignon. The name Ṭodros is written in Hebrew with ṭeth and samek; in Latin and vernaculars, it was changed into Toros, Taurus, even Theodorus.

He composed an antidotary, Sha'are ha-harkabot, partly in Hebrew, partly in Latin. He is probably identical with Maestro Toros of Cavaillon, who was one of three "baylons" or leaders of the Jewish community in Avignon 1400 or 1440.

He is perhaps identical also with Ṭodros ben Moses Yomṭob (in Provençal, Bondia), who translated medical works from Latin into Hebrew c. 1394:

1. A treatise on fevers by Ibn Māsawaih, Mesuë major (IX-1), with commentary by Peter of Spain, Liber de febribus earumque causis, Sefer 'al sibbot ha-qadaḥot, translated 1394.

2. A treatise on digestives and laxatives by Arnold of Villanova (XIII-2), De medicamentis alvum subducentibus, Sefer 'al ha-refuot ha-meriqot.

Criticism. Assemani: Bibliothecae vaticanae catalogus, tomus I (p. 342, 1756). Neubauer-Renan (p. 725, 1893). Steinschneider (p. 717, 783, 1893). H. Gross (p. 539, 1897). S. Kahn (JE 12, 173, 174, 1906), two very short notes.

BENDIG 'AIN

Jewish-Provençal physician (d. not later than 1402).

Bendig 'Ain was a physician in Arles and taught mathematics there (presumably astrological medicine). He entered the service of the Angevine queen of Naples, Giovanna I (ruled 1343–81), who granted him various privileges in 1370. It is said that he knew Arabic, Greek, and Latin, in addition to Hebrew; and that he had foretold astrologically the queen's tragic end (she was dethroned, imprisoned, and finally murdered). By his wife Estes (Esther?) he had four daughters, three of

[49] A papal land enclaved within Provence and forming more than half the present department of Vaucluse. It remained under papal domination until 1791.

whom married physicians, Abraham Abigdor, Thoros Bondias (Ṭodros of Cavaillon?), and Bonsenior Brunelli (?).

Criticism. Neubauer-Renan (p. 451, 1893). Wickersheimer (p. 67, 1936).

B4. Germany

A medical treatise of 1396 in Yiddish

The oldest Yiddish MS known is a single sheet preserved in the archives of the city of Cologne (Hebr. 4), dated end of 1396. It is a short treatise on bloodletting.

My attention was drawn to it by Dr. A. A. Roback, of Cambridge, Mass., in 1935. Salomo Birnbaum: Das älteste datierte Schriftstück in jiddischer Sprache (Beiträge zur Geschichte der deutschen Sprache und Literatur 56, 11–22, 1932), a philological study, completely ignoring the contents of the text; Umschrift des ältesten datierten jiddischen Schriftstücks (Teuthonista 8, 197–207, 1932), transcription of the text. See the same author's study on the problems involved in the transcription of Yiddish, Die Umschrift des Jiddischen (Teuthonista 9, 90–105, 1933).

Moses Gaster: Yiddish literature in the Middle Ages (Essays by divers hands 7, 105–31, London 1927), does not deal with this work but with other Yiddish writings, much later (sixteenth century and later) and not scientific.

According to A. A. Roback: History of Yiddish literature (p. 51–64, New York 1940; suppt., Cambridge, Mass. 1940), the Yiddish language goes back perhaps to the ninth century or even the eighth, but apart from a series of formulae and incantations dating from the thirteenth century or the twelfth, the earliest surviving document is the treatise of 1396 above mentioned.

Note on Early Yiddish Literature

Ancient Yiddish documents were peculiarly liable to destruction, for they were suppressed by Christians on account of the Hebrew script, and could find no place in the synagogue libraries on account of their Yiddishness. How many Latin documents would have come down to us if instead of being preserved in the monastic libraries they had been carefully eliminated from them? Yiddish literature, however, began only in the sixteenth century, its father being the Hebrew grammarian and Masorete Elias Levita (Elijah ben Asher ha-Levi Ashkenazi, 1468–1549; Elijah Baḥur, Elijah Tishbi), who wrote in 1501 the Bovo-buch or Bovo-ma'aseh—that is, a Yiddish version in ottava rima of the "Sir Beues of Hamtoun" tale, version derived from the Italian Buovo d'Antona.[49a] This (Yiddish) text was first printed in an uncertain place c. 1541. Many other books were written in the sixteenth century, the most popular being the Ma'ase Buch, a collection of some three hundred stories derived from Talmudic and other Hebrew writings and from the universal treasure of folk tales. This was first printed in Basel 1602, and often reprinted not only in Yiddish, but in Hebrew, Arabic, German, Latin, English, etc.[50] Another exceedingly popular book was the women's Bible paraphrase by

[49a] That tale is one of the most popular chivalresque romances of the Middle Ages. The Anglo-Norman form of it which has come down to us is of the beginning of the thirteenth century, but is probably older. Versions are found in French, English, Dutch, Cymric, Irish, Scandinavian, Italian, Russian, Yiddish, Roumanian. That romance was especially popular in Italy and Russia. For first orientation see Wells (p. 21–23, 765, 1926, and suppts.) or Mario Pelaez (Enciclopedia italiana 8, 122, 1930).

[50] Gotthold Weil: Ma'aseh books (JE 8, 236–37, 1904). Steinschneider (p. 605–19, 1860).

Jacob ben Isaac Ashkenazi, rabbi of Janow, called Ṣenah u-renah[51] or Teitsh Khumesh, of which there are also innumerable editions, the earliest extant (the fourth?) being that of Basel 1622.

C. SAMARITAN MEDICINE

ABŪ SA'ĪD AL-'AFĪF

Abū Sa'īd (or Sa'd) al-'Afīf (the abstaining one) ibn abī Surūr al-Isrā'īlī al-Sāmarī (al-Sāwī) al-'Asqalānī. Famous Samaritan physician of 'Asqalān (the old Philistine town of Ascalon, on the coast of southern Palestine), who flourished in Cairo, probably toward the end of the fourteenth century.

He wrote two important medical works in Arabic: (1) Kitāb al-lamḥa fī-l-ṭibb (A glimpse of medicine), dealing with acute diseases;[52] (2) Khulāṣat al-qānūn (The essence of the canon), containing extracts from Ibn Sīnā's Qānūn. The first work was the object of a commentary by Ibn al-Amshāṭī. The existence of this commentary is our only clew with regard to the date of Abū Sa'īd's activity.

Muẓaffar al-dīn Maḥmūd ibn Aḥmad al-'Aintābī al-Ḥanafī, commonly called Ibn al-Amshāṭī, was born in 'Aintāb (in the wilāya of Aleppo) or in Egypt (?) in 1407/8. His commentary on the Lamḥa fī-l-ṭibb was entitled Ta'sīs al-ṣiḥḥa (Establishment of health); as usual, it is mixed with the original text.

Criticism. Ḥājjī Khalīfa (3, 166, 1842; 4, 501, 1845; 5, 329, 1850; 6, 253, 1852). Wüstenfeld (p. 159, 1840). Leclerc (2, 265, 291, 1876). Steinschneider (p. 325, 1902). Nothing in Brockelmann.

D. ISLĀM

D1. ANDALUSIA

MUḤAMMAD IBN MUḤAMMAD OF ALMERIA

Abū 'Abdallāh Muḥammad ibn Muḥammad ibn Ja'far, called in Latin Albelbanus. Andalusian Muslim man of letters and physician (d. 1363).

He originated in Almeria, where he was magistrate (quaestor), and he was later governor in Marchena (I cannot identify that locality; in Arabic script the name reads Marshānah). He wrote poems on theology and rhetoric and a treatise on the plague (waba') entitled Islāḥ al-niyyah (Correction of the intention), this being one of the earliest Arabic treatises on the plague.

Criticism. Casiri (2, 74, 1770). The Islāḥ al-niyyah is not mentioned in Brockelmann (1902).

MUḤAMMAD IBN 'ALĪ AL-SHAQŪRĪ

Muḥammad ibn 'Alī ibn 'Abdallāh al-Laqmī[53] al-Shaqūrī. Born in 1326–27, in Segura (Ar., Shaqūra), a town in the hills whence the Segura River flows toward Murcia and Orihuela. Muslim-Andalusian physician.

[51] Go forth [O ye daughters of Zion and behold] (Cant. 3:11). Steinschneider (p. 1216–20, 1860).

[52] According to Ḥājjī Khalīfa (5, 329), the Lamḥa was derived from the writings of al-Īlāqī and other physicians. This must be a reference to Muḥammad ibn 'Alī al-Īlāqī, who flourished in Bākharz, Khurāsān, and died in the battle of Qaṭwān (1141), near Samarqand, when the Saljūq sulṭān Abū-l-Ḥārith Sanjar was defeated by the Qara-Khiṭāi (EI 4, 151; Brockelmann suppt. 1, 887).

[53] I don't understand al-Laqmī, so spelled by Ṭāhā Dinānah (1927). Casiri (2, 89) writes Allakhamita (?) without giving the Arabic form.

He wrote a medical treatise, Tuḥfat al-mutawassil fī ṣan'at al-ṭibb (Gift for the one who wants information on the art of medicine), and an account of the plague which raged in his part of the world in 1348–49. This account may be included in the Tuḥfat or may have been a separate treatise. Casiri (2, 89) mentions two other medical treatises, the one on experiments and the other on the errors of the physicians (so he says, and translates their titles as Major cura and Judaeus perdomitus), but the Arabic titles do not suggest medical contents. They are respectively Al-jihād al-akbar (The greatest appeal to religion and holy war) and Qama'a al-yahūdī 'an ta'adud al-ḥudūd (Knocking of the Jew to prevent him from exceeding the limits); it would seem that these two treatises are devoted rather to the fanning of religious hatred than to medicine.

Criticism. My information is derived exclusively from Casiri (2, 89, 1770). Ṭāhā Dināṇah: Die Schrift von Ibn Khātimah (AGM 19, 27, 1927; Isis 10, 131), simple reference to the plague treatise.

None of the treatises ascribed to him by Casiri are mentioned in Brockelmann (1902). The polemical treatises are not mentioned by Moritz Steinschneider (1877).

D2. Ifrīqīya

IBN ABĪ ḤAJALA

Algerian man of letters, writer on the plague and on chess (1325–75).

Abū-l-'Abbās Aḥmad ibn Yaḥyā Ibn abī Ḥajala al-Tilimsānī al-Ḥanbalī. His grandfather was a famous ṣūfī called Abū Ḥajala (father of the partridge) because a partridge had laid an egg in the sleeve of his cloak. Aḥmad was born in Tlemcen 1325; after having accomplished the Pilgrimage and visited Damascus, he became the head of the ṣūfī monastery established by Manjak[54] near Cairo. He died of the plague on May 2, 1375.

His compositions in prose and poetry are too numerous and not sufficiently relevant to our purpose to be enumerated. He appears to have been influenced chiefly by the great ṣūfī poet Ibn al-Fāriḍ (XIII-1). It is possible that an analysis of his literary works would bring to light materials of interest to us. In the meanwhile we can only cite his writings relative to the plague: (1) Al-ṭibb al masnūn fī daf' al-ṭā'ūn (The sharp medicine for defense against the plague); (2) Jiwār al-akhyār fī dār al-qarār, written in 1362 when his son died of the plague; (3) Daf' al-niqma fī-l-ṣalāt 'alā nabī al-raḥma, apropos of the plague of 1362.

We may also mention his treatise on chess, Kitāb anmūdhaj al-qitāl fī la'b al-shaṭranj (Examples of warfare in the game of chess), or, fī naql al-'uwāl. After an introduction telling the story of early Muslim players, discussing whether the game is licit or not, and the conditions of licitness, there follow eight chapters each ending with five diagrams. Among earlier writers he refers to Muḥammad ibn Yaḥyā al-Ṣulī and Muḥammad ibn 'Ubaidallāh al-Lajlāj (died Shīrāz c. 970).

[54] This is probably the amīr Saif al-dīn Manjak al-Yūsufī (d. 1375), for whom see G. Wiet's edition of Al-manhal al-ṣāfī of Ibn Taghrībirdī (d. 1469) in the Mémoires de l'Institut d'Egypte (vol. 19, Cairo 1932). The ṭarīqa to which that monastery belonged cannot be determined. Many ṣūfī monasteries were founded in or near Cairo by Mamlūk umarā' and others. There is a beautiful mosque of the amīr Manjak near the Citadel in Cairo, and a ruined doorway of his palace, but no trace of a ṣūfī monastery, nor any mention of one in Egyptian topographical writings. Information kindly given to me by my friend Max Meyerhof (letters dated Cairo March 15 and 26, 1940).

Another work of his, the Sukkardān al-sulṭān al-Malik al-Nāṣir, is an anthology illustrating the importance of the number seven in the description and history of Egypt. It was written in 1356, hence during the second rule of the Mamlūk sulṭān al-Nāṣir al-Ḥasan (1354–61).

Criticism. Wüstenfeld (no. 437, p. 17, 1882). Brockelmann (2, 12, 1902; suppt. 2, 5, 1938). Murray (p. 176, 1913). Sarkis (p. 28, 1930).

D3. Mamlūkīya

AL-SHĀDHILĪ

Ṣadaqa ibn Ibrāhīm al-Miṣrī al-Ḥanafī al-Shādhilī. Egyptian ophthalmologist (fl. second half of fourteenth century?).

The dating of al-Shādhilī accepted by Brockelmann (2, 137) and Hirschberg is not sufficiently justified by them; I accept it tentatively. Al-Shādhilī did not live earlier, but he might be a little later. As to the name Shādhilī, it probably refers to the Shādhilīya (or Shādulīya), a religious brotherhood or ṭarīqa founded by the Moroccan shaikh 'Alī ibn 'Abdallāh al-Sharīf al Zarwīlī al-Shādhilī (b. 1197, d. Upper Egypt 1258). See articles by A. Cour and D. S. Margoliouth (EI 4, 246–49, 1926). But it might refer also to the place Shādhila near the Jabal Ẓafrān in Tunisia.

Al-Shādhilī wrote an elaborate treatise on ophthalmology entitled Kitāb al-'umda al-kuḥlīya fī-l-amrāḍ al-baṣarīya (Ophthalmological support for the diseases of the sight organ), extending (in the Munich MS) to almost 3,500 lines. It is divided into five main parts (jumlat): (I) anatomy and function of the eye, (II) medical and ophthalmological generalities, (III) tangible diseases of the eye, diagnosis and treatment, (IV) intangible (or less tangible) diseases, (V) medical and ophthalmological materia medica.

Though al-Shādhilī continues the long tradition of Arabic ophthalmology which goes back to the beginning of the ninth century,[55] yet he was an original observer and investigator and his 'Umda contains various novelties. For example, in part I, faṣl 4, he discusses the embryological origin of the eye. According to Aristotle, he remarks, the heart is formed first; according to Hippocrates, the brain and eyes; according to al-Rāzī, the liver. He then discusses the three theories of vision, inclining, with most of his predecessors down to Galen, to the third, compromising one: vision originates in the lighted object as well as in the eye itself. Referring to an unknown person Ibn Qāḍī Ba'lbakk ("the son of the judge of Ba'lbakk" in the Lebanon), he distinguishes twenty-seven kinds of sensation, and eight conditions of vision. In part I, faṣl 6, we find a beginning of comparative anatomy and physiology of the eye, wherein he considers such questions as the existence or nonexistence of eyes and their comparative size, color, and function in various animals. Then he proceeds to explain the peculiarities of the human eye, also of the human brain, for most eye troubles originate in the brain. He shows the differences between the eyes of various races (Negroes, Turks, Beduins, and city people). This is an interesting chapter of comparative anthropology.

Al-Shādhilī was the first to speak of the prevalence of eye diseases among the Egyptians, which he ascribed to the dust and sand, and also to the weakness of their brains. It is curious that earlier Egyptian oculists like 'Ammār ibn 'Alī (XI-1),

[55] For a brief account of it see Introd. 2, 82; Isis 13, 106–9.

who was an 'Irāqian but flourished in Egypt, did not remark on that important subject. Does it mean that Egyptian eye diseases were relatively less common in earlier days? The earliest European to speak of Egyptian ophthalmia (trachoma, endemic in Egypt) was Prospero Alpini (1553–1617), who observed it c. 1580.

In part III al-Shādhilī deals in turn with the diseases of the eyelid, canthus, conjunctiva, cornea, uvea, and lens. For each of these organs he distinguishes many disorders (36 for the eyelids). He recognizes the four kinds of trachoma as different stages in the development of that disease; observation already made by Paulos Aegineta (VII-1) but missed by 'Alī ibn 'Īsā (XI-1). Other eyelid troubles overlooked by 'Alī ibn 'Īsā but considered by al-Shādhilī are the ikhtilāj ("tic convulsif"), the Persian fire or carbuncle, the lid cancer (saraṭān jafanī), the twitching of the lids.

Whereas 'Alī ibn 'Īsā spoke of only 13 disorders of the conjunctiva, al-Shādhilī (III, 3), following in this Muḥammad ibn 'Alī Najīb al-dīn al-Samarqandī (XIII-1), adds 2 more, nadhra (episcleritis) and bawālṭīn (?). He realized the influence upon the eye of constipation, bad digestion, headaches, menopause. As to the cornea, he recognized only 13 disorders, like 'Alī ibn 'Īsā, but his study of hypopyon is more elaborate than that of his predecessors, Greek or Arabic. The same remark applies to the section on cataract (III, 6).

The materia medica (part V) is arranged alphabetically, much being borrowed, as we should expect, from Ibn al-Baiṭār (XIII-1).

All in all, this treatise is remarkable for its comprehensiveness and relative originality (it is not easy to add many novelties to a general textbook dealing with a very old subject). Each group of diseases is introduced in al-Shādhilī's treatise by pathological generalities. Like Khalīfa ibn abī-l-Maḥāsin (XIII-2), he indicates the seasons and ages of life when certain diseases are more common. He regularly begins the prognosis with the words: This disease is curable, or, it is feared, or, it is incurable.[56]

Al-Shādhilī was pious, witness the morning prayer for physicians which he quotes, and he loved his fellow men; he was obviously an experienced physician, well acquainted with the literature of his profession, yet ready to make experiments.

The treatise is remarkable also as being the last in the great Arabic tradition of ophthalmology, with the partial exception of a treatise Dāḥib al-kusūf fi-l-ṭibb (Remover of eclipses in medicine) written much later (not earlier than the end of the sixteenth century) by the Moroccan Abū Muḥammad 'Abdallāh ibn 'Azūz al-Marrākushī, and largely plagiarized from 'Alī ibn 'Īsā.

Text. The text of the 'Umda is unpublished, but a long analysis of it is given by Hirschberg.

Criticism. Julius Hirschberg: Die arabischen Lehrbücher der Augenheilkunde (Abhandlungen der K. preussischen Akad. der Wissenschaften zu Berlin, 1905, 117 p.; p. 95–150).

AL-MANBIJĪ

Muḥammad ibn Muḥammad al-Manbijī (fl. 1373).

According to his nisba, he was connected in one way or another with Manbij,

[56] This reminds me of the division in the Edwin Smith papyrus (seventeenth century B.C.): "An ailment which I will treat," "An ailment with which I will contend," "An ailment not to be treated." James Henry Breasted: The Edwin Smith surgical papyrus (2 vols., Chicago 1930; Isis 15, 355–67, 1931). Does this indicate the persistence of an Egyptian tradition during thirty-one centuries?

an ancient town in northern Syria (EI 3, 232–36). Apropos of the plague of 1373 he wrote the Tasliyat ahl al-maṣā'ib fī maut al-awlād wal-aqārib.

Text. The Tasliya was printed in Cairo 1929/30.
Criticism. Brockelmann (2, 76, 1902; suppt. 2, 82, 1938).

D4. Yaman

MUḤAMMAD AL-MAHDĪ

Muḥammad al-Mahdī (or Mahdawī?) ibn 'Alī al-Ṣunbūrī (of Sunpūr, Bengal; or is it Ṣubunrī?) al-Yamanī al-Hindī al-Muqrī (of Muqrā inYaman). Author of a medical treatise in Arabic (d. 1412/13).

The man was a Bengali, or at any rate a Hindu, who lived in Yaman. He wrote the Kitāb al-raḥma fī-l-ṭibb wal-ḥikma (Book of mercy, concerning medicine and [medical] wisdom), divided into five parts: (1) physics, (2) foodstuffs and drugs, (3) hygiene, (4) diseases of special parts of the body, (5) general diseases. This book may have been composed in the fourteenth century, or not until the beginning of the fifteenth. It was wrongly ascribed to the Egyptian polygraph al-Suyūṭī (1445–1505).

Text. Printed Cairo 1300, 1302, 1304 H. The edition of 1304 at least includes also the Kitāb al-ṭibb al-nabawī ascribed to al-Dhahabī (XIV-1), and according to Renaud these Egyptian editions contain interpolations, such as magical formulas (kitābāt), of Maghribī origin, witness thereof Berber names of drugs and plants.

Sidi-Siouti: Livre de la miséricorde et de l'art de guérir les maladies et de conserver la santé (84 p., Alger 1856). French translation by Florian Pharaon, revised and annotated by Alphonse Bertherand.

Criticism. Ḥājjī Khalīfa (3, 351, no. 5891, 1842). Brockelmann (2, 189, 1902; suppt. 2, 252, 1938). H. P. J. Renaud and G. S. Colin: Documents marocains pour servir à l'histoire du mal franc (p. 9, Paris 1935; Isis 25, 269). Philip K. Hitti: Catalog of Arabic MSS (nos. 1109, 2169, Princeton 1938).

D5. Anatolia

AL-ĀQSARĀ'Ī

Turkish physician, theologian, and rhetorician writing in Arabic (d. c. 1368–78).

Jamāl al-dīn Muḥammad ibn Muḥammad al-Āqsarā'ī was a great-grandson of Fakhr al-dīn al-Rāzī (XII-2). His nisba refers to a place Āq sarā'i, probably the town some distance southeast of the great salt lake in Qaramān; I say "probably" because there are other places called Āq sarā'i (white palace) in Anatolia, but this is the most important; moreover, we know that he was teaching in the Madrasat al-silsila in Qaramān during the rule of Murād I ('Uthmānlī sulṭān 1360–89). He died in the decade 770–80 (1368–78).

His main work is a commentary on the Mūjiz al-qānūn (or Al-mūjiz fī-l-ṭibb) of Ibn al-Nafīs (XIII-2), itself derived from the Qānūn of Ibn Sīnā.

He annotated the famous Qur'ānic work Al-kashshāf 'an ḥaqā'iq al-tanzīl of al-Zamakhsharī (XII-1), and wrote a commentary on the rhetorical textbook Al-īḍāḥ fī-l-ma'ānī wal-bayān of Khaṭīb Dimashq (XIV-1).

Text. The Ḥall al-mūjiz was printed in Delhi c. 1870, and Lucknow 1877, 1908.
Criticism. Storey (sec. 1, p. 7, 1927). Brockelmann (suppt. 2, 328, 1938). Renaud (p. 45, 1941).

ISḤĀQ IBN MURĀD OF GEREDE

In modern Turkish script Geredeli Ishak bin Murad. Turkish physician writing in Turkish (fl. c. 1388/89). He flourished and perhaps was born in Gerede in northern Anatolia (some 100 km. northwest of Ankara). Gerede was then the chief town of the principality of Qizil Aḥmadlī, south of the Black Sea, corresponding roughly to ancient Paphlagonia.

Two medical writings are ascribed to him: (1) Khulāṣat al-ṭibb, (2) Khawāṣṣ al-adwīya. Both works are said to have been written in Turkish, and are among the earliest Turkish medical writings. They are both dated 1388/89, which suggests that perhaps they are but two titles, or two editions, of the same work. The titles of course are Arabic, but the fact that the text was not in Arabic is confirmed by the absence of the author and of the titles from Brockelmann's elaborate bibliography of Arabic MSS, as well as by the existence of Turkish MSS.

The Khawāṣṣ al-adwīya is a herbal and materia medica combined in the mediaeval manner. The author had obtained some experience of herbs in his excursions in the mountains near Gerede. He deals not only with herbs, but with other plants, and with products of animal and mineral origin. The work is divided into two parts, in the first of which the herbs and drugs are dealt with in alphabetical order; the second part is devoted to the medical applications. The medical properties of each drug are mentioned, and the symptoms and cures of each disease indicated.

There are two MSS of it in Istanbul, one in the Emiri library, no. 109, the other in Topkapu harem library, no. 1693; the second MS is incomplete; there is a third MS in Paris.

Criticism. Galip Ata: Evolution de la médecine en Turquie (Bull. de la Société française d'histoire de la médecine 26, 445, 1932). I. Hakkı Uzunçarşılıoğlu: Anadolu beylikleri (p. 80, Ankara 1937; Isis 32), on Anatolian states, in Turkish; see review also in Turkish by Süheyl Ünver in Tedavi klinigi vol. 8, 5 p., 1938. Aydin M. Sayili: Turkish medicine (Isis 26, 410, 1937). Adnan (p. 15, 1939), Adnan calls the author Murād ibn Isḥāq after a Turkish MS in the Bibliothèque nationale, Paris, A.F. 170, dated 1387. Such inversions are not uncommon in Oriental names. The date 1387 is sufficiently close; if the real date was 790/91, this might be translated 1387/89.

MUḤAMMAD IBN MAḤMŪD

Muḥammad ibn Maḥmūd ibn Ḥājjī al-Shīrwānī, i.e., of the Shīrwān country on the western shore of the Caspian Sea. Turkish (or Caucasian?) physician who wrote for Walī-l-dīn, a grandson of Urkhān ('Uthmānlī sulṭān 1326–60), c. 1397, an Arabic pharmacopoeia, Rauḍat al-'iṭr (li'an yartāḍ al-'aṭṭār). It is divided into 44 chapters preceded by a preface wherein the author explains that he has tried to put in order all the knowledge obtained by him from many books, from the lips of experts, and from his own experience. He gives a list of his main sources, each of which is referred to in the text by means of a distinctive letter. I list these sources in the same order as himself, the names of authors being written in brackets when omitted by him or uncertain (it is sometimes possible that he referred to another work bearing the same title).

Sources enumerated in the preface: Qānūn of Ibn Sīnā (XI-1); Dhakhīrat of Ismā'īl al-Jurjānī (XII-1); Mukhtārāt of Ibn Hubal (XII-2); Irshād [of Ibn Jamī', XII-2]; Malikī of 'Alī ibn 'Abbās (X-2); Mūjiz [of Ibn al-Nafīs, XIII-2]; Mufrādat al-Māliqī (?); Minhāj al-dukkān of al-Kūhīn al-'Aṭṭār (XIII-2); Minhāj of Ibn

Jazla (XI-2); Ḥāwī of Najm al-dīn al-Samarqandī, I suppose the small Ḥāwī of Maḥmūd ibn Ilyās al-Shīrāzī (XIV-1) is meant; Kifāyat [al-ṭabīb of 'Alī ibn Riḍwān, XI-1]; Zahrāwī [probably reference to Abū-l-Qāsim, X-2]; Bustān al-aṭibbā' (?); Aqrābādhīn of Ibn al-Tilmīdh (XII-1); Dastūr māristānī of David ben Solomon (XIII-1); Maqāla of al-Rāzī (IX-2). This Turkish (or Caucasian) compiler certainly had a good medical library!

Criticism. Ḥājjī Khalīfa (3, 504, no. 6657, 1842). Brockelmann (suppt. 2, 327, 1938).

ḤĀJJĪ PĀSHĀ

Khiḍr ibn 'Alī al-Aidīnī, commonly called Ḥājjī pāshā. Turkish physician and theologian writing in Arabic and Turkish (d. 1417).

He was born in Qonya (ancient Iconium) and educated there. He studied law and theology in Cairo. A severe illness directed his attention to medicine, and he did so well in that new field that he finally became chief physician of the great hospital of Cairo, the Bīmāristān al-Manṣūrī (founded by Qalā'ūn c. 1284; Introd. 2, 246). After a while he returned to Qonya, and was then called c. 1395 to Aidīn (the ancient Tralles in Lydia) by the amīr of that district, Aidīnoghlu Meḥmed bey. He settled down in Birgi (ancient Perga; summer residence of the umarā' of Aidīn). He died in Birgi in 1417 and was buried in the cemetery of Hizirlik near by.

He wrote notes to the commentary of Fakhr al-dīn al-Rāzī (XII-2) on the treatise on logic Maṭāli' al-anwār fī-l-manṭiq of al-Urmawī,[57] and he dedicated to 'Īsā bey, son of Aidīnoghlu Muḥammad bey, a commentary on the Anwār al-tanzīl of al-Baiḍāwī (XIII-2). Thus did he prove his interest in logic and in the Qur'ān; other commentaries prove his interest in mysticism and poetry.

His main work was done in the medical field. He wrote in Arabic for 'Īsā ibn Muḥammad (the sulṭān of Aidīn previously mentioned) a medical encyclopaedia, entitled Shifā' al-asqām wa dawā' al-ālām (Cure of diseases and remedies of pains). He completed it c. 1380 in Ephesus (not very far from Aidīn).

Its general plan is the same as that of the Qānūn of Ibn Sīnā, except that it has only four parts: (1) generalities; (2) food and potions; in this part Ibn al-Baiṭār (XIII-1) is often quoted and the author refers frequently also to his teacher (ustādhī) Jamāl al-dīn al-Shubakī (?); (3) diseases relative to particular parts, a capite ad calces; (4) general diseases. In the preface the author explains the great pains he has taken to compose his book, his study of the writings of the great Christian and Jewish doctors, his work under famous teachers, his own clinical experience. The Shifā' contains many personal observations, e.g., a remarkable description of pneumonia, listing a number of objective symptoms similar to those found in modern treatises.

Later Ḥājjī pāshā wrote an abridgment of the Shifā' in Turkish, Tashīl al-ṭibb or Tashīl al-shifā' (Facilitation of medicine, or of health), apologizing in the foreword for his use of the Turkish language instead of the learned Arabic. The Tashīl was written for laymen, hence the use of Turkish was justified.

A third medical work is ascribed to him, the Muntakhab al-shifā', which is another abridgment of the Shifā'. It is also dedicated to 'Īsā bey Aidīnoghlu.

[57] Sirāj al-dīn Abū-l-Thanā' Maḥmūd ibn abī Bakr al-Urmawī (1198–1283), flourished in Mūṣul and Qonya. His Maṭāli' has been commented upon by many authors (Brockelmann 1, 467; suppt. 1, 848).

Text. Adnan mentions a German translation of the Tashīl al-shifā' by Hans Bart (?), which I could not find. My colleague professor Julius Ruska failed to discover it in the Berlin libraries (his card dated Berlin March 27, 1940). Further correspondence with Dr. Adnan (Istanbul May 29, 1940) suggests that that translation does not exist.

Criticism. Ḥājjī Khalīfa (4, 51, no. 7587, 1845). Leclerc (2, 266–67, 1876). Brockelmann (2, 233, 1902; suppt. 2, 326, 1938). Theodor Menzel (EI 2, 206, 1915). A. Süheyl Ünver: Hékim Hadji pacha et l'hôpital de Kalavoun au Caire (Institute of the History of Medicine of the University of Istanbul vol. 6, 7 p., 1937), in Turkish and French. According to the author, the Shifā' was written in Turkish; that may be so, but the Arabic form seems to be the original one. There are Turkish and Arabic MSS of it. I. Hakkı Uzunçarşılıoğlu: Anadolu beylikleri (p. 80–81, Ankara 1937; Isis 32), study of the Anatolian states, in Turkish. Adnan (p. 15–17, 1939).

D6. Iran

AL-RĀMĪ

Sharaf al-dīn al-Ḥasan ibn Muḥammad al-Rāmī. Persian man of letters writing in Persian (fl. third quarter of fourteenth century?).

Al-Rāmī is named as the author of a book Anīs al-'ushshāq (The lover's companion), dedicated to Abū-l-Fatḥ Uwais Bahādur (īlkhānī sulṭān of Ādharbāijān 1356–73). The aim of that book is purely literary, namely, to help poets in finding epithets and similes when describing their beloved. It is divided into 19 chapters, dealing (a capite ad calcem) with the hair, forehead, eyebrows, eyes, eyelashes, face, down on the lips and cheeks, mole or beauty spot, lips, teeth, mouth, chin, neck, bosom, arms, fingers, figure, waist, legs. Arabic and Persian names are given, then all kinds of metaphors. The anatomical interest of that book is, I am afraid, very slight. It is strange that the author was moved to write it after having visited the famous observatory of Nāṣir al-dīn al-Ṭūsī (XIII-2) in Marāgha (Introd. 2, 1004).

Text. Clément Huart: Anīs el-'ochchāq. Traité des termes figurés relatifs à la description de la beauté (114 p., Bibliothèque de l'Ecole des hautes études, sci. phil. 25, Paris 1875), French translation with notes.

Criticism. Browne (2, 19, 83, 1906; 3, 462, 1920). E. Berthels (EI 3, 1114, 1936).

ZAIN AL-'AṬṬĀR

'Alī ibn al-Ḥusain al-Anṣārī, called Ḥājjī Zain al-'Aṭṭār. Persian pharmacist writing in Persian (1329–1403).

His father, Jamāl al-dīn Ḥusain of Iṣfahān, was a physician in Shīrāz c. 1315. One of the ancestors of the family was one of the anṣār, that is, one of the early helpers of the Prophet in Madīna; hence the laqab al-Anṣārī. From his nickname we gather that Ḥājjī Zain al-'Aṭṭār was recognized as a distinguished druggist ('aṭṭār means perfumer, but the man who sold perfumes also sold drugs), and that he had accomplished the Pilgrimage. He was born in Shīrāz in 1329/30; followed in his father's footsteps, and obtained the favor of the Muẓaffarī sulṭān Jalāl al-dīn Shāh Shujā' (ruled 1357–84). It is said that he was attached to the court of Shāh Shujā' for sixteen years. He died in 1403/4.

His main work is a Persian materia medica, Miftāḥ al-khazā'in (Key of the treasures), which he completed on July 23, 1366. It is divided into three discourses (maqālāt): (I) simple drugs, (II) substitutes and correction of drugs, (III) compound drugs. The first two discourses are arranged in alphabetical order of the drugs, the third is divided into 12 chapters.

Three years later (1368/69) he wrote for the princess Badī' al-jamāl a new edition of the Miftāḥ, entitled, after her own name, Ikhtiyārāt-i-Badī'ī (The selections for Badī'). It includes part I of the Miftāḥ, but not part II; as to part III, it is extended from 12 to 16 chapters, dealing respectively with (1) stimulants, (2) sweet electuaries, (3) bitter electuaries, (4) electuaries of myrobalans (astringent), (5) jams, (6) syrups and robs, (7) la'ūqāt, drugs meant to be licked, (8) powders (safūf), (9) pills (ḥabb, ḥubūb), (10) troches or tablets, lozenges (qurṣ, aqrāṣ), (11) purgatives, (12) collyria or eyesalves, (13) various kinds of teriaq, (14) tooth powders, (15) oils, (16) salves and plasters.

The copy of the Miftāḥ al-khazā'in in the Bodleian was written by the author, as is stated in the colophon by another hand (hadhā khaṭṭ li muṣannif). There are many more MSS of the Ikhtiyārāt; one of these at least (Paris) begins with an abundant Arabic-Persian glossary.

Text. Both works are unpublished.
Criticism. Leclerc (2, 324, 1876). Fonahn (p. 85–88, 129, 1910).

MANṢŪR IBN MUḤAMMAD

Manṣūr ibn Muḥammad ibn Aḥmad . . . Ilyās. Persian anatomist and physician, who wrote in Persian (fl. c. 1396–1423).

In 1396 he dedicated to a grandson of Tīmūr, Pīr Muḥammad ibn Jahāngīr ibn Tīmūr (governor of Balkh 1404/5, died two years later), an illustrated treatise on anatomy variously entitled Tashrīḥ-i Manṣūrī, or Tashrīḥ bil-taṣwīr (Anatomy with figures), or Kitāb-i-tashrīḥ-i badan, or Risāla dar tashrīḥ-i-badan-i-insān wa kaifīyat-i awḍā'-i-ān (Letter on the anatomy of the human body and the relative arrangement of its parts). It is divided into an introduction (muqaddama), five chapters (maqālāt), and a conclusion (khātima), dealing respectively with (1) description and division of the organs, (2) bones, (3) nerves, (4) muscles, (5) veins, (6) arteries, (7) composite organs. The most remarkable feature of this treatise is the group of five colored schematic drawings illustrating respectively the bones, nerves, veins, arteries, woman's body with womb containing ripe foetus. The various parts of each drawing are explained by a number of short Persian inscriptions.

In spite of their strange appearance, these five drawings continue an ancient tradition which originated perhaps in Alexandria. These drawings occur in many MSS of Manṣūr's treatise (India Office, London; Bibliothèque nationale, Paris; British Museum, Bodleian, Berlin).

Some time (at least 27 years) later Manṣūr dedicated another Persian treatise, Kifāyat-i-Manṣūrī (The sufficient Mansurian treatise) or Kifāyat-i-mujāhidīya (The sufficient efforts), to Zain al-'ābidīn, sulṭān of Kashmīr (1423–72). It is divided into two main parts. Part or fann I is again divided into two sections, theoretical and practical (qism I, ṭibb naẓarī; qism II, ṭibb 'amalī), subdivided respectively into 4 and 5 maqālāt, as follows: (I, 1) material basis of health, i.e. elements and organs; (2) visible basis of health, i.e. mixtures, qualities; (3) acting basis of health, i.e. air, motion, sleep, eating, drinking, evacuation, etc.; (4) conditions, accidents, and signs (aḥwāl, a'rāḍ, 'alāmāt). (II, 1) preservation of health, general therapeutics; (2) local ailments; (3) fevers; (4) skin troubles; (5) animal poisons.

The second fann is simply divided into two maqāla, (1) simple drugs and foods, (2) compound drugs and their preparation.

Text. Lithographic editions of the Tashrīḥ-i-Manṣūrī, Delhi 1847/48, and of the Kifāyat-i-Manṣūrī, Lucknow 1873/74.

Criticism. Leclerc (2, 325–26, 1876). Sudhoff (p. 52, 57, 1908b). Ernst Seidel and K. Sudhoff: Drei weitere anatomische Fünfbilderserien aus Abendland und Morgenland (AGM 3, 165–87, 347–48, 1 pl., 1909). Fonahn (p. 3–4, 13–15, 129, 1910). Choulant (p. 58, 1920). Browne (p. 93, 1921); also in Renaud's translation (p. 103, 1933).

E. INDIA

MAṄGARĀJA

Canarese physician (fl. 1360).

He wrote a medical treatise in Canarese entitled Khagēndra-maṇi-darpaṇa. This includes quotations from an earlier medical work by Pūjyapāda Devanandin of Mugali, a Canarese Jaina muni (ascetic, yogin) who wrote in Sanskrit on grammar and medicine (fl. fifth–seventh century).

Text. Metrical chapters on medical diagnosis and treatment of diseases and poisons, extracted from the Sāngatya of Sāḷva and the Khagēndra-maṇi-darpaṇa of Maṅga-rāja. Canarese text edited by Yaḷandūru Subbaṇṇa Śāstri (32 p., Mysore 1894). This title is quoted from Lionel David Barnett: Catalogue of Kannada, Badaga and Kurg books in the British Museum (p. 99, 147, London 1910). Sāḷva was a Canarese-Jaina court poet of the middle of the sixteenth century.

Criticism. Edward P. Rice: History of Kanarese literature (p. 45, Calcutta 1921). Winternitz (3, 400, 1922).

For the Canarese language, see my note on Raṭṭa-kavi (XIV-1).

MADANAPĀLA

Hindu prince and pharmacist (fl. 1375).

Madanapāla was a prince of the Ṭāka dynasty, the sixth and last prince of Kāshṭhā or Kāḍhā on the Jumna, north of Delhi.

He compiled (or caused to be compiled) in 1374–75 a dictionary of materia medica called (4) Madanavinodanighaṇṭu or Madanapālavinodanighaṇṭu, containing an enumeration of minerals, plants, animals, foods, and drugs. This work has also been ascribed to his minister Viśveśvara.

This was not by any means the first Sanskrit herbal or medicobotanical dictionary (nighaṇṭu). Much of that kind of knowledge is immemorial, and the oldest medical dictionary extant, the (1) Dhanvantarinighaṇṭu,[58] is older than the Amarakośa, that is, the dictionary of Amara (VI-2). Another one, the (2) Śabdapradīpa, was compiled in 1075 by one Sureśvara or Surapāla, court physician to Bhīmapāla, king of Bengal (I have not been able to identify this king). Finally, the (3) Rājanighaṇṭu was written c. 1235–50 by the Kashmirian Narahari (XIII-1).[59]

[58] Winternitz (p. 553, 1922) followed by Keith (p. 512, 1928) doubts its antiquity or integrity because of the mention of mercury. I do not understand that. Mercury was known to the ancient Hindus, e.g. to Suśruta (VI B.C.). See Introd. 1, 76; 2, 84.

[59] According to Zachariae (p. 39, 1897), the Rājanighaṇṭu would be posterior to the Madanapālavinodanighaṇṭu. These are moot questions, for dictionaries invite interpolations. A late MS of an older text may easily include extracts from a younger text.

Text. 1. Dhanvantarinighaṇṭu or Dhanvantarīyanighaṇṭu, edited together with the Rājanighaṇṭu by Vaidyanārāyaṇa Śarmā Puraṁdare in the Ānandāśrama series (vol. 33, Poona 1896; reprinted 1927).

2. Śabdapradīpa. Unpublished.

3. Rājanighaṇṭu. See no. 1. Other editions, Benares 1883, Calcutta 1899. Partial edition of the mineral part with German translation by Richard Garbe: Die indischen Mineralien, ihre Namen und die ihnen zugeschriebenen Kräfte (114 p., Leipzig 1882). Emeneau (nos. 3229–31, 1935).

4. Madanapālavinodanighaṇṭu. MSS in the Harvard Library and in the Osler Library at McGill University. Poleman (nos. 5300–2, 1938). Editions in Calcutta 1875; with Hindi translation, Benares 1873, Bombay 1910; with Bengali translation, Calcutta 1914; with Gujarati translation, Ahmadabad 1918.

Criticism. Duff (p. 228, 295, 1899). Theodor Zachariae: Die indischen Wörterbücher (Grundriss der indo-arischen Philologie vol. 1, 3 B, p. 38, Strassburg 1897). Julius Jolly: Medizin (ibid. vol. 3, 10, p. 14, 1901). Winternitz (p. 554, 1922). Keith (p. 512, 1928).

For comparison, consult Udoy Chang Dutt: The materia medica of the Hindus compiled from Sanskrit medical works (370 p., Calcutta 1877). Paramananda Mariadassou: Le jardin des simples de l'Inde (288 p., Pondichéry 1913). Chandra Chakraberty: Comparative Hindu materia medica (210 p., Calcutta 1923; Isis 7, 266). There are many more such books; I cite only those available to me.

YOGA-RATNĀKARA

Siṅhalese medical work compiled about the end of the fourteenth century, by an unknown author on the basis of the Pāli treatise Bhesajja-mañjūsā (Casket of medicine), written c. 1267, during the rule of Parākramabāhu II (king 1236–71) by Atthadassi thera, also called Pañca-mūla-pariveṇa-Adhipati. The Bhesajja-mañjūsā is the only Pāli work of its kind extant.

Text. The Yogaratnākara was anonymously edited in the Ānandāśrama series (505 p., Poona 1888; reprinted, 574 p., 1900).

Criticism. G. P. Malalasekera: Pāli literature of Ceylon (p. 215, London 1928).

F. CHINA

WANG LI

Chinese physician (fl. c. 1368).

Wang Li, style An-tao. He was a student of Chu Tan-ch'i (XIV-1) and flourished about the end of the Yüan dynasty, 1368. He wrote a treatise on fevers, I-ching su-hui chi, including a revision of a collection of 397 prescriptions compiled by Chang Chung-ching (II-2). Some of Chang's prescriptions are abandoned, and new ones are introduced, the total number 397 remaining the same. He discusses various kinds of diseases, internal heat, and apoplexy.

Other medical books are ascribed to him, to wit, Pai-ping-kou-yüan, in 20 chüan; I-yün-t'ung-i, in 100 chüan; Piao-t'i-yüan-ping-shih, in 1 chüan.

Criticism. Wylie (p. 99, 1902). Hübotter (p. 25, 1929). Not mentioned by Wong and Wu (1936).

CHIA MING

Chinese physician and theorist of longevity (c. 1268–c. 1374).

Chia Ming, style Chia Wên-ting; fancy name Hua shan lao-jên, meaning old man of the Hua mountain (in Chehkiang). He was born in Hai-ning, Chehkiang. It is said that he lived to be 106 and that he was a centenarian at the time of the accession of the first Ming emperor, Hung Wu (1368–98). Hence one may deduce approximate dates of birth and death.

He was a high official of the Yüan dynasty and became very wealthy and influential; yet he is not dealt with in the Yüan shih.

He wrote a single book, called Yin-shih-hsü-chih or Elements of dietetics. It is said that he presented a draft of it to Hung Wu when he reached the age of a hundred. The emperor asked him, naturally, how he had managed to reach such an old age. Chia answered that his secret was to pay the greatest attention to his diet and regimen. His work was an explanation of that. If that story is true, Chia was the first writer on macrobiotics, far in advance of Luigi Cornaro (1475?–1566), who wrote his Trattato della vita sobria and additions at the age of 75 to 87,[60] not to speak of Christoph Wilhelm Hufeland (1762–1836), who published his Makrobiotik (Berlin 1796) at the ripe age of 34.

The Yin-shih-hsü-chih consists of eight chüan plus a preface written by the author himself. The volumes deal with the following subjects: (1) water and fire, (2) cereals, (3) vegetables, (4) fruits, (5) condiments and dainties, (6) fish, (7) fowl, (8) animals. Most of the information thus presented in a new form is simply derived from the abundant pên ts'ao literature.

Text. The Yin-shih-hsü-chih was edited in the Ssŭ-k'u ch'üan shu vol. 116, p. 28 ff., on the basis of a copy made by Ch'êng Chin-fang. It was printed again in the Hsüeh-hai lai-pien.

Criticism. Wylie (p. 153, 1902). Wieger (p. 324, 542, 1920). T. T. Chang: Chia Ming's Elements of dietetics (Isis 20, 324–34, 1934), analysis of volume 1.

TAI SSŬ-KUNG

Chinese physician (1322–1405).

Tai Ssŭ-kung, style Yüan-li, was born in 1322 at Chin Hua, Chehkiang. He was the outstanding disciple of Chu Tan-ch'i (XIV-1), or, to put it otherwise, the most famous doctor next to the master of the yang yin school. He became physician to the first Ming emperor, Hung Wu (1368–98), and president of the imperial medical college, but in his old age he obtained permission to return to his native place, where he died at the age of 82.

He wrote medical treatises entitled Chêng chih yao chüeh, Chêng chih lei yüan, Lei chêng yung yao, and an account of the teaching of Chu Tan-ch'i, entitled T'ui-ch'iu shih-i or "My teacher's opinions."

A biography of him was written by Li lien, style Ch'uan-fu (born Ch'ang Fu, 1488), in the latter's I-shih, the first extant history of medicine in the Chinese language.[61]

Text. The Chêng chih yao chüeh, 12 chüan, is included in the I t'ung chêng mo ch'üan shu, books 72–73, edition of 1907.

Criticism. Ming shih, chüan 299. Wong and Wu (p. 127–28, 130–31, 1936).

YÜAN KUNG

Yüan kung, style T'ing yü, nicknamed Liu Chuang. Chinese physiognomist (1335–1410).

[60] It was first printed in Padua 1558. See my paper on Hoefer and Chevreul with an excursus on creative centenarians (Bull. of the history of medicine 8, 419–45, Baltimore 1940; p. 440–41).

[61] An earlier work written by Kan Po-tsung in 923–36 is lost. It was entitled Li tai ming i hsing ming, meaning Names of famous physicians; it filled 7 volumes and dealt with 120 physicians from the mythical age of the five rulers to the end of the T'ang dynasty (907).

He wrote a book on physiognomy, Shên hsiang ch'üan pien, which enjoyed some popularity almost until our own days. It should be noted that Chinese physiognomy, hsiang mien, is not concerned so much with the determination of man's character as with the determination of his fortune and longevity.

According to the Ming shih, chüan 299, his son Chung Chê, style Ching Ssŭ, was also a famous physiognomist, who wrote the book on physiognomy Jên hsiang ta ch'êng.

He is sometimes confused with Liu Chang, man of letters and civil servant, who flourished at the beginning of the Sui dynasty (the first Sui emperor, K'ai Huang, ruled 581–601).

Criticism. Giles (no. 2556, also no. 1293, 1898). Henri Doré (S.J.): Recherches sur les superstitions en Chine (no. 34, 1, p. 223–82, Shanghai 1912). Couling (p. 437, 1917). Wieger (p. 483, 1920).

G. JAPAN

YŪRIN

Japanese Buddhist physician (fl. Kyōto c. 1362–67).

There was compiled in 1362–67 a medical collection which has come down to us under the title Yūrin fukuden-hō, Yūrin designating the author, who signed the preface and whose name is otherwise unknown. He was a śramaṇa (sha mên, bonze) in Kyōto.

The Yūrin fukuden-hō[62] is very largely a translation or transcription (with phonetic notes) of Chinese texts. The author refers to more than a hundred Chinese treatises but adds observations of his own. His work is divided into twelve books and begins with a critical examination of the various drugs in popular use. He urges his colleagues to be more careful in their use of them. A chapter is devoted to the moxa technique.

Yūrin classified ailments into twelve main groups, and for each disease he indicated the cause, symptoms, diagnosis, and treatment. He explained the importance of knowing the history of each patient.

Text. The MS dated 1469–77, which formerly belonged to the medical library of the Shōgun, is now in the Imperial Household Museum. A collotype facsimile of it was published, with transcription, in Nihon koden zenshū, collection of ancient Japanese classics (3 vols., Tōkyō 1936).[63]

Criticism. Kokusho kaidai (2, 1848, 1929).

MAJIMA SEIGAN

Japanese eye doctor (d. 1379).

Majima is his family name. Majima Seigan was a Buddhist priest living in the Owari province. He was the founder of the Majima school of ophthalmology.

He cured eye troubles not only with internal remedies, but also by means of acupuncture and moxa and surgical intervention. His method was handed down orally from one generation to another, and was not published until a much later time—in 1558—probably with various interpolations, under the title Majima-ryū ganmoku hiden shō (Secret method of the Majima school of ophthalmology).

Criticism. Fujikawa (p. 31, 77, 1934). Tase (p. 9, 1938).

[62] Hō means prescriptions, fukuden is a Buddhist term = pūṇya-kshetra, meaning holy place, blessings.

[63] My Harvard colleague professor Serge Elisséeff kindly examined that edition for me (Aug. 1943).

CHAPTER XXVI

HISTORIOGRAPHY

(Second Half of the Fourteenth Century)

N.B. Only the main notes are published in this chapter. The historical contributions of many other men, whose main work was done in other fields, are discussed in other chapters. For a general survey of historiography in the second half of the fourteenth century, see section XII of chapter XV. More information on the men referred to in that survey may then easily be found by means of the index.

A. CHRISTENDOM

A1. Hispanic Peninsula

PERE III EL CERIMONIÓS

Peter IV of Aragon, III of Catalonia, and II of Valencia; Pere del Punyalet (Peter of the little dagger). Son of Alfonso IV; born in Balaguer, Lérida in 1319; died in Barcelona 1387. King of Aragon from 1336 to 1387.

He is dealt with here because of his literary and scientific interests and because of the Catalan chronicles written by him or for him. In the history of Catalan historiography, one must put in the place of honor Jaime el Conquistador (XIII-2), Bernat Desclot (XIII-2), Ramón Muntaner (XIV-1), and finally Peter the Ceremonious.

Peter, being inspired by the chronicle of his great-grandfather Jaime el Conquistador, wanted to have a chronicle of his own deeds and instructed his secretary Bernardo Dezcoll (Bernat Des-Coll) to write it. It is now generally agreed that the Crònica de Pere III (1300–80) was written in the Catalan language by the secretary; it is impossible to know to what extent the king inspired and edited it. It is interesting to note that the chronicle does not tell the story of Peter's last years, though Descoll outlived him.

Apparently Peter himself wrote the Crònica de Sant Joan de la Penya (a general chronicle dealing with the origins of Catalonia and Aragon), which was translated into Latin and Castilian, though there are great difficulties in ascertaining the real authorship.

In addition, various poems and treatises (in Latin and Catalan) are ascribed to Peter, and he caused books to be translated from Arabic into Catalan, notably a book of agriculture written for the Moorish kings of Seville, and a Qur'ān which he had obtained from the Franciscans of Mallorca in 1381. He patronized copyists and limners, and founded the library gathered in the famous Cistercian abbey of Poblet (where the kings of Aragon are buried, near Espluga del Francoli, halfway between Tarragona and Lérida).

Text. The chronicle of Peter III (or IV) was first edited by Pere Miguel Carbonell (1434–1517): Chroniques de Espanya fins aci no divulgades (Barcelona 1546). Later editions by Antonio de Bofarull: Crónica del rey de Aragon D. Pedro IV (432 p., Barcelona 1850), and by F. Maspons y Labrós (Barcelona 1885).

The Cronica de San Juan de la Peña (or Pinatense) was edited in Latin and Castilian by Tomás Ximénez de Embún y Val (Zaragoza 1876).

José Coroleu: Documents historichs catalans del sigle XIV, colecció de cartas familars corresponents als regnats de Pere del Punyalet y Johan I (155 p., Barcelona 1889).

Criticism. Rubió y Lluch (1908–21). EUI (42, 1323–28, c. 1921). No information in González Palencia (1928).

LÓPEZ DE AYALA

Don Pedro López de Ayala el Canciller. Spanish (Basque) soldier, statesman, historian, and poet, translator from Latin into Castilian (1332–1407).

Pedro López de Ayala was born at Vitoria, Alava (one of the Basque provinces), in 1332; he held many high offices under four kings of Castile, being finally grand chancellor of Castile in 1398. He fought in wars, acted as a diplomat, and served the kings' interest in many other ways, never forgetting his own interest first. In spite of his cleverness and convenient lack of scruples, he was sometimes out of luck, chiefly at the battle of Aljubarrota (1385),[1] when he was made prisoner and kept for fifteen months in an iron cage in the castle of Oviedes. He died at Calahorra (not far from Logroño, on the upper Ebro) in 1407.

His writings, all in Spanish, include a Spanish chronicle, a treatise on falconry, a satirical poem, and translations, which we shall consider in turn.

The most important of these from the scientific point of view is the chronicle of the four kings of Castile whom he served, Pedro the Cruel, Enrique II, Juan I, Enrique III, and extends from 1350 to 1396. The author was not only a witness of the events which he describes, but an actor; that is, he knew these events from the inside. He may be called the first Spanish historian (vs. chronicler); he is remarkably impartial and candid, his methods are critical, and his style is lively and vigorous. On the basis of his chronicle alone, Pedro López de Ayala should be reckoned the outstanding Spanish writer of his age.

The Libro de las aves de caça is a treatise on falconry composed in 1386, during the author's captivity in Portugal. It is far more elaborate than the Libro de la caza written about sixty years earlier by Don Juan Manuel (XIV-1), and was more popular, witness the existence of at least a dozen MSS. It is divided into 47 chapters, separate ones being devoted to each kind of hawk and to each ailment (and corresponding remedy). Chapter 46 deals with imping, and this, as far as I know, is the earliest mention of imping in any literature. For the sake of readers who are not falconers, it is well to add that to imp (Fr. enter) is to repair a wing or tail with one or more outside feathers in order to increase its flying capacity.[1a]

A third Spanish book on falconry, the Libro de las aves que caçan, written at an unknown date by Juan de Sant Fahagun (Sahagun, Sant-Fagund), was largely and

[1] When Juan I of Portugal defeated his brother-in-law Juan I of Castile and secured the independence of Portugal. The great monastery of Santa Maria da Victoria built near by, at Batalha, to celebrate that victory is a kind of Portuguese pantheon. I visited it in October 1934 (Isis 22, 448).

[1a] Imping is discussed by Casey A. Wood and F. Marjorie Fyfe in their translation of Frederick II's De arte venandi cum avibus (p. 426, 620, Stanford 1943; Isis 35, 182–84), but the emperor did not speak of it. Their definition of imp (imponere) is different from mine and probably better: "to repair by substituting a metal shaft or needle and part of another feather for a broken pinion." Imping-needle (acus): "Metal shaft introduced within the quill to strengthen and repair a broken pinion."

sometimes slavishly derived from López' treatise. Both treatises were commented upon by D. Beltran de la Cueva, first duke of Alburquerque (d. 1492).

The Rimado de palacio (Court rhymes) is a satirical poem written by López de Ayala at intervals and completed c. 1403. It contains a satirical description of court life, and of Spanish life in general. The author castigated impartially clerics, lawyers, merchants, courtiers, politicians, sparing nobody, not even himself, for he denounces his own vices and shortcomings with disarming ingenuity. On account of its irregular composition (stretched over a relatively long period of time with many interruptions), the Rimado is multiform and heterogeneous. In addition to the satire on contemporary types, it includes also long religious and ethical developments and some lyrical parts, particularly in the form of canticles and orations to God and the Virgin.

López translated various Latin books into Spanish, to wit:

1. Livy (I-2 B.C.): Decades I, III, and IV. This was translated from the French version made by Pierre Bersuire c. 1351–55.
2. Valerius Maximus, authorship of the translation uncertain.
3. Boetius (VI-1): Consolatio.
4. Gregory the Great (VI-2): Moralia.
5. St. Isidore of Seville (VII-1): De summo bono.
6. Guido de Columnis (Guy of Colonna), historian and poet who flourished in Messina c. 1276: López translated his Historia trojana, a book of mythology rather than history, which enjoyed considerable popularity in the Middle Ages, and directly or indirectly inspired Boccaccio, Chaucer, Shakespeare.
7. Boccaccio: De casibus virorum illustrium. López' translation of Boccaccio, left incomplete, was finished by the bishop Alonso de Santa Maria de Cartagena (1384–1456), best known as the author of the Doctrinal de los caballeros (princeps 1487, etc.).

The list is important for the history of Spanish humanism. It is interesting to note the French influence to which Spanish letters were submitted; then, and increasingly so, the Italian influences.

Text. The first edition of the chronicle of Pedro the Cruel was printed in Seville 1495. Second edition of that chronicle, and first edition of the rest, Toledo 1526. Third, Seville 1542. Fourth, Pamplona 1591. These early editions are enumerated after Potthast (p. 129, 1896).

Cronicas de los reyes de Castilla por D. Pedro Lopez de Ayala, con las enmiendas del secretario Geronimo Zurita (1512–80) y las correcciones y notas añadidas por D. Eugenio de Llaguno Amirola (2 vols., Madrid 1729–30).

El libro de las aves de caça, con las glosas del Duque de Alburquerque. Published by the Sociedad de bibliófilos, with introduction by Pascual de Gayangos, and glossary (252 p., 3 col., pl., Madrid 1869). Second edition by José Gutiérrez de la Vega, Libro de la caza de las aves et de sus plumages et dolencias, et melecinamientos, in the latter's Biblioteca venatoria (3, 137–359, Madrid 1879).

Albert Frederick Kuersteiner: Poesias del canciller Pero López de Ayala (Hispanic Society of America, 2 vols., New York 1920).

Criticism. Francisco R. de Uhagon: Los libros de cetreria del canciller Pedro Lopez de Ayala, de Juan de Sant-Fahagun y de D. Fadrique de Zuñiga y Sotomayor (30 p., Madrid 1889). The treatise of Zuñiga (or Çuñiga) was first printed in Salamanca 1565. Harting (p. 115–17, 134, 1891).

Friedrich Wilhelm Schirrmacher: Glaubwürdigkeit der Chronik Ayalas (Geschichte von Spanien 5, 510–32, Gotha 1890). Manuel Diaz de Arcaya: El gran canciller D. Pedro López de Ayala (64 p., Vitoria 1900). Hurtado and González Palencia (p. 130–34, 1932).

A2. Italy

FILIPPO VILLANI

Filippo son of Matteo, and thus nephew of Giovanni Villani. Filippo "il solitario." Florentine chronicler and humanist (d. 1405).

As was explained in my note on Giovanni Villani, Filippo wrote the final continuation, for the years 1363 to 1365, of the Florentine chronicle, begun by Giovanni and completed by Matteo. He was less a pure chronicler, and more a rhetorician, than his father and uncle. The chronicle was in Italian, but his main work was a collection of biographies of famous citizens of Florence, written in Latin, Liber de origine civitatis Florentinae et eiusdem famosis civibus. The first part of this book is a fabulous and worthless history; the valuable biographies constitute the second part (the first part remained unpublished).

Filippo was twice chosen to lecture on the Divina commedia, in 1401 and 1404.

Text. For the Istorie fiorentine, see note on Giovanni Villani (XIV-1).

Vitae Dantis, Petrarchae et Boccaccii (Florence 1826).

Cronica di Matteo e Filippo Villani con le Vite d'uomini illustri fiorentini di Filippo e la Cronica di Dino Compagni (Milano 1834).

Liber de civitatis Florentiae famosis civibus, ex cod. Med. Laur. nunc primum editus et de Florentinorum litteratura principes fere synchroni scriptores edited by G. C. Galletti. Accedunt F. Bocchii elogia Florentinorum doctrinis insignium (2 vols., Florence 1847). Ancient Italian translation, Vite d'uomini illustri Fiorentini, edited by Giammaria Mazzuchelli (138 p., Venice 1747). Reprinted Florence 1826, again 1847; also in the complete edition of Giovanni Villani's work by Ignazio Moutier (Florence 1844).

Giuseppe Cugnoni: Il comento al primo canto dell' Inferno (216 p., Città di Castello 1896).

Criticism. Potthast (p. 1092, 1896). Giovanni Calò: F. Villani e il Liber de origine civitatis Florentiae et ejusdem famosis civibus (Rocca S. Casciano 1904).

MICHELE DA PIAZZA

Michael de Platea (or Placia), Michael Platiensis. Sicilian Franciscan chronicler (fl. 1370?).

Michele wrote a Latin chronicle of Sicily from 1337 to 1361. It is unimportant, but deserves to be mentioned here because it contains the earliest description of the plague by an Italian, namely a description of the outbreak at Messina in October 1347. Michele's chronicle was a continuation of the Historia sicula of Niccolò Speciale (Nicolaus Specialis), dealing with Sicilian events from the Vespro (Sicilian vespers, slaughter of all the French in Sicily, 1282) to 1337.

Text. Both chronicles were published by Rosarius Gregorio in his Bibliotheca scriptorum qui res in Sicilia gestas sub Aragonum regno retulere (2 vols., Palermo 1791–92). This was the first edition of Michele's continuation, but the fifth of Niccolò's Historia sicula, the first dating back to 1688.

Criticism. See Potthast (p. 787, 855, 1896).

A3. France

VENETTE

Jean de Venette, French Carmelite, chronicler and poet (d. after 1368).

Jean Fillon (or Fillons), born at Venette, near Compiègne, c. 1308. In 1339 he was already prior of the Carmelite monastery, place Maubert, Paris, and he flourished part of his life (1339, 1356–60, 1364–65) in that city; he traveled in Auvergne, Provence, and Champagne.

He wrote in Latin a chronicle of France from 1340 to 1368, which is incorrectly considered a continuation of Willam of Nangis (XIII-2; d. after 1300). I myself made that mistake (Introd. 2, 1109). That error is due to the fact that in the two extant MSS, Venette's chronicle follows immediately another continuation of Nangis'. There is no evidence even that Venette read the earlier chronicle; it is a continuation of it only in the sense that it is devoted to the period 1340–68, which follows immediately the period dealt with by Nangis and his continuers.

The spirit animating Venette's chronicle is very different from that of his predecessors. He was a man of the people, his sympathies were entirely on their side, and he defiantly accepted the nickname "Jacques Bonhomme" which the gentry applied to the rustics (Géraud's ed., 2, 238, 288). Equal to his love of the poor was his hatred of Englishmen and even more so of the French nobility. There are many violent declamations against the latter in his work. Bad as the English were, they at least protected the people by punishing brigands, whereas the people's own masters were simply betraying it (2, 313). Apropos of this he tells the story of the sheep dog who was secretly in league with the wolf against the sheep (2, 328). He did not ask privileges for the people, and accepted as legitimate all the taxes, impositions, restrictions, and vexations to which they were subjected; but in exchange for their servitude the people were entitled to protection, peace, and the enjoyment of what meager fruits of their labor were left to them. Their seigneurs oppressed them, yet failed to protect them against foreign or domestic lawlessness.

Such were the feelings which caused the Jacquerie, that popular insurrection which broke out in the Beauvaisis in the spring of 1358 and was so terribly repressed. Yet Venette was not a "panégyriste de la Jacquerie" (as it is put in HL 25, 131). He disapproved of the revolution as strongly as of the evils which caused it. He was a proletarian driven to desperation, yet he was also an obedient and humble monk. It is clear, however, that Venette's rude Latin prose struck a new note in the French chronicles.

His chronicle was not a diary; it was written, or at least parts of it were written, retrospectively. It is a little more than a chronicle; the historian begins to appear. He was a witness of many of the events described by him, and he told the story in good faith, giving the facts as known to him and also his own impressions of them. It would seem that part of the chronicle was written in 1360, another part in 1368 or soon after.

In 1348 he observed in Paris the famous meteor (2, 210) which announced the Black Death; he referred to the comets of 1340, 1360, and observed in Reims the comet of 1368 (2, 376, 378; end of the chronicle). He also speaks of plagues, droughts, floods, famines, earthquakes, etc. An analysis of the calamities and meteorologic events recorded by him is desirable.

Venette wrote in French in 1357 a long poem on sacred history, dealing mainly with the three Maries (35,000 octosyllabic lines).[1b]

[1b] The three Maries who witnessed the Crucifixion, that is, the Virgin Mary, Mary Magdalene, and Mary the mother of James and Joses, wife of Clopas (or Cleophas).

Text. The text of Venette's chronicle is printed after that of William of Nangis, by Lucas d'Achery in his Spicilegium (vol. 11, Paris before 1677); and by Hercule Géraud (Société de l'histoire de France, sér. antérieure à 1789, vol. 35; vol. 2 of the Chronique de Guillaume de Nangis, p. 179–378, Paris 1843), well indexed.

Criticism. Géraud's introduction (1, xix–xl, 1843). Victor LeClerc (HL 25, 129–31, 1869). Molinier (4, 20–21, no. 3098, 1904).

DARDEL

Jean Dardel, French historian of Armenia (d. 1384).

Jean Dardel, born at Etampes (Ile-de-France; dépt. Seine-et-Oise), assumed the Franciscan habit, and in 1377 went with Antoine de Monopoli on a pilgrimage to the Holy Land and Mt. Sinai. In Cairo they met Leon V of Lusignan (1342–93), the last king of new Armenia (Cilicia), then a prisoner of the sulṭān of Egypt. Dardel became the confessor and secretary of the king, writing for him innumerable letters to the European sovereigns for the sake of obtaining his deliverance. In 1379 he was sent as the king's confidential agent to the kings of Aragon and Castile to obtain their help, and was able to negotiate the king's liberation after his own return to Egypt in 1382. Leon V and Dardel left Egypt soon afterward (1382), proceeding to Rhodes, where Dardel was appointed chancellor of Armenia, then to Venice, to Avignon, where Clement VII named him bishop of Tortiboli,[1c] to Montpellier, then to Spain. Having failed to obtain assistance for the reconquest of Cilicia, Leon V and Dardel returned to Montpellier and Avignon, and proceeded to Paris (1384).

Dardel died on December 6, 1384, and was buried in his native town, Etampes. As to Leon V, he died in Paris in 1393. He had been the last effective king of Armenia (1374–75), but after his death the kings of Cyprus continued to assume the title (1393–1489).

Jean Dardel is probably the author of a French chronicle of Armenia from Jesus Christ to 1384, divided into 144 chapters. The first 14 chapters, dealing with Armenian history before the fourteenth century, are negligible. The final chapters (116–44), dealing with the period 1377–84, were certainly written by Jean, who had firsthand knowledge of the events recorded by him. For the period preceding 1377, he had probably very little, if any, knowledge of Armenia, but that part of the chronicle was in all probability dictated to him by the king. Thus for that period Jean was simply the scribe or editor. In any case, the history of the last century of the kingdom of Armenia is written in this chronicle on the basis of firsthand knowledge obtained either directly by Jean Dardel or by Leon V, the last Lusignan of Armenia. The work was completed in the second half of 1384.

Text. Dardel's chronicle was first published in the form of an Armenian translation made by mgr. Khorène de Lusignan, Armenian archbishop in Constantinople, for the Tiflis society for the publication of Armenian books (St. Petersburg 1891). First edition of the original French text in the Recueil des historiens des Croisades, Documents arméniens (2, v–xxii, 1–109, Paris 1906). The edition of this second volume, begun in 1879, occupied various editors for almost thirty years.

Criticism. Ulysse Robert: Le chronique d'Arménie de Jean Dardel, évêque de Tortiboli (Archives de l'Orient latin 2, 1–15, Paris 1884), description of the unique anonymous MS discovered in the library of Dôle (Jura) in 1880, by U. Robert, who identified the author. This article is superseded by the introduction to the edition of 1906.

[1c] Tortiboli was a bishopric in Capitanata, a paese on the south Adriatic side of Italy.

A4. Ireland

"PEMBRIDGE"

"Christopher Pembridge." Irish annalist (fl. 1370?).

He may be the author of the Annales Hiberniae from 1162 to 1370, though there is hardly any evidence in support of that ascription. In my book, "Christopher Pembridge" will be a short way of saying "the author of the Irish annals 1162–1370." Christopher is said to have been a native of Dublin.

Later Annales Hiberniae were compiled by James Grace of Kilkenny c. 1538. These annals tally very well with the earlier ones down to 1370; of course that might be due to their being borrowed from a common source; if so, that source is unknown. For the period 1370–1536 Grace's annals consist mainly of obits of members of the Lacy, Burke, Butler, and Fitzgerald families.

Whoever the author of the early annals was, they constitute the main source for English affairs in Ireland for the period 1162 to 1370. They contain meteorological information, e.g. on the extraordinarily dry summer, Dublin 1333.

Text. Chronicon Hiberniae in William Camden (1551–1623): Britannia (London 1586), many times reprinted. Also in English in the translations of Britannia (London 1695), many times reprinted.

John Thomas Gilbert: Chartularies of St. Mary's abbey, Dublin (London 1884).

Grace's chronicle was edited by Richard Butler (Irish Archaeological Society, Dublin 1842).

Criticism. Robert Dunlap (DNB 42, 283, 1895). C. Gross (no. 1688, 1915). Britton (p. 143, 1937).

A5. Scotland

BARBOUR

John Barbour. Scottish poet; father of Scottish poetry and history (by Scottish poetry we mean poetry in Scottish dialect, a dialect akin to the Northumbrian or northern English, "broad Scotch"; not Gaelic of course). In 1357 John was already archdeacon of Aberdeen, as appears on a safe-conduct given to him by Edward III of Windsor for study in Oxford. He obtained similar safe-conducts in 1364, 1365, 1368, whence we conclude that he studied in Oxford and perhaps in Paris. There are many other dated documents concerning his life. For example, he was auditor of the exchequer in 1372, 1382, 1384. In 1377 he received from Robert II the Steward (king of Scotland, d. 1390) a sum of ten pounds. He died in Aberdeen on March 13, 1395.

His main work is the historical poem The Bruce, that is, the history of Robert Bruce, the earliest monument of Scottish literature. It was completed in 1375 and is divided into 20 books, 13,549 four-stress verses in couplets. After a prologue covering the period 1290–1304, the poem begins with the offering of the crown to Robert de Bruce VIII (i.e., Robert I, king and liberator of Scotland, d. 1329) and extends to 1332. Barbour took pains, not always successful, to ascertain his facts, and knew how to tell the stories effectively. Much of the Bruce was assimilated by his successor Andrew of Wyntoun (d. c. 1420) in the latter's Oryginale, a Scottish chronicle from the origin of the world to 1406.

According to Wyntoun, Barbour also wrote a poetical Brut (lost) comparable to that of Layamon (Introd. 2, 453), and the Stewartis orygenalle (the Stewart's genealogy, also lost). On the other hand, Barbour is not, in all probability, the author of the Troy book, of the Legends of the saints, or of the Buik of Alexander. The Troy book and the Legends (or Scottish legendary) are almost literal translations of the Historia destructionis Troiae by Guido da Colonna (fl. 1276) and of the Legenda aurea of James of Voragine (XIII-2).

Text. The Bruce was first printed in Edinburgh 1571. Then again in Edinburgh 1616, 1620, 1648, 1665, 1670, etc. (many more editions). Critical edition by Walter William Skeat (Early English Text Society, 3 vols., 1870–89). Reprinted in 2 vols. (Scottish Text Society, Edinburgh 1894).

New edition by W. M. Mackenzie (London 1909). Translation in modern English by George Eyre-Todd (384 p., London 1907); by Michael Macmillan (276 p., Stirling 1914).

Carl Horstmann: Barbour's Legendensammlung nebst den Fragmenten seines Trojanerkrieges (2 vols., Heilbronn 1881–82). William M. Metcalfe: Legends of the saints in the Scottish dialect of the fourteenth century (Scottish Text Society, 3 vols., Edinburgh 1896).

The Buik of Alexander, edited by R. L. Graeme Ritchie (Scottish Text Society, 4 vols., Edinburgh 1925, 1921–29).

Criticism. Aeneas MacKay: Barbour (DNB 3, 153–56, 1885); Wyntoun (DNB 63, 266, 1900). P. F. H. Buss: Sind die von Horstmann herausgegebenen schottischen Legenden ein Werk Barbere's? (Göttingen thesis, 45 p., 1886). George Eyre-Todd: Early Scottish poetry, Thomas the Rhymer, John Barbour, Andrew of Wyntoun, Henry the Minstrel (224 p., Glasgow 1891). George Neilson: Barbour poet and translator (65 p., London 1900). John T. T. Brown: The Wallace and the Bruce restudied (Bonner Beiträge zur Anglistik, 6, 182 p., Bonn 1900). Fr. W. Mühleisen: Untersuchungen über die Verwandschaft der Überlieferungen von Barbour's Bruce (Bonn thesis, 80 p., 1912). William Henry Schofield: The chief historical error in Barbour's Bruce (Modern Language Association publications 31, 359–78, Baltimore 1916). Wells (p. 202, 795, 1926).

FORDUN

John Fordun. First historian of Scotland (d. after 1384).

Joannes de Fordun was probably a chauntry priest in the cathedral of Aberdeen. Between 1363 and 1383, he traveled considerably in the British Isles to obtain materials for his chronicle, which was the first attempt to give a complete history of Scotland. It extends from Noah to 1383, being particularly valuable, as usual, for the period contemporary with him. He used Scotch, English, Irish documents. He depended naturally on earlier chroniclers, such as William of Malmesbury (XII-1).

John's Chronica gentis Scotorum was completely assimilated and continued by Walter Bower in the latter's Scotichronicon. Walter Bower was an Augustinian, abbot of Inchcolm ("St. Columba's island" in Firth of Forth), died 1449. He wrote the part 1153–1437, making full use of John's notes to 1383.

Text. The Scotichronicon was first published to 1066, by Thomas Gale: Historiae britannicae scriptores XV (p. 563–699, Oxford 1691), and with Bower's continuation to 1437 by Thomas Hearne (5 vols., 1883 p., Oxford 1722); again to 1437 by Walter Goodall (2 vols., Edinburgh 1759).

William Forbes Skene: Johannis de Fordun Chronica gentis Scotorum (2 vols., in Historians of Scotland series, vols. 1, 4, Edinburgh 1871–72). Vol. 1 includes a preface, the Latin text of the chronicle, and other documents; vol. 2 the English translation by Felix J. H. Skene, notes, and index.

Criticism. David Murray: The Black book of Paisley and other MSS of the Scotichronicon with a note upon John de Burdeus or John de Burgundia, otherwise Sir John Mandeville and the pestilence (107 p., Paisley 1885). T. A. Archer (DNB 19, 430–31, 1889). Britton (p. 520–22, 1937), years 1321, 1355, 1358.

A6. England

GEOFFREY LE BAKER

English chronicler (d. c. 1359).

Galfridus le Baker de Swynebroke. Originated in Swinbrook, near Burford, Oxfordshire; in 1347 he flourished at Osney, near Oxford. He was a secular clerk (not an Augustinian Canon in the Osney house).

He wrote a Chronicon dealing with English events from 1303 to 1356, largely based upon Murimuth's chronicle (until 1341) but with many additions, e.g., it ends with a valuable account of the battle of Poitiers (1356). The Vita et mors Edwardi II (1284–1327) often ascribed to Thomas de la More is simply an extract from Baker's Chronicon. Thomas de la More was a squire living in the same district (in Northmoor), and Baker's patron.

In 1347, being in Osney, Baker compiled at the request of Thomas de la More a Chroniculum, a very short and worthless chronicle from the creation to 1336. Every event is dated twice, from Christ's era and backward from 1347 (e.g., death of Edward I, 1307 and 40).

Text. The Chronicon was first edited by John Allen Giles for the Caxton Society (London 1847). Edition by Edward Maunde Thompson (360 p., Oxford 1889). This includes the text of the Chronicon (p. 1–155) and of the Chroniculum (p. 156–74), together with elaborate notes, maps, index.

The Vita et mors Edwardi was published by William Camden in his Anglica (Frankfort 1603) and also edited by William Stubbs in the Chronicles of Edward I and Edward II in the Rolls series (London 1883).

Criticism. T. A. Archer (DNB 3, 6, 1885). Thompson's preface (1889).

ROBERT OF AVESBURY

English chronicler (d. in or after 1359).

Robert was registrar of the court of Canterbury. His will was enrolled in 1359. That is all we know about him.

He wrote a chronicle of Edward III to 1356, very largely restricted to the continental wars, 1339–56. He incorporated original documents in his chronicle, notably letters from Michael de Northburgh (d. 1361), the king's confessor, later bishop of London. Some of these letters give an account of the Crécy campaign.

Meteorological events are noted: contrary winds in the Downs in summer 1355, stormy weather off the Scottish coast in winter 1356, drought in the spring of that year, wet weather in the summer.

Text. First edition of the Historia de mirabilibus gestis Edwardi III by Thomas Hearne (Oxford 1720). Critical edition by Edward Maunde Thompson (Rolls series, 93, 277–315, 1889).

Criticism. C. L. Kingsford (DNB 48, 372, 1896). Britton (p. 142–43, 1937).

KNIGHTON

Henry Knighton (or Cnitthon). English chronicler (d. c. 1366).

Henry Knighton was a canon of St. Mary's, Leicester. He wrote a Compilatio de eventibus Angliae extending from the Norman conquest to 1366, divided into four books. The early part (to 1336) is largely derived from Higden and Hemingburgh. Information on the Black Death.

A fifth book by a continuator, who probably was also a canon of St. Mary's, extends the account from 1377 (not 1367) to 1395. The continuation is more valuable than Knighton's own part. The author of it took sides with the Lancaster party and gives information on (against) Wycliffe. The chronicle and its continuation include valuable meteorological data, e.g. about northern lights (?) in 1355, 1387, 1388, and a "rain of blood" (a colored rain) in 1387.

Text. Robert Twysden and John Selden: Historiae anglicanae scriptores decem (vol. 2, 1652). Edition by Joseph Rawson Lumby in the Rolls series (2 vols., London 1889–95).

Criticism. H. R. Luard (DNB 31, 270, 1892). C. Gross (no. 1807, 1915). Britton (1937).

THORNE

William Thorne. English Benedictine chronicler (d. in or after 1397).

Thorne was a monk in St. Augustine's Abbey, Canterbury (Kent), which was one of the leading Benedictine houses in Europe. He went to Rome in 1387 to obtain the confirmation of a new abbot and for other monastic business, and obtained a good insight into the corruption of the curia. He wrote a history of his abbey from the time of its foundation by St. Augustine (d. 604) down to 1397. Though this is strictly a monastic chronicle—not a history of England from the windows of a monastery—it is of great value for the understanding of monastic development, monastic manners and business. It is especially important because that particular monastery was such an outstanding one.

The earlier part of Thorne's chronicle is naturally derived from earlier ones; it becomes more fundamental for the period beginning in 1272, and includes the text of a long series of charters, title deeds, and other legal instruments. Thorne records strong winds on August 15, 1394 at Canterbury.

Text. Chronicon de rebus gestis abbatum S. Augustini Cantuariae, 578–1397. Included in Twysden and Selden: Historiae anglicanae scriptores decem (2, 1757–2202, London 1652). English translation by A. H. Davis (808 p., Oxford 1934).

Davis' translation includes a very interesting document taken from another chronicle of St. Augustine's, by Thomas of Elmham, a monk of that monastery who died c. 1440 (T. A. Archer, DNB 17, 309, 1889). It is a map of the Isle of Thanet, considered the first cadastral map produced in England (c. 1400).

Criticism. Davis' introduction to his translation, and A. Hamilton Thompson's preface to it. Miss Bateson (DNB 56, 295, 1898). O. G. S. Crawford: Thunor's pit (Antiquity 7, 92–94, 1933), Crawford dates the map 1414. Britton (p. 152, 1937).

CIRENCESTER

Richard of Cirencester. English Benedictine chronicler (d. c. 1401).

Ricardus de Cirencestria was a monk at St. Peter's, Westminster, from 1355 on at least. He obtained leave to make a pilgrimage to Jerusalem in 1391. He died in 1400 or 1401.

He is the author of a mediocre compilation, Speculum historiale de gestis regum Angliae (from 447 to 1066), and would hardly deserve to be dealt with here but for another work, De situ Britanniae, dealing with the topography of Roman Britain, which was wrongly ascribed to him.

It has been conclusively proved by B. B. Woodward (1866–67) and by J. E. B. Mayor (1869) that the De situ Britanniae is a forgery perpetrated in 1747 and following years by Charles Bertram, alias Charles Junius, of Copenhagen (1723–65), and given currency in 1756–57 by the English antiquary William Stukeley (1687–1765). That clever forgery had disastrous consequences, for it introduced a number of imaginary names into English toponymy, many of which continued to appear in Ordnance Survey maps until very recently.

Text. The Speculum was edited by John Eyton Bickersteth Mayor in the Rolls series (2 vols., London 1863–69). It is in vol. 2, p. xvii–cxliv, that Mayor proved Bertram's forgery.

The De situ Britanniae was first edited by Charles Bertram: Britannicarum gentium historiae antiquae scriptores tres, Ricardus Corinensis, Gildas, Nennius (p. 1–60, Copenhagen 1758). English translation by John Allen Giles in his Six English chronicles (Bohn's library, London 1848), reprinted in 1872 after the forgery had already been proved!

Criticism. William Stukeley: An account of Richard of Cirencester and of his works, with his map of Roman Brittain and the itinerary thereof (94 p., London 1757). Bernard Bolingbroke Woodward: A literary forgery (Gentleman's magazine, 3 articles in 1866–67). Mayor's preface (1869). Henry Bradley: Charles Bertram (DNB 4, 412–13, 1885). William Hunt: Cirencester (DNB 10, 365, 1887). H. J. Randall: Splendide mendax (Antiquity 7, 49–60, 1933), with reference to some newly discovered Stukeley MSS.

MALVERNE

John Malverne. English Benedictine, chronicler (d. c. 1415).

The circumstances of his life are obscure. He was a monk in the Benedictine abbey of Worcester (near Malvern), and prior in 1395. He seems to have died in or before 1415.

He wrote the continuation of Higden's Polychronicon from 1346 to 1394. A further continuation from 1395 to 1408, the so-called Liber albus, is by another hand.

Malverne's chronicle contains a number of observations concerning the weather, e.g., earthquakes in 1382, strange solar phaenomena connected with those earthquakes; northern lights (?) in 1385.

The "Vision of Piers Plowman" was erroneously ascribed to him; that poem was probably composed by John's contemporary William Langland (1330?–1400?).

The chronicler John Malverne is different from a contemporary namesake, who was a physician. John Malverne the physician was probably a student in Oriel College, Oxford; he became curate of St. Dunstan's-in-the-East, London, in 1402. He seems to have died c. 1422. He wrote a plague treatise, De remediis spiritualibus et corporalibus contra pestilentiam (or Consilium contra pestem).

Text. Edited in Rolls series, see my note on Higden.

Criticism. C. L. Kingsford (DNB 36, 8, 1893). Britton (1937).

Malverne's plague treatise is not mentioned in Sudhoff's Pestschriften.

WALSINGHAM

English Benedictine, the last of the great English chroniclers (still living in 1421).

Thomas Walsingham came probably from Norfolk; he was educated in St.

Albans (Hertfordshire) and possibly in Oxford, where the novices of that abbey were frequently sent. He held the offices of precentor (1380) and scriptorarius (head of the copying room) in St. Albans until 1394, when he was appointed prior of the cell of Wymondham (Norfolk). In 1396 he returned to St. Albans; he was still living there in 1421.

From 1376 to 1421 (or at any rate before the death of Henry V) he seems to have been busy writing and rewriting chronicles of St. Albans. Criticism of these various chronicles (edited in various forms and under various titles) is difficult, because of the very nature of such work. The task of a monkish chronicler was deemed important enough, but in an anonymous way. It did not awaken any pride of authorship. Hence we cannot be sure that the chronicles of St. Albans were written by Walsingham, or, more exactly, we cannot be sure of the extent of his collaboration. Thus Henry Thomas Riley, who edited the so-called Historia anglicana (1272–1422) for the Rolls series, believed that the later part (1393–1422) was not compiled by Walsingham. On the contrary, the latest editor, V. H. Galbraith, concludes that the chronicle down to 1376 is simply a compilation from earlier chronicles and hence need not detain us; as to the later part, 1376–1422, it constitutes an organic unity, the work of a single author, presumably Walsingham. That later chronicle, 1376–1422, is certainly the work of a contemporary witness. Let us assume that it is Walsingham's. It is a source of fundamental importance for that period, that is, for the reigns of Richard II (1377–99), Henry IV (1399–1413), and Henry V (1413–22). It is one of the main sources for our knowledge of Wycliffe and of the Wat Tyler rebellion (1381); the Peasants' Revolt was particularly ugly in St. Albans, where our chronicler was recording the events. The chronicler was conscientious, but naturally very conservative, that is, anti-Lollard.

He put down many detailed observations of the weather, noting (or copying), e.g., the destructive gales of 1307, 1311, 1390, 1416, the drought of 1325–26, the cold winters of 1338–39, 1407–8, the hot year of 1375, severe thunderstorms in 1384, 1385, 1389, 1416, and a very strange appearance of the sun in July 1391. He had a remarkably good knowledge of the Latin classics, quoting frequently from Ovid, Vergil, Martial, Persius, Lucan, Statius, and Claudian.

Thomas Walsingham (the chronicler?) wrote a musical treatise entitled Regulae de figuris compositis, wherein he criticized the newly introduced crotchet (i.e. noire, Viertel, semi-minim), saying that notes should not be divided beyond the minim.

Text. Chronicon Angliae, edited by Sir Edward Maunde Thompson (Rolls series, 1874).

Gesta abbatum monasterii S. Albani, edited by Henry Thomas Riley (Rolls series, 3 vols., 1867–69).

Historia vitae et regni Ricardi secundi, edited largely from the St. Albans chronicle by Thomas Hearne (1678–1735) (Oxford 1729).

Historia anglicana, or Historia brevis. First edition, very imperfect, by Matthew Parker (1504–75, archbishop of Canterbury) (468 p., London 1574). Second edition by William Camden (1551–1623) in his Anglica, Hibernica, Cambrica a veteribus scripta (Francfort 1603). Critical edition by H. T. Riley (Rolls series, 2 vols., 1863–64). Partly superseded by The St. Albans chronicle, 1406–1420, edited by Vivian Hunter Galbraith (240 p., Oxford 1937).

Ypodigma Neustriae. First edition by Matthew Parker (London 1574). Second in Camden's Anglica (Francfort 1603). Third by H. T. Riley (Rolls series, 1876).

The Regulae de figuris compositis are unpublished (British Museum, Lansdowne MS 763).

Criticism. I. S. Leadam (DNB 59, 242–44, 1899), out of date. Grove (5, 321, 620, 1928). Britton (1937).

BURTON

Thomas of Burton. English Benedictine, chronicler (d. 1437).

Thomas was abbot of the Cistercian abbey of Meaux (or Meux, in the East Riding of Yorkshire; near Hull) from 1396 to 1399. He wrote a chronicle of the abbey from the time of its foundation in 1150 to 1396 (continued by another hand to 1406). The political background of that chronicle is largely borrowed from Higden's Polychronicon. The Chronica monasterii de Melsa is a good example of a monastic chronicle; it is very elaborate and is very valuable for the understanding of the business life of a monastery, and of political and ecclesiastical affairs in their relations with monastic conditions.

Text. Edition by Sir Edward Augustus Bond (Rolls series, 3 vols., London 1866–68).

Criticism. C. Gross (no. 1729, 1915).

GRAY

Sir Thomas Gray the younger, English chronicler (d. c. 1369).

Sir Thomas the younger was the son of Sir Thomas Gray the elder, of Heaton, Norhamshire, Northumberland, who was a distinguished soldier. He succeeded his father in 1345 as lord of Heaton manor and warden of Norham Castle. He took part in the Scottish wars and was carried off as a prisoner in Edinburgh 1355; he was released in 1357. He fought in France with the Black Prince in 1359, and died c. 1369.

During his captivity in Edinburgh he became "curious and pensive" and started writing, in French, a chronicle called Scala cronica (a reference to the scaling ladder in the Gray escutcheon). It is a chronicle of England from the fabulous origins down to 1362. The early part, being completely derived from earlier chronicles, is worthless; some new information begins to appear with the rule of John Lackland, but the chronicle is valuable only for the rule of the Edwards, especially with reference to the Scottish and French wars.

Text. The text has not yet been completely published. Joseph Stevenson has edited the part dealing with the period 1066–1362, Scalacronica, a chronicle of England and Scotland (Maitland Club, Edinburgh 1836), only 108 copies printed.

Partial English translation by Sir Herbert Maxwell: Scalacronica. The reigns of Edward I, Edward II and Edward III (218 p., Glasgow 1907), illustrated with many heraldic shields.

Criticism. T. A. Archer (DNB 23, 21–22, 1890). C. Gross (no. 1784, 1915).

A7. Belgium

LE MUISIT

Gilles Le Muisit, or Li Muisis. Aegidius Li Muisis. Gilles is the same as the English Giles. Belgian Benedictine; Latin chronicler and French poet (1272–1353).

Gilles was born in 1272 in or near Tournai, of a prominent Tournaisien family. In 1289 he assumed the Benedictine habit in St. Martin, Tournai. He struck up an acquaintance with a monk of that abbey, the astrologer John of Harlebeke, who is known only through Le Muisit's chronicle; according to it, John made various political prophecies which were realized (see Lemaître's ed., p. 212). He studied at the University of Paris probably from 1297 to 1301. In 1300 he pilgrimed to Rome on account of the Jubilee. In 1301 he probably returned to his monastery; he was appointed prior of it in 1329, and abbot in 1331, but was not consecrated until the following year. Unfortunately the abbey was so deeply in debt that it was twice excommunicated, and Gilles was unable to free it and himself from endless financial difficulties until 1347. At that time, being seventy-five years of age and almost blind, he began his literary activity! In 1351, the eye surgeon John of Mainz, passing through Tournai, operated upon him for cataract in both eyes. Gilles died in the following year, October 15, 1353, and was buried in the abbatial church.

His historical works, all in Latin, include (1) Tractatus de his quae temporibus suis ante et post promotionem suam in coenobio S. Martini acciderunt, account of the decline and revival of his monastery; (2) De consuetudinibus approbatis . . . , on the old customs of that monastery; (3) chronicle from 1294 to 1348, with brief introduction summarizing previous history; (4) continuation in the form of annals to 1352, including an account of the cataract operations which he underwent in 1351.

The chronicle dictated by the blind old man is largely in the form of reminiscences, but reminiscences based on notes diligently kept through his long life. As is stated in the beginning, "Quod vidimus et audivimus et de illis que in diversis locis manu propria registravimus . . . ad memoriam revocantes, proposuimus et curavimus in unum colligere et unum libellum conficere." Le Muisit had had opportunities of meeting many of the leading men of his time; he was a man of wide experience, critical, scrupulous, and, in spite of being Francophile, remarkably impartial. His chronicle is poorly written but it is a valuable source for the history of the Tournaisis and of Flanders in the first half of the fourteenth century; it is especially interesting from the cultural point of view. It gives a good account of the siege of Tournai in 1340, the flagellants who visited the town in 1349, and the Black Death.

Gilles wrote an abundance of moral and religious French verses of mediocre quality; he was already very old when he dictated them; they reveal a laudator temporis acti, but a good and simple old soul. He criticized gently but keenly the manners of students, of professional people of various kinds, monks, nuns, etc.

Text. Partial edition of the chronicle by J. Goethals-Vercruysse (132 p., Courtrai 1824). More complete edition by the canon J. J. de Smet in Corpus chronicorum Flandriae (vol. 2, Brussels 1841). Henri Lemaître: Chroniques et annales de Gilles Le Muisit, publiées pour la Société de l'histoire de France (370 p., Paris 1906), with elaborate introduction and index. Fragments translated into French by Oct. Delepierre: Chroniques, traditions et légendes des Flamands (p. 205–300, Lille 1834).

Poèmes edited by J. A. Buchon in appendix to his edition of Froissart (Collection des chroniques françaises vol. 24, i.e. vol. 14 of Froissart, 279–466, Paris 1826). Kervyn de Lettenhoven: Poésies de Gilles Li Muisis (2 vols., Bruxelles 1882).

Criticism. Arthur Dinaux: Les trouvères de la Flandre et du Tournaisis (Paris 1839). Auguste Scheler: Etude lexicologique sur les poésies de Gillon le Muiset (Mémoires couronnés de l'Académie de Belgique vol. 37, 1886). Henri Pirenne (Biographie nationale de Belgique 11, 798–806, 1891). Philipp Wagner: Gillon le Muisi (Diss. Berlin, 38 p., Brünn 1896). Wilhelm Schmidt: Untersuchung der Reime in den Dichtungen des Abtes Gilles Li Muisis (Bonn thesis, 76 p., Leipzig 1903). Pansier (fasc. 6, 111, 1908). Langlois (2, 321–73, 1926), including many extracts with commentary. Coulton (2, 394, 397, 1927). Alfred Coville (HL 37, 250–324, 382–86, 1936–38), seen too late to make full use of it.

JEAN LE BEL

Jehan le Bel (li Bials, li Beaulx). Belgian (Liégeois) chronicler, one of the greatest of his time (c. 1290–1370).

Jean Le Bel was born at Liége c. 1290 or a little earlier. He belonged on both sides to prominent Liégeois families; his grandfather, his father, one of his brothers were aldermen (échevins) of the city. He became canon of St. Lambert (in Liége) in 1313 or before. He took part under the leadership of Jean de Hainaut, lord of Beaumont (d. 1357), in the English expedition against the Scots in 1327. In old age he begot twin children whom he recognized and to whom he bequeathed great wealth. He died on February 15, 1370.

He was the forerunner of Froissart, who borrowed considerably from him. He wrote a chronicle of events in France, Belgium, England, Germany from 1326 to 1361. The early part, to 1341, was written after 1352; the rest later, gradually. He was remarkably truthful and neutral, as it was easier for one of his nation to be (than for, say, a Frenchman or an Englishman), but he saw only the surface of things, from the point of view of chivalry and adventure. He was especially interested in Edward III (king of England 1327–77) and John the Blind of Luxemburg, king of Bohemia, who died among the French at Crécy 1346. He took great pains to obtain information and recorded it impartially; for example, in the case of his hero Edward III he does not hesitate to tell stories to the latter's discredit. His historical purpose was not very deep, it was mainly to transmit to posterity the memory of knightly deeds, but his truthfulness and circumspection are much to his honor. He was a better French writer than Froissart, but not so good a storyteller; it is well to bear in mind, however, that some of the stories most admired in Froissart were actually borrowed from Le Bel (e.g., the death of Robert Bruce, king and liberator of Scotland, 1329, and the story of the six heroic burgesses of Calais, 1347).

Le Bel's knowledge was largely derived from oral tradition; he spent much time and money to obtain his information from witnesses of the events described, and in some cases he was himself a witness, e.g., with regard to the Scottish expedition of 1327. In his description of Scotland, he revealed a feeling for nature relatively rare in his time in the West. His chronicle was pillaged not only by Froissart, but also by Jean d'Outremeuse (indeed, the text of it was first rediscovered by Polain, in 1847, in the immense chronicle of Outremeuse).

Text. First complete edition of the Chronicle by Matthieu Lambert Polain (2 vols., 667 p., Bruxelles 1863). New edition prepared for the Société de l'histoire de France by Jules Viard and Eugène Déprez: Chronique de Jean Le Bel (2 vols., Paris 1904–5).

Jules Petit: Li ars d'amour, de vertu et de boneurté par Jehan Le Bel (2 vols., Bruxelles 1867–69). It is now admitted, even by Petit (preface of his vol. 2), that the ascription of this work to Le Bel is untenable; it is now ascribed to Jean d'Arckel (1314–78), bishop of Liége (Biographie nationale de Belgique 10, 314–27, 1889, by Alphonse Le Roy).

Criticism. Henri Pirenne (Biographie nationale de Belgique 11, 518–25, 1891); Histoire de Belgique (3d ed., 2, 466, 1922).

JEAN D'OUTREMEUSE[2]

Chronicler of Liége, compiler of romances (1338–1400).

He unfairly attached himself to the family of De Pré, therefore is often called

[2] Note contributed by Dr. M. C. Welborn (Sept. 1938).

Despreis, Desprez, des Preis, de Pré, etc., but should be known only by the name of d'Outremeuse.

He was born in Liége January 2, 1338, died November 25, 1400. Practically nothing is known about his life. He was a cleric although married; he did not take orders. He was a notary in the court of Liége.

Jean wrote a Myreur des histors, a long chronicle in prose which is a history of the universe beginning with the flood and continuing to the fourteenth century. Much of the material in this work is romance and not history, and a great deal of it was invented by the author himself. He used many sources and in a very indiscriminate manner.

He also wrote a Geste de Liége in verse which contains about the same material as the Myreur (in fact, the Geste was probably written first), except that this work deals only with the history of the country and bishopric of Liége to the fourteenth century. It is written in the style of a chanson de geste, with a country instead of a person as the "hero."

Jean's only scientific work is called the Tresorier de philosophie naturelle des pierres precieuses, which is not yet edited. It is divided into four parts, dealing with (1) philosophy in general, (2) a lapidary, (3) questions mainly astronomical although there is some discussion of stones, (4) technical questions.

Some of his biographers have ascribed a number of poems to him, but it is not yet certain that he wrote them.

Some authors, e.g. P. Hamelius, also claim that Jean was the real author of the famous Voyages of Sir John Mandeville (see note on him). But according to Michel, Jean d'Outremeuse probably did not write the Travels, since Jean copied some of the material for his Myreur from the Travels. Hamelius explains this copying in a different way, that Jean d'Outremeuse used the same facts in both books.

The chronicle of Liége of Jean d'Outremeuse was continued by Jean de Stavelot from 1400 to his death in 1449. This Jean, chronicler, poet, draftsman, painter, was a monk in the abbey of St. Laurent, near Liége. His father had been an alderman in Stavelot (near Spa).

Text. No complete edition has yet been published.

An almost complete edition by Adolphe Borgnet and Stanislas Bormans: Ly myreur des histors, chronique de Jean des Preis dit d'Outremeuse (Collection des chroniques belges inédites, 6 vols., Bruxelles 1864–80); a seventh volume, published in 1887, contains an introduction and table of contents. Each of the 6 volumes contains in the appendix a part of the Geste de Liége.

Criticism. Henri Michelant: Note sur un manuscrit de Jean d'Outremeuse (Bulletin de l'Institut archéologique liégeois, 1870). Auguste Scheler: La Geste de Liége par Jehan des Preis, dit d'Outremeuse. Glossaire (Académie royale des sciences de Belgique, Mémoires vol. 44, 1882). Godefroid Kurth: Etude critique sur Jean d'Outremeuse (Académie royale de Belgique, classe des lettres, Mémoires vol. 7, 1910). Louis Michel: Les légendes épiques carolingiennes dans l'oeuvre de Jean d'Outremeuse (Académie royale de langue et de littérature française de Belgique, Mémoires vol. 10, 1935).

The Chronique de Jean de Stavelot was edited by Adolphe Borgnet (Chroniques belges, 676 p., quarto, Bruxelles 1861). Stanislas Bormans: Table analytique (90 p., 1861).

Alf. Journez: Jean de Stavelot (Biographie nationale de Belgique 10, 419–21, 1889).

HEMRICOURT

Jacques de Hemricourt. Liégeois chronicler, genealogist, historian of political institutions (1333–1403).

Jacques, son of Gilles de Hemricourt, was born at Liége in 1333. In 1353 he was already clerk of the tribunal of aldermen of his native city; at the death of his father, in 1360, he replaced him as alderman (échevin); he occupied various other positions in the city, being finally elected mayor (bourgmestre) in 1389. He was a friend of Jean Le Bel and much influenced by him. Soon after the death of his second wife, in 1397, he became a knight of St. John of Jerusalem.[3] He died at Liége on December 18, 1403.

He wrote three historical works:

1. Miroir des nobles de Hesbaye composé en forme de chronique (Mirror of the noblemen of Hesbaye in the form of a chronicle). Also called Ly traitiez des linages (i.e., lignage, in English lineage). This is a chronicle of Hesbaye (a part of the principality of Liége; a district of central Belgium, high plains between the Meuse and the Scheldt) for the period 1102 to 1398, with special emphasis on the genealogies of the noblemen involved. Hemricourt spent almost half a century (1353–98) collecting his information, and he was very well placed to obtain it through his aristocratic family connections and his high offices in the city of Liége. There was some urgency to the work, because a large part of the Hesbayan nobility was destroyed in the wars of the Awans and the Waroux.[4]

2. Traitiez des guerres d'Awans et de Waroux. Chronicle of the war already referred to, written in the same spirit as the Miroir, i.e., it is a chronicle of the gesta of the noblemen, the common people being of no account.

3. Patron de la temporalité. Begun c. 1360, completed in 1399. This is a history and description of the political and ecclesiastical institutions of Liége. Divided into three books: (I) origin of temporal power, discussion of the author's purpose, history of the institutions of Liége; (II) organization of the commune of Liége, power of the mayor and aldermen; (III) truces and quarantines; criminal jurisdiction of the aldermen and the bishop. The chapters dealing with weights and measures, regulations of some guilds, were added later, namely by Jean de Temploux, called Crule, secretary to the aldermen in 1426. The Patron de la temporalité became a standard reference book, used in the courts even as the statute books. Such a work naturally invited additions and interpolations. It is of great value for the study of Liégeois institutions, manners, and customs.

The language of these three works is a Walloon dialect, sometimes so remote from the purer French dialects of that time that a French translation is needed for their understanding.

Text. The Miroir and the Guerres d'Awans et de Waroux were first published, together with a French translation, by De Salbray (folio, Bruxelles 1673). Some copies have a new title page dated 1715. A new and worse edition was prepared by the canon François Jalheau (Liége 1791). Third edition begun by Antoine Vasse (Bruxelles 1852), only a few parts published and these unsatisfactory.

[3] He was then at least 64. It was not uncommon among men of substance to join a religious brotherhood in extremis in order that they might be shrouded in its habit and better their chances in the hereafter.

[4] A very cruel local war lasting from 1290 to 1335, which began as a quarrel between the village of Awans and a squire of the house of Waroux. It developed into a struggle between the prince-bishop of Liége, taking the Waroux side, and many of his people.

The Patron de la temporalité was edited by Mathieu Lambert Polain at the end of his Histoire du pays de Liége (vol. 2, Liége 1847). New edition in the Recueil des anciennes coutumes de la Belgique, by J. J. Raikem: Coutumes du pays de Liége (Bruxelles 1873).

Criticism. Hilarion de Villenfagne: Essais critiques sur différents points de l'histoire de Liége (1, 208–43, Liége 1808), analysis of the Patron. Leopold August Warnkoenig: Beiträge zur Geschichte und Quellenkunde des lütticher Gewohnheitsrechts (p. 17–22, Freiburg 1838), idem. Alf. Journez (Biographie nationale de Belgique 9, 35–43, 1887). Potthast (p. 637, 1896). Godefroid Kurth: La cité de Liége au Moyen-âge (3 vols., Paris 1910).

FROISSART

Walloon chronicler; the greatest chronicler of his time in the West (c. 1338–c. 1410).

Jean Froissart was born at Valenciennes, on the upper Scheldt, in the county of Hainaut, in 1337–38. It is thus a mistake (often repeated) to call him a Fleming; he was a Hainuyer, that is, a Walloon, and he used Walloon dialectal forms in his writings. The name Froissart, meaning "défricheur" (breaker of new ground, squatter, pioneer), was not uncommon. His family hailed from Beaumont, Hainaut, but his father had moved to Valenciennes. The family was apparently middle class, but Jean, being a precocious and brilliant boy, obtained the protection of Jean de Hainaut, lord of Beaumont, who recommended him to his niece Philippa of Hainaut (c. 1314–69), queen of Edward III. Thus in 1356 he proceeded to the court of England, and his lifelong acquaintance with court circles and leading people was auspiciously begun. In 1360 he was in Avignon, but returned to England in 1361 after an absence of five years. He then presented to Philippa his first historical work (lost), an account of the battle of Poitiers, at which the Black Prince defeated John the Good and made him prisoner (1356). Jean then became queen Philippa's secretary; a little later he spent some months in Scotland, becoming acquainted with David II (David Bruce); then returned to London, where he became secretary to John the Good. A full account of his frequent journeys would be very long and useless; we shall mention only a few more examples. In 1366 he left England, going to Brussels, then to Brittany and southern France. In 1368 he and Chaucer were members of the escort of Lionel duke of Clarence, who traveled to Milano to marry the daughter of Galeazzo Visconti; Petrarch was a guest at the wedding feast! A little later Jean met in Bologna Peter king of Cyprus, who was trying to promote a new crusade. In 1369 Philippa died. Jean's new patrons were the duke of Brabant, Wenceslas of Luxemburg, and Guy de Blois, lord of Beaumont, who appointed him (1373) parish priest of Lestines, near Mons; later still he became canon of Chimay. Guy had married Marie of Namur, and then Jean was brought into touch with her father, Robert count of Namur, who had married Elizabeth of Hainaut, Philippa's sister. The years 1374 to 1386 were probably quietly spent in his parish. In 1386 he resumed his travels, going to Sluys, Ghent, Valenciennes, the south of France, where he was patronized by Gaston Phoebus count of Foix and Béarn, then to Paris, Flanders, etc. About the year 1394 he made a final visit to England, then went back to France, where he witnessed the preparation of the crusade which was to end disastrously at Nicopolis, 1396, when Sigismund of Hungary and his allies were utterly defeated by the 'Uthmānlī sulṭān Bāyazīd I (Bajazet). The final years of his life were largely spent in Valenciennes and Chimay, where he died c. 1410. We have given these details of Froissart's career to illustrate the abundance and importance of his witnesses; he had been brought into personal touch with many of the most prominent political and military leaders of his time, and his winning manners had enabled him to obtain from them all the news he craved for.

His career as a chronicler was apparently begun as early as 1361 (aet. 23). His chronicles, written in French (Walloon dialect), dealt with the events of France, England, Scotland, Spain, Brittany, Gascony, Flanders, and neighboring countries from the year 1322 to the murder of Richard II in 1400. The work is divided into four books. The first deals with the years 1326–76, covering the rule of Edward III; there are three versions of it. Book II, finished in 1388, dealt very fully with the events in Flanders 1382–86. Book III takes us to the Pyrénées, Spain, and Portugal; it was completed in 1389. Book IV contains the chronicles of the following years to 1400. Book I was largely due to Philippa's patronage for its first version, and to that of Robert of Namur for the final version; books II to IV, to that of Guy of Blois.

Froissart had begun his work as a revision and continuation of that of Jean Le Bel, and he incorporated in book I many stories taken bodily out of Le Bel. In fact, some of the best stories credited to him are not his at all, but Le Bel's. In the course of time he emancipated himself gradually from Le Bel's influence and tried to remove traces of it.

Froissart's sources, like Le Bel's, were primarily, if not exclusively, oral, and therefore his direct connections with witnesses and leaders were of great importance. Being neither a Frenchman nor an Englishman, but a son of Hainaut, he could remain singularly impartial as between the great nations, except that he was susceptible to the political ideas of his successive patrons; e.g., as the years go by he becomes less and less friendly to the English, more Bourguignon in his outlook. He was not unbiased as between the classes, for his point of view was absolutely aristocratic; he had no use for the common people; their needs and sufferings did not concern him; yet he could not help reporting their point of view; consider, e.g., his striking account of the socialist preachings of John Ball of York (executed St. Albans 1381; DNB 3, 73). He had a great love of power, of knightly conventions and adventures, and his Chronicles bring that out in a number of impressive stories and vivid portraits; he never saw or cared to see the other side, the black side, of chivalry, the falseness, selfishness, immorality, all the lies conveniently hidden behind the assumption of chivalric "honor." Yet in his time, chivalry was already decadent, especially in contrast with the rising bourgeoisie. The Crusades had put it on the downward path, the Black Death had weakened it considerably, and now the Hundred Years' War was preparing its final decay. In a manner half naïve half cynical he reveals the commercial side of war and chivalry, the tremendous and ugly business of prisoners' ransoms.

His work is very readable, but its philosophy is puerile. It constitutes an excellent mirror (superficial of course, as we expect a mirror to be) of the decadent chivalry of those days, but of little else. Froissart is on the whole remarkably impartial, a good and faithful observer, but uncritical and thoughtless; his style is "primesautier," like that of a reporter; he is less severe than Lebel, more anxious to tell a good story. The vividness of his descriptions was appreciated by Walter Scott; some of his portraits are like medals.

Froissart wrote many poems, the main one being Meliador, the latest poem of the Round Table cycle. Fragments of it were discovered only in 1891 (by Longnon) and the rest was discovered by the same soon afterward. It is enormously long (some 34,000 lines). Froissart wrote the second and final redaction of it for Wenceslas of Luxemburg, duke of Brabant (son of John the Blind, king of Bohemia, killed at Crécy 1346), and inserted into it the lyrical poems of his patron.

Text. The first edition of the Croniques was printed by Antoine Vérard in Paris in an unknown year. Vérard began printing in 1485, and that edition is generally counted among the incunabula (Pellechet 4932), but it may date only from the beginning of the sixteenth century (c. 1503). Later editions are dated 1505, 1514, 1518, 1520, 1574, etc. The early printed editions, as well as the early English translation, represented the first version (the more Anglophile version) of book I.

Oeuvres de Froissart, Chroniques publiées par le baron Kervyn de Lettenhove (25 vols., Brussels 1867–77). Vol. 1, introduction; vols. 2–17, text; vol. 18, pièces justificatives; vol. 19, glossaire by Auguste Scheler; vols. 20–25, tables. Another critical edition by Siméon Luce (12 vols., Paris 1869–99).

The Chronicles were Englished by John Bourchier, baron Berners (1467–1533), and first printed in London 1523–25 (2 vols.), reprinted in 1545. A new translation was prepared by Thomas Johnes (1748–1816) and printed on his own estate (4 vols., Hafod in Wales 1803–5), very often reprinted, e.g. in the series Tudor translations (London 1901), and by the Shakespeare Head Press (8 vols., Oxford 1927 ff.).

Historiarum opus omne, iam primum et breviter collectum et Latino sermone redditum. Latin abbreviation by Johann Philippson Sleidan (1506–56), about whom see NBG (44, 54–56, 1865), first printed Paris 1537 and often reprinted. An epitome of Frossard, compiled by John Sleydane, translated into English by Percival Golding (215 p., London 1608, again 1611); "although published under the name of Percival Golding, the manuscript copy clearly shows that this translation was made by his father Arthur Golding," see Louis Thorn Golding: An Elizabethan Puritan (p. 144, 159–60, New York 1937).

Poésies de Froissart publiées par Auguste Scheler (3 vols., Bruxelles 1870–72). Méliador. Roman comprenant les poésies lyriques de Wenceslas de Bohême, duc de Luxembourg et de Brabant. First edition by Auguste Longnon (3 vols., Paris 1895–99), including glossary in vol. 3.

Criticism. Sainte Beuve: Causeries du lundi (Paris Oct. 24 and 31, 1853). J. Stecher (Biographie nationale de Belgique 7, 317–39, 1883). Mary Darmesteter (née Agnes Mary Robinson): Froissart (174 p., Paris 1894), a gracious book, well documented and pleasantly written; Englished by E. Frances Poynter (New York 1895). Robert Metcalf Smith: Froissart and the English chronicle play (Columbia thesis, 178 p., New York 1915). George Gordon Coulton: The chronicler of European chivalry (London 1930), special winter number of The Studio with many illustrations. Frederick Sidney Shears: Froissart, chronicler and poet (258 p., London 1930). Bartlett Jere Whiting: Proverbs in the writings of Froissart (Speculum 10, 291–321, 1935).

Henry Noel Humphreys: Illuminated illustrations of Froissart, selected from the MSS in the British Museum (36 pl., London 1844); idem from other MSS (London 1845). Arthur Lindner: Der Breslauer Froissart (77 p., 50 pl., 22 ill., Berlin 1912).

JOHN OF YPRES

Flemish chronicler in Latin, translator into French, the "mediaeval Hakluyt" (d. 1383).

Jan De Langhe. Long John. Joannes Longus de Ypra, Iprensis. Born at Ypres in West Flanders, studied in Paris and obtained the degree of doctor decretorum (doctor in canon law), then withdrew to the St. Bertin Benedictine monastery in St. Omer on the river Aa (Pas-de-Calais). He became abbot of that monastery in 1365 and continued to be its abbot until the end of his life, on January 2, 1383.[5]

He wrote a Latin chronicle of his abbey from 590 to 1294. It is copied or derived down to 1229 from earlier chronicles. The later part, 1229 to 1294, is more completely his own. This chronicle contains not only the gesta of fifty-four abbots, but also accounts of many contemporary events. For example, it includes much information on the counts of Flanders and the history of the Netherlands.

Long John was deeply interested in geographical discovery and began a collection of travelers' accounts, which may be considered a prototype of the collections compiled in later times by such men as the Italian Giambattista Ramusio of Treviso (1485–1557), the Englishman Richard Hakluyt (1552?–1616), and many others. He translated from Latin into French the "Livre de l'estat du Grant Caan" (c. 1351). The Latin text (now lost) had been composed between 1328 and 1334, probably by John of Cora. This contains information on Chinese manners and customs, on Lamaism, the Nestorians and Franciscans, on John of Monte Corvino. He also translated into French (1351) Boldensele's account of the Holy Land and Egypt.

Long John speaks in his chronicle of the two journeys of Niccolò and Maffeo Polo, of Marco's participation in the second expedition, of Marco's sojourn of twenty-seven years in the Mongol empire, of his journeys in the emperor's service to various parts of Tartary, India, and the Islands, and of Marco's book in French, of which he (John) had a copy.

He wrote the life of St. Erkembodon, an Irish monk who became abbot of St. Omer and died in 734. The popularity of that saint's cult made it possible to rebuild the cathedral of St. Omer.

Long John should not be confused with another John of Ypres, who was abbot of Lobbes (Hainaut) and died in 1320.

Text. John's chronicle was first published in 1717, in the Benedictine collection edited by Edm. Martène and Ursinus Durand: Thesaurus novus anecdotorum (3, 441–776, Paris 1717). Supplement in the Amplissima collectio of the same editors (6, 613–17, 1724–33).

The Livre de l'estat du Grant Caan was edited by Jacquet (Journal asiatique 6, 57–72, 1830), with glossary.

The life of Erkembodon was edited by father Henschenius for the Acta sanctorum, April 12.

Criticism. Aug. Vander Meersch (Biographie nationale de Belgique 5, 319–20, 1876). Potthast (p. 669, 1896). Beazley (3, 29, 207–10, 394, 1906).

A8. Germany

NORTHOF

Levold von Northof. German (Westphalian) chronicler (b. 1279, d. in or after 1359).

Levold was born on February 5, 1279, of a noble family, probably at Northof, near Hamm, in the county of Marck. He was educated in Erfurt. In 1308 he

[5] John of Ypres was the fifty-eighth abbot of St. Bertin. He was buried in the abbatial church. His two successive tombstones have disappeared, but the epitaphs are preserved. There are two "portraits" of him in MSS of the Library of St. Omer. Information kindly given by Mr. G. Coolen, secretary of the Société des antiquaires de la Morinie in Saint Omer (letter dated March 13, 1939).

continued his studies in Avignon, and after his return received in 1310 the prebend of Boppard (on the Rhine, near Coblenz). In 1313 his patron, Adolf von der Marck, became bishop of Liége, and appointed him, in 1314, canon of St. Lambert (in Liége). He spent the rest of his life mainly in Liége. In 1326 he accompanied count Engelbert II von der Marck to Avignon. He died, probably in Liége, on October 3 (year unknown, 1359 or later).

He wrote a chronicle of the counts of Marck from 1000 to 1358, which is a good example of a chronicle of a small principality of that time. He had served that family and enjoyed its confidence for half a century, and had means of being well informed.

Text. First edition by Heinrich Meibom: Origines marcanae sive Chronica comitum de Marca et de Altena (Hanover 1613). Reprinted by the grandson of the first editor, Heinrich Meibom, jr.: Rerum germanicarum tomus I (p. 371–424, Helmstadt 1688). New edition by C. L. P. Tross (368 p., Hamm 1859). Fourth edition by Fritz Zschaeck: Die Chronik der Grafen von der Mark (Monumenta Germaniae historica, Scriptores, n. s., 6, 194 p., Berlin 1929), with index and glossary.

German translations by Ulrich Verne, chaplain in Hamm, in Joh. Suibert Seibertz: Quellen der westfälischen Geschichte (3 vols., Arnsberg 1857–69; in vol. 1), and by Tross in his edition of 1859.

Criticism. Ernst Fittig: Leopold von Northof (Bonn Diss., 90 p., 1906). Zschaeck's introduction (1929).

TILEMANN

Tilemann Elhen von Wolfhagen. German chronicler (fl. 1347–1402).

Elhen and Wolfhagen are places in Lower Hesse (Niederhessen). We do not know whether Tilemann was born in 1347 or whether his reminiscences can be traced back to that year (that is, he would have been born somewhat earlier). He obtained minor orders in the diocese of Mainz, but apparently spent most of his life in Limburg on the Lahn in West Franconia, in the diocese of Trier (Trèves). He was a city clerk of Limburg and an imperial notary (1370–98). He was married (he is called, in a document of 1398, clericus uxoratus). He died in or after 1402.

Tilemann wrote a chronicle of Limburg for the period 1336–98, which in spite of its local character is one of the most valuable mediaeval chronicles. To begin with, for the period 1347–98 the information is firsthand. Tilemann claims to deal only with things which he has witnessed and experienced. In the second place, he was what would be called today a "cultural" historian; he appreciated the importance of manners and customs and gave valuable information hardly available in other chronicles, concerning such things as art, songs, music, clothes, religion. His recording of the complexities of ordinary life is the more impressive because of its naïveté. He was a well educated man who referred not only to traditional proverbs and to the Bible, but also to the Ethics of Aristotle, Vergil, the Corpus iuris, Buridan, etc. He probably began his work c. 1377, but the unity of it suggests a late redaction, toward the very end of the century.

Though he named himself in his chronicle, he remained unknown for a long while, and the Limburg chronicle was wrongly ascribed to another Tilemann and to one Johann Gensbein.

Text. Fasti limpurgenses (Heidelberg 1617). Reprinted Heidelberg 1619, Wetzlar 1720, Trier 1747, etc. These early editions are cited after Potthast (p. 304).

The 9th edition was prepared by Arthur Wyss for the Monumenta Germaniae historica, Scriptores qui vernacula lingua usi sunt, vol. 4, part 1 (Hannover 1883).

Die Limburger Chronik, eingeleitet von Otto S. Brandt (184 p., 17 fig., Jena 1922). New edition with an introduction, notes, and index, and a translation in modern German by Gottfried Zedler (Limburg an der Lahn 1930).

Criticism. Brandt's introduction. My own attention was called to Tilemann's "small-beer chronicle" by G. G. Coulton: Life in the Middle Ages (2, 78–84, 1929).

CLOSENER

Fritsche Closener. Alsatian chronicler (d. in or after 1372).

Fritsche (or Friedrich) was the son of Sifrid Closener, a Strassburg burgher, and of Margaret Spirer; he was born at the beginning of the fourteenth century, presumably in Strassburg, and became a priest in the cathedral of that city.

He compiled a Latin-German vocabulary, Vocabularium seu nomenclator (lost), and a Directorium chori (1364), this being a collection of the rules and customs of the cathedral chapter. His main work, however, is a chronicle of Strassburg, written in German.

The chronicle begins with a summary of ancient history from the creation, and with lists of popes (the first being Christ!) and emperors. He also gives a list of the Strassburg bishops. The chronicle itself extends from the year 1260 to July 8, 1362, on which day the city was shaken by an earthquake. It deals mainly but not exclusively with Strassburg and Alsace, describing the main political events, wars, conflagrations. There are good accounts of the Black Death in Strassburg, of the terrible persecution of the Jews which followed (they were accused of having caused the plague), of the outbreaks of flagellants (not only after the Black Death, but earlier, in 1261, 1296), of the new religious foundations, etc. Closener is not methodical but honest and clear, and his style is sufficiently individual and impressive in its ingenuousness. It should be noted that this was one of the earliest chronicles to be written in the vernacular. Two chronicles in German prose are earlier still, the Sächsische Weltchronik in Low German extending to 1225 (or 1248), formerly ascribed to Eike of Repgow (XIII-1), and the Oberrheinische Chronik to 1334 (or 1349).[6] Closener's chronicle was used and continued (to 1415) by his younger countryman Jacob Twinger of Königshofen (1346–1420).

Text. First edition of the Strassburgische Chronik by Albert Schott, with a preface by Adam Walther Strobel (141 p., Stuttgart 1842). Second edition by C. Hegel: Chroniken der deutschen Städte (8, 15–151, 1870).

Criticism. Louis Schneegans: Notice sur Closener et Koenigshoven et leurs chroniques allemandes (Code diplomatique de la ville de Strasbourg vol. 1, 60 p., Strasbourg 1842). C. Hegel (ADB 4, 341, 1876). Alois Schutte: Closener und Königshofen (Strassburger Studien 1, 277–99, 1883). Ernest Wickersheimer: La peste noire à Strasbourg et le Régime des cinq médecins strasbourgeois (Proceedings of the Third International Congress of the History of Medicine, London 1922, p. 54–60, Antwerp 1923; Isis 31, 152).

JACOB TWINGER

Jacob Twinger of Königshofen near Strassburg. He is often called Königshofen. Born at Strassburg in 1346, ordained priest in 1382; canon of St. Thomas; died in Strassburg in 1420. German chronicler.

[6] Potthast (p. 305, 1895).

He continued the work of his countryman and elder contemporary Closener, improving and extending it considerably. He first compiled a collection of material in Latin, and in 1382 began the writing of his German chronicle. He wrote it three times; the first version went down to 1390; the second, shorter, to 1391; the third, longer again, to 1415. The longer version contains: (1) a universal history from Adam to Alexander and his followers; (2) history of Rome A.U.C. to the German emperors; (3) history of the Roman church and papacy; (4) history of the church and bishopric of Strassburg; (5) history of Alsace and Strassburg; (6) alphabetic index of historical events with their dates. Aside from its value for local history, Twinger's work is of importance because of its influence upon German historiography. Twinger was trying to reach the layman, witness not only his use of the vernacular, but his easy style. His point of view was German rather than Roman, and bourgeois rather than aristocratic or ecclesiastical. He continued Closener's Latin-German glossary and wrote a treatise on music, Tonarius.

Text. First edition s.l.a. [Augsburg 1474]. Edition by Joh. Schilter (Strassburg 1698). Critical edition by C. Hegel: Chroniken der deutschen Städte (vols. 8, 9, Leipzig 1870). The MSS used by Hegel were destroyed, soon after, during the bombardment of Strassburg in August 1870; the unpublished MS of the glossary was also destroyed.

Franz Xaver Mathias: Der strassburger Chronist Königshofen als Choralist. Sein Tonarius wiedergefunden von Martin Vogeleis (203 p., 2 pl., Graz 1903).

Criticism. C. Hegel (ADB 16, 525–26, 1882). Potthast (p. 1076–78, 1896).

A9. Bohemia

Beneš of Weitmil

Bohemian chronicler writing in Latin (d. 1375).

Benessius Krabice de Waitmuel or Weitmil, canon of Saaz (Žadec on the Eger) and Prague. Died July 27, 1375.

He wrote by order of the emperor Charles IV a Latin chronicle, in four books, of Bohemia from 1283 to 1374. It is especially valuable for the rule of John of Luxemburg,[7] king of Bohemia from 1310 to 1346, and of John's son, Charles IV, i.e. Charles I of Bohemia, king from 1346 to 1378.

Beneš' chronicle enjoyed some fame, being highly praised in the seventeenth century by the great Czech historian, the Jesuit Aloys Boleslas Balbin (1621–88), "Nihil Benessii historia illustrius, nihil etiam verius esse potest."

It has been suggested that Beneš completed the autobiography of the emperor Charles IV, or edited it; it is rather the other way round, for it would seem that Beneš was allowed to incorporate in his chronicle materials accumulated by the king. The Vita Caroli, written in the third person, deals with the years 1331–40 (aet. 15–24), and is thus restricted to Charles' youth, before his coronation. There is a continuation (by another hand?) to 1346. It is a very curious document, one of the most remarkable mediaeval autobiographies. Though Charles had been

[7] Sometimes dubbed the Don Quixote of Bohemia. For the understanding of Czech history and historiography, it is well to remember that John was more German or, rather, more French than Czech. He was an enthusiastic "Parisian." Though he had become blind, he fought with the French against the English and was killed at the battle of Crécy-en-Ponthieu, August 26, 1346. The French poet and musician Guillaume de Machaut (XIV-1; d. 1377) was for thirty years in John's service and thus influenced Czech music and theater.

educated in France—one of his tutors was the Benedictine Pierre Roger (pope Clement VI, 1342–52)—he did not share his father's aloofness, but on the contrary took a deep interest in Bohemia and Moravia and was soon called otec vlastí (pater patriae). Together with Clement VI he founded the University of Prague in 1347, this being the first university in the Empire. He caused various books to be translated into Czech, e.g., an adaptation to Bohemian use of the Golden legend of James of Voragine (XIII-2), called Passionnal. He wrote books on law and ceremony. He employed and patronized Beneš, Pulkava, Marignolli. His famous Bulla aurea (Nüremberg 1356) reorganized the constitution of the Holy Roman Empire.

Text. Benešii de Weitmil Chronicon ecclesiae Pragensis, first edited by Franc. Mart. Pelzel and Joseph Dobrowsky in Scriptores rerum bohemicarum (2, 199–424, Prague 1784). New edition by Josef Emler in the Fontes rerum bohemicarum (4, 460–548, Prague 1884).

Vita Caroli IV imperatoris ab ipso Carolo conscripta. First edition by Reiner Reineccius in Chronicon hierosolymitanum (2, 14–39, Helmstadt 1584). New editions by Marquardus Freher: Scriptores rerum bohemicarum (p. 86–107, Hannover 1602, again 1607), by Joh. Friedr. Böhmer in Fontes rerum germanicarum (1, 228–70, Stuttgart 1843), and by Josef Emler in the Fontes rerum bohemicarum (3, 325–68, 1882). Czech translations edited by Ambros. von Ottersdorf (Olmütz 1555), many times reprinted, finally in the Fontes rerum bohemicarum (3, 369–95, 1882). Old German translation, ibid. (3, 396–417). Translation by L. Oelsner: Kaiser Karls IV. Jugendleben von ihm selbst erzählt (Leipzig 1885):

Criticism. Potthast (p. 144, 1235, 1896). Franz Lützow: History of Bohemian literature (London 1899; again 1907, p. 49); Lectures on the historians of Bohemia (London 1905).

PULKAVA

Bohemian chronicler writing in Latin (d. 1380).

Přibik son of Dluhý of Radenin, surnamed Pulkava, was director of the cathedral school of St. Giles at Prague; later he took orders and became rector of the parish of Chudenic. At the request of the emperor Charles IV he wrote in Latin a chronicle of Bohemia from the flood down to 1330. For the older part he follows Cosmas (XII-1) and explains the dispersion of the Slavs and their arrival across Greece and Turkey to their present settlements. Like Cosmas he describes the arrival of the Czechs in Bohemia under the leadership of Čechus; their first settlement being at the Řip (Georgsberg, a high hill overlooking the Elbe near Roudnice). Pulkava's chronicle is a valuable source for the history not only of Bohemia, but also of Brandenburg. It was promptly translated into Czech.

It has been claimed that Charles IV was the real author of the chronicle, and that Pulkava prepared only the Czech adaptation. That is hardly plausible. The king helped the author, making many documents available to him and perhaps directing and influencing his efforts. A further proof of their cooperation is the fact that Pulkava translated Charles' autobiography into Czech.

Text. Cronica Boemorum first edited by J. B. Mencken in his Scriptores rerum germanicarum (3, 1617–1770, Leipzig 1730). Third edition by Gel. Dobner: Monumenta historica Boemiae (3, 72–290, Prague 1774). Czech translation edited by Fr. Procházky (Prague 1786).

For the Czech translation of the Vita Caroli see my note on Beneš.

Criticism. Potthast (p. 946, 1896). Franz Lützow: History of Bohemian literature (London 1899; again 1907, p. 48–50); Lectures on the historians of Bohemia (p. 20, London 1905).

A10. Poland

JAN CZARNKOWSKI

Joannes de Czarnkowo, Polish chronicler (fl. 1364–84).

This Jan or Janko was archdeacon of Gnesen.[8] He was vice-chancellor to Kasimierz III Wielki (= the great; king of Poland 1333–70). He was holding that office in 1364 and was present at the king's death in 1370. In 1364 he was dean and in 1367 cantor of the cathedral of Włocławek (Russian Vlotslavsk; on the Vistula, 35 miles southeast of Thorn). During Kasimierz' rule, Janko traveled once with other Poles to Avignon, and there met duke Władysław the Wise[9] before the latter's retirement into a monastery. Janko had a brother Simko (Simeon), who was a royal notary in 1368.

Janko is the author of a part of the Chronica Cracoviae, dealing with the period which followed the death of Kasimierz III, that is, with the years 1370–84. The Chronica as published includes seven parts: (1) Cracoviae brevior chronica, to 1135; (2) Ephemerides wladislavienses; (3) Annales poznanienses, 965–1311; (4) Annales gneznenses, 1192–1341; (5) Chronicon anonymi Cracoviae, 730–1376; (6) Janko de Czarnkowo, 1370–84; (7) Continuatio, to 1395. Janko's share in the whole chronicle may be larger than is indicated in this list. He may have edited and revised earlier parts. We meet the same problem with regard to almost every mediaeval chronicle; it is seldom patient of a certain and complete solution.

According to Potthast, the chronicle refers to a disease which might be syphilis (?). I have not been able to locate that passage; the assertion leaves me very skeptical, for there is no mediaeval description of a disease sufficiently clear and unequivocal to bear such an interpretation.

Janko gives a moving account of the sudden blindness which overcame Jaroslaus,[10] archbishop of Gnesen, in 1372 (Sommersberg's ed., p. 107).

Text. Friedrich Wilhelm de Sommersberg: Silesiacarum rerum scriptores (folio, 2, 78–155, Leipzig 1730), only edition available to me. August Bielowski: Monumenta Poloniae historica (2, 619–756, Lwów 1872).

Criticism. Potthast (p. 226, 1895). Heinrich Zeissberg: Die polnische Geschichtschreibung des Mittelalters (Jablonowskische Gesellschaft, Preisschr. no. 17, 452 p., Leipzig 1873; p. 38, 159–61).

A11. Byzantium

JOHN VI CANTACUZENOS

Ἰωάννης ὁ Καντακουζηνός. Byzantine emperor (1341 or 1347 to 1355). Historian, theologian, and interpreter of Aristotelian ethics (c. 1292–1383).

He was born in Constantinople c. 1292 and belonged to the imperial Palaeologos family through his mother. During the rule of Andronicos III (1328–41) he was

[8] Gnesen is 29 miles east by north of Posen. Janko's birthplace, Czarnkow, is probably Czarnikau (38 miles north-northwest of Posen) on the Netze.

[9] I assume this is Władisław the White, duke of Cujavie, who assumed the Cistercian habit at Cîteaux 1356, and was later a Benedictine at Dijon. He was a pretender to the throne of Poland in 1376, 1382; died at Strassburg 1388 (Chevalier p. 4787, 1907).

[10] Jaroslaw Bogurja, bishop of Gnesen 1342–73. It was he who codified the Constitutiones ecclesiarum Poloniae.

at the head of affairs, and when Andronicos died, in 1341, Cantacuzenos was appointed regent and tutor of Andronicos' young son John V Palaeologos (1332–91). Cantacuzenos seized the imperial crown, but little John was recognized by many as the only legitimate emperor. Thus arose a civil war, which was aggravated by all kinds of foreign intrigues with Venetians, Genoese (established at Galata), Serbians,[11] and Turks. John Cantacuzenos married his daughter to Urkhān ('Uthmanlī sulṭān 1326–60), and it was during his reign (in 1354) that the Turks obtained their first foothold in Europe (in Gallipoli). In 1347 his triumph was complete and he was accepted as co-emperor (and sole emperor during his partner's minority), but the empire was weakened, its financial resources almost destroyed. The need of heavy taxation brought his unpopularity to a climax and caused his fall. In 1355, he abdicated in favor of his son Matthew, appointed despot of Mysithra,[12] but the latter was obliged to follow his example in 1357. John Cantacuzenos withdrew to the monastery *τῶν Μαγγάνων* in Constantinople, and soon afterward to Vatopedi on the Holy Mountain, having assumed the name Ἰωσάφ Χριστοδοῦλος. He spent the rest of his life studying and writing, and died in 1383; he was buried at Mysithra.

His main work is a history of Byzance from 1320 to 1356 (1362), four books of Ἱστοριῶν, largely an apology for his own public life. It completes and corrects the history of Nicephoros Gregoras (and vice versa), for the tendencies of the two writers are opposite and their methods and interests very different. This is the only part of Byzantine history written by an emperor, except for the autobiographical fragments included in the *τυπικά* of Michael VIII Palaeologos (XIII-2).

He wrote a paraphrase of the Nicomachean Ethics (books I–V).

As emperor he took a predominant part in the Hesychastic controversy, and later as a monk he wrote many treatises on the subject. Needless to say his point of view was Hesychastic and Athonite, and he wrote treatises against Barlaam and Acindynos, against Prochoros Cydones (brother of the more famous Demetrios Cydones), and against Joannes Calecas, patriarch from 1334 to 1347, who had taken sides with the Barlaamites and lost his see on that account.

Finally, he composed apologetic treatises against Jews and Muslims. His knowledge of the Qur'ān was derived from the Confutatio Alcorani of Ricoldo di Monte Croce (XIII-2), as translated into Greek by Demetrios Cydones.

His son Matthew (Ματθαῖος ὁ Καντακουζηνός) also withdrew to the Athos, wrote commentaries on the Song of songs and the Book of wisdom, and dedicated to his daughter two essays on the love of knowledge (*περὶ φιλομαθίας*) and the three powers of the soul (*περὶ τῶν τριῶν τῆς ψυχῆς δυνάμεων*).

Text. The History was first edited in Latin by the Jesuit Jacob Pontanus (d. 1626) in Ingolstadt (1603). The Greek princeps, together with Pontanus' version and notes by the Jesuit Jacob Gretser (d. 1625), was published in Paris (3 vols.,

[11] The kingdom of Serbia was tremendously developed at about this time by Stephen Nemanieh IX Dushan, born in Albania 1308, king of Serbia in 1331; tsar of the Serbians, Bulgarians, and Albanians in 1346; creator of an immense empire. He tried to conquer Constantinople but failed. He created a Serbian patriarchate independent of that of Constantinople. In order to increase his spiritual power he granted various chrysobulls extending the privileges of the Athos monasteries (the Holy Mountain was entirely in his power). He died in 1355. Dushan's was the third, greatest, and last Slavonic effort to create a Greco-Balkanic empire to replace the Byzantine empire. It failed, but facilitated the Turkish conquests in Europe, which began not long afterward.

[12] Or Mystras in Laconia (ὁ Μυζηθρᾶς, Μυστρᾶς), then a center of letters somewhat comparable to an Italian court of the Renaissance (Krumbacher p. 298, note 1).

1645) and reprinted in Venice 1729. New edition by Ludwig Schopen in the Bonn Byzantine corpus (3 vols., 1828–32) with notes by Niebuhr and Heinrich Grauert. Reprinted in PG (vols. 153, 154, Paris 1865–66).

Many theological treatises against Barlaam, etc., are also in PG (vols. 151, 152, 154, 1865–66).

The paraphrase of the Nicomachean Ethics and the treatise against the Jews, in 9 books, are still unpublished.

The treatise against Islam (in 4 parts) was first edited by Theodore Bibliander (d. 1564) in his large anti-Islamic collection, Machumetis . . . eiusque successorum vitae, ac doctrina, ipseque Alcoran (Basel 1543), Greek text 108 p., Latin text 124 p. It was reprinted in PG (154, 372–692, 1866).

For editions of Matthew's treatises see Krumbacher (p. 489, 1897).

Criticism. An early biography of Cantacuzenos was written in Greek by the physician Joannes Comnenos, last scion of the imperial Comnenoi, bishop of Dristra (d. Bucharest 1719), and edited by Chrysanthos Loparev in St. Petersburg 1888. Gibbon: Decline and fall (ch. 63). Valentin Parisot: Cantacuzène homme d'état et historien (336 p., Paris 1845). Krumbacher (chiefly p. 105–6, 298–300, 1897). Eleutheroudakis encylopaedia (7, 216, 1929).

A12. Armenia

GREGORY OF KHLATH

Armenian poet and historian (c. 1345–c. 1424).

Gregory was born c. 1345 in the city of Khlath, in greater Armenia. He was the son of Zer (hence his name Gregory Zeréntz) and disciple of the vartabed Sarkis. He was a monk and later archimandrite in the monastery of St. Stephen, called Zipna, in Artze (near Erzerum). About 1424 he died a martyr of his faith, being murdered by "Medes" or Kurds; he was buried in Zipna.

He wrote a history of Armenia (lost?), a menology containing brief accounts of the Armenian martyrs, many religious poems called ganz,[13] etc. One of his poems contains an account of all the calamities which visited Armenia in 1386–1421, notably those caused by the archdevil Tīmūr Lang.

Text. French translation of the last-named poem, Récit des désastres qui arrivèrent de notre temps, by Archag Tchobanian: La roseraie d'Arménie (2, 101–20, Paris 1923).

The menology was printed in Constantinople 1706, again 1730.

Criticism. Somal (p. 138, 1829).

C. SAMARITAN

ABŪ-L-FATḤ IBN ABĪ-L-ḤASAN

Abū-l-Fatḥ ibn abī-l-Ḥasan al-Sāmirī. Samaritan chronicler who was one of his people who returned from Damascus to Sichem (Nāblus) in the fourteenth century. In 1355, he wrote in Arabic at the request of the high priest Pineḥas a very conscientious, but very dry, chronicle of the Samaritans. This was based upon Hebrew, Arabic, and Samaritan writings. Like other mediaeval chronicles, this one was gradually enlarged by continuers. It is interesting to note that in this case the process was continued almost to our own days, the latest author being Pineḥas (Ar., Khiḍr[14]) ben Isaac, who died in 1898.

[13] Meaning treasure; compare Arabic kanz, Persian ganj.

[14] Sic. The Samaritans identify Khiḍr (al-Khaḍir) with Pineḥas; the Jews identify him with Elijah. Sarton (Osiris 2, 458–60).

Text. Eduardus Vilmar: Abulfathii Annales samaritani (Gotha 1865), edition of the Kitāb al-ta'rīkh mimmā taqaddama 'an al-aba' . . . (186 p.) and prolegomena (120 p.). The Latin translation announced by the author was not published.

Criticism. Moses Gaster: Samaritan literature (p. 10, 14, 1925), published in the form of a supplement to vol. 4 of EI.

D. ISLĀM

D1. Granada

IBN AL-KHAṬĪB

Hispano-Muslim historian and physician; one of the greatest Muslim scholars of Spain, and the last great one (1313–74).

Lisān al-dīn Abū 'Abdallāh Muḥammad ibn 'Abdallāh al-Salmānī (this refers to a Yamanī ancestor). He was also called Dhū-l-wizāratain (holder of two ministries, war and peace; prime minister). He was born in Loja near Granada on November 15, 1313, was educated in Granada, and, following in his father's footsteps, became a high official at the Naṣrī court; he became wazīr in 1349, and continued in that office until 1359. In that year Muḥammad V was dethroned, and Ibn al-Khaṭīb shared his vicissitudes in Spain and Morocco. When Muḥammad V was re-established, in 1362, Ibn al-Khaṭīb was again wazīr, but in 1371 he was obliged to seek refuge in Ceuta, then in Tlemcen and Fās. During the course of extradition proceedings he was murdered in his prison in Fās 1374.

In spite of these vicissitudes, Ibn al-Khaṭīb managed to write a large number of books, so many that we shall not try to mention them all, but only a few, under the following headings: general history, Spanish history, description and travel, chancellery, medicine.

General history. 1. Al-ḥulal al-marqūma. History of the caliphs East and West.

2. A'māl al-a'lām . . . . Muslim history East and West. The history of Christian Spain, inseparable from that of Muslim Spain, is partly derived from the history of Alfonso el Sabio (XIII-2), made known to the author by the Jew Yūsuf ibn Waqqār of Toledo, who is probably the same as the astronomer Joseph ben Isaac ibn Waqar. The A'māl al-a'lām was composed between 1372 and 1374.

Spanish history. 3. Al-lumḥa al-badrīya fī-l-dawla al-Naṣrīya. History of Granada to 1363.

4. Al-iḥāṭa bi ta'rīkh Gharnāṭa (The comprehensive collection concerning the history of Granada). This is his most important achievement; it is a large collection of biographies of famous men of Andalusia, including himself.

5. Al-tāj al-muḥallā. History of Spain since the beginning of the rule of the Banū-l-Aḥmar, the Naṣrī dynasty, in 1232.

6. Mi'yār al-ikhtiyār. Majālis[14a] written in honor of some hundred famous men of Spain and of her main cities.

7. Mufākharat Mālaqa wa Salā. Rivalry between Malaga and Salā (near Rabāṭ).

7 bis. Al-Ḥulal al-maushīya fī dhikr al-akhbār al-Marrākushīya is apocryphal; author unknown. It is a chronicle of Morocco from the Almohades to the Marinid dynasty. It extends to the beginning of the fifteenth century, that is, far beyond Ibn al-Khaṭīb's lifetime.

[14a] The word majālis, pl. of majlis, is difficult to translate. The meaning here is lessons or discussions or recitations such as would be made in a courtly or friendly circle.

Description and travel. 8. Nufāḍat al-jirāb fī 'ulālat al-ightirāb. Memoirs written in Morocco, including descriptions of Spanish cities, their libraries and learned men.

9. Khaṭrat al-ṭaif fī riḥlat al-shitā wal-ṣaif. Journey in eastern Granada, written in 1347.

Chancellery. 10. Raiḥānat al-kuttāb wa nuj'at al-muntāb. Collection of models of letters. Much of this was reproduced by Aḥmad ibn Muḥammad al-Maqqarī al-Tilimsānī (c. 1591–1632) in the Nafḥ al-ṭīb min ghuṣn al-Andalus al-raṭīb wa dhikr wazīrhā Lisān al-dīn al-Khaṭīb, which is a history of Muslim Spain plus a biography of Ibn al-Khaṭīb.

Medicine. 11. Manfa'at (or Muqni'at) al-sā'il 'an al-maraḍ al-hā'il. Account of the plague which occurred in Granada in 1348. This is one of the earliest accounts of the Black Death; for other early Arabic ones see my note on Ibn Khātimah (XIV-1). It was written practically at the same time as Ibn Khātimah's account. It was composed very rapidly and is distinguished by its clear defense of the idea of contagion. Says Ibn al-Khaṭīb: "The existence of contagion is established by experience, study, and the evidence of the senses, by trustworthy reports on transmission by garments, vessels, ear-rings; by the spread of it by persons from one house, by infection of a healthy sea-port by an arrival from an infected land . . . by the immunity of isolated individuals and . . . nomadic Beduin tribes of Africa . . . . It must be a principle that a proof taken from the Traditions has to undergo modification when in manifest contradiction with the evidence of the perception of the senses" (Meyerhof's version in Legacy of Islam, p. 340). This confirms Ibn Khātimah's views on the subject.

12. 'Amal man ṭabba liman ḥabba. Medical treatise dedicated to the Marīnī sulṭān of Morocco Abū Sālim Ibrāhīm (ruled 1359–61). It is an elaborate treatise divided into two parts: (I) General and special pathology. For each disease a definition of it is given, diagnosis, causes, treatment, drugs, and diet. The information is well arranged and sufficiently brief. The account of eye diseases is particularly full. (II) Fevers, surgery, cosmetics, aphrodisiacs, sexual life, and pediatrics. The final chapter is reserved for delicate questions, concerning things forbidden by law or morality. Ibn al-Khaṭīb justifies the use of wine for Christians and Jews, the use of abortives for women whose life would be endangered by parturition, the use of aphrodisiacs for increasing the population.

13. Manẓūma (or Arjūza) fī-l-ṭibb, medical poem.

14. Al-uṣūl (or, al-wuṣūl) lī-hifẓ al-ṣiḥḥa fī-l-fuṣūl. Regimen for the different seasons of the year.

15. Al-Yūsufī fī ṣana'at al-ṭibb. Large treatise on medicine.

Other medical works are ascribed to him, dealing with the making of the theriaca, embryology, and the veterinary art.

Text. Long extracts from nos. 1, 3, and 4 quoted and translated into Latin by Casiri (2, 71–121, 177–319, 1770).

There are other extracts from the Iḥāṭa (no. 4); the MSS, especially the one in the Academia de la Historia in Madrid, have often been used by historians of Muslim Spain, and there is an abbreviated edition (2 vols. published, Cairo 1319 H.), but we still lack a complete critical edition with indexes and translation.

For partial editions see Brockelmann.

2. E. Lévi-Provençal: Histoire de l'Espagne musulmane, extraite du Kitāb a'māl al-a'lām (Collection de textes arabes publiée par l'Institut des hautes études marocaines vol. 3, Rabat 1934).

3. Al-lumḥa, edited by Muḥibb al-dīn al-Khaṭīb (152 p., Cairo 1347 H.).
4. Iḥāṭa. See above.
6. Mi'yār. The first majlis was edited by Marcus Joseph Müller: Beiträge zur Geschichte der westlichen Araber (München 1866–78; p. 74 ff., 1866), publication which remained unfinished because of the author's death in 1874. Reprint of the Arabic text, Fās 1325 H.
7. Mufākharat. Edited by Müller 1866, together with no. 6. Emilio García Gomez: El parangón entre Málaga y Salé (Al-Andalus 2, 183–96, 1934), in Spanish only.
7 bis. The apocryphal Ḥulal maushīya was printed in Tunis 1327, 1329 H.
10. The Nafḥ al-ṭīb of al-Maqqarī was translated into English by Pascual de Gayangos: The history of the Mohammedan dynasties in Spain (quarto, 2 vols., London 1840–43), with abundant notes and indexes. Many of the diplomatic models of the Raiḥānat al-kuttāb have been edited in Arabic and Spanish by Mariano Gaspar Remiro (Rivista del centro de estudios historicos de Granada, 1912 ff.).
11. The treatise on the plague was edited and translated into German by Marcus Joseph Müller (Sitzungsberichte der K. bayerischen Akad. der Wissenschaften, 1863, 2, 1–34, Munich 1863), the Arabic text fills 10 pages.

Criticism. Pons Boigues (p. 334–47, 1898). Leclerc (2, 285–88, 1876). Wüstenfeld (no. 439, 1882). Brockelmann (2, 260–63, 1902; suppt. 2, 372–73, 1938). C. F. Seybold (EI 2, 397–98, 1918). Auguste Cour: L'opinion d'Ibn al-Khaṭīb sur les ouvrages d'Ibn Khāqān considérés comme source historique (Mélanges René Basset 2, 17–32, Paris 1925), apropos of al-Fatḥ ibn Muḥammad ibn Khāqān, born near Granada, murdered in Morocco c. 1134–40 (Brockelmann 1, 339). Melchior M. Antuña: Obras del poligrafo granadino Abenaljatib existentes en la biblioteca del Escorial (La ciudad de Dios vol. 147, p. 108–20, 161–80, 254–68, Escorial 1926). M. Meyerhof: Science and medicine (Legacy of Islam p. 340, Oxford 1931). Campbell (p. 26–28, 1931). Vera (1, 62–66, 1933). M. M. Antuña: Una versión árabe compendiada de la "Estoria de España" de Alfonso el Sabio (Al-Andalus 1, 105–54, 1933). Mohammed el-Fāsī: Un nouvel exemplaire MS d'un volume de l'Iḥāṭa (Hespéris 24, 132–34, 1937). Farmer (p. 53, 1940), apropos of two musical texts ascribed to Ibn al-Khaṭīb; the second (apocryphal) was edited and Englished by Farmer in his Collection of Oriental writers on music (vol. 1, Glasgow 1933).

D3. Algiers

IBN AL-QUNFŪDH

Abū-l-'Abbās Aḥmad ibn al-Ḥasan (or Ḥusain) Ibn al-Khaṭīb al Qusṭanṭīnī (or Qusanṭīnī), known as Ibn al-Qunfūdh. Algerian historian, mathematician, and astronomer (d. 1407/8).

His grandfather, 'Alī, was a khaṭīb, later a qāḍī, and died in 1332; his father, al-Ḥasan (or Ḥusain), was also a qāḍī and died in 1349. Aḥmad studied in Spain, Morocco, and Tunis and finally became a qāḍī in Constantine, Algeria. He wrote some 27 books, according to his own bibliography (Rabāṭ MS). I list only a few:

1. Al-fārisīya fī mabādī al-daula al-Ḥafṣīya. History of the Banū Ḥafṣ (ruled in Tunis 1228–1534) from 1068 to 1402.
2. Sharḥ al-ṭālib fī asnā'-l-maṭālib. Obituaries of learned men arranged year by year to 1404.
3. Uns al-faqīr wa 'izz al-ḥaqīr. Biography of Abū Madyan Shu'aib ibn al-Ḥasan al-Tilimsānī, a Spanish ṣūfī who became acquainted with 'Abd al-Qādir al-Jīlī (XII-1) in Mecca and helped to diffuse the latter's doctrine (Qādirīya) in the West; he died near Tlemcen c. 1202.

4. Tashīl al-maṭālib fī ta'dīl al-kawākib (Help to the student for the determination of the positions of planets). This is a commentary on the Kitāb al-yasāra fī taqwīm al-kawākib al-sayyāra (Book of ease, tables of the wandering stars) by Ibn al-Bannā' (XIII-2).

5. Ḥaṭṭ al-niqāb 'alā wajh 'amal al-ḥisāb. Commentary on the Talkhīṣ of Ibn al-Bannā'.

6. Commentary on the astrological poem (arjūza) of Ibn abī-l-Rijāl (XI-1); this was written in 1372.

7. Kitāb al-wafayāt. This is probably identical with no. 2.

A fresh study of the Ḥaṭṭ al-niqāb made by H. P. J. Renaud on newly discovered MSS has yielded noteworthy conclusions. Before beginning his explanation of the Talkhīṣ, Ibn al-Qunfūdh considers eight principles (mabādī) or questions: (1) the aim of the book, (2) its utility, (3) its title, (4) the method to be followed in its study, (5) its rank, (6) the author's name, (7) the book's authenticity, and (8) its divisions. From what he says in section 5 it is clear that he regarded the book of Muḥammad ibn 'Abdallāh al-Ḥaṣṣār (XII-2) as very elementary, and Ibn al-Bannā's Talkhīṣ derived from it as of superior rank. The most remarkable feature of the Ḥaṭṭ al-niqāb is the use of many algebraic symbols: the letter shīn (or only the three dots of that letter) for the unknown quantity x (shīn is the initial of shay', a thing, res), the letter mīm lying down for x^2 (mīm is the initial of māl, meaning capital, arithmetical product, or square), the letter lām for equality (lām is the last letter of 'adl, equality), the letter kāf for x^3 (kāf is the initial of ka'b, cube), two letters mīm both lying down for x^4, the letter jīm for root (jīm is the initial of jadr, root). To indicate addition Ibn al-Qunfūdh uses the word wa (and) or ilā (ijtama'a ilā = to add to), or the simple juxtaposition of the numbers to be added; to indicate subtraction, the word illā (less, except) or min (from; ṭaraḥa min = to subtract from); to indicate multiplication, the word fī (ḍaraba 'adadan fī 'adadin = to multiply a number by a number); to indicate division, the word 'alā (qasama 'alā = to divide into). The operations called al-jabr (hence algebra), meaning supplementation, and al-sharf or al-tashrīf, meaning transformation, are symbolized respectively by the words ḥattā (until, so that) and kam (how many). Similar notations are found in another commentary on the same Talkhīṣ, by Ya'qūb ibn Ayyūb ibn 'Abd al-Wāḥid al-Mawāḥidī, who flourished about the middle of the fourteenth century in southern Morocco.[15]

This algebraical symbolism precedes by about a century the one ascribed to the Spanish mathematician Abu-l-Ḥasan 'Alī ibn Muḥammad al-Qurashī al-Basṭī al-Qalaṣādī (born in Basṭa, now Baza, in the province of Granada, flourished in Granada; died in Bāja,[16] Tunisia, December 1486) in his commentary on the Talkhīṣ of Ibn al-Bannā'. This Qalaṣādī was the last important Arabic mathematician, at least in the West; it is significant that some of his efforts were devoted to the explanation of the writings of Ibn al-Bannā', whose influence dominated the last centuries of Maghrib mathematics (see Ibn Khaldūn, Prolégomènes, 3, 132–33, 149).[17]

[15] MS of the middle of the fourteenth century owned by Georges S. Colin in Rabat. There is in the Rabat library (no. 539.3) another MS by the same author, a commentary on Ibn al-Bannā's work on arithmetical inheritance problems.

[16] Ancient Vacca, Βάγα.

[17] Al-Qalaṣādī's arithmetical writings have been made available to Western readers by Franz Woepcke: Traduction d'un traité d'arithmétique d'Aboul Hasan Alkalsadi (Atti de' Nuovi Lincei 12, 230–75, 399–438, 1859); that is the translation of the Kashf al-asrār (or al-astār) 'an 'ilm al-ghubār, Uncovering of the secrets (or the veil) of arithmetic. Woepcke translated

The name of Ibn al-Qunfūdh is strangely reminiscent of that of another Constantinian, Aḥmad ibn al-Ḥasan al-Khaṭīb al-Qusṭanṭīnī, author of the Arjūza fī-l-ṭibb, a medical poem, composed in 1312 (Ḥājjī Khalīfa 1, 247, no. 464). It may be that the date was misread. For a third contemporary Constantinian,[18] see the note on 'Ali ibn abī 'Alī al-Qusṭanṭīnī.

Text. Al-wafayāt edited by Mawlawi M. Hidayat Husain (Journal of the Asiatic Society of Bengal vol. 8, 38 p., Calcutta 1912).

Criticism. Suter (no. 422, p. 170, 1900; p. 178, 1902). Brockelmann (2, 241, 1902; suppt. 2, 341, 1938). E. Lévi-Provençal: Les manuscrits arabes de Rabat (Publication de l'Institut des hautes études marocaines 8, 133, Paris 1921); Les historiens des Chorfa (p. 98, Paris 1922). H. P. J. Renaud: Additions à Suter (Isis 18, 174, 1932); Sur un passage d'Ibn Khaldūn relatif à l'histoire des mathématiques (Hespéris p. 35–47, Rabat 1944; Isis 36, 181).

D4. Tunis

YAḤYĀ IBN KHALDŪN

Tunisian historian, younger brother of the famous Ibn Khaldūn, and man of letters (1333–78).

Abū Zakarīyā Yaḥyā ibn Muḥammad ibn Khaldūn was born in Tunis 1333. Like his brother 'Abd al-Raḥmān, he was educated in Tunis, but unlike him he devoted more attention to belles-lettres and less to philosophy or sociology. In 1356 both brothers were at the court of Abū Salīm, sulṭān of Fās. The latter charged Yaḥyā to accompany two Ḥafṣī princes, his prisoners, from Tlemcen to Bougie, which they were expected to recapture. Yaḥyā acted as chamberlain to one of the princes, the amīr Abū 'Abdallāh, who failed to regain Bougie until later (1363) when Yaḥyā had obtained for him the assistance of the king of Tlemcen, Abū Ḥammū Mūsā II. Soon afterward Yaḥyā was thrown into prison at Bona, but escaped to Biskra; further vicissitudes took him to Tlemcen, Fās, again Tlemcen, where he was murdered in December 1378 or January 1379.

Like his brother, Yaḥyā served different courts and thus obtained much political experience, but his life was much shorter, 46 Muslim years against 76. He wrote a history of the kings of Tlemcen, that is, the Ziyānī dynasty (1235–1393), to 1376, entitled Bughyat al-rūwād fī dhikr al-mulūk min banī 'Abd al-Wād. As Yaḥyā had been the secretary (kātib al-inshā') and adviser of one of those kings, Abū Ḥammū Mūsā II (ruled 1352–86), he was very well documented. His history is less profound than that of his brother, but better written. It gives valuable information on poetry and literary life at the court of Tlemcen.

---

extracts from al-Qalaṣādī's larger commentary on the Talkhīṣ in the two following articles: Mémoire sur la propagation des chiffres indiens (Journal asiatique 1, 27–79, 234–90, 442–529, 1863; p. 58–62), and Passages relatifs à des sommations de séries de cubes (Annali di matematica 5, 147–81, Roma 1863).

F. Woepcke: Notice sur des notations algébriques employées par les Arabes (Journal asiatique 4, 348–84, 1854), important. Auguste Cherbonneau: Notice bibliographique sur Kalaçādi (Journal asiatique 14, 437–48, 1859). Gustav Eneström: Sur une formule d'approximation des racines carrées donnée par Alkalsadi (BM 3, 236–39, 1886). Suter (p. 180–82, 1900; p. 179, 1902). Brockelmann (2, 266, 1902; suppt. 2, 378, 1938). Cantor (1, 810–16, 1907). H. P. J. Renaud: Sur l'origine du nom d'al-Qalaṣādī (Isis 36, 69), the name, which has no meaning in Arabic, is of Spanish origin; it derives probably from one of the many Spanish localities called Calzada; it would be better then, I think, to vocalize it Qalṣādī.

[18] For this third one at least, the place referred to is Constantina between Seville and Cordova, not Constantine in Algiers.

Text. Alfred Bel: Histoire des Beni 'Abd el-Wād (2 vols., Algiers 1904–13), Arabic text with French translation and notes.

Criticism. A. Bel (EI 2, 396, 1918). Brockelmann (2, 241, 1902; suppt. 2, 340, 1938).

IBN KHALDŪN

'Abd al-Raḥmān Ibn Khaldūn. Western Muslim (Tunisian) historian, philosopher, and pedagogue, one of the founders of the philosophy of history and of sociology (Tunis 1332—Cairo 1406).

Contents: (1) Life. (2) Works. (3) Philosophy of history, and sociology. (4) Economics. (5) Geography and anthropology. (6) Spiritism, spiritualism, or metapsychology. (7) Classification and history of science. (8) Pedagogy. (9) Philology. (10) Scientific views. (11) Summary. (12) Influence. (13) Text. (14) Criticism.

1. *Life*

Abū Zaid Walī al-dīn 'Abd al-Raḥmān ibn Muḥammad Ibn Khaldūn al-Tūnisī al-Ḥaḍramī al-Ishbīlī al-Mālikī. His family originated from the South Arabian tribe of Kinda.[19] His ancestor Khālid, also called Khaldūn (whence the family derived its name), emigrated from Yaman to Spain in the ninth century, and some of his descendants established themselves in Seville[20] and Carmona, also across the Straits in Ceuta and Bona. Our Ibn Khaldūn derived from a Sevillan branch which had moved to Tunis in the middle of the thirteenth century; he was born in Tunis on May 27, 1332, and the greater part of his life was spent in Africa. His father died of the plague in Tunis in 1349.

To give a full account of his life would be very long and tedious, and hardly intelligible except to one familiar with the very complex history of the Ḥafṣī dynasty of Tunis (1228–1534), the Ziyānī of Algeria (1235–1393), the Marīnī of Morocco (1195–1470), the Naṣrī of Granada (1232–1492), the Baḥrī Mamlūk (1250–1390) and the Burjī Mamlūk (1382–1517) of Egypt, not to speak of smaller princes, for Ibn Khaldūn witnessed and shared some of their vicissitudes. He was educated in Tunis, and after the Marīnī conquest of that country (1347) he could continue his studies under Moroccan teachers without leaving his native city. He became a royal secretary at the age of 20, and continued in that profession for at least twenty-two years in different courts. Thus we find him established successively in Tunis, Biskra, Fās (1354), Granada (in 1363 the king of Granada sent him as ambassador to Peter the Cruel, in Seville), Bougie, Biskra, Tlemcen, Fās (1372), Granada, Tlemcen . . . . He was acting most of the time as adviser, kātib or qāḍī; sometimes he was in high favor, sometimes under suspicion, sometimes he was thrown into prison, but we may assume that he was all the time collecting information and increasing his knowledge of individual people and of politics.

About 1374 he withdrew to the Qala'at ibn Salāma (Tā'ūghzūt, in the Mina mountains, province of Oran) and remained there four years working at his history.

[19] About that "royal" tribe (Kindat al-mulūk) see F. Krenkow (EI 2, 1018, 1927).

[20] One of the Sevillan members of the Ibn Khaldūn family was Abū Muslim 'Umar ibn Aḥmad ibn Khaldūn al-Ḥaḍramī, who died in Seville in 1057/58 (Suter no. 227, p. 102). 'Umar ibn Aḥmad was learned in philosophy, mathematics, and astronomy, but left no writings. He was a pupil of Maslama ibn Aḥmad al-Majrīṭī (X-2), and his most famous disciple was Ibn al-Ṣaffār (XI-1).

It was in that retreat that he wrote the first draft of his masterpiece, the Muqaddama. In 1378, he went to Tunis to obtain more information in the libraries of that city, and probably with the same purpose in mind he began the great pilgrimage in 1382. He stopped in Alexandria and Cairo, where he studied and taught; and he was appointed chief Mālikī qāḍī in 1384. Soon afterward he lost his family and fortune in a shipwreck, and devoted himself more completely to his studies and good works. In 1401 he followed the sulṭān al-Nāṣir to Damascus in the latter's campaign against Tīmūr.[21] He returned to Cairo, where he died in March 1406.

Though he lived in so many places, it is probable that his scholarly work was done mainly in Tunis, Tlemcen, Tā'ūghzūt, and Cairo.

More details concerning his agitated life may be found in his own autobiography ('Ibar 7, 379–98) and in the writings of some of his contemporaries, chiefly Ibn al-Khaṭīb, whose friendship he had gained at the court of the Banū-l-Aḥmar in Granada (1362–64).

2. *Works*

According to Ibn al-Khaṭīb, Ibn Khaldūn wrote many poems and books, e.g., summaries (talkhīṣ) of some works of Ibn Rushd and of the Muḥaṣṣal (a metaphysical treatise) of Fakhr al-dīn al-Rāzī (XII-2), also treatises on logic and arithmetic, but all these works are apparently lost, and certainly forgotten. He is remembered only, and will always be remembered, because of another work of his, the Kitāb al-'ibar wa dīwān al-mubtada' wal-khabar fī ayyām al-'Arab wal'Ajam wal Berber wa man 'āṣarahum min dhawī'l-sulṭān al-akbar (Instructive examples and collection of origins and information concerning the history of the Arabs, Persians, and Berbers . . .), one of the greatest monuments of Arabic literature. According to a MS which he presented to the mosque of al-Qarawīyīn in Fās, it was dedicated to the Marīnī sulṭān 'Abd al-'Azīz (ruled 1366–72), yet the work was not completed until later (1377 ff.).

The Kitāb al-'ibar is divided into three parts: (1) the Muqaddama[22] (same meaning as prolegomena), a philosophical introduction; (2) history of the Arabs, and of the Nabataeans, Syrians, Persians, Jews, Copts, Greeks, Romans, Turks, and Franks; (3) history of the Berbers and of the Muslim dynasties of North Africa. In the main Arabic edition (7 vols., Būlāq 1867), volume 1 contains the first part, volumes 2–5 the second, and volumes 6, 7 the third. Volume 7 also includes the history of his family and of himself. Leaving out of comparison the philosophical introduction, to which we shall come back presently, the second part is far longer, yet far less important than the third. Indeed, it is largely derived from secondary sources, and that not too well, whereas the history of North Africa is partly based upon the author's very long and intimate acquaintance with many of the peoples and conditions described. Ibn Khaldūn had had the unusual opportunity of obtain-

[21] Ibn Khaldūn had an interview with Tīmūr in Damascus. Tīmūr received him kindly. See French translation of Prolégomènes (1, lxxxvi ff.).

[22] Western Muslim and French scholars prefer to read muqaddima (see, e.g., Goichon p. 301, 1938). Let me explain for non-Arabists that this is simply a moot grammatical point. Muqaddama is a passive participle and muqaddima an active one. The vowel is not indicated in the Arabic script and it is up to the reader to decide whether he will give the word a passive or an active meaning; in most cases no doubt is possible, in this one there is room for a divergence of opinion. According to George Wilhelm Freytag (Lexicon arabico-latinum 3, 411, 1835), muqaddama = anterior pars exercitus; muqaddima = anterior et prior pars rei, praefatio libri, etc. I have used the passive form, equivalent to the Greek passive, prolegomena.

ing evidence not from one court or chancellery, but from many mutually inimical. Yet it is generally admitted that the history of the Berbers is not as good as one might have expected from a man who was so well informed and was one of the greatest theoricians of historiography. That does but confirm, however, a rule of great generality, that the best critic is not necessarily the best creator. Perhaps Ibn Khaldūn was overwhelmed by the very mass, variety, and contradictoriness of his knowledge; this would help to explain his lapses in style and his occasional awkwardness in the presentation of the facts. We must remember also the many vicissitudes of his life; they increased his difficulties as an author in proportion as they multiplied his opportunities as an observer.

3. *Philosophy of history, and sociology*

Before discussing Ibn Khaldūn's views on this great subject, it is well to analyze the Muqaddama, wherein those views are explained. That work was outlined in May–October 1377 during his retreat in the Qala'at ibn Salāma, but elaborated afterward.

The Kitab al-'ibar begins with a preface and introduction explaining the value of historical work in general, the plan of his own work and its main sources, the methods to be followed, and errors to be avoided. The Muqaddama, which follows, deals with the description and discussion of human society in its various aspects (such as nomadic and sedentary life, means of livelihood, sciences and arts, social causes and results). It is divided into six sections, the contents of which are but briefly indicated (a more elaborate discussion of some items will be found in the following chapters):

I. On civilization. Geography and anthropology. Communications with the invisible world insured by seers and prophets; psychology of divination, etc.

II. Discussion of nomadic culture and its contrast with sedentary culture ("the desert and the sown").[23] Sociological and historical causes and consequences of the conflicts arising continually from that fundamental opposition.

III. Dynasties, kingdom, caliphate, order of dignities in a sultanate. Principles of government and administration. Various institutions are discussed, including some of the Christians and the Jews. Much in this section reminds one of the contents of the mediaeval literature "de regimine principum," the development of which can be followed in many languages East and West (Isis 29, 107) and culminates in a strange way in the Prince of Machiavelli.[24] Ibn Khaldūn was not at all a cynic like the latter, but he might be called a realist, though, for him as for most of his contemporaries, the highest as well as the surest and soundest realities were religious.

IV. Observations concerning life in villages and in towns. Ibn Khaldūn comes back here to the argument of section II, but from different angles. How should cities be organized? Descriptions of famous temples. Differences in the costs of life due to urbanism. Wealth tends to be concentrated in fewer and fewer city hands.

V. Means of livelihood, professions, arts and trades, business, agriculture, exportation, building, carpentry, weaving, tailoring, obstetrics, medicine, secretarial work, bookselling, singing . . . .

[23] Title of a remarkable book by Gertrude Bell (1868–1926) describing the desert and towns of Syria (London 1907); the phrase occurs in Edward Fitzgerald's Rubāyāt (no. x, London 1859).

[24] Allan H. Gilbert: Machiavelli's "Prince" and its forerunners. The Prince as a typical book De regimine principum (280 p., Durham, N. C. 1938).

VI. Various kinds of sciences. Psychology of learning and teaching. Classification of sciences.

This summary suggests the encyclopaedic scope of the work, but does not give a sufficient idea of its wealth, nor of its intricacy. The author comes back over and over again to his favorite ideas, which might be considered sociological, political, economic abstractions, but are illustrated here with an abundance of facts and anecdotes.

The Muqaddama is really a treasure of information on all the subjects indicated above and on a great many more, and it is especially valuable to the Western historian or sociologist, because the elements of Ibn Khaldūn's knowledge were so different from those available to Western authors, whether ancient or mediaeval.

I do not hesitate to call it the most important historical work of the Middle Ages. To begin with, it is the mediaeval equivalent of a modern manual on historical method. What are the purpose and validity of historical research; how can one best attain the purpose and increase the extent and precision of one's knowledge; what is the meaning of culture and progress? The author answers such questions as well as he can. Incidentally we are given abundant information on the history of Muslim institutions, private and public, the development of administration, taxation, labor, arts, crafts, and sciences. The information is almost exclusively Islamic (and Berber) and is of special interest for comparison with non-Islamic cultures. For example, Ibn Khaldūn is all the time contrasting not urban and country life, or bourgeois and popular life, as Westerners do, but settled and nomadic life, and trying to explain the paradox involved, for a fixed settlement is the condition of cultural progress, but is also the source of corruption and decadence; it is the origin at once of urbanity and of racial deterioration. The Muqaddama is a melancholy work, for the author was equally conscious of Islām's intrinsic superiority and of the Arabs' shortcomings, and saw the ominous signs of their decadence and fall. This led him to conceive that the life of states and dynasties is similar to that of individuals in that a period of progress is necessarily followed by a period of regress and extinction. Civilization breeds corruption, degeneracy, and ruin, then a new civilization arises, etc. From that point of view Ibn Khaldūn may be considered a forerunner of Oswald Spengler (1880–1936).

He fully realized the social value of religion. He explained what might be called the history and philosophy (or sociology) of arts and trades. For example, he accounted for the progress of agriculture in Muslim Spain by the fact that the best lands were gradually taken by Christians.

His conception of the state was remarkably liberal, his love of freedom being equal to his love of order. That is, he was equally opposed to Beduin anarchy and to tyranny; according to him, the duties of the state were simply to guarantee security, peace, and loyalty in transactions; because of these duties the sovereign had the right to levy moderate taxes. Any other encroachment on individual freedom was as evil for the state as for the individuals themselves. Such a theory of sovereignty and government shows his independence of thought, for he was a pious and orthodox Muslim, and the Muslim state always had strong totalitarian tendencies.

Ibn Khaldūn has been called the father (or one of the fathers) of the philosophy of history and also the father of sociology. There can be no discussion about the first title; the validity of the second depends upon our conception of sociology.

At any rate, his definition of history is a sociological one. Says he (1, 71[25]): "The real aim of history is to help us to understand the social state of man (al-ijmā'u al-insānī), that is, civilization, and to teach us all the phaenomena relative to that, as the softening of customs, the spirit of family and tribe, the different kinds of superiority which people obtain over one another and which lead to the creation of empires and dynasties, the social distinctions, the occupations to which men devote their work and efforts, as the professions, trades, sciences, arts; finally, all the changes which the nature of things may make in the character of society. Now as lies are easily introduced into historical accounts, we should indicate the causes producing them . . . ." And again a little farther on (1, 84) he remarks that man is different from other creatures in special attributes: (1) sciences and arts, (2) need of authority, not instinctive as in the bees, but rational, (3) industry and work providing livelihood, (4) sociability, (5, 6) civilization, which may be nomadic or settled (wa min hadhā-l-'umrān mā yakūn badawiyān . . . wa minhu mā yakūn ḥaḍariyān). In fact, the whole work is full of sociological distinctions or categories. His main interest is in what he called 'ilm al-'umrān, the science of civilization (i.e., analyzing the nature, causes, consequences of civilizations), and that science might be identified with sociology or at least with a branch of it. Ibn Khaldūn was certainly a sociologically minded historian; whether he was the founder of sociology (a title which might be given equally well to Aristotle) is another question.

He was certainly conscious of the originality of his effort (1, 77) and of being the creator of a new science, which might properly be called sociology.

4. *Economics*

Ibn Khaldūn gives considerable importance not only to sociological factors, but also to purely economic ones. He was not the first Arab to do so, witness the Kitāb al-ishāra of Abū-l-Faḍl Ja'far ibn 'Alī al-Dimishqī (XII-2), written before 1175, and the Arabic treatises on ḥisba (function of the police officer, muḥtasib, in charge of markets), e.g., the one by Abū 'Abdallāh Muḥammad al-Saqaṭī of Malaga (written at the end of the eleventh or the beginning of the twelfth century, Isis 19, 528) and the one by 'Abd al-Raḥmān ibn Naṣr (XII-2), composed in Egypt. In addition, economic subjects were occasionally discussed by their philosophers, such as al-Fārābī (X-1), Ibn Sīnā (XI-1), al-Ghazzālī (XI-2), and the Muslim theologians or jurists were obliged to reach conclusions concerning the determination of taxes, the lending of money, the legitimate sources of income, etc. Ibn Khaldūn had been deeply influenced by al-Ghazzālī, and he was a devoted Muslim of the Mālikī sect; within that religious and theological frame he was essentially a liberal, ready to censure every regulation which would restrict economic exchanges. Following al-Ghazzālī in this, he considered labor the cause of wealth, except in the case of real estate, which may produce interest without labor. He praised manual labor at a time when most people despised it. The natural sources of income are provided by agriculture, industry, the liberal professions, trade; on the other hand, the income obtained by civil servants and other servants is unnatural! In opposition to Abū-l-Faḍl al-Dimishqī, he considered the increase of population and the lack of

[25] Such symbols (x, y) refer to the French translation of the Muqaddama by baron de Slane (3 vols., 1862–68). It is easy to pass from the French text to the Arabic text. The French text is admirably indexed, the Arabic not at all; hence to find anything in the Muqaddama the quickest way is to use the French text first and then pass to the Arabic.

excessive wealth as blessings to be aimed at. He did not discuss monetary questions, but gave an outline of the history of money in Islām. He examined such questions as economic needs and their evolution, the merits and demerits of landed property, supply, demand, and price, the importance of labor and the necessity for its division, the classification of trades and professions, the advantages of foreign trade, the productivity of taxes, etc.

5. *Geography and anthropology*

The fact that the beginning of the Muqaddama is devoted to geographical, climatological, and anthropological considerations (some 100 p.) proves that Ibn Khaldūn realized their fundamental importance. His geography was derived from Ptolemy and from the Arabic geographers, particularly al-Idrīsī (1, 93, 99, 106, 112). He continued to believe that the Niger is a branch of the Nile, an error that can be traced back to the time of Vergil (I-2 B.C.)[26] and is probably much older (Egyptian?). He said that the part of the earth's surface uncovered by the ocean was one-half of the whole (1, 91); this conflicts with the opinion of his Syrian contemporary Abū-l-Fidā', according to whom the emerging part is only one-quarter of the whole.

He described the seven climates in the conventional manner and thus led to the discussion of the influence exerted upon men by atmospheric and meteorological conditions, by the original milieu, and by various kinds of food, and though he was bent on exaggerating the action of nurture, he did not neglect that of nature, and of race. He had observed many different nations: Berbers, Sudanese, nomadic Arabs, and urbanized ones, and was thus able to appreciate the problems of race vs. environment; and the extremely complex history of Islām offered him abundant illustrations for his thoughts on the subject. In spite of his Arab ancestry, he was sufficiently Berberized to be impartial. It is noteworthy that in his time the Berber languages were far more popular in Africa than Arabic; at present the situation is reversed (3, 358).

6. *Spiritism, spiritualism, or metapsychology*

Perhaps the most original part of the Muqaddama (section I, 6th discourse, 55 p. in Arabic) is the one dealing with what we should call phaenomena of abnormal psychology, metapsychology, or psychopathology. Explanations of genius, nature of religious revelation, miracles, psychophysiology of prophecy, different kinds of divination and magic, clairvoyance, signification of dreams, evolution from the material world to the supersensible one, etc. It is clear that Ibn Khaldūn, who was intensely religious and ready to accept not only the dogmas of his faith but also many of the superstitions clustering around it, and who had also strong rationalizing tendencies, had given considerable thought to all these puzzling questions, had realized their hidden connections, and had eagerly collected information from all available sources including the Hindu yoginas. For him magic was undoubtedly a part of science, but he was careful to distinguish between legitimate and illegitimate magic. He had but little if any confidence in alchemy and astrology (which he treated at length in another part of the Muqaddama, 3, 207–27, 240–64), and denounced the many vanities and rascalities involved. In general, he discredited material means of divination. Most of the facts mentioned by him were commonplace in Islām, but his synthesis of them was remarkably elaborate, his

[26] See my note on Juba II (Introd. 1, 232) and F. Pellati: Vitruvio e le sorgenti del Nilo (Congrès international de géographie du Caire, 1925, 5, 98–103, 1926; Isis 10, 109); also p. 1158 above

conclusions were original, and he showed much insight. He has given us what is probably the best account of occult science in mediaeval Islām.

7. *Classification and history of science*

The sixth and last section of the Muqaddama, filling a good third of the whole work, deals with the sciences and arts, which are classified in the conventional Islamic way, the author giving information valuable for the history of these sciences; e.g., he quotes many authors and books relative to each science, adding various remarks and criticisms. It deals successively with the Qur'ānic sciences and tradition (ḥadīth), with explanations of the technical terms used in that branch of knowledge; jurisprudence, division of estates ('ilm al-farā'iḍ), dialectics, scholastic theology (kalām); explanation of obscure passages (mutashābih opposed to muḥkam) of the Qur'ān and the sunna, and of difficulties and deviations which those passages have caused; taṣawwuf, interpretation of dreams (ta'bīr al-rū'ya), philosophical sciences developed by the Greeks (logic, physics, metaphysics, mathematics), at the end of this section the author remarks that these philosophical sciences are now (i.e., second half of fourteenth century) said to be flourishing in the lands of the Christians; theory of numbers, arithmetic, algebra, commercial arithmetic (mu'āmalāt),[26a] geometry, optics, astronomy, computation of tables (ḥisāb al-azyāj), logic, physics, medicine, agriculture, metaphysics, magic and talismans ('ulūm al-siḥr wal-ṭilsamāt), occult properties of the letters of the alphabet (asrār al-ḥurūf), alchemy (al-kīmiya), dangers of philosophy, astrology (ṣanā'at al-nujūm). This is followed by a long digression on the methods of studying and teaching, after which Ibn Khaldūn deals with philology and literature.

In another part of the Muqaddama (1, 78) he remarks that the number of sciences and scientists is very large, but that much more knowledge has been lost than has been transmitted to us. What has happened, he asks us, to the knowledge accumulated by the Persians, the Chaldaeans, the Assyrians, the Babylonians, the Copts? we know only the books of Greek science, this being due to the efforts made by al-Ma'mūn (IX-1).

These queries are very interesting in the light of our present knowledge of Babylonian and Egyptian science;[27] it is intriguing that he does not speak of Hindu science, to which the early Muslim scientists paid much attention (Introd. 1, 523), but perhaps that was covered in his mind by the word "Persian." His lack of reference to Egyptian science is less astonishing, because the Muslim invaders of

[26a] On mu'āmalāt see S. Gandz: The rule of three in Arabic and Hebrew sources (Isis 22, 220–22, 1934).

[27] G. Sarton: Remarks on Babylonian mathematics (Isis 31, 398–404, 1940), with bibliography. For Babylonian medicine, see Georges Contenau: La médecine en Assyrie et en Babylonie (Paris 1938; Isis 31, 99–101).

For Egyptian mathematics, see Arnold Buffum Chace: The Rhind mathematical papyrus (Oberlin, Ohio 1927–29; Isis 14, 251–55). For Egyptian medicine, James Henry Breasted: The Edwin Smith surgical papyrus (Chicago 1930; Isis 15, 355–67). B. Ebbell: The papyrus Ebers (Copenhagen 1937; Isis 28, 126–31).

For Hindu influences, in addition to those mentioned in my Introduction (vol. 1, sub vocibus India, Hindu, Sanskrit), Bettina Strauss: Das Giftbuch des Šānāq (Berlin 1934; Isis 23, 446). For Persian and Central Asian influences, Max Meyerhof: Das Vorwort zur Drogenkunde des Bīrūnī (Berlin 1932; Isis 20, 451–54).

More information could easily be obtained by examining the chapters Egypt, Babylonia, India in the critical bibliographies of Isis.

Egypt paid no attention whatsoever to Egyptian antiquities;[27a] it is true he mentions the Copts, but the latter were apparently as indifferent to the ancient Egyptian culture and science as were their Muslim masters. Imperfect as his knowledge of pre-Islamic science was (and how could he have known better?), it is sufficient to show a genuine interest in the origins and history of science. The historians of science of today may thus count him among their very few mediaeval forerunners.

8. *Pedagogy*

The sixth section of the Muqaddama contains abundant evidence that Ibn Khaldūn was a born pedagogue, one of the very few men of his time who were aware of the utter badness of the teaching methods used in the Islamic countries (and which have continued to be used until our own days).[28] He sharply criticized the excessive memorization which was practiced in all the schools, high and low, the lack of concreteness, the love of meaningless summaries and summaries of summaries used for stupid cramming. Following the lead given by the qāḍī Abū Bakr Ibn al-'Arabī (XII-1), he recommends teaching children first of all the Arabic language, then reckoning, and finally the Qur'ān (instead of beginning with the latter). He gives advice on methods of studying, teaching, writing; insists on the value of traveling and sitting at the feet of as many teachers as possible; and he had discovered (long before Napoleon with reference to Laplace!) that learned men ('ulamā') are no good for political administration! (3, 294).

9. *Philology*

Toward the end of the Muqaddama, after having defined and explained the various branches of Arabic letters (grammar, lexicology, rhetoric, literature) and given some account of their particularities and history, he discusses a number of questions of Arabic and comparative philology: evolution of the Arabic language and of its pronunciation (e.g., letter qāf); the best Badwī Arabic is different from the earlier dialects of Muḍar and Ḥimiyar; other dialectal differences; linguistic alterations caused by the pressure of other languages (e.g., Berber in the Maghrib, Spanish in Spain) or by the conditions of urban vs. tent life; phonetic considerations, etc. Apparently Ibn Khaldūn did not know the Berber language, but he was painfully aware of its existence (3, 358), and the difficulties caused by that "jargon" (raṭāna barbarīya) may have sharpened his philological curiosity. He explains the evolution of the Arabic script (3, 266) and describes foreign scripts (Syriac, Hebrew, Latin).

10. *Scientific views*

Ibn Khaldūn had received no scientific training; he was not a physician, but a theologian and a kātib. He had, however, considerable mother wit, and could carry his immense learning without pedantism. His rational views on alchemy and astrology have already been mentioned; they were due, however, to theological prudence rather than to scientific criticism.

There are two chapters on medicine in his Muqaddama (2, 386–91; 3, 162–64),

[27a] A partial exception is the Tuḥfat al-kirām fī khabar al-ahrām, the little treatise on the pyramids, written a century later by Jalāl al-dīn al-Suyūṭī (1445–1505), edited and translated by Leon Nemoy (Isis 30, 17–37, 1939).

[28] I have witnessed the mediaeval method of teaching children the Qur'ān and Arabic in many places, particularly in Damascus, Tlemcen, and Fez.

but they are equally meager; he quotes Galen, al-Rāzī, Ibn Sīnā, Ibn Zuhr. In his History of the Berbers (Cairo ed., 6, 202; de Slane, Histoire des Berbères 2, 115), there is a reference to the sleeping sickness ('illat al-naum) which is probably the earliest in any literature. Ibn Khaldūn tells us that a Mandingo king of Mali, called Jata, died of that disease in 776/77 = 1374/75. Al-Qalqashandī refers to the very same fact, though the date is slightly different, 775 = 1373/74. Ibn Khaldūn's account is probably anterior to that of al-Qalqashandī. In the Muqaddama (1, 66) there is a brief but impressive description of the Black Death (see above, p. 1651); he fully realized that that plague was of such magnitude that it caused a real discontinuity in the history of civilization.

He remarks that the medical prescriptions ascribed to the Prophet in the ḥadīth (3, 164) are not a part of the divine revelation. In such matters the Prophet could easily err, as he did when he forbade the artificial fertilization of the date tree; later he recognized his error.[28a]

His conception of the harmony of the world and of its evolution continues an old Islamic stream of thought, which has often been detected, e.g., in al-Naẓẓām (IX-1), al-Jāḥiẓ (IX-2), al-Mas'ūdī (X-1), Ibn Rushd (XII-2), Niẓāmī-i-'Arūḍī (XII-2), Ramon Lull (XIII-2). For a summary of that see Introd. 2, 61–62 and my preface to M. F. Ashley Montagu: Edward Tyson (Philadelphia 1943; Isis 34, 526).

Some of his views on the influence of the air on men (e.g., the Negroes are gay because the hot air expands their animal spirits), or on the influence of food, may seem childish, but they were the views of his time.

11. *Summary*

Ibn Khaldūn was not a mathematician nor a physician, nor a man of science, nor yet a philosopher, and from the purely scientific point of view he was as far below the level of al-Bīrūnī and Ibn Sīnā as his time was inferior to theirs. He was distinctly anti-intellectualist, but he had considerable experience and common sense and a grasp of political and social realities amounting in his days to genius. Not himself a great historian, he is the greatest theorician of history, the greatest philosopher of man's experience, not only of the Middle Ages, but of the whole period extending from the time of the great classical historians down to that of Machiavelli (1532), Bodin (1576), and even Vico (1725). Badly composed as the Muqaddama is, with many repetitions, and poorly written sometimes to the point of obscurity, it remains one of the noblest and most impressive monuments of mediaeval thought. A comparison between Ibn Khaldūn and Machiavelli is not to the disadvantage of the earlier writer.

In order to understand him one must always bear in mind his theological background. In that sense one may say that the basis of his thought is not sociological, but religious. That would apply to every good Muslim, and he was one, a follower of al-Ghazzālī. According to Muslim opinion, the success or failure of a man or of a tribe or state is largely determined by his, or its, obedience or nonobedience to the sharī'a, the religious law (there is no other law in Islām), and by God's will; even economic matters are so determined.

Hence his originality should not be exaggerated; he could be original only within the frame of Muslim theology; yet within that frame he did not hesitate to ask

[28a] Alfred Guillaume: The traditions of Islam. An introduction to the study of hadith literature (p. 154, Oxford 1924).

himself questions and to try to answer them in a scientific way. He was far ahead of his time and of his tools. The tools needed for the best kind of historical work were not yet available then; they have become available only within recent times, and some of them are still missing.

12. *Influence*

Ibn Khaldūn's historical writings were immediately appreciated, but the Muqaddama was too disturbing to be popular in Arabic countries. Strangely enough, the first scholars to pay due attention to it were Turks,[23b] Ḥāfiẓ al-dīn Muḥammad ibn Aḥmad al-'Ajamī (d. 1550), Aḥmad ibn Muṣṭafā' Tashköprüzāde (d. 1561), and Ḥājjī Khalīfa (d. 1657), who referred to it frequently; and it was translated into Turkish by the shaikh al-Islām Muḥammad Pīrīzāde (d. 1749). That translation was studied by other Turkish scholars during the following hundred years and later.

The West was relatively slow in hearing of the Muqaddama, which appeared too late to be immediately translated (the time of translations from the Arabic was long past). Various Orientalists of the seventeenth century knew of Ibn Khaldūn, but they knew very little. The first fully to realize his importance was Hammer-Purgstall, who called him in 1812 "an Arabic Montesquieu." The rest of the Western story is told below in our list of editions and translations. The Muqaddama was finally introduced into world literature by baron de Slane's French translation (3 vols., 1862–68).

The present interest and pride in Ibn Khaldūn which may be witnessed in every Arabic country and is an intrinsic part of the Arabic renaissance is to some extent a result of his discovery and praise by Western scholars. To illustrate that interest I shall mention three facts:

(1) The Khaldūnīya was created in Tunis 1897, a philomathic society supplementing the University of Tunis, organizing Arabic lectures, the teaching of history and science to adults, etc. It publishes the Nashrat al-jami'īya al-Khaldūnīya; the volume of 1930 (148 p.) was reviewed in Revue tunisienne (3, 129, 1932).

(2) The sixth centenary of Ibn Khaldūn's birth was celebrated in Tunis in 1932, perhaps also in other places, though the celebrations of that year would naturally be due to Western, Christian, initiative. As Ibn Khaldūn was born on 1 Ramaḍān 732 = 27 May 1332, the Muslim sixth centenary was on 1 Ramaḍān 1332 = 24 July 1914. I do not know whether it was celebrated or not.

(3) Not only are popular editions of the Muqaddama published in Arabic, but I have one which is completely vocalized. This is done only for holy books, poetry, or books of great importance.

The admiration felt in the modern Arabic world for Ibn Khaldūn is especially remarkable because of the latter's very outspoken criticism of the Arabs. It would be easy to compile from his work the most devastating account of the Arabic character and deeds, indeed, so devastating that a non-Arab would hardly dare make it.

He was aware of the great qualities of the Beduins, but also of their shortcomings: hardness, cruelty, excessive generosity, fanatic hatred, insane jealousy, "point of honor" carried to criminal consequences; he realized that their central virtue was

[23b] It is true the Turks would have a national or colonial interest in Ibn Khaldūn, because Tunis was taken in 1534 by the famous Turkish corsair and beglerbeg of Algiers, Khair al-dīn Barbarossa (d. 1546, aet. 63).

'aṣabīya, something at its best like patriotism, at its worst like the animal solidarity ḥolding together a tribe or a gang.[29]

Here are a few of his statements concerning the Arabs: "Any land conquered by the Arabs is soon ruined" (1, 310); "Most of the learned men among Muslims were of foreign birth" (3, 296); "Arabs are generally incapable of creating a kingdom except after having received some kind of religious dye from a prophet or saint" (1, 313); "Of all peoples Arabs are the least able to govern" (1, 314); "they have the least disposition for the arts" (2, 365); "they are a race of plunderers and brigands" (1, 309); "most of their buildings fall to pieces" (2, 274). And finally, to those boasting of the great Islamic victories he would answer, "The least civilized peoples make the most extensive conquests" (1, 303). Ibn Khaldūn, we should bear in mind, had suffered much; he was a disgruntled man watching the decadence of Islamic power; maybe he relieved himself by blaming the tragedy on the Arabs, but in so doing he was on the whole unfair even when right in the details, for the Islamic decadence was due to many causes. To those so forcibly indicated by him should have been added others, of which he did not think, such as scholasticism divorced from life, theological obscurantism, etc.

Modern Arabic commentators (e.g., Abū Khaldūn Sāti'u bey al-Ḥuṣrī in the Beirūt weekly al-Amālī, 1, 1614–18, 1939) point out that Ibn Khaldūn's criticism of the Arabs is really directed against the Beduins. That is true, yet the difference between nomadic Arabs and settled ones was less, especially in those days, a difference of race than a difference of circumstances, like the difference between rich and poor with us. Hence Ibn Khaldūn's criticism concerns not only Beduin circumstances, but the Arabic people in general. There never were two races of Arabs, nomadic and settled; every urbanized Arab was proud of his tribal ancestry if he could prove it, and the nostalgia of the desert was deep in his heart.[30]

13. *Text*

Many extracts were published or/and translated by Silvestre de Sacy, the very first in his Chrestomathie arabe (Paris 1806), and by other scholars.

The first complete edition of the whole Kitāb al-'ibar was published in 7 vols. at Būlāq, Cairo in 1867. A new revised edition, also in 7 vols., is being prepared by the amīr Shakīb Arslān, who is adding abundant notes (Cairo). I have received undated prospectus of vol. 1 (439 p., plus 408 p. of notes).

The first edition of the History of the Berbers (i.e., vols. 6, 7 of the Kitāb al-'ibar) was published by William McGucken de Slane (Algiers 1847–51).

The first edition of the Muqaddama was published by Etienne Quatremère (3 vols., Notices et extraits, Paris 1858). There are many Oriental editions of the Muqaddama; I have two, a Cairene one undated (456 p.), and a Beirūt one, vocalized (588 p., 1879, reprinted 1886, 1900).

[29] This is not the place to discuss his views, but the best modern picture of the Arab character may be found in that great classic of English literature, Charles Montagu Doughty (1843–1926): Travels in Arabia deserta (2 vols., Cambridge 1888, often reprinted). See also the Récit du séjour de Fatalla Sayeghir chez les Arabes errans du grand désert, appended to Alphonse de Lamartine: Souvenirs, impressions, pensées et paysages pendant un voyage en Orient, 1832–33 (4, 39–285, Paris 1835). Hitti (p. 23–29, 1937).

[30] There is an interesting ḥadīth connected with this. Arabs suffered periodically from 'aima (that is, a thirst for milk), they were longing for their camels and camel milk. The Prophet asked God to be saved from that longing; for his people he feared milk above aught else, and explained his fear to his companions, saying, "Your passion for milk will cause you to abandon the towns and resume your nomadic life." Henri Lammens: La Bādia et la Ḥīra sous les Omaiyades (Mélanges de la Faculté orientale de Beyrouth 4, 91–112, 1910).

Baron de Slane translated into French the autobiography (Journal asiatique, 1844); the history of the Berbers (4 vols., Algiers 1852–56), revised edition by Paul Casanova (2 vols., Paris 1925–27); and the Muqaddama (3 vols., Notices et extraits 1862, 1865, 1868). It was the last-named translation which revealed Ibn Khaldūn to the public, not only in the West but even in the East. It contains abundant notes, indexes, glossaries. It has recently been reprinted (3 vols., Paris 1932–33). Duncan B. Macdonald: Selection from the Prolegomena (Semitic study series 4, 117 p., Leiden 1905).

The history of the Banū-l-Aḥmar, kings of Granada, was translated into French by Gaudefroy-Demombynes (Journal asiatique vol. 12, 1898).

Carl Johan Tornberg: Narratio de expeditionibus in terras Islamismo subjectas (154 p., Upsala 1840), Arabic and Latin.

There is no English translation, except of the short text relative to Yaman by Henry Cassels Kay: Yaman, its early mediaeval history (London 1892).

The Turkish translation of the Muqaddama by Pīrīzāde, mentioned above, was done in 1730–31; he died in 1749 before finishing the sixth section. It was completed in 1860. A part of the history of the East was also translated into Turkish (4 vols., Istanbul 1860).

14. *Criticism*

The main source of course is Ibn Khaldūn's autobiography in vol. 7 of the Kitāb al-'ibar. French translation by baron de Slane (Journal asiatique, 1844), also in vol. 1 of the Prolégomènes (p. vi–xciii, 1862), including additional information culled from Arabic literature.

Count Jacob Gräberg of Hemsö (Gotland): Notizia intorno alla famosa opera istorica d'Ibn Khaldun (Firenze 1834), also appended to Filippo de Bardi: Storia della letteratura araba (2, 257–303, 1846). R. Dozy: long review of Quatremère and de Slane's edition of the Muqaddama (Journal asiatique 14, 133–218, 1869). A. von Kremer: Ibn Chaldun und seine Culturgeschichte (Sitzungsberichte der Kais. Akad. der Wissenschaften in Wien, phil. Cl., 93, 581–634, 1879). Robert Flint: Historical philosophy (p. 155–71, 1894). T. J. De Boer: Geschichte der Philosophie im Islam (p. 177–84, 1901), also available in English and Arabic translations. Brockelmann (2, 242–45, 1902; suppt. 2, 342–44, 1938). Macdonald (1909); (1911). C. H. Becker: Ältester geschichtlicher Beleg für die afrikanische Schlafkrankheit (Der Islam 1, 197, 1910; reprinted in his Islamstudien, 2, 149–50, Leipzig 1932; Isis 6, 559–61). Simon van den Bergh: Umriss der muhammedanischen Wissenschaften nach Ibn Khaldūn (Diss. Freiburg i.B., Leiden 1912). Ferrand (2, 459–61, 1914). T. Hussein: Etude de philosophie sociale d'Ibn Khaldoun (thèse, 228 p., Paris 1917). Alfred Bel (EI 2, 395–96, 1918). E. Lévi-Provençal: Note sur l'exemplaire du Kitāb al-'ibar offert par Ibn Khaldūn à la bibliothèque d'al-Qarawīyīn à Fès (Journal asiatique 203, 161–68, 1923), apropos of a MS based upon the author's original and offered by himself to that library; it is unfortunately incomplete. Giuseppe Gabrieli: Saggio di bibliografia e concordanza della storia d'Ibn Khaldūn (Rivista degli studi orientali 10, 169–211, 1924). Emile Felix Gautier: L'islamisation de l'Afrique du Nord (Paris 1927). René Maunier: Mélanges de sociologie nord africaine (220 p., Paris 1930). Mohammed Kamil Ayad: Die Geschichts- und Gesellschaftslehre Ibn Khaldūns (220 p., Stuttgart 1930). Gaston Bouthoul: Ibn Khaldoun. Sa philosophie sociale (94 p., Paris 1930). Francesco Gabrieli: Il concetto della 'aṣabiyyah nel pensiero storico di Ibn Khaldūn (Atti della R. Accad. di Torino 45, 473–512, 1930). Nathaniel Schmidt: Ibn Khaldun (68 p., New York 1930; Isis 18, 345; 19, 535). Erwin Rosenthal: Ibn Khalduns Gedanken über den Staat (126 p., München 1932; Isis 20, 525). Sobhi Mahmassani: Les idées économiques d'Ibn Khaldoun (230 p., Lyon 1932; Isis 25, 202). H. A. R. Gibb: The Islamic background of Ibn Khaldūn's political theory (Bull. School of Oriental Studies 7, 23–31, London 1933; Isis 20, 524). Vera (1, 102–8, 1933). José Ortega y Gasset: Abenjaldún nos revela el secreto (Revista de occidente 8, 9–53, Madrid 1934; Al-Andalus 2, 433–36). L. Buret: Un pédagogue arabe du XIVe siècle (Revue tunisienne 5, 23–32, 1934). T. Khemiri: Der 'aṣabīya-Begriff in der Muqaddama (Der Islam 23, 163–88, 1936). Hitti (1937). Max Meyerhof: An early mention of sleeping sickness in Arabic chronicles (Journal of the Egyptian medical association 24, 284–86, Cairo 1941; Isis 36, 181). H. P. J. Renaud: Divination et histoire nord-africaine au temps d'Ibn Khaldūn (Hespéris 30, 213–21, 1943); Sur un passage d'Ibn Khaldūn relatif à l'histoire des mathématiques (Hespéris p. 35–47, Rabat 1944; Isis 36, 181). Gustave E. von Grünebaum: As-Sakkākī on milieu and thought (Journal of the American Oriental Society vol. 65, p. 62, 1945), claiming that al-Sakkākī (XIII-1) in his Miftāḥ al-'ulūm anticipated Ibn Khaldūn's views on nomadic vs. sedentary life and on their respective influence on thought.

The list just given includes the names of various Oriental students which I have written as they wrote them themselves in their Western publications; these are generally doctor's theses in French or German universities. In addition, there is an abundant modern Arabic literature, of which I shall cite only a few items for the sake of curiosity. To begin with, the French thesis (1917) of Ṭāhā Ḥusain has been published in Arabic; its author has since become one of the leaders of Egyptian thought. The Arabic translator of that book, Muḥammad 'Abdallāh 'Unān, has written another Arabic book on Ibn Khaldūn's life and intellectual legacy (190 p., Cairo 1933; Isis 23, 500). Finally, in the many Arabic histories of literature, philosophy, or sociology, a large place is given to him. A recent (c. 1938) Arabic treatise on sociology, Kitāb 'ilm al-ijtimā', by Muṣṭafā Fahmī, devotes much space to him as founder of sociology.

D5. Yaman

IBN WAHHĀS

Abū-l-Ḥasan 'Alī ibn al-Ḥasan Ibn Wahhās al-Khazrajī (related to the Arabian tribe Khazraj) al-Nassāb (the genealogist). Historian of Yaman (d. 1409).

He collected materials concerning the history of Yaman (Tawārīkh al-Yaman) and arranged them in three forms: (1) annals, (2) dynastic order, two-thirds being devoted to the Rasūlī dynasty to 1400 (ruled 1229–1454), (3) alphabetic order of proper names.

The dynastic history is entitled Kitāb al-kifāya wal-i'lām . . . , and the main part, relative to the Banū Rasūl, exists separately under the title Al-'uqūd al-lu'lu'īya fī akhbār al-daula al-Rasūlīya (The pearl strings concerning the stories of the Rasūlī kingdom). The dictionary, called Ṭirāz a'lām al-zaman fī ṭabaqāt a'yān al-Yaman, is partly derived from al-Janadī (XIV-1).

The history of the Rasūlī dynasty is traced back to mythical beginnings; Ibn Wahhās explains how they came to Yaman and gives an account of the kingdom of Saba' (Sheba, Sabaeans) in southwestern Arabia, of the great dam which existed near their capital, Ma'rib, and of the catastrophe of its destruction (sail al-'arim, Qur'ān 34, 14–15). That dam had been constructed in very early days, before the time of Bilqīs (queen of Sheba, who visited Solomon), and its destruction about the middle of the sixth century is one of the main events of pre-Islamic history in Islamic chronicles. See elaborate article by Adolf Grohmann: Ma'rib (EI 3, 280–94, 1930). Thus Ibn Wahhās' history not only deals with the thirteenth and fourteenth centuries, but is a cross section of Arabic antiquities from the Rasūlī angle. It ends with the rule of al-Ashraf Ismā'īl I (1376–1400), at whose court the author flourished.

Text. The pearl strings, Arabic text with translation, introduction, annotations, index, tables, and maps by Sir James William Redhouse. Edited by shaykh Muḥammad 'Asal, E. G. Browne, R. A. Nicholson, and A. Rogers (Gibb memorial series no. 3, 5 vols., London 1906–18). Splendid edition very conveniently arranged; vols. 1 and 2 contain the English translation with full index; vol. 3, 1,673 notes; vols. 4 and 5, the Arabic text with full Arabic index.

Criticism. Ḥājjī Khalīfa (2, nos. 2148, 2344, 1837). Wüstenfeld (no. 459, 1882). Brockelmann (2, 184, 1902; suppt. 2, 238, 1938). Kammerer (1, 159, 1929).

D6. Mamlūkīya

MUFAḌḌAL IBN ABĪ-L-FAḌĀ'IL

Coptic historian writing in Arabic (fl. at least until 1358).

Mufaḍḍal wrote a historical chronicle of the Baḥrī Mamlūk dynasty in Egypt from 1260 to 1349, i.e., from Baibars (ruled 1260–77) to al-Nāṣir Nāṣir al-dīn al-Ḥasan (first rule 1347–51). It was meant as a sequel to the Kitāb al-majmū' al-mubārak of al-Makīn Ibn al-'Amīd (XIII-2), according to a statement in his own preface and to the title Kitāb al-nahj al-sadīd wal-durr al-farīd fī mā ba'd ta'rīkh Ibn al-'Amīd, but its fortune was very different. Al-Makīn was very well known in the East and was one of the earliest Arabic chroniclers to be known in the West, whereas Mufaḍḍal remained practically unknown. The latter's work was represented by a single MS (Bibliothèque nationale, Paris, MS arabe 4525), apparently the very MS prepared under his own direction. It was ignored by later Arabic historians such as Yūsuf ibn Taghrībirdī (d. 1412) and al-Maqrīzī (d. 1442).

According to its own explicit, the MS was completed on September 16, 1358. We may assume that the author was then an old man; the date of his death is unknown, but was certainly anterior to 1381/82. He says that he wrote the chronicle for himself, narrating events which he had witnessed or which had been told to him by witnesses.

He quotes a number of sources, such as Baibars al-Manṣūrī (XIV-1), but he does not quote by name the main one, al-Nuwairī (XIV-1). His abundant summaries extracted from al-Nuwairī always begin "Qāla-l-mu'arrikh" (Said the historian), which may be construed as a very fine tribute to the author of the Nihāyat al-arab.

Though the circumstances of Mufaḍḍal's life are unknown, the names of four members of his family have come down to us, to wit his father, an uncle, a grandfather, a great-grandfather. The name of the last mentioned, Amīn al-mulk, suggests that he was employed in the Mamlūk treasury (a traditional office for Copts).

There is no doubt that Mufaḍḍal was a Copt, but the strange mixture of Christian and Muslim formulas in his chronicle is perplexing. It expresses a kind of dual personality.

Mufaḍḍal's chronicle is of value not only for Mamlūk history, but also for the history of the Coptic patriarchate, the Muslims of Arabia and India, and the Tatars.

Text. Text edited and translated into French with notes by Edgar Blochet: Histoire des sultans mamlouks (Patrologia orientalis 12, 345–550, 1919; 14, 375–672, 1920; 20, 1–270, 1928; in all, 776 p.), this includes the chronicle to 1316; to be completed.

Criticism. Brockelmann (1, 348, 1898; suppt. 1, 590, 1937). G. W. (EI 2, 1002, 1927).

IBN SHĀKIR

Ibn Shākir al-Kutubī. Syrian Muslim historian (d. 1363).

Ṣalāh al-dīn (or Fakhr al-dīn) Muḥammad Ibn Shākir al-Ḥalabī al-Dimashqī al-Kutubī, educated in Aleppo and Damascus; was originally poor but became rich as a bookseller (kutubī) and died in June or July 1363.

He wrote a collection of love poems (ghazal), and a history of the caliphs and learned men centered upon Damascus, 'Uyūn al-tawārīkh (Sources of the histories). He is best known because of his Fawāt al-wafayāt, which is a continuation of the biographical dictionary, Wafayāt al-a'yān, of Ibn Khallikān (XIII-2).

Text. The Fawāt was printed at Būlāq in 1866 and again in 1881. Two MSS of the Escorial contain many biographies not included in the Būlāq editions.

Criticism. Wüstenfeld (no. 422, 1882). Brockelmann (2, 48, 1902; suppt. 2, 48, 1938). Melchior M. Antuña: El suplemento de Abenxákir el Cotobi según dos codices del Escorial (La ciudad de Dios vol. 144, p. 113–22, Escorial 1926). M. Plessner (EI 2, 1172, 1928). Otto Spies: Beiträge zur arabischen Literaturgeschichte (p. 73–76, Leipzig 1932).

'ABD AL-WAHHĀB AL-SUBKĪ

Egyptian Shāfi'ī theologian and historian (1327–70).

Tāj al-dīn Abū Naṣr 'Abd al-Wahhāb ibn 'Alī al-Subkī, son of Taqī al-dīn 'Alī al-Subkī (XIV-1), was born in Cairo in 1327, studied in Cairo and Damascus, and like his father was a teacher, preacher, and judge, in both cities. He succeeded his father in 1355 as qāḍī, but was deposed two years later. In 1368 he was accused of having embezzled trust money and spent three months in jail, then was rehabilitated. He died of the plague in June 1370.

Fewer writings are ascribed to him than to his father, but three of them are very important:

1. Kitāb jam' al-jawāmi' fī-l-uṣūl, a collection of all the collections concerning the principles of Muslim jurisprudence (uṣūl al-fiqh[31]), completed near Damascus in 1358. There are a number of commentaries, glosses, abstracts in prose and verse which testify to the importance attached to that work in the Shāfi'ī community.

2. Mu'īd al-ni'am wa mubīd al-niqam (Restorer of favors and restrainer of chastisements). A book setting forth how the divine grace can be reobtained when lost. There are three methods, study of the causes of one's fall from grace, contrition, prayer. One can pray with one's heart or tongue or deeds (bil-qalb wal-lisān wal af'āl). The argument is illustrated by some 110 examples wherein the duties of every profession or estate, from beggar to caliph, are shown. This is a valuable document for the history of Muslim culture.

3. Ṭabaqāt al-Shāfi'īya. Biographies of Shāfi'ī theologians, existing in three recensions, larger, intermediate, and smaller. The larger recension contains also historical information of a more general kind, e.g., concerning the destruction of Baghdād by the Mongols.

Text. The Mu'īd al-ni'am was edited by David W. Myhrman with introduction and notes (Luzac's Semitic texts, 300 p., London 1908). Abridged and translated into German by Oscar Rescher (Constantinople 1925). German translation of a

[31] On uṣūl see Joseph Schacht (EI 4, 1054–58, 1932).

few extracts by E. Wiedemann in his review of Myhrman's book (Mitt. 10, 410–16, 1910).

Criticism. Wüstenfeld (no. 431, 1882). Brockelmann (2, 89–90, 1902; suppt. 2, 105–7, 1938). Adolf Grohmann (EI 4, 494, 1927). Giorgio Levi Della Vida: A Christian legend in Moslem garb (Byzantion 15, 144–57, Boston 1941), story told in the Ṭabaqāt al-Shāfi'īya apropos of the death of the last caliph, al-Musta'ṣim, in 1258; the caliph's wife played a trick on Hūlāgū which enabled her to save her honor at the expense of her life.

IBN KATHĪR

Abū-l-Fidā' Ismā'īl ibn 'Umar Ibn Kathīr 'Imād al-dīn ibn al-Khaṭīb al-Buṣrawī al-Qurashī al-Shāfi'ī. Syrian historian and traditionist (1301–73).

Ibn Kathīr was born in Damascus 1301, and was a disciple of the Ḥanbalī revivalist Ibn Taimīya (XIV-1), whose sufferings he shared when the latter was persecuted. He taught tradition in Damascus, first in the Umm al-Ṣāliḥ, later in the Ashrafīya. He died in January or February 1373.

His main work is a general history in ten volumes from the creation to 1365, entitled Kitāb al-bidāya wal-nihāya (The beginning and the end); down to 1338 it is largely derived from the chronicle of al-Birzālī (XIV-1). It is an enormous compilation, of which there is no complete MS. The Bidāya was continued by Aḥmad ibn 'Alā al-dīn al-Dimashqī (d. 1413), by Aḥmad ibn abī Bakr al-Ṭabarānī al-Kāmilī (d. 1431), and by Taqī al-dīn ibn Qāḍī Shuhba (d. 1448).

He wrote commentaries on the Qur'ān, on Muslim tradition, etc.

Text. A few extracts from the Bidāya have been published by J. F. L. George: De Aethiopum imperio in Arabia felice (Berlin 1833).

Criticism. Wüstenfeld (no. 434, 1882). Brockelmann (2, 49, 1902; suppt. 2, 48, 1938); (EI 2, 393, 1918). Otto Spies: Beiträge zur arabischen Literaturgeschichte (p. 78, 84, Leipzig 1932).

MUḤAMMAD IBN QĀSIM AL-NUWAIRĪ

Muḥammad ibn Qāsim al-Nuwairī al-Mālikī al-Iskandarī. Egyptian historian (fl. 1337–74).

This al-Nuwairī should not be confused with the more famous al-Nuwairī, Aḥmad ibn al-Wahhāb (also Egyptian, 1279–1332) (XIV-1).

Muḥammad came to Alexandria c. 1337 as a pilgrim, but liked the city so well that he established himself there as a scribe. He witnessed[32] the terrible siege of the city by Peter I of Lusignan in 1365. Though it lasted only seven days (October 9–16), the wealthy city was thoroughly sacked and ruined. After the departure of the Crusaders the Egyptians revenged themselves upon the Christians of Egypt and Syria. Muḥammad began to write an account of these events in February 1366 and finished it in May 1374. The account is entitled Al-ilmām bil-i'lām fīmā jarat bihi al-aḥkām wal-umūr al-maqḍīya fī waq'at al-Iskandarīya. The author's original purpose was to describe the Alexandrian siege and sack, but he could not resist the temptation to add a considerable amount of materials, which, however irrelevant to the main story, are of great interest to the historian of contemporary culture. Thus, in the first volume of al-Ilmām (out of three), we are given much information on Arab ships and nautical knowledge, and in the third volume an account of the Cypriot attack on Tripoli (of Syria) in 1365.

[32] More exactly, he fled the city when the siege began but came back soon after it was ended and witnessed the effects of the siege and sack.

Text. An Arabic edition is being prepared in Ḥaidarabād, and a French version of the text relative to Alexandria is being prepared by Etienne Combe.

Criticism. Brockelmann (2, 35, 1902; suppt. 2, 34, 1938). Atiya (p. 319–78, 1938).

IBN ḤABĪB

Badr al-dīn Abū Muḥammad al-Ḥasan ibn 'Umar Ibn Ḥabīb al-Dimashqī al-Shāfi'ī. Syrian historian and man of letters (1310–77).

Ibn Ḥabīb was born in Damascus in October–November 1310; he was educated in Damascus and Aleppo, where his father had become muḥtasib (inspector of the markets) and teacher of tradition. The father died in 1326. Ibn Ḥabīb accomplished the Pilgrimage at least twice, in 1332 and 1338, and on those occasions visited Palestine and Egypt. He was a civil servant of some kind, and in 1344 traveled all over Syria with the amīr Sharaf al-dīn. In 1354 he was established in Ṭarābulus (Tripoli of Syria); later he lived in Damascus and Aleppo, where he died on August 27, 1377.

Some eleven works, historical and literary, are ascribed to him, the main one being the Durrat al-aslāk fī mulk al-atrāk, which is a history in rhyming prose of the Bahrī Mamlūk dynasty of Egypt-Syria from its beginning in 1250 to 1375; that dynasty was of Turkish origin, which explains the words mulk al-atrāk (kingdom of the Turks) in the title. It is written in the form of annals, the events and deaths of distinguished people being given year by year. There is also some information concerning neighboring countries. It was continued to 1398 by his son Zain al-dīn Ṭāhir. It was used by the famous Egyptian historian al-Maqrīzī (1364–1442).

His Juhainat al-akhbār fī mulūk al-amṣār is a more ambitious history, dealing with kings and judges from the time of the Jews to Qalā'ūn (ruled 1279–90); the Tadhkirat 'an nabīhi fī aiyām al-Manṣūr wa banīhi is a history of Qalā'ūn and his sons. He continued the chronicle of Abū-l-Fidā' (XIV-1).

The Nasīm al-ṣabā is a collection of descriptions of natural and human scenes in rhyming prose mixed with verse. He also put together models of official letters and documents (what were called in the Latin West dictamina) under the title Kashf al-murūṭ 'an maḥāsin al-shurūṭ.

Text. Extracts from the Durrat al-aslāk were edited by Albertus Meursinge and Hendrik Engelinus Weijers (Orientalia 2, 196–489, Amsterdam 1840) and by Pontus Leander (Le monde oriental 7, 1–82, 242–43, Uppsala 1913).

There are many Oriental editions of the Nasīm al-ṣabā (Alexandria 1873, Beirūt 1883, Constantinople 1885; Būlāq 1290 H., Cairo 1289, 1302 H.).

Criticism. Wüstenfeld (no. 440, 1882). Brockelmann (2, 36, 1902; suppt. 2, 35, 1938). EI (2, 379, 1916).

IBN AL-FURĀT

Muḥammad ibn 'Abd al-raḥīm Ibn al-Furāt al-Miṣrī al-Ḥanafī. Egyptian historian (1334–1405).

Ibn al-Furāt was born in Cairo in 1334–35, studied Islamic law and traditions, died on April 2, 1405. He wrote an elaborate chronicle of Islām centered on Egypt, Ta'rīkh al-duwal wal-mulūk (Annals of countries and kings). He wrote it backward beginning with his own time, but was able to cover only three or four centuries, instead of eight. The (autograph?) incomplete MS of Vienna in 9 volumes covers the period 1107 to 1397; other MSS in Paris and Cairo are derived from it.

This compilation has some importance because of literal quotations from earlier lost writings.

Text. There is no complete edition, but an edition is being gradually prepared by the American University in Beirut, which has thus far published the following parts: (1) vol. IX-1, dealing with the years 1387–90, 257 p., 1936; (2) vol. IX-2, dealing with the years 1390–97, 355 p., 1938; (3) vol. VIII, dealing with the years 1284–96, 290 p., 1939.

The editor is Costi K. Zurayq, who has been assisted for parts 2 and 3 by Miss Najlā' 'Izz al-dīn.

Criticism. Wüstenfeld (no. 454, 1882). Brockelmann (2, 50, 1902; suppt. 2, 49, 1938).

IBN DUQMĀQ

Egyptian historian and biographer (d. 1407).

Ibrāhīm ibn Muḥammad Ibn Duqmāq Ṣārim al-dīn al-Ḥanafī al-Miṣrī. The name duqmāq is said to be derived from the Turkish ṭūqmaq, hammer. The dates of birth and death are uncertain; he was still alive but old in 1390/91; he died probably in June 1407.

He flourished in Egypt, probably close to the Burjī Mamlūk court, in 1382 and following years.

He wrote annals of Muslim Egypt to 1377, completed to 1382, in twelve volumes, Nuzhat al-anām fī ta'rīkh al-Islām. As the title indicates, it is a history of Islām, but almost exclusively restricted to Egypt. The sulṭān Barqūq (first Burjī ruler, 1382–98) ordered him to write a history of the salāṭīn of Egypt, Al-jauhar al-thamīn fī siyar al-khulafā' wal-salāṭīn, later extended to 1402 and to 1500.

He had planned to devote a large work to the ten main cities of Islām, Kitāb al-intiṣār li-wāsiṭāt 'iqd al-amṣār, but that plan was not completely realized or else part of the work is lost. We have only the account of the two Egyptian capitals, Cairo and Alexandria, Kitāb al durra al-muḍī'a fī faḍl Miṣr wal-Iskandarīya.

He compiled two biographical collections, the one dealing with taṣawwuf (lost), the other devoted to theologians and jurists of the Ḥanafī school, Naẓm al-jumān fī tabaqāt aṣḥāb imāmnā al-Nu'mān. It fills three volumes and begins with the biography of the founder of that school, Abū Ḥanīfa al-Nu'mān (VIII-1). It is said that the author was imprisoned for a time because of his anti-Shāfi'ī prejudices.

Two other books should still be mentioned, a very large one on the organization of the army, Tarjumān al-zamān fī tarājim al-a'yān, and a treatise on the interpretation of dreams, Farā'id al-fawā'id.

Ibn Duqmāq's chronicles were used by the Syrian historian Maḥmūd ibn Aḥmad al-'Ainī (1360–1451) and by the Palestinian Ibn Ḥajar al-'Asqalānī (1372–1449), but apparently not by his pupil the Egyptian al-Maqrīzī (1364–1442). For some Egyptian matters, Ibn Duqmāq's sources were apparently better than those of al-Maqrīzī.

Text. The remaining part of the Kitāb al-intiṣār (vols. 4 and 5 out of 10) was edited by Carl Vollers: Description de l'Egypte (2 vols., Cairo 1893).

Criticism. Wüstenfeld (no. 457, 1882). Brockelmann (2, 50, 1902; suppt. 2, 49, 1938). J. Pedersen (EI 2, 374, 1916).

IBN AL-SHIḤNA

Abū-l-Walīd Muḥammad ibn Muḥammad Ibn al-Shiḥna al-Ḥalabī. Syrian historian and textbook writer (1348–1412).

Qāḍī al-quḍāt (chief judge) of the Ḥanafī rite in Aleppo and Damascus. He got into trouble with the Mamlūk sulṭān Barqūq in 1391 and with al-Nāṣir in 1410; having regained the latter's favor, he accompanied him to Damascus and was appointed chief qāḍī in Egypt. After Nāṣir's death (1412) he returned to Aleppo, and died there on July 22, 1412.

He wrote an abridgment of the Mukhtaṣar ta'rīkh al-bashar of Abū-l-Fidā' (XIV-1) and continued it to 1403; this work is entitled Rauḍat al-manāẓir fī 'ilm al-awā'il wal-awākhir.

He composed a whole series of short textbooks in verse, called manẓūmāt. Manẓūma means verse (not poetry!) versus manthūra, prose. For example, there is a manẓūma of his fī uṣūl al-dīn (theology), others on taṣawwuf (mysticism), uṣūl al-fiqh (jurisprudence), farā'iḍ (laws of inheritance), ijmā' (theological consensus), manṭiq (logic), ṭibb (medicine), naḥw (syntax), bayān (rhetoric), sīrat al-rasūl (life of the Prophet). Some of these versified compendia have been commented upon by other writers.

Criticism. Brockelmann (2, 141, 1902; suppt. 2, 176, 1938).

AL-QALQASHANDĪ

Egyptian encylopaedist (1355–1418).

Abū-l-'Abbās Shihāb al-dīn Aḥmad ibn 'Alī al-Qalqashandī al-Miṣrī, also called Ibn abī Ghudda. The nisba under which he is best known is derived from the place where he was born, in 1355/56, Qalqashanda near the modern Delta barrage. He was of pure Arabic stock and belonged to a learned family; he seems to have spent his life in the chancellery of the Mamlūk government. He died on July 15, 1418.

His main work is a kind of encyclopaedia of historical, geographical, administrative, and secretarial information composed by him for the use of Egyptian officials, after 1387, completed in February 1412. It is entitled Ṣubḥ al-a'shā fī ṣinā'at al-inshā' (Dawn of the weak-sighted on the art of composition). It was not by any means a novelty, for secretarial guides or encyclopaedias constitute a definite genre in Arabic literature. Two of the first models of that kind are the Kitāb adab al-kātib of Ibn Qutaiba (IX-2), and the 'Uyūn al-akhbār of the same; the latest of those available to al-Qalqashandī was the work compiled by his predecessor in the Egyptian dīwān al-inshā', to wit, Shihāb al-dīn ibn Faḍlallāh al-'Umarī (XIV-1). Al-Qalqashandī's sources are too abundant to be enumerated here; the main one was certainly al-'Umarī, whom he sometimes copied verbatim.

The Ṣubḥ al-a'shā is an enormous work, divided into twelve parts, that is, an introduction (muqaddama), ten books (maqālāt), and a conclusion (khātima). The main contents follow: (Introduction) generalities on the art of writing and on writers; (I) theoretical and practical knowledge needed by writers (secretaries); (II) geography and history of Islamic countries; (III) forms of documents, such as titles, shape, formulas; (IV) administrative correspondence (mukātabāt); (V) appointment diplomas (wilāyāt); (VI) other writings such as religious warnings, dispensations (of taxes, etc.), dismissals, etc.; (VII) documents concerning fiefs or fees; details concerning the writing, e.g., of the basmala and the ṭughrā (calligraphic emblem of the ruler, see J. Deny in EI 4, 822–26, 38 fig., 1931); (VIII) formulas of oaths; (IX) granting of peace (amānāt); (X) occasional letters; (conclusion) organization of couriers and pigeon post, transportation of snow, alarm posts against the Tatars (manāwir, muḥriqāt).

The information on pigeon post is especially interesting (Arabic text, 14, 389). The author describes the pigeon towers (abrāj) and tells the history of the pigeon post, introduced in Egypt in 1169/70, i.e., toward the end of the Fāṭimī regime, which had established a special bureau (dīwān) ad hoc. He quotes two other books on the subject, Tamā'im al-ḥamā'im by Muḥyī al-dīn ibn 'Abd al-Ẓāhir,[33] and an earlier one written by Abū-l-Ḥasan ibn Mulā'ib al-Fawāris al-Baghdādī for al-Nāṣir ('Abbāsī caliph 1180–1225). Arabs were breeding special pigeons for that purpose; the achievements of some famous pigeons were recorded, as well as the fancy prices paid for them.[34]

When we speak of the Arabic barīd[35] or of ancient and Oriental postal services in general, we should bear in mind that such services were not comparable to ours. Their purpose was simply to enable the rulers to obtain quick information from everywhere and to transmit their orders as quickly as possible. The official couriers were used also to transport merchandise which the rulers might require, such as snow brought from the mountainous districts for refrigeration; or later to satisfy the rulers' financial and commercial needs. The postal service was not in any sense public; it was restricted to the rulers, members of the government and their friends. This was not simply an Oriental institution; every ruler was obliged to organize it, and the need tended to increase with the size of his empire. The barīd organized by the 'Abbāsī caliphs had already begun to suffer neglect in the second half of the tenth century. The Mamlūk sulṭān Baibars (1260–77) began its reorganization at considerable expense as soon as he was in power; the Mamlūk system became gradually more complex and more efficient for the purposes of peace and war, and it was combined with the pigeon post and with the use of optical signals; it was almost destroyed by Tīmūr's invasion in 1400, and by 1421 it had practically ceased to function. While it lasted the ṣāḥib al-barīd (literally, the

[33] Text included in the Berlin MS of the Qahwat al-inshā', collection of letters and diplomas of the Egyptian chancellery, put together by Taqī al-dīn Abū Bakr ibn 'Alī called Ibn Ḥijjah al-Ḥamawī (Ḥamāh 1366–1434). Brockelmann (2, 15–17; suppt. 2, 8–9).

[34] In an article on the carrier or homing pigeon (al-ḥamām al-zājil) written by Hubert Bird in Al-mustami'a al-'arabī (vol. 4, no. 7, London, July 7, 1943) information is given derived from a work Al-rawḍ al-mi'ṭār, which I cannot identify, that title having been used many times; see Ḥājjī Khalīfa (vol. 3, nos. 6597–98), Brockelmann (2, 41; suppt. 2, 38). The third 'Abbāsī caliph, al-Mahdī (775–85), was the first to use pigeons for postal service. Pigeons were so much esteemed that registers were kept of their genealogy, and fancy prices paid for the best, as much as 700 or 1,000 dīnār per bird, and 20 dīnār for a single egg (the dīnār was the unit of *gold* currency). They were especially valuable for the protection of caravans crossing the desert, being used by the caravan leaders even as they are used today by airmen. They were, however, relatively far more precious then than now, for they afforded the only means of rapid communication. Pigeon houses were established in a great many places for the postal service. See also Christina Phelps Grant: The Syrian desert (p. 241–45, London 1937; Isis 29, 143–45). The Mamlūk rulers made considerable use of the pigeon post for administrative purposes. It is curious that the art of using pigeons for the quick transmission of news was not noticed by the Crusaders and other Europeans; no reference was made to it in Western books before the sixteenth century, and the art was not practiced in Europe until much later still.

[35] The word barīd is not an original Arabic word, nor is it of Persian origin. It is derived from Latin veredus, post horse, courier's horse (Codex Justinianus; Ausonius); veredarius, courier. Du Cange (6, 773, 1846).

postmaster) was feared by government officials all around, for he was really a kind of spy, or secret agent of the central government. Gaston Wiet: L'Egypte arabe (p. 164, Paris 1937). Jean Sauvaget: La poste aux chevaux dans l'empire des Mamelouks (96 p., 21 fig., 8 pl., Paris 1941; Isis 37), elaborate study based upon the works of Ibn Faḍlallāh al-'Umarī (XIV-1) and al-Qalqashandī, upon contemporary literature and archaeological evidence. For the sake of comparison see description of the Mongol postal services in the Yule-Cordier edition of Marco Polo (1, 433–38; 2, 480, 1926).

The Ṣubḥ al-a'shā is full of historical data, but these are naturally more concentrated in the second maqālah, dealing with geography and history and divided as follows (Arabic text, 3, 227 to 5, 422): geography; generalities; history of the caliphate; description of Egypt; brief history of Egypt; Egyptian finances and institutions. Other parts of the Dār al-Islām are dealt with in the same way but more briefly: Syria, Ḥijāz, the lands of Chingiz Khān, Arabia, India, North Africa, Andalusia, Sūdān, the lands north of Egypt, including information on the Byzantine empire, etc., and the Bilād al-Cherkes, etc., that is, Slavonic countries.

The account of the Sūdān includes (5, 297) one of the two earliest references in any literature to the sleeping sickness ('illat al-nawm, trypanosomiasis); that disease was first mentioned in European medical literature in 1734 by the English naval surgeon John Atkins (1685–1757).[36] Al-Qalqashandī speaks of one of the Mandingo rulers of Mali, sulṭān Mārī Jāza (meaning the lion prince; also spelled Jata, Diata), who died c. 1373–75. Curiously enough, there is in the history of the Berbers of Ibn Khaldūn another reference to the same fact.

Al-Qalqashandī's other writings need not detain us very long. He completed in 1409/10 a genealogy and history of the Arab tribes before the time of Islām, Nihāyat al-arab fi ma'rifat qabā'il al-'Arab, and six years later he wrote a supplement to that work entitled Qalā'id al-jumān fī-l-ta'rīf bi qabā'il 'Arab al-zamān.

Najm al-dīn Muḥammad ibn Aḥmad al-Qalqashandī imitated his father's two works, the Ṣubḥ under the title Qalā'id al-jumān fi muṣṭalaḥ mukātabāt ahl al-zamān, and the Nihāyat under the title Nihāyat al-arab fī ma'rifat ansāb al-'Arab (c. 1442).

Text. A beautiful and elaborate edition of the Ṣubḥ was published by the National Library of Egypt (14 vols., Cairo 1913–20). The editor, Muḥammad 'Abd al-Rasūl Ibrāhīm, has given in vol. 14 an account of the undertaking, a summary of the work, and a biography of al-Qalqashandī. The publication of an index is contemplated.

Parts of the text are available in Western languages. F. Wüstenfeld: Geographie und Verwaltung von Aegypten (Abhandlungen der K. Gesellschaft der Wissenschaften zu Göttingen vol. 25, 225 p., 1879). Henri Sauvaire: Extraits de l'ouvrage intitulé Lumière de l'aurore pour l'écriture des hommes (Mémoires de l'Académie de Marseille 1886–87), dealing with coins, weights, and measures. Gaudefroy-Demombynes (1923). Eugène Tisserant and Gaston Wiet: La liste des patriarches d'Alexandrie dans Qalqachandi (Revue de l'orient chrétien 23, 123–43, 1923).

Sabā'ik al-dhahab fī ma'rifat qabā'il al-'Arab. Rearrangement of the Nihāyat with additions relative to the caliphs and sultans, by Abū-l-Fawz Muḥammad ibn Amīn al-Suwaidī (1814). Lithographic editions (120 p.) Baghdād 1864, Bombay 1879.

Criticism. Wüstenfeld (no. 467, 1882). Brockelmann (2, 134, 1902; suppt. 2,

[36] H. Harold Scott: History of tropical medicine (p. 456, London 1939; Isis 32).

164, 1938); (EI 2, 699, 1924). Stanley Lane-Poole: History of Egypt in the Middle Ages (vol. 6 of Sir Flinders Petrie's History of Egypt, London 1901; 2d revised ed. 1924; reprinted 1924, 1925). Walther Björkman: Beiträge zur Geschichte der Staatskanzlei im islamischen Ägypten (224 p., Hamburg 1928), elaborate analysis of the Ṣubḥ, should be shelved close to the Arabic edition for quicker use of the latter. F. Krenkow: Arabische Berichte über Goldgruben und Schlafsucht im Nigerlande (Sitzungsberichte der Physikalisch-medizinischen Sozietät in Erlangen 58, 344–47, 1928; Isis 14, 483), apropos of gold mining in 1334 (Arabic text, 5, 289–90) and sleeping sickness in 1373 (5, 297). Sarkis (col. 1521–23, 1930). Otto Spies: An Arab account of India in the fourteenth century (Bonner orientalistische Studien vol. 14, 78 p., Stuttgart 1936; Isis 27, 127). Max Meyerhof: An early mention of sleeping sickness in Arabic literature (Proceedings of the R. Society of Medicine, hist. sec., 30, 670–71, London 1937; Isis 31, 522). A. N. Poliak: The influence of Chingiz Khān's Yāsa upon the general organization of the Muslim state (Bull. London School of Oriental Studies 10, 862–76, 1942).

G. CHINA

T'O-T'O

Chinese-Mongol public servant and historian (1313–55).

T'o-t'o, style Ta yung, was of Mongol origin, his father being a prominent officer in the service of the Yüan dynasty. He himself rose quickly to the top, and proved his loyalty to the government when he squashed the rebellion of his uncle Po-yen against Tughān Tīmūr, last emperor of the dynasty (ruled 1333–68). In 1341 he became a minister of state, but ill health obliged him to retire three years later. In 1347 he accompanied his father in banishment. In 1350 he was again minister, and distinguished himself fighting rebellious subjects as well as the rebellious Yellow River. In spite of that, in 1355 he was banished to Yünnan and poisoned. In 1363 his reputation was vindicated and his titles posthumously restored.

He edited the official histories of the Sung (960–1279), Liao (907–1125), and Chin (1115–1260) dynasties. The Liao were Eastern Tatars or Ch'i-tan, K'itan (hence Cathay!); their capital was Liao yang and later Peking. The Chin were Nü Chên Tatars, the "Golden horde"; their capital was the old Sung capital, K'ai-fêng fu.

The Sung shih (in 496 books) is an inferior production, full of metaphysical digressions and factual errors. The absolute value of the Liao shih (in 116 books) is smaller still, because the greater part of the Liao records had been destroyed. The Chin shih (in 134 books) is far more valuable than the two previous works. These three enormous works form respectively the twentieth, twenty-first, and twenty-second of the Twenty-five histories. Books 68–84 of the Sung shih form a treatise on time measurement; books 85–98 deal with the geography of China; books 485–96 with the geography of foreign countries.

Text. Chinese editions of the Sung shih (496 chüan in 100 vols., Chehkiang 1875), of the Liao shih (116 chüan in 16 vols., Kiangsu 1872), of the Chin shih (134 chüan in 20 vols., Kiangsu 1873).

The Library of Congress has two other editions of these histories.

The Liao shih was translated into French and annotated by Rolf Stein (T'oung pao 35, 1–154, 1939).

Criticism. Wylie (p. 22, 1902). Giles (no. 1944, 1898).

SUNG LIEN

Chinese historian and lexicographer (1310–81).

Sung Lien, style Ching Lien, was born in Chin-hua, Chehkiang, 1310; he devoted his life to study and declined public service, except that in 1367 he was tutor to the son of the emperor; later he was president of the Han-lin yüan; in 1380 he fell under suspicion and was banished to Mao chou; he died in 1381. He was canonized as Wên Hsien.

He was one of the originators of the phonetic dictionary Hung Wu chêng yün, which was completed in 1375. It contains about 12,000 words classified under 76 rhymes. The first phonetic dictionary, Ch'ieh yün, had been completed in 601 by Lu Fa-yen (VII-1), and the words in it were classified under 204 rhymes. In 1038, Ting Tu (XI-1) compiled a smaller dictionary, Li pu yün lüeh, containing only 10,000 characters; this was revised in 1252 by Liu Yüan, who reduced the 206 rhymes to 107. The diminution in the number of rhymes illustrates the wear and tear on the language. Manchu and modern dictionaries are based on 106 rhymes, which is more than were used by Sung Lien, and is almost the same number as that used in 1252.

In 1358 Sung Lien published the Chu tzŭ pien, wherein he discussed the authenticity of some fifty philosophical writings. It is not by any means the first effort of its kind (one could cite at least ten predecessors), but one of the most notable.

In 1369, he and Wang Wei were commissioned by the first Ming emperor to edit the history of the Yüan dynasty. The first part of the Yüan shih was completed in eight months. Because the documents relative to the rule of Shun Ti (or Hui Tsung) (1333–68), the last period of the dynasty, were incomplete, the emperor ordered Ou yang yu to go to Peking to collect the missing records. The whole work was completed in six more months. The Yüan shih is an inferior work, but very elaborate; it was not superseded until our own times (see below). Chapters 48–49 deal with astronomy, 58–63 with geography of the empire, 64–66 with the waterways, 67–71 with music, 78–92, 102–5 with government and law, 93–97 with economics, 98–101 with military organization, 208–10 with neighboring countries, etc.

An interesting illustration of the strength and continuity of Chinese tradition is afforded by the fact that a new history of the Yüan dynasty, Hsin Yüan shih, was published at the expense of Hsü Shih-ch'ang, president of the Chinese Republic from 1912 to 1922. The author, Ko Shao-min, who took the chin shih degree and became a member of the Han-lin academy in 1886, spent many years in the preparation of it. He made full use of the large set of the Yung Lo ta tien which was then available in the Han-lin library, and of a collection of some three thousand rubbings of Yüan inscriptions accumulated by himself. The Hsin Yüan shih is especially valuable for the accounts of the reigns of Chingiz Khān (XIII-1) and Kublai Khān (XIII-2). It fills 257 chüan bound in 60 volumes.

Thus far twenty-five dynastic histories or chêng shih have been officially recognized by the Chinese nation. For a list of nos. 1 to 24 see Cordier (p. 600–3, 1904), this includes the Chinese characters; for nos. 1 to 19 see Introd. 1, 797. For 20, Sung shih, 21, Liao shih, and 22, Chin shih, see my note on T'o-t'o above. No. 23 is the Yüan shih, edited by Sung Lien. No. 24 is the Ming shih. The Ming dynasty lasted from 1368 to 1644, and the compilation of its history was ordered in 1679; it was completed c. 1724 under the direction of Chang T'ing-yü (1670–1756,

Giles no. 115), and canonized in 1739. No. 25 is the Hsin Yüan shih, added to the canon by order of president Hsü Shih-ch'ang before 1922.

To complete this account, the Republic of China, continuing the old traditions, ordered the compilation of a history of the fallen Manchu dynasty. The Ch'ing shih kao, "draft of Ch'ing history," was hurriedly prepared by some sixty scholars in 1914–27, but failed to be canonized.[37]

I should have mentioned that according to the Chinese tradition the history of a dynasty can only be written after its fall. It is remarkable that documents were steadily accumulated during the existence of each dynasty by official historiographers, whose work nobody was allowed to see, least of all the ruling emperors. Thus were the Chinese officials preparing materials to be used eventually by representatives of a new order inimical to their own!

In addition to the works already quoted, Sung Lien wrote the three following:

(a) Hung Wu shêng cheng chi, in 2 chüan, dealing with the political history of the Hung Wu period (1368–99).

(b) P'u yang jên wu chi, in 2 chüan, biographies of 27 men and 2 women.

(c) Lung mên tzŭ ning tao chi, in 2 chüan, dealing with Taoism.

Text. Chinese text of the Yüan shih (210 chüan in 40 vols., Kiangsu 1873). The Library of Congress has three editions of the Twenty-four histories, and has a copy of the twenty-fifth.

The Chu tzŭ pien, repunctuated and prefaced by Ku Chieh-kang, was printed in modern form in 1926.

The Library of Congress has a Ming edition of the Hung Wu chêng yün (16 chüan, bound in 5 vols.) with a preface dated 1375.

Criticism. Wylie (p. 23, 1902). Giles (no. 1836, 1898). Couling (p. 232–33, 300, 1917). Arthur W. Hummel: The autobiography of a Chinese historian (p. xxv, 151, Leyden 1931; Isis 33, 132). Trollope (p. 22–30, 1932). Gardner (1938).

LI SHAN-CH'ANG

Li Shan-ch'ang, style Pai shih, canonized as Hsiang Min. Chinese statesman and historian (1314–90).

He was born in 1314 at Ting-yüan, Shensi. He was adviser to Chu Yüan-chang (1328–99) at the time of the latter's revolt against the Yüan dynasty, and he was the head of the delegation which visited Yüan-chang and asked him in 1367 to assume the imperial style Hung Wu. He was the first minister of this first Ming emperor, 1368, but later fell into disgrace and was finally executed, together with more than seventy members of his family, in 1390.

In 1369 he was appointed chief editor of the Yüan shih, or official history of the Yüan dynasty, for which see my note on Sung Lien.

Criticism. Giles (no. 1186, 1898). Wieger (p. 338, 1920).

WU HAI

Chinese historian and Confucianist, who flourished under the Yüan and Ming dynasties and died in 1391.

[37] As it was considered a "reactionary" work, its sale was even forbidden in 1928, but permitted again ten years later. For an analysis, see Erich Haenisch: Das Ts'ing-shi-kao und die sonstige chinesische Literatur zur Geschichte der letzten 300 Jahre (Asia major 6, 403–44, Leipzig 1930; Isis 24, 260).

Wu Hai was styled Chao Tsung and nicknamed Lu k'o. He was employed by the first Ming rulers as a historian, but is more noteworthy because of his aggressive Confucian orthodoxy. He strongly opposed Buddhism and Taoism and urged that the people be forbidden to own heterodox books of any kind, and booksellers to handle them! His writings were collected under the title Wên kuo chai chi, in 6 chüan.

Criticism. Giles (no. 2329, 1898). Wieger (p. 374, 1920).

HSIA WÊN-YEN

Chinese historian of painting (fl. 1365).

Hsia Wên-yen, also called Shih liang, was born in Hu-chou fu, Chehkiang, but lived in Sung-chiang, near Shanghai, toward the end of the Yüan dynasty.

He compiled a history of Chinese painting, entitled T'u hua pao chien, from mythical times to his own, containing short biographies of more than 1,500 painters. The preface is dated 1365. In the course of time more chapters were added by various writers, carrying the story down to the seventeenth century.

This work was not a novelty; it continued a Chinese tradition going back at least to the sixth century. In fact, some earlier works are better, but the T'u hua is one of the best sources for the painters of the Southern Sung and Yüan dynasties (1127–1368).

Hsia Wên-yen had about sixteen predecessors, and many followers. His most important forerunners were: (1) Chang Yen-yüan, who completed in 847 the "Records of famous painters during the various generations," Li tai ming hua chi, dealing with 370 artists (16 of whom were anterior to the third century, when one begins to be on more solid ground), arranged in chronological order down to 841; (2) Chu Ching-hsüan,[38] who wrote c. 1000 the "Records of the celebrated painters of the T'ang dynasty," T'ang chao ming hua; (3) Kuo Jo-hsü, who in the T'u hua chien wên chih continued the work of Chang Yen-yüan from 841 to 1074; and (4) Têng Ch'un, who carried still farther the work of (1) and (3) in his "Continuation of pictorial art," Hua chi, down to 1167. To these might be added T'ang Hou (XIV-1), though the latter is perhaps to be considered an older contemporary rather than a precursor.

Text. The Library of Congress has a Ming edition of T'u hua pao chien. The text occurs also in two ts'ung shu.

Criticism. Wylie (p. 137, 1902). Friedrich Hirth: Scraps from a collector's notebook (p. 105–14, Leiden 1905). Herbert A. Giles: An introduction to the history of Chinese pictorial art (p. 79, 172, London 1918). Wieger (p. 307, 535, 1920). Arthur Waley: Index of Chinese artists (118 p., British Museum 1922).

[38] His real name was Chu Ching Yüan; but Kuo Jo-hsü listed him in T'u hua chien wên chih as "Chu Ching-hsüan," since in Kuo's time the use of the word "yüan" was prohibited, being a part of the imperial name.

CHAPTER XXVII

LAW AND SOCIOLOGY

(Second Half of the Fourteenth Century)

N.B. Only the main notes are published in this chapter. The legal and sociological contributions of many other men, whose main work was done in other fields, are discussed in other chapters. For a general survey of law and sociology in the second half of the fourteenth century, see section XIII of chapter XV. More information on the men referred to in that survey may then easily be found by means of the index.

A. ISLĀM

A1. Maghrib

MŪSĀ (II) IBN ZIYĀN

Abū Ḥammū Mūsā (II) ibn Yūsuf Ibn Ziyān al-'Abdwādī. Ruler of Algeria from 1352 to 1386, author of an Arabic treatise on politics and administration.

Mūsā ibn Yūsuf was one of the last kings of the Ziyānī dynasty (1235–1393), whose capital was Tlemcen (Tilimsān). These kings belong to the Banū 'Abd al-Wād, a part of the great Berber tribe Zanāta; the family is also called Banū Ziyān, after their ancestor Ziyān or Zaiyān (A. Bel in EI 1, 64, 1908).

His treatise is entitled Wāsiṭat al-sulūk fī siyāsat al-mulūk, and is divided into 4 chapters: (1) recommendations for right and just conduct, including (in the fourth and last part) advice as to means of keeping the good will of officers and soldiers; (2) the four pillars on which rests the royal power: intelligence, administration, justice, and the combination of wealth with military power; (3) the four qualities which symbolize and enhance the royal dignity: courage, liberality, toleration, and mercy; (4) physiognomy, as a means of good administration; conclusion. The book is addressed to his son, and was written for his education as a good man and as a just and powerful ruler.

Text. The Wāsiṭat al-sulūk was edited by Maḥmūd Kābādu and Muḥammad Bashīr al Tuwātī (180 p., Tunis 1862).

Spanish translation by Mariano Gaspar: El collar de perlas (Colección de estudios árabes vol. 4, 524 p., Zaragoza 1899).

Criticism. Brockelmann (2, 254, 1902; suppt. 2, 363, 1938).

B. CHRISTENDOM

B1. Italy

ALBORNOZ

Gil Alvarez Carrillo de Albornoz, Spanish soldier, diplomat, and legislator (d. 1367).

Gil (English Giles) was his Christian name; the other names were family names, and he might be classified under Alvarez or Carrillo as well as under Albornoz. Aegidius Albornotius. Born of royal blood in 1310 at Cuenca on the upper Jucar;

educated at Toulouse. He became a chaplain to Alfonso XI of Castile, then archbishop of Toledo (1337). In 1340 he took part in a crusade against the Moors in Africa and southern Spain, fighting at the king's side. When Pedro the Cruel ascended the Castilian throne in 1350, Albornoz was soon obliged to admonish him, and thus incurred his wrath and was forced to leave the country. He went to Avignon, where Clement VI appreciated his military valor, appointed him a cardinal legate in 1350, and employed him to re-establish the potestas temporalis in Italy, power which had disintegrated on account of the residence of the popes in Avignon since 1309.

The Italians were divided into two great parties, the Ghibellines and Guelphs. The Ghibellines represented grosso modo the imperial, feudal, and country policies; the Guelphs, the papal, bourgeois, city policies. The Ghibellines represented the great agricultural estates; the Guelphs, the new industrial and commercial traditions growing vigorously in the cities. That major party division was complicated and sometimes obliterated by a great complexity of local combinations and animosities. Albornoz was an experienced soldier and a resourceful diplomat; he made such good use of his German, French, Hungarian mercenaries on the one hand and of the rivalries and internal difficulties of his enemies on the other hand that he was able in a few years' time to reconstruct the papal dominion in Italy.

Albornoz established his residence at Ancona and consolidated the papal gains by the promulgation of a new code of law, at Fano, April 1357 (see Matteo Villani VII, 61). The Constitutiones aegidianae, as the code was called, is one of the most interesting mediaeval codes, as well as the one that lasted longest, for it remained the basis of administration in the papal states until 1816. Albornoz succeeded in breaking the power of the free companies of mercenary soldiers, and he tried to suppress the parties. He organized a kind of totalitarian state which was at its time a step forward toward the unification of Italy. There is no doubt that his achievements were the main cause in the ending of the French influence on the papacy and of the "Babylonian captivity." His crowning triumph was the return of Urban V to Viterbo in May 1367. (Urban returned to Avignon, however, in 1370, the year of his death, and Avignon remained the papal center until 1376.) Albornoz died at Viterbo in August 1367; his remains were translated to Toledo, where a monument was built to his memory in the cathedral.

Albornoz founded the Spanish college in Bologna.

Text. The earliest edition of the Constitutiones aegidianae was printed at Jesi 1473. There are 10 more editions down to 1605. Critical edition by Pietro Sella: Costituzioni egidiane dell' anno MCCCLVII (Corpus statutorum italicorum 1, 285 p., Rome 1912), with elaborate index.

Criticism. Juan Ginés de Sepulveda: Historia de bello administrato in Italia per annos XV et confecto ab ill.mo Aegidio Albornotio (48 fol., Bologna 1559; again 1628). Hermann Joseph Wurm: Cardinal Albornoz, der zweite Begründer des Kirchenstaates (296 p., portrait, Paderborn 1892). Emerton (p. 197–251, 1925), selections in English with introduction.

BARTOLUS

Bàrtolo da Sassoferrato (1314–57). Italian jurist; one of the greatest jurists of the Middle Ages. Born at Sassoferrato, in the March of Ancona, in 1314; studied law at Perugia under Cino of Pistoia 1327, then in Bologna, obtaining his doctor's degree in the latter place in 1334; legal assessor in Todi and Pisa, and from

1343 on, professor in Perugia, where he died in 1357. There is a beautiful monument to his memory in the church of San Francesco in Perugia.

From 1343 on, he taught civil law in the school of Perugia, which became under his inspiration the rival of the school of Bologna. He wrote a commentary on the Code of Justinian, and many treatises on legal questions. Considering the brevity of his life, his activity was prodigious. His genius was quickly recognized, he was considered an "Accursius redivivus." He developed the dialectical method, introduced by Accursius' pupil Odofredus, and applied his genius to almost every legal problem of his time (Introd. 2, 689).

Said Vinogradoff: "He adapted and developed Roman conceptions of the authority of the people as a source of power, of the part played by coercion in the creation of law (vis coactiva), of the delegation of political authority and jurisdiction by the Emperor, and the like. His commentaries on the subject became the basis of the public law of central Europe, and it is significant that the professors of Roman Law in Germany appropriated his doctrine in preference to the teaching of Justinian's Code itself. The modern elements of Bartolus's teaching made it the more acceptable for the solution of problems arising out of the tangled web of affairs in fifteenth-century Germany. It is in its Italian garb that Roman Law was received by the Germans, and this modification explains to a great extent the reason of the comparative ease of its adoption."

His influence continued until the seventeenth century, not only in Italy and Germany, but wherever Roman law was cultivated.

Text. Opera quae nunc extant omnia, additionibus eruditissimis illustrata et quasi nova facta. Accesserunt loci communes novi et uberrimi ordine literario et methodo singulari ad usum forensem accommodati, by Pieter Cornelis van Brederode (11 vols., Basel 1588–89); the loci communes fill vol. 11. Other collected editions, Lyon 1481/82, Venice 1570/71, 1590, 1602/3, 1615.

The incunabula editions of his separate works are too numerous to list here; see GW (3, 454–547, 1928). There are also innumerable sixteenth-century editions. Later editions are:

Tractatus de insigniis et armis, in Sebastian Faeschi dissertatio de insignibus (Altdorf 1727). Tractatus de insigniis et armis, mit Hinzufügung einer Uebersetzung und der Citate, edited by F. Hauptmann (Bonn 1883).

Commentarius de summaria cognitione, in Joannis Faxioli et Bartoli de Saxoferrato De summaria . . . (92 p., Erlangen 1843).

Commentaria in Codicem, appended to Friedrich Karl von Savigny: Private international law (Edinburgh 1880).

On the conflict of laws, Englished by Joseph Henry Beale (86 p., Harvard Press, Cambridge, Mass. 1914). English translations of De tyrannia and De Guelphis et Gebellinis in Emerton (1925).

Criticism. Girolamo Tiraboschi: Storia della letteratura italiana (5, 273–77, 1783). Friedrich Karl von Savigny (1779–1861): Geschichte des römischen Rechts im Mittelalter (6 vols., Heidelberg 1815–31; 2d ed., 7 vols., Heidelberg 1834–51; chiefly 6, 137–84, 1850, and by index in vol. 7). Carlo Negroni: Dante e Bartolo (Il Alighieri, 7 p., 1890). Gaetano Salvemini: Studi storici (Florence 1901). Paul Vinogradoff: Roman law in mediaeval Europe (p. 124, 1909), see also p. 116 apropos of one of the so-called "trials of Satan"[1] ascribed to Bartolus. Cecil

[1] That is, an exposition of the doctrine of salvation in the form of a fictitious trial. Satan appears before the tribunal of Christ under the name Mascaron and presents a complaint against mankind. The text contains much information about questions of procedure; in addition to its theological intention, it was used to acquaint students with technical terms and fundamental forms of pleading, such as summons, default, equity, possessory and petitory action, exceptions, replication, count, fraud, etc.

Nathan Sidney Woolf: Bartolus of Sassoferrato, his position in the history of medieval political thought (438 p., Cambridge 1913). Francesco Ercole: Da Bartolo all' Altusio.[2] Saggi sulla storia del pensiero publicisto del rinascimento italiano (429 p., Florence 1932; Speculum 11, 405–9). Josephus Lodewijk Johannes Van de Kamp: Bartolus de Saxoferrato (310 p., 16 pl., Amsterdam 1936), elaborate study of his life, works, significance, and of his influence in Italy, Spain, Portugal, France, the Netherlands, and Germany. Anna T. Sheedy: Bartolus on social conditions in the fourteenth century (Studies in history no. 495, 268 p., Columbia University, New York 1942).

BALDO

Baldo degli Ubaldi. Italian jurist; the greatest of his time perhaps, next to Bàrtolo (d. 1400).

Baldo de' Ubaldi (de' Baldeschi). Baldus de Ubaldis. Member of a noble family of Perugia. His father, Francesco, had three sons, Baldo, Angelo, and Pietro, all of whom became eminent jurists. Baldo is the most famous. He was born at Perugia in 1327, or perhaps before (1319?). He studied Roman and canon law in his native city and obtained his doctorate under Bàrtolo, perhaps as early as 1344 (which is easier to reconcile with the birth year 1319 than with the later one). He taught law in many cities: three years in Bologna, thirty-three in Perugia, one in Pisa, six in Florence, three in Padua, ten in Pavia; and he died in the last-named city on April 28, 1400. His tombstone was decorated with his statue in low relief; he is shown holding an open book in each hand; it is preserved at the University of Pavia.

Baldo was very learned in every field of law, Roman, canon, feudal, commercial, penal, international, and he had obtained in the service of his city considerable experience as a judge, ambassador, and administrator. He also had opportunities for obtaining commercial experience, being frequently consulted by the great merchants of Perugia. He was one of the first to give legal opinions concerning bills of exchange, and wrote a Summula respiciens facta mercatorum. He is chiefly known to posterity by his commentaries on the Corpus iuris, Decretales, and Liber feudorum (1391), and on the treaty of peace of Constance (between the Lombard cities and the emperor, 1183). A treatise of his, De commemoratione famosissimorum doctorum, dealing with the history of law, has disappeared, but was used by Tommaso Diplovatazio of Corfu (1468–1541) in the latter's own work on the subject.

Baldo was famous for his learning and experience and also for his love of polemics, and his talent as a dialectician. His opinions (consilia) on many questions were treasured, and collections of them were repeatedly printed (from 1489 on). Among his pupils were Pierre Roger of Beaufort (Gregory XI) and cardinal Zabarella.[3] When Gregory XI died (1378), Urban VI consulted Baldo with regard to his fight against the antipope Clement VII of Avignon. In 1380, Urban VI called him to Rome and ordered him to prepare a new consultation together with Giovanni da Legnano.

[2] Johannes Althusius (1557–1638), German jurist, defender of democracy, critic of witchcraft trials. Carl Joachim Friedrich: Politica methodice digesta of Johannes Althusius (Harvard University, Cambridge 1932; Isis 20, 533), text of the Politica with elaborate introduction. First edition of the Politica, Herborn 1603; third and final author's edition, Herborn 1614. Later editions are reprints.

[3] Francesco Zabarella (1360–1417) of Padua was made a cardinal by Gregory XII in 1411. He took an active part in the preparation and steering of the council of Constance and in the healing of the Great Schism. He died in Constance during the council. Enrico Carusi (Enciclopedia italiana 35, 857, 1937).

Text. Baldo's commentaries have been frequently printed together with the texts commented upon, for example, in many of the fifteenth- and sixteenth-century editions of the Corpus iuris, of the Decretales, of the Liber feudorum, and of the Liber de pace Constantiae.

There are many early editions of the Consilia: at least 5 incunabula (Milan 1489, etc.) and many others during the sixteenth century.

Thomae Diplovatatii opus de praestantia doctorum, partial edition by Gustav Pescatore (232 p., Berlin 1890). Diplovatazio's De claris iuris consultis, edited by Hermann Kantorowicz and Fritz Schulz (Berlin 1919).

These indications are very incomplete. A complete Baldo bibliography would be long and difficult and somewhat out of place here.

Criticism. F. K. de Savigny: Histoire du droit romain (4, 233-36, Paris 1839). Torquato Cuturi: Baldo degli Ubaldi in Firenze (Boll. d. Deputazione di storia per l'Umbria vol. 6, 30 p., Perugia 1900). Biazio Brugi: Per una storia della giurisprudenza italiana. La facoltà giuridica di Padova e le onoranze a Baldo in Perugia, 28 aprile 1900 (Atti del R. istituto veneto 60, part 2, 239-38, 1900), apropos of the fifth centenary of Baldo's death.

GIOVANNI DA LEGNANO

Bolognese jurist and publicist, one of the founders of international law (d. 1383).

Life. Giovanni da Legnano or Johannes de Lignano. The family originated in the little town of Legnano near Milano. His father, Giacomo, was conte degli Oldrendi. Giovanni was born in Milano early in the century; he is first heard of in 1350, when the new ruler of Bologna, Giovanni Visconti, appointed him lecturer in law and member of a commission for the repatriation of men exiled by the former rulers. Giovanni was then already legum doctor. In 1351, he was doctor utriusque iuris, and reader in canon law at the university; he became a full professor in 1360. In 1366, he purchased from the executors of his predecessor a lecture room with the professor's chair and benches for the students, complete! In 1368, he was made a count palatine by the emperor Charles IV. On December 13, 1377, he became papal vicar in Bologna, and soon afterward was made a hereditary citizen of that city. He enjoyed the full confidence of four successive popes, and it is said that the last of these, Urban VI, would have given him a cardinal's hat if his wife had been willing to retire to a convent.

He died in Bologna on February 16, 1383; a monument erected to him in San Dominico is now in the Museo civico of Bologna.

In the prologue of the Clerk's tale Chaucer coupled Giovanni's name with that of Petrarca.

Writings. In addition to the De bello (1360) and the two astrological treatises dealt with below, he wrote a number of treatises on theology, commentaries on the Decretum, Decretals, Clementines, etc., on civil law, on general politics (popes vs. emperors, ecclesiastical vs. civil authority, with special reference to Bologna), on the Great Schism. Those devoted to the last-named topic were written in favor of Urban VI: Epistola ad Cardinalem de Luna (the future Benedict XIII) August 18, 1378; De fletu ecclesiae (Tractatus pro Urbano) 1379, which provoked various replies from the Paris doctors, e.g., De planctu bonorum by the abbot of St. Vedast; Pro Urbano tractatus secundus.

A treatise beginning Audite somnium per quod vidi solem et stellas, and consisting of a dialogue between a clerk and a soldier upon the respective prerogatives of pope and emperor, was written by him in 1373 and dedicated to the pope. It remained unpublished, but a distorted version of it dedicated to Charles V of France (king 1364–80) was printed in French (Le songe du vergier, princeps 1491) and later in Latin (Somnium viridarii, princeps 1516).

Astrological treatises. He wrote two astrological treatises, which are unimportant in themselves, but are interesting as illustrations of astrology applied to politics. The first deals with a conjunction of Saturn and Jupiter in Scorpio in October 1365 (not 1355), the second with the comet of April 1368.

The second treatise is divided into 5 chapters: definition of a comet, different kinds, physical explanation and astrological significance in relation to planets and constellations, list of notable comets. It is less elaborate than the treatises of Geoffrey of Meaux on the comets of 1315 and 1337, and of Jacobus Angelus on that of 1402. According to Giovanni, the comets are sublunar and their influences are twofold, meteorological and astrological. History shows the dependence of wars and other calamities on comets.[4] It is very difficult, however, to determine a comet's position with reference to the zodiac and the planets, and hence definite prophecies are equally difficult. This argument was used against astrologers; on the other hand, it provided them with convenient loopholes.

Giovanni's main astrological sources are the Quadripartitum and Centiloquium, Abū Ma'shar (IX-1), 'Alī ibn Riḍwān (XI-1), Michael Scot (XIII-1), and Leopold of Austria (XIII-2). His conscience was not quite clear on the subject, and he also quoted St. Augustine's writings against astrology and the laws of Justinian De maleficiis et mathematicis.

In addition to these astrological treatises we find astrological digressions in his political treatises, which show even more convincingly how his political thought was permeated with astrological beliefs. In his letter of August 18, 1378 to the Spanish cardinal Pedro de Luna (1328?–1424) he gives him astrological warnings against the impending schism. The introduction to his De bello contains an astrological history of Bologna from 1350 to 1360, the horoscopes of the main events being described.

De bello. We now come to his main work, the treatise first called De civitate Bononiae et de bello, later Tractatus de bello, de represaliis et de duello. It was completed in Bologna 1360, when mismanagement of the city had reached a climax and the only solution seemed to be a surrender to papal authority. The book is dedicated to the great papal captain, cardinal Gil Albornoz (1310–67). It is important as "the earliest attempt to deal, as a whole, with the group of rights and duties which arise out of a state of war" (T. E. Holland).

After the dedication to Albornoz and the astrological introduction already referred to, the De bello itself begins, being divided into three treatises: (I) definition of war; (II) classification of wars (these two first parts are quite short); (III) principal treatise, dealing more lengthily with different kinds of war, as follows: (1) heavenly spiritual war, arising from Satan's rebellion; (2) human spiritual war, conflict between duty and egoism; (3) universal corporeal war, i.e., war as we commonly understand it; (4) corporeal private war, in self defense; (5) corporeal private war, in defense of the state, i.e., reprisals (De particulari bello quod fit ob

[4] As to wars, it is clear that when a sufficient number of powerful people believed that comets cause wars, then the appearance (or prediction) of a comet might easily cause or precipitate one; indeed, it induced irritability and fear, even panic, and the bolder men would take the offensive for fear of being outmatched by their rivals.

defensam corporis mystici, quod "Represaliae" nuncupatur); (6) corporeal private war, for clearing one's character, i.e., the duel.

The main value of the book lies in its discussion (chiefly in III, 3; 68 chapters out of a grand total of 174) of such topics as "the lawful causes of war, the authority by which it may be declared, the distinction between war and reprisals, the distribution of booty, the employment of stratagems, the treatment of prisoners, of noncombatants, of enemy troops who have surrendered and, in particular, of enemy commanders." It is clear that the general subject was not well understood at that time, and in consequence the De bello contains many items which would today be considered irrelevant—but we must remember it was the first treatise of its kind.

The sources of the De bello include the Bible, Aristotle ("the philosopher"), the Corpus iuris civilis, and above all the Corpus iuris canonici; then also the Usus feudorum, Lex lombarda, Lex Friderici, and many jurists and fathers of the church chiefly as quoted in the canon law and its commentaries.

Text. The earliest edition was prepared by the great-grandson of the author, Paulus Antonius de Lignano, who took considerable liberties with the text, emending, adding, subtracting (folio, 75 p., double columns, Bologna 1477). Often reprinted: Pavia 1484, 1487, Milano c. 1500, 1515, Torino 1525. Also included in the Tractatus tractatuum of Venice 1584 (not in that of 1549).

There are also separate editions of the De represaliis (Pavia 1484, 1487) and of De duello (Milano s.a., again 1508, and in the Tractatus tractatuum of 1549).

A sumptuous edition, the first integral one, of the De bello was prepared by Thomas Erskine Holland for the Classics of international law edited by James Brown Scott and published by the Carnegie Endowment for International Peace (quarto, 492 p., Oxford and Washington 1917). It includes: a collotype of the earliest MS, Bologna c. 1390; the text of the same as "extended" and otherwise revised by the editor; a translation of the text, as so extended and revised, by James Leslie Brierly; a facsimile reproduction of the imperfect princeps; introduction and notes.

Criticism. Luigi Rossi: Dagli scritti inediti giuridico-politici di G. da Legnano (Bologna 1898). Filippo Bosdari: Giovanni da Legnano, canonista e uomo politico del 1300 (141 p., Bologna 1901). Albert Stanburrough Cook: Chauceriana II, Chaucer's "Linian" (Romanic review 8, 353-82, 1917). Giuseppe Ermini: I trattati della guerra e della pace di G. da Legnano (Studi e memorie per la storia dell' Università di Bologna 8, 1-154, Bologna 1924). Zinner (p. 205, 462, 1925). Thorndike (3, 592-97; 4, 94, 1934).

B5. Netherlands

PHILIP OF LEIDEN

Philippus de Leyden. Dutch jurist and publicist (d. 1382).

Philip was born in Leiden, was educated for the clergy, and in 1345 went to Orléans to continue his legal studies. After the death of Willem IV (count of Holland 1337-45) he returned to Holland and became a counselor to the future Willem V (count 1349-89). He was sent on a mission to Avignon, was made canon of St. Mary, Condé; then in 1359 canon of St. Peter, Middelburg. In 1369 he obtained the degree of doctor decretorum in Paris. In 1371 he was appointed vicar-general to the bishop of Utrecht. After another mission to Avignon he settled down in his native city and spent there the last decade of his life.

He had accumulated a large library, the integrity of which he tried to preserve by his will for the use of scholars. By the end of the sixteenth century, however, it had already ceased to exist, though the house in which it had been kept was still called Solomon's Temple.

His immortality is based on a single treatise, the Tractatus de cura reipublicae et sorte principantis, which he began in 1346; the first redaction was completed c. 1358, but he continued to correct it until 1375. He wrote it for the education of Willem V.[5] It is not a systematic account, but a discussion of 85 "cases" on the basis of civil and canon law, ancient and mediaeval literature. It is interesting to compare that "case method" as applied to law with the same method applied a little later to medicine in the Consilia of Ugo Benzi. Philip's collection is much more than the usual speculum regale or eruditio principum; it is a treatise on government. Philip realized the need of territorial continuity and unity, as against feudal aberrations, and he often quoted the principle "utilitas sive salus rei publicae" (raison d'état) as a clinching argument. His main idea was, in his own words, "Imperialem decet sollertiam, ita rei publicae curam gerere et subjectorum commoda investigare, ut regni utilitas incorrupta persistat et singulorum status iugiter servetur illaesus" (casus IX, 27).

Philip of Leiden wrote a Compilatio brevis sive tabula of his famous Tractatus, and other books, De formis et semitis reipublicae utilius et facilius gubernandae, De modo et regula rei familiaris facilius gubernandae.

Text. First edition of Tractatus de cura reipublicae, Leiden 1516. Later edition with biography by Franciscus de Vroede (Amsterdam 1701). Critical edition by Robert Fruin and Philip Christiaan Molhuysen (524 p., The Hague 1900), including all the treatises, his two wills, and the Disposicio librorum (1372), a catalogue of his library.

Criticism. J. van Kuyk (Nieuw nederlandsch biografisch woordenboek 1, 1273-74, 1911). Hans Wilfert: Philipp von Leyden. Ein Beitrag zur Vorgeschichte des modernen Staates (Beihefte zur Vierteljahrschrift für Sozialgeschichte no. 5, 42 p., Stuttgart 1925).

C. INDIA

VIŚVEŚVARA

Viśveśvara Bhaṭṭa. Hindu jurist (fl. 1375).

He was patronized by prince Madanapāla, and this determines his own floruit. It is probable, for the same reason, that he flourished in Kāshṭhā north of Delhi.

He compiled for his sovereign a code of law dealing with religious duties and rules of inheritance. It is called Madanapārijāta and contains abundant quotations from earlier works.

Text. The Madanapārijāta was edited by paṇḍit Madhusúdana Smṛitiratna (Bibliotheca indica, work 114, in 11 parts, 1047 p., Asiatic Society, Calcutta 1893).

Criticism. Julius Jolly: Recht und Sitte (Grundriss der indo-arischen Philologie vol. 2, part 8, p. 32, 36, 1896). Duff (p. 228, 295, 1899). Winternitz (3, 503, 1922). Keith (p. 448, 1928). Emeneau (no. 2397, 1935).

[5] More exactly, for the future Willem V, who in 1346 was only 16 years old. His mother, Margaretha, wife of Ludwig IV the Bavarian, ruled until 1349, when Willem V became count of Holland.

D. CHINA

HUNG WU

First Ming emperor, ruled from 1368 to 1398.

Hung Wu was his imperial name or title. His own name was Chu Yüan-chang. He was born at Chung-li, Anhui, in 1328; he spent his childhood and youth in great poverty, was for a time a Buddhist monk, and after many vicissitudes ascended the throne in 1368 (the last Yüan emperor, Shun Ti, died at Karakorum in 1370); he died in 1399.

He is dealt with here not because of his military genius, nor even because of his great administrative abilities, but rather because he was a liberal patron of education and learning.

He laid down wise principles for the government of China; reorganized the system of examinations; published a penal code and a kind of Domesday Book for the distribution of taxation; reformed the calendar (1384); reorganized the currency; prohibited eunuchs from holding offices; restored the dress of the T'ang dynasty; made Taoism and Buddhism state religions.

He ordered the compilation of a new phonetic dictionary, the Hung Wu chêng yün, completed in 1375, which is discussed in the note on Sung Lien.

As to the reorganization of the currency, this was a perennial task to which every strong emperor was obliged to address himself. We may recall that paper money was used in China as early as the beginning of the ninth century; by the middle of the tenth century large quantities were in circulation. In the time of Wang An-shih (XI-2) this was already causing grave difficulties, and a rapid inflation set in at the end of the eleventh century.[6] In 1236 Yeh-lü Ch'u-ts'ai (XIII-1) prevailed on the great khān Ogotāy (ruled 1227–41) strictly to limit an issue of paper money. In 1294, bank notes, ch'ao, were printed in Tabrīz in Chinese and Arabic. Kublai Khān (XIII-2) reorganized the paper currency; Marco Polo noticed the bank notes but did not realize that they were printed, or that printing deserved to be mentioned! It is said[7] that the earliest bank note in existence is one dating from the rule of Hung Wu (British Museum). That is possible, but we have seen that by that time paper money had been used in China for more than half a millennium and had often been abused, and that notes had been printed for perhaps as long a time, and certainly for a couple of centuries.

Text. E. Chavannes: Les saintes instructions de l'empereur Hong Wou (1368–98) publiées en 1587 et illustrées par Tchong Houa-min (i.e., Chung Hua-min) (Bull. de l'Ecole française d'Extrême Orient 3, 549–63, 1903), with French translation.

Criticism. Hung Wu shih lu (official record of his reign) in MS, Cambridge collection B 1870–76 (vol. 1 missing; no date). Giles (p. 192–94, 1898).

[6] For the sake of comparison, remember that banking operations began in the Christian West in the second half of the twelfth century (Introd. 2, 317).

[7] Ball (p. 64–66, 168, 1926). The early Ming bank note is reproduced in the Yule-Cordier edition of Marco Polo, where a good account of Chinese paper money will be found (1, 423–30, 1926). Cordier's Addenda (p. 71–73, 1920). For Marco Polo the use of paper money was a definite trait of the Yüan empire. He often makes statements of this kind: "The people are Idolaters; and since they were conquered by the Great Kaan they use paper-money" (book 2, ch. 76).

LIU WEI-CH'IEN

Chinese jurist (fl. c. 1374).

According to Ming shih, chüan 138, Liu Wei-ch'ien was minister of the board of punishments under the first emperor of the Ming dynasty, year title Hung Wu, for six years. The code of the Ming dynasty, Ta Ming lü, was compiled under his direction. This code has had much influence in the Far East; it has been translated into Korean, Japanese, and Manchu.

Criticism. Wieger (p. 253, 357, 523, 1920).

CHAPTER XXVIII

PHILOLOGY

(Second Half of the Fourteenth Century)

N.B. Only the main notes are published in this chapter. The philological contributions of many other men, whose main work was done in other fields, are discussed in other chapters. For a general survey of philology in the second half of the fourteenth century, see section XIV of chapter XV, summarizing the facts concerning more than thirty-one languages. More information on the men referred to in that survey may then easily be found by means of the index.

The following notes deal only with ten kinds of philologists: Latin, Italian, Catalan, Greek, Czech, Zyrian, Hebrew, Arabic, Canarese, and Chinese.

LATIN AND ITALIAN

GIOVANNI BOCCACCIO

Florentine writer and humanist. One of the founders of Italian prose. The first Greek humanist in Western Europe (1313–75).

Contents: (1) Life. (2) The foundation of Italian prose: the Decamerone. (3) His Latin works. (4) His study of Dante. (5) His humanism. (6) His scientific knowledge. (7) His character.

(8) Bibliographic guides and indexes. (9) Text. (10) Biographies and general criticism. (11) Criticism of the Decamerone. (12) Studies on the Latin writings. (13) His influence. (14) His scientific knowledge. (15) Varia.

1. *Life*

Johannes Boccaccii de Certaldo. Giovanni the son of Boccaccio di (i.e., the son of) Chelino (Michelino) da Certaldo. The father, Boccaccio, was born at Certaldo (some 20 miles from Florence), went to Florence, and was established there as a tavoliere[1] (money-changer); later he was associated with the great Bardi banking house and became in 1324 the consul of the guild of money-changers. He spent a few years in Paris (1310–14), and during that time Giovanni was born of a Parisian woman in Paris 1313. The father returned with the child to Florence and married another woman. Though Giovanni was Parisian by birth and through his mother, Certaldo was his ancestral home and became more and more completely his spiritual home.

Giovanni received his elementary education in Florence, spent six years as an apprentice in a commercial house, studied canon law for five or six years (1331–36) in Naples. Naples being as Guelph as Florence, and these two cities the main supports of papal politics in Italy, there were naturally many communications and exchanges between them. During his stay in Naples (c. 1331–39), Giovanni met the astronomer Andalò di Negro and was his pupil; he may have met Giotto, who

[1] The tavoliere is a man using a tavola (table) for money-changing. Compare the *τραπεζίτης* using a *τράπεζα*, e.g. in Matthew 21:12 and Mark 11:15, *τὰς τραπέζας τῶν κολλυβιστῶν*. That usage can be observed in the Near East and in Islamic lands to this day.

was there in 1330-32.[2] In 1339 his father was suddenly impoverished because of the bankruptcy of the Bardi and Peruzzi banks. Giovanni returned to Florence toward the end of 1340. More disasters occurred in Florence during the forties (bankruptcies, poor harvests, plague), and Giovanni was often absent. His father's death in 1349 brought him back home, and the rest of his life was spent in Florence and Certaldo, though he traveled considerably. As contrasted with Petrarca, who remained a wandering exile and was an Italian "avant la lettre," Boccaccio was primarily a Florentine. He served the republic as a civil servant and a representative on special missions. For example, he was sent on a mission to Romagna in 1350 (during the course of which he presented in the name of the city ten golden florins to Beatrice, Dante's daughter, then a nun in Ravenna); in 1362 we find him in Naples; in 1363 in Venice, in 1365 at the curia in Avignon (in May 1367 he approached Urban V again in Viterbo, later in Rome); in 1367 he was in Ravenna, in 1368 in Venice, in 1370 in Naples. From 1373 to his death he did not move from Certaldo except for short visits to Florence; toward the end of his life he suffered from scabies sicca and other ailments; he died in Certaldo on December 21, 1375 (seventeen months later than his master Petrarca).

His Certaldo house still exists, and there is a cenotaph dedicated to him in the church of Sts. Michel and James in that city.

2. *The foundation of Italian prose: the Decamerone*

Boccaccio is often called "the father of Italian prose," even as Dante and Petrarca are considered "the fathers of Italian verse"; these two phrases being subject to similar qualifications.

His immortality as a writer rests almost exclusively on his Decameron (princeps, 1469 or 1470), a collection of a hundred tales, which is and has remained, and deservedly so, one of the most popular books of the whole of mediaeval literature. He composed it largely during the years 1344 and 1350, but it was not completed and published until 1353. The frame of the collection is this: Seven young ladies and three gentlemen decide to spend the terrible days of the plague in a villa near Florence, and in order to while away the time and cheer themselves up, they tell one another tales. Each evening a king (or queen) is selected to preside over the next day's meeting. Each day ten tales are told, and there were all together ten days (decamerone). The frame is somewhat artificial and the narrators remain shadowy, in great contrast with the very typical and living narrators of the Canterbury tales.

The prologue, forming a dramatic contrast with the tales, includes a description of the plague which broke out in Florence in the spring of 1348. This description has often been compared with Thucydides' account of the plague of Athens (430–425 B.C.), for which see Introd. 1, 107. The style of the Decamerone is vigorous and racy; the tales are realistic but on the whole less brutal than many others of the same age. There are strong anticlerical tendencies, which are not isolated symptoms but are found in many writings, especially in the vernacular writings, of that century. In spite of this there is but little bitterness in the book, the spirit of which is remarkably jovial and lighthearted. As opposed to Dante's otherworldliness, Boccaccio's primary concern was with the life of this earth, and the prose of this

[2] As to other influences to which Boccaccio may have been subject at the court of Robert the Wise (ruler of Naples 1309–43), see Cornelia C. Coulter: The library of the Angevin kings at Naples (Transactions of the American Philological Association 75, 141–55, 1944; Isis 36, 180).

life. In contrast with the Commedia divina, the Decamerone might be called a "commedia umana." It is a magnificent mirror of Italian life in the trecento.

Many efforts have been made to trace the sources of these tales. Some of the motives have been connected with those of Oriental, even Sanskrit tales. It is hardly possible to give a complete account of the transmission, but that proves nothing, for the popular tradition—especially that concerning tales—was primarily oral, the written transmission being secondary and accessory.[3]

The Decamerone was completely or partly translated into too many languages to be listed here. Sometimes the individual tales were transmitted by way of adaptations instead of translations. In any case, the influence of the Decamerone can be traced in almost every European literature. An interesting example is the Yiddish translation of seven stories by Joseph ben Jacob Maarssen, included in his Schöne artliche Geschichten (Amsterdam 1710), probably derived from the Dutch Decamerone printed in Haarlem 1564, and again in Amsterdam 1644. The translator was careful to use as few Hebrew words as possible in order to avoid profaning them. See Richard Gottheil in JE (3, 279, 1902).

The existence of a Japanese translation (which might be assumed on account of the strong erotic tendencies of the Japanese people) was recently brought to the author's attention in a curious way. A copy of a cheap Japanese edition of the Decamerone was found on a captured atoll of the Pacific; that copy is now in the Harvard Library. It bears the rubber stamp of a military censor in English, "Examined in the field; passed by joint intelligence."

3. *His Latin works*

In addition to his Italian writings, Boccaccio composed four works in Latin, the influence of which was quite considerable.

(a) *De casibus virorum illustrium.* A historical and moral treatise divided into nine books. The purpose is to tell the vicissitudes of many men, from Adam on, who were great and whose fall was equally great. It was completed in 1356-60, and dedicated by Boccaccio in 1363-64 to Mainardo dei Cavalcanti, a Florentine knight established in Naples. That work was very popular in those troubled days when there was neither security nor peace even for the powerful and the fortunate; it appealed to educated people for the same reason as Petrarca's Remedia utriusque fortunae, but was more popular than Petrarca's book because of its greater concreteness and realism. As it offered a general view of world history from the time of Adam to the middle of the fourteenth century[4] and was full of curious and dramatic stories, it provided the great of the world with the most interesting reading in their good days and with comforting reading in their hours of trial.

Two versions of the De casibus are represented in the printed editions. The princeps of the first version appeared in Strassburg c. 1474; it was reprinted in Paris c. 1507. The second version was printed only once, Augsburg 1544.

The book was soon translated into five vernaculars, and the number of MSS of these translations, some of them sumptuous, proves their popularity. A French translation was made by Laurent de Premierfait (d. Paris 1418) and dedicated by

[3] The vastness and complexity of the oral tradition has been well illustrated by Stith Thompson in his Motif-index of folk-literature (6 vols., Indiana University, Bloomington, Ind. 1932-36; Isis 20, 607; 28, 602).

[4] More exactly, until John the Good, king of France, was made prisoner by Edward, the Black Prince, near Poitiers (1356), and taken to England.

him on November 13, 1400 to Louis, duke of Bourbon. This literal version was printed by Colard Mansion, Bruges 1476, then again in Lyon 1483. After 1400 Laurent prepared a new French version containing a mass of additional information and extending to more than double the original length; this was completed c. 1405–9 and dedicated to Jean, duke of Berry (1340–1416), brother of Charles V, an evil man but a great patron of artists, one of the most magnificent princes of his time. This second version was transmitted in a number of MSS, some of which are very precious, especially the one illustrated by Jean Foucquet (c. 1415–85). It was first printed in Paris 1483, then again in the same city 1494, 1506?, 1515, 1538. A third French version, by Cl. Witart, was printed in Paris 1578.

A German translation by Hieronymus Ziegler (d. 1562) was published in Augsburg 1545. The Italian translation by Giuseppe Betussi was printed in Venice 1545, 1551, Florence 1598. The Spanish translation by Pero López de Ayala and Juan García, dean of Santiago, was printed in Seville 1495, Toledo 1511, Alcalà de Henares 1552.

Finally, an English version was made by John Lydgate (1370?–1451?), a disciple of Chaucer's. His Fall of princes was a rhymed paraphrase (36,365 lines) of the second version in French prose, Des cas des nobles hommes et femmes, by Laurent de Premierfait. Lydgate wrote it in 1431–38 and dedicated it to Humphrey, duke of Gloucester (1391–1447), the so-called "good duke Humphrey," as much of a rascal as the duke of Berry but like the latter a great patron of letters. There are thirty MSS of the Fall of princes, of which about nine are contemporary with the author and almost all are fifteenth century. The text was first printed by Richard Pynson, London 1494, reprinted by him 1527; other editions London 1554, London 1555?, etc. Critical edition by Henry Bergen (4 vols., Carnegie Institution of Washington, 1923–27; Isis 33, 361).

To summarize, before the middle of the sixteenth century Boccaccio's De casibus had been printed in six languages. There are seven incunabula in four languages, plus fifteen sixteenth-century editions.

(b) *De claris mulieribus.* This is a work similar to the preceding, a collection of historical anecdotes brought together with a moralizing tendency. Completed at the end of 1362, and dedicated to the contessa d'Altavilla, sister of Andrea degli Acciaiuoli, great seneschal of Naples; revised between 1370 and 1374. It was as popular as the study of illustrious men, if not more. It was promptly vulgarized into Italian, "retranslated" into "Florentine"; translated into German by Heinrich Steinhöwel (1412–82, princeps Ulm 1473); into English by Henry Parcare (i.e. Parker), eighth baron Morley (1476–1556); into French (princeps 1493); into Spanish. There are all together eight incunabula editions: three in Latin, one in French, and four in German.

(c) *De genealogiis deorum.* A treatise on classical mythology, which occupied Boccaccio for thirty years (completed in 1370–71 but revised at the end of his life), and was the first great treatise of its kind. Dedicated to Hugh IV of Lusignan, king of Cyprus from 1324 to 1359.

It is divided into a proem and fifteen books. Book XIV is a defense of poetry, and book XV a defense of the work itself. Books I to XIII constitute the genealogies, for Boccaccio's idea was to classify all the mythological lore in the form of genealogical tables (the MSS and editions include drawings of genealogical trees).

This is the most important of Boccaccio's Latin writings, a learned work wherein his sources were carefully indicated. In his interpretation of the ancient myths, he used historical, natural, and moral explanations. By "natural" we mean here the interpretation of myths with reference to natural phaenomena. Boccaccio was one of the earliest scientific mythologists, and his book, crude as it was, remained throughout the Renaissance a standard book on the subject. There are thirty to forty MSS of the fourteenth and fifteenth centuries and at least six incunabula Latin editions (princeps, Venice 1472), plus a French one (Paris 1498).

In book IV, chapter 68 (after the edition of Venice 1494), Boccaccio describes the discovery of a giant in a cave of Trápani (western Sicily); its body when touched fell to dust, but there remained a few bones (tres dentes monstruosae grandiciei, partem cranei anteriorem, os alterius cruris). The gigantic teeth were deposited in the Santuario dell' Annunziata (founded 1315). Boccaccio's account is one of the few early references to fossil bones. A much earlier one, somewhat related to Boccaccio's, was made by Phlegon of Tralles (fl. under Hadrian, emperor 117–38) in the *περὶ θαυμασίων*.[5] A. Pogo: Phlegon, Boccaccio and Kircher (Isis 33, 341, 1941).

(d) *De montibus, sylvis, fontibus, lacubus, fluminibus, stagnis seu paludibus, et de diversis nominibus maris liber.*. A short geographical dictionary, also the first of its kind, wherein the names of mountains are arranged in one alphabetical order, then the names of forests, etc. The mountains are dealt with first because of their altitude, then the forests which are found on their slopes, and the springs, the lakes, the rivers, the marshes in the low regions, and finally at the lowest level the seas. Whereas Petrarca was almost exclusively interested in historical geography, Boccaccio exhibits a remarkable curiosity about natural phaenomena, such as the killing of fishes by sulphurous exhalations near Pozzuoli, the white shells found along the river Elsa, and the calcareous films deposited by that river on various objects. However, in his articles on the river Arno and the fountain of Vaucluse (s.v. Sorgia), he speaks lengthily of his master Petrarca. There are at least five incunabula editions of this little book, but no incunabula translations. An Italian translation by the Venetian canon Niccolò Liburnio (1474–1557) was printed probably in Venice c. 1520.

Boccaccio used extensively but not exclusively the late Roman geographical glossary named after Vibius Sequester (fourth or fifth century).[6] Whether he "plagiarized" it or not is partly a matter of opinion; in any case, he failed to mention this, his primary source.

It should be noted that these four Latin works were composed simultaneously by Boccaccio, and that each, especially the third, occupied him for a relatively long part of his life.

4. *His study of Dante*

Boccaccio's Italian writings do not concern the historian of science, except the Decamerone because of its intrinsic importance and wide repercussions, and the Vita di Dante. The latter is a small book composed c. 1360, revised and shortened

[5] At a much earlier date still, Xenophanes (VI B.C.) referred to fossils but not to the bones of men. Arthur Stanley Pease: Fossil fishes again (Isis 33, 689–90, 1942).

[6] The Liber de fluminibus, de fontibus, de lacubus, de nemoribus, de paludibus, de montibus, de gentibus, de regionibus, de origine urbis Romae, etc. First edition by Jacob Mazzocchi (20 leaves, Rome 1505). Many times reprinted either separately or with other geographical books such as Pomponius Mela. Critical editions by Jeremias Jacob Oberlin (Strasbourg 1778); by Louis Baudet, with French translation (67 p., Paris 1843); by Conrad Bursian (program, 23 p., Zürich 1867). Albert Pueschel: De Vibii Sequestri libelli geographici fontibus et compositione (55 p., Halis Saxonum 1907).

by the author sometime later. The book was well documented and charmingly written. Modest as it is, it is a landmark in the history of biography; it might be called one of the first modern biographies. It was first printed in 1477.

On August 12, 1373, the republic of Florence instituted an annual course of public lectures (Lectura Dantis) to be devoted to the explanation of the Divina commedia, and a fortnight later Boccaccio was appointed the first lecturer. He lectured on the Divina commedia in the Benedictine church of Santo Spirito from October 23, 1373 until the spring of 1375, when his health broke down entirely. The fact that these lectures were needed and appreciated shows that by this time, half a century after Dante's death, the magnitude of Dante's work was already realized, even in his own birthplace. Indeed, Dante's fame had become a kind of superstition, and some people objected to the popularization of the Divina commedia as to a kind of desecration!

Boccaccio was one of the first defenders of Dante's legitimate fame (as against the superstitious perversions of it); he explained his work, tried to increase the number of MSS of it and their diffusion; awakened Petrarca's interest, and was one of the pioneers of "Dantology." He thus created a new kind of humanism, "Italian humanism," in addition to the classical humanism of his master Petrarca.

5. *His humanism*

Boccaccio was deeply influenced by Petrarca, who remained throughout his life his spiritual guide and guardian angel. His first meeting with him, in Florence 1350, was one of the main events of his life.

Petrarca infused him with the love of ancient letters. Boccaccio collected MSS, some of which he gave to Petrarca; some of them he copied with his own hand (e.g., the Terence of the Laurentian library). He visited many libraries in search of MSS and witnessed the ruinous condition and scandalous neglect of the Monte Cassino library. He was especially influenced by Livy and Tacitus. Many texts were discovered or first cited by him, the most important being Varro and Tacitus.

He bequeathed his MSS to the convent of Santo Spirito in Florence. The Florentine humanist Niccolò Niccoli (1363–1437) took care of that collection; according to a catalogue made in 1451, it contained 106 MSS.

He lacked the critical spirit of Petrarca as well as his poetical genius, and devoted himself to humbler philological tasks, the creation of some of the earlier philological tools, crude dictionaries of ancient mythology and geography.

He was the first modern European to study Greek to the extent of being able to read it. He obtained his knowledge from Paolo da Perugia, librarian to king Robert of Naples, and from the Greek-speaking Calabrian Leontius Pilatus, whom he kept in his own Florentine home for three years (1360–62). They read Homer together. Boccaccio's study of Greek was empirical and very imperfect, yet more direct than that of the average Greek scholar of today, and to that extent superior to it.

Like Petrarca, Boccaccio was looking backward rather than forward, yet he was helping to usher in a new age. He was the father of the new Greek learning, as well as the father of Italian humanism. He introduced us to Tacitus and to Homer.

6. *His scientific knowledge*

Boccaccio was not in any sense a scientist, but he took pains occasionally to obtain scientific information from the best sources available to him. He was influenced by the astronomer Andalò di Negro and the geometer Paolo Dagomari. An idea of his scientific knowledge may best be given by quoting his main sources: Aristotle (in Latin), Vitruvius, Pliny, Seneca (Natural questions), Pomponius Mela, Ptolemy's Quadripartitum with the commentary of 'Alī ibn Riḍwān, then Solinus, Orosius, Macrobius, Fulgentius,[7] Hrabanus Maurus, Abū Ma'shar, 'Alī ibn Riḍwān, St. Anselm, Albert the Great, Vincent of Beauvais. He was not acquainted with Roger Bacon.

An opuscule of Boccaccio (not published until 1827), De Canaria et de insulis reliquis ultra Hispaniam in Oceano noviter repertis, gives an account of an expedition to the Canary Islands led in 1341 by the Genoese Nicoloso da Recco (XIV-1). That opuscule, the MS of which was written in Boccaccio's own hand, includes the first description of those islands. It is interesting to recall that an earlier expedition to them by another Genoese, Lanzarote Malocello (c. 1270-75), was referred to by Petrarca.

7. *His character*

Boccaccio was a realist, somewhat cynical, but gentle, kind, and quiet. Some of his contemporaries called him "Giovanni della tranquillità." He was singularly modest. When praising Dante and Petrarca, he did not in the least realize that posterity would place him at their sides, and that his Decamerone would become one of the classics of Italian letters even as the Commedia divina and the Canzoniere. In fact, as he grew older he became a little ashamed of the Decamerone, and did not mention it to Petrarca until 1374.

One has the impression that Petrarca's influence lifted him as it were above himself. He could not, however, be a pure poet nor religious like his master. He was pious in the conventional manner; in 1362, after the visit of a mysterious personage, he experienced a sort of conversion, and his piety increased naturally with the gradual approach of death. His conscience was sometimes tormented because of his irrepressible curiosity about human frailties and pagan myths, but these anxieties were far more superficial than those which assailed Petrarca.

8. *Bibliographical guides and indexes*

Alberto Bacchi della Lega: Serie delle edizioni delle opere di Giovanni Boccacci latine, volgari, tradotte (162 p., Bologna 1875). Guido Traversari: Bibliografia boccaccesca. I. Scritti intorno al Boccaccio e alla fortuna delle sue opere (1,126 items, 284 p., Città di Castello 1907), no more published. Leo S. Olschki: Boccaccio (38 p., Florence 1920), only 196 titles.

There are no modern indexes or concordances, but vocabularies were published early by Lucilio Minerbi (Venice 1525), Fabricio Luna (Naples 1536), Antonio Brucioli (Venice 1538), Alberto Acariso (Cento 1543), Francesco Alunno (Venice 1543), Francesco Sansovino (Venice 1546), Girolamo Ruscelli (Venice 1552, 1553, 1557), etc.

For the Latin writings, see below in section 12.

9. *Text*

Collected edition of the Italian writings. Opere volgari (octavo, 6 vols., Florence 1723-24), edition dated Florence, but printed in Naples. Ignazio Moutier: Opere volgari corrette su i testi a penna (17 vols., Florence 1827-34). This includes the

[7] Fabius Planciades Fulgentius, Latin grammarian and mythologist, fl. c. 480-550.

Decamerone in vols. 1–5, and the Vita di Dante in vol. 15. Thus the Italian writings not referred to above fill more than 11 volumes.

Decamerone. First edition without place or date [Florence? 1469 or 1470]. Some 14 additional editions appeared in the fifteenth century. The best early edition is that printed by the Giunta in Florence 1527. An edition expurgated according to the decisions of the council of Trent appeared in Florence 1573. The expurgation consisted mainly in replacing disorderly monks and priests by laymen! Better editions by Pietro Antonio Guadagni and Angelo Maria Bandini (Lucca 1761) and by Pietro Fanfani (3 vols., Florence 1857). This last mentioned is as it were the vulgate.

German translation (Augsburg 1490, Ulm c. 1471). Bocace des cent nouvelles, French translation by Laurens de Premierfait (Paris 1485), often reprinted. Spanish translation (Sevilla 1496). Dutch translation by Dirick Coornher (Haarlem 1564). English translation, The Decameron containing an hundred pleasant novels (2 vols., London 1620). Vol. 1 was reprinted in 1625, under a new title, The modell of witt, mirth, eloquence and conversation.

De casibus virorum illustrium. Princeps s.a.l. [Strasbourg c. 1474/75]. Second edition, Paris after 1507. Third edition, Augsburg 1544.

Princeps of the French translation by Laurent de Premierfait, Bruges 1476. Eight French editions from 1476 to 1578.

John Bochas descrivinge the falle of princis princessis and other nobles translated by John Ludgate, monk of the monastery of Seint Edmundes Bury. First edition, London 1494; three or four times reprinted within sixty years (1527, 1554, 1555?, 1558).

Italian translation, Venice 1545, 1551, Florence 1598. Spanish translation, Seville 1495, Toledo 1511, Alcalà de Henares 1552. German translation, Augsburg 1545.

Total: at least 22 editions within a century, in six languages.

De claris mulieribus. Princeps, Ulm 1473. Other editions, one undated [Strasbourg c. 1474/75], Louvain 1487, Basel 1531, Bern 1539.

French translation, Paris 1493, 1538, Lyon 1551. Henry Parker's English translation, dedicated to Henry VIII, was printed in London 1789. Italian translation, princeps Venice 1506, seventh Milano 1841. Spanish translations, Zaragoza 1494, Seville 1528. German translation, Ulm 1473, Augsburg 1479, Strassburg 1488 (a fourth incunabula edition cannot be exactly dated and placed), fifth and sixth editions Augsburg 1541, 1543.

In all, 24 editions in six languages, 21 of which are anterior to the seventeenth century.

De genealogiis deorum and *De montibus.* These two works have generally been printed together. However, the two earliest editions—the one without place or date, the other Venice 1472—contain only the Genealogiae. The princeps of De montibus, Venice 1473, is also separate. After that date the two treatises were always printed together, as follows: Reggio 1481, Vicenza 1487, Venice 1494, 1497, 1511, Paris 1511, Basel 1532. A compendium of books 1–13 of the Genealogies was printed at Cologne c. 1472.

In addition, the Genealogies were twice printed in French (Paris 1498, 1531), and 11 times in Italian, all Venetian editions ranging from 1547 to 1644. The De montibus was twice printed in Italian: s.l.a. [Venice 1520?], Florence 1598.

Total: 22 editions of the Genealogiae in three languages, 19 of these editions being anterior to the seventeenth century; 10 editions of De montibus in two languages, all anterior to the seventeenth century.

De Canaria et de insulis reliquis. See my note on Nicoloso da Recco (XIV-1).

Vita di Dante. First edition (15 leaves folio), in the seventh edition of the Commedia divina, printed by Vendelin de Spiera in Venice 1477. Very often reprinted, in Dante's works, in Boccaccio's, or separately. English translations of Boccaccio's life of Dante by G. R. Carpenter (186 p., New York 1900); by James Robinson Smith (163 p., New York 1901); by Philip Henry Wicksteed (174 p., London 1904).

Commento della Divina commedia. First edited by Anton Maria Salvini (Firenze 1723–24), forming vols. 5 and 6 of the Opere volgari of Florence 1723–24. Often reprinted. Il commento alla Divina commedia e gli altri scritti dal Boccaccio intorno a Dante, a cura di Domenico Guerri (3 vols., Bari 1918).

Francesco Corazzini: Le lettere edite e inedite del Boccaccio tradotte e commentate con nuovi documenti (622 p., Firenze 1877).

De vita et moribus Domini Francisci Petrarchae secundum Johanem Bochacii, in Domenico de' Rossetti: Petrarca, Giulio Celso e Boccaccio (p. 316–24, Trieste 1828). Marquis de Valori: Document historique de Boccace sur Pétrarque, MS de la bibliothèque de Saint Marc, publié pour la première fois (78 p., Avignon 1851). This is the same text as the one published in 1828. Many times reprinted.

Oskar Hecker: Boccaccio-Funde; Stücke aus der bislang verschollenen Bibliothek des Dichters, darunter von seiner Hand geschriebenes Fremdes und Eigenes (336 p., 22 pl., Braunschweig 1902).

10. *Biographies and general criticism*

The first biography to be printed was the one by Hieronymo Squarzafico (or Squarciafico) of Alexandria, which appeared in appendix to Boccaccio's Filocolo (Venice 1467); often reprinted. This was followed by a number of grammatical and lexicographical studies which show that Boccaccio was very much esteemed in the sixteenth century. In Traversari's bibliography there is 1 fifteenth-century title, and 31 sixteenth-century titles, all Italian.

A great step forward was made by Giovanni Battista Baldelli: Vita di G. Boccaccio (444 p., Firenze 1806). Marcus Landau: Boccaccio (273 p., Stuttgart 1877). Gustav Koerting: Boccaccio (753 p., Leipzig 1880). Leonardo Bruni Aretino (1369–1444): Dialogus de tribus vatibus florentinis (Dante, Petrarca, Boccaccio) edited by Karl Wotke (32 p., Wien 1889). Emmanuel Rodocanachi: Boccace (256 p., Paris 1908). Edward Hutton: Boccaccio (454 p., London 1909). Henri Hauvette: Boccace (520 p., Paris 1914). Thomas Caldecot Chubb: The life of Boccaccio (298 p., New York 1930). Letterio Di Francia: elaborate illustrated article in Enciclopedia italiana (7, 219–29, 1930). Catherine (MacFarlane) Carswell: The tranquil heart. Portrait of Boccaccio (360 p., New York 1937).

11. *Criticism of the Decamerone*

Domenico Maria Manni: Istoria del Decamerone (708 p., Florence 1742), still fundamental in spite of Manni's lack of criticism; he imagined that there was a historical basis for each story, except those borrowed from ancient writers. Giovanni Lami: Appendice all'illustrazione istorica sul Decamerone, scritta da D. M. Manni (Milano 1820). Marcus Landau: Die Quellen des Dekameron (166 p., Wien 1869); second edition considerably enlarged (363 p., Stuttgart 1884). Giacomo Marcocchia: Una novella indiana (Çukasaptati,[8] textus simplicior XVI) nel Boccaccio e nel Molière (22 p., Spalatro 1905). A. Collingwood Lee: The Decameron, its sources and analogues (380 p., London 1909). Gustav Gröber: Die

[8] That is the Śukasaptati (the seventy stories of a parrot), one of the most popular collections of stories in Sanskrit literature, edited and translated by Richard Schmidt, Textus simplicior (Sanskrit, Leipzig 1897; German, Kiel 1894), Textus ornatior (Sanskrit, Munich 1901; German, Stuttgart 1899). Winternitz (3, 342–48, 1922). Emeneau (nos. 1458–76, 1935). The Persian version of those tales, Ṭūṭī-nāma, has been discussed above (p. 465).

Quellen von Boccaccio's Dekameron (102 p., Strassburg 1912). Otto Löhmann: Die Rahmenerzählung des Decameron (Romanistische Arbeiten no. 22, 240 p., Halle a.S. 1935).

12. *Studies on the Latin writings*

Attilio Hortis: Studj sulle opere latine del Boccaccio, con particolare riguardo alla storia della erudizione nel medio evo e alle letterature straniere, aggiuntavi la bibliografia delle edizioni (quarto, 976 p., Trieste 1879). Though this work is more than half a century old, it is still unsurpassed. It is fundamental. The author was born in Trieste in 1850, and died there in 1926. See notice by Mario Menghini in Enciclopedia italiana (18, 569, 1933, with portrait). He wrote many other papers on Boccaccio, e.g.: M. T. Cicerone nelle opere del Petrarca e del Boccaccio. Con lettere inedite di Matteo d'Orgiano e di Coluccio Salutati a Pasquino de Capellis (102 p., Trieste 1878); Le Additiones al De remediis fortuitorum di Seneca . . . La Corografia di Pomponio Mela attribuita falsamente a Boccaccio (56 p., Trieste 1879).

Emil Koeppel: Laurents de Premierfait und John Lydgates Bearbeitungen von Boccaccios De casibus virorum illustrium (112 p., Munich 1885). Julius Zupitza: Über die mittelenglische Bearbeitung von Boccaccios De claris mulieribus in der Handschrift der British Museum add. 10.304 (Festschrift . . . des deutschen Neuphilologentages p. 93–120, Berlin 1892). Paul Durrieu: Le Boccace de Munich, reproduction des 91 miniatures (130 p., 30 pl., Munich 1909), apropos of a MS of the translation of the De casibus by Laurent de Premierfait. Henry Martin: Le Boccace de Jean sans Peur des cas des nobles hommes et femmes. Reproduction des 150 miniatures du MS 5193 de l'Arsenal (86 p., 39 pl., Bruxelles 1912). Ernest Hatch Wilkins: The trees of the Genealogia deorum of Boccaccio (folio, 29 p., 24 pl., Chicago, Caxton Club 1923), edition de luxe, reproducing (pl. 2–14) the genealogical trees from the MS of the Genealogia deorum prepared for and owned by Coluccio Salutati and now in the library of the University of Chicago. Cornelia C. Coulter: Boccaccio's archaeological knowledge (American journal of archaeology 41, 397–405, 1937). Dorothy M. Robathan: Boccaccio's accuracy as a scribe (Speculum 13, 458–60, 1938).

13. *His influence*

Giovanni Papanti (editor): I parlari italiani alla festa del V centenario di Messer Giovanni Boccacci (750 p., Livorno 1875), includes the life of Boccaccio written by Filippo Villani (first printed in Florence 1826). Bernardo Sanvisenti: I primi influssi di Dante, del Petrarca e del Boccaccio sulla letteratura spagnuola, con appendici di documenti inediti (480 p., Milano 1902). Caroline Brown Bourland: Boccaccio and the Decameron in Castilian and Catalan literature (Bryn Mawr thesis 1902; Revue hispanique vol. 12, 242 p., ill., Paris 1905). Società storica della Valdelsa: Studii su G. Boccaccio (Castelfiorentino 1913).

14. *His scientific knowledge*

Attilio Hortis: Accenni alle scienze naturali nelle opere di G. Boccacci, e più particolarmente del libro De montibus, silvis, etc. (Boll. della Società adriatica di scienze naturali, anno 3, no. 2, 124 p., Trieste 1877). Gregorio Chil y Naranjo: Estudios historicos . . . de las Islas Canarias (Las Palmas, Gran-Canaria 1879). Beazley (3, 424–27, 1906). Dr. Bugiel: Boccace et la médecine (Comptes rendus du 2e Congrès international d'histoire de la médecine, Paris 1921, p. 544–51, Evreux 1922). H. Vorwahl: Die Medizin bei Boccaccio (AGM 28, 125–27, 1935).

15. *Varia*

Henri and Renée Kahane: Akritas and Arcita, a Byzantine source of Boccaccio's Teseida[9] (Speculum 20, 415–25, 1945), showing that Boccaccio was acquainted with the Byzantine popular epic Digenis Acritas, probably through oral account given to him by some Greek-speaking Italian. This completes the very elaborate study of Henri Grégoire: *Ὁ Διγενὴς Ἀκρίτας, ἡ βυζαντινὴ ἐποποιία στὴν ἱστορία καὶ στὴν ποίηση* (λη' + 336 p., New York 1942; Isis 34, 263). The Digenis Acritas should have been discussed in Introd. vol. 1 on the same grounds as the Chanson de Roland, but the author failed to do so because he did not then appreciate the importance of that subject (Krumbacher p. 827–32, 1897) and was inhibited by chronological doubts.

BENVENUTO DE' RAMBALDI

Italian humanist. The most important early commentator on Dante (d. 1390).

Benevenutus de Rambaldis. Benvenuto of the Rambaldi family, often called Benvenuto da Imola after the place Imola in Emilia (ancient Romagna, halfway between Bologna and Forli), where he was born c. 1336–1340. His father, Compagno, notary and lecturer on law, died in Imola before 1364. Benvenuto studied in Bologna and Florence, and during his stay in the latter city (1357–60) became acquainted with Boccaccio. He was in Bologna again in 1361–62, and in 1364, when he met Petrarca. In 1365 he was a member of the mission sent to Avignon by the Anziani of Imola to bespeak the good offices of Urban V. In Avignon he met his future patron, Niccolò II marquis of Este, and renewed his acquaintance with Boccaccio, delegate of Florence, one of many representatives of Italian cities who were beseeching the pope to return to Rome. Judging from various reminiscences of his (e.g., commentary on Inferno XIX), he was impressed and shocked by the corruption of the curia; he identified Avignon with Babylon! He remained in Provence probably until 1367, when he may have returned to Italy in the train of Urban V, going to Viterbo and Rome. During the following years he appears to have been out of favor in Imola, and to have spent most of his time teaching Latin and Italian letters in Bologna. In 1377 he was forced to take refuge in Ferrara, and spent the rest of his life there under the protection of Niccolò II d'Este, lord of Ferrara and Modena from 1361 to 1388. He died in 1390 (not 1380), probably in Ferrara.

Benvenuto's world was thus largely restricted to Imola, Bologna, Florence, and Ferrara, but he was acquainted with other cities, such as Rome and Venice. In Avignon he had learned to dislike the French, and he had come back intensely Italian. The main guides of his thought were Petrarca and Boccaccio.

He helped to revive the study of Latin literature in Bologna and Ferrara. He wrote a number of books in Latin, books of history and commentaries.

His historical works are: (1) Romuleon, a textbook on Roman history ab urbe condita to Diocletian. It was written at the request of Gomez Albornoz, governor of Bologna 1361–62, nephew of the famous cardinal Albornoz (q.v.). It has been ascribed also to a contemporary, Roberto da Porta of Bologna. It was soon translated into Italian, and also into French by Jean Melot, canon of Lille, for Philip duke of Burgundy. (2) Augustalis libellus. Lives of the emperors from Julius

[9] A critical edition of the Teseida was recently published by Salvatore Battaglia (545 p., Florence 1938; Speculum 14, 373–76). For the return influence of the Teseida on Greek writers see note on Theodoros Meliteniotes.

Caesar to Wenceslaus (1385). Written for Niccolò II d'Este. Sometimes wrongly ascribed to Petrarca. (3) De urbe mediolani.

More important are his commentaries on Latin writers of the first century, on Petrarca, and, above all, on Dante. He composed commentaries on the Pharsalia of Lucan (1378), the tragedies of Seneca, and the Dicta et facta memorabilia of Valerius Maximus (1388); on the Latin eclogues of Petrarca (before 1374).

All these works are practically forgotten, and Benvenuto himself would be forgotten, but for his great commentary on the Divina commedia, which was the most learned early commentary and has remained the foundation of all later discussions on Dante. The commentary of another trecentist, Francesco da Buti, is grammatical, whereas Benvenuto's is historical.

In 1373 Florence had established a Dante lectureship, the first lecturer being Boccaccio. Benvenuto went to Florence in that year (or in 1374) to listen to him. Not long afterward, in 1375, Bologna imitated the example given by Florence, and Benvenuto was invited to lecture on Dante. His elaborate Commentum was begun in Bologna and was even anterior to his public lectureship, for the draft of it was completed in 1373; it was amplified in Ferrara; the latest date referred to in it is 1379.

A commentary on Dante is bound to be as encyclopaedic as Dante himself, and hence Benvenuto's Commentum is an important source for fourteenth-century thought. It is not likely to be overlooked, as the substance of it has been integrated into later commentaries, e.g. those of William Warren Vernon (1834–1919), much used by English readers.

To illustrate the interest which that commentary may have for historians of science, two examples will suffice: Apropos of Inferno XXIX, Benvenuto discusses alchemical theories (2, 400 f.). As all metals are derived from mercury and sulphur, their differences are accidental, not essential; every metal is imperfect except gold and sulphur. Transmutation may not be theoretically impossible, yet all those who have tried to accomplish it have failed.

More important and more unexpected is the discussion of probabilities apropos of Purgatorio VI, giuoco della zara. This is the earliest mention of probabilities in world literature. It concerns the throwing of three dice. The lowest and highest throws, 3 and 18, can occur in only one way; the same is true of the throws next to the lowest and highest, 4 and 17, which can also occur only in one way, (1, 1, 2) or (6, 6, 5). This is incorrect. The commentator did not distinguish between permutations and combinations; in this case it is the permutations that count, and there are three ways of throwing (1, 1, 2) or (6, 6, 5). It should be noted that this passage does not occur in the Latin text edited by Lacaita (3, 166 f.) nor in Tamburini's version (2, 124). The first to draw attention to it was Libri (1838), who quoted the relevant text from a MS of his, but is that text Benvenuto's or that of Jacopo della Lana? In either case, this earliest problem of probabilities dates from the end of the fourteenth century, and Todhunter was right in beginning his history with it.[10] The next step in that theory, in the form of two more problems of probabilities, wrongly solved, was taken a full century later in the Summa de arithmetica of Luca Pacioli (Venice 1494); these were the very first problems of their kind to appear in print.

Dante's giuoco della zara started another discussion concerning the word zara (ad azarum, ludum azari). Libri derived it from the Arabic 'asīr (difficult); it is

[10] Isaac Todhunter: History of the mathematical theory of probability (Cambridge 1865).

more probably connected with the Arabic word zahr (pl. azhār), meaning dice. Cf. Spanish azár (an unfortunate throw at dice, accident), our own word hazard and its equivalents in other European languages.

In the commentary on Inferno XXIX there are references to the great plagues which devastated Italy in 1348 and 1362.

Text. Benvenuto's commentary on the Divina commedia was supposed to have been edited for the first time by Cristoforo Berardi da Pesaro and printed in Spires 1477. That text was used by the Accademia della Crusca as a genuine Benvenuto text. It has since been shown, however, that it was the work of Jacopo della Lana, a Bolognese trecentist; it has been reprinted in Milano 1865, and again by Luciano Scarabelli (Bologna 1866). I have not seen these editions.

Passages of historical interest were extracted from Benvenuto's commentary by Lodovico Antonio Muratori and included in his Antiquitates italicae medii aevi (1, 1027–1298, Milano 1738). A very poor Italian translation of the whole commentary, based upon the very MS used by Muratori, was made by Giovanni Tamburini: Benvenuto Rambaldi da Imola illustrato nella vita e nelle opere e di lui commento latino sulla Divina commedia voltato in italiano (3 vols., Imola 1855–56).

First integral edition of the Latin text made at the expense of William Warren Vernon by Jacobo Philippo Lacaita (5 vols., Florence 1887). The Dante Society of Cambridge, Mass. had contemplated the publication of Benvenuto's Commentary, and published in 1881 a circular relative to that project (cf. series of MS documents ad hoc, dated 1863 to 1882, in the Harvard Library).

Giuseppe Guatteri: Il Romuleo di Mess. Benvenuto da Imola volgarizzato nel buon secolo e messo per la prima volta in luce (2 vols., Bologna 1867–68). Henry Martin: La Romuléon (Paris 19—), album containing 18 p. of text plus 60 fig. on 40 pl., reproducing illustrations of MS 667 of the Bibliothèque de l'Arsenal (Les joyaux de l'Arsenal no. 2, Paris in or before 1915).

Liber augustalis. First printed in Petrarchae opera (Basel 1496, again 1581). Edition by Laur. Abstemius (Strassburg 1505); and by Marquardus Freher: Rerum germanicarum scriptores (vols. 1–3, 1600–11; 2, 1–15), reprinted with the supplement of Aeneas Sylvius (Pius II, 1405–1464), down to emperor Friedrich III (1440), in the new edition of Freher's collection prepared by Gotth. Struve (2, 1–24, Strassburg 1717).

Petrarchae Bucolicum carmen cum commentario Benevenuti Rambaldi Imolensis (Venice 1516).

Criticism. Libri (2, 188–89, 1838). Luigi Rossi-Casè: Di maestro Benvenuto (232 p., Pergola 1889). Cantor (2, 327, 1899). Paget Toynbee: Benvenuto and the Iliad and Odyssey (Romania 29, 403–15, 1900); Benvenuto and his commentary on the Divina commedia (An English miscellany presented to Dr. Furnivall on his 75th birthday p. 436–61, Oxford 1901); Index of authors quoted by Benvenuto in his commentary (Dante Society, Cambridge, 18th and 19th annual reports 1901). Vincenzo Ussani: Di una doppia redazione del commento di Benvenuto al poema di Lucano (Rendiconti della R. Accad. dei Lincei, sci. mor., vol. 11, Roma 1902). Michele Barbi: Il testo della "lectura" bolognese di Benvenuto nel cosidetto Stefano Talice da Ricaldone[11] (Bull. della Società dantesca italiana 15, 213–36, 1908). Fausto Ghisalberti: Le chiose virgiliane di Benvenuto (Studi virgiliani, celebrazione bimillenaria, R. Accad. virgiliana, 77 p., Mantova 1930). Thorndike (3, 632, 1934), about alchemy.

[11] Stefano Talice, who flourished c. 1474, wrote a commentary on the Divina commedia. It was published for the first time with the Commedia, by Vincenzo Promis and Carlo Negroni (Torino 1886).

MARSIGLIO OF FLORENCE

Florentine Augustinian, one of the founders of the humanistic revival, friend and commentator of Petrarca (d. 1394).

Luigi Marsiglio (or Luigi de' Marsigli, de' Marsili), Ludovicus Marsilius, was born in the first third of the fourteenth century, and died on August 21, 1394. He was an Augustinian monk and had become a master of theology in Paris. After having traveled in France and Italy, he came back to Florence about 1379, and the monastery of Santo Spirito, where he resided, soon became, thanks to him, the seat of a kind of academy and a center of humanistic influence. In 1382 he was sent as ambassador to the duke of Anjou. He was a friend of Petrarca, who urged him to write "contra canem illum rabidum Averroim," yet could not convince him; on the other hand, he was very deeply interested in classical literature, was familiar with Cicero, Vergil, and Seneca, and discussed the Odyssey. He influenced such men as Coluccio Salutati and Niccolò de' Niccoli.

He wrote commentaries on two canzoni of Petrarca and on three sonnets written by the latter against the court of Avignon.

His importance to us lies in his being a forerunner of the Florentine revival of learning. He prefigures two essential characteristics of the Renaissance: on the positive side, the love of classical literature (Greek, Latin, even Italian); and on the negative side, the hatred of logic, scholasticism, Averroism.

Criticism. Francesco Selmi: Documenti cavati dai trecentisti circa al potere temporale della chiesa (Rivista contemporanea 30, 91-137, 1862), includes a letter written by Luigi Marsigli in Paris 1375. Symonds (1, 73, 1877). Arnaldo della Torre: Storia dell' Accademia platonica di Firenze (876 p., Firenze 1902; p. 173-90). Sandys (2, 10, 17, 1908).

SALUTATI

Coluccio Salutati. Italian humanist (1331-1406). He must be named immediately after Petrarca (1304-74) and Boccaccio (1313-75) as one of the founders of the Italian renaissance on the literary side.

Lino Coluccio son of Piero dei Salutati was born on February 16, 1331, at Stignano, in the Valdinievole, which had made a compact with Florence in 1329 but been conquered by Lucca in the following year. Piero, who had been the instigator of that compact, had taken refuge in Bologna, where his wife joined him in 1331 with Coluccio and the other children. Thus Coluccio was educated as an exile in Bologna, his main teacher being Pietro da Muglio. His primary interest was already literary, but in 1346 he was registered as a notary apprentice at the University of Bologna. He remained in Bologna until c. 1351. By that time, Florence having reconquered the Valdinievole, he established himself as a notary in his native place. From 1351 to 1374, he performed the duties of notary and judge in various cities: Stignano, Todi, Rome (in the service of the apostolic secretary, Francesco Bruni), Lucca, etc. In 1374 he entered the service of the republic of Florence and became its chancellor or Latin secretary in the following year. The rest of his life was splendidly devoted to that office. He died in Florence on May 4, 1406.

Salutati was first and last a humanist, and his chief distinction is to have introduced humanism into politics. He substituted in his briefs, reports, and letters the use of classical (Ciceronian) Latin for that of mediaeval Latin, which by that time had terribly degenerated. His example was gradually imitated in all the chancelleries of Europe, and the study of classical Latin became a professional necessity. Salutati's own letters were used as models by ambitious clerks, e.g., Sbignew Olesnicky, bishop of Cracow in 1423 and secretary to the king of Poland.

Salutati was a correspondent of Petrarch and Boccaccio. He ordered and owned a beautiful illustrated MS of the latter's Genealogia deorum (now in the University of Chicago). Under the influence of these predecessors, and especially of Petrarch, he collected Latin MSS. He sought vainly for the lost books of Livy and for complete MSS of Curtius and Quintilian, but he obtained many others discovering Cato's Agricultura and (in 1392) a part of Cicero's correspondence, the letters Ad familiares, unknown to Petrarch. The letters Ad Atticum, etc., were represented by the Verona MS, the letters Ad familiares by the Vercelli MS, both in Milano; the copies of both MSS made for Salutati are now in the Laurentian of Florence (together with the Vercelli original). We may say that Salutati was the first modern to know the whole of Cicero's correspondence.

In addition, he was one of the first to collate MSS and to develop the methods of textual criticism. This caused him to complain of the many imperfections of the available copies of Latin and Italian classics; it enabled him to recognize the spuriousness of the De differentiis ascribed to Cicero. He collated MSS of Seneca and St. Augustine. He encouraged younger men, such as Leonardo Bruni (Leonardo Aretino, c. 1374–1444) and Poggio Bracciolini of Florence (1380–1459), to work in the same direction. Though he was not himself a Greek scholar, he used his great influence for the promotion of Greek studies. He encouraged Giacomo da Scarperia to go to Constantinople and search for Greek MSS. He was largely responsible for the creation of the first chair of Greek in Florence and the appointment of Manuel Chrysoloras (1396–1400).

He wrote a large number of letters which are of great interest for the study of his time, and a few treatises, which are somewhat in the nature of rhetorical exercises (this being the unavoidable reverse of humanism). For example, in 1399 he wrote a tract De nobilitate legum et medicinae, wherein he discusses whether medicine is superior to law or not; this seems to have been a favorite theme of disputation in the fourteenth and fifteenth centuries in Florence. Salutati's treatise was one of the oldest and longest of its kind; it throws some light on the medical profession and its peculiar problems.

Another tract of his, composed in 1400, deals with tyranny, a painful subject which was as timely in his days as it is today. Salutati was a Guelph, and during his long administration of Florentine foreign policy, his main concern was to check Milanese imperialism. The De tyranno was based upon a similar treatise by Bàrtolo da Sassoferrato, but Salutati dealt with that burning question from the humanistic rather than from the purely legal point of view.

By the end of the century Salutati was the foremost defender of so-called pagan letters against Christian ones. He claimed that the rulers of states should have a secular as well as a religious education. He developed the Boccaccian theme "Veritas sub cortice falsitatis." Secular learning strengthens the faith because "Veritas a quocumque dicatur a Deo est." The pagan sciences are needed to understand metaphysics and even the Scriptures; the latter contain only a part of the truth, not the whole of it, etc. His arguments were clearly restated, then refuted one by one in the scholastic manner, by the Dominican Giovanni Dominici (1356-1419) in the Lucula noctis (1405).[12]

His views on astrology are set forth in a poem and letter in answer to Iacobo Allegretti of Mantua, a contemporary poet, physician, and astrologer; in a treatise De fato et fortuna libri III; and passim in his correspondence. His attitude is rather against than for astrology, but he was too prudent to commit himself on a subject about which he realized his fundamental ignorance. To be sure, the burden of proof was on the shoulders of the astrologers, but they evaded it by endless equivocations, and how could a man of letters prove their error? It must be said to Salutati's credit that he resisted astrological superstition instead of encouraging it; we could not expect more from him.

To conclude, it should be remarked that though Salutati's humanism was largely a matter of style, it went much deeper. It revealed a new attitude of the soul with regard to such fundamental subjects as liberty vs. tyranny, common sense vs. superstitions, religion vs. bigotry.

Text. Tractatus de nobilitate legum et medicinae, Venice 1542.

Alfred von Martin: Salutati's Traktat vom Tyrannen. Eine kulturgeschichtliche Untersuchung nebst Textedition (140 p., Berlin 1913). Francesco Ercole: Tractatus de tyranno (Quellen der Rechtsphilosophie 1, Berlin 1914). Emerton (p. 25-116, 287-377, 1925), contains translation of the De tyranno and of Salutati's letters in defense of liberal studies, with introductions.

Francesco Novati: Epistolario di Coluccio Salutati (4 vols. in 5, Roma 1891-1911). Published by the Istituto storico italiano in the collection Fonti per la storia d'Italia, epistolari. This is fundamental for the study of Salutati and his environment. The last volume (IV, 2, 1911) contains elaborate indexes, incipits of all the letters, glossaries. The index of proper names is a precious tool for the study of that period.

Criticism. Alfred von Martin: Mittelalterliche Welt- und Lebensanschauung im Spiegel der Schriften Salutatis (176 p., München 1913); Salutati und das humanistische Lebensideal (308 p., Leipzig 1916). Ernest Hatch Wilkins: The trees of the Genealogia deorum of Boccaccio (29 p., 24 pl., Chicago 1923), apropos of the MS written and limned for Salutati.

Lynn Thorndike: Medicine versus law in late medieval and Medicean Florence (Romanic review 17, 8-31, 1926; Isis 9, 155), reprinted in: Science and thought in the fifteenth century (p. 24-58, New York 1929; Isis 14, 235-40); History of magic (3, 515-17, 1934); Salutati on disputations (p. 266-69, 1944), urging the practice of disputations on the young humanists of Florence.

Theodore P. Rich: Giovanni da Sanminiato and Coluccio Salutati (Speculum 11, 386-90, 1936), illustrating Salutati's defense of poetry and literature.

GIOVANNI DA RAVENNA (II)

Giovanni di Iacopo Malpaghini. Italian humanist, born at Ravenna c. 1346, died in Florence 1417. Studied under the grammarian Donato degli Albanzani, first in Ravenna, then in Venice. While Petrarca was residing in that city, in 1364, Giovanni became his secretary and helped him to edit his correspondence and verse, and copied for him the translation of Homer by Leonzio Pilato (MS now in the Bibliothèque nationale, Paris). In 1368, he left Petrarca and entered the service

[12] The Lucula noctis was circulated in MSS but remained unpublished until recently. First edition by Remi Coulon (Paris 1908); new edition by Edmund Hunt (Notre Dame, Ind. 1940; Isis 36, 27).

of the apostolic secretary, the Florentine Francesco Bruni; he accompanied the curia to Avignon when Urban V returned there (1370). In 1394, we find him in Florence, where he delivered the Dante lectures for a few years and where he spent the remainder of his life.

In spite of the fact that there are no works bearing his name, he is doubly important in the history of humanism, first as Petrarca's assistant, and secondly as the inspirer of the so-called Florentine school, out of which issued such men as Giacomo d'Angelo (d. after 1410), Leonardo Bruni (d. 1444), and Poggio (d. 1459).

He should not be confused (as has been the case until recently) with another Giovanni da Ravenna, Giovanni di Conversino.

Criticism. Pierre de Nolhac: Pétrarque et l'humanisme (new ed., 2 vols., Paris 1907; 1, 74, 118, 270). Remigio Sabbadini: Giovanni da Ravenna, insigne figura d'umanista, da documenti inediti (270 p., Como 1924).

VERGERIO

Pietro Paulo Vergerio, il Vecchio. Italian humanist and educator writing exclusively in Latin (1370–1444).

The elder Vergerio was born in Capo d'Istria (not far from Trieste) on July 23, 1370 (not in 1349 as is often repeated). He studied in the grammar school in Padua 1385, and in the following year began to teach dialectics in Florence. There he made the acquaintance of Coluccio Salutati and Francesco Zabarella (1360–1417), later cardinal. From 1388 to 1390 he taught logic in Bologna and studied physics and medicine. From 1390 to 1397 we find him again in Padua, teaching logic, continuing his studies of medicine and law, and frequenting the circle of the chancellor Giovanni di Conversino da Ravenna, famous rhetorician. In 1398–1400, he read Greek in Florence under Manuel Chrysoloras, then returned to Padua to continue his studies and obtained in 1405 the doctorate in the arts, medicine, canon and civil law! The years 1405–9 were spent in the Roman curia under Innocent VII and Gregory XII. He attended the council of Constance 1414–18. He met there the emperor Sigismund, and returned with him to Bohemia, being the first Italian humanist to enter the service of a foreign prince. The rest of his life was apparently spent in the emperor's service as secretary and humanist. He traveled with the emperor in Bohemia and Hungary, translated for him into Latin Arrian's Anabasis (II-1) and perhaps Herodian (III-1), wrote letters, etc. Very little is known of his life during that final period. It is possible that after Sigismund's death (in 1437) he withdrew into a monastery in Budapest. He died in that city on July 8, 1444.

His earliest work (Bologna c. 1389) was a Terentian comedy, Paulus. In Padua 1395 he edited Petrarca's epic poem Africa, and wrote a short biography of the poet; at about the same time, he composed a treatise on prosody, De arte metrica, with Zabarella, and wrote a few other dissertations: De republica Venetorum, De situ Iustinopolis, and perhaps the De principibus carrariensibus (on the condottieri of the Carrara family, lords of Padua). His main work and his best title to remembrance is the treatise De ingenuis moribus et liberalibus studiis, which was probably written in Padua (c. 1401) immediately after his second return from Florence, when he was still strongly under Chrysoloras' influence. An earlier date (1392) has been suggested (e.g., by Sandys) for the same work, but is less plausible. The De ingenuis moribus was dedicated to the young Ubertino da Carrara (b. 1390), and it referred frequently to Francesco II Novello da Carrara (signore di Padova from 1388 on). It is a treatise on the liberal arts for young aristocrats, wherein much attention is paid also to moral education and to physical education centered on military training. It tried to harmonize humanism with religion. It was the earliest systematic treatise wherein the necessity for the study of Latin literature was explained, as well as the fundamental importance of style, especially on the Ciceronian pattern; its influence throughout the Renaissance was very great. Vergerio wrote the first modern introduction to the study of Quintilian (I-2). This must have been after 1416, when a MS of the Institutio oratoria was discovered by Poggio (1380–1459) in St. Gall.

At the council of Constance, after the forced abdication of John XXIII (1415), he defended the urgent need of reforms of the church in capite et membris, urging with the imperial party that that reform should precede the election of a new pontiff. In this he opposed the Latin group of prelates, in particular his old friend cardinal Zabarella.

Pietro Paolo Vergerio il Vecchio should not be confused with Pietro Paolo Vergerio il Giovane, also of Capo d'Istria, born in 1498, a Catholic bishop who became a Lutheran, flourished at Tübingen, and died there in 1565. For students of the Reformation the younger Vergerio is naturally the greater, if not the only one.

Text. Paulus. Comoedia ad iuvenum mores corrigendos. Edited by Karl Müllner (Wiener Studien vol. 22, 1900). Also edited by A. C. Pierantoni in appendix to his work on Vergerio seniore (Chieti 1920).

De ingenuis moribus. Venice 1470, Rome c. 1474, Florence c. 1481, Venice 1491, 1493, etc. At least 40 editions appeared before 1600. English translation by William Harrison Woodward in his Vittorino da Feltre (p. 93–118, Cambridge 1897).

De republica veneta fragmenta. Nunc primum in lucem edita. Edited by Emanuele Antonio Cicogna (25 p., Venice 1830).

C. A. Combi: Epistole (Venezia 1887). Leonardo Smith: Epistolario del Pier Paolo Vergerio (Fonti per la storia d'Italia, epistolari, secolo XIV–XV, 618 p., Roma 1934).

Criticism. Sandys (2, 48, 1908). Conrad Bischoff: Studien zu P. P. Vergerio dem Älteren (Abhandlungen zur mittleren und neueren Geschichte no. 15, 108 p., Berlin 1909). K. A. Bopp: Vergerio, der erste humanistische Pädagoge (Lucerna 1893). G. Jachino: Del pedagogista Vergerio (Firenze 1894). Leonardo Smith: Note chronologiche vergeriane (Archivio veneto tridentino 10, 149–57, 1926; Archivio veneto, 5th ser., 4, 92–141, Venezia 1928).

DIETRICH VON NIEM

German teacher of chancellors, historian, and reformer (c. 1343–1418).

Theodericus de Nyem. Dietrich (Theoderich) was born in Niem or Nieheim, Westphalia, between 1338 and 1348. He became a notary of the papal rota in Avignon and followed the curia to Rome in 1376; he was then appointed abbreviator of the papal chancery; bishop of Verden 1395; died at Maestricht on the Meuse in 1418.

He composed two treatises dealing with the methods of chancellery, Stilus palatii abbreviatus (c. 1378–89) and Liber (sive Formula) cancellariae apostolicae (1380), but is chiefly remembered for a number of pamphlets on matters of ecclesiastical politics.

The vicissitudes of the Great Schism had made him realize the urgent need of ecclesiastical reform, and he was one of the main artisans of the council of Constance. His main works are the Nemus unionis (1408) and the treatise on the schism, De scismate libri III (1410), of which his biography of John XXIII (Baldassarre Cossa, pope 1410-15, died 1419) was a sort of continuation. The purpose of these works was controversial rather than historical, yet their historical value is considerable.

He was essentially orthodox and moderate, anxious for union even more than for reform, yet the abuses of the curia had stirred him so deeply that he felt obliged to describe them. Mind you, the conditions which he was describing were those of the time of Urban VI and later, that is, Roman, not Avignonese. He showed how the cardinals neglected their duties, he explained the wretched finances of the church, the greed of Boniface IX, the despicableness and nepotism of John XXIII, their crooked politics, etc. As the popes and cardinals could not be expected to surrender their power, the only way out was for the emperor to depose both popes. As years went on his accusations became bolder. The popes and cardinals should be deprived of their wealth and of their scandalous means of increasing it. He denounced the financial abuses, the immorality of the clergy, but insisted that the main evil of the church was in its head, the pope and sacred college.

Text. For a long time the Nemus unionis was wrongly considered to be the fourth book of De scismate (in reality it is an earlier work), and it was published many times as such. First edition of De scismate alone, Nuremberg 1532-36. First edition of both works together by Simon Schardius, Basel 1566, reprinted Nuremberg 1592, Strassburg 1609, 1629. Georg Erler: De scismate libri III (362 p., Leipzig 1890), critical edition with notes and index.

Historia de vita Johannis XXIII. First edition by the elder Heinrich Meibom (Francfort 1620). Later editions by the younger Heinrich Meibom: Rerum germanicarum tomi III (1, 1-50, 1688) and by Hermann von der Hardt: Magnum oecumenicum constantiense concilium (2, 335-460, 1697).

Hermann Heimpel: Dialog über Union und Reform der Kirche 1410, De modis uniendi et reformandi ecclesiam in concilio universali, mit einer zweiten Fassung 1415 (152 p., Leipzig 1933).

Georg Erler: Der Liber cancellariae apostolicae (1380) und der Stilus palatii abbreviatus (266 p., Leipzig 1888). New fragments of that Liber have been edited by Wilhelm Altmann (Neues Archiv der Gesellschaft für ältere deutsche Geschichtskunde 15, 418-22, 1890).

For other writings, see Potthast (p. 1051-55, 1896).

Criticism. Theodor Lindner (ADB 23, 671, 1886). Georg Erler: Dietrich von Nieheim (552 p., Leipzig 1887). Willem Johannes Maria Mulder: Dietrich von Nieheim, zijne opvatting van het concilie en zijne kroniek (Leiden thesis, 362 p. in 2 vols., Amsterdam 1907). Flick (1, 338-40, 1930). Hermann Heimpel: Dietrich von Niem (Münster i.W. 1932).

CATALAN

BERNAT METGE

Catalan writer (c. 1350-c. 1410).

Bernat Metge was born in Barcelona c. 1350; though metge is the Catalan form of the word medicus, it does not follow that he was a physician. He was a courtier and secretary in the service of En Joan (= Don Juan), son of Pere III el Cerimoniós; when En Joan became king Joan I el Caçador in 1387, Bernat continued to enjoy his favor, and was secretary to the queen Na Violante (= Doña Violante). After the king's death he fell into disgrace, and was even thrown for a time into prison (c. 1398). Later he was restored to favor, and was the secretary of Marti I l'Humà from 1403 to 1410. After that year he is no longer heard of.

He was one of the best Catalan writers of his time, and exerted much influence not only upon Catalan letters, but also upon Spanish ones; he was the main channel through which Italian letters reached the Peninsula. His first work, c. 1381, was the poem entitled Libre de fortuna e prudencia. About 1388 he translated the last story of the Decamerone from the Latin elaboration of it by Petrarca, Historia de Valter e Griselda (this was the first appearance of a part of the Decamerone in the Peninsula). His largest and most important work was written in prison 1398, Del sompni (= somnus, dream), which is in some respects comparable to Il corbaccio o il laberinto d'amore of Boccaccio. It reveals his ironical point of view and his erudition, e.g., in his discussion of the immortality of the soul. Metge was somewhat of a doubter and satirist, sharing fully the misogynic feelings prevalent in his time (cf. Boccaccio, Chaucer, Froissart).

Metge was not a philosopher, but his cultural influence was so great that he deserves to be dealt with in this volume together with the men just mentioned. He was the perfecter of the Catalan language, and placed it on as high a level as French and Italian.

Text. Joseph Michel Guardia: Le songe de Bernat Metge. Publié et traduit en français (452 p., Paris 1889). Les obres d'En Bernat Metge. Textes autèntichs publicats envista detots els manuscrits coneguts per R. Miquel y Planas (252 p., Barcelona 1910).

Criticism. EUI (34, 1254–55). Anfós Par: Sintaxi catalana segons los escrits en prosa de Bernat Metge, 1398 (590 p., Halle 1923).

The "Fundació Bernat Metge, collecció catalana dels autors grecs i llatins" was established in Barcelona, c. 1923, for the publication of a series of classics in Greek (or Latin) and in Catalan. Admirable monument to the spiritual energy and deep humanity of the Catalan people. For information about that great effort see E. Allison Peers: Catalonia infelix (p. 182, London 1937). At the time of Peers' writing, 85 scholarly volumes had already been published.

GREEK

DIASSORINOS

Neilos Diassorinos or Diasorenos, Νεῖλος ὁ Διασσωρινός or Διασωρηνός. Byzantine theologian and rhetorician (d. in or after 1376).

He came from Chios, and his original name was Nicetas, but he assumed the name Neilos when he became a monk. He took sides with the Palamites, that is, the mystical party, and against the Latins or Latinizing party. In 1357 he was consecrated metropolitan of Rhodes, and in 1366 the patriarch Philotheos made him his prefect (ἔξαρχος); in 1369 he was driven away from Rhodes by the knights of St. John; he was deposed by Macarios (patriarch 1376–79, 1390–91); hence he was still living in 1376.

His main work seems to be a treatise on grammar, rhetoric, and logic which he entitled Πηγὴ γνώσεως (Fountain of knowledge). This was somewhat pretentious, for that is the very title of a famous work by John of Damascus (VIII-1). He wrote a summary of the nine oecumenical councils according to the Orthodox tradition (the ninth being the Palamite council of 1341), Διήγησις συνοπτικὴ περὶ τῶν ἁγίων καὶ οἰκουμενικῶν συνόδων, various religious books and rhetorical exercises, and a few technical treatises, περὶ λίθων (on stones), περὶ γεννήσεως τεχνικῆς (artificial generation?), περὶ κατασκευῆς μύρου Μωσαϊκοῦ (preparation of the Mosaic ointment), *περὶ χρόνου βισέκτου* (intercalary, bissextile, time). These technical writings are practically unknown (Escorial MS).

Text. The *Διήγησις* has been published many times, e.g., by Guillaume Voel and Henri Justel (1620–93): Bibliotheca iuris canonici veteris (2, 1155–60, Paris 1661); by Jean Hardouin (1646–1729): Conciliorum collectio regia maxima (5, 1479–86, Paris 1715).

Partial edition of the *Πηγή* by Gustav Uhlig: Appendix artis Dionysii Thracis (50 p., Leipzig 1881).

Criticism. Krumbacher (p. 560, 1897). V. Grumel (DTC 11, 674, 1931). A. Revilla: Catálogo de los códices griegos de el Escorial (1, no. 56, 1–2, Madrid 1936), apropos of the lapidary.

CHRYSOLORAS

Manuel Chrysoloras, Μανουὴλ ('Εμμανουὴλ) Χρυσολωρᾶς. Byzantine humanist, one of the founders of Greek humanism in the West (d. 1415).

Manuel was born at Constantinople about the middle of the century. It is said that he was related to the Palaeologoi; in any case, he was familiar with Manuel II Palaeologos (emperor 1391–1425), who sent him on a mission to Venice in 1394/95 to obtain help against the Turks. Giacomo d'Angelo returned with him to Constantinople and was thus launched in his own career as a collector of Greek MSS. The signory of Florence invited Chrysoloras to become a teacher of Greek, and he began his lectures in February 1397, continuing them until 1400, and attracting to Florence many students, even from foreign countries. These Florentine lectures on Greek language and literature (1397–1400) mark the true beginning of Greek humanism in Western Europe. He occasionally gave lectures in other Italian towns, and attained an immense influence as a teacher, second only to that of Giovanni da Ravenna.

His main disciples were Giacomo d'Angelo da Scarperia (d. after 1410), Coluccio Salutati (1331–1406), Niccolò de' Niccoli (1363–1437), Roberto de' Rossi, Palla degli Strozzi (1370–1462), Pietro Paulo Vergerio il Vecchio (1370–1444), Guarino Veronese (c. 1370–1460), Leonardo Bruni (c. 1374–1444), Poggio Bracciolini (1380–1459), Ambrogio Traversari (1386–1439), but he influenced directly or indirectly a great many others.

In 1400 he accompanied Manuel Palaeologos to Pavia, and remained in Lombardy to continue his Byzantine propaganda (political as well as literary), while the emperor proceeded to France and England; in 1403 he returned with the emperor to Constantinople. He made short visits to Venice in 1404 and 1406, and in 1407 left Constantinople for the last time, going to Venice, France (1408), England (1409), Spain (1410). In that same year 1410 he met John XXIII (pope 1410–15) in Pavia, and from that time on he remained attached to the curia, which he followed to Rome (1411) and other places. In 1413 John XXIII delegated him to the emperor Sigismund to fix the date of a new council. Chrysoloras attended the council of Constance (1414–18), but died not long after the beginning of it, on April 15, 1415, in Constance.

His influence was much greater as a teacher than as a writer. He wrote a catechism of Greek grammar, 'Ερωτήματα, the earliest Greek grammar used in the West. There are many letters of his. He began a Latin translation of Plato's Republic, which was completed after his death by one of his disciples, Uberto Decembrio (1370–1427). A revision of that translation was dedicated in 1440 by the latter's son Pier Candido Decembrio (1399–1477) to Humphrey duke of Gloucester (1391–1447).

Manuel Chrysoloras should not be confused with his contemporary Demetrios Chrysoloras of Salonica, who was also a friend and correspondent of Manuel Palaeologos, but was primarily a theologian and definitely anti-Latin, his main adversary being another Salonican, Demetrios Cydones. Demetrios Chrysoloras wrote many theological treatises.

Text. The Ἐρωτήματα was first published in Florence c. 1484 and in Venice 1484. There is at least a third incunabula edition, Florence c. 1496. Many more editions, either Greek or Greco-Latin, in the sixteenth century: Venice 1512, Alcala 1514, etc.

Epistolae tres de comparatione veteris et novae Romae, edited by Peter Lambeck (1628–80), in appendix to a work of Georgios Codinos (Γεώργιος ὁ Κωδινός ὁ κουροπαλάτης, that is, an imperial major-domo), shadowy figure of the last Byzantine days (Paris 1655, again 1729). Reprinted in PG (vol. 156, 1866).

Criticism. Very little in Krumbacher (1897) and in Sandys (vol. 1, 3d ed., 1921; vol. 2, 1908).

Symonds (2, 79–82, 1877). Emile Legrand: Bibliographie hellénique aux XVe et XVIe siècles (1, xix–xxx, 1885; vols. 2–4, 1885–1906). A. Palmieri (DTC 2, col. 2420–23, 1923). Eleutheroudakis encyclopaedia (12, 973, 1931). Vasiliev (2, 428–30, 1932).

MANUEL II PALAEOLOGOS

Μανουὴλ ὁ Παλαιολόγος. Byzantine emperor (1391–1425), rhetorician, moralist, and apologist.

Manuel was born at Constantinople in 1348, being the son of Joannes V Palaeologos and Helena Cantacuzena; he became emperor in 1391; died in 1425 in the monastery of the Pantocrator, where he had spent the last year of his life in retirement, and where he was buried.

He had received a very elaborate literary and theological education, and was a humanist who found opportunities for writing considerably and elegantly in spite of endless political troubles. He lived for a time (c. 1390) as a hostage at the court of Bāyazīd I ('Uthmānlī sulṭān 1389–1402). After the failure of the Nicopolis crusade (1396), the situation became more ominous, and he traveled in 1399–1402 to Italy, France, and England with the hope of obtaining Catholic help against the Turks. These hopes did not materialize, but Tīmūr Lang's (Tamerlane's) successful invasion of Anatolia in 1401[13] gave Manuel some respite, and diplomatic intrigues enabled him to stave off the ruin of the empire until the accession of Murād II in 1421, when matters became much worse again. Manuel's voyage to the West and particularly his long stay in Paris (almost two years) is a landmark in the history of humanism; it is one of the many events which prepared and accelerated the Greek renaissance in Western and Catholic Europe.

He wrote many letters, orations, and rhetorical exercises, but we remember him here only because of an apologetical dialogue, Διάλογος περὶ τῆς τῶν Χριστιανῶν θρησκείας πρός τινα Πέρσην, which is the most elaborate defense of Orthodox Christianity against Islām. It originated out of religious discussions in which Manuel had engaged with a Turkish theologian in Ankara 1390, but was written a little later and dedicated to his brother Theodoros (d. 1407), despot of Peloponnesos.

[13] Bāyazīd was defeated and taken prisoner by Tīmūr near Ankara on July 20, 1402.

It is an unmethodical discussion of a number of theological questions, divided into 26 chapters.

Manuel composed many moral treatises, the main and best-known being a kind of ethical testament which he wrote for his son Joannes, Ὑποθῆκαι βασιλικῆς ἀγωγῆς, before 1417. It is divided into 100 chapters and explains the rules of conduct of a Christian prince. It is the Byzantine counterpart of the many Latin treatises regimen principum, eruditio regum, etc.,[14] a commonplace and universal type of mediaeval literature.

Among the many other treatises of the emperor Manuel, it will suffice to mention a long one on the procession of the Holy Spirit, written in Paris (1400) in answer to a French theologian, and a short one on dreams, περὶ ὀνειράτων, addressed to one Andreas Asanes.

Text. All the texts quoted above, except the treatise on the procession of the Holy Spirit, which is still unpublished, are included in PG (vol. 156, 1866).

Only the first 2 parts of the apologetical dialogue with a Turkish 'ālim, out of 26, have been edited, by Carl Benedict Hase in the Notices et extraits des MSS de la bibliothèque impériale (8, part 2, 309–82, 1810). There is no more in Migne (156, 126–73).

The Praecepta educationis regiae ad filium Joannem and other treatises were first edited by Ioannes Leunclavius (Basel 1578), with Latin translation.

The De insomniis and other texts were first edited by Jean François Boissonade: Anecdota nova (p. 247, Paris 1844).

Letters edited by Emile Legrand (vol. 1, Paris 1893), no more published.

Criticism. Krumbacher (p. 111, 489–92, 1897). Gustave Schlumberger: Un empereur de Byzance à Paris et à Londres (Revue des deux mondes, Dec. 15, 1915). L. Petit (DTC 9, col. 1925–32, 1927).

CZECH

FLAŠKA Z PARDUBIC

Jan Smil Flaška z Pardubic (d. 1403). Lord of Pardubic, on the Elbe, in Bohemia. Nephew of the first archbishop of Prague, Ernest of Pardubic.

Flaška is the first writer in the Bohemian (Czech) language who is personally known. He was born about the middle of the fourteenth century. In 1395 he joined the union of nobles defending their privileges against the king of Bohemia, Wácslaw (Wenceslas) IV (ruled 1378–1419). He was killed in a skirmish near Kutná-Hora (Kuttenberg) in 1403, fighting against the king's forces.

He wrote a collection of Czech proverbs, a poem entitled Advice of a father to his son; and later, in 1394 or 1395, a beast epic, The new council, with satirical intentions. These works are valuable, not only from the point of view of Bohemian literature, but even more for the study of the Bohemian culture of that time.

Text. Der neue Rath des Herrn Smil von Pardubic; eine Thierfabel aus dem 14. Jahrhundert, nebst dessen übrigen Dichtungen und einer Auswahl aus seiner Sprüchwörtersammlung. Nach dem böhmischen Originaltext zum ersten Male deutsch bearbeitet von Joseph Wenzig (93 p., Leipzig 1855).

The Czech original may be found in Vijbor z literatury české (vol. 1, Prague 1845).

Criticism. Franz Lützow: History of Bohemian literature (p. 35–41, 1907).

[14] Isis 29, 107.

ZYRIAN

ST. STEPHEN OF PERM

Apostle of the Zyrians, inventor of the Zyrian alphabet (c. 1340-96).

Svyatoi Stefan Permskii was born in Ustyug (Vologda government) c. 1340, the son of a sexton. He went to Rostov in 1365, studied theology, Greek, Zyrian, inventing and using a new alphabet for that language (1372). He began his missionary work among the Zyrians in 1379, displaying great administrative abilities, became the first bishop of Perm in 1383, and died in Moscow in 1396.

A biography (zhitie) of St. Stephen was written by his contemporary Epifani Premudry (d. c. 1420). According to Lytkin, a native Zyrian philologist, St. Stephen's translations reveal that he was thinking in Zyrian, not in Russian, and that one of St. Stephen's parents must have been of Zyrian descent.

The Zyrian language is one of the Finno-Ugrian family, which includes many others such as Finnish and Hungarian (to mention only the best-known), and is also related to the group of Samoyed languages (of arctic Siberia). The Zyrian territory in northern Russia includes the governments of Archangel, Vologda, Viatka, and Perm. A. Meillet and Marcel Cohen: Les langues du monde (p. 153-83, Paris 1924). Holger Pedersen: Linguistic science in the nineteenth century (p. 104, Harvard Press, Cambridge, Mass. 1931).[15]

Biography. The "zhitie," by Epifani Premudry, was edited by N. Kostomarov and published in G. Kushelev-Bezborodko's Pamyatniki starinnoi russkoi literatury (Monuments of ancient Russian literature) (4, 119 bis—171, St. Petersburg 1862); this text is printed in Russian type, after a sixteenth-century MS of the Synod Library. A critical edition of the "zhitie," based on the earliest and best MS (fifteenth-sixteenth cent.) of the Synod Library, with variae lectiones from three MSS of the Public Library, was prepared by V. G. Druzhinin and published by the Archaeographic Commission of the Academy of Sciences, St. Petersburg 1897; this text is printed in Slavonic type.

Criticism. The life and work of St. Stephen are discussed in great detail by G. S. Lytkin in Zyrianski krai pri episkopakh permskikh i zyrianski yazyk (The Zyrian territory under the bishops of Perm and the Zyrian language) (St. Petersburg 1889); this book contains facsimiles of Zyrian inscriptions in St. Stephen's alphabet, and a reproduction, in colors, of an icon of St. Stephen. The Finnish professor A. Hämäläinen has written a long memoir in Finnish in the review Suomi (Annual of the Finnish Literary Society), ser. 4, vol. 6, 60 p., Helsinki 1909.

This note was written with the assistance of my Danish colleague Holger Pedersen (letter dated Hellerup, June 13, 1938), and of Dr. A. Pogo.

HEBREW

PEREẒ TRABOT

Pereẓ Trabot, or Trabotti, Trévôt, ha-Naqdan (the punctuator, i.e., a scribe who adds the vowel points). The name Travot or Trevot is written in Hebrew with two ṭeth, Ṭraboṭ. It is probably derived from the place Trévoux in Burgundy (Ain).

[15] These documents concerning St. Stephen are exceedingly rare with regard not only to the Zyrian language but also to the whole Finno-Ugrian family. There is a Hungarian sermon of the thirteenth century, but Hungarian texts are rare before 1500. Finnish and Esthonian literatures begin only in the sixteenth century.

The fact that our Pereẓ calls himself Ẓarfati and Qaṭalano would refer, then, not to the native home of his family or his own, but to their place of exile.

This Pereẓ Trabot is probably the author of the Hebrew dictionary entitled Maqre dardeqe (He who causes children to read). He was exiled from the French kingdom in 1395, and moved to the south, Catalonia and possibly Italy. He compiled his dictionary for the sake of Biblical studies, but instead of explaining the Hebrew words in the order in which they occur in the Bible, as had been done before, he classified them in the Hebrew alphabetical order, and thus created a genuine Hebrew dictionary. He gave for each word Arabic and French or Catalan equivalents, and added rabbinical explanations, many taken from Rashi (XI-2) together with the latter's la'azim, and from David ben Joseph Qimḥi (XII-2).

Adaptations of the Maqre dardeqe, originally Hebrew-Catalan (or French), were soon made not only in Italian, but also in French (or Catalan), Spanish, German, and even English. The first adaptation to Italian (wherein the Catalan vocabulary was replaced by Italian) was made very soon, either by the author himself[16] or by one Jehiel or Yaḥya. The Italian edition superseded the original one and was printed in 1488. It is valuable for the study of trecento Italian.

Text. Maqre dardeqe. First edition in 1488, Naples?, small folio. Includes Arabic and Italian equivalents of Hebrew words, all printed in Hebrew type.

Criticism. Moïse Schwab: Le Maqré dardeqé (Revue des études juives 16, 253–68, 1888, etc.), gives briefly the Hebrew words with Italian equivalents. Neubauer-Renan (p. 713–16, 1893). H. Gross (p. 219, 576, 1897). Short notes in JE (8, 274, 1904; 12, 215, 1906).

MENAHEM BEN ABRAHAM BONAFOS

Menahem ben Abraham, called Bonafos Abraham of Perpignan. Also Bonfos or Bonafoux Abraham of Perpignan. Judeo-Catalan philosopher, who flourished at Perpignan (then in Aragon) at the end of the fourteenth or beginning of the fifteenth century. He compiled a Hebrew dictionary of technical and philosophical terms, with special reference to the Moreh nebukim of Maimonides. That dictionary, entitled Miklal yofi (Perfection of beauty) or Sefer ha-gederim (Book of definitions), is in alphabetical order, but for each letter the terms are divided into six groups: ethics and politics, logic, metaphysics, natural sciences, mathematics and astronomy, medicine. It includes brief and imperfect references to Arabic.

The date of the Miklal yofi has not been determined exactly: it may fall in the fifteenth as well as in the fourteenth century. A critical study of the book, of its sources and use, might enable one to date it.

Text. The Miklal yofi was first edited by Isaac ben Moses ben Arroyo (Salonica 1567) with a few additions. Second edition with additional commentary by Isaac ben Moses Satanow (Berlin 1798).

Criticism. Neubauer-Renan (p. 740, 1893). H. Gross (p. 476, 1897). B. Suler (EJ 4, 933, 1929).

ARABIC

AL-FĪRŪZĀBĀDĪ

Persian lexicographer of the Arabic language, writing in Arabic and Persian (1329–1414).

[16] That is, if the author emigrated to Italy. That hypothesis is supported by the fact that there were in the following centuries (fifteenth to seventeenth) a number of Italian Jews (some of them distinguished scholars) bearing the name of Trabot or Trabotti.

Abū-l-Ṭāhir Muḥammad ibn Ya'qūb Majd al-dīn al-Shīrāzī al-Shāfi'ī al-Fīrūzābādī. His family originated in Fīrūz-ābād in Fārs, but he himself was born at Kāzirūn, near Shīrāz, in 1329. He traveled extensively in the Eastern lands; his movements from country to country can be followed grosso modo, but there is no point in describing them. A few indications will suffice. He studied in Shīrāz, Wāsiṭ, and Baghdād, then in Damascus (1349) and Jerusalem under 'Alī al-Subkī (XIV-1). Jerusalem remained his residence for ten years. He spent five years in Dihlī, India. He was honored by Tīmūr in Shīrāz, 1393. He traveled in Anatolia, Syria, Egypt, and Persia. He made very long stays in Mecca, the longest from c. 1368 to 1382. In 1395 he was appointed chief qāḍī of Yaman, and did not leave that country any more except for the Pilgrimage. He died in Zabīd, Yaman, in December 1414.

In addition to his literary activities, he was a teacher; we know that he taught in Jerusalem and Mecca, and he probably taught in many other places.

His main work, immortalizing his name, is the great Arabic dictionary, al-Qāmūs (the Ocean), upon which all our modern dictionaries are directly or indirectly based. Its name "qāmūs"[17] has become equivalent in meaning to "dictionary." That work was naturally derived from earlier ones, e.g., those of al-Jauharī (X-2), Ibn Sīda (XI-2), al-Ḥasan ibn Muḥammad al-Ṣaghānī (d. 1252), but also from his own experience and intercourse with a great many scholars in Eastern lands. In particular, he introduced many words used in South Arabian dialects. His purpose was rather to illustrate the exuberance of the Arabic language than to act as a critical lexicographer. For example, he had counted more than 80 words to designate honey, and 1,000 to mean a sword (I say "to mean" because most of these words are metaphors, the number of which can be increased indefinitely).[18]

The Qāmūs has been frequently copied, translated, commented upon (in Arabic, Persian, and Turkish), and edited. The most important commentary is the Tāj al-'arūs (Crown of the bride) of the Egyptian scholar Muḥammad al-Murtaḍā al-Zabīdī (1732–91).

Both the Qāmūs and the Tāj al-'arūs include proper names (persons and places); not so the Lisān al-'arab of Ibn Manẓūr (XIII-2).

Fīrūzābādī wrote other books dealing with Arabic lexicography, e.g., one on the words which can be spelled indifferently with sīn or shīn. He wrote in Persian a life of the Prophet, Sifr al-sa'āda; this was translated into Arabic in 1401 by Muḥammad ibn Maḥmūd al-Makhzūmī al-Miṣrī.

Text. The Qāmūs has been printed a good many times, in 1 to 4 volumes. The first edition was the Calcutta one of 1817, 2 vols., with an English preface by Matthew Lumsden. This is the only edition with which I am familiar. Later editions: Bombay 1855, 1881–82, Teheran? 1859, 1860, Cairo 1863–64, Būlāq 1872, Lucknow 1872, 1881.

A Persian translation, Tarjumān al-lugha, was printed in Teheran 1857, 1860.

A Turkish translation, Al-uqiyānūs al-basīṭ, was printed in Constantinople 1815–17, 1887–88, 1888; also in Būlāq 1834.

[17] Qāmūs, pl. qawāmīs. The word is used chiefly for linguistic dictionaries, but also for technical ones, e.g., Qāmūs al-aṭibba' fī-l-mufradāt, dictionary of simples by Madyan ibn 'Abd al-Raḥmān al-Qawṣūnī (chief physician in Cairo, d. c. 1634), and the Qāmūs al-sharī'a, dictionary of Ibāḍī fiqh composed c. 1650 by Jumaiyil ibn Khāmis al-Sa'dī of 'Umān.

[18] Joseph von Hammer-Purgstall (Das Kamel, Wien 1854) counted 5,744 Arabic words concerning the camel! Ernest Renan: Histoire générale des langues sémitiques (5th ed., p. 387, Paris 1878).

The Tāj al-'arūs was printed in Cairo 1869–70, incompletely, only 5 vols. First complete edition, 10 vols., Cairo 1889–90.

Criticism. Ḥājjī Khalīfa (4, no. 7714, 1845). Brockelmann (2, 181–83, 1902; suppt. 2, 234–36, 1938); (EI 2, 113, 1914). Browne (3, 357–58, 1920).

CANARESE

ABHINAVA MAṄGARĀJA

Canarese lexicographer (fl. end of fourteenth century).

He compiled c. 1398 the new dictionary Abhinava-nighaṇṭu, giving the Canarese meanings of Sanskrit words. It was derived from the Vastu-kōśa of Nāgavarman II (Jaina grammarian fl. c. 1145). Both works were of course derived from the fundamental source of Sanskrit lexicography, the Amarakōśa of Amarasiṃha (VI-2), which was well known to the learned men of the Canarese country in its original Sanskrit form and also through the Canarese commentary, Amara-kōśa-vyākhyāna, of the Jaina Nāchirāja (c. 1300).

There was also compiled about the middle of the century a Canarese dictionary of 676 articles or 1,416 words, the Karṇāṭaka-śabda-sāra.

Text. The Karṇāṭaka-śabda-sāra was edited in the monthly magazine Karṇāṭaka kāvya-mañjarī (no. 18, 32 p., Mysore 1897).

Criticism. Edward P. Rice: History of Canarese literature (p. 112, Calcutta 1921).

For the Canarese language, see my note on Raṭṭa-kavi (XIV-1).

CHINESE

CHAO HUI-CH'IEN

Chinese lexicographer (1352–95).

Chao Hui-ch'ien, whose original name was Ku tsê, was born at Yü yao, Chehkiang, in 1352; being a poor orphan, he was educated at the local temple; then he wandered far and wide to study Confucianism, poetry, and music. In 1379 he visited the Ming capital (Nanking), and later he was a magistrate in Kuangtung. He died in 1395, and is best known as K'ao ku hsien shêng, the antiquarian.

His main work is a Chinese dictionary, Liu-shu pên-i, in 12 chüan, wherein the words are classified under 360 radicals. In order to understand the meaning of this, it is necessary to summarize the history of that type of lexicography.

The earliest dictionary of this kind (i.e., classification by radicals) is the Shuo wên chieh tzŭ, by Hsü Shên (II-1), completed c. 120. The Shuo wên contains 10,500 characters classified under 540 radicals.

Two great discoveries made lexicographical progress possible. The first was the spelling system fan ch'ieh, a method of representing the pronunciation of a character by means of two others suggesting the initial and final sounds; that system was invented under Sanskrit influence by Sun Yen (III-2). The other was ssŭ shêng, the indication of the four tones, introduced by Shên Yo (V-2).

On the basis of Shuo wên, fan ch'ieh, and ssŭ shêng, Ku Yeh-wang (VI-1) completed in 543 a new dictionary, Yü p'ien, wherein the words are classified under 542 radicals. The Yü p'ien is lost, and we know it only as revised in 674 by Sun Ch'iang and in 1013 by Ch'ên P'êng-nien (XI-1). Some five hundred years after the first appearance of the Yü p'ien, the historian Ssŭ-ma Kuang (XI-2) published the Lei p'ien, containing over 31,000 characters arranged under 544 radicals.

Apparently further progress implied the reduction of the characters to a smaller number of radicals. In the Liu-shu pên-i it was reduced to 360; somewhat later during the same dynasty (i.e., before 1644), in the anonymous dictionary Tzŭ hui, the number of radicals was further reduced to 214. That smaller number has been maintained in later works, notably in the great Ch'ing dictionary, K'ang-hsi tzŭ tien, completed in 1716, and in Giles' Chinese-English dictionary (1912).

To return to Chao Hui-ch'ien, he composed another lexicographic work, the rhyming dictionary Shêng-yin wên-tzŭ t'ung, which was soon afterward incorporated in the Yung Lo ta tien (1409).[19] According to the Ming shih, chüan 96, the Shêng-yin consists of 100 chüan, but only 32 of them are extant, being included in the Ssŭ k'u chüan shu.

Criticism. Wylie (p. 10, 1922). Giles (no. 162, 1898). Couling (p. 298–301, 1917). Wieger (p. 413, 508, 1920).

TING HAO-NIEN

Ting Hao-nien, often called Ting hsiao tzŭ because of his filial piety. Chinese poet (1335–1424).

We speak of him here as a curious example of assimilation. He was of Central Asian and Muslim origin, his grandfather having served under Kublai Khān (XIII-2). He was brought up at Wu-ch'ang, Hupeh, and lived there until the Ming attacked the city in 1364, and the family fled to Chinkiang. His mother died there, and he lived a life of abstinence for five years (hence his nickname). Then he moved to Chehkiang and Kiangsi, until the return of peace enabled him to take office as a civil servant in his native place, Wu-ch'ang. Yet he remained loyal to the memory of the Yüan dynasty, and wrote a collection of patriotic poems entitled Hai ch'ao chi. Toward the end of his life he became a Buddhist!

Criticism. Giles (no. 1931, 1898). Wieger (p. 436, 1920).

[19] For that great encyclopaedia see my note on Wang Chên (XIV-1).

ADDENDA

Addenda should be avoided as much as possible, but the long duration of printing made the following necessary and excusable. That duration was abnormally extended because of the great size of the book and of war and postwar difficulties.

Every item is indexed. Readers are advised to use the index and to consult not only the main articles, but also the addenda which may refer to those articles and eventually complete and correct them.

These addenda were closed in May 1947. Others will appear periodically in the critical bibliographies of Isis, beginning with the seventy-first in volume 38, in shā' allāh ta'ālā'.—G. S.

Thanks (p. 28). I received help on some Persian items from major Edward Stewart Kennedy, now professor at the American University of Beirūt.

Chinese transcriptions (p. 31). The Giles system of transcription has been followed, except that ordinary apostrophes have been used instead of inverted ones, to indicate aspiration (Introd. 1, 48). The Chinese characters will be easily found in the Chinese index.

John XXII's fiscality (p. 44 note 6). N. Denholm-Young: The merchants of Cahors (Medievalia et humanistica 4, 37–44, 1946).

Byzantine and Eastern churches (p. 52, 95). For comparison of their theology with Catholic theology, see Martin Jugie: Theologia dogmatica Christianorum orientalium ab ecclesia catholica dissidentium (5 vols., Letouzey, Paris 1926–35). Vols. 1–4 are devoted to Byzantine and Russian theology, as follows: vol. 1 (1926), origin, history, sources; vol. 2 (1933), simple theology, de oeconomia; vol. 3 (1930), sacraments; vol. 4 (1931), de novissimis, de ecclesia. Vol. 5 (1935) describes the theological ideas of Nestorians and Monophysites. These volumes are based on an abundant documentation and are very carefully indexed. Jugie's documentation, however, is Greek, Latin, Western, rather than Oriental (Arabic, Syriac, Coptic, etc.). During the war father Jugie published a more popular work, Le schisme byzantin (488 p., Paris 1941; Isis 37), which summarizes the history of the schism from the fourth century on and the doctrines, rites, and usages of the Orthodox churches.

Armenian church (p. 54). Leon Arpee: History of Armenian Christianity from the beginning to our own time (400 p., New York 1946); the author is an Armenian Protestant.

Coptic church (p. 55). Sawīrus ibn al-Muqaffa': History of the patriarchs of the Egyptian church, edited by Yassā 'Abd al-Masīḥ and O. H. E. Burmester (Publications de la Société d'archéologie copte, Le Caire). The second volume began to appear in 1943 (Journal of the Royal Asiatic Society, p. 99–100, 1946).

The descriptions of the Coptic church and people in Edward William Lane's classic "An account of the manners and customs of the modern Egyptians" (5th ed., 2, 273–302, London 1871; first edition 1836) are not only too brief, but inaccurate. Better account by S. H. Leeder: Modern sons of the Pharaohs. A study of the manners and customs of the Copts of Egypt (372 p., ill., London 1918); the modern conditions dealt with have not completely replaced the mediaeval and ancient ones. Gaston Wiet: Qibṭ (EI 2, 990–1003, 1927).

Persecution of the Jews (p. 56). Joshua Starr: The mass conversion of Jews in southern Italy 1290–93 (Speculum 21, 203–11, 1946).

Armengaud Blaise and Jean Blaise (addition to p. 61 and to vol. 2, p. 831, 893). The following information is derived from René Verrier: Etudes sur Arnaud de Villeneuve (87 p., 6 pl., Leiden 1947). A sister of Arnold of Villanova (XIII-2) married Z. Blaise, and they had two sons, Armengaud Blaise and Jean Blaise.

Armengaud was born in Montpellier in the sixties of the thirteenth century; he studied in Montpellier but in 1289 failed to obtain his license; this failure was partly caused by a bitter quarrel between the bishopric and the town. Soon afterward (Oct. 26, 1289) Nicholas IV granted the bull creating the University (studium generale) of Montpellier.[1] Armengaud did probably obtain his license later. He practiced in Montpellier, Barcelona (1303–5), and Avignon. His translations were very probably made from the Hebrew. His knowledge of Hebrew was such that he was believed to be a Jew. He died c. 1312.

His puisne brother, Jean Blaise (c. 1275–1341), was also born in Montpellier; he was in Venice from c. 1285 to 1295, studied medicine in Montpellier, and in 1305 was established as a physician and surgeon in Marseille. He became physician to Robert the Wise, was probably with him in Naples from 1310 to 1319, then returned with him to Provence and remained in his service until 1324. He then settled in Marseille while the king returned to Naples. Documents of 1333 and 1341 enumerate the books of his library and some of his medical and surgical instruments. After his second settlement in Marseille (1324), Jean became a capitalist and investor, acquiring mortgages on noble estates. He died in 1341 in Villeneuve-lès-Vence (now called Villeneuve-Loubet, between Antibes and Nice) and bequeathed his goods partly to his wife, partly to the hospital of the Holy Ghost of Marseille.[2]

There has been much discussion concerning the origin of Arnold of Villanova (Catalan, Languedocian, or Provençal?). Villanova may be his place of origin, but that name is not uncommon. Verrier suggests that the Villanova after which Arnold is named is Villeneuve-lès-Vence, where his nephew died.

Nominalism vs. realism (p. 83). A good exposition of that problem has been published recently by Meyrick H. Carré: Realists and nominalists (136 p., Oxford 1946). Carré does not tell the whole history of that crucial conflict of mediaeval philosophy; that would be very tedious; instead, he discusses the views of four men: St. Augustine (V-1), fountainhead of mediaeval realism; Peter Abaelard (XII-1), defender of conceptualism; St. Thomas Aquinas (XIII-2), who, having the advantage of a deeper knowledge of Aristotle, explained a new kind of realism, moderate and tradi-

[1] For the early history of the University of Montpellier see Introd. (2, 352; 3, 247, 341, etc.).

[2] The Hospitaler Order of the Holy Ghost had been founded in Montpellier c. 1145 (see p. 294); the Hospital of the Holy Ghost in Marseille was founded in 1188 (it was called Hôtel-Dieu in 1593).

tional; finally William Occam (XIV-1), founder of nominalism. The conflict between realism and nominalism is not restricted to mediaeval times; it began in the fourth century B.C. and permeates the development not only of philosophy, but also of science and of politics, down to our own days. Modern science was largely influenced by nominalism, as well as by skepticism and increasing anti-Aristotelianism; modern individualism and democracy developed under similar auspices.

Japanese science and technology (p. 109). Three volumes published in Japan during the war have remained thus far inaccessible to me, and I know them only from a reference in the Library of Congress quarterly (4, 26, 1947). Two of them are vols. 13 and 14 of Gendai Nihon bummei-shi (History of modern Japanese civilization), Tōkyō 1940—: vol. 13, Kagaku-shi (History of science), by Jun Ishihara (1942); vol. 14, Gijutsu-shi (History of technology), by Hiroto Saegusa (1940). The third is a part of a larger series in more than 25 volumes, Taikan Nihon bunka-shi sensho (Comprehensive collection of Japanese cultural histories), Tōkyō 1940—: Nihon kōgyō-shi (History of Japanese industry), by Yasuhiro Nagusa (1942).

Germanic and Scandinavian astronomy (p. 117–19). Otto Sigfrid Reuter has investigated a large number of Scandinavian and Germanic documents of the Middle Ages, and published the results in his book Germanische Himmelskunde. Untersuchungen zur Geschichte des Geistes (783 p., 86 ill., Munich 1934).

Babylonian traits in the Jewish calendar (p. 130). According to al-Bīrūnī's (XI-1) Vestiges of the past,[3] the Jews began some 200 years after Alexander to compute the time of the new moon in a new way in order to avoid difficulties due to poor visibility of the crescent. Al-Bīrūnī's statement is indirectly confirmed by the explanation given by Maimonides (XII-2) in the Mishneh Torah, part 3 (Zemanim).[4]

Maimonides' rules for the computation of the visibility of the new crescent lead to an excellent numerical agreement with values found in a Chaldaean ephemeris of 133 B.C. It is not known how that Chaldaean information reached Maimonides in Egypt, but it is not surprising that the Chaldaean astronomical knowledge was partly preserved by the Jewish communities of Mesopotamia and transmitted by them to other Jewish communities.[5] It would be interesting to follow that Chaldaean tradition in the Jewish calendric treatises posterior to Maimonides.

David Sidersky: Le calcul chaldéen des néoménies (Revue d'assyriologie 16, 21–36, Paris 1919). Otto Neugebauer: History of ancient astronomy (Publications of the Astronomical Society of the Pacific 58, 17–43, 104–42, San Francisco 1946; see p. 42–43). According to Neugebauer, the details of Sidersky's calculations are wrong or unreliable.

[3] Eduard Sachau's edition (p. 52–59, Leipzig 1878) or his English translation (p. 62–69, London 1879).

[4] The Mishneh Torah was composed by Maimonides in Cairo between 1170 and 1180 and completed on Nov. 28, 1180. The Book of festivals (Sefer zemanim) was written in 1178. Solomon Gandz is preparing an English translation of Zemanim which will be published, together with an astronomical discussion by Otto Neugebauer, in the Judaica research series of Yale University in 1948.

[5] Al-Bīrūnī refers to the Chaldaean (or Babylonian) tradition of the Jews (Sachau's version, p. 65).

Arabic astronomy (p. 131). The student of Arabic astronomy should refer to the Arabic treatise of Carlo Alfonso Nallino (1892–1938): 'Ilm al-falak, ta'rīkhuhu 'inda al-'Arab fī-l-qurūn al-wustā' (371 p., Rome 1911–12), or to the Italian translation by his daughter Maria in the Raccòlta of his writings (5, 88–329, Roma 1944; Isis 37). It is easier to consult the Arabic text, which is well indexed, whereas the Italian translation is not. One may also consult Qadrī Ḥāfiz Ṭūqān: Turāth al-'Arab al-'ilmī fīl-riyāḍiyyāt wal-falak (268 p., Cairo 1941; Isis 36, 140–42).

Chinese astronomy (p. 137). We owe the most elaborate studies of our time on Chinese astronomy to Léopold de Saussure (1866–1925): Les origines de l'astronomie chinoise (Paris 1930; Isis 17, 267–71; 27, 286–305, portrait), and to Wolfram Eberhard. The latter wrote at least ten articles on the subject (see, e.g., Isis 24, 258–59; 35, 223). These articles have not been collected, but an index to them was published in Monumenta serica (7, 242–66, Peiping 1942).

Apropos of the astronomical instruments of 1279, see Introd. (2, 1022) and Martin Christopher Johnson: Greek, Moslem and Chinese instrument design in the surviving Mongol equatorials of 1279 A.D. (Isis 32, 27–43, 1940). Johnson concludes that those instruments are closer to the Alexandrian tradition, as known during the Han dynasty, than to the Muslim; they even include Babylonian elements.

Some information on astrology in the Mongol empire may be found in Marco Polo. See Yule-Cordier's edition, passim, by index s.v. astrology, astronomical instruments. The most important people at the Mongolian court, outside of the generals and priests, were "the leeches, the astrologers, and the falconers" (1, 405). A special chapter (book 2, ch. 33) is devoted to the astrologers of the city of Cambaluc (1, 446–56). Discussion of taqwīm[6] (1, 448). Cordier's Addenda (p. 73, 1920).

The textile industry in England (p. 157). The making of woolen cloth was the first important industry of England; it was developed during the fourteenth century, being stimulated by government patronage. "The earliest known instance of a royal grant to foreigners is the letters of protection given to John Kempe and his company, Flemish weavers, by King Edward III in 1331. Similar letters were issued to two Brabant weavers in 1336. This policy was confirmed by a statute in 1337 which enacted that all cloth workers of other countries would be given special franchises and privileges if they settled in England and practised and taught their arts" (Journal of the Patent Office Society vol. 18, no. 7, p. 20, Federalsburg, Md. 1936). This John Kempe is otherwise unknown to me.

Sumer is icumen in (p. 160). This early musical composition was classified (Introd. 2, 634) under XIII-1. According to a new study, its real date is a century later, c. 1310, and the original script was in duple time. Manfred F. Bukofzer: Sumer is icumen in, a revision (University of California publications in music vol. 2, no. 2, vi p. plus p. 79–114, Berkeley 1944), reviewed in Medium aevum (13, 78–81). This includes a full account of the method of notating duple time in English fourteenth-century music, and an excursus on Walter Odington.

Byzantine music (p. 163). René Aigrain: Musicologie byzantine (Revue des études grecques 54, 81–121, 270–74, 1941).

[6] About taqwīm, see also Isis (10, 490–93).

Liber sacerdotum (p. 165). James Corbett: Catalogue des MSS alchimiques latins de Paris (p. 21, 294–309, Bruxelles 1939; Isis 32, 211).

Oil painting (p. 170). Valuable information concerning the early use of oils and resins will be found in Rutherford J. Gettens and George L. Stout: Painting materials (p. 42–44, 56–59, New York 1942).

Catalan portolani (p. 182). It is a curious fact that the early portolani or rutters that have come down to us are all in Italian, though the early nautical charts were produced in Catalonia and Majorca as well as in Italy. Yet there must have been Catalan rutters as well as charts. In October 1323, a rutter was bought and paid for for Jaume II, king of Aragon from 1291 to 1327. Pere IV, king from 1336 to 1387, ordered in 1352 that each ship should carry two nautical charts. In 1373, the infante Joan asked for a nautical chart complete in all its details. In the library of Marti I, king from 1395 to 1410, there was a rutter in Catalan written on Jativa paper (Rubió i Lluch 1, 251; 2, 395, 1908–21; Reparaz-Ruiz p. 284, 286, 293, 1940).

The end of the Norse colonies in Greenland about the middle of the fourteenth century (p. 196). Much information on mediaeval Greenland has appeared in the Meddelelser om Grønland published (since the beginning, 1879) in Copenhagen. The ending of the Norse colonies has been explained in a new way by Knud Fischer-Møller. He suggests that the colonists were not killed off by malnutrition, disease, inability to breed, or by the Eskimos, that they did not lose their identity by interbreeding with the Eskimo population, but that they probably emigrated in mass to the shores of Newfoundland and Labrador, and even to the regions of the Hudson Bay and of the Great Lakes. The latest studies on the mediaeval Norse settlements appeared in vols. 89 and 90 of the Meddelelser (Copenhagen 1941–44; Nature vol. 158, p. 803, 1946).

Earthquakes in China (p. 217). Herbert A. Giles: Earthquakes (Adversaria sinica no. 9, 277–79, Shanghai 1911).

Earthquakes in Japan (p. 217). For generalities see Nicholas Hunter Heck: Japanese earthquakes (Bulletin of the Seismological Society of America vol. 34, 1944; Smithsonian report for 1945, p. 201–17, 4 maps, 3 pl., Washington 1946), but this does not deal with mediaeval events; list of destructive earthquakes, 1596–1944.

Herbals (p. 221). An important herbal was compiled at the end of the thirteenth century by the Italian Rufinus. Its importance was first underlined by Lynn Thorndike (Isis 18, 63–76, 1932), who has finally completed an exemplary edition of it on the basis of the unique MS in the Laurentiana of Florence, with the assistance of Francis S. Benjamin, jr. Thanks to many indexes, this edition is an excellent instrument for the study of mediaeval Latin herbals. This note was the more necessary because Rufinus was not included in our vol. 2, being still unknown at that time. Lynn Thorndike: The herbal of Rufinus (520 p., University of Chicago 1945; Isis 36, 256–57, 1 pl.).

Pên ts'ao kang mu (p. 224). Jacques Roi (S.J.): Plantes médicinales chinoises d'après le Pên ts'ao kang mu (Collectanea commissionis synodalis 14, 687–721; 15, 1–142, 1941–42).

Plant iconography (p. 225). Reference should have been made to the magnificent floral decoration carved in limestone in the York minster and Southwell minster,[7] the decoration in both places being of about the same date, the end of the thirteenth century and the beginning of the fourteenth. The carving of foliage is so realistic, especially in Southwell, that the plants represented can be identified. This has been done for Southwell by Albert Charles Seward (Proceedings of the Cambridge Antiquarian Society 35, 1–32, 1935). Nikolaus Pevsner: The leaves of Southwell (King Penguin book, London 1945), including 32 excellent photographs. The Southwell carvings are in the chapter house and in its portal, built at the very end of the thirteenth century.

Buddhist and Taoist botany (p. 226). Buddhism considerably increased popular interest in certain plants; this influenced botanical iconography and to some extent horticulture. The most sacred plants from the Buddhist point of view are the pipal or sacred fig tree (Ficus religiosa), the sacred lotus (Nelumbium Nelumbo), the tulsi or holy basil (Ocimum sanctum), the sāla (Shorea robusta), the Citrus medica, whose fruit is called fo-shou (Buddha's hand), the pomegranate (Punica granatum). Other plants were connected with other religions. For example, in China the fungus of immortality or plant of long life (ling chih), Fomes japonicus, is a Taoist emblem, often associated with an Artemisia leaf. That fungus grows on tree trunks and becomes woody and enduring.

Arthur de Carle Sowerby: Nature in Chinese art (p. 129–44, New York 1940; Isis 34, 68). Isaac Henry Burkill: On the dispersal of the plants most intimate to Buddhism (Journal of the Arnold Arboretum 27, 327–39, Jamaica Plain, Mass. 1946).

Falconry in Provence (p. 231). This is an addition to Introd. 2, 648 as well as to this section. Alexander Herman Schutz has recently published The romance of Daude de Pradas called Dels auzels cassadors (236 p., Ohio State University, Columbus, Ohio 1945; Isis 37, 100–3). To this critical edition of the Provençal text of the first half of the thirteenth century, based on the five known MSS, Schutz has added an English summary, abundant notes, and glossary.

Arabic falconry (p. 232). The Oriental treatises Moamin and Ghatrif (Introd. 2, 648–49) have been investigated by Håkan Tjerneld: Moamin et Ghatrif. Traités de fauconnerie et des chiens de chasse (446 p., 3 pl., Stockholm 1945). There are two Moamin treatises, dealing respectively with falconry and with hounds, both written originally in Arabic; Ghatrif's treatise, much shorter (43 p. against 168 for the two others), was originally written in Persian. The Moamin treatises were translated into Latin by Theodore of Antioch (XIII-1) and corrected by the latter's patron, the emperor Frederick II, in 1240–41. We do not know who translated the Ghatrif treatise. Both texts were translated from Latin into French by Daniel

[7] The word minster in both cases means cathedral; one also speaks of Beverley minster, without monastic implications.

Deloc of Cremona for Enzo (Enzio, or Enrico), king of Sardinia, natural son of Frederick II. Enzo was his father's best captain against the papal armies, but he was defeated by the people of Bologna at the battle of Fossalta in 1249 and taken prisoner to Bologna. He remained a captive in that city until his death on March 14, 1272. Daniel's translation was made during Enzo's captivity and revised after Enzo's death. It is one of the earliest French works written by an Italian; the Régime du corps of Aldobrandin of Siena (XIII-2), written c. 1256, may be earlier. Its language offers many peculiarities. Tjerneld's edition is based on the unique French MS in San Marco, Venice; it is accompanied by an elaborate study of the text, the Latin, French, Italian MSS, the language, and by French and Latin glossaries. The French text contains many words of Arabic origin, but these have not been listed separately. See review of Tjerneld's edition by Hans J. Epstein (Isis 37, 100-3).

Locust plagues (p. 239). For the modern point of view on them the best authority is Boris Petrovich Uvarov: Locusts and grasshoppers. A handbook for their study and control (366 p., London 1928). First published in Russian (Moscow 1927). Or see Uvarov's short paper The locust plague (Smithsonian report for 1944, p. 331–46, 1945).

Animal stories (p. 239, 1190). The best general account of the distribution and classification of folk tales in general and animal tales in particular will be found in Stith Thompson: The folktale (520 p., New York 1946; Isis 37).

Urine of pregnant women (p. 269 note 36). Martin Krebs: Der menschliche Harn als Heilmittel (112 p., Hippokrates-Verlag, Stuttgart 1942), not seen, review in Mitt. (40, 282). The gonadotropic properties of the urine of pregnant women were discovered by Bernhard Zondek and Selmar Aschheim in 1927. Emile Guyénot: La dualité des "prolans" urinaires (Experientia 1, 1–6, Basel 1945). J. Plesch: Urine therapy experiments (Experientia 2, 501–2, 1946).

Chinese physiognomy (p. 270). For Chinese views on this subject see Herbert A. Giles: Phrenology, physiognomy, and palmistry (Adversaria sinica no. 6, p. 178–84, 3 fig., Shanghai 1908).

Babylonian physiognomy (p. 270). For comparison with Babylonian views see Fritz Rudolf Kraus: Texte zur babylonischen Physiognomatik (Archiv für Orientforschung, Beiheft 3, 35 p., 65 pl., Berlin 1939).

John, count of Luxemburg and king of Bohemia (p. 273). After many vicissitudes, John's remains were buried in 1838 by order of the prince of Prussia (later king Frederick William IV) in the Klause, a chapel in Castell, valley of the Saar. One of the curious aftermaths of the war was their removal in 1946 from Castell to the cathedral of Notre Dame, Luxemburg, Grand Duchy of Luxemburg. Thus were they returned to his native soil, exactly six hundred years after his death.

John, king of Bohemia from 1310 to 1346, was succeeded by his son, who ruled Bohemia from 1346 to 1378 under the name Charles I, but is better known as the emperor Charles IV. See my note on Beneš of Weitmil (p. 1757).

Johann Schötter: Johann Graf von Luxemburg und König von Böhmen (2 vols.,

Luxemburg 1865); for the burial in Castell and the protests of the people of Luxemburg see vol. 2, p. 304–20. Emil Ficken: Johann von Böhmen. Eine Studie zum romantischen Rittertum des 14. Jahrhunderts (178 p., Göttingen 1932).

Chinese ophthalmology (p. 274). Chinese ophthalmology was not discussed, because I did not come across any fourteenth-century writing ad hoc. Chinese eye doctors of that century were probably using the Yin hai ching wei written by Sun Ssŭ-mo (VII-2) and said to be the earliest Chinese treatise restricted to ophthalmology. It may be later than the ascription to Sun Ssŭ-mo suggests. The title means "Exhaustive survey of the silver sea" (silver sea is a Buddhist term for eye). Some 81 kinds of eye diseases are described, but it is not possible to identify them all. Some observations concern prolapse of iris, iridocyclitis, interstitial keratitis, and glaucoma. Curiously enough, there is no mention of cataract, nor of presbyopia. The latter was perhaps considered a normal physiological development rather than a disease.

H. T. Pi: Résumé of an ancient Chinese treatise on ophthalmology, Yin hai ching wei (National medical journal of China 17, 131–49, Peiping 1931; Isis 36, 174). Wong and Wu (p. 223–25, 1936).

Geographical distribution of leprosy (p. 276). The distribution of leprosy both in the fourteenth century and now is very puzzling. When a bacterial disease is as little contagious as leprosy and as curiously distributed, one is driven to admit that (1) the causative organism is connected with the soil of definite countries, is a part of their regular flora, and (or) that (2) the disease is somewhat hereditary, that is, that a certain susceptibility to it is inherited.[8] According to Merrill (1929), the leprosy bacillus is not a true bacterium, but rather a primitive fungus of the genus Actinomyces, a soil organism of very wide distribution. According to Gates, the inheritance of a susceptibility to leprosy is proved by a number of familial investigations. Both theories help to account for the racial, regional, and familial distribution of leprosy.

Elmer Drew Merrill: Leprosy bows to science (Review of reviews vol. 80, p. 79–80, 1929; reprinted in Merrilleana, Chronica botanica 10, 237–38, 1946). Reginald Ruggles Gates: Human genetics (p. 319–23, New York 1946; Isis 37).

Famines in India (p. 283, 1237). Two recent publications may be useful to the historian though they deal only with modern conditions. Kali Charan Ghosh: Famines in Bengal, 1770–1943 (Calcutta 1944). Final report of the Famine Inquiry Commission (Delhi 1945).

Veterinary medicine (p. 284, 1238). The student of veterinary medicine in the Middle Ages must always return to the Greek classics available in the critical edition of Eugen Oder and Karl Hoppe: Corpus hippiatricorum graecorum (2 vols., Teubner, Leipzig 1924–27). He should also take into account the investigations published since 1932 by the Swedish scholar Gudmund Björck concerning those texts and their mediaeval tradition. One of the main Greek writers is Apsyrtos (IV-1), whom Björck would place in a somewhat earlier period, c. 150–250; another was

[8] Before the bacterial nature of leprosy had been established (by A. Hansen in 1871), James Y. Simpson claimed in 1842, and Danielssen and Boeck in 1848, that it was a hereditary disease. Gates (p. 320, 382).

Theomnestos, who was probably a contemporary of Apsyrtos, but whose work is lost. These writings were transmitted to Arabic readers by Ḥunain ibn Isḥāq (IX-2) or his school, and their contents reappear in Arabic treatises such as the Kitāb al-falāḥa of Ibn al-'Awwām (XII-2). It is possible that some of the lost Greek treatises may still be found translated in Arabic MSS. Björck has investigated the tradition of Greek hippiatrics in Latin and Italian MSS. He has found points of contact in the Clavis sanationis of Simon of Genoa (XIII-2) and in the Trattati di mascalcia edited by Pietro Delprato, for which see my notes on Uberto di Cortenova, Lorenzo Rusio, Maurus and Marcus (p. 857–59).

Gudmund Björck: Zum Corpus hippiatricorum graecorum (Uppsala Universitets Årsskrift, 1932, Filosofi 5, 91 p., Uppsala 1932); Le Parisinus grec 2244 et l'art vétérinaire grec (Revue des études grecques 48, 505–24, 1935); Griechische Pferdeheilkunde in arabischer Übersetzung (Monde oriental 30, 1–12, 1936); Apsyrtus, Julius Africanus et l'hippiatrique grecque (Uppsala Universitets Årsskrift, 1944:4, 70 p.; Isis 37), chiefly ch. 4, dealing with the Western mediaeval tradition, and ch. 7, with hippiatric magic.

San Spirito in Rome (p. 294). One of the most valuable MSS in the Archivio di Stato in Rome is an illustrated MS of the Sienese school of the second half of the fourteenth century containing the rule of San Spirito. It has recently been edited and commented upon by A. Francesco La Cava: Liber regulae S. Spiritus, with a preface by Adalberto Pazzini (216 p., 62 pl., Milano 1947).

International trade and credit (p. 324). Stress should have been laid upon the difference between the organization of trade in Italy and its organization in northern countries (such as Flanders and England). Italian trade gave birth to the bills of exchange (cambiali); northern trade was facilitated by bills of credit (lettres de foire). A collection of about 8,000 lettres de foire dating from 1249 to 1291 was found in the archives of Ypres and analyzed by Guillaume des Marez: La lettre de foire à Ypres au XIIIe siècle. Contribution à l'étude des papiers de crédit (Mémoires couronnés publiés par l'Académie de Belgique, collection in 8°, vol. 60, 292 p., 1 pl., Bruxelles 1900). For a general introduction to the study of such questions see James Westfall Thompson: Economic and social history of the Middle Ages (p. 565–602, New York 1928), ch. 23, Merchant travel, markets, the Champagne fairs, the conduct of trade.

Black book of the Admiralty (p. 324 note 7). This is a code of rules for the government of the navy, said to have been compiled in the reign of Edward III (1327–77). These rules were derived from those obtaining in the isle of Oléron, off the French Atlantic coast, which Eleanor of Aquitaine had brought as her dowry when she married Henry II Plantagenet in 1152. The island was not reunited to the French crown until 1370 under Charles V the Wise. The Jugements or Rôles d'Oléron were collected in the eleventh or twelfth century; their collection has been ascribed to queen Eleanor, to her husband, Henry II (king 1154–89), and also to Richard Coeur-de-Lion (king 1189–99); it was probably a local coutumier which the English rulers sanctioned.

Church vs. trade (p. 326). Ecclesiastical objections to trade and usury do not tally with the Parabola talentorum sive mnarum in the Gospels (Matthew 25:14–30;

Luke 19:12–27). It is true I have never been able to understand those parables in their setting, and perhaps churchmen preferred to overlook them.

St. Thomas' views on usury or interest are clarified by Etienne Gilson: Le thomisme (5th ed., p. 451–53, Paris 1945).

Economic power of the church (p. 328). Yves Renouard: Les relations des papes d'Avignon et des compagnies commerciales et bancaires de 1316 à 1378 (Bibliothèque des Ecoles françaises d'Athènes et de Rome no. 151, 722 p., Paris 1941; Speculum 21, 355–59), elaborate study based upon the archives of the Vatican and of Florence. The popes used the service of the Florentine firms Bardi, Peruzzi, and Acciaiuoli until 1342, when these banks failed; from 1342 to 1362 they had to depend upon many smaller companies such as the Malabaila of Asti; after 1362, the services of a larger firm, the Alberti antichi of Florence, became available.

Dutch the original language (p. 350). Ben Jonson (1573?–1637) in The alchemist, acted in 1610 and first published in 1612, has the following dialogue (act 2, scene 1):

> I'll shew you a Booke, where Moses and his Sister,
> And Salomon have written, of the Art,
> I, and a Treatise penn'd by Adam. SUR. How!
> MAM. O' the Philosophers stone, and in high Dutch.
> SUR. Did Adam write, Sir, in high Dutch? MAM. He did:
> Which proves it was the Primitive tongue. . . .

(Quotation taken from the facsimile copy of the first edition, 1612, published in London 1927.)

Such conceits existed in many countries, each people fancying his tongue as the best and the original one. A good example is that of the great mathematician Simon Stevin (1548–1620), who claimed that Dutch was the best language for scientific purposes (Isis 21, 251). What is more remarkable is to find that delusion shared by Stevin's younger contemporary Ben Jonson, who was an Englishman!

Arabic letter writing (p. 373, 1326). The art of letter writing, comparable to the Latin ars dictaminis (p. 332) or to the Chinese (p. 386), was very much developed in the Dār al-islām. It is impossible to discuss here all the implications of that subject; it must suffice to say that literature or the Arabic humanities (adab) played a very important part in Islamic culture. Witness this astounding ḥadīth, "Kāda 'l-adab an yakūn thulthayi 'l-dīn" (One can almost say that adab equals two-thirds of religion). See Ignaz Goldziher: adab (EI 1, 122, 1908); Gustave E. von Grunebaum: Medieval Islam (p. 250–57, Chicago 1946).

Importance of the Persian language in Asia (p. 377). From the Middle Ages on, the Persian language assumed growing importance throughout Asia, not only as a literary idiom but also as a diplomatic and commercial one. That importance reached its climax probably in the eighteenth century. At the end of that century Persian had become a kind of lingua franca in Asia, even as English is today. Its literary prestige was great not only in Asia, but also in Europe. Sylvain Lévi: Les origines d'une chaire, l'entrée du Sanscrit au Collège de France (Le Collège de France, Livre jubilaire p. 329–44, Paris 1932; see p. 332).

Mediaeval Turkish (p. 378). Much work on old Turkish is being done at the Türkiyat enstitüsü headed by Rahmeti Arat in Istanbul, and in Ankara. "A series of books on Seljuk history, published in Ankara, includes an edition of the letters of Jalāl al-dīn Rūmī and the Dīwān-i-Sulṭān Veled. The important Dīwān lughat al-Turk by Maḥmūd Kāshgarī has been issued in five volumes including a photo-static copy of an Istanbul manuscript and extensive indices. Work on the Kudatqu bilik, and a complete index of it under the supervision of Rahmeti Arat, continues.[9] A valuable collection of all Orkhon Turkish inscriptions has been assembled from scattered European publications." Information culled from Richard N. Frye: Oriental studies in Turkey during the war (Journal of the American Oriental Society 65, 204–6, 1945).

Polyglottism of the Yüan dynasty (p. 379). The polyglottism of the Mongol empire is well illustrated by the inscriptions engraved in 1345 at the village of Keuyung Kwan, 40 miles north of Peiping on the road to Kalgan. Those inscriptions were made in six languages, viz., Sanskrit, Tibetan, Mongol, Bāshpah, Uighūr, Chinese, and an unknown one. They were published by prince Roland Bonaparte: Documents de l'époque mongole (Paris 1895, 1896). Elaborate bibliography ad hoc in the Yule-Cordier edition of Marco Polo (1, 28–30, 2 ill., 1926) and Cordier's addenda (p. 13, 1920). Say the editors (1, 29, 1926): "The orders of the great kaan are stated to have been published habitually in six languages, viz., Mongol, Uighūr, Arabic, Persian, Tangutan (Si-Hia), and Chinese. Ghāzān Khān [ruled 1295–1303] is said to have understood Mongol, Arabic, Persian, something of Kashmiri, of Tibetan, of Chinese and a little of the Frank tongue (probably French)."

The Sino-Mongolian inscriptions of Shun Ti (p. 381). During the rule of Shun Ti or Tughān Tīmūr (Cauldron iron), the last Mongol emperor of China (1333–68), five inscriptions were engraved in Chinese and Mongolian. They are dated respectively 1335, 1338, 1340, 1346, 1362, and are important documents for the study of the Mongolian language. These documents were investigated by Francis Woodman Cleaves, but the majority of his rubbings, documents, and notes were impounded by the Japanese in Kōbe in 1941. Fortunately, he was able to bring back the Mongolian text, in Uighūr script, of the last inscription, the one engraved in 1362. Paul Pelliot found it in Kansuh as early as 1908, obtained a rubbing of it, but left it unpublished. The first edition and discussion of it constituted Cleaves' doctoral thesis presented to Harvard University in 1942. A typescript of that thesis, entitled A Sino-Mongolian inscription of 1362 (188 p.. Cambridge, Mass. 1942), is preserved in the Harvard library. Summaries of theses (p. 130, Cambridge, Mass. 1946).

Mongolian and Manchu (p. 381). The study of these languages in the West is almost as old as that of Chinese. See interesting considerations ad hoc by Henri Maspero: La chaire de langues et littératures chinoises et tartares-mandchoues (Le Collège de France, Livre jubilaire p. 355–66, Paris 1932).

Mahābhārata (p. 384 note 107). A critical edition by Vishnu S. Sukthankar is being published by the Bhandarkar Oriental Research Institute in Poona 1927—. Dr.

[9] Three volumes of photostatic copies of the manuscripts of Vienna, Cairo, and Ferghana have appeared.

Sukthankar died on Jan. 21, 1943 and was replaced in April 1943 by Shripad Krishna Belvalkar. The latest installment to appear was the Sabhāparvan, being the second book . . . edited by Franklin Edgerton, forming fascicles 13 and 14 of the whole work (Poona 1944). Journal of the Royal Asiatic Society (p. 111–12, 1946). Journal of the American Oriental Society (66, 267–69, 1946).

For other editions, see Emeneau (nos. 554–717, 1935). For the Bhagavad Gītā, see Isis (36, 71–73).

Oracle bones (p. 385 note 111). A general introduction to the subject was published in Chinese by Kêng Jung (College of arts, Peita 1943); the analytical bibliography included in that introduction was translated by Max Loehr: Eine Bibliographie der wichtigen Werke über die Orakeltexte der Shang-Zeit (Sinologische Arbeiten 3, 114–51, Peiping 1945). A dictionary of oracle-bone inscriptions was compiled during the war by Kao Ming-K'ai and J. M. de Kermadec at the Centre franco-chinois d'études sinologiques, but is not yet published.

Development of the Chinese colloquial language (p. 387). The literary revolution initiated by Hu Shih dates from 1917, but Chinese authors continued for many years to write in an intermediate style which was neither classical nor modern. The first book written entirely in a modern way was perhaps Chao Yuenren's translation of Alice in Wonderland (1921), frequently reprinted. Chao Yang Buwei: Autobiography of a Chinese woman (p. 187, New York 1947).

Abner of Burgos (p. 418). I. F. Baer: Abner's treatise Minḥat qinaot and its influence upon Ḥasdai Crescas (Tarbiz 11, 188–206, 1940), in Hebrew.

Alphonsus Bonihominis (p. 419). Gilles Meersseman: La chronologie des voyages et des oeuvres de frère Alphonse Buenhombre O.P. (Archivum fratrum praedicatorum 10, 77–108, 1940), discussed by Millàs Vallicrosa (Sefarad 2, 205–8, 1942). P. Atanasio López: Obispos en el Africa septentrional desde el siglo XIII (p. 74–78, Tangier 1941; Sefarad 4, 427).

The Aḥmadīya ṭarīqa (p. 420, item 4). F. W. Hasluck: Christianity and Islam under the sultans (2, 663–70, Oxford 1929).

Hasluck's work and his letters edited by his widow in 1926 contain much information also on the Baktāshī and Mawlawī orders. Refer to his indexes under Bektashi and Mevlevi.

Judah Bonsenyor (p. 427). José Cardoner Planas: Nuevos datos acerca de Jafuda Bonsenyor (Sefarad 4, 287–93, 1 pl., 1944).

Niccolò da Reggio (p. 448). Thorndike's study has appeared not in Byzantion, but in Byzantina metabyzantina (1, 213–35, New York 1946).

Samuel Benveniste (p. 451). Antonio Cardoner Planas: El médico judío Benvenist Samuel y su parentesco con Samuel Benvenist de Barcelona (Sefarad 1, 327–45, 1941).

David Bonjorn (p. 452). Alfonso IV, king of Aragon from 1327 to 1336, employed one David Bonjorn de Barris of Collioure (in Roussillon; Pyrénées Orientales) who was a cosmographer, and maker of astrolabes and astronomical tables; in February 1332, he authorized him to marry a woman of Gerona. Reparaz-Ruiz (p. 291, 1940).

Prégent de Coëtivy (p. 458). Prégent de Coëtivy (c. 1400–50) was an admiral of France, who fought the English and died at the siege of Cherbourg. He had married the daughter of the infamous marshal Gilles de Retz (1404–40).[10] Poets and men of letters, especially the chronicler Georges Chastellain, did much to increase his posthumous fame. The Fleming Georges Chastellain (1404–75) was historiographer to the dukes of Burgundy.

Bartholomew of Bologna (p. 460). Leon Arpee: History of Armenian Christianity (p. 157 f., New York 1946).

Robert Mannyng (p. 462). Ethel Seaton: Robert Mannyng of Brunne in Lincoln (Medium aevum 12, 77, 1943).

Al-Nakhshabī (p. 464–65). The translator of Gladwin's Persian-English version was the Alsatian Emile Muller (1885–1932). Another edition of the Persian text was prepared by Leonidas Stanislas Bogdanov (1881–1945), who published also a French translation, Les contes du perroquet, texte persan traduit pour la première fois [?] en français (Les joyaux de l'orient vol. 9, 77 p., Paris 1938–39). That French text is published without explanation, table, or notes of any kind. Bogdanov was born in St. Petersburg and became an authority on the Persian dialects of Afghanistān and India. He was attached to the French legation in Kābul. In 1932, he was naturalized as a French citizen and changed his name to Dugin. He died in Kābul in November 1945 (Richard N. Frye in Moslem world 36, 278, 1946).

Kanjur and Tanjur (p. 468). Kenneth K. S. Ch'en: The Tibetan tripitaka (Harvard journal of Asiatic studies 9, 53–62, 1946), a translation of Mochizuki: Bukkyō Daijiten (4, 3618–19), with added footnotes.

Apropos of Dante's lucciole (p. 487). For the sake of comparison note the impression which fireflies made on John Ruskin (1819–1900). He wrote to his mother from Siena on June 26, 1870, "[The fireflies] are almost awful in the twilight, as bright as candles, flying in and out of the dark cypresses." And nineteen years later, when his own life was darkening, the shining of those Sienese fireflies remained bright in his soul: "How they shone! moving like fine-broken starlight through the purple leaves." These words are taken from the closing paragraph of Praeterita—1889. Eduard Tyas Cook: Life of John Ruskin (2, 205, London 1911). How is it that Dante was the first mediaeval poet to notice those marvels?

Dante. General studies (p. 497). Robert L. John: Dante (280 p., Vienna 1946; American historical review 52, 558, 1947).

[10] The criminal life of Gilles de Retz is said to have given the inspiration for the tale of Bluebeard to Charles Perrault (1628–1703). That cannot be completely true, for the story is an old folkloric motive. Stith Thompson: Motif-index of folk-literature (6 vols., Bloomington, Ind. 1932–36; Isis 20, 607; 28, 602; see Thompson's index, vol. 6, p. 58).

Dante's astronomical views (p. 497). Rudolf Palgen: Dantes Sternglaube. Beiträge zur Erklärung des Paradiso (84 p., 3 fig., Heidelberg 1940), known to me only through Rudolph Zaunick's review (Mitt. 39, 324–25, 1940).

Dante, philosopher (p. 499). Etienne Gilson: Dante et la philosophie (Etudes de philosophie médiévale no. 28, 352 p., Paris 1939).

Robert of Anjou (p. 505). Robert of Anjou, king of Naples (1309–43), is often mentioned in this volume, but I have not dwelt sufficiently upon his patronage of the arts and humanities. He was called the Wise or the Good and was himself a poet, a preacher, and a humanist. The Moralia or Trattato delle virtù morali ascribed to him and often published under his name (Rome 1642, Torino 1750, Naples 1863) was probably written by his contemporary Graziolo Bambagliuoli of Bologna. Petrarca and Boccaccio praised him after his death.

Walter Goetz: Robert von Neapel, seine Persönlichkeit und sein Verhältniss zum Humanismus (76 p., Tübingen 1910), including a list of 289 Latin sermons and addresses made by Robert, and the text of one. Romolo Caggese: Roberto d'Angiò e i suoi tempi (2 vols., Florence 1922–30). Cornelia C. Coulter: The library of the Angevin kings at Naples (Transactions of the American Philological Association 75, 141–55, 1944; Isis 36, 180).

Bernat Oliver (p. 520). Francisca Vendrell (de Millás): La obra de polémica antijudaica de fray Bernardo Oliver (Sefarad 5, 303–36, 1945). This includes the text of the Tractatus Bernardi Oliuarii contra perfidiam (caecitatem) Iudeorum, edited from MS 37, fol. 12 of San Cugat del Vallès. Francisco Cantera has found another MS in the cathedral library of Burgo de Osma which will be discussed in a later number of Sefarad.

Guillaume Vorilong (p. 531). This Vorilong (Vorillon, Vorlion) was a Franciscan in Dinan, Lower Brittany, c. 1450; he died in Rome in 1464. He wrote a commentary on the Sentences, inspired by St. Bonaventure (XIII-2) and Duns Scot (XIII-2), which enjoyed some popularity, witness at least three incunabula editions (Padua c. 1487, Lyon 1489, Venice 1496) and later editions (Paris 1503, Venice 1519). See Werner (vol. 4, 1887).

Celestial vs. terrestrial mechanics (p. 543). The controversy between pure and "impure" mechanics did not end in Newton's days, but took another aspect. As late as 1855, William John Macquorn Rankine (1820–72)—one of the three founders of theoretical thermodynamics, the two others being Rudolf Clausius and William Thomson (Kelvin)—read before the University of Glasgow a Latin discourse De concordia inter scientiarum machinalium contemplationem et usum. A summary of that discourse was included in his Manual of applied mechanics (Glasgow 1858; 20th ed. 1919).

Occam's physics (p. 550). The term philosophia naturalis (sive physica) had been used by Isidore of Seville (VII-1) to designate the quadrivium; that is, of course, a meaning different from Occam's and from ours. Ernest Brehaut: An encyclopaedist of the dark ages (p. 267, New York 1912). See the remarks made apropos of Jean d'Outremeuse (p. 1165).

Occam's mechanics (p. 553). Philotheus Boehner (O.F.M.): The tractatus De successivis attributed to William Ockham edited with a study on his life and works (Franciscan Institute publication no. 1, 134 p., New York 1944). This is a compilation from Occam's writings presumably made by someone else. It is divided into three parts dealing respectively with motion, space, and time. The second part (de loco) is found verbatim in all the printed editions of Occam's Summulae in octo libros Physicorum (or Philosophia naturalis). The three parts are found with but few modifications in Occam's Expositio super libros Physicorum. The edition has been carefully prepared on all the known MSS but lacks an analysis or index.

William of Occam. Special studies (p. 556). L. Baudry: Les rapports de Guillaume d'Occam et de Walter Burleigh (Archives d'histoire doctrinale et littéraire du Moyen âge 9, 155–73, Paris 1934); A propos de la théorie occamiste de la relation (ibid p. 199–203, 1934); Sur trois manuscrits occamistes (ibid. vols. 10–11, p. 129–62, 1936).

Meister Eckhart (p. 569). The edition of Eckardi opera latina by father Théry and R. Klibansky was stopped by the Nazi persecution and the war. It will be continued as soon as possible. Page 569, line 7 from bottom, add the word magisterio between Eckardi and adiunxit.

(Page 570.) For general criticism see also Henri Delacroix: Essai sur le mysticisme spéculatif en Allemagne au XIVe siècle (302 p., Paris 1900). Giuseppe Fagin: Meister Eckhart e la mistica tedesca preprotestante (396 p., Milano 1946). The first part of the book deals with Eckhart; the second, with Tauler, Suso, and the Theologia Deutsch; long bibliography and index.

Meister Eckhart and modern science (p. 571). Modern biology may lead to conclusions very close to those of the Vedānta; indeed, a certain amount of mysticism is perfectly consistent with scientific rationalism. Erwin Schrödinger: What is life? (100 p., Cambridge 1945; Isis 36, 229); read the epilogue (p. 87–91) on determinism and free will.

Engelbert of Admont (p. 575). George B. Fowler, who is preparing a thesis on Engelbert for Columbia University, suggested the following corrections to me on Aug. 6, 1945. Engelbert was abbot of St. Peter's in Salzburg from 1288 to 1297.

De mundo appears now to be apocryphal according to William Laughton Lorimer: The text of pseudo-Aristotle, De mundo (St. Andrew's University publications nos. xviii, xxi, 108 p., 160 p., Oxford 1924–25).

De inundatione Nili seems to be a genuine work of Aristotle according to Josef Partsch: Des Aristoteles Buch über das Steigen des Nil (Abhandlungen der Sächsischen Gesellschaft der Wissenschaften, phil. Kl., 27, 551–600, Leipzig 1909). This article was noted with approval by Werner Jaeger: Aristotle (p. 331, Oxford 1934). See also Isis 14, 461.

Ruysbroeck (p. 582). André Combès is devoting his life to the study of Jean Gerson. His first books on the subject are entitled Gerson, commentateur dionysien (750 p., Paris 1940); Jean de Montreuil[11] et le chancelier Gerson (Paris 1942). During

[11] Joannes de Monsterolio, named after Montreuil-sur-mer (Pas-de-Calais). Born c. 1361 (or 1354?), provost of St. Peter in Lille, died in 1418.

the war he completed an enormous supercommentary discussing Gerson's views on Ruysbroeck, Essai sur la critique de Ruysbroeck par Gerson. Vol. 1, Introduction critique et dossier documentaire (900 p., Paris 1945); vol. 2, La première critique gersonienne de Ruysbroeck et son évolution spontanée; vol. 3, L'apologie de Groenendael et ses suites. I have not yet seen those books and do not even know whether vols. 2 and 3 have actually appeared (February 1947).

Greek spoken in mediaeval Italy (p. 583). Peter Charanis: On the question of the Hellenization of Sicily and southern Italy during the Middle Ages (American historical review 52, 74–86, 1946).

Gregorios Palamas (p. 589). Elaborate articles on Palamas, Palamitism, and Hesychasm by Martin Jugie (DTC vol. 11, 2, col. 1735–1818, 1932).

Levi ben Gerson as a musician (p. 597). The musical views included in the De numeris harmonicis are discussed by Eric Werner and Isaiah Sonne in The philosophy and theory of music in Judaeo-Arabic literature (16, 251–319, Hebrew Union College, Cincinnati 1941; 17, 511–73, 1942–43; see p. 564–72; contents of the whole memoir summarized in Isis 37). Philip of Vitry (to whom the Latin text of Levi's book was dedicated in 1343) could not accomplish his task as long as some ambiguities of the ars antiqua were not removed. Levi helped him to remove them and to create the ars nova. The authors conclude: "Through all of these illustrations, we sense the rational mathematical spirit of the Ars Nova which must have exerted a powerful appeal upon such a mathematician and naturalist as Gersonides. The data are dissected into rigidly bounded units and these are then linked with one another by logical abstractions. This new, mathematically grounded theory of musical measurement proved serviceable to the hitherto blocked development of musical notation."

Immanuel ben Solomon (p. 616). The best presentation of Immanuel's social background will be found in Cecil Roth: The history of the Jews of Italy (592 p., 20 ill., Philadelphia 1946; Isis 37). I take advantage of this note to draw attention to Roth's excellent work.

'Āshiq pāshā (p. 623). For a description of his mausoleum or turba, still existing in Qirshahr, see Walter Rubin: Monuments of Selçuk in Kirşehir (Indian arts and letters 19, 57–59, ill., 1945).

Yūnus Emre (p. 625). A critical edition of his Dīwān (or Divan in new Turkish spelling) was published by Bay Burhan Toprak (2 vols., Istanbul 1943). It includes over 300 poems in approximate chronological order; it does not include a great many other poems which are apocryphal. The same author published four articles on Yūnus Emre in the Jumhuriyet (Istanbul, June 1943), summarized in English by F. Lyman MacCallum (Moslem world 36, 156–69, 1946).

Al-Ījī's discussion of miracles (p. 629). Muslim theologians discussed the nature of miracles for centuries. They distinguished between mu'jiza, the miracle of a prophet after his call, and karāma, the miracle of a saint. Neither word occurs in the Qur'ān. Al-jī' sconclusions concerning mu'jiza are summarized by Gustave E.

von Grunebaum: Medieval Islam (p. 96, Chicago 1946). For other views on miracles see J. A. MacCulloch (ERE 8, 676-90, 1916).

Muḥammad ibn Maḥmūd al-Āmilī on music (p. 632). H. G. Farmer: Ghosts. An excursus on Arabic musical bibliographies (Isis 36, 123–30, 1946; p. 128). Al-Āmilī did not write a separate book on music, but dealt with music in his Persian encyclopaedia, Nāfā'is al-funūn (1334–42).

Cecco d'Ascoli and the Inquisition (p. 645). Lynn Thorndike: More light on Cecco d'Ascoli (Romanic review, Dec. 1946, p. 293–306), "Since the commentary on the Sphere was the prime object of attack by the Inquisition, while the commentary on De principiis was apparently not noticed in either the process at Bologna or that at Florence, it seems probable that he was delivering the former publicly in lectures in 1324 to which objection was taken and had not yet begun to deliver the latter, although it also is divided into lectiones or lectures, but would have proceeded to deliver the lectures upon it the next term, or so soon as the lectures on the Sphere were finished."

Trepidation of the equinoxes (p. 646). The belief that the precession was not continuous, belief due to faulty observations, can be traced back to Theon of Alexandria (IV-2), who spoke of it as an idea not of his own but of old astrologers (*οἱ παλαιοὶ τῶν ἀποτελεσματικῶν*). That idea was entertained also by Hindu astronomers such as Āryabhaṭa (V-2); it was revived by Thābit ibn Qurra (IX-2) and was accepted by most of the Arabic astronomers, al-Battānī (IX-2) being an exception. The most advanced Western astronomers accepted it down to and including Copernicus. Even Tycho Brahe and Kepler had doubts concerning the continuity and regularity of the precession, but they finally rejected the false notion of trepidation.

For further study of trepidation consult the indexes of Introd. (vols. 1, 2, 3). Carlo Alfonso Nallino: Albatenii opus astronomicum (Arabic text, p. 190–92, Milano 1899; Latin text, p. 126–28, 298–304, 1903). Dreyer (1906).

Jean de Meurs' astronomy (p. 654). Among the astronomical instruments mentioned by him we find the turquet, the history of which was outlined in Introd. (2, 1005). Franco of Liége (XI-2) is mentioned in that outline as one of the inventors; according to Thorndike, the inventor was another Franco, Franco de Polonia, who flourished in the thirteenth century (Isis 36, 6, 1945).

Geoffroi of Meaux's cometary studies (p. 659). For the sake of comparison consult Lynn Thorndike: Peter of Limoges and the comet of 1299 (Isis 36, 3–6, 1945), wherein the author corrects some statements concerning Peter made in Introd. (2, 1029) and gives the text of Peter's treatise in Latin and English.

Bradwardine (p. 671). Curt F. Bühler: A new manuscript of the Middle English tract on proportions (Speculum 21, 229–33, 1946), the text suggests comparison with the De proportionibus of Bradwardine; it is not a musical text, as was formerly believed when it was ascribed to one Chilston, unknown English musician (Chevalier p. 906, 1905); the matter needs further investigation.

Nicolaos Artabasdos Rhabdas (p. 682). First edition of his letter on finger notation, Nic. Smyrnaei Artabasdae "Εκφρασις numerorum notationis per gestum digitorum, with Latin translation, by Frédéric Morel, together with Bede's De indigitatione et manuali loquela (23 p., Paris 1614). Often reprinted (Tannery, Mémoires 4, 74).

Muḥammad ibn al-Jazūlī (p. 695). In Suter (no. 412) the nisba is spelled Ghazūlī. According to Brockelmann (2, 252 n. 1, 1902), the first letter is a Berber g, which is confused with jīm, ghain, and even with qāf; in his supplement (2, 364, 1938) he decided in favor of jīm. So did Moh. ben Cheneb (EI 1, 1031).

Al-muqanṭarāt (p. 697). Carlo Alfonso Nallino: Raccòlta di scritti editi e inediti (5, 399–403, Roma 1944; Isis 37).

Jaghmīnī's astronomy (p. 700). C. A. Nallino (Zeitschrift der Deutschen morgenländischen Gesellschaft 48, 120–22, 1894), reprinted in his Raccòlta di scritti editi e inediti (5, 404–7, 1944).

Chu Shih-chieh (p. 702). Cancel lines 5 to 10, from "For example" to "gave no proofs."

Pai fu t'ang suan hsüeh ts'ung shu (p. 703 note 51). The mathematical collection analyzed by father Van Hée in 1914 is the Pai fu t'ang suan hsüeh edited about 1872–76 by Ting Ch'ü-chung of Changsha (Hummel p. 479, 1943) and referred to in my own text (p. 703).

For the Ch'ou-jên chuan of Juan Yüan see the article by Fang Chao-ying (Hummel p. 399–402, 1943).

Kamāl al-dīn al-Fārisī (p. 708). Muṣṭafā Naẓīf bey devoted one of the memorial Ibn al-Haitham lectures to Kamāl al-dīn and his views on optics. The Arabic text of that lecture was published by the university Fu'ād al-Awwal (55 p., Cairo 1945). Professor Naẓīf bey was well prepared for that study by his investigations of the work of Ibn al-Haitham (2 vols., Cairo 1942–43; Isis 34, 217–18; 37).

Muslim vs. ancient metrology (p. 712). Some of the functions of the muḥtasib were comparable to those of the Roman mensor, especially the mensor in charge of the annona (yearly produce, market), but he had many other duties. Standards of weights and measures were sometimes available in or near the ancient market places. It is said that a πῆχυς or cubitus was sometimes engraved in a wall or column of the market. I do not know any example of πῆχυς, but there are various examples of σήκωμα or mensa ponderaria, the best-known perhaps being the one from Pompeii in the Museum of Naples. See the measures of capacity in Athenian shops referred to by Judeich (p. 373, 1931). A fine example of five standards of dry measures excavated from the market place of Assos[12] is on view in the Boston Museum of Fine Arts. It is described by Frank Bigelow Tarbell: A mensa ponderaria from Assos (American journal of archaeology 7, 440–43, 1 fig., 1891), and by Francis H. Bacon: Investigations at Assos (part 1, p. 73, fig. 26, Cambridge, Mass. 1902). Tarbell gives a list of similar monuments (p. 440, 1891).

[12] Assos in the Troad, opposite to Lesbos.

The main sources of information for ancient metrology are Friedrich Hultsch: Metrologicorum scriptorum reliquiae (2 vols., Leipzig 1864–66); Griechische und römische Metrologie (2d ed., Berlin 1882). See also in the Dictionnaire des antiquités of Daremberg and Saglio, articles "mensor" by René Cagnat and "mensura" by P. Tannery (3, 1726–31, 1902; Mémoires 3, 51–67, 1915).

For an example in Western Europe in the fourteenth century, the Avignon standard of length inserted in the wall of the palace of Arles, see p. 1499.

Chinese metrology (p. 713). The late John Calvin Ferguson (1866–1945) made an elaborate study of the Chinese foot measure from the Chou dynasty onward (Monumenta serica 6, 357–82, 8 pl., Peiping 1941). The whole of that volume of Monumenta serica is dedicated to him, and includes his biography by R. H. Van Gulik (6, 340–56, 1941).

Peter the Stranger (p. 714). The earliest edition of the Epistola of 1269 is generally supposed to be that of Augsburg 1558 (Introd. 2, 1031). An earlier one was discovered in 1936 by the bookdealers Davis and Orioli of London and advertised by them. That earlier edition, entitled "Raymundus Lulius de virtute magnetis" (without place or date), contains the same text, with slight variations, that was edited by the imperial physician Achilles Pirmin Gasser in 1558. It was prepared by Salvator Gavellus of Spoleto and was printed in Rome, not after 1520. See Davis and Orioli catalogue no. 73, p. 3, or Isis 37.

Early Scandinavian use of compass (p. 715). Further information may be obtained by means of Otto Sigfrid Reuter: Germanische Himmelskunde (783 p., 86 ill., Munich 1934; p. 48, 726–31).

The early Scandinavian navigators took advantage of bird migrations or bird flights to discover new lands or islands (see example cited at the top of p. 715, referring to the year 874). Centuries later, Columbus made his first American landfall by noting the southwesterly direction taken by great flocks of birds. Samuel Eliot Morison: Admiral of the Ocean Sea (2, 66, passim, Boston 1942; Isis 34, 169–72). James Hornell: The role of birds in early navigation (Antiquity 20, 142–49, 1946).

History of the compass (p. 716). I forgot to mention in the bibliography Edmund O. von Lippmann: Geschichte der Magnetnadel bis zur Erfindung des Kompasses gegen 1300 (Quellen und Studien zur Geschichte der Naturwissenschaften vol. 3, no. 1, 49 p., Berlin 1932), conclusions quoted in extenso in Isis 19, 440.

Measurement of time in mediaeval Europe (p. 717). The fullest account is in Ginzel (3, 88–287, 1914), with elaborate bibliography.

The Dover castle clock (p. 721, 723). Article by A. C. Kay of Dover (The connoisseur vol. 118, p. 118–19, London, Dec. 1946), discrediting the date 1348 as a forgery perpetrated in 1851; according to Kay the clock was found in a French village by the officer of a Highland regiment returning home after Waterloo. I have no means of appraising the value of Kay's information.

Canal locks (p. 735). The most ancient lock of which we have historical records was the one built by Ptolemy II Philadelphos (reigned 285–247 B.C.) at the end of the canal joining the Nile to the Red Sea, at Arsinoë (Gulf of Suez).

As early as the Middle Kingdom (2160–1788), a canal had been dug from Bubastis, on the Tanitic arm of the Nile, along the Wādī al-Ṭumīlāt to Lake Timsāḥ. The second king of the 26th, Saitic, dynasty, Necho (ruled 609–593), ordered the continuation of that canal to the Amari lacus and the Gulf of Suez. According to Herodotos (2, 158), 120,000 Egyptians perished in the undertaking, which had to be abandoned before completion. The canal was completed by Darius (king of Persia and Egypt 521–485); it was wide enough for two triremes to pass each other, and its length was four days' sailing. The great event was commemorated by various inscriptions near the canal, some fragments of which still exist. According to Strabo (I-2 B.C.) and Diodoros of Sicily (I-2 B.C.), the canal ended at Arsinoë and was closed there by a double door to stop the euripos[13] and enable ships to pass from the river to the sea or vice versa.

Claude Bourdon: Anciens canaux, anciens sites et ports de Suez (Mémoires de la Société royale de géographie d'Egypte, vol. 7; folio, 174 p., 7 pl., 9 maps, Cairo 1925; see p. 59–64). Monuments of Ramses II, Darius, and Ptolemy II are reproduced on pl. 1 and 2.

Swineshead (p. 738). Marshall Clagett, of Columbia University, is preparing a critical edition of the Calculationes together with a general study of Swineshead's thought.

John the Canon (p. 740). L. Baudry: En lisant Jean le Chanoine (Archives d'histoire doctrinale et littéraire du Moyen âge 9, 175–97, Paris 1934; Isis 36, 180). John the Canon was also called John Marbres.

Manuel Bryennios (p. 746). See letter of Henry Omont to Paul Tannery, 1889 in Tannery: Mémoires (16, 140–41, 310, 1943). Pierre de Fermat: Notes critiques sur les Harmoniques de Manuel Bryenne (Oeuvres de Fermat, éditées par P. Tannery et Charles Henry, vol. 1, p. xviii, 374, 394–409, Paris 1891). Fermat (1601–65) studied Bryennios' work in the Greek MS 2460 (Bibliothèque nationale, Paris).

Cyranides (p. 754). The following book published in Belgium during the war could not be examined by me until too late. Louis Delatte: Textes latins et vieux français relatifs aux Cyranides (Bibliothèque de la faculté de philosophie de Liége no. 93, 364 p., Liége 1942).

Muslim pottery (p. 755). Dr. Mehmet Aga-Oglu kindly drew my attention (letter dated New York, April 8, 1947) to a passage dealing with pottery in the Mu'jam al-buldān of Yāqūt (XIII-1), Wüstenfeld's edition (3, 455, l. 16); that passage may be derived from the Arabic poet Mis'ar al-Muhalhil,[13a] who flourished at the court of the Sāmānī ruler Naṣr II ibn Aḥmad (ruled 913-42) in Transoxiana and traveled in India and China. Dr. Aga-Oglu is planning a deeper investigation of these matters.

[13] Εὔριπος, any strait or canal where the flux and reflux is violent. So called after the narrow strait separating Euboea from Boeotia, where the tidal currents were particularly strong, up to eight knots.

[13a] C. Brockelmann (EI 3, 519, 1932).

Angelino Dulcert (p. 766). Reparaz-Ruiz (p. 299–304, 1940).

Chinese cartography (p. 808). For the K'un-yü wan-kuo ch'üan-t'u see Hummel (p. 452, 895, 1943–44). An elaborate edition of documents concerning Matteo Ricci with all the necessary Chinese references is being prepared by the Sinologist, father Pasquale M. d'Elia (S.J.), under the title Fonti Ricciane (Roma 1942—; Isis 37).

The study of Chinese cartography will be greatly facilitated by two publications of the Catholic University of Peiping, in their Monumenta serica, monograph series. Walter Fuchs: Der Jesuiten-Atlas der Kanghsi-Zeit, seine Entstehungsgeschichte nebst Namensindices für die Karten der Mandjurei, Mongolei, Osttürkestan und Tibet mit Wiedergabe der Jesuiten-Karten in Originalgrosse (Monumenta serica 3 and 4, 1943); The Mongol atlas and the Kuang-yü t'u (ibid. 8, printing). These publications are known to me thus far only through the Harvard journal of Asiatic studies (9, 344, 1947).

Conrad of Megenberg (p. 817). Wilhelm Kraft: Die Heimat des Konrad von Megenberg (Mitt. 40, 321–25, 1942). The author claims that Conrad originated not in Mainberg, but in Megenberg (now called Mäbenberg) near Spalt, not far from Nürnberg.

Ibn Luyūn (p. 827). For the study of his botany and even more of his linguistic knowledge, it will be useful to compare Ibn Luyūn's work with the 'Umdat al-ṭabīb fī ma'rifat al-nabāt li kull labīb. In MS no. 40 of the Gayangos collection of Madrid, the 'Umda is definitely ascribed to Ibn Buṭlān (XI-1), but that ascription is wrong, for Ibn Buṭlān was a Baghdādī who never left the East, whereas the author of the 'Umda was a Moor familiar with the Andalusian flora and with many Hispanic and Moroccan localities; he often repeats the phrase 'indanā bil-Andalus and quotes a large number of Castilian words. Many references to Ibn Baṣṣāl and Ibn al-Luengo (d. 1095) determine his date, for he speaks of both as contemporaries and of the latter as his teacher. Now Abū 'Abdallāh Muḥammad ibn Ibrāhīm ibn Baṣṣāl flourished in Toledo under al-Ma'mūn ibn Dhī-l-Nūn (ruled 1037–74), and after the fall of Toledo (1085), if not before, in Seville under al-Mu'tamid ibn 'Abbād (ruled 1068–91). Abū-l-Ḥasān 'Alī ibn 'Abd al-Raḥmān al-Anṣārī al-Sā'idī, known as Ibn al-Luengo (son of the big one; note the Spanish Arabic form), was a physician, disciple of Ibn Wāfid of Toledo (XI-1), who died c. 1074; before the Christian reconquest of Toledo, Ibn al-Luengo settled in Badajóz, later in Seville; in 1094, he moved to Cordova, where he died in the following year. Ibn Baṣṣāl and Ibn al-Luengo were both agriculturists; they were not dealt with in Introd. (vol. 1), because their works are lost. Millàs Vallicrosa has found a Castilian version of Ibn Baṣṣāl's treatise on agriculture in the cathedral of Toledo (p. 91–103, pl. 6, 1942).

The 'Umda was written in Seville after 1095 and probably not long after that date. The Arabic text contains a large number of Castilian and Romance terms which have been carefully listed by Miguel Asín Palacios in his last work, Glosario de voces romances registradas por un botánico anónimo hispano-musulmán, siglos XI–XII (476 p., Madrid 1943; Isis 37), with indexes in Latin, Castilian, Arabic, and Greek.

Yung Lo ta tien (p. 830 note 18). According to Dr. Arthur W. Hummel (letter dated Oct. 4, 1946): "The latest census of known and existing Yung Lo ta tien volumes is the one compiled by Dr. Yüan T'ung-li, Director of the National Library of Peiping, and published in September 1939 in the Chinese Edition of the Quarterly Bulletin of Chinese Bibliography (T'u shu chi k'an) new series vol. I, no. 3, pp. 246–286. It lists a total of 367 volumes, with the numbers of each volume; the rhyme series of the word that is treated; the word itself (the encyclopaedia being arranged like a dictionary); the institution or person who owns the volume; and the chapter (or chüan) numbers which the volume covers.

"Mr. Yüan probably could not get a complete report for his census, for in 1940 we acquired a volume not listed by him (see Annual Report for that year, p. 157)."

Giovanni della Penna (p. 859). His long connection with the University of Naples is attested by Renzi (p. 550–51, 1857) and by G. M. Monti in the Storia della Università di Napoli written by Francesco Torraca (not Torraco) and others (p. 85, Naples 1924), but it is denied by Wickersheimer (p. 461, 1936). According to the latter, Giovanni belonged to a noble Neapolitan family or he originated from La Penne in the county of Nice [?]. He was canon of Capua. He did not die in Naples in 1388 to be buried in the church of the Celestines; he died before July 4, 1348 [?]. According to Tommaso del Garbo (XIV-2), the same Franciscus de Gianellis (XIV-2) who presented one of Giovanni's plague consilia to the University of Perugia had a controversy with him de animatione seminis.

I wonder whether Giovanni della Penna and the jurisconsult Luca da Penne (c. 1325–90) were connected. See note on the latter below (referring to p. 1798). In the story of the University of Naples by Torraca and others, they are called respectively Giovanni da Penne and Luca da Penne, but no family connection between them is suggested.

Bernard of Gordon (p. 873). Take note that the title of Bernard's main work, Lilium medicinae, is sometimes given to the Compendium medicinae of Gilbert the Englishman (XIII-1). Thus, in the index to vol. 2, the words Lilium medicinae are followed by two references (p. 658, 1026), the first of which concerns Gilbert, the second, Bernard.

John of Gaddesden on epilepsy (p. 882). Further discussion on this subject in the excellent book of Owsei Temkin: The falling sickness (Baltimore 1945; Isis 36, 275–78).

Acupuncture in modern China (p. 906 note 42). A successful application of acupuncture to cure incipient blindness is described by the patient, Chao Yang Buwei, in her Autobiography of a Chinese woman (p. 25, New York 1947).

Chaulmoogra (p. 908). Joseph F. Rock: The Chaulmoogra tree and some related species. A survey conducted in Siam, Burma, Assam, and Bengal (U. S. Department of Agriculture, bulletin no. 1057, 30 p., 16 pl., 1922), includes a preface by David Fairchild and a chapter on chaulmoogra oils by Frederick B. Power. The author of this paper is the agricultural explorer now established in Yünnan, who is making a thorough study of Na-khi or Mo-so tribes (in northwestern Yünnan), their religious ceremonies, their language, hieroglyphic script, and literature.

Polidoro Vergilio (p. 921). John F. Fulton: Hand list of editions of Polydore Vergil's De inventoribus rerum (15 p. typescript, New Haven, Conn. 1944; Isis 36, 29).

Nicholas Trevet (p. 944). Ruth Dean: The earliest known commentary on Livy (Medievalia et humanistica 3, 86–98, 1945; 4, 110, 1946; Isis 36, 180).

Chronicle of Morea (p. 948). The name gasmulos is used by Marco Polo (book 1, ch. 59): "And there is also here a class of people called Argons, which is as much as to say in French Guasmul, or, in other words, sprung from two different races . . . ." Argon is the Turkish or Mongolian word Arghūn. The word gasmulos is discussed at length by Yule-Cordier (1, 284, 289–92, 1926). See also Du Cange's Greek glossary (col. 181, 1688), s.v. *βασμοῦλοι*.

Text. A new edition of the Greek text was prepared by P. P. Kalonaros: *Τὸ Χρονικὸν τοῦ Μορείος. Τὸ Ἑλληνικὸν κείμενον* (432 p., Greece 1940), with 64 photographs of Frankish sites in Greece.

Criticism. William Miller (d. 1945): Essays on the Latin Orient (Cambridge University 1921).

Nicephoros Gregoras as a geographer (p. 951). Gregoras may have participated in the making of new maps for Ptolemy's Geographia, and may be responsible with Isaac Argyros (XIV-2) for the 68 maps of version B. Leo Bagrow: The origin of Ptolemy's Geographia (Geografiska annaler 27, 318–87, Stockholm 1945; Isis 37).

Aethiopian historiography (p. 957). George Fraser Black: Ethiopica & Amharica (87 p., 2 pl., New York Public Library, 1928).

Al-Dhahabī as a musician (p. 967). The treatise on the knowledge of melodies (Kitāb fī ma'rifat al-anghām) ascribed to him was more probably written by another al-Dhahabī, Shams al-dīn al-Ṣaidāwī also called al-Dimashqī. H. G. Farmer: Ghosts. An excursus on Arabic musical bibliographies (Isis 36, 125, 1946).

The letters of Rashīd al-dīn (p. 973, sec. 6, item 7). According to Reuben Levy, the letters are apocryphal, probably of no earlier date than the fifteenth century and possibly of Hindu origin; their purpose was to glorify Rashīd al-dīn (Journal of the Royal Asiatic Society, p. 74–78, 1946).

Marsiglio's Defensor pacis (p. 986). The popularity of that work is illustrated by Lynn Thorndike: The problem of the composite MSS (Miscellanea Giovanni Mercati vol. 6, 12 p., Vatican 1946; see p. 4).

Ibn al-Ukhuwwa and the treatises on ḥisba (p. 999). Max Meyerhof: La surveillance des professions médicales et para-médicales chez les Arabes (Bulletin de l'Institut d'Egypte 26, 119–34, Le Caire 1944; Isis 36, 219), dealing with the medical aspects of ḥisba and translating relevant chapters from the treatise of 'Abd al-Raḥmān ibn Naṣr al-Shaizarī (XII-2). In Introd. (2, 463) this author was called mistakenly Shairazī; he hailed probably from Shaizar, in northern Syria, and should be called Syrian rather than Egyptian.

Arabic books on ḥisba should be compared with the Book of the prefect or governor (τὸ ἐπαρχικὸν βιβλίον) ascribed to the emperor Leon VI the Philosopher (ruled 886–911), for which see Introd. (1, 617).

Abū Ḥaiyān (p. 1011). He was not only a grammarian and theologian, but also a distinguished poet, who composed many verses, including muwashshaḥāt (verses with double rhymes). Specimens of his verses are transcribed and translated by Alois Richard Nykl: Hispano-Arabic poetry and its relations with the old Provençal troubadours (444 p., Baltimore 1946; Isis 37). Abū Ḥaiyān is dealt with on p. 358–60, but one should read the whole chapter covering the Granada period, if not the whole book, in order to place him as a poet in his proper background.

Cumani and Polovtzi (p. 1016). Alexander Alexandrovich Vasiliev: The Goths in the Crimea (Mediaeval Academy, Cambridge, Mass. 1936).

Apropos of Grønbech's facsimile edition see Monde oriental (31, 89–90, 1937).

The government of the church (p. 1035). A new history of the papacy was published in Switzerland during the war by Gaston Castella: Histoire des papes (quarto, 3 vols., ill., Zürich 1943–45), with Catholic imprimatur. I have read various parts of it, notably the one dealing with the fourteenth century (1, 256–86), and find that the author's conclusions are not essentially different from mine.

Orthodox saints (p. 1044). For Orthodox views on sainthood see Martin Jugie: Le schisme byzantin (p. 449–60, 1941).

Manichaeism in conflict with the Orthodox church (p. 1058). The note on Mānī (III-2) contains a brief account of Manichaeism; more information on its world-wide repercussions may be found in the Introd., passim by means of the indexes (s.v. Manichaeism, Albigenses, Cathari). There were two waves of Manichaeism in Europe, the first from the third century to the seventh, the second from the ninth century to the fourteenth. The second wave was largely stopped by the persecution of the Albigenses initiated by Innocent III (pope 1198–1216). In the meanwhile, a similar heresy had been started in Bulgaria about the middle of the tenth century by Bogomil.[14] When the first Bulgarian empire fell, in 1018, Bulgaria became and remained until 1186 a province of the Byzantine empire, and Bogomilism invaded other provinces and even Constantinople. That invasion was put an end to c. 1110, when the leading Bogomils were imprisoned and their leader, Basil, burned at the stake. Bogomilism was then pressed back into Bulgaria, where a combination of economic difficulties with ecclesiastical nonchalance and of bodily miseries with spiritual confusion and despair favored its growth for a full century. It had less success in Serbia, where it was finally repressed by St. Sava or Sabbas (c. 1169–1237), first archbishop and organizer of the Serbian church (1221–37).[15] The Bulgarian Bogomils were condemned at the council meeting at Tirnovo (capital of the new Bulgarian empire) in 1211 by order of the tsar Boris III (Boril). The coincidence of this Bulgarian persecution of the Bogomils with that of the Albi-

[14] Bogomil is the Slavonic equivalent of Theophilos.

[15] He it was who helped the old Stephen Neman (one of the founders of the Serbian Nemania dynasty, ruled 1151–95) to found the Serbian monastery Chilandari on Mt. Athos.

genses in the West is not accidental. The Bogomils were not beaten, however, witness the necessity of a new condemnation at the council of 1350, organized by St. Theodosios of Tirnovo, Bulgarian champion of Orthodoxy and Hesychasm. They continued to exist precariously until the end of the second Bulgarian empire in 1393.

The main sources for the study of Bogomilism and of contemporary heresies of the Orthodox church are the Sermon against the heretics written soon after 972[16] by the Bulgarian priest St. Cosmas; the Synodicon of the tsar Boril (that is, the acts of the council of Tirnovo); the Dogmatic panoply (Πανοπλία δογματική) of Euthymios Zigabenos (Εὐθύμιος Ζιγαβηνός or Ζιγαδηνός);[17] and the Alexiad of Anna Comnena (XII-1).

General accounts by Fred. J. Powicke (ERE 2, 784–85, 1910) and by Dimitri Obolensky: The Bogomils (Eastern churches quarterly, Oct.–Dec. 1945, 23 p.), including abundant references to Slavonic as well as to other publications.

Introduction to ḥadīth (p. 1067). (Mawlawī) Muḥammad 'Alī of Lahore: A manual of ḥadīth (419 p., Lahore, s.a., recent). This is a very convenient selection of the traditions which are of practical interest to the Muslims of today; the traditions are quoted in Arabic and English, well annotated, and their sources briefly indicated. The author is well known because of his excellent edition of the Qur'ān[18] and many books of Muslim apologetics in English and Urdū, written in connection with the Aḥmadīya movement (EI 1, 206, 1909). He should not be confused with another Muslim apologist, his contemporary namesake, Mawlānā Muḥammad 'Alī of Rampur (1878–1931), whose autobiographical sketch, My life, was edited by Afḍal Iqbāl (285 p., portrait, Lahore 1942).

The three holy ones (p. 1070). Attempts were made from time to time to syncretize the three main religions. Images of the san shêng or three holy ones (Confucius, Buddha, Lao Tzŭ)[19] may be seen in temples and even in special chapels, san shêng an. Such tentatives appealed to the feelings of religious-minded Chinese (except the Confucian doctrinaires), and thus were fairly successful. There were so many such chapels or at least such images that the Confucian magistrates felt obliged to condemn them. Periods of toleration alternated, however, with periods of repression. For example, the emperor Yung chêng (1723–36) provided for the repair not only of the Buddhist temples on the holy island of Puto-shan,[20] but also of

[16] That Sermon is one of the earliest monuments of Bulgarian literature.

[17] Euthymios was a monk of the monastery περὶ Περιβλέπτου in Constantinople, in the service of Alexios Comnenos (emperor 1081–1118), much admired by the latter's daughter, Anna Comnena (Krumbacher p. 82–85, 1897).

[18] The holy Qur'ān. Containing the Arabic text with English translation and commentary by Maulvi Muhammad Ali (2d ed., 1392 p., Ahmadiyya anjuman-i-ishāat-i-Islam, Lahore 1920), preface dated 1916. This is the handiest edition of the Qur'ān for English-Arabic readers; well indexed.

[19] Take note that the expression san shêng sometimes designates three other persons or ideas in Chinese religion or mythology, e.g., three Buddhist or three Confucian ones. See Giles (no. 9892, 1912). Couling (p. 554, 1917). Chinese Catholics use the term shêng san for the Trinity.

[20] More correctly P'u t'o lo ka, the sacred island of the Buddhists in the Chusan archipelago, off the north coast of Chehkiang within easy reach of both Shanghai and Ningpo. The name is derived from the Sanskrit Potaloka, the hill from which Avalokiteśvara looks down. An account of the monasteries of that island and their history is given by Reginald Fleming Johnston: Buddhist China (London 1913). Couling (p. 468, 1917). Soothill and Hodous (p. 478, 1937).

Confucian and Taoist temples in other localities. In 1744, the Board of Rites forbade the practice of the "triple religion"; according to its decree of that date there were then over 590 san shêng an in Honan alone. A final decree of the same kind was issued in 1837.

Edward Harper Parker: Studies in Chinese religion (p. 292–96, London 1910). John Shryock: The temples of Anking and their cults (p. 132–35, Paris 1931; Isis 19, 287).

Manichaeism in China (p. 1071). Mo ni chiao hsia pu tsan, The lower (or second) section of the Manichaean hymns, translated by Tsui Chi (Bulletin of the School of Oriental and African Studies 11, 174–217, London 1943); to the translation is added much information on the Chinese Manichaean writings and their bibliography.

The Jewish Castilian Bible (p. 1077). José Llamas: La antigua biblia castellana de los Judios españoles (Sefarad 4, 219–44, 11 pl., 1944).

Chinese examinations (p. 1083). Hsu Tao-ling has published a name index of the holders of the degree chin shih during the various dynasties. I have not seen it, and know of it only through a note by Joseph Needham in Science and culture (p. 342, Calcutta, Jan. 1946). I cannot quote the title of the book and am not sure of the author's name, because Needham does not give the Chinese characters nor explain his peculiar transcription of them.

Ssŭ-i-kuan (p. 1084). Norman Wild: Materials for the study of the Ssŭ-i-kuan, bureau of translators (Bulletin of the School of Oriental and African Studies 11, 617–40, London 1945), documents derived from Chinese sources concerning the functioning of that office from the fifteenth to the seventeenth century.

In the Zubdat al-tawārīkh (Cream of histories) of the Persian historian Ḥāfiẓ Abrū (a contemporary of Tīmūr and of the latter's son Shāh-rukh) we are given an account of an embassy sent by Shāh-rukh to Yung Lo in 1420. The Tīmūrī embassy was led by Qāḍī Yūsuf, who introduced the Muslim envoys to the Ming emperor and was able to speak not only Chinese, Persian, and Arabic, but also Turkish, Mongol, and Kalmuk. Browne (3, 424–26, 1928). Douglas M. Dunlop: Ḥāfiẓ-i Abrū' version of the Timurid embassy to China in 1420 (Transactions of Glasgow University Oriental Society 11, 15–19, 1946).

Henry of Lancaster (p. 1091). To the mystical writings by Englishmen of this time might be added the Anglo-Norman Livre de seyntz medicines, a devotional book composed in 1354 by Henry of Lancaster, first duke of Lancaster 1351, who died of the plague in 1361. For the biography of that captain, administrator, diplomat see Froissart and DNB (26, 101–6). His book was edited by Emile Jules Arnould (Anglo-Norman texts no. 2, 260 p., Oxford 1940; Isis 36, 181).

This first duke of Lancaster was the father of Blanche of Lancaster, who married John of Gaunt, duke of Lancaster (1340–99), and was the ancestress of the house of Lancaster. The first duke should not be confused with his father and namesake, Henry of Lancaster (1281?–1345), who was earl, not duke, of Lancaster, nor with another contemporary namesake, Henry of Lancaster, earl of Derby, also called Henry of Bolingbroke, who became Henry IV (king 1399–1413) and is mentioned on p. 1150.

Early observations of sunspots (p. 1121). The early Chinese observations of sunspots are not as extraordinary as they may seem if one bears in mind that many sunspots are easily visible with the naked eye at sunset or sunrise or reflected on the surface of still waters. A spot about 30,000 miles or 4 earth-diameters across is large enough to be seen without telescope, and many spots are much larger; on rare occasions they may be almost 20 earth-diameters across. Western astronomers could not see them, because they were blinded by prejudices; those prejudices were still so strong c. 1611 that when Galileo and Christopher Scheiner announced the reality of sunspots, their statements were met with incredulity and opposition.

The Scheiner and Galileo writings concerning sunspots and other notes ad hoc are gathered in Antonio Favaro's edition of Galileo's Opere (5, 1–260, Firenze 1895). John Joseph Fahie: Galileo (p. 128–32, London 1903). Rudolf Wolf: Geschichte der Astronomie (p. 177–78, 389–95, München 1877). Grant McColley: Christopher Scheiner and the decline of neo-Aristotelianism (Isis 32, 63–69, 1 fig., 1940).

Since the writing of this note, I have discovered definite references to sunspots in mediaeval literature (the earliest in the years 807 and 840) and have published the texts ad hoc in the form of a question, Early observations of sunspots? (query no. 111, Isis 37, 69–71, 1947), with the hope of eliciting similar observations. In every case, the sunspots were explained as due to transits of the inferior planets, in spite of the fact that such transits are very rare and brief, whereas sunspots are relatively frequent and may remain visible for weeks on end.

A large amount of knowledge concerning sunspots has accumulated during recent years, and much more will be obtained if only because the improvement of radio communications requires it. Not only have many spots been described, photographed, and followed day after day for weeks or even months, but a certain periodicity in their occurrence has been detected (11-year period, sunspot cycle). Sunspots create magnetic storms and may influence our lives in many ways. It is possible, e.g., that droughts (and famines) are indirectly caused by them. There may be correlations between sunspots and human events, but such correlations have not yet been established and I wonder whether it is possible to establish them without ambiguity. It is just as well that the mediaeval astrologers were not given a chance to speculate on such matters.

Olof André Åkesson: The motion and distribution of the sun-spots (Lunds Universitets årsskrift, afd. 2, vol. 10, no. 10, 100 p. quarto, 1 pl., Lund 1914). Charles Greeley Abbot: Sun spots and weather (Smithsonian miscellaneous collections vol. 87, no. 18, 10 p., 5 fig., Washington 1933). Harlan True Stetson: Sun spots and their effects (216 p., ill., New York 1937). Henry Helm Clayton: The sunspot period (Smithsonian miscellaneous collections vol. 98, no. 2, 18 p., 1 pl., Washington 1939); The 11-year and 27-day solar periods in meteorology (ibid. vol. 99, no. 5, 20 p., ill., 1940). John Adam Fleming: The sun and the earth's magnetic field (Smithsonian report for 1942, p. 173–208; see p. 174). Loyal Blaine Aldrich: The solar constant and sunspot numbers (Smithsonian miscellaneous collections vol. 104, no. 12, 5 p., 1 fig., 1945).

The following item is added for the sake of curiosity. Carlos Garcia-Mata and Felix I. Shaffner: Solar and economic relationships (Quarterly journal of economics vol. 49, 51 p., 12 charts, 1934), reprinted by the Foundation for the study of cycles, Riverside, Conn. (51 p., New York 1945).

Comets' tails (p. 1122). Nicholas Theodore Bobrovnikoff wrote recently in Isis (36, 268, 1946): "The observation associated with Peter Apian, that the tails of comets point away from the sun, is and always was a dangerous half-truth. For the axis of the tail to be directed exactly opposite the sun, the repulsive force acting on the particles of the tail should be infinitely great, or else the earth should be in the plane of the orbit of the comet. All tails deviate from this exact direction more or less, sometimes very much, and the amount of deviation allows us to compute the magnitude of the repulsive force. Astronomers should be grateful that Tycho Brahe, accepting Apian's dictum, was less dogmatic than the author, and gave us a good description of the tail."

Musical teaching in England (p. 1128). A curious Middle English poem, Lament of the monk (52 lines; MS Arundel 292), was probably written c. 1350–80; it describes the struggles of a young monk with his French music master and his lesson in solmization, and provides many of the earliest English occurrences of musical terms. Francis Lee Utley: The chorister's lament (Speculum 21, 194–202, 1946), including text of the poem.

Musical theories and practice in the West (p. 1129). André Pirro (1869–1943): Histoire de la musique de la fin du XIVe siècle à la fin du XVIe (370 p., 32 pl., Paris 1940), including many musical examples.

Chinese music at the beginning of the Ming period (p. 1129). Some general information on Chinese music was given above (p. 162 note 35), and it was added that no Chinese treatises on music of the first half of the fourteenth century were known to the author. The situation seems to have improved in the second half of the fourteenth century and the first half of the fifteenth.

The following treatises are cited on the basis of the list published by Wu Kwang Tsing (= Kuang Ch'ing): Books on East Asiatic music in the Library of Congress, reprinted from the Supplement to the Catalog of early books on music (p. 121–33, Library of Congress, Washington 1944).

1. Ch'in-chien t'u-shih (The ch'in illustrated), by T'ao Tsung-i (fl. c. 1368) in his collectanea Shuo-fu, printed in 1647. "The first three illustrations show the lute, or ch'in, in three dimensions. There are twenty-six illustrations, with brief descriptions, of lutes supposed to have been owned by famous men of history." Mr. Wu remarks: "The name ch'in is generally translated into English as 'lute,' but actually the instrument resembles the psaltery or zither. It consists of an oblong, convex sounding board, over which are stretched seven silk cords of equal length but of differing thickness, tuned GAĆDEGA. It was used formerly in state ceremonies and was played exclusively by the educated classes. Owing to the fact that it is a very difficult instrument to master, the ch'in was never widely popular and today there are even fewer players. The tablature is especially complicated. Each note is made up of several simple symbols indicating for each tone the pitch, string, finger position and direction of plucking."

2. Ch'in-shêng shih-liu fa (Sixteen rules governing the tonal qualities of the ch'in). These rules were formulated by a member of the Board of Music called Lêng Ch'ien (late 14th cent.), styled Lung-yang-tzŭ, and were printed in the T'an chi ts'ung shu (1697), where they are wrongly ascribed to Chuang Chên-fêng (17th cent.). Translated in Robert Hans van Gulik: The lore of the Chinese lute (p. 105–13, Tōkyō 1940).

3. Ku-ch'in lun (Discussion of ancient ch'in), by Ts'ao Chao (late 14th cent.), included in 1388 in his Ko-ku yao-lun. Printed in the Wan-li period (1573–1620).

Explaining construction of the ch'in, its use and care, means of identifying ancient types.

4. Ching-shan yüeh-lu (Ching-shan's book of music), by Mao Ch'i ling,[21] printed in the latter's collected works in 1790. Mao dedicated this book to his father, whose tzŭ was Ching-shan. It is a treatise on musical theory based on the treatise concerning flutes by Chu Ch'üan (d. 1448), son of the first Ming emperor. It deals with music of the T'ang dynasty, the classical period of "modern" Chinese music, as opposed to the "old" music already well developed in Confucius' time.

5. We might still add the Lü-lü hsin-shu (New book of music), by Ts'ai Yüan-ting (1135–98), included in the Philosophical collection, Hsing-li ta-ch'üan, compiled by imperial decree in 1414–15 by Hu Kuang and others (copy in Library of Congress dated 1553). The Lü-lü hsin-shu is divided into two parts: (1) principles of music, (2) examples illustrating those principles. Preface by Chu Hsi (XII-2). Says Mr. Wu: "The term lü-lü derives from the name of an ancient musical instrument which was used, in the manner of a pitch-pipe, to determine the twelve chromatic semitones of the octave. It consisted of twelve bamboo tubes of graduated lengths, six tubes representing the positive tones (yang), called lü, and six representing the negative tones (yin), called lü.[22] Hence this instrument received the name lü-lü, meaning 'law,' or 'principle.' The first and longest of the tubes measured nine inches and was called huang-chung. The sound it produced, known as kung, was the keynote of the chromatic scale. In time the term lü-lü became more or less synonymous with music in general."

With regard to the musical tube huang-chung see G. Sarton and James R. Ware: Were the ancient Chinese weights and measures related to musical instruments? (Isis 37, 73, 1947).

The apparent revival of music under the early Ming is not surprising. The Ming tried their best to revive the old Chinese culture, which had been partly submerged by foreign traditions during the Yüan dynasty. The best models of that culture had been given during the T'ang dynasty (618–907). The T'ang period and more particularly the rule of the sixth emperor, Hsüan Tsung (713–56),[23] was the golden age of Chinese music. As music was an essential part of T'ang culture, a revival of that culture implied naturally a revival of music.

The Catalan or Majorcan school of cartography (p. 1140). Much information on that school has been gathered by Gonçal de Reparaz-Ruiz and published by him in Catalan, Spanish, and French, e.g., in Catalunya a les mars (Barcelona 1930; Isis 16, 173), La época de los grandes descubrimientos españoles y portugueses (Barcelona 1931; Isis 16, 558), Essai sur l'histoire de la géographie de l'Espagne (1940). In the latest of these publications Reparaz-Ruiz deals not only with Dalmau Ces-Planes, William Soler, Abraham Cresques and his son Judah (Jacme de Malhorca), Judah ben Moses Mosconi, to all of whom notes are devoted in this volume, but also to others such as Isaac Nafuci (fl. 1359–73), who made astronomical instruments for Pere IV and was chief rabbi of Majorca in 1362, Ephraim Vidal, Aaron Cohen, Ephraim Bellshoms, and the Italian Ubriachi, who was the representative of the Florentine merchant Francesco Datini in Barcelona. Many

[21] Mao Ch'i-ling (1623–1716). Hummel (p. 563–65, 1943).
[22] These two lü are respectively nos. 7548 and 7520 in Giles (1912).
[23] Introd. (1, 508). Giles (no. 1172, 1898).

of the Majorcan geographers were also astronomers and makers of astrolabes, and they helped to translate books from Arabic into Catalan. Thus, Isaac Nafuci and Ephraim Bellshoms were charged in 1380 by the infante Joan to translate al-Farghānī (IX-1). In 1362, Pere IV demanded communication of an astronomical MS in the library of the crown of Aragon, which was written in Arabic and Catalan.

The fourteenth century was the golden age of the school of Majorca, but that school continued to exist in Palma until the seventeenth century. At the end of the fifteenth century Ferdinand the Catholic appealed to Majorcan cartographers to help him draw the new line of demarcation between Portugal and Spain established by the treaty of Tordesillas (June 7, 1494).

Reparaz-Ruiz (1940).

The Imago mundi of Pierre d'Ailly (p. 1148). Columbus' hopes were increased not only by the overestimate of the length of Eurasia, but also by the underestimate of the size of the earth. The almost correct measurement of the circumference of the earth by Eratosthenes (III-2 B.C.), 252,000 stadia,[24] had been reduced by Posidonios (I-1 B.C.) to 180,000 stadia, and that reduced estimate was transmitted to posterity by Strabo (I-2 B.C.) in his Geography (2, 2, 2) and by Ptolemy. Columbus was acquainted with it directly or indirectly.

Natural philosophy (p. 1165). For the use of that phrase and its equivalents in other languages, see above, the addition concerning Occam's physics (addendum relative to p. 550).

Iron pillar in Delhi (p. 1175). The Iron pillar standing in the courtyard of the Quwwat al-Islām mosque bears an inscription in Gupta script in honor of one king Chandra, who is probably Chandragupta II (ruled c. 380–415); its dating is based on this assumption. According to Murray Thompson it is made of "pure malleable iron of 7.66 specific gravity." There is also a Rajput inscription on that pillar. Science and culture (12, 345, Calcutta 1947). According to Sir Robert Hadfield, the specific gravity is 7.81; there is very little sulphur (0.006 per cent), little phosphorus (0.114 per cent), no manganese. Murray's Handbook for travellers in India (p. 252, London 1913; Isis 2, 402).

The mediaeval fame of Hindu steel is illustrated by the adjective andanicum occurring in Marco Polo and other texts of the thirteenth and fourteenth centuries. See notes on steel in Marco Polo (p. 93–94, 1926) and Cordier (p. 19, 1920). H. D. Austin, Henry and Renée Kahane: Byzantine *ἰνδανικὸς σίδηρος*, Frankish andanicum (Byzantina metabyzantina 1, 181–87, 1946).

Hunger and history (p. 1182). In addition to the book of Drummond and Wilbraham, one should consult also E. Parmalee Prentice: Hunger and history. The influence of hunger on human history (268 p., New York 1939; Isis 32, 227–29).

Menageries (p. 1189). Reference should have been made to menageries in Muslim lands. See the description of the Park of the wild beasts in Baghdād in 917 during

[24] We should remember that there are uncertainties concerning the value of the stadion. See Aubrey Diller (Isis 27, 513; 28, 493).

the rule of al-Muqtadir (908–32) in Gustave E. von Grunebaum: Medieval Islam (p. 28, Chicago 1946), where the sources are duly cited. It is probable that there are other descriptions of menageries in Arabic literature.

Medicine in Denmark (p. 1208). Henrik Harpestraeng (XIII-1), who introduced Salernitan medicine into Denmark and the rest of Scandinavia, had no followers of any importance in mediaeval times. Danish (and Scandinavian) medicine in the fourteenth century remained essentially on the Harpestraeng level or below. The investigation of skeletal remains in mediaeval cemeteries, especially in that of the monastery for Augustinian canons in Aebelholt (northeastern Sjaelland), founded in the twelfth century, has enabled V. Møller-Christensen to draw certain conclusions. No traces of syphilis or actinomycosis have been found; on the other hand, evidences of tuberculosis are frequent, and of ergotism (ignis sacer) not uncommon. The skeleton of a leper was found in 1944. It should be noted that the segregation of lepers was not enforced in Denmark until the latter part of the thirteenth century.

Vilhelm Møller-Christensen: Middelalderens laegekunst i Danmark (Acta historica scientiarum naturalium et medicinalium vol. 3, 250 p., 35 ill., Copenhagen 1944; Isis 37). This book dealing with mediaeval medicine in Denmark contains very little concerning the fourteenth century specifically.

Chinese Jews (p. 1213). There is a single reference to Jews in Marco Polo (book 2, ch. 5). See discussion of it in Yule-Cordier's edition (1, 343, 346–47, 1926). There are many more references to them in Yule-Cordier: Cathay and the way thither (4 vols., 1913–16), see index s.v. Jews. William Charles White: Chinese Jews (3 vols., Toronto 1942; Isis 35, 257).

A story comparable to that of the salvation of baby Moses from the river is found in early Chinese writings. This may be due to folkloric convergence or to an early Chinese familiarity with the Pentateuch. It is said that some Jews drifted to China after the Babylonish captivity (6th cent. B.C.) and that Jews founded a colony in Honan in A.D. 72. That tradition is unproved but not implausible. Herbert A. Giles: Adversaria sinica (no. 3, 55–57; no. 4, 115, Shanghai 1906).

Rudolf Löwenthal: The nomenclature of Jews in China (Collectanea commissionis synodalis 17, 354–70, 1944); An early Chinese source on the K'ai-fêng Jewish community by Chang Hsiang-wên (to be published in the Folklore studies of the Catholic University of Peiping).

Dwarfs (p. 1228). Felix Speiser: Die Pygmäenfrage (Experientia 2, 297–302, 1946).

For latest information on dwarfs and giants from the genetical point of view, see Reginald Ruggles Gates: Human genetics (p. 1310–41, New York 1946; Isis 37).

Franz Weidenreich: Apes, giants and men (130 p., University of Chicago 1946).

Dance macabre (p. 1231). The etymology of the word macabre is obscure. French lexicographers would connect that word with Maccabees or with the name of a French painter of such dances, Macabré.

Jean Le Fèvre[25] in his poem Respit de la mort (1376) refers to an earlier composi-

[25] This Jean Le Fèvre was an advocate in the Parliament of Paris and member of Charles V's chancery; he should not be confused with the contemporary physician of Montpellier dealt with below (p. 1695), nor with the contemporary poet born in Thérouanne (near Saint-Omer, Pas-de-Calais), author of Latin and French poems against women which were duly castigated

tion of his entitled "la dance de Macabré." Gaston Paris: La dance Macabré de Jean Le Fèvre (Romania 24, 129–32, 1895). According to OED that is the earliest use of that phrase. In English the dance macabre was called dance of Machabree or dance Macaber; in Latin, chorea Machabaeorum (Du Cange).

Edward Frank Chaney: La dance macabre des charniers des Innocents (Manchester University Press, 1946), containing the illustrations, French text in verse taken from the Paris editions of 1485 and 1486, English version. Ernst Moritz Manasse: The dance motive of the Latin dance of death (Medievalia et humanistica 4, 83–103, 1946).

Consilia of Ferrari da Gradi (p. 1239). These consilia were very popular, seven printed editions of them appearing between 1480 and 1535. French translations of many of them are included in Henri Maxime Ferrari: Une chaire de médecine au XVe siècle. Un professeur à l'université de Pavie de 1432 à 1472 (334 p., 6 fig., Paris 1899; see pp. 185–241).

Regimina sanitatis (p. 1239). To the regimina listed on p. 285 and 1239 might be added for the sake of comparison the "Régime pour garder santé de corps et d'âme et parvenir à belle et plaisante vieillesse" written c. 1437–60 by the Norman master Héronchel (Pierre Aronchel of Genève?), otherwise unknown. It was written at the request of François Rossyn (or Russin), lord of Allaman, pays de Vaud, for Louis, duke of Savoy from 1434 to 1465. The MS of it is preserved in the old library of Burgundy in Brussels. It is a French translation of the Regimen sanitatis ad regem Aragonum composed by Arnold of Villanova in 1307. Eugène Olivier: Un régime pour garder santé (Gesnerus 1, 117–32, 1944), followed by a very incomplete list of other mediaeval regimina.

Early town physicians in Basel (p. 1244). Karl Leuthardt: Das Stadtarztamt zu Basel. Seine Entwicklungsgeschichte bis zum Jahre 1529 (Zürcher medizingeschichtliche Abhandlungen no. 16, 60 p., Zürich 1940). According to Rudolph Zaunick's review (Mitt. 39, 269, 1940), the first lay physician in Basel was one Magister Symon medicus at the beginning of the fourteenth century; in 1330–55 there was a medical family called Atzo, one of whose members, Wilhelmus Atzo, was from 1355 the first town physician in Basel. There were also Jewish town physicians, called Jocetus and his son Jehiel Gutleben.

Early Ming censuses (p. 1268). The Library of Congress has obtained a microfilm of a book preserved in Peking, the Hou-hu chih (10 chüan, with maps and illustrations), describing the methods of national census. It was first compiled by Chao Kuan in 1514, but additions were made at various dates down to 1621. Beginning in 1381 a census was taken every ten years. "The whole population was then registered by the local officials, the tabulations being recorded in two sets of census books on yellow paper; one for local reference, the other for presentation to the Ministry of Census. The returns of each census were placed in the island[26] deposi-

---

by Christine de Pisan; nor with the chronicler Jean Le Fèvre (Abbeville c. 1396—Bruges 1468), seigneur de Saint-Rémy, etc., counselor to Philip the Good, duke of Burgundy (Biographie nationale de Belgique 11, 664–75, 1891).

[26] Islands in a lake immediately outside the T'ai p'ing gate in the east wall of the city of Nanking. Those islands were regarded as safe places for the preservation of national archives.

tories and as many as 1,200 students were called from the National Academy at Nanking to compare the new returns with the census taken ten years previously." A. Hummel in the Library of Congress quarterly journal (3, no. 2, 19–21, 1946).

Al-jihād al-akbar (p. 1274). The Muslims divided the world into two parts, the Dār al-Islām and the Dār al-ḥarb, or the world of peace and faith and the world of war, or the Muslim world and the infidel one. It was a Muslim duty to carry war against the infidels and try to diminish their world. Muslim theologians gave moral interpretations of these ideas. This reminds us of the Spiritual exercises of St. Ignatius of Loyola, fourth day of the second week (De dos banderas, De duobus vexillis). The spirit animating St. Ignatius in that meditation is very similar to the Muslim spirit at its best, faithful and militant; in both cases such a spirit can never be too militant for self-discipline, but it easily becomes incompatible with the toleration of other faiths and with simple humanity.

Humanism in Italy (p. 1292). To the fin-de-siècle humanists named in this section should be added of course Leonardo Bruni, also called Leonardo Aretino. Born in Arezzo, in 1369; died in 1444. Secretary of the popes (1405–15) and later (1427–44) of the Florentine Republic. He had learned Greek under Chrysoloras, and his main titles to fame are many translations from Greek into Latin (Plato, Xenophon, Aristotle, Polybios, Plutarch, Procopios, etc.). His main original work is an elaborate Latin history of Florence; he also wrote in Latin and Italian on the Italian classics, Dante, Petrarca, Boccaccio. C. 1422–29 he composed the De studiis et litteris for donna Battista de Montefeltro (1384–1448), who was then the wife of Galeazzo Malatesta; this is perhaps the first humanistic initiation written for women.

Sandys (2, 45–47, 1908). Franz Beck: Studien zu Lionardo Bruni (88 p., Berlin 1912). Mariano David: La prima "institutio" umanistica femminile. De studiis et litteris (30 p., Torino 1935). Berthold Louis Ullman: Bruni and humanistic historiography (Medievalia et humanistica 4, 45–61, 1946).

Nō drama (p. 1333). For music and rhythmic speech in nō, see the Japanese books referred to by Shio Sakanishi in the Supplement to the Catalog of early books on music (p. 132–33, Library of Congress, Washington 1944).

An ambitious collection of books dealing with nō was published in Japan during the war under the editorship of Toyoichirō Nogami: Nōgaku zensho (1942—). The Library of Congress has received only vols. 2 to 5, out of at least 6 volumes.

Solomon ben Isaac ha-Levi (p. 1343). Luciano Serrano (O.S.B.): Don Pablo de Santa Maria, gran rabino y obispo di Burgos (Burgos 1941; Sefarad 1, 451–52; 4, 441).

Life of St. Birgitta (p. 1356). The saint's earliest biography was written by two of her confessors soon after her death. The MS of it was completed on Nov. 13, 1378 (only five years after her death). A facsimile edition of it has just been published with an English and Swedish preface by Isak Collijn: Liber de miraculis Beate Brigide de Suecia, Roma 1378, Codex S. Laurentii de Panisperna (Corpus codicum suecicorum medii aevi vol. 7, Copenhagen 1946).

Ācārya (p. 1366). On that title, meaning master or doctor, see Monier-Williams (p. 131, 1899); article ajari in Hōbōgirin (p. 17-18, 1929); Soothill and Hodous (p. 292, 1937).

Jacob ben Isaac Carsono (p. 1375). The astrological treatise which Pere Engelbert and Dalmau Ces-Planes wrote in Catalan with Jacob's collaboration was edited by J. Massó y Torrents (Barcelona 1890).

Lady Margaret's foundations (p. 1402 note 7). Lady Margaret (1443–1509) was Margaret Beaufort, daughter of John, first duke of Somerset; she married Edmund Tudor, earl of Richmond, and later Thomas Stanley, earl of Derby, hence she is sometimes called Margaret countess of Richmond and Derby. After 1485 she lived in retirement, being guided by the saintly and scholarly John Fisher (1459, beheaded 1535). She endowed the Lady Margaret foundations in Oxford and Cambridge, as well as Christ's College (1505) and St. John's College (1508) in Cambridge. She translated part of the Imitatio Christi and other books of devotion from French into English, and was a patron of the early English printers William Caxton and Wynkyn de Worde.

DNB (2, 48–49). Enid M. G. Routh: Lady Margaret, countess of Richmond and Derby, mother of Henry VII (135 p., portrait, London 1924).

Poor scholars (p. 1403). To call Winchester a charity school seems paradoxical, but I have before me an indenture (dated 1946) wherein Harvard College is defined as "a charitable corporation organized under the laws of Massachusetts." That is legal terminology, and it corresponds to some reality, for the students privileged to attend such schools receive considerably more than they pay for.

Libraries (p. 1406). Many references to fourteenth-century libraries and collections of books will be found passim in this work. Add to them Pearl Kibre: Intellectual interests in 14th and 15th century libraries (Journal of the history of ideas 7, 257–97, 1946).

"*Langland*" (p. 1413). Nevill Coghill: The pardon of Piers Plowman (Lecture, British Academy, London 1945).

Cats in English literature (p. 1422). For the sake of comparison, the earliest mention of cats in European literature is to be found in Herodotos (2, 66), who dealt with Egyptian cats (*αἴλουρος*). Aristotle has not much to say about cats, though his remarks on their pairing suggest direct observation (Historia animalium 540a10). The ancient Egyptians were probably the first people who domesticated (and idolized) cats, but wild cats existed in Asia and Europe. Domesticated cats were brought from Egypt to other parts of the Roman empire, possibly also to England. The English (and other European) cats are the offspring of the wild European cats and possibly also of Egyptian cats.

The Greeks and Romans fought mice not with cats, but with some kind of weasel (weasel, marten, polecat, foumart) which they called *γαλέη* or *γαλῆ*, mustela. Remains of cats have been found in Romano-British sites, but it is not possible to decide with certainty whether those cats were wild or domestic. In two letters (dated London, Jan. 24, Feb. 10, 1947) Mr. E. M. M. Alexander has kindly sent me a summary of the evidence available; he concludes, "the domestic cat was known in Roman Britain and this is the view now generally held."

There are various references to cats in the laws of Howel Dda or the Good, early Welsh king (d. 950).

No cat is mentioned in the Bible.

For Egyptian cats see Neville and B. Langton: The cat in ancient Egypt (104 p., 19 pl., Cambridge University 1940).

For Roman Britain, A. W. G. Lowther: Surrey archaeological collection (vol. 38, pl. 4, 1929). George Macdonald: The Roman wall in Scotland (2d ed., p. 214, pl. 31, Oxford 1934). Robin George Collingwood and John Nowell Linton Myres: Roman Britain and the English settlements (2d ed., p. 221, 1937).

For the laws of Howel Dda see Aneurin Owen: Ancient laws and institutions of Wales (p. 835, 862, folio, London 1841). Arthur Wade Wade-Evans: Welsh medieval law, being a text of the laws of Howel the Good (Oxford 1909).

Chaucer. Special criticism (p. 1426). George R. Coffman: Chaucer and courtly love once more. The wife of Bath's tale (Speculum 20, 43–50, 1945). Margaret Schlauch: Chaucer's doctrine of kings and tyrants (Speculum 20, 133–56, 1945).

Gregory of Tathev (p. 1441). Leon Arpee: History of Armenian Christianity (p. 175–86, New York 1946).

Yosippon (p. 1451). Luitpold Wallach: Yosippon and the Alexander romance (Jewish quarterly review 37, 407–22, 1947).

The Shādhilīya fraternity (p. 1452). In the notes of this volume devoted to the Islamic fraternities or ṭuruq (p. 153, 420–21, 1068), only the most important could be mentioned. Perhaps mention should have been made of the Shādhilīya, founded by 'Alī ibn 'Abdallāh al-Shādhilī (born near Ceuta in Morocco or in Shādhila, Tunisia, c. 1196, died in Upper Egypt c. 1258). His mystical views have deeply influenced not only the fraternity named after him, but some thirteen others derived from it. The Shādhilīya is represented to this day by many zawāyā (sing. zāwiya; monastery) chiefly in North Africa, west of Egypt.

The late Don Miguel Asín y Palacios became interested in the Shādhilīya because of Ibn 'Abbād, then devoted longer studies to them published under the title Šaḏilīes y alumbrados (Andalus 9, 321–45, 1944; 10, 1–52, 1945; 11, 1–67, 263–74, 1946); the alumbrados are a Spanish group of illuminati, Christian mystics, about whom see also Henry Charles Lea: Chapters from the religious history of Spain (Philadelphia 1890). Asín's memoir of 1933 was translated into French by Mme L. N. de Céligny and published in the Etudes carmélitaines (p. 113–67, Paris, April 1932). Jean Baruzi: Problèmes d'histoire des religions (p. 111–51, Paris 1935).

Incorruptibility of bodies as a proof of sainthood (p. 1466). Martin Jugie: Le schisme byzantin (p. 449, Paris 1941). A letter from C. W. Adams dated London 14 April 1947, discussing the statement made in Isis (32, 187), came too late for its conclusions to be included in my text, but it made me realize more keenly the great complexity of this question. He refers chiefly to John Cuthbert Lawson: Modern Greek folklore and ancient Greek religion (632 p., Cambridge 1910); ERE (3, 211,

735, 1911); Montague Summers: The vampire, his kith and kin (372 p., London 1928).

Jade (p. 1471). Herbert A. Giles: Jade (Adversaria sinica no. 9, 312–22; no. 10, 327–28, 4 fig., Shanghai 1911–13). Berthold Laufer: Jade, a study in Chinese archaeology and religion (384 p., 204 fig., 68 pl., Field Museum, Chicago 1912). Photographic reprint of Laufer's classic (South Pasadena 1946). Yule-Cordier's edition of Marco Polo (1, 191–94, 1926), Cordier's addenda (p. 46, 1920).

Tīmūr Lang (p. 1474). René Grousset: L'empire des steppes. Attila, Gengis-Khan, Tamerlan (640 p., 30 maps, 20 fig., Paris 1939). Though only a small part (60 p.) of this book deals directly with Tīmūr, the whole of it is an excellent description and explanation of the Mongol and Turkish invasions which recurred for ten centuries, and of which the Tīmūrī invasion was the main climax. The military superiority of the Mongols was due to their hardiness and to the excellence of their archery on horseback; that decisive technical advantage was lost to them when firearms were sufficiently improved. Ivan the Terrible, tsar of Muscovy, defeating the last inheritors of the Golden Horde (Kazan 1552) and Hsüan-yeh (second Ch'ing emperor, ruling from 1661 to 1722 under the reign title K'ang-hsi), cowing the Kalmuck (a Mongol people) into submission, put an end to those invasions. Grousset's book is based on a very rich documentation, but unfortunately lacks an index.

Dorotheos of Sidon (p. 1481 note 2). Dorotheos of Sidon was an astrologer, probably contemporary of Marcus Manilius (I-1). Viktor Stegemann: Die Fragmente des Dorotheos von Sidon (Quellen und Studien zur Geschichte und Kultur des Altertums und des Mittelalters, Lief. 1–2, Heidelberg 1939, 1943), reviewed by A. J. Festugière (Revue des études grecques 56, 263, 1943).

Dalmau Ces-Planes (p. 1485). *Text.* Tractat d'astrologia o sciencia de les steles, edited by J. Massó y Torrents (Barcelona 1890). Original Catalan text of the astrological treatise composed for Pere III el Cerimoniós by Pere Engelbert, Dalmau Ces-Planes, and Jacob ben Isaac Carsono.

Criticism. Reparaz-Ruiz (second part, 1940). Lynn Thorndike: Dalmatius again (Isis 36, 158), notes derived from Rubió y Lluch.

Isaac Argyros as a geographer (p. 1511). Some of the 68 maps of version B of Ptolemy's Geographia may perhaps be ascribed to Nicephoros Gregoras (XIV-1) and to Argyros. Leo Bagrow: The origin of Ptolemy's Geographia (Geografiska annaler 27, 318–87, Stockholm 1945; Isis 37).

Finger reckoning and archery (p. 1533). The relation between these apparently unconnected subjects was traditional. See Arab archery, an Arabic MS of c. 1500, "A book on the excellence of the bow and arrow and description thereof" translated and edited by Nabih Amin Faris and Robert Potter Elmer (193 p., 7 fig., Princeton 1945; Isis 36, 219). In spite of its title this book contains only the English version, not the Arabic text. The anonymous author was a Moroccan. Chapter 8, dealing with "things the archer should know," explains finger reckoning. The translator's preface is extremely meager and does not attempt to compare this text with other

Oriental texts on archery; in particular, no mention is made of the Ghunyat al-ṭullāb or of Ṭaibughā al-Ashrafī al-Baklamishī.

Korean star map of 1395 (p. 1537). It would be interesting to compare this Korean star map with the map prepared in 1193, engraved on stone in 1247, and preserved to this day in the Wên miao of Su-chou. That Sung map was first reproduced by Edouard Chavannes, who translated the accompanying text into French (Paris 1913; Introd. 2, 423). A new edition of it with English translation of the text has just been published. W. Carl Rufus (1876–1946) and Hsing-chih Tien: The Soochow astronomical chart (quarto, 24 p., Ann Arbor, Mich. 1945; Isis 37). This includes the identification as far as possible of the 1440 stars joined in 313 asterisms.

Bellifortis (p. 1550). Franz Denk: Zwei mittelalterliche Dokumente zur Fluggeschichte und ihre Deutung (Sitzungsberichte der Physikalisch-medizinischen Sozietät in Erlangen 71, 1939, 353–68, 4 fig., Erlangen 1940; Mitt. 40, 175); concerning the draco volans (flying dragon) in Konrad Kyeser's Bellifortis, and another dragon in a Viennese MS (National Library, Cod. 3064) of c. 1450.

The Westminster effigies (p. 1561). Victoria and Albert Museum: An exhibition of the royal effigies, sculpture and other works of art prior to their being re-installed in Westminster Abbey, November 1945 (24 p., 4 pl., Society of Antiquaries of London, 1945).

Wall paintings in Mt. Athos (p. 1584). Richard McGillivray Dawkins: The arrangement of wall-paintings in the monastery churches of Mt. Athos (Byzantina metabyzantina 1, 93–105, New York 1946).

Chinese Muslims (p. 1586–90). A Russian study on the Chinese literature of the Muslims by the archimandrite Palladius[27] was published by the Russian archaeological society (40 p., St. Petersburg 1874); a new edition much enlarged was published by the hieromonachos Nicolai (Adoratski) in the Trudy of that society (part 18, p. 163–496, 1886–87; reprinted 1909–10). Translation by Rudolf Löwenthal (Collectanea commissionis synodalis 16, 187–204, 1943).

Catalan cartography (p. 1591). For the notes on the Catalan mappemonde of 1375, William Soleri, and the Cresques, see Reparaz-Ruiz (1940). Apropos of Soleri he remarks that the name should be read Soler, a good Catalan name (Soleri is a Latin genitive or an Italianization). He also refers to the three anonymous Catalan maps of the end of the fourteenth century. Two of them are preserved in the National Libraries of Florence and Naples. The third has been recently discovered by Marcel Detombes in the Top kapu Sarai of Istanbul; it is a fragment of an immense Catalan mappa mundi, contained in a circle of one-meter radius; the fragment represents Siberia to its extreme north, which is not represented in the Catalan atlas of 1375.

Artificial incubation (p. 1596 note 3). The Tagalog (a Malayan tribe of the Philippines) incubate duck eggs, not by means of special ovens as the Chinese do, but by the use of human heat, some of their servants functioning as hatchers. A

[27] Petr Ivanovich Kafarov (1817–78), Couling (p. 420, 1917).

description of this will be found in Paul de La Gironière: Twenty years in the Philippines (p. 358, 362, New York 1854). La Gironière was a Breton physician who lived in the Philippines from 1819 to 1839. A briefer relation of his adventures was first published in French (Paris 1853); the revised text, published in English translation in 1854, appeared in French the following year (Paris 1855).

Runes (p. 1609 note 11). The most interesting example of the use of runes for ceremonial purposes (somewhat like our use of Roman numerals and the modern Arabic use of Kūfī) was given by Linnaeus. On a big boulder near Hammarby he had engraved in runic letters "Riddar Karl Linné köpte Hammarby-Säfja 1758" (The knight Carl Linné bought Hammarby and Säfja in 1758). Benjamin Daydon Jackson: Linnaeus (p. 327, London 1923; Isis 6, 420–23). The statue of Leif Ericsson (X-2) in Boston, erected a few years after 1880, bears a runic inscription.

Jean Bruyant (p. 1633). Also called Jacques Bruant, notary to the king in the Châtelet of Paris, wrote in 1342 a poem, Le livre du chastel de labour de povreté et de richesse (more usually called Le chemin de povreté et de richesse), 2,634 lines. An adaptation of it by Pierre Gringore was first printed in Paris in 1499. English translation, The castle of labour, by Alexander Barclay (1475?–1552) (Paris 1503, London 1505, 1506). The Wynkyn de Worde edition of 1506 was reprinted with the French text of 1501 and with an introduction by Alfred W. Pollard (Roxburghe Club, Edinburgh 1905). Francis William Bourdillon: Le livre du chastel de labour. Description of an illuminated MS belonging to George C. Thomas (46 pl., Philadelphia 1909).

Al-Damīrī (p. 1641). Joseph de Somogyi: Biblical figures in ad-Damīrī's Ḥayāt al-ḥayawān (Dissertationes in honorem Dr. Eduardi Mahler, p. 263–99, Budapest 1937).

Chu Hsiao (p. 1649). Walter T. Swingle: Our agricultural debt to Asia, in Arthur E. Christy: The Asian legacy and American life (p. 84–114, New York 1945, chiefly p. 100; Isis 37).

Public health in Milano (p. 1659). A. Francesco La Cava: Igiene e sanità negli statuti di Milano del sec. XIV (100 p., 1 pl., Milano 1946). Information derived from a MS of the Ospedale maggiore of Milan dated 1481, reproducing regulations of the previous century. Those regulations concern medical teaching and practice, pharmacy, hospitals, and the protection of health in houses, water sources and ducts, sewers, cesspools, prisons, cemeteries, markets.

The plague and Islām (p. 1664). David Neustadt: The plague and its effects upon the Mamlūk army (Journal of the Royal Asiatic Society, p. 67–73, 1946), showing that the plague played a considerable part in weakening that army, not only the Black Death and other plagues of the fourteenth century, but later plagues, from 1416 to 1514, even more. The Mamlūk regime came to an end in 1517, when Egypt and Syria became parts of the Ottoman empire.

Dancing mania (p. 1668). A. H. W. H. Liebscher: Ein kartographischer Beitrag zur Geschichte der Tanzwut (22 p., Zeulenrode 1931).

Dancing as a cure (p. 1668). Richard Brown (fl. 1674–94), M.D., apothecary of Oakham, wrote a book entitled Medicina musica, or a mechanical essay on the effects of singing, music and dancing on human bodies; with an essay on the nature and cure of the spleen and vapours (London 1674; new ed., 142 p., London 1729). William Munk: Roll of the Royal College of physicians (1, 390, 1878). DNB (7, 55).

St. Anthony's fire (p. 1668). Henry Chaumartin: Le mal des ardents et le feu Saint Antoine (43 pl., 204 p., published by the author in Vienne, Isère, Dauphiné 1946), largely devoted to the legends of St. Anthony and the Hospitaler Order of Saint Antoine du Viennois, founded in 1095. George Barger: Ergot and ergotism (296 p., 41 ill., London 1931).

John Arderne and Sven Hedin (p. 1704). More details about this in John F. Fulton's excellent biography of Harvey Cushing (p. 575, 580–82, Springfield, Ill. 1946; Isis 37, 92–93).

Rain of blood (p. 1743). G. Sarton: Was Peiresc the first (in 1608) to offer a rational explanation of the rains of blood? (Isis 38). The earliest reference to a rain of blood in that article is taken from the Historia Francorum of Gregory of Tours (VI-2), Paris 582.

Ibn al-Khaṭīb as a poet (p. 1762). Specimens of his poetry are transcribed and translated by A. R. Nykl: Hispano-Arabic poetry and its relations with the Old Provençal troubadours (p. 363–66, Baltimore 1946; Isis 37). It might be worth while to consult Nykl for the other Moors dealt with by me; almost every learned Moor was, or claimed to be, a poet.

Banū Khaldūn (p. 1767). The leading families of Seville in the eleventh century were the Banū Khaldūn and the Banū Ḥajjāj, both of Yemenite origin. The latter belonged to the tribe of Lakhm and were descended in the female line from Witica, the last but one Visigothic king. The Banū Khaldūn came from Ḥaḍramaut; they lived in Seville and in the Axarafe, where they had castles (burj, pl. burūj or abrāj). Reinhart Dozy: Spanish Islam (p. 338, 341, 349, 371, London 1913).

Ibn Khaldūn's Arabic forerunners (p. 1779). Gustave E. von Grunebaum in his excellent book Medieval Islam (p. 339, Chicago 1946) has pointed out not only that al-Sakkākī (XIII-1) had discussed the influence of milieu on thought before Ibn Khaldūn, but, what is even more striking, that the latter's basic problems were already outlined in Al-tanbīh wal-ishrāf of al-Mas'ūdī (X-1). Of course, this does not diminish in the least Ibn Khaldūn's exceptional merit, even if he read the Tanbīh, which is uncertain.[27a] By the way, we find in the Tanbīh a remark suggesting that al-Mas'ūdī believed in the possibility of unlimited scientific progress, a belief unique in Arabic letters. Grunebaum (ibid. p. 347).

Luca da Penne (p. 1798). Mention should have been made of this great Neapolitan jurisconsult if only to remove the impression that legal studies flourished only in

[27a] Al-Mas'ūdī is quoted four times in the Muqaddama, but it is possible that Ibn Khaldūn was acquainted only with the Murūj al-dhahab, not with the Tanbīh.

the north of Italy and not in the south. To be sure, Bologna was the greatest law school, and the schools of Perugia, Siena, Pavia, Padua were at times equally brilliant, yet Luca gave fame to the school of Naples.

Luca da Penne (Lat., Lucas de Penna) was born c. 1325 at Penne, Abruzzo adriatico, not far from Pescara. He studied law in Naples,[28] where he graduated in 1345, and possibly also in Toulouse. He was not a teacher of law, but practiced it as an advocate and judge, held government offices in southern Italy, and toward the end of his life was employed by the Roman curia. He died in 1390 and was buried in his native town, where a monument was erected to his memory in 1625.

His main work is an enormous commentary on the three last books (X to XII) of the Codex. In spite of its title, it is much more than a commentary, but to a large extent an original work wherein he explains his views on justice, law, equity, constitutional law, criminal procedure, regulations of war and peace, etc. He undertook the writing of it upon the suggestion of Paolo da Perugia, who had arrived in Naples in 1332 to be the librarian of king Robert[29] and complained that books X to XII of the Codex had been neglected by commentators; most of the work was probably done after Paolo's death of the plague in 1348, and it was continued until after 1358.

Luca was primarily a civilian; he was familiar not only with the Roman law and the canon law, but also with customary law, Sicilian and Lombard (Introd. 2, 267, 576). In addition to legal sources, he often referred to Plato, Aristotle, Cicero, St. Augustine, St. Thomas, St. Giles of Rome, etc., and was much influenced by the Polycratus of John of Salisbury (XII-2). He was more deeply concerned with the substantiality of the law than with dialectics.

The ultimate basis of all law is the law of God and of nature. God is also the ultimate source of power, whether ecclesiastical or secular. The pope and the sovereign hold their authority primarily and independently from God; thus his view of sovereignty is dualistic, not monistic like that of Bartolus.[30] The rulers are merely trustees; their power must end when they abuse their trust; tyrannicide may be justifiable. According to Roger Bacon and to Bartolus, canon law was superior to civil law;[31] from Luca's point of view, however, civil law, the ius commune of humanity, is anterior and superior to canon law, and its application is imperative in all courts secular or ecclesiastical; it must yield to canon law only in spiritual causes. Luca's modernity or his devotion to Roman vs. mediaeval ideas (note the Renaissance touch) appears equally well in his definition of sovereignty. The ruler is not simply a judge as was explained, e.g., by Alvaro Pelayo (XIV-1) in his De planctu ecclesiae, but a lawgiver. This new, Roman, point of view was developed by Andrea Alciati (1492–1550), and more fully in the République (1576) of Jean Bodin.

In his legal study of war and peace Luca anticipated Alberico Gentili (1552–1608) and even in some respects Hugo Grotius (1583–1645).

The most modern, and to my mind the most admirable, part of his work is the one dealing with criminal law. According to Luca, crime is a public wrong and

[28] The University of Naples was founded in 1224 by Frederick II, partly to offset the papal University of Bologna (Introd. 2, 575). Rashdall (2, 21–26, 1936).

[29] Cornelia C. Coulter: The library of the Angevin kings of Naples (Transactions of the American Philological Association 75, 141–55, 1944; Isis 36, 180).

[30] According to Bartolus, the pope holds his power from God, and the secular ruler from the pope; according to Luca, they both hold it directly from God.

[31] Said Bartolus, "nam iurisconsulti erant pagani et de praemio aeternae vitae non cogitabant."

accusations have to be preferred by the public authorities rather than by the wronged party. Legal presumptions should be avoided. The purpose of criminal law must be justice, not vengeance. No truth can be obtained by the use of torture. He had to express such views with great caution, for they implied a condemnation of the inquisitorial procedure then in force and favor. In order to realize the importance of Luca's criticism of torture, it is well to remember the following facts. The use of torture to elicit evidence from an accused person or from a witness, to obtain confessions and denunciations, and finally as a means of punishment, was recognized and regularized by Nicholas Eymeric and Tomás de Torquemada (1420–98) and remained an integral part of inquisitorial procedure as long as that procedure was suffered to exist. It was vigorously denounced by the "philosophers" of the eighteenth century; Cesare Beccaria's little book Dei delitti e delle pene (Livorno 1764) was perhaps the most effective arraignment of it in spite of its moderation.[32] It was because of Beccaria's influence and of Voltaire's that Ekaterina II recommended the suppression of torture in her empire in 1776. Torture continued to be used in France until 1789. It was abolished by a papal bull in 1816. It must be added with shame and sorrow that it was revived in various European countries within our own century.

Du Cange s.v. quaestio, quaestionare, quaestionarius (5, 539, 1845). Henry Charles Lea: Superstition and force (4th ed., p. 429–590, Philadelphia 1892); Lea's other works (listed p. 1051) contain abundant examples. George Neilson (ERE 12, 391–93, 1922). Article by James Williams and G. W. Keeton (Encyclopaedia britannica, 14th ed., 22, 311–14, 1929).

Luca's views were not appreciated until later, in the fifteenth century by his fellow Neapolitan Paris de Puteo, and in the sixteenth by the jurisconsults of the Renaissance. His criticism of judicial torture was hardly countenanced before the eighteenth century.

Text. Commentaria in tres posteriores libros Codicis Justiniani. First edition, Paris 1509. Later editions, s.l. 1538, Lyon 1597 (a folio volume of 1050 p.).

Criticism. M. M. Wronowski: Luca da Penne e sua opera (Pisa 1925). Francesco Calasso: Studi sul commento ai Tres libri (Rivista di storia del diritto italiano 5, 395–458, 1932). Walter Ullmann: The medieval idea of law as represented by Lucas de Penna (260 p., London 1946), with bibliography.

Oral traditions (p. 1804 note 3). See also Stith Thompson's more recent work, The folktale (520 p., New York 1946), and the splendid synthesis of the two Chadwicks, man and wife, Hector Munro and Norah Kershaw Chadwick: The growth of literature (3 vols., Cambridge 1932–40; Isis 29, 196). Solomon Gandz: The dawn of literature (Osiris 7, 261–515, 1939).

Fossil fishes (p. 1806 note 5). A discussion on the subject begun by Sarton and Eugene Willis Gudger (Isis 33, 56–58, 1941) was continued not only by Pease, but also by Frank D. Adams (Isis 33, 335), Eugene V. Prostov and L. Carrington Goodrich (Isis 34, 24), Robert Eisler (Isis 34, 363), and Richard C. Rudolph: Early Chinese references to fossil fish (Isis 36, 155, 1946).

[32] **Sarton: Beccaria, 1738–94 (Bulletin of the history of medicine, suppt. no. 3, 283–308, 13 ill., Baltimore 1944).**

Trévoux (p. 1825, last line). Trévoux was the capital of the principality of Dombes. It is immortalized by the activities of the Jesuit fathers who published there from 1701 to 1775 the Mémoires pour l'histoire des sciences et des beaux arts (better known under the name Journal de Trévoux) in order to emulate the Journal des savants and to battle with the "encyclopédistes" and the "philosophes." A methodical table was edited by father Carlos Sommervogel (3 vols., Paris 1864–65). The Jesuits of Trévoux also published the Dictionnaire universel françois et latin, generally called Dictionnaire de Trévoux (first edition 1704; seventh and last edition, 8 vols. folio, Paris 1771). Both works are indispensable for the study of eighteenth-century letters and thought in France and elsewhere.

GENERAL BIBLIOGRAPHY

The following list is printed for the purpose of reducing the length of bibliographical references to a minimum and saving space. For example, a reference like Delatte (2, 435, 1939) is perfectly clear in spite of its brevity. It suffices to look up Delatte in the list below.

The books mentioned in this list are not necessarily more important than those not listed. The list is supposed to include the books which are referred to more frequently, but even that is not completely true. Indeed, the most frequently cited books or papers could have been determined only after this work was completed, and that determination would have required considerable labor. Some books were listed here because the author thought he would be obliged to refer to them very often, and then the opportunities for such reference did not occur. No great harm was done in including these books, but the reader is warned not to attach to this list more importance than it deserves. It is simply a matter of convenience.

Abrahams, Israel (1858–1925)
1896 Jewish life in the Middle Ages. xxvi + 452 p. Macmillan, New York.

Adams, Frank Dawson (1859–1942)
1938 The birth and development of the geological sciences. 506 p. Williams & Wilkins, Baltimore. (Isis 32, 218–20.)

Adelung, Johann Gustav (O.S.B.) (1732–1806)
1840–50 See Du Cange.

Adivar, A. Adnan
1939 See Adnan.
Adıvar is Dr. Adnan's new name. Note that the i of Adıvar is undotted.

Adler, Cyrus (1863–1940)
1901–6 See Jewish encyclopedia. (Isis 34, 60.)

Adnan, Abdulhak (= 'Abd al-ḥaqq 'Adnān)
1939 La science chez les Turcs Ottomans. 174 p. Maisonneuve, Paris. (Isis 32, 186–89.)

Allgemeine deutsche Biographie
1871–1912 56 vols. Leipzig.
Abbr. ADB.

Amann, mgr. Emile (1880——)
1903—— See Dictionnaire de théologie catholique.

Amano, Kageyas W.
1934 See Fujikawa.

Andrews, Michael C.
1926 The study and classification of medieval mappae mundi. (Archaeologia 75, 61–76, London.) (Isis 14, 515.)

Anglade, Joseph (1868–1930)
1921 Histoire sommaire de la littérature méridionale au Moyen âge, des origines à la fin du XVe siècle. xii + 274 p. E. de Boccard, Paris.

Archeion
1928—— See Archivio di storia della scienza.

Archiv für Geschichte der Medizin
1908—— Edited by Karl Sudhoff. Barth, Leipzig.
Vol. 1 is dated 1908 but began to appear in Sept. 1907.
Abbr. AGM.

ARCHIVIO DI STORIA DELLA SCIENZA
1919—— Diretto da Aldo Mieli.
Beginning with vol. 9, 1928, the title was changed to Archeion. The journal was first published in Rome, then in Paris, later in Santa Fe (República argentina). The latest issue received was no. 2/3 of vol. 25, Santa Fe 1943. It is planned to continue its publication in Buenos Aires. Aldo Mieli is still the editor.

ARNOLD, SIR THOMAS WALKER (1864–1930)
1896 The preaching of Islam. A history of the propagation of the Muslim faith. xvi + 388 p. Constable, Westminster.
1913 2d ed. xvi + 467 p. Constable, London.
1908–38 See ENCYCLOPAEDIA OF ISLAM.

ASÍN PALACIOS, MIGUEL (1871–1944)
1931 El Islam cristianizado. Estudio del sufismo a través de las obras de Abenarabi de Murcia. 541 p., 2 pl., 1 map. Editorial Plutarco, Madrid. (Isis 17, 271–73.)
Though dealing more especially with Ibn 'Arabī (XIII-1), it covers the whole subject taṣawwuf vs. Christian mysticism.

ATIYA, AZIZ SURYAL (= 'AZĪZ SURYĀL 'AṬIYA)
1938 The crusade in the later Middle Ages. xviii + 604 p., ill., maps. Methuen, London. (Isis 32.)

BĀBAR (c. 1482–1530)
1921 Memoirs of Zehīr al-dīn Muhammed Bābur, emperor of Hindustan, written by himself in the Chaghatāi Tūrki and translated by John Leyden and William Erskine. Annotated and revised by Sir Lucas King. 2 vols. Oxford University Press, London.

BÄCHTOLD-STÄUBLI, HANNS (1886–1941?)
1927–38 See HANDWÖRTERBUCH.

BAGCHI, PRABODH CHANDRA
1927–38 Le canon bouddhique en Chine. Les traducteurs et les traductions. (Sino-indica, publications de l'Université de Calcutta, vols. 1, 4.) 2 vols. Vol. 1, lii + 436 p., 1927; vol. 2, p. 437–742, 1938.
A third volume announced to contain Chinese index has not yet appeared. (Isis 11, 506.)

BAILLIE, G. H.
1929a Watches. Their history, decoration and mechanism. xxiv + 384 p., 75 pl. Methuen, London.
1929b Watchmakers and clockmakers of the world. xvi + 416 p. Methuen, London.
Both volumes belong to the Connoisseur's library. My references are always to the first, except when the second is explicitly mentioned.

BALL, JAMES DYER (1847–1919)
1926 Things Chinese. Or notes connected with China. 5th ed., revised by E. Chalmers Werner. iv + 766 p. Murray, London.
First edition, London 1892.

BASSET, RENÉ (1855–1924)
1908–38 See ENCYCLOPAEDIA OF ISLAM.

BAUDRAND, MICHEL ANTOINE (1633–1700)
1697 See FERRARI.

BAUMGARTNER, MATTHIAS (1865——)
1915 See UEBERWEG.

BAUMSTARK, ANTON (1872——)
1922 Geschichte der syrischen Literatur, mit Ausschluss der christlich-palästinensischen Texte. xvi + 378 p. Marcus and Weber, Bonn. (Isis 5, 160–62)

BEAZLEY, SIR CHARLES RAYMOND (1868——)
1897–1906 The dawn of modern geography. A history of exploration and geographical science. 3 vols. Murray, London.
1897 Vol. 1, to A.D. 900.
1901 Vol. 2, 900–1260.
1906 Vol. 3, 1260–1420.

BELL, AUBREY FITZ GERALD (1882——)
1922 Portuguese literature. 375 p. Clarendon Press, Oxford.

BENEDICT, SUZAN ROSE (1873–1942)
1914 Comparative study of the early treatises introducing into Europe the Hindu art of reckoning. vi + 126 p. Michigan thesis.

BERGEN, HENRY (1873——)
1923–27 See LYDGATE.

BEZOLD, CARL (1859–1922)
1926 See BOLL.

BIBLIOTHECA MATHEMATICA
1884–1914 30 vols. edited by Gustav Eneström. First series, 3 vols., published in Stockholm 1884–85. Second series, 13 vols., published in Stockholm, Berlin, Paris, 1887–99. Third series, 14 vols., published by Teubner, Leipzig 1900–14. (Isis 2, 135–36.)
Abbr. BM.

BIDEZ, JOSEPH (1867–1945)
1924–32, 1939—— See CATALOGUE. (Osiris 6, p. v–ix.)

BIOGRAPHISCHES LEXIKON DER HERVORRAGENDEN AERZTE ALLER ZEITEN UND VÖLKER
1884–88 1st ed. by E. Gurlt, A. Wernich, and August Hirsch. 6 vols. Wien.
1929–35 2d ed. by W. Haberling, F. Hübotter, and H. Vierordt. 5 vols., suppt. Urban & Schwarzenberg, Berlin und Wien.
1929 Vol. 1. 1932 Vol. 4.
1930 Vol. 2. 1934 Vol. 5.
1931 Vol. 3. 1935 Suppt.
Abbr. BL.

BIRGE, JOHN KINGSLEY (1888——)
1937 The Bektashi order of dervishes. 292 p., 32 ill. Hartford Seminary Press, Hartford.

BLACHÈRE, RÉGIS
1932 Extraits des principaux géographes arabes du Moyen âge. (Bibliotheca arabica de la Faculté des lettres d'Alger, vol. 7.) 392 p. Imprimerie catholique, Beyrouth. (Isis 24, 447–49.)

BLOCH, MOÏSE (1854–1901)
1897 See GROSS, HEINRICH.

BLOCHET, EDGAR (1870——)
1911 See OLLONE.

BLUM, ANDRÉ (1881——)
1935 Les origines du papier, de l'imprimerie et de la gravure. 252 p., 80 ill. La Tournelle, Paris.

BODENHEIMER, FRIEDRICH SIMON (1897——)
1928–29 Materialien für Geschichte der Entomologie bis Linné. 2 vols. Vol. 1, x + 498 p., 1928; vol. 2, vi + 486 p., ill., 1929. W. Junk, Berlin. (Isis 13, 388–92; 14, 454–56.)

BOLL, FRANZ (1867–1924)
1903 Sphaera. Neue griechische Texte und Untersuchungen zur Geschichte der Sternbilder. Mit einem Beitrag von Karl Dyroff. xii + 564 p., 6 pl., 19 fig. Teubner, Leipzig.
1926 Sternglaube und Sterndeutung. Die Geschichte und das Wesen der Astrologie. Unter Mitwirkung von Carl Bezold. Dritte Aufl., hrsg. von W. Gundel. xii + 211 p., 48 fig. Teubner, Leipzig. (Isis 9, 476–77.)
First edition 1917; second edition 1919. (Isis 3, 482.)

BOVILL, E. W.
1933 Caravans of the old Sahara. An introduction to the history of the Western Sudan. 300 p., 13 maps. International Institute of African Languages and Cultures, London. (Isis 25, 267.)

BRAUNMÜHL, ANTON VON (1853–1908)
1900 Vorlesungen über Geschichte der Trigonometrie. Vol. 1, viii + 260 p. Teubner, Leipzig.

BRETSCHNEIDER, EMILII VASILYEVICH (1833–1901)
1888 Mediaeval researches from Eastern Asiatic sources. Fragments towards the knowledge of the geography and history of Central and Western Asia from the 13th to the 17th century. 2 vols. Trübner, London.
1910 Photographic reprint. 2 vols. Kegan Paul, London.

BRINKLEY, FRANK (1841–1912), and KIKUCHI DAIROKU
1914 A history of the Japanese people from the earliest times to the end of the Meiji era. xi + 784 p. Encyclopaedia Britannica, London.

BRITTON, CHARLES ERNEST
1937 Meteorological chronology to A.D. 1450. (Meteorological Office, Geophysical memoirs, no. 70, vol. 8, part 1.) 178 p. London. (Isis 28, 520–22.)

BROCKELMANN, CARL (1868——)
1898–42 Geschichte der arabischen Litteratur.
1898 Vol. 1, xii + 528 p. Felber, Weimar.
1902 Vol. 2, xii + 714 p. Felber, Berlin.
1937 Suppt. vol. 1, xx + 973 p. Brill, Leiden.
1938 Suppt. vol. 2, xx + 1045 p. Brill, Leiden.
1939–42 Suppt. vol. 3, xii + 1326 p. Brill, Leiden.
This volume deals with modern Arabic literature but includes (p. 1191–1326) addenda and errata to vols. 1 and 2.
1943—— Geschichte der arabischen Litteratur. Zweite den Supplementbänden angepasste Auflage. Brill, Leiden.
1943 Vol. 1, x + 676 p.
1944 Vol. 2, parts 1–4, 256 p., to be continued.
Not used. This is mainly what the title says, a reprint of the first edition, the additions of the supplements being inserted in their proper places. When referring to Brockelmann one should consult vol. 1 or 2, then suppt. vol. 1 or 2, then suppt. vol. 3, p. 1191 f., then the second edition.

BROWN, JOHN PORTER (1844–72)
1927 The darvishes or Oriental spiritualism. Edited with introduction and notes by Horace Arthur Rose. xxiv + 496 p., 23 ill. Oxford University Press, London.
Brown's preface to the original edition (London 1868) was dated Constantinople, October 1867. The book deals mainly with Turkish conditions.

BROWNE, EDWARD GRANVILLE (1862–1926)
1906–24 Literary history of Persia. 4 vols. University Press, Cambridge.
1908, reprinted 1909 Vol. 1, From the earliest times until Firdawsī.
1906, reprinted 1915 Vol. 2, From Firdawsī to Sa'dī.
1920, reprinted 1928 Vol. 3, Tartar dominion. 1265–1502.
1924, reprinted 1928 Vol. 4, Modern times. 1500–1924.
1921 Arabian medicine. Being the Fitzpatrick lectures delivered at the College of Physicians in November 1919 and November 1920. viii + 138 p., 1 pl. University Press, Cambridge. (Isis 4, 349–50.)
1933 La médecine arabe. Edition française mise à jour et annotée par H. P. J. Renaud. xii + 174 p. Larose, Paris. (Isis 21, 435.)

BRUN, ROBERT
1928 Avignon aux temps des papes. Les monuments, les artistes, la société. 288 p., 8 pl., 1 plan. Colin, Paris.

BURNELL, ARTHUR COKE (1840–82)
1903 See YULE.

CAMPBELL, ANNA MONTGOMERY (1888——)
1931 The Black Death and men of learning. xii + 210 p. Columbia University Press, New York. (Isis 18, 195–97.)

[CANIBELL, EUDALD]
1918 Bibliografia medical de Catalunya. Inventari primer. Quarto, xxxii + 478 p. Associació general de metges de llengua catalana, Barcelona.
No author is named, but Canibell wrote the explanatory introduction.

CANTOR, MORITZ (1829–1920)
1899–1907 Vorlesungen über Geschichte der Mathematik. 2 vols. Vol. 1, 3d ed., 1907; vol. 2, 2d ed., 1899–1900 (used reprint of 1913). Teubner, Leipzig.

CAPPELLER, CARL (1840–1925)
1899 See MONIER-WILLIAMS.

CARBONELLI, GIOVANNI (1859–1933)
1914–19 Bibliographia medica typographica pedemontana saeculorum XV et XVI. Folio, 436 p. Fieramosca Centenari, Rome 1914 (printing protracted until 1919).
1925 Sulle fonti storiche della chimica e dell' alchimia in Italia. Small folio, 228 p., 242 fig., 2 pl. Istituto nazionale medico farmacologico, Rome. (Isis 8, 465–76.)

CARLYLE, SIR ROBERT WARRAND (1859–1934), and ALEXANDER JAMES CARLYLE (1861——)
1903–36 History of mediaeval political theory in the West. 6 vols. Blackwood, Edinburgh.
1927 Vol. 1, The second century to the ninth.
1928 Vol. 2, The political theory of the Roman lawyers and the canonists, from the tenth to the thirteenth century.
1916 Vol. 3, Political theory from the tenth to the thirteenth century.
1922 Vol. 4, The theories of the relation of the empire and the papacy from the tenth century to the twelfth.
1928 Vol. 5, The political theory of the thirteenth century.
1936 Vol. 6, Political theory from 1300 to 1600.
The dates indicated are those of the editions used by me. Second edition or impression in the case of vols. 1 and 2. Though the name of R. W. Carlyle appears on every volume, the fifth was the first containing a direct contribution of his; the sixth volume was edited after his death by his puisne brother, Alexander James.

CARPENTIER, PIERRE (O.S.B.) (1697–1767)
1840–50 See DU CANGE.

CARRA DE VAUX, BERNARD BARON (1867——)
1921–26 Penseurs de l'Islam. 5 vols. Geuthner, Paris.
1921 Vol. 1, Les souverains. L'histoire et la philosophie politique (Isis 4, 618).
1921 Vol. 2, Les géographes, les sciences mathématiques et naturelles (Isis 5, 165–67).
1923 Vol. 3, L'exégèse. La tradition et la jurisprudence (Isis 7, 272).
1923 Vol. 4, La scolastique, la théologie et la mystique. La musique (Isis 8, 598).
1926 Vol. 5, Les sectes. Le libéralisme moderne (Isis 10, 245).

CARTER, THOMAS FRANCIS (1882–1925)
1925 The invention of printing in China and its spread westward. xx + 282 p., 40 ill. Columbia University Press, New York. (Isis 8, 361–73.)
1931 Revised ed. xxvi + 282 p., 40 ill. Columbia University Press, New York. (Isis 19, 426.)

CASIRI, MIGUEL (1710–91)
1760–70 Bibliotheca arabico-hispana escurialensis. Folio, 2 vols. Madrid. (Isis 34, p. 34.)

CATALOGUE
1924–32 Catalogue des manuscrits alchimiques grecs, publié sous la direction de J. Bidez, F. Cumont, J. L. Heiberg et O. Lagercrantz. (Union académique internationale.) 8 vols. Lamertin, Bruxelles.
1924 Vol. 1, Les Parisini décrits par Henri Lebègue. Les MSS des Coeranides et tables par Marie Delcourt. x + 319 p. (Isis 7, 507–11.)
1927 Vol. 2, Les MSS italiens par Carlo Oreste Zuretti († 1931). Les MSS des Coera-

nides par Zuretti. Excerpta par J. L. Heiberg et Zuretti. Über das Verhaltnis des Cod. Paris 2327 zum Cod. Marc. 299 von Otto Lagercrantz (see also vol. 4, p. 399–432). vi + 369 p. (Isis 11, 244.)

1924 Vol. 3, Les MSS des Iles britanniques, par Dorothea Waley Singer. Les recettes alchimiques du Codex Holkhamicus par Otto Lagercrantz. 84 p. (Isis 7, 507–11.)

1932 Vol. 4, Les MSS d'Allemagne, d'Autriche, de Danemark, de Hollande et de Suisse par Günther Goldschmidt. Die Diatribe des Thomas Reinesius [1587–1667] aus Cod. Gothanus A 242 herausgegeben von G. Goldschmidt. xxvi + 447 p. (Isis 20, 598.)

1928 Vol. 5, Les MSS d'Espagne par C. O. Zuretti. Les MSS d'Athènes par Albert Severyns. vi+175 p. (Isis 13, 547.)

1928 Vol. 6, Michel Psellus. Epître sur la Chrysopée. Opuscules et extraits sur l'alchimie, la météorologie et la démonologie, par Joseph Bidez. En appendice, Proclus sur l'art hiératique; Psellus, choix de dissertations inédites. xiv + 246 p. (Isis 12, 165–68.)

1930 Vol. 7, Anonymi De arte metallica seu De metallorum conversione in aurum et argentum edidit C. O. Zuretti. lx + 466 p., 2 pl. (Isis 15, 410.)

1932 Vol. 8, Alchemista signa digessit et explanavit C. O. Zuretti. viii + 84 p., 17 pl. (Isis 19, 440.)

1939—— Catalogue des manuscrits alchimiques latins. Publié sous la direction de J. Bidez, Fr. Cumont, A. Delatte, Sir Frederic Kenyon, V. de Falco. Vol. 1, MSS de Paris décrits par James Corbett, 1939. Union académique internationale, Bruxelles. (Isis 32, 211.)

CATALOGUS

1898—— Catalogus codicum astrologorum graecorum. 11 vols. (incomplete) edited by F. Cumont and others. Lamertin, Bruxelles. (Isis 6, 206; 15, 295.)

1898 Vol. 1, Codices florentinos descripsit Alexander Olivieri. Accedunt fragmenta selecta primum edita ab Francisco Boll, Francisco Cumont, Guilelmo Kroll, Alexandro Olivieri. vii + 182 p., 1 pl.

1900 Vol. 2, Codices venetos descripserunt G. Kroll et A. Olivieri. Accedunt fragmenta selecta etc. viii + 224 p., 1 pl.

1901 Vol. 3, Codices mediolanenses descripserunt Aemygdius Martini et Dominicus Bassi. 60 p.

1903 Vol. 4, Codices italicos praeter florentinos, venetos, mediolanenses, romanos descripserunt D. Bassi, Fr. Cumont, Aem. Martini, A. Olivieri. viii + 192 p., 2 pl.

1904–40 Vol. 5, Codices romanos partem priorem descripserunt Fr. Cumont et Fr. Boll; viii + 256 p., 1904. Partem secundam descripsit G. Kroll; 163 p., 1 pl., 1906. Partem tertiam descripsit Josephus Heeg; viii + 160 p., 1910. Partem quartam descripsit Stephanus Weinstock. Accedit Porphyrii philosophi Introductio in Tetrabiblum Ptolemaei ab Aemilia Boer et St. Weinstock edita; viii + 253 p., 1940. (Isis 37.)

Parts 2 to 4 deal with the Vatican MSS, part 1 with those in other Roman libraries.

1903 Vol. 6, Codices vindobonenses descripsit G. Kroll. viii + 122 p.

1908 Vol. 7, Codices germanicos descripsit Fr. Boll. viii + 268 p., 2 pl.

1911–29 Vol. 8, Codicum parisinorum partem primam descripsit Fr. Cumont. Appendix, De libris astrologicis testimonia nova; vi + 292 p., 1 pl., 1929. Partem secundam descripsit Carolus Aemilius Ruelle. Accedunt Hermetica edita ab J. Heeg; viii + 195 p., 2 pl., 1911. Partem tertiam descripsit Petrus Boudreaux; viii + 222 p., 1912. Partem quartam descripsit P. Boudreaux [obiit 1914], edidit appendice suppleta Fr. Cumont; viii + 283 p., 1921.

[Vol. 9, to be devoted to the MSS in British, Dutch, Danish, and Swedish libraries, has not yet appeared (April 1947).]

1924 Vol. 10, Codices athenienses descripsit Armandus Delatte. viii + 291 p. (Isis 15, 295.)

1932–34 Vol. 11, Codices hispanenses descripsit Carolus Orestes Zuretti. Pars prior, codices scorialenses; viii + 288 p., 1932. Pars altera, codices scorialenses, matritenses, caesaraugustani; viii + 217 p., 1934.

(Continued on page 1878)

1936 Vol. 12, Codices rossicos descripsit Mstislav Antonini F. Šangin. viii + 268 p., 6 pl. (Isis 26, 483–84.)

These volumes contain first editions of a large number of astrological texts, even when these texts are not mentioned in the titles.

CATHOLIC ENCYCLOPEDIA

1907–12 15 vols. edited by Charles G. Herbermann and others. Appleton, New York. Index, Encyclopedia press, New York 1914.

Abbr. CE.

CHARLES, ROBERT HENRY (1855–1931)

1913 The Apocrypha and pseudepigrapha of the Old Testament in English. Quarto, 2 vols. Vol. 1, Apocrypha; vol. 2, Pseudepigrapha. Clarendon Press, Oxford.

CHEIKHO, LOUIS (S.J.) (1859–1927)

1924 Catalogue des MSS des auteurs arabes chrétiens depuis l'Islam. 2 + 286 p. en Arabe. Tiré de la revue Al-machriq. Imprimerie catholique, Beyrouth. (Isis 19, 282.)

CHEVALIER, ULYSSE (1841–1923)

1894–1903 Répertoire des sources historiques du Moyen âge. Topo-bibliographie. 2 vols. Montbéliard.

1905–7 Répertoire des sources historiques du Moyen âge. Bio-bibliographie. 4832 col. in 2 vols. Picard, Paris.

Both works used, the former seldom, the latter frequently. Used mostly like dictionaries without reference.

CHOULANT, [JOHANN] LUDWIG (1791–1861)

1841 Handbuch der Bücherkunde für die ältere Medizin. Zweite Aufl. xxii + 434 p. Leopold Voss, Leipzig.

First edition 1828. I refer to the edition of 1841, available to me in anastatic reprint 1911.

1920 History and bibliography of anatomic illustration in its relation to anatomic science and the graphic arts. Translated and edited by Mortimer Frank. xxvii + 435 p. University of Chicago Press, Chicago. (Isis 4, 357–59.)

German edition, Leipzig 1852.

CLAPHAM, SIR JOHN HAROLD (1873–1946), and EILEEN POWER

1941 The Cambridge economic history of Europe from the decline of the Roman empire. Vol. 1, The agrarian life of the Middle Ages. xvii + 650 p., 9 pl., 3 maps. University Press, Cambridge. (Isis 34, 262, 373.)

CLAUDIN, ANATOLE (1833–1906)

1900–14 Histoire de l'imprimerie en France aux XVe et XVIe siècles. 4 vols. Imprimerie nationale, Paris.

CLAY, ROTHA MARY

1909 Mediaeval hospitals of England. With a preface by the Lord Bishop of Bristol. (The antiquary's books.) xxii + 357 p., 78 ill. Methuen, London.

COHEN, MARCEL (1884——)

1924 See MEILLET.

COLLES, HENRY COPE (1879–1943)

1927–28 See GROVE.

COMBARIEU, JULES (1859–1916)

1913 Histoire de la musique. Vol. 1, Des origines à la fin du XVIe siècle. x + 651 p. Colin, Paris.

CONNOLLY, JAMES LOUIS

1928 John Gerson, reformer and mystic. xxii + 408 p., 3 fig. Université de Louvain. (Isis 34, 244.)

COOLIDGE, WILLIAM AUGUSTUS BREVOORT (1850–1926)

1904 Josias Simler [1530–76] et les origines de l'alpinisme jusqu'en 1600. xxii + cxcii + 307 + 327 + 99 p., ill. Allier, Grenoble.

Corbett, James [Arthur] (1908——)
1939 MSS alchimiques latins des bibliothèques publiques de Paris, antérieurs au XVIIe siècle. 367 p. Union académique internationale, Bruxelles. (Isis 32, 211.)

Cordier, Henri (1849–1925)
1903 See Marco Polo.
1904–24 Bibliotheca sinica. Dictionnaire bibliographique des ouvrages relatifs à l'empire chinois. 2d ed. (1st ed. 1878–85, suppt. 1895; used less frequently). 5 vols. Vols. 1–4, Guilmoto, Paris; vol. 5, Paul Geuthner, Paris.
1904 Vol. 1, xvi + 764 col.
1905–6 Vol. 2, col. 765–1576.
1906–7 Vol. 3, col. 1577–2380.
1907–8 Vol. 4, col. 2381–3252 (general table at end, col. 3239–52).
1922–4 Vol. 5, col. 3253–4428 (table col. 4429–39).
This volume is called "Supplément et index," but there is no index; probably the index failed to be realized because of the author's death in 1925.
The work is divided into five parts: (I) China proper: generalities, geography, names, anthropology, climate, natural history, population, government, law, history, religion, sciences and arts (col. 1363–1576, 3137–56, 3789–3849), language and literature, manners and customs. (II) Foreigners in China. (III) Relations between foreigners and Chinese. (IV) Chinese abroad. (V) Tributary countries: Tartary (Manchuria, Mongolia), Central Asia, Tibet, Korea, Loo Choo (liu ch'iu) islands.
1912–32 Bibliotheca indosinica. Dictionnaire bibliographique des ouvrages relatifs à la péninsule indochinoise. (Publications de l'Ecole française d'Extrême-Orient.) 5 vols. Ernest Leroux, Paris.
1912 Vol. 1, Birmanie, Assam, Siam, Laos. vii + 1104 col.
1913 Vol. 2, Péninsule malaise. Col. 1105–1510.
1914 Vol. 3, Indochine française. Col. 1511–2280.
1915 Vol. 4, Indochine française, Cambodge, Laos, Tchampa. Col. 2281–3030.
1932 Vol. 5 (par Mme M. A. Roland-Cabaton), Index des auteurs et des matières, 309 p.
First edition of volume 1, Birmanie et Assam only, in T'oung pao 1903–8. Reprinted Leiden 1908. **Not used.**
1912 Bibliotheca japonica. Dictionnaire bibliographique des ouvrages relatifs à l'empire japonais. (Publications de l'Ecole des langues orientales.) xii + 762 col., index. Ernest Leroux, Paris.
1913–16 See Yule.
1920 Ser Marco Polo. Notes and addenda to Sir Henry Yule's edition. x + 161 p. Murray, London; Scribner, New York. (Isis 4, 136.)

Couling, Samuel (1859–1922)
1917 The encyclopaedia sinica. viii + 633 p. Oxford University Press, London.

Coulton, George Gordon (1858–1947)
1923–36 Five centuries of religion. 3 vols. University Press, Cambridge.
1923 Vol. 1, St. Bernard, his predecessors and successors, 1000–1200 A.D.
1927 Vol. 2, The friars and the dead weight of tradition, 1200–1400.
1936 Vol. 3, Getting and spending.
Index to each volume.
1930 Life in the Middle Ages. University Press, Cambridge.
First edition in 1 volume, 1910, Constable, London. Second edition in 4 volumes, 1928, reprinted in 1 volume, 1930, University Press, Cambridge.
The volume of 1930 is divided as follows: (I) Religion, folklore and superstition, 246 p. (II) Chronicles, science and art, 154 p. (III) Men and manners, 168 p. (IV) Monks, friars and nuns, 362 p. Indexes, p. 363–446.
1938a Inquisition and liberty. xiii + 354 p. Heinemann, London. (Isis 30, 558–60.)
1938b Medieval panorama. The English scene from Conquest to Reformation. xiv + 802 p., ill. University Press, Cambridge.
1940 Europe's apprenticeship. A survey of medieval Latin with examples. **288 p. Thos.** Nelson, London.

COURANT, MAURICE (1865——)
1894–1901 Bibliographie coréenne. Tableau littéraire de la Corée jusqu'en 1890. (Publications de l'Ecole des langues orientales vivantes, vols. 18–21.) Leroux, Paris.
1894 Vol. 1, ccxvi + 502 p., nos. 1–1044, 11 facs.
1895 Vol. 2, x + 538 p., nos. 1045–2331, 13 facs.
1896 Vol. 3, x + 446 + clxxviii (indexes) p., nos. 2332–3240, 15 facs.
1901 Suppt. (to 1899), x + 122 p., nos. 3241–3821.
This is far more than a bibliography of some 4,000 items; it is a catalogue raisonné containing much information about the contents and intrinsic (not mere bibliographical) particularities of these books. Some 40 excellent large facsimiles. The indexes are rich but inconvenient.

COUSSEMAKER, EDMOND DE (1805–76)
1864–76 Scriptores de musica medii aevi. Nova series a Gerbertina altera. 4 vols. Durand, Paris.
1864 Vol. 1. 1869 Vol. 3.
1867 Vol. 2. 1876 Vol. 4.
There is a photographic reprint issued by the Bollettino bibliografico musicale, Milano 1931.

COWLEY, SIR ARTHUR ERNEST (1861–1931)
1929 Concise catalogue of the Hebrew printed books in the Bodleian library. vii + 816 p. Clarendon Press, Oxford.

CROOKE, WILLIAM (1845–1923)
1903 See YULE and BURNELL.

CULTURAL HERITAGE
c. 1936 The cultural heritage of India. Sri Ramakrishna centenary memorial. Quarto, 3 vols., ill. Belur Math, Calcutta. (Isis 29, 245.)

CUMONT, FRANZ (1868——)
1898—— See CATALOGUS.
1924–32, 1939—— See CATALOGUE.

CURTZE, MAXIMILIAN (1837–1903)
1902 Urkunden zur Geschichte der Mathematik im Mittelalter und der Renaissance. (Abhandlungen zur Geschichte der mathematischen Wissenschaften, vols. 12, 13.) 2 vols. Teubner, Leipzig.

DAÏ HYAKKA JITEN
1935 (Great encyclopaedia.) In Japanese. 28 vols. Heibonsha, Tōkyō.

DAREMBERG, CHARLES VICTOR (1817–72)
1852–59 See RENZI.

DARMSTAEDTER, LUDWIG (1846–1927)
1908 Handbuch zur Geschichte der Naturwissenschaften und der Technik. Zweite umgearbeitete und vermehrte Aufl. xii + 1264 p. Springer, Berlin.
Chronological summary year by year. The first edition, published in 1904 under a different title (4000 Jahre Pionier-Arbeit in den exakten Wissenschaften), was much smaller (v + 389 p.).

DASGUPTA, SURENDRA NATH (1887——)
1922–40 History of Indian philosophy. 3 vols. University Press, Cambridge.
1922 Vol. 1.
1932 Vol. 2.
1940 Vol. 3.

DELATTE, ARMAND (1886——)
1927–39 Anecdota atheniensia. (Bibliothèque de la Faculté de philosophie et lettres de l'Université de Liége.) 2 vols.
1927 Vol. 1, viii + 740 p. (Isis 12, 328–30).
1939 Vol. 2, viii + 504 p. (Isis 33, 274–78).
1932 Un manuel byzantin de cosmologie et géographie. (Bulletin de l'Académie de Belgique, classe des lettres, 18, 189–222, Bruxelles.) (Isis 23, 563.)

1936 Herbarius. Recueil sur le cérémonial usité chez les anciens pour la cueillette des simples et des plantes magiques. (Bulletin de l'Académie de Belgique, classe des lettres, 22, 227-348, Bruxelles.) (Isis 27, 531-32.)
1938 Herbarius. 2e éd. revue et augmentée. 177 p. Université de Liége. (Isis 30, 395.)
1939—— See CATALOGUE.

DEMIÉVILLE, PAUL
1929—— See HŌBŌGIRIN.

DERENBOURG, HARTWIG (1844-1908)
1884-1903 Les MSS arabes de l'Escurial. (Ecole orientale des langues vivantes.) Vol. 1, 1884; vol. 2, fasc. 1, 1903. Leroux, Paris.
1941 Vol. 2, fasc. 2, ed. by H. P. J. Renaud.
1928-29 Vol. 3, ed. by Evariste Lévi-Provençal. (Isis 34, p. 34.)

DE WAARD, CORNELIS (1879——)
1936 L'expérience barométrique, ses antécédents et ses explications. 198 p. Thouars. (Isis 26, 212-15.)

DE WULF, MAURICE (1867——)
1926 History of mediaeval philosophy. Translation by Ernest C. Messenger based upon the fifth French edition (1924-25). 2 vols. Longmans, Green, London.

DEY, NUNDO LAL
1927 Geographical dictionary of ancient and mediaeval India. (Calcutta Oriental series, no. 21, E. 13.) 2d ed. Quarto, x + 262 p. Luzac, London.
First edition, Calcutta 1899. Second edition printed in sheets in The Indian antiquary, issued as a volume by Quaritch, London 1921. The edition of 1927 was printed in Bombay; the preface is dated Chinsurah 1922.

DICKSON, LEONARD EUGENE (1874——)
1919-23 History of the theory of numbers. 3 vols. Carnegie Institution, Washington.
1919 Vol. 1, Divisibility and primality (Isis 3, 446-48).
1920 Vol. 2, Diophantine analysis (Isis 4, 107-8).
1923 Vol. 3, Quadratic and higher forms (Isis 6, 96-98).

DICTIONARY OF NATIONAL BIOGRAPHY
1885-1900 Edited by George Smith and Sir Sidney Lee. 63 vols. Oxford University Press, London.
Abbr. DNB.

DICTIONNAIRE DE THÉOLOGIE CATHOLIQUE
1903—— Edited by A. Vacant, E. Mangenot, E. Amann. Letouzey et Ané, Paris.
Thus far 14 double volumes have appeared and the 15th is printing, the first part of it reaching the article "théologie" (1943).
Abbr. DTC.

DIEFENBACH, LORENZ (1806-83)
1857 See DU CANGE.

DIEHL, CHARLES (1859——)
1925-26 Manuel d'art byzantin. 2e éd. revue et augmentée. xvi + 746 p., ill. Picard, Paris.

DILLON, EDWARD (d. 1914)
1907 Glass. (Connoisseur's library.) xxviii + 374 p., 49 pl. Dent, London.

DREYER, JOHN LOUIS EMIL (1852-1926)
1906 History of the planetary systems from Thales to Kepler. xii + 432 p. University Press, Cambridge. (Isis 21, 131-44.)

DU CANGE, CHARLES DUFRESNE (1610-88)
1840-50 Glossarium mediae et infimae latinitatis conditum a Carolo Dufresne domino Du Cange, cum supplementis integris monachorum ordinis S. Benedicti D. P. Carpenterii, Adelungii, aliorum, suisque digessit G. A. L. Henschel. Firmin-Didot, Paris.

(*Continued on page 1882*)

1840 Vol. 1, A–B. 1845 Vol. 5, P–R.
1842 Vol. 2, C–D. 1846 Vol. 6, S–Z.
1844 Vol. 3, E–K. 1850 Vol. 7.
1845 Vol. 4, L–O.

Vol. IV continet indices monetarum et monogrammatum; vol. VII, glossarium gallicum, tabulas, indices auctorum et rerum, dissertationes.

Du Cange's Latin glossary was first printed in 3 volumes folio (Paris 1678). Reprinted Francfort a.M. 1679–81. New edition much enlarged by Benedictines (6 vols., Paris 1733–36; reprinted Venice 1737, Basel 1762). Supplement by Carpentier (4 vols. folio, 1766).

I did not use Du Cange's Glossarium mediae et infimae graecitatis (2 vols. folio, Lyon 1688). It includes an Appendix ad glossarium . . . latinitatis, and an Etymologicon vocabulorum linguae gallicae (316 col. with separate numbering in vol. 2).

Biography of Du Cange and other documents concerning him in this edition (vol. 7, 1850). Reviews of this edition by Jean Marie Pardessus (vol. 7, ix–xvi) and by Henry Charles Lea: Minor historical writings (p. 371–74, Philadelphia 1942) (Isis 34, 235).

1857 Vol. 8, Supplementum. Glossarium latino-germanicum mediae et infimae aetatis . . . concinnavit Laurentius Diefenbach. Joseph Baer, Frankfurt a.M.

DUFF, C. MABEL (MRS. W. R. RICKMERS)
1899 Chronology of India from the earliest times to the beginning of the sixteenth century. xi + 409 p. Constable, Westminster.

DUHEM, PIERRE (1861–1916)
1905–6 Origines de la statique. 2 vols. Hermann, Paris.
1906–13 Etudes sur Léonard de Vinci. Ceux qu'il a lus et ceux qui l'ont lu. 3 vols. Hermann, Paris.
1906 Vol. 1, viii + 356 p.
1909 Vol. 2, iv + 474 p.
1913 Vol. 3, Les précurseurs parisiens de Galilée, xiv + 605 p.
1908 Σῴζειν τὰ φαινόμενα. Essai sur la notion de théorie physique de Platon à Galilée. (Extrait des Annales de philosophie chrétienne.) 144 p. Hermann, Paris.
1913–17 Le système du monde. Histoire des doctrines cosmologiques de Platon à Copernic. 5 vols. Hermann, Paris. (Isis 2, 203–4; 3, 125.)
1913 Vol. 1. 1916 Vol. 4.
1914 Vol. 2. 1917 Vol. 5.
1915 Vol. 3.

Le système du monde was meant to fill nine volumes. The fifth volume extends to the second half of the thirteenth century. Volumes 6 to 9 were ready in MS at the time of Duhem's death, but are still unpublished. (Isis 26, 302–3, 1936.)

DUVAL, RUBENS (1839–1911)
1907 La littérature syriaque. Troisième éd. xviii + 430 p. Lecoffre, Paris.
First edition 1899, xv + 426 p. Second edition 1900.

DWIGHT, HARRISON GRAY OTIS (1803–62)
1853 Catalogue of all works known to exist in the Armenian language of a date earlier than the seventeenth century (read October 22, 1851). (Journal of the American Oriental Society 3, 241–88, New York.)

DYROFF, KARL (1862——)
1903 See BOLL.

ECHARD, JACQUES (1644–1724)
1719–21 See QUÉTIF.

ELIADE, MIRCEA
1936 Yoga. Essai sur les origines de la mystique indienne. (Bibliothèque de philosophie roumaine.) ix + 246 p. Geuthner, Paris.

The book is more comprehensive than its title indicates, for it contains a comparative study of yoga theories and practices, not only in India but all over the world.

EMDEN, ALFRED BROTHERSTON (1888——)
1936 See RASHDALL.

Emeneau, Murray Barnson (1904——)
1935 Union list of printed Indic texts and translations in American libraries. xv + 540 p. American Oriental Society, New Haven, Conn. (Isis 25, 258.)

Emerton, Ephraim (1851–1935)
1925 Humanism and tyranny. Studies in the Italian trecento. x + 377 p. Harvard University Press, Cambridge, Mass. (Isis 11, 177.)

Enciclopedia universal
1912–39 Enciclopedia universal ilustrada europeo-americana. 84 vols. Espasa-Calpe, Bilbao, Barcelona, and Madrid.
1912–30 Main work, 70 vols.
1930–33 Appendice, 10 vols.
1934–39 Suplemento anual, 4 vols.
Abbr. EUI.

Encyclopaedia judaica
1928–34 10 vols. published (to Lyra). Edited by Jacob Klatzkin. Eschkol, Berlin.
Abbr. EJ.

Encyclopaedia of Islam
1908–38 A dictionary of the geography, ethnography and biography of the Muhammedan peoples. Edited by M. Th. Houtsma, T. W. Arnold, R. Basset, R. Hartmann, A. J. Wensinck, W. Heffening, E. Lévi-Provençal, H. A. R. Gibb. 4 vols. plus supplement. Brill, Leiden; Luzac, London.
1908–13 Vol. 1, A–D, 1088 p.
1913–28 Vol. 2, E–K, iv + 1176 p.
1928–36 Vol. 3, L–R, viii + 1190 p.
1924–34 Vol. 4, S–Z, ii + 1243 + 15 p.
1934–38 Supplement, A–Z, xvi + 268 p.
Abbr. EI.

Encyclopaedia of religion and ethics
1908–27 Edited by James Hastings. 13 vols. Scribner, New York.
Abbr. ERE.

Eneström, Gustav (1852–1923)
1884–1914 See Bibliotheca mathematica. (Isis 8, 313–20.)

Errera, Carlo (1867–1936)
1926 L'epoca delle grandi scoperte geografiche. Terza ed. rinnovata. xxviii + 505 p., 22 fig. Hoepli, Milano. (Isis 13, 556.)
First edition, Milano 1902; second edition, Milano 1910.

Erskine, William (1773–1853)
1921 See Bābar.

Fabricius, Johann Albert (1668–1736)
1734–46 Bibliotheca latina mediae et infimae aetatis. 6 vols. Hamburg.
1754 Idem. Editio prima italica. 6 vols. Padua.
1858–59 Idem. Revised ed. 6 vols. in 3. Florence.

Falco, Vittorio de
1939—— See Catalogue.

Farmer, Henry George (1882——)
1940 The sources of Arabian music. An annotated bibliography of Arabic MSS which deal with the theory, practice and history of Arabian music. 98 p. Issued privately, Bearsden, Scotland. (Isis 32.)

Felder, Hilarin (1867——)
1904 Geschichte der wissenschaftlichen Studien im Franziskanerorden bis um die Mitte des 13. Jahrhunderts. xi + 557 p. Herder, Freiburg i.B.

Feldhaus, Franz Maria (1874——)
1914 Die Technik der Vorzeit, der geschichtlichen Zeit und der Naturvölker. xvi + 1400 col., 873 ill. Engelmann, Leipzig.
1931 Die Technik der Antike und des Mittelalters. 442 p., 452 ill., 15 pls. Athenaion, Potsdam. (Isis 16, 167–69.)

FERGUSON, JOHN (1811–83)
1906 Bibliotheca chemica. A catalogue of the alchemical, chemical and pharmaceutical books in the collection of the late James Young. 2 vols. Maclehose, Glasgow.

FERRAND, GABRIEL (1864—c. 1935)
1913–14 Relations de voyages et textes géographiques arabes, persans et turcs relatifs à l'Extrême Orient traduits et annotés. 2 vols., xii + 743 p. Leroux, Paris.

FERRARI, FILIPPO (d. 1626)
1697 Novum lexicon geographicum. (1st ed. Milan 1627; later ed. Paris 1670, folio, 2 vols.) New ed. by Michael Antonius Baudrand. 2 vols., 1695–97, bound in 1. Jacobus de Cadorinis, Patavii.
Cited as Ferrari and Baudrand (1697).

FISCHER, HERMANN (1884——)
1929 Mittelalterliche Pflanzenkunde. viii + 326 p., 70 ill. Münchner Drucke, München. (Isis 15, 367–70.)

FISCHER, THEOBALD (1846–1910)
1871–81 Raccolta di mappemondi e carte nautiche del XIII. al XVI. secolo. 15 parts. Ongania, Venezia.
Contents in Phillips (1, no. 249, 1909).

FLICK, ALEXANDER CLARENCE (1869–1942)
1930 The decline of the medieval church. 2 vols. Knopf, New York.

FLÜGEL, GUSTAV (1802–70)
1835–58 See ḤĀJJĪ KHALĪFA.

FONAHN, ADOLF (1873–1940)
1910 Zur Quellenkunde der persischen Medizin. vi + 152 p. Barth, Leipzig.
1922 Arabic and Latin anatomical terminology chiefly from the Middle Ages. (Norwegian Academy, hist. class., 1921, no. 7.) ii + 174 p. Jacob Dybwad, Kristiania. (Isis 5, 170–72; 37, 81.)

FRANK, MORTIMER (1874–1919)
1920 See CHOULANT.

FUJIKAWA YU
1934 Japanese medicine. Translated from the German (Tōkyō 1911) by John Ruhräh. With a chapter on the recent history of medicine in Japan by Kageyas W. Amano. (Clio medica.) xiii + 114 p., 8 ill. Hoeber, New York.

GAMS, PIUS BONIFACIUS (O.S.B.) (1816–92)
1873 Series episcoporum ecclesiae catholicae quotquot innotuerunt a beato Petro apostolo. Quarto, xxiv + 963 p. Manz, Ratisbonae.

GARCÍA SILVESTRE, MANUEL
1932 Historia sumaria de la literatura catalana. Pròleg i bibliografia de Manuel de Montoliu. xvii + 424 p. Balmes, Barcelona.

GARDNER, CHARLES SIDNEY (1900——)
1938 Chinese traditional historiography. (Harvard historical monographs, vol. 11.) xvi + 120 p. Harvard University Press, Cambridge, Mass. (Isis 33, 132.)

GARRISON, FIELDING H. (1870–1935)
1929 Introduction to the history of medicine. 4th ed., revised and enlarged. 996 p., ill. Saunders, Philadelphia. (Isis 13, 137–38.)
First edition 1913; second edition 1917; third edition 1921 (Isis 4, 554–56).

GAUDEFROY-DEMOMBYNES, MAURICE (1862——)
1923 La Syrie à l'époque des Mamelouks d'après les auteurs arabes. cxx + 288 p. Geuthner, Paris. (Isis 6, 561–63.)

GAUTHIER, HENRI (S.J.)
1913 See HOANG.

GAYANGOS Y ARCE, PASCUAL DE (1809–97)
1840–43 The history of the Mohammedan dynasties of Spain. (Oriental Translation Fund of Great Britain.) Quarto, 2 vols. W. H. Allen, London.

Extracts from the Nafḥ al-ṭīb min ghuṣn al-Andalus al-raṭīb wa dhikr wazīrhā Lisān al-dīn Ibn al-Khaṭīb, by Aḥmad ibn Muḥammad al-Maqqarī al-Tilimsānī al-Mālikī (c. 1590–1632). See Brockelmann (2, 296–97, 1902; suppt. 2, 407–8, 1938); Sarkis (col. 1776–78, 1930). See my note on Ibn al-Khaṭīb (XIV-2).

GEIGER, WILHELM (1856——)
1933 See LAW, B. C.

GERBERT, MARTIN (1720–93)
1784 Scriptores ecclesiastici de musica sacra. 3 vols. St. Blasien in the Black Forest.
Facsimile reprint, Graz, Styria, 1905. Second facsimile reprint, Milano 1931.

GÉROLD, THÉODORE (1866——)
1936 Histoire de la musique des origines à la fin du XIVe siècle. 424 p., ill. Laurens, Paris. (Isis 28, 494–502.)

GESAMTKATALOG DER WIEGENDRUCKE
1925—— Hiersemann, Leipzig.
Volume 7 appeared in 1938, and part 1 of vol. 8 in 1940 (to Federicis, Stephanus de). Abbr. GW.

GIACOSA, PIERO (1853–1928)
1901 Magistri salernitani nondum editi. xxxiv + 723 p., atlas of 40 p. Bocca, Torino.

GIBB, ELIAS JOHN WILKINSON (1857–1901)
1900–9 History of Ottoman poetry. 6 vols. Luzac, London.

GIBB, HAMILTON ALEXANDER ROSSKEEN (1895——)
1908–38 See ENCYCLOPAEDIA OF ISLAM.

GILES, HERBERT ALLEN (1845–1935)
1898 Chinese biographical dictionary. xii + 1022 p. Kelly and Walsh, Shanghai.
1912 Chinese-English dictionary. 2d ed., revised and enlarged. Quarto, xviii + 84 + 1711 p. Kelly and Walsh, Shanghai.
First edition, Shanghai 1892.

GILES, LIONEL (1875——)
1911 An alphabetical index to the Chinese encyclopaedia Ch'in ting ku chin t'u shu chi ch'êng. Quarto, xx + 102 p. British Museum, London.

GILSON, ETIENNE (1884——)
1921 Etudes de philosophie médiévale. (Publications de la Faculté des lettres de Strasbourg, no. 3.) vii + 292 p. Strasbourg.
1937 Medieval universalism and its present value. 22 p. Sheed and Ward, New York.

GINZEL, FRIEDRICH KARL (1850–1926)
1906–14 Handbuch der mathematischen und technischen Chronologie. Das Zeitrechnungswesen der Völker. 3 vols. Hinrichs, Leipzig.
1906 Vol. 1, Zeitrechnung der Babylonier, Ägypter, Mohammedaner, Perser, Inder, Südostasiaten, Chinesen, Japaner und Zentralamerikaner. xii + 584 p., 6 fig., tables and map.
1911 Vol. 2, Zeitrechnung der Juden, der Naturvölker, der Römer und Griechen, sowie Nachträge zum 1. Bande. vii + 597 p.
1914 Vol. 3, Zeitrechnung der Makedonier, Kleinasier und Syrer, der Germanen und Kelten, des Mittelalters, der Byzantiner (und Russen), Armenier, Kopten, Abessinier, Zeitrechnung der neueren Zeit, sowie Nachträge zu den drei Bänden. vii + 445 p., 6 fig., 1 pl., chronological tables.

GOICHON, AMÉLIE MARIE
1938 Lexique de la langue philosophique d'Ibn Sīnā. xiv + 496 p. Desclée De Brouwer, Paris.
1939 Vocabulaires comparés d'Aristote et d'Ibn Sīnā. xvi + 50 p. Desclée De Brouwer, Paris. (Isis 33, 326–29.)

GOLUBOVICH, GIROLAMO (O.F.M.) (1865——)
1906–27 Biblioteca bio-bibliografica della Terra Santa e dell' Oriente francescano. 5 vols. Collegio di S. Bonaventura, Quaracchi.

(*Continued on page 1886*)

1906 Vol. 1, 1215–1300.
1913 Vol. 2, Addenda al sec. XIII, a fonti pel sec. XIV, 3 carte geogr. dell' Oriente francescano de' secoli XIII–XIV.
1919 Vol. 3, 1300–1332.
1923 Vol. 4, 1333–1345.
1927 Vol. 5, 1346–1400.

GONZÁLEZ PALENCIA, ANGEL (1889——)
1926–30 Los Mozárabes de Toledo en los siglos XII y XIII. Folio, 3 vols. and preliminary vol. Instituto de Valencia de Don Juan, Madrid. (Isis 15, 183–87.)
1930 Preliminary vol. 1926 Vol. 2.
1926 Vol. 1. 1928 Vol. 3.
1928 Historia de la literatura arábigo-española. 356 p. Colección Labor, Barcelona.
1932 See HURTADO.

GREITH, CARL JOHANN (1807–82)
1861 Die deutsche Mystik im Prediger-Orden (1250–1350) nach ihren Grundlehren, Liedern und Lebensbildern aus handschriftlichen Quellen. viii + 456 p. Herder, Freiburg im Breisgau.

GROSS, CHARLES (1857–1909)
1915 The sources and literature of English history from the earliest times to about 1485. 2d ed. xxiii + 820 p. Longmans, Green, London.
First edition 1900.

GROSS, HEINRICH (1835–1910)
1897 Gallia judaica. Dictionnaire géographique de la France d'après les sources rabbiniques. Traduit sur le MS de l'auteur par Moïse Bloch. (Publication de la Société des études juives.) x + 766 p. Cerf, Paris.

GROUSSET, RENÉ (1885——)
1929 Histoire de l'Extrême-Orient. 2 vols., 789 p., 32 pl., 7 maps. Geuthner, Paris. (Isis 14, 437–41.)

GROVE, SIR GEORGE (1820–1900)
1927–28 Dictionary of music and musicians. 3d ed., edited by H. C. Colles. 5 vols. Macmillan, London.

GUBERNATIS, ANGELO CONTE DE (1840–1913)
1872 Zoological mythology. 2 vols. Trübner, London.

GÜNTHER, SIEGMUND (1848–1923)
1887 Geschichte des mathematischen Unterrichts im deutschen Mittelalter bis zum Jahre 1525. (Monumenta Germaniae paedagogica, vol. 3.) vi + 408 p. Hofmann, Berlin.

GUNDEL, WILHELM (1880——)
1926 See BOLL.

GUNTHER, ROBERT THEODORE (1869–1940)
1920–45 Early science in Oxford. 14 vols. Printed for the author, Oxford.
1920–23 Vols. 1, 2 (Isis 6, 449–53). 1932 Vol. 9 (Isis 20, 537).
1925 Vol. 3 (Isis 8, 375–77). 1935 Vol. 10 (Isis 25, 466–70).
1925 Vol. 4 (Isis 13, 118–19). 1937 Vol. 11 (Isis 29, 525).
1929 Vol. 5 (Isis 14, 233–35). 1939 Vol. 12 (Isis 31, 533).
1930 Vols. 6, 7 (Isis 15, 174–77). 1938 Vol. 13 (Isis 31, 441–42).
1931 Vol. 8 (Isis 16, 498). 1945 Vol. 14 (Isis 37, 82).
Volume 1 was published in parts; part 1, dated 1921, appeared in 1920; the whole volume is dated 1922 or 1923.
The only volumes concerning mediaevalists are vols. 1, 2, 3, 5, 11. Vol. 1 deals with chemistry, mathematics, physics, and surveying; vol. 2 with astronomy; vol. 3 with biology and medicine; vol. 11 with the Oxford colleges; vol. 5 contains Chaucer's treatise on the astrolabe. The other volumes concern science in the seventeenth century: vols. 4, 12 deal with the Philosophical Society of Oxford; vols. 6, 7, 8, 10, 13 with Robert Hooke; vol. 9 with Richard Lower; vol. 12 with Robert Plot; vol. 14 with Edward Lhwyd.
1932 The astrolabes of the world. Quarto, 2 vols., ill. University Press, Oxford.

Vol. 1, The Eastern astrolabes; vol. 2, The Western astrolabes (Isis 20, 310–16, 492–95).
1937 Early science in Cambridge. xii + 513 p. Printed for the author, Oxford. (Isis 28, 134.)

GURLT, ERNEST (1825–99)
1884–88 See BIOGRAPHISCHES LEXIKON.
1898 Geschichte der Chirurgie. 3 vols., ill. Hirschwald, Berlin.

GUYARD, STANISLAS (1846–84)
1883 See REINAUD.

HABERLING, WILHELM (1871–1940)
1929–35 See BIOGRAPHISCHES LEXIKON.

HAESER, HEINRICH (1811–84)
1875–82 Lehrbuch der Geschichte der Medizin und der epidemischen Krankheiten. Dritte Bearbeitung. 3 vols. Fischer, Jena.
1875 Vol. 1, Alterthum und Mittelalter.
1881 Vol. 2, Neuere Zeit.
1882 Vol. 3, Epidemische Krankheiten.

ḤĀJJĪ KHALĪFA (c. 1609–1657)
1835–58 Lexicon bibliographicum et encyclopaedicum a Mustafa ben Abdallah . . . compositum, instruxit Gustavus Flügel. Quarto, 7 vols. Oriental Translation Fund of Great Britain, Leipzig.
1835 Vol. 1. 1850 Vol. 5.
1837 Vol. 2. 1852 Vol. 6.
1842 Vol. 3. 1858 Vol. 7.
1845 Vol. 4.
Volume 7 contains the catalogues of the libraries of Cairo, Damascus, Aleppo, Rhodes, and Constantinople, and commentaries and indexes to volumes 1–6.
Arabic text, with Latin translation on same pages, of the Kashf al-ẓunūn fī asāmī-l-kutub wal funūn, by the great Turkish bibliographer Muṣṭafā ibn 'Abdallāh Kātib Čelebī Ḥājjī Khalīfa. Partly superseded by Brockelmann (1898–1942), yet still to be consulted. It is an immense treasure of Arabic bibliography. See Brockelmann (2, 427–29, 1902; suppt. 2, 635, 1938).

HALLBERG, IVAR
1906 L'extrême Orient dans la littérature et la cartographie de l'Occident des XIIIe, XIVe et XVe siècles. viii + 573 p. Göteborg.
In the form of a geographical dictionary.

HALLIWELL [-PHILLIPS], JAMES ORCHARD (1820–89)
1839 Rara arithmetica. A collection of treatises on the mathematics and subjects connected with them from ancient unedited MSS. viii + 120 p. Parker, London.
1841 2d ed. viii + 120 p. Maynard, London. (Isis 18, 127–32.)

HANDWÖRTERBUCH
1927–38 Handwörterbuch des deutschen Aberglaubens, hrsg. von E. Hoffmann-Krayer, H. Bächtold-Stäubli, usw. 9 vols. De Gruyter, Berlin.
Abbr. HDA.

HARTING, JAMES EDMUND (1841–1928)
1891 Bibliotheca accipitraria. Catalogue of books relating to falconry with notes, glossary and vocabulary. xxviii + 289 p., 26 pl. Quaritch, London.

HARTMANN, RICHARD (1881——)
1908–38 See ENCYCLOPAEDIA OF ISLAM.

HARTSHORNE, ALBERT (1839–1910)
1897 Old English glasses. An account of glass drinking vessels in England from early times to the end of the eighteenth century. Folio, xxiii + 490 p., 67 pl., 366 ill. Arnold, London.

HASTINGS, JAMES (1852–1922)
1908–27 See ENCYCLOPAEDIA OF RELIGION AND ETHICS.

HAURÉAU, BARTHÉLEMY (1812–96)
1872–80 Histoire de la philosophie scolastique. 2 vols. in 3 (vol. 2 in 2 parts). Durand et Pedaune-Lauriel, Paris.
First published in 2 volumes, 1850.

HEATH, SIR THOMAS LITTLE (1861–1940)
1921 History of Greek mathematics. 2 vols. Clarendon Press, Oxford. (Isis 4, 532–35.)
1931 Manual of Greek mathematics. xvi + 552 p. Clarendon Press, Oxford. (Isis 16, 450–51; Osiris vol. 2.)

HEFFENING, WILLI (1894——)
1908–38 See ENCYCLOPAEDIA OF ISLAM.

HEIBERG, JOHAN LUDVIG (1854–1928)
1912–43 See TANNERY, PAUL.
1924–32 See CATALOGUE. (Isis 11, 367–74.)

HENNIG, RICHARD (1874——)
1938 Terrae incognitae. Eine Zusammenstellung und kritische Bewertung der wichtigsten vorcolumbischen Entdeckungsreisen an Hand der darüber vorliegenden Originalberichte. Vol. 3, 1200–1415. x + 389 p., 14 pl. Brill, Leiden.
Volume 2 of this work was reviewed in Isis 29, 188–89.

HENSCHEL, G. A. LOUIS (1806–52)
1840–50 See DU CANGE.

HENSCHEL, G. E. T.
1852–59 See RENZI.

HERBERMANN, CHARLES GEORGE (1840–1916)
1907–12 See CATHOLIC ENCYCLOPEDIA.

HEYD, WILHELM VON (1823–1906)
1879 Geschichte des Levantehandels im Mittelalter. 2 vols. Cotta, Stuttgart.
1885–86 Histoire du commerce du Levant au Moyen âge. Ed. refondue, augmentée. 2 vols. Harrassowitz, Leipzig.
Reprinted Leipzig 1923.

HIME, HENRY WILLIAM LOVETT (1840–c. 1931)
1915 The origin of artillery. viii + 231 p., 1 pl. Longmans, Green, London.

HIRN, YRJÖ (1870——)
1912 The sacred shrine. A study of the poetry and art of the Catholic church. xv + 574 p. Macmillan, London.
First published in Swedish, 1909.

HIRSCH, AUGUST (1817–94)
1884–88 See BIOGRAPHISCHES LEXIKON.

HISTOIRE LITTÉRAIRE
1733—— Histoire littéraire de la France. Vol. 1, Paris 1733.
Work undertaken by the Benedictine congregation of St. Maur, but continued (vols. 13 ff., 1814——) by the Académie des inscriptions. Volumes 24 ff. (1862——) deal with the fourteenth century; the last volume published is vol. 37 (1936–38); the first half of the fourteenth century is completed, the second half remains to be done.
Abbr. HL.

HITTI, PHILIP KHURI (= ḤITTĪ, PHĪLĪB KHŪRĪ) (1886——)
1937 History of the Arabs. xviii + 767 p., many ill., maps. Macmillan, London. (Isis 28, 503–4.)
The revised edition issued by the same publisher in 1940 contains the same number of pages plus an errata slip.

HOANG, PIERRE (1830–1909)
1909–13 Catalogue des tremblements de terre signalés en Chine d'après les sources chinoises (1767 B.C.—1895 A.D.). (Variétés sinologiques, nos. 28, 28 bis.) 2 vols. Vol. 1, 1909; vol. 2, 1913, edited by J. Tobar and H. Gauthier. Mission catholique, Shanghai.

HŌBŌGIRIN
1929—— Dictionnaire encyclopédique du Bouddhisme d'après les sources chinoises et japonaises, édité par Sylvain Lévi, J. Takakusu et Paul Demiéville. Quarto. Maison franco-japonaise, Tōkyō.
Last issue seen, no. 3, to p. 298, 1937.
1931 Fascicule annexe. Tables du Taishō issaikyō, nouvelle édition du canon bouddhique chinois publiée sous la direction de J. Takakusu et K. Watanabe [55 vols., Tōkyō 1924–29]. 202 p. Maison franco-japonaise, Tōkyō.

HOBSON-JOBSON
1903 See YULE and BURNELL.

HODOUS, LEWIS (1872——)
1937 See SOOTHILL.

HOEFER, FERDINAND (1811–78)
1852–66 See NOUVELLE BIOGRAPHIE GÉNÉRALE.
1866–69 Histoire de la chimie. 2e ed., revue et augmentée. 2 vols. xii + 452 p., vi + 615 p. Firmin Didot, Paris.
First edition 1842–43. See Sarton: Hoefer and Chevreul (Bulletin of the history of medicine 8, 419–45, 1940).

HOERNLE, AUGUST FRIEDRICH RUDOLF (1841–1918)
1907 Studies in the medicine of ancient India. Part 1, Osteology. xii + 252 p. Clarendon Press, Oxford.

HOFFMANN-KRAYER, EDUARD (1864–1936)
1927–38 See HANDWÖRTERBUCH.

HONIGMANN, ERNST (1892——)
1929 Die sieben Klimata und die πόλεις ἐπίσημοι. Eine Untersuchung zur Geschichte der Geographie und Astrologie im Altertum und Mittelalter. 247 p., 4 fig. Winter, Heidelberg. (Isis 14, 270–76.)

HOOPS, JOHANNES (1865——)
1911–19 See REALLEXIKON.

HOPFNER, THEODOR (1886——)
1928—— See PATROLOGIA GRAECA.

HORNSTEIN, XAVIER DE
1922 Les grands mystiques allemands du XIVe siècle, Eckart, Tauler, Suso. Etat présent des problèmes. (Thèse de l'Université catholique de Fribourg, Suisse.) xvi + 293 p. Raeber, Lucerne.

HOUTSMA, MARTINUS THEODORUS (1851——)
1908–38 See ENCYCLOPAEDIA OF ISLAM.

HOWGRAVE-GRAHAM, ROBERT PICKERSGILL (1880——)
1927 Some clocks and jacks with notes on the history of horology. (Archaeologia 77, 257–312, 12 pl., London.) (Isis 14, 548.)
Abbr. HG.

HOWLAND, ARTHUR CHARLES (1869——)
1942 See LEA.

HÜBOTTER, FRANZ (1881——)
1924 A guide through the labyrinth of Chinese medical writers and medical writings. 74 p., mimeographed. Kumamoto. (Isis 7, 259.)
1929 Die chinesische Medizin zu Beginn des XX. Jahrhunderts und ihr historischer Entwicklungsgang. 356 p., mimeographed. Asia Major, Leipzig. (Isis 14, 255–63.)

(*Continued on page 1890*)

Though I have always consulted Hübotter's writings, the facts given by me often disagree with his.

1929–35 See BIOGRAPHISCHES LEXIKON.

HUGHES, THOMAS PATRICK (1838–1911)

1885 A dictionary of Islam. Being a cyclopaedia of the doctrines, rites, ceremonies and customs, together with the technical and theological terms of the Muhammadan religion. viii + 750 p., with index in Arabic script, p. 719–50. W. H. Allen, London.

I have used photographic reprint, London 1935.

HUMMEL, ARTHUR WILLIAM (1884——) (EDITOR)

1943–44 Eminent Chinese of the Ch'ing period, 1644–1912. Vol. 1, xii + 604 p., 1943 (Isis 34, 519–22); vol. 2, p. 605–1103, 1944 (Isis 36, 47). U. S. Government Printing Office, Washington.

HUNT, CHARLES

1932 See TROLLOPE.

HURTADO Y JIMÉNEZ DE LA SERNA, JUAN (1875——); with ANGEL GONZÁLEZ PALENCIA

1932 Historia de la literatura española. Tercera ed. xvi + 1140 p. Madrid. (Isis 19, 606.)

Cited as Hurtado and González Palencia. First edition 1921, second 1925.

HUSIK, ISAAC (1876——)

1916 History of mediaeval Jewish philosophy. lii + 462 p. Macmillan, New York.

HYMA, ALBERT (1893——)

1924 The Christian renaissance. a history of the Devotio moderna. xviii + 501 p., facs. Reformed Press, Grand Rapids, Mich.

1938 Church and politics. A history of the principles and struggles of church and state. 331 p. Lippincott, Philadelphia.

IRSAY, STEPHEN D' (1894–1934)

1933–35 Histoire des universités françaises et étrangères des origines à nos jours. 2 vols. Auguste Picard, Paris.

1933 Vol. 1, Moyen âge et Renaissance.

1935 Vol. 2, Du XVIe siècle à 1860 (Isis 24, 370–74).

ISIS

1913—— Revue consacrée à l'histoire et à l'organisation de la science. Publiée par George Sarton. Wondelgem-lez-Gand, Belgique; Max Drechsel, Bern, Schweiz.

That is the subtitle of vol. 1. That subtitle has changed many times, being printed in English from vol. 3 on, the general meaning remaining the same. The latest volume, 37 (nos. 107–10), 1947, bears the subtitle An international review devoted to the history of science and civilization. Official quarterly of the History of Science Society [since vol. 6, 1924]. The editor is still G. Sarton, but assisted by A. Pogo until recently, now by I. Bernard Cohen, and many associate editors.

JAMES, MONTAGUE RHODES (1862–1936)

1924 The apocryphal New Testament. Being the apocryphal gospels, acts, epistles and apocalypses with other narratives and fragments. Newly translated. xxxi + 584 p. Clarendon Press, Oxford.

I have used the impression of 1926.

JENSEN, HANS (1884——)

1925 Geschichte der Schrift. Quarto, viii + 231 p., 303 fig. Orient-Buchhandlung, Hannover.

1935 Die Schrift in Vergangenheit und Gegenwart. viii + 418 p., 445 fig. Orient-Buchhandlung, Hannover. (Isis 30, 132–37.)

Revised edition of the earlier work.

JEWISH ENCYCLOPEDIA

1901–6 12 vols. edited by Cyrus Adler, Isidore Singer, etc. Funk and Wagnalls, New York.

Abbr. JE.

JUDEICH, WALTHER (1859——)
1905 Topographie von Athen. (Handbuch der klassischen Altertumswissenschaft, 3. Bd., 2. Abt., 2. Hälfte.) xii + 416 p., 48 ill. Beck, München.
1931 2. Aufl. xii + 473 p., 24 pl., 56 fig., 4 maps.

JUSSERAND, JEAN JULES (1855–1932)
1884 Les Anglais au Moyen âge. La vie nomade et les routes d'Angleterre au XIVe siècle. 306 p. Hachette, Paris.

KAMMERER, ALBERT (1875——)
1929–35 La Mer rouge, l'Abyssinie et l'Arabie depuis l'antiquité. (Mémoires de la Société royale de géographie d'Egypte, tomes 15, 16.) Folio, 2 vols., ill. Le Caire.
1929 Vol. 1, divided into 3 parts, dealing respectively with Alexandria, Arabia, and Abyssinia.
1935 Vol. 2, Les guerres du poivre. Les Portugais dans l'Océan indien et la Mer rouge au XVIe siècle. Histoire de la cartographie orientale.
Heavy folio volumes richly illustrated. Each is generally bound in two parts.

KARLGREN, BERNHARD (1889——)
1917 A mandarin phonetic reader in the Pekinese dialect with an introductory essay on the pronunciation. (Archives d'études orientales, vol. 13.) 188 p. Leroux, Paris; Norstedt, Stockholm, 1918.
Chinese words have been romanized in my book according to the system of Sir Thomas Francis Wade (London 1867), as modified—very slightly—by H. A. Giles in his Chinese-English dictionary (2d ed., 1912). Karlgren's list (p. 10–18) will enable the reader to find corresponding forms in other transcriptions, to wit, (2) C. W. Mateer, (3) A. Vissière in Bulletin de l'Ecole française d'Extrême-Orient (French system), (4) F. Lessing and W. Othmer (German system, Tsingtau 1912), (5) Dmitrii Alekseyevich Peshchurov (Russian system, 1887).

KARPINSKI, LOUIS CHARLES (1878——)
1911 See SMITH, D. E.

KEITH, ARTHUR BERRIEDALE (1879——)
1921 Indian logic and atomism. An exposition of the Nyāya and Vaiçeṣika systems. 291 p. Clarendon Press, Oxford. (Isis 4, 535–36.)
1928 History of Sanskrit literature. xxxvi + 575 p. Clarendon Press, Oxford.

KENYON, SIR FREDERIC GEORGE (1863——)
1939—— See CATALOGUE.

KIBRE, PEARL (1903——)
1937 See THORNDIKE.

KIKUCHI DAIROKU (1855–1917)
1914 See BRINKLEY.

KIMBLE, GEORGE HERBERT TINLEY (1908——)
1938 Geography in the Middle Ages. xii + 272 p., 20 pl. Methuen, London. (Isis 30, 540–42.)

KING, SIR LUCAS (1856——)
1921 See BĀBAR.

KLATZKIN, JACOB (1882——)
1928–34 See ENCYCLOPAEDIA JUDAICA.

KLEBS, ARNOLD CARL (1870–1943)
1938 Incunabula scientifica et medica. Short title list. (Osiris 4, 1–359, Bruges.)
Describing briefly more than 3,000 editions of 1,058 scientific incunabula. Our citation Klebs (no. 815, 1938) refers to a definite text; nos. 815.1, 815.2, etc. refer to separate editions of that text.
This first part of Osiris 4 really appeared in 1937.

KLEBS, ARNOLD CARL, and KARL SUDHOFF
1926 Die ersten gedruckten Pestschriften. Faksimile von Steinhöwel's Büchlein der Pestilenz, Ulm 1473. 264 p., 24 pl. Münchner Drucke, München. (Isis 9, 430–33.)

KOKUSHO KAIDAI
1929 Annotated bibliography of Japan. In Japanese. 3d ed., in 2 vols. Yoshikawa Kobunkan, Tōkyō.

KREMERS, EDWARD (1865–1941) and GEORGE URDANG
1940 History of pharmacy. x + 466 p., 30 ill. Lippincott, Philadelphia. (Isis 33, 307–8.)

KRETSCHMER, KONRAD (1864——)
1909 Die italienischen Portolane des Mittelalters. Ein Beitrag zur Geschichte der Kartographie und Nautik. viii + 688 p., map. Mittler, Berlin.

KRONENBERG, MARIA ELIZABETH (1881——)
1923–40 See NIJHOFF.

KRUMBACHER, KARL (1856–1909)
1897 Geschichte der byzantinischen Litteratur von Justinian bis zum Ende des Oströmischen Reiches, 527–1453. (Handbuch der klassischen Altertumswissenschaft, 9. Bd., 1. Abt.) Zweite Aufl. xx + 1193 p. Beck, München.
First edition 1891, xii + 494 p.

LAGERCRANTZ, OTTO (1868——)
1924–32 See CATALOGUE.

LAIGNEL-LAVASTINE, MAXIME (1875——)
1936? 1938? Histoire générale de la médecine, de la pharmacie, de l'art dentaire et de l'art vétérinaire. Quarto, 2 vols., ill. Michel, Paris, undated.
This work is remarkable for the richness of its illustrations, though many are unconnected with the text or irrelevant.

LAMMENS, HENRI (1862–1937)
1926 L'Islam, croyances et institutions. 288 p. Imprimerie catholique, Beyrouth.

LANE-POOLE, STANLEY (1854–1931)
1893 The Mohammedan dynasties. xxviii + 301 p., 2 tables. Constable, Westminster.
Photographic reprint, Geuthner, Paris 1925.

LÁNG, PAUL HENRY (1900——)
1941 Music in Western civilization. xvi + 1107 p., ill., maps. Norton, New York. (Isis 34, 182–86.)

LANGLOIS, CHARLES VICTOR (1863–1929)
1926–28 La vie en France au Moyen âge de la fin du XIIᵉ au milieu du XIVᵉ siècle. 4 vols. Hachette, Paris.
1926 Vol. 1, D'après des romans mondains du temps. Nouv. éd. (1st ed. 1903).
1926 Vol. 2, D'après des moralistes du temps. Nouv. éd. (1st ed. 1908).
1927 Vol. 3, La connaissance de la nature et du monde.
1928 Vol. 4, La vie spirituelle. Enseignements, méditations et controverses.

LA RONCIÈRE, CHARLES DE (1870——)
1925–27 La découverte de l'Afrique au Moyen âge. Cartographes et explorateurs. (Mémoires de la Société royale de géographie d'Egypte, vols. 5, 6, 13.) 3 vols. Le Caire.
1925 Vol. 1, L'intérieur du continent.
1925 Vol. 2, La périple du continent.
1927 Vol. 3, Un explorateur français du Niger. Les débuts de Christophe Colomb. Un peintre italien à la cour d'Abyssinie.
Volume 3 deals mainly with the fifteenth century but contains the index to the three volumes.

LAUFER, BERTHOLD (1874–1934)
1907 Skizze der mongolischen Literatur. (Keleti szemle, Revue orientale pour les études ouralo-altaïques 8, 165–261, Budapest.)

LAW, BIMALA CHURN (1892——)
1933 A history of Pāli literature. With a foreword by Wilhelm Geiger. 2 vols. Vol. 1, xxvii + 342 p.; vol. 2, vii + p. 343–691. Kegan Paul, London.

LAW, NARENDRA NATH (1889——)
1916 Promotion of learning in India during Muhammadan rule, by Muhammadans. xlviii + 260 p., ill. Longmans, Green, London.

LEA, HENRY CHARLES (1825–1909)
1840–50 See DU CANGE.
1942 Minor historical writings and other essays, edited by Arthur C. Howland. x + 414 p. University of Pennsylvania, Philadelphia. (Isis 34, 235–36.)

LEACH, ARTHUR FRANCIS (1851–1915)
1915 The schools of medieval England. xv + 349 p., 43 ill. Methuen, London.
I have used the second edition, 1916.

LECLAINCHE, EMMANUEL (1861——)
1936 Histoire de la médecine vétérinaire. xv + 812 p. Office du Livre, Toulouse. (Isis 27, 360–63.)

LECLERC, LUCIEN (1816–93)
1876 Histoire de la médecine arabe. 2 vols. Leroux, Paris. (Isis 2, 448.)

LEE, SIR SIDNEY (1859–1926)
1885–1900 See DICTIONARY OF NATIONAL BIOGRAPHY.

LE QUIEN, MICHEL (1661–1733)
1740 Oriens christianus in quatuor patriarchatus digestus, quo exhibentur ecclesiae, patriarchae, caeterique praesules totius orientis. Opus posthumum. Folio, 3 vols. Typographia regia, Paris.

LE STRANGE, GUY (1854–1933)
1890 Palestine under the Moslems. A description of Syria and the Holy Land from 650 to 1500. Translated from the works of the mediaeval Arab geographers. xxiii + 604 p., ill., 2 maps. Houghton Mifflin, Boston.
1900 Baghdad during the Abbasid caliphate from contemporary Arabic and Persian sources. xxxi + 381 p., 8 plans. Clarendon Press, Oxford.
Photographic reprint 1924.
Though the 'Abbāsī caliphate ended in 1258, this book is necessary for Baghdād history and topography in the fourteenth century.
1905 The lands of the Eastern caliphate. Mesopotamia, Persia and Central Asia from the Moslem conquest to the time of Timur. xviii + 536 p., 10 maps. University Press, Cambridge.
Very precious book, of which I have made considerable use.

LEUMANN, ERNST (1859–1931)
1899 See MONIER-WILLIAMS.

LÉVI, SYLVAIN (1863–1935)
1929—— See Hōbōgirin.

LÉVI-PROVENÇAL, EVARISTE
1908–38 See ENCYCLOPAEDIA OF ISLAM.
1928–29 See DERENBOURG.

LEYDEN, JOHN (1775–1811)
1921 See BĀBAR.

LIBRI, GUILLAUME (1803–69)
1838–41 Histoire des sciences mathématiques en Italie depuis la renaissance des lettres jusqu'à la fin du dix-septième siècle. 4 vols. Renouard, Paris.
1838 Vol. 1. 1840 Vol. 3.
1838 Vol. 2. 1841 Vol. 4.

LIPPMANN, EDMUND O. VON (1857–c. 1941)
1919–31 Entstehung und Ausbreitung der Alchemie, mit einem Anhange zur älteren Geschichte der Metalle. 2 vols. Vol. 1, xvi + 742 p., 1919 (Isis 3, 302–5); vol. 2, vii + 257 p., 1931 (Isis 16, 462–63). Springer, Berlin.

LITTLE, ANDREW GEORGE (1863–1945)
1892 The Grey Friars in Oxford. xvi + 369 p. Clarendon Press, Oxford.

LITTMANN, ENNO (1875——)
1907 Geschichte der äthiopischen Litteratur. (In Geschichte der christlichen Litteraturen des Orients p. 185–269, 277–81.) Amelang, Leipzig.

LORIA, GINO (1862——)
1912–43 See TANNERY, PAUL. (Osiris 7, 1939.)

LUCE, SIMÉON (1833–1892)
1876 Histoire de Bertrand du Guesclin et de son époque. La jeunesse de Bertrand, 1320–64. 624 p. Hachette, Paris.
Reprinted in 1882 without notes. 420 p.

LYDGATE, JOHN (1370?–1451?)
1923–27 The fall of princes. Edited by Henry Bergen. 4 vols. Vols. 1–3, 1923; vol. 4, 1927. Carnegie Institution, Washington. (Isis 33, 361.)

LYNCH, HARRY FINNIS BLOSSE (1862–1913)
1901 Armenia. Travels and studies. Quarto, 2 vols., abundant ill. Longmans, Green, London.
This excellent work has helped me to solve some of the very difficult problems of mediaeval Armenian topography.

MABILLEAU, LÉOPOLD (1853——)
1895 Histoire de la philosophie atomistique. viii + 560 p. Imprimerie nationale, Alcan, Paris.

MACDONALD, DUNCAN BLACK (1863–1943)
1903 Development of Muslim theology, jurisprudence and constitutional theory. ix + 366 p. Scribner, New York.
1909 The religious attitude and life in Islam. Being the Haskell lectures on comparative religion of 1906. ix + 317 p. University of Chicago Press, Chicago.
1911 Aspects of Islam. ix + 375 p. Macmillan, New York.

MALLET, ROBERT (1810–81)
1852 Catalogue of earthquakes from 1606 B.C. to 1755. (Report of the 22d meeting of the British Association for the Advancement of Science, held at Belfast in 1852, p. 1–176, London.)

MANGENOT, EUGÈNE
1903—— See DICTIONNAIRE DE THÉOLOGIE CATHOLIQUE.

MANGET, JEAN JACQUES (1652–1742)
1702 Bibliotheca chemica curiosa, seu rerum ad alchemiam pertinentium thesaurus instructissimus. Folio, 2 vols. Cologne and Geneva.
Contents in Ferguson (2, 68–71, 1906).

MANITIUS, MAXIMILIAN (1858–1933)
1911–31 Geschichte der lateinischen Literatur des Mittelalters. (Handbuch der klassischen Altertumswissenschaft, 9. Bd., 2. Abt., 1–3.) C. H. Beck, München.
1911 Vol. 1, Von Justinian bis zur Mitte des 10. Jahrhunderts. xiii + 766 p.
1923 Vol. 2, Von der Mitte des 10. Jahrhunderts bis zum Ausbruch des Kampfes zwischen Kirche und Staat. x + 873 p.
1931 Vol. 3, Vom Ausbruch des Kirchenstreites bis zum Ende des 12. Jahrhunderts. xiii + 164 p.

MANN, JACOB (1888–1940)
1931–35 Texts and studies in Jewish history and literature. 2 vols. Vol. 1, xvi + 684 p., 27 facs., 1931; vol. 2, xxiii + 1596 p., 4 facs., 1935. Hebrew Union College, Cincinnati, Ohio.
Volume 2 is devoted exclusively to Qaraitica.

MARCO POLO (XIII-2; Introd. 2, 1056–61)
1903 The book of Ser Marco Polo. Translated and edited by Sir Henry Yule. Revised by Henri Cordier. 2 vols. John Murray, London.

First edition, London 1871. Second edition, much increased, 2 vols., London 1874–75. The third (posthumous) edition of 1903 was reprinted in 1921 and 1926. I have generally used the reprint of 1926.
See Cordier (1920).

MARGOLIS, MAX LEOPOLD (1866–1932), and ALEXANDER MARX
1927 History of the Jewish people. xxii + 823 p., 15 maps. Jewish Publication Society of America, Philadelphia.

MARX, ALEXANDER (1878——)
1927 See MARGOLIS.

MASPERO, HENRI (1883–1945)
1937 Les procédés de "nourrir le principe vital" dans la religion taoïste ancienne. (Journal asiatique, vol. 229, p. 177–252, 353–430.) (Isis 33, 278–79.)
The numbers of the Journal asiatique are dated avril-juin 1937, juillet-septembre 1937; yet they were not published until 1938, being received in Cambridge, Mass. in May and November of that year.

MASSON-OURSEL, PAUL
1923 La philosophie comparée. 203 p. Alcan, Paris. (Isis 6, 99–104.)

MCGOVERN, WILLIAM MONTGOMERY (1897——)
1923 Manual of Buddhist philosophy. Vol. 1, Cosmology (no more published). 205 p. Kegan Paul, London.

MEILLET, ANTOINE (1866–1936), and MARCEL COHEN (EDITORS)
1924 Les langues du monde, par un groupe de linguistes. (Collection de linguistique publiée par la Société de linguistique de Paris, vol. 16.) xvi + 811 p., 18 maps. (Isis 10, 298.)

MEYER, ERNST HEINRICH FRIEDRICH (1791–1858)
1854–57 Geschichte der Botanik. 4 vols. Bornträger, Königsberg.
1854 Vol. 1. 1856 Vol. 3.
1855 Vol. 2. 1857 Vol. 4.

MEYER-STEINEG, THEODOR (1873–1936), and KARL SUDHOFF
1928 Geschichte der Medizin. Dritte Aufl. x + 446 p., 217 fig. Fischer, Jena. (Isis 11, 561.)
First edition 1921 (Isis 4, 368–69). Second edition 1922 (Isis 5, 188).

MEYERHOF, MAX (1874–1945)
1940 Un glossaire de matière médicale de Maimonide, édité et traduit. (Mémoires présentés à l'Institut d'Egypte, vol. 41.) lxxvi + 258 p., 70 p. in Arabic. Institut français d'archéologie orientale, Le Caire. (Isis 33, 527–29.)

MICHALSKI, KONSTANTYN, ABBÉ
1920 Les courants philosophiques à Oxford et à Paris pendant le XIVe siècle. (Bulletin international de l'Académie polonaise des sciences, p. 59–88, Cracovie.)
1925a Le criticisme et le scepticisme dans la philosophie du XIVe siècle. (Bulletin international de l'Académie polonaise des sciences, p. 41–122, Cracovie.)
1925b Les courants sceptiques et critiques dans la philosophie du XIVe siècle. (Bulletin international de l'Académie polonaise des sciences, p. 192–242, Cracovie.)
1927 La physique nouvelle et les différents courants philosophiques au XIVe siècle. (Bulletin international de l'Académie polonaise des sciences, p. 93–164, Cracovie.)
1937 Le problème de la volonté à Oxford et à Paris au XIVe siècle. (Studia philosophica 2, 233–365, Leopoli = Lwów.)

MIELI, ALDO (1879——)
1919—— See ARCHIVIO DI STORIA DELLA SCIENZA.
1939 La science arabe et son rôle dans l'évolution scientifique mondiale. xix + 388 p. Brill, Leiden. (Isis 30, 291–95.)

MIGNE, JACQUES PAUL (1800–75)
1844–64 See PATROLOGIA LATINA.
1857–86 See PATROLOGIA GRAECA.

MIKAMI YOSHIO
1913 The development of mathematics in China and Japan. (Abhandlungen zur Geschichte der mathematischen Wissenschaften, Heft 30.) viii + 347 p. Teubner, Leipzig.
1914 See SMITH, D. E.

MILLÀS VALLICROSA, JOSÉ MARIA (1897——)
1931 Assaig d'història de les idees físiques i matemàtiques a la Catalunya medieval. Vol. 1 (no more published), xvi + 351 p., 20 pl. Institució Patxot, Barcelona. (Isis 18, 203–4.)
1942 Las traducciones orientales en los manuscritos de la Biblioteca Catedral de Toledo. Quarto, 373 p., 17 pl. Instituto Arias Montano, Madrid. (Isis 34, 518–19.)

MILLINGEN
See VAN MILLINGEN.

MINŌ KŌJUN
1930 See TOKIWA.

MITTEILUNGEN ZUR GESCHICHTE DER MEDIZIN UND DER NATURWISSENSCHAFTEN
1902–40 39 vols. Leipzig.
Abbr. Mitt.

MÖBIUS, MARTIN (1859——)
1937 Geschichte der Botanik. Von den ersten Anfängen bis zur Gegenwart. vi + 458 p. Fischer, Jena. (Isis 30, 304–6.)

MOLINIER, AUGUSTE (1851–1904)
1903–4 Sources de l'histoire de France des origines aux guerres d'Italie (1494). Picard, Paris.
1903 Vol. 3, Les Capétiens, 1180–1328. 248 p.
1904 Vol. 4, Les Valois, 1328–1461. 354 p.

MONIER-WILLIAMS, SIR MONIER (1819–99)
1899 A Sanskrit-English dictionary etymologically and philologically arranged with special reference to cognate Indo-European languages. New edition greatly enlarged with the collaboration of E. Leumann and C. Cappeller. Quarto, xxxvi + 1333 p. Clarendon Press, Oxford.

MONTESSUS DE BALLORE, FERNAND COMTE DE (1851–1923)
1923 Ethnographie sismique et volcanique, ou Les tremblements de terre et les volcans dans la religion, la mythologie et le folklore de tous les peuples. vii + 206 p. Champion, Paris.

MONTOLIU, MANUEL DE (1877——)
1932 See GARCÍA SILVESTRE.

MORGAN, JACQUES DE (1857–1924)
1919 Histoire du peuple arménien. xviii + 410 p., ill. Berger-Levrault, Nancy.

MOTTELAY, PAUL FLEURY (1841–1922)
1922 Bibliographical history of electricity and magnetism, chronologically arranged. xx + 673 p. Griffin, London. (Isis 6, 104–7.)

MOULE, ARTHUR CHRISTOPHER (1873——)
1930 Christians in China before the year 1550. xvi + 293 p., 22 fig. Society for Promoting Christian Knowledge, London. (Isis 15, 458.)

MOULÉ, LÉON (1849–1922)
1891–1911 Histoire de la médecine vétérinaire. (Extraits du Bulletin de la Société centrale de médecine vétérinaire, Paris.) 684 p.
1891 Part 1, Antiquité. 200 p.
1896 Part 2, Médecine vétérinaire arabe. 125 p.
1900 Part 3, Moyen âge en Europe. 178 p.
1911 Part 4, XVIe siècle. 180 p.

MOURAD, YOUSSEF (= YŪSUF MURĀD)
1939 La physiognomonie arabe et le Kitāb al-firāsa de Fakhr al-dīn al-Rāzī. 162 p. in French, 90 in Arabic. Geuthner, Paris. (Isis 33, 248–49.)

MUNK, SALOMON (1803?–67)
1859 Mélanges de philosophie juive et arabe. xii + 536 p. + 72 p. in Hebrew. Franck, Paris.
I have used facsimile reprint. Paul Catin, Paris 1927.

MURĀD, YŪSUF
1939 See MOURAD.

MURRAY, HAROLD JAMES RUTHVEN
1913 History of chess. 900 p., ill. Clarendon Press, Oxford.

NANJIŌ BUNYIŪ (1848–1927)
1883 Catalogue of the Chinese translation of the Buddhist Tripiṭaka, the sacred canon of the Buddhists in China and Japan. Quarto, xxxvi p. + 480 col. Clarendon Press, Oxford.
I have used a facsimile reprint made in Tōkyō, 1930. See Ross (1910); Tokiwa (1930).

NANSEN, FRIDTJOF (1861–1930)
1911 In northern mists. Arctic exploration in early times. Quarto, 2 vols., ill. Heinemann, London.

NASH, VERNON
1936 Trindex. An index to three dictionaries. Giles' Chinese-English dictionary, K'ang hsi tzu t'ien, P'ei wen yun fu. lvii + 586 p. Yenching University, Peiping.
Cited as the best means of identifying Chinese characters by the use of the numerical system (kuei hsieh) and cross references to the Giles numbers. In addition, simplest means of passing from the Wade to the French transcription, and identifying Chinese words quoted by French scholars.

NEEDHAM, JOSEPH (1900——)
1934 History of embryology. xviii + 274 p., 16 pl., ill. University Press, Cambridge. (Isis 27, 98–102.)

NEUBAUER, ADOLPH (1832–1907)
1877, 1893 See RENAN.

NEUBURGER, MAX (1868——)
1906–11 Geschichte der Medizin. Vol. 1, viii + 408 p., 1906; vol. 2, part 1, 528 p., 3 pl., 1911 (no more published). Enke, Stuttgart.

NEUMANN, CARL FRIEDRICH (1793?–1870)
1836 Versuch einer Geschichte der armenischen Literatur nach den Werken der Mechitaristen frei bearbeitet. xii + 308 p. Johann Ambrosius Barth, Leipzig.
Unfortunately without index, but the Somal books whence it is very largely derived are indexed. See Somal.

NIHON BUNGAKU DAI-JITEN
1937 (Great literary lexicon.) In Japanese. 7 vols. Shinchōsha, Tōkyō.

NIHON HYAKKA DAI-JITEN
1917 (Encyclopaedia japonica.) In Japanese. 10 vols. Sanseido, Tōkyō.

NIJHOFF, WOUTER (1866——), and M. E. KRONENBERG
1923–40 Nederlandsche bibliographie van 1500 to 1540. 2 vols. Vol. 1, xliv + 1002 p., 1923; vol. 2, 1083 + 6 p., 1936–40. Martinus Nijhoff, 's Gravenhage.

NORDENSKIÖLD, ADOLF ERIK (1832–1901)
1897 Periplus. An essay on the early history of charts and sailing directions. Folio, x + 208 p., 100 ill., 60 maps. Norstedt, Stockholm.

NORDSTRÖM, JOHAN
1933 Moyen-âge et Renaissance. Essai historique. Traduit du suédois par T. Hammar. 238 p. Stock, Paris.
Swedish original text in Norstedt Världshistoria utgiven av Sven Tunberg och S. E. Bring (vol. 6, Stockholm 1929).
Excellent synthesis of the French and Provençal origins of the Italian Renaissance.

NOURRY, EMILE (1870–1935)
1930 See SAINTYVES.

NOUVELLE BIOGRAPHIE GÉNÉRALE
1852–66 46 vols. edited by Ferdinand Hoefer. Firmin Didot, Paris.
Vol. 1, 1855.
Abbr. NBG.

OGIWARA UNRAI
1930 See TOKIWA.

OLLONE, COMMANDANT D' (1865——)
1911 Recherches sur les Musulmans chinois. Etudes de A. Vissière, E. Blochet, etc. xii + 472 p., map, ill. Ernest Leroux, Paris.

OPPOLZER, THEODOR VON (1841–86)
1887 Canon der Finsternisse. (Denkschriften der Akademie der Wissenschaften in Wien, vol. 52.) xxxvi + 378 p., 160 maps.

OSIRIS
1936—— Studies on the history and philosophy of science and on the history of learning. Edited by George Sarton, with the cooperation of Alexander Pogo. Saint Catherine Press, Bruges.
Beginning with vol. 5, 1938, the subtitle is in Latin (for the sake of internationalism), Commentationes de scientiarum et eruditionis historia rationeque.
Latest volume published, 7, 1939. (Isis 33, 630.)

OSLER, WILLIAM (1849–1919)
1923 Incunabula medica. xi + 140 p., 16 facs. Oxford University Press, London. (Isis 7, 199; 8, 358–61.)

OXFORD ENGLISH DICTIONARY
1888–1928 10 vols. in 12. Clarendon Press, Oxford.
Abbr. OED.

PANSIER, PIERRE (1864–1934)
1903–33 Collectio ophtalmologica veterum auctorum. Fasc. 1–7 (no more published). Baillière, Paris.
For fasc. 7, see Isis 24, 198, 212.

PAPINOT, EDMOND
1909 Historical and geographical dictionary of Japan. xiv + 842 p., 300 ill., maps. Sansaisha, Tōkyō.
Published in French, Sansaisha, Tōkyō, 1906?

PARDESSUS, JEAN MARIE (1772–1853)
1850 See DU CANGE.

PASTOR, LUDWIG VON (1854–1928)
1901 Geschichte der Päpste seit dem Ausgang des Mittelalters. Vol. 1, Im Zeitalter der Renaissance bis zur Wahl Pius' II [1458]. 4te. Aufl. Herder, Freiburg i.Br.
First edition began to appear in 1886.
1891 History of the popes from the close of the Middle Ages. Vol. 1. Hodges, London.

PATCANIAN, M.
1860 Catalogue de la littérature arménienne depuis le commencement du IVe siècle jusque vers le milieu du XVIIe. (Bulletin de l'Académie impériale des sciences de Saint Pétersbourg 2, 49–91.)

PATROLOGIA GRAECA
1857–86 Patrologiae cursus completus, etc. Patrologia graeca (graece et latine) accurante J. P. Migne. Tomus 1–161 in 165 vols. Paris.
Abbr. PG.
Brief index in Potthast (p. CI–CVI, 1895).
1928—— Theodorus Hopfner: Index locupletissimus. Geuthner, Paris.
1928–34 Tomus 1, contents of vols. 1–99. 541 p.
1936–39 Tomus 2, fasc. I–III, contents of vols. 100–57. p. 542–828.

PATROLOGIA LATINA
1844–64 Patrologiae cursus completus, etc. Patrologia latina accurante J. P. Migne. Tomus 1–221. Paris.
Abbr. PL.
Brief index in Potthast (p. XCIV–CI, 1895).
Very elaborate indexes will be found in PL (vols. 218–21). There are no less than 24 indexes, the last one (vol. 221, 429–1129) dealing with sciences and arts, inventions, astronomy, meteorology, geology, anatomy, medicine, etc.

PAULY, AUGUST (1796–1845)
1894–1939 See PAULY-WISSOWA.

PAULY-WISSOWA
1894—— Pauly's Real-Encyclopädie der classischen Altertumswissenschaft. Neue Bearbeitung herausgegeben von Georg Wissowa. Metzler, Stuttgart.
1894–38 First series, 38 half volumes, Aal to Philon.
1914–39 Second series, 13 half volumes, Ra to M. Tullius Cicero.
1903–35 Supplement, 6 vols.
Abbr. PW.

PETIT DE JULLEVILLE, LOUIS (1841–1901)
1896 Histoire de la langue et de la littérature française des origines à 1900. Vols. 1–2, Moyen Age. Colin, Paris.

PHILLIPS, PHILIP LEE (1857–1924)
1909–20 A list of geographical atlases in the Library of Congress. 4 vols. U. S. Government Printing Office, Washington.
1909 Vol. 1, Atlases. xiv + 1208 p.
1909 Vol. 2, Author list; index. p. 1209–1659.
1914 Vol. 3, Supplement, titles 3266–4087. cxxxvii + 1030 p.
1920 Vol. 4, Second supplement, titles 4088–5324. clviii + 639 p.
Vol. 4 includes author list and index to the whole work, all the titles listed being numbered consecutively from 1 to 5324.

PINES, SALOMON (1908——)
1936 Beiträge zur islamischen Atomenlehre. 150 p. Heine, Berlin. (Isis 26, 557.)

PLESSNER, MARTIN (1900——)
1928 Der οἰκονομικός des Neupythagoreers "Bryson" und sein Einfluss auf die islamische Wissenschaft. Edition und Übersetzung der erhaltenen Versionen, nebst einer Geschichte der Ökonomik im Islam mit Quellenproben in Text und Übersetzung. (Orient und Antike, vol. 5.) xii + 297 p. Winter, Heidelberg. (Isis 13, 529.)

POGO, ALEXANDER (1893——)
1913—— See ISIS.
1936—— See OSIRIS.

POLEMAN, HORACE IRVIN (1905——)
1938 Census of Indic manuscripts in the United States and Canada. xxix + 542 p. American Oriental Society, New Haven, Conn. (Isis 31, 215.)

POLLARD, ALFRED WILLIAM (1859–1944), and G. R. REDGRAVE
1926 Short-title catalogue of books printed in England, Scotland and Ireland and of English books printed abroad 1475–1640. Quarto, xvi + 610 p. Bibliographical Society, London.
Abbr. STC.

PONS BOIGUES, FRANCISCO
1898 Ensayo bio-bibliográfico sobre los historiadores y geógrafos arábigo-españoles. 514 p. San Francisco de Sales, Madrid.

POOLE, REGINALD LANE (1857–1939)
1884 Illustrations of the history of medieval thought in the departments of theology and ecclesiastical politics. viii + 376 p. Williams and Norgate, London.
1920 Revised ed. xiii + 327 p. Society for Promoting Christian Knowledge, London.

POTTHAST, AUGUST (1824–98)
1895–96 Bibliotheca historica medii aevi. Wegweiser durch die Geschichtswerke des europäischen Mittelalters bis 1500. CXLVIII + 1750 p. W. Weber, Berlin.

POUZYNA, I. V.
1935 La Chine, l'Italie et les débuts de la Renaissance (XIIIe–XIVe siècles). Quarto, 102 p., 16 pl. Editions d'art et d'histoire, Paris. (Isis 25, 253.)

POWER, EILEEN (1889–1940)
1941a The wool trade in English medieval history. (Ford lectures.) viii + 128 p. Oxford University Press, London.
1941b See CLAPHAM.

POWICKE, FREDERICK MAURICE (1879——)
1936 See RASHDALL.

PRANTL, CARL VON (1820–88)
1855–70 Geschichte der Logik im Abendlande. 4 vols. Hirzel, Leipzig.
1855 Vol. 1. 1867 Vol. 3.
1861 Vol. 2. 1870 Vol. 4.

PUCCINOTTI, FRANCESCO (1794–1872)
1850–66 Storia della medicina. 3 vols. in 4.
1850 Vol. 1, Medicina antica. Wagner, Livorno.
1855 Vol. 2, part 1, Medio evo. Wagner, Livorno.
1859 Vol. 2, part 2, Medio evo. Wagner, Livorno.
1866 Vol. 3, Moderna. Giachetti, Prato.

PULLÉ, FRANCESCO LORENZO
1905 La cartografia antica dell'India. Parte 2, Il medio-evo europeo e il primo rinascimento. (Studi italiani di filologia indo-iranica, no. 5.) xvii + 140 p., 4 appendixes, 6 maps. Carnesecchi, Firenze.

QUÉTIF, JACQUES (1618–98), and JACQUES ECHARD
1719–21 Scriptores ordinis Praedicatorum recensiti, notisque historicis et criticis illustrati, etc. Folio, 2 vols. Paris.

RADCLIFFE, WILLIAM (1856——)
1921 Fishing from the earlier times. xviii + 478 p., ill. Dutton, New York. (Isis 4, 568–71.)

RĀMAKṚISHṆA, SRI (1836–86)
See CULTURAL HERITAGE.

RAMBAUD, JOSEPH (1849–1919)
1909 Histoire des doctrines économiques. 3e éd. rev. 2 + 816 p. Larose, Paris.

RASHDALL, HASTINGS (1858–1924)
1936 The universities of Europe in the Middle Ages. New ed. in 3 vols. by F. M. Powicke and A. B. Emden. Clarendon Press, Oxford.
Vol. 1, Salerno, Bologna, Paris. Vol. 2, Italy, Spain, France, Germany, Scotland, etc. Vol. 3, English universities. Student life.
First edition 1895, 2 vols. in 3.

RATHGEN, BERNHARD (1847–1927)
1928 Das Geschütz im Mittelalter. Quellenkritische Untersuchungen. xx + 718 p. 16 pl. Verein deutscher Ingenieure, Berlin. (Isis 13, 125–27.)

RAY, PRAPHULLA CHANDRA (1861–1944)
1903–9 History of Hindu chemistry from the earliest times to the middle of the sixteenth century with Sanskrit texts, etc. 2 vols. Vol. 1, 1903, in a 2d ed., rev. and enlarged, including preface to 1st ed., dated 1902; vol. 2, 1909. Bengal Chemical Works, Calcutta. (Isis 3, 68–73.)

REALLEXIKON
1911–19 Reallexikon der germanischen Altertumskunde, hrsg. von Johannes Hoops. 4 vols. Trübner, Strassburg.
Dictionary of English, High and Low German, and Scandinavian antiquities down to the eleventh century in the South and to the twelfth century in the North.
Abbr. RGA.

REDGRAVE, GILBERT RICHARD (1844——)
1926 See POLLARD.

REESE, GUSTAVE (1899——)
1940 Music in the Middle Ages. xvii + 502 p., 8 pls., many ill. Norton, New York. (Isis 34, 182–86.)

REINAUD, JOSEPH TOUSSAINT (1795–1867)
1848–83 Géographie d'Aboulféda. 2 vols. in 3. Bibliothèque nationale, Paris.
1848 Vol. 1, Introduction générale à la géographie des orientaux.
1848 Vol. 2, part 1, Première partie de la traduction.
1883 Vol. 2, part 2, Fin de la traduction; index général.
This part of the work (viii + 320 p.) was done by Stanislas Guyard.

RENAN, ERNEST (1823–92)
1852 Averroès et l'Averroïsme. Calmann Lévy, Paris.
Second edition 1861, considerably modified. Third edition 1869, with more modifications; then stereotyped. New additions in later editions. I used the so-called seventh edition, 1922.
1877 Les rabbins français. (Histoire littéraire 27, 431–776.)
1893 Les écrivains juifs français. (Histoire littéraire 31, 351–830.)
Both works cited as Neubauer-Renan. Indeed, all the ground work was done by Neubauer, as is acknowledged in HL 27, p. iii–iv, and 31, p. i. Renan died before the publication of HL 31, and the proofs of the article written by him on the basis of Neubauer's elaborate investigations were emended by M. Steinschneider. These acknowledgments are very clear, yet may easily escape the reader's attention because they are made not at the beginning of the Neubauer-Renan articles, but at the beginning of large volumes containing other articles as well.

RENAUD, HENRI PAUL JOSEPH (1881–1945)
1933 See BROWNE.
1941 Les MSS arabes de l'Escurial. Décrits d'après les notes de Hartwig Derenbourg. Vol. 2, fasc. 2, Médecine et histoire naturelle. xi + 125 p. Geuthner, Paris. (Isis 34, p. 34–35.)

RENZI, SALVATORE DE (1800–72)
1852–59 Collectio salernitana. Ossia documenti inediti e trattati di medicina appartenenti alla scuola medica salernitana, raccolti ed illustrati da G. E. T. Henschel, C. Daremberg, E. S. de Renzi, premessa la storia della scuola. 5 vols. Filiatre Sebezio, Napoli.
1852 Vol. 1. 1856 Vol. 4.
1853 Vol. 2. 1859 Vol. 5.
1854 Vol. 3.
1857 Storia documentata della scuola medica di Salerno. 2d ed. XVI + 608 + clxxxiv p. Nobile, Naples.
This is an enlarged and corrected edition of the Collectio salernitana, vol. 1, p. 1–416, 1852.

REPARAZ-RUIZ, GONÇAL DE (= GONÇAL DE REPARAZ, FILL) (1901——)
1940 Essai sur l'histoire de la géographie de l'Espagne de l'antiquité au XVe siècle. (An-

nales du Midi, Revue de la France méridionale, 52e année, no. 206, p. 137–89; nos. 207–8, p. 280–341, Toulouse.) (Isis 37.)

RICCARDI, PIETRO (1828–98)
1887–93 Biblioteca matematica italiana. (Memorie della Accademia delle scienze, Bologna.) p. 1–656, 1–676, 1–54.
Six series of additions and corrections.

RICCI, SEYMOUR DE (1881–1942), and WILLIAM JEROME WILSON
1935–40 Census of medieval and renaissance MSS in the United States and Canada. 3 vols. Vols. 1, 2, xxiii + 2343 p., 1935–37; vol. 3, indexes, vii + 222 p., 1940. Wilson, New York. (Isis 33, 719–20.)

RICKARD, THOMAS ARTHUR (1864——)
1932 Man and metals. A history of mining in relation to the development of civilization. 2 vols., xiii + 1068 p., ill. Whittlesey House, New York. (Isis 21, 334–36.)

RICKMERS, MRS. W. R.
1899 See DUFF.

ROBERTSON, JOHN DRUMMOND (1857——)
1931 Evolution of clockwork. With a special section on the clocks of Japan and a comprehensive bibliography of horology. xvi + 358 p., 101 ill. Cassell, London. (Isis 27, 179.)

RÖHRICHT, REINHOLD (1842–1905)
1890 Bibliotheca geographica Palaestinae. Chronologisches Verzeichniss der auf die Geographie des heiligen Landes bezüglichen Literatur von 333 bis 1878 und Versuch einer Cartographie. xx + 744 p. Reuther, Berlin.

ROSE, HORACE ARTHUR (1867——)
1927 See BROWN.

ROSS, SIR EDWARD DENISON (1871–1940)
1910 Alphabetical list of the titles of works in the Chinese Buddhist Tripiṭaka, being an index to Nanjiō's catalogue and to the 1905 Kyōto reprint of the Buddhist canon. xcvii p. Archaeological Department of India, Calcutta.
No Chinese type.

ROVIRA I VIRGILI, ANTONI (1882——)
1922–34 Història nacional de Catalunya. 7 vols. Edicions Pàtria, Barcelona.
1928 Vol. 5.
1931 Vol. 6.

RUBIÓ I LLUCH, ANTONI (1855–1937)
1908–21 Documents per l'històrìa de la cultura catalana mig-eval. 2 vols. Institut d'estudis catalans, Barcelona.
Dealing with the period 1275 to 1406.

SABBADINI, REMIGIO (1850——)
1905–14 Le scoperte dei codici latini e greci ne' secoli XIV e XV. 2 vols. Sansoni, Firenze.

SAINTYVES, P. (= EMILE NOURRY)
1930 En marge de la Légende dorée. Songes, miracles et survivances. Essai sur la formation de quelques thèmes hagiographiques. viii + 596 p. E. Nourry, Paris.

ṢĀLIḤ ZEKĪ
1911 See ZAKĪ.

SANDYS, SIR JOHN EDWIN (1844–1922)
1903–8 History of classical scholarship. 3 vols. University Press, Cambridge.
1903 Vol. 1, From the VIth century B.C. to the end of the Middle Ages. (I used 3d ed., 1921.)
1908 Vol. 2, From the Revival of learning to the end of the eighteenth century.
1908 Vol. 3, The eighteenth century in Germany and the nineteenth century in Europe and the United States.

SAPEGNO, NATALINO (1901——)
1934 Il Trecento. vii + 642 p. Vallardi, Milano.

SARKIS, JOSEPH ELIAN (= YŪSUF IBN ILYĀN IBN MŪSĀ SARKĪS AL-DIMASHQĪ)
1928–30 Dictionnaire encyclopédique de bibliographie arabe. Large quarto, 6 p., 2024 col., 170 p. Librairie Sarkis, Le Caire.
In Arabic exclusively.

SARTON, GEORGE (1884——)
1913—— See ISIS.
1927–31 Introduction to the history of science. 2 vols. in 3. Vol. 1, From Homer to Omar Khayyam, xi + 839 p., 1927; vol. 2 (in 2 parts), From Rabbi ben Ezra to Roger Bacon, xxxv + 1251 p., 1931. Carnegie Institution of Washington Publication 376. Williams & Wilkins, Baltimore.
Abbr. Introd.
1934–35 Simon Stevin of Bruges. The first explanation of decimal fractions and measures (1585). Together with a history of the decimal idea and a facsimile of Stevin's Disme. (Isis 21, 241–303, 1934; 23, 153–244, 1935, 52 fig., 30 p. facs.)
1936—— See OSIRIS.
1938 The scientific literature transmitted through the incunabula. (Osiris 5, 41–245, 60 facs., Bruges.)
Study based on Klebs (1938).

SAVAGE, ERNEST ALBERT (1877——)
1911 Old English libraries; the making, collection and use of books during the Middle Ages. (The antiquary's books.) xv + 298 p., 35 pl. Methuen, London.

SAVIGNY, FRIEDRICH KARL VON (1779–1861)
1839 Histoire du droit romain au Moyen âge, traduite de l'allemand et précédée d'une notice sur la vie et les écrits de l'auteur par Charles Guenoux. 4 vols. Hingray, Paris.
First German edition, 6 vols., Heidelberg 1815–31; second, 7 vols., Heidelberg 1834–51. English translation, Edinburgh 1929 (vol. 1 only; not continued). Italian translation, 3 vols., Torino 1854–57.

SAXL, FRITZ (1890——)
1915–27 Verzeichnis astrologischer und mythologischer illustrierter Handschriften des lateinischen Mittelalters. (Sitzungsberichte der Heidelberger Akademie der Wissenschaften, phil. Kl. 1915, no. 6, 1925–26, no. 2.) C. Winter, Heidelberg.
1915 Vol. 1, In römischen Bibliotheken. 143 p., 21 pl., 18 ill. (Isis 5, 277.)
1927 Vol. 2, Die Handschriften der National-Bibliothek in Wien. 254 p., 17 pl. (Isis 11, 497.)

SCHELENZ, HERMANN (1848–1922)
1904 Geschichte der Pharmazie. xii + 935 p. Julius Springer, Berlin.

SCHMALZL, PETER (1889——)
1929 Zur Geschichte des Quadranten bei den Arabern. 142 p. Salesianische Offizin, München. (Isis 15, 462.)

SCHROETER, JENS FREDRIK (1857——)
1923 Spezieller Kanon der zentralen Sonnen- und Mondfinsternisse, welche innerhalb des Zeitraums von 600 bis 1800 n. Chr. in Europa sichtbar waren. xxiv + 305 p., 300 maps. Dybwad, Kristiania. (Isis 6, 208.)

SCIENTIFIC JAPAN
1926 Scientific Japan past and present. Prepared in connection with the Third Pan-Pacific Science Congress. Preface by Joji Sakurai. 14 chapters by various authors. Maruzen, Tokyo. (Isis 10, 83–88.)

SHAIKHŪ
1924 See CHEIKHO.

SINGER, CHARLES (1876——)
1924 See SUDHOFF.

(Continued on page 1904)

1925 The Fasciculo di medicina, Venice 1493. With an introduction . . . and atlas. Small folio, 2 vols. R. Lier, Florence. (Isis 8, 350.)
1926 The evolution of anatomy. A short history of anatomical and physiological discovery to Harvey. xii + 209 p., 22 pl., 117 fig. Knopf, New York. (Isis 10, 521–24.)
1927 The herbal in antiquity. (Journal of Hellenic studies 47, 1–52, 10 pl., 46 fig.) (Isis 10, 519–21.)

SINGER, DOROTHEA WALEY (1882——)
1928–31 Catalogue of Latin and vernacular alchemical manuscripts in Great Britain and Ireland dating from before the sixteenth century. (Union académique internationale.) 3 vols., xxvi + 1180 p. Lamertin, Brussels.
1928 Vol. 1 (Isis 12, 168–69).
1930 Vol. 2 (Isis 15, 299).
1931 Vol. 3 (Isis 18, 398).

SINGER, ISIDORE (1859—c. 1939)
1901–6 See JEWISH ENCYCLOPEDIA.

SMITH, DAVID EUGENE (1860–1944)
1908 Rara arithmetica. A catalogue of the arithmetics printed before MDCI with a description of those in the library of George Arthur Plimpton of New York [now in Columbia University]. xvi + 507 p. Ginn, Boston.
1939 Addenda. x + 52 p. Ginn, Boston. (Isis 32.)

SMITH, DAVID EUGENE, and L. C. KARPINSKI
1911 The Hindu-Arabic numerals. vi + 160 p. Ginn, Boston.

SMITH, DAVID EUGENE, and YOSHIO MIKAMI
1914 A history of Japanese mathematics. viii + 288 p. Open Court, Chicago. (Isis 2, 410–13.)

SMITH, GEORGE (1824–1901)
1885–1900 See DICTIONARY OF NATIONAL BIOGRAPHY.

SMITH, VINCENT ARTHUR (1848–1920)
1923 Oxford history of India. From the earliest times to 1911. 2d ed., revised to 1921. xxiv + 814 p. Clarendon Press, Oxford.

SOMAL, PLACIDO SUKIAS (= SOMALIAN) (1776–1848)
1825 Quadro delle opere di vari autori tradotte in Armeno. 46 p. Tipografia armenia di S. Lazzaro, Venezia.
1829 Quadro della storia letteraria di Armenia. xx + 241 p. Tipografia armenia di S. Lazzaro, Venezia.

SOOTHILL, WILLIAM EDWARD (1861–1935), and LEWIS HODOUS
1937 Dictionary of Chinese Buddhist terms, with Sanskrit and English equivalents and a Sanskrit-Pali index. Quarto, xx + 510 p. Kegan Paul, London.

STEINSCHNEIDER, MORITZ (1816–1907)
1860 Catalogus librorum hebraeorum in Bibliotheca bodleiana. cxxxii + 3104 col., LL p. Friedlaender, Berlin.
1877 Polemische und apologetische Literatur in arabischer Sprache zwischen Muslimen, Christen und Juden. (Abhandlungen für die Kunde des Morgenlandes, vol. 6, no. 3.) x + 456 p. Brockhaus, Leipzig.
1893a Die hebraeischen Uebersetzungen des Mittelalters und die Juden als Dolmetscher. Ein Beitrag zur Literaturgeschichte des Mittelalters meist nach handschriftlichen Quellen. xxxiv + 1077 p. Bibliographisches Bureau, Berlin.
1893b See RENAN.
1902 Die arabische Literatur der Juden. liv + 348 + 32 p. Kauffmann, Frankfurt a.M.
1904–5 Die europäischen Übersetzungen aus dem Arabischen bis Mitte des 17. Jahrhunderts (Sitzungsberichte der Kais. Akademie der Wissenschaften in Wien, phil. Kl., vol. 149, no. 4, 84 p.; vol. 150, no. 1, 108 p.)

STILLMAN, JOHN MAXSON (1852–1923)
1924 The story of early chemistry. xiii + 566 p. Appleton, New York. (Isis 7, 295; 34, 142–46.)

STILLWELL, MARGARET BINGHAM (1887——)
1940 Incunabula in American libraries. A second census of the fifteenth century books owned in the United States, Mexico and Canada. xlv + 619 p. Bibliographical Society of America, New York. (Isis 33, 96.)

STOKVIS, A. M. H. J.
1888–93 Manuel d'histoire, de généalogie et de chronologie de tous les états du globe. 3 vols. Brill, Leiden.
1888 Vol. 1, Asie, Afrique, Amérique, Polynésie.
1889 Vol. 2, Europe.
1893 Vol. 3, Europe.

STOREY, CHARLES AMBROSE (1888——)
1927—— Persian literature. A biobibliographical survey. Luzac, London.
1927 Sec. 1, Qur'ānic literature.
1935, 1936, 1939 Sec. 2, History.

STREIT, ROBERT (O.M.I.) (1875——)
1928 Bibliotheca missionum. Vierter Band, Asiatische Missionsliteratur, 1245–1599. (Veröffentlichungen des internationalen Instituts für missionswissenschaftliche Forschung.) 24 + 626 p. Missionsdruckerei, Aachen.

SUDHOFF, KARL (1853–1938)
1908—— See ARCHIV FÜR GESCHICHTE DER MEDIZIN.
1908a Deutsche medizinische Inkunabeln. (Studien zur Geschichte der Medizin, nos. 2/3.) xxiv + 278 p., 40 fig. J. A. Barth, Leipzig.
1908b Beitrag zur Geschichte der Anatomie im Mittelalter, speziell der anatomischen Graphik nach Handschriften des 9. bis 15. Jahrh. (Studien zur Geschichte der Medizin, no. 4.) 94 p., 3 fig., 24 pl. J. A. Barth, Leipzig.
1914–18 Beiträge zur Geschichte der Chirurgie im Mittelalter. Graphische und textliche Untersuchungen in mittelalterlichen Handschriften. (Studien zur Geschichte der Medizin, nos. 10–12.) 956 p., ill., 95 pl. J. A. Barth, Leipzig.
1924 The Fasciculus medicinae of Johannes de Ketham. Facsimile of the first (Venetian) edition of 1491 with introduction. Translated and adapted by Charles Singer. Large folio, 60 p., 13 pl. R. Lier, Milano. (Isis 6, 547–49.)
1926 See KLEBS.
1928 See MEYER-STEINEG.

SUTER, HEINRICH (1848–1922)
1900 Die Mathematiker und Astronomen der Araber und ihre Werke. (Abhandlungen zur Geschichte der mathematischen Wissenschaften, Heft 10.) x + 278 p. Teubner, Leipzig.
1902 Nachträge und Berichtigungen. (Abhandlungen zur Geschichte der mathematischen Wissenschaften, Heft 14, p. 155–85.) Teubner, Leipzig. (Isis 5, 409–17; 18, 166–83.)

SUZUKI DAISETZ TEITARO (1870——)
1927–34 Essays in Zen Buddhism. Luzac, London.
1927 First series, x + 423 p., 10 pl.
1933 Second series, xii + 326 p., ill., 25 pl.
1934 Third series, xiv + 392 p., 33 pl.

SYMONDS, JOHN ADDINGTON (1807–71)
1875–86 Renaissance in Italy. 7 vols. John Murray, London.
1875 Vol. 1, Age of the despots. 1881 Vols. 4, 5, Literature.
1877 Vol. 2, Revival of learning. 1886 Vols. 6, 7, Catholic reaction.
1877 Vol. 3, Fine arts.
Stereotyped text 1897–98 was used.

TAFRALI, ORESTE (1876–1937)
1912 Thessalonique au XIVe siècle. Thèse, Paris. Leroux, Paris. (Byzantion 13, 761–63, 1938.)

TAKAKUSU JYUN (1869——)
1929——, 1931 See HŌBŌGIRIN.

TANNERY, MARIE (1862–1945)
1912–43 See TANNERY, PAUL. (Osiris 4, 706–9, 1938.)

TANNERY, PAUL (1843–1904)
1912–43 Mémoires scientifiques. Edited for Mme. (Marie) Tannery by J. L. Heiberg, H. G. Zeuthen, Gino Loria, Joseph Pérès, Marie Tannery, A. Diès, Pierre Louis. Quarto, 16 vols., all published by Edouard Privat, Toulouse, and Gauthier-Villars, Paris. (Osiris 4, 633–89, 1938.)
1912 Vol. 1 (Isis 1, 145).
1912 Vol. 2 (Isis 1, 759).
1915 Vol. 3 (Isis 4, 338–41).
1920 Vol. 4 (Isis 4, 342–45).
1922 Vol. 5 (Isis 6, 431–35).
1926 Vol. 6 (Isis 9, 472–76).
1925 Vol. 7 (Isis 9, 127–30).
1927 Vol. 8 (Isis 10, 92–94).
1929 Vol. 9 (Isis 14, 426–30).
1930 Vol. 10 (Isis 16, 155–57).
1931 Vol. 11 (Isis 19, 515–16).
1933 Vol. 12 (Isis 24, 162–63).
1934 Vol. 13 (Isis 24, 162–63).
1937 Vol. 14 (Isis 29, 157–58).
1939 Vol. 15 (Isis 32).
1943 Vol. 16 (Isis 37).
Vol. 17, including biography, addenda, varia, and indexes, edited by Pierre Louis, was ready for publication about the end of 1946.

TASE SUKESHIGE
1938 Shumi no nihon kagaku shi (Popular history of Japanese science). In Japanese. Keibunsha, Tōkyō.

THOMPSON, DANIEL VARNEY (1902——)
1936 The materials of medieval painting. 240 p. Allen & Unwin, London. (Isis 27, 340.)

THOMPSON, JAMES WESTFALL (1869–1941)
1939 The medieval library. viii + 682 p. University of Chicago Press, Chicago. (Isis 32, 175–77.)

THORNDIKE, LYNN (1882——)
1923–41 History of magic and experimental science. 6 vols. Columbia University Press, New York.
1923 Vols. 1, 2, First thirteen centuries of our era (Isis 6, 74–89).
Originally published by Macmillan and reprinted by them with corrections in 1929, later taken over by Columbia University.
1934 Vols. 3, 4, Fourteenth and fifteenth centuries (Isis 23, 471–75).
1941 Vols. 5, 6, The sixteenth century (Isis 33, 691–712).
1944 University records and life in the Middle Ages. (Records of civilization, no. 38.) xvii + 476 p., 1 map. Columbia University Press, New York. (Isis 36.)
This book was not available to me until May 1945, when half of this work was already proofread, hence I could not use it as fully as I should have wished. I was able to insert a few references to it in the part dealing with the second half of the fourteenth century.

THORNDIKE, LYNN, and PEARL KIBRE
1937 Catalogue of incipits of mediaeval scientific writings in Latin. Quarto, xvi p. + 926 col. Mediaeval Academy of America, Cambridge. Supplement in Speculum (17, 342–46, 1942). (Isis 29, 140–41.)

TOBAR, JÉRÔME
1913 See HOANG.

TOKIWA DAIJŌ, OGIWARA UNRAI, and MINŌ KŌJUN
1930 Japanese alphabetical index of Nanjiō's Catalogue of the Buddhist Tripiṭaka with supplements and corrections. ix + 142 p. Nanjiō-hakushi kinen kankōkwai, Tōkyō.
Includes a beautiful portrait of Bunyiū Nanjiō.

TORRES AMAT, FELIX (1772–1847)
1836 Memorias para ayudar a formar un diccionario critico de los escritores catalanes y dar alguna idea de la antigua y moderna literatura de Cataluña. xliv + 719 p. Verdaguer, Barcelona.

TRINDEX
1936 See NASH.

TROLLOPE, MARK NAPIER (1862–1930)
1932 Corean books and their authors. (Transactions of the Korea branch of the Royal Asiatic Society 21, 1–104, ill., Seoul.)
Summary of lectures given by bishop Trollope before that society in 1929–30 and edited posthumously by Charles Hunt, of the English Church Mission in Seoul. The bishop had collected some 10,000 Korean books, which now are preserved in the Bishop Trollope Memorial Library in Seoul. Necrology by H. H. Underwood (same series, vol. 20, 7 p., 1931).

TROPFKE, JOHANNES (1866–1939)
Geschichte der Elementar-Mathematik in systematischer Darstellung mit besonderer Berücksichtigung der Fachwörter.
1930 Vol. 1^3, Rechnen.
1933 Vol. 2^3, Allgemeine Arithmetik.
1937 Vol. 3^3, Proportionen, Gleichungen.
1923 Vol. 4^2, Ebene Geometrie.
1923 Vol. 5^2, Ebene Trigonometrie, Sphärik und sphärische Trigonometrie.
1924 Vol. 6^2, Analysis. Analytische Geometrie.
1924 Vol. 7^2, Stereometrie. Verzeichnisse.
First edition, 2 volumes, Veit, Leipzig 1902–3. Second edition, 7 volumes, Vereinigung wissenschaftlicher Verleger, Berlin 1921–24 (Isis 5, 182–86, 553; 6, 229; 7, 314). Third edition of volumes 1 to 3, W. De Gruyter, Berlin 1930–37 (Isis 21, 451; 29, 167–69).
I cite the number of the volume with an exponent indicating the edition.

ṬŪQĀN, QADRĪ ḤĀFIẒ
1941 Turāth al-'arab al-'ilmī fīl-riyāḍiyyāt wal-falak (The scientific heritage of the Arabs in mathematics and astronomy). In Arabic. 268 p. Al-Muqtaṭaf wal-Muqaṭṭam, Cairo. (Isis 36, 140–42.)

UEBERWEG, FRIEDRICH (1826–71)
1915 Grundriss der Geschichte der Philosophie der patristischen und scholastischen Zeit. Zehnte Aufl. hrsg. von Matthias Baumgartner. xvii + 658 + 266 p. Mittler, Berlin.
1928 11th ed. Mittler, Berlin.

URDANG, GEORGE (1882——)
1940 See KREMERS.

USHER, ABBOTT PAYSON (1883——)
1929 History of mechanical inventions. xi + 401 p. McGraw-Hill, New York. (Isis 24, 177–80.)

VACANT, A.
1903—— See DICTIONNAIRE DE THÉOLOGIE CATHOLIQUE.

VAN DEN WYNGAERT, ANASTASIUS (1884——)
1929 Sinica franciscana. Vol. 1, Itinera et relationes fratrum minorum saeculi XIII et XIV. cxviii + 637 p., map. Quaracchi, Ad claras aquas.

VANDERKINDERE, LÉON (1842–1906)
1879 Le siècle des Artevelde. Etudes sur la civilisation morale et politique de la Flandre et du Brabant. 445 p. Lebègue, Bruxelles.

VAN MILLINGEN, ALEXANDER (1840–1915)
1899 Byzantine Constantinople. The walls of the city and adjoining historical sites. xi + 361 p., ill. Murray, London.
1912 Byzantine churches in Constantinople. Their history and architecture. xxix + 352 p., 116 fig., xcii pl. Macmillan, London.

VASILIEV, ALEKSANDR ALEKSANDROVICH (1867——)
1932 Histoire de l'empire byzantin. Traduit du russe. 2 vols. A. Picard, Paris.

VERA, FRANCISCO (1888——)
1933–34 La cultura española medieval. Datos bio-bibliográficos para su historia. 2 vols. Gongora, Madrid. (Isis 20, 579; 23, 561.)

VIERORDT, HERMANN (1853——)
1929–35 See BIOGRAPHISCHES LEXIKON.

VINOGRADOFF, SIR PAUL (1854–1925)
1909 Roman law in mediaeval Europe. Small size, III + 136 p. Harper, London.

VISSIÈRE, ARNOLD (1858–1930)
1911 See OLLONE.

WALSH, JAMES JOSEPH (1865——)
1913 The popes and science. The history of the papal relations to science during the Middle Ages and down to our own time. Knights of Columbus edition. xii + 431 p. Fordham University, New York.
First printed 1908.

WATANABE KAIKIOKU
1931 See HŌBŌGIRIN.

WEDEL, THEODORE OTTO (1892——)
1920 The mediaeval attitude toward astrology, particularly in England. (Yale studies in English, no. 60.) viii + 160 p. Yale University Press, New Haven, Conn. (Isis 4, 186.)

WEEKS, MARY ELVIRA (1892——)
1933 The discovery of the elements. (Reprinted from the Journal of chemical education.) iii + 363 p., ill. Mack Printing Co., Easton, Penna. (Isis 21, 455.)
Fifth edition, enlarged and revised, 1945. Chinese translation, Shanghai 1940. (Isis 35, 264.)

WEINDLER, FRITZ
1908 Geschichte der gynäkologisch-anatomischen Abbildung. xvi + 186 p., 122 ill. Zahn und Jaensch, Dresden.

WELLS, JOHN EDWIN (1875–1943)
1926 A manual of the writings in Middle English, 1050–1400. (Connecticut Academy of Arts and Sciences.) 1763 p. Yale University Press, New Haven, Conn.
First published 1916. Fourth printing 1926, sixth printing 1937. Supplements 1, 1919; 2, 1923; 3, 1926; 4, 1929; 5, 1932; 6, 1935; 7, 1938; 8, 1941.
Pagination continuous throughout the volumes, hence indication of the page suffices.

WENSINCK, ARENT JAN (1882–1939)
1908–38 See ENCYCLOPAEDIA OF ISLAM.

WERNER, EDWARD CHALMERS (1864——)
1926 See BALL.

WERNER, KARL (1821–88)
1881–87 Die Scholastik des späteren Mittelalters. 4 vols. Braumüller, Wien.
1881 Vol. 1, Johannes Duns Scotus.
1883 Vol. 2, Die nachscotistische Scholastik.
1883 Vol. 3, Der Augustinismus.
1887 Vol. 4, Der Endausgang.

WERNICH, AGATHON (1843–96)
1884–88 See BIOGRAPHISCHES LEXIKON.

WHITE, ANDREW DICKSON (1832–1918)
1896 History of the warfare of science with theology in Christendom. 2 vols. Appleton, New York.
Often reprinted, and translated into French (1899).

WHITE, LYNN, JR. (1907——)
1940 Technology and invention in the Middle Ages. (Speculum 15, 141–59.)

WICKERSHEIMER, ERNEST (1880——)
1936 Dictionnaire biographique des médecins en France au Moyen âge. viii + 869 p. Paris. (Isis 26, 187–89.)

Abundant biographical and bibliographical data concerning a large number of physicians, apothecaries, surgeons, barbers, midwives, quacks, abortionists, etc. The great majority of these notes do not concern the historian of science at all, but only the student of the medical profession.

WIEGER, LÉON (S.J.) (1856–1933)
1911–13 Taoïsme. 2 vols. Imprimerie de Hien-hien (Ho-kien-fou), Chine.
1911 Vol. 1, Le canon taoïste. Les index officiels et privés. 338 p.
1913 Vol. 2, Les Pères du système taoïste. Lao Tzŭ [VI B.C.], Lieh Tzŭ [IV-2 B.C.], Chuang Tzŭ [III-1 B.C.]. 521 p.
Text and French translation.
1920 La Chine à travers les ages. Hommes et choses. 548 p. Imprimerie de Sien hsien (= Hsien hsien).
References to this book are given to enable the reader to find easily the French transcription of a Chinese name. The same purpose can be attained by means of Karlgren (1917) or Nash (1936).

WILLIAMS, ARTHUR LUKYN (1853——)
1935 Adversus Judaeos. A bird's-eye view of Christian apologiae until the Renaissance. xvii + 428 p., front. Cambridge University Press, Cambridge.

WILSON, WILLIAM JEROME (1884——)
1935–40 See RICCI.
1939 Catalogue of Latin and vernacular alchemical MSS in the United States and Canada. (Osiris 6, 854 p.) (Isis 32.)

WINTERNITZ, MORIZ (1863–1937)
1907–22 Geschichte der indischen Litteratur. 3 vols. Amelang, Leipzig.
1907 Vol. 1, Einleitung. Der Veda. Die volkstümlichen Epen und die Purāṇas. Zweite Ausgabe. xiv + 505 p.
1920 Vol. 2, Die buddhistische Litteratur und die heiligen Texte der Jainas. x + 406 p.
1922 Vol. 3, Die Kunstdichtung. Die wissenschaftliche Litteratur. Neuindische Litteratur. Nachträge zu allen drei Bänden. xii + 698 p.
1927–33 A history of Indian literature. English translation by Mrs. Shridar Venkatesh Ketkar and her sister, Helen Kohn, revised by the author. University of Calcutta.
1927 Vol. 1, Introduction. Veda, national epics, purāṇas and tantras. xix + 634 p.
1933 Vol. 2, Buddhist and Jaina literature. xx + 673 p.

WISSOWA, GEORG (1859–1931)
1894—— See PAULY-WISSOWA.

WONG K. CHIMIN and WU LIEN-TEH
1932 History of Chinese medicine. Being a chronicle of medical happenings in China from ancient times to the present period. XVIII + 706 p., 93 ill., map. Tientsin Press, Tientsin. (Isis 20, 480–82.)
1936 2d ed. xxviii + 906 p. National Quarantine Service, Shanghai. (Isis 27, 341–42.)
Though I have always consulted Wong and Wu, I often disagreed with them. For Wong, see Chinese index, Wang Chi-min.

WRIGHT, JOHN KIRTLAND (1891——)
1925 Geographical lore of the time of the Crusades. xxi + 563 p. American Geographical Society, New York. (Isis 7, 495–98.)

WRIGHT, WILLIAM (1830–89)
1894 Short history of Syriac literature. (Corrected reprint of article in Encyclopaedia britannica, vol. 22, 1887.) 296 p. Adam and Black, London.

WU LIEN-TEH (1879——)
1932, 1936 See WONG K. CHIMIN.
See Chinese index, Wu Lien-tê.

WÜSTENFELD, FERDINAND (1808–99)
1840 Geschichte der arabischen Aerzte und Naturforscher. xvi + 167 + 16 p. Vandenhoeck und Ruprecht, Göttingen.
1881–82 Die Geschichtschreiber der Araber und ihre Werke. (Abhandlungen der Kgl. Gesellschaft der Wissenschaften zu Göttingen, vols. 28, 29.) 2 parts. Part 1, nos. 1–408, VIII + 170 p., 1881; part 2, nos. 409–590, 139 p., 1882.

WYLIE, ALEXANDER (1815–87)
1867 Notes on Chinese literature: with introductory remarks on the progressive advancement of the art; and a list of translations from the Chinese into various European languages. viii + xxviii + 260 p. American Mission Press, Shanghai.
Reprinted 1902, again 1922. xxx + 307 p. Presbyterian Mission Press, Shanghai. Photographic reprint, Peking 1939.
This book is not yet superseded; it is still valuable in spite of many imperfections. The transcription of Chinese words used is annoying, but at least one is given the Chinese characters. The reprints of 1902, 1922, and 1939 are apparently identical with the original edition, but unfortunately the pagination is different. I have used the original edition, and later the reprints. Wylie's fine library was the nucleus of the Royal Asiatic Society Library in Shanghai (Couling, p. 610, 1917).

YIN I CHU
1939 See YOUN.

YOUN, EUL SOU (ABBÉ LAURENT YOUN)
1939 Le Confucianisme en Corée. x + 198 p. Geuthner, Paris.
Called misleadingly second edition, the first edition being the printing of the same text in the form of a Paris thesis.

YOUNG, JAMES (1811–83)
1906 See FERGUSON.

YULE, SIR HENRY (1820–89)
1866 Cathay and the way thither, being a collection of medieval notices of China. 2 vols. Hakluyt Society, London.
1913–16 New edition revised throughout by Henri Cordier. 4 vols., ill. Hakluyt Society, London.
1915 Vol. 1, Preliminary essay on the intercourse between China and the western nations previous to the discovery of the Cape route. xxiv + 318 p.
1913 Vol. 2, Odoric of Pordenone. xiv + 367 p.
1914 Vol. 3, Missionary friars. Rashīduddīn. Pegolotti, Marignolli. xv + 269 p.
1916 Vol. 4, Ibn Batuta. The journey of Benedict Goës from Agra to Cathay (1602–7). Index. xii + 359 p.
1903 See MARCO POLO.
1920 See CORDIER.

YULE, HENRY, and A. C. BURNELL
1903 Hobson-Jobson. A glossary of colloquial Anglo-Indian words and phrases. New edition by William Crooke. xlviii + 1022 p. John Murray, London.
First edition 1886.

ZAKĪ, ṢĀLIḤ
1911 Athār-i-bāqiya (A history of Arabic mathematics). In Turkish. 2 vols., 512 p. Maṭba'a-i-'Āmira, Istanbul. (Isis 19, 506–15.)

ZAMBAUR, EDOUARD DE (1866——)
1927 Manuel de généalogie et de chronologie pour l'histoire de l'Islam. Quarto, 2 vols. Heinz Lafaire, Hanover.

ZEKĪ
1911 See ZAKĪ.

ZEN, SOPHIA HÊNG-CHÊ (= CH'ÊN) (EDITOR)
1931 Symposium on Chinese culture. 480 p. China Institute of Pacific Relations, Shanghai.

ZETZNER, LAZARUS
1659–61 Theatrum chemicum. 6 vols. Zetzner, Strassburg.
1659 Vols. 1–4.
1660 Vol. 5.
1661 Vol. 6.
First edition, in 4 volumes, Ursel 1602; reprinted Strassburg 1613 (4 vols.); fifth volume added in 1622. Then came the edition of 1659–61 (6 vols.). Contents in Ferguson (2, 436–39, 1906).

ZEUTHEN, H. G.
1912–43 See TANNERY, PAUL.

ZINNER, ERNST (1886——)
1925 Verzeichnis der astronomischen Handschriften des deutschen Kulturgebietes. Folio, 544 p., lithographed. Beck, München. (Isis 8, 801; 15, 193–95.)
1931 Die Geschichte der Sternkunde. xi + 673 p. Springer, Berlin. (Isis 16, 161–67.)

ABBREVIATIONS

ADB, Allgemeine deutsche Biographie
AGM, Archiv für Geschichte der Medizin
BL, Biographisches Lexikon der hervorragenden Aerzte aller Zeiten und Völker
BM, Bibliotheca mathematica
CE, Catholic encyclopedia
DNB, Dictionary of national biography
DTC, Dictionnaire de théologie catholique
EI, Encyclopaedia of Islam
EJ, Encyclopaedia judaica
ERE, Encyclopaedia of religion and ethics
EUI, Enciclopedia universal ilustrada
GW, Gesamtkatalog der Wiegendrucke
HDA, Handwörterbuch des deutschen Aberglaubens
HG, Howgrave-Graham, Some clocks and jacks
HL, Histoire littéraire de la France
Introd., Sarton, Introduction to the history of science
JE, Jewish encyclopedia
Mitt., Mitteilungen zur Geschichte der Medizin
NBG, Nouvelle biographie générale
OED, Oxford English dictionary
PG, Patrologia graeca
PL, Patrologia latina
PW, Pauly-Wissowa
RGA, Reallexikon der germanischen Altertumskunde
STC, Pollard, Short-title catalogue

GENERAL INDEX

INTRODUCTORY REMARKS

Scholars using this book are advised to read the following remarks, which will help them to get more benefit out of it.

1. *Index to volumes 1 and 2 and to volume 3.* This index is relatively complete so far as volume 3 is concerned, but is very rudimentary concerning volumes 1 and 2. For these two volumes it simply lists the main personalities dealt with, indicating for each his time, the page of the main article (in italic type), and the pages of the two indexes (of volumes 1 and 2) where the other references may be found. For example, Archimedes (III-2 B.C.), v. 1, *169*, 791; v. 2, 1149; v. 3, etc. (When the index pages contain but one or two references in addition to the main one, these references are given instead of the index page. When references are to volume 3 only, "v. 3" is omitted.)

This index is thus a limited index to the three volumes, and it will often suffice to consult it, but it will always be worth while also to consult the indexes to volumes 1 and 2.

It illustrates a statement often made by me, that no part of the past can be isolated from the preceding ones. Though this volume is devoted to mediaeval science, it contains very many references to ancient science; though it deals primarily with men of science and learning of a single century, men of earlier ages pop in constantly. For all practical purposes, Aristotle, Hippocrates, or Ptolemy was as alive in the fourteenth century as Occam, Chauliac, or Wallingford. Consequently an index to the thought of the fourteenth century must contain brief references to the men of earlier ages who helped to build that century and to animate it.

2. *Personal names.* The major difficulty in indexing mediaeval people lies in the multiplicity and instability of their names. The idea of surname or family name was very slow in developing and has not yet completely emerged in certain countries even now. My purpose has been to collect all the references concerning one person under one heading, with as many cross references to that heading as is desirable or possible. I hope to have succeeded in the great majority of cases; but I must have failed sometimes. To illustrate the slow acceptance of surnames it will suffice to cite the following facts. Surnames were legalized in France under Francis I (1539); French Jews were obliged to assume a family name by Napoleon (1808); such names became compulsory in Turkey only in 1934, when the dictator Mustafa Kemal pasha promulgated a law to that effect, he himself assuming the surname Atatürk (Father of the Turks); surnames are still unknown or unstabilized in many Muslim or Arabic countries.

The mediaeval practice, say in Christian lands, was to give a child a personal name, consecrated by the sacrament of baptism. As that name was insufficient to define him outside his family and close acquaintance, it was necessary to qualify it by adding his father's name or another patronymic (John the son of Peter, John of Peter, John Macdonald) or an indication of place (John of Chester) or a professional designation (John the Taylor) or a nickname (John the Lame). Modern surnames were derived more or less rapidly from those qualifications. The surname can be said to exist only when such a qualification has become stabilized; the stability cannot be completed without legal sanction.

The learned judge Sir Edward Coke (d. 1634) found it still necessary to explain the supreme value from the legal point of view of the baptismal name, "for that a man cannot have two names of baptism as he may have divers surnames."[1] The legal point of view has changed since the seventeenth century, but the church still insists, with good logic, that a man's baptismal name is his true name. It is possible that similar ideas obtain in the Jewish and Muslim world and wherever religious convictions have not yet been displaced by legal formalities. In the following sections we shall consider more particularly the Christian, Jewish, and Muslim names in this index.

3. *Christian names.* A Christian living before the sixteenth century is generally listed under his "given" name, qualified in one way or another, most frequently by an indication of place. If he is one of the main personalities dealt with in this book, his identification is completed by the indication of time. For example, Thomas Bradwardine (XIV-1), Roger of Salerno (XII-2), Siger of Courtrai (XIV-1).

As far as it was feasible, the almost endless forms of each Christian saint's name have been reduced to one. Thus, all the Johns—whether they were called John, or Joannes, or Giovanni, or Jan—are put together. That is simply a matter of convenience; I do not suggest that an Italian should be called John instead of Giovanni, but as the forms of each name are innumerable (there are many variants in each language),[2] it is simpler for the reader to have to look only under one heading or under a few. If more than one form has been used in my index, cross references will lead the reader from one to the other. Though convenience was my main concern, the unification of, say, all the Johns under one form of that name is justified by the fact that all these Johns are really named after one person, St. John the Baptist. (Their patron may be another St. John, but all the St. Johns were originally named after John the Baptist.)

Christian names were often translated by the people bearing them. For instance, an Italian would call himself Joannes or Johannes in Latin, Giovanni in Italian, Jean in French. Hence, he himself recognized that the particular form of his name was not essential, but its meaning. It is better therefore never to abbreviate mediaeval (or modern) Christian names, for the initial letters may vary from language to language (e.g., Hieronymus, Geronimo, Jerome; three different initials would hide the identity of the three names).

In exceptional cases, the main heading chosen by me is not the "given" name, because another name is far better known, for example, Boccaccio, Petrarca, Occam; it would have been pedantic to oblige the reader to refer to John, Francis, or William. In those cases, the procedure is simply reversed; instead of referring from Boccaccio to John, we refer from John to Boccaccio.

In my selection of the best form (for my purpose) of each "given" name I have been helped by the excellent little book of Miss Elizabeth Gidley Withycombe: The Oxford dictionary of English Christian names (172 p., Oxford 1945).

4. *Jewish names.* Jewish names are generally indexed under the given name followed by the father's given name, as Abraham ben Samuel; an indication of locality or another qualification is usually added. The main difficulty for Jewish names

[1] As quoted by Miss Withycombe in her book mentioned below.

[2] In mediaeval times the variants were multiplied endlessly by accidental misspellings or by orthographic nonchalance, the same person spelling his own name in various ways in the same book or even in the same document. Among the European nations the Portuguese were perhaps the most inconsistent in this respect. See Aubrey F. G. Bell: Portuguese literature (p. 18, Oxford 1922).

(as well as for Muslim names) stems from the fact that the immediate patronymic tended to be displaced by one more illustrious but more distant. Those distant patronymics become almost like surnames, the only difference between them and real surnames (and it is an essential one) is that their use was never obligatory or systematized; it might be frequent, but it remained always arbitrary. Consider our old friend Rabbi ben Ezra. His given name was Abraham and his father's name not Ezra but Meïr, yet he is generally called Abraham ben Ezra. Every Jew (or Muslim) who had an illustrious ancestor was likely to include the latter's name in his own, or his friends would do so. Thus arose "family" names, such as Ibn Zuhr, Gershon, Crescas, Qalonymos, which are not family names in the legal meaning of today and cause much confusion. In order to minimize that confusion, I have tried to mention the father's name as well as the more distant patronymic.

5. *Muslim (Arabic) names.* Some of the reflections made in the preceding section apply equally well to this one. Our standard way of naming an Arabic (or Persian, or Turkish) writer is "Aḥmad ibn Muḥammad al-Bahāniqī (XIV-2)." There is considerably more variety in the Arabic names than in the Hebrew ones, and some illustrious Muslims are so well known under a name of a definite form that it would be pedantic to call them in any other way. Thus, the historian of science who understands at once, without ambiguity, the names Abū-l-Fidā', Ibn Khaldūn, Nāṣir al-dīn al-Ṭūsī, al-Battānī, would be much embarrassed to recognize these men under their "standard" names, which are, respectively, Ismā'īl ibn 'Alī al-Aiyūbī (XIV-1), 'Abd al-Raḥmān ibn Muḥammad al-Tūnisī (XIV-2), Muḥammad ibn Muḥammad al-Ṭūsī (XIII-2), Muḥammad ibn Jābir al-Ḥarrānī (IX-2).

As I always prefer to be inconsistent rather than pedantic, I have simply reversed my procedure in all these cases. The more popular name becomes the main heading, and the "standard" form appears in the index for the sake of cross reference to that heading.

Jews and Christians living in the Dār al-Islām and writing in Arabic have been generally dealt with like the Muslims. Their scientific writings are indistinguishable from the Muslim ones, except for the initial doxology and occasional quotations which do not affect their main substance. Such books are generally classified with the Muslim books rather than with the Jewish or Christian ones.[3]

The words ibn (ben) meaning son, and abū meaning father, are abbreviated b. and a. The article al (ha in Hebrew) is generally left out, except when it is grammatically impossible to do so (as in phrases like Kamāl al-dīn or Saif al-dawla).

6. *Perplexities of indexing.* The preceding sections have already made it clear that no rule of indexing could be observed rigorously without foolishness in a book as complex as this one. The author has introduced as many cross references as might be necessary, in his opinion, to satisfy the needs of scholars. It is difficult yet possible to satisfy those needs; on the other hand, it is impossible to satisfy the needs of the ignorant. For example, the Oriental names are written consistently according to definite and well known systems of transliteration. A person having read an Oriental name transliterated according to another system will look for it in vain in this index under that form. For example, he may have read about al-Ḥadschdschādsch in a learned German book, but in mine that word could be found only under the form Ḥajjāj. The phrase Kamāl al-dīn mentioned above would be transcribed by other scholars Kamāluddīn in order to represent more closely the good pronunciation; the same scholars would write 'Abdurraḥmān and Nāṣirud-

[3] That is done even in the Vatican library (Isis 36, 274).

dīniṭṭūsī for the names which I spell 'Abd al-Raḥmān and Nāṣir al-dīn al-Ṭūsī. None of these words could be found in my index. Remember that our transliterations (except of Hebrew, for which we let ourselves be guided by the King James Bible) aim to reproduce the foreign orthography, which is stable, rather than the orthophony, which may vary considerably according to time or place (Introd. 2, 100).

If scholars fail to find a heading which they expected to find, I beg of them to try other ways of interrogating the index. In some cases, the elaborate table of contents will be their surest guide.

7. *Modern names.* The classification of postmediaeval names is much easier than that of mediaeval names, yet there remain ambiguities. During the Renaissance it was often fashionable to translate not only one's given name but even one's surname into Latin and into Greek. Many Latin and Greek surnames existing to this day in Europe are the relics of that fashion. For a time at least, a man or his family might have two surnames, the original in his own vernacular, and the Latin or Greek translation. It is sometimes difficult to choose between the two. Here again, consistency is impossible. It was pedantic for Philip Schwarzerd to call himself Melanchthon, but it would be even more pedantic today to revive the old name. Other cases are not so clear.

Surnames connected with the given name by particles are very troublesome, because it is very difficult in many cases to determine the nature of the connection. Should we write Delavigne, de La Vigne, or de la Vigne? Is the first letter of the name d, l, or v? Usage varies not only within a single family, but also for a definite member of the family. The particle de, de la, von, etc. was often stressed in peaceful times for the sake of snobbishness, and glossed over or even suppressed during a revolutionary storm.[4] My method has varied, as it must, but I have tried to abide by the following compromise. If Delavigne, de La Vigne, and de la Vigne are classified under d, then they must come together as if there were only one word in the three cases (i.e., they cannot be separated from one another by other words). I hope that the reader will be patient enough to try the index in many ways. If he does not find de la Vigne under d, let him try l or v.[5]

In short, modern surnames, though stabilized, are not completely stabilized. In the seventeenth century it was not uncommon for a man to spell his own surname differently on different occasions; the same instability still exists in some European countries, such as Portugal.[6] Snobbishness and other fancies may cause a man to change the spelling of his family name from time to time. These variations tend to diminish, however, for legal and banking reasons. A man is expected to sign checks and other documents always in the same way.

8. *Topics.* Thus far, I have spoken only of proper names. Titles of books have been listed irregularly; there are too many of them to include them all, and their

[4] See my remarks about Lagrange's name in Lagrange's personality (Proceedings of the American Philosophical Society 88, 457–96, 1944, footnote on p. 457).

[5] There is no ambiguity when the particles were occasionally translated. E.g., Alexander von Humboldt signed Alexander de Humboldt when he wrote in Latin, French, or Spanish, hence it would be as unwise to classify him under "von" or "de" as it would be to classify John of London under "of."

[6] In a number of Petrus Nonius (vol. 6, fasc. 1–2, Lisboa 1943) dedicated to the memory of Leite de Vasconcellos, the name is spelled Vasconcellos by some authors and Vasconcelos by others. This is due to the vagaries of the Refôrma ortográfica, for which see A. R. Nykl in Hispanic review (15, 225–26, 1947).

number is artificially increased by variants. The variants of Latin titles are well known to bibliographers, for the incunabula editions of one treatise frequently appear under somewhat different titles.[7] The same ambiguities occur in Hebrew and Arabic. Mediaeval authors did not expect the titles of their books to be more stabilized than their own names.

As to other topics, I have tried to imagine the headings which the scholar would look for, but obviously I could not imagine them all. The table of contents should guide him for the larger divisions such as mathematics and astronomy; the index is meant to help him for smaller items or more specialized ones (say, mercury, equinoxes, bloodletting, urine). Some headings have been introduced in order to reveal items which might be overlooked, as was done for the last edition of Ducange (vol. 7, 547, 1850) in the "index rerum quas in glossario delitescere non autumaret lector."

9. *Index-judex.* In addition to its practical value, which is great and increases rapidly with the size of a book and its complexity, the index is also the best tool for judging a work and discovering rapidly its weaknesses. The index reveals repetitions, inconsistencies, and even contradictions which might have remained hidden without it. Critics may base their judgment on such discoveries, but in fairness to the author, they should remember that no man can be expected to remain invariably consistent during twenty years or more, or during the slow composition of many thousands of pages. They should remember that repetitions or contradictions which are so easy to discover by means of a good index could not have been discovered without it, even by the author himself.

The fault-finding value of an index is salutary and important. If there be errors in this book, the sooner they are revealed, the sooner will it be possible to correct them.

10. *Greek, Chinese, and Japanese indexes.* These three indexes are supplementary to the general index but do not replace it. They serve partly as glossaries. The Greek proper names occur also in the general index, but not so the Chinese and Japanese names, except in a very few cases where the Chinese characters corresponding to them remained unknown. The Latinized forms of Chinese names (such as Confucius) may be found in the general index, but in such cases more abundant references would probably be obtained in the Chinese index under the original name.

11. *How the index was compiled.* Headings to be marked on cards were underlined on the page proofs, and additional headings written in the margins. The cards of the general index were written by the author's secretary, Miss Frances Siegel; the Greek, Chinese, and Japanese cards, by himself. The cards of the general index were roughly classified by Miss Siegel, then more elaborately by the author, who added the cross references which occurred to him. If all the cards of the general index were piled in a single column, that column would be thirty feet high; their number may be estimated to be almost fifty thousand.

The general index was typed by Miss Siegel; the typescript and proofs were read by Professor A. R. Nykl, who suggested various corrections.

G. S.

[7] The difference may consist only in the permutation of some words or the addition of an adjective, but that is enough to separate variants widely in any alphabetical list.

INDEX

Aagesön, *see* Svend
Aaron of Alexandria (VII-1), v. 1, *479*, 462, 463
Aaron the Bookseller, 368
Aaron Cohen, 1858
Aaron b. Elijah the Qaraite (XIV-1), *617*, 56, 73, 101, 131, 368
Aaron b. Joseph the Qaraite (XIII-2), v. 2, *875*, 729, 805; v. 3, 101, 256, 368
Aaron Levi of Barcelona (XIII-2), v. 2, *884*, 731
Aaron b. Meshullam of Lunel (XIII-1), v. 2, *625*, 19, 506
abacus, 1484, 1585
abacus arithmetic (XI-2), v. 1, *756*, 787
Abaelard, *see* Peter
Abano, *see* Peter
Abano, springs, 1240, 1677
Abarbanel, *see* Isaac b. Judah; Samuel
Abarqūh, *see* Muḥammad
abba, title of honor, *see name following, e.g.* Arika; Mari
'Abbād, b., *see* Muḥammad b. Ibrāhīm
Abbagnano, Nicola, 556
Abbār, b., *see* Muḥammad b. 'Abdallāh
'Abbās b. 'Alī Rasūlī (XIV-2), *1637*, 1168, 1180
'Abbās Īrānshahrī, a., 149
'Abbas, *see* Judah b. Samuel
'Abbās Nabātī, a., *see* Aḥmad b. Muḥammad
'Abbās b. Sa'īd (IX-1), v. 1, *562*, 545
'Abbās, *see* Samū'īl b. Yaḥyā
'Abbās Sibtī, a. (XII-2), v. 2, *361*, 287; v. 3, 1118
Abbassi, *see* Jacob b. Moses
Abbeville, *see* Gerald
Abbo of Fleury (X-2), v. 1, *671*, 787; v. 3, 1533
Abbot, C. G., 1856
abbreviationes, 79
'Abbūd a. Rāshid, 491
'Abdallāh b. 'Abdallāh al-Tarjumān, 1341
'Abdallāh b. 'Abd al-'Azīz, *see* Bakrī
'Abdallāh b. 'Abd al-'Azīz Sīwāsī (XIV-1), *897*, 257
'Abdallāh b. 'Abd al-Raḥmān b. 'Aqīl, 1015
'Abdallāh b. 'Abd al-Raḥmān Dārimī, 1066
'Abdallāh b. Aḥmad, *see* b. Baiṭār
'Abdallāh b. Aḥmad Nasafī (XIII-2), v. 2, *1133*, 801; v. 3, 106, 321, 1454
'Abdallāh b. Aḥmad Tijānī (XIV-1), *806*, 202, 257, 296, 307
'Abdallāh b. 'Alī Kāshānī (XIV-1), *755*, 179, 210, 214, 1133
'Abdallāh b. Amājūr, *see* b. Amājūr
'Abdallāh b. As'ad Yāfi'ī (XIV-1), *619*, 102, 163, 1067, 1454, 1459
'Abdallāh b. 'Azūz Marrākushī, 1724
'Abdallāh b. Bay Tamir, 1249
'Abdallāh bey, shaykh, 1342
'Abdallāh b. Faḍlallāh Waṣṣāf of Shīrāz (XIV-1), *977*, 310, 969
'Abdallāh Fārisī Rundī, 1452
'Abdallāh b. Ibāḍ (VII-2), v. 1, *492*, 488, 490
'Abdallāh b. Khalīl Māridīnī (XIV-2), *1530*, 1120, 1129, 1528
'Abdallāh Lakhmī of Cordova, 1636
'Abdallāh b. Maḥmūd Buldajī, 1454
'Abdallāh al-Ma'mūn Suhrawardī, 1455
'Abdallāh b. Muḥammad Baṭalyūsī (Baṭalyawsī) (XII-1), v. 2, *182*, 117, 848; v. 3, 416, 591, 1096, 1376
'Abdallāh b. Muḥammad, *see* b. Faraḍī
'Abdallāh b. Muḥammad Harawī, 626, 627
'Abdallāh b. Muḥammad b. Juzayy (XIV-2), *1636*, 1167, 1185, 1635
'Abdallāh b. Muḥammad b. Khaddām, 707
'Abdallāh b. Muḥammad b. Rushd, 603
'Abdallāh b. Muḥammad Wafā'ī, 1526
'Abdallāh b. Muḥammad b. Yāsmīnī (XII-2), v. 2, *400*, 295; v. 3, 1528
'Abdallāh b. Muqaffa', *see* b. Muqaffa'
'Abdallāh b. Muslim, *see* b. Qutaiba
'Abdallāh b. Ṭaiyib (XI-1), v. 1, *730*, 810; v. 2, 561
'Abdallāh b. 'Umar, *see* Baiḍāwī
'Abdallāh b. a. Yāsir b. 'Amīd, Makīn (XIII-2), v. 2, *1122*, 796, 797; v. 3, 306, 363, 1260, 1780
'Abdallāh b. Yūsuf b. Hishām (XIV-1), *1010*, 373, 759
'Abd al-'Azīz b. 'Abd al-Qādir, 1571
'Abd al-'Azīz Huwārī (XIV-1), *694*, 132
'Abd al-'Azīz b. Jamā'a, 998
'Abd al-'Azīz b. Sarāyā Ḥillī (XIV-1), *749*, 136, 164
'Abd al-Azīz b. Tammām 'Irāqī, 760
'Abd al-'Azīz b. 'Uthmān, *see* Qabīsī
'Abd al-Bāsiṭ b. Khalīl, 203
'Abd al-Dā'yim b. 'Abd al-'Azīz (XIV-1), *616*, 101
'Abd al-Ghaffār b. 'Abd al-Karīm Qazwīnī, 963, 1011
'Abd al-Ḥakam, b. (IX-2), v. 1, *616*, 588, 590
'Abd al-Ḥaqq, 1477
'Abd al-Ḥaqq b. 'Abdallāh, 805
'Abd al-Ḥaqq 'Adnān, 1872
'Abd al-Ḥaqq b. Ibrāhīm b. Sab'īn (XIII-1), v. 2, *598*, 1225

'Abd al-Ḥaqq Islāmī (XIV-2), *1365*, 1065
'Abd al-Karīm b. Ibrāhīm Jīlī (XIV-2), *1459*, 1100
'Abd al-Karīm b. Muḥammad Sam'ānī (XII-2), v. 2, *444*, 1227
'Abd al-Laṭīf b. Yūsuf (XIII-1), v. 2, *599*, 1141; v. 3, 200, 227, 282, 1650
'Abd al-Malik b. Hishām (IX-1), v. 1, *579*, 809
'Abd al-Malik b. Muḥammad Shīrāzī (XII-2), v. 2, *400*
'Abd al-Malik b. Quraib, *see* Aṣma'ī
'Abd al-Malik b. Zuhr (XII-1), v. 2, *231*, 1248; v. 3, 62, 437, 850, 1640, 1675, 1678, 1694, 1719, 1775
'Abd al-Mu'min b. 'Abd al-Ḥaqq (XIV-1), *805*, 201
'Abd al-Mu'min b. Faqīr Ṣafī al-dīn (XIII-2), v. 2, *1034*, 1226; v. 3, 163, 373, 746, 749, 1129, 1461, 1571
'Abd al-Mu'min b. Khalaf Dimyāṭī (XIII-2), v. 2, *1072*, 60, 780; v. 3, 210, 239, 271, 1274
'Abd al-Qādir Afrāmī, 963
'Abd al-Qādir b. 'Alī b. Sha'bān (XIV-2), *1533*, 1121
'Abd al-Qādir b. Ghaibī (XIV-2), *1570*, 1129, 1473
'Abd al-Qādir Jīlī (XII-1), v. 2, *164*, 113; v. 3, 420, 1459, 1764
'Abd al-Qāhir b. 'Abdallāh Suhrawardī, 420
'Abd al-Qāhir b. Ṭāhir (XI-1), v. 1, *706*, 810; v. 2, 249
'Abd Rabbihi, b., 807
'Abd al-Raḥīm b. Ḥasan Isnawī (XIV-2), *1453*, 1046, 1099, 1169, 1170
'Abd al-Raḥīm b. 'Umar Jawbarī (XIII-1), v. 2, *635*, 1189; v. 3, 998
'Abd al-Raḥmān b. 'Abdallāh, *see* b. 'Abd al-Ḥakam
'Abd al-Raḥmān b. Aḥmad Ījī (XIV-1), *628*, 106, 1461, 1462, 1845
'Abd al-Raḥmān b. Aḥmad b. Rajab (XIV-1), *623*, 103
'Abd al-Raḥmān b. 'Alī b. Jauzī (XII-2), v. 2, *362*, 1188; v. 3, 965
'Abd al-Raḥmān b. a. Bakr Suyūṭī, 806, 962, 966, 1640, 1725, 1774
'Abd al-Raḥmān b. a. Ghālib Jādarī (XIV-2), *1524*, 1118
'Abd al-Raḥmān b. Hudhail, *see* 'Alī b. 'Abd al-Raḥmān
'Abd al-Raḥmān b. Ibrāhīm b. Firkāḥ, 804
'Abd al-Raḥmān b. Ismā'īl a. Shāma (XIII-2), v. 2, *1119*, 796, 1131; v. 3, 307, 958
'Abd al-Raḥmān Khāzinī (XII-1), v. 2, *216*, 1193; v. 3, 632
'Abd al-Raḥmān III b. Muḥammad (X-1), v. 1, *628*, 620, 680
'Abd al-Raḥmān b. Muḥammad Bisṭāmī, 1101, 1267
'Abd al-Raḥmān b. Muḥammad Ḥanbalī, 1528
'Abd al-Raḥmān b. Muḥammad b. Khaldūn, *see* b. Khaldūn
'Abd al-Raḥmān b. Muḥammad, *see* b. Wāfid
'Abd al-Raḥmān Nasā'ī, 1065
'Abd al-Raḥmān b. Naṣr Shaizarī (not Shairazī) (XII-2), v. 2, *463*, 1141; v. 3, 998, 1771, 1852
'Abd al-Raḥmān b. Naṣrallāh Shīrāzī (XII-2), v. 2, *431*, 1141
'Abd al-Raḥmān b. 'Umar Ṣūfī (X-2), v. 1, *665*, 649, 654; v. 2, 1141
'Abd al-Raḥmān b. a. Wafā' b. Anbārī (XII-2), v. 2, *469*, 318; v. 3, 373
'Abd al-Rashīd b. Ṣāliḥ Bākuwī (XIV-2), *1623*, 1161
'Abd al-Razzāq b. Aḥmad Shaibānī b. Fūṭī (XIV-1), *968*, 309
'Abd al-Razzāq b. Isḥāq Samarqandī, 627
'Abd al-Razzāq Kāshānī (XIV-1), *627*, 105, 374, 626
'Abd al-Wahhāb b. 'Alī Subkī (XIV-2), *1781*, 964, 1099, 1264, 1454
'Abd al-Wahhāb b. Ibrāhīm Zanjānī, 14f3
'Abd al-Wāḥid b. 'Alī Marrākushī (XIII-1), v. 2, *681*, 527
'Abd al-Wāḥid b. Muḥammad (XIV-2), *1530*, 1120
'Abd al-Wāḥid b. Muḥammad Juzjānī, 1530
'Abdarī, *see* Muḥammad b. Muḥammad
abdominal muscles, 440
'Abdūn, b., 998
Abel, Armand, 757
Abenguefit, *see* b. Wāfid
Abenragel, *see* b. a. Rijāl
aberration, spherical, 707
Abharī, *see* Mufaḍḍal b. 'Umar
'Abhd-Īshō' b. Bĕrīkhā (XIII-2), v. 2, *979*, 1142; v. 3, 97, 358
Abhidhānaratnamālā, 383
abhidharma, 468
Abhidharma-piṭaka, 466
Abhinava Maṅgarāja (XIV-2), *1828*, 383, 1330
Abhinava-nighaṇṭu, 1828
Abicht, Rudolf, 963
Abigdor, *see* Abraham b. Meshullam; Solomon b. Abraham
Ablijn, Cornelis, 955
Abner of Burgos (XIV-1), *417*, 55, 57, 130, 246, 338, 608, 1841
Aboab, *see* Isaac
abortion, 851, 853, 1763
Abraham b. Alexander of Cologne (XIII-2), v. 2, *888*, 732
Abraham Alfaquin of Toledo (XIII-2), v. 2, *844*, 718, 1142; v. 3, 436, 1119
Abraham of Aragón (XIII-1), v. 2, *665*, 83, 523
Abraham, Armenian, 1222

Abraham b. Azriel of Bohemia (XIII-1), v. 2, *556*, 488, 532
Abraham de Balmes, 432, 434, 435, 436, 1119
Abraham Bibago, 432
Abraham Cabret, 1211, 1220, 1384
Abraham Cresques (XIV-2), *1592*, 1141, 1305, 1591, 1858
Abraham b. David Caslari (XIV-1), *893*, 255, 607, 1375
Abraham b. David ha-Levi (XII-2), v. 2, *368*, 1142; v. 3, 1096, 1097, 1376, 1448, 1451
Abraham b. David of Posquières (XII-2), v. 2, *365*, 1142; v. 3, 609, 612
Abraham Ecchellensis, 1640
Abraham b. Ezra (XII-1), v. 2, *187*, 1142; v. 3, 55, 67, 68, 113, 366, 368, 398, 418, 429, 437, 439, 442, 445, 451, 453, 590, 591, 594, 596, 597, 603, 617, 894, 1008, 1096, 1097, 1117, 1364, 1365, 1376, 1378, 1385, 1449, 1450, 1451, 1452, 1489, 1518, 1521, 1522, 1635, 1718
Abraham b. Ḥiyya (XII-1), v. 2, *206*, 1142; v. 3, 128, 131, 366, 416, 590, 792, 1382, 1443, 1516, 1517, 1518
Abraham b. Isaac Bedersi, 255, 366, 593
Abraham b. Isaac ha-Levi, 1522
Abraham b. Isaac of Narbonne (XII-2), v. 2, *477*, 365, 476
Abraham b. Judah b. Ḥayyim (XIII-2), v. 2, *1041*, 1142; v. 3, 168, 363
Abraham b. Meïr, *see* Abraham b. Ezra
Abraham of Memmingen, 1319, 1551
Abraham b. Meshullam Abigdor (XIV-2), *1380*, 877, 1074, 1097, 1212, 1221, 1380, 1690, 1720
Abraham b. Nathan ha-Yarḥi (XIII-1), v. 2, *555*, 488, 492; v. 3, 1062
Abraham Pesaro, 606
Abraham Profiat, 593
Abraham Qirimi (XIV-2), *1365*, 1064
Abraham b. Reuben Amilabi, 1374
Abraham b. Samuel Abulafia (XIII-2), v. 2, *881*, 1142
Abraham b. Samuel b. Ḥasdai (XIII-1), v. 2, *563*, 1142
Abraham b. Samuel Zacuto, 595, 600, 1516
Abraham Shalom b. Isaac, 1435, 1437
Abraham b. Shem-ṭob of Tortosa (XIII-2), v. 2, *1096*, 1142; v. 3, 61, 67
Abraham b. Solomon Conat, 1451
Abrahams, Israel, 592, 614, 615, 792, 1872
Abravanel, *see* Abarbanel
abrīz, 754
abscess, *see* apostemes
absolute values, 76
Abstemius, Laur., 1814
abū, *see next word*
Abudraham, *see* David b. Joseph
abujad numerals, 132, 133, 134
Abulafia, *see* Abraham b. Samuel; Moses b. Joseph; Samuel ha-Levi; Ṭodros b. Joseph
Abulcasis, *see* a. Qāsim
Abulī, *see* Muḥammad b. Ibrāhīm
abūnā, 55
Abyssinia, *see* Aethiopia
Academy (IV-1 B.C.), v. 1, *113*, 787; v. 2, 1142
Acaia, *see* James
Acariso, Alberto, 1808
ācārya, 1863
acceleration, constant, 1488
Acciaiuoli, 948, 1839
Acciaiuoli, *see* Andrew; Nero
Accorso, *see* Francis
accounting, 124, 1111
accounts, Hebrew, 125
accounts, *see* popes
Accursius, *see* Francis
Achatius of Constantinople, St., 1666
Achéry, Luc d', 943, 1739
Achilles Tatios (III-1), v. 1, *322*, 315
Achillini, *see* Alexander
Achillini, G. F., 1345
Achrida, *see* Theophylactos Bulgaros
Acindynos, *see* Gregory
Acominatos, *see* Nicetas
aconite, 846
acoustic vases, 1129, 1569
Acritas, *see* Digenis
Acron of Agrigentum (V B.C.), v. 1, *102*, 83
Acropolites, *see* George
Acta sanctorum, 292, 1042
action at a distance, 148, 538, 553, 602
actione elementorum, De, 565
Acton, Lord, 1051
Actuarios, *see* John
actuarius, 889
actus sorbonicus, 530
acupuncture, 260, 906, 1733, 1851
'Ād, tribe, 1227
adab, 1839
Ādāb al-murīdīn, 420
Adalbertus Ranco ab Ericinio, 1348, 1432
Adam de Anglia, 550, 557
Adam of Bremen (XI-2), v. 1, *767*, 788; v. 2, 1143; v. 3, 194, 1609
Adam de Brome, 474
Adam of Cremona (XIII-1), v. 2, *653*, 88, 519; v. 3, 285
Adam, *see* Gaspard; George; Gerald
Adam Le Lièvre, 1202
Adam, Lucien, 381
Adam Marsh (XIII-1), v. 2, *583*, 1143; v. 3, 91
Adam Murimuth (XIV-1), *945*, 303, 1742
Adam Rous, 1204
Adam of Sodbury, 720
Adam of Usk, 1423
Adam, *see* William

Adam Wodeham (XIV-1), *557*, 82, 91, 550, 1432
Adamantios Sophista (IV-1), v. 1, *356*, 788; v. 3, 270, 1104
Adamī, b., *see* Muḥammad b. Ḥusain
Adamites, 574
Adams, C. W., 1864
Adams, F. D., 214, 930, 1870, 1872
Adam's footprint, 782
Adam's Peak, 423, 782, 1617
Addington, M. H., 1333
Adelard of Bath (XII-1), v. 2, *167*, 1143; v. 3, 120, 192, 439, 548
Adelbold of Utrecht (XI-1), v. 1, *714*, 788
Adelung, J. C., 351
Adelung, J. G., 1872
Adfuwī, *see* Ja'far b. Tha'lab
Adhémar of Chabannes (XI-1), v. 1, *733*, 700, 702
Adhikaraṇaratnamālā, 1367
Adhyāya, 1368
Ādi granth, 1475
'Adīm, *see* 'Umar b. Aḥmad
Adıvar, A. A., 1872
Adler, Cyrus, 1872, 1890
Adler, E. N., 793, 1009
Adler, J. G. C., 799
Adlerblum, N. H., 606
Admetus de Aureliana, 741
Admont, *see* Engelbert; Henry
Adnan, Abdülhak, 975, 1872
'Adnān b. Naṣr 'Ainzarbī (XII-1), v. 2, *234*, 1143
Adolphe de La Marck, 221, 1755
Adorno, *see* Antonniotto; Jerome
Adrastos of Aphrodisias (II-1), v. 1, *271*, 267, 352; v. 3, 745
Adret, *see* Solomon b. Abraham
Adrian and Epictetos, 1498
Adrian VI, 1360
'Aḍud al-Dawla, Buwayhī (X-2), v. 1, *658*, 788
'Aḍud al-dīn Ījī, 633
Advayavajra, 59
advocatus, *see* avoué
advowson, 473, 1601
Aebischer, Paul, 1176
Aeger, *see* Henry
aegidiana, schola, 82
Aegidius, *see* Giles
Aelfric grammaticus (X-2), v. 1, *692*, 788; v. 2, 1143; v. 3, 1165
Aelianos, Claudios (III-1), v. 1, *326*, 788; v. 2, 1143; v. 3, 825
Aelips, dame, 1227
Aelius Paetus, Sextus (II-1 B.C.), v. 1, *189*, 179
Aelschker, Edmund, 934
Aeneas Sylvius, 1036, 1335, 1814
Aeneas Tacticos (IV-1 B.C.), v. 1, *119*, 112, 213
Aeschylos, 997, 1005
"Aesculapius" (VI-1), v. 1, *434*, 417
Aesop, 579, 824
Aethicus Ister (VII-2), v. 1, *495*, 489; v. 2, 958, 1050
Aethiopia, 362, 782, 784, 803, 1143, 1451, 1596, 1606, 1667, 1852, 1891, 1892, 1894
Aethiopic, 362, 364, 437, 1355
Aëtios of Amida (VI-1), v. 1, *434*, 788; v. 2, 1102; v. 3, 1208
Afḍal Iqbāl, 1854
Afendopoulo, *see* Caleb
Afflacius, *see* John
Affò, Ireneo, 1566
'Afīf b. a. Surūr Sāmarī (XIV-2), *1721*, 1213, 1215
Aflaḥ ha-Saraqosṭi, a., 1521
Africa, discovery, 1892
Africa, epic, 506
Africanus, *see* Leo
Aga-Oglu, Mehmet, 1849
Agathangelos, 950
Agatharchides of Cnidos (II-1 B.C.), v. 1, *185*, 178, 179
Agatharchos of Samos (V B.C.), v. 1, *95*, 82; v. 3, 1105
Agathinos, Claudios (I-2), v. 1, *260*, 244
Agen, *see* Foy
Aggavaṃsa (XII-2), v. 2, *472*, 320; v. 3, 382, 423
aggregatio scientiae stellarum, 484
aggregatio stellarum, 484
Aggregator brixiensis, 1670
Aggregator paduanus, 1670
Agha Mahdi Ḥusain, 41
Agilinus, *see* Walter
Agnes, *see also* Anežka
Agnes of Navarre, 1629
Agnolo Gaddi, 1131
Agnus Dei, 292
Agobard, St. (IX-1), v. 1, *555*, 544, 549
Agostino, *see* Augustine
Agramont, *see* James
Agreda, *see* Mary
Agricola (Georg Bauer), 1137, 1139, 1174, 1554
Agricola, *see* Rodolph
agricultural implements, 830
agriculture, 1163, 1168, 1180
agrimensores, 1110, 1498
Agrippa, Camillo, 1160
Agrippa, Marcus Vipsanius (I-2 B.C.), v. 1, *223*, 219
Agrippa v. Nettesheim, H. C., 443, 445
Agron, 366, 1008
Aguiló, Estanislau, 927
Aguiló y Fúster, Marian, 1306
Ahimaaz b. Paltiel (XI-2), v. 1, *776*, 743, 745

Aḥiṭub b. Isaac of Palermo (XIII-2), v. 2, *855*, 1143; v. 3, 491, 616, 1373
ahl al-lithām, 1617
ahl al-ṭarīq, 153
Ahlwardt, Wilhelm, 967, 1007, 1514
Aḥmad b. 'Abdallāh Ḥabash Ḥāsib (IX-1), v. 1, *565*, 806; v. 2, 624
Aḥmad b. 'Abdallāh Iṣfahānī, 966
Aḥmad b. 'Abdallāh Khazrajī, 964
Aḥmad b. 'Abdallāh Rāzī, 958
Aḥmad b. 'Abdallāh b. Ṣaffār (XI-1), v. 1, *716*, 695, 702; v. 2, 1226; v. 3, 1767
Aḥmad b. 'Abd al-Ḥalīm b. Taimīya (XIV-1), *421*, 58, 103, 619, 901, 1012, 1782
Aḥmad b. 'Abd al-Raḥīm 'Irāqī, 966
Aḥmad b. 'Abd al-Wahhāb Nuwairī (XIV-1), *620*, 103, 133, 200, 203, 209, 308, 321, 620, 1264, 1780
Aḥmad b. 'Alā al-dīn Dimashqī, 1782
Aḥmad b. 'Alī 'Asqalānī, 1099, 1265
Aḥmad b. 'Alī Bāqilānī (XI-1), v. 1, *706*, 694, 702; v. 2, 764; v. 3, 149
Aḥmad b. 'Alī Būnī (XIII-1), v. 2, *595*, 1157; v. 3, 119
Aḥmad b. 'Alī Khaṭīb Baghdādī (XI-2), v. 1, 777, 813; v. 2, 1193
Aḥmad b. 'Alī b. Khātimah (XIV-1), *896*, 852, 1722, 1763
Aḥmad b. 'Alī, *see* Maqrīzī
Aḥmad b. 'Alī, *see* Muḥammad b. 'Alī b. Waḥshīya
Aḥmad b. 'Alī, *see* Qalqashandī
Aḥmad b. 'Alī b. Sā'ātī, 1454
Aḥmad b. 'Alī Tamīmī, 1515
Aḥmad b. Amīn Shinqīṭī, 806
Aḥmad Badawī, Sīdī, 420
Aḥmad b. a. Bakr Ṭabarānī, 1782
Aḥmad Bījān, 1464
Aḥmad Burhān al-dīn, 1216
Aḥmad-i Dā'ī, 1328, 1465
Aḥmad b. Dā'ūd, *see* Dīnawarī
Aḥmad b. Faḍlān, *see* b. Faḍlān
Aḥmad Firīdūn Tawqī'ī, 1473
Aḥmad b. Ghulāmallāh al-Kūm, 1525
Aḥmad, *see* Gülshehrī
Aḥmad b. Ḥamdān b. Shabīb (XIV-1), *804*, 201, 203, 209, 963
Aḥmad b. Ḥanbal, *see* Aḥmad b. Muḥammad
Aḥmad b. Ḥasan b. Bāṣa, 132, 696
Aḥmad b. Ḥasan Jārabardī (XIV-1), *1010*, 106, 373
Aḥmad b. Ḥasan Khaṭīb, 1766
Aḥmad b. Ḥasan (or Ḥusain) b. Qunfūdh (XIV-2), *1764*, 1118, 1262
Aḥmad b. Ibrāhīm Aḥmedī (XIV-2), *1464*, 1101, 1216, 1328
Aḥmad b. Ibrāhīm, *see* b. Jazzār
Aḥmad b. Idrīs Qarāfī (XIII-2), v. 3, *708*, 141, 707
Aḥmad 'Īsā bey, 1249
Aḥmad b. Khalīl (XIII-1), v. 2, *703*
Aḥmad Miṣrī, Warrāq, 800
Aḥmad b. Muḥammad b. 'Abd Rabbihi, 164
Aḥmad b. Muḥammad b. 'Arabshāh, 1265, 1266, 1272, 1328, 1329, 1469, 1470, 1473
Aḥmad b. Muḥammad Bahāniqī (XIV-2), *1524*, 1118
Aḥmad b. Muḥammad, a. Bakr, *see* Aḥmad b. Muḥammad Rāzī
Aḥmad b. Muḥammad, *see* Baladī
Aḥmad b. Muḥammad b. Bannā' (XIII-2), v. 2, *998*, 1153; v. 3, 132, 1118, 1515, 1765
Aḥmad b. Muḥammad b. Faqīh (X-1), v. 1, *635*, 621, 624
Aḥmad b. Muḥammad, *see* Farghānī
Aḥmad b. Muḥammad Ghāfiqī (XII-2), v. 2, *424*, 1176; v. 3, 289
Aḥmad b. Muḥammad b. Hā'im (XIV-2), *1527*, 1119
Aḥmad b. Muḥammad b. Ḥanbal (IX-1), v. 1, *551*, 809; v. 3, 1066
Aḥmad b. Muḥammad Ḥaufī (XII-2), v. 2, *462*, 296, 316
Aḥmad b. Muḥammad, *see* b. Khallikān
Aḥmad b. Muḥammad Kīlānī (XIV-1), *897*, 257
Aḥmad b. Muḥammad Maidānī (XII-1), v. 2, *271*, 142; v. 3, 373, 1639
Aḥmad b. Muḥammad Maqdisī (XIV-2), *1623*, 1160
Aḥmad b. Muḥammad Maqqarī, 306, 1763, 1885
Aḥmad b. Muḥammad b. Maskawayh (X-2), v. 1, *687*, 810
Aḥmad b. Muḥammad Nabātī (XIII-1), v. 2, *650*, 1141
Aḥmad b. Muḥammad Nahāwandī (IX-1), v. 1, *565*, 545
Aḥmad b. Muḥammad Qudūrī, 1267
Aḥmad b. Muḥammad Rāzī, a. Bakr (X-1), v. 1, *643*, 622, 624; v. 3, 344
Aḥmad b. Muḥammad Ṣāghānī (X-2), v. 1, *666*, 828
Aḥmad b. Muḥammad Sarakhsī (IX-2), v. 1, *597*, 584
Aḥmad b. Muḥammad Shādhilī, 1453
Aḥmad b. Muḥammad Sijzī (X-2), v. 1, *665*, 648, 654; v. 2, 401
Aḥmad b. Muḥammad Ṭabarī (X-2), v. 1, *677*, 650, 654; v. 2, 1144
Aḥmad b. Muḥammad Ṭaḥāwī, 1454
Aḥmad b. Mūsā, *see* Mūsā, Banū
Aḥmad b. Muṣṭafā Ṭashköprüzāde, 900, 1101, 1263, 1464, 1776
Aḥmad Paraclet, 1341
Aḥmad Qabā'ilī, 1366
Aḥmad b. Qāsim, *see* Uṣaibi'a
Aḥmad b. Rahat, 1249
Aḥmad b. Rajab b. Majdī (XIV-2), *1528*, 1119, 1530

Aḥmad b. Sahl Balkhī (X-1), v. 1, *631*, 793; v. 2, 775, 1009; v. 3, 801
Aḥmad b. Sarrāj Ḥamawī, 1525
Aḥmad b. Sīrīn (IX-1), v. 1, *558*, 788; v. 2, 348; v. 3, 952
Aḥmad Ṭabīb Naḥḥās, 1473
Aḥmad b. Ṭaiyib Sarakhsī, 998
Aḥmad Ṭīnī (XIV-1), *799*, 200, 801
Aḥmad b. 'Umar Niẓāmī-i-'Arūḍī (XII-2), v. 2, *363*, 1210; v. 3, 212, 1775
Aḥmad b. 'Umar b. Rusta (X-1), v. 1, *635*, 810; v. 3, 1108
Aḥmad b. 'Uthmān Juzjānī (XIV-1), *700*, 136
Aḥmad b. 'Uthmān Qaisī (XIII-1), v. 2, *704*, 82, 521
Aḥmad b. Yaḥyā, *see* Balādhurī
Aḥmad b. Yaḥyā Ḍabbī (XII-2), v. 2, *444*, 311
Aḥmad b. Yaḥyā b. Faḍlallāh 'Umarī (XIV-1), *802*, 103, 200, 209, 3(8, 321, 621, 802, 1161, 1264, 1326, 1787, 1785
Aḥmad b. Yaḥyā b. a. Ḥajala (XIV-2), *1722*, 1098, 1100, 1118, 1214
Aḥmad b. Yaḥyā Jābir, *see* Balādhurī
Aḥmad b. a. Ya'qūb, *see* Ya'qūbī
Aḥmad b. Yūsuf b. Kammād (XII-2?), v. 3, *1514*
Aḥmad b. Yūsuf Miṣrī (IX-2), v. 1, *598*, 585, 590; v. 2, 1144; v. 3, 431
Aḥmad b. Yūsuf Ṣafadī, 257, 961
Aḥmad b. Yūsuf Tīfāshī (XIII-1), v. 2, *650*, 1239
Aḥmad Zakī pāshā, 201, 308, 622, 734, 803, 961
Aḥmadīya, 420, 1841, 1854
Ahmed Issa bey, 293
Aḥmedī, *see* Aḥmad b. Ibrāhīm
Ahrendt, E. H., 1228
Ahuys, *see* Henry
Aidīn, *see* 'Īsā b. Muḥammad
Aidīnī, *see* Ḥājjī Pāshā
Aidīnoghlu Meḥmed bey, 1727
Aigrain, René, 1833
Ailly, *see* Peter
'aima, 1777
Aimeric de' Giuliani, 521
Aimerich, 704
Aimoin of Fleury (XI-1), v. 1, *732*, 788
'Ain mishpaṭ ha-derushim, 435
'Ainī, *see* Maḥmūd b. Aḥmad
'Aintābī, *see* Maḥmūd b. Aḥmad
'Ainzarbī, *see* 'Adnān b. Naṣr
Aïri-vankh, *see* Mekhitar
airs and climates, 1651
Airy, G. B., 1166
Aitareya brāhmaṇa, 1369
Aitareyāraṇyaka, 1369
Aitareya saṃhitā, 1368
Aix, *see* Albert; John
'ajā'ib, 965
ajall, sayyid, 1587
'Ajam, 376
'Ajamī, *see* Muḥammad b. Aḥmad
Ājurrūm, b., *see* Muḥammad b. Muḥammad
Ājurrūmīya, 1009
Akbar, 465, 1026, 1329
Åkesson, O. A., 1856
Akfānī, b., *see* Muḥammad b. Ibrāhīm
Akhbār al-Ṣīn wal-Hind, 1587
Akhiyya al-fityān, 154
Akhmîm papyrus (VI-2), v. 1, *449*, 354, 444
'Akkā, *see* Isaac b. Samuel
Akkadian, 364
Akuta, 381
'Alā' al-dīn Tabrīzī, 1469
'Alā' Ma'arrī, a., 79, 490, 962
'Alā' Zuhr, a., *see* Zuhr b. a. Marwān
Alabanti, *see* Anthony
Alain, Alains, *see* Alan, Alans
A'lam, 'Alī b. Ḥusain b. (X-2), v. 1, *666*, 649, 654; v. 2, 1006
'Alam al-dīn Sanjar Jawlī, 1249
Alan Chartier, 745
Alan of Lille (XII-2), v. 2, *383*, 1144; v. 3, 1418
Alans, v. 2, 773, 982; v. 3, 387, 776, 781
Alaric, 229
Alaric, *see* Breviarium
Albalag, *see* Isaac
Alban, E. L., 1667
Albans, Chronicles of St., 1255, 1745
Albanzani, *see* Donato
Albarello, 1134
Albategnius, *see* Battānī
Albé, Edmond, 406
Albelbanus, 1721
Albergheti, *see* Peter
Alberico da Rosciate (XIV-1), *984*, 177, 313
Albero Doneldey, 1711
Albert of Aix, 1603
Albert I of Austria, 285, 577
Albert II of Austria, 933
Albert III of Austria, 1678
Albert IV of Austria, 1193
Albert of Bohemia, 1428
Albert of Bologna, 852, 1690
Albert Brouat, 1690
Albert, *see* Dürer
Albert d'Este, 1400
Albert, F. R., 1040
Albert de Fiesque, 393
Albert del Giudice, 124
Albert the Great (XIII-2), v. 2, *934*, 1144; v. 3, 66, 79, 166, 179, 214, 268, 270, 341, 410, 450, 461, 499, 536, 548, 568, 750, 754, 811, 813, 816, 817, 858, 1165, 1171, 1229, 1353, 1400, 1409, 1412, 1431, 1442, 1481, 1494, 1576, 1579, 1582, 1674, 1808
Albert de Helmstede, *see* Albert of Saxony
Albert of Hohenberg, 935
Albert, Master, 265, 284, 852
Albert of Parma (XIV-1), *888*, 251, 351, 852
Albert, Paul, 1344

Albert Porzello, 1132
Albert, pseudo, 1104
Albert of Ricmestorp, *see* Albert of Saxony
Albert of Saxony (XIV-2), *1428*, 150, 399, 539, 541, 545, 555, 563, 564, 1086, 1091, 1093, 1106, 1112, 1126, 1127, 1166, 1170, 1194, 1398, 1428, 1435, 1489, 1496, 1539, 1565
Albert Tossignano, 1681
Albert of Trebizond, 548
Albert of Würzburg, 252, 1245
Albert de' Zancari (XIV-1), *852*, 244, 266, 293, 1690
Albertano of Brescia (XIII-1), v. 2, *697*, 530, 927; v. 3, 341, 453, 1633
Alberti antichi, 1839
Alberti, *see* Bernard; Leo Battista; Paradiso
Albertin de Virga, 1597, 1598
Albertino Mussato (XIV-1), *917*, 87, 298, 315, 333, 505, 919, 986
Albertino Rainoldi de Salso, 1678
Albertis, *see* John
Alberto, *see* Albert
Albertotti, Giuseppe, 857, 1234
Alberts, Otto, 378
Albic, *see* Sigismund
Albigenses, 339, 341, 345, 404, 405, 412, 1853
Albin, Eleazar, 1642
Albino da Montecaliero (XIV-1), *855*, 244, 285
Albinus, *see* Albino
Albion, 720
Albizzi, *see* Bartholomew
Albo, *see* Joseph
Albohazen, Alboacen, *see* b. a. Rijāl
Albornoz, *see* Gil Álvarez; Gómez
Albrecht, *see* Albert
Albubather, *see* Aḥmad b. Muḥammad Rāzī
Albucasis, *see* a. Qāsim (X-2)
Albumasar, *see* a. Ma'shar
Alcadino of Syracuse, 287
Alcalá de Henares, 73
Alcalá, *see* Peter
Alchamus, 451
Alchandrus (X-2), v. 1, *671*, 649; v. 2, 343; v. 3, 369
alchemists, 167, 406, 981, 983
alchemy, 165, 521, 559, 801, 901, 973, 1135, 1338, 1422, 1472, 1772, 1813, 1876, 1893, 1894
alchemy, instruments, 761, 973, 1573, 1578
alchemy, MSS, 1876, 1877, 1879, 1904, 1909
alchemy, *see* medicine
alchemy, Muslim (X-2), v. 1, *673*
alchemy operations, seven, 1573
alchemy, signs, 1877
alchemy, *see* transmutation
Alcherius, *see* John
Alciati, Andrea, 1869
Alcmaeon of Crotona (VI B.C.), v. 1, *77*, 66
"Alcoatim" (XII-2), v. 2, *430*, 83, 305; v. 3, 1234, 1688
alcohol, distillation (XII-2), v. 2, *408*, 1145
Alcuin (VIII-2), v. 1, *528*, 789; v. 2, 496, 609
Aldabi, *see* Meïr b. Isaac
Alderotti, *see* Taddeo
Aldgate, *see* William
Aldhelm, St. (VII-2), v. 1, *492*, 488, 490
Aldo Manuzio, 512, 1336
Aldobrandin of Siena (XIII-2), v. 2, *1083*, 1145; v. 3, 68, 270, 286, 340, 345, 1104, 1196, 1703, 1836
Aldobrandino, *see* Dino
Aldrevandinus, 171
Aldrich, L. B., 1856
Aldridge, H. R., 1706
Aldrovandi, Ulisse, 1163
Alembert, d', 335
Alençon, *see* Philip
Alessandria, *see* Alexandria, Italy
Alexander Achillini, 1127
Alexander, alchemist, 1583
Alexander of Alexandria (XIV-1), *517*, 87
Alexander of Aphrodisias (III-1), v. 1, *318*, 789; v. 2, 1145; v. 3, 64, 98, 146, 242, 434, 439, 441, 591, 608
Alexander Arnauld, 427
Alexander de Bernai, 232
Alexander, E. M. M., 1864
Alexander Fassitelli, 988
Alexander the Great (IV-2 B.C.), v. 1, *127*, 789; v. 2, 1122; v. 3, 560, 777, 1101, 1465, 1467
Alexander of Hales (XIII-1), v. 2, *582*, 1145; v. 3, 79, 91, 398, 517
Alexander Neckam (XII-2), v. 2, *385*, 1145; v. 3, 332, 714
Alexander Nevski, 39
Alexander of Paris, 232
Alexander Piccolomini, 1127, 1336
Alexander the Pilgrim (XIV-2), *1614*, 1156, 1322
Alexander III, pope (XII-1), v. 2, *268*, 1145
Alexander IV, pope, 374
Alexander V, pope, *see* Peter of Crete
Alexander, romance, 232, 305, 458, 912, 1254, 1261, 1519, 1741, 1864. *See also* Iskandar-nāma
Alexander Sermoneta, 1413
Alexander of Spain (XIV-1), *860*, 245, 285, 921
Alexander della Spina, 921
Alexander of Tralles (VI-2), v. 1, *453*, 789; v. 2, 1145; v. 3, 816, 1208, 1688
Alexander de Villedieu (XIII-1), v. 2, *616*, 1145; v. 3, 66, 116, 119, 331, 410, 1003, 1004, 1404
Alexandre, *see* Alexander
Alexandria, Egypt, 229, 1891
Alexandria, Egypt, *see* Catherine; Clement; Cyril; Stephen

Alexandria, Italy, *see* Alexander; Benzo Cona; Peter
Alexandrides, Demetrios, 799
Alexios Calochetos, 585
Alexios Comnenos, 746, 1854
Alexios Spanos, 995
Alexios II of Trebizond, 63, 123, 438
Alf laila wa-laila, 164, 805, 925, 1214, 1606, 1640
Alfandari, *see* Jacob
Alfasi, Isaac b. Jacob (XI-2), v. 1, *751*, 789; v. 2, 1186; v. 3, 590, 1062, 1364
Alfidius, 166, 1573
Alfīya, 962
Alfonso, *see also* Alonso; Alphonse
Alfonso Álvarez de Villasandino, 1307
Alfonso III of Aragón, 427
Alfonso IV of Aragón, 427
Alfonso Bonihominis, 418, 1841
Alfonso of Burgos, 417
Alfonso X of Castile, *see* Alfonso X el Sabio
Alfonso XI of Castile, 73, 402
Alfonso Converso, 417
Alfonso of Cordova (XIV-1), *861*, 246, 852
Alfonso of Cordova, astrologer in Seville in 1498, 861
Alfonso Giraldez, 344
Alfonso de Palencia, 1302
Alfonso, *see* Peter
Alfonso III of Portugal, 343
Alfonso X el Sabio (XIII-2), v. 2, *834*, 1145; v. 3, 61, 68, 73, 159, 166, 300, 337, 342, 344, 374, 436, 718, 1108, 1514, 1762. *See also* Alphonsine tables
Alfonso de Spina, 418, 1384
Alfonso da Vadaterra, 1355
Alfonso of Valladolid, 57, 417, 1385
Alfonso Vargas of Toledo (XIV-1), *520*, 89
Alfraethi íslenzk, 1114, 1583
Alfraganus, *see* Farghānī
Alfred the Great (IX-2), v. 1, *595*, 789; v. 2, 1145; v. 3, 194, 1148, 1389
Alfred of Sareshel (XIII-1), v. 2, *561*, 1145; v. 3, 166, 1576
Algazel, *see* Ghazzālī
algebraic symbols, 1765
algebrista, 895
Algizar, *see* b. Jazzār
algorism, 116, 869
algorism, French (XIII-2), v. 2, *992*
algorism, Hanover Latin (XIII-1), v. 2, *619*, 505
algorism, Oxford French (XIII-1), v. 2, *619*, 505
algorism, Salem Latin (XIII-1), v. 2, *619*, 505
Alguadez, *see* Meīr b. Solomon
Alḥadib, *see* Isaac b. Solomon
Alhazen, *see* b. Haitham
'Alī b. 'Abbās Majūsī (X-2), v. 1, *677*, 789; v. 2, 1145; v. 3, 288, 850, 870, 879, 881, 1205, 1206, 1229, 1235, 1691, 1707, 1726
'Alī b. 'Abdallāh Shādhilī, 1453, 1723, 1864
'Alī b. 'Abdallāh b. a. Zar' (XIV-1), *957*, 307
'Alī b. 'Abd al-Kāfī Subkī (XIV-1), *622*, 103, 258, 622, 1453, 1781, 1827
'Alī b. 'Abd al-Raḥmān b. Hudhail (XIV-2), *1635*, 1167, 1185
'Alī b. 'Abd al-Raḥmān Sa'īdī, 1850
'Alī b. Aḥmad, *see* Asadī
'Alī b. Aḥmad, *see* b. Ḥazm
'Alī b. Aḥmad b. Hubal (XII-2), v. 2, *430*, 1183; v. 3, 1726
'Alī b. Aḥmad 'Imrānī (X-1), v. 1, *632*, 621, 669; v. 2, 126, 177
'Alī b. Aḥmad Mujtabā, 1533
'Alī b. Aḥmad Nasawī (XI-1), v. 1, *719*, 821; v. 2, 1003; v. 3, 113
'Alī b. Aidamur Jildakī (XIV-1), *758*, 180
'Alī al-A'lā, 1460
'Alī b. a. 'Alī Qusṭanṭīnī (XIV-2), *1523*, 1118, 1766
'Alī b. Anjab Baghdādī, 968
'Alī b. a. Bakr Harawī (XII-2), v. 2, *413*, 35, 300
'Alī b. a. Bakr Marghīnānī (XII-2), v. 2, *464*, 288, 316; v. 3, 1454
'Alī b. Dā'ūd, *see* Mujāhid 'Alī Rasūlī
'Alī Faraḍī, *see* Nūr al-dīn
'Alī Hamadhānī, 1475
'Alī b. Ḥasan b. 'Asākir (XII-2), v. 2, *446*, 1150; v. 3, 307
'Alī b. Ḥasan b. Wahhās (XIV-2), *1779*, 1264, 1637
'Alī b. a. Ḥazm b. Nafīs (XIII-2), v. 2, *1099*, 1208; v. 3, 267, 961, 1215, 1221, 1725, 1726
'Alī b. Ḥusain, *see* b. A'lam
'Alī b. Ḥusain Anṣārī, 1728
'Alī b. Ḥusain Baihaqī, 1465
'Alī b. Ḥusain, *see* a. Faraj Iṣfahānī
'Alī b. Ḥusain, *see* Mas'ūdī
'Alī b. Ḥusain, *see* Zain al-'Aṭṭār
'Alī b. Ibrāhīm b. Shāṭir (XIV-2), *1524*, 1118, 1526
'Alī b. 'Īsā (XI-1), v. 1, *731*, 789; v. 2, 82, 1101; v. 3, 899, 1724
'Alī b. 'Īsā b. 'Alī, fl. end 9th, 1638
'Alī b. 'Īsā Aṣṭurlābī (IX-1), v. 1, *566*, 545, 601
'Alī b. Ismā'īl, *see* Ash'arī
'Alī b. Ismā'īl b. Sīda (XI-2), v. 1, *782*, 810; v. 2, 1136; v. 3, 372, 1639, 1827
'Alī Kāma of Khurāsān, 1644
'Alī Khaiyāṭ, a. (IX-1), v. 1, *569*, 546; v. 2, 1146
'Alī b. Manṣūr, 233
'Alī b. Muḥammad b. Athīr (XIII-1), v. 2, *682*, 1151; v. 3, 794, 801, 962, 964, 965, 967, 968, 971
'Alī b. Muḥammad Bukhārī, 629

'Alī b. Muḥammad Darbandī, 1525
'Alī b. Muḥammad b. Duraihim (XIV-2), *1638*, 1168, 1179
'Alī b. Muḥammad Jurjānī (XIV-2), *1461*, 163, 628, 1100, 1120, 1129, 1266, 1328, 1457, 1473
'Alī b. Muḥammad Māwardī (XI-2), v. 1, *780*, 744, 746; v. 2, 141; v. 3, 997, 998, 1271
'Alī b. Muḥammad Pazdawī, 628
'Ali b. Muḥammad Qalaṣādī, 134, 1765
'Alī b. Muḥammad Qūshchī, 1120
'Alī b. Muḥammad Raba'ī, 804
'Alī b. Muḥammad of Tamgrūt, 807
'Alī b. Mukhliṣ Ilyās, 623
'Alī Munawī, Nūr al-dīn, 899
'Alī b. Mūsā Andalusī, 1012
'Alī b. Mūsā b. Arfa' ra'sahu (XII-2), v. 2, *408*, 1149; v. 3, 759, 1012
'Alī b. Mūsā b. Sa'īd Maghribī (XIII-2), v. 2, *1065*, 1226; v. 3, 200, 1158
'Alī b. Riḍwān Miṣrī (XI-1), v. 1, *729*, 789; v. 2, 1146; v. 3, 254, 264, 432, 870, 1727, 1797, 1808
'Alī b. a. Rijāl, *see* b. a. Rijāl
'Alī b. Sahl Rabbān Ṭabarī (IX-1), v. 1, *574*, 789; v. 2, 82; v. 3, 608, 1449
'Alī b. a. Sa'īd, *see* b. Yūnus
'Alī shāh, 969
'Alī Shaṭranjī, 1469
'Alī b. Shihāb al-dīn Ḥusainī (XIV-2), *1458*, 1100, 1328
'Alī b. Sulaimān (XII-1), v. 2, *275*, 190
'Alī b. a. Ṭālib, 106, 623
'Alī Ṭawāshī Yamanī, 619
'Alī b. 'Umar Kātibī (XIII-2), v. 2, *868*, 1146; v. 3, 146, 630, 1462
'Alī b. Yūsuf b. Qifṭī (XIII-1), v. 2, *684*, 1220; v. 3, 960, 964, 1263
'Alī b. Zaid Baihaqī (XII-2), v. 2, *445*, 1146
Alice in Wonderland, 1841
Alighieri, *see* Antonia; Beatrice; Dante; James; Peter
Alimentus, L. Cincius (III-2 B.C.), v. 1, *176*, 166
aljamiadas,[1] 360
Aljubarrota, battle of, 1021, 1306
Alkemade, Cornelis van, 938
Alkindus, *see* Kindī
All Souls College, 1402
Allacci, Leone, 996, 1156, 1513
Allegretti, *see* James
Allemagne, H. R. d', 1563
Allen, H. E., 567

[1] Alois Richard Nykl: A compendium of Aljamiado literature, with the text of an Aljamiado version of the Alexander romance (reprinted from Revue hispanique 77, 409–611, Paris 1929).

Allen, P. S., 375, 1325
Allen, Thomas, 116
Allix, Petrus, 992
Allyn, H. B., 1663
Almagest, *see* Ptolemy, astronomy and mathematics
Almagest, translation (XII-2), v. 2, *403*
Almagià, Roberto, 1598, 1671
Almagro y Cárdenas, Antonio, 827
Almain, Jacob, 555
Almāligh, 781, 785, 833
Almanach perpetuum Prophatii, 128
almanacs, 138, 1123, 1528
Almarche y Vásquez, Francisco, 927
Almeida, *see* Lewis
Almería, 896
Almogávares, 925
Almond, J. C., 395
Almosnino, *see* Moses b. Baruch
almucantars, 1528, 1533
Aloisius, 1240
Alonso de Santa María de Cartagena, **1736**
Alós, Ramón d', 1342
Alovid, *see* Thomas
Alp Arslān Qarā balī, 1644
Alpetragius, *see* Biṭrūjī
alphabet, Korean, 1562
Alphabetum, 1708
Alphanus of Salerno (XI-1), v. 1, ***727***, **374**, 699; v. 3, 1708
Alpharabius, *see* Fārābī
Alphiatus, 1576
Alphidius, 1576, 1578
Alphita, 1222
Alphonse of Poitiers, 341
Alphonsine tables, 112, 115, 118, 133, **797**, 1107, 1115, 1375, 1486, 1516
Alphonso, *see* Alfonso
Alpini, Prospero, 1724
Alpinism, 1163, 1171, 1628, 1878
Alston, M. N., 266, 1440
Altandäptär, 970
Altavilla, contessa d', 1805
Alten, D. v., 788
Alter, F. C., 305
Althusius, Johannes, 1795
Altmann, Wilhelm, 1820
alum, 750
alumbrados, 1864
aluminibus et salibus, De, 165
Alunno, Francesco, 1301, 1808
Alured of Canterbury, 1569
Alvar García de Santa María, 1250, 1343
Álvaro Paes, 988
Álvaro Pelayo (XIV-1), *401*, 50, 51, **315**, 1401, 1869
Alvarus Thomas, 737
Alvastra, *see* Peter Olafsson
Alvin, Fréd., 725
Alvin, général, 476

Alvise Cadamosto, 190, 1159
Alwis, J. d', 423
Aly, *see* Haly
Alzano, *see* Bartholomew
Amajūr, 'Abdallāh b. (X-1), v. 1, *630*, 620, 624
'amal bil-kura (vulg. Ar.: kurra), 426
Amandus, *see* Suso
Amann, mgr. Emile, 1872, 1881
Amano, Kageyas W., 1872
Amar, Emile, 961, 968
Amara (VI-2), v. 1, *458*, 445; v. 3, 382, 383, 1730, 1828
Amarakośa, 1730, 1828
Amaranātha Jhā, 1585
Amarasiṃha, *see* Amara
Amari, Michele, 806
Amasia, 1216, 1248
Amauri de Lusignan, 452
Amaury of Bêne (XIII-1), v. 2, *551*, 487, 568; v. 3, 22, 402
Amberg, 1553, 1554
Ambrogio, *see* Ambrose
Ambroise, *see* Ambrose
Ambrose Camaldolese, 1289
Ambrose the Jongleur (XII-2), v. 2, *479*, 476
Ambrose Leo of Nola, 891
Ambrose Lorenzetti, 111
Ambrose de' Migli, 1294
Ambrose, *see* Paré
Ambrose Traversari, 1289, 1292, 1321, 1325, 1363, 1822
Ambrose of Treves, St. (IV-2), v. 1, *362*, 359; v. 2, 593, 927; v. 3, viii
'Amda Ṣion (XIV-1), *956*, 306, 320, 362
Amedeo of Savoy, 1035, 1713
amen, 122
Amenophis III, 1187
Amerbach, *see* John
America, Buddhist discovery (V-2), v. 1, *410*
America, Icelandic discovery (XI-1), v. 1, *724*; v. 3, 194
America, *see* Scandinavian exploration
Amerigo Vespucci, 1141
Ames, P. W., 1426
Amharic, 362, 1143
amicable numbers, 134, 429, 707, 1118
'Amīd, b., *see* 'Abdallāh b. a. Yāsir, Makīn
Amidaism, 312, 424
Āmidī, *see* Muḥammad b. Muḥammad
Āmilī, *see* Muḥammad b. Maḥmūd
Amīn, 154
Amiot, Joseph Marie, 162, 381
Amitāyurdhyānasūtra, 311
'Ammār b. 'Alī (XI-1), v. 1, *729*, 790; v. 2, 1147; v. 3, 899, 1723
Ammianus Marcellinus (IV-2), v. 1, *375*, 361; v. 3, 1291
Ammonios, son of Hermias (VI-1), v. 1, *421*, 790; v. 3, 589
Ammonios the Lithotomist (I-2 B.C.), v. 1, *230*, 220; v. 3, 1236
Ammonios Saccas of Alexandria (III-1), v. 1, *320*, 315; v. 2, 366
'Ammud be-shoroshe, 432
'Ammude kesef, 590
Amodeo, Federico, 1488, 1566
Amodio, *see* Andrew
Amos (VIII B.C.), v. 1, *57*, 52; v. 3, 227
Ampère, André Marie, 77
Ampère, Jean-Jacques, 77
Amplonius v. Berka, 1399, 1706
amputation, 871
'Amr b. 'Abd al-Raḥmān Karmānī (XI-1), v. 1, *715*, 813; v. 3, 1341
'Amr b. Baḥr, *see* Jāḥiẓ
'Amr b. Mattā (XIV-1), *956*, 55, 306
'Amr b. 'Uthmān, *see* Sībawaihi
Amrāḍ al-ḥādda, 437
Amrhein, G. L., 325
Amshāṭī, b., 1721
'amūd al-ṣalīb, 487
amulets, 1104
Anacharsis the Scythian (VI B.C.), v. 1, *75*, 65
anaesthesia, 277, 883
analysis, indeterminate, 1535, 1881
Anan b. David (VIII-2), v. 1, *524*, 520; v. 3, 56, 365, 617
Anand, M. R., 377
anaphrodisiacs, 296
Anaritius, *see* Nairīzī
Anastase Marie de St. Elie, 901, 1284
Anastasius, librarian (IX-2), v. 1, *614*, 790
Anatoli, *see* Jacob b. abba Mari
Anatolios of Alexandria (III-2), v. 1, *337*, 790
Anatolius of Beirut Vindonius (IV-2), v. 1, *370*, 790
Anatomia Cophonis (XII-1), v. 2, *237*, 437
Anatomia Mundini, 842
Anatomia porci (XI-2), v. 1, *770*, 742; v. 2, *237*, 135, 238
anatomy, 265, 1223, 1878, 1884, 1904, 1905, 1908
anatomy, dissection, 840, 1193
anatomy, iconography, 1729
anatomy, poetic, 1728
anatomy, *see* Salerno
'Anav, *see* Benjamin b. Abraham; Jehiel b. Jekuthiel
Anaxagoras of Clazomenae (V B.C.), v. 1, *86*, 790; v. 3, 148, 1105, 1621
Anaximander of Miletos (VI B.C.), v. 1, *72*, 65
Anaximenes of Miletos (VI B.C.), v. 1, *73*, 65
anbā, title, *see* Yuḥanna of Samannūd
Anbārī, b., *see* 'Abd al-Raḥmān b. a. Wafā'
Ancklitzen, *see* Constantine
Ancona, Alessandro d', 913
Ancona, *see* Ciriaco
Ancyra, council, 275

Andalò di Negro (XIV-1), *645*, 112, 188, 243, 515, 1409, 1802, 1808
Andalò da Savignone (XIV-1), *780*, 187, 337
Andalusī, *see* Ṣā'id b. Aḥmad
andanicum, 1859
Andersen, Dines, 423
Andersen, H. C., 925
Andersson, Ingvar, 1275
Āndra-bhārata, 466
André, *see also* Andrew
André (fl. 1336), 781
André, Marius, 1304
Andrea, *see* Andrew
Andreae, *see* Anthony
Andreas Asanes, 1824
Andreas Berengarius, 863
Andreas Darmarios, 122
Andreas Libadenos (XIV-1), *790*, 53, 198, 304
Andreoli, *see* George; John; Salimbene; Vincent
Andrew, *see also* Andreas
Andrew degli Acciaiuoli, 1805
Andrew Amodio or Amoglio, 1163
Andrew the Apostle, St., 1036
Andrew Bianco, 185, 1592
Andrew Dandolo (XIV-1), *916*, 297, 313, 1658
Andrew Ghini dei Malpighi, 834
Andrew of Longjumeau (XIII-1), v. 2, *642*, 1147
Andrew de Nassio, 387
Andrew Orcagna, 1231
Andrew degli Organi, 1655
Andrew of Perugia (XIV-1), *780*, 54, 187, 204, 776
Andrew Pisano, 727, 1105
Andrew de Rampinis, 985
Andrew della Ròbbia, 1134
Andrew Rublev, 1583
Andrew da Sommeria (XIV-2), *1482*, 1106
Andrew of Wyntoun, 1254, 1315, 1740
Andrews, A. C., 231
Andrews, M. C., 1872
Andrivet de Bressé, 1302
Andromachos the Elder (I-2), v. 1, *261*, 244
Andromachos the Younger (I-2), v. 1, *261*, 244
Andronicos I Comnenos, 414
Andronicos II, 123, 951
Andronicos III, 583
Andronicos of Constantinople (XIV-1), *414*, 53
Andronicos Oinaiotes, 1511
Andronicos of Rhodes (I-1 B.C.), v. 1, *203*, 201
Anesaki, Masaharu, 1018
Anežka of Štítný, 1353
Angeli, *see* John
Angeli da Scarparia, 1321
Angelica (or Angelina) the Greek, 1467
Angelico of Siena, 1335
Angelino de Dalorto, 182, 765
Angelino Dulcert, 182, 765, 1850
Angelino del Tegghia de' Corbizzi, 768
Angelitti, Filippo, 497
Angellino, *see* Angelino
Angelo Catone da Sepino, 817
Angelo da Clareno (da Cingoli), 396
Angelo Corraro or Corrér, *see* **Gregory XII**
Angelo of Florence, 225
Angelo, *see* James
Angelo Poliziano, 1327
Angelo Salvetti, 1335
Angelo degli Ubaldi, 1795
Angelucci, Angelo, 913
Angkor-Vat, 1030
Anglade, Joseph, 340, 1872
Anglic de Grimoard, 1694
Anglo-Indian, 1910
Anglo-Norman, 334
Anglo-Saxon, *see* botany
Anglure, *see* Ogier
Angoulême, *see* Hugh
Ångström, A. J., 709
angular velocity, 146
Ānī, *see* Samuel
Anianus (XIII-2), v. 2, *992*, 1147
Añíbarro y Rives, M. M., 1344
Aniciae Iulianae, Codex, 442
animalculists, 1229
animals, criminal proceedings against, **238**
animals, *see* cycle of twelve
animals, folklore, 824
animals impregnated by wind, 805
animals, mythology, 1886
animals, power, 157
animals, properties, 1638
animals, stories, 1836
Anīs muṭrib, 957
Anjou, *see* Charles; Lewis; Robert
Ankara, 1464
Ankara, *see* Ṣalāḥ al-dīn
Anna of Auvergne, 1713
Anna of Bohemia, 1076, 1322, 1348, 1561
Anna of Braunschweig, 1104
Anna Comnena (XII-1), v. 2, *250*, 1147; v. 3, 252, 353, 1854
Anna Palaeologa, *see* Anna da Savoia
Anna da Savoia, 53, 584, 1439
Anna Sracimir, 1155
Annam, 205, 978, 1176
Annamite dynasties, 979
annates, 38
Annibaldo of Ceccano, 887
annona, 1847
Annunzio, Gabriele d', 924
anointing, 286
Anonymus Byzantinus (VI-1), v. 1, *430*, 416
Anonymus de rebus bellicis (VI-1), v. 1, *430*, 416
Anquetil-Duperron, 376
Anschel, Asher, 1450
Anse, *see* Estienne

Anselm of Havelberg (XII-1), v. 2, *180*, 1147
Anselm, St. (XI-2), v. 1, *748*, 790; v. 2, 1147; v. 3, 81, 551, 552, 1075, 1388, 1423, 1808
Anselm Turmeda (XIV-2), *1341*, 1046, 1052, 1065, 1072, 1087, 1306, 1328
Anthemios of Tralles (VI-1), v. 1, *427*, 790
Anthimus (VI-1), v. 1, *433*, 417
Anthoni Lucian, 1499
Anthony, *see also* Anthoni; Antoinette; Antonia; Antonius; Antonniotto
Anthony Alabanti, 519
Anthony Andreae (XIV-1), *519*, 89
Anthony Augustine of Saragossa, 894
Anthony Bartoli, 1143
Anthony Beccadelli, 715
Anthony Branca, 1233
Anthony Canals, 1306
Anthony Casini, 1684
Anthony Cermisone, 1196, 1238, 1243
Anthony de Compendio, 1132
Anthony da Fermo, 493
Anthony Genebreda, 1306
Anthony Guainerio, 1565
Anthony de La Salle, 1277
Anthony de Monopoli, 1739
Anthony da Montulmo (XIV-2), *1481*, 1106
Anthony du Moulin, 1573
Anthony of Novgorod (XII-2), v. 2, *421*, 35, 302
Anthony da Padua, 1669
Anthony de' Reboldi, 186
Anthony da Rio, 1243
Anthony, St. (IV-1), v. 1, *346*, 344
Anthony of Toledo, 1582
Anthony Tossignano, 1681
Anthony du Viennois, St., 1868
Anthony Woodville, 1303
Anthony Zeni (XIV-2), *1593*, 1300
Anthony's fire, St., 1247, 1668, 1868
anthracite, 220
anthrax, 874, 1664
antichthons, *see* antipodes
Antidotarium ad aromatorios, 446
Antidotarium Nicolai (XII-1), v. 3, 340, 1208, 1228
Antidotarium parvum, 288
Antimaco, Giulio, 1301
antimony, 289
Antioch, 185
Antioch, *see* Aphthonios; Chanson; Christopher; Erasmus; Fetellus; John; Margaret; Stephen; Theodore
antiperistasis, 543
Antiphon (V B.C.), v. 1, *93*, 82, 352
antipodes, 193, 197, 391, 515, 782
Antoine, *see* Anthony
Antoinette Bourignon, 23
Antonelli, Giovanni, 497
Antoni, *see* Anthony
Antonia Alighieri, 500
Antonio, *see* Anthony
Antonius, *see also* Anthony
Antonius Castor, 224
Antonius a Sala, 564
Antonius Silvester, 1413
Antonniotto Adorno, 1034, 1505
ants, surgical use, 844
Antuña, M. M., 1514, 1764, 1781
Antwerp, *see* Elizabeth; Lionel
Antwerp, tariff, 1111
Antyllos (II-1), v. 1, *280*, 268; v. 3, 1233
Anurādhapura, 59, 422, 977
anwār, 365
anwār wa marāqib, 56
Anziani of Imola, 1812
Anziani, Niccolò, 1291
aphrodisiacs, 296, 1763. *See also* anaphrodisiacs
Aphrodisias, *see* Alexander
Aphthonios of Antioch, 947
Apian, Peter, 1122, 1581, 1856
"Apicius," 1632
apiculture, *see* bees
Apion of Oasis, 1656
Apocaucos, 889
Apocrypha, 1878, 1890
Apollo, 1659
Apollodoros of Athens (II-2 B.C.), v. 1, *198*, 192
Apollodoros of Damascus (II-1), v. 1, *278*, 268
Apollonios of Citium (I-1 B.C.), v. 1, *215*, 790
Apollonios Dyscolos of Alexandria (II-1), v. 1, *286*, 269, 440
Apollonios of Perga (III-2 B.C.), v. 1, *173*, 791; v. 2, 1148; v. 3, 128, 430, 738, 900, 1487
Apollonios of Tyana, 759, 1074, 1382
apoplexy, 1731
apostemes, 869
apostles, pseudo, 404
apothecaries, 290
apothecary shop, 1248
Apotheker, 1666
Appian (II-2), v. 1, *311*, 290
Appius Claudius Caecus (IV-2 B.C.), v. 1, *143*, 126, 127
Aprenos, *see* John
Apros, metropolite, 951
Apsyrtos (IV-1), v. 1, *356*, 791; v. 3, 1837
Apuleius, Lucius (II-2), v. 1, *296*, 253, 289; v. 3, 270, 1104
Apuleius, pseudo (V-1), v. 1, *392*, 379, 421; v. 2, 132, 226
'Aqīl, b., 1015
'aql wa ma'qūl, 431, 594
'Aqnīn, *see* Joseph b. Judah
aqrābādhīn, 443, 836
'Aqrish, Isaac, 1523
Āqsarā'ī, *see* Muḥammad b. Muḥammad
aqua regia, 177

aqua et terra, 483
Aquario, baths of, 1240
aquavitae fathers, 1036
Aquila, *see* John
Aquileia, *see* Bertrand
Aquin, L. H. d', 604
Aquin, Philippe, 594
Aquinas, *see* Thomas
Aquino, Carlo d', 482
aqwāl kāfīya, 827
'Arabī, b., *see* Muḥammad b. 'Abdallāh; Muḥammad b. 'Alī
Arabia, 1891
Arabian nights, *see* Alf laila
Arabic, 364, 367, 370, 561, 1904
Arabic, *see* astronomy; dosimetry; falconry
Arabic-Jewish literature, 1904
Arabic-Latin glossary (XI-2), v. 1, *782*
Arabic letter writing, 1839
Arabic literature, 1875, 1887, 1903
Arabic MSS, 1878, 1881, 1883. *See also* iconography
Arabic, *see* mathematics; medicine; music; numerals
Arabic philology (VII-1), v. 1, *485*, 463
Arabic, *see* science
Arabic-Spanish literature, 1886, 1900
Arabs, *see* navigation
'Arabshāh, b., *see* Aḥmad b. Muḥammad
Arachiel (Arakel) of Sunik, 1095, 1323, 1442
Aramaic, 356, 364, 367
Aratos of Soli (III-1 B.C.), v. 1, *157*, 791; v. 2, 616
arba' ṭurim, 100, 320, 614
Arc, *see* Joan
Arceo, Francisco, 1704
Arcerianus, Codex (V-1), v. 1, *397*, 379
archaei. 905
archaeology, Chinese (XII-1), v. 2, *262*
Archagathos the Peloponnesian (III-2 B.C.), v. 1, *175*, 166
Archelaos of Athens (V B.C.), v. 1, *87*, 81, 82
Archer, J. C., 1476
Archer, T. A., 115, 562, 564, 1742, 1746
Archerius, 1131
archery, 1865. *See also* bows and arrows
Archeion, 1872
Archigenes of Apamea (II-1), v. 1, *280*, 791; v. 3, 871
Archiloge Sophie, 1411
Archimatthaeus of Salerno (XII-1), v. 2, *238*, 1149
Archimede, *see* James Mariano
Archimedes (III-2 B.C.), v. 1, *169*, 791; v. 2, 1149; v. 3, 128, 145, 147, 430, 431, 735, 738, 900, 1031, 1126, 1487, 1518, 1566
architecture, Byzantine, 1907
architecture, *see* Gothic
Archiv für Geschichte der Medizin, 1872
Archivio di storia della scienza, 1873
Archytas of Tarentum (IV-1 B.C.), v. 1, *116*, 111, 112; v. 3, 158, 738
Arckel, *see* John
Arcone, *see* Cecco
arctic exploration, 1897
arctic regions, 1145
Arderiu, Enric, 862
Arderne, *see* John
Arendt, W. W., 726
Arensberg, Walter, 492, 500
areometer, 1566
Aretaeos of Cappadocia (II-2), v. 1, *307*, 289; v. 3, 275
Arethas (IX-2), v. 1, *618*, 588, 589
Arezzo, *see* Bernard; Guido; Leonard Bruni; Minuccio; Ristoro
Arfa' ra'sahu, b., *see* 'Alī b. Mūsā
Argelata, *see* Peter
Argelati, Philip, 854
Argentina Spinola, 458
Arghūn (īl-khān), 202, 833
Arghūn Kāmil, 1249
Arghūn (name), 1852
Arghūn Nāṣirī, 173
Argons, 1852
Argote de Molina, Gonzalo, 925, 1142, 1474
Argyros, *see* Isaac
Ari Fróthi Thorgilsson (XII-1), v. 2, *259*, 1149; v. 3, 303, 352, 715
Arianism, viii
Arias, Gino, 499
'Arīb b. Sa'd (X-2), v. 1, *680*, 791; v. 2, 341, 1118
'arīf, 154
Arika, abba (III-1), v. 1, *317*, 314
Arios (IV-1), v. 1, *348*. *See also* Arianism
Arisi, Francesco, 1680
Aristaces the Grammarian (XIII-1), v. 2, *699*, 532; v. 3, 356
Aristaeos (IV-2 B.C.), v. 1, *140*, 125
Aristarchos of Samos (III-1 B.C.), v. 1, *156*, 150, 602; v. 2, 1002, 1008
Aristarchos of Samothrace (II-1 B.C.), v. 1, *189*, 179, 183
Aristippus of Catania (XII-2), v. 2, *346*, 1149
Aristophanes of Athens, 997, 1005, 1495
Aristophanes of Byzantium (II-1 B.C.), v. 1, *189*, 179, 657
Aristotelian tradition (XIII-1), v. 2, *567*, 859; (XIII-2), v. 2, *859*
Aristotle (IV-2 B.C.), v. 1, *127*, 791; v. 2, 1149; v. 3, x, 13, 14, 36, 61, 62, 64, 65, 66, 77, 80, 81, 82, 83, 114, 134, 141, 142, 145, 146, 147, 148, 197, 208, 211, 214, 216, 242, 266, 268, 318, 331, 378, 398, 399, 400, 428, 434, 435, 440, 442, 452, 484, 488, 497, 501, 507, 508, 517, 518, 520, 529, 532, 534, 535, 540, 547, 550, 552, 558, 560, 562, 563, 568, 574, 577, 584, 589, 590, 704, 709, 736, 738, 739, 750, 751, 753, 792, 801, 812, 828, 836,

840, 843, 844, 847, 849, 856, 870, 873, 879, 881, 885, 937, 952, 990, 992, 1004, 1074, 1075, 1085, 1086, 1087, 1088, 1091, 1094, 1095, 1096, 1123, 1144, 1148, 1171, 1192, 1201, 1220, 1229, 1230, 1235, 1243, 1271, 1275, 1307, 1321, 1377, 1381, 1384, 1387, 1393, 1404, 1429, 1432, 1433, 1434, 1447, 1451, 1452, 1465, 1487, 1490, 1492, 1495, 1504, 1519, 1539, 1564, 1568, 1596, 1637, 1639, 1640, 1673, 1683, 1694, 1710, 1714, 1723, 1755, 1759, 1771, 1798, 1808, 1831, 1844, 1862, 1863, 1869, 1885
Aristotle, *see* Lapidary
Aristotle, pseudo, 1104
Aristotle, *see* Theology
Aristotle's masterpiece, 1229
Aristoxenos of Tarentum (IV-2 B.C.), v. 1, *142*, 126, 426; v. 3, 161, 745
Aristyllos of Alexandria (III-1 B.C.), v. 1, *156*, 150
arithmetic, 1887, 1904
arithmetic, commercial, 1484
Arkhangelsk, 194
Arler, *see* Henry
Arles, *see* Giles
Arles, Roman, 1498
Arlt, K. E., 879
Armagh, *see* Roland; Walter
Armagnac, *see* Bernard
Armagnac, count of, 1629
Armana prouvençau, 1303
Armengaud, son of Blaise (XIII-2), v. 2, *831*, 1149; v. 3, 61, 65, 67, 254, 792, 1374, 1831
Armenia, 1894, 1896
Armenian, 356, 415, 1882, 1897, 1898, 1904
Armenian church, 392, 1830
Armenian Gospel, 235
Armenians, 776, 996
Armenians of Cilicia, 54
Armenopulos, *see* Constantine
Armentières, *see* Peronnelle
Armitage, Frederick, 153
arms and armor, 144, 722, 1125, 1547, 1555
Arnáiz, Greg., 1589
Arnald, Arnaldo, *see* Arnold
Arnaud, Arnaut, *see* Arnold
Arnauld, *see* Alexander
Arnauld, Pierre, 1577
Arnold of Bruxelles, 1565
Arnold of Cologne, 935
Arnold Doneldey, 1205, 1319, 1711
Arnold of Naples, 836
Arnold Pannartz, 399
Arnold del Puey, 1499
Arnold of Quinquempoix (XIV-1), *453*, 65, 67, 68, 113, 346, 442
Arnold of Saxony (XIII-1), v. 2, *592*, 1150
Arnold, T. W., 1179, 1873, 1883
Arnold, Thomas, 1349
Arnold of Villanova (XIII-2), v. 2, *893*, 1150; v. 3, 22, 44, 60, 65, 89, 119, 166, 178, 245, 247, 254, 264, 273, 278, 285, 315, 375, 396, 412, 426, 449, 750, 752, 754, 834, 853, 854, 856, 873, 876, 877, 878, 892, 983, 1074, 1116, 1117, 1199, 1211, 1212, 1219, 1221, 1242, 1243, 1374, 1381, 1382, 1383, 1499, 1572, 1576, 1578, 1579, 1669, 1705, 1714, 1719, 1831, 1861
Arnold Winkelried, 1021
Arnould, E. J., 462, 1855
Arntz, Helmut, 1609
Aronchel, *see* Peter
Arpee, Leon, 1830, 1842, 1864
Arqam, b., *see* Muḥammad b. Riḍwān
arqām hindīya, 798
Arquà, *see* James
Arquà Petrarca, 505
Arragel, *see* Moses
Arras, 727
Arras, *see* Thomas
Arrian the Historian, Arrianus Flavius (II-1), v. 1, *284*, 791; v. 2, 395; v. 3, 1818
Arrian the Meteorologist (II-1 B.C.), v. 1, *184*, 178
arrows, *see* bows
Arroyo, *see* Isaac b. Moses
ars amatoria, 296
ars antiqua, 743, 1845
ars contrapunctus, 742
ars dictaminis, *see* dictamen
ars navigativa spiritualis, 393
ars notaria, 1295
ars nova, 159, 346, 740, 1567, 1845
ars parva, 431
ars perfecta, 742
ars praedicandi, 1040
ars vetus, 534
arsenic, 289, 754
Arsenios, bishop, 826
Ārsheyabrāhmaṇa, 1369
art, 20
art, Byzantine, 1881
art, Christian (XIII-2), v. 2, *824*, 713
Artachaees the Persian (V B.C.), v. 1, *95*, 82
arte illuminandi, De, 168
arte metallica, De, 1877
arte metallorum, De, 44
Artelt, Walter, 266
Artemidoros Daldianos (II-2), v. 1, *295*, 289, 558; v. 3, 952, 1640
Artemidoros of Ephesos (II-2 B.C.), v. 1, *196*, 192
"Artephius" (XII-1), v. 2, *219*, 1150; v. 3, 1577
artesian wells (XII-1), v. 2, *217*, 28, 128
Artevelde, *see* James; Philip
artha, 1000
arthaśāstra, 1000
arthritism, *see* gout

Arthur, J. P., 1361
Articella, 844
articuli, 132, 1483, 1533
artillery, 38, 1888
artisans, portraits of, 1128
Artois, comte d', 1152
Artois, *see* Matilda
'Aruk, 366
Arundel, *see* Thomas
Āryabhaṭa (V-2), v. 1, *409*, 792; v. 2, 213; v. 3, 1535, 1846
Arzachel, *see* Zarqālī
'aṣabīya, 1777
As'ad b. Khaṭīr b. Mammātī (XII-2), v. 2, *464*, 316
As'ad Maḥallī, *see* Ya'qūb b. Isḥāq
Asadī of Ṭūs (XI-2), v. 1, *783*, 792; v. 2, 142; v. 3, 376
Asakawa, K., 989
'Asākir, b., *see* 'Alī b. Ḥasan
āsana, 96
Asanes, *see* Andreas
Asaṅga (IV-1), v. 1, *350*, 344
Asaph Judaeus (IX-2), v. 1, *614*, 588, 683; v. 3, 1008
Asās al-qawā'id, 707
Asbagh b. Muḥammad b. Samḥ (XI-1), v. 1, *715*, 695, 702; v. 2, 837; v. 3, 128, 432, 1138
Asbeck, Melline d', 582
Ascania, *see* Conrad
Ascelin of Lombardy (XIII-1), v. 2, *641*, 37, 513
Ascheim, Selmar, 1836
Asclepiades of Bithynia (I-1 B.C.), v. 1, *214*, 203, 239; v. 3, 836
Asclepiodotos (I-1 B.C.), v. 1, *213*, 202; v. 3, 214
Asclepiodotos of Alexandria (V-2), v. 1, *405*, 399
Asclepios of Tralles (VI-1), v. 1, *423*, 415, 416
Ascoli, *see* Belardo; Cecco; Graziadei; John
Asfuzārī, *see* Muẓaffar b. Ismā'īl
Ash'arī (X-1), v. 1, *625*, 792; v. 2, 165; v. 3, 102, 422, 619, 627
Ashdown, C. H., 726
Ashendon, *see* John
Asher, A., 792
Asher, Ben, 365
Asher b. David of Posquières (XIII-1), v. 2, *607*, 502, 729
Asher b. Jehiel (XIII-2), v. 2, *888*, 732, 887; v. 3, 62, 100, 368, 613, 791, 1062, 1442
Asher b. Moses Valabrègue, 1692
Ashi (V-1), v. 1, *384*, 378, 380; v. 3, 365
'Āshiq pāshā (XIV-1), *623*, 105, 379, 1845
'Āshiq pāshā zāde, 625
Ashkenazi, *see* Eliezer
Ashmole, Elias, 1428
Ashraf Bars-bey, 1329
ashṭaka, 1368
Ashṭāṅgahṛidayasaṃhitā, 259, 1585
Ashṭāṅgasaṃgraha, 1585
Ashton, John, 1604
Ashurbanipal (VII B.C.), v. 1, *62*, 60
Aṣīl al-dīn Ḥasan, 134
'Āṣim, b., *see* Muḥammad b. Muḥammad
Asín Palacios, Miguel, xv, 85, 490, 569, 612, 1341, 1342, 1453, 1850, 1864, 1873
Aṣma'ī, (VIII-2), v. 1, *534*, 523, 524; v. 3, 376, 1636
aṣnāf, 421
Aśoka, Maurya king (III-2 B.C.), v. 1, *167*, 165
Aśoka script, 383
Asolik, *see* Stephen
'Asqalānī, *see* Aḥmad b. 'Alī
ass of Buridan, 542
ass, dispute, 1341
Assaf, S., 73
'Assāl, *see* Isḥāq
Assam, 1879
Assassins (XI-2), v. 1, *752*, 593, 739; v. 2, 1180; v. 3, 779, 969
Assemani, 487, 613, 1717, 1719
Assisi, *see* Francis
Asson, Michelangelo, 498
Assos, 1847
Assyrian-Babylonian, 364
Assyrian, *see* chemistry
Assyrian learning (VII B.C.), v. 1, *62*. *See also* Babylonian
Astegiano, Giovanni, 1671
asthma, 65, 274, 451
Asti, *see* Boniface Rotario; Malabaila
Aston, John, 779
Aston, W. G., 388, 389, 980, 1002, 1018, 1270, 1563
astrolabe, 444, 830, 951, 1114, 1375, 1378, 1421, 1498, 1512, 1515, 1517, 1525, 1527, 1530, 1637, 1886, 1903
Astrolabium Ptolemaei, 1114
Astrologia Hippocratis, 441
astrologia, Libro di, 68
astrology, 16, 17, 112, 339, 409, 430, 456, 509, 537, 539, 557, 559, 602, 900, 1338, 1640, 1772, 1797, 1817, 1833, 1874, 1889, 1903, 1908
astrology, Greek MSS, 1877
astrology, medicine, 263, 1219, 1243
astrology, meteorology, 115
astrology, music, 136, 164, 749
astronomy, 1882, 1911
astronomy, Arabic, 1833, 1905, 1907
astronomy, *see* Babylonian
astronomy, Chinese, 1833
astronomy, Germanic, 1832
astronomy, instruments, 1485, 1524
astronomy, MSS, 1911
astronomy, Roman (I-1 B.C.), v. 1, *213*
astronomy, Scandinavian, 1832

Astruc, 427
Astruc Francisco Dios Carna, 1521
Astruc b. Judah Bonsenior, 427
Astruc ha-Levi, 1061
Astruc of Lunel, 99
Astruc de Noves, Sen, 429, 434
Astruc Rimok, 1377, 1523
Astruc Samiel d'Escola, 1520
Astruc, *see* Samuel; Solomon
Astruch Bonsenyor, 427
Aśvaghosha (II-1), v. 1, *269*, 792; v. 3, 59, 312, 466
Aśvinīkumāra, 1584
Aswad Du'ālī, a. (VII-2), v. 1, *501*, 490; v. 3, 372, 1621
Ata, Galip, 1726
'Aṭā' b. Aḥmad Samarqandī (XIV-2), *1529*, 1119, 1531
'Aṭā' Malik b. Muḥammad Juwainī (XIII-2), v. 2, *1123*, 1191; v. 3, 310, 971, 977
Atalay, B., 1014
Athanasios of Alexandria, St., viii, 55, 1438
Athanasios Nikitin, 1292
Athanasios of Qūṣ, 1006, 1008
Atharvasaṃhitā, 1369
Athenaeos of Attalia (I-2), v. 1, *260*, 244; v. 3, 889
Athenaeos, mechanician (II-2 B.C.), v. 1, *196*, 191, 224
Athenaeos of Naucratis (III-1), v. 1, *326*, 316; v. 3, 353
Athenaeum, vii
Athens, 1597, 1891
Athens, plague of, 1650
Athens, *see* Stephen
Athīr, b., *see* 'Alī b. Muḥammad; Majd al-dīn
Athonism, 585, 1466
Athos, Mount, 96, 169, 584, 585, 824, 1439, 1466, 1583, 1613, 1760
Athos, wall paintings, 1866
Atīsha, 1070, 1371
'Aṭīya, A. S., 1035, 1873
Atkins, John, 1787
Atlantica, 370
atlases, 1899
atomic time, 1417, 1464
atomism, 13, 149, 180, 547, 1891, 1894, 1899
atomism, Buddhist, 149
atomism, Jaina, 149
atomism, Muslim, 1463
atra mors, 887, 1191
Ātreya (VI B.C.?), v. 1, *76*, 66, 284
Attalia, *see* Athenaeos
Attaliates, *see* Michael
Attalos III, Philometor (II-2 B.C.), v. 1, *198*, 192
'aṭṭār, 1728
'Aṭṭār, *see* Judah b. Jacob; Kūhīn
Atthadassi thera, 1731
Atticism, 353
Atticus, T. Pomponius, 333
Attila, 1101, 1474, 1865
Atumanos, *see* Simeon
aṭwāl wal-'urūḍ, 200
Atzo, medical family, 1861
Atzo, *see* William
Aubanel, Théodore, 1303
Aubenton, *see* Peronne
Auber, *see* Stephen
Aubernon, *see* John
Aucher, Jean Baptiste, 955
Audin de Rians, Etienne, 501
Auer, Albert, 1434
Auerbach, I. R., 594
Aufenstein, *see* Conrad
Aufrecht, Theodor, 1369
Augsburg, *see* David
Augustine of Canterbury, St., 1743
Augustine Dini, 1669
Augustine of Tagaste, St. (V-1), v. 1, *383*, 792; v. 2, 1151; v. 3, viii, 49, 86, 95, 164, 193, 211, 242, 401, 482, 489, 507, 511, 518, 529, 530, 551, 558, 562, 572, 574, 575, 578, 704, 873, 942, 981, 1056, 1059, 1075, 1083, 1088, 1093, 1107, 1277, 1288, 1308, 1322, 1353, 1363, 1387, 1388, 1390, 1417, 1490, 1506, 1706, 1797, 1816, 1831, 1869
Augustine of Trent (XIV-1), *648*, 112, 243
Augustine Trionfo (XIV-1), *985*, 113, 130, 314
Augustinianism, 1908
Augustinians (XIII-1), v. 2, *550*, 487; v. 3, 84, 212, 1359
Aungerville, *see* Richard
Aura, *see* Ekkehard
aura, medicine, 875
Aureliana, *see* Admetus
Aurelius Antoninus, Marcus (II-2), v. 1, *297*, 792
Aurelius, physician (VI-1), v. 1, *434*, 392, 417
Aurillac, *see* Durand; Gerbert
Auriol, Blaise, 991
Auriol, *see* Peter
Aurispa, *see* John
aurochs, 1190
aurora borealis (XIV-1), *709*, 142, 143, 560, 1123, 1743, 1744
aurum musicum, musivum, 169
Ausías March, 511
Ausonius of Bordeaux (IV-2), v. 1, *369*, 360, 361; v. 2, 47; v. 3, 922, 1288, 1786
Austin, H. D., 1859
Austria, *see* Leopold
Autolycos of Pitane (IV-2 B.C.), v. 1, *141*, 792; v. 2, 1151; v. 3, 900
autopsies, 265, 848, 1224, 1699
Autrecourt, *see* Nicholas
Autun, *see* Honorius
Auvergne, *see* Durand; Peter; William
Auvray, Lucien, 495
Auxerre, *see* Guy; Lambert; Remi

Auxon, *see* Peter
Auzels cassadors, 339
Avadhūta, 425
Avalokiteśvara, 1854
Avalon, Arthur, 1070
Avanzio Colle, 1668
Avelingh, G. H. Van S., 458
Avena, A., 922
Avencebrol, *see* b. Gabirol
Avendagot, *see* Joseph b. a. Ayyūb
Avenel, Georges d', 249, 284, 291, 1245, 1284
Averardo, *see* Eberhard (the English form is Everard)
Averill, Mary, 1332
Averroës, *see* b. Rushd
Averroism, 13, 82, 83, 443, 507, 562
Aversó, *see* Lewis
Avesbury, *see* Robert
Avesta, 376
Avicebron, *see* b. Gabirol
Avicenna, *see* b. Sīnā
Avienos, Rufus Festus (IV-2), v. 1, *371*, 258, 360
Avienus, Jacobus, 189
Avignon, 44, 57, 328, 1875
Avignon, *see* Isaac b. Ṭodros; John; Pelegrin; Raymond
Avignon, University, 72, 470, 1079
Avkerian, priest, 955
avogario, 750
avoué, 1601
'Awad, Girgis Filoteos, 1007
Awans and Waroux, 1750
'Awfī, *see* Muḥammad
'Awwām, *see* Yaḥyā b. Muḥammad
Axon, W. E. A., 458
Ayad, M. K., 1778
Ayala, *see* López
Ayās, 44, 1035
Ayenbite of inwyt, 68, 462, 1314
Aymus, H., 562
Ayuli Palpata, 42, 386
Āyurveda, 259, 262, 265, 1217
Ayuthia, 1030
Ayyangar, H. S., 383
Ayyangar, S. K., 41
Ayyar, L. K. A., 360
Ayyūb Ruhāwī Abrash (IX-1), v. 1, *574*, 547, 549
Ayyub, *see* Solomon b. Joseph
Ayyūbī dynasty, 102
Azaïs, Gabriel, 339
'Azariah b. Joseph b. abba Mari, 451
'Azīz Suryāl, *see* 'Aṭīya
Azo of Bologna (XIII-1), v. 2, *689*, 1152; v. 3, 319
Azores islands, 184, 786, 1156, 1591
Azraqī, *see* Ibrāhīm b. 'Abd al-Raḥmān
Azriel b. Menaḥem (XIII-1), v. 2, *606*, 1152
azulejo, 757, 1134
Ba'albek, 1619
Ba'ale ḥayyim, 432
Baas, J. H., 1244
Bābar-nāma, 1272, 1472
Bābar, Ẓahīr al-dīn, 999, 1026, 1329, 1468, 1473, 1873
Babbage, C., 1166
Babcock, W. H., 1592, 1595
Babel, tower of, 777, 782
Babelon, Ernest, 508, 1282, 1284
Babinger, Franz, 900, 1101, 1263, 1266, 1267, 1464, 1465
Babington, B. G., 1667
Babington, Churchill, 946
Babli, *see* Eleazar b. Nathan
Bābūya, b., *see* Muḥammad b. 'Alī
Babylonian, 20, 113, 120, 122, 364, 365, 711, 712, 1103, 1113, 1658, 1773, 1832, 1833, 1836. *See also* Assyrian
Babylonian astronomy (VI B.C.), v. 1, *71*
Babylonian captivity, 44, 1019
Babylonian, *see* chemistry
baccalarius formatus, 79
Bacchi della Lega, Alberto, 775, 1808
Bacci, Orazio, 913, 983
Bacci, Peleo, 171, 983
Bacher, Wilhelm, 593, 1009, 1523
Backer, Louis de, *see* Baecker
backgammon, 1640
backstaff, *see* cross-staff
Bacon, F. H., 1847
Bacon, Francis, 576
Bacon, *see* John; Roger; Thomas
Baconthorpe, *see* John
baculus Jacobi, *see* cross-staff
Bade, Josse, 545
bādhahanj, 1528
Badī' Aṣṭurlābī, *see* Hibatallāh b. Ḥusain
Badī' al-jamāl, princess, 1729
Badoer, *see* Jacob
Badr, b., *see* Muḥammad b. 'Umar
Badr al-dīn, *see* b. Mundhir, 828
Badr al-munīr, 758
Badt-Strauss, Bertha, 1523
Baechtold, J., 574
Bächtold-Stäubli, Hanns, 1873, 1887
Baecker, Louis de, 776, 955
Baeda, *see* Bede
Baer, Fritz, 419, 428, 1385, 1593
Baer, I. F., 1841
Baethcke, Hermann, 1232
Bäumer, Eduard, 288
Bagchi, P. C., 382, 468, 1873
Bagenal, Hope, 1570
Baghdād, 1893
Baghdād, sack, 1264
Baghdād, *see* Simeon
Baghdādī, *see* Aḥmad b. 'Alī Khaṭīb; 'Alī b.

Anjab; Muḥammad b. 'Abd al-Bāqī; Muḥammad b. Ḥamdūn
Baglivi, Giorgio, 1220, 1299, 1666
Bagnolo, *see* Guido; Leo
Bagrow, Leo, vii, 1852, 1865
Bahā' al-dīn Aḥmad, 622
Bahāniqī, *see* Aḥmad b. Muḥammad
Bahir, 363, 1522
Bahlūl a. Ḥasan, b. (X-2), v. 1, *689*, 793; v. 3, 358
Bahmanī dynasty, 1237
baḥr al-muḥīṭ, 58
Baḥtawī, *see* Joseph
Baḥya b. Asher of Saragossa (XIV-1), *416*, 55, 100, 208, 212
Baḥya b. Joseph b. Paquda (XII-1), v. 2, *184*, 1152; v. 3, 1443
Baibars Manṣūrī (XIV-1), *961*, 308, 1006, 1780
Baibars, sulṭān, 379
Baiḍāwī, 'Abdallāh b. 'Umar (XIII-2), v. 2, *870*, 1152; v. 3, 971, 976, 1011, 1067, 1727
Baihaqī, *see* 'Alī b. Ḥusain; 'Alī b. Zaid
Bailak b. Muḥammad Qabajaqī (XIII-2), v. 2, *1072*, 1152; v. 3, 714
Bailey, T. G., 1477
Baillie, G. H., 1873
Baillie-Grohman, Wm. A. and F., 1631
Bain, D. C., 921
Baisio, *see* Guido
Baist, Gottfried, 925
bait, 154
bait midrash, 254
Baiṭār, b., 'Abdallāh b. Aḥmad (XIII-1), v. 2, *663*, 1152; v. 3, 289, 898, 1222, 1724, 1727
baiṭara, 622
Baiṭarname, *see* Bayṭarname
baitim, 419
Bājja, b., *see* Muḥammad b. Yaḥyā
Baker, Augustine, 1416, 1417
Baker, E. A., 456
Baker, *see* Geoffrey Le Baker
Bakhshāli manuscript (XII-1), v. 2, *214*, 128
Bakhtyashū', b., *see* Jirjis b. Jibrīl; 'Ubaidallāh b. Jibrīl
Baklamishī, *see* Ṭaibughā b. 'Abdallāh
Bakr b. Aḥmad b. Shuhba, a., 1265, 1266
Bakr b. 'Alī b. Ḥijjah of Ḥamāh, a., 1640, 1786
Bakr b. Badr al-dīn, a., *see* b. Mundhir
Bakr b. Bashrūn, a., 1138
Bakr, a., caliph, 106
Bakr, Ḥasan b. Khaṣīb, a. (IX-2), v. 1, *603*, 585, 590; v. 2, 126, 562
Bakr b. Muḥammad Karakī, a. (XIV-1), *697*, 134
Bakr b. Muẓhir, a. (XII-2), v. 2, *365*
Bakr Rāzī, a., *see* Aḥmad b. Muḥammad Rāzī
Bakr Ṭurṭūshī, a., *see* Muḥammad b. al-Walīd
Bakrī of Cordova, 'Abdallāh b. 'Abd al-'Azīz (XI-2), v. 1, *768*, 793; v. 3, 801, 1158
Baktāsh, Ḥājjī, 105, 420, 623, 625, 1460
Baktāshī, 1460, 1841, 1874
Baktāshī cosmology, 213
Baktāshīya, 57, 105, 155, 212, 420, 1068
Bākuwī, *see* 'Abd al-Rashīd b. Ṣāliḥ
Balaban, M., 56
Balādhurī, Aḥmad b. Yaḥyā (IX-2), v. 1, *616*, 588, 590
Baladī, Aḥmad b. Muḥammad (X-2), v. 1, *679*, 651, 654
Balaguer y Merino, Andreu, 1375
balance foliot, 144, 718, 720, 1545
balance, *see* wheel
Bālāsāghunī, *see* Muḥammad
Balau, Sylvain, 221, 1395
Bālāvatāra, 1371
Balawī, *see* Khālid b. 'Īsā
Balbān, 803
Balbi, *see* John
Balbi, Melchiorre, 741
Balbin, A. B., 1352, 1757
Balboa, *see* Gonzalve
Balbus (II-1), v. 1, *271*, 793
Balch, T. W., 1496
Bald, leechbook (X-1), v. 1, *633*, 621
Baldass, Ludwig, 336
Baldassare, *see* Balthasar
Baldasseroni, F., 1686
Baldelli, G. B., 1810
Baldenstetten, *see* Henry
Baldi, Bernardino, 587, 1127
Baldo degli Ubaldi (XIV-2), *1795*, 470, 1273, 1277
Baldovino, *see* Baldwin
Baldwin II of Courtenay, astrologer to (XIII-2), v. 2, *991*, 750
Baldwin Jacopi, 124
Baldwin, king of Jerusalem, 266
Baldwin of Steinfurth, 788
Bale, John, 942, 1500, 1569
Balearic Jews, 199
Bali, 1177, 1624
Balì, *see* Nerses
Bàliol, *see* Edward
Balkh, *see* Muḥammad Badr al-dīn
Balkhī, b. (XII-1), v. 2, *221*, 39, 130
Balkhī, *see* Aḥmad b. Sahl
Ball, J. D., 1873
Ball, *see* John
Ballard, J. F., 419, 876, 1689
Ballardini, Gaetano, 1134
Ballester y Castell, Rafael, 927
ballistic, 1554
Balme, François, 784
Balmes, *see* Abraham
balneis, De, 850

balneology, 286, 1240
Balsamo, A., 493
Balthasar Cossa, 1033, 1224, 1440
Balthasar degli Embriachi, 1187
Balthasar Pavone, 1234
balzanes, 829
Balzani, Ugo, 915
Bambagliuoli, *see* Graziolo
Bamberg, *see* Frederick; Frutolf
bamboo books (III-1 B.C.), v. 1, *163*, 150, 342
bamboos, 226
Banākatī, *see* Dā'ūd b. Muḥammad
Banda Nawāz, *see* Muḥammad
Bandini, A. M., 1809
Bandini, *see* Dominic
Bandino Bianco, 1409
Banerjea, J. N., 1584
Bang, Willy, 1017
bank notes, 730
banking, international, 324
banks, state, 524
Bannā', b., *see* Aḥmad b. Muḥammad
Banus y Comas, Carlo, 927
Bāpata, K. S., 1585
baptism, compulsory, 1059
Baptist, *see* Battista
Baqā', a., *see* Ṣāliḥ b. Ḥusain
Bāqilānī, *see* Aḥmad b. 'Alī
bar, *see next word*
Baradai, *see* Jacob
barakāt, 292
Barakāt, a. (XIV-1), *1005*, 55, 97, 308, 361, 962
Baralli, D. Raffaello, 740
baraṣ, 280
Barba, Barbe, *see* John
Barbara, St., 1666
barbarian law (V-2), v. 1, *412;* (VI-1), v. 1, *439;* (VII-1), v. 1, *484;* (VIII-1), v. 1, *517;* (IX-1), v. 1, *580;* (X-1), v. 1, *643;* (XI-2), v. 1, *778*
Barbaveri, *see* Samuel b. Judah of Marseille
barbers, 272
Barbi, Michele, 492, 493, 495, 1814
Barbier de Meynard, A., 1014
Barbier de Meynard, Jules, 632
Barbieri, Luigi, 463, 858
Barbosa Machado, Diogo, 862
Barbot, André, 1689
Barbour, *see* John
Barcellos, *see* Peter
Barcelona, *see* Blase; Martin
Barclay, Alexander, 955, 1867
Bardāī, *see* Chand
Bardesanes (II-2), v. 1, *298*, 289, 332
Bardi bank of Florence, 37, 324, 772, 913, 1273, 1300, 1802, 1839
Bardi, Filippo de, 1778
Bardi, *see* Simon
Barduccio di Piero Canigiani, 1335
Barduzzi, Domenico, 1686
Barfat, *see* Isaac b. Sheshet Perfet
Barger, George, 1650, 1868
Bargès, J. J. L., 612
Barhebraeus, *see* a. Faraj Yūḥannā
barīd, 1617, 1786
Bārjīnī, *see* Maḥmūd b. Muḥammad
Barkamānī, *see* Japheth b. a. Ḥasan
Barker, Thomas, 237
Barlaam (XIV-1), *583*, 53, 95, 122, 123, 161, 355, 507, 515, 587, 588, 826, 950, 951, 952, 994, 1377, 1395, 1512, 1760
Barlaam and Ioasaph, v. 1, 507; v. 3, 340, 579, 924, 1451
Barnabas, epistles, 1341
Barnabas of Reggio (XIV-1), *856*, 244, 273, 844
Barnabò Visconti, 834, 1659
Barnes, W. H., 761
Barnett, L. D., 384, 466, 1476, 1730
Barnikol, Ernst, 1361
barometer, 1881
Barqamānī, *see* Japheth b. a. Ḥasan
Barqūq, *see* Ẓāhir
Barraclough, Geoffrey, 327, 328, 333
Barrillon, *see* John
Barrois, J., 1152
Barrow, Isaac, 737
Barthélemy, L., 1382, 1542
Barthélemy Saint-Hilaire, Jules, 146
Barthold, W., 378, 794, 1017, 1026, 1035, 1120
Bartholinus fiascarius, 171
Bartholomew de' Albizzi, 1680
Bartholomew da Alzano, 1336
Bartholomew of Bologna (XIV-1), *459*, 54, 63, 67, 97, 356, 1842
Bartholomew, *see* Breviarium
Bartholomew of Bruges (XIV-1), *885*, 94, 250
Bartholomew Casini, 1684
Bartholomew the Englishman (XIII-1), v. 2, *586*, 1153; v. 3, 91, 248, 340, 579, 1075, 1076, 1088, 1090, 1224, 1313, 1390, 1393, 1417, 1630
Bartholomew Fazio, 1233
Bartholomew dei Granchi, 1680
Bartholomew of Lucca, 314
Bartholomew, master, 1711, 1712
Bartholomew of Messina (XIII-2), v. 2, *829*, 1153; v. 3, 64, 270. 1104, 1123, 1393
Bartholomew Montagnana, 1196, 1239
Bartholomew Orologiarius, 144, 719
Bartholomew of Parma (XIII-2), v. 2, *988*, 1153
Bartholomew Perestrello, 183
Bartholomew da Pisa (XIV-2), *1680*, 1193
Bartholomew of Pisa the Elder, 87
Bartholomew of Prague, 1582
Bartholomew Prignano, 1032
Bartholomew, *see* Ptolemy of Lucca
Bartholomew of Reggio, 1234

Bartholomew of Salerno (XII-1), v. 2, *239*, 1153, 1711
Bartholomew, St., 295, 1248
Bartholomew, St., hospital, 1202, 1704
Bartholomew de San Concordio, 87, 1680
Bartholomew da Santa Sofia, 1193
Bartholomew della Scala, 346, 480, 1391
Bartholomew Siginulfo, 65
Bartholomew dalli Sonetti, 1600
Bartholomew da Tivoli, 1143
Bartholomew da Varignana (XIV-1), *841*, 244, 265, 838, 1679
Bartoli, *see* Anthony
Bartolini, Niccolò, 1290
Bartolino da Novara, 1656
Bàrtolo da Sassoferrato (XIV-2), *1793*, 176, 470, 481, 981, 982, 990, 1273, 1277, 1816, 1869
Bartolommeo, *see* Bartholomew
Bartolus, *see* Bàrtolo
Barton, *see* John
Bartsch, K., 580
Baruzi, Jean, 1864
Barzizza, *see* Cristoforo; Gasparino
Bāṣa, b., *see* Aḥmad b. Ḥasan; Ḥasan b. Muḥammad
Bascour, Hildebrand, 569
Basel, 1861
Basel, *see* Nicholas
Basevorn, *see* Robert
Bashkuwāl, b., *see* a. Qāsim b. 'Abd al-Malik
Bāshpah, 1840
Basil the Bogomil, 1853
Basil the Great, St. (IV-2), v. 1, *361*, 347, 359; v. 2, 348, 593; v. 3, viii, 825, 1513
basil, holy, 778, 1835
Basil of Novgorod, St., 728
basilica, 995
Basingstoke, *see* John
Basnage, Jacques, 414, 788, 790
Baṣra, *see* Solomon
Baṣṣāl, b., *see* Muḥammad b. Ibrāhīm
Bassanus Politus, 737, 739
Basset, René, 958, 1873, 1883
Bassi, Dominicus, 1877
Bassigny, *see* John
Bassoles, *see* John
Basṭ madad al-taufīq, 155
Batallas de Dios, 418
Baṭalyūsī (Baṭalyawsī), *see* 'Abdallāh b. Muḥammad
Bate, *see* Henry
Bateman, *see* William
Bates, W. H., 1708
Bateson, Mary, 558, 1502, 1743
Bath, *see* Adelard
Bath, order, 1039
baths, 276, 849, 1240
Bāṭinīya, 965
Batman, Stephen, 1394
Baṭrīq (VIII-2), v. 1, *537*, 793
Battaglia, Felice, 989
Battaglia, Salvatore, 1812
Battal, Aptullah, 1014
Battānī (IX-2), v. 1, *602*, 793; v. 2, 1153; v. 3, 193, 1116, 1515, 1518, 1846
Battista Beccario, 1141
Battista de Montefeltro, donna, 1862
Battistini, Mario, 1686
Baṭṭūṭa, b. (XIV-2), *1614*, 154, 283, 422, 628, 731, 756, 757, 764, 778, 802, 804, 1082, 1157, 1161, 1167, 1170, 1182, 1262, 1470, 1570, 1614, 1636, 1651, 1910
Battuti, 50
Baṭuvantuḍāve, Andris de Silva, 978, 1371
Bauchant, *see* James
Baud-Bovy, S., 160
Baudet, Louis, 1806
Baudrand, M. A., 1873, 1884
Baudry, L., 556, 1844, 1849
Bauer, Max, 1051
Baumann, Friedrich, 455
Baumgartner, Leona, 1658
Baumgartner, Matthias, 1873, 1907
Baumstark, Anton, 1007, 1873
Baverio de Baverii, 1239
Bāyazīd, 1025, 1209, 1249, 1345, 1467, 1823
Baye, *see* Nicholas
Baylaender, Heinrich, 403
Bayle, Pierre, 541, 1504, 1574
Bayley, C. C., 516
Bayon, H. P., 269
Bayṭarname, 1238
Bazin, Fr., 265
Bazmavep, 827
Bāz-nāma, 232, 1643
Bāz-nāma-yi nāṣirī, 233
Bazoches, *see* Guy
Beale, J. H., 1794
beasts of venery, five, 1630
beatific, *see* vision
Beatrice Alighieri, 500, 1803
Beatrice Portinari, 480, 482
Béatrice of Provence, 341
Beatrice of Savoy, 286, 924
Beatus, St. (VIII-2), v. 1, *536*, 522, 768
Beatus maps, 193, 767
Beaucaire, *see* Moses b. Solomon; Tanḥūm b. Moses
Beauchamp, *see* Simon
Beaudouin, Frédéric, 873
Beaufort, *see* John; Peter Roger
Beaugendre, Antoine, 228
Beaumanoir, *see* Philip
Beaumier, Auguste, 958
Beaumont, E. T., 728
Beauvais, *see* Peter; Vincent
Beauval, *see* Firmin
Beazley, C. R., 1141, 1598, 1874
Bebenburg, *see* Leopold

Beccadelli, *see* Anthony
Beccaria, Cesare Bonesana, 1339, 1656, 1870
Beccaria family, 766
Beccario, *see* Battista
Beccario Beccaria of Genoa, 493
Beccos, *see* John
Bechada, *see* Gregory
Beck, C., 742
Beck, Franz, 1862
Beck, Friedrich, 493
Beck, Heinrich, 859
Beck, W. v., 1471
Becker, C. H., 1778
Becket, *see* Thomas
Beckherrn, Carl, 933
Beckman, Natanael, 1114
Bede (VIII-1), v. 1, *510*, 793; v. 2, 1154; v. 3, 2, 116, 192, 215, 229, 369, 461, 1114, 1121, 1464, 1533, 1650, 1847
Bedersi, *see* Abraham b. Isaac
Bedford, duc de, 1202
Beduins, 1776
Beebe, William, 1520
beer, 1239
bees, 238, 306, 813, 1188
Beghards, 13, 49, 403, 574, 1032, 1054, 1089
beguines, 49, 404, 581
Béguinot, Augusto, 498
Behaim, *see* Martin
Behanan, K. T., 96
Beḥinat ha-'olam, 593
Behrend, Benzion, 1446
Beirut, *see* Anatolius; Gregory
Beis, Magdeleine, 525
Bekker, Im., 952
Bektashi, *see* Baktāshī
Bel, Alfred, 806, 1445, 1767, 1778, 1792
Bela of Styria, 933
Belardo d'Ascoli (XII-1), v. 2, *223*, 35, 131
Beldomandi, *see* Prosdocimo
Belgrano, L. T., 765
Bell, A. F. G., 1251, 1874
Bell, Charles, 1372
Bell, Gertrude L., 1458, 1769
Bell, H. I., 876
Bellanger, Justin, 1631
Belleforest, *see* Francis
Bellemère, *see* Giles
Bellenden, John, 455
Belleperche, *see* Peter
Belleval, *see* Firmin de Beauval
Bellifortis, 1550, 1866
Belloni, Antonio, 515
bells, church, 144, 219
bells, founding, 727
Bellshom, *see* Ephraim; Ephraim Gerondi
Belon, Pierre, 229, 1241
Beltrán de la Cueva, 1736
Beltrando di San Genesio, 856
Belvalkar, S. K., 1841
Belvisi, *see* James
Bembo, *see* Peter
ben, *see next word*
Benastruc, 427
Bennattibus, *see* 'Abdallāh b. Ṭaiyib
Benaya, *see* Solomon
Benci, Antonio, 915
Bencivenni, *see* Zucchero
Bendig 'Ain (XIV-2), *1719*, 1212
Bene, *see* Francis
Bêne or Bennes, *see* Amaury
Benecke, G. F., 580
Benedetti, Giambattista, 1126, 1127
Benedetto Rinio, 1163, 1176, 1177, 1182
Benedict of Mantua, 1671
Benedict XI, pope, 43, 412
Benedict XII, pope, 45, 49, 387, 402, 471, 585
Benedict XIII, pope, 1032, 1061, 1142, 1339, 1440, 1796
Benedict, S. R., 1874
Benedict, St. (VI-1), v. 1, *419*, 783; v. 2, 155, 1087; v. 3, 395
Benedictine order, decline of (XII-1), v. 2, *154*, 1154
Beneš of Weitmil (Weitmühl) (XIV-2), *1757*, 1259, 1322, 1836
Benevento, *see* Marc
Benevenutus, *see also* Benveniste; Benvenuto
Benevenutus Grassus (XII-1), v. 2, *243*, 1154; v. 3, 340, 451, 883, 1234
Bengālī, 1330
Bengesla, *see* b. Jazla
Bengt Knutsson, 1687
Benincasa, *see* James
Benini, R., 498
Benjacob, Isaac, 592
Benjamin b. Abraham 'Anav (XIII-2), v. 2, *1118*, 1154
Benjamin, F. S., jr., 1834
Benjamin b. Isaac of Carcassonne (XIV-2), *1383*, 1074, 1212, 1604
Benjamin b. Jonah of Tudela (XII-2), v. 2, *414*, 1154; v. 3, 777, 793, 1379
Benjamin b. Moses Nahawendi (IX-1), v. 1, *550*, 820; v. 3, 56
benoîts, livres, 347
Bensa, Enrico, 774
Benson, A. B., 1612
Benveniste, *see also* Benevenutus; Benvenuto
Benveniste, *see* Samuel; Sheshet b. Isaac; Vidal b. Labi
Benveniste della Caballeria, 1377
Benveniste b. Solomon b. Labi, 1377
Benvenuto, *see also* Benevenutus; Benveniste
Benvenuto dei Campesani, 919
Benvenuto da Imola, 1812
Benvenuto da Pizzano, 1480
Benvenuto de' Rambaldi (XIV-2), *1812*, 494, 1052, 1086, 1105, 1135, 1210, 1288, 1299
Benz, Ernst, 570

Benzi, *see* Francis; Hugh; Socino
Benzo Cona d'Alessandria (XIV-1), *922*, 299, 912
benzoin, 1620
Berakya b. Naṭronai ha-Naqdan (XII-2), v. 2, *349*, 1154; v. 3, 366, 439, 714, 1450
Berardelli, D. M., 1164
Berardi, *see* Cristoforo
Beraud, P., 1578
Berber, 367, 764, 1617, 1725, 1768, 1772, 1774
Berchem, Max v., 795, 1589
Berchorius, *see* Peter Bersuire
Berengario da Carpi, Jacopo, 440, 844
Berengarius, 68
Berengarius, *see* Andreas
Berengarius of Compostela, 583
Berengarius Eymericus de Valentia, 863
Bérenger of Frédol, 593
Bérenger of Montpellier, 246
Berenger of Thumba (XIV-1), *863*, 246
Berenguier of Noya, 341
Berg, *see* Henry
Bergamo, *see* Moses
Bergen, *see* Hákon
Bergen, Henry, 47, 1805, 1874, 1894
Bergendoff, Conrad, 1356
Berger, Claude?, 17
Berger, Elie, 847
Berger, Ernst, 170
Berger, Samuel, 346, 458, 1389, 1390
Bergeron, Pierre, 184, 955
Bergler, Stephan, 1156
Bergsträsser, G., 431, 1456
Bergström, Rich., 575
Bergthórsson, *see* Bjarni
beriberi, 905
Berkeley, lord of, 1393
Berlaer, *see* Mary
Berliner, Abraham, 1452
Berlinghieri, *see* Francis
Bernai, *see* Alexander
Bernard Alberti (XIV-2), *1690*, 851, 1074, 1200, 1212, 1222, 1381
Bernard di Alemagna, 1709
Bernard of Arezzo, 546
Bernard d'Armagnac, 1022
Bernard Barlaam, *see* Barlaam
Bernard of Chartres (XII-1), v. 2, *195*, 1154; v. 3, 870
Bernard of Clairvaux, St. (XII-1), v. 2, *155*, 1154; v. 3, 239, 395, 532, 574, 860, 990, 1879
Bernard Colle, 1668
Bernard Délicieux (XIV-1), *412*, 51
Bernard Desclot (XIII-2), v. 2, *1108*, 794; v. 3, 300, 342, 926, 949, 1734
Bernard Dezcoll, 1734
Bernard of Frankfurt (XIV-2), *1709*, 1113, 1205, 1219
Bernard of Gordon (XIV-1), *873*, 248, 278, 608, 836, 866, 879, 880, 881, 882, 883, 892, 1074, 1205, 1212, 1221, 1235, 1243, 1375, 1379, 1380, 1664, 1683, 1688, 1690, 1697, 1703, 1705, 1709, 1851
Bernard Gui (XIV-1), *403*, 50, 301, 318, 401, 459, 1052, 1075, 1338, 1392
Bernard, Henri, 140, 808
Bernard the Lombard, 525
Bernard Metge (XIV-2), *1820*, 1087, 1304
Bernard Oliver (XIV-1), *520*, 89, 1305, 1843
Bernard Português, 246
Bernard of Provence (XII-2), v. 2, *440*, 309
Bernard de Pujol, 246
Bernard a Rey, 995
Bernard Rike?, 1428
Bernard of Rostock, 888
Bernard of Saxony, 888
Bernard of Seminara, *see* Barlaam
Bernard Silvester (Sylvester) of Tours (XII-1), v. 2, *198*, 1154; v. 3, 192, 1418
Bernard de So, 1305
Bernard Thesaurarus, 185
Bernard Tolomei, 47, 395
Bernard Torius, 1685
Bernard of Treves, 1131, 1137, 1480, 1579
Bernard of Trilia (XIII-2), v. 2, *989*, 749, 758
Bernard of Verdun (XIII-2), v. 2, *990*, 1154; v. 3, 114, 398, 524, 1112, 1436
Bernard, *see* William
Bernard the Wise (IX-2), v. 1, *605*, 586, 589
Bernard Wittepennig, 1246
Bernardin, *see* Bernardino; Naddino?
Bernardino of Siena, St., 397
Bernardino Ugolini, 124
Bernat, *see* Bernard
Bernelinus of Paris (XI-1), v. 1, *714*, 793
Berners, *see* Juliana
Berossos the Babylonian (III-1 B.C.), v. 1, *162*, 150, 262
Berr, Michel, 594
Berridge, W. A., 324
Berry, *see* John
Bersman, Gregor, 826
Bersuire, *see* Peter
Bertaldi, G. L., 1196
Bertalot, Ludovicus, 493
Bertharius (IX-2), v. 1, *607*, 587, 589
Berthelet, T., 556, 1394
Berthelot, Marcellin, 1551
Berthels, E., 975, 1459, 1728
Bertherand, Alphonse, 1725
Berthold of Bucheck, 934
Berthold of Freising, 1508
Berthold of Mosburg (XIV-1), *568*, 92, 118
"Berthold der Schwarze" (XIV-2), *1581*, 1137, 1319
Berthold of Strassburg, 935
Berti, *see* Michael
Bertin, L. E., 980
Bertin monastery, St., 1753
Bertoni, G., 336, 493, 1292

Bertram, *see also* Beltrán; Beltrando; Bertrand
Bertram, Charles, 1744
Bertrand of Aquileia, 933
Bertrand Boysset (XIV-2), *1498*, 1110, 1189, 1254, 1302
Bertrand de Got, 43, 1031
Bertrand du Guesclin, 1020, 1021, 1022, 1894
Bertrand, Léon, 1630
Bertrand, *see* Peter
Bertruccio, *see* Nicholas
Bertuccio, 727
Berwick and Alba, duke of, 490, 1077
Besalù, *see* Raymond Vidal
Besançon, *see* Gerland; Stephen
Beshiẓi, *see* Elijah b. Moses
Bessarion, cardinal, 587, 1036
Besseler, Heinrich, 743
Bessnitzer, *see* Ulreuch
Besso, Marco, 561
Bestes, *see* Theodore
bestiaries, 239, 824, 1178
betel, 1620
Béthencourt, Galien de, 184
Béthencourt, *see* John
Béthune, *see* Eberhard; Robert
Bett, Henry, 355
Bettinus, *see* Gabranus
Betussi, Giuseppe, 1805
Beues of Hamtoun, 1720
Beukels, *see* Gillis; William
Bevan, Frances, 572
Beveridge, W., 995, 1350
Bezdechi, St., 952
Béziers, 255
Béziers, *see* Jedaiah b. Abraham; Matfre Ermengaut; Raymond; Solomon b. Joseph b. Ayyub
Bezold, Carl, 1874
Bhagavadgītā, 384, 1367, 1475, 1841
Bhāgavatapurāṇa, 1367
bhakti, 425
Bhāratītīrtha, 1367
Bhāskara (XII-1), v. 2, *212*, 1155; v. 3, 1121, 1535
Bhāskara, Telugu poet, 107, 384, 634
Bhāṭṭasāra, 1367
Bhesajjamañjūsā, 1731
Bhīmapāla, 1730
Bhujanga Rao Bahadur, R. M., 384, 466
Biagi, Guido, 492, 493
Biagi, Vincenzo, 494
Biagio, *see* Blase
Bianchi, 37, 480
Bianco, *see* Andrew
Bibago, *see* Abraham
Bībī Khānum, 1470
Bible, 79, 437
Bible, Jewish Castilian, 1855
Bible, women's, 1720
Biblesworth, *see* Walter
Bibliander, Theodore, 1388, 1761
Biblical encyclopaedia, 454
biblicus ordinarius, 79
Bibliotheca mathematica, 1874
Bibowiẓ, Naḥmu, 1520
Bichr Farès, 308
Bickell, J. W., 991
Bicknell, Herman, 1458
Bidez, Joseph, xv, 376, 1874, 1876
Bielowski, August, 1759
Bientinesi, Giuseppina, 411
Bierne, *see* Gerald
Bigongiari, Dino, 499
Bigourdan, G., 561
Bihl, Michael, 397
Bihlmeyer, Karl, 574
Bījagaṇita, 1535
Bījagaṇitāvataṃsa, 1535
Biklārish, b., *see* Yūsuf b. Isḥāq
Bila, *see* David b. Yom-ṭob
Bilancioni, Guglielmo, 499
Bilfinger, Gustav, 722
bills of credit, 1838
bills of exchange, 1273, 1279, 1795, 1838
Bilmanis, Alexander, 932
Bilqīs, 1779
Bīmāristān al-Manṣūrī, 828, 1248, 1727
Bindi, Enrico, 983
Bindoni, Giuseppe, 496
Bingen, *see* Hildegard
Biörnonis, Stephanus, 1114
Biographisches Lexikon, 1874
Biondo, *see* Flavio
Biot, Edouard, 1121, 1122
Birch, T. B., 556
Birch-Hirschfeld, Adolf, 1428
Birchington, *see* Stephen
Bird, Hubert, 1786
Bird, Otto, 838
birdlime, *see* fowling
birds, domestic, 862
birds, invasions, 239
birds in navigation, 1848
birds, *see also* ornithology; volucraries
Birge, J. K., 625, 1874
Birger Persson, 1354
Birgitta of Sweden, St. (XIV-2), *1354*, 1036, 1042, 1056, 1319, 1322, 1353, 1416, 1862
Biringuccio, Vannoccio, 1174, 1554
birkat al-mallāḥa, 1187
Birkenmajer, Alexander, 534, 706, 1005, 1708
Birkenmajer, Ludwik, 1510
Birnbaum, Salomo, 1326, 1720
Birs-i-Nimrūd, 777
Bīrūnī (XI-1), v. 1, *707*, 794; v. 2, 1155; v. 3, xi, 105, 133, 200, 202, 213, 377, 970, 1584, 1775, 1832
Birzāla, 958

Birzālī, *see* Fāṭima b. Qāsim; Qāsim b. Muḥammad
Bischoff, Conrad, 1819
Bishop collection, 1471
Bishop, Morris, vi
bishops, list, 1884
Bishr, b., *see* Mufaḍḍal b. Mājid
Bisliches, M. L., 610
bismuth, 1137
bison, 1190
Bisṭāmī, 1101, 1263
Biṭrūjī (XII-2), v. 2, *399*, 1155; v. 3, 114, 129, 440, 497, 539, 544, 599, 1430
Bitschin, *see* Conrad
bitumen, 797
Bi'ur 'al ha-Torah, 416
Bizyenos, G. T., 1247
Bjarnason, Björn, 232
Bjarni Bergthórsson (XII-2), v. 2, *404*, 1155; v. 3, 1114
Björck, Gudmund, 1837
Björkman, Erik, 579
Björkman, Walther, 804, 1788
Björn Einarsson, Jórsalafarer (XIV-2), *1608*, 1154, 1319
Björn the Rich, 1608
Björnbo, A. A., 1155
Bjork, D. K., 1021
Blacas de Laprade, 1200
Blachère, Régis, 799, 1263, 1620, 1874
Black, G. F., 1051, 1852
Black book of the Admiralty, 324, 1423, 1838
Black Death (XIV-2), *1650*, 39, 196, 215, 274, 608, 914, 1019, 1191, 1621, 1876. *See also* plague
Blades, William, 1166
Blaeu, Jan, 1158
Blagden, C. O., 1627
Blaise, *see* Blase
Blake, R. P., 28, 305
Blakeslee, A. F., 1048
Blakiston, H. E. D., 1423
Blanca, infanta Doña, 418
Blanche, *see also* Blanca
Blanche de Bourbon, 1021
Blanche de La Marche, 541
Blanche of Lancaster, 1855
Blanche of Namur, 1354
Blanche of Navarre, 1393
Blanchet, Augustin, 176
Blandy, *see* John
Blanes, *see* James Ferrer III
Blas y Buysa, 190
Blase of Barcelona, 1130
Blase de Forlivio, 1246
Blase, *see* John
Blase Pelacani (XIV-2), *1564*, 739, 1086, 1106, 1123, 1126, 1127, 1488
Blase of Sebaste, St., 1666
Blasius, *see* Blase
blast furnaces, 220, 1174
Blastares, *see* Matthew
Blau, Ludwig, 1519
Blemmydes, *see* Nicephoros
blind persons, 959
Bliss, H. E., 77
Bloch, Iwan, 892
Bloch, Marc, 872
Bloch, Moïse, 1874, 1886
Bloch, Philipp, 417
Bloch, Samson, 594
Blochet, Edgar, 490, 974, 975, 1179, 1216, 1530, 1639, 1780, 1874, 1898
block printing, *see* printing, block
Bloedner, August, 1689
Blois, François-Louis de, 582
Blois, *see* Guy; Mary
Blommaert, Ph., 940, 1438
blood, abhorrence of, 271
blood accusation, 1656
blood, circulation, 265, 267, 498
blood, prognostic, 1209
blood, rain, 1123, 1743, 1868
blood vessels, twelve larger, 902
bloodletting, 112, 426, 579, 854, 890, 892, 893, 899, 1208, 1228, 1239, 1379, 1541, 1678, 1720
bloodstone, 1242
Bloom, A., 275
Bloomfield, Maurice, 1370
Bloomfield, Morton W., 1415
Blosius, *see* Blois, F. L. de
Bluebeard, 1842
Blum, André, 1874
Blumentrost, Meister, 1207
Blumhardt, J. F., 1396
Blunt, J. H., 1356
Boardman, S. L., 561
Bobrovnikoff, N. T., 1856
Boccaccio, John (XIV-2), *1802*, 37, 40, 47, 110, 183, 188, 197, 228, 355, 456, 472, 482, 493, 496, 505, 506, 508, 510, 584, 585, 768, 853, 925, 943, 1052, 1076, 1086, 1144, 1145, 1152, 1163, 1171, 1198, 1222, 1252, 1263, 1286, 1288, 1294, 1295, 1298, 1299, 1301, 1304, 1313, 1315, 1320, 1335, 1377, 1407, 1409, 1418, 1425, 1427, 1513, 1652, 1690, 1736, 1737, 1815, 1816, 1821, 1843, 1862
Boccafuoco, Costanzo, 529
Bocchio, F., 1737
Bocchoris the Wise (VIII B.C.), v. 1, *59*, 53
Bochart, Samuel, 1640
Bock, A. W., 873
Bock, Friedrich, 1128
Bode, M. H., 634
Bode, Wilhelm, 1134
Bodenheimer, F. S., 1874
Bodhidharma (VI-1), v. 1, *420*, 414; v. 2, 490, 559; v. 3, 59, 387
Bodin, Jean, 1262, 1280, 1775, 1869
Bodman, *see* John

Bodmer, J. J., 580
Boë, Jacques, 1303
Boeck, K. W., 881, 1837
Boeheim, Wendelin, 726
Böhmer, Aloys, 533
Böhmer, Friedr., 1758
Boehmer, G. H., 216, 1172
Boehmer, J. F., 918, 934, 935
Böhner, Konrad, 811
Boehner, Philotheus, 1844
Boendale, *see* John
Boer, Aemilia, 1049, 1877
Boerhaave, 286
Boernave, *see* John
Boethius, *see* Boetius. The spelling Boethius is generally preferred.
Boetius, A. M. S. (VI-1), v. 1, *424*, 794; v. 2, 1155; v. 3, 65, 81, 82, 95, 101, 158, 331, 338, 357, 398, 450, 451, 452, 482, 519, 534, 551, 558, 573, 577, 705, 745, 840, 942, 944, 1075, 1076, 1077, 1088, 1090, 1128, 1243, 1296, 1387, 1389, 1404, 1418, 1431, 1434, 1633, 1700, 1706, 1736
Boetius of Dacia (XIII-2), v. 2, *970*, 1155; v. 3, 331, 552, 1004
Boetius of Dalmatia, 1384
Boetius, translator, 1384
Böttger, J. F., 758
Boetus, Lazare, 445
Bofarull, Antonio de, 926, 1734
Boffito, Giuseppe, 497, 1484
Bogdanov, L. S., 1842
Bogomil, 1853
Bogurja, *see* Jarosław
Bohdanowicz, L., 1026
Boḥairī dialect, 361
Bohemia, *see* John
Bohigas, Pere, 520
Bohner, Hermann, 1002
Bohun, *see* Humphrey
Boiardo, *see* Matthew Maria
Boileau, *see* Stephen
boils, 861
"Bois Protat," 1563
Boisset, *see* James
Boissier, Alfred, 1103
Boissonade, J. F., 588, 888, 997, 1824
Bok, B. J., 17
Bolbec, *see* Gillet
Boldensele, *see* William
Bolfi, Domingo, 917
Bolingbroke, *see* Henry
Bolkestein, H., 294
Boll, Franz, 953, 1049, 1874, 1877
Bolland, John, 1042
Bollandists, 292, 359, 1042
Bollinger, Otto, 1227
Bologna, 152, 1244
Bologna, *see* Albert; Azo; Bartholomew; Fioravante; Francis; Francis Accorso; Gerald; Gratian; Hugolinus; Irnerius; John d'Andrea; Joshua; Odofredus; Onesto; Robert da Porta; Thomas; Urban
Bologna, University (XII-2), v. 2, *351*, 1156; v. 3, 245, 316, 375, 1080, 1244, 1273, 1900
Bombe, Walter, 1686
Bombelen, *see* John
bona fortuna, 537
Bonaccorsi banking houses, 913
Bonacosa (XIII-2), v. 2, *831*, 1156
Bonafos Abraham of Perpignan, 1826
Bonafos, *see* Menahem b. Abraham
Bonafous de Largentera, 589
Bonaparte, Lucien, 1304
Bonapartè, Napoléon, 1642
Bonaparte, Roland, 203, 762, 1840
Bonard, *see* Diomedes
Bonatti, *see* Guido
Bonaventura de' Castelli (XIV-1), *857*, 245, 287
Bonaventura da Demena, 453
Bonaventura de Iseo of Brescia, 166
Bonaventure, St. (XIII-2), v. 2, *922*, 1156; v. 3, 79, 85, 91, 340, 422, 462, 517, 531, 1056, 1093, 1322, 1353, 1412, 1416, 1843
Bonaventure, *see* Nicholas
Boncompagni, B., 606, 1431
Bond, E. A., 1746
Bondavi, En, 434
Bondi, E., 592
Bondol, *see* John
bone of stag's heart, 860, 861
Bonemant, abbé, 1499
Bonenfant of Milhau, 892
Boner, *see* Ulrich
Bonet, *see* Abraham b. Meshullam Abigdor
Bonet, Abram, 593
Bonet Bonjorn, *see* David
Bonet, *see* David b. Jacob; Jacob b. David b. Yom-ṭob; Nicholas
Bonet Profiat, 593
Boneti, *see* Nicholas
Bonfed, *see* Solomon
Bonfils, *see* Immanuel b. Jacob; Joseph b. Eliezer; Joseph ha-Sephardi
Bonfos, 589
Bongars, Jacques, 411, 771
Bongodas Cohen, 1375
Bongodas, maestro, 1374
Bongodas, Nathan Crescas, 1375
Bongoron, *see* David b. Yom-ṭob
Boni, *see* Peter Antonio
Boniface Ferrer, 1306, 1339
Boniface of Gerace (XIII-2), v. 2, *1093*, 1156; v. 3, 284
Boniface of Montferrat, 948, 1095
Boniface III, pope, 470
Boniface VIII, pope, 12, 37, 43, 46, 47, 266, 406, 408, 470, 985

Boniface IX, pope, 1032
Boniface Rotario d'Asti (XIV-2), *1628*, 1163, 1171, 1300
Bonihominis, *see* Alfonso
Bonino Mombrizio, 1337
Bonirac, *see* Solomon
Bonis, Frères, 125
Bonjorn, *see* David b. Yom-ṭob
Bonmatteo Mainardino, 986
Bonn, *see* Ephraim b. Jacob
Bonnardot, François, 864, 1602
Bonne de Bourbon, 1207, 1713
Bonne of Luxemburg, 744
Bonnejoy, M., 857
Bonnemain, 1597
Bonnet, *see* John
Bonnet, Max, 447
Bonnetty, A., 192
Bonsenior Brunelli, 1720
Bonsenior Salomon, 1380
Bonsenior b. Yaḥya (XIV-2), *1449*, 1097
Bonsenyor family, 427
Bonsenyor, *see* Judah b. Astruc
Bonsignori, bank, 124
Bontier, *see* Peter
"book, white," 313
bookkeeping, *see* double-entry
books, cheaper, 410
Boots, J. L., 162, 1561
Bopp, K. A., 1819
borax, 756
Borchardt, Paul, 1593
Borchert, Ernst, 545, 556, 1432, 1489
Borchling, Conrad, 1711
Bordeaux, *see* Ausonius; John
Borelli, G. A., 1220
Borghesi, Peter, 516
Borgia map, 1592
Borgnet, Adolphe, 1749
Borgo San Donnino, *see* Gerald
Borgognoni, 272
Borgognoni, *see* Hugh; Theodoric
Boris III (Boril), 1853
Borlandi, Franco, 774
Bormans, J. H., 940
Bormans, Stan., 937, 1749
Bòrmio, baths of, 1240
Borodin, A. P., 1016
Borrell, *see* James
Borrow, George, 1142
Borso of Este, 1146
Borton, Hugh, 980
Bos, Alphonse, 872
Bosanquet, E. F., 1124
Bosch, *see* Jerome
Bosdari, Filippo, 1798
Bose, P. N., 1584
Bosone da Gubbio, 501
Bosone Raffaelli, 615
Bossert, H. T., 1553
Bossu, Louis, 249
Bossuat, André et Robert, 1630
Bossuet, 413
Boston, *see* John
botanic garden, 816, 895, 1170, 1177
botanic glossaries, 221
botanic iconography (XII-1), v. 2, *226*, 1217 (*under* plant illustrations)
botany, 1884, 1895, 1896
botany, Anglo-Saxon (X-1), v. 1, *633*
botany, Buddhist, 1835
botany, Taoist, 1835
Botarel, *see* Moses; Moses Farissol; Moses b. Leon
Botero, Giovanni, 770
Botoner, *see* William
Botticelli, Sandro, 492
bottomry loans, 324
Bouchacourt, Léon, 253
Bouché-Leclerc, L. A. T., 1103
Boucher, P. B., 325
Boucher, *see* William
Bouchet, Guillaume, 279
Bouchon, J. A. C., 930
Bouchot, Henri, 1563
Boucicault, *see* John
Boucicault, marshal of France, 1345
Boudreaux, Petrus, 1877
Bouillon, *see* Godfrey
Boulogne, *see* Joan
Boulting, William, 1622
Bourbon, *see* Blanche; Bonne; Joan; Stephen
Bourbonnais, *see* Mary
Bourchier, *see* John
Bourdillon, F. W., 1867
Bourdon, Claude, 1849
Bourgain, Louis, 1040
Bourgogne, *see* Joan; John; Margaret
Bourian, *see* Vidal
Bouriant, Urbain, 1265
Bourignon, *see* Antoinette
Bourland, C. B., 1811
Boutaric, 411
Boutell, Charles, 728
Bouthoul, Gaston, 1778
Bouvat, Lucien, 1014, 1120, 1474
Bouvy, E., 1389
Bouyges, Maurice, 433
Bovattieri, *see* Naddino
Bovenschen, Albert, 1605
Bovill. E. W., 1875
Bowen, W. H., 1310
Bower MS (V-1), v. 1, *393*, 379
Bower, *see* Walter
Bowie, William, 1166
Bowman, N. H., 1218
bows and arrows, 1550, 1635, 1641, 1643. *See also* archery
bows, *see* crossbows; longbowmen; longbows
Boyce, G. C., 472

Boyd, Henry, 493
Boyer, C. B., 738
Boyle, Robert, 167
Boym, Michael, 902
Boysset, *see* Bertrand
Bozzelli, Roberto, 815
Brabant, 1907
Brabant, *see* Michael; Siger
Bracey, Bertha L., 571
Bracton, *see* Henry
Bradley, Henry, 347, 1415, 1423, 1744
Bradwardine, *see* Thomas
Brae, A. E., 1424
Brahe, Tycho, 600, 1846, 1857
Brāhma-Samāj, 1475
Brahmagupta (VII-1), v. 1, *474*, 794; v. 2, 213
Brāhmi alphabet, 382
Brahui language, 383
brain, 840, 844, 847, 891
Bramante, Donato, 1043
Bramley, H. R., 567
Brampton, C. K., 555, 989
Branca, *see* Anthony
Branca family, 1233
Brand, Walter, 1706
Brandes, Jan, 1624
Brandicanus, king, 1607
Brandt, C. J., 575
Brandt, O. S., 1756
Brandt, Walther I., 411
Brandt, Wilhelm, 359
Brant, *see* Sebastian
brasses, monumental, 144, 728
Braun, Joseph, 1045
Braunmühl, Anton v., 1875
Braunstein, Baruch, 1060
Braunsvalde, *see* Gerald
Brazil, island, 1592
brazilwood, 1620
Bréal, Michel, 352, 390
Breasted, J. H., 464, 1724, 1773
Breda, *see* Roland
Brederode, P. C. van, 1794
Bredon, *see* Simon
Breede, Ellen, 1232
Brehaut, Ernest, 1464, 1843
Bréhier, Louis, 953, 1041
Breit, Ḥayyim b. D., 417
Breitinger, J. J., 580
Bremen, 153
Bremen, *see* Adam
Bremen Arzneibuch, 1205, 1711
Bremis, *see* Henry
Brémontier, N. T., 207
Brennan, W. A., 1693
Brenner, Oscar, 710
Brer Rabbit, 464
Brescia, *see* Bonaventura de Iseo; John; William Corvi
Breslau, *see* Henry; Thomas
Breslau Salernitan corpus, 1236
Bresnier, L. J., 1010
Bressé, *see* Andrivet
Bretagne, *see* Peter
Breteuil, *see* Geoffrey
Brethren of the Common Life, *see* Brothers
Brethren of the Free Spirit, 574, 581
Brethren of Purity (X-2), v. 1, *660*, 794; v. 2, 1185 (*under* Ikhwān al-ṣafā'); v. 3, 134, 432, 1341
Brethren of Purity, rasā'il, 154, 596, 1072
Bretschneider, E. V., 1875
Brettle, Sigismund, 1340
Breviari d'amor, 339
Breviarium Alarici (VI-1), v. 1, *438*, 412; v. 2, 141, 267
Breviarium Bartholomei, 1705
Breviarium mozarabicum, 174
Březová, *see* Laurence
Bridget of Ireland, St., 1354
Bridget of Sweden, 1354. *See* Birgitta
Bridrey, Emile, 411, 544, 545, 1496
Brie, F. W. D., 1255
Brie, *see* John
Brièle, Léon, 295
Brienne, 746
Brierly, J. L., 1798
Bright, A. H., 1415
Bright, Richard, 875
Brigittines, 1036, 1355
Bṛihatsaṃhitā, 215, 1584
Brill, W. G., 938
Brindisi, *see* James
Bring, S. E., 1898
Brinjal, 1637
Brinkley, Frank, 1875
Brissot, Pierre, 890
Bristol, 194
Brit, *see* Walter
Britten, F. J., 722
"Britton," 319, 348
Britton, C. E., 1875
Brixen, *see* Matthew
Brocard, pseudo (XIV-1), *391*, 46, 54, 186, 189, 318, 416, 457
Brock, Edmund, 943
Brockelmann, Carl, xii, 106, 360, 925, 961, 1014, 1875, 1887
Brockhaus, Hermann, 1458
Broderius, J. R., 1228
Brodrick, G. C., 882
Brody, H., 1635
Broeckx, Corneille, 883
Broekhuizen, Daniel van, 1574
Brøgger, A. W., 194
Broker, *see* Nicholas
Bromby, C. H., 494
Brome, *see* Adam
Bromehead, C. N., 1176
Bromyarde, *see* John

bronze doors, 1105
Broomhall, Marshall, 1589
Brosset, M. F., 305
Brothers, *see also* Brethren
Brothers of the Common Life, 350, 581, 1038, 1081, 1358
Broussaleux, S., 1439
Brouwers, D. D., 887
Brown, Alfred, 1704
Brown, Carleton, 566, 1280, 1428
Brown, Edward, 1574
Brown, J. P., 1875
Brown, J. T. T., 1741
Brown, Richard, 127, 1111, 1868
Browne, E. G., 465, 632, 975, 1875
Browne, Sir Thomas, 1570, 1704
Broydé, Isaac, 420, 429, 435, 436, 437, 452, 593, 1375, 1378, 1380, 1383, 1384, 1449, 1516, 1520
Bruce, the, 1254, 1740
Bruce, *see* David; Robert
Bruce, J. P., 210
Brucioli, Antonio, 1808
Brue, André, 1159
Bruel, Alexandre, 540
Brüll, Nehemias, 593
Bruges, 152, 323, 347
Bruges, *see* Bartholomew; James; John Grise; Lewis; Peter; Rodolph
Brugi, Biazio, 1796
Bruins, J. G., 1412
Brun, Robert, 1201, 1875
Brunel, Clovis, 1303
Brunelleschi, *see* Philip
Brunet, Gustave, 456
Brunet, J. L., 1345
Brunetto Latini (XIII-2), v. 2, *926*, 1157; v. 3, 68, 341, 345, 490, 501, 1603
Brunfels, Otto, 1347
Bruni, *see* Francis
Brunn, F. J., 1153
Brunn, Walter v., 1693
Brunne, *see* Robert
Bruno del Garbo, 837
Bruno, Giordano, 1096, 1447
Bruno da Longoburgo (XIII-2), v. 2, *1077*, 1157; v. 3, 274, 883, 1683, 1698
Brunot, Ferdinand, 345, 1308
Bruns, Ivo, 435
Brunschvig, R., 203
Brunswick, *see* Otto
Brunton, *see* Thomas
Brusch, Gaspard, 577
Brusendorff, Aage, 1425
Brussels, *see* Bruxelles
Brusseri, *see* Philip
Brut, Roman de, 1500
Brute, Chronicles of, 1254
Brute, *see* Walter
Brutus, 1254, 1274
Bruun, F. J., 1142
Bruxelles, 152, 153
Bruxelles, *see* Arnold; Gerald; Henry
Bruyant, *see* James; John
Bryan, W. F., 1426
Bryennios, *see* Joseph; Manuel; Nicephoros
Brygg, *see* Thomas
Bryson of Heraclea (V B.C.), v. 1, *93*, 82
Bryson, neo-Pythagorean, 1072, 1096, 1374, 1899
Buber, Solomon, 1718
Bucardus, 391
Buch, *see* John; Nicholas
Bucheck, *see* Berthold
Buchheit, Gert, 1232
Buchon, J. A. C., 926, 928, 949, 1591
Buchthal, Hugo, 1178, 1179
Buda, University, 1400
Buddensieg, Rudolf, 1349
Buddha (VI B.C.), v. 1, *68*, 65, 332; v. 2, 826; v. 3, 81, 109, 423, 971
Buddha, foot, 423
Buddhadatta, 382
Buddhaghosha (V-1), v. 1, *384*, 794; v. 3, 382, 423, 1477
Buddhism, x, 85, 139, 382, 423, 636, 729, 1069, 1070, 1171, 1370, 1873, 1889, 1895, 1904
Buddhism, Chinese (VII-1), v. 1, *469*, 508, 552
Buddhism, development (VII-1), v. 1, *466*
Buddhism, Japanese, v. 3, 424; (VI-2), v. 1, *448;* (VII-1), v. 1, *470;* (VII-2), v. 1, *491;* (VIII-1), v. 1, *509;* (IX-1), v. 1, *552;* (XII-2), v. 2, *336*, 558, 827; (XIII-1), v. 2, *558;* (XIII-2), v. 2, *827*
Buddhism, Korean (IV-2), v. 1, *364*
Buddhism, *see* Lamaist; lamaseries
Buddhism, Mongolian, v. 2, 827
Buddhism, Tibetan (VII-1), v. 1, *466;* (VIII-2), v. 1, *525;* (XIII-2), v. 2, *827*
Buddhist, *see* atomism; botany; elements
Buddhist literature, 1909
Buddhist, *see* medicine; pilgrims
Budge, E. A. W., 357, 780, 1105
Bühler, C. F., 292, 1846
Büttner, Hermann, 573
Bufini, *see* Margaret
Bughyat al-khabīr, 759
Bugiel, V., 246, 1811
Buḥrân, 436
Bukhārā, 794, 1026, 1470, 1473, 1618
Bukhārī, *see* 'Alī b. Muḥammad
Bukhārī, Muḥammad b. Ismā'īl (IX-1), v. 1, *551*, 794; v. 2, 1066; v. 3, 1065, 1067, 1267
Bukhārī, *see* Muḥammad b. Mubārakshāh; Muḥammad b. Muḥammad Bahā al-dīn; 'Ubaidallāh b. Mas'ūd
Bukka, 41, 1366
Bukofzer, Manfred, 158, 1833
Bulgarian, 356, 1854

Bulgaris, Eugenios, 746
Bulghār, 1618
Bulliot, J., 545
Bulloch, William, 1653
Bullokar, William, 1316
Bundahishn (XII-2), v. 2, *396*, 294
Bundārī, *see* Fatḥ b. 'Alī
Būnī, *see* Aḥmad b. 'Alī
Bunim, M. S., 1105
Bunyan, John, 533
Buono, *see* Peter
Buovo d'Antona, 1720
burāq, 1639
Burchard of Mount Sion (XIII-2), v. 2, *1052*, 1157; v. 3, 391, 769, 770
Burchard of Strassburg (XII-2), v. 2, *420*, 1157
Burckhard, Georg, 1230
Burdach, Konrad, 516, 923
Burdeana, *see* Jacob
Buret, L., 1779
Burgess, J. S., 156
Burgh, *see* Elizabeth; William
Burgo, *see* Nicholas
Burgos, *see* Abner; Alfonso; Paul; Paul of Santa María; Solomon
Burgos chronicle, 299, 1392
Burguburu, Paul, 713
Burgundio of Pisa (XII-2), v. 2, *348*, 1157; v. 3, 441, 813
Burgundy, *see* Bourgogne
burhān fī asrār, 759
Burhān al-dīn Aḥmad, 1216
Burhān al-dīn, *see* Zarnūjī
Buridan, John (XIV-1), *540*, 82, 90, 114, 147, 150, 207, 270, 318, 739, 1086, 1093, 1127, 1194, 1278, 1283, 1429, 1431, 1435, 1489, 1495, 1540, 1565, 1755
Buridan, *see* ass
Burkill, I. H., 1177, 1835
Burlamacchi, Federigo, 1336
Burley, *see* Walter
Burma, 1030, 1084, 1879
Burmese, *see* law
Burmester, O. H. E., 1830
Burn, Richard, 1476
Burne-Jones, 1424
Burnell, A. C., 1367, 1368, 1369, 1875
Burnham, *see* John
burning, three degrees of, 1199
Burns, C. D., 411, 556
Buron, Edmond, 1148
Burr, G. L., 12, 1049, 1051, 1262
Burrell, Arthur, 1415
Bursian, Conrad, 1806
Burton, R. F., 234
Burton, *see* Thomas
burūj al-aflāk, 136
Bury, *see* John Boston; Richard
Burzio, *see* Nicholas
Burzūya (VI-2), v. 1, *449*, 435, 443; v. 2, 590; v. 3, 376
Busbecq, 198, 292, 442
Buscarello de' Ghizolfi (XIII-2), v. 2, *1054*, 1157; v. 3, 202
Busch, *see* John
Busetto, Natale, 499
Busnelli, G., 493, 499
Buss, P. F. H., 1741
Bussey, W. H., 597
Busson, Arnold, 915, 931
Buti, *see* Francis
Buṭlān, b. (XI-1), v. 1, *730*, 809; v. 2, 1157; v. 3, 1850
Butler, A. J., 1602
Butler, Charles, 1316
Butler, H. R., 711
Butler, Pierce, 734, 1564
Butler, R. U., 461
Butler, Richard, 947, 1740
Butler-Bowdon, W., 1315
Buṭrus b. a. Karam, *see* Qibṭī
Buttenwieser, Moses, 1446
butterflies, 1188
Butterworth, C. C., 1350
buttons, 157
Buxtorf I, Johannes, 1063, 1717
Buxtorf II, Johannes, 1063
Buzurg b. Shahriyār (X-2), v. 1, *674*, 794
Byker, *see* John; Patrick; William
Byrhtferth of Ramsey (XI-1), v. 1, *714*, 695, 702; v. 3, 1534
Byron, Robert, 1439, 1613
Byzantine, *see* architecture; art; chronology; cosmology; law
Byzantine literature, 1892
Byzantine, *see* logic; military science; music; science
Byzantium, 1907
Byzinius, *see* Laurence

Caballeria, *see* Vidal b. Labi
Cabasilas, *see* Neilos; Nicholas
Cable, E. M., 727
Cable, Mildred, 1586
Cabral, *see* Gonçalo Velho
Cabret, *see* Abraham; Isaac b. Abraham; Jacob b. Judah
Caccini, *see* John
Cacqueray, *see* Philip
Cadamosto, *see* Alvise
Cadman, S. P., 1349
Cadmos of Miletos (VI B.C.), v. 1, *79*, 66
Cadwalader, king, 462, 1650
Cadwalader, pest of, 1650
Caelius (III-2), v. 1, *340*, 331
Caelius Aurelianus (V-1), v. 1, *392*, 794
Caesar, *see* John
Caesar, Julius (I-1 B.C.), v. 1, *216*, 794; v. 2, 973; v. 3, 250, 303, 506, 912, 1252, 1274

Caetani, Leone, 960
Caetani, Michele Angelo, 500
Cafa, 1035
Caferoğlu, Ahmet, 1014
Caffarini, *see* Thomas
Caggese, Romolo, 1843
Cagnat, René, 1848
cagots, 275, 278, 318
Cahors, 44, 1830
Cahors, *see* Hugh Géraud
Cahors, University, 72, 471
Caillat, G. de, 1225
Caillet, A. L., 1104
Caillet, Robert, 1499
Caius, John, 475
Cajani, A., 756
Cajori, Florian, 1488, 1534, 1628
Calabria, *see* Charles
Calais, burgesses, 1748
calamine, 219, 727
Calasso, Francesco, 1870
Calcar, *see* Gerald v. Kalkar; Henry
Calcar, J. S. van, 1357
calculator, 737
calculosum languorem, Contra, 393
calculus, *see* exponential; probabilities
Caldara, painter, 1163
Caldwell, R., 384
Caleb Afendopoulo, 618
Calecas, *see* John; Manuel
calendar, 115, 123, 420, 960, 1062, 1107, 1109, 1111, 1121, 1444, 1516, 1529, 1800
calendar, Chinese, 1537
calendar, Jewish, 130, 417, 419, 1522, 1832
calendar, moralized, 767
calendar, reform, 45, 951
Calgacus, 1101
Caliergis, 1583
calificadores, 24
Calimala, Arte di, 124
Calistenus, 166
Calixtinus, codex (XII-1), v. 2, *254*, 138, 143
Callierges, Zacharias, 997
calligraphy, 385
Callinicos of Heliopolis (VII-2), v. 1, *494*, 489; v. 2, 1039
Callippos of Cyzicos (IV-2 B.C.), v. 1, *141*, 125
Callisthenes, 166, 1519
Callistos, *see* Nicephoros
Callistus I, 588
Calo Calonymos, *see* Qalonymos b. David the Younger
Calò, Giovanni, 1674, 1737
Calo, maestro, 433
Calochetos, *see* Alexios
Calogerà, Angiolo, 1164
Caloria, *see* Thomas
Calveras, Josep, 1306
Calvet, Augustin, 1343
Calvin, 164, 268, 477
Camateros, *see* John
cambiali, 1838
Cambogia, 294, 1030, 1879
cambric, 727
Cambridge, colleges, 72, 475, 1079, 1402
Cambridge University, 473, 1079, 1402, 1887
Camden, William, 1740, 1742, 1745
camel membranes, 103, 623
camels, 788, 827
camera obscura, 602, 707
Camerarius, Joachim, 514, 826
Camerino, *see* Francis
Cameron, K. W., 1605
"camino francés," 343
camisia, 157
Cammelli, Giuseppe, 1388
Camões, 1160
Camoys, *see* Margaret
Campagnac, E. T., 1316
Campano, 1252
Campano, *see* John
Campbell, A. M., 1663, 1876
Campesani, *see* Benvenuto
camphor, 1620
Campi, Giuseppe, 486, 494
Campione, *see* James; Marc
Can Grande della Scala, 480, 494, 615, 917, 919, 943
Canal, Grand, 735, 777
Canal, *see* Martin
canals (XIV-1), *735*, 1126
Canals, *see* Anthony
Canamusali, *see* 'Ammār b. 'Alī
Canappe, Jean, 1693
Canarese, 383, 1330
Canary islands, 183, 510, 765, 768, 786, 1144, 1147, 1409, 1808
cancer, 1683, 1691, 1697
cancioneiros, 344
Caṇḍeśvara (XIV-1), *1000*, 322, 382
Candia, *see* Crete
Caṅgadeva (XIII-1), v. 2, *625*, 213, 507
Canibell, Eudald, 1876
Canisius, Henricus, 414, 788, 790
Canistris, *see* Opicinus
cannon, 219, 1547
cannon, earliest type of, 724
canon law (XIII-1), v. 2, *688*, 1195; v. 3, 318
canonical books, six, 964
canonization, processes of, 1246
Cantacuzena, *see* Helena; Theodora
Cantacuzenos, *see* John VI; Matthew
Cantelupe, *see* Thomas
Cantera Burgos, Francisco, 1344, 1843
Canterbury, 1743
Canterbury, *see* Alured
Canterbury, archbishops of, 1255
Canterbury, *see* Augustine

Canterbury College, 1079
Canterbury, *see* Gervase; Jordan
Canterbury Hall, 1401
Canterbury tales, 1418
Canterbury, *see* Thomas
cantharides, 296
canticles, 419
Cantigas de Santa Maria, 159, 344
Cantimpré, *see* Thomas
Canton, 156
Cantor, Moritz, 1876
Canutus, 1687
Cão, *see* Diago
Cao, G. B., 191
Capart, Jean, 1584
Capecelatro, Alfonso, 1337
Capella, Martianus Mineus Felix (V-2), v. 1, *407*, 795; v. 2, 1200; v. 3, 192
Capelle, Wilhelm, 214
Capelli, L. M., 514
Capellis, *see* Pasquino
Capestang, *see* Peter
Capistrano, *see* John
capital and labor, 152
capitali, Libro a, 124
Caplan, Harry, 1040
Capocci, *see* James
Cappa-Legora, Antonio, 499, 989
Cappeller, Carl, 1876
Capponi, *see* Gino; Neri
Cappuyno, Maiolus, 569
Capréole, *see* John
Caprotti, Giuseppe, 1168
Capsalo, *see* Richard
Capua, *see* John; Raymond; Samuel b. Jacob
Capuano, *see* Giambattista
Caradog of Llancarvan (XII-1), v. 2, *257*, 1158
Caraka of Kashmir (II-1), v. 1, *284*, 269
caravans, 1875
Caravida, *see* Solomon
Carbondala, *see* John
Carbonell, *see* Peter Miguel
Carbonelli, Giovanni, 270, 855, 1876
Carbonnières, Ramond de, 279
carbuncle, 899
Carcassonne, *see* Benjamin b. Isaac; Leo Joseph
Cardano, Gerolamo, 148, 715, 738, 1127, 1489, 1566
Cardan's suspension, 715
Cardo of Milan (XIV-2), *1674*, 1192
Cardona, Enrico, 926
Cardone of Pavia, 1674
Cardoner Planas, Antonio, 1717, 1841
Cardoner Planas, José, 1841
Carducci, Giosuè, 515, 741, 918, 983, 1567
Caresini, *see* Rafaino
Carignano, *see* John
Carinthia, *see* Henry
Cariyā-piṭaka, 1370
Carle, *see* William
Carlebach, Joseph, 606, 607
Carlo, *see* Charles
Carlowitz, H., 876
Carlyle, A. J., 1876
Carlyle, R. W., 1876
Carlyle, Thomas, 1414
Carmelites (XIII-1), v. 2, *549*, 486
Carmoly, Eliacin, 793
Carnap, Rudolf, 331
Carnegy, F. A. R., 1415
Carnicer, J. L., 1379
Carolina constitutio criminalis, 266
Carolus, Jean, 883
Carpenter, G. R., 1810
Carpentier, Pierre, 1876
Carpi, *see* Berengario
Càrpine, *see* John Pian
Carra de Vaux, Bernard, 759, 797, 925, 965, 1463, 1527, 1876
Carrara, Enrico, 515
Carrara family, 1818
Carrara, *see* Francis; Francis II Novello; Ubertino
Carré, M. H., 1831
Carrick, J. C., 1349
carriers, 880
Carsono, *see* Jacob b. Isaac
Carsovia, 932
Carswell, C. M., 1810
carta mercatoria, 38
Cartagena, *see* Alonso de Santa María
carte pisane, 182, 764
Cartellieri, Alexander, 988
Cartellieri, Otto, 1075, 1202
Carter, T. F., 1876
"cartes moralisées," 767
Carthusians (XII-1), v. 2, *153*, 110
cartography, 1884, 1887, 1892, 1897, 1899, 1900, 1902
cartography (XI-2), v. 1, *767*
cartography, Catalan, 1834, 1866. *See also* mappemonde of 1375
cartography, Chinese (XII-2), v. 2, *423*, 1159; v. 3, 1850
Carusi, Enrico, 1795
Cārvāka, 1366
Cary, H. F., 491, 493
Casa giocosa, 1081, 1290
Casale, *see* John
Casanova, Paul, 1265, 1778
casibus virorum illustrium, De, 1804
Casimir the Great, 1021, 1398, 1759
Casini, *see* Anthony; Bartholomew; Francis; John; Thomas
Casiri, Miguel, 165, 1722, 1763, 1876
Caslari, *see* Abraham b. David; Crescas Vidal; David b. Abraham; Israel b. Joseph
Caspar, Max, 1112
Cassel, David, 614

Cassianos Bassos (VI-2), v. 1, *452*, 444, 657; v. 3, 825, 859, 1637
Cassianus Eremita, *see* John
Cassino, Monte, 395, 1288
Cassiodorus, senator Flavius Magnus Aurelius (VI-1), v. 1, *426*, 795; v. 2, 96; v. 3, 813, 1240
Cassios the Iatrosophist (III-1), v. 1, *324*, 315; v. 3, 64, 242, 441
Cassius Dionysius (I-1 B.C.), v. 1, *213*, 197, 202
Cassius Felix (V-1), v. 1, *392*, 379; v. 2, 1085; v. 3, 816
Cassius, Longinus, 1274
Cassius Parmensis, 1565
Cassius the poet, 1565
Casso, *see* John
Cassuto, Umberto, 433, 449, 492, 616, 1452
Castagnoli, P., 569
Castan, Auguste, 1393
Castañeda, Vicente, 1342
Castel Fabri, 412
Castella, Gaston, 1853
Castelli, *see* Bonaventura; James
Castellieri. Otto, 1275
Castello, *see* Hugh; Peregrine
Castelnou, *see* Joan
castes, 155, 425
Castiglioni, Arturo, 446, 498, 1196, 1674, 1676
Castiglioni, Pietro, 1032
Castilian (Spanish), 337
casting out, *see* sevens, etc.
casting type, 1564
Castor, *see* Antonius
Castor and Pollux, 864
Castor of Rhodes (I-1 B.C.), v. 1, *216*, 203
castration, 1632
Castries, Henry de, 807
Castro, *see* James
Catala, *see* Jordan
Catalan, 342, 1876, 1906
Catalan, *see* cartography
Catalan company, 300, 926
Catalan literature, 1884
Catalan, *see* mappemonde; science
Catalonia, 1902
cataract, 426, 844, 883, 1235, 1724, 1747, 1837
Caterino Zeno, 1594
Cathari (XII-1), v. 2, *157*, 1159; v. 3, 23, 404
Catharic ritual, 339
Cathay, 1910
cathedrals, rise of (XII-1), v. 2, *159*, 713
Catherine of Alexandria, St., 576, 1210, 1596, 1666
Catherine Colombini, 1037
Catherine monastery, Sinai, 306, 769
Catherine Ruffini, 1681
Catherine of Salisbury, 1403
Catherine of Siena, St. (XIV-2), *1334*, 1032, 1042, 1047, 1052, 1056, 1086, 1299, 1340, 1355. 1416, 1684
Catherine of Sweden, St., 1036, 1042, 1056, 1319, 1336, 1355
cathodic rays, 710
Catholicon, 332, 936
Catlin, George, 1612
Cato the Censor (II-1 B.C.), v. 1, *186*, 795; v. 2, 779, 973; v. 3, 301, 811, 813, 1288, 1700, 1816
Catone, *see* Angelo
Catrarios, *see* John
cats, 1186, 1189, 1422, 1863
Catton, *see* Walter
Catullus, 922
Caturmahārāja, 1018
causality, principle of, 90, 534, 542, 546
causis, Liber de (V-2), v. 1, *404*, 135, 399; v. 2, 1159; v. 3, 65, 101, 450
cauterization, 273
Cavaillon, *see* Ṭodros
Cavalcanti, *see* Guido; Mainardo
Cavallari, Elizabetta, 492
cavalry tactics, 1643
Cavenari, Demetrio, 241
Caxton, *see* William
Ceccano, *see* Annibaldo
Ceccarelli, Alfonso, 776
Cecchetti, Bartolomeo, 857, 1672
Cecco d'Arcone, 1482
Cecco d'Ascoli (XIV-1), *643*, 23, 88, 112, 177, 193, 336, 406, 444, 498, 501, 837, 1409, 1600, 1846
Čechus (Čech), 1758
Cecily, St., 1421
Cecily, duchess of York, 1416
Ceffons, *see* Peter
Cele, *see* John
Čelebī, *see* Muḥammad shāh
Celelles, *see* Francis
celestial, *see* mechanics; planisphere; sphere
Céligny, Mme L. N. de, 1864
Cellino di Nese, 313, 982
Celsos (II-2), v. 1, *294*, 795; v. 3, 825
Celsus, Aurelius Cornelius (I-1), v. 1, *240*, 795; v. 2, 638, 1085; v. 3, 816, 871, 1233, 1236, 1292
Celsus, Julius, 1810
Cencio, maestro, 1134
Cennino Cennini, 168, 1131, 1135, 1300
Cennino da Colle, 1132
Censorinus (III-1), v. 1, *322*, 315
census, Chinese, 1268, 1861
centaur, 487
centenarians, 1732
Centeno, Amaro, 955
center of gravity of universe, 1539
Centiloquium, *see* Ptolemy
Ceolwulf, 2
ceramics, *see* glaze; porcelain; pottery
cereal crops, five, 1626
cereals, 830

Cermisone, 1194
Çermisone, *see* Anthony
Černý, Jan, 1167
certainty, degrees of, 547
Certaldo, 1803
Certaldo, *see* Michelino
Cerulli, Enrico, 802
Ceruti, Antonio, 232
Cervantes, 73
Cervera, *see* William
Cervia, *see* Theodoric Borgognoni
Cesareo, G. A., 515
Cesena, *see* Michael
Cessoles, *see* James
Ceylon, 1616, 1617. *See also* Siṅhalese
Chabaneau, Camille, 340, 1499
Chabannes, *see* Adhémar
Chace, A. B., 1773
Chadwick, Dorothy, 1415
Chadwick, H. M., 1870
Chadwick, N. K., 1870
Chagatāy, 1467
Chaghatāi Tūrki, 1329, 1873
Chaillan, Marius, 1406
Chaix, Paul, 799
Chakraberty, Chandra, 1217, 1731
Chalcidius (IV-1), v. 1, *352*, 795; v. 2, 991; v. 3, 548
Chalcondyles, *see* Laonicos
Chalmel, *see* Raymond
chamār, 425
Chamber, John, 586
Chambers, R. W., 229, 483, 1415
Champa, 1879
Champagne, 928
Champagne, fairs, 124
Champeaux, *see* William
Champier, Symphorien, 445
Champlitte, *see* William
Champollion, J. J., 360
Chand Bardāī (XII-2), v. 2, *480*
chaṇḍālas, 280
Chandragupta II, 1859
Chandrenos, general, 996
Chaney, E. F., 1861
Chang, T. T., 1732
Chanoch, Irene, 436
Chanson d'Antioche, 339
Chanson de la croisade, 339
Chanson de Roland (XI-2), v. 1, *773*, 796; v. 2, 1160; v. 3, 345, 1812
Chanson de Sainte Foy, 338
Chao, Celia, 1538
chaos, 149
Chapeauville, Jean de, 937, 1395
Chapman, F. T., 1609
Chapman, John, ix
Charanis, Peter, 1260, 1389, 1845
Charavay, Etienne, 1184
charity, 19, 22
Charland, T. M., 1040
charlatans, *see* quacks
Charlemagne (VIII-2), v. 1, *527*, 796; v. 2, 1160; v. 3, 24, 231, 350
Charles II of Anjou, Naples, 65, 341
Charles I of Bohemia, *see* Charles IV of Luxemburg
Charles of Calabria, 446
Charles V, emperor (Charles Quint), 266, 822, 1037
Charles IV of France, le Bel, 44
Charles V of France, the Wise, 1075, 1136, 1141, 1202, 1293, 1406, 1490, 1128
Charles VI of France, 1129, 1201, 1236, 1467
Charles IX of France, 471
Charles IV of Luxemburg, emperor, 471, 508, 511, 1020, 1076, 1259, 1322, 1757, 1836
Charles de Montegraneli, 1037
Charles, R. H., 1878
Charles of Valois, 480
Charmoy, F. B., 1474
Charpentier, Jarl, 780, 784
charta bombycina, 174
charta damascena, 174
Chartier, *see* Alan
Chartres, *see* Bernard; Theodoric
Chartreuse, 1031
Chassanion, Jean, 1227
Chastel de labour, 1867
Chastellain, *see* George
Châtillon, *see* Guy
Chaucer, Geoffrey (XIV-2), *1417*, 126, 407, 463, 475, 533, 559, 715, 880, 943, 1047, 1048, 1076, 1077, 1090, 1110, 1124, 1136, 1166, 1186, 1204, 1279, 1311, 1312, 1315, 1412, 1414, 1427, 1501, 1506, 1736, 1751, 1796, 1821, 1864, 1886
Chaucer, *see* John
Chaucer Society, 1424
Chauchat, *see* Peter
Chauliac, Guy de (XIV-2), *1690*, 267, 274, 277, 279, 293, 426, 583, 847, 857, 866, 869, 870, 871, 874, 878, 880, 882, 1110, 1194, 1195, 1200, 1202, 1219, 1223, 1224, 1231, 1233, 1235, 1254, 1309, 1379, 1652, 1659, 1694, 1703
chaulmoogra, 261, 280, 289, 908, 1851
Chaumartin, Henry, 1668, 1868
Chavannes, Edouard, 139, 233, 1800, 1866
checks, 127
cheetahs, 1641
Cheikho, Louis, 748, 900, 1007, 1878
Chelebi, *see* Muṣṭafā b. Aḥmad. *See also* Muḥammad shāh Čelebī
chemical papyri (III-2), v. 1, *339*
Chemin de povreté, 1867
chemise, 157
chemistry, 1884, 1889, 1904, 1908, 1911
chemistry, Assyrian, 757
chemistry, Babylonian, 757

chemistry, Hindu, 1901
Chenchiah, P., 384, 466
Cheneb, Moḥ. b., *see* Muḥammad b. Shanab
Cherbonneau, Auguste, 967, 1766
Chéreau, Achille, 872
cherry tree, 790
Chersiphron of Cnossos (VI B.C.), v. 1, *75*
chess, 314, 317, 393, 457, 559, 1097, 1099, 1449, 1469, 1640, 1722, 1897. *See also* shaṭranj
chessboard, 744
chess moralities, 393
Chester, *see* Robert
Chesterton, G. K., 1425
Chevalier, Ulysse, 1044, 1878
Chevreul, Eugène, 301
Chew, S. C., 1046
Chiappelli, Alberto, 1194, 1246
Chiappelli, Luigi, 983, 1248
Chiarini, *see* George di Lorenzo
Chīchaklī, Tawfīq, 794
Chiengmai, 1030
Chieti, *see* Nicholas Vernia
chil nāmūs, 465
Chil y Naranjo, Gregorio, 768, 1811
Chilandari, 1853
Child, F. J., 1424, 1425
Chilmark, *see* John
Chilston, 1846
Chimay, 1751
Chiminelli, Piero, 492
China, 1873, 1876, 1879, 1885, 1889, 1890, 1896, 1900, 1907, 1909, 1910
Chinese, 31, 385, 1885, 1891, 1897, 1904
Chinese, *see* archaeology; astronomy; Buddhism; calendar; cartography; census; chronology; compass; dietetics; earthquakes; epigraphy; examinations; exploration; eye diseases; glass; historiography; hours; itineraries; Jews
Chinese lexicography (V B.C.), v. 1, *110*, 797 (*under* Chinese dictionary)
Chinese, *see* libraries
Chinese literature, 1910
Chinese, *see* maps; materia medica; medicine
Chinese-Mongolian inscriptions, 1840
Chinese, *see* music; Muslims; Nestorianism; ornithology; painting; physiognomy; printing
Chinese radicals, 1828
Chinese, *see* rivers and waters
Chinese self-complacency, 24
Chinese, *see* silk; sphragistics; technology; typography; weights and measures
Chingale, *see* Robert
Chingiz Khān (XIII-1), v. 2, *608*, 1161; v. 3, 40, 380, 954, 971, 975, 1101, 1250, 1467, 1469, 1587, 1788, 1789, 1865
Chiòboli, Ezio, 513
Chioniades, *see* Gregory
Chiovenda, Emilio, 815
Chiquot, A., 572
chiromancy, 835, 1104
chirurgus, 273
Chishti family, 1476
chivalry, 12, 239, 1654, 1752. *See also* cavalry
Chivasso, *see* Dominic de Clavasio
Chloë, 1188
Choisy, Auguste, 1570
cholera (XIV-2), *1664*
Cholmeley, H. P., 882
Choniates, *see* George
chorale, 742
chorea, 1667
Chorea Machabaeorum, 1861
Chorene, *see* Moses
chorioid plexus, 844
Chosroës, 40
Chotzner, Joseph, 616
Choulant, J. L., 1878
Chrétien Legouais, 48, 346, 743
Christ Church College, 1401
Christ, Karl, 570
Christ, orders of, 394, 1038
Christendom, 1908
Christensen, C. H., 1356
Christian, *see* art; era; iconography; mysticism
Christian Orient, 1893
Christian of Prachatice, 1114, 1167, 1176, 1207, 1239, 1322
Christian of Prague, 1208
Christianity, 1879, 1884, 1888
Christianization of Buddhist Asia (XIII-2), v. 2, *823*
Christianization of Europe (V-1), v. 1, *380*
Christians in China, 1896
Christians of the girdle, 1602
Christine de Pisan, 1088, 1308, 1392, 1412, 1480, 1861
Christodulos, *see* Joseph
Christofalo Soligo, 185
Christology, 357
Christopher, *see also* Christophorus; Cristoforo
Christopher of Antioch, St., 1666
Christopher Columbus, 143, 183, 188, 484, 715, 1036, 1109, 1148, 1671, 1848, 1859, 1892
Christopher Pembridge (XIV-2), *1740*, 1254
Christophorus de Honestis (XIV-2), *1679*, 836, 1193, 1220, 1242, 1681
Christ's College, 1863
Christy, A. E., 1867
Christy, Miller, 1595
chromosomes, 271
Chronica Hispaniae, 299
Chronicles, books of (III-1 B.C.), v. 1, *163*, 150
Chronicon salernitanum (X-2), v. 1, *685*
Chroniques de France, 300
chronology, 1885. *See also* era

chronology, Byzantine, 123
chronology, Chinese (VI-1), v. 1, *429*, 797
Chrysanthos, Philippidos, 790
Chrysippos of Cnidos (IV-1 B.C.), v. 1, *121*, 112
Chrysippos of Soli (III-2 B.C.), v. 1, *169*, 166
Chrysococces, *see* George; Gregory; Michael
Chrysogonus, St., 1248
Chrysoloras, *see* Demetrios; Manuel
Chrysostomos, *see* John
Chubb, T. C., 1810
Chuetas of Majorca, 1060
Chumnos, *see* John; Nicephoros
Chuquet, *see* Nicholas
Church, F. J., 494
church, economic power, 1839
church, government, 1853
church and state, 402, 483, 1890
church, trade, 1838
churches, round, 1613
Ciampi, Sebastiano, 768, 983
Ciampoli, Domenico, 512
Ciasca, Raffaele, 499, 1245
cicada, 1187. *See also* cricket
Cicciaporci, Antonio, 838
Cicero, apes, 1327
Cicero, Marcus Tullius (I-1 B.C.), v. 1, *206*, 798; v. 2, 1162; v. 3, 9, 112, 299, 326, 333, 402, 507, 577, 942, 990, 1103, 1288, 1289, 1291, 1292, 1294, 1295, 1418, 1434, 1482, 1490, 1811, 1815, 1816, 1819, 1869
Cicogna, E. A., 1819
Cid, Poema del (XII-2), v. 2, *450*, 294, 313
Cilicia, *see* springs; Theophile; Thomas
cinchona, 289
Cingoli, *see* Angelo da Clareno; James Palmerio
cinnabar, 760, 1140
cinnamon, 1620
Cinnamos, *see* John
Cino of Pistoia (XIV-1), *982*, 87, 268, 313, 315, 335, 615, 849, 850, 990, 1482, 1793
Cino Sighibuldi, 983
Cioffarri, Vincenzo, 498
ciompi, tumulto, 1251, 1334
Cipolla, Carlo, 496, 919, 992
Circa instans, 1375
circle, *see* pi
circular motions, 147, 537
circulation, *see* blood
circumcision, 414
circumnavigation, 1603
Cirencester, *see* Richard
Ciriaco, *see also* Cyriacus
Ciriaco of Ancona, 1321
Ciriaco de' Pizzicolli, 1290
Cis, *see* John
Cisneros, *see* Moses Botarel
Cistercian reform in 1116 (XII-1), v. 2, *154*, 1162; v. 3, 395, 1070
Cistercian rule (XII-1), v. 2, *155*; v. 3, 717
Cîteaux, *see* Cistercian
Città di Castello, *see* Hugh
Civezza, Marcellino la, 779
Cividale, *see* Mondino Friulano; William
civilization, 1769
Claes Zannekin, 1023
Clagett, Marshall, 738, 1849
Clairvaux, *see* Bernard
Clamanges, *see* Nicholas
Clapham, J. H., 1180, 1878
Clare College, 72
Clare Hall, 475
clarea, De, 168
Clarence, *see* Lionel
Clareno, *see* Angelo
Clari, *see* Robert
Clarificatorium, 1696
claris mulieribus, De, 1805
claritatis, Liber, 165
Clarke, H. W., 1458
classical scholarship, 1902
classification of the sciences, 76, 899, 1263, 1461, 1770, 1773
Claud, *see* Claudius
Claudianus, 1745
Claudin, Anatole, 1878
Claudius Caecus, *see* Appius
Claudius Claussøn Swart, 1155
Claudius Clavus, 1146, 1155, 1501
Claudius Marcellus, 1031
Claudius Niger, 1155
Clausius, Rudolf, 1843
Clavasio, *see* Dominic
clavibus sapientie, De, 166
clavier, 1567
Clavijo, *see* González
Clavis sanationis, 288
Clay, R. M., 1878
clay, 727, 756
Clayton, H. H., 1856
Cleanthes of Assos (III-1 B.C.), v. 1, *152*, 149
Cleaves, F. W., 1840
Clémanges, *see* Nicholas
Clement of Alexandria, viii
Clement V, pope, 44, 46, 54, 61, 247, 375, 394, 408, 470, 985
Clement VI, pope, 45, 50, 57, 115, 471, 951, 1656
Clement VII, pope, 472, 1032, 1334
Clement VIII, pope, 330, 1033
Clementinum, 472
Clements of Durham, Mrs., 230
Clemow, F. G., 1659
Cleomedes (I-1 B.C.), v. 1, *211*, 202; v. 3, 123
Cleostratos of Tenedos (VI B.C.), v. 1, *72*, 65
clepsydra, 716, 717, 718, 1546
Clerc, *see* John
Clergué, Georges, 77
Clerk, *see* Roger

Clerke, A. M., 563
Cleyer, Andrew, 902
climata, 1889
climates, seven, 794, 800, 1772
Cline, Walter, 217, 220
Clingenberg, *see* John
clinical spirit, 1197
clock, 151, 1676, 1889, 1902. *See also* clepsydra
clock, astronomical, 1497
clock, chamber, 719
clock divided into 24 parts, 1542, 1544, 1546
clock, house, 1546
clock of Strassburg, 1240
clocks, mechanical (XIV-1), *716*, 498; (XIV-2), *1540*, 1124, 1510, 1669
Clodd, Edward, 239
Closener, *see* Frederick
cloth manufacturing, 323
Cloud of unknowing, 1314, 1416
clove, 1620
Cluny, *see* Odo; Peter the Venerable; Richard
Cluny, reform of (X-1), v. 1, *624*, 798; v. 2, 110; v. 3, 395, 991
Clyn, *see* John
clysteribus et colica, De, 431
coagulum, 751
coal, 220, 323
coal measures, 219
coal mining, 1173
coal, sea, 1173
coal, seam on fire in 25 B.C., 220
Coates, H. H., 425
cobalt, 756
Cobb, W. F., 291
Cobham, C. D., 1210
Cobham, *see* Thomas
Cocceius Auctus, L. (I-2 B.C.), v. 1, *223*, 219
Cocchi, Antonio, 287, 870
Cocharelli family, 1634
Cocharelli, *see* Pelegrino
Cocheris, Hippolyte, 561
Cochin, Henri, 505, 514
Cochran-Patrick, R. W., 221
cockchafers, 238
coconut, 1620
coconut fiber, 782
Codex, Justinian, 982, 985, 990, 1869
Codi, 339
Codinos, *see* George
Codrington, H. W., 423
Coedès, George, 294
Coelestinus, 1492
Coeranides, *see* Cyranides
Coëtivy, *see* Prégent
Coëtmohan, *see* William
Coeur de philosophie, 548
Coffman, G. R., 1864
Coghill, Nevill, 1863
cognitione primi principi, De, 522
Cohen, I. B., 29, 1890
Cohen, *see* Kohen
Cohen, Marcel, 1825, 1878, 1895
co-hong, 156
Coimbra, 73
coitus, defectum, 426
Col, *see* Gontier; Peter
Cola di Rienzo (XIV-1), *922*, 37, 88, 299, 315, 333, 511, 516, 937, 1022, 1677
Colard Mansion, 1496
Coldingham, *see* Geoffrey
Cole, G. D. H., 152
Colette, St., 1035
Colin, G. S., 1636, 1725, 1765
Collard de Marke, 126, 1111
Colle, *see* Avanzio; Bernard; Cennino; Dionisio; Francis; George; John; Tiziano; Vivenzio
Colle, F. M., 838, 839, 841, 1670, 1677, 1678, 1681, 1684
Collège des dix-huit, 476
Collège de France, 369, 477
College, Venerable English, 1248
Colles, H. C., 1878, 1886
Collett, Robert, 1191
Colliget astrologiae, 115
Collignano, *see* Francischino
Collijn, Isak, 1356, 1700, 1704, 1862
Collin de Plancy, 1045
Collingwood, R. G., 1864
Collins, A. J., 567
Collins, Henry, 1090, 1417
Collyrium adversus haereses, 50, 402
Cologne, 192
Cologne, *see* Abraham b. Alexander; Arnold; Franco; Ragimbold
Cologne, University, 1400
Colomb de Batines, Paul, 494
Colombini, *see* Catherine; John
Colombo, Alessandro, 847
Colonna, *see* Guido; Landolfo; Oddone; Sciarra
coloribus, De, 169, 704
coloribus illuminatorum, De, 169
Coluccino, *see* James
Coluccio Salutati (XIV-2), *1815*, 1107, 1145, 1274, 1288, 1298, 1388, 1395, 1811, 1815, 1818, 1822
Columbum, *see* Quilon
Columbus, *see* Christopher
Columella, Lucius Junius Moderatus of Gades (I-2), v. 1, *256*, 244; v. 3, 813, 1291
Colybos, 1511
Comani, *see* Cumani
Combarel, E., 1010
Combarieu, Jules, 1878
Combe, Etienne, 1783
Combéfis, François, 1438
Combès, André, 1844
Combi, C. A., 1819
combinatorial analysis, x, 129, 596, 1108, 1487

Combitis atlas, 1144, 1599
Combitis, *see* Nicholas
Côme, frère, 864
Comenge y Ferrer, Luis, 246
Comenius, 1297, 1354
Comestor, *see* Peter
comet of 1299, 1846
comet of 1337, 818
comet of 1368, 1106, 1504, 1510, 1738, 1797
comet of 1402, 1145
comet of 1680, 1504
comet, Halley's, 1122
comets, 705, 1654, 1797
comets of 1340 and 1360, 1738
comets, tails, 1122, 1856
commenda, 125
commendatione cleri, De, 1401
commentatores, 87, 313, 982
commerce, 1888. *See also* trade
commercial law, 1272
Comminges, *see* Eleanor
Common Life, *see* Brothers
commonplace book, 124
common sense, 844
communes, 12
Communiloquium, 317
Comnenos, *see* Alexios; John; Manuel
Compagni, *see* Dino
compagnie di ventura, 1022
compagnies, grandes, 1022
compagnonnages, 153
companies, free, 1793
compass (XIII-1), v. 2, *629*, 1163; (XIV-1), *714*, 143, 151, 818, 824, 1124, 1848
compass card, 715
compass, Chinese (XI-2), v. 1, *764*, 741, 756
compass roses, 763
Compendio, *see* Anthony
Compendium de epidimia, 896
Compendium salernitanum (XII-2), v. 2, *433*
Comper, F. M. M., 567
Compiègne, *see* Roscelin
complexe significabile, 518
complexions, 270, 548, 855, 860
compline, 716
compositione alchimiae, De, 165
Compositiones ad tingenda (VIII-2), v. 1, *533*, 522; v. 3, 168, 1131
Compostela, *see* Berengarius; Santiago
compurgators, 1044
computations, 586
computations, *see* mental
computus, 334, 548
Comte, Auguste, 77, 1262
Comtino, *see* Mordecai b. Eliezer
Cona, *see* Benzo; Jacob
Conant, J. B., 29
Conat, *see* Abraham b. Solomon; Estellina
conception, 1229
Conception, *see* Immaculate
conceptualism, 82
Conches, *see* William
conciliar theory, 320, 554, 992, 1034, 1055, 1350, 1508
Conciliator differentiarum, 439
Conciliator, *see* Peter
Concordia de las leyes, 418
concordia temporum, De, 302
condottieri, 1022
Confessio amantis, 1427
Confirmatio cartarum of 1297, 38
Confucian classics, printed, 138
Confucian rationalism, 262
Confucianism, 109, 386, 1070, 1910
Confucius (VI B.C.), v. 1, *67*, 798; v. 2, 460; v. 3, 162, 280, 311. *See also Chinese index*, K'ung fu-tzŭ
Congenis, *see* William
Congo river, 1158, 1159
congruence equations, 1121, 1536
Conigrano, *see* Francischi
conjunctions of planets, 444, 886, 914, 1106, 1109, 1113, 1505, 1519, 1521, 1654
Connolly, J. L., 1878
Conon of Samos (III-2 B.C.), v. 1, *173*, 166
conosçimiento, Libro del (XIV-1), *786*, 190, 196, 338, 1142, 1592
Conrad of Ascania, 252
Conrad of Aufenstein, 933
Conrad Bitschin, 932
Conrad v. Gelnhausen (XIV-2), *1350*, 1055, 1276, 1277, 1400, 1508
Conrad of Heinrichau (XIV-1), *1004*, 118, 332
Conrad v. Jungingen, 1112
Conrad Kyeser, 1125, 1550, 1866
Conrad of Masovia, 932
Conrad of Megenberg (XIV-1), *817*, 48, 49, 51, 66, 93, 118, 207, 215, 251, 302, 319, 351, 725, 988, 1206, 1645, 1850
Conrad Mendel, 1128
Conrad of Rotenberg, 930
Conrad Spechtshart, 741
Conrad Sweynheim, 399
Conrad, master-general of Teutonic Knights, 932
Conrad Verniger, 542
Conrad Waldhauser, 1056, 1351
conservation of mass and energy, 565
consilia, 285, 844, 848, 1238, 1707, 1861
Consistori de la gaya sciensa, 340
consolat de mar, Llibre del, 315, 324, 325, 343, 1140, 1423
Consolatio theologiae, 1433
consolation, books of, 1434
Constance, *see also* Constanza
Constance, council in, 1033, 1278
Constantine the African (XI-2), v. 1, *769*, 798; v. 2, 1164; v. 3, 247, 374, 442, 870, 877, 881, 884, 1205, 1206, 1375, 1422, 1685, 1705, 1707
Constantine Ancklitzen, 1581

Constantine III, Armenian catholicos, 54, 67
Constantine Armenopulos (XIV-1), *995*, 53, 97, 320, 355
Constantine I the Great, 1325
Constantine Lascaris, 1321
Constantine Lucytes, 438
Constantine Manasses (XII-2), v. 2, *450*, 1164
Constantine the Philosopher, 1323
Constantine VII Porphyrogennetos (X-2), v. 1, *656*, 798; v. 3, 957, 995
Constantinople, 39, 415, 1617, 1907
Constantinople, College, 355, 374
Constantinople, *see* Cyril; Stephen of Byzantium
Constanza Miquel, 1339
constitutional theory, 319
Constitutiones aegidianae, 1793
Constitutiones clementinae, 984
consubstantiation, 992
consulado, 153
Consultatio (V-2), v. 1, *412*, 400
contagion, 880, 896, 1214, 1640, 1658, 1664, 1763
contagious, *see* diseases, eight
Contarini, *see* James; Secondo
Contemplatio de gratia Dei, 393
contemptu mundi, De, 507
Contenau, Georges, 1773
Conti, *see* Nicholas
Conti, Vicenzo, 1444
continuity, 75, 518, 542, 1488
contracts, 1508
contradiction, principle of, 546
Contreras, *see* González
Controne, *see* Pancius
Conty, *see* Evrard
Convenevole da Prato, 502
conventuals, 397
convergence, cultural, 292
convergence, infinite series, 737
Conversino, *see* John
conversos, 1060
Convivio, 483
Cook, A. S., 1425, 1798
Cook, E. T., 1842
Coolen, G., 1754
Coolidge, Julian, 1488
Coolidge, W. A. B., 189, 1878
Coomaraswamy, A. K., 173, 571, 1030, 1656
Cooper, Sonoma, 1689
coordinates, geographical, 797
Coornaert, Emile, 153
Coornher, Dirick, 1809
Copernicus, 15, 129, 600, 1108, 1284, 1399, 1489, 1490, 1495, 1496, 1525, 1846, 1882
Copho of Salerno (XII-1), v. 2, *237*, 1164; v. 3, 875
Copho, *see* Anatomia
Copinger, W. A., 1361
Copland, Robert, 1691, 1693
copper, 220, 727
copper mine, 219
Coppo, *see* John
Coptic, 360, 732, 1365, 1780, 1831
Coptic-Arabic vocabulary, 1006
Coptic church, 55, 1606, 1830
Coptic grammar, 1006
Coptic, *see* medicine
Coptic monasteries, 1601
Coptic, *see* numerals
Coptic patriarchate, 363, 1260
Coptic, *see* steelyard
Coptic theology, 1006
Copts, 709, 1046, 1454, 1768, 1773
Coq, *see* Robert
Coquebert de Montbret, Eugène, 784
Cora, *see* John
corals, 212
Corazzini, Francesco, 1810
Corbara, *see* Peter
Corbechon, *see* John
Corbeil, *see* Giles; Isaac b. Joseph
Corbett, James, 1138, 1583, 1834, 1877, 1879
Corbett, M. D., 1708
Corbian, *see* Peter
Corbizo, *see* Nicholas
Corcos, see Solomon b. Abraham
Cordeyro, Antonio, 1156
Cordier, Henri, xii, 779, 784, 1071, 1591, 1879, 1894, 1910
Cordova, *see* Alfonso; Bakrī; Isaac b. Nathan; Khashkhāsh
Corin, A. L., 572
Corinth, *see* Gregory
Corinth, isthmus, 736
Coris, 1688
Cormac Mac Duinntshleibhe, 873, 882
cormorant fishing, 234, 778, 1603
Cornaro, Luigi, 301, 1218, 1732
Cornelio, Flaminio, 1095
Cornelius Nepos, 1290
Cornet, *see* Raymond
Cornish mines, 219
Cornut, Etienne (S.J.), 1304
Cornwall, *see* John; Peter Gaveston
Coroleu, José, 926, 1735
Coromandel coast, 383
coroner, duties, 904
Corpus Christi, Cambridge, 473, 1079, 1402
Corpus iuris, 995
Corpus iuris canonici, 983
Corradini, Francesco, 513
Correctorium corruptorii, 526, 992
Correggio, *see* Simon
Corsi, Giuseppe, 1601
Corsini, Andrea, 1248
Corsini, Tommaso, 765
Corsinis, *see* Thomas
Cortenova, *see* Uberto
Cortez, Martin, 716, 844
Cortone, *see* Peter

Corvey, *see* Widukind
Corvi, *see* William
Cosenza, Mario Emilio, 516, 924
Cosenza, *see* Telesforo
Cosimo de' Medici, 500, 1289
Cosmas, brotherhood of St., 247
Cosmas, College of St., 272, 291, 863, 865
Cosmas Indicopleustes (VI-1), v. 1, *431*, 417; v. 3, 358, 363
Cosmas of Prague (XII-1), v. 2, *259*, 139; v. 3, 941, 1758
Cosmas, St., 863, 1247
Cosmas, St., Bulgarian, 1854
cosmetics, 869
Cosmo, *see also* Cosmas
Cosmo Megliorati, 1032
cosmology, 1882
cosmology, Byzantine, 123
Cossa, *see* Balthasar
cossantes, 343
Costomiris, A. G., 892
Cott, P. B., 1187
cotton, 228, 832, 1622
cotton, Japanese (VIII-2), v. 1, *535*
cotton paper, 833
cotton shroud, 833
Coucy, *see* Moses b. Jacob
Couderc, Camille, 1630
Couling, Samuel, 1879
Coulon, Remi, 1817
Coulter, C. C., 1803, 1811, 1843, 1869
Coulton, G. G., 52, 333, 404, 481, 1046, 1336, 1362, 1404, 1425, 1654, 1656, 1663, 1753, 1756, 1879
council, general, *see* conciliar theory
counterpoint, 743
Couplet, Philippe, 902
Cour, Auguste, 1723, 1764
Courant, Maurice, 162, 389, 1880
Courcy, *see* Haiton
Cournot, A. A., 1262
Courtecuisse, *see* John
Courtenay, *see* Baldwin; Richard; William
Courtrai, *see* Siger
Cousin, Louis, 952
Coussemaker, Edmond de, 1880
Couvin, *see* Simon
Covarrubias y Orozco, Sebastián de, 1302
Coville, Alfred, 50, 880, 887, 1276, 1277, 1295, 1346, 1652, 1660, 1747
Cowell, E. B., 1367, 1368, 1369
Cowley, A. E., 1324, 1693, 1880
Cowper, J. M., 462
cowries, 1622
Cowton, *see* Robert
Coxe, H. O., 1428
Coyecque, E., 295
Cracow, *see* Demetrios; Vincent
Cracow, University, 1078, 1398
Cranstoun, David, 1413
Crateros the Macedonian (III-1 B.C.), v. 1, *161*, 150
Crates of Mallos (II-1 B.C.), v. 1, *185*, 178, 179; v. 3, 192
Cratevas (I-1 B.C.), v. 1, *213*, 202, 296; v. 3, 225
Crawford, O. G. S., 1743
Crawfurd, Raymond, 1659, 1663
creatio ex nihilo, 1449
creation, 84, 569, 604
creationism, 488
Crécy, 38
credit, *see* bills
creditori e debitori, libro dei, 124
Creeny, W. F., 728
Creighton, Mandell, 561
Crémieux, Ad., 1382
Cremona, *see* Adam; Daniel Deloc; Gerald; Liudprand; Theophile
Cremonini, Cesare, 539
Cremonini, Pia, 1051
Crescas, *see* Ḥasdai b. Abraham; Meïr; Solomon b. Nathan
Crescas Vidal Caslari, 449
Crescenzi, *see* Giambonino; Peter
Cresques, *see* Abraham; Judah b. Abraham
Cresques the Jew, 1592
Cressy, R. F. S., 1090
Cressy, Serenus, 1416
crestiaa, 279
Crete, 448, 1095
Crete, *see* Peter
cretins, 279
Creutz, Rudolf, 1222
Creutzer, Peter, 710
cricket, 1188. *See also* cicada
Cricklade, *see* Robert
Crimea, 1365, 1853
Crimea, *see* Abraham Qirimī
Crisp, Frank, 815
Crispus (VII-2), v. 1, *497*
Cristofano Dini, 1669
Cristoforo, *see also* Christopher
Cristoforo da Barzizza, 1289
Cristoforo Berardi da Pesaro, 1814
Cristoforo Landino, 1567
criticism, textual, 1816
Critobulos, 919, 1552
Critopulos, *see* Nicholas Cunales
Crivelli, *see* Taddeo
Croatia, *see* Melandino
Crocioni, Giovanni, 501
crocodiles, 1642
Croissant, Jeanne, 1094
Croix, *see* Peter
Cromwell, Thomas, 988
Crooke, William, 1217, 1880, 1910
Crosby, Ruth, 1425
Cross, Invention of the, 1043
crossbows, 725, 1547

cross-staff, 129, 600, 601
Cruickshank, William, 1117
Crule, *see* John
Crum, W. E., 362
Crummer, Le Roy, 845
crusade, *see* Chanson
Crusades (XII-1 and others), v. 2, *163*, 1165; v. 3, 45, 327, 339, 392, 408, 415, 421, 1873, 1909
Crusca, Accademia, 1301, 1302
Ctesias of Cnidos (V B.C.), v. 1, *107*, 83
Ctesibios of Alexandria (II-1 B.C.), v. 1, *184*, 178, 180; v. 3, ix
cubit, 712
cubitus, 1847
cucumbers, 1620
Cuenca, *see* John
Cues (or Cusa), *see* Nicholas
Cueva, *see* Beltrán
Cugnières, *see* Peter
Cugnoni, Giuseppe, 1737
Cuilly, Jacques de, 399
Cūlavaṃsa, 977, 1370
Culley, D. E., 1351
Cultus ruris, 811
Cuman dialect, 379
Cumani, 785, 1016, 1853
Cumanicus, Codex, 379, 1015
Cumba, *see* Giraldus
Cumming, John, 1619
Cumming, W. P., 1356
Cummings, H. M., 1425
Cumont, Franz, 124, 139, 330, 376, 1876, 1877, 1880
Cunales Critopulos, *see* Nicholas
cuneiform, 359
Cunningham, William, 1497
Cuno of Falkenstein, 1578
cupping glasses, 869
Curialti of Tossignano, 1681
Curialtis, *see* Peter Albergheti
Curio, Valentin, 988
currency, *see* money
Curry, W. C., 1426
Curschmann, Fritz, 283
cursor, 79
cursus, rhythmical, 1295, 1327
Curtayne, Alice, 496
Curti, *see* William
Curtius Rufus, Quintus (I-1), v. 1, *241*, 236; v. 3, 1288, 1816
Curtze, E. L. W. M., 1496
Curtze, Maximilian, 606, 607, 735, 1113, 1482, 1483, 1488, 1880
Curzon, Robert, 584
Cusanus, *see* Nicholas
Cushing, Harvey, 1704, 1868
Cuspinian, 935
Cust, K. I., 533
customs, 1617
Cuturi, Torquato, 1796
Cuvier, Georges, 1406
Cybo of Hyères (XIV-2), *1633*, 1164, 1177, 1178
cycle of twelve animals (I-1), v. 1, *238*, 235
cyclopes, 1227
Cydones, *see* Demetrios; Prochoros
cylinders, 432
Cyprian of Kiev, 1613
Cyprianus of Carthage, St., viii, 1294
Cyprus, 40, 772, 1025, 1036, 1210, 1672
Cyprus, *see* Famagusta; Gregory; Henry II; John; Peter
Cyranides, 754, 838, 856, 1849, 1876
Cyriacus, *see also* Ciriaco
Cyriacus of Gandzak (XIII-2), v. 2, *1114*, 1165
Cyriacus of Rome, St., 1666
Cyril of Alexandria, St., viii, 488, 1438, 1441, 1513
Cyril of Constantinople, 924
Cyril of Thessalonica, St. (IX-2), v. 1, *590*, 583, 589; v. 2, 104; v. 3, 355
Cyrillos of Chios, 169
Cyrus, education, 314
Czarnkowski, *see* John; Simeon
Czech, 31, 355

Da'at, 594
Da'at ha-qiddum, 435
Ḍabbī, *see* Aḥmad b. Yaḥyā
Dabi, b., *see* Meïr b. Isaac
Dabry de Thiersant, 1586, 1587, 1589
Dacia, *see* Peter
Dadré, Jean, 399
Dagomari, *see* Paul
Dahhān, b., *see* Muḥammad b. 'Alī
Dahlerup, Verner, 352
Dahlgren, F. A., 1509
Dahmus, J. H., 1350
Dair al-ṭīn, 708
Daivatabrāhmaṇa, 1369
Dalai Lāma, 1371
Daland, Judson, 735, 1563
Dalbon, Charles, 170
Dalechamp, Jacques, 1695
Dalen, *see* John
Dalgairns, J. D., 1416
Dalimil, chronicle, 302, 355, 940, 1322
Dalimil Mezeřický, 940
dallaka, 288
Ḍallana (XII-1), v. 2, *247*, 68, 137
Dallari, Umberto, 845
Dalmatia, 1659
Dalmatia, *see* Herman; Jerome, St.
Dalmau Ces-Planes (XIV-2), *1485*, 1074, 1107, 1115, 1305, 1375, 1858, 1863, 1865
Dalorto, *see* Angelino
Dalton, *see* John
Dalton, O. M., 1187
Dam, b. a., *see* Ibrāhīm b. 'Abdallāh
dam with movable door, 1552

Damascios (VI-1), v. 1, *421*, 799
Damascus in 1344, 803
Damascus, blades, 1175
Damascus, *see* John; Nicholas
Dambach, *see* John
Damian, St., 863, 1247
Damianos (IV-1), v. 1, *354*, 345
Damīrī, Muḥammad b. Mūsā (XIV-2), *1639*, 1099, 1104, 1119, 1168, 1186, 1214, 1219, 1223, 1326, 1867
Damnastes (XI-1), v. 1, *727*, 699
Damocrates Servilius (I-2), v. 1, *261*, 244
Da Mosto, A., 1595
Damouzy, *see* Peter
dance, *see* death; macabre
dancing mania (XIV-2), *1665*, 1192, 1867
dancing procession, 1667
Dancus, king (XIII-2), v. 2, *1071*, 779; v. 3, 231, 1185
Dandin, *see* John
Dane James, 1336
Daniel, book of (II-1 B.C.), v. 1, *180*, 177; v. 3, 364, 398
Daniel Deloc of Cremona, 345, 1835
Daniel, F. S., 163
Daniel of Kiev (XII-1), v. 2, *224*, 1166; v. 3, 1155
Daniel of Morley (XII-2), v. 2, *385*, 293
Daniel, prophet, 1104
Daniel de Roucliffe, 1582
Daniels, Augustinus, 570
Danielssen, D. C., 881, 1837
Danish, 352
Danszon, 1699
Dante Alighieri (XIV-1), *479*, 18, 36, 37, 43, 47, 66, 72, 86, 101, 111, 187, 193, 238, 242, 268, 299, 313, 333, 335, 370, 446, 472, 505, 508, 530, 532, 542, 615, 720, 918, 919, 923, 943, 982, 989, 992, 1086, 1144, 1145, 1210, 1274, 1286, 1299, 1300, 1301, 1304, 1321, 1334, 1336, 1418, 1427, 1456, 1482, 1601, 1737, 1794, 1803, 1806, 1812, 1842, 1843, 1862
Dante societies, 495
Daphnis and Chloë, 1188
Dapiera, *see* Solomon b. Immanuel; Solomon b. Meshullam
Daqīq, b., *see* Muḥammad b. 'Alī
Dār al-ḥarb, 1862
Dār al-Islām, 1862
Dār al-salām, 309
Dār al-Shifā', 970, 1457, 1461
Darbandī, *see* 'Alī b. Muḥammad
Darby, John, 1474
Dardel, *see* John
Daremberg, C. V., 1880, 1901
dargah, 1476
Darmarios, *see* Andreas
Darmesteter, James, 56
Darmesteter, Mary, 1753
Darmstaedter, Ernst, 1174
Darmstaedter, Ludwig, 1880
darvishes, 153, 155, 420, 1875
darvishes, dancing, 420
Das, S. C., 1372
Dasent, G. W., 943
Dasgupta, S. N., 1880
Dastin, *see* John
Dasypodius Conradus, 586, 1541
date palms, 212, 417, 1637, 1775
Dāṭhāvaṃsā, 1370
Datini books, 126
Datini, *see* Francis
Datta, Bhagavad, 1370
Datta, Bibhutibhusan, 137, 1535
Dā'ūd, *see also* David
Dā'ūd b. 'Alī Ẓāhirī (IX-2), v. 1, *592*, 583; v. 3, 1011
Dā'ūd b. Maḥmūd Qaisarī (XIV-1), *626*, 105
Dā'ūd b. Muḥammad Banākatī (XIV-1), *976*, 203, 309, 377, 387, 731, 971
Daude de Pradas, 339, 1835
Daudet, Alphonse, 1116
Dauphin, 184, 1344
Davey, Henry, 1569
David, *see also* Dā'ūd
David b. Abraham Caslari (XIII-2), v. 2, *857*, 723; v. 3, 366, 893
David b. Abraham of Fez (X-2), v. 1, *690*, 653, 655; v. 2, 275; v. 3, 365, 1008
David the Armenian (XII-1), v. 2, *244*, 83, 135
David of Augsburg, 404
David Bonet Bonjorn, 1521, 1522, 1841
David Bruce, 1751
David of Dinant (XIII-1), v. 2, *551*, 487, 568
David, J. B., 582
David b. Jacob Bonet, 1516
David of Jaén, 1233, 1717
David b. Joseph Abudraham (XIV-1), *417*, 55, 131
David b. Joseph Qimḥi (XII-2), v. 2, *470*, 1166; v. 3, 366, 1008, 1522, 1826
David b. Joshua b. Maimon, 1364
David, Mariano, 1862
David b. Merwan (X-1), v. 1, *626*, 620, 623
David b. Samuel Kokabi (XIV-1), *419*, 56
David, *see* Solomon b. David
David b. Solomon Qaraite (XIII-1), v. 2, *665*, 1166; v. 3, 1727
David b. Solomon b. Ya'īsh (XIV-2), *1373*, 1072, 1096
David b. Yaḥya, 1523
David b. Yom-ṭob b. Bila (XIV-1), *451*, 55, 65, 100, 130, 255
David b. Yom-ṭob Bongoron (or Bonjorn), 452, 1450
David-Neel, Alexandra, 1372
Davids, T. W. R., 423
Davidsohn, R., 913
Davidson, Thomas, 1117

Davies, Oliver, 217
Davis, A. H., 1743
Davis, John, 601
Davis, L. M., 711
Davis, T. L., 180, 761, 1140, 1480
Davison, Charles, 216, 1172, 1346
Davy, M. M., 1040
Davy, William, 1472
da'wah, 134
Dawkins, R. M., 1466, 1866
Dawson, W. H., 472
days, *see* Egyptian
Dazzi, M. T., 918
Dean, A. L., 909
Dean, Bashford, 1561
Dean, R. J., 943, 944, 1852
Deanesly, Margaret, 567, 1349, 1362
death, dance, 1231
death, signs, 801
De Boer, Tjitze, 150, 1778
Deborah, Song, 363
Decamerone, *see* Boccaccio
Decembrio, *see* Peter Candido; Uberto
decimal basis, 129
decimal fractions, 1107, 1112, 1116, 1120, 1518, 1903
decimal idea, 113
decimal measures, 1903
decimal numbers, 1535, 1610
decimal scale in charts, 764
Deckelmann, Henry, 1388
declination, magnetic, 143, 183, 715, 1124, 1506
Decretales, 983, 984
Decretum, 983
decubitu ex mathematica scientia, De, 441
Dee, John, 1501
Defensor minor, *see* Marsiglio of Padua
Defensor pacis, *see* Marsiglio of Padua
Defensorium vitae, 426
deficiency diseases, 261, 268
Defrémery, C., 1595, 1622
degeneration, physical, 1675
Degli Azzi, G., 1686
De Goeje, M. J., 622
De Groot, J. J. M., 156
Degryse, R., 822
Deguilleville, *see* William
Dehérain, Henri, 802
Deinard, *see* Ephraim
De Jong, Pieter, 966
De Keyser, Paul, 939
De Korne, J. C., 156
Delaborde, H. F., 930
Delacotte, Joseph, 533
Delacroix, Henri, 1844
Delacrut, *see* Mattithiah b. Solomon
Delafosse, Maurice, 41, 803
De Langhe, *see* John
Delatte, Armand, 104, 124, 197, 755, 953, 1512, 1877, 1880
Delatte, Louis, 1849
Delaunay, Paul, 17, 1227, 1299, 1699
Delaville le Rouex, J., 392
Delcourt, Marie, 1876
Delécluze, Etienne Jean, 514
Delehaye, Hippolyte, 292, 865, 1041, 1042, 1045
Delepierre, Octave, 940, 1747
Delestre, *see* Jourdain
Delft, 756
Delft, *see* John Lietuyt
Del Guerra, G., 1654
Délicieux, *see* Bernard
De Lint, J. G., 1693
Delisle, Guillaume, 1158
Delisle, Léopold, 928, 1003, 1392, 1690
Delitzsch, Franz, 618
Della Porta, Giovanni Battista, 812
Della Torre, Arnaldo, 502, 1815
Del Lungo, Isidoro, 499, 913, 983
Del Monte, G. U., 1127
Deloc, *see* Daniel
Delorme, F., 531
Delprato, Pietro, 858, 859, 1669, 1838
Del Sotto, Is., 1605
De Maria, Michael, 559
Demena, *see* Bonaventura
Demetrios of Apamea (II-2 B.C.), v. 1, *198*, 192
Demetrios Chrysoloras, 1094, 1320, 1823
Demetrios of Cracow, 1582
Demetrios Cydones (XIV-2), *1387*, 585, 587, 746, 1058, 1075, 1320, 1363, 1386, 1439, 1760, 1823
Demetrios Galanos, 465
Demetrios, king, 1643
Demetrios Pepagomenos (XIII-2), v. 2, *1095*, 1166; v. 3, 252, 274, 888, 1643
Demetrios Phalereos, 224, 353
Demetrios of Scepsis (II-1 B.C.), v. 1, *190*, 179
Demetrios Triclinios (XIV-1), *1005*, 353, 355, 997
De Meyer, J., 6
Demiéville, Paul, 1881, 1889
Democedes of Crotona (VI B.C.), v. 1, *77*, 66
Democritos of Abdera (V B.C.), v. 1, *88*, 81, 82; v. 2, 76; v. 3, 148, 149, 751, 1235, 1640
Democritos, pseudo (I-1), v. 1, *238*, 800
demons, 849
demonstrator, 842
Demosthenes, Philalethes (I-2), v. 1, *260*, 244, 245; v. 2, 1085
Dempster, Germaine, 1425
Den-sa sum, 1371
Dene, *see* William
Denholm-Young, Noël, 1296, 1830
Denifle, F. H. S., 574
Denifle, Heinrich, 534, 570, 572

Denis, *see also* Dinis; Dino; Dionisio; Dionysios; Dionysius
Denis, Ferdinand, 785
Denis Foulechat (XIV-2), *1390*, 1075, 1088, 1277, 1307
Denis d'Hormes, 1183
Denis of Paris, St., 1666
Denis, St., chronicle, 300, 1253
Denison, Alfred, 1166
Denk, Franz, 1866
Denk, V. M. O., 1306
Denmark, *see* medicine
Denomy, A. J., 1496
dental instruments, 1692
dentistry, 1892
Deny, Jean, 378, 381, 1026, 1327, 1786
Déodat Jordan, 1406
deontology, chiefly medical, 292, 853, 869, 872, 883, 1700, 1706
Deoprepio, *see* Nicholas
De Pauw, J. C., 826
De Pauw, Napoléon, 1556
Deprès, des Prés, *see* Josquin
Déprez, Eugène, 1748
Dept, G. G., 822
derash, 398
derashot, 417
Derby, *see* Henry
Derek ḥilluq, 1518
Derenbourg, Hartwig, 360, 958, 967, 1881, 1901
"derivation," Byzantine, 890
dermatology, *see* skin ailments
Dernehl, P. H., 498
Der Nersessian, Sirapie, 827, 1178
De Roover, F. E., 124
De Roover, Raymond, 126, 127, 128, 774, 1111
De Sagher, E., 884
De Slane, W. McGuckin, 1777, 1778
Des Marez, Guillaume, 153, 1838
descant, 160, 744
Descartes, 5, 142, 149, 705, 1220, 1487, 1489, 1566
Deschamps, *see* Eustache
Desclot, *see* Bernard
Desimoni, Cornelio, 765, 771, 775
Desmaze, Charles, 1392
De Smet, J. J., 1747
Desnos, E., 892, 1236
Despaux, Albert, 1284
Després, *see* Peter
Destrez, Jean, 1297
Destructio destructionis, 429
determinant, 140
Deters, Friedrich, 726
Detombes, Marcel, 1866
De Toni, Ettore, 1164
Deubner, Ludwig, 864
Deulacres, *see* Hagin
Deuteronomy (VII B.C.), v. 1, *62*, 107
Deutsche Sphaera, 819
De Van, Guillaume, 745
Devanāgarī alphabet, 382, 384
Devatādhyāyabrāhmaṇa, 1369
Develay, Victor, 513
Deventer, 1297, 1317, 1360
Devī, 1237
devil, 405, 1050
De Vis, H., 305
devito e richolti, libro a, 124
Devlin, M. A., 1040
devotio, moderna, 1057, 1081, 1085, 1093, 1297, 1317, 1359, 1361, 1408, 1890
De Vreese, Willem, 582, 939
De Vries, M., 940, 1607
De Vroede, Franciscus, 1799
De Waard, Cornelis, 821, 1881
De Weert, *see* John
De Wulf, M., 1004, 1881
Dey, Nundo Lal, 1881
Deycks, Ferdinand, 789
Deza, *see* Diego
Dezcoll, *see* Bernard
Deztany, Lluis, 1689
dhahab kibrīt, 753
Dhahabī, *see* Lājīn b. 'Abdallāh
Dhahabī, Muḥammad b. Aḥmad (XIV-1), *963*, 163, 257, 308, 619, 1266, 1725, 1852
Dhahabī, *see* Muḥammad b. Muḥammad; Shams al-dīn
Dhammakitti, 310, 977
Dhammakitti IV (XIV-2), *1370*, 1069, 1330
Dhammakitti V (XIV-2), *1370*, 423, 1069, 1102, 1267, 1330
Dhammakitti Mahāsāmi, 1371
Dhammānanda, 423
Dhammapāla, 382
Dhanvantarinighaṇṭu, 1730
Dhar, Nil Ratan, 1175
dharma, 81, 1000
Dharmakīrti, Ācārya (VII-1), v. 1, *473*, 461, 463
dharmaśāstra, 1000, 1367
Dhātuvṛitti, 1367
dhawāt al-khamsa, 612
dhikr, 96
dhimma, 997
dhirā', 712
dhubbān al-hind, 296
Dhū-l-nūn (IX-2), v. 1, *592*, 800; v. 2, 874; v. 3, 759
dhurrāḥ, 296
Dhyāna, 59, 189, 423, 1332
diabetes, xi
Diaconos, *see* Leo
diaeta acutorum, 437
Diago Cão, 1159
dialogo, 1335
Dialogus creaturarum, 835
Diamond ṣūtra, 729

Dias, *see* Dinis
Diassorinos, Diasorenos, *see* Neilos
Diatessaron, 357, 1058, 1513
Díaz de Arcaya, Manuel, 1737
dībāj, 709
Dicaearchos of Messina (IV-2 B.C.), v. 1, *145*, 126
dice, 1813
Diceto, *see* Ralph
Dichos de sabios, 427
Dickens, Charles, 488
Dickmann, Arnold, 1412
Dickson, L. E., 1881
dictamen, 332, 386, 1295, 1296, 1839
dictamina, 1783
dictatores, 1296
Dictionarium iuris, 985
Dictionarius, 332
Dicuil (IX-1), v. 1, *571*, 546
Didot, A. F., 930, 1570
Didron, A. N., 169
Didymos of Alexandria (I-2 B.C.), v. 1, *233*, 220
Didymos of Alexandria (IV-2), v. 1, *370*, 360, 452
Diefenbach, Lorenz, 1881
Diego Deza, 1343
Diehl, Charles, 1881
Diels, H., 158, 441, 718
Diemeringen, *see* Otto
Diepenbrock, Melchior v., 574
Diepgen, Paul, 879, 1244, 1712
Dieppe, sailors, 1147, 1159
Dier, *see* Rodolph
Dietarium, 426
Dieterici, Friedrich, 435, 1342
dietetics, Chinese, 906
Diethalm Schilter, 1153
Dietrich, *see* Theodoric; Theodore
Differentia nostrae translationis, 398
diffusion of cultural items, 151
Di Francia, Letterio, 1810
Digenis Acritas, 1812
Digest, 985
Digestum novum, 981
digits, 1483
Dignāga Ācārya (IV-2), v. 1, *366*, 800
Dijksterhuis, E. J., 545, 1432, 1489
Dijon, *see* Nicholas
Diller, Aubrey, 197, 1501, 1859
Dillmann, August, 1355
Dillon, Edward, 1881
Dilucidatorium, 837
Dimand, M. S., 173
Dimashqī, *see* Ḥasan b. 'Umar b. Ḥabīb; Ja'far b. 'Alī; Muḥammad b. 'Abd al-Raḥmān; Muḥammad b. Ibrāhīm; Ṣadaqa b. Munaja'
dimensions, four, 1487
Dinānah, Ṭāhā, 897, 1721, 1722
Dīnānātha, Rāmacandra, 1585
dinanderie (XIV-1), *727*, 144; (XIV-2), *1561*, 1125
Dinant, *see* David
Dinaux, Arthur, 1747
Dīnawarī (IX-2), v. 1, *615*, 800
Dingle, H., 83
Dingler, Hugo, 1497
Dini, *see* Augustine; Cristofano; Dino; Peter
Dini-Traversari, Alessandro, 1290
Dinis Dias, 1159
Dinis o Lavrador, king of Portugal (XIII-2), v. 2, *844*, 1167; v. 3, 61, 68, 73, 184, 207, 228, 344, 862, 1038
Dīnkart (IX-2), v. 1, *591*; v. 3, 376
Dinkelsbühl, *see* Nicholas
Dino Compagni (XIV-1), *912*, 207, 214, 297, 313, 336, 337, 914, 917, 1737
Dino Dini of Florence (XIV-2), *1669*, 1192, 1238, 1300
Dino del Garbo (XIV-1), *837*, 143, 207, 243, 712, 840, 1192, 1672
Dino da Mugello, 981
Dinostratos (IV-2 B.C.), v. 1, *140*, 125
Diocles of Carystos (IV-1 B.C.), v. 1, *121*, 112, 126; v. 3, ix
Diocles, mathematician (II-1 B.C.), v. 1, *183*, 177, 178; v. 2, 342
Diocletian, 1659
Diodoros of Sicily (I-2 B.C.), v. 1, *231*, 220; v. 2, 760; v. 3, 1073, 1291, 1849
Diogenes of Apollonia (V B.C.), v. 1, *96*, 82
Diogenes the Babylonian (II-1 B.C.), v. 1, *181*, 177, 179; v. 3, 331
Diogenes Laërtios (III-1), v. 1, *318*, 314; v. 3, 224, 326, 563, 1321
Diomedes Bonard, 447
Dion Cassios (III-1), v. 1, *327*, 316, 775; v. 2, 1167
Dionisio II Colle (XIV-2), *1668*, 852, 1192
Dionisio of Milan, 1132
Dionysia de Monchensi, 348
Dionysios, *see also* Denis
Dionysios, Aelios (II-1), v. 1, *286*, 269, 313
Dionysios the Areopagite (V-2), v. 1, *406*, 800; v. 2, 1167; v. 3, 81, 460, 530, 584, 1095, 1323, 1416, 1438, 1439
Dionysios of Halicarnassos (I-2 B.C.), v. 1, *232*, 220
Dionysios Periegetes (I-2), v. 1, *258*, 800; v. 2, 1167
Dionysios of Phurna, 169, 1583
Dionysios of Tell-Maḥrē (IX-1), v. 1, *579*, 437, 548
Dionysios Thrax (II-2 B.C.), v. 1, *200*, 192, 424; v. 2, 998; vol. 3, 356, 1822
Dionysius, *see also* Denis
Dionysius Exiguus (VI-1), v. 1, *429*, 800
Dionysius de Rubertis, 87, 112

Dionysodoros of Amisos (II-1 B.C.), v. 1, *182*, 177
Diophantine analysis, *see* analysis, indeterminate
Diophantos of Alexandria (III-2), v. 1, *336*, 800; v. 2, 1168; v. 3, ix, 14, 119
Dioscorides of Anazarbos, Pedanios (I-2), v. 1, *258*, 800; v. 2, 1168; v. 3, 288, 442, 445, 608, 816, 836, 846, 856, 881, 883, 898, 1205, 1603, 1685
Dioscuri, 864
Diplovatazio, Tommaso, 1795
Directorium ad passagium, 391, 416, 775
Directorium vitae humanae, 464
Dirr, A., 305
Discordantium canonum concordia, 400
discoveries, 145
discoveries, *see* simultaneity
diseases, eight contagious, 874
Dispensarium ad aromatorios, 288, 446
Disputationes adversus astrologos, 439
dissections (XIII-2), v. 2, *1081*, 1168; v. 3, 265, 842, 848, 1223, 1394, 1440
distilling sea water, 881
Dit de bigamie, 865
Dittamondo, 1600
diver, 1552
divination, 103, 1103, 1458, 1537, 1769, 1772. *See also* chiromancy; dreams; geomancy; palmistry; physiognomy; qiyāfa; sorcerers; spasmatomancy; urinomancy
dīwān, 997
Dīwān lughat al-Turk, 378
dīwānī, 134
Ḍiyā al-dīn, *see* Nakhshabī
Dobner, Gelasius, 782, 1758
Dobrowolski, Kazimierz, 222
Dobrowsky (Dobrovský), Joseph, 1758
Docimasta, Eleutero, 918
Dock, George, 882
Doctrina communis Thome, 84
Doctrina de compondre dictats, 343
Doctrina puerilis, 73
Doctrinal de trobar, 343
Dodd, W. G., 1428
Dodds, E. R., 706
Dodwell, H., 41
Doe, Janet, 1233
Dölger, Franz, 1513
Dönne, F., 925
Doenniges, Wilhelm, 913, 918, 920
Dörfler, S., 618
Doering, *see* Matthew
Dōhi, Keizo, 293
Doinel, Jules Stanislas, 528
Dolce, Lodovico, 952
dolce stil nuovo, 335, 338, 615, 982
Dolci, Giulio, 509
Dolcino of Novara, 23
Dolfin, *see* Michael
Dols, J. M. E., 1361
Dombay, Franz v., 958
Dombelay, *see* John
Dombrowski, Ernst v., 1185
Domenichelli, Teofilo, 779
Domenico, *see* Dominic
Domesday book (XI-2), v. 1, *779*, 744; v. 3, 199
Domingo, *see* Dominic
Dominic di Bandini (XIV-2), *1409*, 583, 921, 1086, 1106, 1145, 1163, 1170, 1288
Dominic de Clavasio (XIV-1), *641*, 111, 112, 1539
Dominic Doria, 803
Dominic Gundisalvo (XII-1), v. 2, *172*, 1168; v. 3, 431
Dominic, St. (XIII-1), v. 2, *546*, 573
Dominic Savi, 23
Dominicans (XIII-1), v. 2, *546*, 1168; v. 3, 47, 374, 473, 1886, 1900
Dominici, *see* John; Peter
Dominicus, *see* Dominic
Dominis, *see* Marc Antonio
Domninos of Larissa (V-2), v. 1, *408*, 400
dōms, 784
Donado Soranzo, 126
Donaldson, D. M., 633
Donati, *see* Gemma di Manetto
Donati, Marcello, 848
Donatists, 1059
Donato degli Albanzani, 1407, 1817
Donatus, Aelius (IV-1), v. 1, *358*, 801; v. 2, 1168; v. 3, 331, 340, 350, 410, 552, 1004, 1311, 1358
Donatz proensals, 340
Dondaine, Antonius, 569
Dondi, *see* James; John
Dondua, K. D., 1120
Doneldey, *see* Albero; Arnold
Donet, 1311
Dongola, 1143
Donin, *see* Nicholas
Donis projection, 1146
Donkin, R. S., 1159
Doppelmayr, Gabriel, 820
Doré, Henri, 262, 1733
Doria, *see* Dominic; Lucian; Taddeo
Dormans, *see* John
Dorn, Gerard, 1577
Dorotheos of Sidon, 1481, 1865
Dorp, *see* John
Dortous de Mairan, J. J., 709
Dorveaux, Paul, 251, 347
dosimetry, Arabic, 1211
Dottrinale, 86, 501
Douai, 323
Douais, Célestin, 404
double-entry bookkeeping, 124, 126, 1111
Douce, Francis, 456
Douët-d'Arcq, Louis Claude, 1202, 1633

Doughty, C. M., 1777
Dover castle clock, 723, 1848
Dowling, Thady, 947
Dozy, R., 807, 1778, 1868
Dragomanni, F. G., 915
dragon, flying, 1866
dragon of Ghent, 1561
Drake, F. S., 1071
Drake, Francis, 1595
Drane, A. T., 1337
Draper, W. H., 513
Dravidian languages, 383
dreams, 103, 537, 963, 1093, 1094, 1099, 1103, 1104, 1206, 1421, 1507, 1640, 1641, 1772, 1784, 1821
Dreiling, Raymundus, 529
Dreyer, J. L. E., 497, 1500, 1881
Drioux, Georges, 404
Drogheda, *see* William
Drogio, 1594
Droste, Max, 1340
droughts, 227, 965
Droz, Eugénie, 1661
Druce, Gerald, 1167
Drummond, J. C., 231, 1182, 1236
Drury, A. G., 498
Dryden, H., 1630
Dsordsor, *see* Zacharias
Dubaithī, b., *see* Muḥammad b. Sa'īd
Du Bois, Jacques, 427
Dubois, *see* Peter
Dubs, H. H., 220, 1140
Du Bus, Charles, 183
Duc, Fronton du, 947
Du Cange, 826, 928, 930, 1165, 1177, 1284, 1458, 1632, 1786, 1881
Ducas, 1553
Dudo of St. Quentin (XI-1), v. 1, *733*, 700, 702; v. 2, 453
Dübner, Friedrich, 825
duel, 1798
Dünner, J. Z., 366
dürbäldzin (square), 380
Dürer, Albrecht, 1105, 1231, 1238, 1584
Duèse, *see* James
Duff, C. M., 978, 1882, 1902
Du Four, *see* Vital
Dugin, 1842
Duguet, Firmin, 1665
Duhairī, b., 1006
Duhem, Pierre, 5, 82, 83, 146, 147, 487, 531, 540, 1428, 1431, 1490, 1882
Dukes, E. J., 1537
Dulaf, a., *see* Mis'ar b. Muhalhil
Dulaurier, E., 955
Dulcert, *see* Angelino
Dullaert, *see* John
Dumas, Alexandre, 541
Dumbar, Gerhard, 1361
Dumbleton, *see* John
Dumont, P. E., 29
Dunash b. Labraṭ (X-2), v. 1, *690*, 653, 655; v. 3, 366
Dunbar, H. F., 500
Dunham, Dows, 1596
Dunham, W. H., jr., 719
Dunlap, Robert, 1740
Dunlop, D. M., 1855
Dunning, T. P., 1415
Duns Scotus, *see* John Duns Scot
duple time, 1833
Du Plessis d'Argentrée, Charles, 534
Dupuy, P., 411
Duqmāq, b., *see* Ibrāhīm b. Muḥammad
Duraid, b., *see* Muḥammad b. Ḥasan
Duraihim, b., *see* 'Alī b. Muḥammad; Muḥammad b. 'Abd al-'Azīz
Duran, *see also* Durand; Durant
Duran, *see* Profiaṭ; Simeon b. Ẓemaḥ; Solomon
Durand d'Aurillac (XIV-1), *526*, 89, 413
Durand d'Auvergne, 885, 1493
Durand, D. B., 1153, 1497
Durand, P., 169
Durand of Saint Pourçain (XIV-1), *522*, 82, 84, 89, 90, 114, 326, 401, 413, 521, 526, 529, 991, 992
Durand, Ursin, 1337, 1754
Durand de Valdac, 23
Durand, *see* William
Durandellus, 525, 526
Durant le Jeune, *see* William
Durant of Mende, *see* William
Durgā Devi, famine of, 1237
Durham, *see* Clements, Mrs.; Simeon
Durlabharāja (XII-2), v. 2, *397*, 294
Durr al-maknūn, 759
Durr al-manthūr, 759
Durr al-naẓīm, 900
Durrieu, Paul, 1811
Durus Durandus, 523
Dusburg, *see* Peter
Dussieux, Louis, 803
Dutch, 349, 1839, 1897
Dutt, M. N., 1369
Dutt, U. C., 1731
Dutton, *see* Hugh
Duval, Rubens, 1882
Duvignay, *see* John
Duyvendak, J. J. L., 234
Dvina river, 194
Dvivedi, M. N., 1367
dwarf upon shoulders of giant, 870
dwarfs, 1227, 1860
Dwight, H. G. O., 1882
Dynameron, 64, 288
dynamics, Aristotelian, 147
Dyroff, Adolf, 446, 1428, 1432
Dyroff, Karl, 1874, 1882
dysentery, 928

Dzegli Eristavta, 305
Dziewicki, M. H., 1349

Eadmer of Canterbury (XII-1), v. 2, *275;* v. 3, 942
Earle, John, 348
ears, cagot, 279
earth, diurnal motion, 146, 147, 487, 530, 544, 736, 1108, 1490
earth, *see* land and water; land sphere
earth, shape, 112, 794, 800, 1568, 1603
earth, sphere, 1539
earthquake council, 1346
earthquakes, 198, 215, 515, 800, 818, 861, 905, 962, 965, 1166, 1172, 1348, 1654, 1744, 1756, 1889, 1894, 1896
earthquakes in China, 1834
earthquakes in Japan, 1834
East, Thomas, 1604
Easter, 123, 951
Easter Chronicle (VII-1), v. 1, *482*, 462
"Eastern settlement" in Greenland, 195
Eastern thought, 19, 20
Eastlake, C. L., 170
Ebbell, B., 1773
Ebbers, Meinolf, 1200
Eben boḥan, 430
Ebendorfer, *see* Thomas
Eberhard, *see also* Evrard; Evrart
Eberhard of Bethune (XIII-1), v. 2, *695*, 487, 530; v. 3, 331, 410, 1004, 1404, 1418
Eberhard Hicfelt, 1184
Eberhard de' Medici, 1686
Eberhard v. Wampen (XIV-1), *578*, 93, 207, 251, 351
Eberhard, Wolfram, 1833
Eberstadt, Rudolph, 152
Eboli, *see* Peter
Eccard, Joh. Georg, 820, 911, 934
Eccelino III da Romano, 917
eccentrics, 440, 487, 524, 539, 544, 706
Ecchellensis, *see* Abraham
Ecclesiastes (II-1 B.C.), v. 1, *180*, 59, 177; v. 2, 385; v. 3, 363
Ecclesiasticus (II-1 B.C.), v. 1, *180*, 177
Echard, Jacques, 1882
Echeneis, 818
Echternach, 1667
Eckhart (XIV-1), *568*, 22, 45, 85, 93, 334, 351, 571, 573, 580, 581, 706, 1056, 1091, 1358, 1844, 1889
eclampsia, 875
eclipses, 215, 434, 586, 599, 602, 707, 861, 950, 1409, 1486, 1517, 1537, 1546, 1654, 1898 **1903**
ecliptic, obliquity, 440, 1118, 1524
economic self-sufficiency, 323
economics, 1878, 1899, 1900
Ecphantos of Syracuse (IV-1 B.C.), v. 1, *118*, 112
Edda (XII-1), v. 2, *202*, 1169; v. 3, 352
Edelmann, Ẓebi Hirsch, 792
Edelstein, 579
Edelstein, Ludwig, 441
'Eden 'aruk, 492
Eder, Robert, 1302
Edessa, 357
Edessa (Ruhā'), *see* Ayyūb Ruhāwī; Jacob; Jacob Zanzalus; Matthew; Vahram
Edgar, C. C., 122, 152, 353
Edgerton, Franklin, 1841
Edib, Halidé, 377
Edmund Gonville, 475
Edmund, St., 1248
education, public, 410
education of women, 410
educational code, earliest, 73
Edward de Baliol, 1254
Edward the "Black Prince," 1278, 1556
Edward the Confessor, laws of (XI-2), v. 1, *779*, 774
Edward I of England, 43, 45
Edward II of England, 474
Edward III of England, 37, 38, 39, 474, 1034, 1129, 1310
Edward of Norwich, 1630
Edward Plantagenet, 1165, 1184, 1315, 1630
Eelsingh, H. F., 1369
Efros, Israel, 432
Egen, *see* Laurence
eggplant, 1637
Eglentyne, Madame, 1312
Eglesfield, *see* Robert
Egmond, Chronicle of, 937
Eguarás (better Eguaras), Joaquina, 827
Egypt, 111, 199, 1584
Egyptian, 20, 120, 364, 712, 825, 1103, 1365
Egyptian days, 1712
Egyptian, *see* Fathers; ink; law; medicine; printing, block; science
Eḥad, 429, 450
Ehrle, Franz, 412, 559, 944, 1085, 1440, 1499
Eichendorff, Joseph v., 925
Eichholtz, Martin, 876
Eichler, Albert, 1316
Eichler, Hans, 851
eider duck, 196
Eike of Repgow (XIII-1), v. 2, *692*, 1169; v. 3, 351, 993, 1756
Eilers, Wilhelm, 463
Einhard (IX-1), v. 1, *576*, 801; v. 3, 933
Einstein, Albert, v, 1463
Eis, Gerhard, 1715
Eisenhart, 993
Eisenstein, Judah David, 73, 793, 1522
Eisler, Robert, 930, 1870
Eiximènis, *see* Francis
ekāgratā, 96
Ekkehard of Aura (XII-1), v. 2, *258*, 1169

Elbogen, Ismar, 437, 449
Eldad ha-Dani, 366
Eleanor of Aquitaine, 1838
Eleanor Comminges, 1629
Eleanor, queen of France, 822
Eleanor of Provence, 1311, 1561
Eleazar b. Judah of Worms (XIII-1), v. 2, *608*, 1169
Eleazar b. Nathan ha-Babli (XIV-2), *1365*, 1064
electricity, 1896
element, celestial, 138
elements, 139, 262, 579, 751, 1492, 1504, 1539, 1568, 1573, 1908
elements, Buddhist, 262
elenchi, 82
elephant, 239, 775, 824, 825, 827, 1142, 1186, 1606, 1621
elephantiasis, 1622
Elḥanan b. Abraham (XIV-1), *612*, 100
Elhen, *see* Tilemann
Elia, Pasquale M. d', 1850
Elia of Venice, 1222, 1672
Eliade, Mircea, 1882
Elias, *see also* Elia; Elio; Hélie
Elias Levita, 1720
Elias b. Shīnāyā (XI-1), v. 1, *735*, 801; v. 3, 358
Elias of Ṭīrhān (XI-1), v. 1, *737*, 701, 702; v. 3, 358
Elie, Hubert, 518
Eliezer Ashkenazi, 592, 609
Eliezer Ashkenazi II, 1717
Eliezer b. Hyracanus ha-gadol, 1444
Eliezer b. Judah, 368
Eliezer ha-Sephardi, b., 1364
Eliezer b. Solomon Ashkenasi, 452
Elijah b. Abraham Mizraḥi, 1518
Elijah b. Asher ha-Levi Ashkenazi, 1720
Elijah b. Joseph Ḥabillo, 550
Elijah b. Judah of Montpellier, 792
Elijah del Medigo, 432, 537
Elijah b. Moses Beshizi, 1378
Elijah b. Moses de Vidas, 616
Elijah Shubshi b. Judah Gibbor, 1520
elimination, method of, 140
Elio Antonio de Nebrija, 1302
Elisha b. Abraham b. Mattithiah, 1523
Elisséeff, Serge, 28, 389, 1733
elixir, 751, 752, 754, 755, 1584
élixir des philosophes, 44
Elizabeth, *see also* Isabeau; Isabel; Isabella
Elizabeth of Antwerp, 1417
Elizabeth de Burgh, 475
Elizabeth of Hainaut, 1751
Elizabeth Stagel, 573
Ellenbrechtskirchen, *see* Wolfger
Ellinwood, Leonard, 1567
Ellis, F. S., 1424
Elluchasem Elimithar, *see* b. Buṭlān
Elmer, R. P., 1865
Elmham, *see* Thomas
Eloi's ailment, St., 872
Elton, Charles, 1190
Elwe, J. B., 1158
Elwin, Verrier, 1175
Elyot, Sir Thomas, 332
Ely, 39
Elysian fields, 193
emanation, x, 611
Emanuelli, Pio, 497
Embriachi, *see* Balthasar
embryology, 268, 844, 1229, 1897
embryology, theological, 488
Embún y Val, Ximénez de, 1735
Emden, A. B., 1882
Emeneau, M. B., 1883
Emerton, Ephraim, 989, 1883
Emery, Clark, 1230
Emil, *see* Melis
Emler, Josef, 782, 1758
Emmanuel, *see also* Immanuel; Manuel
Emmanuel de Monticulo, 776
Empedocles of Acragas (V B.C.), v. 1, *87*, 802; v. 3, 435
empire and papacy, *see* pope and emperor
Emre, A. C., 1015
encyclopaedism, 75, 88
Enea Silvio de' Piccolomini, *see* Aeneas Sylvius
Enelow, H. G., 1446
Eneström, Gustav, 113, 607, 1766, 1874, 1883
Enfant sage, 339, 1498
Engelbert of Admont (XIV-1), *575*, 93, 143, 160, 301, 319, 1491, 1844
Engelbert II v. der Marck, 1755
Engelbert, *see* Peter
Engelhardt, J. G. V., 582
Engelhart, *see* Jacob
Enghien, *see* Jonathan
engineering work in northern Italy (XII-2), v. 2, *406*, 27
England, 1891, 1893, 1908
English, 349, 1908
English, basic, 331
English books, 1899
English College, 294
English, *see* glass
English history, 1886
engraving, 1874
Enlart, Camille, 1570, 1597
Ennius Quintus (II-1 B.C.), v. 1, *187*, 802; v. 3, 296
Enoch, 1519
Enrico, *see* Henry
Enrigetto da Rio, 1243
Enrique, *see* Henry
Enseignemens of St. Louis, 929
Enteren, *see* Ralph
enthusiastic, 1094

entomology, 1874
entrata e uscita, 124
Enzo, king of Sardinia, 1836
Ephesos, *see* Artemidoros
Ephesos, ruins of, 1321
Ephoros of Cyme (IV-2 B.C.), v. 1, *146*, 126
Ephraim Bellshom, 1858
Ephraim Deinard, 1448
Ephraim Gerondi, Bellshom, 1116
Ephraim b. Israel b. Naqawa, 1096, 1446
Ephraim b. Jacob of Bonn (XII-2), v. 2, *448*, 312
Ephraim b. Shabbethai ha-Melammed, 1365
Ephraim the Syrian, 360
Ephraim Vidal, 1858
épices, 230
Epicharmos (V B.C)., v. 1, *84*, 81
Epictetos (II-1), v. 1, *270*, 802; v. 3, 339
Epicurean, 588
Epicuros of Samos (IV-2 B.C.), v. 1, *137*, 802
epicycles, 440, 487, 524, 539, 544, 599, 1504
epidemics, 1887
Epifani Premudry, 1825
epigraphy, 311, 385, 1290
epigraphy, Chinese, 1017
epilation, 287
epilepsy, 874, 1247, 1664, 1666, 1851
Epiphanios, St. (IV-2), v. 1, *362*, 359; v. 3, viii, 305
epistaxis, 1247
Eppenstein, Simeon, 1635
Epstein, H. J., 232, 1426, 1836
Epstein, Isidore, 1063
equations, 1535
equations, linear, 140
equations, numerical, 140
equinoxes, precession, 440, 443, 487, 600, 1436, 1846
equinoxes, trepidation, 440, 487, 600, 1112, 1436, 1846
era, Christian (I-1), v. 1, *236*, 429
Erasistratos of Julis (III-1 B.C.), v. 1, *159*, 802; v. 2, 77, 1081; v. 3, 842
Erasmus, 51, 375, 477, 505, 507, 1082, 1093, 1297, 1321, 1325, 1327, 1360, 1395
Erasmus of Antioch, St., 1666
Eratosthenes of Cyrene (III-2 B.C.), v. 1, *172*, 802; v. 2, 1170; v. 3, 197, 1859
Erben, K. J., 1354
Ercole, Francesco, 499, 1795, 1817
Erdmann, Franz, 975
Eremita, *see* John
Erfurt, *see* Thomas
Erfurt, University, 1079, 1399
ergotism, 1650, 1668, 1860, 1868
Erhard, St., 819
Erhardt-Siebold, Erika v., 270
Eric Gnupsson, 1609, 1613
Eric VIII of Pomerania, 1703
Eric the Red (X-2), v. 1, *675*, 650, 655; v. 3, 194, 1609
Erigena, *see* John Scotus
eristavni, 305
Erkembodon, St., 1754
Erlanger, Rodolphe d', 163, 1461
Erlendsson, *see* Haukr
Erler, Georg, 1296, 1820
Erman, Adolf, 1596
Ermini, Giuseppe, 1798
Ernest (Arnošt) of Pardubice, 1824
Ernoul (XIII-1), v. 2, *672*, 1171
Erotianos (I-2), v. 1, *264*, 245
erotics, 296
Erpenius, Thomas, 1010
Errāpragaḍa (XIV-1), *465*, 69, 107, 384
Errera, Carlo, 1883
Erseng, *see* George
Erskine, William, 1873, 1883
Eruditio principum, 1271
Ervine, St. John, 1321
erysipelas, 874, 1664, 1668
Erzinjān, *see* George; John
escapement, 144, 718, 1540
escapement, verge, 721, 1545
Esclot, *see* Bernard Desclot
Escola, *see* Samuel Astruc
Escorial, 1037, 1876, 1881, 1901
Esdras, 188
Eskimos, 196, 1608, 1834
Esperial, *see* Samuel
espiègle, 1190
Esposito, Mario, 1628
Essenwein, August, 726, 1553
Essling, *see* Masséna
Estat du Grant Caan, 775
Este, *see* Albert; Borso; Nicholas
Este mappa mundi, 190, 786, 1592
Estelle, St., 1303
Estellina Conat, 594
Esther, story of, 449
Esthonian, 1825
Estienne, *see also* Stephen
Estienne d'Anse, 339
Estienne, *see* Henry
Estienne, Robert, 332
Estienne, R. I., 1310
Estori b. Moses ha-Parḥi (XIV-1), *791*, 65, 128, 131, 198, 254, 256, 793
Estotiland, 1594
esṭrangelā, 359, 378
Etablissements de Saint Louis (XIII-2), v. 2, *1128*, 800
Eternal Evangel (XIII-2), v. 2, *821*, 1171; v. 3, 396, 483
eternity, 336
eternity of matter, 604
eternity of the world, 521, 538, 547, 592
Ethé, Hermann, 633

Ethiopia, *see* Aethiopia. In vol. 2, *see* Abyssinia
Etienne, *see* Estienne; Stephen
Etna, Mount, 789
Eton College, 1403
Ettinghausen, Richard, 757, 1178
Eucharist, 51, 581, 991, 1346
Euclid of Alexandria (III-1 B.C.), v. 1, *153*, 802; v. 2, 1171; v. 3, 80, 111, 120, 128, 129, 141, 430, 434, 501, 586, 590, 596, 597, 629, 705, 738, 745, 900, 937, 953, 1112, 1115, 1511, 1518, 1565
Euclid, book XV (VI-1), v. 1, *427*, 415, 421
Euclid of Megara, vii
Eudemos of Alexandria (III-1 B.C.), v. 1, *160*, 150
Eudemos of Rhodes (IV-2 B.C.), v. 1, *140*, 802
Eudes, *see also* Oddone; Odo; Otto
Eudes IV de Bourgogne, 1152
Eudes, *see* Richard
Eudoxos of Cnidos (IV-1 B.C.), v. 1, *117*, 111, 112
Eudoxos, Papyrus of (II-1 B.C.), v. 1, *184*, 178
Eugene of Palermo (XII-2), v. 2, *346*, 1171
Eugenius IV, 470
Euhemeros of Messina (IV-2 B.C.), v. 1, *136*, 125, 126; v. 3, 296
Eulenspiegel, 1190
Eunapios (V-1), v. 1, *393*, 379, 380
Eupalinos of Megara (VI B.C.), v. 1, *76*, 65
Euphemia of Norway, 578
Euripides, 997, 1395
Euryphon of Cnidos (V B.C.), v. 1, *102*, 83
Eusebios of Caesarea (IV-1), v. 1, *357*, 802; v. 2, 1171; v. 3, 791, 825, 947
Eustache Deschamps (XIV-2), *1410*, 742, 1047, 1049, 1053, 1075, 1088, 1110, 1201, 1245, 1308
Eustachius of Nicaea, St., 1666
Eustathios, St., 1441
Eustathios of Thessalonica (XII-2), v. 2, *395*, 1171
Eustratios of Nicaea, 1431
Euthesia, 166
Euthymios Zigabenos, 1854
Eutocios (VI-1), v. 1, *427*, 415, 599; v. 2, 342; v. 3, 128, 431
Eutyches, 55
Eutychianism, 55, 357
Eutychios (X-1), v. 1, *640*, 622, 623; v. 2, 122; v. 3, 1583
evacuatio, 426
Evagrios Scholasticos (VI-2), v. 1, *455*, 445; v. 3, 1650
Evangel, *see* Eternal
evangelical poverty, 51, 407, 412, 549, 558
Evans, Allan, 774
Evans, C. de B., 569
Evans, Joan, 930, 1171, 1178, 1906
Evelt, Von, 789
Evenos of Paros, 1188
Everett, Dorothy, 1605
Everard, *see* Eberhard
Evers, R. W., 463
Evershed, Mrs. John, 497
Evert v. Wampen, 578
Evliyā Čelebī, 154
Evliyā efendi, 154
Evno of Würzburg (XIV-2), *1510*, 1113
Evola, N. D., 495
evolution, 13, 1168, 1170, 1775
evolution, creative, 211
evolution, cycle, 213
evolution, emergent, 564
Evrard de Conty (XIV-2), *1393*, 1075, 1123, 1201, 1220, 1309
Evrart de Trémaugon, 1276, 1346
Evreux, *see* Joan
examen leprosorum, 276
examinations, Chinese, 1855
examinations, *see* medicine
exchange, *see* bills
Excitatorium mentis ad Deum, 520
excommunications, 1047, 1049
exempla, 93, 920
exempla naturarum, 583
Exemple du riche homme et du ladre, 1275
Exeter, 474
Exeter Cathedral, 1403
Exeter College, 72
Exmew, William, 1416
Exodus, 238, 405
experimenta, 17
experimental method, 706
experimental point of view, 17
exploration, 1874. *See also* itineraries
exploration of 747, Chinese (VIII-1), v. 1, *515*
explosive substance, 1551
exponential calculus, 1116
exponents, fractional, 1108, 1487
Expositio bonitatis purae, 450
Expositor Avicennae, 837
Expositorium Decreti, 400
Eybe, *see* Lewis
eye, anatomy, 899
eye, diagrammatic sections, 274
eye diseases, 273, 1234, 1898
eye diseases, Chinese, 1837
eye shield, 1553
eyeglasses, *see* spectacles
Eymeric, *see* Nicholas
Eyquem, Pierre, 1087
Eyre-Todd, George, 1741
'Eẓ ḥayyim, 617
Ezekiel (VI B.C.), v. 1, *70*, 65; v. 3, 141, 191
Ezra (V B.C.), v. 1, *108*, 83, 150; v. 3, 364

Ezra, b., *see* Abraham
Ezra, Apocalypse, 188
Ezra, book of (III-1 B.C.), v. 1, *163*
Ezra, b., *see* Moses b. Jacob
Ezra b. Solomon Gatigno, 1061, 1373, 1634

Faber, Hugo, 1239
Faber, *see* John Faure
Fabre, Jean Henri, 510
Fabri, *see* Castel; Felix
Fabriano, papers, 175
Fabrica corporis mistici, 393
Fabricius, J. A., 1883
faburden, 159
Fabvre, B., 156
Faḍl b. Ḥātim, *see* Nairīzī
Faḍl b. Mubārak, a., 465
Faḍl b. Naubakht (VIII-2), v. 1, *531*, 521, 524; v. 2, 343
Faḍlallāh b. ʿImād, *see* Rashīd al-dīn
Faḍlallāh b. a. Muḥammad Ḥurūfī (XIV-2), *1459*, 1068, 1100, 1328
Faḍlallāh of Tabrīz, 1460, 1473
Faḍlallāh ʿUmarī, b., *see* Aḥmad b. Yaḥyā
Faḍlān, b. (X-1), v. 1, *636*, 621; v. 2, 869
Faeschius, Sebastian, 1794
Fages, P. H. O., 1340
Fagin, Giuseppe, 1844
Fagnan, Edmond, 1455
Fahagun, *see* John de Sant
Fahie, J. J., 1856
Fāʾida fī tawallud, 749
Faidit, *see* Uc
faïence, 179, 755, 1133
Fairchild, David, 1851
faith healing, 260, 291, 849, 1246
Faitusi, Jacob b. Abraham, 606
Fakhr al-dīn b. Aḥmad b. Aḥmad b. Mawlā, 828
Fakhr al-dīn ʿĪsā, 967
Fakhr al-dīn Rāzī, *see* Muḥammad b. ʿUmar
fakhrī fī-l-ādāb, Kitāb al-, 967
Falaquera, *see* Nathan b. Joel
Falaquera, b., *see* Shem-ṭob b. Joseph
Falcandus, *see* Hugh
Falco, *see* Paliano
Falco, Vittorio de, 1877, 1883
Falcon, *see* Nicholas
falconers, 1120, 1833
falconry, 339, 342, 1163, 1169, 1183, 1632, 1641, 1643, 1735, 1835, 1887
falconry, Arabic, 1835
falconry, Muslim and Jewish (XII-2), v. 2, *425*
falconry, treatises of (XII-1), v. 2, *227*, 1172; (XIII-1), v. 2, *648*
falcons, 195, 231, 924
falcons, breeding, of, 900
Falcucci, 1194
Falcucci, *see* Nicholas

falghamūnī, 899
Falk, Hj., 194
Falkenstein, *see* Cuno
Fall of princes, 1805
fāl-nāma, 1457
Falun, 219
Famagusta, 40, 772, 1025, 1210, 1569
famines, 227, 281, 905, 965, 1237. *See also* hunger
famines in India, 1837
Fanārī, *see* Muḥammad b. Ḥamza; Muḥammad Shāh
Fanfani, Pietro, 913, 983, 1809
Fanianus, J. C., 981, 984
Fano, *see* Martin
Fantuzzi, Giovanni, 460, 845, 848, 854, 1680
Faqīh, b., *see* Aḥmad b. Muḥammad
faqīr, 421
Faquin, *see* Joseph
Fārābī (X-1), v. 1, *628*, 803; v. 2, 1172; v. 3, 61, 62, 98, 163, 164, 431, 435, 590, 591, 594, 597, 1138, 1381, 1568, 1571, 1771
Faraday, 147
Faraḍī, b., ʿAbdallāh b. Muḥammad (XI-1), v. 1, *734*, 700, 702; v. 2, 137, 250
farāʾiḍ, 419
Faraj b. ʿAssāl, a., 1006
Faraj Iṣfahānī ʿAlī b. Ḥusain, a. (X-1), v. 1, *642*, 787; v. 2, 1136
Faraj b. Salīm (XIII-2), v. 2, *833*, 1172; v. 3, 273
Faraj, a., Yūḥannā b. ʿIbrī (XIII-2), v. 2, *975*, 1172; v. 3, 97, 289, 358, 367, 794, 956, 1006
Faraudo de Saint-Germain, Luis, 1221
Farbman, Michael, 1583
Farges, *see* Raymond
Farghānī (IX-1), v. 1, *567*, 803; v. 2, 1172; v. 3, 61, 111, 463, 484, 501, 590, 600, 819, 1115, 1443, 1516, 1859
Farhang-i Jahāngirī, 1534
Farḥi, *see* Estori b. Moses
Farḥūn, b., 709
Farīd al-dīn ʿAṭṭār, *see* Muḥammad b. Ibrāhīm
Fāriḍ, b., *see* ʿUmar b. ʿAlī
Farinata, 1600
Farinator, *see* Matthew
Farinelli, Arturo, 491, 492, 499, 516
Faris, N. A., 1865
Fārisī, *see* Kamāl al-dīn; Muḥammad b. a. Bakr; Muḥammad b. Ḥasan
Farlati, Daniele, 416
Farmer, H. G., 164, 165, 741, 1571, 1846, 1852, 1883
Faroe islands, 1594
Farr, William, 283
Fās, *see* Fez
Fasciculo di medicina, 1904
Fasciculus medicinae, 270, 1223, 1905
fascination, 143, 576, 1491

Fasi, *see* Alfasi
Fāsī, *see* Muḥammad
Fasoli, Gina, 152
Fassbinder, Franz, 455
Fassitelli, *see* Alexander
fatalism, 1214
fate, 418
Fatḥ b. 'Alī Bundārī (XIII-1), v. 2, *686*, 1157
Fatḥ b. a. Ḥasan, a. (XIV-2), *1761*, 1261
Fatḥ, a., *see* Maḥmūd b. Muḥammad Iṣfahānī
Fatḥ b. Muḥammad b. Khāqān, 1764
Fathers of the church, v. 1, 13, 367; v. 3, viii, 192, 990
Fathers, Egyptian, 1392
Fāṭima, 106
Fāṭima b. Qāsim Birzālī, 958
Fatio, Edmond, 795
Fattorini, Mauro, 839, 841, 1680
fatwā, 16, 1099
Faucon, Maurice, 771
Faure, *see* John
Faust, 949
faux-bourdon, 159
Favaro, Antonio, 446, 515, 1106, 1292, 1856
Favé, Ildefonse, 726
Faversham, *see* Simon
fawā'id al-Bahā'īya, 707
Fawtier, Robert, 1337
Faxiolus, Joannis, 1794
Fay, E. A., 495
Fay, H. M., 281
Fazārī, *see* Ibrāhīm b. Ḥabīb; Muḥammad b. Ibrāhīm
Fazio, *see* Bartholomew
Fazio degli Uberti (XIV-2), *1600*, 1086, 1144, 1145, 1300
Fedanzola, *see* John
feet, binding of women's, 778
Fehse, Wilhelm, 1232
Felains, *see* John
Felder, Hilarin, 1883
Feldhaus, F. M., 157, 1549, 1551, 1553, 1582, 1883
Feldhaus, Wilhelm, 882
feldspar, 756
Felibrejado, 1303
Felipa Perestrello e Moniz, 183
Felix Fabri, 574
Feltre, *see* Vittorino
Feltrino da Montefeltro, 1600
Fenn, John, 1337
Fenollosa, Ernest, 1333
Ferabrich, *see* Richard
Ferckel, Christoph, 285
Ferdinand of Aragon, 1304
Ferdinand III, emperor, 472
Feret, abbé Pierre, 1497
Ferguson, C. W., 1048
Ferguson, Ian, 1051
Ferguson, John, 921, 922, 1550, 1884
Ferguson, John C., 181, 1848
Fermat, Pierre de, 1566, 1849
ferment, 751
Fermo, see Anthony
Fernach, *see* John
Fernández, Benignus, 520
Fernando, San, 1250
Fernando Pecha, 1037
Fernão Lopes, 1250, 1307
Ferrand, Gabriel, 416, 1624, 1884
Ferrara Bible, 1077
Ferrara, *see* Riccobaldo
Ferrara, University, 1080, 1400
Ferrari, Filippo, 1884
Ferrari da Gradi, Gianmatteo, 1573, 1861
Ferrari, H. M., 1861
Ferrarii, *see* John Martini
Ferraro, Francesco, 232
Ferrato, Pietro, 1674
Ferrer, *see* Boniface
Ferrer of Gerona, 1716
Ferrer, *see* James; Vincent; William
Ferreto de' Ferreti (XIV-1), *919*, 87, 298, 496
Ferreto Vicentino, 919
Ferretti, Giovanni, 497
Ferretti, Lodovico, 1336
Ferretti, P. L., 1337
Ferri, Giovanni, 86
Ferrières, *see* Henry
fertilization, artificial, 1775
fertilizers, 1637
Festa, Nicola, 513
Festugière, A. J., 1865
Fetellus of Antioch (XII-2), v. 2, *421*, 1173
Fétis, F. J., 746, 1569
Feuardent, François, 399
feudal institutions, 1020
feudal, *see* law
fever, first to be identified, 274
Feyerabend, Sigmund, 789
Fez, 174
Fez, *see* Alfasi; David b. Abraham; Muḥammad al-Fāsī
Ffoulkes, Charles, 726, 1556
Ffrancesch, *see* Francis
Fiacchi, Luigi, 1596
Fiadeiro, Joaquim, 862
Fibonacci, *see* Leonard
Ficino, *see* Marsiglio
Ficken, Emil, 1837
Fidā' Ismā'īl b. 'Alī, a. (XIV-1), *793*, 103, 133, 135, 136, 200, 203, 209, 216, 229, 308, 373, 621, 756, 962, 1000, 1158, 1160, 1264, 1772, 1783, 1785, 1901
fiḍḍat kibrīt, 753
Fiertz, G. B., 1339
Fiesque, *see* Albert
Fife, R. H., jr., 1605
fig tree, sacred, 1835
Figarola, *see* Peter

Figdor, Albrecht, 1598
Figgis, J. N., 1276
Figueroa, *see* Laurence Suárez
Figulus Publius Nigidius (I-1 B.C.), v. 1, *207*, 201
figura alchata, 431
figura secans, 431
figura sectoris, 432
Filastre, *see* William
Filchner, W., 259, 1372, 1589
Filelfo, *see* Francis
filigranes, 176
Filippa, *see* Philippa
Filippi, Giovanni, 920
Filippini, F., 845
Filippino degli Organi, 1655
Filippino degli Scopoli, 1672
Filippo, *see* Philip
Fillon, *see* John
Fina, Santa, 921
Finck, F. N., 1222
Finé, Oronce, 549, 1492
finger notation, 120, 1847
finger reckoning, 1121, 1533, 1865
finger symbolism, 1483
fingerprints, 271
Finke, Heinrich, 986
Finkelscherer, Bruno, 593
Finley, J. H., jr., 1650
Finnish, 1825
Finno-Ugrian, 1825
Finsen, N. R., 881
Fioravante of Bologna, 736
Fiorello Capocci, 915
Fiorilli, Matilde, 1336
Fiortifiocca, *see* Thomas
fiqh, 1000
firāsa, 270, 271, 800, 1897
Firdawsī (XI-1), v. 1, *705*, 803; v. 2, 1173; v. 3, 305, 310, 376, 631, 1456, 1465
fire, *see* Greek
firearms (XIV-1), *722*, 770, 818, 1547, 1900. *See also* cannon; gun borer; gunpowder; guns; gunsmiths; harquebusery
fireflies, 238, 487, 1842
Firkāḥ, b., *see* Ibrāhīm b. 'Abd al-Raḥmān
firmān, 1327
Firmicus Maternus, Iulius (IV-1), v. 1, *354*, 803
Firmin de Beauval (XIV-1), *657*, 45, 115, 540, 951, 886
Fīrūz Shāh (1351–88), 137
Fīrūz Shāh Taghlaqī, 1237
Fīrūzābādī, Muḥammad b. Ya'qūb (XIV-2), *1826*, 200, 1266, 1326, 1328
Fischel, W. J., 975
Fischer, Alfons, 286, 1245, 1622
Fischer, Clyde, 711
Fischer, Heinrich, 1471
Fischer, Hermann, 1884
Fischer, J. F., 891
Fischer, Joseph, 1147
Fischer, Theobald, 763, 1592, 1598, 1599, 1884
Fischer-Møller, Knud, 1834
Fisher, *see* John
fishes, viii
fishes, flying, 1607
fishing, viii, 1165, 1185, 1900
fishing reel, 237
fishshuṭ, 598
Fiske, Willard, 495, 512
fistula, 892, 1700
Fittig, Ernst, 1755
fityān, 154
Fitzgerald, Edward, 1458, 1769
Fitzherbert, Sir Anthony, 814
Fitzherbert, John, 1181
Fitzneal, *see* Richard
Fitzralph, *see* Richard
Fitzsimon, *see* Simon
Flaccus Verrius (I-2 B.C.), v. 1, *234*, 220
Flacius Illyricus, 1497
flagellants (XIII-2), v. 2, *821*; v. 3, 13, 50, 742, 914, 1747, 1756
Flamel, *see* Nicholas; Pernelle
Flamma, *see* Galvaneus
Flanders, 1907
Flanders, *see* Flemish; Margaret
Flaška, *see* John
Flateyjarbók, 1609
Flaumbaum, Isidoro, 571
Flavio Biondo, 510, 715
Flavio Gioja, 715
Flavius Avianus, 579
Flavius, *see* Joseph
flax, 323
Fleischer, H. L., 799
Fleischhacker, Robert, 1203
Fleischhauer, Werner, 1556
Fleming, J. A., 711, 1856
Fleming, *see* Richard
Flemish weavers, 1833
Fleta, 319, 1279
Flete, *see* William
Fleur des histoires, 953
Fleuret, Fernand, 1277
Fleury, *see* Aimoin
flexus formae, 553
Flick, A. C., 1884
Flint, Robert, 77, 1778
Flodoard of Reims (X-2), v. 1, *684*, 651, 655
Floki Vilgerdarson, 715
Flor, *see* Roger
floral games, 341, 344
Florence, 152, 1248
Florence, budget, 914
Florence, history of, 914
Florence, *see* Bardi bank; Dino Dini; Francis; Frescobaldi bank; Jacob; James; John; Marsiglio; Peruzzi bank; Peter; Poggio Bracciolini; Raggio

Florence Radewijns, 1057, 1317, 1358, 1362
Florence, University, 72, 472, 1244
Florence of Worcester (XII-1), v. 2, *255*, 139
Florentinos (III-1), v. 1, *323*, 315
Florentios, 952
Florenz, Karl, 1002, 1018
Florenz, Landmann, 1040
Flores chronicorum, 404
Flores Geberti, 1138
Flores historiarum, 303
Flores musice, 741
Flori, Ezio, 499
Floriarium Bartholomei, 1705
florin, 1282
Floris V of Holland, 937
Floris, *see* Joachim
Flors del gay saber, 341
Florus, 1582
Flos medicinae, 579
Flotte, *see* Peter
flower arrangement, 1332
Flower, R., 1482, 1634
Flügel, Gustav, 1101, 1461, 1884
fluens, 737
fluxion, 14, 737
fluxus, 737
fluxus formae, 1127, 1488
flying, *see* dragon
Flynn, V. J., 294
Foà, Cesare, 492
Förster, Wendelin, 579
Foillet, Jacques, 752
Foix, *see* Gaston; Gaston Phoebus
Foixà, *see* Jofre
Foligno, Cesare, 500
Foligno, *see* Gentile
foliot, *see* balance
folk literature, 1804
folk medicine, 252
folklore, 1879, 1896
folktale, 1836
Follini, Vincenzio, 915
Fonahn, Adolf, 1884
Fons memorabilium, 583, 1409
Fontaines, *see* Godfrey; Peter
Fontana, Domenico, 1160
Fontana, *see* John
Fontanus or Fonteyn, Nicolaus, 853
Fonte, *see* William
Fontenelle, 301
Forbes, E. W., 170
Forbes, M. D., 475
Forbes, Rosita, 1470
force, 737
forces, composition of, 707
Fordun, *see* John
forensic medicine, *see* medicine, law
forgeries, detection, 979
Forgue, Emile, 272
Forke, Alfred, 467, 1139
forks, table, 157
Forlì, *see* James
Forlivio, *see* Blase
Forma celi (IX-1), v. 1, *569*, 546
forma fluens, 553, 1488
forma totius, 564
Formatio corporis humani, 242
formication, 277
Formiggini, Saul, 491
forms, 518, 522, 558
forms, increase and decrease, 117, 148, 737
forms, intensio et remissio, 148
forms, intensity of, 565
forms, latitudes of, 1112
Formularium audientie contradictarum, 332
Formularium instrumentarum notariorum, 332
Formularium notariorum curie, 327, 332
Formularium pro notariis, 332
Forshall, Josiah, 1349
Forster, E. S., 1220
Forster, John, 488
Forsyth, C., 159
Fortalitium fidei, 418
Forti, Achille, 1164
fortifications, 1550
Fosseyeux, Marcel, 498
fossil, 214
fossil bones, 1806
fossil fishes, 929, 1870
fossils, trade in, 1187
Foster, F. A., 946
Fotheringham, F. G., 1394
Foto, *see* Samuel
Foucquet, *see* John
Foulché-Delbosc, Raymond, 1342
Foulechat, *see* Denis
Four Masters (XIII-2), v. 2, *1088*, 1220 (*under* quattuor magistri)
Fourment, *see* Peter Fromont
Fournier, August, 934
Fournier, *see* James
Fournier, Marcel, 879
Fournier, Paul, 43, 401, 526, 528, 534, 990, 991
Fournival, *see* Richard
Fowler, G. B., 1844
Fowler, Mary, 495, 512
Fowler, R. E., 1428
fowling with birdlime, viii, 1641
Fox, G. G., 1428
Foy, Ste., *see* Chanson
Foy of Agen, Ste., 338
Fracassetti, Giuseppe, 242, 513
Fracastoro, Gerolamo, 1658, 1682
fractions, 113, 122
fractions, *see* decimal
fractions, Roman, 1483
fractions, sexagesimal, 1511, 1525, 1529
Fraehn, C. M., 805
Frameinsberg, *see* Rodolph

Franc-Gontier, 743
France, 1892, 1896, 1908
Francesc, *see* Francis
Francesca, *see* Peter
Franceschini, Ezio, 943
Francesco, *see* Francis
Francis, *see also* Francischi; Francischino; Franco
Francis Accorso of Bologna (XIII-1), v. 2, *689*, 266, 528; v. 3, 1273, 1794
Francis II Accorso, 982
Francis of Assisi, St. (XIII-1), v. 2, *543*, 1174; v. 3, 81, 86, 91, 396, 1336, 1601
Francis de Belleforest, 1452
Francis del Bene, 124, 1196
Francis Benzi, 1196
Francis Berlinghieri, 1146
Francis of Bologna, 512, 1669
Francis Bruni, 1815, 1818
Francis da Buti, 1813
Francis Caecus, 1567
Francis da Camerino, 584
Francis di Carrara, 1681
Francis I of Carrara, 508, 511, 1407
Francis II Novello of Carrara, 508, 1818
Francis Casini (XIV-2), *1684*, 1193, 1242
Francis Celelles, 325
Francis da Colle, 982
Francis Datini, 124, 774, 1273, 1858
Francis Eiximènis (XIV-2), *1410*, 1087, 1306
Francis Filelfo, 852, 1252
Francis of Florentia, 1567
Francis I of France, 342, 1310
Francis of Gianellis (XIV-2), *1669*, 860, 1192, 1851
Francis Giorgi, 186
Francis Landino (XIV-2), *1567*, 1128, 1300
Francis of Lapacino, 1145
Francis of Madrid, 507
Francis of Marchia (XIV-1), *738*, 114, 147, 148, 543, 1580
Francis of Marco, 1684
Francis of Meyronnes (XIV-1), *529*, 45, 90, 114, 1283
Francis Nelli, 505
Francis de Neritono, 519
Francis II Novello of Padova, 1407
Francis, *see* Pegolotti
Francis Pelacani, 1565
Francis di Petracco, 502. *See* Petrarca
Francis, *see* Petrarca
Francis de' Piccolomini, 1336
Francis di Piedimonte (XIV-1), *835*, 243, 288
Francis da Pignano, 738
Francis Pipinus, 186
Francis Pizigano (XIV-2), *1598*, 1144, 1300
Francis of Prague, 934
Francis Rossyn, 1861
Francis de Santa Fé, 1717
Francis of Siena, 1240, 1684
Francis Traini, 84, 87, 1231
Francis degli Ubaldi, 1795
Francis di Ugo, 1684
Francis des Valers, 183
Francis Villon, 541, 743, 1080
Francis Xavier, St., 1546
Francis Ximenes, *see* Francis Eiximènis
Francis Zabarella, 1795, 1818
Franciscans (XIII-1), v. 2, *543*, 1174; v. 3, 47, 396, 473, 1883, 1885, 1894, 1907
Franciscans, *see* Spirituals
Francischi de Conigrano, 1675
Francischino de Collignano (XIV-2), *1675*, 1192
Franck, Adolphe, 556, 1390
Franco, Augusto, 775
Franco of Cologne (XII-2), v. 2, *406*, 1174; v. 3, 160, 740, 741, 743
Franco of Liége (XI-2), v. 1, *757*, 740, 745; v. 2, 1174; v. 3, 1846
Franco de Polonia, 1846
Franco Sacchetti, 1023
François, *see* Francis
Frank, Mortimer, 1878, 1884
Frank, Philipp, v
Frank, S. L., 269
Frankfurt, *see* Bernard
Frankfurter, Moses, 1446
Franklin, Alfred, 153
Franklin, Benjamin, 1303, 1550
Franz, *see also* Francis
Franz, Joannes, 586
Frassetto, Fabio, 500
Frati, C., 815
Frati, Lodovico, 815, 839, 845, 854, 1680
fraticelli, 44, 47, 396, 404, 481
Frechulph of Lisieux (IX-1), v. 1, *577*, 548
Fredegarius Scholasticus (VII-2), v. 1, *499*, 489
Frederick of Austria, 38, 471
Frederick of Bamberg, 741
Frederick Closener (XIV-2), *1756*, 1258, 1319
Frederick II Hohenstaufen (XIII-1), v. 2, *575*, 1174; v. 3, 195, 231, 337, 374, 709, 1189, 1238, 1481, 1534, 1630, 1634, 1735, 1869
Fredericq, Paul, 50, 52, 582, 1051
Frédol, *see* Bérenger
free thought, 84, 490
free will, 90, 617
freemasons, 153
Freher, Marquardus, 1758, 1814
Freiberg, *see* Theodore
Freidank, *see* Henry
Freimann, A., 1717
Freind, John, 882
Freising, *see* Berthold; Otto; Ruprecht
Fremont, Charles, 722
French, 44, 344, 1899
French, *see* algorisms

French in England, 347
French, Francesca, 1586
French prosody, 1411
French, R. D., 1425
Frenkl, D., 1062
Frescobaldi bank of Florence, 218, 324
Frescobaldi, *see* Leonard
Frese, Franz, 1412
Freshfield, E. H., 996
Freuler, Bernhard, 936
Fréville, Ernest de, 1023, 1490
Frey, Johann, 1581
Freybe, Albert, 1232
Freytag, G. W., 1768
friars, 1879
friars, *see* fraticelli
Friars Minor, 47
Friars Preachers, 47
Fricz, Joseph, 941
Friedberg, Emil, 986
Friedensburg, Walter, 918, 919, 934
Friedländer, Joseph, 1523
Friedrich, *see also* Frederick
Friedrich, C. J., 1795
Friemar, *see* Henry
Friends of God, 85, 93, 571, 581
Frisch, Christian, 600, 1112
Fritsche, *see* Frederick
Fritz, Hermann, 709
Friuli, *see* Mondino Friulano
Frobisher, M., 194, 1501
Froehner, Reinhard, 829
Froissart, Jean (XIV-2), *1751*, 38, 929, 1023, 1024, 1129, 1135, 1251, 1253, 1256, 1257, 1308, 1541, 1548, 1629, 1696, 1748, 1821, 1855
Fromont, *see* Peter
Frontinus, Sextus Julius (I-2), v. 1, *255*, 804; v. 3, 1291, 1482
Frothingham, A. W., 171
Fruin, Robert, 1799
Frumentios of Tyre, 55
Frutolf of Bamberg (XI-2), v. 1, *763*, 741, 745; v. 2, 129
Fruytier, J., 1435, 1437
Frye, R. N., 379, 794, 1840, 1842
Fuchs, Walter, 381, 932, 1850
Fück, Johann, 1456
Fünfkirchen, 1399
Fuensanta del Valle, Marqués de la, 299
Fürstenthal, R. J., 1446
Fuhr, Karl, 1008
fūlādh, 1175
Fulgentius, 1075, 1388, 1808
Fulin, R., 771, 916
Fulton, A. S., 902
Fulton, J. F., 1550, 1658, 1852, 1868
Fumagalli, Giuseppina, 515
Funk, A. L., 1024
Funke, Otto, 1316
Funkhouser, H. G., 1487, 1488
Furāt, b., *see* Muḥammad b. 'Abd al-Raḥīm
Furiettus, J. A., 1289
furnace, cupola, 220
furnaces, *see* blast furnaces
Furnivall, F. J., 462, 533, 567, 943, 1424
furs, precious, 323
furūsīya, 1636, 1643
Fusoris, *see* John
Fuṣūl Mūsā, 287
Fuṣūl wa-ghāyāt, 79
Fūṭī, b., *see* 'Abd al-Razzāq b. Aḥmad Shaibānī
futūwa, kutub al-, 154, 421
futuwwetnāme, 154
Fuẓūlī, *see* Muḥammad b. Sulaimān
Fyfe, F. M., 231, 1735
Fyslawe, *see* Thomas

Gabet, Joseph, 1372
Gabi'a kesef, 591
Gabirol, b. (XI-1), v. 1, *704*, 809; v. 2, 1175; v. 3, 367, 427, 430, 450, 612, 1443, 1444
Gabranus Bettinus, 1399
Gabriel, *see also* Jibrīl
Gabriel of Milhaud, 893
Gabriel, treatise, 892
Gabriel de Vallsecha, 1141, 1305
Gabrieli, Francesco, 1778
Gabrieli, Giuseppe, 490, 961, 1778
Gabrielli, Annibale, 923
Gace de la Bigne, 1164, 1183, 1309, 1630
Gaḍalādeṇi sanne, 1371
Gaḍalādeṇivihāra, 1370
Gadd, C. J., 757
Gaddesden, *see* John
Gaddi, *see* Agnolo; Taddeo
Gadifer de La Salle, 184, 1147
Gadla ḥawāryāt, 438
Gadla samā'etāt, 438
Gaetani, *see* James
Gaetano, Cajetan, 521
Gaetano da Thiene, 519, 566, 1413, 1540
Gaetano, *see* Thomas
Gagnier, John, 799
Gaibī, 757
Gaillac, *see* William Bernard
gain of one day when traveling around world, 797
Gairdner, James, 230
Gaius (II-2), v. 1, *311*, 804
Gajah Mada, 42
Gakhig, 1441
Galḁnos, *see* Demetrios
Galbiati, Iohannes, 512
Galbraith, V. H., 1256, 1745
Gale, J. S., 1563
Gale, Thomas, 942, 1741
Galeazzo Malatesta, 1862
Galeazzo da Santa Sofia, 1193, 1207, 1224

Galeazzo Visconti, 454, 766, 1672, 1751
Galen of Pergamum (II-2), v. 1, *301*, 804; v. 2, 1175; v. 3, x, 5, 61, 62, 64, 242, 243, 245, 247, 248, 254, 255, 264, 266, 268, 285, 426, 428, 431, 436, 437, 441, 447, 501, 575, 608, 738, 750, 792, 816, 826, 828, 836, 837, 839, 840, 841, 843, 844, 846, 847, 849, 850, 853, 856, 857, 860, 870, 875, 878, 879, 881, 883, 884, 885, 889, 890, 1192, 1194, 1195, 1201, 1205, 1209, 1220, 1223, 1229, 1235, 1243, 1321, 1374, 1380, 1385, 1389, 1422, 1451, 1603, 1621, 1640, 1671, 1673, 1674, 1675, 1676, 1677, 1678, 1681, 1683, 1685, 1688, 1691, 1699, 1703, 1705, 1707, 1710, 1712, 1714, 1716, 1719, 1723, 1775
Galeotto Tarlati, 1294, 1295
Galician revival, 344
Galik alphabet, 380
Galileo, 14, 15, 114, 146, 542, 1127, 1430, 1487, 1489, 1856, 1882
Galipapa, *see* Ḥayyim b. Abraham
Gall, St., 224
gall bladder, 843
galls, 818
gallstone, 267, 848
Galland, Pierre, 249
Gallée, J. H., 1711
Gallego, *see* Peter
Gallemart, Jean, 399
Galletti, G. C., 1674, 1737
Galliano, *see* Moses b. Judah
Galloppes, *see* John
Galloway, R. L., 221, 1173
Gallus, *see* Laurence
Gallus de Strahov (XIV-2), *1712*, 1207, 1228, 1239, 1241, 1322
Gallus, *see* Thomas
Galpin, S. L., 533
Galvaneus Flamma or Fiamma, 719, 721
Galvano de Levanto (XIV-1), *392*, 46, 185, 245, 314, 317
Galvano de' Zancari, 853
Gambacorta, *see* Peter
Gams, Pius Bonifacius, 1884
gan 'Eden, 591
Gand, *see* Ghent
Ganden Truppa, 1371
Gandersheim, *see* Hrosvitha
Gandhi, Mahātmā, 1475
Gandolfo persiano, 232
Gandz, Solomon, x, 132, 208, 212, 417, 1518, 1519, 1520, 1522, 1534, 1773, 1832, 1870
Gandzak, *see* Cyriacus
Gaṇeśa, 1535
Ganges, 1617
Gaṅgeśa (XII-2), v. 2, *396*, 294
Gaṇita-pāṭi-kaumudī, 1535
Ganscyniec, R., 854
Gansfort, *see* John
Ganshof, F. L., 1111, 1180
Gantin, Jules, 632
Ganzenmüller, Wilhelm, 1134, 1138
Gao, *see* Muḥammad
Gaon, *see* Shem-ṭob b. Abraham; Sherira
Garaḥot, 1232
Garbasso, Antonio, 497
Garbe, Richard, 1731
Garbo, *see* Bruno; Dino; Thomas
Garce, M. M., 1340
Garci Ferrandez de Gerena, 1307
García Gómez, Emilio, 1519, 1764
García, *see* John
García, Manuel, 301
García-Mata, Carlos, 1856
García Silvestre, Manuel, 1884
Garcias, *see* Mary
Garcin de Tassy, 1342
Gardar Svavarsson, 1154, 1610
garden, *see* botanic
garden, experimental, 1170
Gardiner, A. H., 314, 1103
Gardner, Alexander, 1203
Gardner, C. S., 1884
Gardner, E. G., 496, 1337, 1417
Gardner, J. S., 220
Gardthausen, Viktor, 123
Gargiolli, Carlo, 186, 1595, 1596
Gariopontus (XI-1), v. 1, *726*, 699; v. 2, 1085; v. 3, 881, 1688
Garland, *see* John
Garosi, A., 1685
Garrison, F. H., 1884
Garrow, Joseph, 493
Garshūnī, 360
Garter, order, 1038, 1403
Garzoni, *see* John
Gas, *see* Peter
Gascoigne, *see* Thomas
gases, 1506
Gask, G. F., 1204
gasmulos, 948, 1852
Gaspar y Remiro, Mariano, 1792
Gaspar of Sarnana, 1671
Gaspard Adam, 414
Gasparino da Barzizza, 300, 1289
Gasquet, F. A., 294, 330, 1248, 1663
Gass, W., 1439
Gasser, A. P., 1848
Gaster, Moses, 1324, 1720, 1762
Gaster, T. H., 29, 1324
Gaston II of Foix, 340
Gaston III of Foix, 1629
Gaston Phoebus of Foix (XIV-2), *1629*, 231, 1164, 1165, 1184, 1294, 1309, 1751
Gates, R. R., 1837, 1860
Gathorne-Hardy, G. M., 1609
Gatigno, 1187
Gatigno, *see* Ezra b. Solomon; Solomon Astruc

Gaudefroy-Demombynes, Maurice, 803, 999, 1778, 1884
Gaudio, Antonino del, 498
gauging, 1318, 1580
Gaugiricus, D., 399
Gaunt, *see* John
Gaurico, Luca, 1482, 1483
Gauthier, Henri (S.J.), 1884, 1889
Gauthier, Léon, 545, 1211
Gauthiez, Pierre, 496
Gautier, *see also* Walter
Gautier, E. F., 1778
Gautier, L., 706
Gautier, Théophile, 1188
Gavellus of Spoleto, Salvator, 1848
Gaveston, *see* Peter
Gayangos y Arce, Pascual de, 464, 925, 1736, 1764, 1884
gazetteers, 1268
Gazzata, *see* Guido
Ge-lug-pa, 1331, 1371
Geber, 165, 751, 753, 1138, 1573, 1576, 1578. For Arabic original *see* Jābir b. Ḥaiyān
Geber, Latin treatises (XIII-2), v. 2, *1043*, 769
Gebhard, Heinrich, 1415
Gebhardt, Oscar, 1395
Gebhart, August, 1605
Gedun-ḍub, 1371
Geert, *see also* Gerald
Geert Groote (XIV-2), *1356*, 574, 580, 581, 1038, 1049, 1056, 1081, 1093, 1112, 1297, 1316, 1408
Geete, Robert, 1356
Ge'ez language, 306, 362
Geiger, Abraham, 1523
Geiger, Wilhelm, 423, 978, 1885
Geist, S. H., 269
Geldenhauer, Gerhard, 710
Gelder, *see* Henry
gelding of horses, 1669
Gelenije, *see* Řehoř (z Jelení)
Gelenius, *see* Gregory
Gellius, Aulus (II-2), v. 1, *311*, 290
Gellrich, Paul, 913
Gelnhausen, *see* Conrad
Gem, S. H., 1361
Gemārā, 357
gematria, 363, 616, 1068, 1366, 1460
Gembloux, *see* Sigebert
gemellum, 159
Geminos of Rhodes (I-1 B.C.), v. 1, *212*, 804; v. 2, 341, 849
Gemistos Pletho, 1095, 1320
Gemma di Manetto Donati, 480
Gemunden, *see* Henry Arler; John
Genazzano, *see* Paul
Génébrard, Gilbert, 1452
Genebreda, *see* Anthony
generation, 753
generation, spontaneous, 1229, 1506
Genesis, 141, 364, 399
Genesius, Joseph, 1156
Geneva, *see* Robert
Gengis-Khan, *see* Chingiz
genius, 18, 1772
Genoa, aqueduct of, 735
Genoa, *see* John; Massari; Simon
Genoa, traders, 769
Gensbein, *see* John
Gent, *see* Ghent
Gentile da Foligno (XIV-1), *848*, 244, 245, 266, 268, 285, 287, 857, 859, 862, 896, 982, 1239, 1240, 1243, 1381, 1685, 1686, 1690, 1707, 1709
Gentile degli Mainardi (XIV-2), *1482*, 1106, 1300
Gentili, Alberico, 470, 1869
Genty, Achille, 1135
geodesy, 1436
Geoffrey Le Baker (XIV-2), *1742*, 1255
Geoffrey of Breteuil, 192
Geoffrey, *see* Chaucer
Geoffrey de Coldingham, 560
Geoffrey the Grammarian, 1316
Geoffrey de La Tour-Landry (XIV-2), *1406*, 1080, 1309
Geoffrey of Meaux (XIV-1), *659*, 115, 248, 1546, 1797, 1846
Geoffrey of Monmouth (XII-1), v. 2, *256*, 1176; v. 3, 941, 1310
Geoffrey of Paris (XIV-1), *927*, 300, 346
Geoffrey of Saint Victor, 192
Geoffrey Starkey, 1316
Geoffrey, *see* Villehardouin
Geoffroi, *see* Geoffrey
geography, 1874, 1875, 1883, 1884, 1888, 1889, 1891, 1901, 1909
geography, biological, 1623
geography, dictionary, 1887
geography, *see* medicine
geoheliocentrical hypothesis, 440, 446
geological problems, 1163
geological theories, 1170
geology, 1872
geomancy, 123, 339, 443, 1421, 1537
Geometria culmensis, 1112
geometry, analytic, 1487
geometry, axiomless, 597
Geoponica, 813, 858, 859
George, *see also* Jirjīs
George Acropolites (XIII-2), v. 2, *1113*, 1176; v. 3, 303
George Adam, 414
George Andreoli of Pavia, 1134
George, bishop of the Arabs (VII-2), v. 1, *493*, 805
George Chastellain, 1842
George Choniates (XIV-1), *438*, 63, 252
George Chrysococces (XIV-1), *688*, 63, 123, 197, 1117, 1378, 1511
George Codinos, 1823

George Colle, 1668
George of Erseng, 1095, 1323, 1441
George of Erzinjān, 1441
George V of Georgia, 305
George Gucci (XIV-2), *1595*, 1143, 1300
George Hermonymos, 1321
George, J. F. L., 1782
George of Kolozsvár, 1561
George Lapethis (or Lapithes), 586
George di Lorenzo Chiarini, 773
George Mèrula, 922
George Metochites, 95
George the Monk (IX-1), v. 1, *578*, 548, 686; v. 2, 261; v. 3, 305
George, order of St., 1039
George Pachymeres (XIII-2), v. 2, *972*, 1176; v. 3, 97, 119, 120, 161, 239, 303, 363, 745, 746, 825, 927, 950
George, St., Martyr, 416, 1601, 1666
George Scholarios, 589
George Syncellos (IX-1), v. 1, *577*, 482, 548
George de Utra, 184
George Valla, 952
Georgia, 305
Georgia, *see* George
Georgian, 356
Georgian alphabet, 304
Georgian annals, 305
Georgios, *see* George
Gerace, *see* Boniface
Gerald, *see also* Giraldes; Giraldez; Giraldus
Gerald of Abbeville, 48
Gerald Adam, 414
Gerald Bierne, 876
Gerald of Bologna (XIV-1), *518*, 87, 525
Gerald da Borgo San Donnino, 483
Gerald v. Braunsvalde, 932
Gerald of Bruxelles (XIII-1), v. 2, *629*, 1176; v. 3, 146
Gerald of Cremona (XII-2), v. 2, *338*, 1176; v. 3, 166, 430, 431, 434, 450, 484, 602, 613, 705, 898, 1381, 1484
Gerald v. Kalkar, 1503
Gerald de Lacombe, 1234
Gerald de La Palu, 526
Gerald Odonis, 402, 785, 1431
Gerald Petrarca, 510
Gerald of Sabbioneta (XIII-2), v. 2, *987*, 1176; v. 3, 1112, 1433, 1500
Gerald de Schueren, 1317
Gerald de Solo (XIV-1), *876*, 248, 878, 1074, 1212, 1221, 1243, 1379, 1381
Gerald van Voorne, 938
Gerald the Welshman (XII-2), v. 2, *417*, 1176; v. 3, 192, 333
Gerald of Zaiton, 776
Gerald Zerbolt (XIV-2), *1362*, 1039, 1057, 1093, 1297, 1317, 1360
Gerald van Zutphen, 1362
Geraldus, *see* Gerald
Gerard, Gérard, *see* **Gerald (the two names were originally different but have so often been confused that a distinction between them leads to repetitions)**
Gerasimos, bishop of Cerasus, 790
Géraud, Hercule, 1739
Géraud, *see* Hugh
Gerbert of Aurillac (X-2), Sylvester II, v. 1, *669*, 805; v. 2, 2, 4; v. 3, 1031
Gerbert, Martin, 1885
Gerede, *see* Isḥāq b. Murād; Murād b. Isḥāq
Gerhard, *see* Gerald
Gerini, G. E., 1627
Gerlach v. Homburg, 1400
Gerland of Besançon (XI-2), v. 1, *758*, 805; v. 2, 1176
Germain, Alexandre, 1241, 1243
Germain de Calberte, college of Saint, 1406
German, 350
Germanic antiquities, 1901
Germanic, *see* astronomy; law
germination, 269
Gernardus (XIII-1), v. 2, *616*, 504
Gérold, Théodore, 1885
Gerona, 39
Gerona, *see* Ferrer; Moses b. Naḥman
Gerondi, *see* Nissim b. Reuben
Geronimo, *see* Jerome
Gerosa, Pietro Paolo, 515
Gerrans, B., 465
Gerrare, Wirt, 726
Gerretsen, J. H., 1358
Gerrit, *see* Geert
Gershon, *see also* Gerson
Gershon b. Hezekiah, 1212
Gershon b. Solomon (XIII-2), v. 2, *886*, 1176; v. 3, 595, 1443
Gershon Soncino, 616
Gerson, *see* John; Levi; Solomon
Gervase of Canterbury (XIII-1), v. 2, *676*, 1176
Gervase, *see* Riccobaldo
Gervase of Tilbury (XIII-1), v. 2, *637*, 1176; v. 3, 457, 1409
Gervasio, *see* Gervase
Gervinus, G. G., 915
Gesamtkatalog, 1885
Gesenius, 365
Gesner, Conrad, 188, 1207
Gesprächbüchlein, 347
Gessin, Paul, 941
Gessler, E. A., 1555
Gessler, Jean, 251, 347
Gesta Francorum (XII-1), v. 2, *252*, 138
Gesta Romanorum, 317, 455
Gettens, R. J., 1834
Ge'ullah, 453
Geuschmied, *see* Henry; Margaret
Gévaudan, 413
Geyer, Bernhard, 570
Geyl, A., 251

Gezerah, 418
ghaḍārah, 755
Ghāfiqī, *see* Aḥmad b. Muḥammad
ghārah, 925
Gharīb-nāma, 623
Ghāyat al-maṭlūb, 749
Ghāyat al-surūr, 759
Ghāzān Khān, 1249, 1840
Ghāzān Maḥmūd, 969, 975
Ghāzī Bahādur Khān, a., 104
Ghazūlī, 1847
Ghazzālī (XI-2), v. 1, *753*, 805; v. 2, 1176; v. 3, x, 61, 62, 84, 99, 100, 101, 163, 422, 428, 436, 608, 610, 849, 998, 1072, 1097, 1138, 1374, 1377, 1380, 1447, 1452, 1492, 1639, 1771, 1775
Ghent, 152, 153, 323, 1557, 1558, 1559
Ghent, *see* Henry; John; Simon
Gherard, *see* Gerald
Gherardi, Alessandro, 1674, 1676
Ghibellines, 315, 480
Ghiberti, *see* Laurence
Ghidola Malaspina, 1600
Ghillebert, *see* Gilbert
Ghisalberti, A. M., 923
Ghisalberti, Fausto, 455
Ghiyāth al-dīn, 629
Ghiyāth al-dīn b. Rashīd al-dīn, 969
Ghizolfi, *see* Buscarello
Ghosh, K. C., 1837
ghubār numerals, 132, 134, 1483
Ghudda, b. a., 1785
ghufrān, 490
Ghunyat al-ṭullāb, 1866
Giacomo, *see* James
Giacosa, Piero, 1684, 1885
Giacotto di Francesco Malespini, 915
Giambattista Capuano, 1127
Giambattista de' Guarini, 1292
Giambattista da Monte, 1196
Giambonino dei Crescenzi, 811
Giambullari, P. F., 1301
Gian Francesco II Gonzaga, 1290
Gian Galeazzo Visconti, 508, 1025, 1440, 1541, 1655, 1676, 1681, 1682
Gianani, Faustino, 768
Gianellis, *see* Francis
Gianmatteo Ferrari da Gradi, 1239
Giannini, Crescentino, 915
giants, 1227, 1806, 1860
Gibb, E. J. W., 1885
Gibb, H. A. R., 1622, 1778, 1883, 1885
Gibbon, Edward, 586, 914, 950, 1650, 1761
Gibertuzzi, *see* Ugolino Marini
Gibraltar, map of, 1157, 1620
Gibson, H. E., 385
Gibson, Thomas, 241
Gideon Zographos, 1511
Giese, Friedrich, 625
Gifford, *see* John Gyfford
Giggeius, Antonius, 606
Gigli, Girolamo, 1336
Gil Álvarez Albornoz (XIV-2), *1792*, 520, 1019, 1022, 1032, 1273, 1797
Gilbert, A. H., 499, 1769
Gilbert the Englishman (XIII-1), v. 2, *658*, 1177; v. 3, 274, 276, 278, 880, 881, 883, 1074, 1205, 1374, 1688, 1703, 1705, 1708, 1851
Gilbert, J. T., 1740
Gilbert de Lannoy, 1151, 1309
Gilbert de La Porrée (XII-1), v. 2, *197*, 1177; v. 3, 517, 519, 534
Gilbert Maghfeld, 126
Gilbert, *see* Peter Engelbert
Gilbert, physician to king of France, 1449
Gilbert of Sempringham, St., 461
Gilbert of Tournay (XIII-2), v. 2, *864*, 725, 801
Gilbertine canons, 461
Gildas (VI-2), v. 1, *455*, 445; v. 3, 1744
Giles, *see also* Gillis
Giles of Arles, 1375
Giles Aycelin de Montaigut, 476, 1227, 1404
Giles de Bellemère, 1277
Giles of Corbeil (XII-2), v. 2, *440*, 1177; v. 3, 251, 270, 849, 850, 881, 1104, 1703
Giles of Greece, St., 1666
Giles, H. A., 235, 904, 980, 1791, 1834, 1836, 1860, 1865, 1885, 1891
Giles de Hemricourt, 1750
Giles, J. A., 1742, 1744
Giles of Lessines (XIII-2), v. 2, *946*, 1177; v. 3, 94, 302
Giles, Lionel, 174, 1885
Giles Le Muisit (XIV-2), *1746*, 50. 1235, 1257, 1309
Giles Malet, 1202
Giles, master, 546
Giles Muñoz, 1033
Giles de Retz, 1842
Giles of Rome (XIII-2), v. 2, *922*, 1177; v. 3, 87, 89, 112, 141, 242, 268, 314, 402, 450, 457, 518, 577, 578, 1075, 1076, 1088, 1090, 1112, 1277, 1280, 1390, 1392, 1394, 1431, 1436, 1482, 1494, 1869
Giles de Thebaldis, 1383
Gilfillan, S. C., 157
Giliberti, 837
Gillert, Karl, 742
Gilles, *see* Giles
Gillet de Bolbec, 1493
Gillies, H. C., 1239
Gillis Beukels, 823
Gilman, Alfred, 289, 909
Gilson, Etienne, 78, 85, 1839, 1843, 1885
gimbals, 715
Gimlette, J. D., 1177
Ginés de Sepúlveda, Juan, 1793
Gino Capponi, 1251, 1275, 1300
Ginsburg, Jekuthial, 1116
Ginsburger, M., 1551

Ginzberg, Louis, 1444
Ginzburg, B., 146, 1432, 1489
Ginzel, F. K., 1885
Gioja, *see* Flavio
Giordano, *see* Jordan
Giorgi, *see* Francis
Giorgi, Giorgio, *see* George
Giotto, 37, 169, 225, 485, 500, 1131, 1132, 1802
Giovanna, *see* Joan
Giovanni Battista, *see* Giambattista
Giovanni, *see also* Gian; John
Ciovanni, V. di, 927
Giovio, Paolo, 976
Giqaṭilia, *see* Joseph b. Abraham
giraffe, 239, 363, 775, 1142, 1189, 1606, 1627
Giraldes, Mestre (XIV-1), *862*, 207, 228, 246, 284, 344
Giraldez, *see* Alfonso
Giraldus de Cumba, 1234
Girard, I., 1136
Girolamo, *see* Jerome
Gisburn, *see* Walter Hemingburgh
Gíslason, Konráð, 1191
Gismondi, Henry, 956
Gīsū Darāz, 1476
gitano, 279
Giudice, *see* Albert
Giuffre, Liborio, 499
Giuntini, Francesco, 399
Giuseppe, *see* Joseph
Gjandschezian, Esnik, 1222
Glaber, *see* Raoul
Gladwin, Francis, 465
glands, 871
Glanville, *see* Ranulf
Glasenapp, Helmuth v., 1584
Glasgow, 39
glass, 1881
glass beads, 781
glass, Chinese, v. 1, *389*, 378; v. 3, 758
glass, enameled, 173
glass, English, 1887
glass, *see* glaze
glass manufacture (XIII-2), v. 2, *1040*, 1177
glass painting, *see* stained glass
Glaston, *see* John
Glatz, *see* Henry
Glaucias of Tarentum (I-1 B.C.), v. 1, *215*, 203
glaucoma, 1837
Glaucon, 441
Glaucos of Chios (VI B.C.), v. 1, *75*, 65
glaze, ceramical, 179, 752, 756, 1133
Glazemaker, J. H., 955
Glazer, Sidney, 1015
Glettner, J., 948
globes, celestial, early Arabic (XIII-2), v. 2, *1014*, 1233 (*under* spheres)
Glogau, *see* John
Gloria, Andrea, 839, 918, 1670, 1677, 1678, 1681, 1684
glossary, *see* botanic
glossatores, 87, 313, 982
Gloucester, 39
Gloucester, *see* Humphrey; Robert
glowworms, *see* fireflies
Glueck, Nelson, 287
Glycas, *see* Michael
Glycys, *see* John XIII
Gmelin, Julius, 395
Gmünd, *see* Gemunden
gnomon, 138, 1118
Gnudi, M. T., 1174, 1555
Gnupsson, *see* Eric
Gobi desert, 1586
Goblot, Edmond, 77
Goddam, *see* Adam Wodeham
Godefroi, *see* Godfrey
Godfrey de Bouillon, 788
Godfrey of Fontaines (XIII-2), v. 2, *947*, 740; v. 3, 90, 94, 400, 521, 534
Godfrey Prest, 1561
Godfrey, Thomas, 601
Godfrey of Viterbo (XII-2), v. 2, *452*, 1177; v. 3, 192, 369
Godshouse, 1402
Göbler, Justinus, 996
Gölpinarli, Baki, 975
Goemaere, Francis, 989
Görres, Joseph, 574
Goës, Benedict, 1471, 1910
Goethals-Vercruysse, J., 1747
Goethe, 496, 1458
Goette, J. A., 1472
Göttingen, *see* John Hake
Goetz, Walter, 1843
Goetze, Fritz, 533
Gog and Magog, 1227
Goguyer, A., 1010
Gohory, Jacques, 1310
Goichon, A. M., 81, 374, 1768, 1885
Goidelic, 250
gold mining, 1176, 1788
gold, mosaic, 169
gold-silver ratio, 1283, 1494
Goldast, Melchior, 555, 989, 992, 1345
Golden Bull, 1020, 1258, 1541
Golden Fleece, order, 1151, 1403
Golden Horde, 1025
Golden Legend, 1254. *See also* Legenda aurea
golden number, 1610
golden spurs, 37, 938
Goldenthal, Jacob, 435, 492, 609
Golding, Arthur, 1753
Golding, L. T., 1753
Golding, Percival, 1753
Goldschmidt, Adolph, 1187
Goldschmidt, Günther, 1877
Goldstücker, Theodor, 1367
Goldziher, Ignaz, 1839
Golein, *see* John

Golenishchev-Kutuzov, Ilya, 1346
Goliards (XII-2), v. 2, *391*, 294
Goliath, 1227
Golius, Jacob, 1474
Gollancz, Hermann, 616
Gollancz, Israel, 1413
Golodik, *see* John
Golubovich, Girolamo, 776, 780, 1885
Gómez Albornoz, 1812
Gonçalo Velho Cabral, 184
Gonçalves, *see* Nuno
Gonçalves Zarco, *see* John
Gonesse, *see* Nicholas
Gongo Mūsā, 41, 803
Gonnard, René, 544, 1284, 1496
Gonsalvo Transtorna, 785
Gontier Col, 1294
Gonville, 72, 475
Gonville, *see* Edmund
Gonzaga, *see* Gian Francesco
González de Clavijo, Ruy, 232, 1142, 1300, 1467, 1474
González de Contreras, Diego, 1468
González de Mendoza, Juan, 1597
González de Mendoza, Pero, 1671
González Palencia, Ángel, 67, 130, 431, 1886
Gonzalo de Hinojosa, 299, 1253, 1392
Gonzalo de Santa María, 1061
Gonzalve de Balboa, 570
Good Men of Grammont (XII-1), v. 2, *153*, 110
Goodall, Walter, 1741
Goodenough, Anna, 927
Goodman, Louis, 289, 909
Goodman, Tobias, 594
Goodrich, L. C., 28, 211, 386, 832, 833, 930, 1028, 1071, 1549, 1870
goose, 1640
Gordin, Jakob, 593, 1448
Gordlevskiĭ, V., 1068
Gordon, *see* Bernard
Gordon, C. H., 359
Gordon, M. B., 275, 1658
Gore, A. A., 1704
Gores, 206
Goro, *see* John
Gorp, Jan van, 1227, 1318
Gortyn, laws (V B.C.), v. 1, *109*, 62, 83
Goshkevich, I., 1590
gospel, Infancy, 339
Gospel, *see* Nicodemos
Gospels, 346, 357
Gossouin, 510
Got, *see* Bertrand
Gotha Arzneibuch, 1205, 1711
Gothic architecture (XII-2), v. 2, *334*, 281
Gottesfreunde, 1081
Gottheil, Richard, 1516, 1719, 1804
Gough, A. E., 1367
Gough, J. W., 219
Gough, Richard, 191
goupillon, 1190
Goupylus, Jac., 891
gout, 252, 274, 285, 602, 1197, 1198, 1201, 1236, 1247, 1408, 1411, 1673, 1695, 1703, 1706
government, *see* constitutional theory
government, theory of, 1277
Govind Singh, 1475
Govindarāja (XII-1), v. 2, *269*, 142
Gower, *see* John
Gowland, William, 727, 1176
Gozbert, 224
Graal, Saint, 1313
Grabadin, 288, 443, 836
Grabig, Hans, 220
Grabmann, Martin, 146, 332, 563, 570, 992
grace, 49
Grace, James, 1740
Gracian, *see* Shealtiel
Gradi, *see* Gianmatteo Ferrari
Gräber, S. E., 606
Gräberg, Jacob, 1778
Graefe, E., 1143
Graetz, Heinrich, 615
Graevi, J. G., 918
grafting, 813, 1637
gragas, 352
Graham, Stephen, 1470
grammar, *see* Hebrew
grammar, speculative, 331, 1003
Grammateus, *see* Henry
Grammont, *see* Good Men
Granada, 1762
Granada, Alhambra, 1021
Granchi, *see* Bartholomew
Grancsay, S. V., 1175, 1555
Grandaur, Georg, 935
Grandgent, C. H., 496
Grandison, *see* John
Grandmontains, *see* Good Men
Grandson, *see* Othon
Grandville, *see* John; Peter
Granet, Marcel, 138
Grant, C. P., 1786
granth, 1476
Granth ṣāḥib, 1476
graph, 1108, 1487
graphical representation, 117, 737
Gras, L. J., 219
Gras, N. S. B., 283, 1024
grasshopper, 1187, 1621
Grassmann, Herrmann, 1368
Grassus, *see* Benevenutus
Gratarolo, Guglielmo, 1573, 1576
Gratian the alchemist, 166
Gratian of Bologna (XII-1), v. 2, *268*, 1178; v. 3, 316, 400, 403, 991, 1277
Gratius, Orthvinus, 1574
Grattan, J. H. G., 1415
Grauert, H. H., 499

Grauert, Heinrich, 1761
Grauert, Hermann, 820, 1113, 1695
Gravier, Gabriel, 184, 786
Gravina, Domenico, 516
Gravina, G. V., 583
gravitas secundum situm, 1566
gravitation, 14, 1127
gravity, 538, 543, 565, 1436, 1488, 1568
gravity, *see* center
gravity potential, 146, 147, 1566
gravity, specific, 735
Gray, J. M., 474
Gray, L. H., 1247, 1512
Gray, *see* Thomas
Graystanes, *see* Robert
Graziadei d'Ascoli (XIV-1), *517*, 87
Graziolo Bambagliuoli, 1843
Graziolo, Ser, 86, 335, 500
Greatham, *see* Robert
Greaves, John, 799
Greaves, Paul, 1316
Greek, 31, 352, 364, 371, 561, 1845
Greek, *see* astrology
Greek church, 392
"Greek fire," 725, 1643, 1700, 1703
Greek, *see* law; mathematics
Greene, Belle da Costa, 745
Greener, William, 726
Greenland, 194, 232, 710, 1146, 1154, 1155, 1608, 1834
Grégoire, *see also* Gregory
Grégoire, Henri, 941, 1228, 1812
Gregor, *see* Gregory
Gregoras, *see* Nicephoros
Gregorio, *see also* Gregory
Gregorio, Rosarius, 1737
Gregorios, *see* Gregory
Gregorovius, Ferdinand, 295
Gregory Acindynos (XIV-1), *587*, 66, 95, 586, 588, 826, 995, 1386, 1760
Gregory Bechada, 339
Gregory of Beirut (III-2), v. 1, *343*, 331, 438
Gregory VII, catholicos, 54
Gregory Chioniades (XIV-1), *438*, 63, 123, 1512
Gregory Chrysococces, 438
Gregory of Corinth (XII-2), v. 2, *471*, 319
Gregory of Cypros, 587
Gregory Gelenius, 506
Gregory of Hungary, 781
Gregory the Illuminator, 66
Gregory, James, 737
Gregory of Khlath (XIV-2), *1761*, 1260, 1323
Gregory of Nazianzos, St., viii, 947
Gregory Novelli, 518
Gregory of Nyssa, St., viii, 1513
Gregory Palamas (XIV-1), *588*, 53, 95, 96, 584, 586, 587, 995, 1386, 1388, 1438, 1845
Gregory da Pistoia, 1194
Gregory I, St., pope (VI-2), v. 1, *445*, 443; v. 2, 916; v. 3, ix, 238, 574, 1042, 1044, 1076, 1736
Gregory VII, pope, 43
Gregory IX, pope, 334, 405
Gregory XI, pope, 1032, 1334, 1795
Gregory XII, pope, 1032, 1440
Gregory XIII, pope, 951, 1107, 1242
Gregory da Rimini (XIV-1), *518*, 92, 87, 110, 559
Gregory Sinaites, 96
Gregory of Tathev (XIV-2), *1441*, 1095, 1260, 1323, 1441, 1864
Gregory Tifernas, 1321
Gregory of Tours (VI-2), v. 1, *456*, 445; v. 2, 623; v. 3, 1650, 1868
Gregory Zeréntz, 1761
Greith, C. J., 571, 1886
Grenefeld, *see* William
Grenoble, University, 72, 471
Gresham's law, 1283, 1495
Grethenios (XIV-2), *1614*, 1156, 1322
Gretser, Jacob, 587, 820, 1387, 1760
Greven, Joseph, 49
Griera, A., 1306
Grierson, G. A., 425, 1476
Griese, *see* John
Griesinger, Jacob, 172
Griffet, Henri, 1059
Griffith, D. D., 1424
Grillo, Girolamo, 499
Grimaldi, *see* John; Rainier
Grimm, F. M., 1426
Grimoard, *see* Anglic; William
Gringore, *see* Peter
Grion, Giusto, 1601
Grise, *see* John
Gröber, Gustav, 1310, 1810
Grønbech, K., 1016
Grohmann, Adolf, 1010, 1779, 1782
Groote, *see* Geert; Werner
Gross, Charles, 1886
Gross, Heinrich, 1718, 1886
Grossberg, Menasseh, 613, 1376
Grosseteste, *see* Robert
Grossmann, Karl, 1509
Grotefend, C. L., 788
Grotius, Hugo, 1869
Grottanelli, Francesco, 1337
Grousset, René, 1865, 1886
Grove, Sir George, 1886
Grube, Karl, 1361
Grünewald, Käte, 572
Grünhut, Lazarus, 792
Grumel, V., 1822
Grunebaum, Gustave E. v., 1779, 1839, 1846, 1860, 1868
Gruner, C. G., 839, 851
Grynaeus, Simon, 955
Guadagni, P. A., 1809
Guadalupe, 1037

Guainerio, *see* Anthony
Gualterus, *see* Walter
Guardia, J. M., 1821
Guareschi, Icilio, 168
Guarimbertus, *see* Matthew
Guarini, *see* Giambattista
Guarino da Verona, 1073, 1081, 1145, 1252, 1291, 1292, 1321, 1407, 1822
Guatteri, Giuseppe, 1814
Gubbio, *see* Bosone
Gubernatis, Angelo, 1886
Gucci, *see* George
Gudger, E. W., 778, 818, 1603, 1870
Gudmarsson, *see* Ulf
Gudule, miracle of St., 1059
Guelfs, 315, 480
Gülshehrī (XIV-1), *625*, 64, 105, 379
Guénon, René, 500
Guenoux, Charles, 1903
Günther, Siegmund, 607, 711, 1488, 1886
Günzburg, David v., 1719
Guericke, Otto v., 1127
Guerra, Giorgio del, 291
Guerri, Domenico, 913, 1810
Guerrini, Olindo, 168
Gueruccius, 68, 112
Guesclin, *see* Bertrand
Guest, A. R., xi, 1265
Guglielmo, *see* William
Gui, *see* Bernard; Guy
Guiard des Moulins, 1493
Guiard or Guiart, *see* William
Guibert of Nogent (XII-1), v. 2, *253*, 138, 252; v. 3, 266, 1045
Guicciardini, Francesco, 821
Guichard of Troyes, 406
Guichardan, P. S., 589
Guidi, Ignazio, 1010, 1455
Guidi, L., 362
Guido, *see also* Guy
Guido of Arezzo, bishop, 1669
Guido of Arezzo, musician (XI-1), v. 1, *720*, 791; v. 3, 160, 741, 746
Guido of Arezzo, oculist (XIV-1), *855*, 244, 273
Guido da Bagnolo (XIV-2) *1672*, 1192, 1210, 1222, 1298
Guido Baisio, 401
Guido Bonatti (XIII-2), v. 2, *988*, 1178; v. 3, 65, 113, 456, 1409, 1481
Guido Cavalcanti, 482, 837
Guido of Colonna, 1076, 1418, 1736, 1741
Guido Gazzata, 1672
Guido the Geographer (XII-1), v. 2, *222*, 43, 131
Guido, *see* Lanfranchi
Guido II de Mello, 52
Guido da Montefeltro, 920
Guido de Papia, 846
Guido de Perpignan, 400
Guido da Pisa, 86, 335, 500
Guido of Reggio, 856
Guido da Vigevano (XIV-1), *846*, 46, 207, 244, 266, 285, 844, 1550
"Guido's hand," 742
Guidotto, 777
Guignes, Joseph de, 805, 1623
Guigues, Pierre, 817, 898
guilds, 152, 325
Guileville, *see* William Deguilleville
Guilhem, Guilherme, *see* William
Guilhiermoz, Paul, 713
Guilland, Rodolphe, 952, 1439
Guillaume, *see also* William
Guillaume, Alfred, 1066, 1775
Guillelmus, Guillem, Guillermo, *see* William
Guinet, Léon, 6
Guiot of Provins (XIII-1), v. 2, *589*, 1178; v. 3, 714
Guittone, Guittoncino, *see* Cino
Guittone de' Sinibaldi, 982
Guiu, *see* Guy
Gujarātī, 1330, 1474
Gul-Chīn, 1534
Gulandām, *see* Muḥammad
Gulideolus Mordicus, 441
Gulleghem, *see* Siger
gun borer, 1554
Gundel, Wilhelm, 453, 1874, 1886
Gundert, Hermann, 384
Gundisalvo, *see* Dominic
Gune, P. D., 1370
gunpowder, invention of (XIII-2), v. 2, *1036*, 1178; v. 3, 722, 1554, 1581, 1700
guns, 151
gunsmiths, 1174
Gunther, R. T., 1424, 1886
Gūr-i-Mīr, 1471
Gurjistān, 305
Gurlt, E., 1874, 1887
guru, 1475
Gutenberg, *see* John
Gutiérrez de la Vega, José, 925, 1736
Gutleben, *see* Jehiel
Gutleuthäuser, 276
Gutmann, Jehoshua, 1519
Guttmann, Georg, 1605
Guttmann, Jacob, 450
Guttmann, Julius, 607, 1448
Guttmann, Oscar, 726, 1582
Guy, *see also* Guido
Guy, Arthur, 1458
Guy of Auxerre, 52
Guy de Bazoches, 510
Guy de Blois, 1751
Guy de Châtillon, 452, 885
Guy, *see* Chauliac
Guy de Lusignan, 413, 994
Guy I of Luxembourg, 1246
Guy of Montpellier, 294

Guy, R. E., 1416
Guy of Saint Pol, 475
Guy Terrena (XIV-1), *400*, 50, 89, 315, 525, 527
Guyard, Stanislas, 627, 799, 1887, 1901
Guyénot, Emile, 1836
Guyon, madame, 23
Gwynn, Aubrey, 1350
Gyfford, *see* John
gymel, 159
gynaecology, *see* women, diseases
gypsies, 279

Haarbrücker, Theodor, 901
Habakkuk (VII B.C.), v. 1, *64*, 60
Ḥabash Ḥāsib, *see* Aḥmad b. 'Abdallāh
Haberling, Wilhelm, 499, 1874, 1887
Ḥabīb Dimashqī, b., *see* Ḥasan b. 'Umar
Ḥabib, *see* Moses b. Shem-ṭob
Ḥabīb, b., *see* Ṭāhir b. Ḥasan
Ḥabillo, *see* Elijah b. Joseph
Hadassi, *see* Judah b. Elijah
Hadfield, Robert, 1859
hadīth, 209, 421, 489, 964, 1065, 1466, 1639, 1854
Hadley, John, 601
Hadrian, emperor, vii, 339
Haebler, Konrad, 1124
Häfliger, J. A., 290
Hämäläinen, A., 1825
haemoglobinuria, 891
haemorrhoids, 274, 1700
Hänel, Kurt, 275
Haenisch, Erich, 1790
Haerynck, H., 940
Haeser, Heinrich, 1887
Haffner, August, 360
Ḥāfiẓ (XIV-2), *1456*, 1100, 1328, 1473
Ḥāfiẓ Abrū, 1855
Ḥafṣ, Banū, 101
haft rang, 756
Hagen, Paul, 1362
Hagerty, 223
Haggai (VI B.C.), v. 1, *70*, 65
Hagia Sofia, 790
Hagin Deulacres (XIII-2), v. 2, *857*, 1179; v. 3, 67, 68, 442, 453, 1489
Ḥagiz, Jacob b. Samuel, 1446
Haguenauer, M. C., 206
Hahn, L., 864
hai'at al-'ālam, 436
Hailperin, Herman, 400
Hā'im, b., *see* Aḥmad b. Muḥammad
Hainaut, *see* Elizabeth; John; Philippa; Yolande
Hainfogel, Konrad, 820
Haitham, b. (XI-1), v. 1, *721*, 809; v. 2, 1179; v. 3, 62, 111, 114, 118, 130, 141, 142, 436, 524, 602, 705, 707, 993, 1119, 1525, 1847
Haiton de Courcy, 953
Ḥaiyān, a. (XIV-1), *1011*, 58, 179, 307, 363, 373, 377, 379, 381, 759, 959, 1009, 1010, 1329, 1453, 1853
Ḥaiyān, b. (XI-1), v. 1, *734*, 700, 702
Ḥaiyān b. Khalaf, *see* b. Ḥaiyān
Ḥajala, b., 1722
Ḥajala, b. a., *see* Aḥmad b. Yaḥyā
Ḥajar 'Asqalānī, b., 964, 1784
ḥajar al-aswad, 1621
Hájek, Thaddeus, 1167
Ḥājib, b., *see* 'Uthmān b. 'Umar
ḥājim, 896
Ḥajjāj, Banū, 1868
Ḥajjāj Uqṣurī, 1619
Ḥajjāj b. Yūsuf (VIII-1), v. 1, *518*, 506
Ḥajjāj b. Yūsuf b. Maṭar (IX-1), v. 1, *562*, 273, 545; v. 2, 976, 1003
Ḥājjī Bairām, 1464
Ḥājjī, *see* Baktāsh
Ḥājjī Khalīfa, 900, 1101, 1263, 1515, 1776, 1887
Ḥājjī Pāshā (XIV-2), *1727*, 1067, 1101, 1215, 1223, 1248, 1328, 1464, 1465
Ḥakam II [al-Mustanṣir] of Cordova (X-2), v. 1, *658*, 647, 654
Hake, *see* John
Hakkı Uzunçarşılıoğlu, I., 1464, 1465
Hakluyt, Richard, 779, 1151, 1258, 1501, 1594, 1754
Hákon of Bergen, 1607
Hakonarson, *see* John
Ḥalabī, *see* Yūsuf b. Rāfi'
ḥalaqim, 131
Halász, P., 1017
Halāyudha, 383
halçahahny, 427
Halecki, Oscar, 1152
Hales, *see* Alexander
Hales, J. W., 1415
Halidé Edib, 155
Hall, Anthony, 943, 945
Hall, J. C., 1001
Hall, J. J., 722, 1174
Hall, K., 96
Hallager, Fr., 1689
Hallberg, Ivar, 1887
Haller, 816, 844
Halley, Edmund, 324, 710
Halliwell [-Phillips], J. O., 221, 1203, 1315, 1604, 1887
hallucinations, 1206, 1507
halo, 705, 1123, 1490
Halper, Benzion, 594, 1523
Haly Abbas, *see* 'Alī b. 'Abbās
Haly Eben Rodan, *see* 'Alī b. Riḍwān
Hamadhānī, *see* 'Alī Hamadhānī
Ḥamāh, 795
Ḥamāh, *see* a. Fidā'
Ḥamawī, *see* Aḥmad b. Sarrāj
Hamberger, Julius, 572

Hamburger, S., 594
Ḥamdallāh b. a. Bakr Mustawfī Qazwīnī (XIV-1), *630*, 106, 133, 135, 202, 203, 210, 259, 310, 377, 381
Hamdānī (X-1), v. 1, *637*, 806
Ḥamdūn, b., *see* Muḥammad
Hamelius, Paul, 1605, 1749
Ḥāmid b. 'Alī Wāsiṭī (IX-2), v. 1, *601*, 585, 590
Ḥāmid b. Khiḍr Khujandī (X-2), v. 1, *667*, 813; v. 3, 897
Hamilton, G. H., 169
Hamilton, H. C., 942
Hamilton, M. P., 1426
Hamilton, Mary, 292, 1247
Ḥammād, b., *see* Muḥammad b. 'Alī
ḥammām, v. 2, *631*, 1179; v. 3, 287, 288
Hammar, T., 1898
Hammer-Purgstall, Joseph v., 154, 627, 799, 829, 977, 1458, 1464, 1644, 1776, 1827
Hammett, F. S., 1217
Hammond, E. P., 1424
Hamy, E. T., 765, 1591, 1593
Ḥamza b. Ḥasan (X-2), v. 1, *687*, 652, 654; v. 3, 376
Ḥanafī rite, 1099
Ḥanbal, b., *see* Aḥmad b. Muḥammad
Ḥanbalī school, 901, 1099
hand, *see* Guido's
Ḥandali, *see* Moses
Handerson, H. E., 882, 1244
Handlo, *see* Robert
Handlyng synne, 68, 462, 1314
hanhagat ha-beri'ut, 449
Ḥanīfa, a. (VIII-1), v. 1, *507*, 787; v. 3, 107, 1462, 1784
Ḥanina, R., x
Hanka, Věnceslav, 941
Hann, G. R., 1583
Hanno (V B.C.), v. 1, *103*, 83; v. 3, 1159
Hannover, Emil, 1134
Hanns (Hans) = Johannes, *see* John
Hanover Latin, *see* algorism
Hansa, 823
hanse of London, 323
Hanseatic League (XIII-2), v. 2, *1063*, 38, 774; v. 3, 125, 323, 727, 728, 1020
Hansen, A., 275, 1837
Hansen, Joseph, 1051
Hantsch, Victor, 1607
haphṭarah, 367
Happalat ha-happala, 428
Hapsburg, *see* Rodolph
Harada, Jirō, 1333, 1570
Harasiṃha, 1000
Haraszti, Zoltán, 492, 742, 1600
Harawī, *see* 'Alī b. a. Bakr
Harcigny, *see* William
Harden, J. M., 438
Harding, *see* Stephen
Hardoon, Mr. and Mrs. S. A., 467
Hardouin, Jean, 1822
Hardt, Hermann v. der, 1820
Hardy, T. D., 561
Hardy, W. J., 942
Harford, Dundas, 1090
Harihara, 41
Ḥarīrī, *see* Qāsim b. 'Alī
Harivaṃśa, 466
Ḥarizi, *see* Judah b. Solomon
Harkavy, Abraham de, 56
Harlebeke, brothers, 1561
Harlebeke, *see* John
Harmenopulos, *see* Constantine Armenopulos
harnessing in file, 157
Harpestraeng, *see* Henry
harquebusery, 1553
Ḥarrānī, *see* Jābir b. Ḥaiyān; Jābir b. Sinān
Harrison, P. W., 1622
Harrow College, 1403
Harting, J. E., 1642, 1887
Hartknoch, Christopher, 932
Hartley, P. H.-S., 1706
Hartmann v. Aue, 281
Hartmann, Martin, 1589
Hartmann, Richard, 803, 1883, 1887
Hartmann Schedel, 1197, 1290
Hartner, W., 162
Hartshorne, Albert, 1887
Hartwig, Otto, 915, 1509
Hārūn al-Rashīd (VIII-2), v. 1, *527*, 521, 525; v. 2, 27
Harvey, Ralph, 567
Harvey, Wm., 268, 269
Ḥasan b. 'Abdallāh Hāshimī, 961
Ḥasan b. 'Abdallāh Ṣafadī, 201
Ḥasan b. Aḥmad, *see* Hamdānī
Ḥasan 'Alī b. Maghribī, a., 1533
Ḥasan b. 'Alī Marrākushī (XIII-1), v. 2, *621*, 1180; v. 3, 1514, 1526
Ḥasan b. 'Alī, *see* Niẓām al-mulk
Ḥasan Bahmanī, 1027
Ḥasan Čelebī b. Muḥammad shāh Fanārī, 1466
Ḥasan Gāngū, 1026
Ḥasan b. Ghazāl, a. (XIII-1), v. 2, *666*, 523
Ḥasan b. Ḥasan (or Ḥusain), *see* b. Haitham
Ḥasan Ḥusnī 'Abdalwahhāb, 804
Ḥasan of Jerusalem, a., 367
Ḥasan b. Khalīl Karādisī, 1533
Ḥasan b. Khaṣīb, *see* a. Bakr
Ḥasan b. Muḥammad b. Bāṣa (XIV-1), *696*, 132
Ḥasan b. Muḥammad Rāmī (XIV-2), *1728*, 1217, 1232, 1328
Ḥasan b. Muḥammad Ṣaghānī, 1827
Ḥasan b. Muḥammad Wazzān, 1158
Ḥasan b. Mulā'ib al-Fawāris, a., 1786
Ḥasan b. Mūsā, *see* Mūsā, Banū
Ḥasan b. Nūḥ Qumrī (X-2), v. 1, *678*, 651, 654
Ḥasan Rammāḥ (XIII-2), v. 2, *1039*, 1180

Ḥasan Ṣīrāfī, *see* a. Zaid
Ḥasan b. 'Umar b. Ḥabīb Dimashqī (XIV-2), *1783*, 794, 1264
Ḥasan b. Yūsuf Muṭahhar Ḥillī (XIV-1), *626*, 105
Ḥasdai b. Abraham Crescas (XIV-2), *1446*, 605, 1061, 1062, 1096, 1261, 1364, 1377, 1384, 1521, 1522, 1841
Ḥasdai, b., *see* Abraham b. Samuel
Ḥasdai b. Shapruṭ (X-2), v. 1, *680*, 806; v. 2, 1180
Ḥasdai, b., *see* Yūsuf b. Aḥmad
Hase, C. B., 1824
Haselden, R. B., 1415
Hāshimī, *see* Ḥasan b. 'Abdallāh
ḥashīsh, 175, 1620
Ḥashīshīyūn, *see* Assassins
Ḥasid, *see* Judah b. Samuel
Haskell, D. C., 1304
Haskins, C. H., 165
Haslewood, Joseph, 835, 1165
Hasluck, F. W., 1044, 1247, 1461, 1841
Hasluck, M. M., 1044
Hasner, Jos. Ritter v., 1713
Ḥaṣṣār, *see* Muḥammad b. 'Abdallāh
Hastings, James, 1883, 1888
Hastiri, *see* John
Haswell, J. E., 722
Hatherly, S. G., 162
Hattala, Martin, 1354
Ḥaufī, *see* Aḥmad b. Muḥammad
Haugen, Einar, 1609
Haukr Erlendsson (XIV-1), *678*, 66, 94, 119, 303, 352, 1609, 1610
Haupt, Iosef, 1153
Hauptmann, F., 1794
Hauréau, Barthélemy, 228, 392, 406, 407, 412, 458, 459, 535, 547, 706, 854, 991, 1888
Hausherr, Irénée, 96
Hauvette, Henri, 586, 1378, 1810
Havelberg, *see* Anselm
ḥāwī, 288
ḥāwī fī 'ilm al-tadāwī, 898
ḥāwī al-ṣaghīr, 898
Hawkwood, *see* John
Ḥawqal, b., *see* Muḥammad
Hayakawa, S. I., 253, 331
Hayam Wuruk, 1624
ḥayāt al-ḥayawān, 1168, 1639
Haydon, F. S., 1542
Haye, Jean de la, 399
Haymo of Rochester, 1653
Hayton I of Armenia (XIII-2), v. 2, *1063*, 1180; v. 3, 827, 953
Hayton II of Armenia, 827, 953
Hayton the Monk (XIV-1), *953*, 46, 54, 189, 301, 304, 346, 356, 415, 731, 1603
Ḥayyim b. Abraham b. Galipapa, 1652
Ḥayyim b. Joseph Vital, 616
Ḥayyim b. Judah b. Mūsā, 398
Ḥayyim, *see* Levi b. Abraham
Ḥayyuj, Judah b. David (X-2), v. 1, *691*, 653, 655; v. 2, 1191; v. 3, 366, 1008, 1522
hazard, 1814
Ḥazm, b. (XI-1), v. 1, *713*, 809; v. 2, 1180; v. 3, 1012
Haẓẓalat ha-nefesh, 435
ḥazzan, 367
health, *see* public
Hearn, Lafcadio, 1188, 1189
Hearne, Thomas, 462, 942, 1741, 1742, 1745
heart, 843
Heath, Sir T. L., 1888
Heather, P. J., 214
Heawood, Edward, 766
Hebraeomastix, 399
Hebrew, 363, 561
Hebrew, *see* accounts
Hebrew alphabet, x
Hebrew books, 1904
Hebrew grammar, 590, 1522
Hebrew history (VII B.C.), v. 1, *63*; (VI B.C.), v. 1, *79*
Hebrew history and law (V B.C.), v. 1, *107*
Hebrew, *see* Jewish
Hebrew law (VII B.C.), v. 1, *62*
Hebrew-Persian dictionary, 1008
Hebrew philosophy (V B.C.), v. 1, *90*
Hebrew, *see* plant names
Hebrew printed books, 1880
Hebrew roots, 590
Hebrew Scriptures (X-1), v. 1, *624*, 619
Hebron, 1160
Hecataeos of Miletos (VI B.C.), v. 1, *78*, 66
Heck, N. H., 1834
Hecker, J. F. K., 891, 1663, 1667
Hecker, Oskar, 1810
Hedfors, Hjalmar, 168
Hedin, Sven, 1142, 1704, 1868
Hedley, Geoffrey, 758
Heeg, Joseph, 1512, 1513, 1877
Heelu, *see* John
Heerklotz, J. G. A., 1195
Hefele, Hermann, 514
Heffening, W., 1883, 1888
Hefner-Alteneck, J. H. v., 726, 1555
Hegel, C., 1756, 1757
Hegel, Karl v., 913, 1580
Hegetor (II-2 B.C.), v. 1, *198*, 192
Heiberg, J. L., 120, 953, 1512, 1876, 1888
Heidegger, Martin, 571
Heidelberg, University, 1079, 1400
Heiden, *see* John
Heidingsfelder, Georg, 564, 1432
Heiliggeistspitäler, 295
Heilpern, Phinehas, 1523
Heimbach, K. W. E., 996
Heimpel, Hermann, 1820
Heine, Dietrich, 1349
Heine, H., 101, 615

Heinrich, *see also* Henry
Heinrich, Fritz, 1203
Heinrichau, *see* Conrad
Heiser, V. G., 909
Heitz, Paul, 1124, 1661
Helena, St., 952, 1043
Helena Cantacuzena, 1823
Heliand, 350
Helias or Hélie, *see* Peter
Hélie de Talleyrand-Périgord, 788
Hélin, Maurice, 1104
heliocentrical hypothesis, *see* geoheliocentrical
Heliodoros the Alchemist (VIII-1), v. 1, *514*, 505
Heliodoros, son of Hermias (VI-1), v. 1, *429*, 416
Heliodoros the Surgeon (II-1), v. 1, *281*, 268
Hell, Father, 17
hell-fire sermons, 405
Heller, Josef, 56, 419, 1377, 1380, 1383, 1450, 1521, 1717
Heller, Nikolaus, 574
Hellman, C. D., 710, 821
Hellmann, Gustav, 706, 710, 711, 715, 820, 1124
Hello, Ernest, 94, 582
Helluland, 1608
Helm, Erhart, 1581
Helm, Rudolf, 1232
Helmold of Holstein (XII-2), v. 2, *455*, 314
Helmont, J. B. van, 1220
Ḥelo, *see* Isaac b. Joseph
Helperic (X-2), v. 1, *671*, 807
Hélyot, Pierre, 864
Hemacandra (XII-2), v. 2, *473*, 1181; v. 3, 382, 1330
Hemādri (XIII-2), v. 2, *1133*, 1181; v. 3, 259, 322, 382
Hemerken, *see* Thomas
Hemingburgh, *see* Walter
Hemricourt, *see* Giles; James
hemshelim, 450
Ḥen, *see* Shealtiel
Hendel, M. b. S., 417
Henkin, L. J., 1426
Henley, *see* Walter
henna, 999
Hennig, Richard, 1888
Henri, Henricus, Henrik, *see* Henry
Henry of Admont, 930
Henry Aeger, 1357
Henry Ahuys of Münster, 1361
Henry Arler v. Gmünd, 1655
Henry, Aurelia, 494
Henry v. Baldenstetten, 1234
Henry Bate of Malines (XIII-2), v. 2, *994*, 1181; v. 3, 68, 94, 118, 119, 442, 453, 1489
Henry v. Berg, 573
Henry of Bolingbroke, *see* Henry IV of England
Henry Bracton (XIII-2), v. 2, *1130*, 687, 801; v. 3, 319, 348
Henry of Bremis, 1710
Henry VI of Breslau, 1708
Henry of Bruxelles, 118
Henry of Calcar, 1081, 1357
Henry of Carinthia, 933, 940
Henry III of Castile, 1142, 1467, 1697
Henry, Charles, 1849
Henry II of Cyprus, 452
Henry of Derby, 1150
Henry VII, emperor, 494
Henry II of England, 1838
Henry IV of England, 1150, 1347, 1467, 1855
Henry VIII of England, 394, 475
Henry Estienne, 1513
Henry, F. P., 1200
Henry de Ferrières, 1183
Henry Freidank, 251
Henry v. Friemar, 1509
Henry III of Gelder, 1280
Henry Geuschmied, 1579
Henry of Ghent (XIII-2), v. 2, *946*, 739, 925; v. 3, 398, 521
Henry v. Glatz, 777, 779
Henry Grammateus, 1580
Henry Harpestraeng (XIII-1), v. 2, *659*, 1181; v. 3, 352, 579, 1208, 1860
Henry of Hessen, jr., 1092, 1278, 1503
Henry of Hessen, sr., 1092, 1278, 1502
Henry of Huntingdon (XII-2), v. 2, *456*, 314, 455; v. 3, 942
Henry Knighton (XIV-2), *1742*, 1123, 1203, 1255, 1655
Henry Kraemer, 1049, 1338
Henry Lamme, 1243
Henry of Lancaster, 1150, 1855
Henry v. Langenstein (XIV-2), *1502*, 1055, 1091, 1112, 1127, 1137, 1166, 1170, 1206, 1230, 1276, 1278, 1325, 1351, 1398, 1432, 1433, 1496
Henry of Latvia (XIII-1), v. 2, *679*, 526
Henry the Lion, 727
Henry of Lubelck, 888
Henry Martellus, 1146
Henry of Mayence (XII-1), v. 2, *222*, 1181
Henry the Minstrel, 1741
Henry, *see* Mondeville
Henry the Navigator, 183, 785, 1022, 1140, 1141, 1151, 1159, 1593
Henry of Oyta (XIV-2), *1432*, 557, 1091, 1503
Henry v. Pfolspeundt, 1234
Henry Ribbenicz (XIV-2), *1710*, 1205, 1707
Henry of Saxony, 888
Henry Schreiber, 1580
Henry Steinhöwel, 1805, 1891
Henry Stromer, 1579
Henry, *see* Suso
Henry, T. H., 50

Henry Thopping (XIV-2), *1706*, 1205, 1236, 1238
Henry Totting, 542, 1399, 1432
Henry Trastamara, 1021, 1022
Henry Van den Bogarde, 581
Henry de Vick, 1542
Henry Vrigedanch, 251
Henry v. Wiek, 1546
Henry der Wundarzt, 252
Henschel, A. W. E. Th., 817, 839, 841, 877, 1005, 1674, 1684, 1685, 1695, 1708
Henschel, G. A. L., 1888
Henschel, G. E. T., 1888, 1901
Henschen, Godfrey, 1345
Henschenius, 1754
Henslow, George, 348, 1203
Hephaestion of Alexandria (II-1), v. 1, *287*, 269
Hephaestion of Thebes (IV-2), v. 1, *368*, 360
Heptameron, 443, 445
Her, *see* Mekhitar
Heraclides of Pontos (IV-2 B.C.), v. 1, *141*, 125, 272; v. 2, 1181
Heraclides of Tarentum (I-1 B.C.), v. 1, *215*, 203, 215–16
Heraclitos of Ephesos (V B.C.), v. 1, *85*, 81
Heraclius (X-2), v. 1, *673*, 649; v. 2, 769; v. 3, 168, 170, 1131
heraldry, 1165, 1312
Herāt, 1473
herbal, printed, 222
herbals, 1176, 1834, 1904
herbarium, 1177
Herbarius, 1881
Herben, S. J., jr., 1426
Herbermann, C. G., 1878, 1888
Herbert, J. A., 1634
herborizations, 1169
Herbst, Adolf, 1386
herbularius, 224
Heredia, *see* John Fernández; Paul
heredity, 18
Hereford, *see* Nicholas; Roger
heresies, 50, 275, 394, 401
Herff, F. v., 837
Hériger of Lobbes (X-2), v. 1, *685*, 807
Herman de Allemania, 218, 1174
Herman the Dalmatian (XII-1), v. 2, *173*, 1181
Herman the German (XIII-2), v. 2, *832*, 1181; v. 3, 369, 1077
Herman Kerstken, 1408
Herman the Lame (XI-2), v. 1, *757*, 807; v. 2, 121, 173; v. 3, 933
Herman of Nieder-Altaich (XIII-2), v. 2, *1110*, 794; v. 3, 301
Herman de Przeworsko (XIV-2), *1510*, 1114
Herman Schedel, 1197
Herman Warendorp, 125
Herman Wittenborg, 125
Hermannsson, Halldór, 1610
hermaphrodites, 1169, 1454
Hermes, 166, 453, 501, 751, 753, 754, 828, 1519, 1573, 1576, 1578, 1620, 1640
Hermetica, 1460, 1877
Hermodoros of Salamis (II-2 B.C.), v. 1, *196*, 191
Hermogenes of Tarsos, 947
Hermogenianus (IV-1), v. 1, *357*, 807
Hermonymos, *see* George
hernia, 844, 881, 1622, 1692
Hero of Byzantium (X-1), v. 1, *632*, 621, 623
Herodianos, Aelios, grammarian (II-2), v. 1, *312*, 286, 290
Herodianos, historian (III-1), v. 1, *326*, 316; v. 3, 120, 1818
Herodicos of Selymbria (V B.C.), v. 1, *96*, 83
Herodotos of Halicarnassos (V B.C.), v. 1, *105*, 83, 535; v. 2, 395, 450; v. 3, 214, 219, 1158, 1321, 1849, 1863
Herodotos of Rome (I-2), v. 1, *262*, 244; v. 3, 904
Herolt, *see* John
Heron of Alexandria (I-1 B.C.), v. 1, *208*, 807; v. 2, 1181; v. 3, ix, 122, 586, 1115, 1511
Héronchel, 1861
Herophilos of Chalcedon (III-1 B.C.), v. 1, *159*, 149, 150; v. 2, 1181; v. 3, 268, 842
Herr, Michael, 955
Herrad of Landsberg (XII-2), v. 2, *389*, 293
Herrera, Gabriel Alonso de, 814
Herrick, J. B., 1425
herring, 151, 237, 1654
herring preservation, 821
Herringham, Christiana J., 1132
Herron, Francis, 1089
Herrtage, S. J. H., 456
Herschel, 1166
Hersfeld, *see* Lambert
Hershman, A. M., 1062
Hertrich, Henry, 1496
Hervé Nédélec (XIV-1), *521*, 51, 89, 178, 525, 527, 529, 987, 989, 991
Hervey de Stanton, 475
Hervieux, Léopold, 464
Herzog, Emil, 996
Hesdin, *see* Simon
Hese, *see* John Witte
Heseltine, G. C., 567
Heseltine, J. E., 1425
Ḥeshbon ha-mahlakot, 590
Hesiod (VIII B.C.), v. 1, *57*, 807; v. 3, 997, 1005
Hess, Wilhelm, 1124
Hessen, *see* Henry
Hessians, 1023
Hesychasm, Hesychasts, 53, 95, 584, 950, 995, 1058, 1094, 1363, 1386, 1511, 1760, 1845

Hesychios of Alexandria (V-1), v. 1, *398*, 379
Hesychios of Miletus (VI-1), v. 1, *436*, 417, 418
Hetum, 953
Hetum II, 827
Heuckenkamp, Ferdinand, 1277
Heusden, *see* John
Heuser, A., 1356
Hexabiblos, 53, 995
Hexapla, 358
Hexateuch (V B.C.), v. 1, *107*, 83
Heyd, Wilhelm v., 1888
Heylen, P. J., 821, 823
Heylwig van der Basselen, 1357
Heyne, Johann, 1005, 1708
Heyrons of London, 1425
Heytesbury, *see* William
Heyton, *see* Roger
Hezekiah (VIII B.C.), v. 1, *59*, 53
Hezekiah b. Ḥalafta (XIV-1), *450*, 65, 100
Hezekiah ha-Miliabi (XIV-1), *892*, 65, 254, 255
Hibatallāh b. 'Alī b. Malkā (XII-2), v. 2, *382*, 1181; v. 3, 146, 545
Hibatallāh b. Ḥusain Badī' (XII-1), v. 2, *204*, 13, 123
Hibatallāh b. Sa'īd b. Tilmīdh (XII-1), v. 2, *234*, 1239; v. 3, 1727
Hibatallāh b. Zain b. Jamī' (XII-2), v. 2, *432*, 1188; v. 3, 1726
Hicetas of Syracuse (V B.C.), v. 1, *94*, 82
Hidāyat Ḥusain, M., 759, 1766
hides, 323
Hierocles (IV-2), v. 1, *372*, 807; v. 2, 89, 829
hieroglyphics, 359, 360
Hieronymites, 1037
Hieronymo, Hieronymus, *see* Jerome
Hieropais, Nicolaos, 826
Hierophilos the Sophist (XII-1), v. 2, *236*, 88, 134
Hierozoicon, 1640
higayon, 449, 452
Higden, *see* Ranulf
Ḥijjah, b., *see* a. Bakr b. 'Alī
ḥikmat al-ishrāq, 106
Hilāl Ḥimṣī (IX-2), v. 1, *598*, 585, 664; v. 2, 401
Hilāl b. Muḥsin Ṣābī, 967
Hildebert of Lavardin, 228
Hildebrand, *see* Aldobrandin; Dino
Hildegard of Bingen (XII-2), v. 2, *386*, 1182; v. 3, 278, 1505, 1508
Hilgenberg, Luise, 259, 280
Hill, G. F., 127
Hill, John, 1230
Hill, Nathaniel, 533
Hillebrand, Karl, 913
Hillel II (IV-2), v. 1, *368*, 318, 360
Hillel b. Samuel of Verona (XIII-2), v. 2, *886*, 1182; v. 3, 450, 615, 1443
Ḥillī, *see* Ja'far b. Muḥammad
Hilliard, Katherine, 493
Hillyer, Robert, 710
Hilton, *see* Walter
ḥilyat al-insān, 1013
Hime, H. W. L., 724, 1888
Himilco (V B.C.), v. 1, *104*, 83, 371
Ḥimṣī, *see* Hilāl
Hīnayāna, 59, 262, 293, 466
Hinckaert, *see* John
Hindī, 377, 1330, 1476, 1477
Hindī, *see* 'Umar b. Isḥāq
Hindu, *see* chemistry; law; medicine, India
Hindu-Arabic, *see* numerals
Hindushāh b. Sanjar Kīrānī, 967
Hindūstānī, 377, 1477
Hingene, *see* John
Hingham, *see* Ralph
Hinojosa, *see* Gonzalo
Hipparchos of Nicaea (II-2 B.C.), v. 1, *193*, 808; v. 2, 1182; v. 3, 544, 600
Hippias of Elis (V B.C.), v. 1, *92*, 82
hippiatry, 1635
Hippocrates of Chios (V B.C.), v. 1, *91*, 82
Hippocrates of Cos (V B.C.), v. 1, *96*, 808; v. 2, 1182; v. 3, 62, 243, 248, 257, 264, 288, 426, 437, 445, 447, 501, 792, 800, 801, 816, 828, 836, 837, 841, 844, 846, 847, 849, 853, 860, 863, 870, 871, 877, 881, 883, 884, 885, 897, 990, 1075, 1193, 1194, 1195, 1201, 1205, 1209, 1211, 1220, 1229, 1235, 1240, 1243, 1321, 1380, 1384, 1389, 1422, 1451, 1452, 1597, 1603, 1640, 1677, 1681, 1698, 1707, 1710, 1712, 1714, 1716, 1719, 1723
Hippocratic, 64, 285, 1664
Hippocratic treatises (IV-1 B.C.), v. 1, *119*, 112
Hippodamos of Miletos (V B.C.), v. 1, *95*, 82
hippology, 239, 1185
Hippolytos, St. (III-1), v. 1, *320*, 314, 316
Hippon (V B.C.), v. 1, *86*, 81
hippopotamus, 237, 1186, 1642
Hireçon, *see* Thierry
ḥirfa, 154
Hirn, Yrjö, 1888
Hirsau, *see* William
Hirsch, August, 1874, 1888
Hirsch, E. G., 1448
Hirsch, E. b. Z., 432
Hirsch, Theodor, 932
Hirschberg, Julius, 274, 892, 901, 1724
Hirschberg, *see* Pancratius Sommer
Hirsche, Karl, 1361
Hirschfeld, Hartwig, 611
Hirschfeld, Joseph, 594
Hirth, Friedrich, 980, 1625, 1791
ḥisāb al-'uqūd, 1533
ḥisba, 154, 321, 998, 1271, 1771, 1852. *See also* muḥtasib
Hishām, b., *see* 'Abdallāh b. Yūsuf; 'Abd al-Malik

Hishām b. Muḥammad (VIII-2), v. 1, *541*, 523, 524; v. 2, 140
Ḥishbon 'ibbur ḥodshe, 420
Histoire littéraire, 1888
Historia Hierosolymitana, 769
Historia scholastica, 79
historical geography, 188
historiography, Chinese, v. 1, 163; v. 3, 1884
Hitchcock, C. B., 191
Hitti, P. K., 28, 360, 491, 1216, 1725, 1888
Hittite, 364, 1103
Hiver de Beauvoir, 1202
ḥizb, 154
Hjaltelín, J. J., 280
Hjörter, O. P., 710
Hoang, Pierre, 217, 1889
Hobson, R. L., 758
Hobson-Jobson, 1889
Hoccleve, *see* Thomas
Hoche, Richard, 1512
Hochstetter, Erich, 556
Hocsem, *see* John
Hodgkin, Thomas, 1240
Hodoeporicon, 787
Hodous, Lewis, 382, 468, 1889
Hoefer, Ferdinand, 1889, 1898
Höffler, Constantin v., 1259, 1352
Höeg, C., 162
Hoeniger, Robert, 1663, 1695
Hoepffner, Ernest, 745, 1412
Hoernle, A. F. R., 1889
Höttges, Valerie, 1228
Hoffmann, Gerda, 269
Hoffmann v. Fallersleben, A. H., 347
Hoffmann-Krayer, E., 1887, 1889
Hofmeister, Adolf, 935
Hog, Thomas, 943, 945
Hohlfeld, Gerhard, 1239
ḥokmat ha-tishboret, 597
Holand, H. R., 1611, 1612, 1613
Holbein, Hans, 1231
Holbrook, R. T., 488, 498, 500
Holcot, *see* Robert; Thomas
holidays, 1043
Holl, Karl, 1094
Hollaenderski, L., 1450
Holland, T. E., 1798
Hollmann, H. T., 909
Holmyard, E. J., 760
Holobolos, *see* John; Manuel
Holstein, *see* Helmold
Holter, Kurt, 1178
Holtsmark, Anne, 352
Holweck, F. G., 253
Holy Ghost hospital, 294
Holy Ghost, order, 1831
Holy Ghost, procession, 585, 1388
Holy Land, *see* Palestine
Holy Mountain, *see* Athos
Holzapfel, Heribert, 525
Holzschuher, 125
Homburg, *see* Gerlach
Homer (IX B.C.), v. 1, *53*, 808; v. 2, 395, 939; v. 3, 352, 507, 751, 952, 1073, 1299, 1321, 1377, 1395, 1413, 1513, 1807, 1814, 1815, •1817
Homeyer, C. G., 994
Hommel, R. P., 158
homocentric spheres, 484
homosexuality, 960
Honestis, *see* Christophorus
"honi soit qui," 1403
Honigmann, E., 793, 1889
Honorius of Autun (XII-1), v. 2, *200*, 1183; v. 3, 340, 996
Honorius Inclusus (XI-2), v. 1, *749*, 739, 745; v. 2, 1183; v. 3, 548
Honorius Philadelphus, 1576
Honorius IV, pope, 374
Hoogenhout, N. M., 939
Hooke, Robert, 601, 1886
hoopoe, 626, 1636
Hoops, Johannes, 1889, 1901
Hoormaert, H., 49
Hoover, H. C., 1137, 1174, 1555
Hoover, L. H., 1555
Hope, W. H. St. John, 1556
Hopf, Karl, 771, 949
Hopfner, Theodor, 997, 1005, 1103, 1889, 1899
Hôpital, *see* Mary
Hopkin, C. E., 1052
Hopkins, A. J., 754
Hopkins, E. W., 1395
Hoppe, Edmund, 566
Hoppe, Karl, 1837
Hopper, V. F., 1117, 1461
Horace, 512, 933, 1144, 1294, 1706
Horapollon of Nilopolis (IV-1), v. 1, *358*, 346; v. 3, 361, 825, 1006
Hormayr, Joseph v., 790
Hormes, *see* Denis
hormones, 269
Horn, Gabriel, 96
Hornby, St. John, 492
Horneck, *see* Ottokar
Hornell, James, 380, 1848
Hornstein, Xavier de, 1889
Horodetzky, S. A., 417, 452, 1365
Horologgi, Joseppe, 955
horologium, 717
Horovitz, J., 490
Horowitz, I. Z., 793
Horrell, Joe, 1426
horror vacui, 150
horse collar, 157
horses, 209, 1167. *See also* cavalry tactics; hippiatry; hippology
horses, breeding of, 827
horseshoe, 157, 1669
Horstman, Carl, 567, 1741

Hort, Greta, 1415
Hortis, Attilio, 514, 586, 1378, 1811
Hortolanus, 1575
hortus, 224
Hortus sanitatis, 1228
Horwitz, H. T., 1552
Hosea (VIII B.C.), v. 1, *58*, 53; v. 2, 470
Hoshaya, R., x
Hoshino, Sanenori, 702
Hosie, Alexander, 1122
Hospice des enfants bleus, 295
hospital, *see* hôtel-Dieu
Hospitalers, 294, 393, 864. *See also* John of Jerusalem
hospitals (XII-1), v. 2, *245*, 1183; (XIV), v. 3, 280, 293, 972, 1247, 1878
Hosstka, *see* Sulko
Host, desecration, 1364, 1384, 1446
host tragedy, 1059
Ḥotam toknit, 366
hôtel-Dieu, 293, 295, 1831
Houdas, Octave, 1453
hounds, 1835
hours, Chinese, 1547
hours, equal, 1125
hours, Japanese, 1547
Houtsma, M. T., 622, 1014, 1883, 1889
Houzeau, J. C., 1152
Howard, G. E., 290
Howden, *see* Roger
Howel Dda, 1864
Howell, A. G. F., 492, 493
Howell, James, 1451
Howgrave-Graham, R. P., 720, 1545, 1889
Howland, A. C., 1051, 1889, 1893
Howorth, H. H., 138
Hrabanus Maurus (IX-1), v. 1, *555*, 808; v. 2, 222, 927; v. 3, 350, 369, 1229, 1319, 1808
Hrosvitha of Gandersheim (X-2), v. 1, *658*, 808
Hsü, *see* Paul
Hsü Tao-ling, 1855
Huart, Clément, 155, 175, 757, 968, 977, 1014, 1460, 1461, 1728
Ḥubaish b. Ḥasan (IX-2), v. 1, *613*, 587, 612; v. 2, 896
Hubal, b., *see* 'Alī b. Aḥmad
Huber, A., 742
Hubert, *see* Uberti; Ubertino; Uberto
Huc, E. R., 1372
Hucbald of Saint Amand, 746
Hude, *see* Nicholas
Hudhail, b., *see* 'Alī b. 'Abd al-Raḥmān
Hudleston, Roger, 1090
Hudson Bay, 1834
Huebner, F. M., 582
Hübotter, F., 1874, 1889
Huelsen, Christian, 1291, 1551
Huerter, *see* Job
Huesca in Aragón, University, 1397
Huete, *see* John de Cuenca
Hufeland, C. W., 1732
Huffnagl, J. G. T., 577
Hufnagel, Alfons, 993
Hugh, *see also* Ugone
Hugh of Angoulême, 943
Hugh Benzi, 1194, 1195, 1220, 1222, 1238, 1300, 1684, 1799
Hugh Borgognoni (XIII-1), v. 2, *654*, 1183; v. 3, 871, 1244
Hugh of Città di Castello, 112, 243
Hugh of Cyprus, *see* Hugh of Lusignan
Hugh Dutton, 473
Hugh Falcandus (XII-2), v. 2, *452*, 1183
Hugh Géraud of Cahors, 23, 406
Hugh Illuminator, *see* Hugh the Limner
Hugh of Ireland, 1501
Hugh of Leven, 1256
Hugh the Limner 191, 787
Hugh of Lucca, 883
Hugh II of Lusignan, 314
Hugh IV of Lusignan, 952, 1805
Hugh of Newcastle (XIV-1), *406*, 51, 91
Hugh of Reutlingen, 741
Hugh Ripelin of Strassburg, 1442
Hugh of Saint Cher (XIII-1), v. 2, *554*, 1183; v. 3, 457, 1063
Hugh of Saint Victor (XII-1), v. 2, *193*, 1183; v. 3, 150, 398, 530, 990, 1416
Hugh of Santalla (XII-1), v. 2, *174*, 1183; v. 3, 166
Hugh da Siena, 1195, 1685
Hugh Spechtshart (XIV-1), *741*, 160, 302, 331
Hugh of Sutton, 473
Hugh Teralh, 125
Hugh van der Goes, 1359
Hughes, T. P., 1890
Hugo, *see* Hugh
Hugolinus of Bologna (XIII-1), v. 2, *689*, 528
Hugonin, abbé, 1416
Hugues, *see* Hugh
Hugutio of Pisa (XII-2), v. 2, *472*, 1184; v. 3, 1004
Huizinga, J. 11
Hūlāgū, 40, 380, 970, 1101, 1467, 1469
Hulbert, H. B., 1085
Hulme, W. H., 567
Hult, O. T., 1689
Hultman, J. E. E., 533
Hultsch, Friedrich, 713, 1848
Humām, b., *see* Muḥammad b. Muḥammad
humanism, 87, 88, 1883
humanity of science, 19, 20
Humbert II, dauphin du Viennois, 184, 1053, 1344
Hume, 84, 546
Humiliati (XII-2), v. 2, *331*, 280
Hummel, A. W., 28, 204, 222, 223, 233, 310, 469, 713, 755, 832, 904, 909, 1268, 1269, 1479, 1626, 1627, 1649, 1790, 1851, 1862, 1890
humors, 843, 849, 869, 1421

Humphrey of Bohun, 1313
Humphrey of Gloucester, 1805, 1823
Humphreys, H. N., 1753
Ḥunain b. Isḥāq (IX-2), v. 1, *611*, 809; v. 2, 1184; v. 3, 248, 254, 264, 273, 358, 430, 431, 433, 436, 590, 855, 856, 857, 877, 885, 1303, 1639, 1838
Hundred Years' War, 39, 1020
Hungarian, 1825
Hungary, *see* Gregory; Mary; Sigismund; Stephen
Hungary, master of, 1024
hunger and history, 1859
Hunt, A. S., 122, 152, 353
Hunt, Charles, 1890, 1907
Hunt, Edmund, 1817
Hunt, William, 945, 1744
Hunter, Dard, 177, 1580
hunting, viii, 1183, 1186. *See also* beasts of venery
Huntingdon, *see* Henry
Huntington, George, 1667
Ḥurr Riyāḥī, 630
Hurry, J. B., 1247
Hurtado y Jiménez de la Serna, Juan, 1890
ḥurūf al-jumal, 798
Ḥurūfī, *see* Faḍlallāh b. a. Muḥammad
Hus, John, 1048, 1056, 1089, 1093, 1114, 1322, 1348, 1352, 1353, 1400, 1433
Ḥusain, A. M., 1623
Ḥusain b. 'Abdallāh, *see* b. Sīnā
Ḥusain b. 'Abd al-Raḥmān Ahdal, 958, 1264
Ḥusain b. Aḥmad b. Raḥat, 1249
Ḥusain b. 'Alī Ṭughrā'ī (XII-1), v. 2, *218*, 31, 129; v. 3, 759, 1138
Ḥusain b. Ibrāhīm (X-2), v. 1, *678*, 650, 654; v. 2, 79
Ḥusain Jamāl al-dīn of Iṣfahān, 1728
Ḥusain b. Manṣūr b. Bayqarā, 1473
Ḥusain b. Mas'ūd Farrā', 1067
Ḥusain, b., *see* Muḥammad
Ḥusain Qulī Khān, 305, 1120
Ḥusain b. 'Umar, 1587
Ḥusainī, *see* 'Alī b. Shihāb al-dīn
Ḥusām al-daula Taimūr Mīrzā, 233
husbandry, *see* agriculture
Huser, Johannes, 1227
Husik, Isaac, 1890
Hussein, T., 1778
Husung, M. J., 561
Huttich, Johann, 955
Hutton, Edward, 1810
Huxley, Aldous, 1708
Huy, *see* Regnier
Huydecopers, Balthazar, 938
Huyttens, Jules, 153
Hyamson, A. M., 1071
Hyde, T. A., 582
Hyde, Thomas, 1450, 1458
Hyderabad, 1477
hydrometer, *see* areometer
hydrophobia, 1671
hydrostatics, 735, 1126, 1566
Hyères, *see* Cybo
Hyginus, agrimensor (II-1), v. 1, *271*, 809
Hyginus, C. Julius (I-2 B.C.), v. 1, *226*, 219, 220
Hyma, Albert, 545, 1361, 1363, 1890
Hypatia (V-1), v. 1, *386*, 378, 380; v. 3, 1439
hyperboloidal lenses, 707
hypopyon, 1724
Hypsicles (II-1 B.C.), v. 1, *181*, 809; v. 2, 1184; v. 3, 128, 430, 434
Hystaspes, 376
hysteria, 1666

i, *see also* j
Iacopo, *see* James
Iamblichos (IV-1), v. 1, *351*, 809; v. 3, 134, 737
iatrochemistry, 1218, 1220
iatromathematics, 1114, 1208, 1219
Ibach, Helmut, 821
Ibāḍ, b., *see* 'Abdallāh
'ibar, Kitāb, 1768
Ibdā' al-malāḥa, 827
Iberian, 356
ibn, *see next word*
Ibrāhīm b. 'Abbād, 1452
Ibrāhīm b. 'Abdallāh b. a. Dam (XIII-1), v. 2, *683*, 527
Ibrāhīm b. 'Abd al-Raḥīm b. Jamā'a, 998
Ibrāhīm b. 'Abd al-Raḥmān Azraqī, 966
Ibrāhīm b. 'Abd al-Raḥmān b. Firkāḥ (XIV-1), *804*, 163, 201
Ibrāhīm b. Faraj, a. Isḥāq (XII-2), v. 2, *471*, 1187
Ibrāhīm b. Ḥabīb Fazārī (VIII-2), v. 1, *530*, 521, 524
Ibrāhīm Ḥāsib (XIV-2), *1529*, 1119
Ibrāhīm, a. Isḥāq, 366
Ibrāhīm b. Maḥmūd 'Aṭṭār, 959
Ibrāhīm b. Muḥammad b. Duqmāq (XIV-2), *1784*, 1099, 1103, 1264, 1271
Ibrāhīm b. Muḥammad, *see* Istakhrī
Ibrāhīm b. Muḥammad b. Ṭarkhān (XIII-1), v. 2, *661*, 1237
Ibrāhīm b. Rashīd al-dīn, 969
Ibrāhīm b. Ṣāliḥ, 372
Ibrāhīm b. Sinān (X-1), v. 1, *631*, 620, 624
Ibrāhīm Ṭabāṭabā, 967
Ibrāhīm b. Waṣīf Shāh, 805
Ibrāhīm b. Yaḥyā, *see* Zarqālī
Ibrāhīm b. Ya'qūb (X-2), v. 1, *675*, 650, 654
ibrīz, 754
Iceland, 194, 216, 1154
Iceland, discovery of (IX-2), v. 1, *605*, 586
Icelandic, 32, 351
Icelandic discovery, *see* America
Icelandic republic, 194, 1319

iconography, anatomical and medical, 269, 1230
iconography, animals and plants, 1638
iconography, Arabic manuscripts (XIII-2), v. 2, *1073*
iconography, *see* botanic
iconography, Christian, 1138
iconography, plant and animal, 1177, 1638
ideas, theory of, 81
Ideler, J. L., 891
'Idhārī, b., Marrākushī (XIII-2), v. 2, *1118*, 630, 796, 957
idrāk lilisān al-Atrāk, 1013
Idrīs, 1620
Idrīsī, 229
Idrīsī, Muḥammad b. Muḥammad (XII-2), v. 2, *410*, 1184; v. 3, 801, 803, 1133, 1158, 1772
Ifhām ṭā'ifat al-Yahūd, 418
Ighāthat al-umma, 282
Ignatios the Greek, 728
Ignatius of Loyola, St., 477, 1036, 1057, 1297, 1360, 1362, 1509, 1862
Ignatius of Smolensk (XIV-2), *1613*, 1156, 1322
ignis sacer, 1668
iḥāṭa, 1762
iḥṣā' al-'ulūm, 431
iḥtifāl fī istīfā', 830
Iijima, Ikuzō, 1415
ijāza, 1009
ijāza 'āmma, 1620
Ījī, *see* 'Abd al-Raḥmān b. Aḥmad; 'Aḍud al-dīn
ijmā', 421
ikhtilāj, 960
ikhtiṣāṣ wa-durrat, 759
ikhwān, 421
Ikhwān al-ṣafā', *see* Brethren of Purity
iksīr, 755
Īlāqī, *see* Muḥammad b. 'Alī; Muḥammad b. Yūsuf
Ildukuz Ayyūbī, 965
Ilg, Albert, 1132
'illot, 431, 450
'ilm jābir, 1138
'ilm al-miftāḥ, 759
'ilm al-mīzān, 759
'ilm al-muktasab, 759
'ilmain, 616
Ilyās, *see* Manṣūr b. Muḥammad
'Imād al-dīn Faqīh of Kirmān, 1473
'Imād al-dīn Iṣfahānī, *see* Muḥammad b. Muḥammad
imām, 997
Imām al-dīn Nasīmī, 1460
Imbriani, Vittorio, 502
Imitatio Christi, 85, 1083, 1088, 1092, 1297, 1317, 1359, 1415, 1507
Immaculate Conception, 48, 528, 1405
Immanuel, *see also* Emmanuel
Immanuel b. Jacob Bonfils (XIV-2), *1517*, 1116, 1117, 1261, 1383, 1515, 1718, 1719
Immanuel b. Solomon of Rome (XIV-1), *615*, 101, 335, 368, 429, 449, 491, 1845
immortality, 84, 96, 99, 604, 1443
Imola, *see* Anziani; Benvenuto
impanation, 992
impetigo, 1664
impetus, 146, 542, 543, 545, 738, 1430, 1488
imping, 1735
impotence, *see* sexual
impregnation, 268, 1200, 1229, 1230
'Imrānī, *see* 'Alī b. Aḥmad
Ina, West Saxon king, 294
incense, 1620
inceptor, 554
incipits, catalogue of, 1906
inclined plane, 146
incorruptibility of saintly bodies, 1466, 1864
incubation, eggs, 1596, 1866
incubation, rite, 864, 1247
incubi, 849
incunabula, 10, 1885, 1891, 1898, 1903, 1905
indeterminate, *see* analysis
India, 1880, 1881, 1882, 1893, 1900, 1904
Indian, *see* literature; medicine; mysticism; philosophy
Indic manuscripts, 1899
individualism, 553
individuation, 81
Indo-China, 205, 294
Indonesia, 1879
induction, *see* mathematical
indulgences, 327, 393, 407, 413, 1256
Indus river, 213
industry and learning, history, 1253
inertia, 146, 149, 543, 738, 1488. *See also* impetus
inertia, human, 127, 129, 142, 150, 151, 1666
Infancy, *see* gospel
infinity, 75, 518, 524, 542, 559
infusionism, 488
Inge, W. R., 1090
Ingeborg Bengtsdotter, 1354
Ingeborg of Sweden, 578
Ingelmark, B. E., 1555
Inghen, *see* Marsilius
Inglis, J. B., 561
Ingrassia, G. F., 851
Inguimbert, mgr. d', 1498
inheritance problems, 1119, 1527
inḥirāf, 135, 1526
Injū, *see* Jamāl al-dīn Ḥusain
ink, 181, 1139
ink cakes, 1590
ink, Egyptian, 760
ink, invention of real black (IV-2), v. 1, *369*, 441; v. 3, 760
ink manufacturers, 311, 760, 1585

ink, oily, 1564
ink, red, 760
Innocent III, 50, 317, 405, 1853
Innocent IV (XIII-1), v. 2, *690*, 1185; v. 3, 374, 405, 470
Innocent VI, 1031
Innocent VII, 1032
Innocent VIII, 301, 1049
Inns of Court, 38
inoculation, 274
Inquisition, 301, 403, 404, 412, 444, 1050, 1060, 1304, 1879
Inquisition, organization of the (XIII-1), v. 2, *552*, 1185
inquisitorial procedure, 1338, 1870
inquisitorial trials, 394, 403
insects, 238, 1164, 1634
insidentibus aquae, De, 145, 735
Institutes, Justinian, 990
instruments, *see* astronomy; music; surgical; etc.
Insulae flandricae, 185
Insulae flemengorum, 185
insurance, commercial, 324
insurance, life, 324
insurance, marine, 324, 914
interest, 111, 326, 530. *See also* usury
interest, tables of, 125, 773, 1111
intermediate beings, 849
international life, 26
internationalism of trade, 322, 1273, 1838
internationalism of universities, 322
Introductorium juvenum, 877
inventio medii, 542
inventions, history, 151, 298, 921
Iolanda of Montferrat, 458
Ion Gardener, Mayster, 1181
Iorga, Nicolae, 927, 1148, 1323, 1345
Iovan Shishman III, 1025
Īqā'āt, 741
Iqriṭi, *see* Shemariah b. Elijah
Īrān, 106
Iranian, 20
Iranian history (VI-2), v. 1, *457*
Īrānshahrī, 149
'Irāq, 105
'Irāqī, *see* Muḥammad b. Aḥmad
Irbilī, *see* Muḥammad b. 'Alī Khaṭīb
Ireland, *see* James
Irenaeos of Smyrna, St. (II-2), v. 1, *294*, 288; v. 3, viii
Iriki, documents of, 980
iris, 704, 1647
Irish, *see* law
Irnerius of Bologna (XII-1), v. 2, *265*, 1186
iron, 219, 220, 1174, 1175
iron, medicine, 1241
iron ore, 1637
iron pillar, 1859
irrationality, 1430, 1535
irrigation system, 1469
Irsay, Stephen d', 887, 1191, 1658, 1663, 1890
Irshād al-qāṣid, 74, 899
'Īsā bey Aidīnoghlu, 1727
'Īsā the Mongol (XIII-2), v. 2, *1021*, 1186
'Īsā b. Muḥammad of Aidīn, 1727
'Īsā tarjamān (tarjumān, turjumān), 137, 261
'Īsā b. Yaḥyā b. Ibrāhīm (IX-2), v. 1, *613*, 587
'Īsā b. Yaḥyā a. Sahl Masīḥī (X-2), v. 1, *678*, 651, 654; v. 2, 76
Isaac Aboab (XIII-2), v. 2, *878*, 729; v. 3, 1445
Isaac b. Abraham the Blind (XII-2), v. 2, *366*, 1186; v. 3, 363
Isaac b. Abraham Cabret, 1074, 1211, 1221, 1384
Isaac b. Abraham b. Laṭīf of Toledo (XIII-1), v. 2, *607*, 502, 527; v. 3, 1443
Isaac b. Abraham of Tretz, 892
Isaac Albalag (XIII-2), v. 2, *877*, 719, 729; v. 3, 62, 99, 592, 608, 1374, 1381, 1448
Isaac Argyros (XIV-2), *1511*, 123, 951, 1094, 1115, 1320, 1852, 1865
Isaac b. Crispin (XII-2), v. 2, *477*, 476
Isaac Denaḥna, 428
Isaac Efodi, 1521
Isaac Ḥazzan, *see* Isaac b. Sid
Isaac Israeli the Elder, *see* Isḥāq b. Sulaimān
Isaac Israeli the Younger (XIV-1), *691*, 62, 130, 132, 198, 306, 368, 598, 1443, 1516
Isaac b. Jacob, *see* Alfasi
Isaac b. Jacob ha-Kohen (XIV-1), *611*, 100
Isaac b. Jacob Lattes (XIV-2), *1718*, 893, 1097, 1211
Isaac b. Joseph of Corbeil, 1718
Isaac b. Joseph Ḥelo (XIV-1), *793*, 198
Isaac b. Joseph b. Israel, *see* Isaac Israeli the Younger
Isaac b. Joseph b. Pulqar (XIV-1), *693*, 57, 62, 130, 338, 418
Isaac Judaeus, *see* Isḥāq b. Sulaimān Isrā'īlī
Isaac b. Judah Abravanel, 398, 592, 605, 1376, 1523
Isaac b. Judah Lattes (XIV-1), *893*, 99, 255, 419, 605, 1718
Isaac Kohen Sholal, 792
Isaac b. abba Mari (XII-2), v. 2, *464*, 1186
Isaac b. Melchizedek (XII-2), v. 2, *365*, 289
Isaac b. Moses b. Arroyo, 1826
Isaac b. Moses ha-Levi, *see* Profiaṭ Duran
Isaac Nafuci, 1858
Isaac b. Nathan of Cordova (XIV-1), *436*, 62, 99, 1448
Isaac b. Nathan of Majorca, 436
Isaac Nathan b. Qalonymos, 1063, 1716
Isaac b. Samuel of 'Akkā (XIV-1), *616*, 100, 101
Isaac b. Sheshet Perfet (or Barfat), 605, 611, 1062, 1343, 1376, 1377, 1446, 1515
Isaac b. Sid Ḥazzan (XIII-2), v. 2, *843*, 1186

Isaac b. Solomon b. Alḥadib (XIV-2), *1515*, 1115, 1124, 1516
Isaac b. Solomon, Qaraite, 1520
Isaac of Stella (XII-2), v. 2, *384*, 293; v. 3, 419
Isaac Tarphon, 1523
Isaac b. Ṭodros of Avignon (XIV-2), *1718*, 612, 1211
Isaac Tzetzes (XII-1), v. 2, *192*, 1187
Isaac b. Vidal of Tolosa, 611
Isabeau of Bavaria, 1227
Isabel of Lancaster, 1298
Isabel Moniz, 183
Isabella of Castile, 1304
Isaiah (VIII B.C.), v. 1, *58*, 53; v. 2, 188, 470; v. 3, 460
Isaiah b. Elijah of Trani (XIII-2), v. 2, *887*, 556, 732
Isaiah b. Joseph of Tabrīz (XIV-2), *1450*, 1098
Isaiah b. Mali of Trani (XIII-1), v. 2, *556*, 488, 887
Isaiah b. Moses b. Solomon, 428
Isaiah of Nik, 1441
Iseo, *see* Bonaventura
Iṣfahān, *see* Ḥusain Jamāl al-dīn
Iṣfahānī, see Aḥmad b. 'Abdallāh; Maḥmūd b. Muḥammad
Isḥāq b. 'Assāl, a., 1006
Isḥāq b. Barūn (XII-1), v. 2, *272*, 142; v. 3, 367
Isḥāq b. Ḥunain (IX-2), v. 1, *600*, 811; v. 2, 1187; v. 3, 434, 1638
Isḥāq Ibrāhīm, a., *see* Ibrāhīm b. Faraj
Isḥāq b. Ibrāhīm Tadmurī, 1160
Isḥāq b. Murād of Gerede (XIV-2), *1726*, 1169, 1176, 1215, 1328
Isḥāq b. Mūsā b. Jundī, 1455
Isḥāq b. Sulaimān Isrā'īlī (X-1), v. 1, *639*, 811; v. 2, 1187; v. 3, 248, 251, 374, 450, 813, 1235, 1719
Isḥāq b. Tāj al-dīn Multānī (XIV-1), *633*, 58, 107, 373, 377, 633
Ishizuka, Ryūgaku, 425
Ishmael b. Elisha, 608
Ishmael, tanna, 604
Ishrāqīya, 420
Isidore of Charax (I-2 B.C.), v. 1, *230*, 220
Isidore of Seville (VII-1), v. 1, *471*, 811; v. 2, 1187; v. 3, 191, 192, 401, 813, 836, 857, 933, 946, 1004, 1076, 1146, 1464, 1600, 1706, 1736, 1843
Isidoros I, patriarch, 588, 790
Isis, 1890
Iskandar-nāma, 1465, 1519
Iṣlāḥ al-majisṭī, 61, 128, 432
Islām, beginning (VII-1), v. 1, *464*, 460
Islām, varia, 1873, 1876, 1883, 1888, 1890, 1892, 1893, 1894, 1897, 1899, 1910
Islands of the Blessed, 193
Islip, *see* Simon
Ismā'īl b. 'Abbād (X-2), v. 1, *688*, 652, 654; v. 3, 372
Ismā'īl b. 'Alī, *see* a. Fidā'
Ismā'īl b. Ḥammād, *see* Jauharī
Ismā'īl b. Ḥusain Jurjānī (XII-1), v. 2, *234*, 1187; v. 3, 1210, 1726
Ismā'īl b. Ibrāhīm Māridīnī (XIII-1), v. 2, *703*; v. 3, 1530
Ismā'īl b. Razzāz Jazarī (XIII-1), v. 2, *632*, 510; v. 3, 1456
Ismā'īl b. 'Umar b. Kathīr (XIV-2), *1782*, 1264
Ismā'īlī, 149, 969, 971, 975
Ismā'īlī propaganda (IX-2), v. 1, *593*, 811; v. 2, 113, 1045
Ismā'īlīya, *see* Assassins
isnād, 1262
Isnard, M. Z., 340
Isnawī, *see* 'Abd al-Raḥīm b. Ḥasan
Isolani, Isidoro, 1430, 1431
isoperimeter, 1485
isostasy, 1166, 1170, 1430
isrā', 489
Israel, 1883, 1886, 1890, 1894, 1895, 1897, 1901, 1909
Israel b. Joseph Caslari (XIV-1), *449*, 62, 65, 254
Israel b. Joseph Israeli, 373
Israel b. Joseph b. Naqawa (XIV-2), *1445*, 1096
Israel b. Samuel Ma'arabi (XIV-1), *419*, 56, 131
Israeli, *see* Israel b. Joseph
Issa bey, *see* Ahmed
Isserles, Moses b. Israel, 614
Istakhrī, Ibrāhīm b. Muḥammad (X-2), v. 1, *674*, 650, 654
istibṣār, 709, 1067
istiqṣā' wal-ibrām, 895
Īśvarakṛishṇa (IV-1), v. 1, *351*, 811
Italian, 335
italic type, 512
Italy, 1900, 1902, 1905
itch, 874, 1247, 1664
itineraries, 202
itineraries (IV-2), v. 1, *371*, 811
itineraries, Chinese (III-1), v. 1, *324*
itineraries, Roman (III-1), v. 1, *323*
Ivan I Kalita, 39
Ivan IV the Terrible, 1865
Ivar Bártharson, the Greenlander (XIV-2), *1607*, 196, 1154, 1319
Ives, S. A., 1178
Ivins, W. M., jr., 1552
Iviron on Mount Athos, 305, 306
ivory, 1186

j, *see also* i
Jabal al-qamar, 1158
Ja'barī, *see* Ṣāliḥ b. Thāmir

Jābir b. Aflaḥ (XII-1), v. 2, *206*, 1187; v. 3, 61, 114, 128, 129, 432, 434, 738, 598, 1516, 1525
Jābir b. Ḥaiyān (VIII-2), v. 1, *532*, 811; v. 2, 1187; v. 3, 165, 431, 759, 1138. For Latin tradition *see* Geber
Jābir b. Sinān Ḥarrānī (IX-2), v. 1, *602*, 585
jabr, 895
Jachino, G., 1819
Jack Straw, 1279
jacks, 717, 1541, 1545, 1889
Jackson, A. V. W., 1458
Jackson, B. D., 1867
Jackson, Isaac, 1605
Jackson, J. H., 875
Jackson, W. A., 1146
Jackson, W. W., 493
Jacme, *see* James
Jacob, *see also* James; Ya'qūb. The form James is reserved for Christians (as in English NT); the form Jacob, with a few exceptions, for Jews (as in English OT), and writers in Hebrew; the form Ya'qūb for Muslims (as in the Qur'ān), and writers in Arabic.' The distinction is sometimes difficult or arbitrary.
Jacob Alfandari, 895
Jacob the Armenian (XIV-2), *1715*, 1210, 1710
Jacob b. Asher (XIV-1), *614*, 100, 320, 417, 618
Jacob Badoer, 127, 358
Jacob Baradai, 358
Jacob Burdeana, 358
Jacob Çadique, 427
Jacob Cona, 1132
Jacob b. David b. Yom-ṭob Bonet (XIV-2), *1516*, 452, 1115, 1116, 1515, 1520, 1521
Jacob the Dragoman (XIV-1), *460*, 67, 97, 356, 1095
Jacob of Edessa (VII-2), v. 1, *500*, 811; v. 2, 977; v. 3, 358
Jacob Engelhart, 1145
Jacob of Florence, 110, 337
Jacob b. Isaac Ashkenazi, 1721
Jacob b. Isaac Carsono (XIV-2), *1375*, 1072, 1074, 1115, 1863, 1865
Jacob b. Joseph ha-Levi (XIV-1), *892*, 65, 254
Jacob b. Judah Cabret (XIV-2), *1383*, 1074, 1116, 1211, 1219, 1382
Jacob b. Judah of Lorraine, 56
Jacob Köbel, 1580
Jacob of Königshofen, 1756
Jacob b. Maḥir b. Tibbon (XIII-2), v. 2, *850*, 1188; v. 3, 61, 67, 98, 99, 128, 131, 208, 240, 434, 436, 437, 597, 601, 610, 791, 792, 1116, 1119, 1516
Jacob of Mainz, 935
Jacob Mantino, 432, 603
Jacob b. abba Mari Anaṭoli (XIII-1), v. 2, *565*, 1187; v. 3, 366, 598, 600, 609, 1443, 1445, 1516, 1521
Jacob b. Meïr (fl. 1322), 436
Jacob b. Meïr Tam (XII-1), v. 2, *190*, 1188; v. 3, 1364
Jacob b. Moses b. Abbassi (XIII-2), v. 2, *853*, 720, 729
Jacob b. Nathaniel ha-Kohen (XII-2), v. 2, *415*, 301; v. 3, 1156
Jacob of Paris (XIII-2), v. 2, *1064*, 35, 774
Jacob Po'el, 1116, 1516
Jacob Qafanton, 894
Jacob b. Reuben the Qaraite, 1385
Jacob b. Shakkō (XIII-1), v. 2, *603*, 1188; v. 3, 358
Jacob b. Solomon Ẓarfatī (XIV-2), *1449*, 1097, 1212, 1326
Jacob b. Ṭafīruh, 131
Jacob of Ulm, 172
Jacob Ẓaddīq, 427
Jacob Zanzalus, 358
Jacobi, Hermann, 150, 180
Jacobi, *see* John
Jacobite, 358
Jacobitz, Karl, 997
Jacobs, J. H., 1438
Jacobs, Joseph, 1593, 1656
Jacobus, *see* James
Jacoby, Felix, 1519
Jacoli, Ferdinando, 1431
Jacopi, *see* Baldwin; Riccomanno
Jacopo, *see* James
Jacopone da Todi, 50, 86, 335
jacquemart, 717
Jacquerie, 1024, 1279, 1654, 1738
Jacques, *see also* James
Jacques Bonhomme, 1024, 1164, 1738
Jacquet, E., 776, 1754
Jādarī, *see* 'Abd al-Raḥmān b. a. Ghālib
jade, 1169, 1171, 1471, 1865
Jade mountains, 1472
jadwal, 1526
Jadwiga of Poland, 1325
Jäck, J. H., 788
Jaeger, Werner, ix, 1844
Jaén, *see* David
Jähns, Max, 726
Ja'far b. 'Alī Dimashqī (XII-2), v. 2, *462*, 1188; v. 3, 998, 1771
Ja'far Khāzin, a. (X-2), v. 1, *664*, 648, 654; v. 2, 205
Ja'far b. Muḥammad Ḥillī (XIII-2), v. 2, *1132*, 801, 1011
Ja'far b. Muḥammad, *see* Ja'far Ṣādiq; a. Ma'shar
Ja'far b. Muḥammad Mustaghfirī, 966
Ja'far Ṣādiq (VIII-1), v. 1, *508*, 503, 505
Ja'far b. Tha'lab Adfuwī (XIV-1), *959*, 103, 163, 307
jafr, 103, 623
Jagaddeva (XII-2), v. 2, *397*, 294, 310
Jaghmīnī, *see* Maḥmūd b. Muḥammad

Jagič, I. V., 1323
Jagiello, *see* Ladislas
Jagiello, grand duke of Lithuania, 1021
Jagiello son of Olgerd, 1325
Jagmandar-lāl Jainī, 1584
Jagow, Kurt, 823
Jāḥiẓ (IX-2), v. 1, *597*, 586, 590; v. 2, 62, 632; v. 3, 802, 1639, 1775
Jahn, Albert, 952
Jahn, Karl, 971, 975
Jahuda, *see* Judah
Jaihānī (X-1), v. 1, *635*, 811
Jaime, *see* James
Jaiminīyanyāyamālāvistara, 1366
Jaina, 180, 383, 1069, 1102, 1366, 1474, 1584, 1909
Jaina, *see* atomism; Mahāvīra
Jakobson, Roman, 941
Jalabert, Denise, 1178
Jalāl al-dīn Mirān shāh, 969
Jalāl al-dīn Muḥammad Rūmī (XIII-2), v. 2, *874*, 1188; v. 3, 105, 163, 379, 420, 624, 625, 1840
Jalāl al-dīn b. Sulaimān Dā'ūd, 966
Jalheau, François, 1750
Jamā'a, b., *see* Muḥammad b. a. Bakr; Muḥammad b. Ibrāhīm
Jamāl al-dīn, chief physician, 1473
Jamāl al-dīn, Chinese, 137
Jamāl al-dīn Ḥusain Injū, 1534
Jamāl al-dīn Ḥusain Subkī, 622
Jamāl al-dīn b. Muhannā, 1013
Jamāl al-dīn Shubakī, 1727
Jamālī Muḥammad Ganja, 1644
Jamatus, *see* John
James, *see also* Jacob; Ya'qūb
James di Acaia, 855
James d'Agramont (XIV-1), *862*, 246, 343, 852
James Albinus de Montecalerio, 855. *See* Albino
James Alighieri (XIV-1), *600*, 86, 88, 335, 336, 1600
James Allegretti, 1817
James d'Angelo, 1073, 1145, 1155, 1289, 1597, 1797, 1818, 1822
James I of Aragón, Conquistador (Conqueridor) (XIII-2), v. 2, *1107*, 1188; v. 3, 300, 325, 342, 427, 1162, 1250, 1734
James II of Aragón, 61, 89, 342, 427
James da Arquà (XIV-2), *1676*, 1192, 1220, 1238, 1243, 1713
James van Artevelde, 38, 940, 1907
James Bauchant (XIV-2), *1391*, 1075, 1307
James de Belvisi, 470
James Benincasa, 1334
James Boisset, 1498
James Borrell, 1306
James di Brindisi, 859
James of Bruges, 184
James Bruyant, 745
James da Campione, 1656
James Capocci, 402
James de' Castelli, 857
James de Castro, 246
James de Cessoles, 317, 393, 457, 579, 1394
James di Coluccino, 1194, 1246
James Contarini, 916
James de' Dondi (XIV-2), *1669*, 144, 721, 1105, 1125, 1144, 1163, 1171, 1192, 1240, 1241, 1243, 1685
James Duèse, 44, 1031
James Ferrer (XIV-1), *785*, 190, 1599
James Ferrer II, 785
James Ferrer III de Blanes, 785
James of Florence, 54, 780
James da Forlì, 1195, 1197
James Fournier, 44, 1031
James Gaetani, cardinal, 887
James the German, 172, 1582
James de Hemricourt (XIV-2), *1750*, 1257, 1280, 1309
James of Ireland, 777
James della Lana, 1813, 1814
James of Lausanne, 525, 991
James Legrand, 1411
James de Liége, 160
James, M. R., 232, 560, 1297, 1890
James van Maerlant (XIII-2), v. 2, *947*, 1188; v. 3, 66, 68, 302, 349, 817, 937, 938, 939, 1092, 1317, 1437, 1465
James of Majorca, 375, 1141, 1306, 1593, 1858
James Mangiatroja, 838
James March, 1304
James Mariano Taccola, 1552
James de Molay, 153, 394, 415
James of Montecalvo, 1679
James de Navernia, 741
James de Nouvion, 1294
James degli Oldrendi, 1796
James Olivier, 125
James dall' Orologio, 1670
James of Padua, 1676
James Palmerio da Cingoli, 1234
James Paradisi, 1676
James Pavieta, 721
James Pipìno (XIV-1), *859*, 245, 290
James Poggio, 1253
James da Prato (XIV-2), *1686*, 1193, 1233
James de Revigny, 990
James Ribes, 1141, 1593
James de Sanatis, 1676
James da Scarparia, 1073, 1145, 1816
James Sprenger, 1338
James della Torre, 564, 1194, 1195, 1196, 1220
James Twinger (XIV-2), *1756*, 1258, 1319
James da Varaggio, 403
James of Venice (XII-1), v. 2, *179*, 1188
James of Verona (XIV-1), *768*, 46, 185, 1210
James of Viterbo, 402

James of Vitry (XIII-1), v. 2, *671*, 1188; v. 3, 398, 579, 714, 770, 1603
James of Voragine (XIII-2), v. 2, *1106*, 793; v. 3, 353, 457, 946, 1041, 1042, 1305, 1418, 1741, 1758
Jametel, Maurice, 1590
Jāmi', 1065
Jāmi' al-funūn, 804
Jamī', b., *see* Hibatallāh b. Zain
Jāmi' al-tawārīkh, 970
Jamshīd b. Mas'ūd, 1120, 1328
Jan, Carl v., 586, 953
Jan, *see* John
Janadī, *see* Muḥammad b. Ya'qūb
Janāḥ, b. (XI-1), v. 1, *736*, 809; v. 2, 1188; v. 3, 366, 590, 792, 1008, 1522
Jandun, *see* John
Janicsek, Stephen, 1623
janissaries, 155, 1460
Jannequin, Claude, 1159
Jannottaro, *see* Matthew
Janov, *see* Matthew
Janovez, *see* Nicholas
Japan, 1875, 1879, 1892, 1896, 1897, 1898, 1902
Japanese, *see* cotton; earthquakes
Japanese historiography (VIII-1), v. 1, *516;* (IX-2), v. 1, *617;* (XI-2), v. 1, *778*
Japanese, *see* hours; law; mathematics; medicine; printing; science; tea; technology
Japheth b. a. Ḥasan Barqamānī (XIII-1), v. 2, *704*
Japheth b. Ẓaghir, 419
Jārabardī, *see* Aḥmad b. Ḥasan
jarīd, 1643
Jarosław Bogurja, 1759
Jarrett, Bede, 411
jasada, 1139
jasmin, 1303
Jāṭ, 425
Jata, 1775, 1787
Jātaka, 1370
Játiva, 375
Játiva, *see* paper
Jauharī Ismā'īl b. Ḥammād (X-2), v. 1, *689*, 652, 654; v. 2, 1136; v. 3, 372, 1639, 1827
Jaume, *see* James
Jauzī, b., *see* 'Abd al-Raḥmān b. 'Alī; Sibṭ
Jāvaka, 1624
jawāhir al-'arā'is, 755
Jawāhir al-niẓām, 746
Jawālīqī, b., *see* Mawhūb b. a. Ṭāhir
Jawbarī, *see* 'Abd al-Raḥīm b. 'Umar
jawhar, 149
Jawrī, poet, 1464
Jawzīya, *see* Muḥammad b. Qayyim
Jayakar, A. S. G., 1641
Jayaswal, Kashi-prasad, 1000
Jayavarman, king, 294
Jayme, *see* James
Jazarī, *see* Ismā'īl b. Razzāz; Muḥammad b. Muḥammad
Jazla, Yaḥyā b. 'Īsā b. (XI-2), v. 1, *772*, 742, 746; v. 2, 1189; v. 3, 797, 1727
Jazūlī, b., *see* Muḥammad
Jazzār, Aḥmad b. Ibrāhīm b. (X-2), v. 1, *682*, 651, 654; v. 2, 1189; v. 3, 274, 877, 1650, 1707
Jean, *see also* John
Jean, René, 171
Jeanne, *see* Joan
Jeanroy, Alfred, 533
Jeanselme, Edouard, 252, 281, 1209
Jedaiah b. Abraham Bedersi, Penini (XIV-1), *593*, 61, 98, 255, 431, 608, 1450
Jefferson, B. L., 1425
Jeffery, Arthur, 1442
jegar shahadritha, 364
Jehan, Jehanne, *see* John, Joan
Jehiel b. Asher, 1523
Jehiel Gutleben, 1861
Jehiel b. Jekuthiel 'Anav (XIII-2), v. 2, *887*, 732
Jehiel b. Solomon, 606
Jehudah, *see* Judah
Jekuthiel b. Solomon of Narbonne (XIV-2), *1380*, 874, 1074, 1212, 1221, 1379
Jelinek, H., 941, 1354
Jellinek, Adolph, 1437
Jellinek, M. H., 351
Jellouschek, C. J., 516
Jenkin, A. K. H., 219
Jenkins, J. T., 823
Jenkins, Rhys, 220, 1174
Jensen, Hans, 1890
Jeremiah (VII B.C.), v. 1, *63*, 60; v. 3, 227
Jernenski, M. E., 1516
Jerome Adorno, 1292
Jerome Bosch, 405
Jerome of Dalmatia, St. (IV-2), v. 1, *363*, 811; v. 2, 1189; v. 3, viii, 330, 369, 488, 579, 984, 1037, 1075, 1325
Jerome of the Holy Faith, 399, 1046, 1053, 1061
Jerome Manfredi, 1224
Jerome of Prague, 1348, 1433
Jerome de Santa Fé, 1716
Jerome da Santo Stefano, 1292
Jerome Savonarola, 1198, 1336
Jerome Squarzafico, 1810
Jeroschin, *see* Nicholas
Jerrold, M. F., 514
Jerusalem, Knights of St. John, *see* John
Jerusalem, Stations, 1150
Jerusalem, *see* Tanḥum b. Joseph
Jeshua, *see* Joshua
Jespersen, Otto, 31
Jesu Haly, see 'Alī b. 'Īsā
Jesuati, 1036, 1092
Jesus College, 1402
Jewish, *see* calendar
Jewish life, 1872

Jews, Chinese, 833, 1071, 1860
Jews, expulsion from England (XIII-2), v. 2, *825*
Jews, persecutions, 1523, 1580, 1656, 1756, 1831
Jews of Spain, conversion (XIII-2), v. 2, *825*, 584, 805
Jibrīl, *see also* Gabriel
Jibrīl b. Bakhtyashū' (IX-1), v. 1, *573*, 547, 549; v. 3, 1235
jihād, 997, 1065, 1274, 1635, 1643, 1722, 1862
Jīlānī, *see* Jīlī
Jildakī, *see* 'Alī b. Aidamur
Jīlī, *see* 'Abd al-Karīm b. Ibrāhīm; 'Abd al-Qādir
Jiménez de la Espada, Marcos, 787
Jinagupta (VI-2), v. 1, *447*, 443; v. 3, 378
Jinnī, b., *see* 'Uthmān
Jireček, Josef, 941
Jirjīs, *see also* George
Jirjis b. Jibrīl b. Bakhtyashū' (VIII-2), v. 1, *537*, 522, 526
Jirjīs Makīn, *see* 'Abdallāh b. a. Yāsir
Jivanmuktiviveka, 1367
Jñānarāja, 1535
Joachim, Erich, 1190
Joachim of Floris (XII-2), v. 2, *332*, 1189; v. 3, 396, 483, 924
Joachimite, 396, 400, 1350
Joan of Arc, 23, 1020, 1079, 1307
Joan de Boulogne, 1152
Joan of Bourbon, 1184, 1237, 1389
Joan of Bourgogne, 397, 457, 541, 846
Joan de Castelnou of Toulouse, 341, 343
Joan of Evreux, 1235
Joan of France, 249, 1152
Joan de Laval, 532
Joan I of Naples, 1212, 1719
Joan of Navarre, 406, 464, 476, 743, 928, 1632
Joan of Poitiers, 541
Joan, pope, 585
Joan de Santa María, 1343
Joan of Toulouse, 341
Joan of Wales, 1502
Joanna, *see* Joan
Joannes, *see* John
Joannissiany, Abgar, 1222
João, *see* John
Job, book of (V B.C.), v. 1, *90*, 82, 83; v. 2, 846; v. 3, 402
Job Huerter, 184
Jocetus, 1861
Joël, Manuel, 607, 1448
Joel, rabbi, 464
Jörg Tyrman, 1580
Jørgensen, Johannes, 1356
Jofre de Foixà, 343
Johanan, *see* John; Yūḥannā
Johann, Johannes, *see* John
Johannitius, *see* Ḥunain b. Isḥāq
John, *see also* Gian; Ion; Jack; Yaḥyā; Yūḥannā. The form John (representing a large number of variants) is reserved for Christians (as in English NT); the form Yūḥannā for Muslims and Arabic writers. On account of unavoidable ambiguities, it is advisable to consult the two forms.
John Actuarios (XIV-1), *889*, 252, 288, 1208
John Afflacius (XI-2), v. 1, *769*, 742, 745; v. 2, 1143
John d'Aix, 1695
John de Albertis, 1674
John Alcherius, 1131, 1136, 1300, 1308
John the Almoner, 219
John de Altre, 251
John Álvarez Salamiellas, 246, 284
John Amerbach, 512
John d'Andrea (XIV-1), *983*, 177, 313, 401, 470, 981, 1397
John Andreoli, 1134
John Andrew of Corsica, 399
John Angeli, 444
John of Antioch (VII-1), v. 1, *482*, 812
John XIV Aprenos, 1439
John of Aquila (XIII-2), v. 2, *1088*, 78, 784
John I of Aragón, 1129
John d'Arckel, 1748
John Arderne (XIV-2), *1700*, 293, 1166, 1176, 1202, 1231, 1233, 1317, 1868
John d'Ascoli, 1482
John of Ashendon (XIV-1), *672*, 117, 249, 1500, 1546
John of Asia (VI-2), v. 1, *457*, 445
John d'Aubernon, 728
John Aurispa, 922, 1194, 1197, 1236, 1321
John of Austria (Oosterroyck), 1153
John of Avignon, 873, 1240, 1378
John Bacon, 561
John Baconthorpe (XIV-1), *561*, 92, 400, 529, 1431
John Balbi of Genoa (XIII-2), v. 2, *1135*, 803; v. 3, 332, 345, 1136, 1309
John Ball, 1024, 1279, 1752
John Baptist, *see* Giambattista
John the Baptist, St., 338, 460
John the Baptist, dance of St., 1665
John ad Barbam (à la Barbe), 1166, 1176, 1202, 1309, 1603
John Barbour (XIV-2), *1740*, 725, 1254, 1315
John Barrillon, 1136
John Barton, 1311
John Basingstoke (XIII-1), v. 2, *567*, 1189
John of Bassigny, 115
John of Bassoles (XIV-1), *549*, 91, 249
John Beaufort, 1150
John Beccos, 95, 588
John, duc de Berry, 744, 1075, 1202, 1293, 1391 1629, 1805
John of Béthencourt, 184, 786
John Blaise, 1831
John de Blandy, 1404

John, *see* Boccaccio
John v. Bodman, 1153
John van Boendale (XIV-1), *939*, 94, 302, 350, 1317, 1437
John Boernave, 1541
John of Bohemia, king, 273, 744, 887, 1235, 1258, 1692, 1748, 1757, 1836
John Bombelen, 1578
John Bondol, 533
John Bonnet (XIV-1), *547*, 90, 346
John of Bordeaux, 1200, 1203, 1603
John Boston of Bury, 1569
John of Boucicault, 1474
John Bourchier, 1753
John III, duke of Brabant, 939
John of Brescia (XIII-2), v. 2, *831*, 1189
John of Brie (XIV-2), *1631*, 1164, 1181, 1309
John of Bromyarde, 456
John Bruyant, 1633, 1867
John v. Buch (XIV-1), *993*, 319, 351
John, duc de Bourgogne, 1074, 1200, 1203, 1212, 1274, 1383, 1603, 1660
John Briefmaler, 1580
John Buchdrucker, 1580
John, *see* Buridan
John Burnham, 1314
John Busch, 1359, 1408
John Byker, 1547
John Caesar, 847
John de' Caccini, 1686
John Calecas, 588, 1363, 1760
John Camateros (XII-2), v. 2, *402*, 20, 296
John di Ser Cambio, 1194
John Campano (XIII-2), v. 2, *985*, 1189; v. 3, 399, 484, 1409, 1430, 1540, 1568
John the Canon (XIV-1), *739*, 150, 1849
John VI Cantacuzenos (XIV-2), *1759*, 40, 584, 889, 995, 1058, 1094, 1259, 1320, 1386, 1512, 1652
John da Capistrano, 397
John Capréole, 521
John of Capua (XIII-2), v. 2, *856*, 1189; v. 3, 464
John of Carbondala (XIII-2), v. 2, *1079*
John di Carignano (XIV-1), *764*, 182, 337
John da Casale (XIV-1), *739*, 148, 1127
John Casini, 1684
John Cassianus Eremita, 1392
John de Casso (XIV-1), *856*, 244, 273
John Catrarios (XIV-1), *690*, 123
John Cele (XIV-2), *1408*, 1082, 1317
John Chaucer, 1417
John Chilmark, 565, 1089
John Chrysostom, St., viii, 947, 1321, 1438, 1513
John Chumnos (XIV-1), *888*, 97, 252, 285, 996
John Cinnamos (XII-2), v. 2, *450*, 313; v. 3, 63
John de Cis, 1389
John de Clerc, 939
John Clingenberg, 125
John Clyn (XIV-1), *947*, 303
John Colombini, 1036
John Colle, 1668
John's College, St., 1863
John Comnenos, 1209, 1761
John di Conversino, 1080, 1198, 1407, 1818
John Coppo, 920
John of Cora (XIV-1), *775*, 186, 346, 780, 1754
John Corbechon (XIV-2), *1390*, 814, 1075, 1088, 1307
John Cornwall, 1314
John Courtecuisse, 1295
John of the Cross, St., 92, 1098, 1453
John Crule, 1750
John de Cuenca of Huete, 1428
John of Cypros (XIV-2), *1438*, 738, 1094, 1320, 1387
John Czarnkowski (XIV-2), *1759*, 1259
John van Dalen, 1408
John de Dalton, 566
John of Damascus (VIII-1), v. 1, *507*, 812; v. 2, 1190; v. 3, ix, 551, 753, 755, 1438, 1513, 1821
John of Dambach (XIV-2), *1433*, 1092, 1296
John Dandin (XIV-2), *1390*, 507, 1075, 1088, 1277, 1307, 1493, 1496
John Dardel (XIV-2), *1739*, 1253, 1260, 1309
John Dastin (XIV-1), *752*, 178
John the Deacon, 916
John De Langhe, 1151
John De Weert (XIV-2), *1437*, 1092, 1317
John Dombelay (XIV-2), *1578*, 1135, 1136, 1576
John Dominici, 1817
John de' Dondi (XIV-2), *1676*, 242, 509, 1163, 1171, 1192, 1240, 1243, 1541, 1546, 1685
John de Dormans, 1202
John Dorp, 541, 545
John Dullaert, 536, 545
John of Dumbleton (XIV-1), *564*, 92, 1089
John Duns Scot (XIII-2), v. 2, *967*, 1190; v. 3, 79, 81, 91, 116, 166, 332, 399, 401, 407, 519, 521, 528, 529, 530, 532, 549, 552, 558, 563, 589, 738, 739, 1004, 1400, 1437, 1568, 1843, 1908
John Duvignay, 457
John Engel, *see* John Angelo
John Eremita, 1075
John the Englishman (Anglicus), 459, 880
John of Erzinjān (XIII-2), v. 2, *997*, 1190; v. 3, 54, 67, 97, 119, 356
John's evil, St., 1247
John Faure (XIV-1), *989*, 316
John Fedanzola, 186
John de Felains, 1545
John v. Fernach, 1655
John Fernández de Heredia, 949, 1250, 1305
John Ferrarius of Salerno (XII-2), v. 2, *439*, 1190
John Fillon, 1738
John Fisher, 1863

John Flaška of Pardubice (XIV-2), *1824*, 1167, 1190, 1322
John of Florence, 459, 781, 1576
John de' Fontana, 1551
John Fordun (XIV-2), *1741*, 1254
John Foucquet, 1805
John II of France, le Bon, 249, 1181, 1183, 1202
John Francis, *see* Gian Francesco
John, *see* Froissart
John Fusoris (XIV-2), *1497*, 1110, 1125, 1308
John of Gaddesden (XIV-1), *880*, 178, 249, 278, 838, 874, 1205, 1222, 1688, 1703, 1705, 1709, 1851
John Galloppes, 532
John Gansfort, 1399
John García, 1805
John Garland (XIII-1), v. 2, *695*, 1190; v. 3, 331, 332, 552, 741, 1004, 1411, 1575
John Garzoni, 854
John of Gaunt, 1021, 1501, 1855
John v. Gemunden, 1112
John of Genoa, 112, 245
John Gensbein, 1755
John the German (Allemanno), 592, 611
John Gerson, 413, 454, 476, 581, 1033, 1034, 1053, 1085, 1088, 1109, 1275, 1276, 1277, 1295, 1309, 1359, 1509, 1844, 1878
John of Ghent, 535
John of Glaston, 720
John of Glogau (XIV-2), *1707*, 1113, 1114, 1205
John XIII Glycys, 438, 949
John Golein (XIV-2), *1392*, 299, 988, 1075, 1253, 1277, 1307
John Golodik, 460, 1095, 1323
John Gonçalves Zarco, 183
John de Goro, 920
John Gower (XIV-2), *1427*, 462, 1048, 1055, 1090, 1149, 1256, 1295, 1312, 1315, 1412
John the Grammarian (VII-1), v. 1, *480*, 812; v. 2, 1073; v. 3, x
John Grandison, 1403
John de Grandville (XIV-2), *1713*, 1207, 1242
John Griese, 887
John Grimaldi, 776
John de Grise (of Bruges?), 232
John Gutenberg, 1564
John Gyfford, 231, 348, 1165, 1184, 1315, 1630
John de Hainaut, 1748, 1751
John Hake of Göttingen (XIV-1), *887*, 251, 852
John Hakonarson, 1609
John of Harlebeke, 1746
John Hastiri, 752
John Hawkwood, 1022
John van Heelu, 939
John den Heiden, 1361
John Herolt, 456
John de Heusden (XIV-2), *1502*, 1112
John Hinckaert, 580
John van Hingene, 1542
John de Hocsem (XIV-1), *936*, 118, 302, 320
John Holobolos, 746
John of Holywood, *see* Sacrobosco
John, *see* Hus
John Jacobi (XIV-2), *1687*, 881, 1072, 1199, 1220, 1234, 1236, 1243, 1696, 1698, 1719
John Jamatus (XIII-1), v. 2, *654*, 73, 519
John of Jandun (XIV-1), *535*, 22, 51, 90, 114, 147, 148, 150, 315, 443, 550, 739, 819, 986, 988, 1346
John of Jerusalem, Knights of St. (XII-1), v. 2, *160*; v. 3, 40, 393, 421
John, *see* Joinville
John Jouvence, 1542
John of Karīn, 54, 67, 97, 356, 459, 460
John Kempe, 1833
John of Ketham, 1228, 1682, 1805
John Krichpaum, 541
John Lackland, 1034
John de La Fontaine (1413), 1135, 1308
John of La Rochelle (XIII-1), v. 2, *589*, 1190; v. 3, 1040
John le Bègue, 455, 1136, 1308
John Le Bel (XIV-2), *1748*, 1257, 1309, 1750, 1752
John Le Ferron, 317, 1695
John Le Fèvre (XIV-2), *1695*, 1201, 1236, 1860
John da Legname, 911
John da Legnano (XIV-2), *1796*, 1052, 1106, 1273, 1276, 1345, 1504, 1795
John Le Lièvre (XIV-2), *1699*, 1201, 1224, 1309
John Lemoine, 476
John Le Verrier, 184, 786
John Lichtenberger, 710, 1153
John Liefray, 1699
John Lietuyt de Delft, 1541
John de Linières (XIV-1), *649*, 114, 115, 118
John of Livania (XIV-2), *1510*, 1092, 1113, 1137
John of London (XIII-1), v. 2, *582*, 1190
John, Long, *see* John of Ypres
John of Louvain, 1059
John Lucae e Camerino (John del maestro Lucha dell' abaco), 1517
John Ludgate, 1809
John of Luxemburg, *see* John of Bohemia
John Lydgate, 47, 92, 197, 533, 1046, 1253, 1311, 1313, 1315, 1421, 1423, 1805, 1811, 1894
John of Mainz, 1235, 1747
John, *see* Malalas
John di Malpaghini, 1817
John Malverne (XIV-2), *1744*, 946, 1166, 1172, 1202, 1255
John Mandeville (XIV-2), *1602*, 40, 778, 779, 788, 1076, 1149, 1150, 1166, 1171, 1176, 1200, 1202, 1203, 1210, 1259, 1308, 1383, 1742, 1749
John Mansionario of Verona, 920
John Manuel (XIV-1), *924*, 73, 207, 231, 246, 300, 315, 338, 375, 1735
John Manzini, 1676
John Marbres, 1849

John de' Marignolli (XIV-1), *781*, 187, 204, 229, 297, 358, 532, 1143, 1259, 1758, 1910
John Marliani, 738
John of Marseille, 1392
John Martini de' Ferrarii, 1679
John de Matociis (XIV-1), *920*, 87, 298
John Matthew, *see* Gianmatteo
John Mauduith (XIV-1), *660*, 116, 560, 665, 667
John Maynus, 461
John Meliteniotes, 1513
John Melot, 1812
John Melton, 1403
John Merlin, 1202
John of Meung (XIII-2), v. 2, *932*, 1190; v. 3, 52, 90, 166, 249, 345, 346, 453, 457, 718, 929, 1135, 1410, 1418, 1465
John of Meurs (XIV-1), *652*, 45, 114, 115, 145, 147, 160, 886, 951, 952, 1128, 1518, 1846
John Micaele Savonarola, 445, 839, 1194, 1197, 1198, 1222
John Mielot, 391
John Mignot, 1656
John of Milano, 207, 225, 1233, 1683
John of Mirecourt (XIV-1), *533*, 84, 90
John of Mirfeld (XIV-2), *1704*, 1202, 1222, 1248
John da Modena, 1132
John Molinier (XIV-2), *1698*, 1201, 1234
John Mondino da Cividale, *see* Mondino Friulano
John de Montbron, 990
John de Montecorvino (XIII-2), v. 2, *1054*, 1190; v. 3, 54, 71, 186, 204, 207, 229, 358, 363, 380, 776, 780, 935, 1754
John de Montreuil, 511, 1294, 1844
John de Monzón, 1405
John Muret, 1294
John of Naples (XIV-1), *516*, 84, 87, 523, 525, 527
John de Narbonne, 23
John v. Neumarkt, 1708
John Newton, 567
John the Norman, 1132
John de Northampton, 1423
John da Noto, 1194, 1197, 1236. *See* John Aurispa
John, *see* Ocreatus
John Orchard, 1561
John of Orodn (XIV-2), *1441*, 1095, 1323
John d'Outremeuse (XIV-2), *1748*, 1149, 1165, 1170, 1171, 1257, 1309, 1602, 1843
John of Padua, 507, 509
John V Palaeologos, 584, 1022, 1058, 1760, 1824
John of Paris (XIV-1), *991*, 51, 89, 141, 142, 318, 707, 1350
John of Parma (XIII-2), v. 2, *1083*, 783; v. 3, 847, 876
John Pataran (XIV-2), *1694*, 1200, 1229
John Pauli, 451
John pauperum, 1573
John Peckham (XIII-2), v. 2, *1028*, 1190; v. 3, 91, 141, 398, 602, 707, 1123, 1433, 1506, 1509, 1565
John Pediasimos (XIV-1), *682*, 97, 122, 123, 161, 252, 268
John della Penna (XIV-1), *859*, 245, 852, 1669, 1851
John de la Penya, 1734
John de Peratallada, 1572
John Petit, 1274
John Petrarca, 502
John Philoponos (VI-1), v. 1, *421*, 824; v. 2, 1190; v. 3, x, 145, 149, 543, 589, 951, 1115, 1488, 1511
John Phocas (XII-2), v. 2, *416*, 1190
John Pian del Càrpine (XIII-1), v. 2, *640*, 1190; v. 3, 380, 784, 954, 1603
John Picard, 557
John Pico della Mirandola, 439, 444, 591, 600, 611, 737, 1448, 1482, 1491, 1517
John de Piscis, 877
John Pitart (XIV-1), *865*, 247, 346, 452, 864, 866, 871
John de Planis (XIV-1), *461*, 67, 246, 370
John Platearius, *see* Platearius
John III Platearius, *see* Platearius
John Plige, 126
John Pontii, 427
John Portinari, 125
John XXI, pope, *see* Peter of Spain
John XXII, pope, 44, 45, 49, 51, 67, 84, 86, 115, 159, 167, 178, 370, 392, 396, 401, 406, 412, 426, 470, 473, 475, 501, 523, 526, 527, 550, 562, 743, 752, 763, 912, 983, 986, 1189, 1242, 1277, 1830
John XXIII, pope, 1033, 1440, 1820, 1822. *See* Balthasar Cossa
John I of Portugal de Boa Memória, 1021, 1108
John de Pouilli (XIV-1), *534*, 48, 90, 527
John da Prato, 228, 1567
John des Preis, 1749
John, Prester (XII-2), v. 2, *416*, 1190; v. 3, 363, 782, 786, 1143, 1596, 1606
John of Příbram, 1351, 1352
John da Procida (XIII-2), v. 2, *1076*, 782; v. 3, 245, 836, 1303
John Prouville (XIV-1), *452*, 65, 246, 346, 452
John de Ptraccia, 1683
John Purvey, 1347
John Quidort, 991
John, R. L., 1842
John de Raigecourt, 1147
John da Ravenna (I) (XIV-2), *1407*, 1080, 1198, 1236, 1288
John da Ravenna (II) (XIV-2), ***1817*, 1288, 1299**
John of Reading, 944, 1255
John Reger, 1146
John de Regina de Neapoli, **516**
John Reuchlin, 591, 1292, 1321
John Rhenanus, 1579
John v. Ringgenbern, 579

John Rodington (XIV-1), *557*, 91
John de Roquetaillade, 1572
John de Roussines, 990
John Rucherath, 1399
John of Rupescissa (XIV-2), *1572*, 1130, 1136, 1510
John van Ruysbroeck (XIV-1), *580*, 85, 94, 350, 574, 1056, 1081, 1297, 1316, 1357, 1408, 1844
John, *see* Sacrobosco
John of Saint Albans, 1149
John of Saint Amand (XIII-2), v. 2, *1089*, 1190; v. 3, 250, 287, 878, 881, 1074, 1211, 1221, 1374, 1384
John de Saint Denys, 788
John of Saint Paul (XII-2), v. 2, *439*, 1190
John of Salisbury (XII-2), v. 2, *466*, 1190; v. 3, 317, 509, 577, 870, 1075, 1088, 1262, 1277, 1308, 1390, 1490, 1494, 1869
John Salvati, 370, 397
John da San Gimignano (XIV-1), *920*, 298, 314
John da San Miniato, 1817
John de Sant Fahagun (Sahagún), 1735
John da Santa Sofia (XIV-2), *1677*, 839, 1192, 1193, 1220
John the Saracen, *see* John Afflacius
John Sarrazin (XII-2), v. 2, *347*, 1190; v. 3, 530, 1417
John Saval, 125
John of Saxony, 115, 117, 118, 251, 1206
John Schiltberger, 1152, 1319, 1474
John Schlippacher, 1343
John of Schönbach, 1005
John Schoenfelder, 933
John van Schoonhoven, 581
John Scotus Erigena (IX-2), v. 1, *594*, 802; v. 2, 1190; v. 3, 355, 530
John Scylitzes (XI-2), v. 1, *776*, 743, 745
John of Seville (XII-1), v. 2, *169*, 1190; v. 3, 113, 213, 484, 1113, 1374, 1381, 1444, 1498, 1518
John of Sicily (XIII-2), v. 2, *987*, 1190
John Somer (XIV-2), *1501*, 1111, 1421
John of Spain, 451
John Spiesshaymer, 935
John Sporer, 1580
John Standonck, 476
John de Stavelot, 1749
John of Stendal, 1113, 1498
John Stephani, 427
John, *see* Stobaeos
John Stokes, 1348
John Surrel, 1406
John de Sy (XIV-2), *1389*, 1039, 1053, 1075, 1088
John Tauler (XIV-1), *571*, 85, 93, 351, 573, 580, 1056, 1091, 1358, 1844, 1889
John de Temploux, 1750
John Thórdarson, 1609
John v. Tiffen, 1234
John Tölner, 125
John of Toledo, 1113, 1695
John Tolomei, 395
John of Torquemada, 1356, 1552
John de Tournemire (XIV-2), *1696*, 876, 1074, 1200, 1212, 1221, 1235, 1236, 1243, 1247, 1380, 1688, 1719
John Trevenant, 1501
John of Trevisa (XIV-2), *1393*, 556, 946, 1038, 1039, 1055, 1076, 1090, 1256, 1280, 1311, 1313, 1349
John Trithemius, 1510
John of Tynemouth, 942
John Tyrus of Toledo, 752
John Tzetzes (XII-1), v. 2, *192*, 1190; v. 3, 825, facing 1019
John of Utrecht, 1151
John da Uzzano, 773
John Vanagan (XIII-1), v. 2, *680*, 526, 1114
John da Varignana, 841
John de Venette (XIV-2), *1738*, 300, 1253, 1309
John of Venice, 721
John of Vicenza (XIII-1), v. 2, *553*, 1190
John of Victring (XIV-1), *933*, 301
John de Vignai (XIV-1), *457*, 65, 317, 346, 391, 393, 457
John Villani (XIV-1), *913*, 215, 297, 313, 337, 496, 917, 919, 1198, 1251, 1283, 1482, 1737
John del Virgilio, 481, 918, 1482
John Visconti, 1796
John Voet, 1151
John Vrieman, 1541
John of Wales, 407
John of Waleys, 317
John v. Wesel, 1399
John of Willoughby, 560
John of Winterthur (XIV-1), *935*, 302
John Witte de Hese (XIV-2), *1606*, 1150
John Wittenborg, 125
John of Würzburg (XII-2), v. 2, *419*, 1191; v. 3, 1230
John, *see* Wycliffe
John, *see* Xiphilinos
John Yperman (XIV-1), *882*, 250, 272, 278, 293, 350, 1233, 1437
John of Ypres (XIV-2), *1753*, 775, 777, 779, 788, 953, 1075, 1151, 1258, 1309
John Zonaras (XII-1), v. 2, *251*, 137, 143
Johnes, Thomas, 930, 1753
Johnson, A. F., 513
Johnson, M. C., 1833
Johnson, O. S., 1139
Johnson, R. P., 168
Johnsson, J. W. S., 1659, 1689
Johnston, R. F., 779, 1018, 1854
Joinville, Jean de (XIV-1), *928*, 52, 57, 214, 229, 248, 301, 347, 464
Jolly, Julius, 1000, 1585, 1731, 1799
Jón, *see* John
Jonathan of Enghien, 1059

Jonckbloet, W. J. A., 938, 939, 940, 1438
Jondet, Gaston, 229
Jones, C. M., 1045
Jones, Dorothy, 1416
Jones, G. P., 1403
Jones, I. B., 250
Jones, R. M., 50, 572, 1416
Jones, W. H. S., 238
Jones, William, 627, 1458
Jonson, Ben, 1316, 1839
Jónsson, Finnur, 352, 1608
Jónsson of Skardsá, Björn, 1608
Jordan, *see also* Jordanes; Jordanus; Jourdain
Jordan of Canterbury, 1204
Jordan Catala de Sévérac (XIV-1), *783*, 189, 358
Jordan da Rivalto, 921
Jordan Ruffo (XIII-2), v. 2, *1076*, 89, 782; v. 3, 340, 813, 815, 858, 1669
Jordanes (VI-2), v. 1, *455*, 426, 445
Jordanes de Turre (XIV-1), *877*, 248
Jordanus, axiom, 146
Jordanus Nemorarius (XIII-1), v. 2, *613*, 1191; v. 3, 113, 145, 146, 147, 1432, 1487, 1489, 1565
Jorga, *see* Iorga
Jorge, *see* George
Jórsalafarer, *see* Björn Einarsson
Jorz, *see* Thomas
Joseph, *see also* Yūsuf. The form Joseph is generally used for Christian and Jewish names, the form Yūsuf for Arabic names.
Joseph Abraham b. Abraham, 1522
Joseph b. Abraham Giqaṭilia (XIII-2), v. 2, *882*, 730; v. 3, 100
Joseph b. Abraham Naḥmias, 894
Joseph v. Abraham ha-Ro'eh (XI-1), v. 1, *703*, 694, 751
Joseph b. Abraham b. Waqar (XIV-1), *613*, 62, 100, 255
Joseph Albo, 1447
Joseph of Arimathie, 1313
Joseph b. a. Ayyūb ha-Rofe, 451
Joseph Baḥtawi, 365
Joseph Bryennios, 746, 1058, 1209, 1320, 1363
Joseph Christodulos, 1094, 1260
Joseph b. David ha-Yewani (XIV-1), *1008*, 369, 1452
Joseph b. Eliezer Bonfils (XIV-2), *1364*, 1060, 1064, 1156
Joseph Faquin, 198
Joseph Flavius (I-2), v. 1, *262*, 245; v. 2, 1191; v. 3, 367, 1451, 1656
Joseph Flavius, pseudo, 1451
Joseph b. Gorion, 1009, 1451
Joseph b. Isaac Israeli, 67, 130, 198
Joseph b. Isaac Qimḥi (XII-2), v. 2, *344*, 1191; v. 3, 366, 427, 1385
Joseph b. Isaac b. Waqar (XIV-2), *1514*, 1115, 1762
Joseph b. Jacob b. Ẓaddīq (XII-1), v. 2, *186*, 118
Joseph b. Japhet ha-Levi, 1117
Joseph b. Joseph Naḥmias, 130, 132, 1523
Joseph b. Joshua ha-Kohen, 1384, 1652
Joseph b. Joshua I ha-Lorqi (XIV-2), *1373*, 1072, 1096
Joseph b. Joshua II ha-Lorqi (XIV-2), *1373*, 1072, 1211, 1221, 1380, 1385
Joseph b. Judah b. Aqnīn (XII-2), v. 2, *380*, 1191; v. 3, 62, 99, 432, 602
Joseph b. abba Mari Kaspi (XIV-1), *589*, 56, 73, 74, 98, 368, 428, 429, 1635
Joseph b. Meïr b. Zabara (XII-2), v. 2, *381*, 291, 307
Joseph b. Moses Kilti (XIV-2), *1452*, 1098, 1117
Joseph Orabuena, 1343, 1377, 1384
Joseph, philosopher, 888, 889, 996
Joseph the Priest, *see* Yūsuf Khūrī
Joseph Rhacendytes, 889, 891
Joseph b. Samson (XIII-1), v. 2, *699*, 532; v. 3, 345, 366
Joseph b. Samuel b. Naqawa, 1445
Joseph Sapiens (X-2), v. 1, *672*, 649, 655
Joseph b. Saul Qimḥi, 1516
Joseph ha-Sephardi called Bonfils, 1364
Joseph b. Shem-ṭob b. Shem-ṭob, 594, 1447, 1522, 1523
Joseph b. Sheshet, 1523
Joseph b. Simon Qara, 397
Joseph, T. K., 358
Joseph b. Vidal Labi, 1377, 1716
Joseph b. Yaḥya, 1523
Joseph, *see* Yūsuf b. Aḥmad b. Ḥasdai
Josephus, *see* Joseph
Joshua of Bologna, 1669
Joshua b. David ha-Kohen, 876
Joshua b. Joseph ha-Lorqi, 399, 1053, 1373
Joshua b. Joseph II ha-Lorqi (XIV-2), *1716*, 1211, 1240, 1377
Joshua b. Judah (XI-2), v. 1, *751*, 739, 745
Josippon, 1451
Josquin des Prés, 744
Josse van den Berg, 184
Jostes, Franz, 570
Joubert, Laurent, 279
Jouguet, Pierre, 1007
Jourdain, Amable, 1384
Jourdain, Charles, 374, 476, 944, 1491, 1494, 1495
Jourdain Delestre, 1545
Jourdain, P. E. B., 556
Jourdanne, Gaston, 1304
journal, business, 128
Journal des savants, 1871
Journal de Trévoux, 1871
Journez, Alf., 1749, 1751
Jouvence, *see* John
Joyce, *see* Thomas

Joz Dutra, 184
Juan, *see* John
Juba II of Mauretania (I-2 B.C.), v. 1, *232*, 220; v. 3, 1158, 1772
Jubair, b., *see* Muḥammad b. Aḥmad
Jubilee of 1300 (XIII-2), v. 2, *823*; v. 3, 37, 43, 393, 1247
Jubinal, Achille, 249
Jūd, a., *see* Muḥammad b. Laith
Judah b. Abraham Cresques (XIV-2), *1593*, 1141, 1858
Judah b. Asher (XIV-1), *613*, 100, 130
Judah b. Asher II, 130, 614, 1445, 1515
Judah b. Astruc Bonsenyor (XIV-1), *427*, 61, 255, 343, 427, 1841
Judah b. David, *see* Ḥayyuj
Judah b. Elijah Hadassi (XII-1), v. 2, *190*, 119
Judah ha-filosof, 449
Judah b. Isaac Kohen (XIV-1), *609*, 98, 434, 850
Judah b. Jacob b. 'Aṭṭār, 1452
Judah b. Jehiel Rophe, 594
Judah ha-Levi (XII-1), v. 2, *186*, 1191; v. 3, 1521
Judah b. Moses b. Daniel (XIV-1), *449*, 65, 101, 370, 429, 449
Judah b. Moses Kohen (XIII-2), v. 2, *842*, 1191; v. 3, 1383
Judah b. Moses Mosconi (XIV-2), *1450*, 957, 1009, 1098, 1213, 1261, 1858
Judah ha-Nasi (II-2), v. 1, *295*, 288, 384; v. 2, 208; v. 3, 419, 1062
Judah b. Nissim b. Malkah (XIV-2), *1444*, 1096
Judah b. Quraish (IX-1), v. 1, *581*, 811; v. 2, 142, 272; v. 3, 366
Judah Romano, *see* Judah b. Moses b. Daniel
Judah b. Samuel b. 'Abbas (XIII-1), v. 2, *606*, 1191
Judah b. Samuel ha-Ḥasid (XIII-1), v. 2, *607*, 1191
Judah b. Saul b. Tibbon (XII-2), v. 2, *345*, 1191; v. 3, 366, 368, 590, 596
Judah b. Solomon Ḥarizi (XIII-1), v. 2, *604*, 1191; v. 3, 590, 615, 1303
Judah b. Solomon ha-Kohen (XIII-2), v. 2, *603*, 1191; v. 3, 1008, 1450
Judah b. Solomon b. Labi (XIV-2), *1377*, 1072, 1074, 1384, 1716
Judah b. Solomon Nathan (XIV-2), *1374*, 608, 1072, 1074, 1097, 1212, 1221, 1448, 1717, 1719
Judah b. Verga, 1448
Judaism, development (VII-1), v. 1, *471*
Judeich, Walther, 1891
Judges, book of (VI B.C.), v. 1, *79*; v. 3, 363
Jugie, Martin, 358, 1830, 1845, 1853, 1864
Julian the Apostate (IV-2), v. 1, *365*, 812
Julian, Salvius, jurist (II-1), v. 1, *285*, 269
Juliana Berners, 1165, 1184, 1185, 1315
Juliana of Norwich, 1089
Julianos of Laodicea (V-2), v. 1, *410*, 400
Julien des ménétriers, St., 1129
Julien, Stanislas, 976
Julios Africanos (III-1), v. 1, *327*, 812; v. 3, 1838
Julius Alexandrinus de Neustain, 891
Julius, *see* Caesar
Juljul, b. (X-2), v. 1, *682*, 809; v. 2, 79, 663
Jull Hindī, 1636
Jullien, Ernest, 1185
Jullien, M., 1428, 1432
Jumaiyil b. Khāmis Sa'dī, 1827
jumar, 455
Jundī, b., *see* Isḥāq b. Mūsā; Khalīl b. Isḥāq
Jundīshāpūr, school (VI-1), v. 1, *435*, 812; v. 3, 357, 376
Jundt, Auguste, 572
Jungingen, *see* Conrad
Jupiter, 444, 1489
jurisprudentia, 1000
Jurjānī, *see* 'Alī b. Muḥammad; Ismā'īl b. Ḥusain; Sa'īd Ḍarīr
Jurji, E. J., 1271
Jusserand, J. J., 1413, 1415, 1891
Justel, Henri, 1822
Justinian I, the Great (VI-1), v. 1, *439*, 812; v. 2, 1191; v. 3, 39, 995, 1797
Justinian, *see* Codex; Institutes
Justinian, plague, 1650
Justinos II, 378
Justinos Martyr, St. (II-2), v. 1, *293*, 288; v. 3, viii
juvamentis, De, 844
Juvenal, 1418
Juwainī, *see* 'Aṭā Malik b. Muḥammad; Muḥammad b. Muḥammad
Juynboll, T. G. J., 806
Juynboll, Th. W., 1066, 1262
juz' wāḥid, 149
Juzayy, b., *see* 'Abdallāh b. Muḥammad; Muḥammad b. Muḥammad
Juzī'yāt wa kullīyāt, 465
Juzjānī, *see* 'Abd al-Wāḥid b. Muḥammad; Aḥmad b. 'Uthmān

Ka'b b. Zuhair, 1010
Kabar, b., *see* a. Barakāt
Kabīr, 154, 425, 1475
Kabīr panth, 1475
Kabīrpanthī, 425
Kaccāyana, 382, 423, 1371
Kaccāyanappakaraṇa, 423
Kad ha-qemaḥ, 100, 417
kadaḷi pāka, 465
Kämpf, Hellmut, 411
Kaempfer, Engelbert, 906
Kafa, *see* Cafa
Kafarov, P. I., 1866
Kāfī fī 'ilm al-dīn, 1067
Kaftor u-feraḥ, 791

kāghad, 175
kāghad khāna, 175
Kah-dam-pa, 1371
Kahane, Henri, 1812, 1859
Kahane, Renée, 1812, 1859
Kahn, S., 428, 449, 1382, 1719
Kahrie jami, 97, 950. *See also* Saviour in Chora, Saint
Kaiser, Hans, 1351
Kaiser, Rudolf, 252
kalām, 149
Kalbe, *see* Rülein
Kalbfleisch, Karl, 447
Kalhaṇa (XII-1), v. 2, *261*, 140
Kālidāsa, 1366
Kalīla wa-Dimna, 68, 305, 464, 925, 1639
Kalkar, *see* Calcar
Kalm, Per, 1612
Kalmar, Union, 1021
Kalmuk, 380, 1865
Kalonaros, P. P., 1852
Kålund, Kristian, 1114, 1583
Kaluza, Max, 1424, 1425
kāma, 1000
Kamāl al-dīn 'Abd-al-Razzāq, 1292
Kamāl al-dīn Fārisi (XIV-1), *707*, 134, 141, 142, 705, 1847
Kamāl al-dīn, *see* Mūsā b. Yūnus
kāmaśāstra, 296, 465, 1000
Kamil, Murad, 957
Kāmil, a., *see* Shujā' b. Aslam
Kāmil al-sinā'atain, 828
Kamintus, 1689
Kammād, b., *see* Aḥmad b. Yūsuf
Kammerer, Albert, 1891
Kammūna, b., *see* Sa'd b. Manṣūr
Kanfe nesharim, 1517
Kanjur (VII-1), v. 1, *467*, 538, 593; v. 3, 59, 69, 71, 259, 380, 384, 468, 1842
Kankan Mūsā, 803
Kannaḍa, 383
Kannaḍa Ṭīke, 383
Kansi, *see* Samuel b. Simeon
Kantorowicz, H. U., 850, 1796
Kappot kesef, 592
Kara-khōja, 833
Kara Khoto, 203
Karā, *see* Muḥammad b. 'Īsā
Karabaček, Josef, 175
Karādīsī, *see* Ḥasan b. Khalīl
Karak, 393
kāraka, 1371
Karakī, *see* a. Bakr. b. Muḥammad
karāma, 623, 1845
Karīn, 459
Karīn, *see* John
Karkhī, *see* Muḥammad b. Ḥasan
Karlgren, Bernhard, 1891
Karlsefni, *see* Thorfin
Karmānī, *see* 'Amr b. 'Abd al-Raḥmān
Karmapradīpikā, 1535
Karnak, 1187
Kārnāmak (VI-2), v. 1, *457*, 445
Karṇāṭakaśabda-sāra, 1828
Karpinski, L. C., 1110, 1312, 1426, 1891
Karrer, Otto, 570
Karshūnī, 360
Karslake, J. B. P., 191
Karst, J., 305, 1222
Kartlis tzkhovreba, 305
ka's al-futūwa, 154
kashaf, 405
Kāshān wares, 756
Kāshānī, *see* 'Abdallāh b. 'Alī; 'Abd al-Razzāq; Ya'qūb b. Aḥmad
Kashf al-asrār, 760
Kashf al-rain, 899
Kashf al-sutūr, 759
Kashf al-wail, 828
Kāshgar, *see* Maḥmūd
kāshī, 756
kāshī-kārī, 757
kāshī-paz, 757
kāshī-sāzī, 757
Kashmīr, 1475
Kashmir, *see* Caraka
Kashmīrī, 1330, 1476, 1840
Kaspi, 589
Kaspi, *see* Joseph b. abba Mari; Mari b. Joseph; Solomon b. Joseph
Kastner, Georges, 1231
Kāśyapa-Mātaṅga (I-2), v. 1, *246*
Kāthī, *see* Muḥammad b. 'Abd al-Malik
Kathīr, b., *see* Ismā'īl b. 'Umar
Kātib, a., 1385
Kātib Qaiṣar, b., 1006
Kātibī, *see* 'Alī b. 'Umar
kattān, 175
Katzenellenbogen, M. E. v. H., 430
Kaufmann, D., 419, 1376, 1443
Kaufmann, J., 1522
Kausler, Eduard v., 1438
Kauṭilya (IV-2 B.C.), v. 1, *147*, 126, 127
Kautzsch, Rudolf, 1407
Kavi-bhūshaṇa, 1396
Kavirājamārga, 383
Kaviratna, Hariśchandra, 1585
kavitraya, 466
Kawi, 1331, 1624
Kay, A. C., 1848
Kay, H. C., 958, 1778
Kayserling, Meyer, 419, 449, 1344, 1386, 1523, 1717
Kayserling, Moritz, 1377, 1385
kayyasa, 288
Kazan, 1026
Keane, A. H., 281
Keats, 1188
Keay, F. E., 1476
Kebra nagast, 957

Keeton, G. W., 1870
Kégl, Sándor, 1641
Kehrmann, Alexander, 1407
Keith, A. B., 1117, 1369, 1891
Kekelídze, K. S., 305
Kelal qaṭan, 451
Keller, Ferdinand, 224
Kellermann, Benzion, 606
Kelsen, Hans, 499
Kempe, Anders, 370
Kempe, *see* John; Margery
Kempis, *see* Thomas
Keniston, R. H., 491, 492
Kennedy, A. G., 1425
Kennedy, E. S., 1830
Kensington inscription, 1155, 1610
Kenyon, Frederic G., 1877, 1891
Kēphā, *see* Moses bar
Kepler, Johann, 17, 215, 543, 600, 705, 746, 1112, 1846, 1881
Kerenbes, 1143
Kermadec, J. M. de, 1841
Kern, G. J., 111
Kern, Hendrik, 1624, 1627
Kern, R. A., 1627
Kerniensis, *see* John of Karīn?
Kerstken, *see* Herman
Kervyn de Lettenhove, 1023, 1747, 1753
keshafim, 405
Keskinto inscription (II-2 B.C.), v. 1, *195*
Kethābā dheskōlyōn, 139
Ketham, *see* John
Ketkar, Mrs. Shridar Venkatesh, 1909
Kettlewell, Samuel, 1361
Kéza, *see* Simon
Khabbāzī, *see* 'Umar b. Muḥammad
Khaddām, b., 134
Khadduri, Majid, 1274
Khagēndramaṇidarpaṇa, 1730
Khair al-dīn Barbarossa, 1776
khāl, 960
khalā wa-malā', 149
Khalaf b. 'Abbās, *see* a. Qāsim
Khaldūn, b., 'Abd al-Raḥmān b. Muḥammad (XIV-2), *1767*, 18, 134, 373, 957, 1010, facing 1019, 1082, 1098, 1104, 1118, 1138, 1157, 1167, 1170, 1214, 1236, 1264, 1271, 1274, 1284, 1463, 1515, 1618, 1651, 1765, 1766, 1868
Khaldūn, Banū, 1262, 1868
Khaldūn, b., *see* 'Umar b. Aḥmad; Yaḥyā b. Muḥammad
Khaldūnīya, 1776
Khālid b. 'Abd al-Malik Marwarrūdhī (IX-1), v. 1, *566*, 545, 550
Khālid b. 'Īsā Balawī (XIV-1), *807*, 202, 307
Khālid b. Yazīd (VII-2), v. 1, *495*, 489, 490; v. 2, 1193; v. 3, 165, 759, 1138
khalīfa, 106, 154
Khalīfa b. a. Maḥāsin of Aleppo (XIII-2), v. 2, *1101*, 82, 789; v. 3, 1724
Khalīl b. Aḥmad (VIII-2), v. 1, *541*, 523, 524; v. 2, 701; v. 3, 372, 435, 1637
Khalīl b. Aibak Ṣafadī (XIV-1), *959*, 134, 201, 257, 271, 308, 1262
Khalīl b. Isḥāq b. Jundī (XIV-2), *1455*, 1099
Khalīl b. Shāhīn Ẓāhirī, 1265
Khalīlī, *see* Muḥammad b. Muḥammad; Mūsā b. Muḥammad
Khaljī, 40
Khallāl, *see* Muḥammad b. Sālim
Khallikān, Aḥmad b. Muḥammad b. (XIII-2), v. 2, *1120*, 1193; v. 3, 308, 619, 958, 960, 1264, 1781
Khalwatī, *see* 'Umar
Khalwatīya, 1069
Khan, M. A. R., 1623
Khānbaliq, 773, 777
Khāqān, king, 1644
Kharaqī, *see* Muḥammad b. Aḥmad
Khardal, 230
Kharīdat al-'ajā'ib, 805, 963
Khashkhāsh of Cordova, 803
Khaṭīb Baghdādī, *see* Aḥmad b. 'Alī
Khaṭīb Dimashq, *see* Muḥammad b. 'Abd al-Raḥmān
Khaṭīb Irbilī, *see* Muḥammad b. 'Alī
Khaṭīb, b., Muḥammad b. 'Abdallāh (XIV-2), *1762*, 307, 827, 830, 852, 896, 897, 1157, 1213, 1261, 1635, 1636, 1768, 1868, 1885
Khātimah, b., *see* Aḥmad b. 'Alī
Khaṭṭāb b. Aḥmad b. Raḥat, 1249
Khayyām, *see* 'Umar
Khazars, 415
Khāzin, *see* a. Ja'far
Khāzinī, *see* 'Abd al-Raḥmān
Khazrajī, *see* Aḥmad b. 'Abdallāh
Khemiri, T., 1779
Khiḍr, 1324, 1761
Khiḍr b. 'Alī Aidīnī, 1727. *See* Ḥājjī Pāshā
khirqa, 619
khirqat al-taṣawwuf, 154
Khitrovo, Mme B. de, 791, 1613
Khlath, *see* Gregory
Khmer, 1030
Khuastuanift, 378
Khudā Yār Khān Dā'ūd 'Abbāsī, 232
Khudhāy-nāmak (VII-1), v. 1, *482*, 540; v. 3, 376
Khujandī, *see* Ḥāmid b. Khiḍr; Muḥammad b. Muḥammad
Khull, K., 788
khunthā, 1169
Khurdādhbih, b. (IX-2), v. 1, *606*, 810
khutzuri (ecclesiastical), 304
Khwaja Banda Nawāz, 1476
Khwārizmī. *see* Luqmān; Muḥammad b. Aḥmad

Khwārizmī, Muḥammad b. Mūsā (IX-1), v. 1, *563*, 813; v. 2, 1193; v. 3, xi, 738, 1158
kiat-hāne, 175
Kibre, Pearl, 166, 1863, 1891
kibrīt, 753
Kienbusch, C. O. v., 1556
Kiepert, Heinrich, 774
Kiesewetter, R. G., 1571
Kiessling, Th., facing 1019
Kiev, 39
Kiev, *see* Cyprian; Daniel; Nestor
Kīlānī, *see* Aḥmad b. Muḥammad
Kilti, *see* Joseph b. Moses
Kilwardby, *see* Robert
Kimble, G. H. T., 1592, 1598, 1891
Kinda, tribe, 1767
Kindī (IX-1), v. 1, *559*, 813; v. 2, 1193; v. 3, 128, 164, 200, 245, 264, 431, 453, 501, 738, 749, 836, 1211
King, F. H., 210
King, Sir Lucas, 1873, 1891
Kings, books of (VI B.C.), v. 1, *79*; v. 2, 858; v. 3, 227
King's College, 72, 1402
King's Hall, 475
Kingsbury, *see* Thomas
Kingsford, C. L., 183, 462, 552, 558, 738, 944, 945, 946, 1316, 1394, 1500, 1742, 1744
Kingsley, Charles, 572
Kinney, B. A., 882
Kīrānī, *see* Hindushāh b. Sanjar
Kirby, T. F., 1403
Kircher, Athanasius, 1007, 1667, 1806
Kirchheim, Raphael, 592
Kirfel, Willibald, 259, 280
Kirkby, *see* Margaret
Kirkup, Seymour, 485
Kirsch, J. P., 1356
Kirsten, Peter, 1010
Kitāb, 372
Kitayama, Junyu, x
Kittredge, G. L., 354, 745, 1124, 1425
Klapper, Joseph, 252
Klaproth, Jules, 975, 976, 1016
Klatzkin, Jacob, 1719, 1883, 1891
Klebel, Ernst, 934
Klebs, A. C., xv, 28, 241, 862, 1103, 1241, 1661, 1891
Klein, Gustav, 1207
Klein, Salomon, 452
Kleinhans, Arduinus, 375
Klemm, Kurt, 1369
Klemming, G. E., 1356
Klett, Werner, 1415
Klibansky, R., 11, 515, 569, 1844
Klimas, Petras, 1152
Klinckowstroem, Carl v., 1551
Knapp, Hermann, 993
Kneer, August, 1351, 1509
knighthood, *see* religious orders
Knighton, *see* Henry
Knobel, E. B., 1120
Knötel, August, 1160
Knoll, Oskar, 915
Knoop, Douglas, 1403
Knott, C. G., 1586
Knox, Francis, 575
knowledge lost, 1773
Knust, Hermann, 564, 925, 1303, 1428
Knutsson, *see* Paul
Koch Hugo, 1439
Koch, Joseph, 524, 535, 557, 570
Koch, Robert, 1665
Koch, T. W., 495
Köbel, *see* Jacob
Koehler, J. B., 622, 799, 805
Köhler, Johannes, 1709
König, C., 1623
König, Dietrich, 404
Königshofen, *see* Jacob
Königssaal, *see* Peter
Köpke, Ernst, 458
Koeppel, Emil, 1811
Köprülü, Mehmed Fuat, 104, 1014
Körting, Gustav, 514, 1810
Kofler, Hans, 998
Kohen, *see* Jacob b. Nathaniel; Joseph b. Joshua; Joshua b. David; Judah b. Isaac; Judah b. Moses; Judah b. Solomon; Perez b. Isaac
Kohen, S. b. M., 437
Koheḥ, *see* Solomon; Solomon b. Paṭer
Kohen-Ẓedeq, Joseph, 792, 1523
Kohler, Charles, 392, 393, 416, 956
Kohler, Joseph, 499
Kohler, Kaufmann, x, 56, 417, 1071, 1444
Kohn, Helen, 1909
Kokabi, *see* David b. Samuel
Kokan, engraver, 424
Kokaśāstra, 465
Kokkoka, 465
Koldewey, Robert, 778
Kollert, Erna, 876, 1698
Kolozsvár, *see* George; Martin
Komai, Kazuo, 906
Komroff, Manuel, 779
Kondakov, N. P., 1583
Konow, Sten, 384
Konrad, *see* Conrad
Konstantinides, A., 170
Konungs skuggsjá (XIII-1), v. 2, *594*, 1193; v. 3, 352, 709, 1187
Koo, V. K. W., 1589
Korea, 1879, 1880, 1907, 1910
Korean, 32, 387
Korean, *see* alphabet
Korean influence on Japanese medicine (VI-2), v. 1, *454*
Korean, *see* star map; typography
Koryu dynasty, 1478
Korzybski, Alfred, 331

Kosegarten, J. G. L., 618, 789
Kostanecki, Anton v., 499
Kostomarov, N., 1825
Kowalewski, J. S., 381
Kowalski, Tadeusz, 1017
Kozlov, P. K., 203
Kraemer, *see* Henry
Kraft, Wilhelm, 1850
Krall, Jakob, 175
Kramer, Stella, 153
Kramers, J. H., 63, 771, 1099, 1160
Krapf, Eugenio, 925
Kraus, F. R., 1836
Kraus, Paul, 165, 292
Krause, F. E. A., 956
Krauss, Samuel, 364
Krazer, Adolf, 738, 1488, 1567
Krebs, Engelbert, 522, 706
Krebs, Martin, 1836
Krebs, Werner, 153
Kremer, A. v., 1778
Kremers, Edward, 290, 860, 1892
Kremsier (Kroměříž), *see* Milič
Krenkow, F., 622, 961, 1788
Kretschmayer, Heinrich, 917
Kretschmer, Konrad, 771, 1892
Krichpaum, *see* John
Kriegk, G. L., 1716
Kṛishṇa, 466
Krist, Gustav, 1470
Kristeller, Paul, 580
Kṛittivāsa (XIV-2), *1395*, 1077, 1330
Kṛityacintāmaṇi, 1000
Kroll, Wilhelm, 150, 1877
Kronenberg, M. E., 1892
Kroschel, H. G., 820
Krüger, Gustav, 55, 358
Krumbacher, Karl, 1892
Kublai Khān (XIII-2), v. 2, *980*, 1194; v. 3, 42, 69, 137, 162, 205, 211, 380, 384, 386, 468, 634, 730, 832, 970, 971, 978, 1027, 1029, 1624, 1789, 1800, 1829
kūcha-i-'ulamā', 970
Kudatku bilik, 378, 1015, 1840
Kühnöl, C. G., 1388
Kühtmann, Alfred, 556
Künssberg, Hans, 1433
Künstle, Karl, 1041, 1232
Kuersteiner, A. F., 1736
Kürzinger, Josef, 521
Kugler, Lothar, 556
Kūhī, *see* Wījan b. Rustam
Kūhīn 'Aṭṭār (XIII-2), v. 2, *1097*, 1194; v. 3, 1726
Kuhl, E. P., 1425
Kuhns, L. O., 498
Kulamaṇḍana, 1330, 1474
Kuleserian, B. E., 1442
Kulīnī, *see* Muḥammad b. Ya'qūb
Kumārajīva (V-1), v. 1, *384*, 814; v. 3, 468
Kumārila (VIII-1), v. 1, *512*, 504, 1366
Kumbum, 1371
kumiss, 1621
Kummer, Bernhard, 1230
Kunnāsh, 797, 895
Kunstmann, Friedrich, 771, 783, 784
kunya, 961
Kunz, Alfred, 462
Kunz, G. F., 1471
Kupka, Paul, 1232
Kurdian, Haroutiun, 784, 789
Kurth, Godefroid, 937, 1605, 1749, 1751
Kurz, Otto, 1178
Kushelev-Bezborodko, G., 1825
Kūshyār b. Labbān (XI-1), v. 1, *717*, 696, 702
Kutná Hora, 472
Kutub pillar, 1175
kutub al-sitta, 1065, 1639
Kutubī, *see* Muḥammad b. Shākir; Yūsuf b. Ismā'īl
Kuun, Géza, 1016
Kybal, Vlastimil, 1352
kybrit, 753
Kyeser, *see* Conrad
Kyngeston, *see* Richard
Kyrkby, *see* Margaret

la'azim, 345, 397, 1826
Labanca, Baldassare, 516, 989
Labande, L. H., 1032
Labbe, Philippe, 952
Labi, *see* Joseph Vidal; Judah b. Solomon; Solomon
labor, specialization, 152
labor troubles, 13, 1580
Laborde, A. de, 1552
Labouret, H., 41, 803, 1617
Labrador, 1154
La Brière, 1631
Labrosse, H., 399, 400, 1344
labsān, 230
lac virginis, 1573
Lacaita, J. P., 1814
La Cava, A. F., 1838, 1867
La Cerda, *see* Lewis
Lacinio, Giano, 752
Lackland, *see* John
Lacnunga (X-1), v. 1, *634*, 621
Lacombe, *see* Gerald
lacquer, 170
Lacroix, Paul, 1080, 1632
Lactantius, viii, 193, 1294
ladder, spiritual, 581
Ladhdhat al-nisā', 465
Ladislas Jagiello, 1325, 1398
Ladislas the Wise, 1759
Lafont, *see* William
La Fontaine, 929, 1135
La Fontaine, *see* John
Lagarde, Georges de, 989

Lagercrantz, Otto, 755, 1876, 1892
La Gironière, Paul de, 1867
Lagrange, 335, 1489
La Horbe, *see* Nicholas
Lahore, *see* Muḥammad 'Alī
Laignel-Lavastine, Maxime, 1217, 1892
Lailā wa Majnūn, 305
Lailavoix, Louis, 1425
Lajard, Félix, 317, 458, 463, 992
Lājīn b. 'Abdallāh Dhahabī, 210, 239, 1169, 1642
Lajlāj, *see* Muḥammad b. 'Ubaidallāh
Lajos I, 1480
Laking, G. F., 1556
Lakshmaṇa Śāstrī, 423
Lakshmīdhara (XII-1), v. 2, *269*, 142
Lal Ded (XIV-2), *1475*, 1102, 1330
Lallā-vākyāni, 1475
Lallā Yōgīshwarī, 1475
Lām-rim, 1371
Lamaist, 468
La Marche, *see* Blanche
La Mare, *see* Thomas; William
Lamartine, Alphonse de, 1777
Lamas, pseudonym, 1385
lamaseries, 1371
Lamb, Harold, 1474
Lambeck, Peter, 1823
Lambert of Auxerre, 552
Lambert, F. A., 582
Lambert of Hersfeld (XI-2), v. 1, *775*, 743, 745
Lambert of Saint Omer (XII-1), v. 2, *222*, 1194; v. 3, 192, 193
Lambert li Tors, or le Tort, 232
Lambertenghi, *see* Leo
Lambourne, *see* Reginald
Lambrecht, Joos, 349, 1318
Lambros, *see* Lampros
Lami, Giovanni, 1810
Lami, Vittorio, 915
Lamme, *see* Henry
Lammens, Henri, 803, 1035, 1461, 1777, 1892
Lampros, Spyridōn, 120, 1260
Lana, *see* James
Lancaster, *see* Blanche; Henry; Isabel; Thomas
land sphere, 483
land and water areas, 188, 797, 1148
Landa, *see* Nicholas
Landau, L., 1717
Landau, Marcus, 1810
Landau, *see* Nicholas
Landauer, Gustav, 570
landed property, 327
Lander, John, 1159
Lander, R. L., 1159
Landino, *see* Cristoforo; Francis
Landnámabók, 303
Landolfo Colonna, 987, 989
Landrechtsbuch, 993
Landry, Adolphe, 1496
Landry, B., 494
Landsberg, *see* Herrad
Landsberger, Julius, 432
Lane, E. W., 288, 805, 1830
Lane, W. C., 495
Lane-Poole, Stanley, 1788, 1892
Lanercost, Chronicon de, 1256
Lanfranchi (XIII-2), v. 2, *1079*, 1194; v. 3, 244, 247, 272, 274, 278, 865, 866, 870, 881, 882, 883, 1194, 1203, 1243, 1699, 1703, 1705
Lanfranchi of Milano, *see* Lanfranchi
Lang, Albert, 1432
Láng, P. H., 1892
Langdon, Courtney, 493
Lange, Gerson, 606
Lange, Hugo, 1422, 1426
Langenstein, *see* Henry
Langer, W. L., 37
Langham, *see* Simon
Langkavel, Bernhard, 826
Langland, *see* William
Langlès, L. M., 1473
Langlois, C. V., 400, 407, 411, 457, 531, 535, 546, 549, 784, 886, 955, 1676, 1892
Langlois, E. H., 1231
Langlois, Ernest, 452, 458
Langmantel, Valentin, 1153
Langtoft, *see* Peter
Langton, Neville, 1186, 1864
language, 1895
"langue d'oc," 338
"langue d'oīl," 338
langues de serpent, 1242
languier, 1242
Langus, Joannes, 947
Lanz, K. F. W., 926
Lanzarote Malocello (XIII-2), v. 2, *1062*, 36 773; v. 3, 183, 510, 768, 1808
Lao Thai, 1029
Laonicos Chalcondyles, 919, 1553
Laos, 1879
Lapa di Puccio Piagenti, 1334
Lapacino, *see* Francis
La Palu, *see* Gerald; Peter
Lapethis, *see* George
lapidaries, 1165, 1166, 1171, 1208, 1749, 1822. *See* also stones, precious
Lapidary of Aristotle (IX-1), v. 1, *572*; v. 3, 801
lapide philosophico, De, 398, 560
lapis lazuli, 756
Laplace, 1489
La Porrée, *see* Gilbert
Lappe, Joseph, 547
Laprade, *see* Blacas
laqab, 961
Largentera, *see* Bonafous

Larned, W. C., 281
La Roche, *see* Othon
La Rochefoucauld, barony of, 990
La Rochelle, *see* John; Nicholas Donin
La Roncière, Charles de, 771, 1892
Larsen, Henning, 1208
Larson, L. M., 710
La Salle, *see* Anthony; Gadifer
Lascaris, *see* Constantine; Theodore
Las Casas, 1671
Lasinio, Fausto, 436
Lassus, Roland de, 744
Lasswitz, Kurd, 1464
Last, Isaac, 592
Lateran council, 276
Latham, C. S., 494
Laṭīf, b., *see* Isaac b. Abraham
Latimer, *see* William
Latin, 330, 371, 1881, 1883, 1894
Latin MSS, 1902, 1903
Latin, *see* mathematics and astronomy; medicine
Latin, mediaeval, 1879
Latin-Persian-Coman dictionary, 1016
Latini, *see* Brunetto
latitudes and longitudes, 135, 1436, 1487
La Torre, Felice, 268
La Tour-Landry, *see* Geoffrey
Lattes, *see* Isaac b. Jacob; Isaac b. Judah
Latvia, *see* Henry
Laudesi, 50
Laue, Max, 920
Laufer, Berthold, 181, 233, 237, 381, 716, 758, 778, 780, 833, 1187, 1188, 1561, 1586, 1590, 1865, 1892
Laufer, Heinrich, 259, 1331
Launay, Louis de, 151
Launoy, Jean de, 476
Laura de Noves, 514
Laura, Petrarca's, 335, 502
Laurence, *see also* Rienzo
Laurence (Vavřinec) of Březová, 1076, 1093, 1103, 1259, 1322
Laurence Byzinius, 1076
Laurence, Dominican, 340, 349, 462, 463
Laurence Egen, 1153
Laurence Gallus, 462
Laurence Ghiberti, 1105, 1300
Laurence il Magnifico, 1301
Laurence Mònaci, 916
Laurence de Premierfait, 1294, 1313, 1804, 1809, 1811
Laurence Rusio (XIV-1), *858*, 245, 284, 859, 1669, 1838
Laurence of Stokes, 720
Laurence Suárez de Figueroa, 427
Laurenstein, Dietrich, 1177
Laurent, *see also* Laurence
Laurent, Henry, 1496
Laurent, J. C. M., 779
Laurent, M. H., 569
Laurentian atlas, 1144
Laurentius, *see* Laurence
Laurie, A. P., 1132
Lausanne, *see* James
Lautenbach, *see* Manegold
Lauterbach, J. Z., 713, 1062
Lautrey, Louis, 1242
Laval, *see* Joan
Lavallée, Joseph, 1630
La Vallée Poussin, Louis de, 1070, 1367
Lavardin, *see* Hildebert
La Vérendrye, 1612
Lavignac, Albert, 162
Law, B. C., 1892
Law, N. N., 1893
law, *see* barbarian
law book, Syriac-Roman (V-2), v. 1, *412*, 400
law, Burmese, 382
law, Byzantine (VIII-1), v. 1, *517;* (IX-2), v. 1, *617*
law, *see* canon law; commercial
law, criminal, 1869
law, Egyptian (VIII B.C.), v. 1, *59*
law, feudal (XII-1), v. 2, *267*, 141, 800
law, Germanic, 993
law, Greek (VII B.C.), v. 1, *62;* (V B.C.), v. 1, *109*
law, *see* Hebrew; Hebrew history and law
law, Hindu, 382
law, Irish (V-1), v. 1, *397*
law, Japanese (VII-1), v. 1, *485;* (VII-2), v. 1, *500;* (VIII-1), v. 1, *518;* (IX-1), v. 1, *581;* (IX-2), v. 1, *618;* (XIII-1), v. 2, *693*
law, *see* lex; leys
law, Lombard, 1869
law, *see* medicine
law, Roman, 1273, 1903, 1908
law, Roman (V B.C.), v. 1, *109*, 508, 779; (VI-1), v. 1, *438*
law, Roman, in East (VI-1), v. 1, *440*
law, Roman, in France and England (XII-1), v. 2, *267*, 1195
law, Sicilian, 1869
law, Visigothic (VII-2), v. 1, *500*, 837
law, *see* wager
law, Welsh, 1864
Lawī, b., *see* Mūsā
Lawrence, *see* Laurence
Lawson, J. C., 1864
laxatives, 427, 1228
Layamon, 1740
Layard, Arthur, 1605
lazar houses, 276
Lazar of Serbia, 1025
lazaretti, 276, 293
Lazarus, 1275
lāzhuward, 757
Lazi, Jekuthiel b. Nahum, 1376
Lazzarini, Vittorio, 1671, 1677

Lea, Henry Charles, 52, 239, 328, 395, 1044, 1047, 1051, 1060, 1077, 1140, 1339, 1347, 1601, 1864, 1870, 1882, 1893
Leach, A. F., 1893
lead, 219
lead poisoning, 889
Leadam, I. S., 1746
Leaf, Walter, 1458
Leander, Pontus, 1783
Lebègue, Henri, 1876
Le Bègue, *see* John
Le Bel, *see* John
Le Cerf, 575
Lechler, G. V., 1348, 1349
Lechner, Karl, 1663
Leclainche, Emmanuel, 1893
Leclerc, Lucien, 1893
Le Clerc, Victor, 22, 392, 476, 1601, 1739
Le Court de la Villethassetz, F., 232
Lecoy de la Marche, Albert, 168, 1040
ledger, 128
Lee, A. C., 1810
Lee, Charles, 1549
Lee, Samuel, 1622
Lee, Sidney, 1279, 1428, 1881, 1893
leeches, 869, 1621, 1640
Leeder, S. H., 1831
Leeds, J. W., 1349
Leeser, Isaac, 792
Lefebvre des Noëttes, 156
Le Ferron, *see* John
Le Fèvre, *see* John
Lefranc, Abel, 355, 369, 1321, 1323
Le François, 17
Legenda aurea, 300, 403, 1076, 1254, 1902
Leger, Louis, 941
Legge, M. D., 1312
legitimacy of a child, 849
Legname, *see* John
Legnano, *see* John
Legouais, *see* Chrétien
Legouis, Emile, 1425
Legouis, Henry, 1349
Le Gournaix, *see* Poince
Legrand, Emile, 1823, 1824
Legrand, *see* James
Le Grand, Léon, 280, 1597
Lehmann, Hermann, 448
Lehmann, Max, 567
Lehmann-Haupt, Hellmut, 1178
Leibniz, 140, 148, 738, 771, 1318
Leibniz, G. W., 935
Leiden, *see* Philip
Leif Ericsson (X-2), v. 1, *676*, 814; v. 3, 194, 1608, 1867
Leigh, Gertrude, 496, 500
leipsanothecas, 1045
Leland, John, 720, 728
Lelewel, Joachim, 1151, 1594
Le Lièvre, *see* Adam; John
Le Long, Isaac, 938
Lemaître, Henri, 1747
Le May, Reginald, 1031
Le Miesier, *see* Thomas
Le Mire, *see* William
lemmings, 1190
Lemoine, cardinal, 72
Lemoine, Collège du cardinal, 476
Lemoine, *see* John
Lemoisne, P. A., 1564
lemosina, lenga, 338, 342
Le Muisit, *see* Giles
Lenglet, A., 399
Lenin, 1466
Lennox, W. G., 876, 882
Leo, *see also* Judah
Leo Africanus, 1158
Leo III of Armenia, 54, 67
Leo VI of Armenia, 1035
Leo de Bagnols, 595
Leo Battista Alberti, 736, 1105
Leo III, Byzantine emperor, the Isaurian (VIII-1), v. 1, *517*, 505, 617
Leo VI, Byzantine emperor, the Wise, 824, 1853
Leo de (Ser) Daniele, 449
Leo Diaconos (X-2), v. 1, *686*, 652, 655
Leo Joseph of Carcassonne (XIV-2), *1379*, 875, 877, 1074, 1212, 1221, 1381, 1697
Leo Lambertenghi, 922
Leo V of Lusignan, 1253, 1309, 1739
Leo Magentinos (XIV-1), *589*, 97
Leo of Mantua, 605
Leo, mathematician (IV-1 B.C.), v. 1, *116*, 111
Leo medico, 451
Leo, Messer, 594
Leo of Montpellier, 886
Leo of Naples, 1519
Leo of Ostia (XII-1), v. 2, *255*, 139
Leo X, pope, 397, 470
Leo (Leone) Romano, *see* Judah b. Moses b. Daniel
Leo of Thessalonica (IX-1), v. 1, *554*, 814; v. 2, 27
Leo Tuscus of Pisa (XII-2), v. 2, *348*, 284, 292
Leon, Leone, *see* Leo
León, *see* Moses b. Shem-ṭob
Leonard Bruni Aretino, 455, 496, 1252, 1810, 1816, 1818, 1822, 1862
Leonard Fibonacci of Pisa (XIII-1), v. 2, *611*, 1195; v. 3, 110, 126, 127, 1484
Leonard, forerunner of, 1565
Leonard Frescobaldi (XIV-2), *1595*, 1143, 1300
Leonard of Maurperg (XIV-2), *1582*, 1137
Leonard da Vinci, 142, 147, 188, 214, 242, 267, 511, 545, 707, 1105, 1127, 1223, 1301, 1489, 1540, 1554, 1566, 1568, 1584, 1882

Leonardo, *see* Leonard
Leonhardt, Kurt, 851
Leonides of Alexandria (II-2), v. 1, *309*, 290
Leoninus of Paris (XII-1), v. 2, *217*, 25, 129
Leonti Mroveli, 305
Leontios Machairas, 952
Leonzio Pilato (XIV-2), *1377*, 472, 507, 1073, 1321, 1807, 1817
Leopardi, 515
Leopold of Austria (XIII-2), v. 2, *996*, 1195; v. 3, 1481, 1797
Leopold de Bebenburg, 819
Leopold of Weltingen, 933
Le Paige, C., 937
leper, office of exclusion, 277
lepers, 275, 318, 430, 1656, 1860
"Lepraschaubriefe," 277
Le Preux, 514
leprosy, 261, 289, 851, 860, 871, 874, 878, 881, 883, 908, 909, 1247, 1664, 1676, 1692, 1705, 1837
leprosy, white, 279
Le Quien, Michel, 1893
Le Rat, *see* Simon
Lerchundi, José, 827
Lérida, 1397
Le Roux de Lincy, 540
Le Roy, Alphonse, 184, 1227, 1748
Le Roy, Edouard, 83
Le Roy, Julien, 1542
Leroy, Maurice, 356
lesāna tārik, 957
Lespinasse, René de, 153, 864
Lessines, *see* Giles
Lessing, F., 1891
Lessing, G. E., 580, 1711
Le Strange, Guy, 632, 1142, 1474, 1893
Le Touzé, *see* William
Letteris, Max, 1652
Letteris, Me'ir, 1450
letters, mathematical use, 1487
lettres de foire, 1838
Leucippos of Miletos (V B.C.), v. 1, *88*, 81
leucodermia, 279
Leumann, Ernst, 1893
Leunclavius, Joannes, 996, 1824
Leuthardt, Karl, 1861
Levanto, *see* Galvano
Levati, Ambrogio, 514
level, xi
Leven, *see* Hugh
lever, xi, 146
Le Verrier, *see* John
Levi b. Abraham b. Ḥayyim (XIII-2), v. 2, *885*, 1196; v. 3, 98, 128, 602
Levi, Benedetto, 491
Levi b. Gerson (XIV-1), *594*, 18, 45, 56, 73, 98, 99, 116, 128, 130, 141, 142, 368, 434, 592, 609, 708, 886, 1096, 1116, 1364, 1448, 1516, 1518, 1521, 1845
Levi, Guido, 913
Lévi, Israël, 1452, 1519, 1520
Levi, *see* Joseph b. Japhet; Judah; Samuel (Abulafia); Samuel b. Joseph; Solomon b. Isaac
Lévi, Sylvain, 174, 1839, 1889, 1893
Levi, *see* Zeraḥiah b. Isaac
Levi Della Vida, Giorgio, 732, 1168, 1602, 1782
Lévi-Provençal, Evariste, 307, 1763, 1766, 1778, 1881, 1883, 1893
Levis, J. H., 162
levitation, 1621
Leviticus, 208, 405
Levold v. Northof (XIV-2), *1754*, 1258
Levonian, Lootfy, 1442
Levy, J. J., 594
Levy, Raphael, 454
Levy, Reuben, 975, 999, 1383, 1852, 1906
Lévy-Bruhl, L., 253
Lewin, Louis, 1242
Lewis de Almeida, 906
Lewis d'Anjou, 1407
Lewis d'Aversó, 1305
Lewis IV of Bavaria, emperor, 38, 44, 401, 501, 550, 917, 985, 986
Lewis II of Bourbon, 1035, 1150, 1207, 1242, 1713, 1805
Lewis of Bruges, 547
Lewis de la Cerda, 183
Lewis, D. B. W., 1407
Lewis v. Eybe, 1554
Lewis II of Flanders, de Male, 1316, 1502
Lewis IX of France, St., 45, 52, 57, 295, 928, 1189
Lewis XIV of France, 38
Lewis, Harry S., 616
Lewis I of Hungary, 1676
Lewis Marsigli, 509, 1815
Lewis de Nevers, 1316
Lewis d'Orléans, 1184, 1274, 1391
Lewis of Provence, 1499
Lewis Pulci, 1301
Lewis Rinio, 1163
Lewis of Spain (Luiz de España), 183
Lewis van Velthem (XIV-1), *938*, 66, 68, 302, 350
Lewysohn, Ludwig, 488
Lex septimo mense, 849
Lex Wisigothorum renovata (VII-2), v. 1, *500*
Lexa, François (František), 1103
Leyden, John, 1873, 1893
Leys, A. M., 395
Leys d'amors, 340
Lhwyd, Edward, 1886
Libadenos, *see* Andreas
libās al-futūwa, 154
Liberius, pope, 238
Libero, Don, 1051
libraries, 117, 970, 1192, 1200, 1202, 1222, 1297, 1344, 1391, 1399, 1406, 1436, 1451, 1500,

libraries—*continued*
1672, 1677, 1734, 1763, 1768, 1798, 1807, 1831, 1863, 1903, 1906
libraries, chained, 474, 1298
libraries, Chinese, 77
Libri, Guillaume, 1893
Liburnio, *see* Nicholas
licentia docendi, 154
Lichtenberger, Henri, 570
Lichtenberger, *see* John
Lichtenstein, Franz, 931
Lichtenstein, *see* Otto
Liebenau, Theodor v., 1021
Liebscher, A. H. W. H., 1867
Liefray, *see* John
Lieftinck, G. J., 572
Liége, 221, 1173, 1749, 1750
Liége, *see* Franco; James; Notger; Ralph; Renier
lies, detecting, 576
Lietuyt, *see* John
life, prolonging, *see* macrobiotics
light, dispersion, 142
light, origin, 704
light, reflection, 704
light, refraction, 135, 704, 707
light, speed, 142, 707
light, uncreated, 95, 584
light, wave theory, 707
Lightfoot, *see* Peter
Lignano, *see* Paul Antonius
Lignipedes, 397
Līlāvatī, 1535
Lilium medicinae, 873, 1851
Lille, *see* Alan
Limborch, Philip van, 404
Limburg chronicle, 1755
limning, 395
Limoges, *see* Peter
Limousin, 342
limpieza, 24, 1140
Lincoln College, 1402
Lindkvist, Harald, 567
Lindner, Arthur, 1753
Lindner, B. M., 578
Lindner, Theodor, 1820
Lindsay, James, 556
linen, bed, 276
linen, *see* paper
linen, use, 157
liṅga, 383
Liṅgayat, 383
linguarum mater, 363
linhagens, Livro de, 344
Linières, *see* John
Linköping, *see* Matthew
Linnaeus, 1642, 1867
Lionel of Antwerp, 1417
Lionel of Clarence, 1751
lions, 914
Lipari islands, 214
Liphard of Tuscany, 1582
lipi, brāhmī, 383
Lippmann, E. O. v., xv, 178, 498, 515, 531, 726, 755, 1064, 1137, 1553, 1848, 1893
Lippmann, Gabriel, 1064
Lipschitz, J., 453
Lisân al-'arab, 373, 1827
Lisbon, University, 73
Lisieux, *see* Frechulph; Nicholas
Litania maior, 238
"Literary digest," vi
literature, Indian, 1883
lithotomy, *see* stone, medicine
Lithuanians, 932, 1150
Little, A. G., 407, 1501, 1502, 1894
Littmann, Enno, 55, 1894
Littré, Emile, 6, 279, 873, 876, 878, 887, 1633
Liucci, *see* Neri Franzoli
Liuccio di Luzzi, 842
Liudprand of Cremona (X-2), v. 1, *684*, 652, 655
Livania, *see* John
liver, 843
livery companies, 126
Livet, C. L., 1310
Livi, Giovanni, 496
Livi, Ridolfo, 1672
Livingstone, David, 1159
Livinius of Middelburg, 108
"livre tournois," 1283
Livy (I-2 B.C.), v. 1, *233*, 220, 775; v. 3, 65, 298, 346, 454, 507, 511, 917, 919, 942, 944, 1075, 1144, 1288, 1294, 1482, 1736, 1807, 1816, 1852
Lizerand, Georges, 395
Llabrés y Quintana, Gabriel, 428
Llaguno Amirola, Eugenio de, 1736
Llamas, José, 1855
Llancarvan, *see* Caradog
Lloyd, A., 727
Lluis, *see* Lewis
Lobbes, *see* Hériger
Locard, Edmond, 253, 265
Locatelli, Boneto, 539
locks, canal, 1848
locks and sluices, 735
Lockwood, D. P., 1239
Locock, K. B., 533
locusts, 239, 818, 821, 905, 1167, 1187, 1634, 1836
Locy, W. A., 270, 820
Lodewijk, *see* Lewis
Lodge, J. E., 237, 757
Lodi, *see* Oldrado
Lodovico, *see* Lewis
Loeb, Isidore, 125, 1384
Loeffs, Rodolph, 513
Löhmann, Otto, 1811
Loehr, Max, 1841
Loenertz, Raymond, 459, 1038

Löwenklau, 996
Löwenthal, Rudolf, 1589, 1860, 1866
Löwy, Moritz, 437
logarithms, 1107
logic, 551, 1900
logic, Byzantine, 551
logica antiqua, 82
logica nova, 82, 534, 552
logical terminism, 331
Loise, Ferdinand, 1152
Loisel, Gustave, 915, 1189
Lokadīpasāra, 634
Lokert (or Lockhart), George, 545, 1540
Lollard, *see* Walter Lolhard
Lollards, 13, 49, 91, 566, 1024, 1039, 1046, 1048, 1054, 1089, 1347, 1655, 1745
Lombard, 326
Lombard, *see* law; Peter
Lombardo della Seta, 503
Lombroso, Giacomo, 514
Lomonosov, M. V., 711
London, 153
London, accounts, 126
London, *see* hanse; John; Moses ha-Naqdan
London pest, 1653
London tables (XIII-1), v. 2, *620*, 1197
Long, W. R., 955
longbowmen, 38
longbows, 725
Longfellow, H. W., 493
Longhena, Mario, 912, 1292
longitudes, *see* latitudes
Longjumeau, *see* Andrew
Longnon, Auguste, 1602, 1753
Longnon, Jean, 949
Longoburgo, *see* Bruno
Longré, Ephrem, 570
Longus, 1188
loose-leaf books, 128
Lo Parco, Francesco, 448, 515, 586
Loparev, Chrysanthos, 1761
Lopes, David, 41
Lopes, Duarte, 1160
Lopes, *see* Fernão
López, A. R., 418, 1841
López de Ayala, Pedro (XIV-2), *1735*, 1075, 1163, 1184, 1250, 1251, 1301, 1805
Lorenz, *see also* Laurence
Lorenz, Ottokar, 931, 934, 938
Lorenzen, Markus, 1605
Lorenzetti, *see* Ambrose
Lorenzi, Marcello, 859
Lorenzo, *see* Laurence; Rienzo
Loret, Victor, 1007
Loreto, 1043
Lorey, Eustache de, 974
Lori, *see* Vardan
Loria, Gino, 111, 497, 1106, 1894
Lorimer, Peter, 1349
Lorimer, W. L., 1844
Lorqi family, 1343
Lorqi, *see* Joseph b. Joshua; Joshua b. Joseph
Lorraine, *see* Jacob b. Judah
Lorris, *see* William
Lortholain, 1135
Losch, Philipp, 1023
Loserth, Johann, 934, 1349
loshon ha-qodesh, 363
Lot-Borodine, M., 1439
Lothier, Guillaume, 1695
lotus, 999, 1835
lotus sūtra, 311, 729
Lotze, Alfred, 570
Louhans (or Louens), *see* Renaud
Louis, *see* Lewis
Louise of Savoy, 1713
Lounsbury, T. R., 1425
Louvain, *see* John; Nicholas
Louve, *see* Nicholas
Louys, Pierre, 1277
lovage, 231
Loveday, Alexander, 284
Lovering, Joseph, 709
Lowe, W. H., 1457
Lower, Richard, 1886
Lowes, J. L., 1412, 1425, 1428
Lowth, Robert, 1403
Lowther, A. W. G., 1864
Loxius, 442
Loyola, 1045
Loyola, *see* Ignatius
Luard, H. R., 945, 1743
Lubelck, *see* Henry
Lubin, Antonio, 497
Lubūdī, b., *see* Yaḥyā b. Muḥammad
Luca Pacioli, 111, 126, 773, 1111, 1565, 1813
Luca da Penne, 1851, 1868
Luca della Ròbbia, 1134
Luca, Santo, Ospedale, 1194
Lucae, *see* John
Lucan, 1482, 1745, 1813
Lucańor, Conde, 924
Lucas, F. W., 1595
Lucas, H. S., 940
Lucca, *see* Bartholomew; Hugh; Ptolemy; Riccardi bank
Lucca, baths, 287, 849, 1240, 1686
Lucca, trumpeters, 1129
lucciole, 487, 1842
Luce, Siméon, 1753, 1894
Luchino Visconti, 1600
Lucian of Antioch (IV-1), v. 1, *349*, 344
Lucian Doria, 1022
Lucidarium, 740
Lucidarius (XII-2), v. 2, *386*, 200, 293
Lucidator astronomiae, 440
Lucifer, 1034
Luciferi, Epistola, 1497
Lucilius, Letters to, 65, 1391
lucina sine concubitu, 1230

Lucretius Carus, Titus (I-1 B.C.), v. 1, *205*, 816; v. 2, 1197; v. 3, 215, 1229, 1289, 1291, 1457
Lucytes, *see* Constantine
Ludgate, *see* John
Ludolf of Saxony, 1092
Ludolf of Suchem, 775
Ludolf of Sudheim (XIV-1), *788*, 192, 351, 1210
Ludwig, *see also* Lewis
Ludwig, Emil, 1160
Ludwig, Friedrich, 745
Lüdy, Fritz, jr., 1139
Luengo, b., 1850
Lütjens, August, 1228
Lützow, Franz, 941, 1259, 1352, 1354, 1758, 1824
Lugano, Placido, 395, 851
Lughat-i-Furs, 376
Luḥot, 599
Luigi, *see* Lewis
Luiso, Francesco Paolo, 501
Luiz, *see* Lewis
Luke, *see* Luca
Lull, *see* Raymond
Lullian art, 167, 1130, 1135
Lullian tradition, 1032, 1087
Lumby, J. R., 946, 1743
Lumen animae, 94, 582
Lumsden, Matthew, 1827
Luna, Fabricio, 1301, 1808
Luna, *see* Peter
Luncz, Abraham Moses, 792
Lunel, *see* Abraham b. Nathan ha-Yarḥi; Mari b. Moses; Meshullam b. Jacob; Shelemyah; Simon b. Joseph
Lunis, *see* William
Lunt, W. E., 328
Lupara, *see* Thomas
Lupo d'Olmedo, 1038
Luqmān, 1464
Luqmān Khwārizmī, 1216
Lusignan, 40, 1025
Lusignan, *see* Guy; Hugh; Leo; Peter of Cyprus
Lusignan, Khorène de, 1739
Lusner, Ludwig, 463
luster technique, 1133
lute, 1857
Luther, 51, 80, 93, 164, 399, 409, 554, 570, 572, 1057, 1089, 1297, 1348, 1360, 1399
Luxemburg, *see* Bonne; Guy; John of Bohemia; Mary; Peter; Sigismund
Luxor, 1619
Luyūn, b., *see* Sa'd b. Aḥmad
Luẓqi, Simḥa (Isaac) b. Moses, 618
Luzzatto, S. D., 1523
Luzzi, 842
Luzzi, *see* Liuccio; Mondino
Lyceum (IV-2 B.C.), v. 1, *127*, 124; v. 2, 1197; v. 3, 224
Lydgate, *see* John
Lydius, J. M., 1294
Lyell, Charles, 494
Lyell, J. P. R., 1298
Lyly, John, 567
Lynch, H. F. B., 1894
Lynn, 194
Lynn, *see* Nicholas
Lyon, D., 1604
Lyon, John, 1403
Lyra, *see* Nicholas
lyre of Mercury, 747
Lysistratos of Sicyon (IV-2 B.C.), v. 1, *142*, 126
Lytkin, G. S., 1825

Ma'ālī, a. (XII-2), v. 2, *433*, 307, 523
Ma'ālim al-qurba, 712, 998
Ma'arabi, *see* Israel b. Samuel
Ma'areket ha-elahut, 450
Ma'ārif-nāma, 623
Maarssen, Joseph b. Jacob, 1804
Ma'ase Buch, 1720
ma'aseh ḥosheb, 596
mabādī', 591, 1765
Mabilleau, Léopold, 1894
Mabillon, 24
Mabo' ha-gadol le refu'ah, 431
macabre, dance, 1860
Macarios, patriarch, 1821
Mac, Mc. Names beginning with Mc are classified as if written Mac.
Macartney, C. A., 976
Macaulay, G. C., 1428
Macauliffe, M. A., 1476
Macbeath, 1239
MacCallum, F. L., 1845
McCann, Justin, 1417
McColley, Grant, 531, 1108, 1490, 1856
McCormick, Wm., 1425
McCroben, G., 496
MacCulloch, J. A., 231, 1045, 1230, 1246, 1846
McCune, G. M., 389, 1270
Macdonald, D. B., xv, 211, 376, 623, 925, 1214, 1274, 1463, 1641, 1778, 1894
Macdonald, George, 1864
Macdonell, A. A., 1370, 1395
Mac Duinntshleibhe, *see* Cormac
Macer, Aemilius (I-2 B.C.), v. 1, *231*, 220
Macer floridus, 1176, 1705, 1711
McGovern, W. M., 1895
Machairas, *see* Leontios
Machaut, *see* William
Machiavelli, 1262, 1280, 1769, 1775
Machin, *see* Robert
McIlwain, C. H., 319
MacKay, Aeneas, 1741
McKenzie, Kenneth, 512
Mackenzie, W. M., 1741
MacKinney, L. C., 446, 1671, 1706
Macklin, H. W., 728

McLaughlin, T. P., 328
Maclean, A. J., 54, 1150
Macleod, H. D., 1495
Macler, Frédéric, 1442
Macmichael, H. A., 1143
Macmillan, Michael, 1741
McNair, J. B., 231
Maconi, *see* Stephen
McPherson, J. W., 421
MacRitchie, David, 1228
macrobiotics, 1732
Macrobius, Ambrosius Theodosius (V-1), v. 1, *385*, 816; v. 2, 1198; v. 3, 192, 1418, 1487, 1565, 1808
macrocosmos, 214, 263. *See also* microcosmos
Mādabā, map (VI-1), v. 1, *432*, 417
Madanapāla (XIV-2), *1730*, 1139, 1218, 1242, 1281, 1330, 1799
Madanapārijāta, 1799
Madanavinodanighaṇṭu, 1730
Madariaga, Salvador de, 188, 484, 1060, 1671
Madaune, J. M. de, 1631
Madden, F., 456, 1349
madder, 323
Madeira, 183, 786
Mādhava (XIV-2), *1366*, 1069, 1102, 1330, 1584
Mādhavakara (VIII-2), v. 1, *537*, 505, 522
Mādhavīyavedārthaprakāśa, 1368
madhhab, 1272
Madhusūdana Smṛitiratna, 1799
Madras, 782
madrasa 'ainīya, 1067
madrasa, first 'Uthmānlī, 105
Madrid, *see* Francis
Madyan b. 'Abd al-Raḥmān Qawsūnī, 1827
Maedge, C. M., 220
Maerlant, *see* James
Maeterlinck, Maurice, 94, 582
Māgadhī, 1477
Magalotti, Lorenzo, 1595
Magee, J. H., 325
Magen wa-romaḥ, 398
Magentinos, *see* Leo
Maghfeld, *see* Gilbert
Maghrūrīn, 803
magia Tropaeensium, 1234
magic, 16, 167, 443, 1411, 1491, 1906
magic squares, 138
Magna Carta (XIII-1), v. 2, *691*, 529; v. 3, 319
Magnaghi, Alberto, 498, 765
Magnani, Luigi, 915
Magnes, J. L., 437
magnet, 538, 818, 840, 871, 1447
magnetic attraction, 531, 1506
magnetic declination, 1422
magnetic influences, 576
magnetic needle, 1573
magnetism, 1124, 1667, 1896
magnetism, animal, 143, 576
Magnino of Milano (XIV-1), *854*, 244, 285
Magninus de Magnis, 834
Magnocavallo, Arturo, 771
Magnus Ericson, king, 578, 1354
Magnus, Olaus, 1610
Magnus Smek, 1154
Magnus Thórhallsson, 1609
Mago (II-2 B.C.), v. 1, *197*, 192, 213
Mahābhārata, 69, 107, 384, 465, 1077, 1330, 1395, 1840
Mahalingam, T. V., 41
Maḥallī, *see* Ya'qūb b. Isḥāq
Mahānāma (V-2), v. 1, *412*, 816; v. 2, 140, 261; v. 3, 977
Mahānī, *see* Muḥammad b. 'Īsā
Mahāsāmi, *see* Dhammakitti
Mahaut, countess of Artois, 227
Mahāvaṃsa, 310, 977
mahāvihāra, 422, 977
Mahāvīra, Jaina apostle (VI B.C.), v. 1, *69*, 65; v. 3, 383, 1584
Mahāvīra, Jaina mathematician (IX-1), v. 1, *570*, 546, 549; v. 2, 128, 215; v. 3, 1535
Mahāyāna, 59, 85, 93, 262, 293, 466, 569
Mahāyānaśraddhotpāda, 312
Maḥberet ha-ṭene, 491
Mahdī, *see* Muḥammad b. 'Alī
Mahmassani, Sobhi, 1778
Maḥmūd b. Aḥmad 'Ainī, 1067, 1267, 1329, 1784
Maḥmūd b. Aḥmad 'Aintabī, 899, 1721
Maḥmūd b. a. Bakr Urmawī, 630, 1727
Maḥmūd b. Ilyās Shīrāzī (XIV-1), *898*, 257, 289, 1727
Maḥmūd Kābādu, 1792
Maḥmūd of Kāshghar, 378, 1014, 1840
Maḥmūd b. Mas'ūd Quṭb al-dīn Shīrāzī (XIII-2), v. 2, *1017*, 1220; v. 3, 58, 106, 134, 135, 141, 142, 146, 202, 203, 257, 280, 705, 707, 1525, 1571
Maḥmūd b. Muḥammad Bārjīnī (XIV-2), *1643*, 1072, 1169, 1185, 1216, 1238, 1328
Maḥmūd b. Muḥammad Iṣfahānī, a. Fath (X-2), v. 1, *664*, 648, 654
Maḥmūd b. Muḥammad Jaghmīnī (XIV-1), *699*, 135, 257, 1120, 1461, 1530, 1847
Maḥmūd b. 'Umar Zamakhsharī (XII-1), v. 2, *271*, 1248; v. 3, 358, 373, 630, 1011, 1067, 1461, 1462, 1725
Mai, Angelo, 1513
Maidānī, *see* Aḥmad b. Muḥammad
Maimon, 461
Maimon, b., *see* David b. Joshua
Maimonides (XII-2), v. 2, *369*, 1198; v. 3, x, 55, 61, 62, 65, 99, 100, 149, 254, 255, 264, 274, 285, 286, 287, 320, 367, 416, 419, 436, 437, 449, 450, 451, 589, 590, 593, 594, 595, 607, 608, 609, 610, 612, 614, 617, 816, 850, 1062, 1072, 1096, 1097, 1247, 1365, 1373, 1381,

Maimonides—*continued*
1443, 1445, 1447, 1451, 1516, 1520, 1521, 1718, 1719, 1826, 1832, 1895
Maimonidism, 83, 893
Mainardi, *see* Bonmatteo; Gentile; Marsiglio of Padua
Mainardo dei Cavalcanti, 1804
Maineri, *see* Maino; Peter
Maino de' Maineri (XIV-1), *834*, 88, 112, 243, 244, 245, 271, 287, 1190
Mainz, *see* Henry; Jacob; John
maiolica, 756, 1133
Maistre, F. X. de, 281
Mājapāhit, empire, 42, 1268, 1624
Majd al-dīn a. Sa'ādat b. Athīr, 801
Majdī, b., *see* Aḥmad b. Rajab
majlis, 1762
Majmū' mubārak, 306, 363
Major, R. H., 184, 786, 892, 1291, 1594, 1608, 1693
Majorca, *see* Balearic; Chuetas; Isaac b. Nathan; James; Muḥammad b. 'Abdallāh Mayurqī
Majorcan school of cartography, 1140, 1858
Majrīṭī, *see* Maṣlama b. Aḥmad
Majūsī, *see* 'Alī b. 'Abbās
Makhzūmī, *see* Muḥammad b. Maḥmūd
Makīn, *see* 'Abdallāh b. a. Yāsir b. 'Amīd
Makkī, *see* Muḥammad b. 'Alī
Malabaila of Asti, 1839
Malabar, coast of, 229, 383, 781
maladreries, 276
Málaga, *see* Muḥammad Saqaṭī
malāḥim, 623
Malaise, Joseph, 1362
Malalas, John (VI-2), v. 1, *454*, 445
Malalasekera, G. P., 423, 978, 1370, 1371, 1731
Malaspina, *see* Ghidola
malastruc, 427
Malatesta, 1684
Malatesta, *see* Galeazzo; Sigismondo
Malay, 205, 1161, 1331, 1624, 1866, 1879
Malayalam, 360, 383
Maldive islands, 1616, 1617
Mâle, Emile, 172, 1041
Malespini, *see* Giacotto di Francesco; Ricordano
Malfūẓāt, 1272
Mali, 765, 803
Maliciones de los Judíos, 418
Malik al-Afḍal, *see* 'Abbās b. 'Alī Rasūlī
Mālik b. Anas (VIII-2), v. 1, *525*, 520, 524; v. 2, 264; v. 3, 1066
Mālik, b., *see* Muḥammad b. 'Abdallāh
Malik Shāh, 233
malikī, Kitāb, 288
Mālikī school, 1099
Malines, *see* Henry Bate; William
Malkā, b., *see* Hibatallāh b. 'Alī
Malkah, *see* Judah b. Nissim
Mallet, Robert, 1894
Malleus maleficarum, 301, 527, 1049
Mallon, Alexis, 1007
Mallory, W. H., 284
Malmesbury, *see* Oliver; William
Malocello, *see* Lanzarote
Malombra, *see* Richard
malos medicos, Libellus in, 419
Malpaghini, *see* John
Malpighi, *see* Andrew Ghini
Malta, knights, 40
Malter, Heinrich, 437
Malvern, *see* Walcher
Malverne, *see* John
Ma'mar b. Muthannā, *see* a. 'Ubaida
Mambelli, G., 482, 491, 495
Mamlūk, 40
Mamlūk army, 1867
Mamlūk citadels, 769
Mammātī, b., *see* As'ad b. Khaṭīr
Ma'mūn, caliph (IX-1), v. 1, *557*, 817; v. 2, 1199; v. 3, 1773
Manāfi' al-ḥayawān, 1168, 1179
Manandian, Agop, 1222
Manasse, E. M., 1861
Manasses, *see* Constantine
Manāẓir, 141, 707
Manbijī, *see* Muḥammad b. Muḥammad
Manchu, 381, 1840
Manchu writing (XII-1), v. 2, *273*; v. 3, 360
Manchuria, 1879
Mandaeans, 359
māṇḍala, 1368
Mandan, 1612
mandarin, 1084
Mandel, Hermann, 573
Mandelli, Fortunato, 1164
Manderstown, William, 1413
Mandeville, *see* John
Mandingo, 41, 201, 803, 1236, 1617, 1775
Mandonnet, Pierre, 499, 526
Mandosio, Prospero, 241
Mandrocles of Samos (VI B.C.), v. 1, *76*, 65
Manegold of Lauterbach (XII-1), v. 2, *264*, 141, 466; v. 3, 193
Manente degli Uberti, 1600
Manethon the Egyptian (III-1 B.C.), v. 1, *161*, 817
Manetti, Giannozzo, 496
Manfred of Sicily (XIII-2), v. 2, *855*, 1199
Manfredi, *see* Jerome
Maṅgarāja (XIV-2), *1730*, 1218, 1330
Mangenot, E., 1881, 1894
Manger, S. H., 1474
Manget, J. J., 1894
Mangiatroja, *see* James
Mānī, the Zindīq (III-2), v. 1, *332*, 817; v. 2, 1199; v. 3, 360, 1853
Manichaean cosmogony, 139
Manichaean script, 360

Manichaeans, 139, 378, 404, 405, 490, 1071, 1107, 1441, 1853, 1855
Māṇikka-Vāśagar, 571
Manilius, Marcus (I-1), v. 1, *237*, 235, 236; v. 3, 444, 1291, 1865
Manitius, Max, 746, 817, 1894
Manjak Yūsufī, 1722
Manly, J. M., 1413, 1415, 1424, 1425
Mann, J. G., 1556
Mann, Jacob, 1894
Manni, D. M., 913, 1252, 1810
Manning, B. L., 1349
Mannyng, *see* Robert
Manoaḥ maẓa ḥen, 417
Manoello Giudeo, *see* Immanuel b. Solomon
Manosque, 340
Manresa, *see* Receptari
Mansa Mūsā, 803
Manser, G. M., 547
Mansfield, M., 921
Mansionario, *see* John
Manṣūr b. 'Alī, a. Naṣr (X-2), v. 1, *668*, 787
Manṣūr, caliph (VIII-2), v. 1, *527*, 521
Manṣūr b. a. Faḍl b. Sūrī (XIII-1), v. 2, *649*, 1235
Manṣūr b. Muḥammad Ilyās (XIV-2), *1729*, 1217, 1227, 1231, 1328
Manṣūr, a., *see* Muwaffaq b. 'Alī
Mantino, *see* Jacob
Manṭiq al-ṭayr, 625
mantra, 425
Mantrabrāhmaṇa, 1369
Mantua, *see* Benedict; Leo; Marcolconi
Manuel, *see also* Emmanuel; Immanuel
Manuel Bryennios (XIV-1), *745*, 161, 1849
Manuel Calecas (XIV-2), *1363*, 1058, 1320, 1388
Manuel Chrysoloras (XIV-2), *1822*, 472, 1073, 1095, 1145, 1292, 1320, 1363, 1816, 1818, 1862
Manuel Comnenos, 996
Manuel Holobolos (XIII-2), v. 2, *858*, 723, 745
Manuel, *see* John
Manuel Moschopulos (XIV-1), *679*, 119, 122, 354, 996, 997, 1005
Manuel II Palaeologos (XIV-2), *1823*, 1035, 1058, 1094, 1103, 1280, 1320, 1467, 1822
Manuel Panselinos, 169, 1583
Manuel Pezagno, 184
Manuel Philes (XIV-1), *825*, 208, 239
Manuel, priest, 63
manure, 812, 1180
manus guidonica, 742
Manuzio, *see* Aldo
Manuzzi, Giuseppe, 463
Manzi, Guglielmo, 1595
manzil, 154
Manzini, *see* John
Manẓūr, b., *see* Muḥammad b. Mukarram
map, relief, 1157, 1620
Mappae clavicula (VIII-2), v. 1, *533*, 522, 723; v. 3, 168, 715, 1131
mappae mundi, 303, 946, 1872
mappemonde of 1375, Catalan (XIV-2), *1591*, 765, 785, 1140
maps of 1137, Chinese (XII-1), v. 2, *225*
maps divided into squares, 807
maps, monastic (XIII-2), v. 2, *1050*, 771
maps, projection, 808
maps, *see* wheel
Maqāṣid al-falāsifa, 608, 610, 1374, 1381
Maqdisī, *see* Aḥmad b. Muḥammad; Muṭahhar b. Ṭāhir
Maqqarī, *see* Aḥmad b. Muḥammad
Maqre dardeqe, 1826
Maqrīzī, Aḥmad b. 'Alī, 199, 203, 282, 306, 1265, 1780, 1783, 1784
Mar, title, follows the name
Marāgha, 134, 309, 377, 972, 1120, 1570
Marakuev, A. V., 714
Marāṣid al-iṭṭilā', 705
Marbais, *see* Michael
Marbode (XI-2), v. 1, *764*, 817; v. 2, 1200; v. 3, 340, 912, 1166, 1385, 1604
Marbres, *see* John
Marc Antonio de Dominis, 705, 1540
Marc Aurelius, *see* Aurelius Antoninus
Marc di Benevento, 555
Marc da Campione, 1655
Marc the Greek (XIII-2), v. 2, *1038*, 1200; v. 3, 859, 1581
Marc de Marchia, 1580
Marc Polo (XIII-2), v. 2, *1057*, 1200; v. 3, xii, 42, 171, 182, 186, 207, 220, 229, 233, 237, 337, 346, 363, 380, 385, 387, 439, 731, 773, 775, 777, 778, 784, 833, 954, 971, 1149, 1157, 1186, 1614, 1618, 1754, 1787, 1800, 1833, 1840, 1852, 1859, 1860, 1865, 1879, 1894
Marc, St., 238
Marc Sanudo II, duke of Naxos, 770
Marc Sinzanogio of Sarnano, 1234
Marc of Toledo (XII-2), v. 2, *344*, 1200; v. 3, 431
Marc, veterinary doctor (XIV-1), *858*, 245
Marca, Pierre de, 279
Marçais, 1267
Marcel, Gabriel, 1592
Marcel, *see* Stephen
Marcellinos (II-2), v. 1, *309*, 290
Marcellos of Side (II-2), v. 1, *308*, 289, 290
Marcellus Empiricus (V-1), v. 1, *391*, 379
Marceriis, G. de, 877
March, *see* Ausías; James
Marchant, Jacques, 821
Marchena, Josef, 1339
Marchetto of Padua (XIV-1), *740*, 159, 1128
Marchia, *see* Francis; Marc
Marco, *see also* Marc
Marco, *see* Francis

Marcocchia, Giacomo, 1810
Marcolconi de Mantua, 446
Marcotti, Giuseppe, 1023
Marcus, *see* Marc
Marcuse, Julian, 288
Mārdīnī, *see* Māridīnī
Marescalcia equorum, 858
Margānīthā, 97
Margaret, *see also* Margery
Margaret of Antioch, St., 1666
Margaret of Bavaria, 1799
Margaret Beaufort, *see* Margaret, Lady
Margaret de Bourgogne, 541
Margaret di (Benno) Bufini, 857
Margaret de Camoys, 728
Margaret of Denmark, 1021
Margaret of Flanders, 1502
Margaret, friend of fra Dolcino, 23
Margaret Geuschmied, 1579
Margaret Kyrkby (or Kirkby), 566
Margaret, Lady, 1402, 1416, 1863
Margaret Poirette (or Porrette), 23, 48, 406, 535
Margaret of Provence, 314, 577
Margaret of Richmond and Derby, *see* Margaret, Lady
Margaret Sbrunen, 1557
Margaret Spirer, 1756
Margaretha, *see* Margaret
Margerie, Emmanuel de, 497
Margery Kempe, 1314
Marghinānī, *see* 'Alī b. a. Bakr
Margoliouth, D. S., 421, 422, 962, 1068, 1264, 1451, 1723
Margolis, M. L., 1895
Margry, Pierre, 184
Marguerite, *see* Margaret
Mari b. Eligdor, abba, 128, 434, 591
Mari, *see* Isaac b. abba
Mari b. Joseph Kaspi, abba, 590
Mari b. Moses of Lunel, abba (XIV-1), *609*, 83, 99, 893
Mārī b. Sulaimān, 306, 956
Maria, *see* Mary
Mariadassou, Paramananda, 280, 1217, 1731
Mariano, *see* James
Mariano di Nanni da Siena, 1552
Marianus Scottus (XI-2), v. 1, *775*, 743, 745; v. 2, 255
Marianus Taccola, 1552
Ma'rib, 1779
Māridīnī, *see* 'Abdallāh b. Khalīl; Ismā'īl b. Ibrāhīm; Māsawaih; Sibṭ
Marie, *see* Mary
Mariétan, Joseph, 77
Mariette pacha, 151
Marignolli, *see* John
Marin, C. A., 781
Marini, Gaetano, 241, 1685
Marīnī dynasty, 101
Marini, *see* Ugolino
Marino Sanudo Torsello il Giovine, 769, 916
Marino Sanudo Torsello il Vecchio (XIV-1), *769*, 46, 182, 185, 298, 303, 313, 415, 763, 916, 949, 953, 1550
Marinos of Alexandria (II-1), v. 1, *281*, 268, 269
Marinos of Sichem (V-2), v. 1, *405*, 399
Marinos of Tyre (II-1), v. 1, *279*, 817
Mark, *see* Marc
Marke, *see* Collard
Markham, Sir Clements, 196, 787, 1142, 1474
Markland, 1608
Markon I, 56, 1365
Marliani, *see* John
Marmardji, A. S., 357
Marmousets, 1201
Marocco, Pietro, 458
Marqaria, Jacob b. David, 605
Marquard v. Stein, 1406
Marquart, J., 1017
Marr, Y. N., 1120
Marra, *see* William
Marracci, Lodovico, 422
Marrākushī, *see* 'Abd al-Wāḥid b. 'Alī
Marre, Aristide, 1534
Marrocco, W. T., 1567
Marseille, *see* John; Raymond; Samuel b. Judah
Marsh, *see* Adam
Marshall, William, 988
Marsigli, *see* Lewis
Marsiglio, *see also* Marsilius; Marsilli
Marsiglio Ficino, 483, 493, 1674
Marsiglio of Florence (XIV-2), *1815*, 1288, 1292
Marsiglio dei Mainardini, *see* Marsiglio of Padua
Marsiglio of Padua (XIV-1), *986*, 22, 38, 51, 88, 315, 402, 403, 499, 511, 536, 550, 819, 918, 985, 986, 1346, 1350, 1852
Marsiglio da Santa Sofia (XIV-2), *1681*, 839, 1193, 1220, 1677
Marsilius van Inghen (XIV-2), *1434*, 150, 539, 738, 1093, 1112, 1126, 1127, 1151, 1350, 1400, 1431
Marsilli b. Judah, 61
Marston, R. B., 1166
Martel, F., 1453
Martellus, *see* Henry
Martène, Edmond, 1290, 1337, 1754
Martialis, Gargilius (III-1), v. 1, *323*, 315, 355; v. 3, 813, 1288, 1745
Martianus, *see* Capella
Martin, Alfred v., 1817
Martin of Aragón, 1397
Martin of Barcelona, 532
Martin Behaim, 185, 600, 1501
Martin, C. T., 1416
Martin da Canal, 916

Martin da Fano (XIII-2), v. 2, *1126*, 726, 798; v. 3, 286
Martin, Henry, 1811, 1814
Martin of Kolozsvár, 1561
Martin Mercz, 1553
Martin Ortholan, 1575
Martin V, pope, 1033, 1057
Martin, *see* Raymond
Martin de Saint-Gilles (XIV-2), *1389*, 1075, 1201, 1220, 1309
Martin Saint Léon, Etienne, 153
Martin, Theodore, 493
Martin of Troppau (XIII-2), v. 2, *1111*, 794; v. 3, 304, 461, 579, 932, 933, 936
Martin, W. E., jr., 1424
Martínez y Martínez, Francisco, 1340
Martini, Emidio, 826, 1877
Martini, *see* John
Martinotti, Giovanni, 845
Martinov, Jean, 1156
Martinovich, N. N., 625
Martinsson, Sven, 1605
Martoni, *see* Nicholas
martyrs, cult, 1042
Marwān, *see* b. Janāḥ
Marwarrūdhī, *see* Khālid b. 'Abd al-Malik
Marx, Alexander, 433, 607, 1009, 1386, 1516, 1520, 1895
Mary d'Agreda, 23
Mary, André, 930
Mary van Berlaer, 938
Mary of Blois, 1391
Mary de Bourbonnais, 413
Mary, daughter of Edward I, 943
Mary Francis Xavier, 231
Mary Garcias, 1037
Mary of Hungary, 822, 1468
Mary de l'Hôpital, 1234
Mary of Luxemburg, 453, 846
Mary Magdalene, St., 1498
Mary of Namur, 1751
Mary of Saint Pol, 348
Mary in Sassia, Santa, 294
Mary, three Maries, 1738
Mary of Valence, 475
Marzials, Frank, 930
Masālik al-abṣār, 802
Masarra, b., *see* Muḥammad b. 'Abdallāh
Māsawaih Mārdīnī (XI-1), v. 1, *728*, 817; v. 2, 1200; v. 3, 243, 273, 288, 443, 836, 841, 844, 853, 870, 876, 1193, 1221, 1679
Māsawaih, Yūḥannā b. (IX-1), v. 1, *574*, 810; v. 2, 1200; v. 3, 849, 856, 870, 1074, 1205, 1212, 1221, 1719
Māshāllāh (VIII-2), v. 1, *531*, 521, 524; v. 2, 1200; v. 3, 501, 1076, 1421, 1424
Mash'ar, a., Ja'far b. Muḥammad (IX-1), v. 1, *568*, 787; v. 2, 1200; v. 3, 123, 444, 453, 501, 1357, 1421, 1481, 1510, 1529, 1674, 1694, 1797, 1808
Maskawayh, b., *see* Aḥmad b. Muḥammad
Maskell, Alfred. 1187
Maskiyot kesef, 590
Maslama b. Aḥmad Majrīṭī (X-2), v. 1, *668*, 817; v. 2, 1200; v. 3, 134, 759, 1138, 1341, 1525, 1767
Mas Latrie, L. de, 416, 745
Masoretes, 364
Masovia, 932
Masovia, *see* Conrad
Maspero, Henri, 1840, 1895
Maspero, Jean, 1265
Maspons y Labrós, F., 1734
mass in four voices, 744
massada, 288
massage (masaḥa), 286, 288
Massari of Genoa, 126
Masseket purim, 430
Masséna, Victor, prince d'Essling, 336, 514
Massignon, Louis, 155, 1069, 1158, 1460
Massmann, H. F., 1231
Massó Torrents, Jaume, 927, 1486, 1863, 1865
Masson-Oursel, Paul, 76, 1370, 1895
Mastino II della Scala, 913
Mas'ūd al-Dahhān, 1451
Mas'ūd of Seville, a. (or b.), 1521
Mas'ūd b. 'Umar Taftāzānī (XIV-2), *1462*, 1100, 1272, 1326, 1328, 1461, 1473
Mas'ūdī, 'Alī b. Ḥusain (X-1), v. 1, *637*, 817; v. 2, 1201; v. 3, 200, 212, 213, 801, 803, 849, 965, 967, 1170, 1652, 1775, 1868
Matarancos, 888
Mateer, C. W., 1891
materia medica, 1895
materia medica, Chinese (VII-2), v. 1, *498*
materia medica, Chinese and Japanese (XII-2), v. 2, *442*
materia medica, German (XIII-2), v. 2, *1092*
materia medica, Mongolian, 972
Matfre Ermengaut of Béziers, 339
mathematical induction, 129, 597
mathematics, 1880, 1886, 1893, 1896, 1902, 1907
mathematics, Arabic, 1905, 1907, 1910
mathematics, Greek, 1888
mathematics, Japanese, 1904
mathematics and astronomy, Latin (IX-1), v. 1, *569*
mathematicus, 112
Mather, Frank Jewett, jr., 485, 500
Mathews, M. M., 1316
Mathias, F. X., 1757
Mathnawī, 624
Mathys, C. H., 891
Matignon, J. J., 262
Matilda of Artois, 546
matins, 716
Matociis, *see* John
matres lectionis, 364
Matsumoto, T., 467

Matsuoka, Gentatsu, 1646, 1649
Mattā b. Yūnus (X-1), v. 1, *629*, 620, 623; v. 2, 339
Matteo, *see* Matthew
Matthaei, Otto, 820
Matthaeus, *see* Matthew
Matthew. All the Matthew and Matthias and their variants are put together, except Mattithiah (the Hebrew original).
Matthew Blastares (XIV-1), *994*, 53, 320, 354
Matthew of Brixen, 933
Matthew Cantacuzenos, 994, 1058, 1094, 1320, 1760
Matthew, Christians of St., 782
Matthew Doering, 1343
Matthew of Edessa (XII-1), v. 2, *251*, 138, 313; v. 3, 356
Matthew, evangelist, 230, 237, 463, 1385
Matthew, F. D., 1349
Matthew Farinator, 583
Matthew Guarimbertus (XIV-2), *1483*, 1106
Matthew (di Giovanni) Jannottaro, 859
Matthew (Matěj) of Janov (XIV-2), *1352*, 1056, 1322
Matthew of Linköping, 1355
Matthew Maria Boiardo, 911
Matthew of Neuenburg (XIV-1), *934*, 302
Matthew d'Orgiano, 1811
Matthew Paris (XIII-2), v. 2, *1109*, 1201; v. 3, 191, 227, 239, 303, 944
Matthew Platearius (XII-1), v. 2, *241*, 1201; v. 3, 225, 340, 813, 1375, 1409
Matthew Sylvaticus (XIV-1), *816*, 207, 221, 225, 244, 288, 898, 1222
Matthew da Varignana, 838, 1679
Matthew de Viladestes, 1141
Matthew Villani, 297, 914, 1198, 1251, 1300, 1652, 1658, 1737, 1793
Matthew Visconti I, 1243
Matthew of Westminster, 944
Matthews, A. N., 1066
Matthews, C. D., 422, 804
Matthias, *see* Matthew
Mattioli, P. A., 898
Mattithiah b. Solomon Delacrut, 199, 1382
Mattiussi, 777
matula, 890
Mauduith, *see* John
Maugin de Richebourg, Jean, 1577
Maunier, René, 1778
Maur, mal St., 1201
Maurer, G. L. v., 993
Maurice, Franciscan, 196
Maurice de Narbonne, 23
Maurice of Nassau, 127
Mauro, Fra, 1592
Mauro Tedesco, 859
Maurolico, Francesco, 129, 597
Maurperg, *see* Leonard
Maurus of Salerno (XII-2), v. 2, *436*, 1201
Maurus, veterinary doctor (XIV-1), *858*, 245, 284, 1838
Mawāḥidī, *see* Ya'qūb b. Ayyūb
Māwardī, *see* 'Alī b. Muḥammad
Mawhūb b. a. Ṭāhir b. Jawālīqī (XII-1), v. 2, *270*, 1188; v. 3, 373
Mawlānā Badr al-dīn, 1615
Mawlawī, 1841
Mawlawīya, 420
mawqif, 628, 629
Mawṣilī, *see* Muḥammad b. Aḥmad
Mawṣulī, *see* Muḥammad b. Daniyāl
maxima and minima, 737, 1108, 1487
Maximilian, emperor, 1644
Maximos Confessor (VII-1), v. 1, *471*, 817; v. 3, 1439
Maximos Planudes (XIII-2), v. 2, *973*, 1201; v. 3, 66, 95, 119, 120, 197, 252, 269, 303, 354, 355, 825, 1115, 1511
Maxwell, Herbert, 1746
Maya civilization, 238
Mayall, M. W., 17
Mayence, *see* Mainz
Ma'yene ha-yeshu'ah, 398
Mayer, Alfons, 340, 820
Mayer, C. F., 1204, 1667
Mayer, L. A., 804, 1178
Mayerne, T. T. de, 241, 1704
Mayers, W. F., 1171
Mayhew, A. L., 1316
Maynus, Jew, 246
Maynus, *see* John
Mayor, J. E. B., 1744
Mazaugues, *see* Thomassin
Mazdak (VI-1), v. 1, *420*, 415
Māzinī, *see* Muḥammad b. 'Abd al-Raḥīm
Mazuello, *see* Vincent
Mazzetti, Serafino, 1680
Mazzini, Giuseppe, 1684
Mazzocchi, Jacob, 1806
Mazzuchelli, G., 848, 1737
Mc. Names beginning with Mc are classified as if written Mac.
mead, 1239
Means, P. A., 1346, 1609, 1611, 1613
measles, 274, 1682
measures, *see* weights and measures
Me'ati, *see* Nathan b. Eliezer; Samuel b. Solomon; Solomon b. Nathan
Meaux, abbey of, 1746
Meaux, *see* Geoffrey
mechanical theories, 1126, 1504
mechanics, celestial, 146, 543, 738, 1127, 1504, 1843
Mecia de Viladestes, 1305
Mecklin, J. M., 327, 1043
Medhaṃkara (XIV-1), *634*, 59, 107, 383
Medicean Atlas, 1351 (XIV-2), *1597*, 785, 1144
Medici accounts, 126, 1111

Medici, *see* Cosimo; Eberhard; Laurence il Magnifico
Medici, Michele, 854
Medicina castellana regia, 1379
Medicina musica, 1868
medicine, 1878, 1884, 1887, 1892, 1895, 1896, 1897, 1900, 1901, 1908
medicine, alchemy, 1219
medicine, Arabic, 1875, 1893, 1896, 1910
medicine, *see* astrology
medicine, Buddhist, 259
medicine, Chinese, 972, 1889, 1909
medicine, Chinese (IV-1 B.C.), v. 1, *122*
medicine, Coptic (IX-2), v. 1, *614*, 588
medicine, Denmark, 1860
medicine, *see* deontology
medicine, Egyptian, 1724
medicine, examinations, 259, 859
medicine, fees, 872
medicine, geography, 199, 894, 896
medicine, Indian, 1889
medicine, Indian (VI B.C.), v. 1, *76*
medicine, Japanese (VII-1), v. 1, *481*, 393; (IX-1), v. 1, *575*
medicine, Latin (VIII-2), v. 1, *536*
medicine, Latin, outside of Salerno (XI-2), v. 1, *770*
medicine, law, 253, 260, 982
medicine, Persian, 1884
medicine, Persian (VI-1), v. 1, *435*
medicine, *see* physicians
medicine, profession, 290, 998, 1242, 1816
medicine, prophetic, 1214
medicine, Roman (I-1), v. 1, *239*
medicine, teaching, 290
medicine, Tibetan (VIII-2), v. 1, *538*, 469
medicine, Welsh (XIII-1), v. 2, *659*
Medicorum astrologia, 441
Medin, A., 918
Medzoph, *see* Thomas
Meech, S. B., 1315
Meerman, Gerard, 976
Meerochs, 1190
Meersseman, Gilles, 1841
Mees, Jules, 185
Megasthenes (III-1 B.C.), v. 1, *161*, 150
Megenberg, *see* Conrad
Meges of Sidon (I-2 B.C.), v. 1, *230*, 220
Megherditeh, 1178
Megliorati, *see* Cosmo
Mehl, Ernest, 915
Mehren, A. F. van, xii, 802
Mehus, Lorenzo, 1290, 1291
Meḥuyab ha-meẓyiut, 436
Meibom, Heinrich, 1755, 1820
Meietus, Paulus, 1673
Meijboom, Adriaan, 533
Meillac, Camille, 1668
Meillet, A., 356, 1825, 1895
Meinert, J. G., 782
Meinong, Alexis, 518
Meinsma, K. O., 1663
Meïr b. Baruch of Rothenburg (XIII-2), v. 2, *887*, 1202
Meïr Crescas, 1521
Meïr b. Isaac b. Dabi or Aldabi (XIV-2), *1442*, 1060, 1096, 1098, 1115, 1156, 1211, 1223
Meïr b. Solomon Alguadez (XIV-2), *1384*, 1074, 1096, 1211, 1302, 1343, 1377, 1522
Meisel, W. A., 430
Meisl, N., 1326
Meisner, H., 789
Meistersänger, 338
Mekhitar of Aïri-vankh (XIII-2), v. 2, *1117*, 795
Mekhitar of Her (XII-2), v. 2, *441*, 1202; v. 3, 1222
Mekong river, 1030
Mela, Pomponius (I-1), v. 1, *239*, 818; v. 3, 1600, 1806, 1808, 1811
malakim, Sefer, 429
Melampus, 960
Melandino, ban of Croatia, 838
Meleager, 1188
Meletios the Monk (VII-2), v. 1, *497*, 459
Melga, Michele, 186, 864
Melgueil, *see* Solomon b. Moses
Meli, Romolo, 1198
Mélibée et Prudence, 453
Melioranski, P. M., 1014
Melis Stoke (XIV-1), *937*, 302, 350
Meliteniotes, 1167, 1171, 1320
Meliteniotes, *see* John; Nicholas; Theodore
Melleus liquor, 860
Melli, M. A. F., 215
Mello, *see* Guido
melons, 1620
melopoeia, 746
Melot, *see* John
Melton, *see* John
Memmingen, *see* Abraham
Menaechmos (IV-2 B.C.), v. 1, *139*, 125
menageries, 1189, 1470, 1859
Ménagier de Paris, 1164, 1182, 1184, 1276, 1632
Menahem b. Aaron b. Zeraḥ (XIV-2), *1444*, 1096, 1115
Menahem b. Abraham Bonafos (XIV-2), *1826*, 1324
Menahem b. Jacob b. Saruq (X-2), v. 1, *690*, 653, 655; v. 2, 190; v. 3, 366
Menam river, 1029
Mencius (IV-2 B.C.), v. 1, *138*, 818
Mencken, J. B., 1758
Mende, *see* William Durand; William Durant
Mendel, *see* Conrad
Mendelsche Zwölfbrüderstiftung, 1128
Mendez, Sola, 419
Mendip district, 219
Mendis, G. C., 423, 978

Mendoza, *see* González
Menecrates, C. Q., of Zeophleta (I-1), v. 1, *241*, 235, 236
Meneghelli, Antonio, 512
Menelaos of Alexandria (I-2), v. 1, *253*, 818; v. 2, 1202; v. 3, 432, 900
Menéndez y Pelayo, Marcelino (not Ramón), 1341
Menges (not Monges), K. H., 381
Menghini, Mario, 1811
Menodotos of Nicomedia (II-2), v. 1, *308*, 290
Menon (IV-2 B.C.), v. 1, *146*, 126, 127
Menorat ha-refu'ah, 437
Menorat kesef, 591
Menorat ha-ma'or, 1008
mensa ponderaria, 1847
Mense, Carl, 280
mensor, 1847
menstruation, 263
mensura, 1848
mensural, *see* music
mental computation, 1527
mental epidemic, 1666
mental inertia, *see* inertia, human
Menut, A. D., 1494, 1496
Menzel, Theodor, 1728
Menzies, J. M., 385
Meorot, 442
Mercati, Giovanni, 587, 1364, 1387, 1388, 1395, 1438, 1512, 1513
Mercator, Gerard, 1501
Mercedarians (XIII-1), v. 2, *550*, 487
Mercier, abbé, 1152
Mercier, C. A., 280
Mercier, Louis, 1635, 1642, 1643
Mercier, Melpo, 162
Mercurian, Eberhard, 574
mercury, element, 167, 289, 751, 753, 797, 1139, 1730
Mercury, lyre, 747
Mercury, planet, 1517
mercury, *see* salivation
Mercz, *see* Martin
Merle, *see* William
Merlin, Book of, 68
Merlin, *see* John
Merrifield, Mary Philadelphia, 168, 1132, 1136
Merrill, E. D., 1837
Mersand, Joseph, 1426
Merseburg, *see* Thietmar
Mersenne, 1566
Merswin, *see* Rulman
Merton College, 92, 116, 141, 473, 1110, 1126
Merton, *see* Walter
Mèrula, *see* George
Merutuṅga (XIV-2), *1584*, 1139, 1218, 1220, 1330, 1366
Merveilles du monde, 300
Mesgnien Meninski, François de, 1458
Meshalim be-tishboret, 433
Meshullam b. Jacob of Lunel, 609
Meshullam b. Jonah, 613
meshullash, 433
Mesmer, F. A., 17, 143
Mesopotamian, *see* Babylonian
Mesrop, St. (V-1), v. 1, *397*, 818; v. 2, 1202; v. 3, 304, 356
Messenger, E. C., 1881
Messiah, 398, 417, 419, 453
Messina, *see* Bartholomew; Thomas Caloria
Mesuë the Elder, *see* b. Māsawaih
Mesuë, junior, *see* Māsawaih Mārdīnī
Mesuë the Third (XIII-1), v. 2, *662*, 1202; v. 3, 65, 254, 264, 272, 892
Mesuë (undefined), 883, 1698
Metagenes of Ephesus (VI B.C.), v. 1, *75*, 65
metallurgy, 1126, 1173
metals, seven, 800, 818
Metaphrastes, *see* Simeon
Metastasio, Pietro, 583
Metcalf, K. DeW., 29
Metcalfe, W. M., 1741
metempsychosis, 452, 488, 973
meteor, 1122, 1738
meteorites, 1122, 1621
meteorology, 117, 1124, 1875
meteorology, *see* astrology
meteorology, optical, 1123
Metge, *see* Bernard
Methley, *see* Richard
Methodios, St. (IX-2), v. 1, *590*, 583, 589
Methodios, pseudo, 1394
Methodus medendi, 889
métiers, Livre des, 251, 347
Metochites, *see* George; Theodore
Meton of Athens (V B.C.), v. 1, *94*, 818
metonic cycle, 1610
Metrodora (II-1), v. 1, *283*, 268
Metrodoros (V-2), v. 1, *408*, 400
metrology, *see* weights and measures
Mets, A. de, 884
Metz, *see* Walter
Meung, *see* John; Odo
Meunier, Francis, 1494, 1497
Meunier, Dom G., 1090
Meurs, *see* John
Meursinge, Albertus, 1783
Meyer, E. H. F., 1895
Meyer, Hermann, 820
Meyer, Jacob, 1474
Meyer, Paul, 249, 458, 1312, 1499, 1632, 1695
Meyer-Steineg, Theodor, 1895
Meyerhof, Max, x, xi, xv, 105, 254, 267, 289, 377, 708, 709, 897, 961, 1637, 1722, 1764, 1773, 1779, 1788, 1852, 1895
Meyronnes, *see* Francis
Mezeřický, *see* Dalimil
Mézières, Alfred, 514
Mézières, *see* Philip

mibḥar, 101
Mibḥar ha-peninim, 427, 430
mibḥarim, 442
Micah (VIII B.C.), v. 1, *58*, 53
Michael Angelo, 1105
Michael Attaliates (XI-2), v. 1, *779*, 792
Michael Berti, 396
Michael of Brabant, 1084
Michael da Cesena, 396, 401, 407, 527, 550
Michael Chrysococces, 1517
Michael Dolfin, 182
Michael the Elder, Mar (XII-2), v. 2, *449*, 1203; v. 3, 358
Michael Glycas (XII-1), v. 2, *251*, 1203; v. 3, 825, 952
Michael of Marbais, 1004
Michael de Northburgh, 1742
Michael of Northgate (XIV-1), *462*, 68, 340, 349, 1314
Michael VIII Palaeologos (XIII-2), v. 2, *1114*, 1203; v. 3, 363, 1760
Michael Panaretos, 790
Michael da Piazza (XIV-2), *1737*, 1253
Michael Psellos (XI-2), v. 1, *750*, 826; v. 2, 1203; v. 3, ix, 288, 353, 552, 589, 755, 1208, 1877
Michael of Roubaix, 1004
Michael Scot (XIII-1), v. 2, *579*, 1203; v. 3, 165, 166, 169, 214, 268, 270, 450, 539, 843, 1104, 1409, 1797
Michael of Smolensk, 1613
Michaelhouse, 72, 475
Michalski, Constantin, 534, 1895
Michaud, 930
Michel, Michele, *see also* Michael
Michel, A., 1246
Michel, André, 1564
Michel, Francisque, 281, 930
Michel, Louis, 1749
Michel, Robert, 721
Michelant, Henri, 232, 347, 1749
Michelet, 405
Michelino da Certaldo, 1802
Michelino di Vesuccio, 1132
Michon, abbé, 1602
Michon, L. A. J., 887, 1663
Mickwitz, Gunnar, 152
microcosmos, 214, 263, 1427. *See also* macrocosmos
Microtegni, 839
Middelburg, *see* Livinius
Middleton, *see* Richard
Midianitic dialect, 364
midrash, 398, 416
midwifery, 836, 1206. *See also* obstetrics
Mieli, Aldo, 497, 1873, 1895
Mielot, *see* John
Miftāḥ al-sa'āda, 900
Migdal David, 419
Migli, *see* Ambrose
Migne, J. P., 1895, 1899
Mignot, *see* John
miḥrāb, 135, 136, 1528
Miklal yofi, 1826
Milá y Fontanals, 926
Milanesi, Gaetano, 1132, 1134
Milano, *see* Cardo; Dionisio; John; Lanfranchi; Magnino
Milemete, *see* Walter
Miles Benjudas, 433
Milham, W. I., 722
Milḥamot Adonai, 418, 595
Milhau, *see* Bonenfant
Milhaud, *see* Gabriel; Hezekiah Miliabi
Milič of Kremsier (Kroměříž) (XIV-2), *1351*, 1056, 1353
military science, Byzantine (VI-1), v. 1, *430*
militia, Liber de, 73
milk, thirst for, 1777
Milky Way, 487
Millar, Eric, 1634, 1704
Millás, Francisca Vendrell de, 1843
Millás Vallicrosa, J. M., 133, 1221, 1306, 1448, 1516, 1841, 1850, 1896
Miller, Emmanuel, 826, 949, 952, 1513
Miller, H. W., 531
Miller, Konrad, 953
Miller, L. R., 433
Miller, Otto, 499
Miller, William, 1852
Millet, Gabriel, 170, 1439
Mills, E. W., 1176
mīnā wash, 756
mīnā'ī ware, 756
mineral waters, 1241
mineralogy, 1167. *See also* stones, precious
mineralogy, glossary, 1513
mineralogy, Muslim (IX-1), v. 1, *572*
Minerbi, Lucilio, 1808
Mingana, A., 360
Minhāj-i-Sirāj (XIII-2), v. 2, *1123*, 797
Minḥat qinaōt, 418
mining, 1126, 1173, 1902
mining, African, 217, 220
mining profession, 218
mining, Roman, 217
Minnesingers (XII-2), v. 2, *392*, 25, 294; v. 3, 338
Minns, E. H., 1555
Minns, G. W. W., 1570
Minns, Susan, 1232
Minoia, M., 918
Minorsky, V., 106, 376
Minuccio of Arezzo, 1669
minucione, De, 285
Miqdash me'aṭ, 491
Miquel, *see* Constanza
Miquel y Planas, R., 1821
Mirabilia descripta, 783
mirabilibus mundi, De, 454

miracles, 1772, 1845
miraculous cures, 291
mi'rāj, 489, 1476, 1639
Mirall de trobar, 341
Miramar, 375
Mīrānshāh, 1468
Mirecourt, *see* John
Mirfeld, *see* John
Mirica, *see* William
miroir du monde, 311
Miroir de Saxe, 23
Mirot, Léon, 774, 1498
mirrors, 311
mirrors, Four, 980
mirrors, Three, 980
Mis'ar b. Muhalhil a. Dulaf (X-1), v. 1, *637*, 787; v. 2, 869; v. 3, 1849
Miṣbāḥ fī asrār, 759
Misciattelli, Piero, 1336
Miserere, 1275
Mishkāt al-maṣābīḥ, 1066
Mishna, 357, 367, 1062
Mishnat ha-middot (XII-1), v. 2, *208;* v. 3, 597
Mishneh Torah, 55, 590, 1832
Mispar, 590, 596
Mispar ha-ḥokmot, 431
missing links, 212
Mistiaen, Emmanuel, 1509
mistletoe, 1241
Mistra, 948, 1583
Mistra, *see* Samuel Foto
Mistral, Frédéric, 1188, 1303, 1499
Mistruzzi, Vittorio, 913
Misyn, *see* Richard
Mitchell, A. C., 1509
Mitchell, J. B., 191
Mitchell, J. M., 823
Mithdridates Eupator (I-1 B.C.), v. 1, *214*, 202
Mithdridates, Flavius, 611
Mithob, Burchard, 1581
mitis, Liber, 855
Mitra, Rājendralāla, 1369
Mitry, *see* Rémion
Mitteilungen zur Geschichte der Medizin, 1896
mīzān, 367
Mizraḥi, *see* Elijah b. Abraham
Miẓri, *see* Obadiah
miẓwah, bar, 367
Mizzī, *see* Muḥammad b. Aḥmad; Yūsuf b. Zakī
mkhedruli, 304
Mliẓah, 1008
Mnesitheos of Athens (IV-2 B.C.), v. 1, *146*, 126
Moamin and Ghatrif, 1835
Mode, P. G., 1663
Modena, *see* John; Thomas
Modestinus, Herennius (III-1), v. 1, *329*, 316, 396
Modi, Jivanji Jamshedji, 632
modi significandi, 331, 1004
modista, 94, 331, 552, 1003
Modjokěrto, 42
modo celebrandi concilii, De, 413
modo Sarracenos extirpandi, De, 391, 415
Modus, king, 231, 1183, 1309
Möbius, Martin, 1896
Moeller, Charles, 394
Møller-Christensen, V., 1860
Mönch, *see* Philip
Moerbeke, *see* William
Möring, Michel, 295
mofet, 432
Moggallāna (XII-2), v. 2, *472*, 320, 472; v. 3, 382, 423
Mogk, Eugen, 1228
Mogul style, 1473
Mohammed, *see* Muḥammad
Moidrey, Joseph de, 1122
Moiliens, *see* Renclus
Moinet, Louis, 1542
Moisé, Filippo, 926
Moladot, 442
Molano, *see* Nicholas
Molay, *see* James
moles of human body, 960
Molhuysen, P. C., 1799
Molière, 272, 1201, 1810
Molières, *see* Raymond
Moliné y Brasés, Ernest, 325
Molinier, Auguste, 1631, 1896
Molinier, Emile, 1134
Molinier, *see* John; William
Mollat, Guillaume, 404
Moller, H. W. E., 582
Mollien, Gaspard, 1159
Molther, Menrad, 955
Mombrizio, *see* Bonino
momentum, linear, *see* impetus
Mommsen, T. E., 515
Mon-Khmer peoples, 1029
Monachos, *see* George the Monk
Mònaci, *see* Laurence
monarchia, De, 483
Monardes, Nicolás, 1379
Moncetti, Giovanni Benedetto, 483, 494
Monchensi, *see* Dionysia
Mondeville, Henry (XIV-1), *865*, 113, 114, 247, 248, 272, 278, 293, 340, 346, 842, 846, 865, 883, 1194, 1223, 1224, 1233, 1632, 1691, 1700, 1703
Mondino Friulano (XIV-1), *840*, 244, 288
Mondino de' Luzzi (XIV-1), *842*, 244, 265, 266, 426, 846, 847, 853, 1223, 1691, 1707
Mondino, *see* Thomas
money, 544, 545, 1276, 1772
money changing, 1802
money, depreciation, 318, 410

money, *see* paper
money, renovation, 1282
money, theory of, 318, 1282, 1493, 1494
Mongan, Elizabeth, 1564, 1659
Mongolia, 379, 972, 1840, 1865, 1879, 1892. *See also* Pax mongolica
Mongolian, *see* Chinese-Mongolian; materia medica
Mongolian script, 360, 469
Monier-Williams, Monier, 1070, 1896
Monin, H., 1578
Moniz, *see* Isabel
monkey, 212
monks, 1879
Monmouth, *see* Geoffrey
Monophysites, 55, 357, 361, 460, 1830
Monopoli, *see* Anthony
Montagnana, *see* Bartholomew
Montagu, M. F. A., 13, 212, 1228, 1230, 1775
Montaiglon, Anatole de, 1407
Montaigne, 929, 1087, 1242, 1251
Montaigu, Collège, 72, 476
Montaigu, *see* Giles Aycelin
Montaigut, *see* Giles Aycelin
Montbron, *see* John
Monte, *see* Giambattista
Montecaliero, *see* Albino
Montecalvo, *see* James
Montecatini, *see* Ugolino
Montecorvino, *see* John
Monte Croce, *see* Ricoldo
Montefeltro, *see* Battista; Feltrino; Guido
Montegraneli, *see* Charles
Montesa, Our Lady of, 394
Montescalerio, 542
Montesquieu, 1776
Montessus de Ballore, Fernand, 1896
Montet, Edouard, 421
Monteverde, Claudio, 1295
Montferrat, *see* Boniface
Montfort, *see* Simon
Montgomery, J. A., 956
Monti, G. M., 152, 815, 837, 860, 983, 1851
Monti, Vincenzo, 1601
monti di pietà, 326, 525
Monticolo, Giovanni, 152
Monticulo, *see* Emmanuel
Montlauzun, *see* William
Montmorency, J. E. G. de, 1362
Montoliu, Manuel de, 1884, 1896
Montpellier, 44, 245, 247, 316, 341, 1079, 1199, 1242, 1244
Montpellier, *see* Bérenger; Elijah b. Judah; Guy; Leo
Montpellier, tables, 67
Montpellier, University (XII-2), v. 2, *352*, 1204
Montreuil, *see* John
Montulmo, *see* Anthony
Monzón, *see* John
Moody, E. A., 545, 556
moon, 131, 441, 1158
moon, folklore, 263
Moore, Edward, 492, 493, 496, 497, 498
Moore, Norman, 295, 882, 1704, 1706
Moore, W. J., 294
Moos, Maria Fabianus, 80
mora, 449
Moralizationes super totam Bibliam, 454
Morandi, Luigi, 1301
Mordecai b. Eliezer Comtino, 1117
Mordecai b. Joshua of Rodez, 1717
Mordecai Nathan, 1063
Mordtmann, J. H., 154
More, Sir Thomas, 554, 1362
Morea, chronicle of (XIV-1), *948*, 303, 346, 354, 770, 1250, 1852
Moreau, Fernand, 1118
Moreh ha-moreh, 591
Moreh nebukim, 398, 428, 590
Moreh ẓedeq, 418
Morejón, A. H., 1379
Morel, Eustache, 1410
Morel, Frédéric, 1847
Morel-Fatio, Alfred, 198, 949
Morelius, G., 589
Morell, Thomas, 1424
Morellet, André, 1339
Morelli, Gonippo, 153
Moreni, Domenico, 1552
Morgan, Evan, 1139
Morgan, Jacques de, 359, 1896
Morgarten, 38
Morghen, Raffaello, 915
Mori, Assunto, 498
Morici, Medardo, 515
Morigni, 22
Moriscos, 1060
Morison, M., 37
Morison, S. E., 183, 1036, 1148, 1848
Morley, *see* Daniel
Morley, S. G., 238
Morley, Thomas, 741
Morossi, Benedetto, 917
Morquelines, *see* Peter
Morris, Manuel, 854
Morris, Richard, 463, 567
Morris, William, 1394, 1424
mors nigra, 886
Morse, E. S., 234, 1188, 1332
Morse, H. B., 156
mortality, tables, 324
Mortara, Mordecai (or Marco), 606
mortmain, 326, 327, 914, 1180, 1508
Morwyng, Peter, 1451
mosaic, *see* gold
Mosburg, *see* Berthold
Moschion (VI-1), v. 1, *433*, 283, 417; v. 2, 1085
Moschopulos, *see* Manuel
Mosconi, *see* Judah b. Moses; Muna

Moscow, 39
Mose, *see* Moses
Moser, Simon, 556
Moses, *see* Mūsā for Arabic names
Moses b. Abraham Ya'ari, 1516
Moses Arragel, 1077
Moses b. Baruch Almosnino, 1382
Moses of Bergamo (XII-1), v. 2, *180*, 116
Moses Botarel of Cisneros, 1383
Moses of Chorene (V-1), v. 1, *395*, 819; v. 2, 449; v. 3, 356
Moses b. Ezra, *see* Moses b. Jacob
Moses Farissol Botarel, 1383
Moses Ḥandali, 1515
Moses b. Isaac ha-Nessiah, 366
Moses b. Isaac da Rieti, 450, 491, 592
Moses b. Jacob ha-Ashkenazi, 618
Moses b. Jacob of Coucy (XIII-1), v. 2, *555*, 488, 557; v. 3, 590, 1718
Moses b. Jacob b. Ezra (XII-1), v. 2, *185*, 118, 137
Moses b. Joseph Abulafia, 1385
Moses b. Joseph Qimḥi of Narbonne (XII-2), v. 2, *469*, 318; v. 3, 366, 609, 1377
Moses b. Joshua of Narbonne (XIV-1), *607*, 56, 98, 255, 418, 592, 610, 893, 1448, 1450, 1719
Moses Judah Galliano, 1526
Moses bar Kēphā (IX-2), v. 1, *596*, 819
Moses b. Leon Botarel, 1383
Moses b. Maimon, *see* Maimonides
Moses Medicus, 451
Moses b. Mordecai Zacuto, 492
Moses b. Naḥman of Gerona (XIII-2), v. 2, *883*, 1205; v. 3, 416, 453, 595, 608, 612, 616, 1008, 1061, 1364, 1376, 1443, 1445
Moses ha-Naqdan of London, 366
Moses of Palermo (XIII-2), v. 2, *833*, 1205
Moses b. Samuel Qala'i, 618
Moses b. Samuel of Roquemaure (XIV-2), *1378*, 873, 1074, 1212, 1240
Moses b. Samuel b. Tibbon (XIII-2), v. 2, *847*, 1205; v. 3, 61, 435, 450, 591, 597, 603, 894, 1123, 1373, 1376, 1516
Moses b. Shem-ṭob b. Ḥabib, 594
Moses b. Shem-ṭob of León (XIII-2), v. 2, *878*, 730; v. 3, 100, 101, 363, 616
Moses b. Solomon of Beaucaire (XIV-1), *428*, 61, 98, 429, 432, 591
Moses b. Solomon of Salerno, 428
Mostrador de justicia, 418
motetus, 159
motion, 146, 149, 553
motion, absolute, 1488
motion, perpetual, 146
motion of projectile, 543
motion, quantity, 543
Moṭoṭ, b., *see* Samuel b. Sa'adia
Mottelay, P. F., 1896
Mottez, Victor, 1132
Moule, A. C., 54, 776, 779, 784, 1071, 1627, 1896
Moulé, Léon, 1896
Moulin, *see* Anthony
Moulins, *see* Guiard
Mount Sion, *see* Burchard
mountain, *see* Alpinism
Moura, *see* Santo Antonio
Mourad, Youssef, 1897
Mouradgea d'Ohsson, Constantin, 975
Mourek, V. E., 941
Mousket, *see* Philip
Moutier, Ignazio, 915, 1808
movement, theory, *see* motion
Mowat, J. L. G., 1222, 1706
moxa, 260, 906, 1733
Mozarabs, 373, 1886
mozarabic, *see* Breviarium
Mroveli, *see* Leonti
Mu'aiyad al-dīn 'Urḍī (XIII-2), v. 2, *1013* 1242; v. 3, 1525
Mu'aiyad billāh, *see* Yaḥyā b. Ḥamza
mu'allim, 154
Muang Thai, 1029
Mubashshir b. Fātik, 1302
Mudawwar, b. (XII-2), v. 2, *432*, 1205
Mudejars (Mudéjares). 373
Mudkhal fīl-ṭibb, 431
Mühleisen, F. W., 1741
Müllendorff, Prosper, 1051
Müller, Andreas, 955
Müller, August, 976
Müller, Carl, 555, 1553
Müller, F. M., 1369
Müller, Friedrich, 1712
Müller, J., 1260
Müller, M. J., 897, 1764
Müller, Marianus, 570
Müller-Hickler, H., 1555
Müller v. Westendorff, Max, 989
Müllner, Karl, 1819
Münster, *see* Henry Ahuys
Münster, Sebastian, 770, 1386, 1451
Münster in Westphalia, 1360
Müntz, Eugène, 336, 514
Mufaḍḍal b. a. Faḍā'il (XIV-2), *1780*, 306, 363, 1260, 1264
Mufaḍḍal b. Mājid b. Bishr (XIII-2), v. 2, *1098*, 788
Mufaḍḍal b. 'Umar Abharī (XIII-2), v. 2, *867*, 1205; v. 3, 134
Mugdhāvabodha, 1474
Mugello, *see* Dino
Mughairibī, 1138
mughāwīr, 925
Mughulṭā'ī b. Qilij, 964
Muglio, *see* Peter
Muḥammad of Abarqūh, 973
Muḥammad b. 'Abdallāh b. Abbār (XIII-1), v. 2, *681*, 527, 796

Muḥammad b. 'Abdallāh b. 'Arabī (XII-1), v. 2, *264*, 1205; v. 3, 1774
Muḥammad b. 'Abdallāh, *see* b. Baṭṭūṭa
Muḥammad b. 'Abdallāh Ḥaṣṣār (XII-2), v. 2, *400*, 1205; v. 3, 1765
Muḥammad b. 'Abdallāh, *see* b. Khaṭīb
Muḥammad b. 'Abdallāh b. Mālik, 1013
Muḥammad b. 'Abdallāh b. Masarra, v. 2, 598; v. 3, 489, 612, 627
Muḥammad b. 'Abdallāh Mayurqī, 1341
Muḥammad b. 'Abdallāh Salmānī, 1762
Muḥammad b. 'Abdallāh Su'ūdī, 1161
Muḥammad b. 'Abdallāh Ṭā'ī, 962
Muḥammad b. 'Abdallāh Tibrīzī, 1066
Muḥammad b. 'Abdallāh Timirtāshī, 1455
Muḥammad 'Abdallāh 'Unān, 1779
Muḥammad b. 'Abd al-'Azīz b. Duraihim, 1638
Muḥammad b. 'Abd al-Bāqī Baghdādī (XI-2), v. 1, *761*, 740, 746; v. 2, 1205
Muḥammad b. 'Abd al-Karīm Shahrastānī (XII-1), v. 2, *249*, 113, 137
Muḥammad b. 'Abd al-Malik Kāthī (XI-1), v. 1, *723*, 698, 702; v. 2, 1044
Muḥammad b. 'Abd al-Malik, *see* b. Ṭufail
Muḥammad b. 'Abd al-Mun'im Ṣinhājī, 306
Muḥammad b. 'Abd al-Raḥīm b. Furāt (XIV-2), *1783*, 1264
Muḥammad b. 'Abd al-Raḥīm Māzinī (XII-2), v. 2, *412*, 1201; v. 3, 1186
Muḥammad b. 'Abd al-Raḥmān Khaṭīb Dimashq (XIV-1), *1011*, 373, 1326, 1463, 1725
Muḥammad 'Abd al-Rasūl Ibrāhīm, 1787
Muḥammad b. 'Abd al-Ṣamad Ṣanbāṭī, 1453
Muḥammad b. 'Abd al-Wahhāb, 422
Muḥammad 'Abduh, 422
Muḥammad b. Aḥmad 'Ajamī, 1776
Muḥammad b. Aḥmad, *see* Bīrūnī; Dhahabī
Muḥammad b. Aḥmad 'Irāqī (XIII-2), v. 2, *1045*, 769
Muḥammad b. Aḥmad b. Jubair (XII-2), v. 2, *412*, 1191; v. 3, 807, 1618
Muḥammad b. Aḥmad Kharaqī (XII-1), v. 2, *204*, 1205
Muḥammad b. Aḥmad Khwārizmī (X-2), v. 1, *659*, 647, 654; v. 3, 374
Muḥammad b. Aḥmad b. Maḥmūd, 972
Muḥammad b. Aḥmad Mawṣilī, 1534
Muḥammad b. Aḥmad Mizzī (XIV-1), *696*, 134
Muḥammad b. Aḥmad Muqaddasī (X-2), v. 1, *675*, 820; v. 3, 756
Muḥammad b. Aḥmad Nasawī (XIII-1), v. 2, *686*, 527
Muḥammad b. Aḥmad Qalqashandī, 1787
Muḥammad b. Aḥmad Qazwīnī (XII-1), v. 2, *182*, 117
Muḥammad b. Aḥmad Riqūṭī (XIII-2), v. 2, *865*, 726, 834; v. 3, 74, 1082
Muḥammad b. Aḥmad, *see* b. Rushd
Muḥammad b. Aḥmad Tamīmī (X-2), v. 1, *679*, 833; v. 2, 371; v. 3, 759
Muḥammad b. Aḥmad Tījānī, *see* 'Abdallāh b. Aḥmad
Muḥammad b. 'Alī b. 'Arabī (XIII-1), v. 2, *596*, 1206; v. 3, 102, 105, 489, 619, 626, 627, 801, 1067, 1100, 1459, 1461, 1462, 1873
Muḥammad b. 'Alī b. Bābūya (X-2), v. 1, *656*, 647, 654; v. 3, 1067
Muḥammad b. 'Alī b. Dahhān (XII-2), v. 2, *462*, 1165
Muḥammad b. 'Alī b. Daqīq, 959, 997
Muḥammad b. 'Alī b. Ḥammād (XIII-1), v. 2, *681*, 527
Muḥammad b. 'Alī Īlāqī, 1721
Muḥammad b. 'Alī Khaṭīb Irbilī (XIV-1), *746*, 105, 163
Muḥammad 'Alī of Lahore, 1854
Muḥammad b. 'Alī Mahdī (XIV-2), *1725*, 1215
Muḥammad b. 'Alī Makkī, 1452
Muḥammad b. 'Alī, a. Muqri' (XIV-1), *695*, 132, 1524
Muḥammad 'Alī of Rampur, 1854
Muḥammad b. 'Alī Samarqandī (XIII-1), v. 2, *661*, 1208 (*under* Najīb); v. 3, 1724
Muḥammad b. 'Alī Shafra (XIV-1), *895*, 209, 225, 228, 257, 273
Muḥammad b. 'Alī Shaqūrī (XIV-2), *1721*, 852, 897, 1065, 1213
Muḥammad b. 'Alī Sipāhīzāde, 797
Muḥammad b. 'Alī b. Ṭiqṭaqā, 309, 321, 967
Muḥammad b. 'Alī b. Waḥshīya (X-1), v. 1, *634*, 621; v. 2, 425; v. 3, 801, 1637
Muḥammad b. 'Alī b. Zuraiq (XIV-2), *1526*, 1118, 1525
Muḥammad Amīn Khānajī, 806
Muḥammad b. Amīn Suwaidī, 1787
Muḥammad b. 'Ammār Mālikī, 1623
Muḥammad b. Aqī Ḥizām Jabalī, 828
Muḥammad b. Ashraf Samarqandī (XIII-2), v. 2, *1020*, 1206
Muḥammad 'Awfī (XIII-1), v. 2, *602*, 1206; v. 3, 631
Muḥammad Bābā Sammāsī, 1068
Muḥammad Badr al-dīn of Balkh, 1644
Muḥammad b. a. Bakr Fārisī (XIII-2), v. 2, *1000*, 753
Muḥammad b. a. Bakr b. Jamā'a, 998
Muḥammad b. a. Bakr Zuhrī (XII-1), v. 2, *221*, 130
Muḥammad Bālāsāghunī, 1644
Muḥammad Banda Nawāz (XIV-2), *1476*, 1102, 1330
Muḥammad Bashīr Tuwātī, 1792
Muḥammad b. Dāniyāl Mawṣulī (XIII-2), v. 2, *872*, 728; v. 3, 103
Muḥammad b. Faḍlallāh Qibṭī, 1249
Muḥammad Fāsī, 1764

Muḥammad Gao, 803
Muḥammad Gulandām, 1457
Muḥammad Ḥāfiẓ, *see* Ḥāfiẓ
Muḥammad b. Ḥamdūn Baghdādī (XII-2), v. 2, *445*, 311
Muḥammad b. Ḥamza Fanārī (XIV-2), *1465*, 1101
Muḥammad b. Ḥasan b. Duraid (X-1), v. 1, *644*, 809; v. 2, 1136; v. 3, 372, 376
Muḥammad b. Ḥasan Fārisī, 707
Muḥammad b. Ḥasan Karkhī (XI-1), v. 1, *718*, 813; v. 2, 211, 401; v. 3, 133, 596, 1518
Muḥammad b. Ḥasan Shaibānī, 1454, 1462
Muḥammad b. Ḥasan Ṭūsī, 1067
Muḥammad Hāshimī Filālī, 957
Muḥammad b. Ḥawqal (X-2), v. 1, *674*, 650, 654; v. 3, 63
Muḥammad b. Ḥusain b. Adamī (X-2), v. 1, *630*, 620
Muḥammad b. Ḥusain b. Farrā', 623
Muḥammad b. Ḥusain Fāṭimī, 957
Muḥammad b. Ḥusain of Granada, 1525
Muḥammad b. Ḥusain a. Ja'far (XI-1), v. 1, *718*, 809
Muḥammad b. Ḥusain b. Muḥammad (XII-2), v. 2, *401*, 10, 296
Muḥammad b. Ibrāhīm b. 'Abbād (XIV-2), *1452*, 1098, 1864
Muḥammad b. Ibrāhīm Abulī (XIV-1), *1118*, 132
Muḥammad b. Ibrāhīm b. Akfānī (XIV-1), *899*, 74, 105, 210, 214, 258, 271, 998
Muḥammad b. Ibrāhīm b. Baṣṣāl, 1637, 1850
Muḥammad b. Ibrāhīm Dimashqī (XIV-1), *800*, 58, 103, 179, 200, 203, 209, 217, 258, 271, 321, 799, 800, 900, 1160, 1158
Muḥammad b. Ibrāhīm Fārid al-dīn 'Aṭṭār (XIII-1), v. 2, *601*, 1172; v. 3, 64, 105, 379, 625
Muḥammad b. Ibrāhīm Fazārī (VIII-2), v. 1, *530*, 521, 524
Muḥammad b. Ibrāhīm b. Jamā'a (XIV-1), *997*, 74, 102, 321, 900
Muḥammad b. Ibrāhīm b. Raqqām (XIV-1), *695*, 132, 1515
Muḥammad b. Ibrāhīm Shalāḥī, 165
Muḥammad b. Ibrāhīm Waṭwāṭ Warrāq (XIII-2), v. 2, *870*, 1245; v. 3, 103, 200, 799
Muḥammad b. Idrīs Shāfi'ī (IX-1), v. 1, *550*, 543; v. 3, 102, 618, 801, 1161
Muḥammad b. 'Īsā b. Karā (XIV-1), *749*, 163
Muḥammad b. 'Īsā Māhānī (IX-2), v. 1, *597*, 816
Muḥammad b. 'Īsā Tirmidhī, 1065
Muḥammad b. Isḥāq a. 'Abdallāh (VIII-2), v. 1, *540*, 523, 524
Muḥammad b. Isḥāq b. a. Ya'qūb Nadīm (X-2), v. 1, *662*, 809
Muḥammad b. Ismā'īl, *see* Bukhārī
Muḥammad b. Jābir, *see* Battānī
Muḥammad b. Jarīr, *see* Ṭabarī
Muḥammad b. Jazūlī (XIV-1), *695*, 132, 1847
Muḥammad Khādim Ḥusain, 966
Muḥammad b. Khair (XII-2), v. 2, *444*, 311
Muḥammad Khalīlī, 1118
Muḥammad b. Laith (better than Līth), a. Jūd (XI-1), v. 1, *718*, 787
Muḥammad b. Lājīn (XIV-2), *1642*, 1169, 1185
Muḥammad oğlu Maḥmūd, 1644
Muḥammad b. Maḥmūd Āmilī (XIV-1), *632*, 106, 259, 628, 1846
Muḥammad b. Maḥmūd Makhzūmī, 1827
Muḥammad b. Maḥmūd b. Najjār, 964
Muḥammad b. Maḥmūd Shīrwānī (XIV-2), *1726*, 1215, 1242
Muḥammad b. Maḥmūd Ṭūsī (XII-2), v. 2, *413*, 1206
Muḥammad b. Mangalī (XIV-2), *1641*, 1169, 1185, 1214, 1238
Muḥammad b. Manṣūr, *see* Zarrīn Dast
Muḥammad b. Ma'rūf Taqī al-dīn, 1525
Muḥammad b. Mu'ādh, 434
Muḥammad b. Mubārakshāh Bukhārī (XIV-1), *699*, 106, 123, 135, 163, 438, 1461, 1512
Muḥammad b. Muḥammad 'Abdarī (XIII-2), v. 2, *1065*
Muḥammad b. Muḥammad b. Ājurrūm (XIV-1), *1009*, 373
Muḥammad b. Muḥammad of Almería (XIV-2), *1721*, 852, 897, 1213
Muḥammad b. Muḥammad Āmidī (XIII-1), v. 2, *598*, 500
Muḥammad b. Muḥammad Āqsarā'ī (XIV-2), *1725*, 1011, 1067, 1215, 1221, 1326
Muḥammad b. Muḥammad b. 'Āṣim (XIV-2), *1453*, 1098, 1271
Muḥammad b. Muḥammad Bahā' al-dīn Bukhārī, 1068
Muḥammad b. Muḥammad Dhahabī, 967
Muḥammad b. Muḥammad, *see* Fārābī; Ghazzālī
Muḥammad b. Muḥammad b. Humām, 1623
Muḥammad b. Muḥammad, *see* Idrīsī
Muḥammad b. Muḥammad 'Imād al-dīn Iṣfahānī (XII-2), v. 2, *447*, 1185 (*under* 'Imād); v. 3, 1644
Muḥammad b. Muḥammad Jazarī (XIV-2), *1455*, 1067, 1100, 1266
Muḥammad b. Muḥammad Juwainī, 707
Muḥammad b. Muḥammad b. Juzayy, 1167, 1618, 1636
Muḥammad b. Muḥammad Khalīlī (XIV-2), *1526*, 1118
Muḥammad b. Muḥammad Khujandī (XIV-1), *897*, 257
Muḥammad b. Muḥammad Manbijī (XIV-2), *1724*, 1214
Muḥammad b. Muḥammad, *see* Nāṣir al-dīn Ṭūsī

Muḥammad b. Muḥammad b. Nubāta (XIV-1), *999*, 321
Muḥammad b. a. Muḥammad Saqaṭī, 998
Muḥammad b. Muḥammad b. Shiḥna (XIV-2), *1785*, 794, 1082, 1264
Muḥammad b. Muḥammad Tabrīzī (XIII-2), v. 2, *871*, 728; v. 3, 62, 99, 437, 1448
Muḥammad b. Muḥammad Taḥtānī (XIV-1), *629*, 106, 1462
Muḥammad b. Muḥammad b. Ukhuwwa (XIV-1), *998*, 143, 321, 712, 1852
Muḥammad b. Muḥammad, *see* a. Wafā'
Muḥammad b. Mukarram b. Manẓūr (XIII-2), v. 2, *1136*, 806; v. 3, 307, 373, 1827
Muḥammad al-Murtaḍā Zabīdī, 1827
Muḥammad b. Mūsā, *see* Damīrī; Khwārizmī
Muḥammad b. Mūsā b. Shākir, *see* Mūsā, Banū
Muḥammad b. Naqīb, 962
Muḥammad Qādirī, 465
Muḥammad b. Qalā'ūn, 199, 204
Muḥammad Qashshāsh, 1342
Muḥammad b. Qāsim Nuwairī (XIV-2), *1782*, 1264
Muḥammad, a. Qāsim, the Prophet (ṣl'm) (VII-1), v. 1, *464*, 819; v. 2, 1206; v. 3, 991
Muḥammad b. Qāsim b. Zākūr Fāsī, 957
Muḥammad b. Qayyim Jawzīya (XIV-1), *901*, 103, 163, 210, 239, 258, 321
Muḥammad b. Rāfi' Sallāmī, 958
Muḥammad Riḍā Shabībī, 431, 968
Muḥammad b. Riḍwān b. Arqam (XIV-1), *830*, 1636
Muḥammad b. Sa'd (IX-1), v. 1, *579*, 548, 550
Muḥammad b. Sa'īd b. Dubaithī, 964
Muḥammad b. Sālim Khallāl (XIV-1), *623*, 104
Muḥammad b. Sālim b. Wāṣil (XIII-2), v. 2, *1119*, 727, 796
Muḥammad b. Sam'ūn, 134
Muḥammad Saqaṭī of Málaga, 1771
Muḥammad Shafra, *see* Muḥammad b. 'Alī
Muḥammad shāh Čelebī, 1101, 1466
Muḥammad Shāh Fanārī, 1530
Muḥammad b. Shākir Kutubī Ḥalabī (XIV-2), *1781*, 308, 960, 1264
Muhammad Shalāḥī of Seville (XIII-1), v. 2, *633*, 26, 510
Muḥammad b. Shanab, 422, 805, 963, 966, 1010, 1455, 1847
Muḥammad b. Sulaimān Fuẓūlī, 1457
Muḥammad b. Taghlaq, 41, 137, 283, 1026, 1616
Muḥammad b. 'Ubaidallāh Lajlāj, 1722
Muḥammad b. Umail Tamīmī, 759
Muḥammad b. 'Umar b. Badr (XIII-1), v. 2, *622*, 506, 753
Muḥammad b. 'Umar Fakhr al-dīn Rāzī (XII-2), v. 2, *364*, 1172; v. 3, 270, 630, 801, 967, 1101, 1104, 1374, 1466, 1571, 1725, 1727, 1768, 1897
Muḥammad b. 'Umar b. Farrukhān (IX-1), v. 1, *568*, 546, 550; v. 2, 170
Muḥammad b. 'Umar b. Qūṭīya (X-2), v. 1, *688*, 652, 654; v. 3, 372
Muḥammad b. 'Umar b. Rushaid (XIII-2), v. 2, *1066*, 1206; v. 3, 202, 208, 307
Muḥammad b. 'Umar Wāqidī (VIII-2), v. 1, *541*, 523
Muḥammad b. Walīd Ṭurṭūshī (XII-1), v. 2, *264*, 118, 137, 141
Muḥammad b. Yaḥyā b. Bājja (XII-1), v. 2, *183*, 1152; v. 3, 286, 608
Muḥammad b. Yaḥyā Ṣūlī, 967, 1722
Muḥammad b. Ya'qūb, *see* Fīrūzābādī
Muḥammad b. Ya'qūb Janadī (XIV-1), *958*, 307, 1263, 1779
Muḥammad b. Ya'qūb Kulīnī, 1067
Muḥammad b. Yazīd Qazwīnī, 1065
Muḥammad b. Yūsuf, *see* a. Haiyān
Muḥammad b. Yūsuf Īlāqī, 632
Muḥammad b. Zakarīyā, *see* Rāzī
Muhannā, b., *see* Jamāl al-dīn
muḥīṭ, 372
muḥtasib, 154, 321, 712, 998, 1847. *See also* ḥisba
Muḥyī al-dīn b. 'Abd al-Ẓāhir, 1786
Muḥyī al-dīn Maghribī, *see* Yaḥyā b. Muḥammad
Muḥyī al-dīn Ṣabrī Kurdī, 435
Muiden, *see* Rodolph Dier
Mu'īn al-dīn Chishtī, 1476
Mu'īn al-murīd, 104
Muisit, Le, *see* Giles
Mu'izz b. Bādīs, 175
Mujāhid 'Alī Rasūlī (XIV-1), *827*, 209, 240, 257, 285, 1637
mu'jiza, 1845
Mukhammas al-mā', 759
Mukhtār b. Ḥasan, *see* b. Buṭlān
Mukhtār al-jawāhir, 427
Mukhtaṣar, 1455
Mukhtaṣar ta'rīkh al-bashar, 794
Mulcaster, Richard, 1316
Mulder, W., 555, 1360
Mulder, W. J. M., 1820
Muller, E., 465, 1842
Muller-Thym, B. J., 571
Mulomedicina, 342, 1669
Multānī, *see* Isḥāq b. Tāj al-dīn
Multifarium, 88, 583
Mummenhoff, Ernst, 1128
Muna Mosconi, 1451
Munaja' b. Ṣadaqa (XII-2), v. 2, *336*. 281
Munḍā, 383
Mundhir, b. (XIV-1), *828*, 210, 240, 257, 285, 827
mundi caelestis terrestrisque constitutione, De (IX-1), v. 1, *569*, 546

mundi fabrica, De, 1409
Mundinus, *see* Anatomia
mundo, De, 1844
Mundy, John, 1113
Munier, Henri, 1007
Munk, J., 251
Munk, Solomon, 1897
Munk, William, 1868
Muñoz, Antonio, 269
Muñoz, *see* Giles
Munqidh, b., *see* Usāmah b. Murshid
Munshi, K. M., 1475
Muntaner, *see* Raymond
Muntner, S., 254
Muqaddama (or Muqaddima), 960, 1006, 1768, 1769
Muqaddasī, *see* Muḥammad b. Aḥmad
Muqaffa', b. (VIII-2), v. 1, *540*, 810
muqanṭarāt, 1530, 1847
Muqri', a., *see* Muḥammad b. 'Alī
Murād b. Isḥāq of Gerede, 1726
Murad Kamil, 1451
Murād, Yūsuf, 1897
Murano, 171
Muratori, L. A., 1252, 1814
Muratov, P. P., 1583
Murchi, Tommaso, 854
Murcia, 375
murdār-sang, 170
Muret, *see* John
Murimuth, *see* Adam
Muris, Murs, *see* John of Meurs
Murray, David, 1605, 1742
Murray, H. J. R., 1897
Murray, M. A., 1051, 1052
Musa, Antonius (I-2 B.C.), v. 1, *231*, 220
Mūsā, *see* Moses for Jewish and Christian names
Mūsā, Banū (IX-1), v. 1, *560*, 793; v. 2, 1207
Mūsā, *see* Gongo; Ḥayyim b. Judah
Mūsā b. Khālid (IX-2), v. 1, *613*, 587
Mūsā b. Maimūn Isrā'īlī, *see* Maimonides
Mūsā b. Lawī, 1385
Mūsā b. Muḥammad Khalīlī, 1118, 1527
Mūsā b. Ṭūbī, 62, 100, 611
Mūsā b. Yūnus Kamāl al-dīn (XIII-1), v. 2, *600*, 1192
Mūsā (II) b. Yūsuf b. Ziyān (XIV-2), *1792*, 271, 1271
Musanda, *see* Peter
musar, 590
Muschketow, J. W. v., 1471
Museum of Alexandria (III-1 B.C.), v. 1, *158*, 150; v. 2, 285, 350
Musharrif al-dīn b. Muṣliḥ al-dīn, *see* Sa'dī
music, 20, 1878, 1880, 1885, 1886, 1892, 1901
music, Arabic, 1883
music, *see* astrology
music, Byzantine, 1833
music, Chinese, 1857
music, instruments, 165
music, mensural, 743, 1128, 1568
music, notation, 162
music, sacred, 1037
music of the spheres, 164
music, teaching, 1857
music, theories, 1128
music, tube, 1858
musicians, guild of, 1129
Muslim, *see* alchemy; Arabic; atomism
Muslim brotherhoods, 420
Muslim, early conquests (VII-1), v. 1, *465*
Muslim b. Ḥajjāj Nīsābūrī (IX-2), v. 1, *592*, 583; v. 2, 1066, 1132; v. 3, 1065
Muslim, *see* mineralogy; ships; weights and measures
Muslims, Chinese, 1586, 1866, 1898
Musnad, 1066
Musnad al-jāmi', 1066
Musre ha-pilosofim, 590
Mussafia, Adolfo, 865
Mussato, *see* Albertino
Muṣṭafā b. Aḥmad Chelebī, 628
Muṣṭafā bey, 1014
Muṣṭafā Fahmī, 1779
Muṣṭafā Naẓīf, 708
Mustaghfirī, *see* Ja'far b. Muḥammad
mustard, 230
Mustawfī, *see* Ḥamdallāh b. a. Bakr
muta'allim, 154
Muṭahhar Ḥillī, b., *see* Ḥasan b. Yūsuf
Muṭahhar b. Ṭāhir Maqdisī (X-2), v. 1, *659*, 820
Mutakallimūn, 150
Mu'tamin, *see* Yūsuf b. Ahmad
mutaṭabbib, 897
mutawassiṭāt, 'ilm al-, 633
Mu'tazila, 617, 619, 629
Mutschmann, Hermann, 448
Muttra plague, 1651
Muwaffaq b. 'Alī, a. Manṣūr (X-2), v. 1, *678*, 787; v. 3, 376, 1222
Muwaffaq al-dawla 'Alī, 969
Muwaffaq al-dīn, *see* Ya'qūb b. a. Isḥāq
Muwaffaq Faḍlallāh b. a. Muḥammad, 308
muwaqqit, 134, 1118, 1524
muwashshaḥāt, 1853
muwaṭṭa', 1066
Muẓaffar b. Ismā'īl Asfuzārī (XII-1), v. 2, *204*, 1207
Muẓaffar b. Muḥammad Ṭūsī (XIII-1), v. 2, *622*, 1207; v. 3, 601
Myamir, 447
Myers, J. G., 1188
Myhrman, D. W., 1781
Mylo, Paul, 1631
Myrepsos, *see* Nicholas
Myres, J. N. L., 1864
Myrtil, *see* Nicholas
mysteries, Greek, 1094

mysticism, v, 14, 17, 75, 84, 1886, 1889
mysticism, Christian, 1873
mysticism, Indian, 1882
mysticism, Muslim, *see* taṣawwuf
mythology, classical, 1805
Mžik, Hans v., xi, 1158, 1622

Nabataean, 1168, 1768
Nabāṭī, *see* Aḥmad b. Muḥammad
Nabokoff, Nicolas, 711
Nāchirāja, 383, 1828
Naddino di Aldobrandino Bovattieri, 1201
Naddino de Prato, 1201
Naddodd the Viking, 1154, 1610
Nadilz, *see* Peter
naevus, 271, 960
Nafā'is al-funūn, 632, 1846
Nafīs, b., *see* 'Alī b. a. Ḥazm
Naftule elohim, 417
Nafuci, *see* Isaac
Nafza tribe, 1011
Nagar, *see* Nathan
Nāgarakṛitāgama (XIV-2), *1624*, 1161
Nāgarī, 382
Nāgārjuna of Kōsala (III-1), v. 1, *316*, 820; v. 3, 59, 466, 1584
Nāgavarma II, 383, 1828
Nagel, F., 1633
Nagtglas, Frederik, 823
Nagusa, Yasuhiro, 1832
naḥash, 451
Nahāwandī, *see* Aḥmad b. Muḥammad
Nahawendi, *see* Benjamin b. Moses
Naḥḥās, b., 1012
Naḥmanides, *see* Moses b. Naḥman
Naḥmias, *see* Joseph b. Abraham; Joseph b. Joseph
Nahum (VII B.C.), v. 1, *64*, 60
Nairīzī (IX-2), v. 1, *598*, 820; v. 2, 341, 836; v. 3, 1526
najāt, Kitāb al-, 435
Najīb 'Āṣim, 972
Najīb al-dīn Samarqandī, *see* Muḥammad b. 'Alī Samarqandī
Najjār, *see* Muḥammad b. Maḥmūd
Najlā' 'Izz al-dīn, 1784
Najm al-dīn Maḥmūd, 898
Najm al-dīn Samarqandī, 1727
Nakayama, T., 906
Na-khi tribes, 1851
Nakhshabī Ḍiyā' al-dīn (XIV-1), *464*, 69, 259, 267, 296, 377, 1842
Nallino, C. A., 421, 1638, 1833, 1846, 1847
Nallino, Maria, 1833
Namur, 220
Namur, *see* Blanche; Mary; Robert
Nāmūs-i-akbar, 465
Nānak, 1475
Nancy map, 1155
Nangis, *see* William
Ñāṇissara, 423
Nanni, *see* Mariano
Nanniah, 466
Nannini or Nanni, Remigio, 507
Nansen, Fridtjof, 196, 1897
Naphtali, 365
Naples, 65, 374
Naples, *see* Arnold; John; Leo
Napoléon III, 726
Napoléon, fate book, 360
Napoleone Orsini, 752, 858
Naqawa, b., *see* Ephraim b. Israel; Israel b. Joseph; Joseph b. Samuel
Naqdan, *see* Moses
naqīb, 154
Nāqid, b. (XII-2), v. 2, *432*, 1208
Naqshbandī, 1272, 1469, 1475
Naqshbandīya, 1068
Narahari (XIII-1), v. 2, *668*, 1208; v. 3, 1330, 1730
Nārāyaṇa (XIV-2), *1534*, 134, 1121, 1330
Narbonne, *see* Abraham b. Isaac; Jekuthiel b. Solomon; John; Maurice; Moses b. Joseph Qimḥi; Moses b. Joshua
Nardi, Bruno, 446, 497, 499
Narducci, Henri, 1484
narm-āhan, 1175
Nasafī, *see* 'Abdallāh b. Aḥmad; 'Umar b. Muḥammad
Nasawī, *see* 'Alī b. Aḥmad; Muḥammad b. Aḥmad
Nash, Vernon, 1897
Nasi, *see* Judah
Nasīmī, *see* Imām al-dīn
Nāṣir al-dīn Ḥasan, 173
Nāṣir al-dīn Ṭūsī, Muḥammad b. Muḥammad (XIII-2), v. 2, *1001*, 1208; v. 3, 133, 134, 377, 598, 626, 630, 707, 968, 969, 971, 972, 1077, 1120, 1461, 1464, 1525, 1530, 1570, 1728
Nāṣir al-dīn b. 'Umar, 1587
Nāṣir-i-Khusraw (XI-2), v. 1, *768*, 821; v. 3, 149, 376
Nāṣir Muḥammad b. Qalā'ūn, 1249
Nāṣir, Nāṣir al-dīn Muhammad, 40
Nāṣirī, Kitāb, 828
Nasmith, James, 787
Naṣr, Banū, 101
Naṣr, a., *see* Manṣūr b. 'Alī
Naṣr b. Ya'qūb (XI-1), v. 1, *706*, 694, 702
Nassau, *see* Maurice
Nassio, *see* Andrew; William
Natā'ij al-fikar, 759
Nathan b. Eliezer Me'ati (XIII-2), v. 2, *853*, 1208; v. 3, 437, 613, 1211, 1220, 1373, 1379, 1385
Nathan b. Jehiel (XI-2), v. 1, *782* (misspelled Jeliel), 821; v. 2, 142, 700; v. 3, xi, 366
Nathan b. Joel Falaquera (XIII-2), v. 2, *1096*, 1208

Nathan, *see* Judah b. Solomon
Nathan Nagar, 1523
Nathan Orgier, 1382
Nathan b. Shelemiah, 1374
nations in universities, 78, 1399
Natorp, Paul, vii
Nattangia, 932
natura rerum, 211
natural philosophy, 550, 1165, 1505, 1843, 1859
nature vs. nurture, 270
Naubakht, b., *see* Faḍl
Naucratis, *see* Athenaeos
Naudé, Gabriel, 445, 1359
Naumann, Leopold, 572
Nava-Medhaṃkara, 634
Navarre, 72
Navarre, *see* Blanche; Joan
Navarre, Collège, 476, 1088
Navernia, *see* James
navigation of the Arabs, 1782
navigation, history of, 770
Naviglio, Grande, 735
Naville, Adrien, 77
Nawawī, *see* Yaḥyā b. Sharaf
Nazianzos, *see* Gregory
Naẓīf, Muṣṭafā, 1847
Naẓīf b. Yumn (X-2), v. 1, *664*, 648, 654
Naẓẓām (IX-1), v. 1, *559*, 544, 546; v. 2, 61; v. 3, 211, 1775
Neander, Theophilus, 1574
Nearchos (IV-2 B.C.), v. 1, *145*, 126, 284
Nebrija, *see* Elio Antonio
Nebuchadnezzar, 1104
Necho (VI B.C.), v. 1, *78*, 66
Neckam, *see* Alexander
Nédélec, *see* Hervé
Needham, Joseph, viii, 906, 1549, 1641, 1855, 1897
Nef, J. U., 221, 1173
Négrier, Paul, 288
negromanti, 406
Negroni, Carlo, 1794, 1814
Negropont, 448
Negus, 55
Neḥamat ha-filosofiya, 451
Nehemiah (V B.C.), v. 1, *109*, 83, 150
Nehemiah, book of (III-1 B.C.), v. 1, *163*
Neilos Cabasilas, 1438, 1439
Neilos Diassorinos or Diasorenos (XIV-2), *1821*, 1094, 1167, 1170, 1171, 1259, 1320
Neilos, patriarch, 746
Neilson, George, 1741, 1870
Nélis, H., 940
Nelli, *see* Francis
Nemesianus, Marcus Aurelius Olympius (III-2), v. 1, *340*, 331
Nemesios of Emesa (IV-2), v. 1, *373*, 361, 727; v. 2, 65, 348; v. 3, 488
Nemorarius, *see* Jordanus
Nemoy, Leon, 56, 365, 367, 1774
Nemus unionis, 1819
Nennius, 1774
Nente, del, 575
Neophyta doctrina, 393
Neophytos, 121, 122, 754
Neophytos Prodromenos (XIV-1), *826*, 53, 208
Neophytus spiritualis, 393
Neoplatonism, 118, 212
Nepal, 59
Ner elohim, 591
Neri (vs. Bianchi), 37, 480
Neri Capponi, 1251
Neri, Ferdinando, 915
Neri di Landoccio Pagliaresi, 1335, 1337
Nerino Franzoli da' Liucci, 842
Neritono, *see* Francis
Nero (I-2), v. 1, *247*, 243, 244
Nero Acciaiuoli, 1025
Nerses Balì (XIV-1), *460*, 67, 253, 288, 304, 356, 826
Nerses the Graceful (XII-2), v. 2, *335*, 1209
nerves, two sets, 840
Nēryōsang, 376
Nese, *see* Cellino
Nessiah, *see* Moses b. Isaac
Nestor of Kiev (XII-1), v. 2, *261*, 1209
Nestorianism, 49, 54, 55, 105, 137, 139, 298, 306, 357, 364, 377, 776, 1071, 1602, 1754, 1830
Nestorianism, Chinese, 358
Nestorianism, Chinese, monument of 781 (VIII-2), v. 1, *526*, 520
Nestorios (V-1), v. 1, *381*, 380; v. 2, 1209
Netherlandish, 349
Neubauer, Adolf, 419, 617, 792, 1449, 1717, 1897, 1901
Neuburger, Max, 1660, 1897
Neuenburg, *see* Matthew
Neugebauer, Otto, 1832
Neuman, A. A., 1063
Neumann, Bernhard, 1553
Neumann, C. F., 1897
Neumann, G. A., 192, 789
Neumann, J., 400
Neumann, K. E., 571
Neumann, K. F., 1153
Neumann, Wilhelm Anton, 190, 1153
Neumarkt, *see* John
Neustadt, David, 1867
Neustain, *see* Julius Alexandrinus
Nève, Félix, 1260
Nevelet, I. N., 579
Nevers, *see* Lewis
Nevins, Allan, 1613
New College, 1079, 1401
Newburgh, *see* William
Newcastle, *see* Hugh
Newcastle-on-Tyne, 406, 1173
Newman, J. H., 1349
Newport Tower, 1613

Newton, 14, 15, 114, 142, 148, 543, 601, 705, 737, 870
Newton, *see* John
Nibelungenlied (XII-2), v. 2, *394*, 1209; v. 3, 351
Nicaea, council, viii
Nicaise, Edouard, 872, 1693, 1695
Nicander of Colophon (III-1 B.C.), v. 1, *158*, 150; v. 2, 1209
Nicanor of Alexandria (II-1), v. 1, *287*, 269
Niccolò, *see* Nicholas
Nicene creed, viii
Nicephoros Blemmydes (XIII-2), v. 2, *971*, 1209; v. 3, 755, 951
Nicephoros Bryennios (XII-1), v. 2, *250*, 143; v. 3, 746
Nicëphoros Callistos Xanthopulos (XIV-1), *947*, 303
Nicephoros Chumnos (XIV-1), *587*, 53, 96, 97, 252, 888, 889, 996
Nicephoros Gregoras (XIV-1), *949*, 53, 96, 97, 123, 161, 197, 217, 304, 354, 585, 586, 587, 588, 1094, 1115, 1259, 1438, 1511, 1652, 1760, 1852, 1865
Nicephoros Patriarches (IX-1), v. 1, *578*, 548
Nicetas Acominatos (XIII-1), v. 2, *680*, 1209; v. 3, 303
Nicetas, physician (IX-2), v. 1, *608*, 821
Nicetas Sacatophoros, 1644
Nicetas Stethatos, 96
Nicholas, *see also* Claes; Cola
Nicholas Adoratski, 1866
Nicholas, *see* Antidotarium Nicolai
Nicholas d'Autrecourt (XIV-1), *545*, 22, 84, 90, 534, 542
Nicholas of Basel, 572
Nicholas de Baye, 1294
Nicholas Bertruccio (XIV-1), *847*, 244, 266, 1223, 1690
Nicholas de Bonaventure, 1655
Nicholas Bonet (XIV-1), *532*, 90, 189
Nicholas Boneti, 781
Nicholas Broker, 1561
Nicholas von Buch, 993
Nicholas di Burgo (XIV-2), *1674*, 1192
Nicholas Burzio, 1565
Nicholas Cabasilas (XIV-2), *1438*, 1094, 1115, 1320, 1388
Nicholas Chuquet, 134, 1116, 1518
Nicholas de Clémanges (or Clamanges), 454, 476, 743, 1054, 1276, 1294, 1295, 1699
Nicholas de Combitis, 1599
Nicholas de' Conti, 41, 1291
Nicholas Corbizo, 774
Nicholas of Cues (or Cusa, Cusanus), 12, 413, 530, 544, 568, 570, 1082, 1297, 1360, 1408
Nicholas Cunales Critopulos, 995
Nicholas Damascenos (I-2 B.C.), v. 1, *226*, 821; v. 2, 1209; v. 3, 432
Nicholas de Deoprepio, 446
Nicholas of Dinkelsbühl (XIV-2), *1432*, 1091, 1112, 1123
Nicholas of Dijon, 814
Nicholas Donin of La Rochelle (XIII-1), v. 2, *557*, 1209; v. 3, 369
Nicholas II of Este, 1812
Nicholas Eymeric (XIV-2), *1338*, 1049, 1052, 1107, 1131, 1574, 1870
Nicholas Falcon, 953, 955
Nicholas Falcucci, 1194, 1222
Nicholas Flamel (XIV-2), *1576*, 1135, 1308
Nicholas the German, 1146
Nicholas de Gonesse, 1075, 1307, 1391
Nicholas of Hereford, 1347
Nicholas de Hude, 192, 789
Nicholas Janovez, 23
Nicholas v. Jeroschin, 932
Nicholas de La Horbe (XIV-1), *456*, 65, 113
Nicholas de Landa, 847
Nicholas v. Landau, 570
Nicholas Liburnio, 1806
Nicholas of Lisieux, 47
Nicholas v. Louvain, 572
Nicholas Louve, 1147
Nicholas of Lynn, Carmelite (XIV-2), *1501*, 1111, 1421, 1500
Nicholas of Lynn, Franciscan, 1148, 1501
Nicholas of Lyra (XIV-1), *397*, 48, 90, 188, 370, 407, 1325, 1343, 1436, 1539
Nicholas di Martoni (XIV-2), *1596*, 1032, 1143, 1210
Nicholas Meliteniotes, 1513
Nicholas of Molano, 781
Nicholas Myrepsos (XIII-2), v. 2, *1094*, 1209; v. 3, 64, 288, 446, 889, 1208
Nicholas Myrtil, 1341
Nicholas de' Niccoli, 1289, 1321, 1807, 1815, 1822
Nicholas Niger, 1155
Nicholas O'Hickey, 881
Nicholas, *see* Oresme
Nicholas di Paganica, 112, 243
Nicholas Panis, 1693
Nicholas da Pavia, 609
Nicholas de Pelhřimov, 1352
Nicholas of Pergamon, 834, 1190
Nicholas da Poggibonsi (XIV-1), *774*, 185, 186, 207, 337
Nicholas of Poland (XIII-2), v. 2, *1092*, 94, 786
Nicholas III, pope, 126
Nicholas V, (anti)pope, 401
Nicholas da Prato, 942
Nicholas Prepositi, 446
Nicholas (Nicoloso) da Recco (XIV-1), *768*, 183, 184, 337, 1144, 1808
Nicholas da Reggio (XIV-1), *446*, 64, 242, 288, 1691, 1841
Nicholas Rhabdas (XIV-1), *681*, 119, 122, 123, 354, 1511, 1847

Nicholas Roccabonella, 1163
Nicholas Rossell, 190
Nicholas Saemundarson (XII-2), v. 2, *421*, 35, 302; v. 3, 196, 1154
Nicholas of Salerno (XII-1), v. 2, *239*, 1209; v. 3, 288, 426, 813, 836, 883, 1222, 1679
Nicholas II of Salerno (XII-2), v. 2, *436*, 309
Nicholas de Sandwych, 1500
Nicholas da Santa Sofia (XIV-1), *839*, 243, 1193, 1677
Nicholas of Soissons, 541
Nicholas Speciale, 297, 1737
Nicholas Trevet (XIV-1), *942*, 92, 301, 303, 348, 1418, 1852
Nicholas Tyngewich, 1705
Nicholas of Udine (XIV-2), *1678*, 1192
Nicholas Vernia da Chieti, 519, 539
Nicholas Zeno (XIV-2), *1593*, 1143, 1300
Nicholson, E. W. B., 1605
Nicholson, R. A., 490, 632
Nicklas, Anna, 575
Nicodemos, Gospel of, 339, 1039, 1055, 1076, 1393
Nicola, Nicolas, *see* Nicholas
Nicolai, Alexandre, 176
Nicolaos, *see* Nicholas
Nicolas, N. H., 1425
Nicole, Nicoletto, *see* Nicholas
Nicole, Jules, 1513
Nicolle, *see* Nicholas
Nicoloso, *see* Nicholas
Nicomachean Ethics, 434
Nicomachos of Gerasa (I-2), v. 1, *253*, 821; v. 2, 1210; v. 3, 128, 430, 745, 951, 1115, 1511
Nicomedes, mathematician (II-1 B.C.), v. 1, *182*, 177
Nicomedes, physician, 826
Nicopolis crusade, 1025, 1036
Nicosia, 40
Nicot, Jean, 1310
Niebuhr, 1761
Nieder-Altaich, *see* Herman
Niedling, Justus, 841, 848, 854, 1674, 1681
Niem, *see* Theodore
Nienhues, *see* Otto
Nifo, Agostino, 433, 1127, 1539
Niger, *see* Nicholas
Niger river, 1158, 1617, 1772
nighaṇṭu, 1730
Niglis, Alfred, 1004
Nigris, *see* Syllanus
Nihāyat al-arab, 620
Nihāyat al-ṭalab, 759
nihilianism, 80
Nijhoff, Wouter, 1897
Nijmegen, *see* Peter
Nik, Armenia, *see* Isaiah
Nikāyasaṅgraha, 1370
Nikitin, *see* Athanasios
Nikolai, Nikolaus, *see* Nicholas
Nikulás, *see* Nicholas
Nile, 227, 229, 282, 785, 885, 929, 1158, 1595, 1596, 1598, 1617, 1844
Nile, exploration of Upper (I-2), v. 1, *258*
Nile, rising, 576
Ni'matullāh b. 'Abdallāh Walī (XIV-2), *1459*, 1100, 1328
Nino, St., 304
Nippoldt, A., 1422, 1426
niqqud, 365
nirukta, 382
Nirvāṇa, 81
Nīsābūrī, *see* Muslim b. Ḥajjāj
nisba, 961
Nissi b. Noah, 365
Nissim b. Jacob b. Shahin, 604
Nissim b. Reuben Gerondi (XIV-2), *1364*, 610, 1061, 1446, 1718
Nitardy, F. W., 290
Nītiratnākara, 1000
nītiśāstra, 1000
nitric acid, 177, 760
Nityanātha, 1584
Nixon, J. A., 1693
Niẓām a'raj, 58, 134, 135, 373
Niẓām al-dīn Shāmī, 1267, 1328, 1473
Niẓām al-Mulk, Ḥasan b. 'Alī (XI-2), v. 1, *780* (misspelled Nidhām), 744, 746; v. 2, 141, 353; v. 3, xi, 376
Niẓāmī-i-'Arūḍī, *see* Aḥmad b. 'Umar
Niẓāmī of Ganja, 626
Nō drama, 1570, 1862
Noël de la Morinière, 823
Noël, Pierre, 571
Nörlund, Poul, 1555
Nogent, *see* Guibert
Nohl, Johannes, 1663
Noix, *see* William
Nola, *see* Ambrose Leo
Nolhac, Pierre de, 503, 510, 514, 586, 1295, 1378, 1818
Noll-Husum, H., 820
nomadism, 1769
nominalism, 75, 81, 99, 522, 523, 1085, 1095
nominalism vs. realism, 1831
nominalism, scientific, 83
nomocanon, 994
nomoụa gherel, 469
nona, 716
Nonnos, *see* Theophanes
"noon" hour, 716
Nordenskiöld, A. E., 1595, 1897
Nordström, Johan, 863, 1293, 1898
nordurseta, 195
Norlind, Arnold, 498
Normands, 1490
Norpoth, Leo, 441, 446
Norrbom, Sven, 1711
North, E. M., 360
Northampton, *see* John

Northburgh, *see* Michael
northern light, *see* aurora borealis
Northgate, *see* Michael
Northof, *see* Levold
Norton, C. E., 493, 500, 1426
Nortquelmes, *see* Peter
Norway, A. H., 496
Norway, *see* Sigurd
Norwegian, 351
Norwich, *see* Edward; Juliana; William
Nossol, Reinhard, 1196
Nostradamus, 1383
notaries, 332
Notary, Julyan, 1394
Notger of Liége (X-2), v. 1, *657*, 647, 655
nothingness, 149
Notker, Labeo (XI-1), v. 1, *703*, 822
Noto, *see* John
Nourry, Emile, 1898
Nouvion, *see* James
Novara, *see* Bartolino; Dolcino
Novati, Francesco, 458, 918, 1499, 1686, 1817
Novelli, *see* Gregory
Novgorod, *see* Anthony; Basil; Stephen
Novgorod letopis, 728
Noya, *see* Berenguier
Nubāta, b., *see* Muḥammad b. Muhammad
Nuciarelli, Gerolamo, 531
Nuḍār, 1012
Nukhbat al-dahr, 800
Nu'mān b. Thābit, *see* a. Ḥanīfa
number 7 (seven), 793, 1521, 1723. *See also* sevens, casting out
number 10 (ten), 1521, 1621
number 40 (forty), 216, 1659
numbers, *see* amicable; decimal; fractions
numbers, negative, 1535
numbers, *see* sexagesimal
numbers, theory, 1881
Numenios of Apamea (II-2), v. 1, *298*, 289
numerals, *see* abujad
numerals, Arabic, *see* numerals, Hindu-Arabic
numerals, Coptic, 134
numerals, diffusion of Hindu (IX-2), v. 1, *601*, 822
numerals, *see* ghubār
numerals, Hindu-Arabic, v. 1, *663*, 882; v. 3, 120, 122, 127, 134, 200, 797, 1438, 1766, 1874, 1904
numerals, new, 129, 132, 133
numerals, *see* "place value"
numerals, Roman, 127
numerals, runic, 1610
numerals in Western Europe, Hindu-Arabic (XIII-2), v. 2, *985*, 1210
numerals, *see* zero
numerology, 138, 1068, 1117, 1118
nummi, 1282
Nuniz, Fernão, 41
Nuno Gonçalves, 1022
nuns, 1879
Nūr al-dīn 'Alī Faraḍī, 1529
Nūr al-'uyūn, 376
Nūrbakhshīya, 420
Nuremberg, 1258, 1579
Nuremberg chronicle, 1197
Nurhachu, v. 2, 273; v. 3, 381, 469
Nūshirwān the Just (VI-1), v. 1, *435*, 822; v. 3, 40, 376, 1644
Nuwairī, *see* Aḥmad b. 'Abd al-Wahhāb; Muḥammad b. Qāsim
Nuzhat al-qulūb, 631
Nyāya, 180, 1366, 1891
Nyāyamālāvistara, 1366
Nykl, A. R., v. 1, 713; v. 3, 28, 827, 925, 1853, 1868
Nyssa, *see* Gregory

Oasis, *see* Apion
Obadiah Miẓri, 1450
Oberlin, J. J., 1806
Obermiller, Eugène, 1372
Oberrheinische Chronik, 1756
Obicini, Thomas, 1010
oblates, 327, 477
Obolensky, Dimitri, 1854
O'Brien, B. J., 40, 1025
observance, 397
obstetrics, 268, 362, 1229. *See also* pregnancy
Occam, William of (XIV-1), *549*, 38, 51, 82, 91, 148, 319, 332, 396, 401, 518, 524, 528, 534, 538, 541, 543, 547, 563, 819, 988, 1280, 1347, 1350, 1394, 1429, 1431, 1435, 1510, 1832, 1843, 1844
Occamism, 13, 82, 1085, 1092, 1504, 1567
Occam's razor, 552
Occleve, *see* Thomas Hoccleve
ochetus, 741
Ochin, 67
Ockenden, R. E., 11, 705, 1540
Ocreatus (XII-1), v. 2, *210*, 1211
oculus berellinus, 874
Oddi, *see* Stjörnu
Oddone, *see also* Eudes; Odo; Otto
Oddone Colonna, 1033
Oder, Eugen, 859, 1837
Odington, *see* Walter
Odložilík, Otakar, 1352
Odo, *see also* Eudes; Oddone; Otto
Odo of Cluny (X-1), v. 1, *625*, 822
Odo of Meung (XI-2), v. 1, *765*, 822; v. 2, 50
Odofredus of Bologna (XIII-1), v. 2, *690*, 528; v. 3, 1794
Odonis, *see* Gerald
O'Donnell, J. R., 547
Odoric of Pordenone (XIV-1), *777*, 187, 204, 207, 237, 298, 337, 385, 457, 731, 783, 1603, 1910
Odysseus, 952

Oeconomos, Lysimachos, 1209
Oefele, Felix v., 1711
Oelsner, L., 1758
Oenopides of Chios (V B.C.), v. 1, *92*, 82
Oesterley, Hermann, 456
Oestrup, Johannes, 925
Offa, king of the Mercians, 294
Oga, Jukichi, 495
Ogden, C. K., 331
Ogier VIII of Anglure (XIV-2), *1601*, 1147, 1210, 1308
Ogotay, 1800
O'Hickey family, 873
O'Hickey, *see* Nicholas
Ohman, Olof, 1609
Ohthere (IX-2), v. 1, *606*, 586; v. 3, 194
oil, linseed, 1564
oil, mineral, 1241
oil painting, 170, 1564, 1834
Okakura, Kakuzō, 1332
Olaf Haraldson, St., 1354
Olafr Thórtharson (XIII-1), v. 2, *698*, 531
old age pensions, 1617
old people, care of, 903
Old Testament, 357, 363, 364, 397, 405
Old Testament, concordance, 1063
Oldenburg, *see* Wilbrand
Oldham, R. D., 183, 763, 766
Oldrado da Lodi, 981
Oldrado da Ponte (XIV-1), *981*, 177, 313, 983, 984
Oldrendi, *see* James
Oléron, isle, 1838
Olešnický, *see* Sbigněw
Oliger, Livarius, 397
Oliva, near Danzig, 932
Oliva, Giovanni, 1291
Oliva, *see* Stanislas
Olivares, Bible, 1077
Oliver, *see* Bernard
Oliver, L. N. d', 926
Oliver of Malmesbury (XI-1), v. 1, *720*, 697, 702
Oliver, Revilo P., 516
olivers, 1174
Olivetans (XIV-1), *395*, 47
Olivi, *see* Peter
Olivier, Eugène, 1176, 1861
Olivier, *see* James
Olivier, Sydney, 127
Olivieri, Alexander, 1877
Ollone, d', 1588, 1898
Olmedo, *see* Lupo
Olmo, Jacob b. Abraham, 492
Olschki, L. S., 1808
Olson, C. C., 1426
Oltmanns, Käte, 570
Olympiodoros (V-1), v. 1, *389*, 378, 379
Olympus, 1583
Oman, Charles, 726
Omar Khayyam, *see* 'Umar Khayyām
Omar Tousson, 282
Omer, Saint, 1258, 1754
Omont, Henry, 189, 416, 949, 1145, 1849
Ōmura, Sōbei, 424
Onasandros (I-2), v. 1, *255*, 244; v. 3, 514
oneirocriticism, oneirology, oneiromancy, *see* dreams
Onesto da Bologna, 1482
Onley, F. G., 1589
ŏnmun, 388
onocentauros, 825
ophthalmology, *see* eye diseases
Opicinus de Canistris (XIV-1), *766*, 182, 189, 297, 314, 333
Opicius de Papia, 766
Oporinus, Joannes, 493
Oppenheim, Paul, 77
Oppert, Gustav, 1607
Oppianos I of Cilicia, viii, 1641
Oppianos II of Syria, viii, 1641
Oppolzer, Theodor v., 1546, 1898
optics, 1123
Opus, *see* Philip
Or Adonai, 1447
Orabuena, *see* Joseph
oracle bones, 385, 809, 1841
Oraḥ ḥayyim, 607
oral, *see* tradition
Orandus, Eirenaeus, 1577
Orange, University, 1079, 1398, 1406
Orbanus Hungarus, 1553
Orbelian family, 98
Orbelian, *see* Stephen
Orcagna, *see* Andrew
Orchard, *see* John
ordeal, 1047
Orderic Vital (XII-1), v. 2, *254*, 138, 252
ordinatio, 79
ores, 323
Oresme, Nicole (XIV-2), *1486*, 14, 66, 118, 318, 351, 410, 455, 476, 507, 540, 544, 565, 576, 736, 737, 739, 988, 1032, 1075, 1086, 1087, 1093, 1108, 1112, 1123, 1126, 1275, 1276, 1278, 1282, 1283, 1307, 1309, 1345, 1429, 1430, 1432, 1435, 1448, 1505, 1506, 1565, 1566, 1568
organ, 161
Organi, *see* Andrew; Filippino; Philip
organum, 160, 744
Orgiano, *see* Matthew
Orgier, *see* Nathan; Solomon
Oribasios of Pergamon (IV-2), v. 1, *372*, 822; v. 2, 1085; v. 3, 288, 836, 871, 1208, 1650
Oriel College, 72, 474
Origen (III-1), v. 1, *317*, 822; v. 3, viii, 356, 488, 825
originibus rerum, De, 583
Orion (V-1), v. 1, *398*, 379
Orkhon Turkish inscriptions, 1840

Orkneys, 1594
Orlando, *see also* Roland
Orlando Bandinelli, *see* Alexander III, pope
Orlando innamorato, 911
Orléans, 316
Orléans, *see* Lewis
ornithology, Chinese (XIII-2), v. 2, *1075*, 60
Orodn, *see* John
Orologio, *see* James
Orontes river, 795
Orosius, Paul (V-1), v. 1, *395*, 822; v. 2, 1212; v. 3, 501, 1808
Orr, Mary Acworth, 497
orrery, 1112, 1125, 1541, 1676
Orseln, *see* Werner
Orsenigo, *see* Simon
Orsini, *see* Napoleone
Ortega y Gasset, José, 1779
Ortelius, Abraham, 1158
Orthodox churches, 1830
Ortholan, *see* Martin; Richard
Orti, M. A., 1340
Ortolanus (XIV-2), *1575*, 1135
Ortolff the Bavarian, 1206, 1319
Oseberg ship, 194
Oshin of Corycos, 953
Osi, F., 918
Osiris, 1898
Osler, William, 1667, 1898
Ossetians, 305
Ostanès, 376
ostensor, 842
Ostermann, Theodor, 491
Ostia, *see* Leo
ostriches, 1189, 1642
Ostrorog, Léon, 925
Othmer, W., 1891
Othon, *see also* Otto
Othon III de Grandson, 1713
Othon de La Roche, 948
otio religiosorum, De, 507
Otloh, 817
Otot ha-shamayim, 432
Ottaviano, Carmelo, 563
otter fishing, 778, 1603
Ottersdorf, Ambros. v., 1758
Otto, *see also* Eudes; Oddone; Odo; Othon
Otto of Brunswick, 728
Otto v. Diemeringen, 1605
Otto, emperor, 727
Otto of Freising (XII-1), v. 2, *258*, 1272; v. 3, 933, 993, 1262
Otto II of Lichtenstein, 930
Otto v. Nienhues, 787
Otto, Rudolf, 571
Otto v. Thüringen, 934
Ottokar of Bohemia and Moravia, 575, 933
Ottokar v. Horneck, 930
Ottokar of Styria (XIV-1), *930*, 301, 351
Ottolenghi, Joseph, 606
Ottsen, Johann, 726
Our Lady, 80
Our Lady of Montesa, order of, 1039
outlawry, 1279
Outremeuse, *see* John
Ovid, 48, 454, 751, 933, 944, 1252, 1294, 1418, 1482, 1706, 1745
Ovid moralized, 48, 743
ovists, 1229
ovulation, 269
Owen, Aneurin, 1864
Owen, D. L., 1415
Owst, G. R., 1040
Oxford, colleges, 72, 473, 1079, 1401
Oxford French, *see* algorism
Oxford University (XII-2), v. 2, *352*, 1212; v. 3, 375, 473, 1401, 1886, 1895
Oyta, *see* Henry
Ozanam, Frédéric, 499

Pablo, *see* Paul
Pachomios, St. (IV-1), v. 1, *347*, 344, 625
Pachymeres, *see* George
Pacioli, *see* Luca
Packard, F. R., 1233
paddle wheels, 1550, 1552
Padmakara Dvivedi, 1535
Padmasaṃbhava, 1371
Padova, *see* Padua
Padrin, Luigi, 918
Padua, *see* Anthony; Francis Novello; James; John; Marchetto; Marsiglio; Paravicius; Rolandino; Salio; William de Marra
Padua, University, 443, 1244
Paes, *see* Álvaro
Paes, Domingo, 41
Paganica, *see* Nicholas
Paganini, C. P., 499
Paganinus de Paganinis, 520
Pagel, Julius, 817, 872, 878, 879, 1660, 1685, 1697, 1709
Pagliaresi, *see* Neri di Landoccio
Pagnini, Gian Francesco, 774
Pahlawī, 376
Pahncke, Max, 570
painting, 1105, 1906. *See also* oil
painting, Chinese, 1791
painting, history, 311, 979
països d'oc, 342
Palaemon, Quintus Remmius (I-2), v. 1, *265*, 245
Palaeologos family, 40
Palaeologos, *see* John; Manuel; Michael; Theodore; Thomas
Palamas, *see* Gregory
Palamites, 95, 1511
Palazuelos, Fernando de, 1467
Palencia, *see* Alfonso
Paleofilon curativus languoris, 393
Palermo, *see* Aḥiṭub b. Isaac; Moses; Paul

Palerne, see William
Paleschi, Filippo, 499
Palestine, 1885, 1893, 1902
Palestine, map, 393
Palestine, topography, 198, 791
Palestrina, 159, 744
Palgen, Rudolf, 497, 1843
Pāli, 382, 1477, 1904
Pāli grammar, 1371
Pāli literature, 1892
Paliano di Falco, 125
Palla degli Strozzi, 1822
Palladios the Iatrosophist (V-1), v. 1, *392*, 379, 608; v. 2, 846, 1080
Palladius archimandrite, 808, 1866
Palladius, Rutilius Taurus Aemilianus (IV-1), v. 1, *355*, 823; v. 2, 1213; v. 3, 812
Pallis, Marco, 1070
Palmerio, *see* James
Palmieri, A., 588, 746, 1389, 1823
palmistry, 271, 835, 1104
Palpata, *see* Ayuli
Palpushtakam, 360
Palquera, *see* Shem-ṭob b. Joseph b. Falaquera
Palu, *see* Peter de La Palu
Pamphila of Epidaurus (I-2), v. 1, *264*, 245
Pamphilos of Alexandria (I-2), v. 1, *264*, 245
Pamphilos the Botanist (I-2), v. 1, *257*, 244
Panaetios of Rhodes (II-2 B.C.), v. 1, *193*, 191, 192
Panaretos, *see* Michael
pañcabhūta, 262
Pañcadaśi, 1366
Pañca-mūlaparveṇa-Adhipati, 1731
Pancius de Controne, 1204
Pancratius Sommer v. Hirschberg, 1246
pancreatic duct, 843
Pandectae of Justinian, 981
pandectae, others, 797, 816, 895
Pāndurang, Shankar, 1369
Paneth, Fritz, 166
Pāṇini (IV-1 B.C.), v. 1, *123*, 823; v. 2, 1213; v. 3, 382, 423, 1366, 1367
Panis, *see* Nicholas
Pannartz, *see* Arnold
Pannier, Carl, 580
Pannier, Léopold, 455, 1906
Panofsky, Erwin, 1105
Panselinos, *see* Manuel
Pansier, Pierre, 241, 249, 406, 427, 838, 851, 856, 857, 877, 879, 1201, 1230, 1235, 1499, 1685, 1689, 1690, 1693, 1695, 1697, 1898
Paṇśīkar, V. S., 1367
Pantaleon of Nicomedia, St., 1666
Pantegni, 1206
pantheism, 569
Paoli, H. J., 1379
Paolo, *see* Paul
Papadopulos, G. I., 162
Papadopulos, J., 438
Papadopulos, N. C., 589
Papanti, Giovanni, 1811
Papencordt, Felix, 924
paper, 181, 1590, 1874. *See also* charta
paper, Játiva, 175, 1834
paper, linen, 1580
paper mill, 1137
paper money, 730, 773, 775, 954, 971, 1617, 1800
Papia, *see* Guido
Papias the Lombard (XI-2), v. 1, *781*, 744, 745; v. 2, 472, 1135; v. 3, 836, 1004
Papini, Giovanni, 491, 492, 496
Papinian (III-1), v. 1, *328*, 823
Papinot, Edmond, 1898
Papirius Sextus (VI B.C.), v. 1, *80*, 66
Pappos of Alexandria (III-2), v. 1, *337*, 823; v. 3, ix, 5, 14
papyri, 122, 152, 174, 175, 176, 326, 353
papyri, *see* chemical
papyri, Edwin Smith, 1724
papyri, medical, 361
papyrus, *see* Akhmîm
Par, Anfós, 1821
Paracelsus, 289, 905, 1139, 1220, 1227, 1666
Paraclet, *see* Aḥmad
pārada, 1584
Paradisi, *see* James
Paradiso degli Alberti, 1567
Parain, Charles, 1181
Parākramabāhu II, 1731
Parākramabāhu IV, 422
paralysis, 285, 1212, 1247, 1719
Paramārtha (VI-2), v. 1, *446*, 823; v. 3, 468
Paramientos de la caza, 924
Pāramīmahāsataka, 1370
pāramit, 1370
Páramo, Luis de, 1339
Paranikas, Matthaios K., 790
Parāśarasmṛiti, 1367
Paraules e dits de savis, 427
Paravicius the Paduan (XIII-2), v. 2, *866*, 1213
parchment, 175, 176
pardes, 593
Pardessus, J. M., 325, 1882, 1898
Pardubice, *see* Ernest (Arnošt); John Flaška
Paré, Ambroise, 279, 871, 1233, 1691
Pareja Casañas, F. M., 317, 1450
Parent, A., 157
parhelia, *see* halo
Parḥi, *see* Estori b. Moses
Parikramaṇabālāvabodha, 1474
Paris, 153, 538
Paris, *see* Alexander; Denis; Geoffrey; Jacob; John; Leoninus; Matthew; ménagier; Perotinus; Peter
Paris, colleges, 72, 476
Paris, University (XII-2), v. 2, *351*, 737;

v. 3, 79, 375, 409, 1050, 1079, 1242, 1244, 1404, 1895, 1900
Paris, Gaston, 462, 464, 930, 1152, 1861
Paris, Paulin, 300, 745, 928, 956, 1390
Paris de Puteo, 1870
Parisot, Valentin, 952, 1761
Park, Mungo, 1159
Parker, E. H., 1855
Parker, Henry, 1805, 1809
Parker, Matthew, 945, 1745
Parlement of the thre ages, 1278
Parliament, Good, 1024
Parliament, Model, 319
Parliament of Westminster, 319
parliamentary institutions, 13, 1024
Parma, *see* Albert; Bartholomew; Cassius; John; Roland; Salimbene; Taddeo
Parmenides of Elea (V B.C.), v. 1, *85*, 81, 82
Parodi, Ernesto Giacomo, 492
parrot, Book of, 465
Parry, C. L., 325
Parsees, 784, 1475
Pārsi dialect, 376
parsimony, law, 552
Parsons, R. G., 49
Parthey, G., 911
Partington, J. R., 169, 170
partnerships, 124
partnerships, limited, 1272
Partsch, Josef, 1844
Pascal, Blaise, 129, 597, 1087, 1165
Pascal (Blaise), triangle, 140
Pascal, Etienne, 1566
Pascal of Vitoria (XIV-1), *785*, 190
Paschal, *see* Peter
Paschal the Roman (XII-2), v. 2, *347*, 284, 292
Pascheles, Wolf, 592
Pascoli, Giovanni, 500
Pascual de Gayangos, *see* Gayangos
Pasquino de Capellis, 1811
Passera, Ercole, 498
Passerin d'Entrèves, Alessandro, 989
Passerini, Giuseppe Lando, 492, 493, 495, 496, 500
Passion of Christ, order of the, 1345
passionibus mulierum, De, 448
Passover, 130
Pasteur, Louis, 1230, 1658
Paston letters, 230
Pastor, Ludwig v., 1898
Pastorello, Ester, 916
pastoureaux, 430, 1024, 1164
Pastrengo, *see* William
paṭala, 1584
Patañjali (II-2 B.C.), v. 1, *199*, 192; v. 3, 96, 1000, 1584
Pataran, *see* John
Patcanian, M., 1898
Patch, H. R., 499, 1425
Pater noster, 463
Paṭer, *see* Solomon
Patrick Byker, 1547
Patrologia graeca, 1899
Patrologia latina, 1899
Patron de la temporalité, 1750
Patronio, 924
Pattloch, Franz, 561
Paucton, A. J. P., 712
Paul dell' Abbaco, 243
Paul Aegineta (VII-1), v. 1, *479*, 824; v. 2, 1085; v. 3, 836, 1208, 1692, 1724
Paul of Alexandria (IV-2), v. 1, *367*, 823
Paul Antonius de Lignano, 1798
Paul of Burgos, 397, 1046, 1053, 1343, 1384, 1521, 1716
Paul Dagomari (XIV-1), *639*, 110, 243, 337, 1808
Paul the Deacon (VIII-2), v. 1, *539*, 824; v. 2, 222
Paul de Genazzano, 518
Paul de Heredia, 591
Paul Hsü, 1646
Paul Knutsson, 1154, 1609, 1613
Paul, monk, 124
Paul of Palermo, 539
Paul of Pergola, 1413
Paul the Persian (VI-2), v. 1, *448*, 443; v. 3, 490
Paul da Perugia, 585, 1807, 1869
Paul al-Rāhib, 709
Paul Ramusio, 1552
Paul, St. (I-2), v. 1, *246*, 823; v. 2, 347; v. 3, 446, 1353
Paul de Santa María, 1250, 1325, 1343. *See also* Paul of Burgos; Solomon b. Isaac ha-Levi
Paul the Syrian, 490
Paul of Thebes, 1602
Paul Uccello, 1105
Paul of Venice, 519, 1086, 1106
Pauli, *see* John
Pauli, Reinhold, 1428
Paulsen, Adam, 710
Paulus, Julius (III-1), v. 1, *328*, 824
Pauly, August, 1899
Pauly-Wissowa, 1899
pauperes Christi, 279
paupertate, De, 528
paupertate Christi, De, 516, 522, 527
Paur, Theodor, 1601
Pausanias Atticista (II-2), v. 1, *312*, 290
Pausanias of Lydia (II-2), v. 1, *300*, 824; v. 2, 1214
Pavia, 766
Pavia, *see* Cardone; George Andreoli; Nicholas; Opicius
Pavia, University, 1078, 1080, 1244, 1397
Pavieta, *see* James
Pavone, *see* Balthasar

pawnbroker, 326
Pax mongolica, 380, 1027, 1161
Payne, E. A., 1070
Payne, J. F., 1704
Payne, John, 1458
Payne, R. C., 571
Payne, *see* Robert
Pāzand, 376
Pazdawī, *see* 'Alī b. Muḥammad
Pazzini, Adalberto, 1838
peace, v, 26, 409, 824
Peacey, Edith, 1356
peacocks, 1189, 1642
Peake, C. H., 735
Pearce, Nathaniel, 1667
pearl fisheries, 1620
Pearson, Hesketh, 127, 1466
Pearson, Karl, 570
Peasants' Revolt, 1654
Pease, A. S., 214, 930, 1806
peccatum originis, 49
Pecci, Bernardino, 1336
Pecha, *see* Fernando
pecia, 1297
Peckham, *see* John
Pécs, University, 1399
Pedersen, Holger, 31, 1017, 1825
Pedersen, Johannes, 1266, 1784
Pediasimos, *see* John
Pedrazzini, C., 499
Pedro, *see* Peter
Peers, E. A., 1410, 1821
Peet, T. E., 365
Peez, J. K., 577
peg of earth, x
Pegolotti, Francesco Balducci (XIV-1), *771*, 125, 185, 337, 731, 1111, 1283, 1300, 1910
Peiginsky, A., 893
Peire, *see* Peter
Peiresc, N. C. Fabri de, 1498, 1868
Peking, 156
Pelacani, *see* Blase; Francis
Peláez, Mario, 1720
Pelagius, Pelagianism (V-1), v. 1, *382;* v. 2, 588; v. 3, 49
Pelayo, *see* Álvaro
Pelegrin of Avignon, 158
Pelegrino Cocharelli, 1634
Pelegrino, *see* Peregrine
Pèlerin de Prusse (XIV-2), *1498*, 1110, 1308
Pèlerinage de la vie humaine, 532
Pelham, R. A., 191
Pelhřimov, *see* Nicholas
pelican, instrument, 881
Pelka, Otto, 1187
Pellati, F., 1772
Pellegrini, Francesco, 837
Pellegrino, E. L., 499
Pellian equations, 1535
Pelliot, Paul, xv, 139, 223, 378, 632, 713, 734, 776, 808, 830, 975, 1017, 1187, 1549, 1840
Pellizzari, Achille, 1601
Pelster, Francis, 559, 570
Pelzel, F. M., 1758
Pelzer, Auguste, 886
Pembridge, *see* Christopher
Pembroke College, 72, 475
Peña, Francisco de, 1339
Peñafort, *see* Raymond
Penceth, *see* Thomas
Pencrych, *see* Richard
pendulum, 718
Penitents, 13
Penna, *see* John; Luca
Penya, *see* John
Pepagomenos, *see* Demetrios
pepper, 229, 781, 1182, 1620, 1891
Pepys, 1659
Peratallada, *see* John
Pérault, *see* William
Perceval, Roman, 1298
Pere, *see* Peter
peregrinantium, Societas fratrum, 1038
Peregrine of Castello (XIV-1), *776*, 54, 187, 204
Peregrinus, *see* Peter the Stranger
Perestrello, *see* Bartholomew; Felipa
Perez b. Isaac Kohen, 450
Pérez de Moya, Juan, 1534
Perez Trabot (XIV-2), *1825*, 1324
perfectione vitae, De, 400
Perfet, *see* Isaac b. Sheshet
perfumes, 323
Pergamon, *see* Nicholas; Oribasios
Pergens, Ed., 1228
Pergola, *see* Paul
Peri ha-niqra meah dibburim, 431
Perigenes (I-2 B.C.), v. 1, *230*, 220
Periplus, 1897
Periplus of Erythrean Sea (I-2), v. 1, *257*, 244
Perkins, P. D., 1333
Perlbach, Max, 933
Perles, Joseph, 429, 593
Perlmann, M., 1366, 1454
Perlmann, S. M., 1071
Perm, *see* Stephen
permutations, *see* combinatorial analysis
Pernelle Flamel, 1577
Permety, Dom, 1578
Pero, *see* Peter
Peronne d'Aubenton, 23
Peronnelle d'Armentières, 745
Perotinus of Paris (XII-1), v. 2, *217*, 25, 129
Perowne, J. J. S., 1010
Perpignan, *see* Bonafos Abraham; Guido
Perpignan, University, 72, 47°
Perrando, G. G., 851
Perrault, Charles, 1842
Perrault, *see* William
Perrinus Vesconte, 763

Perron, A., 828, 829, 966, 1641
Perron, Nicolas, 1455
Perry, A. J., 556, 1394
Perry, G. G., 567
Perry, J. T., 1561
persecution, uselessness, 24
Perseus (II-1 B.C.), v. 1, *182*, 177
Persia, 1875
Persian language, 364, 375, 1839
Persian literature, 1905
Persian, *see* medicine
Persian-Mongol glossary, 1013
Persians, 1773
Persius, 1745
perspectiva communis, 1123, 1433
perspective, 111, 1105
perspective, aerial, 707
Pertis, Teresa de, 362
Perugia, 1795
Perugia, *see* Andrew; Paul
Perugia, University, 72, 470, 1244, 1273, 1795
perush ha-berakot, 417
Peruzzi bank of Florence, 37, 124, 324, 1803, 1839
pesaḥ, 364
Pesaro, *see* Cristoforo Berardi; Sante Ardoino
Pescatore, Gustav, 1796
Peschel, Oscar, 1592
peshaṭ, 416
Peshchurov, D. A., 1891
Pĕshīṭtā, 357, 359
Pessoa, Alberto, 862
pest, *see* London; plague
Petaḥiah b. Jacob of Ratisbon (XII-2), v. 2, *415*, 1214
Petau, Denys, 952, 1511
petechiae, 881
Peter, *see also* Buṭrus
Peter Abaelard (XII-1), v. 2, *194*, 1214; v. 3, 80, 1831
Peter d'Abano (XIV-1), *439*, 64, 68, 88, 112, 186, 242, 243, 406, 453, 519, 537, 578, 839, 840, 848, 849, 850, 1199, 1380, 1671
Peter d'Ailly, 413, 454, 476, 547, 1053, 1088, 1108, 1109, 1148, 1155, 1253, 1276, 1295, 1405, 1859
Peter Albergheti de Curialtis, 1681
Peter de Alcalá, 374
Peter of Alexandria, 598, 606
Peter Alfonso (XII-1), v. 2, *199*, 1214; v. 3, 193, 340, 579, 925, 1449
Peter Alighieri, 86, 500
Peter Antonio Boni, 750
Peter, apostate, 1064
Peter of Aragón, 460, 1095, 1323
Peter of Aragón, Cerimoniós (XIV-2), *1734*, 300, 472, 510, 1072, 1162, 1180, 1191, 1250, 1305, 1375
Peter of Aragón, son of Jaume II el Just, 343
Peter d'Argelata, 1194, 1195, 1224, 1233
Peter Aronchel, 1861
Peter Auriol (XIV-1), *528*, 45, 48, 82, 90, 519
Peter of Auvergne (XIII-2), v. 2, *1127*, 738, 800; v. 3, 90, 316, 1276
Peter d'Auxon (XIV-2), *1699*, 1201, 1238, 1243
Peter de Barcellos, 344
Peter of Beauvais (XIII-1), v. 2, *702*, 43, 58
Peter de Belleperche, 982, 990
Peter Bembo, 1297, 1298, 1300
Peter Bersuire (XIV-1), *454*, 48, 52, 65, 332, 346, 456, 942, 944, 1736
Peter Bertrand, 397, 525
Peter Bontier, 184, 786
Peter de Bretagne, 1583
Peter of Bruges, 725
Peter Buono (XIV-1), *750*, 178, 1134
Peter of Candia, *see* Peter of Crete
Peter Candido Decembrio, 1823
Peter of Capestang (XIII-2), v. 2, *1091*, 785; v. 3, 248, 285, 878
Peter of Castile, the Cruel, 1021, 1022
Peter Ceffons (XIV-1), *736*, 147
Peter Chauchat (XIV-1), *879*, 248
Peter of Cluny, *see* Peter the Venerable
Peter Col, 1295
Peter Comestor (XII-2), v. 2, *453*, 1215; v. 3, 79, 510, 1603
Peter Conciliator, 439
Peter da Corbara, 536
Peter de Corbian, 339
Peter of Cortone, 1669
Peter dei Crescenzi (XIV-1), *811*, 206, 228, 301, 858, 1181, 1409
Peter of Crete (XIV-2), *1440*, 1033, 1073, 1085, 1095, 1195, 1224
Peter de la Croix, 160, 741
Peter de Cugnières, 525
Peter I of Cyprus, 744, 1035, 1253, 1494, 1672, 1751, 1782
Peter of Dacia (XIII-2), v. 2, *996*, 1215
Peter de Damouzy (XIV-1), *879*, 248
Peter the Deacon (XII-1), v. 2, *255*, 139
Peter Després, 454
Peter Dini, 1669
Peter Dominici, 403
Peter Dubois (XIV-1), *407*, 46, 51, 72, 318, 375, 551, 1076, 1283, 1394, 1401
Peter of Dusburg (XIV-1), *931*, 301
Peter the Eater, *see* Peter Comestor
Peter of Eboli (XII-2), v. 2, *438*, 1215; v. 3, 287, 1075, 1201, 1240, 1391
Peter Engelbert (XIV-2), *1485*, 1074, 1107, 1115, 1305, 1375, 1863, 1865
Peter Figarola (XIV-1), *861*, 246
Peter of Florence, 780, 839
Peter Flotte, 408
Peter de Fontaines, 345
Peter della Francesca, 1105
Peter Fromont (XIV-2), *1689*, 1201, 1233, 1309
Peter Gallego (XIII-1), v. 2, *562*, 1215

Peter Gambacorta, 1037
Peter García de Santa María, 1343
Peter Gas, 878
Peter Gaveston, earl of Cornwall, 944
Peter Gilbert, *see* Peter Engelbert
Peter of Grandville, 1713
Peter Gringore, 1867
Peter Hélie, 1003
Peter the Irishman (XIII-2), v. 2, *949*, 740
Peter v. Königssaal, 934
Peter of Langtoft (XIV-1), *941*, 301, 302, 348, 462
Peter de la Palu (XIV-1), *526*, 46, 84, 89, 400, 413, 523, 525
Peter Lightfoot, 144, 719, 720, 1545
Peter of Limoges, 1846
Peter the Lombard (XII-2), v. 2, *382*, 1215; v. 3, 79, 80, 243, 316, 398, 520, 523, 532, 534, 549, 562, 942, 991, 1194, 1362, 1432, 1434, 1435. *See also* Sentences
Peter, *see* López de Ayala
Peter de Luna, 1032, 1339, 1385, 1411, 1440, 1797
Peter of Lusignan, *see* Peter of Cyprus
Peter de Luxembourg, 1246, 1697
Peter de Maineri, 834
Peter, metropolitan, 39
Peter Miguel Carbonell, 1734
Peter of Morquelines, 1601
Peter da Muglio, 1815
Peter of Musanda (XII-1), v. 2, *242*, 1215
Peter de Nadilz (XIV-2), *1694*, 1200, 1229
Peter of Navarre, 1497
Peter of Nijmegen, 571
Peter de Nortquelmes, 1601
Peter Olafsson of Alvastra, 1354
Peter Olafsson of Skeninge, 1354
Peter Olivi (XIII-2), v. 2, *1032*, 1215; v. 3, 22, 146, 147, 148, 396, 400, 527, 1126, 1488
Peter Paolo Vergerio, il Giovane, 1819
Peter Paolo Vergerio, il Vecchio (XIV-2), *1818*, 1052, 1081, 1289, 1407, 1822
Peter de Paris (XIV-1), *452*, 65
Peter Paschal of Valencia (XIII-2), v. 2, *893*, 1215; v. 3, 375
Peter Peregrinus, *see* Peter the Stranger
Peter Philarges, *see* Peter of Crete
Peter, physician, 1708
Peter of Piacenza (XII-2), v. 2, *465*, 316, 352; v. 3, 316
Peter of Pisa, 1037
Peter Plowman, 1048, 1054, 1278, 1315, 1413
Peter del Punyalet, *see* Peter of Aragón, Cerimoniós
Peter de Regio, 1383
Peter Ribera de Perpeja, 299, 342
Peter Roger de Beaufort, 530, 1031, 1032
Peter, St., 358, 446
Peter de Saint Flour (XIV-1), *878*, 248
Peter of Saint Omer (XIII-2), v. 2, *1041*, 1215; v. 3, 168, 1131, 1564
Peter dei Salutati, 1815
Peter II de Samer, 1277
Peter de Sancta Beata, 721, 1542
Peter de Sant Pere, 325
Peter de Santa María, *see* Peter García
Peter Soderini, 1680
Peter of Spain (XIII-2), v. 2, *889*, 1215; v. 3, 44, 65, 82, 100, 285, 375, 450, 551, 856, 861, 881, 1004, 1074, 1086, 1097, 1193, 1194, 1212, 1381, 1437, 1565, 1683, 1719
Peter v. Sparnau, 1153
Peter the Stranger (XIII-2), v. 2, *1030*, 1215; v. 3, 143, 146, 714, 1127, 1848
Peter of Sudheim, 788
Peter of Tarragona, 459
Peter Theoctonicos (XIII-2), v. 2, *1042*, 723, 768; v. 3, 66, 179, 754
Peter of Thomas, 1053, 1087, 1345
Peter Tomacelli, 1032
Peter Torrigiano de' Torrigiani (XIV-1), *839*, 243, 244, 837
Peter da Tossignano (XIV-2), *1681*, 1086, 1192, 1193, 1220, 1221, 1233, 1238, 1240, 1664
Peter de Trabibus (XIII-2), v. 2, *934*, 738, 1033
Peter of Tripoli, 1344
Peter degli Ubaldi, 1795
Peter da Varignana, 838, 1679
Peter of Vaux Cernay (XIII-1), v. 2, *673*, 525, 1108
Peter the Venerable (XII-1), v. 2, *161*, 1215; v. 3, 174, 369
Peter de Verberia, 528
Peter Vesconte (XIV-1), *762*, 182, 337, 498, 767, 770, 771
Peter Vidal, 115
Peter of Vinea or delle Vigne (XIII-1), v. 2, *690*, 529, 571; v. 3, 1335
Peter Virgin, 532
Peter le Viser, 741
Peter Waldo, 339
Peter v. Zittau, 934
Peters, J. L., 237, 1642
Petersen, C. S., 1155
Pétis de la Croix, François, 1474
Petit Jehan de Saintré, 1277
Petit, *see* John
Petit, Jules, 1748
Petit de Julleville, Louis, 1899
Petit, L., 995, 1824
petit mal, 874
Petracco, *see* Francis
Petrarca, Francesco (XIV-1), *502*, 37, 45, 50, 72, 84, 86, 112, 113, 178, 188, 207, 242, 264, 299, 313, 315, 333, 335, 355, 454, 540, 561, 584, 585, 725, 742, 744, 916, 917, 921, 922, 923, 943, 981, 982, 1016, 1031, 1075, 1085, 1088, 1107, 1145, 1171, 1222, 1235, 1252, 1263, 1277, 1286, 1288, 1293, 1299, 1301,

1303, 1304, 1315, 1321, 1334, 1336, 1377, 1391, 1407, 1418, 1483, 1493, 1496, 1567, 1582, 1672, 1673, 1677, 1684, 1737, 1751, 1796, 1803, 1804, 1806, 1807, 1808, 1812, 1813, 1815, 1816, 1817, 1818, 1821, 1843, 1862
Petrarca, *see* Gerald; John
Petrie, Flinders, 713
Petrocchi, Policarpo, 1301
Petrocellus (XI-1), v. 1, *726*, 699; v. 2, 438, 1089
petroleum, 1241
Petronius of Salerno (XII-2), v. 2, *438*, 1215
Petros, Petrus, *see* Peter
Pettus, Sir John, 218
Petzholdt, Julius, 495
Pevsner, Nikolaus, 1835
pewter, 219
Peyron, F., 295
Pez, Bernard, 577, 1509
Pez, Hieronymus, 931, 934
Pezagno, *see* Manuel
Pfalz, *see* Ruprecht
Pfander, H. G., 1040
Pfeffer, Bernhard, 1394
Pfeiffer, Franz, 569, 573, 580, 819
Pfeiffer, R. H., 364
Pfister, Albrecht, 580
Pfister, Friedrich, 1045
Pflaum, Heinz, 497
Pfolspeundt, *see* Henry
Pforzheim, 1114
Phagspa (XIII-2), v. 2, *1137*, 1215; v. 3, 380, 384, 469
Phagspa alphabet, 469
Phalereos, *see* Demetrios
Phanias of Eresos (IV-2 B.C.), v. 1, *144*, 126
Pharaon, Florian, 1642, 1725
Phares, *see* Simon
pharmacy, 152, 288, 1241, 1892, 1903. *See also* apothecaries
pharos, 1619
pheasant, golden, 914
Philagrios of Thessalonica (IV-2), v. 1, *373*, 360, 361
Philarges, *see* Peter of Crete
Philemon, 442
Philes, *see* Manuel
Philip d'Alençon, 1685
Philip van Artevelde, 1020
Philip Beaumanoir (XIII-2), v. 2, *1129*, 800; v. 3, 345
Philip II of Bourgogne, le Hardi, 1020, 1075, 1152, 1202, 1502
Philip Brunelleschi, 1105
Philip Brusseri, 190, 1154
Philip de Cacqueray, 173
Philip IV of France, le Bel, 37, 38, 43, 46, 47, 203, 247, 249, 314, 394, 408, 1283
Philip VI of France, de Valois, 38
Philip of Leiden (XIV-2), *1798*, 1280, 1298
Philip de Mézières (XIV-2), *1344*, 40, 1036, 1053, 1148, 1276, 1280, 1309, 1321, 1323, 1329, 1331, 1350, 1390, 1494, 1609, 1672, 1676
Philip Mönch, 1554
Philip Mousket (XIII-1), v. 2, *675*, 525
Philip of Opus (IV-1 B.C.), v. 1, *118*, 111, 112
Philip degli Organi, 736
Philip of Taranto, 446
Philip of Thaon (XII-1), v. 2, *201*, 1215; v. 3, 333
Philip of Tripoli (XIII-1), v. 2, *563*, 1216
Philip Utenbroeke, 66, 302, 938
Philip Villani (XIV-2), *1737*, 297, 496, 1086, 1251, 1299, 1300, 1600, 1673, 1674, 1811
Philip of Vitry (XIV-1), *742*, 160, 346, 597, 740, 1128, 1568, 1845
Philippa, *see also* Felipa
Philippa of Hainaut, queen of England, 474, 563, 1203, 1751
Philippa, daughter of Henry IV of England, queen of Pomerania, 1703
Philippa of Lancaster, queen of Portugal, 1021
Philippa (Roet?), 1418
Philippa Tossignano, 1681
Philippe, A., 851
Philippines, 1866
Philipps, Thomas, 789
Philistion of Locroi (IV-1 B.C.), v. 1, *120*, 112
Phillips, Dayton, 49
Phillips, P. L., 1899
Phillipps, T., 1630
Phillott, D. C., 233
Philobiblon, 560
Philolaos (V B.C.), v. 1, *93*, 81, 82
Philon of Byzantium (II-2 B.C.), v. 1, *195*, 824; v. 2, 27; v. 3, ix, 715
Philon the Jew (I-1), v. 1, *236*, 824; v. 2, 938; v. 3, 367, 1441
Philonium, 1199
Philoponos, *see* John
philosopher's stone, 754, 751
philosophy, Indian, 1880
philosophy, *see* natural
Philostratos the Athenian (III-1), v. 1, *319*, 314, 315
Philotheos, patriarch, 1386, 1821
Philotinos (IV-2 B.C.), v. 1, *146*, 126
Philoxenian, 358
Philumenos (II-2), v. 1, *308*, 289, 290
phlegmon, 899
Phlegon of Tralles, 1806
Phocas, *see* John
Phoebus, *see* Gaston
Phoenix, 1130
Phoibammon, 1008
phonetics, 349, 382
phosphorescence, 531
Photios (IX-2), v. 1, *594*, 824; v. 3, 353, 994
Phra Chao Rama Tibodi, 1029
Phrynichos (II-2), v. 1, *313*, 290

Phurna, *see* Dionysios
physicians, imperial, 1244
physicians, papal, 241, 1245
physicians, royal, 1244
physicians, town, 1244, 1861
physics, Aristotelian, 146
physiognomy, 103, 258, 270, **321**, **439**, **442**, **800**, 899, 900, 901, 960, 1104, 1232, 1421, 1478, 1635, 1671, 1732, 1792, 1897
physiognomy, Babylonian, 1836
physiognomy, Chinese, 1836
Physiologos (II-2), v. 1, *300*, 289, 765; v. 2, 1216; v. 3, 340, 825
physiology, 267, 1228, 1904
phytopathology, 813
pi, value of, 140, 430, 1430
Piacenza, *see* Peter
Piacenza, University, 1398
Piaget, Arthur, 1713
Pian del Càrpine, *see* John
Piazza, *see* Michael
Picard, abbé, 1488
Picard, *see* John
Piccini, G., 501, 983
Piccoli, Raffaello, 913
piccolo dell' asse, Libro, 124
Piccolomini, *see* Alexander; **Francis**
Piccolpasso, Cipriano, 179, 756
Pichon, Jérôme, 1633
Pichonius, Anthonius, 952
Pick, Friedel, 1715
Pickens, C. L., 1589
Pico, G. F., 1483
Pico della Mirandola, Gianfrancesco, **444**, **1448**
Pico della Mirandola, *see* John
Pictor (III-2 B.C.), v. 1, *176*
Piedimonte, 1876
Piedimonte, *see* Francis
Pier, Piero, *see* Peter
Pierantoni, A. C., 1819
Pierce the Ploughmans Crede, **1414**
Pieri, Marius, 516
Pierre, *see* Peter
pierres d'épreuve, 1242
Piers, *see* Peter
Pierson, J. L., jr., 1332
Piesch, Herma, 570
Pietro, *see* Peter
Pietrobono, Luigi, 495, 500
Pigafetta, Antonio, 929
Pigafetta, Filippo, 1160
Pignano, *see* Francis
Pike, R. E., 1346
Piiate, Acts, 1039
Pilato, *see* Leonzio
pilgrimage, Muslim, 1665
pilgrimages, 46, 1042, 1043
pilgrimages, expiatory, 1047
pilgrims, Buddhist (VII-1), v. 1, *470*
pilgrims to the Holy Land (XII-1), v. 2, *223*; (XII-2), v. 2, *419*; (XIII-1), v. 2, *639*, 1216; (XIII-2), v. 2, *1051*, 1216
Pimen, metropolitan, 1613
Pin y Soler, J., 561
Pindaros, 997, 1005
Pineḥas, 1324, 1761
Pineḥas b. Isaac, 1761
Pinelli atlas, 1144, 1599
Pines, Salomon, 146, 545, 1899
Pinet, M. J., 1481
Pingaud, L., 513
Pingré, A. G., 1122
Pinkhof, H., 894
Pinson, R., 1312
Pintelon, P., 1424
pipal, 1835
Pipino, *see* James
Pipinus, *see* Francis
Piquet, Jules, 395
pīr, 154, 292
pirates, 205, 416, 1021, 1410
pirates, Japanese, 1028, 1176
Pirenne, Henri, 221, 940, 1174, 1257, 1361, 1747, 1748
Pirḥe elahut, 450
Pīrīzāde, Muḥammad, 1776, 1778
Pirqe abot, 590, 1097
Pirqe rabbi Eli'ezer, 1096, 1444
Pirro, André, 1202, 1857
Pisa, *see* Andrew; Bartholomew; Burgundio; carte; Guido; Hugutio; Leo Tuscus; Leonard Fibonacci; Peter; Pratearius; Rustichello
Pisa, University, 72, 471, 1244
Pisan, *see* Christine; Thomas
Pisanello, 1290
Piscis, *see* John
Pistoia, *see* Cino; Gregory
Pitart, *see* John
pitch, sources, 1622
Pits, John, 1569
Piur, Paul, 515, 516, 923
Pius II, *see* Aeneas Sylvius
Pius III, 1336
Pius X, 330
Pius XI, 512
Pius XII, 1034
Pizigano, *see* Francis
Pizigano map, 1143
Pizzano, *see* Benvenuto
Pizzicolli, *see* Ciriaco
"place value," 120, 122, 129
Placides et Timéo, 90, 346, 547
Placitus Papyriensis, Sextus (IV-2), v. 1, *375*, 361
plagal, 162
plague, 112, 818, 848, 860, 861, 862, 874, 886, 896, 962, 1737, 1763, 1775, 1803, 1867, 1891. *See also* Black Death
plague, *see* Athens

plague, Dalmatia, 1659
plague, *see* lazar houses; lazaretti
plague treatises (XIV-2), *1659*, 1664, 852
plague treatises, list, 1661
plain song, 159, 743
Planck, 1463
planctu ecclesiae, De, 51, 402
planetary systems, 1881
Planis, *see* John
planisphere, celestial, 1122, 1537
plant iconography, 1835
plant illustrations (XII-1), v. 2, *226*, 1217
plant names, Hebrew, 791
Plantagenet, *see* Edward
Plantijn, 1318
plantis, De, 208
plants, magic, 1881
Planudes, *see* Maximos
Platearius, Joannes the Younger (XI-2), v. 1, *770*, 742, 745; v. 2, 1190; v. 3, 816, 881, 883, 1206, 1705
Platearius, John III (XII-1), v. 2, *241*
Platearius, *see* Matthew
Plato (IV-1 B.C.), v. 1, *113*, 825; v. 2, 1217; v. 3, 13, 62, 81, 148, 158, 161, 434, 435, 507, 530, 547, 548, 584, 590, 751, 753, 836, 888, 952, facing 1019, 1073, 1095, 1235, 1320, 1321, 1357, 1426, 1464, 1465, 1489, 1637, 1640, 1822, 1862, 1869, 1882
Plato of Tivoli (XII-1), v. 2, *177*, 1217; v. 3, 369, 1518
playing cards, 1563
Plesch, J., 1836
Plessner, Martin, 74, 1374, 1533, 1781, 1899
Pletho, *see* Gemistos
Plige, *see* John
Plimpton, G. A., 1394, 1426, 1904
Plinii, two, 87, 298, 920
Pliny the Elder (I-2), v. 1, *249*, 825; v. 2, 1217; v. 3, 26, 216, 217, 224, 229, 488, 812, 813, 816, 920, 1144, 1158, 1171, 1186, 1292, 1596, 1600, 1603, 1808
Pliny the Younger, 26, 65, 920, 1391
Ploetz, K., 37
Plot, Robert, 1886
Plotinos (III-2), v. 1, *334*, 825; v. 2, 366; v. 3, 96, 569, 570, 588
Plowman, *see* Peter
plurality of worlds, 150, 530, 543, 559, 564
Plusquam commentum, 839
Plutarch of Chaeronea (I-2), v. 1, *251*, 825; v. 3, 825, 1073, 1252, 1292, 1321, 1395, 1862
pluviis imbribus, De, 431
pneumatic school, 889
pneumonia, 1727
Poblet, 1734
Po'el, *see* Jacob
poetical competitions, 1304
Poggendorff, J. C., 716
Poggi, Francesco, 1596
Poggibonsi, *see* Nicholas
Poggio Bracciolini of Florence, 813, 922, 923, 1073, 1155, 1229, 1253, 1291, 1816, 1818, 1819, 1822
Poggio, *see* James
Pognon, Henri, 139
Pogo, A., 29, 1122, 1806, 1825, 1890, 1898, 1899
Poince Le Gournaix, 1147
Poirette, *see* Margaret
poisoner, 1207
poisons, 431, 442, 1241, 1671, 1679, 1685
Poisson, Albert, 1578
Poitiers, *see* Alphonse; Joan; Richard
Polain, M. L., 1748, 1751
Polak, Gabriel b. Isaac, 366
Poland, *see* Franco de Polonia
polar regions, *see* arctic
Polcastro, *see* Sigismondo
Poleman, H. I., 360, 1899
Polemon of Laodicea (II-1), v. 1, *271*, 267, 356; v. 2, 441, 939; v. 3, 270, 442, 801, 1104
Polemon Periegetes (II-1 B.C.), v. 1, *185*, 178, 179
Polentone, *see* Secco
Poliak, A. N., 1788
Polidoro Vergilio, 921, 1550, 1852
Polish, 32, 355
political theory, 1876, 1900
Poliziano, *see* Angelo
Pollard, A. F., 557
Pollard, A. W., 533, 779, 1424, 1605, 1867, 1899
Pollard, H. B. C., 726
Pollio, C. Asinius (I-2 B.C.), v. 1, *222*, 219
Pollus, Julius (II-2), v. 1, *313*, 290
Polo family (XIII-2), v. 2, *1056*, 38, 772; v. 3, 186
Polo, *see* Marc
Polovtzi, 1016, 1853
Polyak, S. L., 274
Polybios (II-1 B.C.), v. 1, *188*, 825; v. 3, 1862
Polybos of Cos (IV-1 B.C.), v. 1, *120*, 112
Polycarpos of Smyrna, St., viii
Polycratus, 317
polyglottism of the Yüan, 1840
polyphony, 159
pomegranates, 825, 1835
Pomerania, *see* Eric
Pomerium, 740, 911
Pomerius, 582
Pompilio Totti, 923
Pomponazzi, Pietro, 737
Pomponius, *see* Mela
Poňatovská (Poniatowska), Christina, 1354
ponderibus, De, 145
pons asinorum, 542
Pons Boigues, Francisco, 1900
Pontanus, Jacob, 1760
Ponte, *see* Oldrado
Pontii, *see* John
Pontius Pilatus, 9

Poole, R. L., 411, 557, 560, 565, 566, 740, 1394, 1501, 1900
Poor Men of Lyon, 404
Poor, *see* Richard
Pope, A. U., 757, 975
pope and emperor, 314, 1876
popes, 1898, 1908
popes, accounts, 327
Poppe, N. N., 381
porcelain, 758, 1617
porcelain, Western transmission of Chinese (XII-2), v. 2, *409*, 1217
Pordenone, *see* Odoric
Poricologos (XII-2), v. 2, *426*, 304
Poridad de poridades, 342
pork, 1589
Porphyry (III-2), v. 1, *334*, 825; v. 2, 1217; v. 3, 81, 97, 517, 534, 550, 555, 563, 589, 603, 1462, 1466, 1877
Porphyry of Gaza, xi
Porretta, Bagni, 287, 850, 857
Porrette, *see* Margaret
Porta, *see* Robert
Porter, A., 1450
Portigliotti, Giuseppe, 266
Portinari bank, 1595
Portinari, *see* Beatrice; John
portolani (XI-2), v. 1, *767*, 742; v. 2, *1047*, 39, 77; v. 3, 182, 510, 715, 786, 1141, 1144, 1591, 1599, 1892
portolani, earliest dated, 762
portolani, first printed, 1600
Portuguese, 343
Portuguese literature, 1874
Porzello, *see* Albert
Posch, Andreas, 577
Posener, S., 1384
Posidonios (I-1 B.C.), v. 1, *204*, 825; v. 3, 214, 1859
Posidonios the Physician (IV-2), v. 1, *373*, 360, 361
positivism, Aristotelian, 83
Posquières, *see* Abraham b. David; Asher b. David
post mortem, 841, 1195
postal services, 1617, 1622
postal services, pigeon, 1786
Postansque, A., 771
Postilla litteralis, 48, 398
Postilla moralis, 398
postillae, 56
postulates, 597
Potaloka, 1854
potash, 756
potestate papae, De, 408
Potter, G. R., 1360
Potter, M. A., 515
pottery, Muslim, 1849
Poṭṭhapāda sutta, 81
Potthast, August, 1900
Potti, 995
Potvin, Charles, 1151
Pouille, *see* Thomas
Pouilli, *see* John
Poujoulat, 930
Poul, *see* Paul
Poulain, Louis, 1407
pouncing process, 1178
Pound, Ezra, 1333
Poutrel, abbé, 65, 246, 346, 452
Pouzyna, I. V., 1900
poverty, 48, 282. *See also* evangelical
Power, D'Arcy, 1704
Power, Eileen, 411, 1180, 1181, 1900
Power, F. B., 1851
Powicke, F. J., 572, 1854
Powicke, F. M., 411, 563, 570, 1900
Poynting, J. H., 150
Poznański, Adolf, 1523
Poznanski, Samuel, 56
Pozzuoli, baths, 1685
Prabandhacintāmaṇi, 1585
Prabandhaparameśvara, 465
Prachatice, *see* Christian
Practica geometriae (XII-2), v. 2, *403*, 1218
Practica della mercatura, 773
Practica officii inquisitionis, 50, 403
praemunire, statute, 1034
Prague, *see* Bartholomew; Christian; Cosmas; Francis; Jerome
Prague, University, 72, 471, 1244
Prajñāpāramitā, 729
Prākrit, 382, 1477
prakṛiti, 1475
prāṇayāma, 96
Prantl, Carl v., 1900
Prapañca, 1161, 1268, 1331, 1624
Pratearius of Pisa, 1576
Pratimāmānalakshaṇa, 1584
Pratirājadeva, 423
Prato, *see* Convenevole; James; John; Naddino; Nicholas
Pratt, A. M., 1051
Pratt, G. D., 336
Pratt, J. H., 1166
Praxagoras of Cos (IV-2 B.C.), v. 1, *146*, 126; v. 2, 76
Préaux, Claire, 454
precession, *see* equinoxes
Prégent de Coëtivy, 458, 1842
Preger, Theodor, 1291
Preger, Wilhelm, 574, 575
pregnancy, 252, 268
pregnancy, length of, 1230
pregnancy of seven months, 1698
Preis, *see* John
Preisendanz, Karl, 1436
Premierfait, *see* Laurence
Premonstrants (XII-1), v. 2, *157*, 111
Premudry, *see* Epifani

Prentice, E. P., 1859
Prepositi, *see* Nicholas
Presles, *see* Raoul
Prester John, *see* John
Pretiosa margarita, 750
Pretzl, Otto, 1456
Previté-Orton, C. W., 989
Přibík Pulkava (XIV-2), *1758*, 1259
Příbram, *see* John
Price, C. S., 1708
Pricke of conscience, 463, 566, 1314
Prieur, Léon, 499
Prignano, *see* Bartholomew
Prihoda, R., 1556
prima, 716
prima et secunda intentione, Liber de, 73
Primat of Saint Denis, 457
primum mobile, 599
principiis naturae, De, 528
printing, 109, 157, 1125, 1874, 1876, 1878. *See also* typography; xylography
printing, block, 729, 971, 974, 976
printing, block, in Egypt, 732
printing, Chinese (VI-2), v. 1, *451;* (IX-2), v. 1, *604;* v. 3, 138, 386
printing, dry, 1563
printing in the East (XIV-1), *729*
printing, Japanese, 637
printing, Muslim, 1588
printing on textiles, 1563
Priscianos of Lydia, philosopher (VI-1), v. 1, *423*, 415; v. 2, 590
Priscianus of Caesarea, grammarian (VI-1), v. 1, *440*, 826; v. 2, 1218; v. 3, 331, 350, 552, 563, 1003, 1358, 1566
Priscianus, Theodorus (IV-2), v. 1, *374*, 826; v. 2, 1085; v. 3, 816
Priscilla, 23
privatio, 564
privilegium practicandi, 859
probabilities, 1105, 1813
probamentum, 1242
Probatio adventus Christi, 398
Problemata, Aristotelian, 537, 1123, 1229
Probos of Antioch (V-2), v. 1, *407*, 826; v. 3, 358
Probst, J. H., 1343
Probus, Philip, 414
Procházka, Fr., 1758
Prochoros Cydones (XIV-2), *1386*, 95, 587, 1058, 1075, 1095, 1320, 1363, 1760
Procida, *see* John
Proclos the Successor (V-2), v. 1, *402*, 826; v. 2, 1218; v. 3, 81, 92, 118, 568, 706, 737, 1115, 1416, 1439, 1511, 1877
Procopios (VI-2), v. 1, *454*, 445; v. 3, 1650, 1862
procreation, 1230
Prodromenos, *see* Neophytos
Prodromos, *see* Theodore
procliis, Historia de, 1261, 1519
Profiat, *see* Abraham
Profiaț Duran (XIV-2), *1520*, 1063, 1097, 1117, 1212, 1221, 1324, 1384, 1385, 1523
Prognostica secundum lunam, 441
prognostication, *see* divination
Prognosticationes, 426
progress, 25, 1770
progress, scientific, 1868
projection, method, 951
Promis, Carlo, 847
Promis, Vincenzo, 1814
propaganda literature, 46
property, *see* landed
prophecy, 1772
proportions, 1487
proprietates terminorum, 552
Prosdocimo de' Beldomandi, 740, 1106, 1170, 1128, 1565
prosody, 1411
Prosper of Aquitania, Tiro (V-2), v. 1, *411*, 399, 400
Prostov, E. V., 214, 930, 1870
Protagoras of Abdera (V B.C.), v. 1, *88*, 83
Protat, *see* Bois
Protat, Jules, 1563
Protospatharios, *see* Theophile
Prouville, *see* John
Provençal, 338, 1872, 1898
Provence, *see* Lewis; Margaret
Provenzali, Dino, 512
Proverbis rimats, 342
Proverbs, books (III-1 B.C.), v. 1, *163*, 150; v. 2, 846; v. 3, 419
Provins, *see* Guiot
provisions, papal, 38
Provisors, Statute, 1034
Pruckner, Hubert, 1496, 1509, 1510
Prüm, *see* Regino
Průšek, Jaroslav, 387
Prutz, Hans, 1150
Pruzhinin, V. G., 1825
Przeworskǫ, *see* Herman
Przyluski, Jean, 1030
Psellos, *see* Michael
pseudepigrapha, 1878
Psichari, Jean, 1513
psoriasis, 275
psychoanalysis, 1434
psychology, 1491, 1507
psychology, abnormal, 1772
Ptolemaic, 116, 1525
Ptolemaic maps, 197
Ptolemaic theories, 112, 114, 1411
Ptolemy, *see also* Tolomei, Tolomeo
Ptolemy (II-1), v. 1, *272*, 826; v. 2, 1219; v. 3, 303, 532, 563, 1321
Ptolemy, astrology, 128, 431, 1005, 1049, 1073, 1481, 1483, 1493, 1519, 1694, 1703, 1707, 1797, 1808, 1877
Ptolemy, astronomy and mathematics, Alma-

Ptolemy, astronomy—*continued*
gest, 120, 123, 430, 434, 440, 484, 487, 501, 539, 544, 595, 705, 706, 792, 801, 950, 951, 1072, 1108, 1115, 1118, 1378, 1421, 1430, 1439, 1451, 1511, 1512, 1521. *See also* Almagest, translation
Ptolemy, Geography, vii, 80, 197, 200, 1145, 1153, 1155, 1158, 1159, 1289, 1597, 1772, 1852, 1859, 1865
Ptolemy, music, 161, 586, 951
Ptolemy, optics, 141
Ptolemy of Lucca (XIII-2), v. 2, *1126*, 1219; v. 3, 298, 404, 577, 932
Ptolemy, pseudo, 431
Ptraccia, *see* John
public health (XIV-2), *1658*, 1867
Puccinotti, Francesco, 1900
Pueschel, Albert, 1806
Puey, *see* Arnold
Puibusque, Adolphe de, 925
Pujol, *see* Bernard
Pūjyapāda Devanandin, 1730
Pūlād-čink-sānk, 970
Pulci, *see* Lewis
Pulkava, 1076, 1259
Pulkava, *see* Přibík
Pullé, F. L., 1900
Pullè, Giorgio, 779
Pulologos, 208, 239, 823
Pulqar, *see* Isaac b. Joseph
pulse, 891, 902, 906, 1228
Pumbedita, 366
Punel, abbé, 452
Puṇṇānanda Swāmi, Samaṇa, 1371
pūṇya-kshetra, 1733
Purāṇa, 1909
Purcell, Victor, 1084
Purchas, Samuel, 955
purgation, 427, 1228
Purim, 430, 449
Pūrṇachandra De, 1396
purusha, 1475
Pūrvamīmāṃsā, 1366
Purvey, *see* John
Puschmann, Theodor, 1244, 1245, 1660
Pusey, W. A., 873, 881, 884
Puteo, *see* Paris
Puteoli, baths, 287, 1240
Puto-shan, 1854
Putti, Vittorio, 845
Puylaurens, *see* William
Puyol, P. E., 1361
pygargus, 1642
pygmy, 212
pyramids, 1606, 1620
Pyrrhon of Elis (IV-2 B.C.), v. 1, *136*, 125
Pythagoras of Samos (VI B.C.), v. 1, *73*, 826; v. 2, 1219; v. 3, 134, 158, 161, 435, 745, 751
Pythagoras, school, 474
Pytheas of Massilia (IV-2 B.C.), v. 1, *144*, 126, 606
qabā'il, 376
Qabajaqī, *see* Bailak b. Muḥammad
qabāla, salt gabelle, 181
qabbala, 85, 100, 212, 613, 616, 793, 1068, 1096, 1098, 1460
qabbān al-qubṭī, 712
Qabīsī, 'Abd al-'Azīz b. 'Uthmān (X-2), v. 1, *669*, 649, 654; v. 2, 125, 170; v. 3, 451, 1421, 1481, 1498
qadar, 1214
Qāḍī Ba'lbakk, 1723
Qāḍī Yūsuf, 1855
Qāḍī Zāde Rūmī, 1119, 1120, 1466
Qādirīya, 420. *See also* 'Abd al-Qādir Jīlī
Qafanton, *see* Jacob
Qaiṣar b. a. Qāsim (XIII-1), v. 2, *623*, 1219
Qaiṣarī, *see* Dā'ūd b. Maḥmūd
Qaisī, *see* Aḥmad b. 'Uthmān
Qā'it-bey, 173
Qala'i, *see* Moses b. Samuel
Qalandarīya, 420
Qalaṣādī, *see* 'Alī b. Muḥammad
Qalā'ūn's hospital (XIII-2), v. 2, *1102*; v. 3, 1727
Qalā'ūn, b., *see* Muḥammad; Nāṣir Muḥammad
Qalonymos b. David Ṭodros (XIV-1), *428*, 61, 98, 428, 433, 609
Qalonymos b. David the Younger, 429
Qalonymos family, 429
Qalonymos, *see* Isaac Nathan
Qalonymos b. Qalonymos (XIV-1), *429*, 62, 67, 98, 128, 134, 208, 240, 254, 428, 434, 451, 589, 591, 596, 603
Qalqashandī, Aḥmad b. 'Alī (XIV-2), *1785*, 306, 621, 1161, 1214, 1236, 1264, 1272, 1326, 1619, 1775
Qalqashandī, *see* Muḥammad b. Aḥmad
Qāmūs, 1326, 1827
Qānūn al-Mas'ūdī, 200
Qara 'Alā' al-dīn, 1466
Qara, *see* Joseph b. Simon
Qara-Kiṭāi, 1721
Qarāfa cemeteries, 1161
Qarāfī, *see* Aḥmad b. Idrīs
Qaraism, Qaraites, 56, 83, 101, 131, 419, 449, 617, 1064, 1365, 1378, 1385, 1517, 1894
Qarmaṭī, 154, 958, 1460
Qaro, Joseph b. Ephraim, 614
Qāsim b. 'Abd al-Malik b. Bashkuwāl, a. (XII-1), v. 2, *249*, 137, 682
Qāsim in Alexandria, a., 1644
Qāsim b. 'Alī Ḥarīrī (XII-1), v. 2, *270*, 1180; v. 3, 373, 615
Qāsim b. 'Asākir, 804
Qāsim b. Ḥasan Shaddād, a., 1118
Qāsim Ḥaufī, a., *see* Aḥmad b. Muḥammad Ḥaufī
Qāsim 'Irāqī, a., *see* Muḥammad b. Aḥmad
Qāsim, a., Khalaf b. 'Abbās Zahrāwī (X-2), v.

1, *681*, 787; v. 2, 1219; v. 3, 62, 246, 255, 264, 272, 275, 277, 280, 340, 607, 613, 863, 870, 883, 884, 895, 1216, 1227, 1683, 1691, 1700, 1727
Qāsim b. Muḥammad Birzālī (XIV-1), *958*, 307, 1782
Qaṣṣāb 'Alī, 1464
Qawānīn al-ṣayyād, 232
qaws quzaḥ, 707
Qawsūnī, *see* Madyan b. 'Abd al-Raḥmān
Qayyim Jawzīya, *see* Muḥammad
qazān, 155
qaẓin b. qaẓin, 428
Qazwīnī, 630
Qazwīnī, *see* 'Abd al-Ghaffār b. 'Abd al-Karīm; Ḥamdallāh b. a. Bakr Mustawfī; Muḥammad b. Aḥmad; Muḥammad b. Yazīd
Qazwīnī, Zakarīyā b. Muḥammad (XIII-2), v.2 , *868*, 1247; v. 3, 631, 707, 1144, 1161, 1175, 1623, 1640
Qebuẓat kesef, 591
qesem, 405
qesheth, 141
qibbuẓ, 618
qibla, 135, 632, 1118, 1526
Qibṭī, *see also* Qifṭī
Qibṭī, Buṭrus b. a. Karam (XIII-2), v. 2, *1121*, 1221
Qibṭī, *see* Muḥammad b. Faḍlallāh
qibuẓim, 428
Qifṭī, b., *see* 'Alī b. Yūsuf
Qimḥi, *see* David b. Joseph; Joseph b. Isaac; Joseph b. Saul; Moses b. Joseph
Qipchaq, 379, 1016, 1615, 1617
Qipchaqī, 1013
qirāḍ, 1272
Qirimi, *see* Abraham
Qirqisānī (X-1), v. 1, *626*, 620, 623; v. 3, 56, 365, 367
qirṭās, 175
Qiryat sefer, 419, 1718
qiyāfa, 271, 801
Qiz-ughlu, b., *see* Yūsuf
Qizil-bāsh, 420
qiẓẓur, 431
Qiẓẓur qaṭan, 590
Qobeẓ al-yad, 438
Qoriyyat II, Judah, 612
Qorsono, 1375
quacks, 273, 855, 869, 884, 1204
quadrangle, college, 473
quadrant, 601, 1524, 1526, 1528, 1530, 1903
quadrature, 1106, 1112
Quadripartitum, 1049
quadrivium, 80
qualities, four, 1492
quarantine, 1659, 1750
Quatremère, E. M., 803, 975, 1265, 1777
Quattuor magistri, 247, 883
Qudāma b. Ja'far Baghdādī (X-1), v. 1, *636*, 621; v. 3, 801
Qudūrī, *see* Aḥmad b. Muḥammad
Queen's College, 72, 474, 1402
Quentin, Charles, 295
Quétif, Jacques, 1900
Queux de Saint-Hilaire, 1412
Quff, b., *see* Ya'qūb b. Isḥāq
Quidort, *see* John
Quietanus, J. R., 600
quietism, 95
Quilon in Travancore, 781, 783
quinine, 289
Quinquempoix, *see* Arnold
Quint, Josef, 570
quintessence, 1573
Quintilian of Calagurris (I-2), v. 1, *265*, 245; v. 2, 532, 701; v. 3, 373, 1288, 1291, 1816, 1819
Quinze joies de mariage, 1277
Quinze-vingt, 295
Qumrī, *see* Ḥasan b. Nūḥ
Qunfūdh, b., *see* Aḥmad b. Ḥasan
Qur'ān, 58, 79, 135, 138, 165, 211, 363, 370, 376, 421, 1774, 1854
Qūshchī, *see* 'Alī b. Muḥammad
Qusṭā b. Lūqā (IX-2), v. 1, *602*, 827; v. 2, 1220; v. 3, 61, 114, 245, 264, 426, 430
Qusṭanṭīnī, *see* 'Alī b. a. 'Alī
Qutaiba, b. (IX-2), v. 1, *615*, 810; v. 2, 1220; v. 3, 1785
Quṭb al-dīn Shīrāzī, *see* Maḥmūd b. Mas'ūd
Qūṭīya, b., *see* Muḥammad b. 'Umar

Rab' i-Rashīdī, 970
Raba'ī, *see* 'Alī b. Muḥammad
rabāb, 163
Rabāb-nāma, 163
rabbinic script, 364
Rabbinism, 83
Rabelais, 477
Rabī' b. Yaḥyā, 430
Rabī' b. Zaid Usquf (X-2), v. 1, *669*, 649, 654; v. 3, 430
rabies, 872
rabw, 451
race vs. environment, 1772
Rackham, Bernard, 290, 756, 1134
Rada, *see* Rodrigo Jiménez
Radcliffe, William, 1166, 1900
Radermacher, L., 1094
Radewijns, *see* Florence
radiation, theory of, 705, 1505
Radlov, V. V., 1015, 1016
Radolf, *see* Ralph
Rae, G. M., 358
Raepsaet, J. J., 823
Rafaino Caresini, 916
Rafī'ī, 1460
rafīq, 155

Rafn, C. C., 1154
Rafn Sveinbjörnsson (XIII-1), v. 2, *637*, 1221; v. 3, 196, 1236
Raggio of Florence, 737
Rāghavānanda, 425
Ragimbold of Cologne (XI-1), v. 1, *715*, 695, 702; v. 2, 11
ragioni, libro delle, 124
Rahere, 295
Rāhib Qibṭī, b., *see* Qibṭī, Buṭrus b. a. Karam
Rahmeti Arat, 1840
Raḥmūn, *see* Salāma b. Mubārak
Raigecourt, *see* John
Raikem, J. J., 1751
Raimond, Raimondo, Raimundo, Raimundus, *see* Raymond
Rainaud, Armand, 193
rainbow, 141, 452, 704, 707, 709, 818, 992, 1123, 1506, 1540
Rainer, archduke, 174, 175, 732
Rainer II Grimaldi, 740
raison, livre de, 124
Rajab, b., *see* 'Abd al-Raḥmān b. Aḥmad
Rājanighaṇṭu, 1730
rājanīti, 1000
Rajasanagara, 1624
Rajna, Pio, 493, 835
Ral-pa-Chan (IX-2), v. 1, *593*, 468, 584
Ralph, *see also* Raoul; Rodolph
Ralph Diceto (XII-2), v. 2, *457*, 314
Ralph of Enteren, 1357
Ralph of Hingham, 719
Ralph of Laon (XII-1), v. 2, *210*, 4, 124
Ralph of Liége (XI-1), v. 1, *715*, 695, 702; v. 2, 11
Ralph Strode (XIV-2), *1412*, 1089
Rāma Rāja, 41
Rāmacandra, 1584
Rāmacaritamānasa, 425
Rāmadatta, 425
Rāmakṛishṇa, 1367, 1900
Rāmānanda (XIV-1), *425*, 60, 1330, 1475
Ramanayya, N. V., 41
Rāmānuja (XI-2), v. 1, *754*, 739, 746; v. 2, 826; v. 3, 60, 425, 1366, 1475
Rāmāwat, 425
Rāmāyaṇa, 384, 1077, 1330, 1395
Ramazzini, Bernardino, 301
Rambaldi, *see* Benvenuto
Rambaud, Joseph, 1284, 1900
Ramboldini, *see* Vittorino
Ramée, Pierre de la, 1316, 1504
Rāmī, *see* Ḥasan b. Muḥammad
"Raminto," 1689
raml, 123
Ramón, *see* Raymond
Rampinis, *see* Andrew
Rampur, *see* Muḥammad 'Alī
Ramsey, *see* Byrhtferth
Ramusio, Giambattista, 779, 955, 1151, 1158, 1291, 1552, 1594, 1754
Ramusio, *see* Paul
Ranco, *see* Adalbertus
Rand, E. K., 496
Randal, *see* Ranulf
Randall, H. J., 191, 1744
range finding, 1554
Ranke, Hermann, 1596
Rankine, W. J. M., 1843
ransoms, 1752
Ranulf Glanville (XII-2), v. 2, *467*, 317, 322
Ranulf Higden (XIV-1), *946*, 190, 303, 348, 1076, 1149, 1256, 1313, 1393, 1743, 1744, 1746
Rao, A. V., 383
Raoul, *see also* Rodolph
Raoul Glaber (XI-1), v. 1, *734*, 805; v. 3, 227
Raoul de Presles (XIV-2), *1390*, 992, 1075, 1088, 1276, 1277, 1307, 1345, 1493
Raoul Renaud le Breton (XIV-1), *534*, 82, 90, 534
Raoul de Ruisseau, 1257, 1395
Raphael, *see* Rafaino
Raphelengius, Franciscus, 431
Raqqām, b., *see* Muḥammad b. Ibrāhīm
rasa, 1139, 1218, 1584
Rasādhyāya, 1584
Rasahṛidaya, 1584
Rasaratnākara, 1584
Rasaratnasamuccaya, 1584
Rasario, G. B., 589
Rasārṇava, 1584
Rasasiddhānta, 1584
Rasavāhinī, 422, 1370
rasāyana, 1584
raṣd, 'ilm, 1526
rasendra, 1584
Rasendracintāmaṇi, 1584
raseśvara, 1366, 1584
raseśvaradarśana, 1584
Raseśvarasiddhānta, 1584
Rashdall, Hastings, 547, 1349, 1900
Rashi (XI-2), v. 1, *752*, 827; v. 2, 1221; v. 3, 56, 364, 368, 370, 397, 400, 416, 614, 615, 1008, 1364, 1826
Rashīd al-dīn (XIV-1), *969*, 74, 106, 179, 203, 210, 228, 256, 258, 261, 264, 309, 377, 380, 387, 629, 630, 731, 755, 902, 976, 977, 1249, 1852, 1910
Rasm al-ma'mūr min al-arḍ, 200
Rasm al-rub' al-ma'mūr, 200
Rasmussen, Harald, 1458
Rasūl, Banū, 102
Rasūlī dynasty, 827, 1117, 1168
Rasūlī, *see* 'Abbās b. 'Alī; Mujāhid 'Alī
Raswan, C. R., 1636
Ratdolt, 111, 444
Rathgen, Bernhard, 726, 1900
Ratio, queen, 231, 1183, 1309
rationalism, 18, 83
Ratirahasya, 465

Ratisbon, *see* Petaḥiah b. Jacob
Raṭṭa-kavi (XIV-1), *634*, 69, 107, 383, 466, 1828
Raṭṭa-mata, 383, 384, 634
Raṭṭahapāla, 423
rauḍ al-qirṭās, 957
Ravaglia, Giuseppe, 857
Ravaisse, Paul, 173, 1265
Ravasini, R., 270
Ravenna, geographer of (VII-2), v. 1, *496*, 324, 489; v. 2, 222; v. 3, 911
Ravenna, *see* John
Rawḍ mi'ṭār, 306
rawk al-Nāṣirī, 199
Rawlings, G. B., 1407
Ray, D. N., 262, 1217
Ray, John, 1642
Ray, P. C., 1585, 1901
Raymond, *see also* Mondino
Raymond d'Avignon, 339
Raymond de Béziers (XIV-1), *464*, 68
Raymond da Capua, 1335, 1336
Raymond Chalmel de Viviers (XIV-2), *1694*, 1200, 1254
Raymond Cornet, 343
Raymond de Farges, 415
Raymond Lull (XIII-2), v. 2, *900*, 1221; v. 3, 23, 46, 49, 73, 89, 119, 141, 166, 178, 212, 245, 300, 315, 342, 363, 375, 410, 412, 546, 750, 753, 770, 879, 924, 1040, 1052, 1327, 1338, 1572, 1574, 1576, 1775, 1848. *See also* Lullian
Raymond of Marseilles (XII-1), v. 2, *210*, 1221
Raymond Martin (XIII-2), v. 2, *892*, 1221; v. 3, 369, 374, 375, 398
Raymond of Molières (XIV-1), *878*, 248, 877, 1690
Raymond Muntaner (XIV-1), *925*, 300, 342, 949, 1734
Raymond of Peñafort (XIII-1), v. 2, *553*, 1221; v. 3, 369, 1338
Raymond Sebonde, 1087
Raymond de Tárrega (XIV-2), *1574*, 179, 1130
Raymond Vidal of Besalù, 340, 343
Raynaud, Gaston, 1412
Rayner, *see* Rainer; Rainier; Regnier; Renier; Reynard
Razes, *see* Rāzī, Muḥammad b. Zakarīyā
Rāzī, *see* Aḥmad b. 'Abdallāh; Aḥmad b. Muḥammad; Muḥammad b. 'Umar Fakhr al-dīn
Rāzī, Muḥammad b. Zakarīyā (IX-2), v. 1, *609*, 827; v. 2, 1221; v. 3, xi, 61, 149, 165, 247, 270, 274, 288, 292, 442, 463, 753, 801, 813, 836, 846, 850, 856, 870, 877, 883, 884, 894, 898, 1104, 1193, 1200, 1205, 1212, 1221, 1229, 1235, 1236, 1379, 1381, 1449, 1514, 1674, 1680, 1681, 1682, 1683, 1685, 1688, 1696, 1699, 1703, 1705, 1710, 1719, 1723, 1727, 1775
Razos de trobar, 340
Razzāq, 'Abd al-, 41
Razzolini, Aloisio, 513
reaction, 737
Read, B. E., 224
Read, John, 1704
Read, T. T., 221
Reade, W. H. V., 499
"Reader's digest," vi
Reading, *see* John; Robert
reading machine, vi
realism, 75, 81, 604, 1348
Réaumur, 1597
rebec, 163
Reboldi, *see* Anthony
Rebouis, H. E., 1652
rebus memorandis, De, 506
Recco, *see* Nicholas
Receptari de Manresa, 246
Rechtsbuch, 993
Reckelbus, Louis, 49
Recorde, Robert, 1483, 1500, 1581
recuperatione Terrae Sanctae, De, 408
Red Hats, 1070, 1371
Red Sea, 788, 1891
red worm, 844
Rede, *see* William
Redgrave, G. R., 1901
Redhouse, J. W., 1780
Redi, Francesco, 1230
Redstone, L. J., 1425
Redstone, V. B., 1425
Reductorium morale, 48, 454
Reeland, Adriaan, 791
Rees, Wm., 191
Reese, Gustave, 1901
Reeve, Henry, 514
Reeves, A. M., 1609
reflection, *see* light
Reformation, 12, 24, 51, 987
refraction, *see* light
Regel, Karl, 1711
Regensburg, *see* Petaḥiah b. Jacob of Ratisbon
Reger, *see* John
Reggio, *see* Barnabas; Bartholomew; Guido; Nicholas
Reggio, I. S., 592
Regimen Judaeorum, 286
Regimen et modus studendi, 286
Regimen principum, 286, 314, 321, 393, 402, 577, 1824
Regimen sanitatis, 245, 285, 834, 1861
Regimen solitarii, 286
regimina, 285, 1238
Reginald Lambourne, 1500
Regino of Prüm (X-1), v. 1, *641*, 827; v. 3, 933
Regio, *see* Peter

Regiomontanus, 129, 142, *444*, *445*, 598, 601, 705, 1106, 1481, 1483, 1546
Regles de trobar, 343
Regnault, Jules, 1051
Regnier of Huy, *727*
regulars vs. seculars (XIII-2), v. 2, *823*, 712; v. 3, 47, 535, 819, 1038
regum qui est geometricus, Liber, 429
Řehoř Hrubý of Gelenije (Jelení), 506
Reichelt, K. L., 312, 1018
Reiffenberg, baron de, 392, 788
Reims, *see* Flodoard; Richer
Reinach, Salomon, 1051
Reinaud, J. T., 622, 632, 799, 1901
reindeer, 1630
Reindl, Joseph, 1190
Reineck, Reiner, 955, 1758
Reinesius, Thomas, 1877
Reischauer, A. K., 312
Reischauer, E. O., 28, 389
Reiske, J. J., 622, 799
Relaxati, 396
relics, 291, 1044. *See also* reliquaries
relics, robbers, 266
religion, 20, 1883
religious orders of knighthood (XII-1), v. 2, *159*
reliquaries, 1045
reliquiae, medicine, 849
Rembrandt, 1056
remediis utriusque fortunae, De, 506
Remi d'Auxerre (IX-2), v. 1, *595*, 827
Rémion de Mitry, 1147
Remiro, M. G., 621, 1764
Remus, Uncle, 464
Rémusat, Abel, 1122
Renan, Ernest, 43, 46, 411, 461, 505, 548, 966, 1322, 1622, 1827, 1901
Renard, Georges, 152
Renaud, H. P. J., xv, 131, 136, 287, 896, 1118, 1461, 1725, 1765, 1766, 1779, 1875, 1881, 1901
Renaud de Louhans, 453, 1633
Renaud, *see* Raoul
Renaudet, Augustin, 490
Renclus de Moiliens, 1275
Renier of Liége, 221
Renier, Rodolfo, 1601
Rennell, James, 1159
rennet, 751
Renou, Louis, 1370
Renouard, Yves, 1839
Renzi, Salvatore de, 1302, 1901
Reparaz-Ruiz, Gonçal de, 1593, 1858, 1901
Repertorium morale, 48, 454
Repgow, *see* Eike
reportationes, 79
Reprobatio operis catalonici, 400
reprobatione iudiciorum astrologiae, De, 115
Res rustica, 813
Resaina, *see* Sergios
Rescher, Oscar, 1781
Reshit ḥokmah, 431, 442
resistance, 1430
respondentia, 324
responsa, 16, 1061
Responsio ad quemdam Judeum, 398
Restori, Vasco, 1301
retina, 274
Retuqot kesef, 590
Retz, *see* Giles
Reuber, J., 918
Reuchlin, *see* John
Reusens, E. H. J., 536
Reuss, professor, 573
Reuter, O. S., 1832, 1848
Reutlingen, *see* Hugh
Reutter de Rosemont, Louis, 290
Revelli, Paolo, 498, 1670
Revigny, *see* James
Revilla, A., 1822
Revius, Jacobus, 1363
revolving bookcases, 107
revolving repository, 734
revolving type cases, 145, 734, 830
"revulsion," Hippocratic, 890
Rewiczki, Charles, 1458
Rey, *see* Bernard
Reynard the Fox (XII-2), v. 2, *393*, 1223; v. 3, 239, 824, 1190
Reynold, *see* Reginald; Regino; Renaud
Rhabdas, *see* Nicholas
Rhacendytes, *see* Joseph
Rhalli, 995
Rhazes, *see* Rāzī, Muḥammad b. Zakarīyā
Rhenanus, *see* John
rhinoceros, 1242, 1621
rhinoplasty, 1233
Rhodes, 40, 1036
Rhodes, *see* Andronicos
Rhodes, Knights, 40
rhythm, 161
Riant, Paul, 1606
ribāṭ, 1635
Ribbenicz, *see* Henry
Ribera de Perpeja, *see* Peter
Ribera y Tarragó, Julián, 159
Riberta y Roqueta, Bartolomé María, 517
Ribes, *see* James
Ricaldone, *see* Stephen Talice
Ricardo, *see* Richard
Riccardi, *see also* Richard
Riccardi bank of Lucca, 324
Riccardi, Pietro, 1902
Riccardo, *see* Richard
Ricci, Corrado, 168, 492, 493, 496
Ricci, Matteo, 140, 205, 808, 1646, 1850
Ricci, Seymour de, 1902
Ricciotti, Giuseppe, 490

Riccobaldo da Ferrara (XIV-1), *911*, 187, 297, 1145
Riccomanno Jacopi, 124
Riccordo, *see* Richard
Rice, E. P., 384, 634, 1730, 1828
Rice, J. V., 1359
Rich, T. P., 1817
Richard d'Aungerville, 560
Richard de Bury (XIV-1), *560*, 92, 333, 559, 563, 1295, 1298
Richard di Capsalo, 555
Richard of Cirencester (XIV-2), *1743*, 1148, 1255
Richard of Cluny, 1500
Richard of Courtenay, 1497
Richard I of England, Lionheart (XII-2), v. 2, *420*, 1223
Richard the Englishman (XIII-1), v. 2, *657*
Richard Eudes (XIV-2), *1391*, 1075, 1201, 1240, 1309
Richard Ferabrich, 1413
Richard Fitzneal (XII-2), v. 2, *467*, 1223; v. 3, 562
Richard Fitzralph, 1038, 1055, 1076, 1394
Richard Fleming, 1347
Richard de Fournival (XIII-2), v. 2, *864*, 1223; v. 3, 345
Richard, fra, 584
Richard de Ghlymi Eshedi, 736
Richard, J. M., 228
Richard Kyngeston, 1150
Richard Malombra, 916
Richard Methley, 1417
Richard of Middleton (XIII-2), v. 2, *951*, 1223; v. 3, 91, 114
Richard Misyn, 566
Richard of Monte Croce, *see* Ricoldo
Richard Ortholan, 1575
Richard Pencrych, 1314
Richard de Poitiers, 1500
Richard Poor, 1423
Richard the Redeless, 1414
Richard Rolle (XIV-1), *566*, 85, 92, 349, 463, 1089, 1314, 1416
Richard of Saint Victor, 582, 1416, 1661
Richard of Salerno (XII-2), v. 2, *436*, 309
Richard Swineshead (XIV-1), *736*, 92, 117, 147, 739, 1086, 1849, 1565
Richard Wallingford (XIV-1), *662*, 116, 129, 144, 278, 720, 1110, 1568
Richard of Wendover (XIII-1), v. 2, *657*, 1223
Richards, I. A., 331
Richardson, H. G., 1296, 1312
Richer of Reims (X-2), v. 1, *685*, 827
Richter, G. M. A., 1584
Richthofen, Karl v., 938
Rickard, T. A., 1902
Rickert, Edith, 1424
Rickmers, C. Mabel (Mrs. W. R.), 978, 1882, 1902
Rico y Sinobas, Manuel, 133
Ricoldo of Monte Croce (XIII-2), v. 2, *1061*, 1223; v. 3, 46, 49, 186, 375, 1045, 1075, 1388, 1760
Ricordano de Malespini, 915
Ricotti, Ercole, 1023
Riḍā Tawfīq, 1460
Riḍwān b. Muḥammad b. Sā'ātī (XIII-1), v. 2, *631*, 1225
Rieck, Wilhelm, 284
Rieder, Karl, 572
Rienzo, *see* Cola
Rieti, *see* Moses b. Isaac
Rieu, Charles, 465, 633, 828
Rieux, A. P., 930
Rifat, K. M., 1014
Rigault, 406
Rigault, Nicolas, 952
Rigg, J. M., 1023
rigging, 157
Righini, Eugenio, 498
Right good lernyng, 347
Rīgistān, 1470
Rigoli, Luigi, 463
Rigord of Saint Denis (XIII-1), v. 2, *674*, 525
Ṛigveda, 1368
Rihani, Ameen, 1327
Rijāl, b. a. (XI-1), v. 1, *715*, 695, 702; v. 2, 1223; v. 3, 960, 1074, 1117, 1118, 1383, 1481, 1485, 1765
Riley, H. T., 1204, 1745
Rimini, *see* Gregory
Rinaldi, Odorico, 525
Ringgenbern, *see* John
Ringhausen, K. W., 214
Rinio, *see* Lewis
Rio, *see* Anthony; Enrigetto; Uguccione
Rio de Oro, 785
Ripelin, *see* Hugh
Ripert, Emile, 1304
Ripley, George, 1165, 1577
Riqūṭī, *see* Muḥammad b. Aḥmad
Risseeuw, J. E., 823
Ristoro d'Arezzo (XIII-2), v. 2, *928*, 737, 749; v. 3, 214, 1106
Ritchie, R. L. G., 1741
Ritschl, Friedrich, 997
Ritter, Gerhard, 1435, 1437
Ritter, Hellmut, 757, 960, 961, 1636, 1643
rivers, conservancy, 809
rivers and waterways of China, 809
Rivola, Francesco, 460
Riẓā Tevfīq, 1460
rizma, 175
Roback, A. A., 1720
robarie, Officium, 416
Robathan, D. M., 922, 1811
Ròbbia, *see* Andrew; Luca
Robbins, F. E., 1049
Robbins, R. H., 566, 1280, 1428

Robert of Anjou, 56, 188, 225, 370, 429, 447, 449, 505, 510, 740, 1303, 1803, 1831, 1843
Robert of Avesbury (XIV-2), *1742*, 1255
Robert de Basevorn, 1040
Robert of Béthune, 526
Robert de Bruce, 278, 1254, 1315, 1740, 1748
Robert de Brunne, 461
Robert of Chester (XII-1), v. 2, *175*, 1223; v. 3, 166, 1378
Robert de Chingale, 1245
Robert de Clari (XIII-1), v. 2, *671*, 525, 670
Robert le Coq, 1024
Robert Cowton, 558
Robert of Cricklade (XII-2), v. 2, *426*, 47, 304
Robert of Eglesfield, 474
Robert the Englishman (XIII-2), v. 2, *993*, 1223; v. 3, 718, 722, 880
Robert of Geneva, 1032, 1335
Robert of Gloucester, 1310
Robert of Graystanes, 560
Robert of Greatham, 334
Robert Grosseteste (XIII-1), v. 2, *583*, 1223; v. 3, 64, 91, 115, 146, 192, 193, 369, 462, 551, 951, 1111, 1310, 1431, 1493
Robert de Handlo (XIV-1), *741*, 160
Robert of Holcot (XIV-1), *559*, 82, 92, 117, 456, 560
Robert Kilwardby (XIII-2), v. 2, *949*, 1224; v. 3, 331, 1003
Robert Machin, 183
Robert Mannyng (XIV-1), *461*, 68, 92, 302, 349, 463, 941, 1314, 1842
Robert of Namur, 1751
Robert of Naples, the Wise, *see* Robert of Anjou
Robert Payne, 1428
Roberto da Porta of Bologna, 1812
Robert de Reading (XIV-1), *944*, 303
Robert de' Rossi, 1822
Robert da Senigallia, 1245
Robert of Sorbon (XIII-2), v. 2, *863*, 725, 738
Robert of Torigny (XII-2), v. 2, *455*, 1224
Robert, Ulysse, 1739
Robert Valturio, 1550, 1552
Robert of York, 117, 178
Roberts, Laurence, 181
Roberts, Lloyd, 495
Robertson, J. D., 1902
Roberval, 1566
Robigalia, 238
Robin Hood, 1279
Robinson, F. N., 1204, 1424
Robinson, J. H., 514
Robinson, William, 289
Rocca, Luigi, 494, 502
Roccabonella, *see* Nicholas
Rocciamelone, 1628
Roch, St., 1246, 1659
Rochas, Victor de, 279, 281
Rochester, *see* Haymo
Rock, J. F., 1851
rockets, 1551
Rockhill, W. W., 810, 1625
Rockinger, Ludwig, 333, 993
Rodd, Rennell, 949
Rodenberg, Julius, 1337
Rodez, *see* Mordecai b. Joshua; Violas
Rodgers, E. C., 1043
Rodianus, 166
Rodier, Georges, 149
Rodington, *see* John
Rodocanachi, Emmanuel, 924, 1810
Rodolph, *see also* Raoul
Rodolph Agricola, 1360
Rodolph II of Bavaria, 1706
Rodolph of Bruges (XII-1), v. 2, *177*, 1225
Rodolph Dier van Muiden, 1361
Rodolph of Frameinsberg (XIV-1), *789*, 192
Rodolph of Hapsburg, 575, 576
Rodolph, magister, 853
Rodolph Schwenninger, 888
Rodrigo Jiménez de Rada (XIII-1), v. 2, *675*, 526; v. 3, 299, 342
Roeder, Fritz, 232
Röder, Kurt, 757
Röding, Anna, 815
Ro'eh, *see* Joseph b. Abraham
Röer, E., 1369
Röhricht, Reinhold, 769, 771, 789, 1902
Roersch, Alphonse, 476
Rofe, or Rophe, *see* Joseph b. a. Ayyūb; Judah b. Jehiel
Roger Bacon (XIII-2), v. 2, *952*, 1224; v. 3, 79, 91, 115, 141, 146, 147, 148, 166, 193, 287, 320, 367, 369, 375, 397, 410, 552, 562, 602, 705, 707, 722, 731, 750, 951, 1052, 1111, 1325, 1442, 1505, 1540, 1808, 1869
Roger Clerk of Wandsworth, 1204
Roger de Flor, 925
Roger of Hereford (XII-2), v. 2, *404*, 1224
Roger de Heyton, 1204
Roger of Howden (XII-2), v. 2, *457*, 1224
Roger, *see* Peter
Roger de Ropford, 144, 718
Roger of Salerno (XII-2), v. 2, *435*, 1224; v. 3, 222, 244, 272, 339, 883, 1375, 1683, 1708
Roger II of Sicily (XII-1), v. 2, *191*, 1224
Roger of Wendover (XIII-1), v. 2, *676*, 1224
Rogers, B. B., 1495
Rogers, J. E. T., 284
Rohlfs, Gerhard, 583
Roi, Jacques, 1835
Roland, *see also* Orlando
Roland of Armagh, 558
Roland of Breda, 1395
Roland-Cabaton, M. A., 1879
Roland, *see* Chanson
Roland of Parma (XIII-1), v. 2, *653*, 1224; v. 3, 272, 883

Roland of Tongres, 1257, 1395
Roland Van den Dorpe, 347
Rolandino of Padua (XIII-2), v. 2, *1105*, 793
Rolandino de' Rolandi, 847
Rolbiecki, J. J., 499
Rolfe, H. W., 514
Rolland, Eugène, 488
Rolle, *see* Richard
Rolleston, J. D., 1426
Roman, *see* astronomy; itineraries; law; medicine; numerals
Roman de charité, 1275
Roman de la rose, 52, 90, 532, 1077, 1090, 1298, 1414, 1418
Romanesque art (XII-1), v. 2, *162*, 112, 334
Romano, *see* Eccelino
Romano, G., 847
Romano, S. M., 845
Romanoff, Paul, 792
Romans, Epistle to, 193
Romberch, Johann, 537
Rome, 1247
Rome, Adolphe, ix, 1439
Rome, *see* Cyriacus; Giles; Immanuel b. Solomon
Rome, Stations, 1150
Rome, University, 72, 375, 470
Romein, Jan, 938
Romocki, S. J. v., 726
Romsey, *see* Thomas
Romuald, St., 395
Romuald of Salerno (XII-2), v. 2, *451*, 313, 434
Rondeau, Philippe, 218
Ronsard, 516
Ronto Matteo, 482
Ronzoni, Cirillo, 444
Roosevelt, Theodore, 1631
root, square, approximation, 586
rope trick, 1491, 1621
Ropford, *see* Roger
Rophe, *see* Rofe
Roquemaure, *see* Moses b. Samuel
Roques, Mario, 332, 345, 453, 1310
Roquetaillade, *see* John
Rorez, L., 771
Rorimer, J. J., 336
Rosa anglica, 880
Rosa medicinae, 880
Rosarius, 752, 1573
Rosarius, *see* Gregorio
Roscelin of Compiègne (XI-2), v. 1, *749*, 739, 745; v. 2, 120, 194; v. 3, 81, 552
Roscher, Wilhelm, 1494, 1495
Rose, H. A., 425, 1476, 1875, 1902
Rosenberg, Bernhard, 1361
Rosenberg, Judah, 614
Rosenmüller, E. F. C., 1459
Rosenthal, Erwin, 1778
Rosenzweig-Schwannau, Vincenz v., 1458
Rosinus, 166
Roskoff, Gustav, 1051
Roslin, *see* T'oros
Rosmini, Carlo de', 1292
Ross, E. D., 465, 1084, 1902
Rossell, *see* Nicholas
Rossetti, D. G., 493, 983
Rossetti, Domenico de', 1810
Rossi, B. de, 592
Rossi, Bastiano de', 815
Rossi, Giovanni, 501
Rossi, Luigi, 1798
Rossi, *see* Robert
Rossi, Vittorio, 513
Rossi-Casè, Luigi, 1814
Rossyn, *see* Francis
Rostagno, Enrico, 493, 512
Rostock, *see* Bernard
Rosweyde, Heribert, 292
Rotario, *see* Boniface
rotation of crops, 227, 1180
Rotenberg, *see* Conrad
Roth, Cecil, 1845
Roth, Emanuel, 1198
Roth, F. W. E., 789, 1509
Roth, Rudolf, 1368
Rothenburg, *see* Meïr b. Baruch
Rothschild, 1137
Rothwell, Fred, 582
Rotours, Robert des, 1084
Roubaix, *see* Michael
Roucliffe, *see* Daniel
Rouffaer, G. P., 1627
Roumanille, Joseph, 1303
Rous, *see* Adam
Roussat, Richard, 845
Rousseau, Alphonse, 807
Roussillon, 1211
Roussines, *see* John
Routh, E. M. G., 1863
Rovira i Virgili, A., 862, 1902
Rubertis, *see* Dionysius
Rubin, Walter, 1845
Rubió i Lluch, Antonio, 300, 1902
Rublev, *see* Andrew
Rubruquis, *see* William
Rucherath, *see* John
Rudbeck, Olof, 370
rudder, 157
Rudianus, 166
Rudolf, Rudolph, *see* Rodolph
Rudolph, R. C., 1870
Rülein v. Kalbe, 1174
Ruelle, C. A., 1877
Ruellius, J., 891
Ruffini, *see* Catherine
Ruffini Avondo, Edoardo, 989
Ruffini-Horner procedure, 140
Ruffo, *see* Jordan

Rufus of Ephesus (II-1), v. 1, *281*, 828; v. 2, 76; v. 3, 843, 1205, 1650
Rufus, W. C., 1533, 1538, 1866
Rugby College, 1403
Ruhāwī, *see* Ayyūb
Ruhräh, John, 1884
Ruisseau, *see* Raoul
rukhkh, 1621
Rulman Merswin, 574
Rūmī, *see* Jalāl al-dīn Muḥammad; Qāḍī Zāde
Runes, D. D., 542
runes, 1155, 1867
runic alphabet, 351, 1609
runic inscription, 196, 1609
runic numbers, 1610
runicus, Codex, 1610
Runtinger, 125
Rupenian dynasty, 54
Rupescissa, *see* John
Ruprecht v. Freising (XIV-1), *993*, 319, 351
Ruprecht v. der Pfalz, 1555
Ruralia commoda, 811
Ruscelli, Girolamo, 1808
Rushaid, b., *see* Muḥammad b. 'Umar
Rushd, b., *see* 'Abdallāh b. Muḥammad
Rushd, Muḥammad b. Aḥmad b. (XII-2), v. 2, *355*, 1225; v. 3, 61, 62, 65, 67, 83, 87, 98, 99, 101, 128, 208, 211, 240, 242, 246, 264, 274, 428, 432, 433, 434, 435, 443, 450, 461, 487, 489, 508, 518, 519, 529, 535, 543, 551, 557, 563, 590, 591, 594, 603, 607, 609, 704, 836, 870, 966, 1074, 1097, 1109, 1211, 1221, 1229, 1235, 1374, 1381, 1431, 1448, 1451, 1490, 1521, 1522, 1640, 1698, 1718, 1719, 1775, 1768, 1815, 1901. *See also* Averroism
Rusio, *see* Laurence
Ruska, J., 165, 166, 431, 498, 752, 757, 759, 829, 1138, 1175, 1426, 1534, 1576, 1578, 1728
Ruskin, John, 1163, 1842
Russell, A. D., 1455
Russell, Bertrand, 518
Russian, 32, 356
Russian Chronicles (XII-2), v. 2, *458*, 273
Rusta, b., *see* Aḥmad b. 'Umar
Rustichelli, *see* Peter Torrigiano
Rustichello of Pisa, 345, 346
rusticus, 273
Rutebeuf, 249, 943
Rutherford, A., 943
rutters, 1834
Ruxton, F. H., 1455
Ruyelle, *see* William
Ruys, H. J. A., 1607
Ruysbroeck, *see* John
Ryckmans, Gonzague, 1118
Rydquist, J. E., 352

S'a-mar, 1371
S'a-ser, 1371
Saadia b. Joseph, Gaon (X-1), v. 1, *627*, 620, 623; v. 2, 1225; v. 3, x, 365, 367, 590, 592, 792, 1008, 1062
Sā'ātī, b., *see* Riḍwān b. Muḥammad
Saba', kingdom, 1779
Sābā, Mār, 305
Sabbadini, Remigio, 1289, 1292, 1408, 1818, 1902
Sabbadini, S., 491
Ṣabbāḥ, b., 163
Sabbas of Servia, St. (XIII-1), v. 2, *639*, 35, 512; v. 3, 1853
Sabbioneta, *see* Gerald
Sabdapradīpa, 1730
Sabellios of Libya, 588
Sābī, *see* Hilāl b. Muḥsin
Sabians, 800, 1460
Sab'īn, b., *see* 'Abd al-Ḥaqq b. Ibrāhīm
sabot, 450
Sabuncuoğlu, 1216
Sābūr b. Sahl (IX-2), v. 1, *608*, 587; v. 2, 84, 234; v. 3, 1235
sābūrqān, 1175
Sacatophoros, *see* Nicetas
Sacchetti, *see* Franco
sacerdotum, Liber, 165, 1834
Sachau, E. C., 1584, 1832
Sachsenspiegel, 319, 351, 993
Sacramentale, 991
Sacrobosco, John (XIII-1), v. 2, *617*, 1190; v. 3, 66, 112, 118, 399, 501, 548, 718, 722, 819, 1074, 1106, 1109, 1112, 1114, 1117, 1382, 1426, 1430, 1433, 1490, 1501, 1565, 1566, 1846
Sacy, Silvestre de, 200
Sa'd b. Aḥmad b. Luyūn (XIV-1), *827*, 209, 228, 373, 1850
Sa'd al-dīn of Warāmīn, 1272
Sa'd b. Manṣūr b. Kammūna (XIII-2), v. 2, *875*, 1192
Sa'd, b., *see* Muḥammad
Sa'd b. a. Waqqāṣ, 1587
Ṣa'da, 102, 1264
Sa'dān, a., 128, 433
Ṣadaqa b. Ibrāhīm Shādhilī (XIV-2), *1723*, 899, 1214, 1235
Ṣadaqa b. Munaja' Dimashqī (XIII-1), v. 2, *666*, 1225; v. 3, 1213
Saddhammasaṅgaha, 1371
Saddhānanda, Nedimāle, 1371
Saddharmālaṅkāra, 1370
Saddharmapuṇḍarīka, 311
Sade, J. F. de, 514
Sa'dī (XIII-2), v. 2, *872*, 1225; v. 3, 626, 1328, 1457, 1463, 1621
Sa'di, Luṭfī M., 1463
Ṣadr al-dīn 'Alī, 134
Ṣadr al-Sharī'a al-awwal, 628
Ṣadr al-Sharī'a al-thānī (XIV-1), *628*, 106, 135, 1462

Sächsische Weltchronik, 1756
Saegusa, Hiroto, 1832
Saeki, P. Y., 54, 298, 358
Saemundarson, *see* Nicholas
Saewulf (XII-1), v. 2, *223*, 1226
Ṣafadī, *see* Aḥmad b. Yūsuf; Ḥasan b. ʻAbdallāh; Khalīl b. Aibak
Safar-nāma, 376
Ṣafawī dynasty, 420
Ṣafawīya, 57, 420
Ṣaffār, b., *see* Aḥmad b. ʻAbdallāh
saffron, 1183
Ṣafī al-dīn, *see* ʻAbd al-Mu'min b. Faqīr
Ṣafī al-dīn Ḥillī, 749
Ṣafī al-dīn, shaikh, 420
ṣafīḥa, 1515
sagas, 194, 352
Ṣāghānī, *see* Aḥmad b. Muḥammad; Ḥasan b. Muḥammad
Sagres, 1140, 1141
Sahara, 764, 1875
Sahdā, b. (IX-1), v. 1, *573*, 547
Ṣaḥīḥ, 1065
Sahl b. Abān (XII-1), v. 2, *221*, 1226
Sahl b. Bishr (IX-1), v. 1, *569*, 828; v. 2, 1226; v. 3, 501
Sahl Masīḥī, a., *see* ʻĪsā b. Yaḥyā
Sahl b. Maẓliah (X-2), v. 1, *690*, 653, 655; v. 3, 365
Sahl Ṭabarī (IX-1), v. 1, *565*, 545, 549
Sahlender, P. M., 1630
Sa'īd ʻAfīf, a., *see* ʻAfīf b. a. Surūr
Ṣā'id b. Aḥmad b. Ṣā'id Andalusī (XI-2), v. 1, *776*, 810; v. 3, 1263, 1620
Sa'īd b. Biṭrīq, *see* Eutychios
Sa'īd Ḍarīr Jurjānī, a. (IX-1), v. 1, *562*, 545, 550
Sa'īd b. Hibatallāh (XI-2), v. 1, *772*, 742, 746; v. 2, 68
Sa'īd Maghribī, b., *see* ʻAlī b. Mūsā
Ṣā'id, b., *see* Ṣā'id b. Aḥmad
Sa'īd, a., *see* ʻUbaidallāh b. Jibrīl
Sa'īd b. Ya'qūb, a. ʻUthmān (X-1), v. 1, *631*, 620, 622; v. 2, 341
Ṣaidana fī-l-ṭibb, 105
Sa'īdī, *see* ʻAlī b. ʻAbd al-Raḥmān
Sa'īdī dialect, 361
Sainson, Camille, 978
Saint. For saints, see under their names; but in place names and surnames, Saint is written out. For example, (the man) Louis, St.; (the place) Saint Louis.
Saint Albans, *see* John
Saint Amand, *see* Hucbald; John
Saint Amour, *see* William
Saint Catherine's College, 1402
Saint Cher, *see* Hugh
Saint Cloud, *see* William
Saint Denis, *see* Primat; Rigord; Suger
Saint Denys, *see* John
Saint Flour, *see* Peter
Saint-Gilles, *see* Martin
Saint-Lager, Dr., 872
Saint Martin, Léandre de, 399
Saint Omer, *see* Lambert; Peter
Saint Paul, *see* John
Saint Peter, *see* Peter de Sant Pere
Saint Pol, *see* Guy; Mary
Saint Pourçain, *see* Durand
Saint Saviour in Chora, *see* Saviour, Saint
Saint Saviour, order of, 1036, 1355
Saint Victor, *see* Geoffrey; Hugh; Richard; Thomas
Sainte-Beuve, 1753
Saintré, *see* Petit Jehan
saints, 292, 1041, 1864
saints, cult, 421
saints, diseases named after, 1411
saints, Orthodox, 1853
Saintyves, P., 1045, 1124, 1230, 1902
Śaiva, 383, 1366
Śaiva yōga, 1475
Sajāwandī, 1461
Sakharov, J. P., 791, 1613
Sakkākī, *see* Yūsuf b. a. Bakr
Saksena, R. B., 1477
Śakti, 1070
Sala, *see* Antonius
sāla, 1835
Saladin, *see* Ṣalāḥ al-dīn
Salado de Tarifa, 38, 344
Ṣalāḥ al-dīn of Ankara, 1215
Ṣalāḥ al-dīn, physician, translator, 1077, 1240
Ṣalāḥ al-dīn, poet (XIV-2), *1464*, 1100, 1119, 1328
Ṣalāḥ al-dīn Saghīr, 173
Ṣalāḥ al-dīn, Saladin, 793, 1601
Ṣalāḥ, b., *see* ʻUthmān b. Ṣalāḥ
Ṣalāḥ al-dīn b. Yūsuf, oculist (XIII-2), v. 2, *1102*, 1226
Salāmā (XIV-1), *437*, 62, 362
Salāma b. Mubārak b. Raḥmūn (XII-1), v. 2, *190*, 119, 134
Salamanca, University, 375
Salamiellas, *see* John Álvarez
Salazaro, Demetrio, 168
Salbray, De, 1750
Salebruche, *see* Simon of Sarrebruck
Salem Latin, *see* algorism
salernitanum, *see* Chronicon; Compendium
Salerno, 247, 266, 579, 840, 1242, 1885, 1900 1901
Salerno, *see* Alphanus; Archimatthaeus; Bartholomew; Copho; Maurus; Moses b. Solomon; Nicholas; Petronius; Richard; Roger; Romuald; Salernus; Zacharias
Salerno, anatomy, first demonstration (XII-1) v. 2, *237;* second demonstration (XII-1) v. 2, *238*, 1226

Salerno, school of (XI-1), v. 1, *725*, 828; (XII-2), v. 2, *351*, 1226
Salernus of Salerno (XII-1), v. 2, *240*, 1226
Saletore, B. A., 41
Ṣalībā b. Yūḥannā, 55, 306, 956
Saliceto, *see* William
Ṣāliḥ b. 'Abd al-Ḥalīm, 957
Ṣāliḥ b. Ḥusain a. Baqā (XIII-1), v. 2, *557*, 490
Ṣāliḥ b. Thāmir Ja'barī, 1529
Ṣāliḥ Zekī, 1902
Salimbene Andreoli, 1134
Salimbene of Parma (XIII-2), v. 2, *1105*, 1227; v. 3, 481, 1650
Salio of Padua (XIII-1), v. 2, *562*, 1227
Salisbury, 39
Salisbury, *see* Catherine; John
salivation caused by mercury, 289, 871
Saljūq, 40, 104, 379
Salkind, I. M., 1382
Sallāmī, *see* Muḥammad b. Rāfi'
Sallet, Albert, 1176
Sallust (I-2 B.C.), v. 1, *231*, 828; v. 3, 298, 912, 919, 1294, 1482
Salmānī, *see* Muḥammad b. 'Abdallāh
Salmawaih b. Bunān (IX-1), v. 1, *573*, 547, 549
salmiac, 754
Salmon, A. A., 269
Salmon, U. J., 269
Salmony, Alfred, 1030
Salomon, Richard, 182, 455, 768, 820
Salonica, 996, 1387, 1905
Salonica (Thessalonica), *see* Cyril; Leo; Solomon b. Elijah
Salsette, island, 783
Salso, Albertino Rainoldi
Ṣalt, a., *see* Umaiya b. 'Abd al-'Azīz
salt, 181
salt gabelle, 761
salt, manufacture, 761
salt, mining, 797
salt of the sea, 800, 1163, 1670
Saltel, J., 1237
Saltonstall, Gurdon, 364, 1508
saltpeter, 722
Salus vitae, 100, 451
Salutati, *see* Coluccio; Peter
Sālva, 1730
Salvati, *see* John
Salvemini, Gaetano, 497, 1794
Salvetti, *see* Angelo
Salvini, A. M., 1810
Salzburg, *see* Virgil
samā' wa-raqṣ, 422
Samakantha, Hitavrata, 1369
Sam'ānī, *see* 'Abd al-Karīm b. Muḥammad
Samannūd, *see* Yūḥannā, anbā
Samanta-kūṭāvaṇṇanā, 423
Samarqand, 174, 794, 1026, 1101, 1119, 1470, 1473
Samarqandī, *see* 'Abd al-Razzāq b. Isḥāq; 'Aṭā' b. Aḥmad; Muḥammad b. 'Alī; Muḥammad b. Ashraf; b. Zuhr
Sāmaśramī, Satyavrata, 1369
Sāmaveda, 1369
Sāmaveda saṃhitā, 1369
Sāmavidhānabrāhmaṇa, 1369
Śaṁbhudāsa, 465
Samer, *see* Peter
Samḥ, b., *see* Aṣbagh b. Muḥammad
Sāṃkhya, 1366
Sammāsī, *see* Muḥammad Bābā
Samoyed languages, 1825
Sampson, *see* Thomas
Samson, Heinrich, 292
Samson b. Solomon (XIV-1), *428*, 61, 254
Samuel, A. M., 823
Samuel Abravanel, 1444
Samuel of Ānī (XII-2), v. 2, *448*, 313, 1117
Samuel Astruc d'Escola, 1520
Samuel Benveniste (XIV-1), *451*, 65, 255, 1841
Samuel, books of (VII B.C.), v. 1, *63*
Samuel Esperial (XIV-2), *1717*, 1211, 1233, 1305
Samuel Foto of Mistra, 1516
Samuel b. Jacob of Capua (XIII-2), v. 2, *854*, 1227
Samuel b. Joseph ha-Levi (XI-1), v. 1, *704*, 694, 701; v. 3, 366
Samuel b. Judah of Marseille (XIV-1), *433*, 61, 62, 98, 128, 590, 609
Samuel b. Judah b. Tibbon (XIII-1), v. 2, *564*, 1227; v. 3, 366, 434, 435, 592, 603, 1451
Samuel ha-Levi Abulafia (XIII-2), v. 2, *843*, 1227
Samuel, Mar (III-1), v. 1, *318*, 817
Samuel Marocanus, 418
Samuel b. Meïr (XII-1), v. 2, *189*, 1227; v. 3, 398, 599
Samuel b. Sa'adia b. Moṭoṭ (XIV-2), *1375*, 1072, 1096, 1364
Samuel b. Samson (XIII-1), v. 2, *643*, 35, 514
Samuel b. Sanah b. Ẓarẓa, 895, 1364, 1376, 1515
Samuel b. Simeon Kansi (XIV-2), *1520*, 1116, 1516
Samuel b. Solomon ha-Me'ati (XIV-1), *437*, 62, 256
Samuel b. Waqar (XIV-1), *894*, 199, 256
Samū'īl b. Yaḥyā b. 'Abbās (XII-2), v. 2, *401*, 1227; v. 3, 418, 596
Samura, b., *see* 'Umar b. 'Alī
San Concordio, *see* Bartholomew
San Genesio, *see* Beltrando
San Gimignano, *see* John
San Miniato, *see* John
San Spirito, 294, 1838
Ṣan'ā, 102, 1215, 1264

Sanad b. 'Alī (IX-1), v. 1, *566*, 828; v. 2, 126, 128
Sanah, b., *see* Samuel
Sanā'ī, 626
Śānāq, 431, 1773
Sanatis, *see* James
Ṣanbāṭī, *see* Muḥammad b. 'Abd al-Ṣamad
Sancho IV of Castile, 401
Sancho I o Povoador, 343
Sancho VI el Sabio (XII-2), v. 2, *427*, 1227; v. 3, 1630
Sancta Beata, *see* Peter
Sand, George, 1141
Sandbach, F. E., 1605
Sanderlin, George, 1423
Sanders, J. H., 1474
Sandwych, *see* Nicholas
Sandys, J. E., 1902
Saṅgama, 41
Sāngatya, 1730
saṅgharāja, 1370
Šangin, M. A. F., 1878
Sanguinetti, B. R., 1595, 1622
Ṣanhāja (Ṣinhāja), 708, 1009
ṣāni', 154
sanitate, Pro conservanda, 531
sanitatis custodia, De, 855
sanitatis, *see* Regimen; regimina
Sañjaya, 1077, 1330, 1396
Śaṅkara (IX-1), v. 1, *561*, 828; v. 2, 826; v. 3, 569, 571, 1102, 1366
Śaṅkaradigvijaya, 1366
Śaṅkarasvāmin, 465
Sanskrit, 380, 382, 383, 385, 1896, 1899, 1901, 1904, 1909
Sanskrit literature, 1883, 1891
Sansom, G. B., 1018
Sansovino, Francesco, 955, 1808
Sant Fahagun, *see* John
Sant Pere, *see* Peter
Santa Casa, 1043
Santa Fé, *see* Francis
Santa María, *see* Gonzalo; Joan; Paul
Santa Sofia family, 1243, 1681
Santa Sofia, *see* Bartholomew; Galeazzo; John; Marsiglio; Nicholas; William
Santalla, *see* Hugh
Sante Ardoino of Pesaro, 1679
Sante Ferrari, 445
Santeler, Josef, 522
Santiago de Compostela, 343
Śāntideva (VII-2), v. 1, *490*, 488, 490
Santillana, David, 1455
Santino, 1552
Santo Antonio Moura, José, 958, 1622
Santo Stefano, *see* Jerome
Santorio, Santorio, 1220
Sanudo, *see* Marc; Marino
Sanvisenti, Bernardo, 516, 1811
Sapegno, Natalino, 1903
Sapienza, 470
saporibus, De, 834
Sapta-kāṇḍa kṛitti-vāsarāmāyaṇa, 1396
Saqaṭī, *see* Muḥammad; Muḥammad b. a. Muḥammad
Sarābī, b. (XII-1), v. 2, *229*, 1229; v. 3, 816, 870, 898, 1205
Sarāfyūn, *see* Yaḥyā
Saragossa, 1379
Saragossa, *see* Anthony Augustine; Baḥya b. Asher; Stephen
Sarakhsī, *see* Aḥmad b. Muḥammad
sarāwīl al-futūwa, 154
Sarepta, *see* Thomas
Sarezana, *see* Ventura
ṣārim al-maslūl, 422
Sarker, E., 594
Sarkis, J. E., 1903
Sarkis of Sunik, 1441
Sarkis, vartabed, 1761
Sarnana, *see* Gaspar
Sarnano, cardinal, 529
Sarnano, *see* Marc Sinzanogio
Śārṅgadhara (XIII-1), v. 2, *667*, 1228
Sarra, Raffaele, 498
Sarradin, Amédée, 1412
Sarrazin, *see* John
Sarre, F., 757
Sarrebruck, *see* Simon
Sarti, Mauro, 839, 841, 1680
Sarton, Mrs. G., 795
Sarton, G., 1858, 1868, 1903
Sarum, 943
Saruq, *see* Menahem b. Jacob
Sarvadarśanasaṃgraha, 1366, 1368, 1584
Sasagawa, Tomooki, 906
Sasanian, 376
Sassoferrato, *see* Bàrtolo
Sastri, K. A. N., 1624
Sastri, Sivanath, 1476
Sastry, K. R. R., 155
Satan, trials of, 1794
Śatananda (XII-1), v. 2, *212*, 127
Satanow, Isaac b. Moses, 1384, 1826
Śatapathabrāhmaṇa, 1369
Satchell, Thomas, 1165
Sathas, Constantino, 952
Sāṭi'u bey al-Ḥuṣrī, 1777
Saturn, 444, 1489, 1529
sauces, 834
saüdade, 343
Saul b. Boṭnit, 1365
Ṣauma, b. (XIII-2), v. 2, *1068*, 1228; v. 3, 358, 956
Saussure, Léopold de, 1833
Sauvaget, Jean, 1787
Sauvaire, H. J., 713. 1528, 1787
Sava, St., 1853
Savage, E. A., 1903
Saval, *see* John

Savastano, Luigi, 815
Savi, *see* Dominic
Savi, V., 780
saviesa, Llibre de, 342
Savignone, *see* Andalò
Savigny, F. K. v., 1794, 1796, 1903
Saville, 374
Saviour in Chora, Saint, 97, 684, 687, 950
Saviour, Saint, order, *see* Saint Saviour
Savonarola, *see* Jerome; John Micaele
Savoy, *see* Louise
Savskan, Judah, 618
Sawīrus b. al-Muqaffa', 1830
Sawles warde, 463
Sawtrey, *see* William
Saxl, Fritz, 1903
Saxo Grammaticus (XIII-1), v. 2, *677*, 1228
Saxony, *see* Arnold; Henry; John; Ludolf
Sayābija, 1624
Sāyaṇa (XIV-2), *1368*, 1069, 1330, 1366
ṣayd, 234
Ṣayd-nāma-i-Malik Shāhī, 233
ṣayd al-samak, 234
Saye, Hymen, 1695
Sayer, E. P., 493
Sayili, Aydin M., 29, 104, 264, 293, 379, 706, 709, 972, 1014, 1217, 1248, 1726
Sayyid al-Ajall, 1071
Sbigněw Olešnický, 1816
Sbrunen, *see* Margaret
scabies, *see* itch
scala, 1006
Scala, della, *see* Bartholomew; Can Grande; Mastino
Scala cronica, 1746
scala naturae, 212, 1168
Scale of perfection, 1314, 1415
Scaliger, 444
Scaligeri, 480, 922, 1600
Scalinci, Noè, 859
Scandinavian, 351
Scandinavian antiquities, 1901
Scandinavian, *see* astronomy
Scandinavian expeditions to White Sea (XIII-1), v. 2, *638*
Scandinavian exploration of North America (XIV-2), *1608*
Scarabelli, Luciano, 1814
scarabs, 1187
Scarparia, *see* Angeli; James d'Angelo; James
Scarperia, *see* William
Scarpini, Modesto, 499
Scartazzini, Giovanni Andrea, 494, 495
Scellinck, *see* Thomas
scenography, 1105
Schacht, Joseph, 734, 1455, 1781
Schacht, Theodor, 931
Schaeder, H. H., 1470
Schäfer, Godeh, 170
Schäfer, K. H., 252, 1245
Schaefer, R. J., 851
Schanazarian, G., 1260
Schannat, J. F., 887
Schard, Simon, 989, 992, 1820
Schedel, *see* Hartmann; Herman
Scheeben, H. C., 1340
Scheffer, Hans, 286
Scheffer, J. E., 854
Scheffer-Boichorst, Paul, 913, 915
Scheiner, Christopher, 1856
Schelenz, Hermann, 1903
Scheler, Auguste, 1747, 1749, 1753
Schetelig, Haakon, 194
Schiltberger, *see* John
Schilter, Joh., 1757
Schirow, Ludwig, 275
Schirrmacher, F. W., 1736
Schism, Great, 1020, 1033
Schlauch, Margaret, 1864
Schlippacher, *see* John
Schloessinger, Max, 435, 1096, 1376, 1452
Schlosser, Max, 1187
Schlumberger, Gustave, 300, 1824
Schmalzl, Peter, 1903
Schmelzer, Heinrich, 515
Schmidt, Carl, 571, 572
Schmidt, Nathaniel, 1778
Schmidt, Richard, 1810
Schmidt, Robert, 171
Schmidt, Wilhelm, 1747
Schmitt, John, 949, 1513
Schmitz, L., 1351
Schmoelders, August, 435
Schmutzer, Richard, 284
Schnabel, Christian, 1010
Schneegans, Louis, 1756
Schneider, Frederick, 493, 497, 934
Schneider, J. G., 1534
Schneider, J. P., 567
Schneider, K. E. C., 513
Schneider, Marius, 743
Schneider, Philipp, 820
Schneider, Rudolf, 726
Schneider, Theophora, 570
Schnell, Eugen, 567
Schniewind, C. O., 1564, 1659
Schnyder, Werner, 153
Schöffler, Herbert, 1203
Schön, Th., 742
Schönbach, *see* John
Schöne, Hermann, 447, 448
Schoenfelder, *see* John
Schoenstedt, Friedrich, 1275
Schoepff, F. G. P., 1361, 1363
Schöppler, Hermann, 252, 820, 1241
Schötter, Johann, 1836
Schofield, W. H., 1741
Schola Anglorum, 294
Schola Saxonum, 294
Scholarios, *see* George

scholars, poor, 1403, 1863
Scholem, Gerhard, 611, 1521
Scholz, Richard, 555, 767, 820, 986, 989
Schomerus, H. W., 571
schools, 1893
schools, cathedral and monastic, 1080
schools, chantry, 1079
schools, grammar, 477
schools, public, 1079, 1403
Schoonhoven, *see* John
Schopen, J., 952
Schopen, Ludwig, 1761
Schopenhauer, 1385
Schott, Albert, 1756
Schottmüller, Konrad, 395
Schoy, Carl, 136, 1526, 1530
Schreger, Odilo, 822
Schreiber, *see* Henry
Schreiber, Manfred, 1676
Schrieke, B., 490
Schrödinger, Erwin, 1844
Schroeter, J. F., 1903
Schrutz, Andreas, 1715
Schub, Pincus, 1117
Schubring, Walther, 1584
Schück, Albert, 716
Schueren, *see* Gerald
Schulhof, Hilda, 925
Schulz, Fritz, 1796
Schulz, H. C., 1415
Schulz, Hugo, 820
Schum, Wilhelm, 876
Schupart, J. G., 618
Schuster, Julius, 225
Schutte, Alois, 1756
Schutz, A. H., 339, 1835
Schwab, Moïse, 1826
Schwabacher, C. H., 594
Schwabenspiegel (XIII-2), v. 2, *1131*, 1228; v. 3, 351, 931
Schwartz, Ida, 913
Schwarz, Ignaz, 1195
Schwarz, Israel, 792
Schwarz, Joseph, 791
Schwarz, Richard, 575
Schweinfurth, Philipp, 1583
Schwenninger, *see* Rodolph
Schwind, Oskar, 1693
Sciarra Colonna, 536
science, Arabic, 21, 1895
science, Byzantine, 1880
science, Catalan, 1896
science, *see* classification
science, Egyptian, 1773
science, *see* humanity
science, Japanese, 1832, 1903
sciences, hundred, 1101
"sciences, seven," 611
scientia scientiarum, 77
Scipio Africanus, major, 506
Scire te volumus, 408
Scola, *see* Schola
Scopoli, *see* Filippino
scorpions, 1621, 1640, 1671
Scotists, 84
Scott, F. R., 1426
Scott, H. H., 929, 1787
Scott, W., 1228, 1752
Scott-Moncrieff, P. D., 55
screws, 718
Scribonius Largus (I-1), v. 1, *241*, 235, 236
script (vs. language), 359
Scriptores rei rusticae, 813
scrofulas, 892
Scrope, *see* Stebin
Scudder, V. D., 1337
sculpture from living model, 1256
scurvy, 928
Scylax of Caryanda (V B.C.), v. 1, *104*, 83, 126
Scylitzes, *see* John
sea, depth, 1208
sea, descent into, 1519
sea, *see* salt
seal oil, 194
seals, engraved, *see* sphragistics
seals, use of, 1621
Seaton, Ethel, 1842
Sebaste, *see* Blase
Sebastian Brant, 1621
Sebastian, St., 1246, 1659
Sébillot, Paul, 221
Sēbōkht, *see* Severus
Sebonde, *see* Raymond
Secco Polentone, 918
Secondo Contarini, 539
secret names, alchemy, 1138
Secret, Petrarca's, 507
Secreta fidelium crucis, 769
Secreta mulierum, 268, 269, 548
Secreta secretorum (IX-1), v. 1, *556*, 136, 544; v. 3, 165, 339, 548, 1427
secrets aux philosophes, Livre des, 90, 346, 547
Secrets, *see* Segreti
Secretum philosophorum, 547
seculars, *see* regulars
Sedacer, *see* William
Sedacina totium alchimiae, 754, 1575
Seddon, J. P., 1426
Seeberg, Erich, 570
Seelmann, Wilhelm, 1232
Seemüller, Joseph, 931
sefirot, x, 613, 1450
Segreti per colori, 168
segullot, 451
Seibertz, Joh. Suibert, 1755
Seidel, Ernst, 269, 901, 1730
Seidler, Elise, 275
seigniorage, 1282
Seiler, Raphael, 1388

seismology, *see* earthquakes
Seitz, Josy, 571
sekel, 594
sekel ha-hayulani, 435
sekel veha-muskal, Ma'amar be-, 431
Selden, John, 1743
Seldes, Gilbert, 1048
Seleucos the Babylonian (II-1 B.C.), v. 1, *183*, 178
self-complacency, 22, 25
Selfe, R. E., 915
Selfridge, H. G., 126
Seligsohn, Max, 1444, 1452
Sella, Pietro, 290, 1793
Selmi, Francesco, 1815
Selvaggia Vergiolesi, 982
semantics, 83, 331
Semerau, Alfred, 1023
semina, 849
seminal forces, 981
Seminara, Bernard of, *see* Barlaam
seminis, de animatione, 1851
Semita, 179
Semita recta, 66, 754
Sempach, 1021
Sempringham, *see* Gilbert
Sen, D. C., 1396
Senart, E., 155
Seneca, Lucius Annaeus of Cordova (I-2), v. 1, *247*, 243, 245; v. 2, 1229; v. 3, 36, 65, 214, 346, 402, 507, 577, 873, 918, 942, 944, 990, 1075, 1144, 1171, 1221, 1288, 1357, 1391, 1418, 1434, 1490, 1808, 1811, 1813, 1815, 1816
Senegal river, 1158, 1159
Senigallia, *see* Robert
Senior, 166, 1426
Senn, Reinhard, 575
sensation, kinds, 1723
Sentences, books, 79, 400, 407, 516, 518, 519, 521, 522, 526, 527, 528, 530, 531, 533, 549, 551, 557, 558, 559, 577, 736, 738, 739, 992, 1085, 1095, 1440, 1503, 1843. *See also* Peter the Lombard
sententiarius, 79
Septuagint (III-1 B.C.), v. 1, *151*, 829; v. 3, 330, 353, 355, 356
sequins, 1282
Serafina, 921
Serapion of Alexandria (II-1 B.C.), v. 1, *186*, 178
Serapion the Elder, *see* Yaḥyā b. Sarāfyūn
Serapion, b., geographer (X-1), v. 1, *635*, 621; v. 3, xi
Serapion the Younger, *see* b. Sarābī
Ser'ata Mangest, 957
Serbia, *see* Stephen
Serenos (IV-1), v. 1, *353*, 345
Serenus Samonicus, Quintus (III-1), v. 1, *324*, 315
serfdom, 326, 1347
Sergios of Resaina (VI-1), v. 1, *423*, 829; v. 2, 87; v. 3, 357, 358
Sergius, St., 39
Sergius Vasciéntz, 460
sericulture, *see* silkworms
series, infinite, 737
series, summation, 1766
Serjeantson, Mary S., 1171
Sermoneta, *see* Alexander
serpente alchemico, De, 559
Serra, Renato, 336
Serrano, Luciano, 1862
Serres, Olivier de, 1597
Serrure, C. P., 1151
serṭō, 359
Sertorius, Q., 1397
Servet, Miguel, 267
Servites (XIII-1), v. 2, *551*, 487
Seta, *see* Lombardo
Seth, *see* Simeon
sevens, casting out, 1527
Sever map, St., 193
Sévérac, *see* Jordan Catala
Severs, J. B., 1426
Severus Sēbōkht (VII-2), v. 1, *493*, 829; v. 3, 358
Severyns, Albert, 1877
Sevillana medicina, 1379
Seville, Alcázar, 1021
Seville, *see* Isidore; John; Mas'ūd; Muḥammad b. Mu'ādh; Muḥammad Shalāḥī
Seward, A. C., 1835
Sewell, Robert, 41
sexagesimal, 113, 120, 122, 596, 1112, 1518
sexagesimal, *see* fractions
sexta, 716
Sextos Empiricos (II-2), v. 1, *299*, 289, 320
Sextus Iulius Africanus (III-1), v. 1, *327*; v. 2, 449
sexual impotence, 269, 527, 1246, 1247
sexuality, plants, 212, 417
sexuality, unborn child, 268
Seymour de Ricci, 1134
Shabbethai b. Abraham Donnolo (X-2), v. 1, *682*, 801; v. 2, 367, 368
Shabbethai b. Solomon, 603
Shabīb, b., *see* Aḥmad b. Ḥamdān
shadd, 154, 164
Shādhilī, *see* Aḥmad b. Muḥammad; 'Alī b. 'Abdallāh; Ṣadaqa b. Ibrāhīm
Shādhilīya, 1453, 1723, 1864
Shaḍviṃśabrāhmaṇa, 1369
Shadwell, C. L., 494
Shaffner, F. I., 1856
Shāfi'ī, *see* Muḥammad b. Idrīs
Shāfi'ī school, 1099
Shafra, *see* Muḥammad b. 'Alī
Shāh Rukh, 1260, 1292, 1459, 1468, 1469, 1473, 1855

Shah-i-Zinda, 1470
Shahin, *see* Nissim b. Jacob
Shāhnāma, 376, 631
Shahrastānī, *see* Muḥammad b. 'Abd al-Karīm
Shaibānī, *see* 'Abd al-Razzāq b. Aḥmad; Muḥammad b. Ḥasan
Shaikhī, 1464
Shaikhū, 1903
Shairazī, *mistake for* Shaizarī
Shaizarī, *see* 'Abd al-Raḥmān b. Naṣr
Shajara-i Tarākima, 104
Shakespeare, 456, 725, 925, 1152, 1736
Shakīb Arslān, 1777
Shākir Kutubī, b., *see* Muḥammad b. Shākir
Shākir b. Rāhib, a., 1006
Shakl al-qaṭṭā', 431
Shakta Hinduism, 1237
Shalāḥī, *see* Muḥammad; Muḥammad b. Ibrāhīm
Shāma, a., *see* 'Abd al-Raḥmān b. Ismā'īl
Shammā' Ḥalabī, b., 965
shams al-akbar, 760
Shams al-dīn Dhahabī, 1852
Shams al-dīn Mīrak, *see* Muḥammad b. Mubārakshāh
Shams al-dīn Ṣāliḥ, 748
Shams al-dīn 'Umar, Sayyid al-Ajall, 1587
Shanqĕlāwī, *see* Simeon
Shapruṭ, *see* Shem-ṭob b. Isaac
Shāpūr II, 376
Shaqūrī, *see* Muḥammad b. 'Alī
Sharaf al-dawla, Buwayhid sulṭān (X-2), v. 1, *659*, 830
Sharaf al-dīn b. 'Alī, 1216, 1248, 1328
Sharaf al-dīn 'Alī Yazdī, 1267, 1473
Sharaf of Urganj, 104
Sharma, Ramkrishna, 1585
Sharshot (or Sharsherot) kesef, 590
Shāstrī, Haraprasāda, 59
shatawīyāt, 803
Shāṭiba paper, 174
Shāṭir, *see* 'Alī b. Ibrāhīm
shaṭranj, 317, 1469
Shaw, G. B., 127, 1466
Shaw, J. E., 496
Shayyāl, J. M., 282
Shealtiel Gracian (or Ḥen), 1521
Shears, F. S., 1753
Shebile emunah, 1442
Shebile di Yerushalim, 793
Sheedy, A. T., 1795
She'elot, 442
she'elot u-teshubot, 1062
sheep, 1181. *See also* shepherdy
Sheldon, E. S., 496
Shelemyah of Lunel, 609
shell, chank, 380
Shelly, Percy Van Dyke, 347, 1425
Shemariah b. Elijah ha-Iqriṭi (XIV-1), *448*, 56, 64, 1365, 1379, 1450
Shem-ṭob b. Abraham b. Gaon (XIV-1), *612*, 100
Shem-ṭob b. Isaac b. Shapruṭ (XIV-2), *1385*, 1060, 1074, 1096, 1211, 1221, 1373, 1523
Shem-ṭob b. Isaac of Tortosa (XIII-2), v. 2, *845*, 1230; v. 3, 613, 1386
Shem-ṭob b. Joseph b. Falaquera (XIII-2), v. 2, *876*, 1230; v. 3, 431, 591, 610, 612
Shem-ṭob, *see* Joseph b. Shem-ṭob
Shem-ṭob b. Shem-ṭob, 605, 1096
Shene ha-meorot, 437
Shepard, Odell, 514'
Shepherd, William, 1292
shepherdy, 1164, 1181, 1631
Sheriff, Laurence, 1403
Sherira Gaon (X-2), v. 1, *687*, 830; v. 2, 368; v. 3, 357
Shesh kenafayim, 1517
Sheshet b. Isaac Benveniste (XII-2), v. 2, *431*, 1230; v. 3, 451
sheṭaḥ, 596
Shī'a, 106, 309, 965, 967, 1065, 1067, 1100
shifā', 1728
Shiḥna, b., *see* Muḥammad b. Muḥammad
Shikand-gūmānīg vījār (Škand-gumānīk vičār) (IX-2), v. 1, *591*; v. 3, 376
Shikār-nāma-i-Īlkhānī, 233
Shilson, J. W., 1182
shipholder, 818
ships, 1617
ships, Muslim, 1782
ships, Viking, 194
Shīrāz, 1456
Shīrāzī, *see* Maḥmūd b. Ilyās; Maḥmūd b. Mas'ūd Quṭb al-dīn
shirb (shurb), 154
Shirley, W. W., 1349
shirts, 276
Shīrwānī, *see* Muḥammad b. Maḥmūd
Shishmarev, V. F., 745
Sholal, *see* Isaac Kohen
shoreshim, 590
shrapnel, 1551
Shrī Sumangala, 423
Shryock, John K., 1281, 1855
Shu'aib b. Ḥasan Tilimsānī, 1764
Shubakī, *see* Jamāl al-dīn; Elijah b. Judah
Shuchirch, *see* William
Shudhūr al-dhahab, 754, 1012
Shuhba, b., *see* a. Bakr b. Aḥmad
Shujā' b. Aslam, a. Kāmil (X-1), v. 1, *630*, 787; v. 2, 1192
Shuja, F. M., 708
Shu'lah, b., 1533
Shulḥan 'aruk, 100, 320, 614
Shulḥan kesef, 591
shu'ūbīya, 154, 376
Shyreswood, *see* William

Siam, 1029, 1879
Siamese, 1084
Sībawaihi (VIII-2), v. 1, *542*, 523, 524; v. 3, 372, 1013
Siberia, 1866
Sibṭ b. Jauzī (XIII-1), v. 2, 705; v. 3, 965
Sibṭ Māridīnī, 1526, 1527, 1530, 1533
Sic et non, 80
Sicca, Maria, 515
Sicilian, *see* law
Sicily, *see* John; Roger
Sīda, b., *see* 'Alī b. Ismā'īl
Sidat-saṅgarāva, 423
Siddhāntas, the (V-1), v. 1, *386*, 830
Siddiqi, M. Z., 1449
siddur queri'at ha-ḥokmot, 432
Sidersky, David, 1832
Sīdī Khalīl, *see* Khalīl b. Isḥāq b. Jundī
Sidrach, romance of (XIII-1), v. 2, *589*, 498, 648; v. 3, 340, 548, 1498
Siebert, Hermann, 1045
Siedel, Gottlob, 573
Siena, 39
Siena, *see* Angelico; Catherine; Francis; Hugh; Mariano di Nanni
siesta, 716
siete partidas, Las, 73
Sigebert of Gembloux (XII-1), v. 2, *257*, 1231
Siger of Brabant (XIII-2), v. 2, *945*, 1231; v. 3, 79, 407, 489, 499, 563
Siger of Courtrai (XIV-1), *1003*, 94, 332, 410
Siger of Gulleghem, 1003
Sigerist, H. E., 269, 287, 528, 1207, 1227, 1659
Sighibuldi, *see* Cino
Sighinolfi, Lino, 845
Siginulfo, *see* Bartholomew
Sigismondo Malatesta, 1552
Sigismondo Polcastro, 1197, 1222
Sigismund Albic (XIV-2), *1713*, 1207, 1239, 1319
Sigismund of Hungary, 1025, 1345, 1467
Sigismund of Luxemburg, emperor, 1244, 1400, 1818, 1822
Sigoli, *see* Simon
Sigrid the Beautiful, 1354
Sigurd of Norway (XII-1), v. 2, *224*, 35, 131; v. 3, 352, 1613
Ṣiḥāḥ, 372
ṣiḥāḥ al-sitta, 1065
siḥr, 623
Sijilmasa, 764, 765
Sijistānī, *see* Sulaimān b. Ash'ath
Sijzī, *see* Aḥmad b. Muḥammad
Sikes, J. G., 556, 569
Sikh religion, 1475
sikka, 1284
silk, Chinese, 912
Silk, E. T., 944
silkworms, 238, 306
Silos, 174
Silva Batuwantudawa, Andris de, 978, 1371
Silva Carvalho, Augusto da, 864
silver mines, 218, 219
Silvester, *see* Antonius; Bernard
Silvester II, *see* Gerbert of Aurillac
Silvestre de Sacy, 134, 967, 1010, 1534, 1641, 1777
Silviera, *see* William
Simeon, *see also* Simon
Simeon Atumanos (XIV-2), *1394*, 584, 1073, 1076, 1320, 1325
Simeon of Baghdād, 436
Simeon Czarnkowski, 1759
Simeon of Durham, 560
Simeon Metaphrastes (X-2), v. 1, *686*, 832; v. 3, 353
Simeon the New Theologian, 96
Simeon Seth (XI-2), v. 1, *771*, 830; v. 2, 53, 95; v. 3, 198, 1208
Simeon Shanqĕlāwī (XII-2), v. 2, *449*, 296, 313
Simeon b. Yoḥai, 616
Simeon b. Ẓemaḥ Duran, 592, 595, 605, 1062, 1097, 1116, 1523
Simeonis, *see* Simon
Simḥa b. Ṣolomon, 618
Simi, Renzo, 1132
sīmiyā', 623
Simler, Josias, 1878
Simocattes, *see* Theophylactos
Simon, *see also* Simeon
Simon de' Bardi, 482
Simon de Beauchamp, 728
Simon Bredon, 117, 566, 1501
Simon da Correggio, 856
Simon of Couvin (XIV-1), *886*, 119, 250, 852
Simon of Faversham (XIV-1), *562*, 92
Simon Fitzsimon, 787
Simon of Genoa (XIII-2), v. 2, *1085*, 1231; v. 3, 61, 67, 244, 288, 332, 816, 836, 840, 898, 1222, 1698, 1838
Simon of Ghent, 1422
Simon de Hesdin (XIV-2), *1391*, 1075, 1307
Simon Islip, 1401, 1500
Simon, J. M., 1689
Simon b. Joseph of Lunel, 609
Simon of Kéza (XIII-2), v. 2, *1111*, 794
Simon Langham, 1401
Simon Le Rat, 452
Simon medicus, 1861
Simon de Montfort, 319, 341
Simon Orsenigo, 1655
Simon of Phares, 816, 1110, 1481
Simon, Richard, 398, 399, 1386
Simon of Sarrebruck, 1210, 1601
Simon Sigoli (XIV-2), *1596*, 1143, 1300, 1595
Simon Simeonis (XIV-1), *787*, 191
Simon Tunsted (XIV-2), *1568*, 399, 742, 1110, 1123, 1128, 1148
Simone, *see* Simon

Simonet, F. J., 827
Simonini, R., 835, 1684, 1710
Simonsfeld, Henry, 771, 917
simony, 1047, 1049, 1508
Simplicios (VI-1), v. 1, *422*, 831; v. 2, 1232; v. 3, 145, 430, 544, 1487, 1493
Simpson, J. Y., 1837
simultaneity of discoveries, 142
Sīnā, b. (XI-1), v. 1, *709*, 810; v. 2, 1232; v. 3, xii, 62, 81, 84, 98, 143, 166, 213, 245, 247, 248, 254, 255, 256, 257, 259, 267, 273, 288, 378, 435, 442, 489, 501, 551, 591, 594, 608, 629, 630, 632, 704, 712, 738, 750, 753, 792, 812, 813, 816, 836, 837, 839, 840, 841, 843, 846, 847, 849, 850, 853, 855, 856, 857, 869, 870, 878, 879, 881, 883, 884, 885, 894, 897, 899, 900, 1072, 1138, 1166, 1192, 1195, 1200, 1201, 1205, 1211, 1213, 1220, 1229, 1235, 1243, 1328, 1373, 1374, 1379, 1381, 1385, 1430, 1451, 1490, 1492, 1514, 1521, 1530, 1573, 1640, 1671, 1673, 1674, 1675, 1676, 1677, 1679, 1681, 1683, 1685, 1686, 1688, 1690, 1691, 1694, 1698, 1699, 1703, 1705, 1707, 1710, 1712, 1714, 1716, 1721, 1725, 1726, 1771, 1775, 1885
ṣināb, 230
Sinaites, *see* Gregory
Sinān b. Thābit (X-1), v. 1, *641*, 831
ṣinf, 154
Singer, Charles, 270, 274, 400, 845, 1209, 1224, 1646, 1683, 1693, 1903
Singer, D. W., 165, 400, 1131, 1138, 1195, 1383, 1605, 1660, 1684, 1689, 1877, 1904
Singer, Isidore, 1890, 1904
Singh, A. N., 1535
Ṣinhājī, *see* Muḥammad b. 'Abd al-Mun'im
Sinhalese chronicles (XIV-1), *1370*
Sinibaldi, *see* Guittone
sinibus, chordis et arcubus, De, 598
sinistral, 380
Sinzanogio, *see* Marc
Sionita, Gabriel, 1451
Sipāhīzāde, *see* Muḥammad b. 'Alī
siphons, 1009
Sirr al-asrār, 270, 286, 801, 1104
Sīs, 54
Sīs, council of, 67
Śiva, 1070
Śivāchār, 383
Sivera, J. S., 1340
Sīwāsī, *see* 'Abdallāh b. 'Abd al-'Azīz
Sixtus IV, 399
Siyāsatnāma, 376
Skeat, W. W., 1317, 1413, 1424, 1425, 1741
Skene, F. J. H., 1741
Skene, W. F., 1741
Skeninge, *see* Peter Olafsson
skin ailments, 871
Skoplye, 39
Skopti Ogmundson, 352
Slane, baron McGuckin de, 799
slaves, buying, 899
slaves, Christian, 1035
Slavonic languages, 355
sleeping sickness, 1214, 1236, 1775, 1787
Sleidan, J. P., 1753
Slonimski, H. S., 1520
sluice building, 145
smallpox, 261, 274, 881, 904, 973, 1682
Smets, G., 913
Smith, A. D. H., 1372
Smith, C. S., 1174, 1555
Smith, D. E., xv, 111, 116, 1484, 1904
Smith, F. P., 224
Smith, George, 792, 1881, 1904
Smith, J. R., 1810
Smith, L. T., 1150
Smith, Leonardo, 1819
Smith, R. M., 1753
Smith, R. S., 153
Smith, Thomas, 738
Smith, V. A., 1027, 1045, 1904
Smolensk, *see* Ignatius; Michael
Smṛitiratnākara, 1000
Smyth, A. H., 1549
Smythe, Barbara, 743
snake bite, 839
snakes, 1642, 1671, 1676
snakeskin, 65, 451
Snel, Willebrord, 142, 705
Snellaert, F. A., 582, 940
Snodham, Thomas, 1604
Snorri Sturluson (XIII-1), v. 2, *677*, 1232; v. 3, 352
snow, transportation, 1786
So, *see* Bernard
soap, 1622
Sobhy, Georgy, 289
socialism, 13
societas maris, 125
society, perfect, 1276
Socino Benzi, 1196
sociology, 1771
Socotra, 391
Socrates (V B.C.), v. 1, *89*, 82, 122; v. 2, 185; v. 3, vii, 509
Socrates of Constantinople (V-1), v. 1, *394*, 379, 380; v. 3, 947
sod, 591
sod ha-'ibbur, 131
sod, Sefer ha-, 428
Sodbury, *see* Adam
Soderini, *see* Peter
Soerensen, Th., 629
Sogdian, 360, 378
Soghd, *see* Sogdian; Sughd
soils, 1637
Soissons, *see* Nicholas
Sŏl Ch'ong, 388
Solagna, *see* William

Soldan, W. G., 1051
Solente, S., 1481
Soler, 1866
Soleri map of 1385, 765
Soleri, *see* William
Solerti, Angelo, 514
Soligo, *see* Christofalo
Solinus, Caius Julius (III-2), v. 1, *341*, 331; v. 2, 1233, 1600, 1603, 1808
Solmi, Arrigo, 499
solmization, 742
Solo, *see* Gerald
Solomon, for Arabic names *see* Sulaimān
Solomon b. Abraham Abigdor (XIV-2), *1382*, 1074, 1116, 1219, 1383
Solomon b. Abraham b. Adret of Barcelona (XIII-2), v. 2, *884*, 1233; v. 3, 83, 100, 255, 416, 593, 610, 612, 893, 1061, 1062, 1364, 1443
Solomon b. Abraham Corcos, 130
Solomon Astruc Gatigno (XIV-2), *1634*, 1061, 1167
Solomon of al-Baṣra (XIII-1), v. 2, *602*, 1233; v. 3, 1188
Solomon b. Benaya, 1117
Solomon Bonfed, 1523
Solomon Bonirac (XIV-1), *436*, 62, 255
Solomon of Burgos, 436
Solomon Caravida, 1717
Solomon b. David Davin (XIV-2), *1382*, 1074, 1117, 1383
Solomon Duran, 1523
Solomon b. Elijah (XIV-2), *1378*, 1064, 1072, 1073, 1117, 1324
Solomon the Frenchman, 1008
Solomon b. Gerson, 599
Solomon b. Immanuel Dapiera, 62, 100, 611
Solomon b. Isaac ha-Levi (XIV-2), *1343*, 1053, 1302, 1339, 1716, 1862
Solomon b. Isaac, *see* Rashi
Solomon b. Joseph b. Ayyub of Béziers (XIII-2), v. 2, *845*, 1233; v. 3, 274, 366
Solomon b. Joseph Kaspi, 73, 590
Solomon b. Judah, *see* b. Gabirol
Solomon Kohen (XIII-2), v. 2, *1098*, 69, 788
Solomon b. Labi (XIV-2), *1376*, 1072, 1097
Solomon b. Meshullam Dapiera, 1384
Solomon b. Moses of Melgueil (XIII-2), v. 2, *858*, 1233
Solomon b. Nathan Crescas (XIV-2), *1382*, 1074
Solomon b. Nathan ha-Me'ati, 437
Solomon Orgier, 1382
Solomon b. Paṭer Kohen (XIV-1), *436*, 62, 130, 1119
Solomon, *see* Proverbs
Solomon b. Samuel the Persian (XIV-1), *1008*, 369, 377, 957
Solomon b. Verga, 1448
Solomon, *see* Wisdom
Solomon b. Ya'ish (XIV-1), *894*, 256, 1373, 1385
Solomon's Temple, 1799
Solon (VI B.C.), v. 1, *79*, 66
Solon Archimedicus, 447
Solon, M. L., 1134
Solvet, Charles, 1459
Somal, P. S., 1904
Somalian, 1904
Somer, *see* John
Sommalius, Henry, 1361
Somme le Roi, 340, 462
Somme des vices et vertus, 462
Sommeria, *see* Andrew
Sommersberg, F. W. de, 1759
Sommervogel, Carlos, 1871
Somnium viridarii, 1276, 1345, 1797
Somogyi, Joseph, 967, 1104, 1641, 1867
Soncino, *see* Gershon
Sonetti, *see* Bartholomew
Song-tsen Gam-po (VII-1), v. 1, *466*, 831; v. 2, 429
Songe verd, 1480
Songe du vergier, 1276, 1345, 1797
Songe du vieil pelerin, 1345
Sonne, I., 430, 1444, 1845
Soothill, W. E., 382, 468, 1904
sopherim, 364, 365
Sophia, widow, 39
Sophocles, 997, 1005, 1395
Sophonias (XIII-2), v. 2, *972*, 745; v. 3, 446
Soranos of Ephesus (II-1), v. 1, *282*, 831
Soranzo, *see* Donado
Sorbelli, Albano, 815, 1340
Sorbon, *see* Robert
Sorbonne, 369, 476
sorcerers, 404
Sorel, Alexandre, 239
Sorg, S., 789
Sorio, Bartolomeo, 815
Sorleone Vivaldo, 186, 190, 337, 786
sortes sanctorum, 1458
sortes vergilianae, 1457
Sossnitz, J. L., 1444
Sostratos of Cnidos (III-1 B.C.), v. 1, *161*, 150
Soto, Domingo de, 544
Sotomayor, Pelayo de, 1467
Sottas, Henri, 361
Soulié, Georges, 162, 906
Soulier, Gustave, 956
sound, 1491
Souques, 472
Southern Cross, 487
Southey, Robert, 1250
Southwell minster, 1835
Souza-Araujo, H. C. de, 909
sovereignty, 314, 1869
Sowerby, A. de C., 211, 233, 386, 1179, 1835
Sozomen of Constantinople (V-1), v. 1, *394*, 379, 380; v. 3, 947

Sozomenos, *see* Sozomen
Spain, 1901, 1907
Spain, history of, 24
Spain, Muslim, 1884
Spain, *see* Peter
Spallanzani, Lazzaro, 1230
Spanish era, 1107
Spanish flies, 296
Spanish literature, 1890
Spanos, Alexios, 995
Sparnau, *see* Peter
spas, 1240
spasmatomancy, 960
Spechtshart, *see* Conrad; Hugh
Speciale, *see* Nicholas
spectacles, 142, 874, 921, 1235, 1708
spectacles, invention of (XIII-2), v. 2, *1024*, 761
spectroscopic observations, 710
Speculator, 413
speculum, 311
Speculum animae, 1507
Speculum grammaticale, 741
Speculum historiale, 65, 66
Speculum hominis, 1427
Speculum morale, 48, 89
Speculum regum, 402
Speculum sanctorale, 403
Speculum virtutum, 577
speed, accelerated, 1430
speed, *see* angular velocity
Speiser, Felix, 1860
Spencer, A. J., 218
Spencer, H., 77
Spengler, Oswald, 1770
Spenser, Edmund, 1428
Speusippos of Athens (IV-2 B.C.), v. 1, *139*, 831
Spezi, Giuseppe, 232
Sphaera, 1874
sphere, astronomical, 1485
sphere, eighth, 441
sphere, solid, 426
sphere, water, 483
spheres, celestial, 147
spheres, eccentricity of earth and water, 1568
spheres, *see* globes; homocentric
sphragistics, 311, 385
sphragistics, Chinese, 1017
spices, 323, 1182
Spiegel, 311
Spiegel, Friedrich, 423
Spieghel historiael, 302
Spielmann, M. H., 1357, 1426
Spies, Otto, 619, 623, 803, 1781, 1782, 1788
Spiesshaymer, *see* John
Spina, *see* Alexander; Alfonso
Spinello Aretino, 225
Spingarn, J. E., 496
spinning, *see* wheel
Spinola, *see* Argentina
Spinoza, 605, 1096, 1447
Spirer, *see* Margaret
"spiritual medicine," 292
Spirituals (XIV-1), *396*, 13, 44, 47, 400, 412, 549, 553, 923, 985, 1038
Spiro, Jean, 1342
spleen, 843
Spölgen, 580
Spoleto, *see* Gavellus
Spooner, R. C., 1140
Spooner, W. A., 1403
Sporer, *see* John
Sporos of Nicaea (III-2), v. 1, *338*, 331
Sprengel, Kurt, 817, 840, 882, 889
Sprenger, Aloys, 627, 900
Sprenger, Jacob, 1049
Sprenger, *see* James
springs, 287, 1163, 1540
springs of Cilicia, 461
springs, hot, 197, 1192, 1677
springs, mineral, 1171
Spurgeon, C. F. E., 1425
Spurs, Battle of the Golden, 37, 938
Squarzafico, *see* Jerome
squinting, 890
Squire, W. B., 741
śramana, 1733
Sreznevski, I., 1142
Śrī Sūrya, 465
Śrī Vaishnava, 425
Śrīdhara (XI-1), v. 1, *719*, 697, 701; v. 2, 213
Śrīvijaya, 1624
Stabat mater, 50
stadion, 1859
staff, Levi's, 601
Stagel, *see* Elizabeth
stained glass, 172, 1655
Stainer, J. F. R., 741
Staley, Edgcumbe, 124, 152
Stalin, 1467
Stamm, Eduard, 542
Stammler, Wolfgang, 1232
standard texts, 1125
Standonck, *see* John
Stanford, C. V., 159
Stanislas of Oliva, 932
Stanley of Alderley, 929
Stanley, H. M., 1159
Stansby, Thomas, 1604
Stanton, *see* Hervey
Stapeldon, *see* Walter
Stapelmohr, Ivar v., 789
staple, merchants of the, 324
Stapleton, H. E., 759
star map, Korean, 1866
Starkey, *see* Geoffrey
Starr, Joshua, 1831
stars, diurnal motion, *see* earth
state accounting, 126
statibus ecclesiae, De, 400

statical equilibrium, 1430, 1566
statical moment, 146
statics, 1566, 1882
statistics, 914
Statius, 505, 917, 1418, 1482, 1745
Staubach, C. N., 1110, 1312
Stavelot, *see* John
Stead, Mrs. Cleves, 1178
Stebin Scrope, 1303
Stecher, J., 1438, 1753
steel, damascened, 1175
Steele, F. M., 1355
Steele, Robert, 1394
steelyard, Coptic, 712
Stefano, *see* Stephen
Stefansson, V., 194, 196, 1155, 1319, 1501, 1608, 1610
Steffen, R., 1356
Steffenhagen, 994
Stegemann, Viktor, 1865
Stegemeier, Henri, 1232
Stein, Sir Aurel, 378, 714, 833
Stein, E. L., 572
Stein, I. H., 1349
Stein, *see* Marquard
Stein, Rolf, 1788
Steinberg, S. H., 742
Steiner, Árpád, 314, 1281, 1605
Steinfurth, *see* Baldwin
Steinhöwel, *see* Henry
Steinilber-Oberlin, H. E., 1018, 1332
Steinschneider, Moritz, 417, 420, 427, 430, 433, 435, 436, 437, 445, 450, 593, 606, 616, 618, 872, 1375, 1450, 1452, 1690, 1901, 1904
Stella, *see* Isaac
Stendal, *see* John
Stengel, Edmund, 1310, 1311
Stenzel, G. A., 1005
Stephan, *see* Stephen
Stephani, *see* John
Stephanides, Michael, 589
Stéphanou, E., 119
Stephen of Alexandria (VII-1), v. 1, *472*, 832
Stephen of Antioch (XII-1), v. 2, *236*, 1234; v. 3, 374
Stephen Arlandi (XIV-1), *426*, 61, 114, 245
Stephen Asolik (XI-1), v. 1, *735*, 700, 702; v. 3, 356
Stephen of Athens (VII-1), v. 1, *478*, 832; v. 2, 87
Stephen Auber, 1031
Stephen, son of Basilios (IX-2), v. 1, *613*, 587; v. 2, 79
Stephen of Besançon, 579
Stephen Birchington, 945, 1255
Stephen Boileau (XIII-2), v. 2, *1128*, 800; v. 3, 153, 345, 347, 864
Stephen de Bourbon, 579
Stephen of Byzantium (VI-1), v. 1, *433*, 417; v. 2, 395
Stephen Harding, St., 369
Stephen of Hungary, 933
Stephen Lazarevich, 1323
Stephen Maconi, 1335, 1337
Stephen Magnetes (XI-1), v. 1, *727*, 699
Stephen Marcel, 1024
Stephen of Novgorod (XIV-1), *790*, 198, 356, 1155, 1614
Stephen Orbelian (XIII-2), v. 2, *1116*, 795; v. 3, 54, 98, 304, 356
Stephen of Perm, St. (XIV-2), *1825*, 1058, 1286, 1324
Stephen of Saragossa (XIII-1), v. 2, *562*, 1234
Stephen of Serbia, Stephen Nemanya, 1853
Stephen Dushan Nemanyich IX, 39, 1760
Stephen Dushan Urosh IV, 994, 1209
Stephen Talice da Ricaldone, 1814
Stephen of Toulouse, 24
Stephens, George, 1203
Stephenson, John, 632, 1641
Stephenson, Mill, 728
Stern, M. E., 594, 616
Stern, S. G., 1448
Stethatos, *see* Nicetas
Stetson, H. T., 1856
Steuart, R. H. J., 1090
Stevart, Pierre, 414
Stevenson, E. L., 1147, 1592
Stevenson, Joseph, 463, 1746
Stevin, Simon, 122, 127, 773, 1111, 1113, 1116, 1126, 1127, 1518, 1525, 1839, 1903
Stewart, Aubrey, 771, 789
Stewart, Charles, 1473
sthāna, 1619
Sticker, Georg, 280, 1663, 1665
Stieglitz, Leopold, 989
Stillman, J. M., 752, 1904
Stillwell, M. B., 1905
Stiso, Sergio, 859
Štítný, *see* Anežka; Thomas (Tomáš)
Stjörnu Oddi (XII-1), v. 2, *212*, 127, 404; v. 3, 352, 1114
Stobaeos, Joannes (V-2), v. 1, *405*, 399; v. 2, 832
Stoddart, J. T., 582
Stögmann, K., 934
Stönner, Heinrich, 1369
Størmer, Carl, 709
stoicism, 585
Stoke, *see* Melis
Stokes, *see* John; Laurence
Stokvis, A. M. H. J., 1905
Stolingwa, Peter, 1407
Stollen, W. G., 752
stomach, 843
stone drums, 386
Stone, Isabella, 583
Stone Man, 1556, 1559
stone, medicine, 844, 853, 881, 1236

stones, precious, 214, 755, 899, 912. *See also* lapidaries; mineralogy
Storck, W. F., 1553
Storey, C. A., 1463, 1905
Storm, Gustav, 1608
Storr, Rayner, 1361
Storrs, R., 40, 1025
Stout, G. L., 1834
Strabo, *see* Strabon; Walafrid
Strabon (I-2 B.C.), v. 1, *227*, 832; v. 2, 1234; v. 3, 214, 736, 1073, 1292, 1849, 1859
Strahov, *see* Gallus
Stralsund, peace of, 1020
Strassburg, 1258, 1756
Strassburg, *see* Berthold; Burchard; Hugh Ripelin; Thomas; Ulrich
Strassburg cathedral, 1541
Strassburg, *see* clock
Strassburg, oaths, 344
Strassburg physicians, 852
Straton of Lampsacos (III-1 B.C.), v. 1, *152*, 832; v. 3, 149
Strauch, Philipp, 570, 574
Strauss, Bettina, 431, 1773
Straw, *see* Jack
Streck, M., 1624
Streeter, B. H., 475, 1298
Streeter, E. C., 1693
streghe, 406
stregoni, 406
Strehlke, Ernst, 932
Streit, Robert, 1905
Strobel, A. W., 1756
Strode, *see* Ralph
Stromer, *see* Henry; Ulman
Strothmann, R., 106, 965, 1067, 1264
Strowski, Fortunat, 1087
Strozzi, *see* Palla
Struve, B. G., 820
Struve, Gotth., 1814
Strycker, E. de, 454
Stuart, G. A., 223
Stubbs, W., 945, 1742
student, guide for, 900
Studer, G., 935
Studer, Paul, 1171
studia generalia, 72, 73
Studnička, F. J., 1114
Stückelberg, E. A., 1045
Stürzinger, Jacob, 533, 1311
Stüve, Erich, 949
Stufler, Johann, 525
Stukeley, William, 1744
Sturla Thórdarson (XIII-2), v. 2, *1112*, 1235; v. 3, 303, 352
Sturluson, *see* Snorri
Suárez, *see* Laurence
Ṣubḥ al-a'shā, 1785
Subkī, *see* 'Abd al-Wahhāb b. 'Alī; 'Alī b. 'Abd al-Kāfī; Jamāl al-dīn Ḥusain
Suchem, *see* Ludolf
Suchier, Hermann, 458
Suchier, Walther, 339
Sūdān, western, 1142, 1617, 1875
Sudheim, *see* Ludolf; Peter
Sudhoff, Karl, 249, 251, 264, 269, 274, 275, 277, **281**, 284, 285, 286, 288, 712, 835, 839, 847, **848**, 850, 851, 854, 855, 860, 861, 862, 864, **865**, 873, 876, 877, 878, 879, 886, 887, 1131, **1195**, 1197, 1203, 1206, 1207, 1219, 1220, **1227**, 1229, 1230, 1239, 1240, 1241, 1244, **1246**, 1605, 1606, 1660, 1661, 1664, 1674, **1675**, 1676, 1677, 1678, 1679, 1684, 1685, **1686**, 1687, 1688, 1689, 1693, 1695, 1697, **1699**, 1704, 1707, 1709, 1710, 1712, 1715, **1716**, 1730, 1891, 1895, 1905
Sūdī, 1457
Suess, Eduard, 497
Süssheim, K., 1458, 1465
Suetonius (II-1), v. 1, *284*, 832; v. 3, 873, 1482
Suez canal, 1849
ṣūfī, *see* taṣawwuf
Suger of Saint Denis (XII-1), v. 2, *161*, 1235; v. 3, 171
Sughd, 378, 794, 1470. *See also* Sogdian
Suhrāb, *see* b. Serapion
Suhrawardī, *see* 'Umar b. 'Abdallāh; Yaḥyā b. Ḥabash
Suhrawardīya, 420, 1069
Suidas (X-2), v. 1, *691*, 832; v. 2, 584
suiipsius et multorum ignorantia, De, 507
Suisset, *see* Richard Swineshead
Śukasaptati, 465, 1810
Sukhāvatīviyūhasūtra, 312
Sukthankar, V. S., 1840
Sulaimān. Jewish and Christian names are generally classified under Solomon.
Sulaimān b. Ash'ath Sijistānī, 1065
Sulaimān b. Ḥaffāẓ Kūhīn, *see* Solomon Kohen
Sulaimān b. Ḥārith, *see* Alcoatim
Sulaimān b. Ḥassān, *see* b. Juljul
Sulaimān the Merchant (IX-1), v. 1, *571*, **546**; v. 2, 409
Sulaimān, a. Rabī, *see* Solomon b. Ya'īsh
Suler, B., 400, 452, 1117, 1373, 1375, 1377, **1516**, 1520, 1521, 1523, 1717
Ṣūlī, *see* Muḥammad b. Yaḥyā
Sulko of Hosstka, 1207, 1319
sullam, 1006
Sullivan, James, 556, 989
Sully, 127
sulphur, 167, 289, 751, 752
sulphuric acid, 1551, 1573
Sulpicius Severus (IV-2), v. 1, *376*, 361
Sulṭān Walad, 105, 163, 379, 624, 626, 1840
Sulūk duwal al-mulūk, 1000
Sulūk fī ṭabaqāt al-'ulamā', 958
Suluvaṃsaya, 977
Sumaṅgala, H., 978

Sumaṅgala, Tibbotuvāvē, 977
Sumatra, 778, 1616
Sumer is icumen in (XIII-1), v. 2, *634*, 25, 510; v. 3, 159, 1833
Summa dictaminis, 332
Summa de haeresibus, 400
Summa perfectionis, 165, 751
Summa sedacina, 754
Summers, Montague, 1049, 1051, 1865
Summulae logicales, 82
sun, apogee, 440
Sunamoto, Etsujirō, 1187
sunan, 1065
sunan al-arba'a, 1066
sundial, 716, 717, 719, 1546
Sunik, *see* Arachiel; Sarkis
sunna, 1065
Sunnī, 106
sunspots, 1121, 1122, 1856
superstition, 16, 45, 1879, 1887. *See also* divination; talismans
Sura, 366
Surapāla, 1730
surds, *see* irrationality
Sure de Syberg, 1706
Sureśvara, 1730
surgeons, 293, 864
surgery, 271, 844, 1232, 1887, 1905
surgery, plastic, 1233
surgical instruments, 872, 1700, 1831
Ṣūrī, b., *see* Manṣūr b. a. Faḍl
Surius, Laurentius, 571, 574, 582
Surrel, *see* John
surveying, 1498
Sūryadāsa, 1535
Suso, Henry (XIV-1), *573*, 85, 93, 351, 572, 1056, 1092, 1358, 1844, 1889
Suśruta (VI B.C.?), v. 1, *76*, 832; v. 2, 84; v. 3, 1233, 1236, 1584, 1730
Suter, Heinrich, 445, 1431, 1534, 1905
sūtra, 467
Sūtrapiṭaka, 466, 468
suttee, 778, 784, 1621
Sutton, *see* Hugh; Thomas
Su'ūdī, *see* Muḥammad b. 'Abdallāh
Suyūṭī, *see* 'Abd al-Raḥmān b. a. Bakr
Suzuki, B. L., 1333
Suzuki, Chokichi, 234
Sven, Swedish master, 119
Svend Aagesön (XII-2), v. 2, *458*, 315, 317
Sviatskiĭ, D. O., 710
Svyatoĭ Stefan, Permskiĭ, 1825
Swan, Charles, 456
Swart, *see* Claudius Claussøn
Sweden, *see* Catherine
Swedish, 352
swelling, *see* boils
Sweynheim, *see* Conrad
Swinburne, *see* Thomas
Swineshead, *see* Richard
Swingle, W. T., 831, 832, 1549, 1649, 1867
Swiss Confederation, 43
Swiss independence, 38
swordsmiths, 1175
Sy, *see* John
Syberg, *see* Sure
Sydenham, Thomas, 252, 1667
Sydenham's chorea, 1667
Syllanus de Nigris (XIV-2), *1680*, 1193, 1221
Sylvaticus, *see* Matthew
Sylvester, *see* Silvester
Symeon, *see* Simeon
Symon, *see* Simon
Symonds, J. A., 1905
Synaxaria, 948
Syncellos, *see* George
Synesios of Cyrene (V-1), v. 1, *388*, 833; v. 2, 974; v. 3, 951, 952, 997, 1577
Synonyma, 816
Syntagma, 53, 994
Syntipas, 925
syphilis, 223, 274, 290, 907, 1384, 1759, 1860
Syracuse, *see* Alcadino
Syria, 1884, 1893
Syriac, 356, 372, 1873, 1882
Syriac Chronicle (VI-1), v. 1, *437*; of 569 (VI-2), v. 1, *457*; (VII-2), v. 1, *499*
Syriac, *see* law, Syriac-Roman
Syriac literature, 1909
Syriac script, 359
Syrianos (V-1), v. 1, *386*, 378. 380
Szalay, B., 1190

Tà-prohm, 294
ta'addud, 1722
ṭabaqāt, 960
Ṭabarī, *see* Aḥmad b. Muḥammad; 'Alī b. Sahl Rabbān
Ṭabarī, Muḥammad b. Jarīr (X-1), v. 1, *642*, 833; v. 2, 1206; v. 3, 794, 965, 970
Ṭabarī, *see* Sahl; 'Umar b. Farrukhān
Ṭabāṭabā, *see* Ibrāhīm
Tabor, Mount, 95, 584, 1386, 1512
Tabrīz, 971
Tabrīz, *see* Faḍlallāh; Isaiah b. Joseph
Tabrīz, school of painting, 974
Tabrīzī, *see* Muḥammad b. 'Abdallāh Tibrīzī; Muḥammad b. Muḥammad; Tāj al-dīn
Tabula smaragdina, 165, 1576
Taccola, *see* James Mariano; Marianus
Tacitus, Cornelius (I-2), v. 1, *263*, 245; v. 2, 932; v. 3, 112, 1101, 1288, 1807
Tacuinum sanitatis, 270
tadbhava, 383
Tadbīr al-abdān, 426
Tadbīr al-siḥḥa, 285
Taddeo Alderotti (XIII-2), v. 2, *1086*, 1236; v. 3, 66, 88, 243, 244, 285, 291, 333, 837, 838, 839, 841, 842, 848, 855, 1192, 1239, 1672
Taddeo de' Crivelli, 1146

Taddeo Doria, 803
Taddeo Gaddi, 500, 1131
Taddeo of Parma, 112, 298
Tadhkira al-aḥbāb, 707
Ta'dīl al-'ulūm, 628
Tadmurī, *see* Isḥāq b. Ibrāhīm
taedium vitae, 1434
Taeschner, Franz, 626, 803, 805
Taeuber, Walter, 1284
Taeusch, C. F., 328
tafā'ul, 1457
Tafel, G. L. F., 916
Tāfīlālt, 182
Ṭafīruh, *see* Jacob
Tafrali, Oreste, 1905
tafsīr, 58, 1065
Taftāzānī, *see* Mas'ūd b. Umar
Tagalog, 1866
Tagaste, *see* Augustine
taggin, 612
Taghlaq, 40
Taghlaq, b., *see* Muḥammad
Taghrībirdī, b., *see* Yūsuf
tagin, Sefer ha-, 1522
Tagore, Rabindranath, 1476
Ṭāhā Ḥusain, 1779
Tahāfut al-tahāfut, 98, 428, 433
Ṭaḥāwī, *see* Aḥmad b. Muḥammad
Tahdhīb al-aḥkām, 1067
Ṭāhir, b., *see* 'Abd al-Qāhir
Ṭāhir b. Ḥasan b. Ḥabīb, 1783
Taḥtānī, *see* Muḥammad b. Muḥammad
Ṭā'ī, *see* Muḥammad b. 'Abdallāh
Ṭaibughā b. 'Abdallāh Baklamishī (XIV-2), *1643*, 1169, 1185, 1274, 1533, 1866
Taillevent, *see* William Tirel
Taimīya, b., *see* Aḥmad b. 'Abd al-Ḥalīm
Taine, Hippolyte, xiv
Taisīr al-manfa'a, 1066
Tait, James, 945, 1303
Taittirīya, 1368
Taittirīyabrāhmaṇa, 1369
Taittirīyāraṇyaka, 1369
Ṭaiyib, b., *see* 'Abdallāh
Tāj al-'arūs, 1827
Tāj al-dīn 'Abd al-Wahhāb, 622
Tāj al-dīn Tabrīzī, 755
Tāj Maḥall, 1473
Tājik, 1442
tajsīm, 1012
Takhjīl ahl al-injīl, 422
Takhjīl man ḥarrafa al-tauriya wal-injīl (XIII-1), v. 2, *557*
Takla Hāmānot, St., 362
takmīl, 154
Talbert, E. W., 1350
Talbot, Eugène, 232
Ṭālib Ḥusainī, a., 1472
Ṭālib Khān, a., 1458
Talice, *see* Stephen
Ta'līm al-muta'allim, 74
talismans, 292, 893
Talkhīṣ fī a'māl al-ḥisāb, 132
Talleyrand-Périgord, *see* Hélie
Talmud (V-2), v. 1, *401*, 833; v. 2, 1237; v. 3, 357, 364, 365, 367, 368, 369, 370, 397, 404, 430
Tam b. David b. Yaḥya, 1451
tamar, Sefer ha-, 1521
Tamara, queen, 305
Tambroni, Giuseppe, 1132, 1814
Tamerlane, *see* Tīmūr Lang
Tamgrūt, *see* 'Alī b. Muḥammad
Tamil, 383
Tamīmī, *see* Muḥammad b. Aḥmad; Muḥammad b. Umail
Tammar Luxoro atlas, 764
Tana, 773, 777, 783
Tanabe, H., 162
Tāṇḍyamahābrāhmaṇa, 1369
Tànfani, Gustavo, 446, 839, 851, 1243, 1671, 1678, 1681
Tanḥum b. Joseph of Jerusalem (XIII-1), v. 2, *700*, 1237; v. 3, 366
Tanḥum b. Judah, 892
Tanḥum b. Moses of Beaucaire, 1380
Tanjur (VII-1), v. 1, *467*, 833; v. 3, 69, 71, 259, 382, 384, 468, 1842
Tānksūqnāmah, 970, 972
Tannery, Marie, xv, 1906
Tannery, Paul, 5, 119, 121, 122, 123, 1848, 1849, 1906
Tannstetter, Georg, 1504
Tanqīḥ al-manāẓir, 707
Tansillo, Luigi, 502
Ṭanṭā, 420
tantra, 1070
tantras, Four, 384
Tantucci, A. A., 1337
Taoism, 109, 180, 636, 1070, 1139, 1895, 1909
Taoist, *see* botany
Taqaz, viceroy, 1249
taqdīr, 1214
Taqī al-dīn b. 'Izz al-dīn Ḥanbalī (XIV-2), *1527*, 1119
Taqī al-dīn b. Qāḍī Shubha, 965, 1782
taqrīb fī-l-asrār, 760
ṭaqṭaqa, 288
taqwīm, 1833
Taqwīm al-abdān, 797
Taqwīm al-buldān, 794
Tārāghāy, 379, 1467
Taranne, 540
Taranta, *see* Valescus
tarantism, 1666
Taranto, *see* Philip
tarantula, 1666
Tarascon, *see* Immanuel b. Jacob Bonfils; Tartarin
tarassul, 1465

Tarbé, Prosper, 743
Tarbell, F. B., 1847
Tardif, Guillaume, 1185
Targūm, 367
Ta'rīf bi-l-muṣṭalaḥ, 802
ta'rīf al-'ulūm, 748
Tarifa of c. 1345, Venetian, 185
Tarifa zoè noticia, Venetian, 773
tariffs, 125, 773
Ta'rīkh-i-guzīda, 630
Ṭarīqa (XIV-1), *420*, 57, 153
Tarjumān al-lugha, 1827
Tarkālankāra, Chandrakānta, 1367
Tarkavācaspati, Tārānātha, 1367
Ṭarkhān, b., *see* Ibrāhīm b. Muḥammad
tarkīb, 836
Tarphon, *see* Isaac
Tarragona, *see* Peter
Tárrega, *see* Raymond
Tartaglia, Niccolò, 1127, 1554
Tartarin de Tarascon, 1116
Taruṇaprabha (XIV-2), *1474*, 1069, 1102, 1330
taṣawwuf, 57, 85, 153, 155, 212, 379, 421, 624, 626, 800, 1099, 1100, 1102, 1457, 1475, 1476, 1873
tashakhkhuṣ, 81
Ṭashköprüzāde, *see* Aḥmad b. Muṣṭafā
Tasso, Torquato, 1037
Tastu, J., 1591
Tatar characters, 1612
Ṭaṭār, sulṭān, 1329
Tatars, 71, 379, 1780
Tatatonga, 380
Tatham, E. H. R., 515
Tathev, *see* Gregory
Tatian (II-2), v. 1, *293*, 834; v. 3, 357
Tatlock, J. S. P., 490, 1045, 1425, 1426
tatsama, 383
Tauler, *see* John
ṭā'ūn, 896
ṭā'ūn al-'āmm, 962
Tavenor-Perry, J., 729
Tawfīq, *see* Chīchaklī
tawḥīd, 436, 1099
Tawney, C. H., 1585
taxation, ecclesiastical, 326
taxes, 327
Taylor, F. H., 336
Taylor, L. W., 715
Tchobanian, Archag, 1442, 1761
Te Winkel, Jan, 1438, 1607
tea ceremony, 1332
tea, Japan (XII-2), v. 2, *429*, 1238
teaching profession, 1242
Ṭe'amim, 442
ṭeba', Sefer ha-, 432
technical improvements, 1127
technology, 1883, 1907, 1908
technology, diffusion of Chinese (VI-2), v. 1, *452*
technology, Japanese (VIII-1), v. 1, *515*
technology, military, 1550
Teetaert, Am., 1440
Tegghia de' Corbizzi, *see* Angelino
tegni Galeni, 431
Teixeira, *see* Tristão Vaz
tekunah, 599
Telesforo of Cosenza, 1505
Telfer, Buchan, 1153
Tell-Maḥrē, *see* Dionysios
Telugu, 383
Temkin, Owsei, 1245, 1851
Tempe, defile, 214
temperaments, 270, 579, 1421
Templars, Knights (XII-1), v. 2, *160*, 111; v. 3, 7, 23, 38, 44, 46, 153, 393, 408, 476, 521, 535, 927, 985, 1038
Templars, trial of (XIV-1), *393*
Temple, R. C., 1476
Temple-Leader, John, 1023
Temploux, *see* John
temptations, Four, 581
temunah ha-ḥittukit, 431, 432
Ten Brink, Bernhard, 1425
Tennstädt, *see* Ulrich
Tennyson, 1188
Teodorico, *see* Theodoric
Teoli, Carlo, 913
Ter Gouw, J., 823
Teralh, *see* Hugh
Terentius, 1288, 1294, 1807
terminism, 82, 552, 554, 1429
terminorum proprietatibus, De, 82
Terpander of Lesbos (VII B.C.), v. 1, *61*, 60
terra nigra, 221
terra sigillata, 292
Terrasse, Henri, 136, 1118
Terrena, *see* Guy
Terrien de La Couperie, A., 1586
tertia, 716
Tertullianus of Carthage, viii, 489
Terumat ha-kesef, 590
Terzieken, near Antwerp, 276
teshubot she'elot nisheal mehem, 436
testament, 430. *See also* Ẓawa'ot
Testament of love, 1423
Tetrabiblos, 1049
tetragrammaton, 591, 1508, 1519
Teutobochus, 1228
Teutonic Knights (XII-2), v. 2, *333*, 245, 281; v. 3, 125, 126, 572, 931, 1020, 1026, 1150, 1190
textile, *see* cloth
textile industry, 1833
Teza, E., 891, 1164
Thābit b. Qurra (IX-2), v. 1, *599*, 834; v. 2, 1238; v. 3, 128, 134, 430, 431, 433, 1525, 1846
Thaddeus, *see* Taddeo
Thai, 1030

Thales of Miletos (VI B.C.), v. 1, *72*, 65; v. 2, 24; v. 3, 563, 714, 1881
Thana, 783
Thanet, Isle, 1743
Thaon, *see* Philip
thawāb, 104
Thawbān b. Ibrāhīm, *see* Dhū-l-Nūn
Theaetetos of Athens (IV-1 B.C.), v. 1, *116*, 111
Thebaldis, *see* Giles
Thebes, *see* Paul
Theinred (XIV-2), *1569*, 1128
Theissing, Eugenie, 49
Themison of Laodicaea (I-1 B.C.), v. 1, *215*, 203
Themistios (IV-2), v. 1, *366*, 834; v. 2, 1238; v. 3, 146
Themon son of the Jew (XIV-2), *1539*, 545, 1091, 1123, 1152, 1429, 1568
Theocritos, 997, 1005
Theoctonicos, *see* Peter
Theodora Cantacuzena, 40
Theodore of Antioch (XIII-1), v. 2, *648*, 1238; v. 3, 1835
Theodore Bestes, 994
Theodore of Cyrene (V B.C.), v. 1, *92*, 82
Theodore, Flemish embroiderer, 1132
Theodore of Freiberg (XIV-1), *704*, 92, 118, 141, 142, 1506, 1540
Theodore b. Kōnī, 139
Theodore II Lascaris (XIII-2), v. 2, *970*, 1238
Theodore Meliteniotes (XIV-2), *1512*, 123, 438, 746, 1058, 1115, 1511, 1812
Theodore Metochites (XIV-1), *684*, 97, 889, 949, 952, 996
Theodore v. Niem (XIV-2), *1819*, 1055, 1278, 1296
Theodore Palaeologos, 320, 458, 1823
Theodore, *see* Priscianus
Theodore Prodromos (XII-1), v. 2, *191*, 120, 1190 (*under wrong heading*, John); v. 3, 825
Theodore of Samos (VI B.C.), v. 1, *75*, 65
Theodore, Shāpūr's physician (IV-2), v. 1, *372*, 360, 435; v. 3, 376
Theodoretos of Cyrus (V-1), v. 1, *394*, 379, 380; v. 3, 947
Theodoric, *see also* Thierry
Theodoric Adamaeus, 995
Theodoric Borgognoni of Cervia (XIII-1), v. 2, *654*, 1238; v. 3, 271, 278, 290, 340, 342, 858, 866, 870, 871, 883, 1375, 1669
Theodoric of Chartres (XII-1), v. 2, *196*, 1238
Theodoric the Hermit, 1351
Theodoric, king of Ostrogoths (VI-1), v. 1, *438;* v. 2, 96; v. 3, 1240
Theodoric the Pilgrim (XII-2), v. 2, *420*
Theodosian, Code (V-1), v. 1, *396*, 379, 438; v. 3, 1044
Theodosios of Bithynia (I-1 B.C.), v. 1, *211*, 834; v. 2, 1238; v. 3, 705
Theodosios II, emperor (V-1), v. 1, *396*, 341
Theodosios of Tirnovo, St., 1854
Theodosios Zygomalas, 995
Theologia Deutsch (XIV-1), *572*, 93, 351, 1092, 1844
Theology of Aristotle (V-2), v. 1, *406*, 834; v. 2, 287
Theomnestos, 1838
Theon of Alexandria (IV-2), v. 1, *367*, 834; v. 2, 1238; v. 3, ix, 1115, 1439, 1512, 1846
Theon of Smyrna (II-1), v. 1, *272*, 267, 268; v. 2, 972; v. 3, 745
Theophanes Confessor (IX-1), v. 1, *577*, 548, 776; v. 2, 858
Theophanes the Cretan, 1583
Theophanes the Greek, 1583
Theophanes Nonnos (X-1), v. 1, *639*, 821; v. 3, 1208
Theophano, princess, 727
Theophile of Cilicia, 943
Theophile of Cremona, 517
Theophile of Edessa (VIII-2), v. 1, *537*, 522
Theophile the Priest (XI-2), v. 1, *763*, 741, 745; (XII-1), v. 2, *219*, 1238; v. 3, 168, 170, 171, 727, 1131, 1564
Theophile Protospatharios (VII-1), v. 1, *478*, 834; v. 2, 1238; v. 3, 251, 843
Theophrastos of Eresos (IV-2 B.C.), v. 1, *143*, 834; v. 2, 1238; v. 3, 220, 224, 816, 836, 1186, 1434
Theophylactos Bulgaros, Achridensis (XI-2), v. 1, *751*, 739, 745
Theophylactos Simocattes (VII-1), v. 1, *481*, 462, 463; v. 3, 825
Theopompos of Chios (IV-2 B.C.), v. 1, *147*, 126
Theresa of Jesus, St., 92
theriaca, 751, 861
thermae, 287
Théry, father, 1844
Théry, Gabriel, 569, 570
Thesaurus religiose paupertatis, 393
Thessalonica, *see* Salonica
Thessalos of Tralles (I-2), v. 1, *262*, 244
Theudios of Magnesia (IV-2 B.C.), v. 1, *140*, 125
Thibault IV of Champagne, 928
Thieme, Ulrich, 1634
Thiene, *see* Gaetano
Thierry, Edouard, 1232
Thierry d'Hireçon, 227, 1181
Thietmar of Merseburg (XI-1), v. 1, *733*, 700, 702; v. 3, 767
Thikötter, Elisabet, 153
Thiriot, G., 575
Thomas de Almaigne, 218, 1174
Thomas of Alovid, 1260, 1267, 1323
Thomas, *see* Alvarus

Thomas Anglicus, 525, 529
Thomas, Antoine, 404, 452, 453, 454, 455, 865, 1389, 1392
Thomas (apostle), St., 358, 1607
Thomas Aquinas, St. (XIII-2), v. 2, *914*, 1239; v. 3, ix, 13, 40, 45, 54, 65, 66, 67, 77, 79, 80, 81, 84, 86, 91, 95, 97, 142, 166, 212, 266, 286, 314, 316, 326, 356, 398, 405, 407, 410, 416, 422, 450, 459, 460, 484, 488, 489, 499, 516, 517, 518, 521, 523, 525, 527, 538, 542, 551, 558, 563, 568, 570, 574, 577, 578, 587, 706, 750, 882, 985, 987, 992, 1004, 1052, 1058, 1075, 1085, 1087, 1095, 1276, 1343, 1346, 1347, 1386, 1388, 1400, 1412, 1431, 1494, 1706, 1831, 1839, 1869
Thomas of Arras, 546
Thomas Arundel, 1427
Thomas Bacon, 562
Thomas à Becket, St., 1421
Thomas of Bologna, 1480, 1579, 1679
Thomas Bradwardine (XIV-1), *668*, 49, 92, 116, 117, 148, 534, 542, 559, 560, 739, 1086, 1418, 1430, 1435, 1496, 1509, 1539, 1565, 1846
Thomas of Breslau, 1708
Thomas Brunton, 1040
Thomas Brygg, 1150, 1606
Thomas of Burton (XIV-2), *1746*, 1255, 1256
Thomas Caffarini, 1336, 1337
Thomas Caloria da Messina, 509, 561
Thomas de Cantelupe, 413
Thomas of Canterbury, St., 1248
Thomas of Cantimpré (XIII-1), v. 2, *592*, 1239; v. 3, 66, 208, 714, 817, 823, 1188
Thomas Casini, 1684
Thomas, Christians of St., 358, 1602, 1607
Thomas of Cilicia (XIV-1), *826*, 208, 356
Thomas de Cobham, 474
Thomas de Corsinis, 856
Thomas, E. C., 561
Thomas Ebendorfer, 1433
Thomas of Elmham, 1743
Thomas of Erfurt, 332
Thomas Fiortifiocca, 923
Thomas Fyslawe, 1416
Thomas, G. C., 1867
Thomas, G. M., 916
Thomas Gaetano, 521
Thomas Gallus, 530
Thomas del Garbo (XIV-2), *1672*, 837, 1086, 1192, 1220, 1222, 1241, 1481, 1679, 1681, 1851
Thomas Gascoigne, 1356
Thomas Gray (XIV-2), *1746*, 1312
Thomas Gray the Younger, 1256
Thomas Hemerken, 1359
Thomas Hoccleve, 1280, 1315, 1394, 1426
Thomas Holcot, 559, 1137
Thomas Jorz or Joyce (XIV-1), *557*, 91, 529
Thomas a Kempis, 1057, 1317, 1359, 1408
Thomas Kingsbury, 1502
Thomas of Lancaster, 563
Thomas de La Mare, 720, 1542, 1742
Thomas Le Miesier (XIV-1), *546*, 90
Thomas de Lupara, St., 476
Thomas Magister (XIV-1), *996*, 303, 320, 354, 355, 889, 1005
Thomas de Medzoph, 1260
Thomas de Modena, 142
Thomas of Mondino, 1481
Thomas Palaeologos, 1036
Thomas Penceth, 519
Thomas, *see* Peter
Thomas de Pisan (XIV-2), *1480*, 1106, 1109, 1131, 1136, 1137, 1579
Thomas de Pouille, 23
Thomas the Rhymer, 1741
Thomas of Romsey, 1403
Thomas, St., country, 782
Thomas of Saint Victor, 1417
Thomas Sampson, 1295, 1299, 1312, 1313
Thomas of Sarepta (XIV-2), *1708*, 1166, 1176, 1177, 1205, 1222, 1234, 1235
Thomas Scellinck (XIV-1), *884*, 250, 272, 350, 883, 1437
Thomas Scotus, 403
Thomas of Štítný (XIV-2), *1353*, 1056, 1092, 1322, 1348
Thomas of Strassburg (XIV-1), *577*, 82, 93, 444, 518
Thomas of Sutton (XIV-1), *558*, 92, 558, 943
Thomas Swinburne (XIV-2), *1606*, 1150
Thomas Torquemada, 1338, 1870
Thomas Usk, 1423
Thomas of Vercelli, 530, 1417
Thomas Waleys, 558, 1040
Thomas Walsingham (XIV-2), *1744*, 1128, 1255, 1279
Thomas of Wilton, 529
Thomas of York (XIII-2), v. 2, *950*, 740; v. 3, 91
Thomassin de Mazaugues, 1498
Thomism, 83, 95
Thompson, A. H., 1743
Thompson, D. V., 168, 169, 1132, 1906
Thompson, D'Arcy W., 488, 826
Thompson, E. M., 945, 1742, 1745
Thompson, J. W., 561, 1838, 1906
Thompson, Murray, 1859
Thompson, R. C., 757
Thompson, S. P., 494
Thompson, Stith, 1804, 1836, 1842, 1870
Thomson, M. H., 222
Thomson, S. H., 91, 1349
Thomson, William (Kelvin), 1843
Thopping, *see* Henry
Thorburn, W. M., 556
Thórdarson, *see* John; Sturla
Thordeman, Bengt, 1555
Thorfin Karlsefni, 194, 1608

Thórhallason, Egill, 196
Thórhallsson, *see* Magnus
Thorndike, L., 28, 115, 166, 270, 311, 392, 393, 427, 444, 448, 477, 532, 546, 717, 718, 721, 722, 835, 845, 857, 861, 878, 1292, 1401, 1486, 1509, 1516, 1567, 1671, 1672, 1677, 1684, 1817, 1834, 1846, 1865, 1906
Thorne, *see* William
Thorning, Hermann, 155
Thornley, J. C., 153
Thoroddsen, Thorvaldur, 1172
Thorold, Algar, 1336
Thoros Bondias, 1720
Thorp, R. W., 1667
Thórtharson, *see* Olafr
thought transference, 1492
three holy ones, 1854
three, rule of, 1773
Thucydides of Athens (V B.C.), v. 1, *106*, 83, 233; v. 3, 1650, 1803
Thüringen, *see* Otto
Thule, ultima, 515, 561
Thumba, *see* Berenger
Thureau-Dangin, F., 122
Thymaridas of Paros (IV-1 B.C.), v. 1, *117*, 111, 352
Thynne, William, 1423
Ṭibb nabawī, 257
ṭibb nabī, 966, 1214
ṭibb rūḥānī, 292
Tibbon, *see* Jacob b. Maḥir; Judah b. Saul; Moses b. Samuel; Samuel b. Judah
Tiberghien, Albert, 250, 1318
Tiberias, 365
Tibet, 380, 382, 384, 779, 1084, 1879
Tibetan, *see* Buddhism; medicine
Tibeto-Burman dialects, 383
Tibrīzī, *see* Tabrīzī
tidal forces, 215
tides, 563, 800, 1106, 1144, 1540, 1573, 1670
Tien, Hsing-chih, 1866
Tīfāshī, see Aḥmad b. Yūsuf
Tifernas, *see* Gregory
Tiffen, *see* John
Tiflis, 305
Tignonville, *see* William
tigretier, 1667
Tigrigna, 362
Tījānī, *see* 'Abdallāh b. Aḥmad
Tikkana Sōmayāji, 466
Tikkanna Yagvi, 466
Tilander, Gunnar, 1183
Tilbury, *see* Gervase
Tilemann Elhen v. Wolfhagen (XIV-2), *1755*, 1258
tiles, 757, 1134, 1473
Tillet, J. du, 1386
Tillyard, H. J. W., 162
Tilmannus Henrici (XIV-2), *1706*, 1174, 1205, 1238
Tilmīdh, b., *see* Hibatallāh b. Sa'īd
Timaeos, lexicographer (III-2), v. 1, *343*, 331
Timaeos of Tauromenium (III-1 B.C.), v. 1, *162*, 835
Timbuktu, 41, 1141, 1142, 1159
time, 537
time, *see* atomic
time measurement, 1788, 1848
time, reality of, 526
times of prayers, 1118
Timirtāshī, *see* Muḥammad b. 'Abdallāh
Timocharis of Alexandria (III-1 B.C.), v. 1, *156*, 150
Timtchenko, J., 738, 1488, 1566
Tīmūr Lang (XIV-2), *1467*, 6, 173, 380, 624, 1019, 1025, 1068, 1101, 1142, 1169, 1209, 1237, 1238, 1260, 1266, 1272, 1328, 1441, 1460, 1461, 1463, 1467, 1570, 1761, 1768, 1823, 1827, 1865
Tīmūrī style, 1473
tin, 727
tin mining, 219
Tinbergen, D. C., 463
tinctures, 754
Ṭīnī, *see* Aḥmad
Ṭiqṭaqā, b., *see* Muḥammad b. 'Alī
Tiraboschi, Girolamo, 839, 1197
Ṭirat kesef, 428, 429, 591
Tirel, *see* William
Ṭīrḥān, *see* Eliās
Tirmidhī, *see* Muḥammad b. 'Īsā
Tirnovo, *see* Theodosios
Tiro, Marcus Tullius (I-1 B.C.), v. 1, *217*, 203
Tiruvalla, copper plates, 358
Tīsaṭācārya (XIII-2), v. 2, *1103*, 789
Tisserant, Eugène, 540, 1007, 1717, 1787
Ṭivoli, *see* Bartholomew; Plato
Tiziano Colle, 1668
Tjerneld, Håkan, 1835
Tkatsch, Jaroslaus, 1622
ṭob ha-gamur, 450
tobacco, 1310
Tobard, Jérôme (S.J.), 1071, 1889, 1906
Todhunter, Isaac, 1813
Todi, *see* Jacopone
Ṭodros de Cavaillon (XIV-2), *1719*, 1212, 1242, 1720
Ṭodros b. Joseph Abulafia (XIII-2), v. 2, *882*, 607, 730
Ṭodros b. Meshullam Ṭodrosi (XIV-1), *435*, 62, 98
Ṭodros b. Moses Yom-ṭob, 1074, 1212, 1221, 1242, 1381, 1719
Ṭodros, *see* Qalonymos b. David
Ṭodrosi, *see* Ṭodros b. Meshullam
Tölner, *see* John
Toepke, Gustav, 1435, 1436
Töply, Ritter v., 851, 876
Töppen, Max, 932
Tofet we-'eden, 615

Tofte 'aruk, 492
Togaï, 781
Togan, A. Zeki Validi, 133
Toledan letter, 1113
Toledo, 1886, 1896
Toledo, *see* Abraham Alfaquin; Alfonso Vargas; Anthony; Isaac b. Abraham b. Laṭīf; John; John Tyrus; Marc; Yūsuf b. Waqqār
Toledo, art of, 1110, 1411
Toledo, blades of, 1175
Toledo tables, 1486
Toledot Alexander, 1519
toleration, 19, 22
Tolomei, Tolomeo, *see also* Ptolemy
Tolomei, *see* Bernard
Tolomei, Claudio, grammarian, 1300, 1301
Tolomei, *see* John
Tolosa, *see* Isaac b. Vidal; Vidal
Tomacelli, *see* Peter
Tomás, *see* Thomas
Tommaseo, Niccolò, 1336, 1291
Tommaso, *see* Thomas
Tongres, *see* Roland
Toprak, B. B., 1845
Tordesillas, treaty, 1859
Torel, *see* William
Torigny, *see* Robert
Torius, *see* Bernard
Torkomian, V., 461, 827
Tornay, S. C., 556
Tornberg, C. J., 805, 957, 1778
T'oros Roslin, 237
Torquemada, *see* John; Thomas
Torraca, Francesco, 496, 1851
Torre, *see* James
Torre, Lelio della, 491
Torres, Francisco, 1438
Torres Amat, Felix, 1574, 1906
Torrey, H. B., 1007
Torri, Luigi, 740
Torricelli, Evangelista, 1430
Torrigiano, *see* Peter
Tors, or Tort, *see* Lambert
Torsello, *see* Marino Sanudo
Tortosa, *see* Abraham b. Shem-ṭob; Shem-ṭob b. Isaac
Tortosa, disputations of, 1716
torture, 405, 1047, 1870
torture, judicial, 394. *See also* Inquisition
tosafot, 56, 397
toscaneggiamento, 337
Tossignano, *see* Albert; Anthony; Curialti; Peter; Philippa
Totti, *see* Pompilio
Totting, *see* Henry
touching, royal, 872
Toulouse, 403
Toulouse, *see* Joan; Joan de Castelnou; Stephen; Vidal de Tolosa
Tour-Landry, *see* Geoffrey
Tournai, 1257, 1746
Tournai, mass, 744
Tournay, *see* Gilbert
Tournebize, François, 1260
Tournebu, Adrien, 1005
Tournemire, *see* John
Tours, *see* Bernard Silvester; Gregory
Tout, T. F., 726, 941
Toxites, Michael, 752
Toynbee, Paget, 481, 491, 492, 494, 495, 496, 500, 1814
Tozer, H. F., 493, 494
Trabibus, *see* Peter
Trabot, *see* Perez
trachoma, 1664, 1724
trade, *see also* commerce; internationalism
trade roads, 770, 773
trade unions, 1654
trade, Venice, 770
tradition, oral, 419, 1804, 1870
traducianism, 242, 488
Traini, *see* Francis
Tralles, *see* Alexander; Anthemios; Asclepios
Trani, *see* Isaiah b. Elijah; Isaiah b. Mali
transmutation, 177, 752, 755, 1573, 1575, 1576, 1577
Transtorna, *see* Gonsalvo
transubstantiation, 992
Trapassi, Pietro, 583
Trapp, O. G., 1556
Trastamara, *see* Henry
Traube, Hermann, 1471
Traversari, *see* Ambrose
Traversari, Guido, 1808
Trebizond, 63, 123, 790
Trebizond, *see* Albert; Alexios II
Trebizond, school, 304, 1512
Tréguier, Collège, 477
Trémaugon, *see* Evrart
Trenchant, Jean, 773
Trent, *see* Augustine
trepidation, *see* equinoxes
Trets College, 1406
Tretz, *see* Isaac b. Abraham
Treu, M., 888
Trevelyan, G. M., 1349
Trevenant, *see* John
Treveris, Peter, 1394
Treves, *see* Ambrose; Bernard
Treves, Naphtali (Hirz) b. Eliezer, 417
Trevet, *see* Nicholas
Trevisa, 1393
Trevisa, *see* John
Trevisanus, 1577
Trevise, University, 72, 471
Trévoux, Dictionnaire, 1871
Trialogus, 1347
tribus principiis rerum naturalium, De, 519
Triclinios, *see* Demetrios

Tricot-Royer, 884
tridosa, 262
Trier, *see* Treves
trigonometry, 117, 129, 1875
Trilia, *see* Bernard
trilingual colleges, 375
Trincavelli, Vittorio, 589
Trindex, 1897
Trinitarians (XII-2), v. 2, *334*, 281, 550
Trinity, 314, 591
Trinity College, 475
Trinity Hall, 72, 475
Trionfi, 335, 506
Trionfo, *see* Augustine
Tripiṭaka, 107, 109, 138, 328, 382, 384, 637, 730, 1842, 1897, 1902, 1906
Tripiṭaka, Chinese (XIV-1), *466*
Tripiṭaka, Mongolian (XIV-1), *468*
triplum parts, 159
Tripoli, *see* Peter; Philip
Trissino, Gian Giorgio, 483, 493, 1300, 1301
Tristão Vaz-Teixeira, 183
Trithemius, *see* John
Tritton, A. S., 1117
trivarga, 1000
Trivero, Camillo, 77
Trivet, *see* Nicholas Trevet
trivium, 80
Trollope, M. N., 1563, 1907
Tromholt, Sophus, 709
Tronchin, Henry, 286
Tronchin, Théodore, 286
Tropfke, Johannes, 177, 1907
Trophimus, St., 1498
Troppau, *see* Martin
Tross, C. L. P., 1755
Trotula (XII-1), v. 2, *242*, 1241
Trotz, Theodor, 1374
Troubadours (XII-2), v. 2, *389*, 1241; v. 3, 338, 342, 1188
Troubetzkoy, N., 356
Trouvères (XII-2), v. 2, *389*, 25, 294; v. 3, 338, 1747
Troy, romance, 912, 1254, 1741
Troyes, 56
Troyes, *see* Guichard
Trucchi, Francesco, 913
Trumpp, Ernst, 1010
Truppa, *see* Ganden
truss, 874
truth, v, 9, 25
Tryphon Euangelides, 438
Tschudi, 1461
T'Sestich, Antoon van, 1318
Tsong Kapa (XIV-2), *1371*, 1069, 1331
tuberculosis, 1664, 1860
Ṭūbī, b., *see* Mūsā
Tucker, E. C., 1349
Tudela, *see* Benjamin b. Jonah; Judah ha-Levi; William
Ṭufail, b., Muḥammad b. 'Abd al-Malik (XII-2), v. 2, *354*, 1241; v. 3, 99, 608
Tughān Tīmūr, 232, 233, 1788
Tughluq, *see* Taghlaq
ṭughrā, 1327, 1785
Ṭughrā'ī, *see* Ḥusain b. 'Alī
Tuḥfat al-'arūs, 806
Tujīb, Banū, 827
Tuke, D. H., 279, 281
Tuki, Raphaele, 362
tulasī or tulsī, 778, 1835
Ṭulasī-Dāsa, 425
Tulasī kṛta Rāmāyaṇa, 425
Tulsī Dās, 425
Tūmart, b. (XII-1), v. 2, *165*, 113; v. 3, 1274
Ṭumlūs, b., *see* Yūsuf b. Muhammad
tumors, 895
Tunberg, Sven, 1898
Tunguz, 381
Tunis, 375
Tunsted, *see* Simon
Ṭūqān, Qadrī Ḥāfiẓ, 1833, 1907
Tūqtāmish Ghiyāth al-dīn, 1026
Turāb 'Alī, M., 759
Turba philosophorum, 165, 751, 1578
Turcs, 1872
Turfan, 378
turjamān (tarjumān, turjumān), 154
Turkish, 32, 378, 1840, 1875
Turkish-Arabic glossary, 1013
Turkish, *see* Chaghatāi
Turkish grammar, 1013
Turkish language, 1460
Turkish poetry, 1885
Turkish states, 624
Turkomānī, 1014
Turlupins, 23
Turmeda, *see* Anselm
turquet, 1846
Turrell, W. J., 1166
Ṭurṭūshī, *see* Muḥammad b. Walīd
ṭuruq, *see* Ṭarīqa
Tuscus, *see* Leo
Ṭūsī, *see* Muḥammad b. Ḥasan; Muhammad b. Maḥmūd; Muẓaffar b. Muhammad; Nāṣir al-dīn
Ṭūṭī-nāma, 465, 1810
Tuzūkāt-i-Tīmūrī, 1272
twelve animals, *see* cycle
Twici, *see* William
Twinger, *see* James
Twiss, Travers, 324, 1423
Twyne, Thomas, 507
Twysden, Robert, 1743
Tyler, *see* Wat
tympanites, 1666
Tynemouth, *see* John
Tyngewich, *see* Nicholas
type, wooden, 830
typography, 144, 830, 1125

typography, Chinese, 733
typography, earliest printed account of invention, 911
typography, Korean, 1562
Typsiles, 1551
tyrannicide, 1274, 1869
tyranny, 1816, 1883
Tyre, *see* William
Tyrman, *see* Jörg
Tyrus, *see* John
Tyrwhitt, Thomas, 1424
Tyson, Edward, 13, 272, 1228, 1775
Tyssen-Amherst, Alicia M., 1181
Tzetzes, *see* Isaac; John

u and v, 463
'Ubaida, a. (VIII-2), v. 1, *541*, 523, 524; v. 3, 376, 1636
'Ubaidallāh b. 'Abdallāh, *see* b. Khurdādhbih
'Ubaidallāh b. Jibrīl b. Bakhtyashū' (XI-1), v. 1, *730*, 700, 701; v. 2, 442; v. 3, 1638, 1639
'Ubaidallāh b. Mas'ūd Bukhārī, 628
Ubaldi, *see* Angelo; Baldo; Francis; Peter
Uberti, 1600
Uberti, *see* Fazio; Manente
Ubertino da Carrara, 848, 1243, 1669, 1818
Uberto di Cortenova (XIV-1), *857*, 245, 284, 1838
Uberto Decembrio, 1440, 1822
Ubriachi, 1858
Uc Faidit, 340
Uccello, *see* Paul
Uchtmann, Allard, 594
'ūd, 163
Udine, *see* Nicholas
Ueberweg, Friedrich, 1907
Ünver, A. S., 972, 975, 1216, 1465, 1474, 1726, 1728
Ugo, *see also* Hugh
Ugo, *see* Francis
Ugolini, 124
Ugolini, *see* Bernardino
Ugolini, Biagio, 420
Ugolino Marini Gibertuzzi, 400
Ugolino de Montecatini (XIV-2), *1686*, 1193, 1222, 1240, 1673, 1685
Ugolino Vivaldo (XIII-2), v. 2, *1062*, 36, 773; v. 3, 186, 190
Ugone di Provenza, 1235
Uguccione da Rio, 1243
Uhagon, F. R. de, 1736
Uhden, Richard, 183
Uhl, Willo, 573
Uhlig, Gustav, 1822
Uighūr, 71, 104, 139, 359, 378, 380, 384, 469, 734, 785, 830, 832, 970, 972, 1009, 1015, 1016, 1084, 1121, 1537, 1562, 1587, 1840
Uilenspiegel, 1190
Ukhuwwa, *see* Muḥammad b. Muḥammad
Ulf Gudmarsson, 1354
Ulfilas (IV-1), v. 1, *349*, 836; v. 3, 351
Ulin Apt, 1206
Uljāi'tū Khudābanda, 203, 970
Ullman, B. L., 1862
Ullmann, Walter, 1870
Ulm, 1114
Ulm, *see* Jacob
Ulman Stromer (XIV-2), *1579*, 176, 1112, 1124, 1137, 1258, 1278, 1318
Ulpian (III-1), v. 1, *328*, 836
Ulreuch Bessnitzer, 1553
Ulric, *see* Odoric
Ulrich Boner (XIV-1), *579*, 93, 351
Ulrich of Strassburg (XIII-2), v. 2, *944*, 739
Ulrich v. Tennstädt, 1153
Ulrich of Vienna, 575
Ulūgh Beg, 1119, 1120, 1466, 1468, 1470, 1473
'ulūm al-ṭarīq, 153
Umaiya b. 'Abd al-'Azīz b. a. Ṣalt (XII-1), v. 2, *230*, 1227; v. 3, 1212, 1221, 1374
'Umar b. 'Abdallāh Suhrawardī (XII-2), v. 2, *363*, 1242; v. 3, 420, 1458
'Umar b. 'Abd al-Raḥmān, *see* 'Amr b. 'Abd al-Raḥmān Karmānī
'Umar b. Aḥmad b. 'Adīm (XIII-1), v. 2, *683*, 1242
'Umar b. Aḥmad b. Khaldūn, 1767
'Umar b. 'Alī b. Fāriḍ (XIII-1), v. 2, *600*, 1172; v. 3, 626, 1454, 1722
'Umar b. 'Alī b. Samura, 619
'Umar b. Farrukhān Ṭabarī (IX-1), v. 1, *567*, 836; v. 2, 1242
'Umar b. Hajjāj, a. (XI-2), v. 1, *766*, 741, 746; v. 2, 56
'Umar b. Ibrāhīm Khayyāmī, *see* 'Umar Khayyām
'Umar b. Isḥāq Hindī (XIV-2), *1454*, 1099
'Umar Khalwatī, 1069
'Umar Khayyām (XI-2), v. 1, *759*, 813; v. 2, 1242; v. 3, 1457
'Umar b. Muḥammad Khabbāzī, 1454
'Umar b. Muḥammad Nasafī (XII-1), v. 2, *164*, 1242; v. 3, 1462
'Umar b. Muḥammad b. Wardī, 805, 963
'Umar b. Muẓaffar b. Wardī (XIV-1), *962*, 103, 201, 257, 308, 373, 794, 805
'Umar b. Yūsuf, sulṭān al-Ashraf, 1637
'Umāra b. 'Alī Yamanī (XII-2), v. 2, *446*, 311; v. 3, 958
'Umarī, *see* Aḥmad b. Yaḥyā b. Faḍlallāh
umbilicanimi, 95, 584
Umbra, *see* Thomas Scellinck
'Umdat al-kuttāb, 175
'Umdat al-ṭabīb, 1850
'umrān, 'ilm, 1771
'umūd fī uṣūl al-ṭibb, 432
'Unān, *see* Muḥammad b. 'Abdallāh
Underhill, Evelyn, 86, 582, 1416, 1476
Underwood, H. H., 1907

Ungerer, Alfred, 722, 1541
Uniat, 54
unicorn, 825, 1186, 1242
United Brethren, 1441
unito et unitate, De, 101
unity, 596
unity of knowledge, 19
unity of mankind, 19, 21
unity of nature, 19
universalism, 1885
universals, 81, 552, 563, 1339. *See also* realism
universities, 78, 1401, 1890, 1900
universities, birth of European (XII-2), v. 2, *350*
universities (XIII-1), v. 2, *570*, 1242
universities, *see* internationalism
University College, 475
university records, 1906
"untori," 1656
Unwin, George, 153
Upādhyāya, Baladeva, 1369
Upanishad, 93, 569, 571
Uqiyānūs al-basīṭ, 1827
Urban of Bologna (XIV-1), *519*, 88
Urban V, pope, 1032
Urban VI, pope, 1032, 1335
Urbani de Gheltof, Giovanni, 1677
urbanism, 152
Urbanists, 1032
Urbano, *see* Urban
Urdang, Georg, 290, 1907
'Urḍī, *see* Mu'aiyad al-dīn
Urdū, 377, 1329, 1330, 1477
Urganj, *see* Sharaf
urine, 289, 843, 890, 1380, 1836. *See also* uroscopy
urine therapy, 1836
urinomancy, 1207
Urkhān, 40, 1025
Urmawī, *see* Maḥmūd b. a. Bakr
uroscopy, 251, 252, 269, 509, 853, 1228
Urso of Calabria (XII-2), v. 2, *437*, 1242
Urstisius, 935
Ursula, St., 1045
Uṣaibi'a, Aḥmad b. Qāsim b. a. (XIII-1), v. 2, *685*, 1242; v. 3, 960, 1263
Usāmah b. Murshid b. Munqidh (XII-2), v. 2, *446*, 1207
Usener, Hermann, 438, 1513
Usher, A. P., 128, 1907
Usk, *see* Adam; Thomas
Uskub (Üsküb), 39
Uso di Mare, 785
Uspenskij, Th., 586
Usque, Abraham, 1444
Ussani, Vincenzo, 1814
uṣūl al-fiqh, 1781
usury, 326, 328, 525, 999, 1494, 1838. *See also* interest
'Uṭārid b. Muḥammad (IX-1), v. 1, *572*, 547, 565; v. 2, 837
Utenbroeke, *see* Philip
uterus, *see* womb
'Uthmān, house of, 40
'Uthmān b. Jinnī (X-2), v. 1, *689*, 652, 654; v. 3, 372, 1010
'Uthmān Muḥammad Amīn, 431
'Uthmān, a., *see* Sa'īd b. Ya'qūb
'Uthmān b. Ṣalāḥ b. Ṣalāḥ (XIII-1), v. 2, *558*, 490, 1132
'Uthmān b. 'Umar b. Ḥājib (XIII-1), v. 2, *700*, 1179; v. 3, 373, 628, 632, 1011, 1455, 1462
utilitate digitorum, De, 448
Utley, F. L., 1857
Utopia, 554
Utrecht, *see* Adelbold; John
Utrecht Arzneibuch, 1205, 1711
Uvarov, B. P., 1836
Uwais Bahādur, 1728
Uyemura, Rokurō, 170
'uyūn al-masā'il, 435
Uzbek Soviet Republic, 1470
Uzunçarşılıoğlu, I. H., 624, 1644, 1726, 1728
Uzzano, *see* John
Uzziel, 1517

Vacant, A., 1881, 1907
Vacarius (XII-2), v. 2, *465*, 1243
Vacca, G., 597
Vaccaro, Leopold, 499
vaccination, 905
vacuum, 148, 537, 539, 543, 547, 559, 564, 604, 739, 1127, 1429, 1436, 1506. *See also* horror vacui
Vadaterra, *see* Alfonso
Vade in pace, 24
Vademecum in tribulatione, 1572
Vadino Vivaldo (XIII-2), v. 2, *1062*, 36, 773; v. 3, 186, 190
Vadstena, 1056, 1354
Vagānu Śāsana, 466
Vāgbhaṭa the Elder (VII-1), v. 1, *480*, 836; v. 2, 1243; v. 3, 259, 280, 1585
Vahram of Edessa (XIII-2), v. 2, *1117*, 335, 795
Vaiçeiṣika, 1891
Vaidyanārāyana Sarmā Puraṁdare, 1731
Vailhé, S., 1363
Vaiśeshika, 180, 1366
Vaishṇava, 60, 1475
Vajrayāna, 59
Vaka, Demetra, 1247
Valabrègue, *see* Asher b. Moses
Valdac, *see* Durand
valence, chemical, 442
Valence, *see* Mary
Valencia, 375

Valencia, *see* Berengarius Eymericus; Peter Paschal
Valenciennes, 1257, 1751
Valentina Visconti, 1699
Valentinus, 1576
Valerius Maximus, 579, 1075, 1391, 1434, 1482, 1736, 1813
Valerius Probus, M. (I-2), v. 1, *265*, 245
Valers, *see* Francis
Valescus de Taranta, 426, 877, 1199, 1222, 1235, 1696, 1697
Valla, *see* George
Valladolid, *see* Alfonso
Vallet de Viriville, 1578
Valli, Luigi, 500
Vallsecha, *see* Gabriel
Vālmīki, 1395
Valois, Noël, 43, 529, 535, 540, 989, 1509
Valori, Marquis de, 1810
Valturio, *see* Robert
values, *see* absolute
Vámbéry, Arminius, 1015
vampire, 1865
Vaṃśabrāhmaṇa, 1368, 1369
Van Aalst, J. A., 162
Vanagan, *see* John
Van Andel, M. A., 1361
Van Arenbergh, Emile, 1391, 1605
Van Arendonk, C., 155, 1099, 1266
Vance, W. R., 325
Van de Kamp, J. L. J., 1795
Vandelli, G., 493
Van den Berg, *see* Josse
Van den Bergh, Simon, 1778
Van den Bogarde, *see* Henry
Van den Dorpe, *see* Roland
Van den Oudenrijn, M. A., 1442
Vandenpeereboom, Alphonse, 884
Vanden Wyngaert, Anastasius, 779, 1907
Van de Put, Albert, 756
Van der Aa, A. J., 938
Van der Basselen, *see* Heylwig
Van der Does, Jan, 937
Van der Goes, *see* Hugh
Vander Haegen, *see* William
Van der Haeghen, Ferdinand, 1183
Vanderkindere, Léon, 1907
Van der Linden, H., 153, 939
Van der Meer, H. J., 1605
Van der Meer, M. J., 1318
Vander Meersch, Aug., 1754
Van de Wijnpresse, Hildegarde, 575
Vandier, Jacques, 282
Van Duyse, Hermann, 1183, 1556
Van Dyck, 241
Van Eyck, 111, 170
Van Ginneken, Jac., 1362
Van Gulik, R. H., 162, 1848, 1857
Van Hamel, A. G., 1275
Van Hée, 1847
Vanini, G. C., 562
Van Kuyk, J., 1799
Van Leersum, E. C., 884, 885
Van Loey, Adolf, 939
Van Millingen, Alexander, 1907
Van Moé, Emile, 1493
Van Oosterzee, H. M. C., 823
Van Otterloo, A. A., 582
Van Rensselaer, Mrs. J. K., 1563
Van Rijnberk, Gerard, 270
Van Roosbroeck, Rob., 823, 1111
Van Schevensteen, A. F. C., 281
Van Schoor, Oscar, 251
Van Slee, J. C., 582
Van Vaernewyck, Marc, 821, 1183
Varaggio, *see* James
Varāhamihira (VI-1), v. 1, *428*, 836; v. 3, 215, 1584
Vardan the Great (XIII-2), v. 2, *1115*, 1243; v. 3, 356
Vardan of Lori, 1178
Varennes, P. G. de, 1612
Vargas, *see* Alfonso
varicella, 881
varices, 1197
Varignana, *see* Bartholomew; John; Matthew; Peter; William
variola, 881
variolation, 261, 289, 905
Varro, Marcus Terentius (I-2 B.C.), v. 1, *225*, 836; v. 3, 812, 813, 1180, 1288, 1807
Vasari, Giorgio, 500
Vasciéntz, *see* Sergius
Vasiliev, A. A., 790, 1853, 1907
Vasse, Antoine, 1750
Vastu-kōśa, 1828
Vasubandhu (IV-1), v. 1, *350*, 836; v. 3, ix
Vattier, Pierre, 435, 1474
Vaucelle, Louis, 1010
Vaucluse, 502
Vaux Cernay, *see* Peter
Vavřinec, *see* Laurence
Vayssière, Aimé, 1633
Vázquez Queipo, Vicente, 713
Veazie, W. B., 1426
Veda, 382, 1369, 1909
Veda-bhāshya-bhūmikā-saṃgraha, 1369
Vedabrāhmaṇa, 1369
Vedānta, 85, 1069, 1366, 1844
Vedāntavāgīśa, Anandachandra, 1369
Vedasaṃhitā, 1369
Vedast, abbot of St., 1796
Vedeha (XIV-1), *422*, 59, 310, 383, 1370
Vegetius, Flavius Renatus (IV-2), v. 1, *368*, 836; v. 2, 932; v. 3, 457, 1313, 1393, 1482, 1493, 1552
Vegetius, Publius Renatus, veterinarian (IV-2), v. 1, *374*, 361; v. 3, 1669
Veith, Ilsa, 260
Velletri, table, 1141, 1144

velocity, *see* angular
Velthem, *see* Lewis
Vendrell (de Millás), Francisca, 1843
venenis eorumque remediis, De, 442
venesection, *see* bloodletting
Venette, *see* John
Venice, 152, 171
Venice, *see* Elia; James; John; Paul; Tarifa; trade; Walter
Venis, Arthur, 1367
Venni, Giuseppe, 779
Ventoux, Mount, 188, 510, 540
Ventura de Sarezana, 776
Venturi, G. B., 706
Venus, 1517
Vera, Francisco, 1907
Vérard, Antoine, 548
Verberia, *see* Peter
Vercelli, Francesco, 497
Vercelli, *see* Thomas
Vercoullie, Jozef, 349, 939
Vercruysse, H., 1004
Verdam, J., 251
Verdun, *see* Bernard
veredus, 1786
Vergerio, *see* Peter Paolo
Vergil, *see* Virgil
Vergilio, *see* Polidoro
Verkade, Willibrord, 1132
Verlinden, Charles, 1663
Vermeylen, August, 956
Verne, Ulrich, 1755
Vernet, F., 586
Vernia, *see* Nicholas
Verniger, *see* Conrad
Vernon, William Warren, 488, 494, 501, 502, 1813, 1814
Verona, *see* Guarino; Hillel b. Samuel; James; John Mansionario; Scaligeri
verre de fougère, 171
Verrier, René, 1831
Verrill, A. H., 230
vertigo, 1212, 1236, 1449
Vesalius, 5, 15, 267, 270, 842, 1223, 1399, 1357
Vesconte, *see* Perrinus; Peter
vespers, 716
Vespucci, *see* Amerigo
Vesuccio, *see* Michelino
veterinary medicine, 284, 1216, 1238, 1837, 1892, 1893, 1896
veterinary medicine in Spain (XIII-2), v. 2, *1091*
Vetter, 746
Vetter, Ferdinand, 571, 575
via antiqua, 554, 1400, 1429
via moderna, 92, 554, 1400, 1429
via nova, 1504
Vian, Alsager, 753
Vianeo family, 1234
Vianey, Joseph, 516
Viard, Jules, 1748
Vibius Sequester, 1806
Vicaire, Georges, 1633
Vicente, *see* Vincent
Vicenza, 919
Vicenza, *see* John
Vicini, E. P., 290
Vick, *see* Henry
Vicko v. Geldersen, 125
Vico, 1262, 1775
Victor, St., 1008
Victor, *see* Vittorino
victoria Christi, De, 407
Victorius of Acquitania (V-2), v. 1, *409*, 837
Victorius, B., 566
Victring, *see* John
Vidal, *see also* Vital
Vidal de Bourian, 1375
Vidal, *see* Ephraim
Vidal b. Labi Benveniste, 1061, 1716
Vidal b. Labi de la Caballeria, 1716
Vidal, *see* Peter; Raymond
Vidal de Tolosa (XIV-1), *610*, 55, 100
Vidas, *see* Elijah b. Moses
Vidyābhūshaṇa, Sati Chandra, 1371
Vidyālaṅkāra, Dīnanātha, 1000
Vidyāmātrasiddhi, 729
Vidyāraṇya, 1366
Vidyāsāgara, Īśvarachandra, 1367
Vidyāsagara, Jībānanda, 1369
Vienna, *see* Ulrich
Vienna, University, 1078, 1398
Vienne, council of, 375
Viennois, *see* Anthony; Humbert
Vierdordt, H., 1874, 1908
Vigevano, *see* Guido
Vigier, Jean, 853
Vignai, *see* John
Vignaux, Paul, 80, 547
Vigne, *see* Peter of Vinea
Vigo, Pietro, 1232
Vigor, Simon, 411
Vijayanagar, 41, 1027, 1069, 1102, 1291, 1366
Vijñāneśvara (XI-2), v. 1, *781*, 744, 746
Vikings, age of (IX-1), v. 1, *576*, 548; v. 3, 194, 715, 716, 1124, 1609, 1612
Vikings, *see* ships
Viladestes, *see* Matthew; Mecia
Vildhaut, H., 931
Villain, E. F., 1578
Villani, *see* John; Matthew
Villani, N., 918
Villani, *see* Philip
Villanova, *see* Arnold
Villard de Honnecourt (XIII-2), v. 2, *1033*, 1243; v. 3, 146, 345, 718, 1177, 1178
Villari, Pasquale, 989, 1198
Villarosa, marchese di, 501
Villasandino, *see* Alfonso Álvarez
Villault de Bellefond, 1147

Villecourt, Louis, 1007
Villedieu, *see* Alexander
Villehardouin, Geoffrey (XIII-1), v. 2, *670*, 1176; v. 3, 928, 948
Villeneuve, *see* Arnold of Villanova
Villenfagne, Hilarion de, 1751
Villiers, Cosmas de, 1392, 1575
Villon, *see* Francis
Vilmar, Eduardus, 1762
Vinario, *see* Raymond Chalmel
vinaya, 468
Vinayapiṭaka, 466
Vincent Andreoli, 1134
Vincent, Auguste, 854
Vincent of Beauvais (XIII-2), v. 2, *929*, 1243; v. 3, 65, 88, 89, 166, 314, 339, 411, 457, 510, 577, 583, 770, 831, 858, 922, 938, 1075, 1088, 1170, 1171, 1265, 1277, 1281, 1391, 1443, 1603, 1630, 1808
Vincent of Cracow (XIII-1), v. 2, *679*, 526
Vincent, Eugène, 262
Vincent Ferrer, St. (XIV-2), *1339*, 1035, 1042, 1060, 1052, 1306
Vincent Mazuello, 533
Vinci, *see* Leonard
Vindicianus (IV-2), v. 1, *374*, 361; v. 2, 237
Vine, Guthrie, 1689
Vinea, *see* Peter
Vineis, *see* Raymond of Capua
vines, 812
Vinogradoff, Paul, 1794, 1908
Viñzamūru Kṛishṇamāchāryulu, 466
Violante, queen, 1820
Violas of Rodez (XIV-2), *1717*, 1211, 1221
Violier des histoires, 456
Viollet, Paul, 414
Vīraśaiva, 383
Virchow, Rudolf, 280, 295
Virga, *see* Albertin
Virgil (I-2 B.C.), v. 1, *221*, 219, 220; v. 3, 253, 299, 481, 507, 512, 751, 813, 933, 942, 1031, 1144, 1149, 1252, 1288, 1294, 1299, 1321, 1418, 1456, 1482, 1706, 1745, 1755, 1772, 1814, 1815
Virgil of Salzburg (VIII-1), v. 1, *516*, 505; v. 2, 45; v. 3, 192
Virgilio, *see* John
Virgin, *see* Peter
virginity, simulation, 872
Viridarium, 426
virtual displacement, 146
virtus motiva, 738
vis medicatrix naturae, 871
Visby, 1555
Visby, battle, 1125
Visconti, *see* Barnabò; Galeazzo; Gian Galeazzo; John; Luchino; Matthew; Valentina
Viser, *see* Peter
"Visierkunst," 1112, 1318, 1580
Visierruthe, 1318, 1580
Visigothic, *see* law
vision, 1492, 1540, 1723
vision, beatific, 44, 45, 49, 401, 524, 526, 527
Viśishṭa-Advaita, 1475
Visitation of Mary, Sisters of the, 1037
Vissière, Arnold, 1586, 1589, 1891, 1898, 1908
Viśveśvara Bhaṭṭa (XIV-2), *1799*, 1218, 1281, 1330, 1730
Vita nuova, 482
vita solitaria, De, 507
Vital, *see also* Vidal
Vital du Four (XIV-1), *531*, 48, 87, 90, 207, 248, 278, 285, 516
Vital, *see* Ḥayyim b. Joseph; Orderic
Vital, physician, 1246
vitamins, 196, 268, 905
Vitanza, Calogero, 497
Vitelo (XIII-2), v. 2, *1027*, 1246; v. 3, 111, 602, 705, 707, 1491
Viterbo, *see* Godfrey; James
Vitoria, *see* Pascal
vitrarii, 171
Vitruvius Pollio, Marcus (I-2 B.C.), v. 1, *223*, 837; v. 2, 27; v. 3, 738, 1171, 1291, 1569, 1772, 1808
Vitry, *see* James; Philip
Vittori, Benedetto, 1430, 1431
Vittorino da Feltre, 1080, 1290, 1292, 1296, 1407, 1565, 1819
Vittorino di Ramboldini, 1290
Vitus, dance of St., 1665
Vivādaratnākara, 1000
Vivaldi, brothers, 186, 786. *See* Ugolino; Vadino
Vivaldo, *see* Sorleone
Vivenzio Colle, 1668
Vives, b., 1373
Vives, Juan Luis, 536, 737
Viviani, Ugo, 515, 855
Viviers, *see* Raymond Chalmel
vivisection, 266
Vizcay, Dom Martin de, 279
Vladimir, St. (X-2), v. 1, *655*, 647; v. 2, 162
Vladislav, *see* Ladislas
Vlekke, B. H. M., 42, 1627
Vocabularium Bibliae, 332
Vögele, H. H., 234
Voel, Guillaume, 1822
Voet, *see* John
Vogel, J. P., 1619
Vogels, Johann, 1605
Voigt, L. G., 514
volcanoes, 216, 1172, 1654, 1896
voles, 1190
Vollers, Carl, 1784
Volpe, Carlo della, 775
Volpe, Galvano della, 570, 1301
Voltaire, 101, 505, 615, 1457, 1870
Voltelini, Hans v., 931

volucraries, 239, 1178
Vonderlage, Balduin, 845
Voorne, *see* Gerald
Vopadeva (XIII-2), v. 2, *1103*, 1244; v. 3, 382, 1474
Voragine, *see* James
Vorilong, *see* William
Vorstius, Conrad, 1387
Vorwahl, H., 1811
Vosem.chastei slova, 355
Vossler, Karl, 496
Vox clamantis, 1427
Vrieman, *see* John; William
Vṛinda (VIII-2), v. 1, *537*, 522
Vuitry, Adolphe, 411
vulgari eloquentia, De, 482
Vulgate, 330, 353, 369, 1321, 1325
Vuylsteke, Julius, 1561
Vyāsa, 1395
Vystijd, M., 931

Waas, Christian, 580
wabā, 895
Wace of Jersey (XII-2), v. 2, *453*, 256, 313; v. 3, 462
Waddell, L. A., 1070, 1372
Wadding, Luke, 7, 739, 784, 785, 1568
Wade, T. F., 1891
Wade-Evans, A. W., 1864
Wadington, *see* William
wafā', 961
Wafā', a. (X-2), v. 1, *666*, 787; v. 2, 621, 1007; v. 3, 598
Wafayāt al-a'yān, 308
Wāfī bi-l-wafayāt, 308, 959
Wāfid, b. (XI-1), v. 1, *728*, 699, 702; v. 2, 1244; v. 3, 287, 1074, 1212, 1221, 1374, 1850
Wagaru (XIII-2), v. 2, *1134*, 801; v. 3, 322, 382
Wagenseil, J. C., 1446
wager of law, 1044
Wagner, Philipp, 1747
Wagner, Wilhelm, 825
Wahb, b., v. 1, 571, 636; v. 3, 1587
Wahb a. Kabsha, 1587
Wahhābī, 58, 103
Wahhābīya, 422
Wahhās, *see* 'Alī b. Ḥasan
Waḥshīya, b., *see* Muḥammad b. 'Alī
waḥy ghair matlū, 1065
Wailly, Natalis de, 411, 458, 927, 930
Waite, A. E., 752, 1316
Wajīh Qalyūbī, 1006
Wakhtang, king, 305, 1120
wakīl, 154
Walad, *see* Sulṭān
Walafrid Strabo (IX-1), v. 1, *570*, 546
Walcher of Malvern (XII-1), v. 2, *209*, 1244
Walcott, M. E. C., 1403
Walde, Bernhard, 1509
Waldemar V of Denmark, 1020
Waldensians (XII-2), v. 2, *331*, 280, 695; v. 3, 404
Waldhauser, *see* Conrad
Waldo, *see* Peter
Wales, *see* Gerald; Joan; John
Waley, Arthur, 235, 1069, 1332, 1333, 1791
Waleys, *see* John; Thomas
walī, 292
Wallach, Luitpold, 1864
Wallachia, Black, 976
Waller Zeper, C. M., 773, 1111
Wallerand, G., 1004
Walleser, Max, 1331
Wallingford, *see* Richard
Wallis, Henry, 1134
Wallis, John, 586, 746
Walpole, H. R., 331
walrus, 194, 1186
Walser, Ernst, 1292
Walsh, J. J., 295, 873, 1908
Walsham, *see* William
Walsingham, *see* Thomas
Walter Agilinus (XIII-1), v. 2, *656*, 784; v. 3, 65, 254, 264, 882, 892
Walter of Armagh, 558
Walter de Biblesworth, 348
Walter Bower, 1254, 1741
Walter Brit (XIV-2), *1500*, 1110, 1203, 1233
Walter Brute, 1054, 1501
Walter Burley (XIV-1), *563*, 92, 150, 303, 560, 1127, 1431, 1494, 1844
Walter Catton, 115, 557
Walter de Hemingburgh (XIV-1), *942*, 303, 1743
Walter of Henley (XIII-1), v. 2, *647*, 1244; v. 3, 345, 814, 1181
Walter Hilton (XIV-2), *1415*, 1089, 1091, 1314
Walter Lolhard, 23
Walter de Merton, 473
Walter of Metz (XIII-1), v. 2, *591*, 1244; v. 3, 199, 510
Walter de Milemete, 725
Walter Odington (XIV-1), *661*, 116, 160, 178, 1568, 1833
Walter de Stapeldon, 474
Walter Venice, 225
Walter Wiburn, 1150
Walton the Irishman (XIII-1), v. 2, *647*
Walton, Izaac, 1166
Walz, A. M., 1038
Wampen, *see* Eberhard; Evert
Wandsworth, *see* Roger Clerk
Wang, C. H., 1140
Waqar, *see* Joseph b. Abraham; Joseph b. Isaac; Samuel
waqf, 200
Wāqidī, *see* Muḥammad b. 'Umar
Waqqār, *see* Yahūda b. Solomon
Waqqāṣ, *see* Sa'd

war, 1797
Warāmīn, *see* Sa'd al-dīn
Waraq, 175
Wardī, b., *see* 'Umar b. Muḥammad; 'Umar b. Muẓaffar
Ware, J. R., 28, 1071, 1858
Ware, *see* William
Warendorp, *see* Herman
Wareru (XIII-2), v. 2, *1134*, 801
Warnecke, F., 1556
Warner, G. F., 1604, 1605
Warner, Langdon, 170, 1472
Warnkoenig, L. A., 1751
Warrack, Grace, 1090
Warrāq, *see* Muḥammad b. Ibrāhīm Waṭwāṭ
Warren, J., 1394
Warren, K. M., 1415
Warthin, A. S., 1232
Wāṣil, b., *see* Muḥammad b. Sālim
Waṣṣāf, *see* 'Abdallāh b. Faḍlallāh
wasters, 757
Wat Tyler, 1024, 1279, 1427, 1745
watches, 1873
watches, pocket, 1546
water classic, 205
water clock, *see* clepsydra
watermarks, 176
waters, medicinal, 834
waters, mineral, 1670
Watkins, M. G., 1166
Watrigant, father, 1509
Watteau, 1135
Waṭwāṭ, *see* Muḥammad b. Ibrāhīm
Wauters, Alphonse, 1502
Wautier d'Aygalliers, Alfred, 582
Waxman, Meyer, 1448
Way, Albert, 1316, 1556
weasel, 1863
weather record, 117
Weber, A., 1369
Weck, Wolfgang, 1177
Weczerzik v. Planheim, Karl, 499
Wedel, T. O., 1908
Weeks, M. E., 177, 1908
Weidenreich, Franz, 1860
Weider, Manfred, 153
Weigel, Oswald, 1051
weight drive, 144, 718
weights and measures (XIV-1), *711*, 111, 773, 791, 837, 840, 844, 998, 1124, 1204, 1499, 1515, 1580, 1637, 1685, 1750, 1787
weights and measures, Chinese, 1848
weights and measures, *see* decimal
weights and measures, Muslim vs. ancient, 1847
weights, medicinal, 712
Weijers, H. E., 1783
Weil, Gotthold, 400, 1720
Weil, Isidore, 607
Weil, Samson, 1376, 1377
Weiland, Ludwig, 935
Weinberg, J. R., 547
Weindler, Fritz, 1908
Weinstock, Stephanus, 1877
Weise, Paul, 815
Weiss, Konrad, 570
Weisse, Joseph, 594
Weitmil (Weitmühl), *see* Beneš
Welborn, M. C., 28, 293, 838, 840, 845, 873, 1704, 1706, 1748
Wellesz, E., 162
Wellhausen, Julius, 1451
Wells, H. W., 1415
Wells, J. E., 1908
Wells cathedral clock, 1543
Welsh, *see* law; medicine
Weltingen, *see* Leopold
Weltzien, G., 918
Wenceslas (Václav) IV of Bohemia, 472, 1258, 1751, 1753, 1824
Wenck, Karl, 887
Wendover, *see* Richard; Roger
Wenemaer, *see* William
Wensinck, A. J., 136, 1066, 1883, 1908
Wentworth, lady, 1636
Wenzig, Joseph, 1824
Werbluner, S. Z., 592
werewolf, 1313
Werlauff, Erich Christian, 196
Werner, E. C., 1873, 1908
Werner, Eric, 1845
Werner Groote, 1357
Werner, Karl, 540, 1908
Werner v. Orseln, 931
Wernich, Agathon, 1874, 1908
Wernsdorf, Gottlieb, 825
Wescott, W. W., 1577
Wesel, *see* John
Wesley, E. A., 1663
Wesley, John, 1349, 1361
Wesselski (not Wesseiski), Albert, 491
Wessely, K., 175
Wessman, N., 1700
West, A. F., 561
Westcott, G. H., 1476
Westenrieder, Lor., 993
Westland, A. M., 1224
Westman, K. B., 1356
Westminster effigies, 1561, 1866
Westminster, *see* Matthew; Parliament
Weston, S., 977
Westwood, Thomas, 1165
Wharey, J. B., 533
Wharton, Henry, 560, 945
Wheatley, L. A., 1361
wheel balance, 718
wheel maps, 767
wheel, spinning, 1553
White, A. C., 494, 496
White, A. D., 1136, 1908

White, J. G., 829
White, Joseph, 1472
White, Lynn, jr., 1908
White, W. C., 221, 233, 758, 833, 1071, 1590, 1860
White Monks, 395
White Sea, 194. *See also* Scandinavian expeditions
Whitehill, W. M., 174, 372
Whitfield, J. H., 515
Whiting, B. J., 1425, 1753
Whiting, M. B., 496
Whitlock, H. P., 1471
Whitmore, M. E., 1425
Whitney, J. P., 1348
Whittlesey, *see* William
Whymant, A. N. J., 381
Wiborg, F. B., 181, 1564, 1586
Wiburn, *see* Walter
Wichert, T. F. A., 918
Wickersheimer, Ernest, 249, 277, 448, 528, 816, 841, 844, 846, 873, 878, 888, 1110, 1196, 1206, 1229, 1239, 1243. 1247, 1656, 1661, 1688, 1689, 1693, 1698, 1707, 1756, 1908
Wickremasinghe, M. de Z., 1370
Wicksteed, P. H., 492, 493, 496, 499, 915, 1810
Widukind of Corvey (X-2), v. 1, *684*, 652, 655
Wiedemann, Eilhard, 622, 708, 709, 760, 901, 1138, 1265, 1526, 1622, 1782
Wiegand, W., 935
Wieger, Léon, 1909
Wiehe, Heinrich, 1415
Wiek, *see* Henry
Wieleitner, Heinrich, 111, 1487, 1488, 1489, 1567
Wiener, Meïr, 1448, 1652
Wieruszowski, Helene, 333, 500
Wieser, Franz v., 1597, 1598
Wiesselgren, Oscar, 1704
Wiet, Gaston, 173, 379, 1007, 1178, 1265, 1722, 1787, 1831
Wigram, W. A., 1474
Wījan b. Rustam Kūhī (X-2), v. 1, *665*, 814; v. 2, 401
Wijnschenk, C. A., 582
Wilbraham, Anne, 231, 1182, 1236
Wilbrand of Oldenburg (XIII-1), v. 2, *639*, 35, 512
Wild, Norman, 1855
Wilfert, Hans, 1799
Wilfrid, St., 1499
Wilhelmus, *see* William
Wilken, Friedrich, 1436
Wilkins, E. H., 496, 515, 1811, 1817
Wilkins, H. J., 1349, 1394
Wilkinson, C. K., 457
will, *see* testament
will (voluntas), 1895
Willard, J. F., 191
Willeke, Franz, 1712
Willem, *see* William
Willems, J. F., 940
William Adam (XIV-1), *414*, 46, 54, 189, 318, 391, 775, 953
William of Aldgate, 1547
William Atzo, 1861
William of Auvergne (XIII-1), v. 2, *588*, 1245; v. 3, 370, 1491
William Bateman, 475
William Bernard de Gaillac (XIV-1), *459*, 66, 1388
William Beukels (XIV-1), *821*, 237
William of Boldensele (XIV-1), *787*, 46, 191, 789, 1210, 1603, 1754
William Botoner, 787
William Boucher (XIV-2), *1698*, 1201, 1238, 1243
William the Breton (XIII-1), v. 2, *674*, 525; v. 3, 332
William de Burgh, 1602
William Byker, 1547
William Carle, 1024
William Caxton, 317, 347, 457, 463, 946, 1149, 1255, 1303, 1311, 1393, 1406, 1424, 1863
William de Cervera, 342
William of Champeaux (XII-1), v. 2, *192*, 120, 194
William de Champlitte, 948
William of Cividale del Friuli, 840
William de Coëtmohan, 477
William of Conches (XII-1), v. 2, *197*, 1245; v. 3, 150, 192, 193, 548, 944, 1229
William of Congenis (XIII-1), v. 2, *656*, 1245; v. 3, 272, 883
William Corvi of Brescia (XIII-2), v. 2, *1087*, 1245; v. 3, 44, 88, 243, 285, 575, 866, 1670
William of Courtenay, 1024
William Curti, 1200
William Deguilleville (XIV-1), *532*, 90, 346
William Dene, 1653
William of Drogheda (XIII-1), v. 2, *692*, 529
William Durand (XIII-2), v. 2, *1127*, 1245; v. 3, 413, 984, 1075, 1392
William Durant le Jeune (XIV-1), *413*, 46, 52, 525, 526
William the Englishman (XIII-1), v. 2, *620*, 1245; v. 3, 1481
William Ferrer, 1339
William Filastre, 1155
William Flete, 1335
William de Fonte, 1200
William the Founder (fusor), 1548
William de Francia, 744
William Grenefeld, 1256
William de Grimoard, 1032
William Guiart or Guiard (XIV-1), *927*, 300, 346
William de Harcigny (XIV-2), *1696*, 1201, 1236

William Heytesbury (XIV-1), *565*, 92, 148, 1126, 1413
William of Hirsau (XI-2), v. 1, *762*, 740, 741; v. 2, 197
William II, count of Holland, 736, 937
William IV of Holland, 1798
William V of Holland, 1798
William de Lafont, 1200
William de La Mare (XIII-2), v. 2, *950*, 741; v. 3, 91, 397, 521, 992
William Langland (XIV-2), *1413*, 1054, 1089, 1182, 1279, 1315, 1744, 1863
William Latimer, 1024
William Le Mire (XII-2), v. 2, *347*, 284
William Le Touzé, 1201
William de Lorris, 228, 1577
William of Lunis (XIII-1), v. 2, *563*, 1245
William de Machaut (XIV-1), *744*, 29, 40, 159, 160, 346, 742, 1128, 1253, 1298, 1410, 1652, 1757
William of Malines, 1688
William of Malmesbury (XII-1), v. 2, *255*, 139, 453; v. 3, 1741
William de Marra of Padua (XIV-2), *1671*, 1192, 1242, 1685
William Merle (XIV-1), *674*, 117, 141, 216, 1510
William de Mirica, 1671
William of Moerbeke (XIII-1), v. 2, *829*, 1245; v. 3, 64, 145, 355, 441, 484, 577, 735, 885, 1276, 1380, 1431, 1493
William Molinier, 340
William de Montlauzun (XIV-1), *990*, 50, 316, 401
William of Nangis (XIII-2), v. 2, *1109*, 794, 1048; v. 3, 300, 398, 457, 937, 1738
William de Nassio, 387
William of Newburgh (XII-2), v. 2, *456*, 314; v. 3, 942
William de Noix, 781
William of Norwich, 475
William, *see* Occam
William of Palerne, 1313
William da Pastrengo (XIV-1), *921*, 298, 583, 981
William Pérault or Perrault, 314, 1349
William practicus, 1246
William of Puylaurens (XIII-2), v. 2, *1108*, 794
William Rede (XIV-2), *1499*, 1110, 1255
William Rubruquis (XIII-2), v. 2, *1053*, 1246; v. 3, 380, 385, 388, 731, 784, 954
William Ruyelle, 126, 1111
William de Saint Amour, 23, 47
William of Saint Cloud (XIII-2), v. 2, *990*, 1246; v. 3, 602
William of Saliceto (XIII-2), v. 2, *1078*, 1246; v. 3, 1708
William da Santa Sofia, 839
William Sawtrey, 1046
William (Lucci) della Scarperia, 1669
William Sedacer (XIV-2), *1574*, 179, 754, 1130
William Shuchirch, 1136
William of Shyreswood, 552
William da Silveira, 184
William da Solagna, 777, 779
William Soleri (XIV-2), *1592*, 1141, 1858, 1866
William Thorne (XIV-2), *1743*, 1048, 1055, 1255
William de Tignonville, 1302
William Tirel Taillevent (XIV-2), *1632*, 1164, 1182, 1309
William Torel, 1561
William of Tudela (XIII-1), v. 2, *673*, 525, 530; v. 3, 339, 345
William Twici, 231, 348, 1165, 1184, 1315, 1630
William of Tyre (XII-2), v. 2, *454*, 1246; v. 3, 229, 398, 770
William van der Haegen, 184
William da Varignana (XIV-1), *838*, 243, 841
William Vorilong, 531, 1843
William Vrieman, 1541
William of Wadington, 462
William Walsham, 720
William of Ware (XIII-2), v. 2, *951*, 741, 750; v. 3, 91, 529
William Wenemaer, 1556, 1558
William Whittlesey, 1500
William Woodward, 1548
William of Worcester, 787
William of Wykeham, 1079, 1401, 1402
Williams, A. L., 1909
Williams, Charles, 1052
Williams, James, 499, 1870
Williams, John, 1122
Williams, S. W., 1176
Willibrord (VIII-1), v. 1, *506*, 503, 529; v. 3, 1668
Willoughby, *see* John
Willshire, W. H., 1563
Wilson, A. D., 948
Wilson, H. H., 1368
Wilson, W. J., 761, 1138, 1565, 1909
Wilton, *see* Thomas
Wimandus de Ruffo Clipeo (XIV-2), *1579*, 1137, 1318
Winchester, 1079, 1402, 1863
wind blowers, 715
wind roses, 143, 715
Winderlich, R., 757
Windesheim Canons, 1038, 1081, 1358
Windle, B. C. A., 1228
Windler, Ernst, 1712
Windsor, treaty, 1022
Windstosser, Maria, 573
wine, 323, 812, 1239, 1374, 1763
Wineland, 194, 1608
Wingate, S. D., 1494
Winkelmann, E., 917
Winkelried, *see* Arnold
Winkler, H. A., 1641

Winkworth, Susanna, 572, 573
Winn, H. E., 1349
Winter, Heinrich, 716, 1124
Winter, J. G., 122
Winternitz, Moritz, 1909
Winterthur, *see* John
wires, metal, 1174
Wirsung, J. G., 843
Wisdom of Solomon (I-1 B.C.), v. 1, *208*, 202; v. 3, 158, 1229
Wissell, Rudolf, 153
Wissler, Clark, 151
Wissowa, Georg, 1909
Wiszniewski, Michal, 932
Witart, Cl., 1805
witchcraft (XIV-1), *405*, 50, 394, 404, 1049, 1338, 1478
Witelo, *see* Vitelo
Withington, E. T., 1704
Witica, 1868
Witte, Carl, 494, 983
Witte, *see* John
Wittenborg, *see* Herman; John
Wittepennig, *see* Bernard
Władysław, *see* Ladislas
woad, 306, 323
Wodeham, *see* Adam
Woepcke, Franz, 1765
Wogihara, Unrai, x
Wohlgemuth, Fritz, 1228
Wolf, Johannes, 743, 1567
Wolf, Rudolf, 1856
Wolfenbüttel Arzneibuch, 1205, 1711
Wolff, Gerhard, 266
Wolff, J. C., 420
Wolff, O. L. B., 1407
Wolfger v. Ellenbrechtskirchen (XIII-1), v. 2, *638*, 35, 512
Wolfhagen, *see* Tilemann Elhen
Wolfsohn, Julius, 1448
Wolfson, H. A., 77, 611, 712, 1448
Wolfstrigl-Wolfskron, M. v., 219
Wolowski, Louis, 1284, 1494, 1496
Wolsey, cardinal, 1401
womb, 268, 843, 1229
women, diseases, 1908
women, humanism, 1862
women, island, 805
women, rights, 318
women, souls, 554
Wong K. Chimin, 1909
Wood, Alex., 1570
Wood, C. A., 231, 1534, 1735
Wood, E. J., 1227
Wood, J. T., 1321
Wood, W. A. R., 1030
Woodbine, G. E., 1311
woodcrafts, 278
Woodforde, Christopher, 172
Woodman, J., 1604
Woodroffe, John, 1070
Woods, J. H., 96
Woodson, W. D., 1667
Woodville, *see* Anthony
Woodward, B. B., 1744
Woodward, R. S., 4
Woodward, W. H., 1290, 1292, 1819
Woodward, *see* William
wool, woolen, 323, 729, 1181, 1833
wool trade, 324, 1900
Woolf, C. N. S., 1795
Woolley, R. M., 567
Worcester, *see* Florence; William
Workman, H. B., 1349
worlds, four, 616
worlds, *see* plurality
Worm, Ole, 1610
Worms, *see* Eleazar b. Judah
worms, parasites, 889, 1247
Worrell, W. H., 362, 1007, 1533
Wotke, Karl, 1810
wounds, 895
wounds, new method of treating, 871
Wright, J. K., 136, 1909
Wright, Jonathan, 497
Wright, Thomas, 221, 348, 941, 1203, 1315, 1407, 1604
Wright, W. A., 533
Wright, W. C., 1658
Wright, William, 1909
writing, 1890
Wronowski, M. M., 1870
Würdtwein, S. A., 934
Würschmidt, Joseph, 706, 708
Würsdörfer, Joseph, 518
Würzburg, *see* Albert; Evno; John
Wüstenfeld, Ferdinand, 427, 806, 966, 1787, 1910
Wulff, Fredrik Amadeus, 516
Wulff, Winifred, 882
Wulfstan (IX-2), v. 1, *606*, 586
Wurm, H. J., 1793
Wurstisen, Christian, 935
Wuruk, *see* Hayam
Wust, Joel b. Joseph, 594
Wutke, Konrad, 219
Wychgram, J., 918
Wyclif Society, 1348
Wycliffe, John (XIV-2), *1346*, 23, 91, 471, 554, 562, 988, 1025, 1039, 1048, 1054, 1076, 1089, 1093, 1149, 1280, 1314, 1352, 1362, 1394, 1400, 1401, 1412, 1414, 1433, 1501, 1743, 1745
Wycliffism, 1024, 1054, 1602, 1121
Wykeham, *see* William
Wylie, Alexander, 1910
Wyman, M. A., 1187
Wynkyn de Worde, 1311, 1394, 1416, 1863
'Wynnere and Wastoure," 1278
Wyntoun, *see* Andrew

Wyse, W. B., 1304
Wyss, Arthur, 1756
Wyss, Georg v., 936

Xanthopulos, *see* Nicephoros Callistos
Xenarchos of Seleucia (I-2 B.C.), v. 1, *222*, 219
Xenocrates of Aphrodisias (I-2), v. 1, *261*, 244
Xenocrates of Chalcedon (IV-2 B.C.), v. 1, *139*, 838
xenodochium, 294
Xenophanes of Colophon (VI B.C.), v. 1, *73*, 65; v. 3, 214, 1806
Xenophon (IV-1 B.C.), v. 1, *122*, 90, 112; v. 2, 450; v. 3, 314, 1073, 1291, 1862
Xiberta, B. F. M., 401
Ximenes (Jiménez), cardinal, 73, 814, 1298
Ximenes, *see* Francis Eiximènis
Xiphilinos, Joannes (XI-2), v. 1, *775*, 838
xylography, 733, 1126, 1563

y, for Biblical names beginning with y, *see* j
Ya'ari, *see* Moses b. Abraham
Yaballaha III, 956
Yāfi'ī, *see* 'Abdallāh b. As'ad
Yahuda, A. S., 365
Yahūda b. a. Isḥāq b. Istīlja, 1514
Yahūda b. Solomon b. Waqqār, 1514
Yaḥyā, *see also* John; Yūḥannā
Yaḥyā b. 'Adī (X-1), v. 1, *629*, 620, 623
Yaḥyā b. Bala'm, 366
Yaḥyā b. Baṭrīq (IX-1), v. 1, *556*, 838; v. 2, 1246
Yaḥyā, Baṭrīq a., *see* Baṭrīq
Yaḥyā b. Ghālib, *see* a. 'Alī Khaiyāṭ
Yaḥyā b. Ḥabash Suhrawardī (XII-2), v. 2, *361*, 218, 1019; v. 3, 106
Yaḥyā b. Ḥamza Mu'aiyad billāh (XIV-1), *619*, 102
Yaḥyā b. 'Īsā, *see* b. Jazla
Yaḥyā, imām, 619
Yaḥyā b. a. Manṣūr (IX-1), v. 1, *566*, 545, 549
Yaḥyā b. Māsawaih, *see* b. Māsawaih, Yūḥannā
Yaḥyā b. Muḥammad b. 'Awwām (XII-2), v. 2, *424*, 1152; v. 3, 228, 813, 1637, 1838
Yaḥyā b. Muḥammad b. Khaldūn (XIV-2), *1766*, 1262
Yaḥyā b. Muḥammad b. Lubūdī (XIII-1), v. 2, *624*, 1197
Yaḥyā b. Muḥammad Muḥyī al-dīn Maghribī (XIII-2), v. 2, *1015*, 1206; v. 3, 379, 1525
Yaḥyā b. Sarāfyūn (IX-2), v. 1, *608*, 587, 590; v. 2, 1246; v. 3, 797, 853, 856, 870, 898, 1205
Yaḥyā b. Sharaf Nawawī (XIII-2), v. 2, *1131*, 728, 801; v. 3, 959, 1012, 1099, 1623, 1639
Ya'īsh, *see* David b. Solomon; Solomon
Yājūj, 1227
Yajurveda, 1369
Yaḷandūru Subbaṇṇa Śāstri, 1730
Yamanī, *see* 'Umāra b. 'Alī; Zechariah b. Sa'īd
yanbaghī an yuqaddama, Kitāb fīmā, 432
Ya'qūb. The form Ya'qūb is generally reserved for Arabic names, James for Christian names, Jacob for Jewish names.
Ya'qūb b. Aḥmad Kāshānī (XIV-1), *698*, 134, 373, 756
Ya'qūb b. Ayyūb Mawāḥidī, 1765
Ya'qūb b. akhī Ḥizām (IX-2), v. 1, *610*, 587
Ya'qūb b. Ibrāhīm, *see* a. Yūsuf
Ya'qūb b. Isḥāq, *see* Kindī
Ya'qūb b. Isḥāq Maḥallī (XIII-1), v. 2, *665*, 1150
Ya'qūb b. a. Isḥāq Muwaffaq al-dīn (XIII-2), v. 2, *1098*, 1207; v. 3, 1213
Ya'qūb b. Isḥāq b. Quff (XIII-2), v. 2, *1098*, 1220; v. 3, 273
Ya'qūb Nadīm, b. a., *see* Muḥammad b. Isḥāq
Ya'qūb b. Ṭāriq (VIII-2), v. 1, *530*, 521, 524
Ya'qūb, a., *see* Yūsuf
Ya'qūbī, Aḥmad b. a. Ya'qūb (IX-2), v. 1, *607*, 838
Yāqūt b. 'Abdallāh (XIII-1), v. 2, *642*, 1247; v. 3, 200, 201, 756, 805, 1144, 1849
Yār Muḥammad, b., 232
Yaroslav the Wise, 39
Yāska (V B.C.), v. 1, *110*, 83; v. 2, 294; v. 3, 382
Yasmīnī, b., *see* 'Abdallāh b. Muḥammad
Yassā 'Abd al-Masīḥ, 1830
Yazdī, *see* Sharaf al-dīn 'Alī
Yazīdī, religion (XII-2), v. 2, *336*, 282
Yāzījī-oghlu (better Yāzijī) Aḥmad, 1464
Yāzījī-oghlu (better Yāzijī) Meḥmed, 1464
Year, Great, 443, 1489
year, Julian, 1107
Yeldham, F. A., 1483, 1534
Yellow Hats, 1069, 1371
Yellow river, 205
yellow of silver, 172
yeñi-cheri, 155
Yersin, Alexander, 1653
yeshivah, 73, 254
Yesod 'olam, 67, 130
yesodot, 1373
Yesodot ha-maskil, 451
Yetts, W. P., 385
Yewani, *see* Joseph b. David
Yeẓirah, v. 2, *367*, 289, 366; v. 3, x, 363, 616, 1096, 1376, 1444, 1522
Yiddish, 1213, 1240, 1325, 1720
yiḥud, 436
Ying-ki, Ignatius, 1071
Yiẓhar family, 449
yoga, 96, 584, 1366, 1475, 1621, 1882

Yoga-Ratnākara (XIV-2), *1731*, 1218
Yoga-sūtra, 96
Yogavāsishṭha, 1367
Yoḥai, *see* Simeon
Yolande of Hainaut, 1313
Yom-ṭob b. Solomon Lipmann, 1063
Yom-ṭob, *see* Ṭodros b. Moses
Yon (XIV-1), *1003*, 331
Yonge, C. D., 945
Yoreh de'ah, 590
York, 39
York, *see* Cecily; Robert; Thomas
York, James, 925
York minster, 1835
Yoshida, H., 170
Yoshinoya, Gonbei, 1646
Yosippon, Sefer, 62, 306, 363, 957, 1009, 1261, 1451, 1864
Youn, Eul sou, 1910
Youn, Laurent, 1910
Young, James, 1910
Young, Karl, 1345, 1426
Young, R. F., 1348, 1403
Youngson, J. W., 1476
Youssef Mourad, 1104
Yperman, *see* John
Ypes, Catharina, 516
Ypotis, 339
Ypres, 39, 251, 323, 1838
Ypres, *see* John Yperman; John of Ypres
Ysowilpe, bishop, 728
Yūhannā. This is the Syriac-Arabic form. For the Arabic proper, see Yaḥyā; for Christian names, John; for Jewish names, Johanan.
Yūḥannā, anbā of Samannūd, 1006, 1008
Yūḥannā b. Ibrī, *see* a. Faraj
Yūḥannā b. Māsawaih, *see* b. Māsawaih
Yule, Henry, 784, 975, 1605, 1616, 1894, 1910
Yūnus, b. (XI-1), v. 1, *716*, 810; v. 2, 1247
Yūnus Emre (XIV-1), *625*, 105, 379, 1845
Yūsuf. This is the Arabic form. Christian and Jewish names are generally classified under Joseph.
Yūsuf, a. (VIII-2), v. 1, *525*, 520, 524; v. 3, 828
Yūsuf b. Aḥmad b. Ḥasdai (XII-1), v. 2, *229*, 1247
Yūsuf b. Aḥmad Mu'tamin, of Saragossa (XI-2), v. 1, *759*, 740, 746; v. 2, 296, 373; v. 3, 960
Yūsuf b. 'Alī b. Muḥammad, 756
Yūsuf b. a. Bakr Sakkākī (XIII-1), v. 2, *701*, 532; v. 3, 373, 628, 1011, 1461, 1463, 1779, 1868
Yūsuf b. Ilyān Sarkīs, 1903
Yūsuf b. Isḥāq b. Biklārish (XII-1), v. 2, *235*, 1155
Yūsuf b. Ismā'īl b. Kutubī (XIV-1), *897*, 257, 289
Yūsuf Kamāl, 183
Yūsuf Khāṣṣ ḥājib, 1015
Yūsuf Khūrī (IX-2), v. 1, *600*, 585, 587
Yūsuf b. Muḥammad b. Ṭumlūs (XIII-1), v. 2, *596*, 500
Yūsuf b. Qiz-ughlu (XIII-1), v. 2, *705*; v. 3, 321
Yūsuf b. Rāfi' Ḥalabī (XII-2), v. 2, *448*, 312, 527
Yūsuf b. Taghrībirdī, 960, 1722, 1780
Yūsuf b. Waqqār of Toledo, 1762
Yūsuf, a. Ya'qūb, 1620
Yūsuf b. Zakī Mizzī, 964
Yver, G., 1098
Yves, friar, 52
Zābaj, 1624
Zabara, *see* Joseph b. Meïr
Zabarella, *see* Francis
Zabīdī, *see* Muḥammad b. Murtaḍā
Zaccagnini, Guido, 983
Zacchia, Paolo, 253, 260
Zachariae, Theodor, 1731
Zacharias, *see also* Zakarīyā; Zechariah
Zacharias of Dsordsor, 67, 356
Zacharias, physiognomist, 442
Zacharias of Salerno (XII-1), v. 2, *244*, 1247
Zacuto, *see* Abraham b. Samuel
Zacuto (Zakkuth), *see* Moses b. Mordecai
zād al-musāfirīn, 149
Ẓaddīq, *see* Jacob; Joseph b. Jacob
Ẓafar-nāma, 631
Zagalia, Giuseppe, 562
Zahel, 501
Ẓāhir Barqūq, 173
Ẓāhirī, *see* Dā'ūd b. 'Alī; Khalīl b. Shāhīn
Ẓāhirī school, 1011
Zahrāwī, *see* a. Qāsim
Zaid, a. (X-1), v. 1, *636*, 787; v. 3, 1587
Zaid b. 'Alī, 619
Zaid b. Thābit (VII-1), v. 1, *465*, 460, 464
Zaidī (Shī'a) rulers, 102
Zaidīya, 619, 1264
Zain al-'Aṭṭār (XIV-2), *1728*, 1217, 1242, 1328
Zainer, G., 789
Zaire river, 1159
Zaiton, *see* Gerald
Zaitūn, 1589, 1616
zaitūna, Jāmi' al-, 1342
Zajączkowski, Ananiasz, 1014
Zakarīyā, *see also* Zacharias; Zechariah
Zakarīyā b. Muḥammad, *see* Qazwīnī
Zakī, *see* Aḥmad
Zakī, Ṣāliḥ, 1910
Zakonnik, 39
Zamakhsharī, *see* Maḥmūd b. 'Umar
Zambaco, D. A., 281
Zambaur, Edouard de, 1910
Zambrini, Francesco, 232, 1605

Zancari, *see* Albert; Galvano
Zanella, Giacomo, 920
Zanjānī, *see* 'Abd al-Wahhāb b. Ibrāhīm
Zannekin, *see* Claes
Zanotti-Bianco, O., 494, 497
Zanotto, Francesco, 1040
Zanzalus, *see* Jacob
Zanzibar, 1186
Zar', b. a., 307
zara, giuoco, 1813
ẓara'at, 275
Zaragoza, *see* Saragossa
Zardo, Antonio, 918
Ẓarfatī, *see* Jacob b. Solomon
Zarncke, Friedrich, 1607
Zarnūjī, Burhān al-dīn (XIII-1), v. 2, *598*, 500; v. 3, 74, 900, 998
Zarqālī (XI-2), v. 1, *758*, 839; v. 2, 1248; v. 3, 128, 193, 434, 1514, 1515
Zarrīn Dast (XI-2), v. 1, *772*, 839; v. 2, 82; v. 3, 376
zarṭafa, 828
Ẓarẓa, *see* Samuel b. Sanah
Zaunick, Rudolph, 1843, 1861
Ẓawa'ot, 590
zāwiya, 154, 1864
Zayton, *see* Zaitūn
Zbyněk Zajíc (not Zajík), 1351
Zebel, M., 429
zebu, 1190
Zechariah, *see also* Zacharias; Zakarīyā
Zechariah (VI B.C.), v. 1, *70*, 65
Zechariah b. Isaac ha-Levi, 1447
Zechariah b. Sa'īd Yamanī, 1451
Zeck, Ernest, 411
Zedler, Gottfried, 1756
Zeiss, Hans, 1610
Zeissberg, Heinrich, 1759
Zeitlin, Jacob, 514
Zekī, *see* Ṣāliḥ
Ẓel ha-'olam, 199
ẓela', 596
Zelanti, 47, 396
Zeller, Renée, 575
ẓemaḥim, 432, 1832
Zemarchos the Cilician (VI-2), v. 1, *453*, 444; v. 3, 378
Zen, Sophia Hêng-chê, 1910
Zend, 304, 376
Zeni brothers, 1593. *See* Anthony; Caterino
Zenker, J. T., 1101, 1263
Zeno of Citum (IV-2 B.C.), v. 1, *137*, 125; v. 3, 331
Zeno of Elea (V B.C.), v. 1, *85*, 81, 82
Zeno, *see* Nicholas
Zeno, St., 920
Zenodoros (II-1 B.C.), v. 1, *182*, 177
Zenodotos of Ephesos (III-1 B.C.), v. 1, *164*, 151
Zephaniah (VII B.C.), v. 1, *63*, 60
Zeraḥ, *see* Menahem b. Aaron
Zeraḥiah b. Isaac ha-Levi, 1072, **1097**, **1377**
Zeraḥiah b. Isaac b. Shealtiel Gracian (XIII-2), v. 2, *846*, 1248; v. 3, **432**, **450**, **603**, **1220**, 1377
Zerbolt, *see* Gerald
Zeréntz, *see* Gregory
zero, 120, 122
zero, operations with, 1535
Ẓeror ha-kesef, 590
Zetterstéen, K. V., 828, 962
Zetzner, Lazarus, 752, 1911
Zeuthen, H. G., 1911
Zichmni, 1594
Ziegler, Hieronymus, 1805
Ziegler, Jacob, 1191
Ziesemer, Walther, 933
Zifroni family, 615
Zifroni, Israel, 1444
zīj, 'ilm al-, 1526
Zilboorg, Gregory, 405, 1666
Zimara, Marco Antonio, 522, 540
zinc, 1139
zindīq, 490
Zingarelli, Nicola, 496, 1499
Zinner, Ernst, 717, 1490, 1546, 1911
Zippel, Giuseppe, 1289
Zirkle, Conway, 455, 632, 826, 1230
Zittau, *see* Peter
Ziyāda, M. M., 282
Ziyān, Banū, 102
Ziyān, b., *see* Mūsā b. Yūsuf
Zobel, M., 366, 449, 450, 593, 893, **1364**, **1380**, 1452
Zoccolanti, 397
Zographos, *see* Gideon
Zohar, 100, 363, 613, 616, 1522
Zonaras, *see* John
Zondek, Bernhard, 1836
Zoroaster (VII B.C.), v. 1, *60*, 332; v. **3**, **376**
Zoroastrianism (IX-2), v. 1, *591*, 839; v. **3**, 1071
Zosimos of Constantinople, alchemist (III-2), v. 1, *339*, 331; v. 3, 166
Zosimos of Constantinople, historian (V-1), v. 1, *394*, 379, 380
Zoubov, V., 820
Zschaeck, Fritz, 1755
Zuccarini, F. A., 1437
Zucchero, Bencivenni (XIV-1), *463*, **61**, **68**, 336, 337, 484
Zuchhold, Hans, 570
Zuckermann, B., 713
Zuhr, b., *see* 'Abd al-Malik
Zuhr b. a. Marwān (XII-1), v. **2**, ***230***, **1144** (*under* 'Alā')
Zuhr, b., Samarqandī, 608
Zuhrī, *see* Muḥammad b. a. Bakr
Zuidema, Sytse Ulbe, 557
zulaij, 757

Zúñiga y Sotomayor, Fadrique de, 1736
Zuntz, Günther, 163
Zunz, Leopold, 1446
Zupitza, Julius, 1811
Zuraiq, b., *see* Muḥammad b. 'Alī
Zurayq, C. K., 1784
Zuretti, C. O., 755, 1139, 1575, 1876, 1877
Zurita, Gerónimo, 1736
Zutphen, *see* Gerald
Zwingli, 164
Zwolle, 1082, 1297, 1317, 1360, 1408
Zycha, Adolf, 218
Zygomalas, *see* Theodosios
Zyrians, 1825

GREEK INDEX

This is rather a glossary than an index, for it refers only to the Greek words occurring in the text in Greek script, and such words were used very sparingly, seldom more than once or twice each. It will thus be necessary to refer to the general index to obtain more information on the men or terms listed in this one. For example, the word *κενόν* in the technical sense of emptiness occurs only once (p. 148), but the general index would give abundant illustrations of the *idea* which that term represents under *vacuum*. The meaning of each Greek term can be easily found by referring to its context. The position of the words in a phrase has sometimes been modified in order to facilitate the finding; thus *περὶ τῆς ἐν Χριστῷ ζωῆς* occurs under *ζωῆς ἐν Χριστῷ*.

Articles and the preposition *περί* have been generally omitted; genitives imply the omitted preposition.

G. S.

July 24, 1947

ἀββᾶ 357
ἀγεωμέτρητος .... facing 1019
ἁγίων καὶ οἰκουμενικῶν συνόδων 1821
'Αγράφων, Διονύσιος ἐξ 1583
ἀέρων ὑδάτων τόπων 1240
ἄζυμα 994
ἄθλων δώδεκα 683
Αἴγυπτος 360
αἴλουρος 1863
αἱματώδη χρώματα 709
αἱμάτων σωτηρίων καὶ ὀλεθρίων 1209
αἱρέσεων 448, 1438
αἰσθήσεως καὶ αἰσθητῶν 684
αἴσθησις 891
αἰτίαι τινές 1209
αἰτίας 890
αἰτίων προκαταρκτικῶν, συνεκτικῶν 447
ἀκαδημία θετικῶν ἐπιστημῶν 438
ἀκάθαρτος 275
'Ακίνδυνος, Γρηγόριος 587
ἀκριβὴς δίαιτα 836
ἀκριδοθήκη 1188
ἀκρίς 1188
'Ακρίτας, Διγενής 1812
ἀκτουάριος 889
'Αλέξανδρος Ε' πάπας 1440
'Αλέξιος Σπανός 995
ἀλήθεια 9
ἁλιευτικά 1641
ἁμάρτημα μητρός μου 1247
ἀμίς 890
'Αμπουλφέδα 'Ισμαήλ 799
ἀνάργυροι 863
ἀνασκευή 683
ἀνασκευὴ τοῦ δόγματος 587
ἀνατοκισμός 326
ἀνατολή 748
ἀνάτριψις 288
'Ανδρέας Λιβαδηνός 790
'Ανδρόνικος Α' Κομνηνός 414
'Ανδρόνικος Οἰναιώτης 1511
ἀνθρακώδης 220
ἄνθραξ 220
ἄνθρωπος διαλεγόμενος μετὰ ψυχῆς 825
ἀντίδοτοι ἐκ Περσίας 438
ἀντιλογία 826
ἀντιπερίστασις 543
ἀοργησίας 1073
'Απίων 'Οασιτικός 1656
ἁπλῆ, γλῶσσα 354
ἁπλοελληνική, γλῶσσα 354
ἀπόδειξις περὶ τῶν 'Ιεροσολύμων 1156
'Απόκαυκος 889
ἀπορίας λύσις 1511
ἀποτελεσματικῶν 1846
ἀποτομή 1526
ἀποτρόπαιος 1666
'Αργυρός, 'Ισαάκ 1511
ἀρθριτικὴ νόσος 1197
ἄρθρων 288
ἀριθμητικὴ εἰσαγωγή 430, 1511
ἀριθμοὶ ἰνδικοί 121
ἀρίστης αἱρέσεως 448
ἀρίστης διδασκαλίας 447
'Αρμενόπουλος, Κωνσταντῖνος 995
ἁρμονικά 586, 745, 951
'Αρτάβασδος 'Ραβδᾶς, Νικόλαος 681
ἀρχεῖον Πόντου 790

ἀρχῶν καθολικῆς πίστεως 1363
ἄσημον 754
ἀσσάρια 122
ἀστρολαβικοῦ ὀργάνου, κατασκευή 1512
ἀστρολάβου, κατασκευή 951
ἀστρολογίας 690
ἀστρονομίαν ὑβριζόντων, τῶν τὴν 951
ἀστρονομίας 951
ἀστρονομικὴ ἐπιστήμη 684
ἀστρονομικὴ τρίβιβλος 1511, 1512
'Ατουμᾶνος 1394
ἀττικῶν, συλλογὴ ὀνομάτων 679
αὐτόχθονες 1188
'Αφθόνιος 947

Βάγα 1765
βαθμῶν 1008
βαραδαῖος 358
Βαρλαὰμ Καλαβρός 583
βασιλείας 996
βασμοῦλοι 948, 1852
Βέκκος (Βέκος, Βέκων), 'Ιωάννης 684
Βησσαρίων 438
βίβλος ἱστοριῶν facing 1019
βίοι ἐν συντόμῳ 403
Βλαστάρης, Ματθαῖος 994
Βλαχέρναι 587, 687
βόθυνοι 709
βουβῶνος 1650
βουλή 120
βραχέα χρονικά 1260
βραχυβιότητος καὶ μακροβιότητος 684
βρεφοτροφεῖον 294
Βρυέννιος, Μανουὴλ 745
βυζαντιακὰ κείμενα 438

γαδάρου, λύκου, ἀλουποῦς διήγησις 824
γαλέη, γαλῆ 1863
γαληνός 682
γάμου 994
γασμοῦλος 948, 1852
Γεδεὼν Ζωγράφος 1511
γενέσεως καὶ φθορᾶς 684
Γενέσιος 1156
γεννήσεως τεχνικῆς 1170, 1821
γεροντοκομεῖον 294
γεωγραφία συνοπτική 951
γεωγραφικὴ ὑφήγησις 197, 1158
Γεώργιος Γεμιστὸς Πλήθων 684
Γεώργιος Κωδινός 1823
Γεώργιος Λαπήθις (Λαπίθης) 586
Γεώργιος Χατζύκης 681
Γεώργιος Χρυσοκόκκης 688
Γεώργιος Χωνιάτης 438
γήρως καὶ νεότητος 684
Γλαύκωνα θεραπευτικά, πρὸς 441
γλῶσσα ἁπλῆ, ἁπλοελληνική, δημοτική, δημώδης, καθαρεύουσα, καθημαξευμένη, καθωμιλημένη, ῥωμαϊκή 354
γονῆς 1229
γραμμαί 683
γραμματικά, ἐρωτήματα 679
γραμματικῆς, ἐπιτομή 679
γραφίδιον 443, 836
Γρηγορᾶς, Νικηφόρος 949
Γρηγόριος 'Ακίνδυνος 587
Γρηγόριος Παλαμᾶς 588, 1438
Γρηγόριος Χιονιάδης 438
γυναικὸς κακῆς, ἀγαθῆς 683
γυναικῶν 994
γύψ 825
γωνίαι 683

Δαβίρ 1718
Δαμασκηνός, Σωφρόνιος 446
Δαυὶδ Παφλαγών, Νικήτας 679
δεήσεων κύριος 681
Δημήτριος Κυδώνης 1387
Δημήτριος Τρικλίνιος 1005
δημοτική, γλῶσσα 354
δημώδης, γλῶσσα 354
διὰ τεσσάρων 1513
διαγνώσεως παθῶν 889, 890
δίαιτα προφυλακτική 888
διαίτης λεπτυνούσης 447
διαίτης ὀξέων 437
διαλεκτικῆς πραγματείας 1387
διαλέξεις 1513
διάνοια 891
διαπλάσεως κυουμένων 448
Διασσωρινός, Νεῖλος 1821
Διασωρηνός, Νεῖλος 1821
διαφορᾶς οὔρων 890
Διγενὴς 'Ακρίτας 1812
διδάσκαλος 1209
διήγησις παιδιόφραστος 824, 1190
διήγησις πωρικολόγου 824
διήγησις συνοπτική 1821
διοικητής, μέγας 888
δίολκος 735
Διονύσιος ἐξ 'Αγράφων 1583
Διόσκοροι 864
δοξαστικόν, μέρος 891
δρουγγάριος 824
δυναμερόν 446
δυσπνοίας 447
δώδεκα ἀθλῶν 683

ἐβραϊστί ... 363
ἐγκοίμησις ... 1247
ἐγκυκλοπαιδικὸν λεξικόν ... 438, 689
ἐθῶν ... 447
εἰκοσάεδρον ... 662
Εἰρηνόπολις ... 309
εἰρμολόγια ... 163
εἰρμολόγιον ... 162
εἰρμός ... 163
εἰσαγωγὴ ἀριθμητική ... 430, 1511
ἔκδοσις ... 1517
ἔκδοσις γεγοννῖα ... 689
ἔκθεσις τῆς βασιλείου τάξεως ... 957
ἔκθεσις στοιχειώδης ῥήσεων θεολογικῶν ... 1438
ἐκκλησία Τραπεζοῦντος ... 790
ἐκλογή ... 680
ἐκλογὴ ὀνομάτων ... 996
ἐκπόρευσις ἁγίου πνεύματος ... 1363
ἔκφρασις ... 1847
ἔκφρασις δακτυλικοῦ μέτρου ... 681
ἐλαιῶν σώματος ... 960
ἔλεγχος πλάνης Λατίνων ... 994
ἐλεημοσυνάριος ... 219
ἐλέφαντος ... 825
Ἐλωΐ, λαμὰ σαβαχθανί ... 357
ἐμβαδά ... 683
Ἐμηλία ... 1513
Ἐμμανουὴλ Πανήλιος Πανσέληνος ... 169
Ἐμμανουήλ, see also Μανουήλ
ἐνεργειῶν ... 889
ἐνεργειῶν καὶ παθῶν τοῦ ψυχικοῦ πνεύματος ... 891
ἔνθεοι ... 1094
ἐνθουσιασταί ... 1094
ἐνιαυσίου χρόνου, περὶ μεγέθους ... 1439
ἐννεαμήνων καὶ ἑπταμήνων ... 683
ἐνυπνίων ... 684, 952
ἐξ φρὴν ἑνός ... 667
ἐξάβιβλος ... 995
ἐξαπτέρυγον, ἰουδαϊκόν ... 689, 1517
ἔξαρχος ... 1821
ἐξήγησις εἰς τὴν σύνταξιν τῶν Περσῶν ... 688
ἐπαρχικόν ... 1853
ἐπιστασίαι μερικαί ... 683
ἐπιτομὴ νέα γραμματικῆς ... 679
ἐπίτομος ἐξήγησις εἰς πλάνας Ὀδυσσέως ... 952
ἑπταμήνων καὶ ἐννεαμήνων ... 683
ἐπωνυμίας πόλεων καὶ τόπων ... 689
ἑρμηνεία τῆς ζωγραφικῆς ... 169, 1583
ἑρμηνεία θείας λειτουργίας ... 1439
ἑρμηνείας ... 331, 589, 683, 1441
Ἕρμιππος ... 690
Ἑρμογένης ... 947
ἐρωτήματα ... 1822
ἐρωτήματα γραμματικά ... 679
Εὔηνος ... 1188
Εὐθύμιος Ζιγαβηνός (Ζιγαδηνός) ... 1854
εὐπόριστα ... 447, 1208
εὕρεμα Παλαμήδους ... 681
εὕρεσις τετραγωνικῶν πλευρῶν ... 1512
εὕρεσις τετραγώνων ἀριθμῶν ... 679
Εὔριπος ... 1849
ἐφόδῳ γεγενημένων, περὶ τῶν ἐν τῇ Ἰταλῶν καὶ Περσῶν ... 996
ἐφφαθά ... 357

Ζιγαβηνός (Ζιγαδηνός), Εὐθύμιος ... 1854
Ζυγομαλᾶς, Θεοδόσιος ... 995
ζυθοπωλῶν ... 152
ζύμη ... 754
ζωγραφικῆς ἑρμηνεία ... 169, 1583
Ζωγράφος, Γεδεών ... 1511
ζωῆς καὶ θανάτου ... 684
ζωῆς ἐν Χριστῷ ... 1439
ζῴων ... 825
ζῴων γενέσεως ... 684
ζῴων ἰδιότητος ... 825
ζῴων κινήσεως ... 684
ζῴων μορίων ... 684
ζῴων πορείας ... 684

ἡγούμενος ... 584
ἦθος ... 161
ἥλιος ... 689
ἡμεροδανειστής ... 326
ἡμεροευρεσίου ... 689
ἡμικρανία ... 1696
ἡσυχασταί ... 584
ἡσυχία ... 96, 584
ἠχεῖα ... 1569

Θαβώριον ... 95
θαυμασίων ... 1806
θείας οὐσίας καὶ θείας ἐνεργείας ... 1363
Θεοδόσιος Ζυγομαλᾶς ... 995
Θεόδουλος μοναχός ... 996
Θεοδώρητος Μελητινιώτης ... 1512
Θεόδωρος Μελητινιώτης ... 1512
Θεόδωρος Μετοχίτης ... 684
Θεόδωρος Τζαβούχης Κλαζομένιος ... 681
Θεοῦ μετοχῆς ... 1511
θεοφανείας ... 1387
θεραπευτικὰ πρὸς Γλαύκωνα ... 441
θεραπευτικαὶ ἰατρεῖαι ... 1209
θεραπευτικὴ μέθοδος ... 889
Θεσσαλονίκη ... 1388
θεωρία ... 588
θηριακῆς ... 447
Θησεὺς καὶ γάμοι τῆς Ἐμηλίας ... 1513

θρησκείας Χριστιανῶν 1823
Θωμᾶς μάγιστρος 996

Ἰακωβίτης 358
ἰατρικὴ σύστασις 447
ἰατρικὴ τέχνη 839
ἰατρικὴ ὕλη 442
ἰατρικῆς μερῶν, τῶν τῆς 447
ἰατρός 689
Ἰβηρία 305
ἱερακοσόφιον 1644
Ἱεροσολύμων 1156
ἰνδανικὸς σίδηρος 1859
ἰνδικὴ ψηφοφορία 120, 681
ἰουδαϊκὸν ἐξαπτέρυγον 689, 1517
Ἰσαὰκ Ἀργυρός 1511
ἱστοριῶν 1760
Ἰταλῶν 996
Ἰωάννης ἀκτουάριος 889
Ἰωάννης Βέκκος 684
Ἰωάννης ἐλεημοσυνάριος 219
Ἰωάννης Καντακουζηνός 1759
Ἰωάννης Κατράριος (Κατράρης) 690
Ἰωάννης Κυπαρισσιώτης σοφός 1438
Ἰωάννης Πεδιάσιμος 682
Ἰωάννης Χαρσανίτης 688
Ἰωάννης Χοῦμνος 888
Ἰωσὰφ Χριστοδοῦλος 1760

Καβάσιλας, Νεῖλος 1439
Καβάσιλας, Νικόλαος 1438
καθαρεύουσα, γλῶσσα 354
καθημαξευμένη, γλῶσσα 354
καθωμιλημένη, γλῶσσα 354
καιρῶν ἐν ταῖς νόσοις 448
καιρῶν ὅλου νοσήματος 448
Καλαβρός, Βαρλαάμ 583
Καλέκας, Μανουήλ 1363, 1388
Καλλίπολις 1388
Κάλλιστος Ξανθόπουλος, Νικηφόρος 947
κανικλείου, ὁ ἐπὶ τοῦ 587
κάννα 725
κανόνες 994
κανόνια τοῦ μήκους καὶ τοῦ πλάτους τῶν ἐπισήμων πόλεων 689, 1889
κανόνιον τοῦ ἡμεροευρεσίου 689
κανονίων, πραγματεία νέων 1511
κανόνων θείων καὶ ἱερῶν 995
Καντακουζηνός, Ἰωάννης 1759
Καντακουζηνός, Ματθαῖος 1760
κανών 162
καρπός 431
Κάστωρ 864
κατασκευή 683
κατασκευὴ ἀστρολαβικοῦ ὀργάνου 1512
κατασκευῆς καὶ γενέσεως ἀστρολάβου 951
κατασκευῆς μύρου Μωσαϊκοῦ 1821
καταφατικοῦ καὶ ἀποφατικοῦ 1387
καταφρονεῖν θάνατον 1388
Κατράριος (Κατράρης), Ἰωάννης 690
Κάφα 1035
κενόν 148
Κερασοῦς 790
κεφάλαια 588
κεφάλαια ἑπτάκις ἑπτά 1209
κεφαλαλγία 1696
Κλαζομένιος, Θεόδωρος 681
κοίλη 843
κοινὴ διάλεκτος 353
κόλλυβα (not κόλυβα) 994
κολλυβιστῶν 1802
Κολυβᾶς 1511
Κομνηνός, Ἀνδρόνικος Α′ 414
κόσμου φύσεως 588
Κουνάλης Κριτόπουλος, Νικόλαος 995
κουροπαλάτης 1823
κρίσεων 436, 879
Κριτόβουλος 1553
Κριτόπουλος, Νικόλαος Κουνάλης 995
Κυδώνης, Δημήτριος 1387
Κυδώνης, Πρόχορος 1386
κύκλος, πῶς ὁ τῆς σελήνης (τοῦ ἡλίου) εὑρίσκεται 689
κύκλου μέτρησις 430
κυλίνδρου 431
κυνηγετικά 1641
κυουμένων διαπλάσεως 448
Κυπαρισσιώτης, Ἰωάννης 1438
Κύπρου, χρονικόν 952
κύριος μέγας 948
Κωδινός, Γεώργιος 1823
κώματος 447
Κωνσταντῖνος Ἀρμενόπουλος 995

λάθε βιώσας 687
Λάμπρος, Σπυρίδων 1439
Λαπήθης (Λαπίθης), Γεώργιος 586
Λατίνων, ἔλεγχος πλάνης 994
λειτουργίας, ἑρμηνεία θείας 1439
λείψανα 1044
Λεόντιος Μαχαιρᾶς 952
λέπρα, λεπρός, λεπρώσας 275, 754
λεπτά 122
λεπτυνούσης διαίτης 447
Λέων Μαγεντῖνος 589
Λιβαδηνός, Ἀνδρέας 790
λίθων 1821
Λόγγος 1188

λογιστική 586
λογοθέτης μέγας, τοῦ γενικοῦ, τῶν σεκρέτων 684, 688
λουτροῦ 288
λύσις ἀπορίας 1511

Μαγγάνων 1058, 1439, 1760
Μαγεντῖνος, Λέων 589
μαθήματα 158
μαθηματικὴ σύνταξις 1439
μαθηματικοῦ εἴδους τῆς φιλοσοφίας 687
Μανουὴλ Βρυέννιος 745
Μανουὴλ Καλέκας 1363, 1388
Μανουὴλ Μοσχόπουλος 679
Μανουὴλ Παλαιολόγος 1823
Μανουὴλ Φιλῆς 825
Μανουὴλ Χρυσολωρᾶς 1822
Μανουήλ, see also Ἐμμανουήλ
μανόν 148
μαντική 1103
μαντικὴ παλμῶν 960
μαντικῆς καθ' ὕπνον 684
Ματθαῖος Βλαστάρης 994
Ματθαῖος Καντακουζηνός 1760
Μαχαιρᾶς, Λεόντιος 952
μεγέθους ἐνιαυσίου χρόνου 1439
Μεθόδιος Ὁμολογητής 1394
μέθοδος τῆς ἱερᾶς προσευχῆς 96
Μελάμπους 960
Μελέαγρος 1188
Μελητινιώτης, Θεοδώρητος 1512
Μελητινιώτης, Θεόδωρος 1512
Μελιτηνιώτης, see Μελητινιώτης
μεμολυσμένος 275
μέρος δοξαστικόν 891
μεσαιωνικὴ βιβλιοθήκη 688
μεταλλικῆς τέχνης 179, 754, 1130, 1575
μετάλλων συστροφῆς 754
μεταμόρφωσις 95, 1511
μεταφράζειν 353
μετεωρολογικῶν 684
Μετοχίτης, Θεόδωρος 684
μετρήσεως καὶ μερισμοῦ γῆς 682
μέτρων 680
μηδεὶς ἀγεωμέτρητος εἰσίτω facing 1019
μητροπολίτης 679
μιάνας 275
μιλιαρήσιον 122
Μιχαὴλ Πανάρετος 790
μνήμης καὶ ἀναμνήσεως 684
μονῳδία ἐπὶ τοῖς ἐν Θεσσαλονίκῃ πεσοῦσιν 1388
Μορείος, χρονικὸν τοῦ 1852
Μορέως, χρονικὰ τοῦ 949
Μοσχόπουλος, Μανουήλ 679

Μουζελίνη 995
Μυζηθρᾶς 1760
μύρου Μωσαϊκοῦ, κατασκευή 1821
Μυστρᾶς 1760

νᾶπυ 230
Νεῖλος Διασσωρινός (Διασωρηνός) 1821
Νεῖλος Καβάσιλας 1439
Νέος Ἑλληνομνήμων 120, 121
Νεόφυτος 690
Νεόφυτος Προδρομηνός 826
Νικήτας Δαυὶδ Παφλαγών 679
Νικηφόρος Γρηγορᾶς 949
Νικηφόρος Κάλλιστος Ξανθόπουλος 947
Νικηφόρος Χοῦμνος 587
Νικόδημος 1393
Νικόλαος Ἀρτάβασδος Ῥαβδᾶς 681
Νικόλαος Καβάσιλας 1438
Νικόλαος Κουνάλης Κριτόπουλος 995
νόμισμα 122
νόμοι 994, 995
νομοκάνων 994
νοσοκομεῖον 294, 1209
νοτάριος 689
νοῦς 891
νοῦς ποιητικός 595

Ξανθόπουλος, Νικηφόρος Κάλλιστος 947
ξενοδοχεῖον 294
ξενῶν 294, 1209

Ὀασιτικός, Ἀπίων 1656
ὀβολός 122
ὄβρυζον 754
ὄγκων, περὶ τῶν παρὰ φύσιν 447
Ὀδυσσεύς 952
οἰκονομικός 1374, 1899
οἰκονόμος 943
οἰκουμενικὸν διδασκαλεῖον 947
Οἰναιώτης, Ἀνδρόνικος 1511
ὀκτάηχος 163
ὀκτὼ μερῶν 355
ὁμηριστής 353
Ὁμολογητής, Μεθόδιος 1394
ὁμολογία πίστεως 790
ὀμφαλόψυχοι 95, 584
ὀνειράτων 1824
ὀνοκένταυρος 825
ὀνομάτων, ἐκλογή 996
ὄργανον 754, 1512
ὀρθογραφίας 952
ὀρφανοτροφεῖον 294
ὅτι τὰ τῆς ψυχῆς ἤθη 447
οὐδεμία μοῖρα 120

οὐδὲν ἐξηκοστόν 120
οὐρανοῦ 684
οὔρων 890
οὐσίας καὶ ἐνεργείας 587, 1386
ὀχουμένων 735

παιδιόφραστος, διήγησις 824, 1190
παίδων ἀγωγῆς 1073, 1292
Παλαιολόγος, Μανουήλ 1823
Παλαμᾶς, Γρηγόριος 588, 1438
Παλαμήδης 681
Παλαμιτικῶν παραβάσεων 1438
παλμῶν μαντική 960
Πανάρετος, Μιχαήλ 790
πανεπιστήμιον 438
Πανήλιος, Ἐμμανουήλ 169
πανοπλία δογματική 1854
Πανσέληνος, Ἐμμανουήλ 169
Παντοκράτωρ 1209
παραγγελίαι 291
παράδοσις 681, 689, 1511
παράδοσις εἰς εὕρεσιν τετραγώνων ἀριθμῶν 679
παράδοσις σύντομος, πρόχειρος 681, 689
παρακλητική 163
παρακλητικὴ περὶ ἀστρονομίας 951
παράκλητος 1341
παρακοιμώμενος μεγάλης σφενδόνης 888
παρανατέλλοντα 444
παραφύλλον 120
πατρότητος καὶ υἱότητος ἐν τῷ Θεῷ 1387
Παῦλος Ῥαβδᾶς 681
Παφλαγών, Νικήτας Δαυίδ 679
Πεδιάσιμος, Ἰωάννης 682
πέντε φωνῶν 517
Περιβλέπτου 1854
περιηγητικὴ ἱστορία 790
περιήθημα 891
περικλυτός 1341
Περσῶν 996
Περσῶν, *σύνταξις τῶν* 123, 688
Πέτρος Φίλαργος (Φιλάργης) 1440
Πέτρος Φιλάρετος 1440
πέψις 891
πηγὴ γνώσεως 1821
πῆχυς 1847
Πιλάτος 1377
πίστεως 1363
Πλήθων, Γεώργιος Γεμιστός 684
πλῆρες 148
πνεῦμα φυσικόν, ζωτικόν, ψυχικόν 891, 905
πνεύματος, ἐκπόρευσις ἁγίου 1363
ποδάγρα 888
πόθος 683
πόλεις ἐπίσημοι 689, 1889

πόλεων καὶ τόπων 689
πόλις γραμμάτων 1718
πολιτείας 996
πολιτικῶν λογαριασμῶν 681
Πολυδεύκης 864
Πόντου, *ἀρχεῖον* 790
πουλολόγος 823
πούσουλα 824
πραγματεία νέων κανονίων 1511
προγιγνώσκειν 447
προγνώσεως 890
προγυμνάσματα 947
Προδρομηνός, Νεόφυτος 826
προκαταρκτικῶν αἰτίων 447
προσευχή 96
πρόσωπον νεκρώδης 802
προσωποποιία 588
πρόχειρον νόμων 995
πρόχειρος 826
πρόχειρος παράδοσις 689
Πρόχορος Κυδώνης 1386
πρώτων καὶ ἁπλῶν σωμάτων 588
πτωχεῖον 294
πυγολαμπίς 488
πωρικολόγου, διήγησις 824
πῶς δεῖ κατασκευάζειν ἀστρόλαβον 951
πῶς ἑπτάμηνος καὶ ἐννεάμηνος τόκος σώζεται 683

Ῥαβδᾶς, Νικόλαος Ἀρτάβασδος 681
Ῥαβδᾶς, Παῦλος 681
ῥαβόλιον 123
Ῥακενδύτης 889
ῥήσεων θεολογικῶν, ἔκθεσις 1438
ῥιζοτομικόν 225
ῥιζοτόμοι 222
Ῥινάλδος τῆς Βιλανόβα 754
ῥύσις 737
ῥωμαϊκή, γλῶσσα 354
ῥωμαϊκὴ ἱστορία 950
Ῥωμαίοις συμβουλευτικός 1388
Ῥωμανίᾳ πολέμων, χρονικὸν τῶν ἐν 948

σακελλάριος 1439, 1512
Σάμψ Μπουχαρής 699
σελήνη 689
σελήνης ὅρος 1158
σήκωμα 1847
σημεῖα 623
σίδηρος ἰνδανικός 1859
σιλεντιάριος 679
σίναπι 230
σοφίας 952
Σπανός, Ἀλέξιος 995
στερεόν 148

στιχηρά 162
στιχηράριον 162
στίχος 162
στοιχείωσις ἐπὶ τῇ ἀστρονομικῇ ἐπιστήμῃ 684
στρατηγικὸς λόγος 514
στρατηγός 305
στρατοπεδάρχης 587
συλλογή 996
συλλογὴ κατὰ στοιχεῖον 826
συλλογὴ ὀνομάτων ἀττικῶν 679
συμβουλευτικοί 1388
Συμεὼν 'Ατουμάνου 1394
Συμεὼν ὁ νέος θεολόγος 96
συμμίκτα 1156
συναγωγή 197
συναξάρια 403
συναξάριον γαδάρου 824
συνεκτικῶν αἰτίων 447
συνθέσεως φαρμάκων 447
συνοδικόν 995
σύνταγμα τῶν θείων καὶ ἱερῶν κανόνων 995
σύνταγμα περὶ ποδάγρας 888
σύνταγμα τῶν τεσσάρων μαθημάτων 119
σύνταξις μαθηματική 1439
σύνταξις τῶν Περσῶν 123, 688
σύντομος ἔκφρασις ἐλέφαντος 825
Συρία 356
συστάσεως ἰατρικῆς 447
σφαίρας καὶ κυλίνδρου 431
σχεδογραφία 679
σχέδος 679, 996
σῴζειν τὰ φαινόμενα 440, 1882
Σωτῆρος, μονὴ τοῦ 584
Σωτῆρος φῶς 1511
Σωφρόνιος Δαμασκηνός 446
σωφροσύνην, εἰς τὴν 1513

ταλιθά, κοῦμι 357
Τάναϊς 783
τάξεως, ἔκθεσις τῆς βασιλείου 957
τεσσάρων μαθημάτων 119
τεσσάρων στοιχείων οὐρανοῦ 755
τετράγωνος ἀριθμός 119, 679
τετραγωνικῶν πλευρῶν, εὕρεσις 1512
τεττιγοφόρος 1188
τέττιξ 1187, 1188
τέχνη ἰατρική 839
τεχνολογία 679
τεχνολογία γραμματικῆς 952
Τζαβούχης, Θεόδωρος 681
τζύφρα 122
τινὲς αἰτίαι 1209
τόκος ἐπίτριτος, πεντώβολος 326
τόκος ἑπτάμηνος καὶ ἐννεάμηνος 683
τόκος τόκου 326
τόκου 1439
τοποτηρητής 746
τράπεζα, τραπεζίτης 1802
Τραπεζοῦντος, ἐκκλησία 790
τρίβιβλος ἀστρονομική 1511, 1512
Τρικλίνιος, Δημήτριος 1005
τρῖψις 288
τριῶν ψυχῆς δυνάμεων 1760
τροπάρια 162
τρόπων 679
τροφῶν δυνάμεως 1209
τυπικόν 1209, 1760
τύπων 447

ὕλης 588
ὕλης ἰατρικῆς 442
ὕπνου καὶ ἐγρηγόρσεως 684
ὑποθέσεις τῶν πλανωμένων 430
ὑποθῆκαι βασιλικῆς ἀγωγῆς 1280, 1824
ὑπομνηματισμοὶ καὶ σημειώσεις γνωμικαί 687
ὑποτύπωσις ἐμπειρική 447

φαντασία 891
φαρμάκων σύνθεσις 447
Φίλαργος (Φιλάργης), Πέτρος 1440
Φιλάρετος, Πέτρος 1440
Φιλῆς, Μανουήλ 825
φιλομαθίας 1760
Φιλόπονος 1512
φιλοσόφου ἱστορίας 448
φλεβοτομίας 431, 447, 891
Φλωρέντιος 952
Φοιβάμμω 1008
φόλλις 122
φρόνησις 891
φύσεως 211
φύσεως κόσμου 588
φυσικῆς ἀκροάσεως 684
φυσιολόγος 824
φύσιος παιδίου 837
φυσιογνωμονικά 270

χαλκοκολλητῶν 152
Χαμαετός 1438
Χαρσανίτης, Ἰωάννης 688
χάρτης 175
χαρτοφύλαξ 682, 746
χάσματα 709
Χατζύκης, Γεώργιος 681
Χιονιάδης, Γρηγόριος 438
χολέρα 1664
χολή 1664
Χοῦμνος, Ἰωάννης 888

Χοῦμνος, Νικηφόρος 587
χρείας μορίων 447
χρήσιμος σαφήνεια 826
Χριστιανῶν, θρησκεία 1823
Χριστοδοῦλος, Ἰωσάφ 1760
Χριστῷ, ζωὴ ἐν 1439
χρονικὰ τοῦ Μορέως 949
χρονικὸν Κύπρου 952
χρονικὸν τοῦ Μορείος 1852
χρονικὸν τῶν ἐν Ῥωμανίᾳ πολέμων 948
χρόνου βισέκτου 1822
χρόνου ἐνιαυσίου 1439
Χρυσοκόκκης 1378
Χρυσοκόκκης, Γεώργιος 688
Χρυσολωρᾶς, Μανουήλ 1822
Χωνιάτης, Γεώργιος 438

ψευδογραφίας καὶ δυσσεβείας 588
ψηφοφορία κατ' Ἰνδούς 120, 681
ψηφοφορικόν 681
ψυχή 447, 488
ψυχὴ θρεπτική, αἰσθητική, διανοητική 905
ψυχῆς 588, 684, 825
ψυχῆς, τριῶν δυνάμεων 1760
ψυχογονία 683

ᾠδαί 162
ὧν οἱ κατὰ καιροὺς αἱρετικοὶ ἔδοξαν 996

CHINESE INDEX AND GLOSSARY TO VOLUMES 1, 2, AND 3

1. As its title suggests, the purpose of the following list is twofold. It is an *index* which will enable the reader to find the pages of volumes 1, 2, 3 where each Chinese personality or subject is dealt with.[1] It is at the same time a *glossary* giving the Chinese characters corresponding to each Chinese name or phrase and a definition, as brief as possible, yet sufficient to guide the reader's attention.

A third purpose may be added, namely, to reveal the very large amount of Chinese materials included in my Introduction. The reader might not be aware of their multiplicity, because those materials are not grouped together, but scattered through 4,000 pages of text dealing as well with many other nations.

2. As Chinese type was not available to me at the time of publication of volumes 1 and 2, each Chinese word in them was followed (at least once) by its Giles numbers (Introd. 1, 47). That method was accurate and absolutely unambiguous, but very inconvenient. Even when a scholar had the Giles dictionary at hand (first edition 1892, or second, 1912), the Chinese characters could not be read except after a tedious process of decoding. What is worst, I had overestimated, if not the value, at least the popularity of Giles' dictionary. A great many Sinologists do not have a copy of it and never had. The French have always been partial to their own excellent dictionary (father Couvreur's);[2] the Germans, the Russians, the Italians have their own dictionaries, and of course Chinese and Japanese scholars, as well as the most advanced Western Sinologists, can use the best and fullest dictionaries of all, exclusively in Chinese, or Sino-Japanese. For anybody lacking the Giles dictionary the Giles numbers are naturally worthless.

In order to correct that shortcoming, the present index gives the Chinese characters of the Chinese words included not only in this volume, but in volumes 1 and 2 as well.

3. The classification follows the alphabetical order of the Wade-Giles romanizations; equal romanizations corresponding to different characters are placed in the same order as in Giles' dictionary. The classification of phrases was made according to the first character; then for each character (not for each romanization) the phrases were classified in the order of the second character, and so forth. As a result, the index is not in strict alphabetical order from the English point of view, but that does not matter much, for it will suffice to glance through a few lines, at most a page, to discover whether any Chinese phrase is included or not. This method has the advantage that identical first characters appear close together; this facilitates the correction of proofs and thus decreases the chances of error.

It is easy for French scholars to pass from the Couvreur romanization to Giles' by means of Karlgren's Mandarin phonetic reader (1917), Nash's Trindex (1936), or otherwise, and hence it will not be very difficult for them to use this index.

[1] In a few cases the page numbers are missing, but the index is still of use to readers coming across the Chinese words in the text and wishing to know the corresponding characters.

[2] Séraphin Couvreur (S.J., 1835–1919): Dictionnaire classique de la langue chinoise. Imprimerie de la Mission Catholique, Ho kien Fou (1st ed., 1890; 2d, 1904; 3d, xii+1144 p., 1911; 4th, 1930). I am using the third edition. The dictionary, largely derived from the K'ang-hsi tzŭ-tien and other Chinese dictionaries, contains a great many examples, the variants of each character, and references to the texts.

4. The four tones (ssŭ shêng) were indicated in volumes 1 and 2 but left out of volume 3, because they are not by any means as fixed as the characters themselves and give a barbarous look to the romanizations. To non-Sinologists they are meaningless; Sinologists can find them in their several dictionaries. For every word used in volume 1 or 2, the tones can be easily found in the text of those volumes.

In my romanizations ordinary apostrophes have been used instead of inverted ones. This was done for the printers' convenience. As only one kind of apostrophe is used, there is no ambiguity, but the reader should remember that each apostrophe represents a strong aspiration.

5. The index includes all the Chinese words of volumes 1 to 3 except place names, the characters of which are easily obtainable in gazetteers, and the names of emperors or other rulers who were mentioned only in a casual fashion. The name of a place, river, mountain, emperor, etc. is included only when the Introduction provides definite information about it; that is, these names are included for the "index" rather than for the "glossary" purpose.

Chinese words in Westernized form (such as Confucius, Mencius) are listed in the general index, not in this one. The same had to be done of necessity for Chinese words the original characters of which remained unknown. That is the case, e.g., for Chinese authors writing in Western languages and transcribing their own names according to their own fancy.

6. Tzŭ and hao. Chinese scholars and men of science were known not only under their own family and personal names (the family name always preceding the personal), but also, and even more frequently, under a style name, tzŭ, a kind of nickname, hao, or a posthumous name, shih hao (Introd. 1, 43). These tzŭ and hao names are listed below in their proper order. If any reader wishes to connect the tzŭ (or hao) with the family and personal names he can easily do so by means of the index.

7. The glossary purpose of this index is satisfied by the insertion of brief explanations. In the case of persons, the explanation consists simply in an indication of time, or in a translation (e.g., the Sanskrit name of some Buddhist personalities).[3] When the time is indicated as follows, (V B.C.) or (XIII-1), it means that an article is devoted to that personality. In all other cases, the time is indicated otherwise, (1325–89), or (d. 1389), or (fl. end 4th), or (fl. 1342).

A phrase of many characters is often self-explaining, but when there are only one or two characters their meaning may remain uncertain without context. Therefore, a short definition or explanation is helpful, the reader being aware that more information can be readily obtained by referring to the pages designated.

No attempt has been made to translate titles of books, except very short ones (these titles, like those of Arabic books, are often metaphorical and meaningless). It is more helpful to indicate the purpose of books, e.g., medical, alchemical, astronomical. The simplest way of identifying Buddhist terms is to give their Sanskrit equivalents, and this has generally been done.

9. The Chinese index is supplementary to the general index. For example, under such headings as Ching chiao or Mo ni chiao one will find references only to the pages containing those very words; for more information the reader should consult in the main index the heading Nestorians or Manichaeans. The same remark applies with special force to technical terms, such as mo, chên fa, ta fêng-tzŭ,

[3] Sometimes references have been added to Giles (1898), Hummel (1943–44), Couling (1917), or Isis.

ssŭ yüan shu, etc. After having checked up the purely Chinese references, one should make a deeper exploration of the subject by consulting in the general index the English terms conveying the same idea, ink, pulse, acupuncture, chaulmoogra, equations, etc.

10. The publication of this index was made possible by the expert and friendly collaboration of my colleague James Roland Ware, associate professor of Chinese in Harvard University. I owe thanks also to the many Chinese scholars who helped me from time to time during more than twenty years. Their names are gratefully recorded in vol. 1, 48, vol. 2, xi, vol. 3, 28. None has helped me more than professor Ware, who tracked down some refractory characters missing in my notes, enabled me to identify others, added cross references the need of which was more obvious to him than to me, and finally assumed the responsibility of reading the proofs of the Chinese column and of checking its congruence with the English column.

G. S.

August 17, 1947

A-jih-fu (Muslim writer), v. 3, 1587 .... 阿日孚
A-lao-wa-ting (XIII-2), v. 2, *1034*, 765; v. 3, 158, 970 .... 阿老瓦丁
A-su (Alans), v. 2, 773, 982; v. 3, 387, 776 .... 阿速
Ai-hsieh (ʿĪsā), v. 2, 1021; v. 3, 137 .... 愛薛
ai-tai (spectacles), v. 2, 1024 .... 靉靆
ai-huo (moxa), v. 2, 78 .... 艾火
An Chih-chai (mathematician), v. 3, 1536 .... 安止齋
An-hsi (Parthia), v. 1, 197 .... 安西
An-jên (tzŭ), v. 3, 979 .... 安仁
An-nan chih-lüeh (history of Annam), v. 3, 978 .... 安南志略
An-tao (tzŭ), v. 3, 909, 1731 .... 安道
An-tun (Marcus Aurelius), v. 1, 297 .... 安敦
An Yü (Korean Confucianist), v. 3, 108, 636 .... 安裕
An-ch'êng, *see* Yen-ch'êng
Ao-po t'u (on salt), v. 3, 761 .... 熬波圖

Cha-ma-lu-ting (XIII-2), v. 2, *1021*, 19, 755, 982; v. 3, 137, 377 .... 札馬魯丁
ch'a (tea), v. 2, 57 .... 茶
Ch'a ching (on tea), v. 1, 535 .... 茶經
Chai kung (hall of abstinence), v. 3, 1472 .... 齋宮
Chai-chih (tzŭ), v. 3, 760 .... 宅之
Ch'ai Yüan, v. 2, 311, 442; v. 3, 1646 .... 柴源
Chan-jan chü-shih wên chi (collected essays), v. 2, 574 .... 湛然居士文集
ch'an (dhyāna), v. 1, 199; v. 3, 189 .... 禪
Ch'an-lin sêng-pao chuan (Buddhist biographies), v. 2, 558 .... 禪林僧寶傳
Ch'an-tsung (Zen Buddhism), v. 1, 48, 420, 447, 552; v. 2, 282, 337, 559; v. 3, 59, 226, 311, 387, 423 .... 禪宗
Ch'an k'o hsin fa (on obstetrics), v. 2, 81 .... 產科心法
Ch'an-yü pao-ch'ing chi-fang (on obstetrics), v. 2, 443 .... 產育寶慶集方
Chang Chan (philosopher, fl. 4th), v. 1, 139 .... 張湛
Chang Chi (*see* Chang Chung-ching, II-2), v. 1, 290, 310 .... 張機
Chang Ch'ien (II-2 B.C.), v. 1, *197*, 192 .... 張騫
Chang Ch'iu-chien (VI-2), v. 1, *450*, 444 .... 張邱建
Chang Ch'iu-chien suan-ching (mathematical), v. 1, 494 .... 張邱建算經
Chang Chu (XIV-1), v. 3, *979*, 310, 810 (Isis 30, 236) .... 張翥
Chang Chung-ching (II-2), v. 1, *310*, 290; v. 2, 76, 87; v. 3, 903, 905, 1731 .... 張仲景
Chang Fêng (fl. 1925) .... 張風
Chang Fu (d. 1449; Giles no. 52), v. 3, 1548 .... 張輔
Chang Hai-p'êng (d. 1816; Hummel p. 36), v. 2, 646 .... 張海鵬
Chang Hêng (II-1), v. 1, *278*, 196, 268, 269; v. 3, 217, 234 .... 張衡
Chang Hsiang-wên (contemporary), v. 3, 1860 .... 張相文
Chang Hsiao-chih, v. 2, 311, 442; v. 3, 1646 .... 張孝直
Chang Hua (period 265–420), v. 2, 1075 .... 張華
Chang I-hsi (fl. 1617), v. 1, 514 .... 張一熙
Chang P'êng-ko (d. 1725; Hummel p. 49), v. 3, 809 .... 張鵬翮
Chang Po-hsing (d. 1725; Hummel p. 51), v. 3, 809 .... 張伯行
Chang Po-tuan (d. 1082; Isis 30, 236), v. 3, 180 .... 張伯端

Chang Shih-ch'êng (Giles no. 103), v. 3, 1017 .... 張士誠
Chang Shou-chieh (fl. 737), v. 1, 476 .... 張守節
Chang Ssŭ-hsün (X-2), v. 1, *672*, 649, 654 .... 張思訓
Chang Sui (*see* I-hsing, VIII-1), v. 1, 514 .... 張遂
Chang Sung (fl. 1370), v. 3, 1268 .... 張松
Chang T'ing-yü (d. 1755; Hummel p. 54), v. 3, 1789 .... 張廷玉
Chang Tsai (d. 1076), v. 1, 755 .... 張載
Chang Ts'ang (II-1 B.C.), v. 1, *183*, 178, 211, 339, 449, 494; v. 2, 626, 1023 .... 張蒼
Chang Tun-jên (d. 1834; Hummel p. 417), v. 1, 474 .... 張敦仁
Chang Tzŭ-ho (XII-2), v. 2, *479*, 71, 79, 92, 476; v. 3, 907 .... 張子和
Chang Wên-ming (*see* I-ching, VII-2), v. 1, 497 .... 張文明
Chang Yen-yüan (fl. 847), v. 3, 1791 .... 張彥遠
Chang Yüan-su (fl. 13th), v. 2, 1104; v. 3, 902, 908 .... 張元素
ch'ang p'u (sweet flag), v. 3, 1647 .... 菖蒲
Ch'ang Ch'ü (fl. 347), v. 3, 204 .... 常璩
Ch'ang Tê (XIII-2), v. 2, *1067*, 37, 776, 797 .... 常德
Ch'ang-an k'o hua, v. 3, 260 .... 長安客話
ch'ang shêng (long life, Taoist term), v. 3, 96 .... 長生
Chang-sun No-yen (fl. 677), v. 1, 486 .... 長孫訥言
Chao-hsien kuo (Korea, Chōsen), v. 3, 1028 .... 朝鮮國
Ch'ao-tsung (*see* Wu hai, XIV-2), v. 3, 1791 .... 朝宗
Chao Kuan-chih (Sung), v. 3, 1590 .... 晁貫之
Chao Shuo-chih (Sung), v. 3, 1590 .... 晁妁之
Chao (Annamese dynasty, 208–111 B.C.), v. 3, 978 .... 趙
Chao Ch'êng, v. 3, 702 .... 趙城
Chao Hsi-ku (Sung), v. 2, 1024 .... 趙希鵠
Chao Hui-ch'ien (XIV-2), v. 3, *1828*, 1331 .... 趙撝謙
Chao I-ch'ing (d. 1764; Hummel p. 76), v. 3, 809 .... 趙一清
Chao Ju-kua (XIII-1), v. 2, *645*, 44, 47, 514, 517; v. 3, 1625 .... 趙汝适
Chao Kuan (fl. 1514), v. 3, 1861 .... 趙官
Chao Yu-ch'in (XIV-1), v. 3, *703*, 140, 761 .... 趙友欽
Chao Yü, v. 3, 1536 .... 趙瑀
Chao Yang Buwei (contemporary), v. 3, 1841, 1851 .... 趙楊步偉
Chao Yüan-ren (Yuen Ren; contemporary), v. 3, 1841 .... 趙元任
Chao Yün-ts'ung (contemporary), v. 3, 180, 761 .... 趙雲從
ch'ao (paper money), v. 2, 764; v. 3, 731, 1800 .... 鈔
Ch'ao Yüan-fang (VII-1), v. 1, *481*, 462, 463, 683 .... 巢元方
Ch'ao Ts'o (II-2 B.C.), v. 1, *196*, 192; v. 3, 217 .... 鼂錯
Chê-tsung (Sung emperor), v. 3, 635 .... 哲宗
Ch'ê Fêng-chao (*see* Wu K'ung, VIII-2), v. 1, 526 .... 車奉朝
Chên-hui lao-jên (hao), v. 3, 1589 .... 眞回老人
Chên kao (Taoist treatise), v. 1, 436 .... 眞誥
Chên-la fêng t'u chi (on Cambodian customs), v. 2, 1067 .... 眞臘風土記
Chên-ti (Paramārtha, VI-2), v. 1, 446 .... 眞諦
Chên-tsung (Sung emperor), v. 1, 713; v. 3, 274 .... 眞宗
Chên-yen tsung (true word, Jap. Shingon; Buddhist sect), v. 1, 508, 553 .... 眞言宗
Chên chia shu yao (medical), v. 3, 907 .... 診家樞要
chên (fourth character in I ching), v. 3, 1645 .... 貞
Chên-i (hao), v. 3, 807 .... 貞一

Chên-i-chai tsa chu (collected essays), v. 3, 808 .... 貞一齋雜著
Chên-kuan chêng-yao (on government), v. 1, 518 .... 貞觀政要
Chên-chiu chia-i-ching (on acupuncture), v. 1, 342 .... 鍼灸甲乙經
Chên-chiu ta ch'êng (on acupuncture), v. 1, 906 .... 鍼灸大成
chên fa (acupuncture) .... 鍼法
Chên-luan (VI-2), v. 1, *450*, 299, 444 .... 甄鸞
Chên-hêng (*see* Chu Tan-ch'i, XIV-1), v. 3, 907 .... 震亨
Ch'ên Huo [Shên Huo is better] (*see* Shên Kua, XI-2), v. 1, 755 .... 沉括
Ch'ên Han (Koma in Korea), v. 1, 364 .... 辰韓
Ch'ên (Annamese dynasty, 1225–1414), v. 3, 978 .... 陳
Ch'ên Chieh (fl. 1843), v. 1, 474 .... 陳杰
Ch'ên Chih (fl. 1078), v. 3, 903 .... 陳直
Ch'ên Ching-i (XIII-2), v. 2, *1073*, 53, 780 .... 陳景沂
Ch'ên Ch'un (XIV-1), v. 3, *761*, 181 .... 陳椿
Ch'ên Fu (XII-1), v. 2, *228*, 56, 133; v. 3, 211 .... 陳敷
Ch'ên Fu-yao (fl. 1688), v. 2, 652 .... 陳扶搖
Ch'ên Hao (XIV-1), v. 3, *635*, 108 .... 陳灝
Ch'ên I (*see* Hsüan-tsang, VII-1), v. 1, 477 .... 陳禕
Ch'ên Jên-hsi, v. 2, 398 .... 陳仁錫
Ch'ên Jên-yü (XIII-1), v. 2, *651*, 57, 517, 524 .... 陳仁玉
Ch'ên, Kenneth K. S., v. 3, 808, 1842 .... 陳觀勝
Ch'ên Kuan-wu (XIV-1), v. 3, *760*, 108, 180, 703 .... 陳觀吾
Ch'ên Kuo-fu (fl. 1942), v. 3, 761 .... 陳國符
Ch'ên Li (d. 1882; Hummel p. 90), v. 3, 809 .... 陳澧
Ch'ên Li (XIV-1), v. 3, *979*, 108, 311 .... 陳櫟
Ch'ên P'an-chih, *see* P'an Chih .... 陳盤之
Ch'ên P'êng-nien (XI-1), v. 1, *737*, 442, 486, 701, 702; v. 3, 385, 1828 .... 陳彭年
Ch'ên Shou (III-2), v. 1, *343*, 331; v. 2, 429 .... 陳壽
Ch'ên shu (9th dynastic history), v. 1, 483 .... 陳書
Ch'ên Tê-an (*see* Chih-i, VI-2), v. 1, 447 .... 陳德安
Ch'ên Tsai-hsin (fl. 1927), v. 3, 703 .... 陳在新
Ch'ên Tzŭ-ming (XIII-1), v. 2, *668*, 81, 524 .... 陳自明
Ch'ên Yen (XII-2), v. 2, *443*, 71, 81, 311 .... 陳言
chêng (positive quantity, right), v. 1, 183, 339 .... 正
Chêng chiao chên ch'üan (apology of Islām), v. 3, 1589 .... 正教眞詮
Chêng fa hua ching (lotus sūtra), v. 1, 447 .... 正法華經
Chêng-i-t'ang ch'üan shu (ts'ung shu), v. 2, 1022 .... 正誼堂全書
chêng shih (dynastic histories), v. 1, 797; v. 3, 310, 1789 .... 正史
Chêng yün (phonetic dictionary), v. 3, 1789, 1800 .... 正韻
Chêng (personal name of Shih huang-ti, III-2 B.C.), v. 1, 168 .... 政
Chêng-ho chêng-lei pên-ts'ao, v. 3, 223 .... 政和證類本草
chêng (harpsichord), v. 1, 175 .... 箏
Chêng A-li (Uighūr astronomer), v. 3, 1121, 1537 .... 鄭阿里
Chêng Ch'iao (XII-2), v. 2, *459*, 315, 983; v. 3, 78, 180, 386 .... 鄭樵
Chêng Mêng-chou (XIV-2), v. 3, *1478*, 636, 1103 .... 鄭蠓周
Chêng chih lei yüan (medical), v. 3, 1732 .... 證治類元
Chêng chih yao chüeh (medical), v. 3, 1732 .... 證治要訣
Chêng-lei pên-ts'ao, v. 2, 52, 137, 247, 248, 1075; v. 3, 223, 908 .... 證類本草
Ch'êng Chin-fang (d. 1784; Hummel p. 114), v. 3, 1732 .... 程晉芳

Ch'êng Hao (d. 1085), v. 1, 755 .... 程顥
Ch'êng I (d. 1107), v. 1, 755; v. 3, 386 .... 程頤
Ch'êng Mo (III-2 B.C.), v. 1, *176*, 166; v. 3, 385, 1017 .... 程邈
Ch'êng tzŭ, *see* Ch'êng Hao .... 程子
Ch'êng-shih tsung (Buddhist sect), v. 1, 470 .... 成實宗
Ch'êng-tsung (Yüan emperor), v. 3, 1027 .... 成宗
Ch'êng-wei-shih lun [not Vidyāmātrasiddhi, but Vijñānamātrasiddhi], v. 3, 729 .. 成唯識論
Ch'êng-i-po wên chi, v. 3, 1537 .... 誠意伯文集
Chi Chung-ching, *see* Chang Chung-ching (II-2) .... 機仲景
chi hsieh, *see* Chung kuo tzŭ kuei hsieh .... 庋擷
Chi Han (III-2), v. 1, *340*, 331 .... 稽含
Chi K'ang (III-2), v. 1, *335*, 336 .... 稽康
chi (belles-lettres), v. 3, 77, 831 .... 集
Chi ku lu (on epigraphy), v. 1, 777 .... 集古錄
Chi-yün (phonetic dictionary, 1039), v. 1, 737 .... 集韻
chi-pei (cotton), v. 3, 833 .... 吉貝
Chi Tsai (Korean), v. 3, 1478 .... 吉再
Chi-i (tzŭ), v. 3, 1590 .... 季一
Chi-yeh (X-2), v. 1, *676*, 650, 654 .... 繼業
ch'i (lacquer), v. 1, 369 .... 漆
Ch'i-tan (Liao dynasty, Tatars), v. 2, 78, 273 .... 契丹
Ch'i-tan kuo-chih (annals of Ch'i-tan dynasty), v. 2, 687 .... 契丹國志
ch'i lüeh (seven outlines of classification), v. 3, 77 .... 七略
ch'i (aura, pneuma), v. 3, 905 .... 氣
Ch'i-fu ts'ung-shu, v. 2, 1067 .... 畿輔叢書
Ch'i-hsin lun (awakening of the faith), v. 1, 270; v. 3, 312 .... 起信論
Ch'i Chao-nan (d. 1768; Hummel p. 129), v. 3, 809 .... 齊召南
Ch'i-min yao-shu (on rural economy), v. 1, 441 .... 齊民要術
Ch'i shu (annals of Ch'i dynasties), v. 1, 438, 483 .... 齊書
Ch'i Tê-chih (XIV-1), v. 3, *907*, 261, 273 .... 齊德之
Ch'i-ku suan-ching (on arithmetic), v. 1, 474 .... 緝古算經
Ch'i-su-nung (Song-tsen Gam-po, VII-1), v. 1, 466 .... 棄蘇農
Ch'i-tsung-lung-tsan (Song-tsen Gam-po, VII-1), v. 1, *466*, 460, 463, 468, 525, 593 . 棄宗弄贊
Chia-chi (hao), v. 2, 459 .... 夾際
Chia-chi i-kao (collected essays), v. 2, 460 .... 夾際遺稿
Chia-i ching (on acupuncture), v. 1, 342; v. 3, 906 .... 甲乙經
chia tzŭ (sexagesimal cycle), v. 1, 673 .... 甲子
Chia, *see* Hui-yüan (IV-2) .... 賈
Chia I (fl. 2d B.C.; Giles no. 321), v. 1, 199 .... 賈誼
Chia K'uei (I-2), v. 1, *254*, 244 .... 賈逵
Chia Kung-yen (early T'ang), v. 1, 571 .... 賈公彥
Chia Ming (XIV-2), v. 3, *1731*, 1218, 1240 .... 賈銘
Chia Ssŭ-hsieh (VI-1), v. 1, *441*, 416, 418 .... 賈思勰
Chia Ssŭ-tao (XIII-1), v. 2, *651*, 60, 517; v. 3, 1188 .... 賈似道
Chia Tan (VIII-2), v. 1, *536*, 522; v. 2, 225; v. 3, 808 .... 賈耽
Chia T'ung (mathematician, fl. 14th?), v. 3, 1536 .... 賈通
Chiang Ch'ên-ying (d. 1699; Hummel p. 135), v. 3, 1029 .... 姜宸英
Chiang Chi (IV-2), v. 1, *368*, 360 .... 姜岌
Chiang T'ing-lü (writer on acupuncture), v. 2, 78 .... 姜廷梠

Chiao Ping-chên (fl. 1696; Hummel p. 329), v. 2, 428 .... 焦秉貞
chiao ch'i (foot spirit, beriberi), v. 3, 905 .... 脚氣
Chieh-ch'ieh (on astronomy), v. 1, 450 .... 竭伽
chieh shêng (knotted cords, cf. quipu), v. 1, 66 .... 結繩
Chieh-ku (tzŭ), v. 3, 908 .... 潔古
Chieh-tzŭ-yüan hua chuan (on painting), v. 2, 1074 .... 芥子園畫傳
Ch'ieh yün (first phonetic dictionary, 601), v. 1, 486; v. 3, 1789 .... 切韻
Chien-chên (*see Japanese index*, Ganjin, VIII-2), v. 1, 539 .... 鑑眞
Ch'ien-kuang (hao), v. 2, 1023 .... 謙光
Ch'ien-chin fang (materia medica), v. 1, 498 .... 千金方
Ch'ien fo tung (caves of thousand Buddhas), v. 1, 604 .... 千佛洞
Ch'ien tzŭ wên (thousand character classic), v. 1, 441; v. 2, 984; v. 3, 386 .... 千字文
Ch'ien I (XI-2), v. 1, *773*, 743, 746; v. 2, 82 .... 錢乙
Ch'ien Lo-chih (V-1), v. 1, *388*, 378 .... 錢樂之
Ch'ien Pao-ts'ung (fl. 1932), v. 3, 701 .... 錢寶琮
Ch'ien shih hsiao-êrh yao-chêng chên-chüeh (on pediatrics), v. 1, 773 錢氏小兒藥證眞訣
Ch'ien Ta-hsin (d. 1804; Hummel p. 152), v. 3, 1586 .... 錢大昕
ch'ien (leading, first part), v. 3, 1645 .... 前
Ch'ien chi (on flowers), v. 2, 1074 .... 前集
Ch'ien-Han shu (2d dynastic history), v. 1, 264; v. 3, 756 .... 前漢書
Ch'ien-lung (Kao-tsung, Ch'ing emperor; Hummel p. 369), v. 2, 983; v. 3, 78, 467, 1472 .... 乾隆
Chih-pu-tsu-chai ts'ung-shu, v. 2, 220, 228, 422, 428, 628, 644, 646, 1074; v. 3, 226, 1536, 1808 .... 知不足齋叢書
Chih-i (VI-2), v. 1, *447*, 443, 553 .... 智顗
Chih-k'ai (*see* Chih-i, VI-2), v. 1, 447 .... 智顗
Chih-shêng (VIII-1), v. 1, *509*, 504 .... 智昇
Chih hsüan p'ien (guide to mystery), v. 3, 180 .... 指玄篇
Chih-ta (period 1308–12), v. 3, 468, 903 .... 至大
Chih-yüan (period 1264–95), v. 3, 903 .... 至元
Chih-hsü (tzŭ), v. 3, 760 .... 致虛
Chih-ho t'u lüeh (on Yellow River), v. 3, 809 .... 治河圖略
Chih-shih kuei chien (on art of government), v. 3, 1001 .... 治世龜鑑
Chih wu ming shih t'u k'ao (botanical, before 1846; Giles no. 2322), v. 3, 224. 植物名實圖考
Chih-ch'uan (tzŭ), v. 1, 355 .... 稚川
chih (technical memoirs appended to dynastic histories), v. 1, 494, 676; v. 3, 713 .... 志
Ch'ih Ch'ên-yüan (fl. 1395), v. 3, 1537 .... 池臣源
ch'ih (foot, place for pulse taking), v. 3, 808, 902 .... 尺
Chin Fu (d. 1692; Hummel p. 161), v. 3, 809 .... 靳輔
Chin chi (Chin dynasty, Ju-chên, 1115–1260), v. 2, 273, 627; v. 3, 381 .... 金紀
Chin Chiu-hsia (fl. 1796), v. 3, 904 .... 金就夏
chin-chung-êrh (golden bell cricket), v. 2, 652 .... 金鐘兒
Chin Hou (fl. 1395), v. 3, 1537 .... 金候
Chin Hsien (fl. 1489), v. 3, 1627 .... 金銑
Chin-kang ching (diamond sūtra), v. 1, 604 .... 金剛經
Chin-kuei kou-yüan (medical), v. 3, 908 .... 金匱鉤元
Chin-kuei yao-fang (medical), v. 1, 355 .... 金匱藥方
Chin-kuei yü han yao lüeh fang lun (on dietetics), v. 1, 310 .... 金匱玉函要略方論
chin-mu (golden-eye, spectacles), v. 2, 1025 .... 金目

Chin shih (history of Chin dynasty), v. 3, 310, 1788 .... 金史
Chin Shu (fl. 1398), v. 3, 1537 .... 金恕
Chin-tan chêng-li ta-ch'üan (Ming alchemical collection), v. 3, 761 .... 金丹正理大全
Chin-tan ta-yao (on alchemy), v. 3, 180, 761 .... 金丹大要
Chin Tui (fl. 1395), v. 3, 1537 .... 金堆
Chin Tzŭ-sui (fl. 1395), v. 3, 1537 .... 金自綏
Chin Yüan ssŭ ta chia (four famous doctors of Chin and Yüan dynasties), v. 3, 907 .... 金元四大家
Chin-nang ch'i mêng (mathematical), v. 3, 1536 .... 錦囊啓蒙
Chin-ch'ing (tzŭ), v. 3, 809 .... 晉卿
Chin shu (5th dynastic history), v. 1, 482 .... 晉書
Chin-chih (tzŭ), v. 3, 902 .... 進之
chin shih (third academic degree, "doctor"; Couling p. 108, 114), v. 2, 1124, 1125; v. 3, 386, 1083, 1855 .... 進士
Ch'in Chan (Sung writer), v. 2, 228 .... 秦湛
Ch'in Chiu-shao (XIII-1), v. 2, *626*, 9, 507, 625, 755, 756; v. 3, 138, 140, 701, 1586 .... 秦九韶
Ch'in Yüeh-jên (*see* Pien Ch'iao, V B.C.), v. 1, 102 .... 秦越人
Ch'in-yu-t'ang sui lu (on schools of philosophy), v. 3, 979 .... 勤有堂隨錄
Ch'in ching (on birds), v. 2, 60, 781, 1075 .... 禽經
ch'in (lute with seven strings), v. 3, 181, 1857 .... 琴
Ch'in-chien t'u-shih (musical), v. 3, 1857 .... 琴箋圖式
Ch'in-shêng shih-liu fa (musical), v. 3, 1857 .... 琴聲十六法
Ch'in ting ku chin t'u shu chi ch'êng, *see* T'u shu, etc. .... 欽定古今圖書集成
ching (classic, canon), v. 1, 797; v. 3, 77 .... 經
Ching-kuei (hao), v. 3, 635 .... 經歸
Ching-shih chêng-lei ta-kuan pên-ts'ao, v. 2, 248; v. 3, 730 .... 經史證類大觀本草
Ching shih ta tien (encyclopaedia, 1329), v. 3, 205, 808 .... 經世大典
Ching tien shih wên (glossary of classics), v. 1, 458 .... 經典釋文
ching tsang (sūtrapiṭaka), v. 3, 468 .... 經藏
Ching yao hsüan ming lun (medical), v. 2, 478 .... 莖要宣明論
Ching chiao (luminous doctrine, Nestorianism), v. 3, 1071 .... 景教
Ching chiao pei (Nestorian monument, 781), v. 1, 527 .... 景教碑
Ching-ching (author of Nestorian inscription, 781), v. 1, 527 .... 景淨
Ching-kao (tzŭ), v. 3, 978 .... 景高
Ching-lien (tzŭ), v. 3, 1789 .... 景濂
ching wu (natural curiosities), v. 2, 423 .... 景物
Ching-chai (tzŭ), v. 2, 627; v. 3, 761 .... 敬齋
Ching Po (VII-1), v. 1, *484*, 462, 463 .... 敬播
Ching-tai pi shu (ts'ung shu), v. 2, 262 .... 津逮祕書
Ching-ling tzŭ (*see* Lu Yü, VIII-2), v. 1, 535 .... 竟陵子
Ching-shan (tzŭ), v. 3, 1858 .... 竟山
Ching-shan yüeh-lu (on music), v. 3, 1858 .... 竟山樂錄
Ching-chên chiao (pure true religion, Islām), v. 3, 1587 .... 淨眞教
Ching-t'u tsung (pure land school, Amidaism), v. 1, 364; v. 3, 312 .... 淨土宗
Ching-ssŭ (tzŭ), v. 3, 1733 .... 靜思
Ch'ing-chao-t'ang ts'ung-shu, v. 3, 1478, 1586 .... 青照堂叢書
Ch'ing-i lu, v. 3, 237 .... 淸異錄
Ch'ing shih kao (draft of Ch'ing history), v. 3, 310, 1237, 1790 .... 淸史稿
Ch'ing-yüan (period 1195–1201), v. 2, 137, 248 .... 慶元

Ch'ing Li (period 1041–49), v. 3, 733 .... 慶歷
Chiu p'u (on alcoholic beverages), v. 1, 723 .... 酒譜
Chiu-chang suan-shu (mathematical), v. 1, 183, 338; v. 2, 626 .... 九章算書
Chiu-ch'êng (tzŭ), v. 3, 1585 .... 九成
Chiu-chih-li (on systems of chronology), v. 1, 513, 514 .... 九執歷
Chiu-fêng (tzŭ), v. 2, 625 .... 九峯
Chiu t'ung (the nine t'ung), v. 2, 983 .... 九通
Chiu-mo-lo (Kumārajīva, V-1), v. 1, 384 .... 鳩摩羅
Chiu-huang pên-ts'ao (famine herbal, 1406), v. 3, 223, 1170, 1176, 1218, 1645, 1646, 1647 .... 救荒本草
Chiu huang yeh-p'u, v. 3, 1649 .... 救荒野譜
Chiu T'ang shu (16th dynastic history), v. 1, 643 .... 舊唐書
Chiu Wu tai shih (18th dynastic history), v. 1, 688 .... 舊五代史
Ch'iu Ch'ang-ch'un (XIII-1), v. 2, *644*, 37, 514, 609, 610, 1067; v. 3, 833 .... 邱長春
Ch'iu Ch'u-chi, *see* Ch'iu Ch'ang-ch'un (XIII-1) .... 邱處幾
Ch'iu K'ai-ming (contemporary), v. 3, 28, 78, 283, 761, 1536 .... 裘開明
Cho kêng lu (collection of essays), v. 3, 1585 .... 輟耕錄
chou (department or political division), v. 1, 676 .... 州
Chou, *see* Chuang tzŭ (III-1 B.C.) .... 周
Chou chi (*see* Hou-Chou shu), v. 1, 483 .... 周紀
Chou Ch'in k'o shih shih yin (on epigraphy), v. 3, 1018 .... 周秦刻石史音
Chou ch'ü-fei (fl. 1178), v. 2, 646; v. 3, 1625 .... 周去非
Chou Hsiao, *see* Chou wang Hsiao .... 周橚
Chou Hsien (fl. 1370), v. 3, 1645 .... 周憲
Chou Hsing-ssŭ (VI-1), v. 1, *441*, 418; v. 2, 984; v. 3, 386 .... 周興嗣
Chou Hsüeh-hai (Hummel p. 903), v. 3, 907 .... 周學海
Chou li t'ien kuan (Chou rituals), v. 3, 259 .... 周禮天官
Chou Li-ching (Ming editor), v. 2, 652 .... 周履靖
Chou pi suan ching (mathematical), v. 1, 494 .... 周髀算經
Chou Po-ch'i (XIV-1), v. 3, *1017*, 385 .... 周伯琦
Chou-shih i-hsüeh ts'ung-shu, v. 3, 907, 909 .... 周氏醫學叢書
Chou Ta-kuan (XIII-2), v. 2, *1067*, 38, 39, 776, 797; v. 3, 1030 .... 周達觀
Chou Ting-wang (posthumous hao), v. 3, 1645 .... 周定王
Chou Ts'ung (XI-2), v. 1, *762*, 741, 746 .... 周琮
Chou Tun-i (XI-2), v. 1, *755*, 27, 739–40, 746; v. 2, 398; v. 3, 108, 636 .... 周敦頤
Chou tzŭ (*see* Chou Tun-i, XI-2), v. 1, 755 .... 周子
Chou wang Hsiao (*see* Chu Hsiao, XIV-2), v. 3, 1170, 1644, 1645 .... 周王橚
Chou Yung (fl. 5th), v. 1, 413 .... 周顒
Chou Yung-nien (1730–91; Giles no. 430), v. 3, 108 .... 周永年
Chou-hou pei-chi fang (medical), v. 1, 355; v. 3, 904 .... 肘後備急方
Ch'ou-jên chuan (biographies of astronomers; Hummel p. 402), v. 3, 703, 1847 .... 疇人傳
ch'ou (computing rods), v. 1, 339 .... 籌
Chu Chih-hsi (d. 1666; Hummel p. 178), v. 3, 809 .... 朱之錫
Chu Ching-hsüan (fl. 1000), v. 3, 1791 .... 朱景玄
Chu Ching-yüan (fl. 1000), v. 3, 1791 .... 朱景元
Chu Ch'üan (d. 1448), v. 3, 1858 .... 朱權
Chu fu-tzŭ (*see* Chu Hsi, XII-2), v. 2, 397 .... 朱夫子
Chu Hsi (XII-2), v. 1, 110, 755, 778; v. 2. *397*, 294, 315, 610, 625, 797, 981; v. 3, 74, 108, 109, 380, 636, 907, 1478, 1858 .... 朱禧
Chu Hsiao (XIV-2), v. 3, *1644*, 223, 1170, 1176, 1177, 1218, 1646, 1867 .... 朱橚

Chu I-chung (XII-1), v. 2, *220*, 130, 145 .... 朱翼中
Chu Shih-chia (fl. 1941), v. 3, 204 .... 朱士嘉
Chu Shih-chieh (XIV-1), v. 2, 9, 755, 756; v. 3, *701*, 138, 139, 140, 1847 .... 朱世傑
Chu Ssŭ-pên (XIV-1), v. 3, *807*, 204 .... 朱思本
Chu Tan-ch'i (XIV-1), v. 2, 248; v. 3, *907*, 261, 280, 289, 1218, 1731, 1732 ... 朱丹溪
Chu tzŭ, *see* Chu Hsi (XII-2) .... 朱子
Chu Yü (fl. after 1100), v. 1, 764 .... 朱昱
Chu Yüan-chang (*see* Hung-wu, XIV-2), v. 3, 1028, 1536, 1800 .... 朱元章
Chu Yün (d. 1781; Hummel p. 198), v. 3, 831 .... 朱筠
chu-suan (abacus arithmetic), v. 1, 299; v. 3, 1586 .... 珠算
Chu-suan chih-tu k'ao (arithmetical), v. 3, 1586 .... 珠算制度考
Chu-ts'ung pieh lu (ts'ung shu), v. 2, 651 .... 珠叢別錄
Chu-ching yao chi (Buddhist ethics), v. 1, 491 .... 諸經要集
Chu fan chih (records of foreign nations), v. 2, 646; v. 3, 1625 .... 諸蕃志
Chu tzŭ pien (on historical method), v. 3, 1789 .... 諸子辨
Chu Fa-lan (fl. 1st), v. 1, 246 .... 竺法蘭
Chu Mu (XIII-2), v. 2, *1124*, 797, 1074 .... 祝穆
Chu t'ien ta tsan chi chieh (Muslim collection), v. 3, 1587 .... 祝天大贊集解
chu (bamboo), v. 3, 226 .... 竹
Chu lin ch'i hsien (seven sages of bamboo grove), v. 1, 335 .... 竹林七賢
Chu p'u hsiang lu (on bamboo), v. 2, 1074; v. 3, 226 .... 竹譜詳錄
Chu shu chi nien (annals of bamboo books), v. 1, 163 .... 竹書紀年
Ch'u san tsang chi chi (catalogue of Buddhist works), v. 1, 420 .... 出三藏記集
Ch'u-chi (*see* Ch'iu Ch'ang-ch'un, XIII-1), v. 2, 645 .... 處幾
chuan (accuracy), v. 1, 35 .... 專
chuan (seal character), v. 1, 286; v. 3, 1017 .... 篆
Ch'uan-fu (tzŭ), v. 3, 1732 .... 川父
Chuang Chên-fêng (fl. 17th), v. 3, 1857 .... 莊臻鳳
Chuang Chou, *see* Chuang tzŭ (III-1 B.C.) .... 莊周
Chuang-hsien wang (king of Korea, 1419–50), v. 3, 1562 .... 莊憲王
Chuang tzŭ (III-1 B.C.), v. 1, *153*, 149; v. 3, 634, 1909 .... 莊子
ch'uang (ulcer), v. 3, 907 .... 瘡
Chui shu (mathematical), v. 1, 410 .... 綴術
Ch'un ch'iu (spring and autumn), v. 1, 67, 777; v. 3, 635 .... 春秋
Ch'un ch'iu shih li t'u ti ming (topographical commentary on Ch'un ch'iu), v. 1, 341 .... 春秋釋例土地名
Chung kuo (middle kingdom), v. 3, 1028 .... 中國
Chung kuo fo chiao shih, v. 3, 469 .... 中國佛教史
Chung kuo jên ming ta tz'ŭ tien (encyclopaedia of Chinese biography), v. 3, 1255 .... 中國人名大辭典
Chung kuo tzŭ kuei hsieh (filing of Chinese characters, system explained in Trindex), v. 3, 1897 .... 中國字庋擷
Chung t'ien chu kuo hsing chi (relation of travel in central India), v. 1, 496 .. 中天竺國行記
Chung tsang ching (medical), v. 1, 325 .... 中藏經
Chung yung (doctrine of the mean, one of the four books), v. 1, 91 .... 中庸
Chung-chü (tzŭ), v. 3, 979 .... 仲舉
Chung Ch'ê (fl. 2d half of 14th), v. 3, 1232, 1733 .... 忠徹
Chung i lu (biographies of devoted officers), v. 3, 979 .... 忠義錄
Chung Hua-min (fl. 1587), v. 3, 1800 .... 鍾化民

Chung-yo (tzŭ), v. 2, 88 .... 鍾繇
Ch'ung-hsiu ko hsiang hsin shu (mathematical), v. 3, 703 .... 重修革象新書
ch'ung hu-huan (mathematical method), v. 2, 1023 .... 重互換
Ch'ung-hsiu kuang yün, *see* Ta Sung ch'ung, etc. .... 重修廣韻
Ch'ung-kuang pên-ts'ao t'u ching, v. 2, 443 .... 重廣本草圖經
Chü-na-lo-t'o (Paramārtha, VI-2), v. 1, 446 .... 拘那羅陀
Chü fang fa hui (medical), v. 3, 908 .... 局方發揮
chü (chrysanthemum), v. 3, 226 .... 菊
Chü yung kuan (in Nan-kow pass), v. 3, 203 .... 居庸關
Chü-shê tsung (Hīnayāna sect), v. 1, 492 .... 俱舍宗
Chü lu (on oranges), v. 2, 428 .... 橘錄
chü jên (second degree examination), v. 2, 1083 .... 舉人
Ch'ü Hsüan-ying (fl. 1930), v. 3, 204 .... 瞿宣穎
Ch'ü Shou-i (fl. end 14th), v. 3, 761 .... 瞿守義
Ch'ü Shou-jên (brother of Ch'ü Shou-i), v. 3, 761 .... 瞿守仁
Ch'ü-t'an (Hindu astronomers, VII-1), v. 1, *475*, 463 .... 瞿曇
Ch'ü-t'an Chuan (fl. 618), v. 1, 475 .... 譔
Ch'ü-t'an Hsi-ta (VIII-1), v. 1, *513*, 504, 514 .... 瞿曇悉達
Ch'ü-t'an Lo (T'ang astronomer), v. 1, 475 .... 羅
Ch'ü T'ien-hsi (son of Ch'ü Shou-i), v. 3, 761 .... 瞿天禧
chüan (volumen) .... 卷
Ch'üan fang pei tsu (botanical), v. 2, 53, 1073 .... 全芳備祖
Ch'üan nêng chi (mathematical), v. 3, 1536 .... 全能集
Ch'üan Tsu-wang (d. 1755; Hummel p. 203), v. 3, 809 .... 全祖望
Ch'üan chih (on coinage), v. 2, 262 .... 泉志
Ch'üan chou (prefecture in Fuhkien, Polo's Zayton), v. 2, 44, 645, 1055; v. 3, 1589 .... 泉州
Ch'üan Chin (d. 1409), v. 3, 1479, 1537 .... 權近
Ch'üan Chung-ho (fl. 1395), v. 3, 1537 .... 權仲和
chün tzŭ (gentleman), v. 3, 226 .... 君子
chün huo (principal fire in the heart), v. 3, 908 .... 君火
Chün-tsai (tzŭ), v. 3, 979 .... 君載
Chün p'u (on mushrooms), v. 2, 651 .... 菌譜

Êrh (ear; name of Lao tzŭ, VI B.C.), v. 1, 66 .... 耳
Êrh ya (earliest Chinese dictionary), v. 1, 84, 110, 353; v. 2, 460; v. 3, 385, 389 .... 爾雅

Fa-ching (VI-2), v. 1, *448*, 443 .... 法經
Fa-hsien (V-1), v. 1, *390*, 377, 378, 380, 414; v. 3, 280, 468, 833 .... 法顯
Fa-hua-ching (lotus sūtra), v. 3, 312 .... 法華經
Fa-shang (Dharmakīrti, VII-1), v. 1, 473 .... 法尙
Fa-yang (Dharmakīrti, VII-1), v. 1, 473 .... 法揚
Fa yüan chu lin (Buddhist encyclopaedia, 668), v. 1, 491 .... 法宛珠林
Fa-yün (XII-2), v. 2, *474*, 282, 321; v. 3, 382 .... 法雲
Fan Liang-fêng (fl. 554), v. 1, 454 .... 繙量豐
Fan-i ming-i chi (Sanskrit-Chinese dictionary), v. 2, 474 .... 翻譯名義集
Fan-i ming-i chi hsüan (Sanskrit-Chinese dictionary), v. 2, 474 .... 翻譯名義集選
Fan Ch'o (fl. 860), v. 1, 536 .... 樊綽
fan ch'ieh (method indicating pronunciation of characters), v. 1, 343, 413, 442; v. 3, 385, 1828 .... 反切

Fan Ch'êng-ta (XII-2), v. 1, 676; v. 2, *422*, 39, 57, 302, 305, 321 .... 范成大
Fan P'êng (1272–1330), v. 3, 109 .... 范梈
Fan tê-chi shih-chi (anthology of poems), v. 3, 109 .... 范德機詩集
Fan ts'un chü p'u (on chrysanthemums), v. 2, 422 .... 范村菊譜
Fan Yeh (V-1), v. 1, *396*, 279, 379 .... 范曄
Fang chih k'ao kao (on gazetteers), v. 3, 204 .... 方志考稿
Fang chou tsa yen, v. 2, 1024 .... 方舟雜言
Fang Hsü (Ch'ing writer), v. 2, 652 .... 方芧
Fang Kuan-ch'êng (d. 1768; Hummel p. 233), v. 3, 809, 833 .... 方觀承
Fang Kuang (fl. before 1536), v. 3, 908 .... 方廣
Fang yen (on Chinese dialects), v. 1, 353 .... 方言
Fang Chao-ying (contemporary), v. 3, 1847 .... 房兆楹
Fang Ch'iao (*see* Fang Hsüan-ling, VII-1), v. 1, 482 .... 房喬
Fang Hsüan-ling (VII-1), v. 1, *482*, 462, 463 .... 房玄齡
fang ying shu (falconry), v. 3, 233 .... 放鷹術
Fei-t'un (tzŭ), v. 2, 1073 .... 肥遯
fêng shui (wind and water, divination), v. 1, 345, 353; v. 3, 1537 .... 風水
fêng tu chiao ch'i (medical term), v. 3, 905 .... 風毒脚氣
fêng (leprosy and other diseases), v. 3, 280 .... 瘋
fêng shan (a kind of sacrifice), v. 1, 199 .... 封禪
Fêng Tao (X-1), v. 1, *633*, 621; v. 3, 729 .... 馮道
Fêng Ying-wang, *see* Fêng Tao (X-1) .... 馮瀛王
Fo chiao (Buddhism), v. 3, 77, 424 .... 佛教
Fo kuo chi (records of Buddhist kingdoms), v. 1, 391; v. 3, 280 .... 佛國記
fo shou (Buddha's hand, fruit of Citrus medica), v. 3, 1835 .... 佛手
Fo so hsing tsan (Buddhacarita, deeds of the Buddha), v. 1, 270 .... 佛所行讚
Fo tsang (Tripiṭaka), v. 3, 108 .... 佛藏
Fo tsu li tai t'ung tsai (history of Buddhism to 1344), v. 3, 423 .... 佛祖歷代通載
Fu-sang (mysterious Eastern country), v. 1, 411 .... 扶桑
Fu Hsi (497–569), v. 3, 107, 734 .... 傅翕
Fu Jên-chün (VII-1), v. 1, *475*, 461, 463 .... 傅仁鈞
Fu Kuang-tsê (Ming author), v. 2, 984 .... 傅光宅
Fu Kung (XI-2), v. 1, *766*, 741, 746; v. 2, 60 .... 傅肱
fu (prefecture), v. 1, 676 .... 府
fu (bowels), v. 2, 1104 .... 腑
Fu-hsi (first emperor), v. 2, 459 .... 伏羲
Fu chou (in Fuhkien) .... 福州
fu (negative quantity), v. 1, 183, 339 .... 負
Fu yung tsu (poetical descriptions), v. 2, 1074 .... 賦詠祖
Fu-jên ta-ch'üan liang-fang (on married women's diseases), v. 2, 668 ... 婦人大全良方

hai (boar, last of the twelve branches; pisces) .... 亥
Hai ch'ao chi (collection of poems), v. 3, 1829 .... 海巢集
Hai-kuo t'u-chih (on historical geography of Asia; Hummel p. 851), v. 3, 808 ... 海國圖志
Hai-nei hua-i t'u (map of China and barbaric countries), v. 1, 536 .... 海內華夷圖
Hai-tao suan-ching (sea-island arithmetic), v. 1, 338 .... 海島算經
Hai-tsang hsien-shêng (hao), v. 3, 902 .... 海藏先生
han (to sweat), v. 2, 478 .... 汗
Han l ai (ts'ung shu), v. 2, 646 .... 函海

han ch'i (cold spirit), v. 3, 905 .... 寒氣
han liang (cooling medicine), v. 2, 478 .... 寒凉
Han Ch'an-chih (XII-2), v. 2, *428*, 57, 305, 322 .... 韓產直
Han Ching (fl. middle 13th), v. 2, 1074 .... 韓境
Han Yü (768–824; Giles no. 632), v. 3, 233, 905 .... 韓愈
Han lin yüan (the old imperial academy), v. 1, 512; v. 2, 627, 807, 981, 1021; v. 3, 42, 386, 634, 730, 809, 1083, 1789 .... 翰林院
Han-chang (tzŭ), v. 3, 810 .... 漢章
Han chi (history of earlier Han), v. 1, 299 .... 漢紀
Han Ch'ing (*see* Chu Shih-chieh, XIV-1), v. 3, 701 .... 漢卿
Han i wên chih (catalogue of Han books), v. 1, 222, 264 .... 漢藝文志
Han shu (history of Han dynasty), v. 3, 310 .... 漢書
hao (nickname, name of a firm), v. 1, 43 .... 號
Hao-ku-t'ang shu-mu (catalogue of rare books; Hummel p. 811), v. 3, 807 .... 好古堂書目
hêng (to be successful, second character of I ching), v. 3, 1645 .... 亨
hêng (crosswise; horizontal comparison), v. 1, 35 .... 橫
Hêng ch'ao (short cut, pure land school), v. 1, 364 .... 橫超
ho (river), v. 3, 809 .... 河
Ho fang t'ung i (on Yellow River), v. 3, 809 .... 河防通議
Ho Ch'eng-t'ien (V-1), v. 1, *388*, 378 .... 何承天
ho-ko (Jap. tanka), v. 3, 1018 .... 和歌
Ho Ch'ung [correct to Ts'ui Ch'ung] (fl. 1068), v. 3, 108
Ho-shan (tzŭ), v. 3, 761 .... 鶴山
Hoang, Pierre, *see* Huang
Hou Hsiang-ch'uan (contemporary), v. 3, 906 .... 侯祥川
Hou-hu chih (on national census methods), v. 3, 1861 .... 後湖志
hou (following), v. 3, 1645 .... 後
hou chi (supplement to book or article), v. 2, 1074 .... 後集
Hou-Chou shu (12th dynastic history), v. 1, 483 .... 後周書
Hou-Han shu (3d dynastic history), v. 1, 396 .... 後漢書
Hou Hsi yu chi (fantastic novel), v. 2, 645 .... 後西遊記
Hsi-cheng kêng-wu yüan li (on reform of calendar), v. 2, 574 .... 西征庚午元曆
Hsi kuo chi, *see* Hsi yu chi .... 西國記
Hsi shih chi, v. 2, 1067 .... 西使記
Hsi wang mu (royal lady of the West), v. 1, 342 .... 西王母
Hsi yu chi (travel diary, novel; *see* Hou Hsi yu chi), v. 1, 477, 496; v. 2, 610, 645 .... 西遊記
Hsi yu lu (journey to the West), v. 2, 574, 644 .... 西遊錄
Hsi yü chi (record of western countries, 648), v. 1, 477; v. 2, 645 .... 西域記
Hsi yü ch'iu fa kao sêng chuan (travels in India), v. 1, 497 .... 西域求法高僧傳
Hsi yü t'u chi (record of western countries), v. 1, 476 .... 西域圖記
Hsi-chai tao jên (hao), v. 3, 226 .... 息齋道人
Hsi-tsung (third Chin emperor), v. 2, 273 .... 熙宗
Hsi-yüan lu (on forensic medicine), v. 2, 668; v. 3, 260, 322, 904 .... 洗寃錄
Hsi yüan lu chi chêng (on forensic medicine), v. 2, 668 .... 洗寃錄集證
Hsi yüan lu chi chêng hui tsuan (on forensic medicine), v. 2, 668 .... 洗寃錄集證彙纂
Hsi yüan lu hsiang i (on forensic medicine), v. 2, 668 .... 洗寃錄詳義
Hsi yüan lu k'o chüeh (on forensic medicine), v. 2, 668 .... 洗寃錄斠訣
Hsia-hou Yang (VI-2), v. 1, *449*, 444 .... 夏侯陽
Hsia Kuei (d. 1230), v. 2, 263 .... 夏珪

Hsia Wên-yen (XIV-2), v. 3, *1791*, 1270 .... 夏文彥
hsia (lower, laxative), v. 2, 478; v. 3, 1645 .... 下
Hsia chên pien (on acupuncture), v. 3, 906 .... 下針砭
hsiang huo (auxiliary fire in liver and kidney), v. 3, 908 .... 相火
hsiang mien (physiognomy), v. 3, 1733 .... 相面
Hsiang-min (posthumous name), v. 3, 1790 .... 襄愍
Hsiang-yang (place of a famous siege), v. 2, 1034 .... 襄陽
Hsiang-chieh chiu-chang suan-shu (mathematical), v. 2, 1023 .... 詳解九章算術
Hsiang ming suan fa (mathematical), v. 2, 1536 .... 詳明算法
Hsiang Hsiu (fl. 3d), v. 1, 335 .... 向秀
hsiang-ch'i (elephant game, chess), v. 1, 451 .... 象棋
Hsiang-shan (hao), v. 2, 398 .... 象山
hsiao chuan (lesser seal script), v. 1, 286; v. 3, 385, 1017 .... 小篆
Hsiao Tzŭ-hsien (VI-1), v. 1, *438*, 417 .... 蕭子顯
Hsiao ching (classic of filial piety), v. 1, 321 .... 孝經
Hsieh Ch'ang-shou (Korean, fl. 1395), v. 3, 1357 .... 偰長壽
Hsieh Ch'ing-shou (brother of Hsieh Ch'ang-shou, fl. 1395), v. 3, 1537 .... 偰慶壽
Hsieh Chi, v. 2, 668 .... 薛己
Hsieh Chü-chêng (X-2), v. 1, *688*, 652, 654 .... 薛居正
Hsieh Ts'ung (fl. 700), v. 3, 108, 388, 636 .... 薛聰
Hsieh Chin (d. 1415), v. 3, 831 .... 解縉
Hsieh p'u (on crabs), v. 1, 766 .... 蟹譜
Hsieh Wei-hsin (XIII-2), v. 2, *1125*, 798 .... 謝維新
Hsieh Ying-fang (XIV-2), v. 3, *1477*, 1102, 1104, 1162 .... 謝應芳
hsien-shêng (teacher), v. 3, 1536 .... 先生
Hsien fo t'ung yüan lun (Taoist Buddhist), v. 3, 761 .... 仙佛同源論
Hsien-yü Wang-jên (fl. 2d), v. 1, 195 .... 鮮于妄人
Hsien chiao (Zoroastrianism), v. 3, 1071 .... 祆教
Hsien lo kuo (Siam), v. 3, 1030 .... 暹羅國
hsien (geographical district), v. 1, 676 .... 縣
Hsin-fa (medical collection), v. 3, 908 .... 心法
Hsin-fa fu-yü (medical collection), v. 3, 908 .... 心法附餘
Hsin chien t'ung jên chên chiu t'u ching (on acupuncture), v. 2, 78 .. 新鑴銅人鍼灸圖經
Hsin-hsiu pên-ts'ao, v. 1, 539; v. 3, 223 .... 新修本草
Hsin i-hsiang fa-yao (astronomical), v. 1, 762 .... 新儀象法要
Hsin lin (collection of predictions), v. 1, 353 .... 新林
Hsin T'ang shu (17th dynastic history), v. 1, 777 .... 新唐書
Hsin Wu tai shih (19th dynastic history), v. 1, 777 .... 新五代史
Hsin Yüan shih (new Yüan annals), v. 2, 610, 982; v. 3, 310, 907, 909, 979, 1001, 1789 .... 新元史
hsing-li (Sung Confucianism), v. 1, 27, 755; v. 2, 294, 398; v. 3, 94, 108, 109, 262, 636, 1103 .... 性理
Hsing-li ta-ch'üan (1415; Hummel p. 913), v. 3, 1858 .... 性理大全
hsing-ming (life), v. 3, 979 .... 性命
Hsing ching (early catalogue of stars), v. 1, 504, 514 .... 星經
Hsing Ping (932–1010), v. 1, 110 .... 邢昺
hsing (apricot), v. 3, 226 .... 杏
hsiu ts'ai (first degree examination), v. 3, 1083 .... 秀才
Hsiung Tsung-li (fl. 1440?), v. 1, 773 .... 熊宗立

Hsü-chai ming t'ao t'u lu (catalogue of pottery), v. 3, 758 .... 虛齋名陶圖錄
Hsü Ch'ieh (920–74), v. 1, 286 .... 徐鍇
Hsü Ching (XII-1), v. 2, *225*, 39, 132, 145; v. 3, 388 .... 徐兢
Hsü Hsüan (916–91), v. 1, 286 .... 徐鉉
Hsü Kuang-ch'i (d. 1633; Giles no. 779), v. 3, 1646 .... 徐光啓
Hsü Shih-ch'ang (d. 1922), v. 2, 610, 982; v. 3, 1789 .... 徐世昌
Hsü Yu-lin (fl. 1796), v. 3, 904 .... 徐有隣
Hsü Yüeh (II-2), v. 1, *299*, 289, 756; v. 3, 1586 .... 徐岳
Hsü Ch'ien (XIV-1), v. 3, *635*, 108, 907 .... 許謙
Hsü Ching-tsung (d. 672; Giles no. 769), v. 1, 484 .... 許敬宗
Hsü Ch'ung (fl. 121), v. 1, 286 .... 許冲
Hsü Hêng (XIII-2), v. 2, *1021*, 755 .... 許衡
Hsü Kuei-lin (fl. 1821; Hummel p. 472), v. 1, 756 .... 許桂林
Hsü Lu-cha chi, *see* Hsü Hêng (XIII-2) .... 許魯渣集
Hsü Shên (II-1), v. 1, *285*, 269, 441; v. 3, 385, 1017, 1828 .... 許愼
Hsü Shih-lien (contemporary), v. 3, 386 .... 許仕廉
Hsü Ch'a ching (on tea), v. 1, 535 .... 續茶經
Hsü Kao sêng chuan (Buddhist biographies), v. 1, 491 .... 續高僧傳
Hsü Ku chai ch'i suan fa (mathematical), v. 2, 1023 .... 續古摘奇算法
Hsü Wên-hsien t'ung-k'ao (botanical), v. 2, 1074 .... 續文獻通考
Hsüan-tsang (VII-1), v. 1, *477*, 350, 367, 461, 462, 463, 470, 484, 488, 496, 604; v. 2, 645; v. 3, 382, 468, 729 .... 玄奘
Hsüan-ying (VII-1), v. 1, *487*, 463; v. 3, 385 .... 玄應
Hsüan-tsung (T'ang emperor, 713–56), v. 1, 508; v. 3, 139, 1858 .... 玄宗
Hsüan-ho fêng shih kao li t'u ching (description of Korea), v. 2, 225 .. 宣和奉使高麗圖經
Hsüan wang (Chou emperor, 827–781 B.C.) .... 宣王
Hsüeh ching t'ao yüan (ts'ung shu), v. 2, 262, 646, 1067; v. 3, 1018 ..... 學津討原
Hsüeh hai lei pien (ts'ung shu), v. 2, 644; v. 3, 1732 .... 學海類編
Hsüeh ku pien (on sphragistics and epigraphy), v. 3, 1017 .... 學古編
hsüeh (places for acupuncture), v. 2, 78 .... 穴
Hsüeh Ts'ung (Korean inventor of ido script), *see* Hsieh Ts'ung .... 薛聰
Hsün Hsü (III-2), v. 1, *342*, 331; v. 3, 77 .... 荀勖
Hsün K'uang (III-2 B.C.), v. 1, *168*, 166 .... 荀況
Hsün Yüeh (II-2), v. 1, *299*, 289, 290; v. 2, 626 .... 荀悅
Hu-ssŭ-hui (XIV-1), v. 3, *905*, 261 .... 忽思慧
Hu Chêng-yen (fl. 1634; Hummel p. 896) .... 胡正言
Hu Cho (fl. 1774), v. 3, 1268 .... 胡琢
Hu Kuang (fl. 1415), v. 3, 1858 .... 胡廣
Hu Shih (contemporary), v. 2, 645; v. 3, 387, 809, 1841 .... 胡適
hu huan (alternate exchange, mathematical term), v. 2, 1023 .... 互換
Hua ching (mirror of flowers), v. 2, 652 .... 花鏡
Hua-ch'uan (tzŭ), v. 2, 88 .... 華川
Hua Hsi-min (fl. 1699), v. 1, 663 .... 華希閔
Hua T'o (III-1), v. 1, *325*, 315 .... 華佗
Hua-yang chên-jên (hao), v. 1, 436 .... 華陽眞人
Hua-yang-kuo chih (oldest gazetteer, 347), v. 3, 204 .... 華陽國志
Hua-shan lao-jên (hao), v. 3, 1731 .... 嘩山老人
Hua chi (history of art), v. 3, 1791 .... 畫繼
Hua chien (history of painting), v. 3, 979 .... 畫鑒

Hua hsüeh hsin yin (ts'ung shu), v. 3, 980 .... 畫學心印
hua pên (spoken text of a story), v. 3, 387 .... 話本
Hua Shou (XIV-1), v. 3, *907*, 103, 261 .... 滑壽
Huai-nan tzŭ (II-2 B.C.), v. 1, *193*, 191, 192; v. 2, 1025; v. 3, 1139 .... 淮南子
Huang chi ching shih shu (commentary on book of changes), v. 1, 755 .... 皇極經世書
Huang-fu Mi [not Huang Fu] (III-2), v. 1, *342*, 331; v. 2, 78; v. 3, 906 .... 皇甫謐
Huang Chin (XIV-1), v. 3, *809*, 204 .... 黃溍
huang-chung (longest musical tube), v. 3, 1858 .... 黃鐘
Huang Fang-kang (contemporary), v. 1, 48 .... 黃方剛
Huang Fang (fl. 1522), v. 3, 1017 .... 黃芳
Huang ho (Yellow River), v. 2, 981; v. 3, 809 .... 黃河
Huang ho yüan wei (description of Yellow River), v. 3, 205, 1001 .... 黃河原委
Huang Mei-wu (*see* Nien-ch'ang, XIV-1), v. 3, 423 .... 黃梅屋
Huang [= Hoang], Pierre (d. 1909), v. 3, 217 .... 黃伯祿
Huang Shu-tu (Ming editor), v. 2, 1125 .... 黃叔度
Huang Tao-p'o (XIV-1), v. 3, *832*, 228 .... 黃道婆
Huang ti (Yellow emperor; Giles no. 871), v. 1, 112, 122 .... 黃帝
Huang ti, *see* Nei ching su wên
Hui-tsung (Sung emperor; Giles no. 145), v. 1, 764; v. 2, 247, 262 .... 徽宗
Hui-ho (Uighūr), v. 3, 1587 .... 回紇
Hui-hui (Muslims), v. 3, 1069, 1586 .... 回回
Hui-hui li (Muslim calendar), v. 3, 1537 .... 回回歷
Hui-hui shih-t'ou (Muslim precious stones), v. 3, 1585 .... 回回石頭
Hui-hui shuo (discourse on Muslims), v. 3, 1587 .... 回回說
hui-kuan (guild house), v. 3, 155 .... 會館
Hui-chiao (fl. 519), v. 1, 343, 491 .... 慧皎
Hui-shên (V-2), v. 1, *410*, 400 .... 慧深
Hui-yüan (IV-2), v. 1, *364*, 359, 469; v. 3, 212 .... 慧遠
Hui-an (*see* Sung Ch'i, XI-1), v. 1, 737 .... 惠安
Hui-hung (XIII-1), v. 2, *558*, 490 .... 惠洪
Hui-shêng (fl. 518), v. 1, 431 .... 惠生
Hui-tsung (Shun ti, last Yüan emperor, d. 1370; Giles no. 1953), v. 3, 1027 .... 惠宗
Hung-fan huang chi nei p'ien (on numerology), v. 2, 625 .... 洪範皇極內篇
Hung Kua (XII-2), v. 2, *460*, 262, 315; v. 3, 385 .... 洪适
Hung Mai (d. 1203), v. 2, 262 .... 洪邁
Hung Tsun (XII-1), v. 2, *262*, 140, 460 .... 洪遵
Hung-wu (first Ming emperor, XIV-2; Giles no. 483), v. 3, *1800*, 731, 1028, 1084, 1162, 1281, 1536, 1644 .... 洪武
Hung Wu, *see* Chêng yün; Shêng cheng chi; Shih lu
Hung-chien (tzŭ), v. 3, 1646 .... 鴻漸
Hung lieh chieh (Taoist cosmology), v. 1, 193 .... 鴻烈解
Hung Chün (fl. 1743), v. 2, 88 .... 弘晙
Hung ming chi (Buddhist history), v. 1, 420 .... 弘明集
Hung Ta (*see* P'ei Chü, VII-1), v. 1, 476 .... 弘大
Huo fa chi yao (medical), v. 3, 908 .... 活法機要
huo ch'i (fiery spirit), v. 3, 905 .... 火氣
Huo chiao (fire religion, Zoroastrianism), v. 3, 1071 .... 火教

I-ch'ieh ching yin i (Buddhist glossary, 649), v. 1, 487 .... 一切經音義
I-hsing (VIII-1), v. 1, *514*, 504; v. 2, 626 .... 一行

I-t'ung chih, *see* Ta Ming i t'ung chih .... 一統志
I-chia-t'ang ts'ung-shu, v. 2, 627, 1023 .... 宜稼堂叢書
I-hsing yao (pottery made at I hsing, Kiangsu), v. 3, 179 .... 宜興窰
I ching su-hui chi (on fevers), v. 3, 1731 .... 醫經溯洄集
I hsüeh fa ming (medical), v. 3, 908 .... 醫學發明
I lei yüan jung (medical), v. 3, 902 .... 醫壘元戎
I shih (history of medicine), v. 3, 1732 .... 醫史
I t'ung chêng mo ch'üan shu (medical), v. 3, 903, 907, 909, 1732 .... 醫統正脈全書
I yün t'ung i (medical), v. 3, 1731 .... 醫韻統一
I-ssŭ-ma-yin (XIII-2), v. 2, *1034*, 765; v. 3, 158, 970 .... 亦思馬因
I mên kuang tu (ts'ung shu), v. 2, 652; v. 3, 1018 .... 夷門廣牘
I-ching (VII-2), v. 1, *497*, 480, 488, 489, 490; v. 3, 59, 382, 468 .... 義淨
I-li chu shih (commentary on I-li, oldest book on rites), v. 1, 571 .... 儀禮注釋
I ku kên yüan (mathematical), v. 2, 1023 .... 議古根源
I-chih (tzŭ), v. 3, 635, 907 .... 益之
I-ku yen tuan (mathematical), v. 2, 627 .... 益古演段
I ching (book of changes), v. 1, 67, 163, 322, 448, 755; v. 2, 460; v. 3, 635, 1645 ... 易經
I yü t'u chih (on geography and natural history), v. 3, 1162, 1169, 1179, 1625, 1626, 1627 .... 異域圖志

Jên Ch'êng-lao (fl. 983), v. 3, 108 .... 任成老
jên (man), v. 3, 701 .... 人
Jên wu chih (on anthropology), v. 1, 321; v. 3, 1281 .... 人物志
Jên hsiang ta ch'êng (on physiognomy), v. 3, 1733 .... 夙相大成
Jên ch'ing (tzŭ), v. 2, 627 .... 仁卿
Jên-tsung (Yüan emperor; Giles no. 13), v. 1, 764; v. 3, 42, 386, 1027 .... 仁宗
Jih sun chai kao (collection of essays), v. 3, 809 .... 日損齋藁
Jih sun chai pi chi (collection of essays), v. 3, 809 .... 日損齋筆記
Ju-chên, *see* Nü-chên
Ju mên shih ch'in (medical), v. 2, 479 .... 儒門事親
Ju tsang (Confucian patrology), v. 3, 108 .... 儒藏
Juan Chi (fl. 3d), v. 1, 335 .... 阮籍
Juan Fu, *see* Yüan Fu
Juan Hsien (fl. 3d), v. 1, 335 .... 阮咸
Juan Yüan (1764–1849; Hummel p. 399), v. 1, 663; v. 2, 1023; v. 3, 703, 1847 .... 阮元
Jung Kêng (contemporary), v. 3, 1841 .... 容庚

kai-t'ien (celestial hemisphere), v. 1, 195 .... 蓋天
K'ai-fêng fu (Sung capital in Honan), v. 3, 833, 1071, 1170, 1177, 1213, 1645, 1788 .. 開封府
K'ai-pao hsiang-ting pên-ts'ao, v. 3, 222 .... 開寶詳定本草
K'ai-yüan (period 713–42), v. 1, 513 .... 開元
K'ai yüan chan ching (on Tantric divination), v. 1, 513 .... 開元占經
K'ai-yüan lu (Buddhist bibliography), v. 1, 509 .... 開元錄
K'ai-yüan shih-chiao lu (Buddhist bibliography), v. 1, 509 .... 開元釋教錄
kan ch'i (liver spirit), v. 3, 905 .... 肝氣
Kan Po-tsung (fl. 923), v. 3, 1732 .... 甘伯宗
K'an yü man hsing (on geomancy), v. 3, 1537 .... 堪嫗漫興
Kang-mu pên-ts'ao, v. 2, 1075 .... 綱目本草
K'ang-chü (Soghdiana), v. 1, 197 .... 康居
K'ang-hsi (1654–1722, second Ch'ing emperor; Hummel p. 327), v. 2, 428, 982, 1024 .. 康熙

K'ang-hsi tzŭ-tien (dictionary), v. 2, 1024; v. 3, 385, 1829, 1897 .... 康熙字典
Kao Chin (d. 1779; Hummel p. 411), v. 3, 809 .... 高晉
Kao Hsiang-hsien (Isis 30, 236), v. 3, 180 .... 高象先
Kao-k'o-li (a Korean kingdom), v. 3, 1538 .... 高句麗
Kao-li (Korea, Jap. Kōrai; Koryu dynasty), v. 3, 1537 .... 高麗
Kao-li kuo (old name of Korea), v. 3, 1028 .... 高麗國
Kao-li shih (Korean annals), v. 3, 734, 1562 .... 高麗史
Kao Ming-k'ai (contemporary), v. 3, 1841 .... 高名凱
Kao P'ing-tzŭ (contemporary), v. 3, 138 .... 高平子
Kao Pin (d. 1755; Hummel p. 412), v. 3, 809 .... 高斌
Kao sêng chuan (Buddhist biographies), v. 1, 343, 491, 673; v. 2, 558 .... 高僧傳
Kao Shao-kung (fl. 1159), v. 2, 311, 442; v. 3, 1646 .... 高紹功
Kao-tsung (T'ang emperor, 650–84; Giles no. 1109), v. 1, 498 .... 高宗
Kao-tsung (S. Sung emperor, 1127–62; Giles no. 166), v. 2, 263 .... 高宗
Kao-tsung (Ch'ien-lung, Ch'ing emperor, 1736–96; Hummel p. 369), v. 2, 983; v. 3, 78, 467, 1472 .... 高宗
K'ao ku hsien shêng (hao), v. 3, 1828 .... 考古先生
Kêng chih t'u shih (on husbandry and weaving), v. 2, 428; v. 3, 211, 1179 .. 耕織圖詩
Kêng Shou-ch'ang (I-1 B.C.), v. 1, *211*, 195, 202, 254 .... 耿壽昌
Ko chih ching yüan (encyclopaedia; Hummel p. 97), v. 1, 451 .... 格致鏡原
Ko chih yü lun (medical), v. 3, 908 .... 格致餘論
Ko-ku yao lun (1388), v. 3, 1857 .... 格古要論
Ko Mu-fu (fl. 1319), v. 3, 226 .... 柯牧甫
Ko Shao-min (d. 1933), v. 2, 610, 982; v. 3, 1789 .... 柯劭忞
Ko Hung (IV-1), v. 1, *355*, 345; v. 2, 84, 667; v. 3, 274, 904 .... 葛洪
Ko hsiang hsin shu (mathematical), v. 3, 703 .... 革象新書
K'o-ta (tzŭ), v. 3, 635 .... 可大
k'o (division of the day), v. 1, 429 .... 刻
k'ou (mouth), v. 3, 1587 .... 口
K'ou Tsung-shih (XII-1), v. 2, *248*, 137; v. 3, 908 .... 寇宗奭
ku chi (archaeological curiosities), v. 2, 423 .... 古蹟
Ku chin ho pi shih lei pei yao (encyclopaedia), v. 2, 1125 .... 古今合璧事類備要
Ku chin hsing shih shu pien chêng (history of clans and families), v. 2, 262. 古今姓氏書辨證
Ku chin shuo hai (ts'ung shu), v. 2, 1067 .... 古今說海
Ku chin t'u shu chi ch'êng (medical), v. 1, 103, 325; v. 3, 756 .... 古今圖書集成
Ku ch'in lun (discussion of ancient lutes), v. 3, 1857 .... 古琴論
ku-pei (cotton), v. 3, 833 .... 古貝
Ku tsê, *see* Chao Hui-ch'ien (XIV-2) .... 古則
Ku yü t'u p'u (catalogue of jade), v. 2, 140, 263, 315; v. 3, 1171 .... 古玉圖譜
Ku Hung-ming (contemporary), v. 1, 68 .... 辜鴻銘
Ku Chieh-kang (contemporary), v. 2, 460; v. 3, 1790 .... 顧頡剛
Ku K'o-hsüeh (fl. 1556), v. 2, 1125 .... 顧可學
Ku Yeh-wang (VI-1), v. 1, *441*, 418, 737; v. 3, 1017, 1828 .... 顧野王
Kua ti chih (geographical), v. 1, 476 .... 括地志
Kuan wu liang shou ching (great book of eternal life), v. 3, 312 .... 觀無量壽經
Kuan wu (on study of phaenomena), v. 1, 755 .... 觀物
kuan (place on wrist for pulse taking, middle pulse), v. 3, 902 .... 關
kuang (light, character tabooed in 1195), v. 2, 248 .... 光
Kuang-chai (T'ang calendar), v. 1, 475 .... 光宅

Kuang Ch'ün fang p'u (pên ts'ao), v. 3, 224 .... 廣羣芳譜
Kuang Hung ming chi (Buddhist bibliography, 664), v. 1, 491 .... 廣弘明集
Kuang shih lei fu (encyclopaedia), v. 1, 663 .... 廣事類賦
Kuang yü t'u (atlas of Chinese maps), v. 3, 807, 1850 .... 廣輿圖
Kuang yün (dictionary), v. 3, 729 .... 廣韻
kuei hsieh, *see* Chung kuo tzŭ kuei (chi) hsieh
Kuei-ch'ien chih (1295), v. 2, 644 .... 歸潛志
kuei ch'ao (tortoise nest), v. 3, 1478 .... 龜巢
Kuei hai yü hêng chih (geography and history of S. China), v. 2, 422 .... 桂海虞衡志
K'uei-chi (VII-1), v. 1, *473*, 461, 463, 491 .... 窺基
K'un yü wan kuo ch'üan t'u (Ricci's map of the world), v. 3, 808, 1850 .... 坤輿萬國全圖
Kung-shun-t'ang ts'ung-shu, v. 3, 832 .... 功順堂叢書
kung-so (public hall, guild), v. 3, 155 .... 公所
Kung-sun Ch'iao (VI B.C.), v. 1, *80*, 66 .... 公孫喬
Kung-sun Hung (d. 121 B.C.), v. 3, 387 .... 公孫弘
Kung-wang (tzŭ), v. 2, 78 .... 公望
Kung (family name of Fa-hsien, V-1) .... 龔
kung (keynote), v. 2, 1858 .... 宮
K'ung An-kuo (II-1 B.C.), v. 1, *181*, 177 .... 孔安國
K'ung Chi (V B.C.), v. 1, *91*, 82, 168 .... 孔伋
K'ung Ch'iu, *see* K'ung fu-tzŭ .... 孔丘
K'ung fu-tzŭ (*see general index*, Confucius, VI B.C.), v. 1, *67*, 65, 66, 252, 755; v. 2, 295, 397, 460 .... 孔夫子
Kuo-ch'ao pao chien (annals of last Korean dynasty), v. 3, 388 .... 國朝寶鑑
Kuo fêng tsun ching, v. 3, 1586 .... 國風尊經
Kuo hsüeh (library in Nanking), v. 3, 904 .... 國學
Kuo hsüeh chi k'an (journal of Sinology), v. 2, 460 .... 國學季刊
Kuo Jo-hsü (fl. 1074), v. 3, 1791 .... 郭若虛
Kuo P'o (IV-1), v. 1, *353*, 110, 345, 764; v. 3, 1537, 1625, 1627 .... 郭璞
Kuo Shou-ching (XIII-2), v. 2, *1022*, 12, 14, 19, 44, 755, 757, 759, 776, 982; v. 3, 137 .... 郭守敬

lan (orchid), v. 3, 226 .... 蘭
Lan shih pi-tsang (medical), v. 2, 1104 .... 蘭室祕藏
Lang T'ing-chi (d. 1715; Hummel p. 441), v. 3, 758 .... 郎廷極
lao (old), v. 3, 903 .... 老
Lao chün, *see* Lao tzŭ (VI B.C.) .... 老君
Lao Tan, *see* Lao tzŭ (VI B.C.) .... 老聃
Lao-ts'an yu-chi (novel; Hummel p. 517), v. 3, 809 .... 老殘遊記
Lao tzŭ (VI B.C.), v. 1, *66*, 65; v. 2, 981; v. 3, 634, 1909 .... 老子
Lei ssŭ ching (on construction of plows), v. 3, 211 .... 耒耜經
Lei-chêng chu-shih ch'ien-shih hsiao-êrh fang-chüeh (medical), v. 1, 773 類證註釋錢氏小兒方訣
Lei-chêng yung yao (medical), v. 3, 1732 .... 類證用藥
Lei p'ien (dictionary), v. 1, 778; v. 3, 385, 1828 .... 類篇
lei-shu (encyclopaedias), list in v. 1, 802 .... 類書
Lêng Ch'ien (fl. late 14th), v. 3, 1857 .... 冷謙
li (third of a mile), v. 1, 536; v. 2, 225; v. 3, 204, 808 .... 里
li ch'i (form and matter), v. 2, 398 .... 理氣

Li-tsung (Sung emperor; Giles no. 199), v. 2, 668, 1074 .... 理宗
Li yüan-lu (on forensic medicine), v. 3, 904 .... 理冤錄
li (plum), v. 3, 226 .... 李
Li, *see* Lao tzŭ (VI B.C.)
Li ch'ao (Korean dynasty, 1392–1910), v. 3, 636, 1028, 1070, 1270, 1479 .... 李朝
Li ch'ao (Annamese dynasty, 1010–25), v. 3, 978 .... 李朝
Li Ch'êng-kuei (founder of Korean dynasty), v. 3, 1537 .... 李成桂
Li Chi (fl. 659), v. 1, 489, 498; v. 3, 222 .... 李勣
Li Chi-fu (IX-1), v. 1, *573*, 547 .... 李吉甫
Li Ch'i-hsien (XIV-1), v. 3, *635*, 108, 1478 .... 李齊賢
Li Chien-yüan (fl. end 16th), v. 3, 223 .... 李建元
Li Chih [better than Li Yeh] (XIII-1), v. 2, *627*, 9, 507, 755, 756; v. 3, 138, 701 .... 李治
Li Chih (fl. 1220), v. 2, 423 .... 李直
Li Chih-ch'ang (fl. beginning 13th), v. 2, 645 .... 李志常
Li Ch'ung Jên (d. 1397), v. 3, 1478 .... 李崇仁
Li Fang (X-2), v. 1, *663*, 648, 654 .... 李昉
Li Hsien (d. 1466; Giles no. 1137), v. 3, 1162 .... 李賢
Li Huang (fl. 1820), v. 1, 474 .... 李潢
Li Jui (d. 1814; Hummel p. 144), v. 2, 628 .... 李銳
Li K'an (XIII-2), v. 2, *1074*, 55, 780; v. 3, 226 .... 李衎
Li Kao (XIII-1; better than XIII-2 as in v. 2, 1104, for he died in 1251, aet. 72), v. 2, *1104*, 789; v. 3, 902, 907 .... 李杲
Li Lien (b. 1488), v. 3, 1646, 1732 .... 李濂
Li Lung-chi (*see* Ming-huang, VIII-1), v. 1, 512 .... 李隆基
Li Ping (III-2 B.C.), v. 1, *175*, 166 .... 李冰
Li Po-yao (VII-1), v. 1, *483*, 462, 463 .... 李伯藥
Li Sê (d. 1396), v. 3, 1478 .... 李穡
Li Shan-ch'ang (XIV-2), v. 3, *1790*, 1268 .... 李善長
Li Shih-chên (d. 1590–96), v. 3, 223, 756, 908, 1645 .... 李時珍
Li Shih-min (*see* T'ai-tsung, VII-1), v. 1, 474 .... 李世民
Li Shun-fêng (VII-2), v. 1, *494*, 183, 338, 450, 489, 490 .... 李淳風
Li Ssŭ (d. 208 B.C.; Giles no. 1203), v. 1, 166, 176; v. 3, 234, 1017 .... 李斯
Li T'ai-tsu (fl. 1380), v. 3, 1176 .... 李太祖
Li T'ai (VII-1), v. 1, *476*, 462, 643 .... 李泰
Li T'ang (fl. 1100–30), v. 2, 263 .... 李唐
Li Tê-lin (d. 590), v. 1, 483 .... 李德林
Li T'iao-yüan (d. 1803; Hummel p. 486), v. 2, 646 .... 李調元
Li Ts'un (fl. beginning 14th), v. 3, 979 .... 李存
Li Yeh, *see* Li Chih (XIII-1), *above* .... 李治
Li Yen-shou (VII-1), v. 1, *484*, 462, 463 .... 李延壽
Li Yen (d. 1945), v. 3, 1536, 1586 .... 李儼
li (third character of I ching), v. 3, 1645 .... 利
Li Tao-yüan (fl. in period 386–535), v. 3, 809 .... 麗道遠
li (to calculate, calendar), v. 1, 476 .... 曆
Li suan ch'üan shu, v. 3, 1585 .... 曆算全書
Li ch'ao t'ung lüeh (history of China), v. 3, 979 .... 歷朝通略
Li tai ming hua chi (history of painting), v. 3, 1791 .... 歷代名畫記
Li tai ming i hsing ming (history of medicine), v. 3, 1732 .... 歷代名醫姓名
Li ch'ao (Annamese dynasty, 981–1009), v. 3, 978 .... 黎朝

Li-hsien (Syria), v. 1, 197 .... 黎軒
Li Pêng (fl. beginning 14th), v. 3, 978 .... 黎琫
Li Tsê (XIV-1), v. 3, *978*, 205, 311 .... 黎崱
Li chi (record of rites), v. 1, 91; v. 3, 635 .... 禮記
Li chi chi shuo (commentary on Li chi), v. 3, 635 .... 禮記集說
Li ching ao chih, v. 2, 460 .... 禮經奧旨
li pu (board of rites), v. 2, 263 .... 禮部
Li pu yün lüeh (rhyme dictionary), v. 1, 737; v. 3, 1789 .... 禮部韻略
Li-yen (d. 792), v. 3, 382 .... 禮言
Li-fang (tzŭ), v. 3, 807 .... 立方
Li t'ien yüan i (mathematical), v. 2, 626; v. 3, 138 .... 立天元一
li fêng (leprosy), v. 3, 280 .... 癘風
Li chih p'u (on litchi, 1059), v. 1, 766; v. 2, 1074 .... 荔枝譜
li tu (Korean script), v. 3, 388 .... 吏讀
Li hsü (on epigraphy), v. 2, 460 .... 隸續
Li shih (on epigraphy), v. 2, 460 .... 隸釋
li shu (early Chinese official script), v. 1, 176, 181; v. 3, 385 .... 隸書
Liang shu (8th dynastic history), v. 1, 483 .... 梁書
Liang Ying-shêng (Ming writer), v. 2, 984 .... 梁應升
Liao ch'ao (Chinese dynasty) .... 遼朝
Liao Chin chi nien (history of Liao and Chin dynasties), v. 3, 1001 .... 遼金紀年
Liao shih (history of Liao dynasty), v. 3, 310, 1788 .... 遼史
Liao-yang (Liao capital) .... 遼陽
Lieh tzŭ (IV-2 B.C.), v. 1, *138*, 125; v. 3, 1909 .... 列子
Lieh Yü-k'ou, *see* Lieh Tzŭ (IV-2 B.C.) .... 列禦寇
Lien yün i ts'ung-shu, v. 2, 645 .... 連筠簃叢書
Lien tsung (lotus school, Buddhist sect), v. 1, 364 .... 蓮宗
Lin I (fl. 1068), v. 1, 342 .... 林億
Lin Hsi-chung (= Lin Yün-ming, fl. 17th), v. 1, 153 .... 林西仲
Lin Yün-ming, *see* Lin Hsi-chung .... 林雲銘
Lin-ch'uan (hao), v. 3, 634 .... 臨川
Lin-tê (calendar, 664), v. 1, 494 .... 麟德
ling (laws), v. 1, 500 .... 令
Ling-hu Tê-fên (VII-1), v. 1, *483*, 462, 463 .... 令狐德芬
ling lung k'ai fang (mathematical method), v. 2, 626; v. 3, 701 .... 玲瓏開方
Ling wai tai ta (geographical), v. 2, 646; v. 3, 1625 .... 嶺外代答
Ling ch'i ching (on divination), v. 3, 1537 .... 靈棋經
Ling-chien-ko ts'ung-shu, v. 2, 574 .... 靈鶼閣叢書
ling chih (plant of long life, fungus on trees), v. 3, 1835 .... 靈芝
Ling hsien (on cosmology), v. 1, 278 .... 靈憲
Ling shu ching (medical), v. 1, 310 .... 靈樞經
Liu-ch'iu (Loochoo, Jap. Ryukyu, islands), v. 3, 1879 .... 琉球
liu-li (colored glass, glaze), v. 1, 389; v. 3, 756 .... 琉璃
Liu-chuang (hao), v. 3, 1732 .... 柳莊
Liu Fang-tsê (fl. 1395), v. 3, 1537 .... 柳方澤
Liu Pin (fl. 883), v. 1, 605 .... 柳玭
Liu An, *see* Huai-nan tzŭ (II-2 B.C.) .... 劉安
Liu Chi (XIV-2), v. 3, *1536*, 1121 .... 劉基
Liu Chih (fl. 1710), v. 3, 1587, 1589 .... 劉智

Liu Ê (d. 1909; Hummel p. 516), v. 3, 386, 809 .... 劉鶚
Liu Hsi (fl. 1700), v. 2, 78 .... 劉錫
Liu Hsiang (fl. 7 B.C.), v. 1, 222; v. 3, 77 .... 劉向
Liu Hsiao-sun (Sung editor), v. 1, 450 .... 劉孝孫
Liu Hsin (I-2 B.C.), v. 1, *222*, 219, 220, 264; v. 3, 77 .... 劉歆
Liu Hsü (X-1), v. 1, *643*, 621, 622 .... 劉昫
Liu Hui (III-2), v. 1, *338*, 331, 494; v. 2, 626 .... 劉徽
Liu Hung (II-2), v. 1, *300*, 289, 338 .... 劉洪
Liu I (fl. 13th), v. 2, 1023; v. 3, 138 .... 劉益
Liu Ling (fl. 3d), v. 1, 335 .... 劉伶
Liu Mêng (fl. early 12th), v. 2, 422 .... 劉蒙
Liu Pin, v. 1, 767 .... 劉份
Liu Shao (III-1), v. 1, *321*, 315; v. 3, 1281 .... 劉劭
Liu-shih chü p'u (on chrysanthemums), v. 2, 422 .... 劉氏菊譜
Liu Sung-nien (fl. 1190–1230), v. 2, 263 .... 劉松年
Liu Tun-chên (contemporary), v. 3, 138 .... 劉敦楨
Liu T'ung, v. 2, 652 .... 劉侗
Liu Wan-su (XII-2), v. 2, *478*, 68, 71, 79, 87, 92, 476; v. 3, 907 .... 劉完素
Liu Wei-ch'ien (XIV-2), v. 3, *1801*, 1281 .... 劉惟謙
Liu Yü (fl. 1259), v. 2, 1067 .... 劉蜮
Liu Yüan (fl. 1252), v. 1, 737; v. 3, 1789 .... 劉淵
liu ch'i (six influences), v. 2, 478, 644 .... 六氣
Liu ching ao lun, v. 2, 460 .... 六經奧論
Liu mên êrh fa (medical), v. 2, 479 .... 六門二法
liu shu (six classes of characters), v. 2, 1137 .... 六書
Liu shu chêng o (on orthography), v. 3, 1017 .... 六書正譌
Liu shu ku (on six classes of characters), v. 2, 1137 .... 六書故
Liu shu pên i (dictionary), v. 3, 1828 .... 六書本義
liu t'i (six styles of writing), v. 2, 1137 .... 六體
Lo Chên-yü (d. 1940), v. 3, 735 .... 羅振玉
Lo Chên-ying (fl. 1931), v. 3, 310 .... 羅振英
Lo Chih-t'i (fl. beginning 14th), v. 3, 908 .... 羅知悌
Lo Hung-hsien (d. 1564), v. 3, 807 .... 羅洪先
Lo-lo (non-Chinese tribe in Yünnan), v. 3, 1030, 1851 .... 羅羅
Lo Ming-hsiang (fl. 1802) .... 羅茗香
Lo Shih-lin (d. 1853; Hummel p. 538), v. 3, 702 .... 羅士琳
Lo-hsia-hung (II-2 B.C.), v. 1, *195*, 191 .... 洛下閎
Lo-yang ch'ieh-lan chi (account of Lo-yang monasteries), v. 1, 431 .... 洛陽伽藍記
Lo-shan (hao), v. 3, 761 .... 樂山
Lo shou t'ang (pavilion of happiness and longevity), v. 3, 1472 .... 樂壽堂
Lou Shou (XII-2), v. 2, *428*, 54, 56, 305; v. 3, 211, 428, 1179 .... 樓璹
lu (official records), v. 3, 904 .... 錄
Lu-k'o (hao), v. 3, 1791 .... 錄客
Lu (Confucius' native state), v. 1, 67 .... 魯
Lu Kuei-chên (contemporary, calling herself Lu Gwei-djen), v. 3, 906 .... 魯桂珍
Lu Ming-shan (XIV-1), v. 2, 780; v. 3, *832*, 211, 228 .... 魯明善
Lu I-chün (fl. 1395), v. 3, 1537 .... 盧乙俊
Lu Chi (III-1), v. 1, *322*, 315 .... 陸績
Lu Chiu-yüan (XII-2), v. 2, *398*, 286, 295; v. 3, 979 .... 陸九淵

Lu Fa-yen (VII-1), v. 1, *486*, 459, 463, 737; v. 3, 385, 1789 .... 陸法言
Lu Kuei-mêng (T'ang writer), v. 3, 211 .... 陸龜蒙
Lu Shên (d. 1544; Giles no. 1427), v. 1, 451 .... 陸深
Lu shih Chou i shu (commentary on I ching), v. 1, 322 .... 陸氏周易述
Lu Tê-ming (VI-2), v. 1, *458*, 445; v. 3, 385 .... 陸德明
Lu T'ing-ts'an (fl. 1735), v. 1, 535 .... 陸廷燦
Lu Tung, v. 3, 1646 .... 陸東
Lu Yu (XIV-1), v. 1, 369; v. 3, *760*, 180, 311 .... 陸友
Lu Yü (VIII-2), v. 1, *535*, 522; v. 2, 429 .... 陸羽
lü (penal law) (*see* Ta Ming lü), v. 1, 500 .... 律
Lü li chih (Chinese chronology), v. 1, 264 .... 律歷志
lü lü (music), v. 3, 1858 .... 律呂
Lü lü hsin shu (on music), v. 3, 1858 .... 律呂新書
lü tsang (vinayapiṭaka), v. 3, 468 .... 律藏
Lü tsung (Buddhist school), v. 1, 469, 491 .... 律宗
Lun hêng (philosophical), v. 1, 252 .... 論衡
lun tsang (abhidharmapiṭaka), v. 3, 468 .... 論藏
Lun yü (Confucian analects), v. 1, 67; v. 3, 109, 280, 637 .... 論語
lun tsang (revolving library), v. 3, 734 .... 輪藏
Lung mên tzŭ ning tao chi (on Taoism), v. 3, 1790 .... 龍門子凝道記
Lung Ta-yüan (fl. 1176), v. 2, 140, 263, 315; v. 3, 1171 .... 龍大淵
Lung wei pi shu (ts'ung shu), v. 2, 428 .... 龍威祕書
Lung-yang-tzŭ (tzŭ), v. 3, 1857 .... 龍陽子
Lung-tsan (Song-tsen Gam-po, VII-1), v. 1, 466 .... 弄贊

Ma An-li (fl. 1878), v. 3, 1587 .... 馬安禮
Ma ha-sha (fl. end 13th), v. 2, 765, 1034; v. 3, 158, 970 .... 馬哈沙
Ma Han (one of the three Korean kingdoms), v. 1, 365 .... 馬韓
Ma Kuo-han (d. 1857; Hummel p. 557), v. 3, 831 .... 馬國翰
Ma-ming (Aśvaghosha, II-1), v. 1, 269 .... 馬鳴
Ma-sha pan (name of some Yüan editions), v. 2, 1125 .... 馬沙版
Ma Tuan-lin (XIII-2), v. 1, 411; v. 2, *983*, 747; v. 3, 388, 1122 .... 馬端臨
Ma Yüan (fl. 1190–1224), v. 2, 263 .... 馬遠
ma-fei-san (anaesthetic), v. 1, 325 .... 麻沸散
ma-huang (ephedrine) .... 麻黃
ma-yao (anaesthetic), v. 1, 325 .... 麻藥
ma-fêng (leprosy), v. 3, 280 .... 痲瘋
Mai-chüeh (on pulse), v. 2, 76 .... 脈訣
Man shu (geographical), v. 1, 536 .... 蠻書
Mao Ch'i-ling (d. 1716; Hummel p. 563), v. 3, 1858 .... 毛奇齡
mei (plum), v. 3, 226 .... 梅
Mei Wên-ting (d. 1721; Hummel p. 570), v. 3, 1585 .... 梅文鼎
mên (door, chapter, cf. Arabic bāb) .... 門
Mêng T'ien (III-2 B.C.), v. 1, *175*, 166, 451; v. 3, 385 .... 蒙恬
Mêng ch'i pi t'an (collection of essays), v. 1, 755 .... 夢溪筆談
Mêng Hung (d. 1246), v. 2, 610 .... 孟珙
Mêng Shên (d. 713), v. 3, 223 .... 孟詵
Mêng tzŭ (Mencius, IV-2 B.C.), v. 1, 138 .... 孟子
Mi-tsung (sacred teaching, Buddhist school), v. 1, 508 .... 密宗

Miao-fa-lien-hua-ching (lotus sūtra), v. 1, 447 .... 妙法蓮花經
mien-hua (cotton flowers) .... 棉花
Mien-tien (Burma) .... 緬甸
Ming i pieh lu (materia medica), v. 1, 436 .... 名醫別錄
Ming-hsiang (hao), v. 3, 702 .... 茗香
Ming hu t'u lu (illustrated account of I-hsing pottery), v. 3, 758 .... 茗壺圖錄
Ming chiao (religion of light, Manichaeism), v. 3, 139 .... 明教
Ming chih (tzŭ), v. 2, 1104 .... 明之
Ming-huang (T'ang emperor, VIII-1), v. 1, *512*, 451, 504; v. 2, 981; v. 3, 730 ... 明皇
Ming i tsa chu (medical), v. 3, 908 .... 明醫雜著
Ming shih (Ming annals), v. 3, 310, 1537, 1645, 1732, 1733, 1789, 1801, 1829 ..... 明史
Ming ti (Han emperor, d. 76; Giles no. 1292), v. 1, 243, 246 .... 明帝
Ming t'ien li (calendar, 1065), v. 1, 762 .... 明天歷
Mo-so (tribes), v. 3, 1851 .... 麼些
Mo ho chih kuan (Buddhist treatise), v. 1, 447 .... 摩訶止觀
Mo ni chiao (Manichaeism), v. 1, 552; v. 3, 139, 1071 .... 摩尼教
Mo ni chiao hsia pu tsan (Manichaean hymns), v. 3, 1855 .... 摩尼教下部讚
Mo-t'êng (Kāśyapa-Mātaṅga, I-2), v. 1, 246 .... 摩騰
Mo Jo, v. 3, 703 .... 莫若
Mo ching (on pulse), v. 1, 342; v. 2, 76; v. 3, 902, 972, 1590 .... 脈經
Mo chüeh chih chang ping shih t'u shuo (medical), v. 3, 908 .... 脈訣指掌病式圖說
Mo yin chêng chih (medical), v. 3, 909 .... 脈因證治
mo (ink), v. 1, 369 .... 墨
Mo ching (on ink), v. 3, 1590 .... 墨經
Mo fa chi-yao (on ink), v. 3, 1139, 1590 .... 墨法記要
Mo hai chin hu (ts'ung shu), v. 2, 645, 651; v. 3, 809, 832 .... 墨海金壺
Mo shih (on ink), v. 3, 760 .... 墨史
Mo Ti (V B.C.), v. 1, *91*, 82 .... 墨翟
Mo tzŭ, *see* Mo Ti (V B.C.) .... 墨子
Mou Ying-lung (fl. 1307), v. 3, 226 .... 牟應龍
Mu-yin (tzŭ), v. 3, 1478 .... 牧隱
Mu-lan-p'i kuo (Andalusia), v. 3, 1625 .... 木蘭皮國
Mu-hu (Zoroastrians), v. 1, 552; v. 3, 1071 .... 穆護
Mu-min (Muslims), v. 3, 1071 .... 穆民
Mu t'ien tzŭ chuan (emperor Mu's visit to the West), v. 1, 342 .... 穆天子傳
Mu wang (Chou emperor, d. 946 B.C.; Giles no. 1559), v. 1, 342 .... 穆王

Nan Ch'i shu (7th dynastic history), v. 1, 438 .... 南齊書
Nan ching (Buddhist academy of), v. 1, 350 .... 南京
Nan fang ts'ao mu chuang (botanical), v. 1, 341 .... 南方草木狀
Nan hua chên ching (Taoist treatise), v. 1, 153; v. 3, 634 .... 南華眞經
Nan shan tsung (southern hill school, Buddhist), v. 1, 469 .... 南山宗
Nan shih (14th dynastic history), v. 1, 484 .... 南史
Nan ching (medical), v. 1, 83, 102, 310 .... 難經
Nan ching pên i (medical), v. 3, 907 .... 難經本義
Nei ching su wên (medical), v. 1, 122, 539; v. 2, 68, 478 .... 內經素問
Nei wai shang pien huo lun (medical), v. 2, 1104 .... 內外傷辨惑論
nêng (ability, Jap. nō), v. 3, 1332 .... 能
nien-hao (reign titles), v. 1, 485; v. 2, 248 .... 年號

Nien-ch'ang (XIV-1), v. 3, *423*, 59, 108, 311 .... 念常
Ning-tsung (S. Sung emperor, d. 1224; Giles no. 170), v. 2, 248, 423 .... 寧宗
Nung chêng ch'üan shu (agricultural), v. 3, 1646 .... 農政全書
nung chia (agricultural books), v. 3, 210 .... 農家
Nung lin hsin pao (journal on agriculture and forestry) .... 農林新報
Nung sang chi yao (agricultural), v. 2, 56, 780, 982; v. 3, 211, 226, 832 .... 農桑輯要
Nung sang i shih ts'o yao (agricultural), v. 2, 780; v. 3, 211, 832 .... 農桑衣食撮要
Nung shu (agricultural), v. 2, 228; v. 3, 211, 228, 734, 830, 1179 .... 農書
Nü-chên [erroneous reading for Ju-chên] (Tatar Chin dynasty, 1115–1260), v. 3, 381 .. 女貞

O-mi-t'o ching (book of Amida), v. 3, 312 .... 阿彌陀經
Ou-yang Hsiu (XI-2), v. 1, *777*, 536, 643, 741, 743, 746; v. 2, 57, 315; v. 3, 385 ... 歐陽修
Ou-yang Yu (fl. 1369), v. 3, 1789 .... 歐陽佑

pa ching (eight illuminations, Taoist term) .... 八景
pa kua (eight diagrams) .... 八卦
Pa-ssŭ-pa (Phagspa, XIII-2), v. 2, 981, 1137; v. 3, 469 .... 巴思巴
Pai-fu-t'ang suan-hsüeh ts'ung-shu, v. 2, 628; v. 3, 703, 1847 .... 白芙堂算學叢書
Pai-hu t'ung (cosmological), v. 1, 264 .... 白虎通
pai-hua (colloquial), v. 3, 387 .... 白話
Pai-ma ssŭ (monastery of the white horse), v. 1, 246 .... 白馬寺
Pai shou wên (white head essay, thousand character), v. 1, 441 .... 白首文
pai-tieh (cotton) .... 白疊
Pai-yün hsien-shêng (hao), v. 3, 635 .... 白雲先生
Pai ch'uan hsüeh hai (ts'ung shu), v. 2, 422, 429 .... 百川學海
Pai ping kou yüan (medical), v. 3, 909, 1731 .... 百病鉤元
Pai-shih (tzŭ), v. 3, 1790 .... 百室
Pai shih lei pien, v. 2, 1024 .... 稗史類編
Pan Ku (I-2), v. 1, *264*, 163, 244, 245; v. 2, 460; v. 3, 77, 220, 310, 388, 809 .... 班固
Pan Piao (father of Pan Ku), v. 1, 264 .... 班彪
Pan lun ts'ui ying (on children's diseases), v. 3, 903 .... 瘢論萃英
P'an Chih [correct to Ch'ên P'an-chih] (fl. 14th), v. 3, 979
p'an chih (small balls of abacus), v. 2, 1585 .... 盤制
P'an chu chi (arithmetical), v. 1, 756 .... 盤珠集
P'ang An-shih (XI-2), v. 1, *773*, 743, 746; v. 2, 87 .... 龐安時
P'ang Yüan-chi (collector of pottery), v. 3, 758 .... 龐元濟
Pao T'ing-po (d. 1814; Hummel p. 612), v. 3, 226 .... 鮑廷博
Pao p'u tzŭ (Taoist treatise), v. 1, 355 .... 抱朴子
Pao ming chi (medical), v. 2, 478 .... 保命集
Pei Ch'i shu (11th dynastic history), v. 1, 483 .... 北齊書
Pei shan chiu ching (on distillation), v. 2, 220 .... 北山酒經
Pei shih (15th dynastic history), v. 1, 484 .... 北史
Pei shih chi (on an embassy to the North), v. 2, 644 .... 北使記
Pei tou ch'i hsing ching (sūtra of the Great Bear constellation), v. 3, 71 .. 北斗七星經
pei ts'ang ying (with black falcons on our arms), v. 3, 234 .... 臂蒼鷹
P'ei Chü (VII-1), v. 1, *476*, 461, 463 .... 裴矩
P'ei Hsiu (III-2), v. 1, *341*, 331; v. 3, 204, 808 .... 裴秀
P'ei-wên yün fu (Hummel p. 741), v. 3, 1897 .... 佩文韻府
Pên-ch'u (tzŭ), v. 3, 807 .... 本初

pên ts'ao (herbal), v. 1, 122, 436, 489, 498, 523, 539; v. 2, 52, 55, 80, 133, 137, 247, 311, 442, 781, 789; v. 3, 222, 223, 226, 289, 729, 905, 1176, 1179, 1218, 1645 .... 本草
Pên ts'ao ching chu (6th cent.), v. 1, 436 .... 本草經註
Pên ts'ao kang mu (1552–78), v. 2, 52, 247, 1075; v. 3, 223, 224, 756, 908, 1645, 1835 .... 本草綱目
Pên ts'ao kuang i, v. 2, 248 .... 本草光義
Pên ts'ao shih i (739), v. 3, 223 .... 本草拾遺
Pên ts'ao yen i (1115), v. 1, 764; v. 2, 137, 248; v. 3, 908 .... 本草衍義
Pên ts'ao yen i pu i, v. 3, 908 .... 本草衍義補遺
Pi chuan hua ching (on crickets), v. 2, 652 .... 祕傳花鏡
Pi-mi-chiao (Tantrism), v. 1, 509 .... 祕密教
Pi, H. T. (contemporary), v. 3, 1837 .... 畢華德
Pi Shêng (XI-1), v. 1, *723*, 698, 702, 703; v. 3, 733, 830 .... 畢昇
pi-yü (deep-green jade), v. 3, 1169, 1471 .... 碧玉
p'i ch'i (spleen spirit), v. 3, 905 .... 脾氣
P'i wei lun (medical), v. 2, 1104 .... 脾胃論
Piao t'i yüan ping shih (Confucian analects), v. 3, 734, 1731 .... 標題源病式
pieh-lu (materia medica), v. 1, 436; v. 3, 77 .... 別錄
Pien Ch'iao (V B.C.), v. 1, *102*, 83; v. 3, 907 .... 扁鵲
Pien Han (Kudara kingdom in Korea), v. 1, 364 .... 弁韓
Pien T'ung (fl. 1406), v. 3, 1645, 1646 .... 卞同
Pien huo p'ien (against superstitions), v. 3, 1104, 1478 .... 辨惑篇
Pin-hu (tzŭ), v. 3, 223 .... 瀕湖
Ping hu mai (mo) hsüeh (on pulse), v. 3, 223 .... 頻湖脈學
ping (disease), v. 3, 262 .... 病
Ping yüan hou lun (medical), v. 1, 481 .... 病源候論
P'ing yang (college), v. 2, 574, 1021 .... 平陽
P'ing yüan lu (on forensic medicine), v. 3, 904 .... 平寃錄
p'ing (mathematical method), v. 1, 494 .... 評
po-li (rock crystal), v. 1, 389; v. 3, 756 .... 玻璃
Po-lo-mo-t'o (Paramārtha, VI-2), v. 1, 446 .... 波羅末陀
po-tieh (fine cotton), v. 3, 833 .... 白疊
Po-ch'ing (tzŭ), v. 3, 634 .... 伯清
Po-hsiu (tzŭ), v. 3, 1,001 .... 伯修
Po-jên (tzŭ), v. 3, 907 .... 伯仁
Po-wên (tzŭ), v. 3, 1017, 1536 .... 伯温
Po-yen (tzŭ), v. 3, 1788 .... 伯顏
Po-yüan (tzŭ), v. 3, 703 .... 伯元
po (cotton) .... 帛
Po mei li kuo (country in South Sea islands), v. 3, 1626 .... 撥枚力國
Po ku t'u lu (archaeological), v. 2, 140, 263 .... 博古圖錄
P'o-lo-mên suan ching (mathematical), v. 1, 450 .... 婆羅門算經
P'o-lo-mên suan fa (mathematical), v. 1, 450 .... 婆羅門算法
P'o-lo-mên t'ien-wên ching (mathematical), v. 1, 450 .... 婆羅門天文經
P'o-lo-mên yin-yang suan ching (mathematical), v. 1, 450 .... 婆羅門陰陽算經
Pu-k'ung (VIII-1), v. 1, *509*, 504, 508; v. 3, 1018 .... 不空
Pu-yin (tzŭ), v. 3, 1478 .... 圃隱
pu i (supplement), v. 3, 1649 .... 補遺
Pu-la (Būlād), v. 2, 1021 .... 布拉

P'u yang jên wu chi (collection of biographies), v. 3, 1790 .... 浦陽人物記
P'u-chên chi wên (local gazetteer), v. 3, 1268, 1269 .... 濮鎮紀聞
P'u-t'i-ta-mo (Bodhidharma, VI-1), v. 1, 420 .... 菩提達磨
p'u (general order of history), v. 1, 35 .... 普
P'u chi fang (medical), v. 3, 1218, 1646, 1649 .... 普濟方
P'u t'o lo ch'ieh (Buddhist island Pootoo, Puto-shan), v. 3, 1854 .... 普陀洛伽

Sa-ha-pa (fl. 632), v. 1, 467 .... 薩哈巴
san chiao (three doctrines), v. 3, 1071 .... 三教
San Han (three kingdoms of old Korea), v. 3, 1538 .... 三韓
San hsiao lun (medical), v. 2, 478 .... 三消論
San Hung (the three brothers Hung), v. 2, 262 .... 三洪
San kuo chih (4th dynastic history), v. 1, 343 .... 三國志
San-lun tsung (Buddhist sect), v. 1, 470 .... 三論宗
San shêng an (chapel of the three holy ones), v. 3, 1854 .... 三聖庵
San-tsang (Tripiṭaka), v. 3, 466 .... 三藏
San t'ung (the three t'ung), v. 2, 983 .... 三通
San t'ung li (calendar), v. 1, 222 .... 三統歷
San tzŭ ching (three character classic), v. 1, 441; v. 2, 727, 983; v. 3, 74, 386 .... 三字經
San yin chi i ping chêng fang lun (medical), v. 2, 443 .... 三因極一柄證方論
San-p'u-la (fl. 632), v. 1, 467 .... 繖菩喇
Sang Ch'in (fl. 1st?), v. 3, 809 .... 桑欽
sao chou hsing (comet), v. 3, 1122 .... 掃箒星
Sêng-hui (fl. 3d), v. 1, 343 .... 僧會
Sêng-yu (VI-1), v. 1, *420*, 415, 491, 509; v. 3, 467 .... 僧祐
Sha K'o-shih (Yüan writer), v. 3, 809 .... 沙克什
Sha Kuo-chên (contemporary), v. 3, 1589 .... 沙國珍
Sha-lo-pa (d. 1314), v. 3, 469 .... 沙羅巴
sha-mên (śramaṇa, Buddhist priest), v. 3, 1733 .... 沙門
Shan hai ching (hill and water classic), v. 1, 353; v. 3, 1625, 1626, 1627 .... 山海經
shan shui (mountain and water), v. 3, 1472 .... 山水
Shan T'ao (fl. 3d), v. 1, 335, 336 .... 山濤
Shan chu ch'iao (bamboo bridge of excellence), v. 3, 1478 .... 善竹橋
shan hsing (good human nature), v. 3, 905 .... 善性
Shan-tao (VII-1), v. 1, *469*, 460, 463 .... 善導
shang (upper), v. 3, 1645 .... 上
Shang-tu (Xanadu), v. 2, 1057, 1067 .... 上都
Shang-yang-tzŭ (tzŭ), v. 3, 760, 761 .... 上陽子
Shang shu (book of history), v. 1, 67, 68; v. 3, 979 .... 尙書
Shang shu chi ch'uan tsuan su (commentary on Shang shu), v. 3, 979 .... 尙書集傳纂疏
Shang shu tsuan yen (commentary on Shang shu), v. 3, 634 .... 尙書纂言
Shang han (medical), v. 2, 478 .... 傷寒
Shang han hsin ching (medical), v. 2, 479 .... 傷寒心經
Shang han chih ko lun (medical), v. 2, 478 .... 傷寒直格論
Shang han hsin yao lun (medical), v. 2, 478 .... 傷寒心要論
Shang han lun (on fever), v. 1, 310; v. 2, 68, 87 .... 傷寒論
Shang han piao mu hsin fa lei ts'ui (medical), v. 2, 478 .... 傷寒標木心法類萃
Shang han tsung ping lun (on fevers), v. 1, 773 .... 傷寒總病論
Shao-chan (tzŭ), v. 2, 610 .... 少詹

Shao-hsing chiao-ting ching shih chêng lei pei chi, v. 2, 52, 55, 442; v. 3, 1646 .... 紹興校定經史證類備急
Shao-hsing pên-ts'ao, *see preceding item* .... 紹興本草
Shao Yung (XI-2), v. 1, *755*, 739, 746 .... 邵雍
Shê-na-chüeh-to (Jinagupta, VI-2), v. 1, 447 .... 闍那崛多
Shê hsien-jên (Sui astronomy), v. 1, 450 .... 捨仙人
Shê-po (Sumatra empire), v. 3, 1624 .... 社薄
Shê-mo-t'êng (Kāśyapa-Mātaṅga, I-2), v. 1, 246 .... 攝摩騰
Shên chien (on government), v. 1, 299 .... 申鑑
shên (spirit, gods), v. 3, 1002 .... 神
Shên hsiang ch'üan pien (on physiognomy), v. 3, 1733 .... 神相全編
Shên-nung (early emperor; Giles no. 1695), v. 1, 112, 122; v. 2, 57 .... 神農
Shên-nung pên-ts'ao, v. 1, 122, 436; v. 2, 247; v. 3, 260 .... 神農本草
Shên Chi-sun (XIV-2), v. 3, *1590*, 1139 .... 沈繼孫
Shên Huai-yüan (fl. 5th), v. 3, 833 .... 沈懷遠
Shên Huo (*see* Ch'ên Huo), v. 1, 755
Shên Kua (XI-2), v. 1, *755*, 723, 740, 741, 743, 746, 764; v. 3, 733, 1621 .... 沈括
Shên Wei-yüan (fl. 1693), v. 1, 103 .... 沈微垣
Shên Yo (V-2, also VI-1), v. 1, *413*, *437*, 400, 401, 417, 442; v. 3, 385, 1828 .... 沈約
Shêng yin wên tzŭ t'ung (rhyming dictionary), v. 3, 1829 .... 聲音文字通
shêng (province), v. 1, 676 .... 省
Shêng cheng chi (historical), v. 3, 1790 .... 聖政記
Shêng san (Trinity), v. 3, 1854 .... 聖三
Shêng yü t'u chieh .... 聖諭圖解
shih (history), v. 3, 77 .... 史
Shih Chêng-chih (fl. 12th?), v. 2, 422 .... 史正志
Shih-chi (historical memoirs), v. 1, 68, 199, 777; v. 3, 234, 310 .... 史記
Shih Chou (fl. 9th B.C.), v. 3, 1017 .... 史籀
Shih Lu (fl. 3d B.C.), v. 1, 168 .... 史祿
Shih shih chü p'u (botanical), v. 2, 422 .... 史氏菊譜
shih chieh (deliverance of the corpse, immortality), v. 3, 96 .... 尸解
Shih K'uang (ancient fabulous writer on birds; probably identical with Giles no. 1717), v. 2, 1075 .... 師曠
Shih chi chuan ming wu ch'ao (commentary on the five classics), v. 3, 635 .... 詩集傳名物鈔
Shih ching (book of poetry), v. 1, 67; v. 3, 635 .... 詩經
Shih-chên, *see* Li Shih-chên .... 時珍
shih ch'ên (divisions of the day), v. 1, 429 .... 時辰
shih yin ch'uang (kind of ulcer), v. 3, 907 .... 濕陰瘡
shih lu, Hung Wu (official annals), v. 3, 1800 .... 實錄
Shih-chia-chai yang hsin lu, v. 3, 1586 .... 十駕齋養新錄
Shih ssŭ ching fa hui (medical), v. 3, 907 .... 十四經發揮
Shih wan chüan lou ts'ung-shu, v. 2, 248; v. 3, 903 .... 十萬卷樓叢書
Shih-hu tz'ŭ (collection of rhymes), v. 2, 422 .... 石湖詞
Shih ku wên (on epigraphy), v. 2, 460 .... 石鼓文
Shih-i tê-hsiao fang (medical), v. 3, 906 .... 世醫得效方
Shih-tsu (Kublai Khān, XIII-2), v. 2, 609, 980 .... 世祖
Shih-tsung (Ch'ing emperor; Giles no. 2577), v. 3, 467 .... 世宗
Shih liao pên-ts'ao, v. 3, 223 .... 食療本草
Shih wu pên-ts'ao, v. 3, 1645 .... 食物本草

Shih tou chên-lun (medical), v. 3, 904 .... 氏痘疹論
Shih huang-ti (emperor, III-2 B.C.), v. 1, *168*, 165; v. 3, 385 .... 始皇帝
Shih chia p'u [not ch'ieh] (history of Buddhism), v. 1, 420 .... 釋迦譜
Shih lei fu (earliest encyclopaedia), v. 1, 663 .... 事類賦
Shih shih tsu (botanical), v. 2, 1074 .... 事實祖
Shih wên lei chü (encyclopaedia), v. 2, 1124 .... 事文類聚
Shih-an (tzŭ), v. 1, 342 .... 士安
Shih-liang (tzŭ), v. 3, 1791 .... 士良
Shih yüan ts'ung-shu, v. 3, 808 .... 適園叢書
shih hao (posthumous name) .... 諡號
Shou-chên (tzŭ), v. 2, 478 .... 守眞
Shou-shan-ko ts'ung-shu, v. 2, 262, 645; v. 3, 979, 1478 .... 守山閣叢書
Shou jih li (on calendar), v. 2, 1022 .... 授日曆
Shou shih li (calendar, 1280), v. 2, 1022; v. 3, 137 .... 授時曆
Shou ch'in yang lao hsin shu (on medical treatment of old people), v. 3, 903 壽親養老新書
Shou shan (mountain of longevity), v. 3, 1472 .... 壽山
Shou-wêng (tzŭ), v. 3, 979 .... 壽翁
shou hsing (animal nature), v. 3, 905 .... 獸性
Shu ching (book of history), v. 1, 67, 483; v. 3, 311, 625, 634 .... 書經
Shu ching chi chuan (commentary on Shu ching), v. 2, 625 .... 書經集傳
shu mu (literary catalogue), v. 1, 37 .... 書目
shu yüan (collegiate chapel), v. 3, 1478 .... 書院
Shu yün kuan (astronomical board), v. 3, 1537 .... 書雲觀
Shu (one of the three kingdoms), v. 1, 343 .... 蜀
Shu hsüeh chiu chang (mathematical), v. 2, 626 .... 數學九章
Shu shu chi i (mathematical), v. 1, 299 .... 數術紀遺
Shu shu chiu chang (mathematical), v. 2, 626 .... 數書九章
Shu shu chiu chang cha chi (mathematical), v. 2, 627 .... 數書九章札記
Shu shu ta lüeh (mathematical), v. 2, 626 .... 數術大略
shu (vertical), v. 1, 35 .... 竪
Shui ching (water classic), v. 3, 205, 809 .... 水經
Shun Yü-i (II-1 B.C.), v. 1, *187*, 178 .... 淳譽意
Shun ti (Hui-tsung, last Yüan emperor, d. 1370; Giles no. 1953), v. 3, 1027, 1800 ..... 順帝
Shuo fu, v. 2, 651, 652, 1068; v. 3, 980, 1478, 1586, 1857 .... 說郛
Shuo wên chieh tzŭ (earliest dictionary arranged by radicals), v. 1, 286, 441; v. 3, 385, 1017, 1828 .... 說文解字
Shuo wên tzŭ yüan (on etymology), v. 3, 1017 .... 說文字原
Ssŭ-ma Ch'ien (II-2 B.C.), v. 1, *199*, 67, 68, 164, 192; v. 2, 460; v. 3, 162, 234, 310 ... 司馬遷
Ssŭ-ma Kuang (XI-2), v. 1, *778*, 67, 744, 745, 746; v. 2, 315, 397, 797, 981; v. 3, 380, 385, 1828 .... 司馬光
Ssŭ-ma Piao (d. 305), v. 1, 396 .... 司馬彪
Ssŭ-ma Ta (fl. 522?), v. 1, 448 .... 司馬達
Ssŭ-ma T'an (d. 110 B.C.), v. 1, 199 .... 司馬談
Ssŭ-ch'ao ch'ao-pi t'u-lu (on printing of paper money), v. 3, 735 .... 四朝鈔幣圖錄
Ssŭ i kuan (college of foreign nations), v. 3, 1084, 1331, 1855 .... 四夷館
Ssŭ k'u ch'üan shu (Manchus' Chinese library), v. 3, 78, 703, 761, 810, 906, 1646, 1732, 1829 .... 四庫全書
Ssŭ k'u ch'üan shu tsung mu (book catalogue), v. 3, 979 .... 總目

ssŭ pu (the four categories), v. 3, 77 .... 四部
Ssŭ pu ts'ung k'an (ts'ung shu), v. 2, 247, 474, 574, 627, 645 .... 四部叢刊
ssŭ shêng (the four tones), v. 1, 413, 442; v. 3, 385, 1828 .... 四聲
Ssŭ shih êrh chang ching (sūtra in 42 chapters), v. 1, 246 .... 四十二章經
Ssŭ shu (the four books), v. 3, 386 .... 四書
ssŭ t'ien wang (the four kings of heaven), v. 3, 1018 .... 四天王
ssŭ yüan shu (mathematical method of four elements), v. 3, 140, 701 .... 四元術
Ssŭ yüan yü chien (mathematical), v. 3, 139, 701 .... 四元玉鑑
Ssŭ yüan yü chien hsi ts'ao (mathematical), v. 3, 703 .... 四元玉鑑細草
ssŭ hui (secret societies), v. 3, 156 .... 私會
Su Ching (T'ang official), v. 1, 498, 539 .... 蘇敬
Su chou (place), v. 2, 39, 422, 423 .... 蘇州
Su I-chien (fl. 986), v. 3, 181 .... 蘇易簡
Su Kung (fl. 7th?), v. 1, 489, 498 .... 蘇恭
Su shên liang fang (medical), v. 1, 755 .... 蘇沈良方
Su Sung (XI-2), v. 1, *762*, 741, 746; v. 3, 1646 .... 蘇頌
Su T'ien-chio (XIV-1), v. 3, *1001*, 205, 311, 322 .... 蘇天爵
Su wên (medical), v. 1, 310, 539; v. 3, 260 .... 素問
Su wên hsüan chi yüan ping-shih (medical), v. 2, 478 .... 素問玄機原病式
Su wên ping chi (medical), v. 2, 478 .... 素問病機
Su hui chi [misspelled Suan] (medical), v. 3, 909 .... 溯洄集
Suan ching (mathematical classic), v. 1, 474, 494; v. 3, 713, 1536 .... 算經
Suan ching shih shu (mathematical), v. 2, 627 .... 算經十書
suan fa (mathematics), v. 3, 1536 .... 算法
Suan hsüeh ch'i mêng (mathematical), v. 3, 701 .... 算學啓蒙
Suan hsüeh ch'i mêng shu i (mathematical), v. 3, 702 .... 算學啓蒙述義
suan-p'an (abacus), v. 1, 299, 741, 756; v. 2, 626; v. 3, 1121, 1585 .... 算盤
sui han san yu (three friends of winter), v. 3, 226 .... 歲寒三友
Sui shu (13th dynastic history), v. 1, 450, 483, 494; v. 3, 77 .... 隋書
sui hsing (comet), v. 3, 1122 .... 彗星
Sun chên-jên ch'ien chin fang (Taoist medical treatise), v. 1, 498; v. 3, 262 .... 孫眞人千金方
Sun Ch'iang (fl. 674), v. 1, 442; v. 3, 1828 .... 孫強
Sun Hsi (editor, date unknown), v. 2, 645 .... 孫錫
Sun Hsing-yen (d. 1818; Hummel p. 675), v. 1, 476 .... 孫星衍
Sun Mien (fl. 751), v. 1, 486 .... 孫愐
Sun Shu-jan (*see* Sun Yen, III-2), v. 1, 343 .... 孫叔然
Sun Ssŭ-mo (VII-2), v. 1, *498*, 489, 490; v. 2, 78; v. 3, 262, 906, 1837 .... 孫思邈
Sun tzŭ (III-1), v. 1, *321*, 315, 449; v. 2, 625; v. 3, 1536 .... 孫子
Sun tzŭ suan ching (mathematical), v. 1, 321; v. 3, 713 .... 孫子算經
Sun Wu (V B.C.), v. 1, *94*, 82 .... 孫武
Sun Yen (III-2), v. 1, *343*, 331, 413, 442; v. 3, 385, 1828 .... 孫炎
Sun p'u (on bamboo shoots), v. 1, 673; v. 3, 226 .... 筍譜
sung (pine), v. 3, 226 .... 松
Sung-t'ing (hao), v. 3, 701 .... 松庭
Sung Ch'i (XI-1), v. 1, *737*, 701, 702, 744, 777; v. 3, 385 .... 宋祁
Sung chih (memoirs of Sung shu), v. 3, 1162 .... 宋志
Sung Ching-ch'ang (fl. 1842; Hummel p. 539), v. 2, 627, 1023 .... 宋景昌
Sung Kao sêng chuan (Buddhist biographies), v. 1, 491, 673 .... 宋高僧傳

Sung Lien (XIV-2), v. 2, 982, 1022; v. 3, *1789*, 703, 1268, 1331, 1800 .... 宋濂
Sung Lin-hsiang (writer on smallpox), v. 2, 88 .... 宋麟祥
Sung shih (Sung history), v. 3, 310, 1788 .... 宋史
Sung shu (6th dynastic history), v. 1, 437 .... 宋書
Sung Tz'ŭ (XIII-1), v. 2, *668*, 97, 524, 530; v. 3, 260, 322, 904 .... 宋慈
Sung yang hui suan fa [delete Sung] (mathematical), v. 2, 1023
Sung Yün (VI-1), v. 1, *431*, 414, 416, 419, 447 .... 宋雲

Ta chin kuo chih (history of Chin Tatars), v. 2, 687 .... 大金國志
Ta ch'in (Roman East, Syria), v. 1, 324, 552; v. 3, 756, 1071 .... 大秦
ta chuan (ancient script), v. 2, 460; v. 3, 1017 .... 大篆
ta fêng-tzŭ (chaulmoogra), v. 3, 908 .... 大楓子
ta fêng (leprosy), v. 3, 280 .... 大瘋
Ta hsia (Bactria), v. 1, 197 .... 大夏
Ta-hsüan (tzŭ), v. 2, 88 .... 大宣
Ta hsüeh (great learning), v. 1, 91; v. 3, 635 .... 大學
Ta-jih ching (sūtra of the sun Buddha), v. 1, 508 .... 大日經
Ta Jih-pên hsü tsang ching (edition of Tripiṭaka, supplement), v. 3, 467.. 大日本續藏經
Ta-kuan (era, 1107–11), v. 2, 247 .... 大觀
Ta-kuan, *see* Chêng-lei pên-ts'ao
Ta Ming i-t'ung chih (Ming geography), v. 3, 1162 .... 大明一統志
Ta Ming lü (Ming code), v. 3, 1281, 1801 .... 大明律
Ta Sung ch'ung-hsiu kuang yün (Sung phonetic dictionary), v. 1, 737... 大宋重修廣韻
Ta T'ang, *see* Hsi yü chi; Hsi yü ch'iu fa kao sêng chuan; K'ai yüan chan ching
Ta t'ung li (Ming calendar), v. 2, 1022; v. 3, 1537 .... 大統歷
Ta yen li (calendar, 721), v. 1, 514 .... 大衍歷
ta yen shu (mathematical method), v. 1, 514; v. 2, 626 .... 大衍術
Ta yüan (Ferghana), v. 1, 197 .... 大宛
Ta yüeh-chih (Indoscythia), v. 1, 197 .... 大月支
Ta-yung (tzŭ), v. 3, 1788 .... 大用
Ta-chai (tzŭ), v. 3, 906 .... 達齋
Ta-fu (tzŭ), v. 3, 807 .... 達夫
Ta-mo (Bodhidharma, VI-1), v. 1, 420 .... 達磨
Tai Chên (d. 1777; Hummel p. 695), v. 1, 183, *449*, 494; v. 3, 809 .... 戴震
Tai Ch'i-tsung (fl. 1331), v. 3, 180 .... 戴起宗
Tai chiao suan ching shih shu (mathematical), v. 1, 183, 450, 474, 494... 戴校算經十書
Tai Ssŭ-kung (XIV-2), v. 3, *1732*, 1218 .... 戴思恭
Tai T'ung (XIII-2), v. 2, *1137*, 806; v. 3, 385 .... 戴侗
Tai Yüan-li (*see* Tai Ssŭ-kung, XIV-2), v. 3, 1732 .... 戴元禮
T'ai chi (great extreme), v. 2, 398 .... 太極
T'ai chi t'u (commentary on I ching), v. 1, 755 .... 太極圖
T'ai-ch'u li (calendar, 104 B.C.), v. 1, 195 .... 太初歷
T'ai p'ing (great peace), v. 2, 984 .... 太平
T'ai-p'ing huan yü chi (geographical), v. 1, 676 .... 太平寰宇記
T'ai-p'ing kuang chi (encyclopaedia), v. 1, 663 .... 太平廣記
T'ai-p'ing san tzŭ ching (edition of three character classic), v. 2, 984 ..... 太平三字經
T'ai-p'ing yü lan (encyclopaedia), v. 1, 663; v. 3, 234 .... 太平御覽
T'ai shih kung (*see* Ssŭ-ma Ch'ien, II-2 B.C.), v. 1, 199 .... 太史公

T'ai ts'ang kung fang (medical), v. 1, 187 .... 太倉公方
T'ai-tsu (founder of Sung dynasty, d. 976; Giles no. 168), v. 1, 552; v. 2, 273, 609; v. 3, 381 .... 太祖
T'ai-tsung (T'ang emperor, VII-1; Giles no. 1196), v. 1, *474*, 460, 461, 462, 463, 477, 482, 484, 518, 663; v. 2, 609; v. 3, 139 .... 太宗
T'ai-tsung (Korean king, 1403), v. 3, 1562 .... 太宗
Tan-ch'i hsien-shêng (*see* Chu Tan-ch'i, XIV-1), v. 3, 907 .... 丹溪先生
Tan-ch'i hsin-fa (medical), v. 3, 908 .... 丹溪心法
Tan ch'i hsin-fa fu yü (medical), v. 3, 908 .... 丹溪心法附餘
tan sha (cinnabar, alchemical term), v. 3, 1140 .... 丹砂
T'an-chi ts'ung-shu (musical), v. 3, 1857 .... 檀几叢書
T'ang Hou (XIV-1), v. 3, *979*, 311, 1791 .... 湯厚
T'ang i ta fa (medical, probably identical with the following), v. 3, 903 .... 湯液大法
T'ang i pên-ts'ao, v. 3, 903 .... 湯液本草
T'ang ch'ao ming hua lu (history of painting), v. 3, 1791 .... 唐朝名畫錄
T'ang hsin pên-ts'ao, v. 1, 498 .... 唐新本草
T'ang pên-ts'ao, v. 1, 498 .... 唐本草
T'ang Shên-wei (fl. 1108?), v. 2, 137, 247, 248 .... 唐愼微
T'ang shu (history of T'ang dynasty), v. 1, 484, 643, 777; v. 3, 380 .... 唐書
T'ang Sung ts'ung-shu, v. 2, 1075 .... 唐宋叢書
T'ang yün (dictionary), v. 3, 729 .... 唐韻
tao (the right path), v. 3, 77, 761 .... 道
Tao-hsüan (VII-2), v. 1, *491*, 420, 441, 446, 460, 463, 469, 488, 490, 509 .... 道宣
Tao p'o, v. 3, 832 .... 道婆
Tao-shih (VII-2), v. 1, *491*, 488, 490, 496 .... 道世
Tao tê ching (Taoist canon), v. 1, 66, 477; v. 2, 981; v. 3, 634, 979 .... 道德經
Tao tsang (Taoist patrology), v. 3, 107, 108, 262 .... 道藏
Tao tsang chi yao (Taoist patrology), v. 2, 645 .... 道藏輯要
tao yin (breathing exercises) .... 導引
Tao chien lu (on famous swords), v. 1, 436 .... 刀劍錄
Tao i chih lüeh (account of Malay archipelago), v. 3, 810 .... 島夷志略
t'ao (peach), v. 3, 226 .... 桃
T'ao Hung-ching (VI-1), v. 1, *436*, 417, 498 .... 陶弘景
T'ao Ku (d. 970; Giles no. 1898), v. 3, 237 .... 陶穀
T'ao Tsung-i (XIV-2), v. 2, 1068; v. 3, *1585*, 1069, 1121, 1139, 1169, 1171, 1331, 1857 .... 陶宗儀
T'ao-yin (tzŭ), v. 3, 1478 .... 陶隱
T'ao Yin-chü (*see* Tao Hung-ching, VI-1), v. 1, 436 .... 陶隱居
Têng Ch'u-chung (Sung editor), v. 1, 325 .... 鄧處中
Têng Ch'un (fl. 1167), v. 2, 262; v. 3, 1791 .... 鄧椿
Têng Ming-shih (XII-1), v. 2, *262*, 140 .... 鄧名世
Têng Ssŭ-yü (contemporary), v. 3, 1084 .... 鄧嗣禹
ti (earth), v. 3, 701 .... 地
ti chih (twelve earthly branches), v. 1, 673 .... 地支
ti li (topographical books), v. 1, 676; v. 2, 422; v. 3, 204 .... 地理
T'iao-chih (Chaldaea), v. 1, 197 .... 條支
t'ieh (iron), v. 3, 1176 .... 鐵
T'ieh ch'in t'ung chien lou Sung Chin Yüan pên shu ying (facsimiles of Sung, Chin, and Yüan printing), v. 3, 735, 1562 .... 鐵琴銅劍樓宋金元本書影

tien shih (palace examination), v. 3, 1083 ... 殿試
t'ien (heaven), v. 3, 701 ... 天
T'ien chu (India), v. 1, 197 ... 天竺
T'ien-fang tzŭ-mu chieh-i (introduction to Islām and to Arabic language), v. 3, 1589 ... 天方字母解義
t'ien-huang (emperor, Jap. tennō), v. 3, 1029 ... 天皇
t'ien kan (ten celestial stems), v. 1, 673 ... 天干
T'ien-ming (Ch'ing emperor, 1616–26; Giles no. 1580), v. 2, 273; v. 3, 381, 469 ... 天命
T'ien shan (celestial mountains), v. 3, 1471 ... 天山
T'ien-t'ai tsung (Buddhist school), v. 1, 447, 553 ... 天台宗
t'ien ti (heaven and earth), v. 2, 398 ... 天地
t'ien-wang t'ang (tien) (hall of heavenly kings, entrance hall of Buddhist temples), v. 3, 1018 ... 天王堂殿
T'ien-wen shuo (astronomical), v. 1, 450 ... 天文說
t'ien yüan (mathematical method of celestial element), v. 3, 701 ... 天元
t'ien yüan shu (mathematical method), v. 2, 9, 507, 626, 627, 755, 1023; v. 3, 138, 140 ... 天元書
T'ien Jun-ch'üan (fl. 1395), v. 3, 1537 ... 田潤權
ting (mathematical method), v. 1, 494 ... 定
Ting-yü (hao), v. 3, 979 ... 定宇
Ting-yü chi (collection of essays), v. 3, 979 ... 定宇集
Ting-yü hsien-shêng (hao), v. 3, 979 ... 定宇先生
Ting ch'ao (Annamese dynasty, 968–91), v. 3, 978 ... 丁朝
Ting Chü (XIV-2), v. 3, *1536*, 1121 ... 丁巨
Ting Ch'ü-chung (fl. 1872; Hummel p. 479), v. 2, 628; v. 3, 703, 1847 ... 丁取忠
Ting Chü suan fa (mathematical), v. 3, 1536 ... 丁巨算法
Ting Hao-nien (XIV-2), v. 3, *1829*, 1331 ... 丁鶴年
Ting Hsiao-tzŭ, v. 3, 1829 ... 丁孝子
Ting Ping (d. 1899; Hummel p. 726), v. 3, 904 ... 丁丙
Ting Tu (XI-1), v. 1, *737*, 701, 702; v. 3, 385, 1789 ... 丁度
Ting Yu-t'o (*see Japanese index*, Tei-Yūda), v. 1, 454 ... 丁有陀
T'ing-yü (tzŭ), v. 3, 1732 ... 廷玉
T'o-t'o (XIV-2), v. 1, 762; v. 3, *1788*, 1161, 1268 ... 脫脫
T'o-yen tz'ŭ (collection of poems), v. 3, 979 ... 蛻巖詞
T'o-pa (fl. 580), v. 1, 447; v. 3, 378 ... 拓跋
Tou chên chêng tsung (on smallpox), v. 2, 88 ... 痘疹正宗
Tou chêng ching yen pi yao (on smallpox), v. 2, 88 ... 痘症精言祕要
Tou P'ing (XI-1), v. 1, *723*, 698, 702; v. 2, 130, 220 ... 竇苹
T'ou lien hsi ts'ao (mathematical), v. 3, 1536 ... 透簾細艸
Tsa tsang (mixed treasure, fourth part of Tripiṭaka), v. 3, 467 ... 雜藏
Ts'ai Ch'ên (XIII-1), v. 2, *625*, 503, 507, 527 ... 蔡沈
Ts'ai Hsiang (XI-2), v. 1, *766*, 741, 746; v. 2, 57, 1074 ... 蔡襄
Ts'ai Lun (II-1), v. 1, *279*, 268; v. 3, 174 ... 蔡倫
Ts'ai Yüan-ting (d [illegible]98), v. 3, 1858 ... 蔡元定
Tsan-ning (X-2), v. [illegible], *373*, 491, 650, 652, 654; v. 3, 226 ... 贊寧
Ts'an t'ung ch'i, v. 3, 761 ... 參同契
Ts'an shu (on sericulture), v. 2, 228 ... 蠶書
tsang (viscera), v. 2, 478, 1104 ... 臟
Ts'ao-lu hsien-shêng (hao), v. 3, 634 ... 草廬先生

Ts'ao-t'ing (tzŭ), v. 2, 1067 .... 草庭
Ts'ao Chao (fl. late 14th), v. 3, 1857 .... 曹昭
Ts'ao ssŭ (water transport), v. 2, 248 .... 漕司
Ts'ê-yüan hai ching (mathematical), v. 2, 627 .... 測圓海鏡
Ts'ê-fu yüan-kuei (administrative encyclopaedia), v. 1, 713 .... 册府元龜
Tsêng-hsiu wu yüan lu yen chieh (on forensic medicine), v. 3, 904 .... 增修無寃錄諺解
Tsêng tzŭ (Confucius' disciple), v. 3, 635 .... 曾子
Tso Ch'iu-ming (Confucius' disciple), v. 1, 67 .... 左丘明
Tso chuan (Confucian treatise), v. 1, 67 .... 左傳
Tsou-p'an chi (arithmetical), v. 1, 756 .... 走盤集
Tsou Hsüan (XIV-1), v. 3, *903*, 261, 286 .... 鄒鉉
Tsou Yen (fl. 4th B.C.; Giles no. 2030), v. 3, 1140 .... 騶衍
Tsu Ch'ung-chih (V-2), v. 1, *410*, 400, 494 .... 祖冲之
Tsu I, v. 3, 703 .... 祖頤
Ts'u chih chih [or ching] (on crickets), v. 2, 651, 652 .... 促織志經
Ts'u chih p'u (on crickets), v. 2, 652 .... 促織譜
Ts'ui Chi (contemporary), v. 3, 1855 .... 崔驥
Ts'ui Chih-yüan (d. 910), v. 3, 108, 636 .... 崔致遠
Ts'ui Ch'ung [not Ho Ch'ung] (fl. 1068), v. 3, 108 .... 崔冲
Ts'ui Jung (fl. 1395), v. 3, 1537 .... 崔融
Ts'ui-lang-kan-kuan ts'ung-shu, v. 3, 909 .... 翠琅玕館叢書
ts'un (inch), v. 3, 902 .... 寸
ts'un k'ou (place for pulse taking), v. 3, 902 .... 寸口
ts'un mo (place for pulse taking), v. 3, 902 .... 寸脈
tsung (religious school or sect), v. 1, 470; v. 2, 827 .... 宗
Ts'ung-chêng (tzŭ), v. 2, 479 .... 從正
ts'ung shu (collection of books or essays), v. 3, 831 .... 叢書
Tu Ch'in (I-2 B.C.), v. 1, *230*, 220 .... 杜欽
Tu Yu (IX-1), v. 1, *581*, 547, 548; v. 2, 983 .... 杜佑
Tu Yü (III-2), v. 1, *341*, 331 .... 杜預
Tu shu ts'ung shuo, v. 3, 635 .... 讀書叢說
Tu ssŭ shu ts'ung shuo (commentary on the four books), v. 3, 635 .... 讀四書叢說
tu ching ch'uang (kind of ulcer), v. 3, 907 .... 妒精瘡
T'u chi (*see* Chên-la fêng), v. 2, 1068 .... 土記
t'u (to vomit), v. 2, 478 .... 吐
T'u ching pên-ts'ao, v. 2, 52, 55, 442; v. 3, 1646 .... 圖經本草
T'u hua chien wên chih (history of painting), v. 3, 1791 .... 圖畫見聞誌
T'u hua pao chien (history of painting), v. 3, 1791 .... 圖畫寶鑑
T'u shu chi ch'êng (encyclopaedia), v. 1, 110, 663; v. 2, 422; v. 3, 224, 1176, 1237, 1590, 1885 .... 圖書集成
T'u shu chi k'an (bulletin of Chinese bibliography), v. 3, 1851 .... 圖書季刊
Tuan Ch'êng-chi (Yüan editor), v. 1, 355 .... 段成己
T'ui-ch'iu shih-i (medical), v. 3, 1732 .... 推求師意
Tun-huang, v. 1, 604; v. 3, 139, 174, 222, 223, 378, 830 .... 敦煌
Tun-mi (fl. 632), v. 1, 467 .... 頓米
Tung-hui-tsê (place name), v. 3, 635 .... 東匯澤
Tung-pi (tzŭ), v. 3, 223 .... 東壁
Tung-shan (hao), v. 3, 978 .... 東山
Tung-yüan (tzŭ), v. 2, 1104; v. 3, 907 .... 東垣

Tung Ping (fl. end 11th), v. 1, 743, 746, 773 .... 董柄
Tung Tso-pin (contemporary), v. 3, 138 .... 董作賓
Tung-lin (predictions), v. 1, 353 .... 洞林
T'ung shan shê (fellowship of goodness, a secret society), v. 3, 156 .... 同善社
T'ung-jên chên chiu ching (on acupuncture), v. 1, 732 .... 銅人鍼灸經
T'ung chien kang mu (history of China), v. 1, 778; v. 2, 397, 610, 797, 981 .. 通鑑綱目
T'ung chih (history of China), v. 2, 459, 983 .... 通志
T'ung-mi (fl. 632), v. 1, 467 .... 通密
T'ung-ming (tzŭ), v. 1, 436 .... 通明
T'ung pao (journal of Sinology), *passim* .... 通報
T'ung shu (neo-Confucian treatise), v. 1, 755 .... 通書
T'ung tien (encyclopaedia), v. 1, 581; v. 2, 983 .... 通典
T'ung tien ch'ing lu, v. 2, 1024 .... 通典清錄
T'ung-yüan suan fa (mathematical), v. 3, 1536 .... 通原算法
T'ung li (on calendar), v. 1, 222 .... 統歷
tzŭ (philosophy, first of twelve branches), v. 3, 77 .... 子
Tzŭ-ch'an (*see* Kung-sun Ch'iao, VI B.C.), v. 1, 80 .... 子產
Tzŭ-ching (tzŭ), v. 2, 398 .... 子靜
Tzŭ-hsia (V B.C.), v. 1, *110*, 84; v. 3, 385 .... 子夏
Tzŭ-hsing (tzŭ), v. 3, 1017 .... 子行
Tzŭ-jung (tzŭ), v. 3, 1646 .... 子容
tzŭ (style or literary name), v. 1, 43 .... 字
Tzŭ hui (dictionary), v. 3, 1829 .... 字彙
tzŭ pu (radicals of Chinese characters), v. 3, 385 .... 字部
Tzŭ-tien, *see* K'ang-hsi tzŭ-tien
Tzŭ chih t'ung chien (history of China), v. 1, 778 .... 資治通鑑
Tzŭ-ch'i hsien-shêng (history of Buddhism), v. 3, 1001 .... 滋溪先生
Tz'ŭ shih nan chih (medical), v. 3, 902 .... 此事難知
Tz'ŭ yüan (dictionary), v. 1, 369 .... 辭源

Wai k'o ching i (essence of surgery), v. 3, 907 .... 外科精義
Wai k'o ching yao (medical), v. 2, 668 .... 外科精要
wai-kuo (foreign nation), v. 3, 1071 .... 外國
Wai t'ai pi yao (medical), v. 1, 538 .... 外汰必要
Wan-li (reign title of emperor Shên-tsung, 1573–1620; Giles no. 452) .... 萬曆
Wan li ch'ang ch'êng (great wall), v. 1, 168 .... 萬里長城
Wan nien li (calendar, 1267), v. 2, 1021; v. 3, 137 .... 萬年曆
Wan yung chêng tsung pu ch'iu jên ch'üan pien ("ask no questions" handbook, popular encyclopaedia), v. 3, 1627 .... 萬用正宗不求人全編
Wang An-shih (XI-2), v. 1, *781*, 744, 745, 746; v. 3, 260, 730, 1800 .... 王安石
Wang Chên *or* Chêng (XIV-1), v. 1, 723; v. 3, *830*, 145, 211, 228, 734, 833, 1179, 1562, 1829 .... 王楨
Wang Chi-min (contemporary; spells his name Wong), v. 3, 1909 .... 王吉民
Wang Chi-hsien (fl. 1159), v. 2, 311, 442; v. 3, 1646 .... 王繼先
Wang Ch'i (fl. 1586), v. 2, 983 .... 王圻
Wang Chieh-chai (fl. 1502), v. 3, 908 .... 王節齋
Wang Chieh (fl. 868), v. 1, 604 .... 王玠
Wang Ch'in-jo (XI-1), v. 1, *713*, 695, 702 .... 王欽若
Wang Chung-min (contemporary), v. 3, 222, 223, 234 .... 王重民

Wang Ch'ung (I-2), v. 1, *252*, 244 .... 王充
Wang Fan (III-2), v. 1, *338*, 331 .... 王蕃
Wang Fu (fl. 1107), v. 2, 140, 263 .... 王黼
Wang Hao-ku (XIV-1; should be XIII-1, for he flourished in 1232–64, not 1308), v. 3, *902*, 261, 906 .... 王好古
Wang Hsi (XIV-1), v. 3, *809*, 205 .... 王喜
Wang Hsiang-chih (XII-2), v. 2, *423*, 39, 302, 315 .... 王象之
Wang Hsiao-t'ung (VII-1), v. 1, *474*, 461, 463 .... 王孝通
Wang Hsien-ch'ien (d. 1918; Hummel p. 140), v. 3, 756 .... 王先謙
Wang Hsüan-ts'ê (VII-2), v. 1, *496*, 489, 490 .... 王玄策
Wang I-jung (d. 1900; Hummel p. 826), v. 3, 386 .... 王懿榮
Wang Jung (fl. 3d), v. 1, 335 .... 王戎
Wang Kuan (XI-2), v. 1, *766*, 741, 746; v. 2, 57 .... 王觀
Wang Kuo-wei (d. 1927; Hummel p. 856), v. 3, 713 .... 王國維
Wang Li (XIV-2), v. 3, *1731*, 909, 1218 .... 王履
Wang Ling (contemporary; Isis 37, 160) .... 王鈴
Wang Lun (fl. 1502), v. 3, 908 .... 王綸
Wang P'an, v. 3, 1646 .... 王磐
Wang Pao-sun (fl. 553), v. 1, 448 .... 王保孫
Wang Ping (VIII-2), v. 1, *539*, 522 .... 王冰
Wang Shih-chêng (d. 1593; Giles no. 2220), v. 3, 223 .... 王世貞
Wang shih shu hua yüan (ts'ung shu), v. 2, 1074 .... 王氏書畫苑
Wang Shu-ho (III-2), v. 1, *342*, 310, 331; v. 2, 76; v. 3, 902, 972, 1590 .... 王叔和
Wang Tai-yü (fl. 1642), v. 3, 1589 .... 王岱輿
Wang Tan (d. 1017; Giles no. 2230), v. 3, 274, 905 .... 王旦
Wang Tao-liang (fl. 553), v. 1, 448 .... 王道良
Wang Tao (VIII-2), v. 1, *538*, 522 .... 王燾
Wang Tê-yüan (fl. 1287), v. 2, 628 .... 王德淵
Wang Wei (d. 1372), v. 3, 703, 1268, 1789 .... 王褘
Wang Wei-tê (XI-1), v. 1, *732*, 700, 702; v. 2, 78 .... 王惟德
Wang Ying-lin (XIII-2), v. 1, 441; v. 2, *983*, 727, 747; v. 3, 74, 386 .... 王應麟
Wang-yu Ling-t'o (fl. 554), v. 1, 454 .... 王有陵陀
Wang Yü (fl. 1308), v. 3, 260, 322, 904 .... 王與
Wang Chê (fl. 1780), v. 2, 81 .... 汪喆
Wang K'ên-t'ang (fl. 1756; Hummel p. 323), v. 3, 909 .... 汪肯堂
Wang Ta-yüan (XIV-1), v. 3, *810*, 205 .... 汪大淵
Wei Chao (d. 273), v. 1, 343 .... 韋昭
Wei Tan (fl. 4th or 5th?), v. 1, 369 .... 韋誕
Wei Yao, *see* Wei Chao .... 韋曜
Wei (one of the three kingdoms), v. 1, 343 .... 魏
Wei Chêng (VII-1), v. 1, *483*, 462, 463, 494 .... 魏徵
Wei lüeh (history written middle 3d cent.), v. 1, 315, 324; v. 3, 756 .... 魏略
Wei Po-yang (fl. 2d; Giles no. 2287), v. 3, 761 .... 魏伯陽
Wei Shou (VI-2), v. 1, *458*, 445 .... 魏收
Wei shu (10th dynastic history), v. 1, 458, 483 .... 魏書
Wei Yüan (d. 1856; Hummel p. 850), v. 3, 808 .... 魏源
Wei I-lin (XIV-1), v. 3, *906*, 261 .... 危亦林
Wên-an (posthumous hao), v. 2, 262, 398 .... 文安
wên chang (classical essays), v. 3, 1083 .... 文章

Wên-chên (*see* Wei Shou, VI-2), v. 1, 458 .... 文貞
Wên-chêng (posthumous hao), v. 2, 1021; v. 3, 634 .... 文正
Wên-ch'êng (posthumous hao), v. 3, 1537 .... 文成
Wên-chien (*see* Ting Tu, XI-1), v. 1, 737 .... 文簡
Wên-chung (*see* Ou-yang Hsiu, XI-2), v. 1, 777 .... 文忠
wên fang (a scholar's study), v. 3, 181 .... 文房
Wên fang ssŭ p'u, v. 3, 181 .... 文房四譜
Wên-hsien (canonical name of Huang Chin, XIV-1), v. 3, 809 .... 文獻
Wên hsien t'ung k'ao (medical), v. 2, 983; v. 3, 1122 .... 文獻通考
Wên-hsien (canonical name of Sung Lien, XIV-2), v. 3, 1789 .... 文憲
Wên-i (canonical name), v. 3, 635, 907 .... 文懿
Wên-i kung (fl. beginning 14th), v. 3, 907 .... 文懿公
wên li (classical language) .... 文理
wên miao (Confucian temple), v. 2, 423; v. 3, 1866 .... 文廟
Wên-mu (canonical name), v. 2, 422 .... 文穆
Wên ti (Sui emperor, d. 605; Giles no. 2367), v. 1, 451 .... 文帝
Wên-ting (tzŭ), v. 3, 1731 .... 文鼎
Wên-jên Kuei (XIV-1), v. 3, *904*, 261 .... 聞人規
Wên-kuo-chai chi (collected writings), v. 3, 1791 .... 聞過齋集
wo k'ou (Japanese pirates), v. 3, 1029 .... 倭寇
Wu ching (five classics), v. 3, 108, 386 .... 五經
Wu ching suan shu (mathematical), v. 1, 450 .... 五經算術
Wu hua ssŭ (monastery of the five flowers), v. 3, 1071 .... 五花寺
Wu shan (five mountains), v. 3, 1171 .... 五山
Wu ts'ao suan ching (mathematical), v. 1, 449 .... 五曹算經
Wu tzŭ (the five philosophers), v. 1, 755; v. 2, 397; v. 3, 108, 386 .... 五子
Wu yüeh, or yo (five mountains), v. 3, 1171 .... 五嶽
wu yün (interaction of the five elements), v. 2, 478 .... 五運
Wu Ch'ung-yao (fl. 1855), v. 2, 423 .... 伍崇曜
Wu Lien-tê (contemporary), v. 3, 1664, 1909 .... 伍連德
Wu-ch'iu Yen (XIV-1), v. 3, *1017*, 311, 385 .... 吾丘衍
Wu-k'ung (VIII-2), v. 1, *526*, 520 .... 悟空
Wu-ku-sun Chung-tuan (fl. 1220), v. 2, 37, 514, 644 .... 烏古孫仲端
Wu-ti (Liang emperor, 502–49; Giles no. 720), v. 1, 436; v. 3, 107, 467. (Han emperor, 140–86 B.C.; Giles no. 1276), v. 3, 387 .... 武帝
Wu-tsung (T'ang emperor, 841–47; Giles no. 1229), v. 1, 552; v. 3, 139, 1071. (Yüan emperor, 1308–12; Giles no. 933), v. 3, 69, 468 .... 武宗
Wu ying tien chü chên pan ts'ung-shu, v. 2, 627, 644; v. 3, 831, 832, 1590 武英殿聚珍版叢書
Wu (one of the three kingdoms), v. 1, 343 .... 吳
Wu Chên (d. 1354), v. 3, 235, 237 .... 吳鎮
Wu Ch'êng (XIV-1), v. 3, *634*, 108, 1001 .... 吳澄
Wu Ch'i-chün (d. 1846; Giles no. 2322), v. 3, 224 .... 吳其濬
Wu Chien (fl. 1349), v. 3, 810 .... 吳鑑
Wu Ching (VIII-1), v. 1, *518*, 505 .... 吳兢
Wu ch'uan lu (travel account), v. 1, 676; v. 2, 422 .... 吳船錄
Wu chün chih (topographical), v. 2, 422 .... 吳郡志
Wu Hai (XIV-2), v. 3, *1790*, 1070, 1268 .... 吳海
Wu Kuang-ch'ing (contemporary; spells his name Kwang Tsing), v. 3, 1857 .. 吳光清

Wu Shu (X-2), v. 1, *663*, 648, 654 .... 吳淑
Wu Ta-ch'êng (d. 1902; Hummel p. 880), v. 2, 263 .... 吳大澂
Wu-liang-shou ching (sūtra of eternal life), v. 3, 212 .... 無量壽經
Wu-tsê (tzŭ), v. 2, 443 .... 無擇
wu wei (Taoist theory of submission), v. 1, 66, 153 .... 無爲
Wu yüan lu (on forensic medicine, duties of a coroner), v. 3, 904 .... 無冤錄
Wu Chao-i (fl. 960), v. 1, 633 .... 毋照裔
wu (things or matter), v. 3, 701 .... 物

Ya-ku (Ya'qūb), v. 2, 765, 1034; v. 3, 158, 970 .... 亞古
Ya shêng (Mencius, IV-2 B.C.), v. 1, 138 .... 亞聖
Ya tung t'u shu kuan (Shanghai publication), v. 2, 645 .... 亞東圖書館
yang hsing (to nourish the vital spirit, Taoist term), v. 3, 96, 180 .... 養性
Yang lao fêng ch'in shu (on medical care of old people), v. 3, 903 .... 養老奉親書
yang yin (to nourish the yin, name of medical school), v. 3, 908, 1732 .... 養陰
Yang chou shao yao p'u (on peony), v. 1, 767 .... 揚州芍藥譜
Yang Hsiung (fl. 14 B.C.), v. 1, 353 .... 揚雄
Yang tzŭ chiang (The River), v. 2, 981, 1028 .... 揚子江
Yang Chi-chou (fl. 16th/17th), v. 3, 906 .... 楊繼洲
Yang Chu (IV-2 B.C.), v. 1, *138*, 125 .... 楊朱
Yang Hsüan-chih (fl. 547), v. 1, 431 .... 楊衒之
Yang Hui (XIII-2), v. 1, 756; v. 2, *1023*, 9, 755, 756; v. 3, 138, 701 .... 楊輝
Yang Hui suan fa (mathematical), v. 2, 1023 .... 楊輝算法
Yang-ts'un (tzŭ), v. 3, 1479 .... 楊村
Yang tzŭ, *see* Yang Chu (IV-2 B.C.) .... 楊子
Yang Wên-ping (epigraphist), v. 3, 1018 .... 楊文昺
yang (positive or male principle), v. 1, 353; v. 2, 478, 1104; v. 3, 262, 908, 1858 .... 陽
Yao Ch'a (fl. 629), v. 1, 483 .... 姚察
Yao Chi-hêng (b. 1647; Hummel p. 811), v. 3, 807 .... 姚際恒
Yao Chien (VII-1), v. 1, *483*, 462, 463 .... 姚簡
Yao Shan-yu (contemporary), v. 3, 283, 1237 .... 姚善友
Yao Ssŭ-lien (*see* Yao Chien, VII-1), v. 1, 483 .... 姚思廉
Yao Shih [read Yo shih] (X-2), v. 1, *676*, 650, 654 .... 樂史
Yao lei fa hsiang (medical), v. 3, 903 .... 藥類法象
Yeh-lü Ch'u-ts'ai (XIII-1), v. 2, *574*, 19, 37, 496, 507, 527, 609, 644, 726, 1021, 1067 耶律楚才
Yeh-lü Hsi-liang (XIII-2), v. 2, *1067*, 38, 776; v. 3, 1800 .... 耶律希亮
Yeh-ts'ai p'u (pên ts'ao), v. 3, 1646, 1649 .... 野菜譜
Yeh-yin (tzŭ), v. 3, 1478 .... 冶隱
Yeh Lung-li (XIII-1), v. 2, *687*, 528 .... 葉隆禮
Yen-ching (Harvard Institute), v. 2, 574, 1025 .... 燕京
Yen Kung (XIV-2), v. 3, *1536*, 1121 .... 嚴恭
Yen pei tsa chih (collection of essays), v. 3, 760 .... 研北雜志
Yen-Hsiu (tzŭ), v. 3, 907 .... 彥修
yen wên (Korean alphabet, ŏnmun), v. 3, 388 .... 諺文
Yen Chih-t'ui (VI-2), v. 1, *459*, 445, 486; v. 3, 385 .... 顏之推
Yen shih chia hsün (on education), v. 1, 459 .... 顏氏家訓
yen tuan so fang (mathematical method), v. 2, 1023 .... 演段鎖方
Yen Hsiao-chung (fl. 1119), v. 1, 773 .... 閻孝忠

Yen-ch'êng [read An-ch'êng?] (fl. 1421), v. 3, 1071, 1213 .... 俺誠
yin (negative or female principle), v. 1, 353; v. 2, 478, 1104; v. 3, 262, 908, 1858 ..... 陰
Yin chêng lüeh li (medical), v. 3, 902 .... 陰証略例
yin shih ch'uang (kind of ulcer), v. 3, 907 .... 陰蝕瘡
yin yang (positive-negative theory), v. 3, 903 .... 陰陽
Yin ch'ao (name of Shang dynasty when its capital was moved to Yin, Honan; cf. Yin bones), v. 3, 386 .... 殷朝
Yin hai ching wei (on eye diseases), v. 1, 498; v. 3, 1837 .... 銀海精微
Yin shan chêng yao (principles of correct diet), v. 3, 905 .... 飲膳正要
Yin shih hsü chih (elements of dietetics), v. 3, 1732 .... 飲食須知
Yin I-chu (contemporary), v. 3, 1910 .... 尹乙洙
Yin Jên-lung (fl. 1395), v. 3, 1537 .... 尹仁龍
yin (name, the 3 or 4 yin in Korea), v. 3, 1479 .... 隱
yin (seal, print), v. 1, 451, 723 .... 印
Ying-kung (fl. 650), v. 1, 498 .... 英公
Yo-chih (tzŭ), v. 3, 908 .... 約之
Yu-ch'ing (tzŭ), v. 3, 634 .... 幼清
Yu-jên (tzŭ), v. 3, 760 .... 友仁
Yü-chung (tzŭ), v. 2, 459 .... 漁仲
Yü ti chi shêng (description of S. China), v. 2, 423 .... 輿地紀勝
yü ti t'u (map of China), v. 3, 807 .... 輿地圖
yü t'u (map of China), v. 3, 204, 807 .... 輿圖
Yü-t'ai (tzŭ), v. 3, 909 .... 宇泰
Yü-wên Kung-liang (fl. 1355), v. 3, 1017 .... 宇文公諒
Yü-wên Mou-chao, v. 2, 687 .... 宇文懋昭
Yü kung hsüeh hui (Ricci's map), v. 3, 808 .... 禹貢學會
Yü-chêng (Mongolian tribe), *see* Ju-chên .... 女貞
yü (jade), v. 3, 1171 .... 玉
Yü hai (sea of jade), v. 2, 727, 983; v. 3, 74 .... 玉海
Yü p'ien (dictionary), v. 1, 441, 442; v. 3, 729, 1828 .... 玉篇
Yü shan (jade mountains), v. 3, 1471 .... 玉山
Yüan-li (tzŭ), v. 3, 1732 .... 原禮
Yüan chien lei han (encyclopaedia), v. 1, 676 .... 淵鑑類函
Yüan-tu (tzŭ), v. 3, 703 .... 緣督
Yüan Chü, v. 2, 88 .... 袁句
Yüan Hung-tao, v. 2, 652 .... 袁宏道
Yüan Kung (XIV-2), v. 3, *1732*, 1218, 1232 .... 袁珙
Yüan T'ung-li (contemporary), v. 3, 1851 .... 袁同禮
yüan (beginning; first character of I ching), v. 3, 1645 .... 元
Yüan ch'ao mi shih (Yüan annals), v. 2, 610 .... 元朝密史
Yüan ch'ao ming ch'ên shih lüeh (biographies of civil servants of Yüan dynasty), v. 3, 1001 .... 元朝明臣事略
Yüan-chên (tzŭ), v. 3, 702 .... 元鎮
Yüan-fêng (period 1078–86), v. 3, 903 .... 元豐
Yüan-ho chün hsien chih (geographical), v. 1, 573 .... 元和郡縣志
Yüan jên hsiao shuo (Yüan annals), v. 2, 1024 .... 元人小說
Yüan shih (Yüan annals), v. 2, 610, 982, 1022, 1067; v. 3, 310, 701, 808, 810, 832, 907, 979, 1001, 1268, 1732, 1789, 1790 .... 元史
Yüan tien chang (Yüan institutions), v. 3, 260 .... 元典章

Yüan-ts'ung (*see* Chou Tun-i, XI-2), v. 1, 755 .... 元從
Yüan Fu, or Juan Fu (fl. 4th/5th), v. 3, 978 .... 阮敷
Yüan Yüan, *see* Juan Yüan .... 阮元
Yung-lo (era of third Ming emperor, 1402–24; Giles no. 471), v. 3, 1644 .... 永樂
Yung-lo ta tien (encyclopaedia), v. 1, 183, 321, 339, 494; v. 2, 1074; v. 3, 211, 226, 469, 761, 808, 830, 903, 1084, 1102, 1162, 1169, 1170, 1176, 1270, 1281, 1331, 1536, *1549*, 1789, 1829, 1851 .... 永樂大典
Yung yao hsin fa (on use of drugs), v. 3, 903 .... 用藥心法
Yüeh chih lüeh (history of Annam), v. 3, 978 .... 越志略
Yün-chuang (hao), v. 3, 635 .... 雲莊
yün (rhyme), v. 1, 486 .... 韻

JAPANESE INDEX AND GLOSSARY TO VOLUMES 1, 2, AND 3

Some of the remarks made at the beginning of the Chinese index apply mutatis mutandis to the Japanese index. There is, however, an essential difference between the two indexes: in the Chinese one, all the phrases beginning with the same character were put together; that method has not been followed in the Japanese index, where it would have created many difficulties. The Japanese phrases are classified in the simple alphabetical order of their romanization, as they would be in a Japanese-English dictionary.

The romanization which has been consistently followed in this work is the one advocated by the Japanese Romanization Society (Rōmaji Kwai) since 1885, not the new romanization officially sponsored in Japan a few years ago.[1]

This index may be called a glossary, because the Japanese terms are defined, proper names by a date, titles of books by an indication of the subject dealt with, other words by an indication of their meaning. In a very few cases references to pages are missing because of accidental loss; in those cases, the index is still valuable for finding the Chinese characters corresponding to a phrase found in the text.

The standardization of the Japanese names and words used in my Introduction was made possible because of the kind cooperation at first of professor Y. Mikami, of Tōkyō, and later of Dr. S. Sakanishi, of the Library of Congress (now back in Japan), and of my Harvard colleague professor Serge Elisséeff. For the preparation and publication of this index, I am deeply indebted to my two Harvard colleagues professor Edwin Oldfather Reischauer, who corrected the MS, and professor James Roland Ware, who corrected the proofs.

August 31, 1947 **G. S.**

[1] Denzel Carr: The new official romanization of Japanese (Journal of the American Oriental Society 59, 99–102, 1939). Kim Yung-kun: Note sur la nouvelle romanisation officielle du Japonais (Bulletin de l'Ecole française d'Extrême Orient 38, 306–8, 1940).

Abe Manao (fl. 808), v. 1, 575 .... 安倍眞直
Abe Nai-shinnō (name of Shōtoku-tennō), v. 1, 529 .... 安倍內親王
Abe Seimei (X-2), v. 1, *672*, 649, 654 .... 安倍正明
ajari (master or doctor), v. 3, 1863 .... 阿闍梨
Ajiki [more correctly Achiki] (Korean, fl. 284?), v. 1, 67, 441 .... 阿直岐
Aji Kishi [more correctly Achi Kishi], *see* Ajiki .... 阿知吉師
Akazome Emon (fl. 1027), v. 1, 778 .... 赤染衛門
Aki Morisada (XIV-1), v. 3, *910*, 263 .... 安藝守定
amabe (guild of fishermen), v. 3, 156 .... 海部
Amida, v. 1, 364, 553; v. 2, 113 .... 阿彌陀
Amidakyō (sūtra), v. 3, 312 .... 阿彌陀經
Amidakyō sho .... 阿彌陀經疏
Ashikaga, v. 3, 42, 636, 1029, 1270 .... 足利
Ashikaga-gakkō (school), v. 3, 1085, 1331, 1408 .... 足利學校
Ashikaga Motouji (1304–67), v. 3, 1408 .... 足利基氏
Ashikaga Yoshikane (1147–96), v. 3, 1408 .... 足利義兼
Azuma-kagami (XIII-2), v. 2, *1125*, 798, 807; v. 3, 389 .... 吾妻鏡

Baizu-kan (illustrations of plants for horse diseases), v. 2, 1104 .... 馬醫圖卷
be (guild), v. 3, 156 .... 部
bettō (superintendent), v. 2, 574 .... 別當
Birushana (Vairocana), v. 1, 510 .... 毗盧遮那
Birushana-butsu, v. 3, 727 .... 毗盧遮那佛
biwa (four-stringed lute), v. 1, 519 .... 琵琶
Bōjō (kuge[2] family name), v. 3, 156 .... 坊城
Bukkyō (Buddhism), v. 1, 448 .... 佛教
Bukkyō daijiten (Buddhist dictionary), v. 3, 1842 .... 佛教大辭典
bunko (library), v. 2, 865; v. 3, 477 .... 文庫
Bunsen-Ō (Confucius, VI B.C.), v. 1, 67 .... 文宣王
bunshō-hakase, *see* monjō-hakase .... 文章博士
Buppō (Buddhism), v. 1, 448 .... 佛法
Bussetsu rokuji shinju ōkyō, v. 3, 729 .... 佛說六字神呪王經
Butsudō (Buddhism), v. 1, 448 .... 佛道
byō (disease), v. 3, 262, 291 .... 病

cha-no-yu (tea ceremony), v. 3, 1332 .... 茶ノ湯
Chikaku (name of Soseki, XIV-1), v. 3, 478 .... 智覺
Chikashige Masumi (contemporary), v. 3, 1139 .... 近重眞澄
Chion-in (temple in Kyōto), v. 2, 337 .... 智恩院
Chishō-daishi (posthumous title of Enchin), v. 1, 552 .... 智證大師
Chi-sō-ki (earliest Japanese treatise on surgery), v. 1, 575 .... 治瘡記
Chitatsu (fl. 658), v. 1, 492 .... 智達
Chitsū (fl. 658), v. 1, 492 .... 智通
Chōsen (Korea), v. 3, 1028, 1538 .... 朝鮮
Chū-ron (sūtra), v. 1, 470 .... 中論

[2] Kuge, nobles of the imperial court, distinct from the military nobles (daimyō).

Daibutsu (gigantic statue of Buddha in Nara), v. 1, 515, 529; v. 3, 727 .... 大佛
Daidō-rui-shiu-hō [better Daidō ruiju hō] (medical), v. 1, 575 .... 大同類聚方
daigaku-bettō (rector of university), v. 1, 539 .... 大學別當
daigaku no kami (rector of university), v. 1, 582 .... 大學頭
daigaku-ryō (University of Nara), v. 1, 513 .... 大學寮
Daihō, *see* Taihō .... 大寶
Dai hyakka jiten (encyclopaedia), v. 3, 1880 .... 大百科事典
Dai-jō (Mahāyāna), v. 1, 448; v. 3, 60 .... 大乘
Daimuryōjukyō (sūtra of eternal life), v. 3, 312 .... 大無量壽經
daimyō (feudal lord), v. 3, 1001, 1029 .... 大名
Dai-nembutsu-ji (Nembutsu monastery), v. 2, 165 .... 大念佛寺
Dainichi-Nyorai (*see* Daibutsu), v. 1, 510; v. 3, 727 .... 大日如來
daishi (great teacher, saint), v. 1, 553 .... 大師
Dai-sōjō (title of Eisai, XII-2), v. 2, 337 .... 大僧正
darani (Skt. dhāraṇī, charm or prayer; one million printed c. 770 for Shōtoku-tennō, VIII-2), v. 1, 529; v. 3, 729 .... 陀羅尼
Daruma (Bodhidharma, VI-1), v. 1, 420 .... 達磨
dengaku (popular show of music and dance), v. 3, 1332 .... 田樂
Dengyō daishi (IX-1), v. 1, *552*, 447, 544, 552 .... 傳教大師
Dōgen (d. 1253), v. 2, 559, 636, 827 .... 道元
Dontetsu-shū (collection of Chinese poems), v. 3, 109 .... 鈍鐵集
Dōsen (fl. 736), v. 1, 504, 510 .... 道璿
Dōshō (d. 700), v. 1, 367, 491 .... 道昭

egoma (vegetable oil), v. 3, 170 .... 荏胡麻
Ehon mushi erami (picture book of insects), v. 3, 1188 .... 繪本蟲選
Eigwa monogatari [commonly Eiga] (XI-2), v. 1, *778*, 744, 745, 746; v. 3, 389 ... 榮華物語
Eihei-ji (Zen monastery), v. 2, 559 .... 永平寺
Eisai (XII-2), v. 1, 552; v. 2, *337*, 57, 282, 305, 429, 490, 559; v. 3, 1332 .... 榮西
eki (relay, station), v. 1, 515 .... 驛
Ekwan [commonly Ekan] (fl. 625), v. 1, 460, 463, 470 .... 慧灌
Enchi, v. 3, 424 .... 圓智
Enchin (d. 891), v. 1, 552 .... 圓珍
Engi-kyaku-shiki (code of law, 907), v. 1, 618 (Engi, nengō 901–23) .... 延喜格式
Engi-shiki (on ceremonies and customs, X-1), v. 1, 644 .... 延喜式
Enkaku-ji (temple in Kyōto), v. 3, 636 .... 圓覺寺
Enkō-daishi (posthumous title of Hōnen-Shōnin, XII-2), v. 2, 337 .... 圓光大師
Enryaku-ji (temple near Kyōto), v. 1, 553 .... 延曆寺
Enshō daishi (posthumous title of Ippen Shōnin, XIII-2), v. 2, 828 .... 圓照大師
Eshin (other name of Genshin, X-2), v. 1, 656 .... 惠心

Fudoki [not Fūdoki] (gazetteers, VIII-1), v. 1, *515*, 505 .... 風土記
Fujikawa Yu [correctly Yū] (contemporary), v. 3, 910, 1884 .... 富士川游
Fujisawa (in Sagami), v. 2, 828 .... 藤澤
Fujiwara, v. 1, 500, 518 .... 藤原
Fujiwara Fuhito (d. 720), v. 1, 518 .... 藤原不比等
Fujiwara Ietada (d. 1136), v. 2, 461 .... 藤原家忠
Fujiwara Michinori (XII-2), v. 2, *405*, 297 .... 藤原通憲
Fujiwara Mototsune (d. 891), v. 1, 517, 617 .... 藤原基經

Fujiwara no Michinaga (d. 1027), v. 1, 778 .... 藤原道長
Fujiwara Otsugu (d. 843), v. 1, 516, 548, 580 .... 藤原緒嗣
Fujiwara Shinzei (religious name of Fujiwara Michinori, XII-2), v. 2, 405 .... 藤原信西
Fujiwara Tadahira (d. after 909), v. 1, 644 .... 藤原忠平
Fujiwara Tamenari (XII-1), v. 2, *263*, 140, 1125; v. 3, 389, 980 .... 藤原爲業
Fujiwara Tokihira (d. 909), v. 1, 517, 617, 644 .... 藤原時平
Fujiwara Tsuginawa (d. 796), v. 1, 516, 541 .... 藤原繼縄
Fujiwara Yoshifusa (d. 872), v. 1, 516, 617 .... 藤原良房
Fukuda Tokuzō (contemporary), v. 3, 714 .... 福田德三
Fukuden-hō (medical), v. 3, 1733 .... 福田方
Furu-kotobumi (records of ancient things), v. 1, 516 .... 古事紀
Fushimi-tennō (ruled 1278–98, d. 1317), v. 3, 424 .... 伏見天皇

Ganjin [better than Kanjin] (VIII-2), v. 1, *539*, 504, 510, 523 .... 鑑眞
Gembō (fl. 736), v. 1, 513 .... 玄昉
Gemmei-tennō (empress 708–14), v. 1, 515 .... 元明天皇
Gen-e (XIV–1), v. 3, *636*, 60, 74, 109, 980 .... 玄惠
Gendai Nihon bummei shi (history of modern Japanese civilization), v. 3, 1832 现代日本文明史
Genji monogatari (romance written 2d half of 10th), v. 3, 1332 .... 源氏物語
Genka-reki (calendar), v. 1, 476 .... 元嘉曆
Genkū (fl. 1175), v. 2, 282, 336, 559; v. 3, 311 .... 源空
Genshin (X-2), v. 1, *656*, 647, 654 .... 源信
Genshō-tennō (empress 724–48), v. 1, 518 .... 元正天皇
Gidō Shūshin (1326–89), v. 3, 478, 637, 1084, 1332 .... 義堂周信
Gijutsu-shi (history of technology), v. 3, 1832 .... 伎術史
Gikū (fl. 815), v. 1, 552 .... 義空
Gion no yashiro (shrine in Kyōto), v. 3, 156 .... 祇園社
Gizan (1648–1717), v. 3, 424 .... 義山
go (game), v. 1, 519 .... 碁
Go-Daigo-tennō (ruled 1319–38), v. 3, 42, 109, 636, 1029 .... 後醍醐天皇
Go-Fushimi-tennō (ruled 1299–1301, d. 1336), v. 3, 60, 424 .... 後伏見天皇
Go-Kameyama-tennō (ruled 1373–92, d. 1424), v. 3, 1029 .... 後龜山天皇
Goki-reki (calendar, 856), v. 1, 476 .... 五紀曆
Go-Komatsu-tennō (ruled 1392–1412; d. 1433), v. 3, 1029 .... 後小松天皇
Go-Murakami-tennō (ruled 1339–68), v. 3, 1002 .... 後村上天皇
Go-Nijō-tennō (ruled 1302–8), v. 3, 424 .... 後二條天皇
Go seibai shikimoku (code of law), v. 2, 694 .... 御成敗式目
Go-Shirakawa-tennō (ruled 1156–58, d. 1192), v. 2, 405 .... 後白河天皇
Go-Uda-tennō (ruled 1275–87, d. 1324), v. 3, 1018 .... 後宇多天皇
go zan (five Zen temples), v. 3, 636 .... 五山
Gozan-han [more commonly Gozamban] (Go-zan editions), v. 3, 1562 .... 五山版
Gyōgi-Bosatsu (VIII-1), v. 1, *510*, 504, 505, 553 .... 行基菩薩
gyōgi-yaki (unglazed porcelain), v. 1, 510 .... 行基燒

Han-Ryōhō (fl. 554), v. 1, 454 .... 潘量豐
Harada Jirō (contemporary), v. 3, 293, 1333, 1570 .... 原田次郎
hasebe (guild of potters), v. 3, 156 .... 長谷部
Heian-kyō (capital of peace, Kyōto), v. 1, 509 .... 平安京

Heijō-tennō (ruled 806–9, d. 824), v. 1, 547, 575 .... 平城天皇
Heike monogatari (romance written 2d half of 12th), v. 3, 1332 .... 平家物語
Henchiin (temple), *see* Seiken (XII-2) .... 遍智院
Hideyoshi, *see* Toyotomi .... 秀吉
Hieda no Are (fl. 711), v. 1, 516 .... 稗田阿禮
Hiei-zan (sacred mountain near Kyōto, Tendai temples), v. 2, 337, 559; v. 3, 980, 1270 .... 比叡山
Hino (family), v. 2, 559 .... 日野
Hi-oki (calendar), v. 1, 476 .... 日置
hiragana (syllabary), v. 1, 519, 553; v. 3, 110, 389 .... 平假名
Hirashio-yama (Buddhist temple) .... 平鹽山
Hirata Atsutane (1776–1843), v. 3, 714 .... 平田篤胤
Hōbōgirin (Buddhist encyclopaedia), v. 3, 467, 1889 .... 法寶義林
Hōjō (family), v. 2, 574, 694, 727, 865; v. 3, 42, 74 .... 北條
Hōjō Akitoki (fl. beginning 14th), v. 2, 865 .... 北條顯時
Hōjō Sanetoki (d. 1275), v. 2, 727, 865; v. 3, 477 .... 北條實時
Hōjō Yasutoki (d. 1242), v. 2, 693 .... 北條泰時
Hōjō Yoshitoki (fl. 1270), v. 2, 865 .... 北條義時
Hōjōji no Kwampaku (d. 1027), v. 1, 778 .... 北條寺關白
Hōjō-ki (annals of ten feet square), v. 2, 687; v. 3, 1018 .... 方丈記
Hokke-kyō (lotus sūtra), v. 1, 448; v. 2, 827; v. 3, 312 .... 法華經
Hokke-shū (Nichiren sect using chiefly lotus sūtra), v. 2, 827 .... 法華宗
Hokkyō Enzen (fl. 1233), v. 2, 694 .... 法橋圓全
Hōkō-ji (temple in Kyōto), v. 1, 452 .... 方廣寺
Honchi-suijaku (Shintō doctrine), v. 1, 553 .... 本地垂迹
Honchō do-ryō-kenkō kō (on weights and measures in Japan), v. 3, 714 .. 本朝度量權衡考
Hōnen-Shōnin (XII-2), v. 2, *337*; v. 3, 60, 110, 311, 424 .... 法然上人
Hongwanji-ha, or Honganji-ha [not Kongwanji-ha] (mother stem of Shin-shū), v. 2, 560 .... 本願寺派
Honzō iroha shō (index of plant names), v. 2, 1075 .... 本草以呂波鈔
Honzō wamyō (materia medica), v. 1, 683 .... 本草和名
Hori Genkō (fl. 1750), v. 1, 325 .... 堀元厚
Hōryū-ji (temple near Nara), v. 1, 470, 529; v. 3, 170 .... 法隆寺
Hossō-shū (Buddhist sect), v. 1, 488, 491 .... 法相宗
Hyaku-ron (sūtra), v. 1, 470 .... 百論

Ichi-dai-kyō-shū (Sanron-shū), v. 1, 470 .... 一代教宗
Ichijō Fuyuyoshi (d. 1514), v. 3, 980 .... 一條冬良
Idzumo Hirosada [correctly Izumo] (fl. 808), v. 1, 575 .... 出雲廣貞
Ikaruga-dera (Hōryū-ji), v. 1, 470 .... 斑鳩寺
ikebana (flower arrangement), v. 3, 1332 .... 生花
Ikkō-shū (Shin-shū), v. 2, 559 .... 一向宗
Ima-kagami (mirror of the present, 12th-cent. chronicle), v. 2, 263 .... 今鏡
Imube Hironari [more correctly Imbe] (IX-1), v. 1, *580*, 548 .... 齋部廣成
Ingen Zenji (fl. 1655), v. 2, 559 .... 隱元禪師
Ippen Shōnin (XIII-2), v. 2, *828*, 715 .... 一遍上人
iroha (first three syllables of kana), v. 1, 554 .... 伊呂波
Ise monogatari (romance written beginning 10th), v. 1, 778; v. 3, 389, 1332 ... 伊勢物語
Ishihara Jun (contemporary), v. 3, 1832 .... 石原純

Ishinhō (medical), v. 1, 683; v. 2, 78 .... 醫心方
Issaikyō (Tripiṭaka), v. 3, 466 .... 一切經

Jikaku daishi (IX-1), v. 1, *554*, 544 .... 慈覺大師
Jimon-shū (branch of Tendai-shū), v. 1, 552 .... 自問宗
Jingō shōtōki, *see* Jinnō shōtō-ki
Jinkō-ki (mathematical), v. 2, 405 .... 塵劫記
Jinnō shōtō-ki (Shintō history of Japan), v. 3, 322, 1002, 1029 .... 神皇正統記
Ji-shū (Buddhist sect, XIII-2), v. 2, *828*, 715; v. 3, 59 .... 時宗
Jitō-tennō (empress 687–96, d. 703), v. 1, 500 .... 持統天皇
Jō-jui shiki ron [not Vidyāmātrasiddhi, but Vijñānamātrasiddhi], v. 3, 729 .... 成唯識論
Jōben (poet), v. 3, 1018 .... 淨辨
Jōdo-shinshū (true Jōdo sect), v. 2, 166, 559 .... 淨土眞宗
Jōdo-shū (Buddhist sect), v. 1, 364, 656; v. 2, 166, 282, 336, 828; v. 3, 60, 110, 311, 424 .... 淨土宗
Jōei shikimoku (code of law, 1232), v. 2, 530, 694; v. 3, 389, 1001 (Jōei, or Tei-ei, nengō 1232–33) .... 貞永式目
Jōgwan-kyaku-shiki [also Jōgan] (code of law, 868), v. 1, 618 (Jōgan, nengō 859–76) .... 貞觀格式
Jōjitsu-shū (Buddhist sect, began 625), v. 1, 460, 470; v. 3, 60 .... 成實宗
Judō (Confucianism), v. 1, 67 .... 儒道
Jufuku-ji (temple in Kamakura), v. 3, 636 .... 壽福寺
Jūkō honzō zukyō [not dsukyō] (herbal, Ch. pên ts'ao), v. 2, 443 .... 重校本草圖經
Jukyō, *see* Judō .... 儒教
Jū-nī-mon-ron (sūtra), v. 1, 470 .... 十二門論
jūni no taka (acceptance of falcons), v. 3, 234 .... 十二ノ鷹
Jūshichi-jō-kempō (constitution, 604), v. 1, 473, 500 .... 十七條憲法
jyō, *see* jō

Kagaku shi (history of science), v. 3, 1832 .... 科學史
kagami (mirror, speculum), v. 2, 263, 798, 1125; v. 3, 311, 389, 980 .... 鏡
kaigen (opening the eyes, inauguration of a statue), v. 1, 515 .... 開眼
Kairitsu (Ritsu-shū), v. 1, 510 .... 戒律
Kaji Hōjun (contemporary), v. 3, 424 .... 梶寶順
Kajiwara Kagetoki (d. 1200), v. 3, 909 .... 梶原景時
Kajiwara Shōzen (XIV-1), v. 3, *909*, 263 .... 梶原性全
Kamakura, v. 3, 42 .... 鎌倉
Kamakura Hōjō, v. 3, 636 .... 鎌倉北條
Kamakura Shikken, v. 2, 693, 865 .... 鎌倉執權
Kamatari (d. 669), v. 1, 500 .... 鎌足
kami (gods), v. 3, 1002 .... 神
kami yo (age of the gods), v. 3, 212 .... 神代
kammu (Ch. kang mu), v. 2, 1075 .... 綱目
Kamo Chōmei (XIII-1), v. 2, *687*, 528; v. 3, 227, 1018 .... 鴨長明
kana (syllabary), v. 1, 519; v. 3, 388, 389, 1562 .... 假名
Kana Nihongi (syllabic chronicle, 714), v. 1, 516 .... 假名日本紀
Kan'ami [better than Kannami] (d. 1384), v. 3, 1332 .... 觀阿彌
Kanazawa-bunko (library, XIII-2), v. 2, *865*; v. 3, 74, 390, 477, 1331 .... 金澤文庫
Kanetsune Kiyosuke (contemporary), v. 3, 162 .... 兼常清佐

Kanjin, *see* Ganjin (VIII-2)
Kano Einō (fl. 1676), v. 2, 428 .... 狩野永納
Kariya Ekisai (d. 1835), v. 3, 714 .... 狩谷棭齋
katakana (syllabary), v. 1, 519, 553; v. 3, 110, 389, 1649 .... 片假名
Katō Shirōzaemon Kagemasa (fl. 1223), v. 2, 636 .... 加藤四郎左衛門景正
Katō Shunkei (XIII-1), v. 2, *636*, 30, 511; v. 3, 757 .... 加藤春慶
Kawase Kazuma (contemporary), v. 3, 735 .... 川瀬一馬
Kegonkyō (Avatamsakasūtra), v. 1, 510 .... 華嚴經
Kegon-shū (Buddhist sect, 736), v. 1, 510 .... 華嚴宗
keishi-zan (mathematical term), v. 2, 297, 405 .... 計子算
Keiun (poet), v. 3, 1018 .... 慶運
Kemmu shikimoku (code of laws, 1336), v. 3, 322, 1001 (Kemmu, nengō 1334–36) 建武式目
Kenchō-ji (temple in Kamakura), v. 3, 636 .... 建長寺
Kenchōji-bune (ships sent to China for Kenchō-ji), v. 3, 205 .... 建長寺船
Kenkō (same as Yoshida Kaneyoshi, XIV-1), v. 3, 1018 .... 兼好
Kennin-ji (Zen temple), v. 2, 337, 559; v. 3, 636 .... 建仁寺
Kenshin-daishi (d. 1268), v. 2, 559 .... 見眞大師
Ki Tsurayuki (X-1), v. 1, *639*, 622 .... 紀貫之
Kibi Makibi, or Kibi no Mabi (VIII-1), v. 1, *519*, 506, 513; v. 3, 389 .... 吉備眞備
Kikuchi Dairoku (d. 1917), v. 3, 1891 .... 菊池大麓
Kimiya Yasuhiko (contemporary), v. 3, 637 .... 木宮泰彦
Kimmei-tennō (ruled 540–71), v. 1, 454 .... 欽明天皇
Kinkaku-ji (golden pavilion), v. 3, 1029 .... 金閣寺
Kin-ki (medical), v. 1, 310 .... 金匱
Kiran-hō (medical), v. 1, 575 .... 金蘭方
Kishinron (awakening of the faith by Aśvaghosha), v. 3, 312 .... 起信論
Kiso-kaidō (road from Kyōto, built 702), v. 1, 515 .... 木曾街道
Kissa-yōjō-ki (on tea), v. 2, 337, 429 .... 喫茶養生記
Kitabatake Chikafusa (XIV-1), v. 3, *1001*, 60, 109, 312, 322, 980, 1029 .... 北畠親房
Kitagawa Utamaro (d. 1806), v. 3, 1188 .... 北川歌磨
Kitasato Shibasaburo (d. 1931), v. 3, 1653 .... 北里柴三郎
Kiyowara Natsuno (IX-1), v. 1, *581*, 548, 623 .... 清原夏野
Kōbō daishi (IX-1), v. 1, *553*, 519, 544, 548, 549, 552; v. 3, 109, 389 .... 弘法大師
Kōbun-in (school, 800), v. 1, 539 .... 弘文院
Kōbun shōsho kōshi den (earliest Chinese classic printed in Japan), v. 3, 637 古文尙書孔子傳
Kogo-shūi (on customs of old Japan, 808), v. 1, 580 .... 古語拾遺
Kōgon-tennō (ruled 1331–33, d. 1364), v. 3, 1029 .... 光嚴天皇
Kojiki (early annals), v. 1, 474, 516, 517; v. 3, 389 .... 古事記
Kojima (d. 1374), v. 3, 980, 1270 .... 小島
Kō yō shō [often read Kō yaku shō] (on perfumes), v. 2, 443 .... 香藥抄
Kōken-tennō (empress 749–58; *see* Shōtoku-tennō, VIII-2), v. 1, 529 .... 孝謙天皇
Kokin-shū (collection of poems), v. 1, 639 .... 古今集
Kokin-wakashū (same as Kokin-shū), v. 1, 639 .... 古今和歌集
Kōkoku do sei kō (on Japanese weights and measures), v. 3, 714 .... 皇國度制考
Kokurui shō (on cereals), v. 2, 443 .... 穀類抄
Kokusai bunka shinkokai (society for international cultural relations), v. 3, 1333 .... 國際文化振興會

Kokusho kaidai (annotated bibliography of Japan), v. 3, 1892 國書解題
Koma (one of the three Korean kingdoms), v. 1, 364, 365, 492; v. 3, 1538 高麗
Kōmyō-kōgō (d. 760), v. 1, 539; v. 3, 293 光明皇后
Kon-Bu (Korean, fl. 1st half of 5th), v. 1, 393 金武
Kondō (part of Hōryū-ji), v. 3, 170 金堂
Kongō-bu-ji (temple on Kōya-san), v. 1, 553 金剛峯寺
Kongwanji-ha, *see* Hongwanji-ha
Kōnin-kyaku-shiki (code of law, 811), v. 1, 548, 581, 618 (Kōnin, nengō 810–24) 弘仁格式
Konoe (kuge family), v. 3, 156 近衞
Koppitsuretsu (Kublai Khān, XIII-2), v. 2, 980 忽必烈
Kōrai (Korea), v. 3, 1028 高麗
Koremune Naomoto (X-1), v. 1, *644*, 623 惟宗直本
Koremune Tomotoshi (XIII-2), v. 2, *1075*, 52, 53, 781 惟宗具俊
Kōshi (Confucius, VI B.C.), v. 1, 67 孔子
ko-saburai-dokoro (military ministry of shōgun), v. 2, 574 小侍所
Kōtoku-tennō (ruled 645–54), v. 1, 463, 485 孝德天皇
Kōya-han (editions of Kōya temple), v. 3, 1562 高野版
Kōya-san (sacred mountain in Kii), v. 1, 553 高野山
Koyomi (calendar), v. 1, 476 曆
Kudara (one of the three Korean kingdoms), v. 1, 364, 448, 454, 476, 492 百濟
Kuga Michichika (fl. beginning 13th), v. 2, 559 久我通親
Kujihongi, or Kujiki (early annals), v. 1, 473, 474 舊事本紀 舊事紀
Kūkai, *see* Kōbō daishi (IX-1) 空海
Kunimiyama (in Iga), v. 3, 1018 國見山
Kuninaka Kimimaro (fl. 747), v. 1, 515 國中公麻呂
Kuon-ji (Nichiren temple), v. 2, 827 久遠寺
Kurodani Shōnin wago tōroku (collection of sermons by Hōnen-Shōnin), v. 3, 110 黒谷上人和語燈錄
Kusha-shū (Buddhist sect), v. 1, 488, 492; v. 3, 60 俱舍宗
Kwammuryōjukyō (sūtra of eternal life), v. 3, 312 觀無量壽經
Kwammu-tennō [also Kammu] (ruled 782–805), v. 1, 509, 513, 522, 535 桓武天皇
kwampaku [also kampaku] (court office), v. 1, 778 關白
kwangaku-den (rice fields helping to support Nara students), v. 1, 513 勸學田
Kwanroku (VII-1), v. 1, *476*, 461, 462, 463, 481 勸勒
Kwanze Kwanami Kiyotsugu (d. 1384), v. 3, 1332 觀世觀阿彌清次
kyaku (official rules), v. 1, 518 格
kyō (mirror), v. 3, 980 鏡
Kyōto, v. 1, 509, 639; v. 3, 156 京都
Kyōto sects, v. 1, 552, 553 京都派

Majima-ryū (medical school), v. 3, 1236, 1332 間島流
Majima ryū ganmoku hiden shō (on eye diseases), v. 3, 1733 間島流眼目秘傳抄
Majima Seigan (XIV-2), v. 3, *1733*, 1218, 1236 間島清眼
Man-an pō (medical), v. 3, 909 萬安方
Manju-ji (Kyōto temple), v. 3, 636 萬壽寺
manyō-gana (syllabary), v. 1, 516, 519; v. 3, 388, 389 萬葉假名
Man-yō-shū (early anthology), v. 3, 389, 1332 萬葉集
Masu-kagami (chronicle to 1333), v. 2, 263; v. 3, 311, 389, 980 增鏡
Matsudaira Naritake (fl. 1810), v. 1, 644 松平齊貴

Metsura Omi (group of men of letters, 6th cent.), v. 1, 448 .... 珍勳臣
Mido Kwampaku (d. 1027), v. 1, 778 .... 御堂關白
Mikami Yoshio (contemporary), v. 3, 162, 702, 1896, 1904 .... 三上義夫
Minabuchi Shōan (fl. 608), v. 1, 463, 485 .... 南淵請安
Minamoto, v. 3, 42 .... 源
Minamoto no Chikafusa (*see* Kitabatake Chikafusa, XIV-1), v. 3, 1001 .... 源親房
Minamoto no Shitagau [properly Shitagō] (X-2), v. 1, *692*, 653, 654; v. 3, 389 .... 源順
Minamoto Yoritomo (d. 1199), v. 3, 42 .... 源賴朝
Minō Kōjun (contemporary), v. 3, 1896 .... 美濃晃順
mitsuda-é (painting technique), v. 3, 170 .... 密陀畫
Mitsu kagami (three chronicles), v. 2, 140, 263; v. 3, 980 .... 三鏡
Miura (family name of Dengyō daishi, IX-1), v. 1, 552 .... 三浦
Miyoshi Yasutsura (fl. 1233), v. 2, 694 .... 三善康行
Mizu-kagami (water mirror, chronicle to 850), v. 2, 263, 315, 461 .... 水鏡
Mochizuki (contemporary), v. 3, 1842 .... 望月
mogasa (smallpox), v. 1, 509 .... 疱瘡
momen (cotton fabrics), v. 1, 535 .... 木綿
Mommutennō (ruled 697–707), v. 1, 518 .... 文武天皇
monjō-hakase [misread bunshō] (professor of literature), v. 1, 582 .... 文章博士
monogatari (romances), v. 1, 778; v. 3, 389 .... 物語
Mononobe Hiroizumi [Monobe is wrong] (IX-1), v. 1, *575*, 547 .... 物部廣泉
Monto-shū (Buddhist sect, *see* Shin-shū, XIII-1), v. 2, 559 .... 門徒宗
Mōshi (Mencius, IV-2 B.C.), v. 1, 138 .... 孟子
Mu-ku jō-kō kyō (vimala nirbhasa sūtra), v. 1, 530 .... 無垢淨光經
Muchū mondō (by Soseki, XIV-1), v. 3, 110 .... 夢中問答
Muromachi (or Ashikaga period, 1336–1568), v. 3, 42 .... 室町
Musō-kokushi (posthumous name of Soseki, XIV-1), v. 3, 110, 478 .... 夢窓國師
myōhō (Chinese law), v. 1, 581 .... 明法
myōhōdō (Chinese law), v. 1, 513 .... 明法道
Myōhō-renge-kyō (lotus sūtra), v. 2, 827; v. 3, 312 .... 妙法蓮華經
Myōō (fl. 1st half of 14th), v. 3, 478, 1084, 1332 .... 明王
Myōshin-ji (Tendai temple), v. 3, 636 .... 妙心寺

Nagao Kagehisa (fl. 1394), v. 3, 1408 .... 長尾景壽
Nakasendō (road built 702), v. 1, 515 .... 中仙道
Nakatomi no Kamako (d. 669), v. 1, 500 .... 中臣鎌子
Nakayama Tadachika (XII-2), v. 2, *461*, 263, 315 .... 中山忠親
Namu Amida butsu (prayer), v. 2, 165 .... 南無阿彌陀佛
Nanjiō Bunyiū [correctly Nanjō Bun'yū], v. 3, 467, 1897 .... 南條文雄
Nan-kyō (medical), v. 1, 310 .... 難經
Nanzen-ji (temple near Kyōto), v. 3, 636, 1084 .... 南禪寺
Nara Daibutsu (great Buddha of Nara), v. 1, 509 .... 奈良大佛
Nara period, v. 1, 504, 505, 509, 513 .... 奈良朝
Nara sects, six, v. 1, 510, 552, 553 .... 奈良六派
Nara university, v. 1, 513 .... 奈良大學寮
Narabi-no-oka no Otodo (*see* Kiyowara Natsuno, IX-1), v. 1, 581 .... 雙岡大臣
Nembutsu-shū (Buddhist sect), v. 2, 113, 165, 282, 336, 828 .... 念佛宗
nengō (era), v. 1, 461, 476, 672; v. 2, 694 .... 年號
Nichiren (XIII-2), v. 2, 827 .... 日蓮

Nichiren-shū (Buddhist sect, XIII-2), v. 2, *827*, 715; v. 3, 59 .... 日蓮宗
Nihon bungaku dai-jiten (great literary lexicon), v. 3, 1897 .... 日本文學大辭典
Nihon hyakka dai-jiten (encyclopaedia japonica), v. 3, 1897 .... 日本百科大辭典
Nihon keizai sōsho (Japanese economic series), v. 3, 714 .... 日本經濟叢書
Nihon kōgyō-shi (history of Japanese industry), v. 3, 1832 .... 日本工業史
Nihon ko insatsu bunka shi .... 日本印刷文化史
Nihon-kōki (histories, IX-1), v. 1, *580*, 516 .... 日本後紀
Nihon koten zenshū [not koden] (collection of ancient Japanese classics), v. 3, 1733 日本古典全集
Nihon koten zenshū kankō-kai (society publishing Nihon koten zenshū), v. 3, 714 日本古典全集刊行會
Nihongi, *see* Nihon shoki .... 日本紀
Nihon shoki (chronicle), v. 1, 516, 517, 575; v. 3, 388, 389 .... 日本書紀
Nimmyō-tennō (ruled 834–50), v. 2, 461 .... 仁明天皇
Ninchō (d. 1711), v. 3, 424 .... 忍徵
Ninsei (d. 1303), v. 3, 263, 280, 293, 909 .... 忍性
nō (drama), v. 3, 1332, 1862 .... 能
Nōgaku zensho (collection of books on nō), v. 3, 1862 .... 能學全書
Nogami Toyoichirō (contemporary), v. 3, 1862 .... 野上豐一郎
Norito, noritogoto (Shintō prayers), v. 1, 644; v. 3, 389 .... 祝詞

Ōanseki (*see Chinese index*, Wang An-shih, XI-2), v. 1, 781 .... 王安石
Ōbaku (branch of Zen), v. 2, 559 .... 黃檗
Ochi Michihide (d. 1289), v. 2, 828 .... 越智道秀
Odawara castle .... 小田原城
Ogiwara Unrai (contemporary; spells his name in English Wogihara), v. 3, x, 1898 荻原雲來
Ōhara-yama (Buddhist temple), v. 2, 687 .... 大原山
Ō-kagami (great mirror, chronicle to 1036), v. 2, 140, 263; v. 3, 389 .... 大鏡
Okakura Kakuzō (d. 1913), v. 3, 1332 .... 岡倉覺三
Oku Saburōbei (fl. 1878), v. 3, 758 .... 奥三郎兵衞
Ōmi ritsu-ryō (code of law, c. 667), v. 1, 490, 500 .... 近江律令
Ōmi ryō (code of law), v. 1, 518, 581 .... 近江令
Ōmura Fukuyoshi (IX-1), v. 1, *575*, 547 .... 大村福吉
Ono no Takamura (d. 852), v. 3, 1408 .... 小野篁
Ōno Yasumaro (fl. 720), v. 1, 505, 516 .... 太安萬侶
osa (interpreters of Chinese and Korean), v. 1, 448 .... 譯
Ōtani Masanobu (contemporary), v. 3, 1189 .... 大谷正信
Ōyū-Ryōda (fl. 554), v. 1, 454 .... 王有陵陀

Pakche (*see* Kudara), v. 1, 364 .... 百濟

Raikō-in (temple in Ōhara), v. 2, 165 .... 來迎院
Rei-sui (medical), v. 1, 310 .... 靈樞
reki (calendar), v. 1, 476 .... 曆
Rekidai teiō hennen goken no zu (chronological table of emperors), v. 3, 109 歷代帝王編年互見之圖
reki-hakase (astronomers), v. 1, 476 .... 曆博士
Ren-in (d. c. 1225), v. 2, 687 .... 蓮胤

Rikkokushi (histories), v. 1, 516, 580, 617 .... 六國史
Riku-kokushi, *see* Rikkokushi
Rinzai-shū (Buddhist sect), v. 2, 559; v. 3, 59, 74, 109, 205, 478 .... 臨濟宗
rin-zō (revolving library), v. 3, 734 .... 輪藏
Risshō ankoku-ron (Nichiren treatise), v. 2, 827 .... 立正安國論
Risshū (Ritsu-shū), v. 1, 510 .... 律宗
rito (Korean script), v. 3, 388 .... 吏道
Ritsu-shū (Buddhist sect), v. 1, 510 .... 律宗
Rokuon-ji (temple in Kyōto), v. 3, 1084 .... 鹿苑寺
Rongo (Confucian analects), v. 1, 67; v. 3, 109 .... 論語
Rongo shūchū (collection of commentaries on the analects), v. 3, 109 .... 論語集注
Rongo shūkai (commentary on the analects), v. 3, 637 .... 論語集解
ryō (code of law), v. 1, 500 .... 令
Ryō no gige (commentary on Japanese law), v. 1, 581, 644 .... 令義解
Ryō no shūge (commentary on Japanese law), v. 1, 644 .... 令集解
Ryōbu-Shintō (two-sided Shintō, i.e. Shintō harmonized with Buddhism), v. 1, 510, 553 兩部神道
Ryōken (fl. 14th), v. 3, 478, 1084, 1332 .... 良顯
Ryōnin (XII-1), v. 2, *165*, 113, 282, 336 .... 良忍
Ryūshin (fl. 13th), v. 3, 424 .... 隆信

Sadaaki (fl. 14th), v. 2, 865 .... 貞明
Saeki Daitarō (contemporary), v. 3, 467 .... 佐伯大太郎
Saeki Yoshio (contemporary), v. 3, 54, 298, 358 .... 佐伯好郎
Saga-tennō (ruled 810–23, d. 842), v. 2, 429 .... 嵯峨天皇
Saichō (d. 822), v. 1, 552 .... 最澄
Saiki (family name of Kōbō daishi, IX-1), v. 1, 553 .... 佐伯
Saimei-tennō (ruled 655–61), v. 1, 500 .... 齋明天皇
Sakaibe Iwazumi (VII-2), v. 1, *502*, 490; v. 3, 389 .... 境部石積
Sakanishi Shio (contemporary), v. 3, 28, 109, 110, 156, 702, 714, 755, 1332, 1333, 1862 坂西志保
Sakurai Jōji (contemporary), v. 3, 1903 .... 櫻井錠二
sampitsu (three calligraphists), v. 1, 554 .... 三筆
samurai, v. 2, 694 .... 士
San-dai-kyaku-shiki (rules of three generations), v. 1, 518, 618 .... 三代格式
Sandai jitsu-roku (true annals of three reigns to 887), v. 1, 517, 617 .... 三代實錄
Sangaku keimō chūkai (mathematical), v. 3, 702 .... 三角啓蒙註解
sangi (computing rods, divination), v. 1, 339 .... 算木
San han (three kingdoms of Korea), v. 1, 364 .... 三韓
San kyō (three mirrors, histories), v. 2, 263; v. 3, 980 .... 三鏡
Sankyō shiki (by Kōbō daishi, IX-1), v. 3, 109 .... 三教指歸
Sanron-shū (Buddhist sect, 625), v. 1, 460, 470 .... 三論宗
sarugaku (popular play), v. 3, 1332 .... 猿樂
Seami Motokiyo (d. 1444), v. 3, 1332 .... 世阿彌元清
Seia (XIII-2), v. 2, *1104*, 55, 90, 781, 789 .... 西阿
sei-i-tai shōgun, v. 3, 42 .... 征夷大將軍
Seiken "Henchiin" (XII-2),[3] v. 2, *443*, 52, 55, 57, 305, 311 .... 成賢遍智院

[3] The data in my note, v. 2, 443, derived from the account by the botanist Shirai Mitsutaro, contain errors. Seiken lived from 1162 to 1231, chiefly at the temple Henchiin.

Seimei (king of Kudara), v. 1, 448 .... 聖明王
Seiwa-tennō (ruled 859–76, d. 881), v. 1, 575 .... 清和天皇
Seki Kōwa [Takakuzu is better reading than Kōwa] (fl. 1683), v. 2, 1023; v. 3, 140, 702 關孝和
Sekitō-ji (temple) .... 石頭寺
Semmei-reki (calendar, 861), v. 1, 476 .... 宣明曆
Senjimon (thousand character essay), v. 1, 441 .... 千字文
Senkō-kokushi (d. 1215), v. 2, 337 .... 千光國師
Seto (in Kasugai, Owari), v. 2, 636 .... 瀬戸
setomono (earthenware), v. 2, 636; v. 3, 757 .... 瀬戸物
Setsuyō-yōketsu (on hygiene), v. 1, 575 .... 攝養要訣
seyakuin (dispensary), v. 3, 293 .... 施藥院
Shaka (Buddha), v. 1, 448 .... 釋迦
Shihonryū-ji (temple of Nikkō), v. 1, 529 .... 四本龍寺
shiki (rites and customs), v. 1, 518 .... 式
shikken (regent), v. 3, 42 .... 執權
Shi-kyō (four mirrors; histories), v. 2, 263; v. 3, 980 .... 四鏡
Shimotsumichi Asomi (*see* Kibi Makibi, VIII-1), v. 1, 519 .... 下道朝臣
Shingon-shū (Buddhist sect), v. 1, 509, 552, 553; v. 2, 165, 827 .... 眞言宗
Shinran-Shōnin (d. 1268), v. 2, 490, 559, 827 .... 親鸞上人
Shinsai (d. 1159), v. 2, 405 .... 信西
Shin-shū (Buddhist sect, XIII-1), v. 2, *559*, 490, 715, 827; v. 3, 59 .... 眞宗
Shintan no Shaka (*see Chinese index*, Chih-i, VI-2), v. 1, 448 .... 震旦釋迦
Shintō, v. 1, 504, 510, 516, 553, 644; v. 3, 42, 60, 322, 389, 1002, 1018, 1332 .... 神道
Shinzei (d. 1159), v. 2, 405 .... 信西
Shiragi (one of the three Korean kingdoms), v. 1, 364, 365, 492 .... 新羅
shi-tennō (the four heavenly kings), v. 3, 1018 .... 四天王
Shōdō-shōnin (temple in Nikkō), v. 1, 529 .... 勝道上人
Shōfuku-ji (temple in Hakata), v. 2, 337 .... 聖福寺
shōgun, v. 2, 574; v. 3, 42 .... 將軍
Shōhei rongo, *see* Rongo (Shōhei, nengō 1346–69) .... 正平
Shōjiroku (genealogies, IX-1), v. 1, *580*, 548; v. 2, 140 .... 姓氏錄
Shō-jō (Hīnayāna), v. 1, 448; v. 3, 60 .... 小乘
Shō-kan-ron (medical), v. 1, 310; v. 2, 87 .... 傷寒論
Shōkō kōtei keishi shōrui bikiū honzō (herbal, Ch. pên ts'ao), v. 2, 443 紹興校定經史證類備急本草
Shōkoku-ji, *see* Sōkoku-ji
Shoku-gen shō (administrative history, after 1339), v. 3, 1002 .... 職原鈔
Shoku Nihongi [Zoku is wrong] (chronicle to 791), v. 1, 516, 523, 541 .... 續日本紀
Shoku-Nihon-kōki [Zoku is wrong] (history to 850), v. 1, 516, 617 .... 續日本後紀
Shōmu-tennō (ruled 749–58), v. 1, 513, 515; v. 3, 293 .... 聖武天皇
Shō-ō-daishi (d. 1132), v. 2, 165 .... 聖應大師
Shōsō-in (in Nara), v. 3, 293, 729 .... 正倉院
Shōtoku-taishi (VII-1), v. 1, *473*, 460, 461, 462, 463, 470 .... 聖德太子
Shōtoku-tennō (empress, VIII-2), v. 1, *529*, 451, 512, 521, 522; v. 3, 637, 729, 1562 稱德天皇
Shōyō-daishi (d. 1253), v. 2, 559 .... 承陽大師
Shōzui [not Shonzui] (fl. 1510), v. 2, 636 .... 祥瑞
shū (religion), v. 1, 470 .... 宗

Shumi no nihon kagaku shi (popular history of Japanese science), v. 3, 1906 趣味ノ日本科學史
Shunjō (d. 1227), v. 3, 109 .... 俊芿
Shunjō Hōin (XIV-1), v. 2, 337; v. 3, *424*, 60, 312 .... 俊乗法院
Shūshin, *see* Gidō
Sōchū-ji (temple at Ikegami), v. 2, 827 .... 宗仲寺
Sōdō-shū (branch of Zen), v. 2, 559, 827 .... 曹洞宗
Soga no Umako (fl. 604), v. 1, 473 .... 曾我馬子
Sōkoku-ji (temple in Kyōto), v. 3, 636 .... 相國寺
So-mon (medical), v. 1, 310 .... 素問
soroban (abacus), v. 1, 756 .... 算盤
Soseki (XIV-1), v. 3, *478*, 75, 110, 1029, 1084 .... 疎石
Sōtō-shū, *see* Sōdō-shū .... 曹洞宗
Sōzu (fl. 602), v. 1, 476 .... 僧都
Sugawara Kiyogimi (IX-1), v. 1, *582*, 548 .... 菅原清公
Sugawara Koreyoshi (IX-1), v. 1, *582*, 548 .... 菅原是善
Sugawara Minetsugu (fl. 865), v. 1, 575 .... 菅原峯嗣
suijaku (passage), v. 1, 553 .... 垂迹
Suiko-tennō (empress 593–628), v. 1, 470, 481 .... 推古天皇
Sunamoto Etsujirō (contemporary), v. 3, 1187 .... 砂本悅次郎
Sushun-tennō (ruled 588–92), v. 1, 452 .... 崇峻天皇
Sutoku-tennō (ruled 1124–41, d. 1164), v. 2, 263 .... 崇德天皇
Suzuki Daisetz Teitaro (contemporary), v. 3, 1905 .... 鈴木大拙貞太郎

Tachibana no Moroe (fl. 750), v. 3, 389 .... 大衍曆
Taien-reki (calendar, 763), v. 1, 476 .... 橘諸兄
Taihei-ki (history to 1368), v. 3, 311, 637, 980, 1270, 1332 .... 太平記
Taihei-ki kōmoku [not sō-moku] (revision of Taihei-ki to 1382), v. 3, 980, 1270 太平記綱目
Taihō (nengō 701–4), v. 1, 518 .... 大寶
Taiho-ryōritsu (code of law, 701), v. 1, 506, 518, 581; v. 2, 694 .... 大寶令律
Taikwa [daika, better taika] (first nengō, 645–50), v. 1, 485 .... 大化
Taikwa no kaishin (constitution of Taikwa era), v. 1, 485 .... 大化改新
taishi (prince), v. 1, 473, 529 .... 太子
Taishin-oshō (d. 763), v. 1, 510 .... 大新和尙
Taishō issaikyō (Tripiṭaka), v. 3, 467, 1889 .... 大正一切經
Taishō shinshū daizōkyō, v. 3, 467 .... 大正新修大藏經
Takakusu Junjirō (contemporary), v. 3, 467, 1889, 1905 .... 高楠順次郎
Takauji (Ashikaga shōgun 1338–58), v. 3, 478 .... 尊氏
Takebe Katahiro (d. 1739), v. 3, 702 .... 建部賢弘
Taketori monogatari (romance written end of 9th), v. 1, 778; v. 3, 389 .... 竹取物語
Tamamushi-no-zushi (in Kondō of Hōryū-ji), v. 3, 170 .... 玉蟲廚子
Tamba Yasuyori (X-2), v. 1, *683*, 651, 654; v. 2, 78 .... 丹波康賴
Tanabe Hisao (contemporary), v. 3, 162 .... 田邊尙雄
tanka (short poem), v. 1, 639; v. 3, 1018 .... 短歌
Tase Sukeshige (contemporary), v. 3, 1906 .... 田制佐重
Teikin ōrai (on ethics and etiquette), v. 3, 637 .... 庭訓往來
Teikyō-reki (calendar, 1684), v. 1, 476 (Teikyō, nengō 1684–88) .... 貞享曆
Tei-Yūda (fl. 554), v. 1, 454 .... 丁有陀

Tenchi-tennō (ruled 662–71), v. 1, 500 .... 天智天皇
Tendai-shū (Buddhist sect), v. 1, 448, 552, 553; v. 2, 165, 827; v. 3, 74, 424 .... 天台宗
tengenjutsu (mathematical method), v. 2, 626; v. 3, 701 .... 天源術
tennō (emperor, empress), v. 1, 529; v. 3, 1029 .... 天皇
Tennō-ki (imperial biographies), v. 1, 473 .... 天皇記
Tenryū-ji (temple in Kyōto), v. 3, 636 .... 天龍寺
Tenryūji-bune (ships used for Tenryū-ji), v. 3, 206, 1029 .... 天龍寺船
Tenryū-ji-seiji (porcelain imported by means of Tenryūji-bune), v. 3, 1029 .. 天龍寺青磁
ten-yaku-ryō (medical department of imperial court), v. 1, 539 .... 典藥寮
Tō-dai-ji (temple in Nara), v. 1, 509, 510, 515 .... 東大寺
Tōfuku-ji (temple in Kyōto), v. 3, 636 .... 東福寺
Tokiwa Daijō (contemporary), v. 3, 1906 .... 常盤大定
Tokudaiji Kintsugu [Kimitsugu is an error] (minister of the left, beginning of 13th), v. 3, 109 .... 德太寺公繼
Tokugawa, v. 3, 1408 .... 德川
Tokugawa Ieyasu (d. 1616), v. 2, 866; v. 3, 478 .... 德川家康
Tokurai (fl. 457), v. 1, 393 .... 德來
Ton-a (d. 1384), v. 3, 1018 .... 頓阿
Toneri-shinnō (d. 735), v. 1, 505, 516 .... 舍人親王
Ton-i shō (medical), v. 3, 909 .... 歎異鈔
Tosa-nikki (diary, 935), v. 1, 639 .... 土佐日記
Tōsho-daiji (temple in Yamato), v. 1, 510 .... 唐招提寺
Toyotomi Hideyoshi (d. 1598), v. 2, 443; v. 3, 701 .... 豐臣秀吉
Tsure-zure-gusa (literary classic, 1st half of 14th), v. 3, 75, 390, 1018 .... 徒然草

Uda-tennō (ruled 888–97, d. 931) .... 宇多天皇
Uesugi Norizane (d. 1466), v. 2, 866; v. 3, 478, 1408 .... 上杉憲寶
Uji (family), v. 1, 500 .... 氏
Ukita Hideiye (fl. 1592), v. 2, 443 .... 宇喜多秀家
Umayado (d. 621), v. 1, 473 .... 厩戶
Unchiku (fl. 1700), v. 3, 424 .... 雲竹
Urabe (family name of Genshin, X-2), v. 1, 656 .... 卜部
Urabe Kenkō (same as Yoshida Kenkō or Kaneyoshi, XIV-1), v. 3, 1018 .... 卜部兼好
uta-dokoro (poetic department of court), v. 2, 687 .... 歌所
Utamaro (d. 1806), v. 3, 1188 .... 歌麿

waka-dokoro, *see* uta-dokoro .... 和歌所
waka shi-tennō (four kings of poetry), v. 3, 1018 .... 和歌四天王
Wake Hiroyo (VIII-2), v. 1, *539*, 523; v. 2, 52 .... 和氣廣世
wakō (pirates), v. 3, 205 .... 倭寇
Wamyōshō (Sino-Japanese dictionary, 2d half of 10th), v. 1, 692; v. 3, 389 .... 和名鈔
Watanabe Kaigyoku (contemporary), v. 3, 467, 1889, 1908 .... 渡邊海旭
Wogihara, *see* Ogiwara .... 荻原

Yakkei-taiso (materia medica), v. 1, 539 .... 藥經大素
Yakoshiso Tamafuru (fl. 602), v. 1, 476 .... 陽胡史祖玉陳
Yakushu shō (on drugs), v. 2, 443 .... 藥種抄
Yamato-bumi (chronicle, 714), v. 1, 516 .... 大和文
Yatsu-mimi no Ōji (d. 621), v. 1, 473 .... 八耳王子

Yengi, *see* Engi-shiki .... 延喜
yoriudo (director), v. 2, 687 .... 寄人
Yōrō-ryōritsu (laws of nengō 717–24), v. 1, 506, 518 .... 養老令律
Yoshida Kaneyoshi (same as Yoshida Kenkō, XIV-1), v. 3, 1018 .... 吉田兼好
Yoshida Kenkō (XIV-1), v. 3, *1018*, 75, 390 .... 吉田兼好
Yoshida Kōyū (fl. 1627), v. 2, 405 .... 吉田光由
Yoshida no Kaneyoshi (same as Yoshida Kenkō, XIV-1), v. 3, 1018 .... 吉田兼好
Yoshimasa (Ashikaga shōgun 1449–74), v. 3, 1332 .... 義政
Yoshimine Yasuyo (IX-1), v. 1, *580*, 548 .... 良岑安世
Yoshimitsu (Ashikaga shōgun 1367–95), v. 3, 478, 1029, 1332 .... 義満
Yoshimochi (Ashikaga shōgun 1395–1423), v. 3, 1029 .... 義持
Yotsu-kagami (four mirrors, chronicles), v. 2, 263; v. 3, 980 .... 四鏡
yūgen (profundity, mystery), v. 3, 1333 .... 幽玄
Yūgyō Shōnin (d. 1289), v. 2, 828 .... 遊行上人
Yui-itsu-shintō (reform of Shintō), v. 3, 1018 .... 唯一神道
Yuishiki (Hossō-shū, Buddhist sect, 654), v. 1, 491 .... 唯識
Yūrin (XIV-2), v. 3, *1733*, 1218, 1242, 1332 .... 有隣
Yūrin fukuden-hō (medical), v. 3, 1733 .... 有林福田方
Yūzū nembutsu-shū (*see* Nembutsu), v. 2, 165 .... 融通念佛宗

Zenko-kokushi, *see* Senkō-kokushi
Zen-ō-ji (temple) .... 善應寺
Zen-shū (Buddhist sect, XIII-1), v. 1, 420, 552; v. 2, *559*, 282, 337, 490, 715, 827; v. 3, 59, 75, 189, 226, 311, 387, 1084, 1332, 1905 .... 禪宗
zō (elephant), v. 3, 1187 .... 象
Zoku, *see* Shoku .... 續